RHS
PLANT
FINDER
2002-2003

RHS
PLANT
FINDER
2002-2003

DEVISED BY CHRIS PHILIP

PRINCIPAL EDITOR
TONY LORD

RHS EDITORS
JANET CUBEY
MIKE GRANT
ADRIAN WHITELEY

COMPILER
JUDITH MERRICK

A Dorling Kindersley Book

Dorling Kindersley

LONDON, NEW YORK, MUNICH, MELBOURNE and DELHI

Published by
Dorling Kindersley Ltd
80 Strand, London WC2R 0RL
A Penguin company

© The Royal Horticultural Society 2002
First edition April 1987
Sixteenth edition April 2002

British Library Cataloguing Publication Data.
A Catalogue record for this book is available from the British Library.

ISBN 0 7513 3705 6
ISSN 0961-2599

Compiled by
The Royal Horticultural Society
80 Vincent Square,
London SW1P 2PE
Registered charity no: 222879

www.rhs.org.uk

Royal
Horticultural
Society

Illustrations by Sarah Young
Maps by Alan Cooper

Printed and bound in England by Clays Ltd, St Ives Plc

The Compiler and the Editors of the *RHS Plant Finder* have taken every care, in the time available, to check all the information supplied to them by the nurseries concerned. Nevertheless, in a work of this kind, containing as it does hundreds of thousands of separate computer encodings, errors and omissions will, inevitably, occur. Neither the RHS, the Publisher nor the Editors can accept responsibility for any consequences that may arise from such errors.

If you find mistakes we hope that you will let us know so that the matter can be corrected in the next edition.

Front cover photographs clockwise from top left: *Papaver orientale* 'Patty's Plum', *Tulipa* 'Cape Cod', *Arisaema candidissimum*, *Arum italicum* 'Marmoratum', *Iris bulleyana*, *Hordeum jubatum*, *Malus* 'John Downie', *Lysichiton americanus*
Back cover photographs clockwise from top left: *Heuchera* 'Purple Petticoats', *Coreopsis grandiflora* 'Badengold', *Corydalis flexuosa*, *Achillea millefolium* 'Sammetriese', *Scabiosa* 'Chile Sauce', *Euphorbia* × *martinii*, *Veltheimia bracteata*, *Amelanchier lamarckii*, *Pelargonium* 'Fair Ellen', *Phillyrea latifolia*
Spine: *Rosa* 'Gruss an Aachen'

See our complete catalogue at

www.dk.com

CONTENTS

INTRODUCTION

The *RHS Plant Finder* exists to put enthusiastic gardeners in touch with suppliers of plants, many of them unusual. The book is divided into two related sections – PLANTS and NURSERIES. PLANTS includes an A–Z Plant Directory of some 70,000 plant names, against which are listed a series of nursery codes. These codes point the reader to the full nursery details contained in the NURSERIES section towards the back of the book.

The *RHS Plant Finder* is comprehensively up-dated every year and provides the plant lover with the richest source of suppliers known to us, whether you are looking for plants locally, shopping from your armchair or touring the country in search of the rare and unusual.

NEW IN THIS EDITION

This year, to help readers pick out plants new to this edition, they are indicated by the word "new" appearing to the right of the plant name (see below). For ease of use, the fonts have been changed to reflect the correct styling of genus and family names. For the first time, common names of fruit, vegetables and herbs are cross-referenced to their botanical names in the Plant Directory.

SYMBOLS AND ABBREVIATIONS

SYMBOLS APPEARING TO THE LEFT OF THE NAME

*   Name not validated. Not listed in the appropriate International Registration Authority checklist nor in works cited in the Bibliography. For fuller discussion see p.749

I   Invalid name. See *International Code of Botanical Nomenclature 2000* and *International Code of Nomenclature for Cultivated Plants 1995*. For fuller discussion see p.749

N   Refer to Nomenclature Notes on p.725

§   Plant listed elsewhere in the Plant Directory under a synonym

×   Hybrid genus

+   Graft hybrid genus

SYMBOLS APPEARING TO THE RIGHT OF THE NAME

✿   National Council for the Conservation of Plants and Gardens (NCCPG) Plant Collection exists for all or part of this genus. Provisional Collections appear in brackets. Full details of the NCCPG Plant Collections are contained in the *National Plant Collections® Directory 2001* available from: NCCPG, The Stable Courtyard, RHS Garden Wisley, Woking, Surrey GU23 6QP

♥^{H4} The Royal Horticultural Society's Award of Garden Merit, see p.12.

(d)   double-flowered

(F)   Fruit
(f)   female
(m)   male
(v)   variegated plant, see p.12
PBR   Plant Breeders Rights see p.12
new   New plant entry in this edition

For abbreviations relating to individual genera see **Classification of Genera** p.734
For **Collectors' References** see p.731
For symbols used in the **Nurseries** section see the reverse of the card insert

SYMBOLS AND ABBREVIATIONS USED AS PART OF THE NAME

×   hybrid species
aff.   affinis (allied to)
agg.   aggregate, a single name used to cover a group of very similar plants, regarded by some as separate species
ambig.   ambiguous, a name used by two authors for different plants and where it is unclear which is being offered
cl.   clone
cv(s)   cultivar(s)
f.   forma (botanical form)
g.   grex
sp.   species
subsp.   subspecies
subvar.   subvarietas (botanical subvariety)
var.   varietas (botanical variety)

AVAILABLE FROM THE COMPILER

APPLICATION FOR ENTRY

Nurseries appearing in the *RHS Plant Finder* for the first time this year are printed in bold type in the Nursery Index by Name starting on p.911.

If any other nursery wishes to be considered for inclusion in the next edition of the *RHS Plant Finder* (2003-04), please write for details to the Compiler at the address below. The closing date for entries will be 31 January 2003.

PLANTS LAST LISTED IN EARLIER EDITIONS

Plants cease to be listed for a variety of reasons. For more information turn to How to Use the Plant Directory on p.10.

A listing of the 23,400 or so plants last listed in earlier editions, and for which we currently have no known supplier, is available from the Compiler. Please send a £1 stamp.

LISTS OF NURSERIES FOR PLANTS WITH MORE THAN 30 SUPPLIERS

To prevent the *RHS Plant Finder* from becoming still larger, if more than 30 nurseries offer the same plant we cease to print the nursery codes and instead list the plant as having 'more than 30 suppliers'. This is detailed more fully in How to Use the Plant Directory on p.10.

If any readers have difficulty in finding such a plant, we will be pleased to send a full list of all the nurseries that we have on file as stockists. All such enquiries must include the full name of the plant being sought, as shown in the *RHS Plant Finder*, together with an A5 size SAE. For more than one plant, please send an A4 1st class SAE.

The above may all be obtained from:
The Compiler,
RHS Plant Finder,
RHS Garden Wisley,
Woking,
Surrey
GU23 6QB

THE RHS PLANT FINDER ONLINE

The *RHS Plant Finder* is available on the Internet. Visit the Royal Horticultural Society's website (**www.rhs.org.uk**) and search the *RHS Plant Finder* database online.

> IT IS NOT WITHIN THE REMIT OF THIS BOOK TO CHECK **that nurseries are applying the right names to the right plants or to ensure nurseries selling plants with Plant Breeders' Rights are licensed to do so.**

ACKNOWLEDGMENTS

There have been several changes in the team responsible for generating this edition of the *RHS Plant Finder* from *BG-BASE*™ this year. Clare Burgh, who took over the compiling of nursery information from *Plant Finder*'s founder Chris Philip and produced the previous four editions, left the RHS in October 2001. We are all grateful to her for managing a time of transition for *Plant Finder* with such skill and efficiency. This year Judith Merrick, together with June Skinner, compiled the nursery information and plant listings and generated the bibliography from *BG-BASE*™ for the first time, a process that makes compilation easier and quicker and results in a slightly different format. Richard Sanford, assisted by Gerda Pope, Emma Cox and Stuart Hallett, worked on the editing of plant names. The horticultural database has been managed by Senior Database Administrator Rupert Wilson. Other parts of the book have been drawn together by Simon Maughan of RHS Publications Department.

The RHS botanists Adrian Whiteley, Janet Cubey and Mike Grant have carried out the preliminary editing of all plant names new to the book and have worked on the reformatting and updating of the bibliography. Our team has again been helped by the efforts of Dr Kerry Walter of *BG-BASE* Inc.

Once again this year I am indebted to my colleagues on the RHS Advisory Panel on Nomenclature and Taxonomy: Chris Brickell,

Susyn Andrews, James Compton, Christopher Grey-Wilson, Stephen Jury, Sabina Knees, Alan Leslie, Simon Thornton-Wood, Piers Trehane and Adrian Whiteley, along with Mike Grant, Diana Miller and Janet Cubey, all of whom have provided much valuable guidance. Scores of nurseries have sent helpful information about asterisked plants which has proved immensely useful in verifying some of the most obscure names, as well as suggesting corrections to existing entries. Some of these suggested corrections remain to be checked and entered in our next edition, though those that contravene the Codes of Nomenclature have had to be rejected for reasons covered in the section on nomenclature.

I am grateful, too, to our regular correspondents and to the RHS International Registrars.

Actaea	J. Compton ('01)
Camellia	T.J. Savige, International Registrar, NSW, Australia ('96)
Cistus	R. Page ('97, '99 & '02)
Clematis	V. Mathews, International Registrar, RHS ('00-'02)
Conifers	P. Trehane, International Registrar, RHS Wisley ('94 & '99)
Cotoneaster	Jeanette Fryer, NCCPG Collection Holder ('99)
Dahlia	R. Hedge, RHS Wisley ('96-'00 & '02)
Delphinium	Dr A.C. Leslie, International Registrar, RHS Wisley ('97-'00 & '02)
Dianthus	Dr A.C. Leslie, International Registrar, RHS Wisley ('91-'00 & '02)
Hebe	Mrs J. Hewitt ('94-'99)
Hypericum	Dr N.K.B. Robson ('94-'97)
Ilex	Ms S. Andrews ('92-'98)
Iris	Mrs J. Hewitt ('95-'99 & '02)
Jovibarba & *Sempervivum*	P.J. Mitchell, International Registrar, Sempervivum Society ('98)
Lavandula	Ms S. Andrews ('92-'99)
Lilium	Dr A.C. Leslie, International Registrar, RHS Wisley ('91-'00 & '02)
Liriope	Dr P.R. Fantz ('99)
Meconopsis	Dr E. Stevens ('02)
Narcissus	Mrs S. Kington, International Registrar, RHS ('91-'00 & '02)
Ophiopogon	Dr P.R. Fantz ('99)
Rhododendron	Dr A.C. Leslie, International Registrar, RHS Wisley ('91-'00 & '02)
Sorbus	Dr H. McAllister ('01)

To all these, as well as the many readers and nurseries who have also made comments and suggestions, we are, once again, sincerely grateful.

Tony Lord, March 2002

TO AVOID DISAPPOINTMENT, WE SUGGEST THAT YOU ALWAYS check with the nursery before visiting or ordering and always use the current edition of the book.

PLANTS

WHATEVER PLANT YOU ARE LOOKING FOR,
MAYBE AN OLD FAVOURITE OR A MORE UNUSUAL
CULTIVAR, SEARCH HERE FOR A LIST OF THE
SUPPLIERS THAT ARE CLOSEST TO YOU.

How to Use the Plant Directory

Nursery Codes

Look up the plant you require in the alphabetical Plant Directory. Against each plant you will find one or more four-letter codes, for example SLan, each code represents one nursery offering that plant. The first letter of each code indicates the main area of the country in which the nursery is situated, based on their county. For this geographical key, refer to the card insert at the beginning of the Nurseries section p.769.

Turn to the **Nursery Details by Code** starting on p.772 where, in alphabetical order of codes, you will find details of each nursery which offers the plant in question. If you wish to visit any nursery, you may find its location on one of the maps (following p.921). Please note, however, that not all nurseries, especially mail order only nurseries, choose to be shown on the maps. For a fuller explanation of how to use the nursery listings please turn to p.769. Always check that the nursery you select has the plant in stock before you set out.

Plants with more than 30 Suppliers

In some cases, against the plant name you will see the term 'more than 30 suppliers' instead of a nursery code. If we were to include every plant listed by all nurseries, the *RHS Plant Finder* would become unmanageably bulky. We therefore ask nurseries to restrict their entries to those plants that are not already well represented. As a result, if more than 30 nurseries offer any plant the Directory gives no nursery codes and the plant is listed instead as having 'more than 30 suppliers'. You should have little difficulty in locating these in local nurseries or garden centres. However, if you are unable to find such plants, we will be pleased to send a full list of all the nurseries that we have on file as stockists. To obtain a list, please see the Introduction on p.7.

Finding Fruit, Vegetables and Herbs

You will need to search for these by their botanical names. Common names are cross-referenced to their botanical names in the Plant Directory.

If you have Difficulty Finding your Plant

If you cannot immediately find the plant you seek, look through the various species of the genus. You may be using an incomplete name. The problem is most likely to arise in very large genera such as *Phlox* where there are a number of possible species, each with a large number of cultivars. A search through the whole genus may well bring success. Please note that, for space reasons, the following are not listed in the Plant Directory: annuals, orchids, except hardy terrestrial orchids; cacti, except hardy cacti.

Cross-references

It may be that the plant name you seek is a synonym. Our intention is to list nursery codes only against the correct botanical name. Where you find a synonym you will be cross-referred to the correct name. Occasionally you may find that the correct botanical name to which you have been referred is not listed. This is because it was last listed in an earlier edition as explained below.

Plants Last Listed in Earlier Editions

It may be that the plant you are seeking has no known suppliers and is thus not listed.

The loss of a plant name from the Directory may arise for a number of reasons – the supplier may have gone out of business, or may not have responded to our latest questionnaire and has therefore been removed from the book. Such plants may well be still available but we have no current knowledge of their whereabouts. Alternatively, some plants may have been misnamed by nurseries in previous editions, but are now appearing under their correct name.

To obtain a listing of plants last listed in earlier editions please see the Introduction on p.7.

Please, never use an old edition

USING THE PLANT DIRECTORY

The main purpose of the Plant Directory is to help the reader correctly identify the plant they seek and find its stockist. Each nursery has a unique identification code which appears to the right of the plant name. Turn to Nursery Details by Code (p.772) for the address, opening times and other details of the nursery. The first letter of each nursery code denotes its geographical region.

Turn to the card insert towards the rear of the book to find your region code and then identify the nurseries in your area.

Another purpose of the Directory is to provide more information about the plant through the symbols and other information. For example, if it has an alternative names, is new to this edition or has received the RHS Award of Garden Merit.

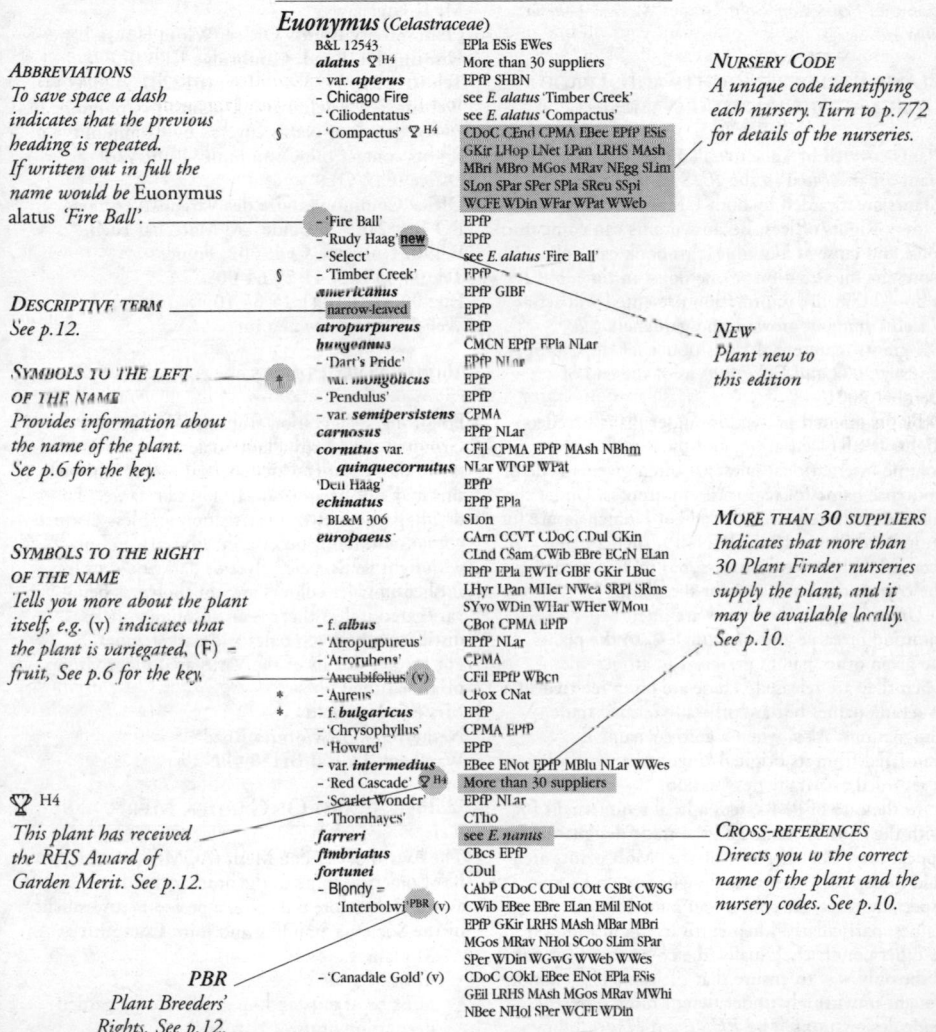

ABBREVIATIONS
To save space a dash indicates that the previous heading is repeated. If written out in full the name would be Euonymus alatus 'Fire Ball'.

DESCRIPTIVE TERM
See p.12.

SYMBOLS TO THE LEFT OF THE NAME
Provides information about the name of the plant. See p.6 for the key.

SYMBOLS TO THE RIGHT OF THE NAME
Tells you more about the plant itself, e.g. (v) indicates that the plant is variegated, (F) – fruit, See p.6 for the key.

♥ H4
This plant has received the RHS Award of Garden Merit. See p.12.

PBR
Plant Breeders' Rights. See p.12.

NURSERY CODE
A unique code identifying each nursery. Turn to p.772 for details of the nurseries.

NEW
Plant new to this edition

MORE THAN 30 SUPPLIERS
Indicates that more than 30 Plant Finder nurseries supply the plant, and it may be available locally. See p.10.

CROSS-REFERENCES
Directs you to the correct name of the plant and the nursery codes. See p.10.

Euonymus (Celastraceae)

B&L 12543	EPla ESis EWes
alatus ♥ H4	More than 30 suppliers
- var. *apterus*	EPfP SHBN
- Chicago Fire	see *E. alatus* 'Timber Creek'
- 'Ciliodentatus'	see *E. alatus* 'Compactus'
§ - 'Compactus' ♥ H4	CDoC CEnd CPMA EBee EPfP ESis GKir LHop LNet LPan LRHS MAsh MBri MBro MGos MRav NEgg SLim SLon SPar SPer SPla SReu SSpi WCFE WDin WFar WPat WWeb
- 'Fire Ball'	EPfP
- 'Rudy Haag' new	EPfP
- 'Select'	see *E. alatus* 'Fire Ball'
§ - 'Timber Creek'	EPfP
americanus	EPfP GIBF
- narrow-leaved	EPfP
atropurpureus	EPfP
bungeanus	CMCN EPfP FPla NLar
- 'Dart's Pride'	EPfP NLar
- var. *mongolicus*	EPfP
- 'Pendulus'	EPfP
- var. *semipersistens*	CPMA
carnosus	EPfP NLar
cornutus var.	CFil CPMA EPfP MAsh NBhm
quinquecornutus	NLar WTGP WPat
'Dell Haag'	EPfP
echinatus	EPfP EPla
- BL&M 306	SLon
europaeus	CArn CCVT CDoC CDul CKin CLnd CSam CWib EBre ECrN ELan EPfP EPla EWTr GIBF GKir LBuc LHyr LPan MIler NWea SRPl SRms SYvo WDin WHar WHer WMou
- f. *albus*	CBot CPMA EPfP
- 'Atropurpureus'	EPfP NLar
- 'Atrorubens'	CPMA
- 'Aucubifolius' (v)	CFil EPfP WBcn
- 'Aureus'	CFox CNat
- f. *bulgaricus*	EPfP
- 'Chrysophyllus'	CPMA EPfP
- 'Howard'	EPfP
- var. *intermedius*	EBee ENot EPfP MBlu NLar WWes
- 'Red Cascade' ♥ H4	More than 30 suppliers
- 'Scarlet Wonder'	EPfP NLar
- 'Thornhayes'	CTho
farreri	see *E. nanus*
fimbriatus	CBcs EPfP
fortunei	CDul
- Blondy = 'Interbolwi' PBR (v)	CAbP CDoC CDul COtt CSBt CWSG CWib EBee EBre ELan EMil ENot EPfP GKir LRHS MAsh MBar MBri MGos MRav NHol SCoo SLim SPar SPer WDin WGwG WWeb WWes
- 'Canadale Gold' (v)	CDoC COkL EBee ENot EPla ESis GEil LRHS MAsh MGos MRav MWhi NBee NHol SPer WCFE WDin

ADDITIONAL PLANT NAME INFORMATION IN THE DIRECTORY

DESCRIPTIVE TERMS

Terms which appear after the main part of the name are shown in a smaller font to distinguish name parts that are common names, collectors' codes and other descriptive terms. This descriptive element gives extra information about the plant, for example where it is from, or what colour it is. For example, *Penstemon* 'Sour Grapes' M. Fish, *Lobelia tupa* dark orange.

PLANT BREEDERS' RIGHTS AND TRADE DESIGNATIONS (SELLING NAMES)

Plants covered by an active Plant Breeders' Rights grant are indicated in the *RHS Plant Finder*. Grants are awarded by both UK and EU Plant Variety Rights offices. Because grants can come into force and lapse at any time, this book can only represent the situation at one point in time, but it is hoped that the information presented will act as a useful guide to growers and gardeners. UK grants represent the position as of the end of January 2002 and EU grants as of the end of October 2001.

Plants granted protection under Plant Breeders' Rights (PBR) legislation, and those with high-volume international sales, are often given a code or nonsense name for registration purposes. Under the rules of the International Code of Nomenclature for Cultivated Plants 1995 (ICNCP), such a name, established by a legal process, has to be regarded as the correct cultivar name for the plant.

Unfortunately, the names are often unpronounceable and meaningless, so the plants are given other names designed to attract sales when they are released. These are often referred to as selling names but are officially termed trade designations. Also, when a cultivar name is translated from its original language, the translation is regarded as a trade designation.

In the case of PBRs, it is a legal requirement for both the cultivar name and the trade designation to appear on a label at point-of-sale. Most plants are sold under only one trade designation, but some, especially roses, are sold under a number of names, particularly when cultivars are introduced to other countries. Usually, the correct cultivar name is the only way to ensure that the same plant is not bought unwittingly under two or more different trade designations. The *RHS Plant Finder* follows the recommendations of the ICNCP when dealing with trade designations. These are always to quote the cultivar name and trade designation together and to style the trade designation in a different typeface, without single quotation marks. The *RHS Plant Finder* takes no responsibility for ensuring that nurseries selling plants with Plant Breeders' Rights are licensed to do so.

For further information on PBR contact:
Mr R Greenaway
Plant Variety Rights Office, White House Lane, Huntingdon Road, Cambridge CB3 0LF
Tel: (01223) 342350   Fax: (01223) 342386.
Website: www.defra.gov.uk/planth/pvs/pbrguide.htm

For details of plants covered by Community Rights contact the Community Plant Variety Office (CPVO):
Office Communautaire des Variétés Végétales, PO Box 2141, 3 Boulevard Maréchal Foch, F-49021 Angers, Cedex 02, France
Tel: 00 33 (02) 41 25 64 00
Fax: 00 33 (02) 41 25 64 10
Website: www.cpvo.eu.int

VARIEGATED PLANTS

Following a suggestion from the Variegated Plant Group of the Hardy Plant Society, we have added a (v) to those plants which are 'variegated' although this may not be apparent from their name. The dividing line between variegation and less distinct colour marking is necessarily arbitrary and plants with light veins, pale, silver or dark zones or leaves flushed in paler colours are not shown as being variegated unless there is an absolutely sharp distinction between paler and darker zones. For further details of the Variegated Plant Group, please write to
Mrs Bee Newbold
Netherbury, 36 Worgret Road
Wareham, Dorset BH20 4PN

♀ THE AWARD OF GARDEN MERIT

The Award of Garden Merit (AGM) is intended to be of practical value to the ordinary gardener, and is awarded therefore only after a period of assessment by the Society's Standing and Joint Committees. An AGM plant:
* must be available
* must be of outstanding excellence for garden decoration or use
* must be of good constitution

- must not require highly specialist growing conditions or care
- must not be particularly susceptible to any pest or disease
- must not be subject to an unreasonable degree of reversion

The RHS publication *AGM Plants 2002* gives a full list of AGM plants with hardiness ratings. Copies can be ordered from **RHS Enterprises** on (01483) 211320. Information about AGM plants is also available on the RHS website at www.rhs.org.uk.

HARDINESS

Hardiness ratings are shown for AGM plants. The categories used are as follows:

H1 = plants requiring heated glass in the British Isles (roughly equivalent to Zones 10 and 11 according to the United States Department of Agriculture [USDA] system).

H2 = plants requiring unheated glass in the British Isles (USDA Zone 9 but sometimes resenting winter wet).

H3 = plants hardy outside in some regions of the British Isles or in particular situations, or which, while usually grown outside in summer, need frost-free protection in winter (e.g. dahlias)(USDA Zones 8 and 9).

H4 = plants hardy throughout the British Isles. (USDA Zone 7. Though most of the British Isles corresponds to USDA Zone 8, to be considered hardy here, plants must tolerate significantly colder than average, i.e. USDA Zone 7, winters.)

SUPPLEMENTARY KEYS TO THE PLANT DIRECTORY

NOMENCLATURE NOTES

These refer to plants in the Directory that are marked with a 'N' to the left of the name. The notes add further information to names which are complex or may be confusing. They start on p.725.

COLLECTORS' REFERENCES

Abbreviations (usually with numbers) following a plant name, refer to the collector(s) of the plant. These abbreviations are expanded, with a collector's name or expedition title, in the section Collectors' References starting on p.731.

A collector's reference may indicate a new, as yet unnamed range of variation within a species; their inclusion in the *RHS Plant Finder* supports the book's role in sourcing unusual plants.

Since the adoption of the *Convention on Biological Diversity* in 1993, collectors are normally required to have prior consent for the acquisition and commercialisation of collected material.

CLASSIFICATION OF GENERA

Genera including a large number of species or with many cultivars are often subdivided into groups, each based on a particular characteristic or combination of characteristics. Colour of flower or fruit and shape of flower are common examples, and, with fruit, whether a cultivar is grown for culinary or dessert purposes. How such groups are named differs from genus to genus.

To help users of the *RHS Plant Finder* find exactly the plants they want, the majority of classifications used within cultivated genera are listed with codes and each species or cultivar is marked with the appropriate code in brackets after its name in the Plant Directory. The codes relating to edible fruits are listed with the more specialised classifications. These apply across several genera. To find the explanation of each code, simply look it up under the genus concerned in the Classification of Genera on p.734.

REVERSE SYNONYMS

It is likely that users of this book will come across names in certain genera which they did not expect to find. This may be because species have been transferred from another genus (or genera). In the list of Reverse Synonyms on p.739, the name on the left hand side is that of an accepted genus to which species have been transferred from the genus on the right. Sometimes all species will have been transferred, but in many cases only a few will be affected. Consulting Reverse Synonyms enables users to find the genera from which species have been transferred. If the right-hand genus is then found in the Plant Directory, the movements of species becomes clear through the cross-references in the nursery-code column.

THE PLANT DIRECTORY

A

Abelia ✿ (Caprifoliaceae)

	biflora <u>new</u> hort.	WWes
	chinensis hort.	see *A.* x *grandiflora*
§	**chinensis** R. Br.	CBcs CPle EBee ECre EPfP MAsh NBlu SMer SPer SPla WFar WHCG WPat WSHC WTel
	dielsii	CPLG CTrw GQui
	'Edward Goucher'	CBcs CDoC CPle EBee ELan ENot EPfP LPan LRHS MGos MHFa MRav NBea NHol SEND SLim SPer SPlb WBod WDin WFar WOld WPat WSHC WWal
	engleriana	CAbP CPLG CPle EBee EPfP SPer WBcn WFar
	floribunda ♀ H3	CBcs CFil CMac CPLG CPle CSBt CSam CTrw CWib ELan EPfP LRHS SIgm SMur SPer SPoG SSta WAbe WBcn WBod WFar WOld WPat
§	x **grandiflora** ♀ H4	More than 30 suppliers
	- **'Aurea'**	see *A.* x *grandiflora* 'Gold Spot'
	- **'Compacta'**	LRHS MAsh WFar
	- Confetti = 'Conti'PBR (v)	More than 30 suppliers
	- dwarf	CDoC
§	- 'Francis Mason' (v)	More than 30 suppliers
§	- 'Gold Spot'	CBcs CDoC CWSG EBee EPfP LHop MAsh MWat SOWG WBrE WLRN WOld WWeb
	- 'Gold Strike'	see *A.* x *grandiflora* 'Gold Spot'
	- 'Goldsport'	see *A.* x *grandiflora* 'Gold Spot'
	- 'Hopleys'PBR (v)	LHop WWeb
	- 'Panache' (v)	CPle
	- 'Prostrata'	WWeb
	- 'Sherwood' <u>new</u>	WPat
	- 'Sunrise' (v)	CAbP CDoC CSBt EBee EHoe ELan EPfP EVFa LRHS MAsh SBod SLim SMur SPer SPla WPat WWeb
	- 'Variegata'	see *A.* x *grandiflora* 'Francis Mason'
	rupestris Lindl.	see *A. chinensis*
	rupestris hort.	see *A.* x *grandiflora*
	schumannii ♀ H4	More than 30 suppliers
	spathulata	WFar
	triflora	CAbP CBot CFil CPLG CPle EBee EPfP LAst LRHS SLon SSta WFar WPat WTel
	zanderi	see *A. dielsii*

Abeliophyllum (Oleaceae)

	distichum	More than 30 suppliers
	- Roseum Group	CBcs CFil CPMA EBee EBre ELan EPfP GBuc GKir LAst LHop LRHS MAsh MRav NSti SBrw SHBN SLon SSpi WPGP

Abelmoschus (Malvaceae)

§	**manihot** CC 3456	CPLG

Abies ✿ (Pinaceae)

	alba	CDul GKir LCon MBar NWea WMou
	- 'Compacta'	CKen
	- 'King's Dwarf'	CKen
	- 'Microphylla'	CKen
	- 'Munsterland'	CKen
	- 'Tortuosa'	CKen
	amabilis	EWTr GKir LCon LRav
	- 'Spreading Star'	LPan NLar
	arizonica	see *A. lasiocarpa* var. *arizonica*
	x **arnoldiana**	MBar
	balsamea	CAgr LCon NWea WEve
	- Hudsonia Group ♀ H4	CDoC CKen CMac EHul GKir IMGH LCon LLin LRHS MAsh MBar MBri MGos MOne NDlv NMen SLim WDin
	- 'Nana'	CKen EBre EHul EOrn GKir LBee LCon LPan LRHS MAsh MBri WDin WStI
	- 'Piccolo'	CKen EHul GKir IMGH SLim WGor
	- 'Prostrata'	ECho EHul LLin LRHS WEve
	- 'Verkade's Prostrate'	CKen
	borisii-regis	LCon
*	- 'Pendula'	CKen
	brachyphylla dwarf	see *A. homolepis* 'Prostrata'
	cephalonica	LCon
	- 'Greg's Broom'	CKen
§	- 'Meyer's Dwarf'	EHul IMGH LCon LLin MAsh MBar SCoo SLim WEve
	- 'Nana'	see *A. cephalonica* 'Meyer's Dwarf'
	concolor ♀ H4	CBcs CDul CTho EHul EMil GKir GWCH LCon LPan LRHS MBar NWea WDin WPat
	- 'Archer's Dwarf'	CKen LCon MGos
I	- 'Argentea'	LCon
	- 'Blue Spreader'	CKen MGos
§	- 'Compacta' ♀ H4	CDoC CKen EOrn GKir IMGH LCon LLin LNet MAsh MBar MGos NLar SCoo SLim SPoG WEve
	- (Lowiana Group) 'Creamy'	CKen
	- 'Fagerhult'	CKen
	- 'Gable's Weeping'	CKen
	- 'Glauca'	see *A. concolor* Violacea Group
	- 'Glauca Compacta'	see *A. concolor* 'Compacta'
§	- 'Hillier's Dwarf'	CKen
	- 'Husky Pup'	CKen
	- Lowiana Group	LCon
	- 'Masonic Broom'	CKen
	- 'Mike Stearn' <u>new</u>	CKen
	- 'Piggelmee'	CKen
*	- 'Swift's Silver'	LBee
§	- Violacea Group	CDoC CKen LCon LLin MAsh MBar
	- 'Wattezii'	CKen LLin

Abromeitiella (Bromeliaceae)

Abrotanella (Asteraceae)

Abutilon ✿ (Malvaceae)

	'Canary Bird' ♀ H2	CBcs CBot CHEx CHal ELan ERea MLan MOak SHBN SYvo WKif WOld
	'Canary Bird' misapplied	see A. 'Golden Fleece'
	'Cannington Carol' (v) ♀ H2	ERea MOak SDys WWol
	'Cannington Peter' (v) ♀ H2	CHal MOak WWol
	'Cannington Sally' (v)	MLan SSte
	'Cannington Sonia' (v)	ERea
	'Cloth of Gold'	LRHS SOWG
	'Cynthia Pike' (v)	LRHS
§	'Feuerglocke'	MOak
	Firebell	see A. 'Feuerglocke'
	'Frances Elizabeth'	LRHS MOak
	globosum	see A. x hybridum
§	'Golden Fleece'	ERea MOak
	'Heather Bennington'	LRHS
	'Helen'	SMrm WWol
	'Henry Makepeace'	LRHS
	'Hinton Seedling'	MOak
§	x hybridum	CHEx
	- 'Savitzii'	see A. 'Savitzii'
	indicum	WPic
	'J. Morris'	LRHS MAsh
	'Kentish Belle' ♀ H2-3	CBcs CHEx CMHG CMac CPle CSev EBee ECot EPfP LRHS MOak SBra SHBN SPer
	'Lemon Queen'	CHal
	'Linda Vista Peach' ♀ H2	MOak
	'Louis Marignac'	MOak
	'Marion' ♀ H2	LRHS MOak SDys SOWG WWol
	'Master Michael'	CMac ERea
	megapotamicum ♀ H3	CBcs CBot CHEx CMHG CPle CRHN CSBt CTrC EBee ELan ENot EPfP EPla ERea GQui LRHS MGos MHer MLan MOak MRav SHBN SMad SOWG SPer SRms WBod WCru WFar WSHC
	- 'Variegatum' (v)	CBcs CBrm CPLG CSBt ELan EPfP GQui IBlr LRHS MAsh MGos MOak SBod SHBN SOWG SPar SPer SSta WFar
	x milleri ♀ H2	CMac CPLG CRHN ELan ERea SHBN SVen WSHC
	- 'Variegatum' (v)	CBcs CHEx CHal CMHG CMac LRHS MOak SEND SHBN
	- 'Ventnor Gold' **new**	SVen
	'Moonchimes' **new**	MOak
	'Nabob' ♀ H2	CHal CTrC ERea LRHS MBri MLan MOak MTis SAga SLdr SOWG SYvo
	'Orange Glow' (v) ♀ H2	MOak
	'Orange Vein'	CHal
	'Patrick Synge'	CMHG CPle EBee ERea LPhx LRHS MOak SOWG SVen
	'Peaches and Cream'	LRHS
§	pictum	ERea SYvo
	- 'Thompsonii' (v)	CHEx CHal ERea MLLN MOak SGar SPar SSte SVen WDyG
	'Pink Lady'	CBcs ERea GQui
	'Red Bells'	GQui MOak SVen
	'Rotterdam'	MOak
§	'Savitzii' (v) ♀ H2	CHal EPfP MOak SOWG SRms SSte SVen
	sellowianum var. marmoratum	ERea
	'Snowfall' **new**	MOak
	'Souvenir de Bonn' (v) ♀ H2	CHal EHol ERea EShb LRHS MLan MOak MTis SAga SMrm SPar SSte
	striatum hort.	see A. pictum
	x suntense	CBcs CHEx CMHG CSBt EPfP ERea LHyd LRHS MWgw NPer SOWG SSta WBod WTel

	- 'Jermyns' ♀ H3	CEnd EPfP LRHS NBur NEgg SPar SSte
	- 'Violetta'	CEnd MAvo
	theophrasti	MSal
	vitifolium	CBcs CBot CDul ECot EPfP ERea ISea MGos MHer NBid NEgg SAga SChu SCro SYvo WKif
	- var. album	CBcs CHEx CMHG CPLG CRHN CTCP EPfP ISea LAst LHyd MAvo MHer SChu SEND SSpi SSta WCru
	- 'Buckland'	CHll
	- 'Ice Blue'	CBot
	- 'Simcox White'	EBee WEas
	- 'Tennant's White' ♀ H3	CAbP CBot ELan EPfP ERea LRHS NBur SOWG WCru
	- 'Veronica Tennant' ♀ H3	ERea MSte SLon WGwG
	'White King' **new**	WWol

Acacia ✿ (Mimosaceae)

	acinacea	SPlb
	adunca	SPlb
	alpina	WCel
	armata	see A. paradoxa
	baileyana ♀ H2	CBcs CSBt CTrC CTrG ECot ELan EMil ERea EShb ESlt GQui IDee ISea LRHS MGol SPar SPlb WPat
	- 'Aurea' **new**	CTrC SPlb
	- 'Purpurea' ♀ H2	CAbb CBcs CBos CDoC CEnd CFil CKno CTbh CTrC CWSG EBee EMil EPfP ERea GQui IDee LHop LRHS MBlu MLan MPre MTis SPar SPer SPlb WFar WMul
	boormanii	CTrC
	cultriformis	ERea
	cyanophylla	see A. saligna
	dealbata ♀ H2	More than 30 suppliers
	- 'Gaulois Astier'	LRHS
*	- subalpina	CCVT LRHS WCel WMul WPGP
	Exeter hybrid	CSBt
	filicifolia	WCel
	floribunda	CTrC
	- 'Lisette'	ELan EPfP LRHS
	frigescens	WCel
	galpinii	WMul
	jonesii	CTrC
	julibrissin	see Albizia julibrissin
	juniperina	see A. ulicifolia
	karroo	CArn WMul
	kybeanensis	CTrC WCel
	longifolia	CAbb CBcs CHEx EBee IDee SPar SPer SRms
	macradenia	SPlb
	maidenii	MGol
	mearnsii	WCel WMul
	melanoxylon	CDul CTrC ISea LRHS WCel WHer
	motteana	ECot ERea
	obliquinervia	WCel
§	paradoxa ♀ H2	CTrC EHol LRHS
	pataczekii	ENot EPfP ERea SSpi
	podalyriifolia	CDoC CFil IDee WPGP
	pravissima ♀ H2-3	More than 30 suppliers
	retinodes ♀ H2	CBcs CDoC CPle CTrC EBee ELan EPfP ERea GQui IDee LRav SEND WCFE WMul
	riceana	CTrC CTrG GQui IDee LEdu LRav SPar WPat
	rivalis	ERea
	rubida	LPan WCel WMul
§	saligna	CAbb CTrC EBee EShb LRHS
	senegal	ELau
	sentis	see A. victoriae
	sophorae	CTrC

	spectabilis	SPlb
	suaveolens	SPlb
§	ulicifolia	CPLG CSBt CTrG
	verticillata	CTrG
§	victoriae	ERea
	xanthophloea	WMul

Acaena (Rosaceae)

	adscendens misapplied	see A. affinis
	adscendens hort.	see A. magellanica subsp. magellanica, A. saccaticupula 'Blue Haze'
	adscendens Vahl	see A. magellanica subsp. laevigata
	- 'Glauca'	CMdw EMan NBir NFor SBla
§	affinis	COIW ECha SDix
	anserinifolia hort.	see A. novae-zelandiae
§	anserinifolia Druce	ECha GGar MGGn MWod NHol WPer WWin
	buchananii	CTri EBee EDAr EGoo EPot GGar GTou MBar MBri MLLN NBro NFor NMGW SRms WCom WPer
	caerulea	see A. caesiiglauca
§	caesiiglauca	CTri GAbr GGar GTou NBid NFor NLon NMRc SBla SCro SGar SVal WCom WEas WHoo WPer
	caespitosa new	EBee
	fissistipula	EHoe GGar WHer
	glabra	MGGn
	glaucophylla	see A. magellanica subsp. magellanica
	'Greencourt Hybrid'	CLyd
	inermis	CLyd EBee EPot GTou MLLN NFla NLAp SPlb WCom WPer
	- 'Purpurea' new	FShb WHoo
§	magellanica	GTou NLon WWin WWpP
	subsp. laevigata	
§	- subsp. magellanica	GTou LEdu MGGn
	microphylla ♀ H4	EBee EBre ECha ESis LBee LRHS MBar MBri MSPs MWat NMen SDes SHFr SIng SPlb SRms SVal WAbe WCer WPer
	- Copper Carpet	see A. microphylla 'Kupferteppich'
	- 'Glauca'	see A. caesiiglauca
§	- 'Kupferteppich'	EBee EHoe EMan GGar GKir MBri MBro MRav MWgw NCat NVic SIng WBea WCom WPat WPer WWpP
	- 'Pewter Carpet'	EGoo
	- 'Pulchella'	EBre FMan LRHS MTdf
	myriophylla	EBee ECho EDAr EGoo EMFP MGGn WPer
§	novae-zelandiae	CTri EBee GGar GTou MGGn SDix SIng WCom WPer
	ovalifolia	CRow EBee EDAr GTou NLAp
	'Pewter'	see A. saccaticupula 'Blue Haze'
	pinnatifida	GTou NBro WPer
	profundeincisa	see A. anserinifolia Druce
	'Purple Carpet'	see A. microphylla 'Kupferteppich'
	saccaticupula	MWgw
§	- 'Blue Haze'	CLyd EBee ECha EDAr EPot GGar GKir GTou LRHS MBar MBro MLLN NChi NPer NVic SIng SPar SPer SPlb SRms WCom WFar WHoo WMoo WPer
	sanguisorbae	see A. anserinifolia Druce
	viridior	see A. anserinifolia Druce

Acalypha (Euphorbiaceae)

| | hispaniolae ♀ H1 | ERea ESlt MOak |
| | hispida ♀ H1 | LRHS MBri |

| | pendula | see A. reptans |
| § | reptans | CHal SPet |

Acanthocalyx see Morina

Acantholimon (Plumbaginaceae)

	new	EMan
	androsaceum	see A. ulicinum
	glumaceum	MDHE MWat NMen WPat
	litvinovii	WLin
§	ulicinum	ECho EPot
	venustum var. venustum	SOkd

Acanthopanax see Eleutherococcus

| | ricinifolium | see Kalopanax septemlobus |
| | sessiliflorus new | GIBF |

Acanthostachys (Bromeliaceae)

| | pitcairnioides new | EMan |

Acanthus ✿ (Acanthaceae)

	balcanicus	see A. hungaricus
	caroli-alexandri	EBlw WHil
	dioscoridis	EBlw LPhx WSel
	- var. perringii	CRDP EBee LPio MSph MSte NChi SBla SIgm SSte WCot WFar WHil WPGP WSel WViv
	- smooth-leaved	SIgm
	hirsutus	EBlw EMar EMon LPhx MAnH MMil SCro SIgm SVal WCot WHil
	- JCA 109.700	MSph SBla
	- f. roseus	SBla SIgm WFar
	- subsp. syriacus	EHrv EMon MAnH
	- - JCA 106.500	LPhy
§	hungaricus	More than 30 suppliers
	- AL&JS 90097YU	EBlw EMon WHil
	- 'Architect' new	LRHS
	longifolius	see A. hungaricus
	mollis	More than 30 suppliers
	- 'Feilding Gold'	see A. mollis 'Hollard's Gold'
	- free-flowering	GCal
	- 'Hollard's Gold'	CBct CFir CHad CKno CRDP CWes EBee EBlw EFou EMan EPPr GBin GCal LPio MAnH MAvo MBri MLLN MTed NPro SDix SIgm SUsu SWat WCom WCot WFar WHil WSel
	- 'Jcffalbus' new	EBlw EMon WHil
	- Latifolius Group	CMGP EBee EBlw EFou EMan EPfP LRHS MRav MSte SClu SDes SPer SRms WCom WHil WHoo WWal
	- 'Pride of Morvan' (v) new	WCot
	- 'Summerdance' new	LHop
	'Rue Ledan'	LPhx MAnH
	sennii new	SIgm
	spinosus ♀ H4	More than 30 suppliers
	- 'Lady Moore' (v)	EBlw EMon IBlr MAvo WCot WHil
	- 'Royal Haughty'	EFou
	- Spinosissimus Group	CBct CMHG EBee EBlw ECha EHrv ELan EMan EOrc GCal LPhx LPio MMil MRav SAga SBla SMad SPar SWat WCot WFar WHil WMnd WSel
	'Summer Beauty' new	WCot
	syriacus	CPom EBlw EMan GCal NLar NPro SAga SVal WHil WViv

Acca (Myrtaceae)

| | sellowiana (F) | CArn CBcs CBrm CDoC CDul CMHG CPle CTrG CWSG EBee |

ELan EPfP ERea ERom GEil GQui
IDee LPan LRHS MCCP MWat
NPSI SLim SOWG SPar SSte WSHC

	- 'Apollo' (F)	CTrC EREa
	- 'Coolidge' (F)	EREa
	- 'Mammoth' (F)	CBcs EREa
	- 'Triumph' (F)	CBcs EREa
	- 'Variegata' (F/v)	EPfP LAst

Acer ❀ (Aceraceae)

	B&SWJ 6024	WHCr
	B&SWJ 6245	WHCr
	B&SWJ 6341	WHCr
	B&SWJ 6373	WHCr
	acuminatum	CMCN WNor
	argutum	CMCN IMGH WCwm WNor
	barbinerve	CMCN EPfP WNor
	buergerianum	CBcs CDul CMCN CPMA ECrN GKir IMGH LRHS MBri STre WCwm WDin WNor
	- 'Goshiki-kaede' (v)	CPMA LNet
	- 'Integrifolium'	see *A. buergerianum* 'Subintegrum'
	- 'Mino-yatsubusa'	WWes
	- 'Mitsubatō-kaede' **new**	WWes
	- 'Miyasama-yatsubusa' **new**	WWes
	- 'Naruto'	CMCN
§	- 'Subintegrum'	CMCN
	- 'Tanchô'	LNet
*	- 'Variegatum' (v)	CMCN
	calcaratum	CMCN
*	*campbelii* var. *fansipanense*	WCru
	B&SWJ 8270 **new**	
	campbellii	LNet
	- subsp. *flabellatum* var. *yunnanense*	CFil
	- subsp. *sinense*	see *A. sinense*
	- subsp. *wilsonii*	see *A. wilsonii*
	campestre ♀ H4	More than 30 suppliers
	- 'Carnival' (v)	CBcs CDul CEnd CMCN CPMA CTho CWib EBee GKir LNet LRHS MAsh MBlu MBri MGos NHol SMad SPer WPGP
	- 'Elsrijk'	CLnd MHFa
	- 'Evenley Red'	MBlu
	- 'Nanum'	WWes
	- 'Pendulum'	CEnd CTho GKir
	- 'Postelense'	CEnd CMCN CPMA GKir LNet MBlu SLim SSpi
	- 'Pulverulentum' (v)	CDoC CEnd CMCN CPMA GKir LNet SLim SMad SPar SSta WBcn
	- 'Queen Elizabeth'	CCVT MHFa
	- 'Red Shine'	MGos
	- 'Royal Ruby'	CMCN CPMA CTho GKir LNet SKee SLim SSta WWes
*	- 'Ruby Glow'	CDoC CEnd CLnd GKir LRHS SPer
	- 'Schwerinii'	CMCN
	- 'Silver Celebration' (v)	CPMA
	- 'William Caldwell'	CEnd CTho GKir LRHS
	capillipes	GKir SLim SSpi SSta
	'Candy Stripe'	
	cappadocicum	CMCN CSam LRHS MDun MLan NBea NWea WDin WNor WWes
	- 'Aureum' ♀ H4	More than 30 suppliers
	- var. *mono*	see *A. pictum*
	- 'Rubrum' ♀ H4	CDul CLnd CMCN ECrN ENot EPfP GKir LBuc LNet LPan LRHS MBlu MGos MHFa MRav SKee SLim SPer WDin WHer
	- subsp. *sinicum*	CFil CMCN EPfP
	carpinifolium	CBrd CMCN CTho LNet SSpi WNor WWes

	- B&SWJ 5086	WHCr
	catalpifolium	see *A. longipes* subsp. *catalpifolium*
§	*caudatifolium*	CFil CMCN CPle EBee WPGP
	- B&SWJ 3531	WCru
	- B&SWJ 6734	WCru WHCr
	- B&SWJ 6761	WHCr
§	aff. *caudatifolium* CC 1744	WHCr
§	*caudatum*	SSpi
	- subsp. *ukurunduense*	CMCN GIBF WNor
	cinnamomifolium	see *A. coriaceifolium*
	circinatum	CBcs CDoC CDul CMCN CPMA CSam EPfP GGGa IDee LNet MLan NBea NFor NHol NLar SHBN SSpi SSta WDin WFar WNor
	- 'Little Gem'	CPMA LNet
	- 'Monroe'	CMCN LNet WWes
	cissifolium	CBcs CDoC CFil CMCN CTho EPfP EPla IArd IMGH WNor WPGP
	x *conspicuum* 'Candy Stripe'	CPMA
	- 'Elephant's Ear'	CPMA EPfP
I	- 'Phoenix'	CEnd CMCN CPMA CTho EPfP GKir LNet LRHS MBlu MBri NLar SSpi
	- 'Silver Cardinal'	see *A.* 'Silver Cardinal'
§	- 'Silver Vein'	CDoC CMCN CPMA EBee EPfP GKir LNet LRHS NLar SSpi SSta
§	*coriaceifolium*	WNor
	crataegifolium	CMCN IMGH WNor
	- 'Veitchii' (v)	CDoC CLnd CMCN CPMA EPfP GKir LNet SSpi WBcn WPGP
	creticum	see *A. sempervirens*
	dasycarpum	see *A. saccharinum*
	davidii	More than 30 suppliers
	- 'Ernest Wilson'	CBcs CDul CMCN LRHS MBlu
	- 'George Forrest' ♀ H4	CBcs CDoC CDul CMCN CTho CWSG EBee ECrN ELan EPfP GKir LPan LRHS MBlu MBri MGos NBea NWea SBod SEND SKee SLim SPer WDin
	- 'Karmen'	CPMA GKir LRHS MBri
	- 'Madeline Spitta'	CMCN
	- 'Rosalie'	EPfP GKir LRHS MBlu MBri WWes
	- 'Serpentine' ♀ H4	CBcs CDoC CEnd CMCN CPMA CTho EPfP GKir LRHS MBlu MBri NLar SSpi WOrn
	- 'Silver Vein'	see *A.* x *conspicuum* 'Silver Vein'
	diabolicum	CMCN
	- f. *purpurascens* **new**	GIBF
	divergens	CMCN
	elegantulum	CMCN WCwm WNor
	erianthum	CDul CLnd CPne SSpi SSta WNor
	fabri	CBcs CMCN WNor
	flabellatum	see *A. campbellii* subsp. *flabellatum*
§	*forrestii*	CDul CMCN CTho EPfP NBea NHol WNor
	- 'Alice'	CBcs CDul CEnd CLnd CMCN CPMA LNet MBlu SSpi SSta WBcn WWes
	- 'Sirene'	CPMA MGos
§	- 'Sparkling'	CPMA GKir LRHS WWes
	x *freemanii* **new**	CMCN
	- 'Armstrong'	LNet WFar
	- Autumn Blaze = 'Jeffersred'	CCVT CDoC CDul CLnd EPfP MBlu SKee SMad WDin WFar
	- 'Autumn Fantasy'	GKir LNet MBlu
	- Indian Summer = 'Morgan'	CEnd CLnd GKir
	fulvescens	see *A. longipes*
	ginnala	see *A. tataricum* subsp. *ginnala*

glabrum	CMCN WNor
globosum	see *A. platanoides* 'Globosum'
grandidentatum	see *A. saccharum* subsp. *grandidentatum*
griseum ♀ H4	More than 30 suppliers
grosseri	CBcs CDul CMCN CTri GKir IArd NEgg WLRN
- var. *hersii* ♀ H4	CCVT CDoC CDul CFil CLnd CPLG CTho CWib EBee ECrN ENot EPfP ESis GGGa GKir IFro LRHS MBri MDun MHFa MRav NBea NWea SLim SPer WCwm WDin WGer WNor
- 'Leiden'	MBlu
heldreichii	CMCN EPfP
henryi	CDul CLnd CMCN ENot EPfP LNet MAsh WCwm WNor
hookeri	CMCN
hyrcanum	CMCN
japonicum	CDul CMCN LNet LRHS MBar NHol SSta WNor
- B&SWJ 5950	WCru
§ - 'Aconitifolium' ♀ H4	More than 30 suppliers
- 'Attaryi'	CMCN WWes
- 'Aureum'	see *A. shirasawanum* 'Aureum'
- 'Ezo-no-momiji'	see *A. shirasawanum* 'Ezo-no-momiji'
- 'Filicifolium'	see *A. japonicum* 'Aconitifolium'
- 'Green Cascade'	CEnd CMCN CPMA ECho WPGP WPat WWes
- 'Laciniatum'	see *A. japonicum* 'Aconitifolium'
- f. *microphyllum*	see *A. shirasawanum* 'Microphyllum'
- 'Ogurayama'	see *A. shirasawanum* 'Ogurayama'
- 'Ô-isami'	CMCN GKir LNet
- 'Ô-taki'	ECho
- 'Vitifolium' ♀ H4	CDoC CEnd CMCN CPMA CSBt ELan EPfP GKir LNet LPan LRHS MAsh NPSI NPal SPar SPer SReu SSpi SSta WPat WWeb
kawakamii	see *A. caudatifolium*
laevigatum	CMCN
laxiflorum	SSta
lobelii Bunge	see *A. turkestanicum*
lobelii Tenore	CLnd CTho NRog
§ *longipes*	CMCN WBcn
§ - subsp. *catalpifolium*	CMCN
macrophyllum	CFil CMCN CTho EPfP IDee ISca LHyd SMad
mandschuricum	CBcs CPMA EPfP IArd LNet MBlu WCwm WDin WNor
§ *maximowiczianum*	CBcs CMCN CSam CTho ELan GIBF LNet LPan SSpi SSta WFar WNor WWes
maximowiczii	CMCN ECrN LRHS NWea WNor
§ *metcalfii*	WNor
micranthum	CFil CMCN EPfP EPla GKir IMGH MBlu MDun SSpi WNor WPGP WWes
miyabei	WBod
mono	see *A. pictum*
monspessulanum	CDul CFil CMCN
morrisonense	see *A. caudatifolium*
negundo	CCVT CDul CLnd CMCN CTho CWib ECrN ENot MHFa NWea SCrf WNor WOrn
- IDS 2000	WHCr
- 'Argenteovariegatum'	see *A. negundo* 'Variegatum'
- 'Auratum'	CMCN MBar WDin WPat
- 'Aureomarginatum' (v) **new**	LBuc
- 'Aureovariegatum' (v)	CBcs MBar SHBN

- subsp. *californicum*	WNor
§ - 'Elegans' (v)	CDul CEnd CLnd CMCN COtt EBee EBre ECrN ENot EPfP LPan LRHS MHFa NHol SHBN SKee SPer
- 'Elegantissimum'	see *A. negundo* 'Elegans'
- 'Flamingo' (v)	More than 30 suppliers
- 'Kelly's Gold'	CBcs CTho CWSG EBee ENot LRHS MAsh MDun MGos MHFa SCoo SKee SLim SPoG WOrn WWeb
§ - 'Variegatum' (v)	CBcs CLnd EBee ECrN ENot LAst LPan LRHS MHFa NBea NWea SPar SPer WDin WFar
- var. *violaceum*	CBcs CEnd CMCN WBcn WWes
nikoense	see *A. maximowiczianum*
oblongum	CMCN
okomotoanum	CMCN
oliverianum	CFil EPfP ESis WNor WPGP
- subsp. *formosanum*	WCru
B&SWJ 6773 **new**	
- - HWJ 628	WCru
opalus	CMCN SSpi WCwm
orientale	see *A. sempervirens*
'Pacific Sunset'	GKir LRHS MBri
palmatum	CDul CMCN CMHG CTho CWib EBee ENot EPfP GIBF LHyr LNet LRHS MBar MBlu MBro MLan NBlu NWea SBrw SHBN SPar SPer SSpi SSta STre WFar WHar WOrn WPat WTel
- B&SWJ 4474	WCru
§ - 'Aka Shigitatsusawa'	CMCN CMac CPMA GKir LNet MAsh MGos SSpi WFar WPat WWeb
§ - 'Akaji-nishiki'	LRHS MAsh MBri
- 'Akane'	LNet
- 'Akegarasu'	CMCN LNet MAsh WWeb WWes
- 'Aôba-jo'	CMCN CPMA WWes
- 'Aoshime-no-uchi'	see *A. palmatum* 'Shinobugaoka'
- 'Aoyagi'	CEnd CMCN CPMA GKir LAst LNet LRHS MAsh NHol WFoF WPat WWes
§ - 'Arakawa'	CEnd CMCN ECho GKir LNet SPar
- 'Aratama'	CMCN CPMA WPat
- 'Ariadne' (v)	CPMA GKir NLar WWes
- 'Ariake-nomura' **new**	WWes
- 'Asahi-zuru' (v)	CBcs CMCN CPMA EBee ECho GKir LNet LPan MGos NHol NLar NPSI SPer WFar WFoF WWes
- 'Atrolincarc'	LNet WPat
- f. *atropurpureum*	More than 30 suppliers
- 'Atropurpureum'	CSBt CTri CWib EBee SPer
- 'Attraction'	CMCN CMac CTho MBri MDun WWes
- 'Aureum'	CMCN CWib ECho EPfP GKir LNet NLar SCoo SSpi WFar
- Autumn Glory Group	CEnd CPMA SSpi WWes
* - 'Autumn Red'	LPan LRHS
* - 'Autumn Showers'	CEnd CPMA
- 'Azuma-murasaki'	CMCN CPMA WWes
* - 'Beni K Sport'	CPMA
- 'Beni-chidori'	ECho
- 'Beni-fushigi' **new**	WWes
- 'Beni-gasa' **new**	CPMA
- 'Beni-hime'	CPMA
- 'Beni-kagami'	CEnd CMCN CPMA GKir LNet MBlu MGos WWes
- 'Beni-kawa'	GKir LNet SSpi WWes
- 'Beni-komachi'	CBcs CEnd CMCN CMac CPMA ECho GKir LNet LRHS MAsh WPat WWeb
- 'Beni-maiko'	CEnd CMCN CPMA EBee GKir LNet LRHS WPGP WPat WWes
- 'Beni-otake'	CBcs CMCN CPMA ECho LNet LRHS MAsh MGos NPSI SPer

	- 'Beni-schichihenge' (v)	CEnd CMCN CPMA CWSG EPfP GKir LNet LRHS MAsh NHol SCoo SMur SSta WPGP WPat WWeb
	- 'Beni-shidare Variegated' (v)	CMCN CPMA LNet
	- 'Beni-shigitatsu-sawa'	see *A. palmatum* 'Aka Shigitatsusawa'
	- 'Beni-tsukasa' (v)	CEnd CPMA ECho GKir LNet LPan LRHS MAsh SSpi WPGP WPat WWes
	- 'Berry Dwarf'	WPat
	- 'Bloodgood' ♀ H4	More than 30 suppliers
	- 'Bonfire'	see *A. palmatum* 'Akaji-nishiki'
	- 'Brocade'	CMCN WPat WWes
	- 'Burgundy Lace' ♀ H4	CBcs CDoC CEnd CMCN CPMA CWib EMil GKir LNet LRHS MAsh MBlu MBri MGos NHol NPSI SPar SPer WFar WPat
	- 'Butterfly' (v)	CBcs CDoC CDul CEnd CFil CMCN CPMA CWSG CWib EBre EPfP GKir LNet LPan LRHS MBar MGos NBea NHol SLdr SLim SPar SRPl SReu SSta WDin WFar WStI WWeb
	- 'Carminium'	see *A. palmatum* 'Corallinum'
	- 'Charlotte'	LNet
	- 'Chirimen-nishiki' (v)	CMCN LNet
	- 'Chishio'	see *A. palmatum* 'Shishio'
	- 'Chishio Improved'	see *A. palmatum* 'Shishio Improved'
	- 'Chitoseyama' ♀ H4	CDoC CEnd CMCN CPMA EPfP GKir LNet LRHS MBar MBri MGos NLar SCoo SLim SMur SSpi SSta WPat WWeb
	- 'Coonara Pygmy'	CMCN CPMA ECho LNet MAsh WFar WPat WWes
	- 'Coral Pink'	CPMA WWes
§	- 'Corallinum'	CBcs CEnd CMCN CPMA GKir LNet MGos SSpi WPat
N	- var. ***coreanum***	CMCN CSam WNor
N	- - B&SWJ 4474	WCru
N	- - 'Korean Gem'	ECho MAsh
	- 'Crippsii'	ECho EMil LRHS MAsh SCoo SPer WFar WWeb WWes
	- 'Deshôjô'	CBcs CMCN LNet LPan MBar MBlu MGos NHol SPar
	- 'Diana' **new**	WWes
	- var. ***dissectum*** ♀ H4	CDoC CEnd CWSG CWib EBee ENot EPfP GKir LBuc LHyd LRHS MBar MBri MGos NBee NHol NWea SBrw SHBN SLim SPar SReu WCFE WDin WFar WNor WPat WStI
	- - 'Ao-shidare' **new**	WWes
	- - 'Baby Lace' **new**	CPMA
	- - 'Baldsmith'	CPMA
	- - 'Berrima Bridge' **new**	CPMA
	- - 'Crimson Queen' ♀ H4	CBcs CDoC CDul CEnd CMCN CPMA CWSG CWib EPfP GKir LNet LPan LRHS MAsh MBar MBri MBro MDun MGos NHol SPar SPer SSta WDin WFar WGer WNor WPat WStI
	- - Dissectum Atropurpureum Group	More than 30 suppliers
	- - - 'Pink Filigree'	LPan WWes
	- - 'Dissectum Flavescens'	CEnd CMCN CMac CPMA MBlu
§	- - 'Dissectum Nigrum'	CPMA CWSG LNet LPan LRHS MGos NBea NHol SSpi WLRN WPat
	- - 'Dissectum Palmatifidum'	LNet LRHS NPSI WFar
	- - 'Dissectum Rubrifolium'	CMCN WWes

§	- - 'Dissectum Variegatum' (v)	CPMA EPfP LNet LRHS SSta
	- - Dissectum Viride Group	CBcs CDul CMCN CPMA CWSG EBee ELan EMui EPfP LNet LPan LRHS MAsh MBro MDun NBea NBlu NPSI NPri SBrw SLim SPar SPer SPla SSta WBod WFar WOrn WWeb
	- - 'Green Globe'	LPan LRHS NLar WWes
	- - 'Green Lace'	LPan NLar
	- - 'Green Mist'	CPMA WWes
	- - 'Inaba-shidare' ♀ H4	CBcs CDoC CEnd CMCN COtt CPMA CWib EBee EMil ENot EPfP GKir IMGH LNet LPan LRHS MAsh MBar MBri MGos NHol SPar SPer SReu SSta WGer WPGP WPat WWeb
*	- - 'Lionheart'	CPMA ECho EMil LNet LRHS MGos NPSI SCoo WFar WWeb
	- - 'Octopus'	CPMA
	- - 'Orangeola'	CPMA LNet WPat WWes
	- - 'Ornatum'	CDoC CMCN COtt CWib EBee ECho IMGH LNet LPan MBar MGos NBea NEgg SBrw SCoo SPar SPer WDin WFar WGer WHar
	- - 'Red Autumn Lace' **new**	WWes
	- - 'Sunset'	CMCN CPMA MDun WPat
	- - 'Watnong' **new**	CPMA
	- - 'Zaaling'	CPMA ECho
	- 'Dragon's Fire'	EMui MDun
	- 'Eddisbury'	CPMA MGos SSta WBod WPat WWes
	- 'Edna Bergman'	CPMA
	- 'Effegi'	see *A. palmatum* 'Fireglow'
	- 'Eimini' **new**	WWes
	- 'Elegans'	ECho EPfP WDin
	- 'Ellen' **new**	WPat WWes
	- 'Enkan' **new**	CPMA WPat WWes
	- 'Ever Red'	see *A. palmatum* var. *dissectum* 'Dissectum Nigrum'
	- 'Fall's Fire' **new**	CPMA
	- 'Filigree' (v)	CDoC CMCN CPMA EPfP GKir LNet LRHS MGos SSpi WPat
	- 'Fior d'Arancio'	CPMA WWes
§	- 'Fireglow'	CDoC CEnd CMCN CPMA CWib ECho EMil LPan LRHS MGos NEgg SCoo WFar WPGP WPat WWeb WWes
	- 'Fjeilheim'	CPMA
	- 'Frederici Guglielmi'	see *A. palmatum* var. *dissectum* 'Dissectum Variegatum'
	- 'Garnet' ♀ H4	More than 30 suppliers
	- 'Ôgon-sarasa'	CPMA
	- 'Golden Pond' **new**	WWes
	- 'Goshiki-kotohime' (v)	CMCN CPMA
	- 'Goshiki-shidare' (v)	CEnd CPMA LNet WWeb
	- 'Green Trompenburg'	CMCN LNet WWes
§	- 'Hagoromo'	CDoC CMCN ECho LNet NPSI SPer WFar
	- 'Harusame' (v)	LNet
	- 'Hazeroino' (v)	CMCN
	- 'Helena' **new**	WWes
	- var. ***heptalobum***	CMCN
§	- 'Heptalobum Elegans'	CMCN LRHS MBlu SHBN SSpi
§	- 'Heptalobum Elegans Purpureum'	see *A. palmatum* 'Hessei'
§	- 'Hessei'	CEnd CMCN ECho GKir LNet LRHS MAsh MBlu WWes
	- 'Higasayama' (v)	CBcs CDoC CEnd CMCN CPMA GKir LNet LRHS MAsh MGos NHol WPGP WPat WWeb WWes
	- 'Hôgyoku'	CMCN CPMA

	- 'Hupp's Dwarf' **new**	WWes
	- 'Ichigyôji'	CDul CEnd CMCN CPMA LRHS MAsh WPGP WWeb
	- 'Improved Shishio'	see *A. palmatum* 'Shishio Improved'
	- 'Inazuma'	CBcs CDoC CMCN ECho MGos WWes
	- 'Japanese Sunrise' **new**	WWes
	- 'Jirô-shidare'	EPfP LNet LRHS MAsh WWeb
	- 'Junihitoe'	see *A. shirasawanum* 'Jûnihitoe'
	- 'Kaba' **new**	WWes
§	- 'Kagiri-nishiki' (v)	CDul CMCN CPMA CWSG ECho LNet LRHS MAsh MGos NHol SCoo SPer WFar WNor
	- 'Kamagata'	CDoC CEnd CMCN CPMA EPfP GKir MAsh MGos NPSI SSta WPGP WPat WWeb
	- 'Kandy Kitchen' **new**	WWes
	- 'Karaori-nishiki' (v)	ECho LNet MBlu
	- 'Karasugawa' (v)	CMCN CPMA LNet
	- 'Kasagiyama'	CEnd CMCN COtt CPMA LRHS WPGP
	- 'Kasen-nishiki'	ECho
	- 'Kashima'	CEnd CMCN CPMA ECho LRHS MBNS WWes
	- 'Katja' **new**	WWes
	- 'Katsura' ♀ H4	CBcs CDoC CEnd CMCN COtt CPMA ELan EPfP GKir LPan MAsh MBlu MBri MGos NBlu NHol SPer SPla SSpi SSta WFar WNor WStI WWeb
	- 'Ki-hachijô'	CMCN CPMA
	- 'Kingsville Variegated' (v) **new**	WWes
	- 'Kinran'	CMCN ECho GKir LNet LRHS MAsh WPat WWeb
	- 'Kinshi'	CEnd CMCN CPMA GKir LNet LRHS MAsh SSta WPat WWeb WWes
	- 'Kiri-nishiki'	CMCN CPMA ECho
	- 'Kiyohime'	CDoC CMCN ECho GKir MBlu WPat
	- 'Ko-chidori' **new**	WWes
	- 'Komache-hime'	CPMA
	- 'Komaru' **new**	NLar
	- 'Komon-nishiki' (v)	CPMA
	- 'Koriba' **new**	NLar
§	- 'Koshimino'	CPMA LPan
	- 'Kotohime'	CMCN CPMA NLar WWes
	- 'Koto-Ito-komachi'	CEnd CPMA ECho NLar WPat
	- 'Koto-no-ito'	CMCN LNet NLar
	- 'Kurabu-yama'	CMCN
	- 'Kurui-jishi'	LNet WPat
	- 'Linearilobum'	CDoC EPfP GKir LHyd LNet MBlu NBea NHol NLar WNor WPat
	- 'Linearilobum Atropurpureum'	LRHS WNor
	- 'Little Princess'	see *A. palmatum* 'Mapi-no-machihime'
	- 'Lutescens'	CMCN ECho
	- 'Mai Mori' (v) **new**	WWes
	- 'Maiko'	CDul CMCN ECho
	- 'Mama'	CMCN WWes
§	- 'Mapi-no-machihime'	CDoC CEnd CMCN CPMA ELan GKir LNet LRHS MAsh NHol SMur WPGP WPat WWeb WWes
	- 'Marjan' **new**	WWes
	- 'Masamurasaki'	WPat
	- 'Masukagami' (v)	CEnd CPMA
	- 'Matsugae' (v) **new**	MAsh
	- 'Matsukaze'	CMCN COtt CPMA GKir WWes
	- 'Melanie'	SSpi
*	- 'Mikasayama'	GKir MAsh WWeb
	- 'Mikawa-yatsubusa'	CMCN CPMA ECho LRHS NBhm WPat WWes

	- 'Mini Mondo' **new**	WWes
	- 'Mirte'	LNet
	- 'Mizuho-beni'	CPMA
	- 'Mizu-kuguri'	CMCN WPat
	- 'Momenshide'	WPat
	- 'Momoiro-koya-san'	WPat
	- 'Mon Papa'	CPMA WWes
	- 'Monzukushi'	CMCN CPMA
	- 'Moonfire'	CDoC CMCN CPMA EPfP GKir LNet LRHS MAsh SSpi WWeb
	- 'Murasaki-kiyohime'	CMCN CPMA ECho WPat
	- 'Mure-hibari'	CMCN CPMA
	- 'Murogawa'	CMCN
	- 'Nathan' **new**	WWes
	- 'Nicholsonii'	CMCN LRHS MBri WPat WWes
	- 'Nigrum' ♀ H4	CMCN LNet WPat
§	- 'Nishiki-gawa'	CEnd CMCN CPMA GKir LNet WPGP
	- 'Nishiki-momiji'	WWeb
	- 'Nomurishidare' misapplied	see *A. palmatum* 'Shôjô-shidare'
	- 'Nomurishidare' Wada	SSpi
	- 'Nuresagi'	CEnd CMCN CPMA LNet
	- 'Ogi Nagashi' (v) **new**	WWes
	- 'Ô-kagami'	CDoC CEnd CMCN CPMA ECho GKir LNet MGos SBod SSta
	- 'Okina' **new**	WWes
	- 'Okukuji-nishiki'	CPMA LNet MAsh WWeb
	- 'Okushimo'	CDoC CEnd CMCN CPMA LNet LRHS NHol NLar WPGP WPat
	- 'Omato'	LNet
	- 'Omurayama'	CDoC CEnd CMCN CPMA ECho EPfP LNet MAsh MGos NBhm NLar SCoo SSta WPat WWeb WWes
§	- 'Ô-nishiki'	CMCN CWib LNet
	- 'Orange Dream'	CEnd CMCN CPMA GKir LNet LPan LRHS MAsh MBlu NLar SCoo WPat WWeb WWes
	- 'Oregon Sunset'	CDul CMCN
	- 'Orido-nishiki' (v)	CBcs CEnd CMCN CPMA ELan EPfP LNet LRHS MAsh MBar MBlu MGos NBea NBee NBlu NEgg SCoo SPar SRPl SSta WWeb
	- 'Ôsakazuki' ♀ H4	More than 30 suppliers
	- 'Ôshio-beni'	CPMA ECho MAsh WWes
	- 'Ôshû-beni'	CMCN
	- 'Ôshû-shidare'	CMCN CPMA WPat
	- 'Oto-hime' **new**	WWes
	- 'Otome-zakura'	CMCN
	- 'Peaches and Cream' (v)	CPMA
	- 'Pendulum Julian'	CMCN
	- 'Pine Bark Maple'	see *A. palmatum* 'Nishiki gawa'
	- 'Pixie'	CMCN CPMA
	- var. **pubescens** B&SWJ 6886 **new**	WCru
	- 'Red Dragon'	CBcs CDoC CPMA ECho LNet LRHS MGos NPSI WPat WWeb
	- 'Red Filigree Lace'	CEnd CMCN CPMA ECho EPfP GKir LNet LRHS MBlu SSta WPat LPan LRIIS
	- 'Red Flash'	
	- 'Red Pygmy' ♀ H4	CBcs CDoC CEnd CMCN COtt CPMA CSam CWib EMil GKir LNet LRHS MAsh MBar MBri MGos NBea NBee SCoo SMur SPer SSpi SSta WFar WPat WWeb
	- 'Red Select' **new**	MGos
	- 'Reticulatum'	see *A. palmatum* 'Shigitatsu-sawa'
	- 'Ribesifolium'	see *A. palmatum* 'Shishigashira'
	- 'Roseomarginatum'	see *A. palmatum* 'Kagiri-nishiki'
	- 'Rough Bark Maple'	see *A. palmatum* 'Arakawa'
	- 'Rubrum'	CMCN
	- 'Rufescens'	CMCN

	Name	Suppliers
	– 'Ryoku-ryu' **new**	WWes
	– 'Ryuzu'	CPMA
	– 'Sagara-nishiki' (v)	CEnd CMCN CPMA ECho
	– 'Samidare'	CMCN CPMA
	– 'Sandra' **new**	WWes
N	– 'Sango-kaku' ♀ H4	More than 30 suppliers
	– 'Saoshika'	CMCN CPMA
	– 'Satsuki-beni' **new**	WWes
	– 'Sazanami'	CEnd CMCN CPMA WNor
	– 'Scolopendriifolium'	WPat
	– 'Seigen'	CEnd CMCN ECho WPat
	– 'Seiryû' ♀ H4	More than 30 suppliers
	– 'Seiun Kaku' **new**	WWes
	– 'Sekimori'	CMCN CPMA WWes
	– 'Sekka-yatsubusa'	CMCN
	– 'Senkaki'	see A. palmatum 'Sango-kaku'
	– 'Septemlobum Elegans'	see A. palmatum 'Heptalobum Elegans'
	– 'Septemlobum Purpureum'	see A. palmatum 'Hessei'
	– 'Sessilifolium' dwarf	see A. palmatum 'Hagoromo'
	– 'Sessilifolium' tall	see A. palmatum 'Koshimino'
	– 'Shaina'	CBcs CPMA LNet LPan MAsh MDun NBhm WFar WPat
	– 'Sharp's Pygmy'	WWes
	– 'Sherwood Flame'	CMCN CPMA CWib LNet LRHS MAsh MBlu MBri MGos NLar WPat
	– 'Shidava Gold'	WPat
§	– 'Shigitatsu-sawa' (v)	CBcs CEnd CMCN CPMA EMil GKir LPan LRHS MGos NLar SCoo WWeb
	– 'Shigure-bato'	CMCN CPMA
	– 'Shigurezome'	CMCN
	– 'Shikageori-nishiki'	WWeb
	– 'Shime-no-uchi'	CMCN LNet
	– 'Shindeshôjô'	CDoC CEnd CMCN COtt CPMA GKir LNet LRHS MAsh MGos NPSI SCoo SHBN SPar SPer SRPl SReu SSta WFoF WNor WOTO WPat WWeb
§	– 'Shinobugaoka'	CMCN CPMA LNet
	– 'Shinonome'	CMCN
§	– 'Shishigashira'	CBcs CDoC CMCN COtt CPMA ECho EPfP LPan LRHS MBar MBlu MBri MGos WPat
§	– 'Shishio'	CMCN ECho GKir LAst LHyd LNet LRHS MAsh SPer SSpi WWeb
§	– 'Shishio Improved'	CEnd CMCN CPMA CTho CWSG LNet MBlu MGos NBhm NLar SSta WOTO
	– 'Shôjô'	CMCN CPMA MBri
	– 'Shôjô-no-mai' **new**	WWes
	– 'Shôjô-nomura'	CAbP CEnd CMCN COtt CPMA LRHS MAsh NLar WPGP
§	– 'Shôjô-shidare'	CEnd ECho WPat
	– 'Skeeters'	CDoC WPat WWes
	– 'Stella Rossa'	CEnd CMCN CPMA LPan MBlu WPat WWes
	– 'Suminagashi'	CDoC CMCN LNet MDun SMur WWeb
	– 'Susan' **new**	WWes
	– 'Takinogawa'	LRHS MAsh WWeb
	– 'Tamahime'	CMCN CPMA ECho LNet WWes
	– 'Tamukeyama'	CMCN CPMA EMil LNet LRHS MAsh MDun SBod SKee SPer WFar WPat WWeb
	– 'Tana'	CMCN CPMA WPat
	– 'Tarô-yama' **new**	WPat WWes
	– 'Tatsuta-gawa'	ECho
	– 'Tennyo-no-hoshi' **new**	NLar
	– 'Tiny Tim'	CPMA WPat
	– 'Toyama-nishiki' (v)	CMCN
	– 'Trompenburg' ♀ H4	More than 30 suppliers
	– 'Tsuchigumo'	CMCN CPMA ECho WWes
	– 'Tsukubane'	CMCN
	– 'Tsukushigata'	CMCN
	– 'Tsuma-beni'	CMCN CPMA EPfP LNet LRHS MAsh WPat
	– 'Tsuma-gaki'	CMCN CPMA ECho WPat
	– 'Tsuri-nishiki' (v)	CPMA ECho
	– 'Ukigumo' (v)	CBcs CEnd CMCN CPMA CWSG ELan EMil GKir LNet MAsh MGos NHol NPSI SBod SCoo SMur SPar SPer WPat WWeb
	– 'Ukon'	CMCN CPMA EMil
	– 'Umegae'	CMCN CPMA
	– 'Utsu-semi'	CMCN CPMA LNet
	– 'Vens Broom'	WPat
	– 'Versicolor' (v)	CMCN CPMA LNet LRHS WWes
	– 'Vic Broom'	WPat
	– 'Vic Pink'	WPat
	– 'Villa Taranto'	CDoC CEnd CMCN CPMA EPfP GKir LNet LRHS MAsh MBlu NLar SCoo SSpi WPGP WPat WWeb
	– 'Volubile'	CMCN ECho EPfP LRHS MAsh SMur SSta WWeb
	– 'Wabito'	CMCN CPMA WWes
	– 'Wakehurst Pink' (v)	CMCN
	– 'Waterfall'	CMCN CPMA LNet WWes
	– 'Wendy' **new**	WWes
	– 'Wilson's Pink Dwarf'	CPMA ECho EPfP LNet NLar
	– 'Winter Flame'	CPMA MAsh WPat
	– 'Wou-nishiki'	see A. palmatum 'O-nishiki'
	– 'Yasemin'	MBri
	– 'Yatsubusa' **new**	WWes
	– 'Yezo-nishiki'	CMCN LRHS MAsh MBri WWeb
	– 'Yûba e'	CMCN MBri
	– 'Yûgure'	CMCN MGos NLar WWes
	papilio	see A. caudatum
	paxii	CMCN
	pectinatum subsp. *forrestii*	see A. forrestii
	– 'Sirene'	see A. forrestii 'Sirene'
	– 'Sparkling'	see A. forrestii 'Sparkling'
	pensylvanicum ♀ H4	CBcs CDul CLnd CMCN CTho EBee ELan EPfP GGGa GKir LBuc LPan LRHS MGos MHFa MRav NBee NBlu NHol NWea SHBN SLim SPer SSpi WDin WFar WNor
	– 'Erythrocladum'	CEnd CMCN CPMA EPfP GKir LNet MBri MGos NBea NHol NLar SLim SMad SRPl SSpi SSta
	pentaphyllum	CMCN GKir LNet SKee SSpi
§	*pictum*	CMCN CTho EPfP GIBF WNor
	– 'Shufu-nishiki'	CMCN
	platanoides ♀ H4	CCVT CDoC CKin CLnd CMCN CTri CWib EBee ECrN ENot EPfP GKir LBuc LHyr LPan MGos MHFa NBee NWea SKee SPer WDin WHar WMou WNor
	– 'Cleveland'	CBcs EBee ENot MHFa
	– 'Columnare'	CDoC CLnd CMCN EBee ECrN ENot EPfP LNet LPan LRHS NBee WOrn
	– 'Crimson King' ♀ H4	More than 30 suppliers
	– 'Crimson Sentry'	More than 30 suppliers
	– 'Cucullatum'	CMCN CTho
	– 'Deborah'	CDul CLnd CTho EBee EWTr LPan MHFa SHBN
	– 'Dissectum'	CTho GKir
	– 'Drummondii' (v)	More than 30 suppliers
	– 'Emerald Queen'	CDoC CLnd CMCN EBee ECrN ENot MHFa SHBN WDin
	– 'Faassen's Black'	LPan
§	– 'Globosum'	CLnd CMCN ECrN ENot LBuc LPan MGos
	– 'Goldsworth Purple'	CLnd CMCN MHFa

	- 'Laciniatum'	CEnd CMCN ENot GKir SHBN
	- 'Lorbergii'	see *A. platanoides* 'Palmatifidum'
	- 'Olmsted'	ENot LNet MHFa
§	- 'Palmatifidum'	CLnd CSam
	- Princeton Gold	CDoC EBee ECrN ELan ENot GKir
	= 'Prigo'PBR	LPan LRHS MBlu MBri MRav SCoo SKee SPoG WWeb
	- 'Reitenbachii'	CDul
	- 'Royal Red'	CDul CMCN EBee ECrN ENot LPan MGos MHFa MRav SKee
	- 'Ruby' **new**	GKir
	- 'Schwedleri' ♀ H4	CDul CLnd CMCN ECrN MGos MHFa NBee NWea SPer WDin
	- 'Tharandt'	CMCN
	- 'Walderseei'	CLnd
	pseudoplatanus	CBcs CCVT CDul CKin CLnd CMCN CSBt CTri ECrN ENot GKir LBuc LHyr LPan MBar MGos MHFa NBee NWea SPer WDin WHar WMou
§	- 'Atropurpureum'	CDoC CDul CLnd CTho ECrN ENot MHFa NBec NWea WDin WOrn
	- 'Brilliantissimum' ♀ H4	More than 30 suppliers
	- 'Corstorphinense'	CMCN MHFa
	- 'Erectum'	ENot MHFa
	- 'Erythrocarpum'	CMCN
N	- 'Leopoldii' (v)	CBcs CDoC CDul CLnd CMCN COtt CTho CWib EBee ECrN ELan ENot EPfP LAst LPan MAsh MHFa NBee SHBN SKee SLim SPer WDin WFar WOrn
	- 'Negenia'	EBee ENot
	- 'Nizetii' (v)	CMCN LRHS
	- 'Prinz Handjéry'	CBcs CDul CEnd CLnd CMCN CTri EBee LNet LPan LRHS MAsh MBar MGos NWea SHBN SPer SSpi
	- 'Simon-Louis Frères' (v)	CCVT CDul CEnd CLnd CMCN CWSG EMui EPfP LNet LPan LRHS MAsh MBar MBri MDun MGos MHFa MWat NBea SKee SLim SPer WFar WFoF WHar WOrn WStI
N	- 'Spaethii' hort.	see *A. pseudoplatanus* 'Atropurpurcum'
	- 'Spring Gold'	MGos
	- 'Worley'	CBcs CDoC CDul CLnd CMCN COtt CSBt CTho EBee ECrN ENot EPfP GKir LPan LRHS MHFa MRav NBee NWea SHBN SKee SLim SPer WDin WHar WOrn WStI
	pseudosieboldianum	CFil CMCN GIBF GKir MBlu SSpi WNor WPGP
	pubipalmatum	WNor
	pycnanthum	CMCN
	robustum	CMCN WNor
	rubescens	CLnd CPne
	- B&SWJ 6710	WHCr
	- B&SWJ 6735	WHCr
	rubrum	CBcs CDoC CDul CLnd CMCN CSBt CTho CTri EBee ECrN EPfP GKir LRHS MGos MHFa MLan MWat NBea NBee NWea SCoo SHBN SLim SPer WDin WFar WNor
	- 'Bowhall'	CMCN SBir
	- 'Candy Ice' (v) **new**	CPMA
	- 'Columnare'	CDul CMCN GKir
	- 'Elstead'	LNet
	- 'October Glory' ♀ H4	CBcs CDoC CDul CEnd CLnd CMCN CPMA CTho EPfP GKir LPan LRHS MBlu MBri NWea SBir SCoo SKee SMad SPer SSpi SSta WFar WPat WWeb
	- Red Sunset	CDoC CDul CEnd CMCN CPMA
	= 'Franksred'	CTho EPfP GKir LPan MBlu SBir SCoo SMad SSpi SSta
	- 'Schlesingeri'	CEnd CLnd CMCN CMac CPMA NLar
	- 'Tilford'	GKir SSta
§	*rufinerve* ♀ H4	CBcs CDoC CDul CFil CLnd CMCN CTho CTri ECrN EPfP EPla LPan LRHS MBri MHFa NBea NWea SKee SPer WDin WGer WNor WOrn WPGP WStI
	- B&SWJ 5108	WHCr
	- 'Albolimbatum'	see *A. rufinerve* 'Hatsuyuki'
	- 'Albomarginatum'	see *A. rufinerve* 'Hatsuyuki'
	- 'Erythrocladum'	CPMA LNet
§	- 'Hatsuyuki' (v)	CDoC CEnd CMCN CPMA GKir LRHS WPGP
	- 'Winter Gold'	CPMA GKir SSpi
§	*saccharinum*	CBcs CCVT CDul CLnd CMCN EBee ECrN ELan ENot EPfP EWTr LHyr MGos MHFa MLan MWat NBee NWea SHBN SKee SPer SRPl WDin WFar WNor WStI
	- 'Fastigiatum'	see *A. saccharinum* f. *pyramidale*
	- f. *laciniatum*	CMCN EBee ENot LRHS MBlu MGos MHFa SPer WDin
	- 'Laciniatum Wieri'	CDul CLnd CMCN CTho LPan MGos NBee WDin
	- f. *lutescens*	CDul CMCN CTho ENot MBlu
§	- f. *pyramidale*	CDoC CLnd CMCN EBee ENot EPfP LPan MHFa SPer WDin
	saccharum	CDul CLnd CMCN CTho EPfP GKir IDee LPan MBlu MLan NWea SPer WNor
	- subsp. *barbatum*	see *A. saccharum* subsp. *floridanum*
§	- subsp. *floridanum*	CMCN
§	- subsp. *grandidentatum*	CMCN
	- subsp. *leucoderme*	CMCN
	- subsp. *nigrum*	CMCN
	- - 'Temple's Upright'	CMCN LNet WWes
	- subsp. *skutchii*	CMCN
	'Scanlon'	CBcs CDoC CDul CEnd CMCN CTho GKir LRHS
§	*sempervirens*	CFil CMCN WPGP
	serrulatum	CMCN
	- B&SWJ 6760	WCri
	- B&SWJ 6773	WHCr
§	*shirasawanum*	CDul CMCN WNor
§	- 'Aureum' ♀ H4	More than 30 suppliers
	- 'Autumn Moon'	CPMA
§	- 'Ezo-no-momiji'	CMCN CPMA
§	- 'Júnihitoe'	WNor
§	- 'Microphyllum'	CMCN LNet WNor
§	- 'Ogurayama'	CPMA LNet
	- 'Palmatifolium'	CMCN CPMA GKir MGos WStI
	- var. *tenuifolium*	GKir WNor
	sieboldianum	CMCN CTho CTri ECho EPfP MDun SSpi WNor
	- 'Sode-no-uchi'	CMCN WPat
	sikkimense	see *A. metcalfii*
	subsp. *metcalfii*	
§	'Silver Cardinal' (v)	CBcs CEnd CMCN CPMA EPfP LNet MBlu MGos NBhm NLar SMad SSpi WWes
	'Silver Vein'	see *A.* x *conspicuum* 'Silver Vein'
§	*sinense*	CMCN GIBF IArd WNor
§	*spicatum*	CMCN WNor
§	*stachyophyllum*	GQui
§	*sterculiaceum*	CFil CMCN EBee EPla GGGa WPGP
	taronense	CMCN
	tataricum	CMCN
	- IDS 97	WHCr

§   – subsp. **ginnala**   CAgr CBcs CDul CLnd CMCN
                             CTho ECrN ENot EPfP GKir LRHS
                             MGos MHFa MRav NBea NWea
                             SHBN SLim SPer WDin WNor
  – – 'Fire'   LNet
  – – 'Flame'   CPMA CWSG ELan EPfP GKir
                             MGos SHBN SKee
  tegmentosum   CMCN CPMA MBlu WNor
  – subsp.
    glaucorufinerve   see *A. rufinerve*
  tenuifolium   CMCN
  tetramerum   see *A. stachyophyllum*
  trautvetteri   CMCN EPfP WNor
  triflorum ♀ H4   CLnd CMCN CTho EPfP IArd
                             IMGH LRHS NLar NWea SSpi
                             WDin WFar WWes
  truncatum   CMCN WNor WOTO
  – 'Akaji-nishiki'   see *A. palmatum* 'Akaji-nishiki'
  – 'Akikaze-nishiki' (v)   CPMA LNet
  tschonoskii   CLnd GQui WNor WWes
  – subsp. **koreanum**   CTho WNor
§   **turkestanicum**   CDul CFil CMCN EBee
  velutinum   CMCN
  villosum   see *A. sterculiaceum*
  'White Tigress'   CTho EBee GKir
§   **wilsonii**   CMCN GIBF WNor
  x **zoeschense**   CMCN
  – 'Annae'   CPMA

Aceras (Orchidaceae)
  anthropophorum   EFEx

Aceriphyllum see *Mukdenia*

x *Achicodonia* (Gesneriaceae)
§   'Cornell Gem'   NMos
  'Dark Velvet'   WDib

Achillea ❀ (Asteraceae)
  ageratifolia ♀ H4   ECha ECtt LBee MTho SRms WFar
§   – subsp. **aizoon**   WPer
§   **ageratum**   CArn CSev ELau GBar GDra GPoy
                             IIve MChe MHer MSal NArg NPri
                             SRms WHHs WHer WJek WLHH
                             WPer WWye
  – 'W.B. Childs'   CPlt CSli CSpe EBee ECha EGle
                             ELan EOrc GBuc MArl MAvo MBct
                             MNrw NDov WCot WEas
  'Alabaster'   CRDP CSli EFou GBuc LPhx MAvo
                             NCiC
  Anthea = 'Anblo'PBR   CKno CMGP EBee EBlw EBre
                             EGle EMan GKir GMaP GSki LRHS
                             MCLN MLLN SCro SMrm SPar
                             WAul WFar
§   'Apfelblüte'   More than 30 suppliers
  Appleblossom   see *A.* 'Apfelblüte'
  'Apricot Beauty'   CFir CFwr EMar NPro SVil
  argentea hort.   see *A. clavennae, A. umbellata*
  argentea Lamarck   see *Tanacetum argenteum*
  aurea   see *A. chrysocoma*
  'Bahama'   EBee EPPr GBuc NBro
  'Belle Epoque' ♀ H4   CSli LPhx
  'Bloodstone'   CSli EMan EPPr EWes EWsh GBar
                             MRav NPPs WBea WWhi
  brachyphylla   EPot
  'Brilliant' **new**   WWeb
  cartilaginea   CSli EFou WFar WMoo
  – 'Silver Spray'   EBee EMan EWTr WWpP
  chamaemelifolia   WHil
  'Christine's Pink' ♀ H4   CDes CSli EBee EPPr
§   **chrysocoma**   ETow GAbr MWat WTel
  – 'Grandiflora'   CHad CHar CKno ECha MGrG
                             NGdn

§   **clavennae**   CBrm EBot ECtt EMlt EPot LPio
                             MLLN MWat NFla SAga SBla SRms
                             WCom WCot WFar
  clypeolata Sibth. & Sm.   CSli EPPr LPio SPlb SRms
  coarctata   NBir WPer
  'Coral Beauty' **new**   EBee
  'Coronation Gold' ♀ H4   CDoC CPrp EBee ECtt EFou ELan
                             EMan ENot EPfP ERou GKir GMac
                             GSki LPVe LPhx LRHS MBri MCAu
                             MCLN MMil MWat MWgw NChi
                             SDes SPer WEas WFar WMnd
  'Credo' ♀ H4   More than 30 suppliers
  'Croftway'   SCro
  decolorans   see *A. ageratum*
  erba-rotta subsp.   ECho NBro
    moschata
  – subsp. **rupestris**   CMea MDHE WPer
§   'Fanal'   More than 30 suppliers
  'Faust'   CDes CMil CSli EBee EFou LPhx
                             SMrm WPGP
  'Feuerland'   More than 30 suppliers
  filipendulina   NSti SYvo WHrl WWpP
  – 'Cloth of Gold' ♀ H4   More than 30 suppliers
  – 'Gold Plate' ♀ H4   CDoC CHad EBre EChP ECha ECtt
                             EFou ELan EPfP ERou GKir GSki
                             MMil MRav MWgw NDov NOrc
                             SCro SHel SPar SPer SRms WCot
                             WFar WMnd
  – 'Parker's Variety' ♀ H4   EBee EMil EMon LRHS MLan
                             NOak WFar WPnP
  Flowers of Sulphur   see *A.* 'Schwefelblüte'
  'Forncett Beauty'   CSli EFou SChu WHil
  'Forncett Bride'   CSli EFou NDov
  'Forncett Candy'   CSli EFou NDov WHil
I   'Forncett Citrus'   CDes CSli EBee EFou WPGP
  'Forncett Fletton'   CSli EBee EFou EGle EMar EPPr
                             GBri LPhx MAvo MBct MCAu
                             MNrw NPPs SAga SCro SHel
                             SMrm STes WCot WHil WViv
  'Forncett Ivory'   CSli EFou LPhx WHil
  fraasii   WPer
  glaberrima hybrid   EMan NDov WCot
  'Gloria Jean' **new**   SHar
  'Gold and Grey'   CSli
§   **grandifolia** Friv.   CBre CFwr CSam EBee EChP EGle
                             EMar EMon EPPr GCal GEdu LPhx
                             MAnH MWgw NBro NPPs NSti
                             SMad SMrm SPer SSvw WBea WFar
                             WHer WHil WMnd WOld WWye
  grandifolia misapplied   see *Tanacetum macrophyllum*
  'Great Expectations'   see *A.* 'Hoffnung'
  'Grey and Gold'   EFou
  'Hannelore Pahl' **new**   EBee
  'Hartington White'   GBuc
  'Heidi' ♀ H4   CSli
  'Helios' **new**   GBin
  'Hella Glashoff' ♀ H4   CSli EBee ECho EGle EMon LPhx
                             MBri NDov SCro WCot WHoo
                             WPrP WWeb
§   'Hoffnung'   CPrp CSli EBee ECtt EGle EMan
                             ERou GSki MBri MRav NPPs SCro
                             SDes SPer SSpe WMnd WPer
                             WRus WWin
  'Huteri'   CLyd CPBP ECtt EDAr EGoo
                             EMNN EPot ENot EPot EChP NJOw NLon
                             MHer MRav NFor NJOw NLon
                             SBla SChu WCom WEas WFar
                             WPer WWin
  'Inca Gold'   CKno CSli EBee EBlw ECha ECtt
                             EGle EHrv EMan EMar GBri
                             MCLN MHar MRav NBro NDov
                             SAga SBla SChu WWpP
  'Jacqueline' **new**   EBee

'Judith'	SDes WWeb
x **kellereri**	MBro MDHE
Kirschkönigin	see *A. millefolium* 'Cerise Queen'
x **kolbiana**	EMan MWat NHol NJOw NMen
	SRms WHoo WLin WPat WWin
§	'Lachsschönheit' ♀ H4	More than 30 suppliers
x **lewisii**	NMen
– 'King Edward' ♀ H4	CMHG CSam EBre ECha EDAr EMlt
	ESis LRHS MTho NBir NJOw
	NMGW SBla SChu SIng WCom WFar
'Libella'	GBuc
ligustica new	WCot
'Lucky Break' ♀ H4	CMdw ECha SDix SMHy SUsu
macrophylla	EBee EMar
'Marie Ann' **new**	ERou MBri MCLN NPro WElm WHil
Marmalade'	CSli EBee EFou SMrm WPGP
'Martina' ♀ H4	CDoC CKno CM&M CSli EBee
	EChP ECha ECtt EFou EGle EGoo
	EMan EMon EPPr EPfP EWTr
	GBuc LAst LHop LRHS MLLN
	MUlv NDov NOrc NPro SCro
	SOkh SVil WBro WPGP
'McVities'	CKno CSli EBee EChP ECtt EFou
	EGle EMan EPPr GBin GMaP LHop
	LPhx MCAu MLLN MSph NDov
	NPPs NPro SDes STes WBea WCot
	WCra WElm WHal WRus WTin
millefolium	CArn COld EFls FFWa ELau GBar
	GPoy GWCH MBow MHer NCWG
	NLan NMir NSco SPlb WHHs WHbs
	WHer WJek WLHH WSel WWyc
– 'Carla Hussey'	WFar
– 'Cassis' **new**	ECoo SWal
§	– 'Cerise Queen'	More than 30 suppliers
– 'Cherry Queen'	LPVe WSan
'Christel' **new**	CSli SUsu
'Christine'	CFwr SDes
– 'Colorado'	CM&M COlW CPen CSam LPVe
	MFir NChi NCiC SMac STes WBea
	WHrl WWeb
– dark red	CSli
– 'Debutante' **new**	WHil
– 'Fire King'	CHal
– 'Harlekin'	CFwr
– 'Kelwayi' ♀ H4	CSli
– 'Lansdorferglut' ♀ H4	CSli EPPr LPhx LRHS MBri MDKP
	MRav NDov NPro SUsu WWpP
– 'Lavender Beauty'	see *A. millefolium* 'Lilac Beauty'
– 'Lemon Curd' **new**	LDai
§	– 'Lilac Beauty'	More than 30 suppliers
*	– 'Lilac Queen'	CMGP CSli MArl SWat
– 'Lollypop' **new**	LDai
– 'Paprika'	More than 30 suppliers
– 'Red Beauty'	CFwr CSli EBee EMan EMar EWTr
	LRHS MTis NBro SRms SWat
– 'Red Velvet' **new**	WCot
– 'Rosie' **new**	GBar
– 'Rougham Beauty'	CSli ERou
– 'Rougham Cream'	CSli
– 'Rougham White'	CSli
– 'Salmon Queen' **new**	WCra
– 'Sammetriese'	CSli EGle ELan EMon GBuc LPhx
	LRHS MCAu MHar MSte NDov
	SMad WElm WFar WHoo WPrP
	WRHF WWpP
– 'Serenade'	CFwr EBee
– 'Summertime'	SBod
– 'Tickled Pink'	NCat WPer
– 'White Queen'	EBee EGle EMar EWTr LBuc MSps
	WPer
'Mondpagode' ♀ H4	CSli EGle EPPr EVFa LPhx NDov
	SAga SAsh SCro SUsu
'Moonlight'	MBro

'Moonshine' ♀ H3	More than 30 suppliers
'Moonwalker'	CAbP EBee LRHS MLLN SIde SMac
	WBVN WFar WPer WWeb WWpP
nana	LPVe
nobilis subsp.	CRDP CSli CSpe EBee EGoo EHrv
	neilreichii	EMon EPPr GBri MCAu MHar
	MLLN MWrn NDov NSti SAga
	SPer WCot WHal WHil
'Old Brocade'	CHea CSli EFou LPhx
'Peter Davis'	see *Hippolytia herderi*
pindicola subsp.	EWes
	integrifolia
I	'Pink Island Form'	CKno
'Prospero'	CMea MSte NDov WBea WCot WCra
ptarmica	CArn CBre CKin ELau EMFW
	GBar IIve MChe MHer MSal NEgg
	NMir SPer WLHH WWye
*	– 'Ballerina'	MWrn NDov NLar WRHF
– Innocence	see *A. ptarmica* 'Unschuld'
– 'Major'	EChP MCAu
– 'Nana Compacta'	CSli CSpe EBee ECha EFou EGle
	EPPr GSki IGor LHop LRHS
	MAnH MCAu MLLN NBir SMrm
	SOkh SPlb SUsu WCFE WCot
	WHil WMaN WOld
– 'Perry's White'	CBre EBee EGle GCal NCat NGHP
	WCot
– 'Stephanie Cohen'	CMdw CStr EBee EFou EGle
	MAnH MDKP MLLN MSph NBhm
	SOkh WCot WFar WHil WMaN
N	– The Pearl Group	CBcs EBre ECha EFou ELan EPar
	seed-raised (d)	GKir LHop MFir NVic SDes SMac
	SPlb SWat WBea WFar WMoo
	WPer WWpP
N	– – 'Boule de Neige'	CHal GSki MBri NPer NSti SPla
	(clonal) (d)	SPla WFar WGwG WHil WLRN
	WMnd WWal
N	– – 'The Pearl' (clonal)	CDes CSbt EBee EPfP ERou MRav
	(d) ♀ H4	MSte MWat MWgw NBid NBir NBro
	NLon SCro SRms WCot WEas WFar
	WHer WHil WOld WPGP WWeb
§	– 'Unschuld'	NBir
I	'Rose Madder'	CDes CSpe EBla EChP EGle EMan
	EMar EPPr EVFa GBin MAvo MLLN
	MSph MSte NCot NPPs SChu SHBN
	SOkh SPla WCot WElm WWpP
'Rougham Bright Star'	CSli
	new
'Rougham Salmon'	CSli ERou
'Sally' **new**	EBee EPPr
'Sandstone'	see *A.* 'Wesersandstein'
'Scarlett O'Hara'	CSli
§	'Schwefelblüte'	NBir SBla SMrm
'Schwellenburg'	CSli
sibirica	LPio WElm
– var. **camschatica**	CBrm CSli EMan EMar EWTr GBar
	'Love Parade'	GMac GSki LPVe LRHS MDKP
	MRav MSps MWrn SGar SOkh
	SSvw STes WBea WBry WMoo
	WSan WViv WWeb WWpP
'Summer Glory'	SCro
Summer Pastels Group	CBri CM&M COlW EBlw EMan
	EMil EShb GKir LHrt LRHS MLan
	NArg NBir NBlu NMir NOrc SDes
	SGar SMac SRms SWal SWat
	WLRN WMnd WPer WRha WWeb
'Summerwine' ♀ H4	More than 30 suppliers
I	'Taygetea'	CBot CSam CSli EBee EChP EFou
	ELan EMan EPPr EPfP EWir GMaP
	MCAu MSte NSti SChu SDix SPer
	WCom WCot WFar WKif WPer
	WRus WSHC
'Terracotta'	More than 30 suppliers

	'The Beacon'	see *A.* 'Fanal'
	tomentosa ♀ H4	CTri ECha ECtt EPfP NEgg
§	- 'Aurea'	CHal ECtt ELau IHMH LPVe NBlu NBro SRms WPer
	- 'Maynard's Gold'	see *A. tomentosa* 'Aurea'
§	***umbellata***	CLyd EMlt ETow WCot
	'Walther Funcke'	More than 30 suppliers
§	'Wesersandstein'	CDes CHar CKno CPlt CSli CWCL EBee EFou EMan EPPr GBar LRHS MAvo MBri MHar MLLN NBir NDov NPro SBod STes SUsu WCot WElm WPGP WPer WWhi
	'Wilczekii'	NChi SRms
	***wilsoniana* new**	WCot
	'Yellowstone'	SDes

x *Achimenantha* (*Gesneriaceae*)

	'Cerulean Mink'	see x *Smithicodonia* 'Cerulean Mink'
	'Dutch Treat'	NMos
	'Ginger Peachy'	NMos
	'Inferno' ♀ H1	NMos WDib
*	'Rose Bouquet'	NMos
	'Royal'	NMos

Achimenes (*Gesneriaceae*)

	'Almandine'	NMos
	'Ambroise Verschaffelt' ♀ H1	LAma NMos WDib
	'Ami Van Houtte'	NMos
	'Ann Marie'	NMos
	'Apricot Glow'	NMos
	'Aquamarine'	NMos
	'Bassenthwaite'	NMos
	'Bernice'	NMos
	'Blauer Planet'	NMos
	'Bloodstone'	NMos
	'Blue Gown'	NMos
	'Brilliant'	NMos
	'Butterfield Bronze'	NMos
	'Buttermere'	NMos
	'Camberwell Beauty'	NMos
	'Cameo Rose'	NMos
	'Cameo Triumph'	NMos
	'Camille Brozzoni'	NMos
	candida	NMos
	'Carmine Queen'	NMos
	'Cascade Cockade'	NMos
	'Cascade Evening Glow'	NMos
	'Cascade Fashionable Pink'	NMos
	'Cascade Rosy Red'	NMos
	'Cascade Violet Night'	NMos
	'Cattleya'	LAma
	'Charm'	NMos
	'Clouded Yellow'	NMos
	'Compact Great Rosy Red'	NMos
	'Coniston Water'	NMos
	'Copeland Boy'	NMos
	'Copeland Girl'	NMos
	'Coral Sunset'	NMos
	'Cornell Favourite 'A''	NMos
	'Cornell Favourite 'B''	NMos
	'Crimson Beauty'	NMos
	'Crimson Glory'	NMos
	'Crummock Water'	NMos
	'Cupido'	NMos
	'Derwentwater'	NMos
	'Dorothy'	NMos
	'Dot'	NMos
	dulcis	NMos
	'Early Arnold'	NMos

	'Elke Michelssen'	NMos
	'English Waltz'	NMos
	erecta	WDib
	'Escheriana'	NMos
	'Flamenco'	NMos
	'Flamingo'	SDeJ
	flava	NMos
	'Fritz Michelssen'	NMos
	'Gary John'	NMos
	'Gary/Jennifer'	NMos
	'Grape Wine'	NMos
	'Grasmere'	NMos
	'Harry Williams'	LAma
§	'Harveyi'	NMos
	'Haweswater'	NMos
	'Hilda Michelssen' ♀ H1	NMos WDib
	'Himalayan Yellow Cloud'	LAma
	'Honey Gold'	NMos
	'Ida Michelssen'	NMos
	'India'	NMos
§	'Jaureguia Maxima'	NMos
	'Jennifer Goode'	NMos
	'Jewell Blue'	NMos
	'Johanna Michelssen'	NMos
	'Jubilee Gem'	NMos
	'Lakeland Lady'	NMos
	'Little Beauty'	NMos WDib
	'Little Red Tiger'	NMos
	longiflora	NMos
	- 'Alba'	see *A.* 'Jaureguia Maxima'
	- 'Major'	NMos
	'Magnificent'	NMos
	'Marie'	NMos
	'Masterpiece'	NMos
	'Maxima'	LAma
	'Menuett '80'	NMos
	'Milton'	NMos
	misera	NMos
	'Moonstone'	NMos
	'Old Rose Pink'	NMos
	'Orange Delight'	WDib
	'Orange Queen'	NMos
	'Pally'	NMos
	'Panic Pink'	NMos
	'Patens Major'	NMos
	'Paul Arnold' ♀ H1	NMos
	'Peach Blossom'	LAma NMos
	'Peach Glow'	NMos
	'Pearly Queen'	NMos
	'Pendant Blue'	NMos
	'Pendant Purple'	NMos
	'Petticoat Pink'	NMos
	'Pink Beauty'	NMos
	'Pinocchio'	NMos
	'Prima Donna'	NMos
	'Purple King'	NMos
	'Quickstep'	NMos
	'Rachael'	NMos
	'Red Admiral'	NMos
	'Red Giant'	NMos
	'Red Top Hybrid'	NMos
	'Robin'	NMos
	'Rosenelfe'	NMos
	'Rosy Doll'	NMos
	'Rosy Frost'	NMos
	'Rydal Water'	NMos
	'Scafell'	NMos
	'Shirley Dwarf White'	NMos
	'Shirley Fireglow'	see *A.* 'Harveyi'
	'Show-off'	NMos
	'Silver Wedding'	NMos
	'Snow Princess'	SDeJ
	'Sparkle'	NMos

'Stan's Delight' (d)	♀ H1	NMos WDib
'Sue'		NMos
'Tango'		NMos
'Tarantella'		NMos
'Teresa'		NMos
'Tiny Blue'		NMos
'Topsy'		NMos
'Troutbeck'		NMos
'Ullswater'		NMos
'Vanessa'		NMos
'Viola Michelssen'		NMos
'Violacea Semiplena'		NMos
'Vivid'		LAma NMos
'Warren'		NMos
'Wastwater'		NMos
'Wetterflow's Triumph'		NMos
'White Admiral'		NMos
'White Rajah'		NMos
'Wilma'		NMos
'Windermere'		NMos

Achlys (Berberidaceae)

californica new	IBlr
japonica	WCru
triphylla	GBuc GGar IBlr WCru

Achnatherum see Stipa

Achyranthes (Amaranthaceae)

bidentata	CArn IIve MSal

Acidanthera see Gladiolus

Acinos (Lamiaceae)

§	alpinus	CAgr CArn CBrm EBee EMan ESis GBar LPVe LPhx LTwo MSPs SBla WJek
	- subsp. meridionalis	EGle
§	arvensis	MHer MSal
§	corsicus	ESis MBro NWCA WHoo WPat WWin

Aciphylla (Apiaceae)

aurea	GCal NWCA SPlb WHil
congesta	EMan NMen
crenulata	WCot
hectorii	NMen WCot
horrida	GCal GCrs
kirkii	GCrs WCot
monroi	GDra LTwo NMen NWCA WCot
montana	NMen
- var. gracilis new	NMen
pinnatifida	GCrs GGar NHar NMen
similis	EMan GGar NMen
simplex	NMen
squarrosa	EMan GCal
subflabellata	GCal GCrs

Acmena (Myrtaceae)

smithii new	EShb

Acnistus (Solanaceae)

australis	see Iochroma australe

Acoelorrhaphe (Arecaceae)

wrightii	CBrP LPal

Aconitum ✿ (Ranunculaceae)

ACE 1449	GBuc
- B&SWJ 2954 from Nepal	WCru
- CNDS 036 from Burma	WCru
alboviolaceum	GCal WCot
- var. albiflorum	WCru
B&SWJ 4105 new	

	anglicum	see A. napellus subsp. napellus Anglicum Group
	anthora	EChP LPio NCat WAul
N	autumnale	NBir
	bartlettii B&SWJ 337	EBee EMan WCru
	'Blue Opal' new	EWes
	'Blue Sceptre'	EBre EMan MCLN WAul WSel
	'Bressingham Spire' ♀ H4	More than 30 suppliers
	x cammarum 'Bicolor' ♀ H4	More than 30 suppliers
	- 'Grandiflorum Album'	EBee ERou LPhx SAga
§	carmichaelii	CArn CBot CBri EBee EFou EMan ETub GKir GSki IBlr LRHS MBri MBro MRav MWgw NChi NFor NOrc SCro SMrm SRms WBod WCom WHoo WPnP WSel
	- 'Arendsii'	More than 30 suppliers
	- 'Pink Sensation' new	MWrn
	- Wilsonii Group	CHar EBee GGar LPhx LRHS MBri MRav MSte MWat MWrn NChi SBla SChu WFar WPer WSel WWin WWye
§	- - 'Barker's Variety'	CPou CRow EBee EChP EGle EMan EPfP GBuc GMac LPhx MAnH MFir NHol NSti SMrm WAul WCot WViv
	- - 'Kelmscott' ♀ H4	EBee ECGN EGle EMon MRav MSte MWgw SAga SDix SMHy WFar WRHF
	- - 'Spätlese'	EBee EChP EGle EMan GCal MAnH MEHN WCot WHHs
	- - 'The Grim Reaper'	EMon
	cilicicum	see Eranthis hyemalis Cilicica Group
	'Eleonara'	CFir EBee EChP EGle EMan EMar EPPr EPfP GBuc GKir LRHS MAvo NGby NLar NSti SDes WAul WFar WWeb
	elliotii	GBin
	elwesii	EBee GGar
	episcopale	CPlN EBee WCru WFar
	aff. episcopale	WSHC
	- CLD 1426	GBuc WFar
	'Faun' new	EBee
	ferox	CPLG EBee
	fischeri hort.	see A. carmichaelii
	fukutomei	WCot WCru
	var. formosanum B&SWJ 3057	
§	hemsleyanum	CBot CBri CPLG CPlN CRHN CRow EBee EPot ETow GEil IBlr LPhx LRHS MFir MNrw MTis NBid SMad WAul WBrE WCot WCru WEas WFar WFoF WOld WWeb WWhi
	- dark blue	CMea
	- latisectum	IBlr
	heterophyllum	LPhx
	hyemale	see Eranthis hyemalis
	'Ivorine'	More than 30 suppliers
	japonicum	EBee
	- subsp. subcuneatum B&SWJ 6228	WCru
	lamarckii	see A. lycoctonum subsp. neapolitanum
	lasianthum new	EBee
	longecassidatum B&SWJ 4105 new	WCru
	lycoctonum	GCrs IKee MCAu SRms
	- 'Dark Eyes'	EBee ECGN WCot
§	- subsp. lycoctonum	GKir MSal SRms
	- subsp. moldavicum	EBee

§ – subsp. **neapolitanum**   EBee EChP ELan EMFP EMan EPfP
                              GCal GSki LRHS MLLN MRav NFla
                              NGHP NHol NLar NSti SSpi SWat
                              WBor WFar WLin WSan
§ – subsp. **vulparia**   CArn ECGN ECha EFou GCal
                              GPoy MBri MSal MTed NMRc
                              WAul WCot WEas WSel WWye
'Matthew Tudor' **new**   NCat
napellus   More than 30 suppliers
– 'Albiflorus'   see *A. napellus* subsp. *vulgare*
                             'Albidum'
– 'Bergfürst'   EBee EGle LPhx LPio MTed
– 'Blue Valley'   EBee EChP EGle EMan EPfP MBri
                             NPSI WHil WLow
– 'Carneum'   see *A. napellus* subsp. *vulgare*
                             'Carneum'
§ – subsp. **napellus**   CRow CSev EBee EChP GBuc IBlr
   Anglicum Group   MSal MSte MWrn NHol WBWf
                             WCot WPen
– 'Rubellum'   EBre EChP EGle EMan EMar EPPr
                             EVFa LAst NBir NBro NPri WAul
                             WHil WPnP
– 'Sphere's Variety'   NOrc
– subsp. **tauricum**   EBee
§ – subsp. **vulgare**   More than 30 suppliers
   'Albidum'
– – 'Carneum'   EBee EGle EMan EMon GKir GMac
                             MLLN MRav NSti WEas WHer WHoo
                             WKif WLin WSel WViv WWin WWye
napiforme   LPio
– B&SWJ 943   WCru
neapolitanum   see *A. lycoctonum* subsp.
                             neapolitanum
'Newry Blue'   CBos CHad ELan EMon ERou GBuc
                             GKir LRHS MBri MRav MWhi NBir
                             NHol SRms WCra WFar WPer WRHF
orientale hort.   see *A. lycoctonum* subsp.
                             vulparia
paniculatum   EBee MBri
– 'Roseum'   CFir LRHS MBNS SPer WFar
pseudolaeve   LPhx
pyrenaicum   see *A. lycoctonum* subsp.
                             neapolitanum
ranunculifolius   see *A. lycoctonum* subsp.
                             neapolitanum
sczukinii   EMon WCru
seoulense B&SWJ 694   WCru
septentrionale   see *A. lycoctonum* subsp.
                             lycoctonum
'Spark's Variety' ♀ H4   More than 30 suppliers
spicatum   EBee
'Stainless Steel'   More than 30 suppliers
'Tissington Pearl'   MTis
x **tubergenii**   see *Eranthis hyemalis* Tubergenii
                             Group
uchiyamai B&SWJ 1216   WCru
variegatum (v)   EMar
vilmorinianum   MFir
violaceum **new**   EBee
volubile hort.   see *A. hemsleyanum*
vulparia   see *A. lycoctonum* subsp.
                             vulparia
yamazakii **new**   WCru

Aconogonon see *Persicaria*

Acorus ✿ (*Acoraceae*)

calamus   CAgr CArn CRow CWat EHon
                             ELau GPoy LPBA MCCP MSal
                             MSta NPer SWat WHer WMAq
                             WWeb WWpP
– 'Argenteostriatus' (v)   CBcs CBen CRow CWat EBee
                             ECha ECtt EHon EMFW EPfP

                             LPBA MSta NBlu NOrc SHel SLon
                             SPar SWal SWat WAul WLeb
                             WMAq WMoo WViv WWpP
  gramineus   CRow EMFW LPBA MLan NPer
                             SWat WHer WWpP
– extra dwarf   CStu
– 'Golden Edge' (v) **new** ENot
– 'Hakuro-nishiki' (v)   More than 30 suppliers
I – 'Licorice'   EBee EPPr IFro IIve LBuc LRHS
                             MBNS MSal WBea WCHb WCot
                             WLeb WWpP
– 'Masamune' (v)   EGle EMan EPla GCal NPro WCot
                             WLeb
– 'Minimus Aureus'   CWCL EVFa
– 'Oborozuki' (v)   CRow EPla NPro WCot
– 'Oborozuki' misapplied   see *A. gramineus* 'Ogon'
§ – 'Ogon' (v)   More than 30 suppliers
– var. **pusillus**   CRow EPla NBro SWal
– 'Variegatus' (v)   More than 30 suppliers
– 'Yodo-no-yuki' (v)   CRow EPla
* **intermedius**   NPer
tatarinowii **new**   EBee

Acradenia (*Rutaceae*)

frankliniae   CBcs CFil CMHG CPLG CPle
                             CTrG GEil GGar IArd IDee LAst
                             LRHS MNes SBrw SSpi WBod
                             WPGP WSHC

Actaea (*Ranunculaceae*)

alba   see *A. pachypoda*, *A. rubra* f.
                             neglecta
arizonica   LPhx SAga
asiatica   EBee GBin
– B&SWJ 616   WCru
biternata   CLAP MSte
cimicifuga   GBin GCal GPoy
– B&SWJ 2966   WCru
cordifolia   EBee EMan GMaP LPhx MSal
                             WCru WPnP
dahurica   EBee GCal GKir LBuc MSal NLar
                             SWat WCru
elata   EBee WCru
erythrocarpa   see *A. rubra*
europaea   LPhx WCru
frigida B&SWJ 2657   WCru
heracleifolia   GKir GSki WCot
japonica   CLAP CRow EBee EBre EChP
                             GCal GKir LPhx LRHS NSti WCot
matsumurae 'Elstead'   CFil CRow ECha EPar GCal LPhx
   ♀ H4   MRav NDov SSpi WPGP
– 'Frau Herms'   ECha GKir LPhx
– 'White Pearl'   More than 30 suppliers
§ **pachypoda** ♀ H4   CBos CBrd CLyd CPom ECGN
                             ECGP ECha EGle EMan EPar GPoy
                             GTou IBlr MFir MSal MSte MTed
                             NBid NLar NSti SSpi WCru WMoo
                             WWye
– f. **rubrocarpa**   EBee
podocarpa   MSal
racemosa ♀ H4   CArn CRow CSam EBre EChP
                             EGol ELan EPfP ERou GCal GKir
                             GPoy LRHS MSal NGdn SPer
                             WCot WFar WMnd WWye
§ **rubra** ♀ H4   CBro CMHG EChP ECha EPar
                             GCal GDra GGar GKir GPoy IBlr
                             MLLN MSte NChi NHol NSti SDes
                             SMad SSpi WCru WEas WFar
                             WMoo WPGP WWin
– **alba**   see *A. pachypoda*, *A. rubra* f.
                             neglecta
§ – f. **neglecta**   EBee EChP EMan GBuc GKir NLar
                             SMad SSpi

simplex   CBot CFil CMea CSam EBee GDea
                                GKir LRHS NPri SPer SWat WCot
- B&SWJ 6355   WCru
- Atropurpurea Group   More than 30 suppliers
- - 'Bernard Mitchell'   MTed
- - 'Brunette' ♀ H4   More than 30 suppliers
- - 'Hillside   CElw EBee EBlw EChP EGle ELan
  Black Beauty'   EMan IPot LHop NBir NGdn SOkh
                                WCot
- - 'James Compton'   More than 30 suppliers
- - 'Mountain Wave' **new**   EBee
§ - 'Prichard's Giant'   CPlt EBee GBuc GCal GKir LPhx
                                LRHS MBri MRav MSte NHol
                                NPPs WCot WFar
- *ramosa*   see *A. simplex* 'Prichard's Giant'
- 'Scimitar'   LPhx
- 'Silver Axe'   GCal
§ *spicata*   GBuc GKir GPoy MSal MSte NLar
                                NSti NWoo WCru
- var. *rubra*   see *A. rubra*
taiwanensis   CDes
- B&SWJ 3413   EBee WCru
- B&SWJ 343   CLAP
yesoensis   GCal
yunnanensis ACE 1880   GBuc

Actinella (Asteraceae)
scaposa   see *Tetraneuris scaposa*

Actinidia ✿ (Actinidiaceae)
arguta   CAgr CFil CPlN MRav SSte WPGP
- (m)   SHBN
- B&SWJ 569   WCru
- 'Dayton' **new**   EBee MRav
- 'Issai' (s-p/F)   EBee ERea LBuc MGos MRav
- LL#2 (f) **new**   CAgr
- LL#3 (m) **new**   CAgr
- 'Weiki'   MGos
callosa   CPlN
- var. *ephippioidea*   WCru
  B&SWJ 1790
- var. *formosana*   WCru
  B&SWJ 3806
chinensis hort.   see *A. deliciosa*
coriacea   CPlN
§ *deliciosa*   CAgr ERom MGos SLon WCru
                                WSHC WStI
- (f/F)   MRav SHBN
- 'Atlas' (m)   MBri SLim
  'Bruno' (f/T)   SLim
- 'Hayward' (f/F)   CBcs CDoC CHEx COtt CSBt EBee
                                EBre ELan EMil EMui EPfP EPla
                                ERea LRHS MBri MGos MWat NPal
                                SDca SHBN SPer SSta WCru WStI
- 'Jenny' (s-p/F)   CSBt EBee GKir LBuc LRHS MCoo
                                MGos SDea
- 'Solo'   CDoC SSte
- 'Tomuri' (m)   CBcs CDoC CHEx COtt CSBt
                                EBee EBre ELan EMil EMui EPfP
                                EPla ERea LRHS MGos MWat NPal
                                SHBN SPer SSta WCru WStI
giraldii   CMac
hypoleuca   WCru
  B&SWJ 5942 **new**
kolomikta ♀ H4   More than 30 suppliers
- B&SWJ 4243   WCru
latifolia B&SWJ 3563   WCru
melanandra   CPlN
pilosula   CFil CPLG CPlN CSPN EMil GCal
                                LHop SBrw SCoo SLon SSte WCru
                                WPGP WPat WSHC
polygama (F)   CPlN SSte WCru
- B&SWJ 5444   WCru

purpurea (F)   CPlN
- (f/F) **new**   CAgr
rubricaulis B&SWJ 3111   WCru
rufa B&SWJ 3525   WCru

Adelocaryum see *Lindelofia*

Adenium (Apocynaceae)
obesum ♀ H1   CRoM

Adenocarpus (Papilionaceae)
decorticans   CArn CTrC

Adenophora ✿ (Campanulaceae)
'Afterglow'   see *Campanula rapunculoides*
                                'Afterglow'
* *asiatica*   WFar
aurita   CBcs CFir CMea CPLG CRDP
                                EBee EChP EHyt EMan EPPr MHar
                                MLLN NSti NWoo SWat WCot
bulleyana   CBri CHar COlW EBre ECGN EGle
                                ELan EWTr EWsh GBuc LRHS MLwd
                                NBid SMac SPet SPlb SRot WBea
                                WCot WFar WGwG WHHs WPer
* *campanulata*   WPer
coelestis   EBee EMan SRot
- ACE 2455   EPot GBuc
confusa   EBee EMan GAbr LHop LRHS
                                MAnH SAsh WFar WHer
cymerae   EBee
divaricata   EMan WFoF
forrestii   CCol WFar
- var. *handeliana*   EBee
himalayana   GBri GDea MAnH MNrw SAga
                                WTcr
khasiana   CBri CFir MAnH MNrw NLar
                                WWin
koreana   EBee
kurilensis   SIng
latifolia hort.   see *A. pereskiifolia*
latifolia Fischer   GBri NBir WElm
liliifolia   CBri CHar CHea ECtt EEls ELan
                                EMan GAbr GCal GEil GMac LHop
                                LRHS NBro NCat NPer NSti SRot
                                SSvw SWat WFar WMaN WPer
§ *nikoensis*   CTCP EBee MNrw NBid NWCA
§ - var. *stenophylla*   WCot
nipponica   see *A. nikoensis* var. *stenophylla*
§ *pereskiifolia*   EBee SEND SHar SPlb WCot
                                WElm WFar WPer
polyantha   CHar EBee EHrv EMan GAbr
                                GBuc GMac LRHS MAnH MNrw
                                SBod SRms WFar WPic WPnP
polymorpha   see *A. nikoensis*
potaninii   CFir CHea EBee EGra EMan EWTr
                                GBuc LBBr MNrw SBla SGar
                                WCHb WFar WHal WPnP
stricta   LRHS MLan WWeb
- subsp. *sessilifolia*   EBee GBuc SPla
sublata   WFar
takedae   MAnH MWrn
- var. *howozana*   EBee LHop
taquetii **new**   GKev MAnH
- B&SWJ 1303   WCru
tashiroi   CLyd CNic CPrp EBee ECtt EPfP
                                GAbr GBri GBuc LHop MNrw
                                MUlv NBro NPro SCro SHel SMac
                                WCHb WGwG WHHs WWeb
triphylla   EMan GCal NBir WCru
- var. *hakusanensis*   EBee
- var. *japonica*   EBee
uehatae   MAnH
- B&SWJ 126   WCru

Adenostyles (*Asteraceae*)
alpina	see *Cacalia hastata*

Adiantum ✿ (*Adiantaceae*)
aethiopicum	WHer WRic
§ **aleuticum** ♀ H4	CFil CLAP CRDP EBee EFer ELan EMon GBin NBro NHol NMar WHal WPGP WRic WTMC
- 'Imbricatum'	EBee ECha LRHS NHar NHol SPla SRms WFar
- 'Japonicum'	CDes CFil CLAP CMil CRDP EBee ELan MBri NBir SBla SMad SRms SSpi WCot WCru WHal WPGP WRic
- 'Laciniatum'	CFil SRms
* - f. **minimum**	SRms
- 'Miss Sharples'	CFwr CLAP EBee LRHS NMar SRms WCru WFar WRic
- 'Subpumilum' ♀ H4	CLAP ELan GBin MRav
capillus-veneris	MWat
- 'Mairisii'	see *A.* x *mairisii*
- 'Pointonii'	NMar
cuneatum	see *A. raddianum*
diaphanum	NMar
formosanum new	WRic
hispidulum	NMar SRms
jordanii	CFil
§ x **mairisii** ♀ H3	NMar
* **monocolor**	MBri
pedatum ♀ H4	CBos CFil CHEx CLAP CRDP EBee EBre ECha EFer ELan ENot EPfP LEur LRHS MBri MWgw NHol SApp SChu SPar SPer SRot SSpi SWat WFar WPGP WTMC
- var. **aleuticum**	see *A. aleuticum*
- Asiatic form	see *A. aleuticum* 'Japonicum'
- 'Japonicum'	see *A. aleuticum* 'Japonicum'
- 'Roseum'	see *A. aleuticum* 'Japonicum'
- var. **subpumilum**	see *A. aleuticum* 'Subpumilum'
peruvianum	MBri
pubescens	MBri NMar
§ **raddianum** ♀ H2	CFil CHal NMar
- 'Crested Majus'	NMar
- 'Crested Micropinnulum'	NMar
- 'Deflexum'	NMar
- 'Double Leaflet'	NMar
- 'Elegans'	NMar
- 'Feltham Beauty'	NMar
- 'Fragrans'	see *A. raddianum* 'Fragrantissimum'
§ - 'Fragrantissimum'	MBri
- 'Fritz Lüthi' ♀ H2	CHal MBri NMar
- 'Gracilis'	see *A. raddianum* 'Gracillimum'
§ - 'Gracillimum'	NMar
- 'Grandiceps'	NMar
- 'Gympie Gold'	NMar
- 'Kensington Gem' ♀ H1	NMar
- 'Legrand Morgan'	NMar
- 'Legrandii'	NMar
- 'Micropinnulum'	NMar
- 'Pacific Maid'	NMar
- 'Pacottii'	NMar
- 'Tuffy Tips'	NMar
- 'Variegated Pacottii' (v)	NMar
- 'Variegated Tessellate' (v)	NMar
- 'Victoria's Elegans'	NMar
- 'Weigandii'	NMar
tenerum 'Green Glory'	NMar
venustum ♀ H4	CBos CFil CHEx CLAP CRDP EFer EGle EHyt ELan EMon GCal LEur NMar NVic SBla SDix SHFr SMad

Adina (*Rubiaceae*)
	SRms SSpi SWat WAbe WCom WCot WEas WFib WPGP WRic
whitei	NMar
rubella new	IArd

Adlumia (*Papaveraceae*)
asiatica new	WCru
fungosa	CHid CPlN CSpe EBre LRHS MCCP

Adonis (*Ranunculaceae*)
amurensis	EBee ECho EPar EPot GCrs GEdr LAma SCnR WCot WLin
- 'Fukujukai'	ECha WFar
- 'Pleniflora' (d)	EBee EPar GKir MBri MTed NLar SBod SPer WCot WFar
brevistyla	EBee EHyt ETow GCrs NLar NMen WAbe WCru
chrysocyathus	EBee
coerulea new	EBee
sutchuenensis	EBee LAma
tianschanica	EBee
vernalis	CPLG EPar GPoy MMHG NEgg

Adoxa (*Adoxaceae*)
moschatellina	CFox CKin NMen WHer WShi WWye

Adromischus (*Crassulaceae*)
cooperi	WEas

Aechmea (*Bromeliaceae*)
distichantha var. **schlumbergerii** new	CFir
fasciata ♀ H1	LRHS MBri

Aegle (*Rutaceae*)
sepiaria	see *Poncirus trifoliata*

Aegopodium (*Apiaceae*)
podagraria	EMon
gold-margined (v) new	
- 'Bengt'	EMon
- 'Dangerous' (v)	CHid CNat WCHb
- 'Lacock Blush'	CNat
- 'Variegatum' (v)	More than 30 suppliers

Aeonium (*Crassulaceae*)
arboreum ♀ H1	CAbb CHEx CTrF EPem EShb MWya SPar WHal WIvy WRos
- 'Atropurpureum' ♀ H1	CHEx CTrF EAmu EBee EPem ERea EShb IBlr MBri MLan MOak MRav NPer SEND SPar WEas
* - 'Magnificum'	EBee EPfP EWll SAPC SArc
- var. **rubrolineatum**	SPar
- 'Variegatum' (v)	EWll LPio NPer SSte
balsamiferum	CHEx CTbh CTrc CTrF EBee EPfP EWll SAPC SArc SChr SPar WHal
canariense	CAbb CHEx CTCP CTrF EBee WHal
§ - var. **subplanum**	CTrF
castello-paivae	CTrF EBee EShb
cuneatum	CTbh CTrF MLan SPar SPet SVen
* **decorum**	WCot
'Variegatum' (v)	
'Dinner Plate'	CHEx
x **domesticum**	see *Aichryson* x *domesticum*
goochiae new	EBee
haworthii ♀ H1	CAbb CHEx CHal CTbh CTrF MLan SPar WWeb
- 'Variegatum' (v)	EBee SChr
holochrysum	CTrF IBlr

lindleyi	CTrF SChr
nobile	CTrF
percarneum	CTrF
rubrolineatum	CTrF
simsii	CHal CTbh CTrF EBee SChr
subplanum	see *A. canariense* var. *subplanum*
tabuliforme ♀ H1	CTrF EPem SPar SSte
- 'Cristatum'	EPem
undulatum ♀ H1	CHEx CTrF
urbicum	CHEx
- 'Zwartkop' ♀ H1	More than 30 suppliers

Aeschynanthus (Gesneriaceae)

'Big Apple'	CHal WDib
Black Pagoda Group	WDib
'Fire Wheel'	WDib
hildebrandii	WDib
'Hot Flash'	WDib
lobbianus	see *A. radicans*
longicalyx	WDib
§ *longicaulis* ♀ H1	LRHS WDib
marmoratus	see *A. longicaulis*
'Mira'	MBri
'Mona'	MBri
parvifolius	see *A. radicans*
§ *radicans* ♀ H1	EBak MBri
- *lobbianus*	see *A. radicans*
speciosus ♀ H1	CHal WDib

Aesculus ✿ (Hippocastanaceae)

arguta	see *A. glabra* var. *arguta*
× *arnoldiana*	CDul CMCN SBir
- 'Autumn Splendor'	CDul
assamica	CFil
§ × *bushii*	CDul CMCN CTho MGos
californica	CBcs CFil CMCN CTho CTrw
	EPfP ERod IArd ISea NPal SMad
	SSpi SSta WPGP
× *carnea*	CDul ELan MBar
- 'Aureomarginata' (v)	ERod SMad WPat
- 'Briotii' ♀ H4	More than 30 suppliers
- 'Planticrensis'	CDul CTho EBee ENot
* - 'Variegata' (v)	CDul CMCN LRHS MGos WDin
chinensis	CMCN
'Dallimorei'	SMad
(graft-chimaera)	
§ *flava* ♀ H4	CFil CMCN CTho ECrN ENot EPfP
	MGag SPer SSpi WPGP
- f. *vestita*	CDoC CDul MBlu
flava × *pavia*	see *A.* × *hybrida*
georgiana	see *A. sylvatica*
glabra	CDul CFil CMCN CTho LRHS
§ - var. *arguta*	CFil CMCN GKir WDin
- 'October Red'	MBlu WPGP
glaucescens	see *A.* × *neglecta*
hippocastanum ♀ H4	More than 30 suppliers
- 'Aureomarginata' (v)	GKir
§ - 'Baumannii' (d) ♀ H4	CDoC CDul CLnd COtt CWib
	EBee ECrN ENot EPfP ERod GKir
	LPan LRHS MBri MGos NBee
	NWea SHBN SPer WDin WStI
- 'Digitata'	CDul CMCN GKir SMad
- 'Flore Pleno'	see *A. hippocastanum*
	'Baumannii'
- 'Hampton Court Gold'	CBcs CDul CEnd CMCN GKir
	NBhm
- 'Honiton Gold'	CTho
- 'Laciniata'	CDul CMCN ERod GKir LRHS
	MBlu SMad
- 'Monstrosa'	SMad
- 'Pyramidalis'	CDul CLnd LPan SMad
- 'Wisselink'	CDul CLnd CMCN MBlu SMad
§ × *hybrida*	CFil SBir SSpi

indica	CDul CHEx CLnd CMCN CTho
	EBee ECrN ELan ENot EPfP GGGa
	IArd LPan LRHS MBri NWea SLdr
	SPer SRPl SSpi WDin WPGP
- 'Sydney Pearce' ♀ H4	CDoC CDul CEnd CFil CMCN
	EBee ERod GKir MBlu MGag
	MGos SBir SMad SPer SSpi WPGP
× *marylandica*	CDul
memmingeri **new**	SBir
× *mississippiensis*	see *A.* × *bushii*
× *mutabilis* 'Harbisonii'	WWes
- 'Induta'	CLnd CMCN EBee EPfP LRHS
	MBlu MBri SSpi WWes
§ - 'Penduliflora'	CBcs CDul CEnd CTho EPfP
	LRHS MBlu NPal
§ × *neglecta*	CBcs CDul CLnd CMCN
- 'Erythroblastos' ♀ H4	CBcs CDoC CDul CEnd CFil CLnd
	CMCN CTho EBee EMil EPfP
	ERod GKir LNet LRHS MBlu SBir
	SHBN SMad SSpi WDin WPat
parviflora ♀ H4	CBcs CDul CFil CMCN CTho
	EBee ELan ENot EPfP IDee LNet
	LPan LPhx MBar MBlu MGos
	MLan NBea NBlu SKee SMad SPer
	SSpi SSta WDin WOrn WPGP
§ *pavia* ♀ H4	CBcs CDul CFil CMCN CTho EPfP
	GKir ISea SSpi WDin WWes
- 'Atrosanguinea'	CDul CEnd CFil CLnd CMCN EPfP
	ERod LRHS MBlu NPal SMad SSpi
- var. *discolor*	CFil WDin
- - 'Koehnei'	CDul LRHS MBlu MBri SPoG WOrn
- var. *flavescens*	NPal
- 'Penduliflora'	see *A.* × *mutabilis* 'Penduliflora'
- 'Purple Spring' **new**	MBlu SMad
- 'Rosea Nana'	CMCN MBlu WPat
splendens	see *A. pavia*
§ *sylvatica*	CFil CTho
turbinata	CBcs CLnd CMCN IDee MBlu
	WBVN
- var. *pubescens*	MBlu SMad WPGP
wilsonii	CBcs CFil
× *woerlitzensis*	CLnd ISea WCwm

Aethionema (Brassicaceae)

armenum	CNic MOne WLin
coridifolium	WPer
§ *grandiflorum* ♀ H4	NBro SBla SRms WBVN WPer
- Pulchellum Group	CLyd EPot GKev GKir MBro
♀ H4	NMen WWin
iberideum	CNic ETow MOne MWat SRms
oppositifolium	CLyd GTou MBro MWat WHoo
pulchellum	see *A. grandiflorum*
§ *saxatile*	CBrm EHyt
'Warley Rose' ♀ H4	CLyd EDAr ELan EPot GKir LHop
	MBro MWat NLon NMen SIng
	SRms WPat WWin
'Warley Ruber'	CLyd EDAr NBir NHol SIng WAbe
	WHoo

Afrocarpus (Podocarpaceae)

falcatus	ECou GCal

Agapanthus ✿ (Alliaceae)

blue **new**	SWal
'Aberdeen' **new**	CPne XDoo
'Adonis' **new**	IBlr
§ *africanus* ♀ H1	CAbb CElw CM&M EBee EHrv
	EPfP EWTr GSki IBlr LRHS MBNS
	MGrG MWgw NBlu NRog SAPC
	SArc SBod SDes SPer SWat WBrE
	WFar WPer
* - 'Albus' ♀ H1	CBcs CDoC CFwr CHad CHid
	EBee EMan ENot EPfP EWTr GKir

	GSki IBlr IKee LRHS MBNS NBlu SBod SDes SEND SYvo WFTG WPer XDoo
* - 'Big Blue'	CKno EBee GGar
'Albatross'	ECha
* 'Albus'	CAvo CBri CSBt MHer SAga SPar WWeb
'Amsterdam'	CFwr XDoo
'Angela'	CPne
'Aphrodite' **new**	IBlr
'Arctic Star'	GSki
Ardernei hybrid	CBot CDes CFil CPne EBee ECha EWes GCal IBlr LPhx LPio MSte MTed NCat SAga SSpi SUsu WCot WPGP XDoo
'Baby Blue'	CLyd CWib IBlr LRHS SApp
'Ballyrogan'	IBlr LPio
'Beeches Dwarf'	EBee
'Ben Hope'	EBee GBuc IBlr WCot
'Bethlehem Star'	GSki SRos
'Bicton Bluebell'	IBlr
'Blue Baby'	LRHS WFar
'Blue Brush'	CAbb CFai EMil SVil
'Blue Cascade'	IBlr
'Blue Companion'	CPne IBlr
'Blue Diamond'	EHrv SRos
'Blue Dot' **new**	EBee EFou EMan NCat
'Blue Fortune'	WGer
'Blue Giant'	CBro CHid CPen EBee EWTr IBal IBlr LRHS MSte SAga SDes SWat WDav WFar
'Blue Globe'	CM&M EBee EChP EMan ERou GMaP MCAu NCat NGdn WLow WMnd WSan WTMC
'Blue Gown'	CPne
'Blue Haze' **new**	SRos
'Blue Imp'	GBuc GSki IBlr LRHS MMHG NHol XDoo
'Blue Méoni'	XDoo
'Blue Moon'	CBro CHad CPen EBee ECha EGle IBal IBlr LRHS MTed NPri SEND WCot
'Blue Skies'	CBcs EBee IBlr SDes WTMC XDoo
'Blue Triumphator'	CHid EBee EPfP EWTr EWll IBlr LBow LPio LRHS SBod SDes SMrm WCot
'Blue Velvet'	CPne
'Bressingham Blue'	CBro CPne CTri EBre GCal IBlr LRHS MRav MSte NVic SChu SPar SSpe SWat
'Bressingham Bounty'	EBre
'Bressingham White'	CPne EBee EBre ECtt EFou EMan LPio LRHS MCLN MRav MTed SOkh SSpe SWat WRus
'Bristol'	CFwr XDoo
'Buckingham Palace'	CBro CDes CFil CKno EBee IBlr WPGP XDoo
Cambourne hybrids	MBri SDes
'Cambridge'	CPne XDoo
§ *campanulatus*	CElw CRDP CWCL EBee EBlw ELan GGar GKir GSki IBlr ISea LRHS SWat SYvo WCot WFar WLRN
- var. *albidus*	More than 30 suppliers
- 'Albovittatus'	CLAP CSam ECho EVFa LPhx
- bright blue	GCal
- 'Buckland'	IBlr
- 'Cobalt Blue'	ECha
- 'Isis'	CAbb CBro CFir CTri CWCL EBre ECha GBuc IBal IBlr LRHS SMrm SRos
- 'Meibont' (v)	WCot
- 'Oxbridge'	IBlr
- 'Oxford Blue'	CFil CPne EBee GBri GBuc IBlr SRos WPGP

- subsp. *patens* ♀ H3	EBee EBla EMan EPfP GBri GBuc LPio SSpi SWat WPGP
- - deep blue	CFir IBlr
- 'Premier'	CFil CPne EBee IBlr WPGP
- 'Profusion'	CBro CWCL EBre ECha IBal IBlr LRHS SRos SSpi WFar
- 'Slieve Donard Variety'	EBee IBlr WFar
- 'Spokes'	IBlr
- variegated (v)	ECha NPer
- 'Wedgwood Blue'	IBlr SApp
- 'Wendy'	IBlr
- 'White Hope'	IBlr SRos
- 'White Triumphator'	WCot
'Castle of Mey'	CFil CPlt EBee EGle IBlr LPhx MTho SBla SRos WPGP XDoo
'Catharina'	CPne XDoo
caulescens ♀ H1	CFil EBee IBlr WBrE
- subsp. *angustifolius*	IBlr WCot
- subsp. *caulescens*	IBro SWat
'Cedric Morris'	ERea IBlr XDoo
'Chandra'	IBlr
'Charlotte' **new**	XDoo
'Cherry Holley'	LPio SRos
'Clarence House'	CBro
coddii	EMan IBlr LPio LRHS SChu
comptonii	CAvo CFil CPou IBlr SYvo WPGP XDoo
- subsp. *comptonii*	SWat
- subsp. *longitubus*	CPne EBee LPio SWat
Danube	see *A.* 'Donau'
'Dawn Star'	XDoo
'Dayspring'	CRow
'Debbie'	CFwr CPne XDoo
'Delft'	IBlr
'Density'	IBlr
'Devon Dawn'	CPne
'Doctor Brouwer' **new**	CPne NGby
§ 'Donau'	CBro CDoC CHid EBee EBlw EMan WFar XDoo
dyeri	CBro IBlr
'Elisabeth' **new**	CPne
'Eve'	EBee IBlr
'Evening Star'	CPne ECha LRHS
'Findlay's Blue'	CFil CLCN EBee GBuc WPGP
'Gayle's Lilac'	CBcs CDoC CElw CFai CFwr CPne CPrp CSam EBee EChP EGle EMan EMil EVFa IBal LPio LRHS MAvo NSti SApp SPoG WCot WGer WWhi
'Glenavon' **new**	CAbb
'Golden Rule' (v)	CDes CFir CRow EBee EHoe GBuc IBlr SAga SSpi WPGP
§ Headbourne hybrids	More than 30 suppliers
'Helen' **new**	IBlr
'Holbeach'	CFwr XDoo
'Holbrook'	CSam
'Hydon Mist'	XDoo
'Ice Blue Star'	SRos
'Ice Lolly'	CBro
inapertus	CBro CFil CRDP LRHS SBla SWat WCot WPGP
- 'Graskop'	SWat
- subsp. *hollandii*	CAvo CPne GCal IBlr MSte SWat
- - 'Lydenburg'	IBlr
- subsp. *inapertus*	IBlr SWat WCot
I - - 'Albus' **new**	IBlr
- - 'Cyan' **new**	IBlr
- subsp. *intermedius*	CFil EBee GCal IBlr SSpi SWat
- - 'Wolkberg' **new**	IBlr
- subsp. *parviflorus*	IBlr
- subsp. *pendulus*	CDes EBee IBlr
'Innocence'	IBlr

I	'Intermedia' **new**	EBee
	'Jack's Blue'	More than 30 suppliers
	'Jersey Giant'	EBee
	'Jodie'	CPne
	'Johanna' **new**	CPne
	Johannesberg hybrids	ECha
	'K. Wiley' **new**	WPrP
	'Kew White' **new**	EWTr
	'Kingston Blue'	EHrv IBlr SMHy SUsu WFar XDoo
	'Kobold'	EBee EGle SBod WFar
	'Lady Edith'	IBlr
	'Lady Moore'	EBee EGle IBlr SUsu
	'Latent Blue'	IBlr
	'Leighton Blue'	MBri
	'Lilac Time'	CPne IBlr
	'Lilliput'	More than 30 suppliers
	'Loch Hope' ♀ H3	CAbb CAvo CBro CCtw CDoC CFil CHid CPne CPrp EBee EBlw EGle EMan LAst SPer WCot XDoo
	'Luly'	CPne XDoo
	'Mabel Grey'	IBlr
	'Magnifico'	IBlr
	'Malvern'	WWeb
	'Marcus' **new**	CPne
	'Mariètte'	CFwr CPne XDoo
*	'Marjorie'	CLCN CWCL
	'Martine'	CFwr CPne XDoo
	'Midnight'	CHad SAga
	'Midnight Blue'	ELan EPfP GBuc GCal GSki IBlr LPhx LPio LRHS MSte SBla WFar
	'Midnight Star'	CBro ECha GSki IBal LRHS MSte SRos WFar WPrP XDoo
	mixed whites	WCFE
I	'Mooreanus' misapplied	CFil EPfP GCal IBlr WPGP XDoo
	'Morning Star'	GSki
	'Naomi'	LAst
	'Navy Blue'	CAbb CCtw CDoC CFai CMdw CPne CPrp EBee FChP EMan EOrc EWll GBin IBal IPot MBri MLLN MNrw MSph NLhi SApp WCot WFlG WMaN WWhi
	New Blue' **new**	CPen ENot
	'Norman Hadden'	IBlr
	'Nottingham'	CFwr XDoo
	nutans	IBlr LRHS WCot
	- 'Albus'	GCal
	'Nyx'	IBlr
	'Oslo'	CFwr CPne XDoo
	Palmer's hybrids	see *A.* Headbourne hybrids
	'Patent Blue'	IBlr
	'Penelope Palmer'	IBlr
	'Peter Pan'	CBcs CBro CElw CFwr CHid CMea COlW CPen CPne CPrp CRow CSWP CTrC EBee ECtt EOrc GBuc GGar GSki IBal LPhx LPio LRHS MCAu MRav SDes SPla WFar WQRN WWeb
	'Phantom'	CPne IBlr
	'Pinchbeck' **new**	CPne XDoo
	'Pinocchio'	CFwr EBee MLan NHol WViv
	'Plas Merdyn Blue'	IBlr
	'Plas Merdyn White'	CFir IBlr
	'Podge Mill'	CLCN CWCL EGle IBlr
	'Polar Ice'	CFir CPne FBec EFou IBlr NHol WFar
	praecox	CFil CLAP EBee IBlr WViv
	- 'Atlas' **new**	IBlr
	- 'Bangor Blue'	IBlr
	- 'Blue Formality'	IBlr
I	- 'Blue Mercury'	IBlr
	- 'Dwarf White'	see *A.* white dwarf hybrids
	- 'Flore Pleno' (d)	CDes CFai CPne EBee ECha ELan EMan IBlr LPhx WCot WFar WPGP
	- subsp. *floribundus*	SWat
	- subsp. *maximus*	CPou IBlr SSpi
	'Albus'	
	- 'Miniature Blue'	SWat
	- subsp. *minimus*	CElw CPne GSki IBlr SWat XDoo
	- - 'Adelaide'	EBee SWat
	- - blue	SWat
I	- - 'Supreme'	IBlr
	- - white	SWat
	- 'Mount Stewart'	IBlr
§	- subsp. *orientalis*	CSut EBee EHrv ERea ETub GGar GSki IBlr IBro NPal SMad SVen SWat WHil WPic
	- - var. *albiflorus*	CBro CPne CPou CSut EBee GSki IBal LBow NPal
	- subsp. *praecox*	IBlr IGor
	- - azure	SWat
	- - 'Silver Sceptre'	IBlr
	- - 'Variegatus' (v) ♀ H1	CDes
	- Slieve Donard form	IBlr
	- 'Storms River'	SWat
	- 'Titan' **new**	IBlr
	- 'Vittatus' (v)	WCot WFar
	'Purple Cloud'	More than 30 suppliers
	'Purple Star'	SVil
	'Queen Anne'	SVen
	'Rhône'	EFou IBlr
	rich blue	XDoo
	'Rosewarne'	CAbb CBcs CPne EBee GQui IBlr NLar SVil WGer XDoo
	'Rotterdam'	XDoo
	'Royal Blue'	CBro CWCL GBuc LPio NHol SVil
	'Sandringham'	CDes CFil CRow EBee IBlr WPGP XDoo
	'Sapphire'	IBlr
	'Sea Coral'	CAbb CBcs CDoC CFai CPne
	'Sea Foam'	CBcs CPne EBee MBNS MCAu NLar
	'Sea Mist'	CBcs
	'Sea Spray'	CPne CTrC
	'Silver Baby' **new**	CAbb
	'Silver Mist'	CPne IBlr
	Silver Moon	EHan ELan EMan ENot EPfP LBuc MBri WWeb
	= 'Notfred' (v)	MBri WWeb
	silver variegated (v)	SMrm
	'Snowball'	CBcs CDoC CFai CLAP COlW CPne CPrp EBee ERea MSte SCro SDes SVen SVil XDoo
	'Snowcloud' **new**	CAbb CPne
I	'Snowdonii' **new**	WAbb
*	'Snowdrop'	CFwr CM&M CPne CPrp EBee FChP EGle EMan EVFa FWll LAst LHop LPio MBri MMil MNrw MSte MTPN SOkh SPer SPla WCot WFar WWhi
	'Snowy Eyes' **new**	EBee
	'Snowy Owl'	CLAP EBee
	'Starburst'	IBlr
	'Stephanie Charm'	XDoo
	'Storm Cloud' (d)	CBro
	'Streamline'	More than 30 suppliers
	'Summer Clouds'	ENot LRHS
	'Summer Skies'	ENot LRHS
	'Sunfield'	CPne LRHS WDav WWeb XDoo
	'Super Star'	XDoo
	'Sylvine'	XDoo
	'Tall Boy'	IBlr
	'Timaru'	CAbb CCtw CElw CFai CFwr CHid CM&M CPne CPrp EBee EChP EGle EMan LAst LHop MBri MLLN MSph MTPN NCat NLar SOkh WCot WMaN WWhi
	'Tinkerbell' (v)	More than 30 suppliers
	'Torbay'	CElw IBlr SBla XDoo
	Tresco hybrid **new**	CHEx

I	'Tresco Select' **new**	EBee
	'Twilight'	IBlr
	umbellatus L'Hérit.	see *A. africanus*
	umbellatus Redouté	see *A. praecox* subsp. *orientalis*
	'Underway'	EFou GCal IBlr
I	'Virgineus'	XDoo
	'Wedgewood Blue' **new**	IBal
	white	GGar SWal
	'White Christmas'	EBee ERea
	'White Dwarf'	see *A.* white dwarf hybrids
§	white dwarf hybrids	CBro CPen CPne EBee ECha EFou EMan EPfP IBal LRHS MBri SMrm WFar
	'White Ice'	CAbb CBcs CPne EBee GQui SDes XDoo
	'White Starlet'	IBal SApp
	'White Superior'	CM&M CPne CSpe EBee EChP EMan ERou GMaP LAst MCAu NGdn SCro WLow WMnd WSan WTMC WWye
	'White Umbrella'	EBee
	'Windlebrooke'	EBee ECha
	'Windsor Castle'	EBee IBlr
	'Windsor Grey'	CDes IBlr WPGP
	'Winsome'	IBlr
	'Wolga'	EBee
	'Yves Klein'	IBlr
	'Zella Thomas'	CPne LHyd

Agapetes (Ericaceae)

	serpens ♀ H1	CBcs CKob CPlN SLon
	- 'Nepal Cream'	SLon
	- 'Scarlet Elf'	SBrw

Agarista (Ericaceae)

| § | **populifolia** | WFar |

Agastache (Lamiaceae)

	B&SWJ 4187 from Korea	WCru
	anethiodora	see *A. foeniculum*
	anisata	see *A. foeniculum*
	'Ankum Summer' **new**	CSpe
	'Apache Sunset' **new**	NPPs
	'Apricot Sprite'	MHar NPPs SMac WCHb WCot WGwG WHHs
	aurantiaca new	LHop
	'Black Adder' **new**	EFou LHop
	'Blue Fortune'	EBee ECtt EMan EMil EMon ENot EPfP GBri IBal LRHS MCLN MHdf SMrm SOkh WFar WWeb
	camphor hyssop	EOHP
§	**cana**	EBee ECtt EMan EOHP LPhx MAnH MDKP MWrn SPoG WCHb WCot WFar WRos WSan
	- 'Cinnabar Rose'	NBir WFar
	- 'Heather Queen'	EOHP
*	**canariensis new**	WCHb
	'Firebird'	More than 30 suppliers
§	**foeniculum**	CAgr CArn CBod CPrp CSev EChP ECha EFou ELan ELau EOHP GMaP GPoy LPhx LRHS MCAu MChe MHer MRav NFor SBla SRms WFar WHHs WMnd WPer WWye
	- 'Alabaster'	CBcs EBee EGoo ELau EMon LPhx SAga WCHb WRus WWye
	- 'Alba'	EFou MLLN SHDw WFar
	'Globetrotter'	LHop
	'Glowing Embers'	EBee ELan ENot LBuc LRHS
	'Honey Bee Blue'	EWll LRHS WWeb
	'Honey Bee White' **new**	WBry
§	**mexicana**	CSev EBee MChe MHar SCro SMHy SMrm WCom WHHs WJek WSan WWeb

	- 'Carille Carmine'	EMan
	- 'Champagne'	EGoo EMan WCHb WPer WRus
	- 'Mauve Beauty'	EBee NNor SMrm WPer
	- pink	MBri
	- 'Red Fortune' PBR	ENot MBri
	- 'Rose Beauty'	SMrm
	- 'Rosea'	see *A. cana*
	- 'Toronjil Morado' **new**	LHop
	neomexicana	WGwG WHHs
	'Lavender Haze' **new**	
	nepetoides	CArn CHar EBee EMan EPPr IIve MSal MWod NLar SMad WCHb WWpP WWye
	'New Blue' **new**	EPfP
	'Painted Lady'	CSpe EBee EMan EVFa LPhx SMrm WCot WWpP
	pallidiflora var. **pallidiflora**	EBee
	palmeri	LHop
	'Pink Panther' **new**	EBee
	pringlei	EChP GEil MWrn NLar SWat WCHb WWpP
	'Purple Candle'	EFou EWes EWll MTis SPla
	rugosa	CArn CBod CFir CSev ELau EMan EOHP GBar GPoy LPhx LRHS MLLN MSal MWrn SSth SWat WHHs WJek WPer WSel WWye
	- pink form	CSam
	- 'Alba'	MCAu MWrn
	- 'Korean Zest' B&SWJ 735	EBee EGoo EMan SUsu WCru WWeb
	rupestris	EBee EChP EMar EShb LHop LPhx MWrn WCot WHil WKif WLin WSan
	scrophulariifolia	EBee EWll NBur WCHb WRos WWpP
	'Serpentine'	EBee EMon
	'Tangerine Dreams'	CSpe EBee EMan LPhx SAga SMrm WCot
	'Tutti-frutti'	EBee EBre EHrv SPoG
	urticifolia	CArn CSpe LRHS MSal WOut
	- 'Alba'	EBee WPer
	- 'Liquorice Blue'	ECtt EWTr LRHS MLan MWgw NBid NDov NGdn NLar SPer SPoG SWat WFar WGer WHHs WPer
	- 'Liquorice White'	CRDP EBee ECtt LRHS MWgw NBur NDov NLar SPer SWat WHHs

Agathaea see *Felicia*

Agathosma (Rutaceae)

| | **crenulata** | ELau |

Agave ✿ (Agavaceae)

	albicans	EOas EPem
	americana ♀ H1	CAbb CBcs CCtw CDoC CHEx CHad CTrC CWSG EAmu EBot ELau EOas GQui IBlr LPal LPan MCCP MSPs NPal NPri SAPC SArc SChr SMad SNew SPar SSte STop WMul
	- 'Marginata' (v)	CBrP CHal CHll EBot EOas IBlr MPRe NPri
	- 'Mediopicta' (v) ♀ H1	CHEx CTbh SAPC SArc SPar STop WEas
§	- 'Mediopicta Alba' (v) ♀ H1	CBrP EAmu EOas MPRe SChr
	- 'Mediopicta' misapplied	see *A. americana* 'Mediopicta Alba'
	- 'Striata' (v)	NBlu
	- 'Variegata' (v) ♀ H1	More than 30 suppliers
	angustifolia var. **marginata** hort. **new**	MPRe
I	**atrovirens** 'Nana'	MPRe
	attenuata	CBrP EOas LRHS SAPC SArc

bracteosa	CTrF EOas EPem MPRe
§ *celsii*	CHEx CTbh EOas SAPC SArc SChr
chrysantha	CAbb CTrC EOas EPem
colorata	CTrF
deserti	CBrP EOas
ferdinandi-regis	see *A. scabra* x *A. victoriae-reginae*
ferox	CAbb EOas MPRe SPar
filifera ♀ H1	CHEx CTrF EOas EPem MPRe SChr
franzosinii	CFir CTrF SPar
ghiesbreghtii	EOas
guadalajarana 'Jalisco'	EOas
havardiana	CTrC EOas
horrida	SChr
kerchovei	EOas
lechuguilla	CTrC EOas SChr
lophantha	CFir
- var. *coerulescens*	EOas
§ - var. *univittata*	EOas
lurida	MPRe
macroacantha new	CFir
mckelveyana	EOas
mitis	see *A. celsii*
§ *mitriformis*	WAbe
montana	CFir EBee
neomexicana	EOas SIgm
nizandensis	CHEx
palmeri	CAbb CTrC EOas EPem IDee SChr
parryi	CAbb CDoC CTrC EOas IDee LEdu SChr SIgm SSte WPGP
- var. *couesii*	see *A. parryi* var. *parryi*
- var. *huachucensis*	CBrP EOas
§ - var. *parryi*	CBrP CFir EOas
parviflora ♀ H1	CTrC SChr
aff. *pelona* new	EBee
potatorum ♀ H1	SChr
salmiana	CTrF
- var. *ferox*	CBrP EOas SAPC SArc SChr
scabra	CTrC EBee EOas
- x *victoriae-reginae*	CFir EPem SChr
schidigera	CBrP CFir GCal
schottii	EOas
shawii	EOas
sisalana	CTrF EOas
striata	CTrC
stricta ♀ H1	EOas MPRe
toumeyana	SChr
univittata	see *A. lophantha* var. *univittata*
utahensis ♀ H1	EOas SEND SIgm
- var. *discreta*	SChr
- var. *eborispina*	EOas
- var. *nevadensis*	EOas
victoriae-reginae ♀ H1	CBrP CTrC CTrF EOas SPar
xylonacantha	EOas

Ageratina see *Eupatorium*

Ageratum (Asteraceae)
corymbosum	CSpe

Aglaonema (Araceae)
§ *crispum*	MBri
- 'Marie'	MBri
'Malay Beauty'	MBri
roebelinii	see *A. crispum*
'Silver Queen' ♀ H1	MBri

Agonis (Myrtaceae)
flexuosa	CTrC
juniperina new	LRav

Agrimonia (Rosaceae)
eupatoria	CArn CKin COld EBee ELau GPoy

	IIve MChe MGas MHer NMir SIde SWat WBri WCHb WHHs WHbs WHer WWye
- 'Topas'	ELau
grandiflora	EBee
gryposepala	EBee
odorata hort.	see *A. procera*
odorata (L.) Mill.	see *A. repens*
pilosa	CArn EBee ELau IIve MSal
§ *procera*	WBWf
§ *repens*	CTCP GBar MSal WCHb

Agropyron (Poaceae)
glaucum	see *Elymus hispidus*
magellanicum	see *Elymus magellanicus*
pubiflorum	see *Elymus magellanicus*
scabrum	see *Elymus scabrus*

Agrostemma (Caryophyllaceae)
coronaria	see *Lychnis coronaria*
githago	GWCH MBow MWgw WHer WJek

Agrostis (Poaceae)
calamagrostis	see *Stipa calamagrostis*
§ *canina* Silver Needles' (v)	CBre CHor EBre EChP EGra EHoe EHul EMan EMon EPPr EWes GCal GKir LRHS MMoz NBir NHol WElm WFar WPnP WRos
karsensis	see *A. stolonifera*
nebulosa	EFWa LIck
stolonifera 'Icy Flames' (v) new	WAlt

Aichryson (Crassulaceae)
§ x *domesticum*	CHEx CHal EBee
- 'Variegatum' (v) ♀ H1	CHal EBak EBee
palmense new	CPLG

Ailanthus (Simaroubaceae)
§ *altissima*	CBcs CDul CHEx CLnd CWlb EBee EBre ECrN EMil ENot EPfP GKir LPan MBlu MGos NBee SAPC SArc SMad SPar SPer SRPl WDin WNor WOrn WStl
- f. *erythrocarpa* new	MBlu
- var. *sutchuenensis*	CFil
- var. *tanakae* B&SWJ 6777	WCru
glandulosa	see *A. altissima*

Ainsliaea (Asteraceae)
acerifolia B&SWJ 4795	WCru
fragrans new	EBee

Aiphanes (Arecaceae)
aculeata	LPal

Ajania (Asteraceae)
§ *pacifica*	CHal CSLe EBee ECtt ELan EMFP EMan LDai LRHS MOak MPWC SPar WWal
pallasiana new	GIBF
tibetica JJH 9308103	NWCA

Ajuga (Lamiaceae)
ciliata var. *villosior*	CFir EBee GCal
genevensis 'Tottenham'	EBee
'Little Court Pink' new	LRHS
metallica hort.	see *A. pyramidalis*
'Monmotaro San'	EMan
'Pink Spires'	EBee NCot
§ *pyramidalis*	CFee CLyd EBee ECha ECho SCro WHer WMoo

	– 'Metallica Crispa'	CRDP CRez EBee EMar EWes GKir MBro NFla NHar NRya SPar WFTG WFar WPnP WWeb WWpP
	reptans	CKin CNic ECtt ELau EWTr GPoy LGro LPBA MChe MHer MSal NMir NSco SGar WFar WHHs WRHF WWpP
	– 'Alba'	CArn CRow EBee ECtt EMan GCal MCAu MNrw NBro NPro NSti SRms WAlt WCHb WFar WHil WLHH WMoo WPer WWye
	– f. *albiflora* 'Silver Shadow'	NPro
	– 'Arctic Fox' (v)	More than 30 suppliers
	– 'Argentea'	see *A. reptans* 'Variegata'
§	– 'Atropurpurea'	More than 30 suppliers
	– 'Braunherz'	More than 30 suppliers
	– 'Burgundy Glow' (v)	More than 30 suppliers
§	– 'Catlin's Giant' ♀ H4	More than 30 suppliers
	– 'Chocolate Chip'	see *A. reptans* 'Valfredda'
	– 'Delight' (v)	ECot SBod WCer WEas
	– 'Ebony' **new**	NPro
	– 'Ermine'	CBgR CFai EBee EChP EGle EMan EMar EMil LAst MBNS MNrw MTPN NCat NCot NLar NSti SPer WCot WLin
	– 'Evening Glow' **new**	CFwr
	– 'Green Splash' **new**	EBee
	– 'Grey Lady'	CBos CMea CSpe EMan GBuc ITer WLin
	– 'John Pierpoint'	WCot
	– 'Julia'	EMon
	– 'Jumbo'	see *A. reptans* 'Jungle Beauty'
§	– 'Jungle Beauty'	CHid CRDP CRow CSev ECtt EMan EPar EPfP GCal IHMH MRav WCer WHen
	– 'Macrophylla'	see *A. reptans* 'Catlin's Giant'
§	– 'Multicolor' (v)	CArn CHEx COkL COlW EDAr ELan EPar IHMH LAst LGro LPBA MBar MLLN MRav NArg NChi NFor SBod SDes SPar SPer SPlb SRPl SRms WCer WFar WHil WMoo WPer WTel EBee GSki LRHS NSti
	– 'Palisander'	
I	– 'Pat's Selection' (v)	EMan
	– 'Pink Elf'	CBcs CBre CLyd CMCo CMHG CRow EMan ENot EOrc EWTr MGrG MHer MRav NBro SHel SIng SUsu SWat WBea WCer WFar WHoo WLin WMoo WPer WWpP
	– 'Pink Splendour'	CBre CMea NChi WBry WCer
	– 'Pink Surprise'	CHid CNic CRow CSpe EBre ECha ECtt EHoe EMar EPri GBar LRHS MHer NRya SCro SRPl SSvw WCHb WEas WFar WMoo WTMC
	– 'Purple Brocade'	CStr ECha EHoe WBro
	– 'Purple Torch'	COlW EBee ESis WCer WEas WOut WTMC WViv WWpP
	– 'Purpurea'	see *A. reptans* 'Atropurpurea'
	– 'Rainbow'	see *A. reptans* 'Multicolor'
	– 'Rosea'	CHal EBee NPro WHil WMoo
	– 'Rowden Royal Purple'	CRow
	– 'Schneekerze'	EBee
	– 'Tricolor'	see *A. reptans* 'Multicolor'
§	– 'Valfredda'	CWes EBee EDAr EMan EWll GBin NLar SHar WCot
§	– 'Variegata' (v)	COkL EBre ECtt EDAr EHoe ELan EMar EPar GDra LGro LHop MHer MLLN NBid NEgg NPPs SBod SPer SPet SRms SWat WCot WEas WFar WMoo

Akebia (Lardizabalaceae)

	longeracemosa B&SWJ 3606	WCru

	x *pentaphylla*	CPIN EMil EPfP ERea GQui LRHS MAsh SBra SPer WBcn WSHC
	– B&SWJ 2829	WCru
	quinata	More than 30 suppliers
	– B&SWJ 4425	WCru
	– 'Alba'	CSPN
	– cream	EPfP LRHS MAsh SBra SPer SSta WCru
	– variegated (v)	WCru
	trifoliata	CBcs CHEx CPIN EBee EPfP GKir LBuc LRHS MDun SLim WBcn
	– B&SWJ 2829	WCru

Alangium (Alangiaceae)

	chinense	CFil EPla LAst SLon WBVN WBcn WPGP
	platanifolium	CBot CFil CMCN EPla IArd IDee MBlu SMad WBod WPGP

Albizia (Mimosaceae)

	distachya	see *Paraserianthes lophantha*
§	**julibrissin**	CArn CFil CTrC ISea LAst MPRe MWat SHFr SPlb WDin WMul WPat
	– 'Ombrella' **new**	NPSI
	– f. *rosea* ♀ H2-3	More than 30 suppliers
	lophantha	see *Paraserianthes lophantha*
	saman	MGol

Albuca (Hyacinthaceae)

	from Lesotho **new**	GCal
	altissima	CStu EBee WCot
	canadensis	CStu WCot
	humilis	CStu ECho ESis ETow NMen WAbe WCot
	juncifolia	EMan WCot
	nelsonii	CAvo EBee LRHS WCot
	setosa	WCot
	shawii	CDes CPen CPrp CStu EBee EMan ERos IFro ITer NSla SAga SBla SOkd WAbe WCot WOBN WPGP WPrP
	spiralis	CDes

Alcea (Malvaceae)

	'Arabian Nights'	WBry
	'Blackcurrant Whirl'	WBry
	'Double Moonlight' (d)	WBry WRHF
	ficifolia	EMan MCCP NPPs NPri WHil WMoo
	– 'Golden Eye'	NBur
	pallida	EMan EMar NPri WHil
§	**rosea**	GWCH LAst MWgw WFar WLRN
	– 'Black Beauty'	EWTr NBur
	– Chater's Double Group (d)	CHad EBre ECtt EPfP GKir LPVe MBri NFor NNor SCoo SRob WGwG WMnd
	– – chamois (d)	WViv
	– – chestnut brown (d)	WViv
	– – pink (d)	ECtt NPri SPer WViv
	– – red (d)	ECtt NPri WViv
	– – salmon pink (d)	NPri WViv
	– – violet (d) **new**	NPri
	– – white (d)	NPri SPer WViv
	– – yellow (d)	ECtt NPri SPer WViv
	– double apricot (d)	NBur
	– double pink (d)	MHer
	– double red (d)	MHer
	– double white (d)	EBee MHer
	– double yellow (d)	EBee MHer
	– 'Lemon Light'	EBee LHop NBur
	– Majorette Group	ECtt
	– 'Nigra'	CArn CHad COlW EBee EChP EGoo EHrv EMar LAst LHop LPVe LRHS MBNS MCAu MHer MSte

		MTis NFor NGdn NPPs NPri SAga
		SGar SMad SPer SRob WCom
		WHHs WHil
	- single	COIW LPVe
	- single pink	LHop LRHS MCAu
	- single white	MCAu
	- Summer Carnival	
	Group	MBow SWal WGor
	- 'Victoria Ann' (v)	CPla MCCP
	- yellow	IHMH MMHG
§	*rugosa*	CHad CSam EMan EOrc MSte
		MWgw NPri SDix SMad WPGP
		WRus
	- *alba*	CBri

Alchemilla ✿ (*Rosaceae*)

§	*abyssinica*	CHid GBuc WBro WHen
	alpina misapplied	see *A. conjuncta*, *A. plicatula*
	alpina L.	CFee CLyd EPar GKir GTou LBee
		LRHS MCLN MRav MTho NChi
		NEgg NFor NLon NMir SHel SIng
		SPar SRPl SRms SWat WCom WFar
		WHHs WMoo WPer WWin
	aroanica	EBee
	arvensis	see *Aphanes arvensis*
§	*conjuncta*	More than 30 suppliers
	elisabethae	ECGP EMon MGrG WCHb
	ellenbeckii	CFee EBee EMon GAbr GBar
		GKir MBar MBct MHer SWat
		WCHb WCom WFar WHen WPGP
		WPer
	epipsila	EBee LPhx MSte NLar WPer
	erythropoda ♀ H4	More than 30 suppliers
	faeroensis	CMCo EGle MBct NChi NLon
		WPer
	- var. *pumila*	CLyd EBee
	filicaulis 'Minima'	CNat
§	*fulgens*	EWTr WHen
	glaucescens	CNat
	koppeana hort.	see *A. plicatula*
	iniquiformis	EBee WPGP
	lapeyrousei	EMon EPPr SIng WTer
	mollis ♀ H4	More than 30 suppliers
l	- 'Auslese'	EWTr LPVe LRHS WHil WWpP
*	- 'Robusta'	EBee ECha EPla LRHS MTho NBur
		SEND SPlb SRPl SWat WFar WMnd
		WMoo WTuP WWpP
*	- 'Senior'	EMil WMnd
	- 'Thriller'	IBal NArg NBur WWeb
	- 'Variegata' (v)	IBlr
	monticola	WPer
	'Mr Poland's Variety'	see *A. venosa*
	pedata	see *A. abyssinica*
§	*plicatula*	WPer
	psilomischa	EBee EMon LRHS
	pumila	EFou MGrG NCot
	saxatilis	WPer
	speciosa	SHel
	splendens misapplied	see *A. fulgens*
	straminea	EFou EMFP
§	*venosa*	EBee SCro
	aff. *venosa*	EPla
	vetteri	EBee
	vulgaris hort.	see *A. xanthochlora*
§	*xanthochlora*	CArn EBee EPPr GBar GGar GPoy
		MSal NLar NSco WHer WPer

Alectryon (*Sapindaceae*)

| | *excelsus* | CHEx |

Aletris (*Melanthiaceae*)

| | *farinosa* | EBee |
| | *spicata* **new** | EBee |

Alisma (*Alismataceae*)

	lanceolatum	SBHF
	plantago-aquatica	CBen CKin CRow EHon EMFW
		LPBA MSta NPer SLon SWat WFar
		WMAq WWeb WWpP
	- var. *parviflorum*	CBen EMFW LPBA MSta SPlb
		SWat WWeb

Alkanna (*Boraginaceae*)

	orientalis	WCot
	tinctoria	CMdw MSal SAga
	- HH&K 345	CMdw

Allamanda (*Apocynaceae*)

§	*blanchetii*	SOWG
	cathartica	EPfP ERea ESlt LRHS MBri
	- 'Birthe'	MBri
	- 'Grandiflora'	CPIN
	- 'Hendersonii' ♀ H1	LRHS SOWG
	neriifolia	see *A. schottii*
§	*schottii* ♀ H1	ESlt LRHS SOWG
	violacea	see *A. blanchetii*

Allardia (*Asteraceae*)

| | *tomentosa* | EHyt |

Alliaria (*Brassicaceae*)

| | *petiolata* | CArn CKin GPoy IIve NLan WHbs |
| | | WHer |

Allium ✿ (*Alliaceae*)

	aciphyllum **new**	EBee LAma
§	*acuminatum*	EHyt GIBF GKir NBir NMen
	acutiflorum **new**	CPom
	aflatunense hort.	see *A. bollandicum*, *A. stipitatum*
	aflatunense B. Fedtsch.	EBee EMon ETub WBrE
	akaka	ETow GCrs
	'Akbulak' **new**	LAma
	albidum	see *A. denudatum*
	albopilosum	see *A. cristophii*
	altaicum	EBee GIBF
	altissimum	NRog
	- 'Goliath'	EBee EMan
	amabile	see *A. mairei* var. *amabile*
	ampeloprasum	CFil EBee ECha GIBF WHer WShi
	- var. *babingtonii*	CArn CAvo CFox CNat GPoy IIve
		ILis MLLN WHer WShi
	amphibolum	EBee
	amplectens	GDra NRog
§	*angulosum*	CMea CPom EBee GIBF MMil
		MSph SDix SMrm SYvo WCot
	angustitepalum	see *A. jesdianum* subsp.
		angustitepalum
	atropurpureum	EBee EBlw ECha EHrv ELan EMan
		EMon EPar ETub GIBF LAma LEdu
		LPhx LRHS MLLN NCcl NDov
		NRog WHrl
	atroviolaceum	EBee GIRF
	azureum	see *A. caeruleum*
	balansae	SOkd
	barszczewskii	EBee
	'Beau Regard' ♀ H4	EBee LAma NRog
	beesianum hort.	see *A. cyaneum*
	beesianum W.W. Smith	CLAP CLyd CMdw EHyt ESis GIBF
		GKir IIve NBir NRya
	blandum **new**	GIBF
	brevicaule	LRHS
	bucharicum JJH 94805	WCot
	bulgaricum	see *Nectaroscordum siculum*
		subsp. *bulgaricum*
§	*caeruleum* ♀ H4	More than 30 suppliers
	- *azureum*	see *A. caeruleum*

caesium ♀ H4	EBee EHyt
callimischon	CBro NRog NRya
- subsp. callimischon	EBee
- subsp. haemostictum	EHyt NMen NRog SBla SIng
canadense	CArn EBee SHar
caricoides new	EBee
§ carinatum	EBee EMar
§ - subsp. pulchellum ♀ H4	More than 30 suppliers
- - f. album ♀ H4	More than 30 suppliers
- - 'Tubergen'	ETub
§ carolinianum	EBee GCrs GIBF
cepa	CPLG NGHP
- Aggregatum Group	ELau ILis
- 'Perutile'	CArn GBar GPoy ILis MHer
- Proliferum Group	CArn CBod CPrp CSev ELau GBar GPoy ILis LEdu MBow MChe MHer NWoo WCHb WCer WHer WJek WLHH WSel
* - 'White Flower'	WCot
cernuum	More than 30 suppliers
§ - 'Hidcote' ♀ H4	CLAP EMon MSte WCot
- 'Major'	see A. cernuum 'Hidcote'
- roseum	CLyd SIng
cirrhosum	see A. carinatum subsp. pulchellum
cowanii	see A. neapolitanum Cowanii Group
crenulatum	EHyt
§ cristophii ♀ H4	More than 30 suppliers
§ cupanii	EBee
§ cyaneum ♀ H4	CArn CGra CHea CLyd CPBP CPom EMlt ERos GCrs GKir LBee LRHS NChi NJOw NMen NRya SBla SRot WBea WCom WFTG WWin
cyathophorum	GCrs NRog NWCA
- var. farreri	CArn CAvo CBre CBro CHea CLyd CNic EBee EMlt EPot ERos ESis GCrs GEdr GGar GIBF GKir GSki LLWP MBro MRav NChi NLAp NLon NMen NRya SIng WCot WWin
decipiens new	EBee
delicatulum	EBee
§ denudatum	EBee
dichlamydeum	CBro CPom EBee ERos NRog
dregeanum	LBow
§ drummondii	EBre ECha
elatum	see A. macleanii
ericetorum	ERos
eusperma new	LAma
falcifolium	CAvo EBee EChP ETow GCrs LAma NMen WCot
farreri	see A. cyathophorum var. farreri
fasciculatum new	LAma
fetisowii	EBee
fimbriatum	EBee
'Firmament'	CAvo CElw CMea EBee EChP EMan EMon LAma LRHS MSte WPnP
fistulosum	CArn CBod EBee ELau GBar GPoy ILis LEdu MChe MHer NFor NGHP NHol NPri SIde WCHb WCer WCot WPer WWye
- red	CBod
- 'Red Welsh'	IIve ILis WJek WLHH
flavum ♀ H4	CArn CAvo CBro CHea CPom EBot ECha EGle EPar ETub GIBF GKir LAma LHop MRav NCel NDov NRog NSd EOrp SHBN SPer SYvo WGor WPer
§ - 'Blue Leaf'	EPot ERos GKir LEdu NBir
- subsp. flavum	EBee LEdu LPhx MBow MNrw
- - var. minus	CNic CStu EPot GDra MTho NWCA
- 'Glaucum'	see A. flavum 'Blue Leaf'
- var. nanum	CNic EPot GEdr GKir
- subsp. tauricum	EBee ECho
forrestii	CLyd GCrs
galanthum	EBee
geyeri	EHyt WCot WLin
giganteum ♀ H4	More than 30 suppliers
'Gladiator' ♀ H4	CBro CFir CHar CPen EBee EChP EMan EMon LAma LRHS MLLN NCel NRog SMad SPer WDav WPnP
glaucum	see A. senescens subsp. montanum var. glaucum
'Globemaster' ♀ H4	CAvo CBro CFir CMea CRDP EBee EHrv ELan EMan ETub LAma LRHS MMHG MSte MWgw NCel SPer WBry WCot WCra WFar WPnP
globosum new	EBee
'Globus'	EBee EMan LAma LRHS
goodingii	CNic CPom EHyt GCrs
grisellum new	EBee
gultschense	GIBF
guttatum	EBee
dalmaticum new	
- subsp. sardoum	EBee ECho
haematochiton	WCot
heldreichii	EBee
* hirtifolium var. album	EBee LAma
'His Excellency'	CFir EBee ECho EMan ETub LAma LRHS NCel WFTG
§ hollandicum ♀ H4	More than 30 suppliers
- 'Purple Sensation' ♀ H4	More than 30 suppliers
hookeri ACE 2430	WCot
- var. muliense new	GEdr
humile	CLyd WCot
hyalinum	EBee EHyt NRog
- pink	EMan WCot
§ insubricum ♀ H4	ECho EHyt ERos GCrs GDra LPhx NBir NMen NSti SIng
jajlae	see A. rotundum subsp. jajlae
japonicum new	GIBF
jesdianum	CBro CPom MLLN
* - album	EBee
- subsp. angustitepalum	EBee
- 'Michael Hoog'	see A. rosenbachianum 'Michael Hoog'
- 'Purple King'	EMan LAma WCot
kansuense	see A. sikkimense
karataviense ♀ H3	More than 30 suppliers
- 'Ivory Queen'	CBro CElw CHar EBee EMar EPyc ETub EVFa LAma LRHS MBow MCCP MCLN MDKP MSph MSte MTed NCel SPer WDav WFar WHil WWeb WWpP
- 'Kara-tau' new	LRHS
ledebourianum	EBee ECho WCra
lenkoranicum new	EBee
libani	WPer
lineare	GIBF IHMH IIve
longicuspis	GIBF
loratum	EPar
'Lucy Ball'	CMea EBee EMan EMon EPot ETub LAma LRHS MLLN MSte NBir NCel NRog WBry
§ macleanii	CArn CMil EBee ELau EMan EMon EPar LAma LRHS NRog WDav
macranthum	CLyd CPom EBee EBre GDra GEdr MSte WLin
macrochaetum	LAma
mairei	CElw CLyd EBee EHyt ERos LHop LLWP LRHS MBar NMen NRya WGwG WTin
- var. amabile	CLyd ERos ETow GDra GEdr GIBF LTwo NChi NWyn NWCA SIng WCot

'Mars'	CFir CMea EBee LRHS MLLN NCel
maximowiczii	EBee ECho EWes
meteoricum **new**	LRHS
moly	CArn CBri CBro EPar EPfP ETub
	GBuc CBri GDra LAma MBow MBri
	MRav NCel NJOw NRog NRya
	NSti SRms SWal SYvo WCHb
	WCom WCot WPer WWin WWpP
- 'Jeannine' ♀ H4	CBro CMea EBee EPot LAma LPhx
	MLLN NCel
'Mont Blanc'	CMea EBee ELan LAma NCel
'Mount Everest'	CAvo CBro CHar CPen EBee EChP
	EMan EMar EPot ETub LAma LRHS
	MBow MSte NCel SPer WDav WPnP
multibulbosum	see *A. nigrum*
murrayanum Reg.	see *A. acuminatum*
murrayanum	see *A. unifolium*
misapplied	
narcissiflorum hort.	see *A. insubricum*
§ *narcissiflorum* Villars	CLyd CPom GCrs GIBF NChi
	NMGW NSla NWCA WCot
neapolitanum	CAgr CArn EBee EPar EPot LAma
	LRHS MBri NCel NRog NSti SPer
	SRms WPer
§ - Cowanii Group	CBro CHar EBee EHrv ERos GIBF
	LRHS MNrw NCel SYvo WCot
	WCra WFTG WLin
- 'Grandiflorum'	EBee LRHS MLLN MNrw NRog
	WBrE
nevskianum **new**	LAma
§ *nigrum*	CArn CBro CFwr CHea CPLG EBee
	EBlw EHrv EMan EMar EMon EPar
	EPot ETub GIBF LAma LPhx LRHS
	MBow MLLN MNrw MRav NBir
	NCel NRog SWal WCot WFTG
nutans	CBod EBee EHol HHMH IIve LEdu
	NGHP SHDw WHal WJek WPrP
nuttallii	see *A. drummondii*
§ *obliquum*	EBee ECha ECho EGle GSki LRHS
	WCot WTin
odorum L.	see *A. ramosum* L.
oleraceum	WHer
olympicum	SScr
§ *oreophilum*	CArn CAvo CBro CMdw CNic
	ECha ECtt EHyt EPar EPfP GSki
	LAma LRHS MBow MLLN NCel
	NJOw NMGW NRog NRya SPer
	SRms SYvo WCot WPer WWpP
- 'Zwanenburg' ♀ H4	CBro CMea EBee ECho EMar EPot
	GEdr LPhx NMen NRog WCot
oreoprasum	EBee GIBF LAma
orientale	GIBF
ostrowskianum	see *A. oreophilum*
pallasii	EBee LAma
pallens	CBre CHea MTho NBir
§ *paniculatum*	CAvo EChP EHyt GKir LEdu MMil
	NRog
paradoxum	EBee LRHS NBir NRog
- var. *normale*	CBro CRDP EBee EHyt EMan
	EMon WCot
pedemontanum	see *A. narcissiflorum* Villars
peninsulare	WCot
platyspathum **new**	EBee
plurifoliatum	EBee LAma
polyphyllum	see *A. carolinianum*
polyrhizum **new**	EBee
przewalskianum	EBee GKir
pskemense	GIBF
pulchellum	see *A. carinatum* subsp.
	pulchellum
pyrenaicum hort.	see *A. angulosum*
pyrenaicum	ELan EMan
Costa & Vayreda	

ramosum Jacquin	see *A. obliquum*
§ *ramosum* L.	LAma NGHP WJek WPer
'Rien Poortvliet'	CArn EBee EMan LAma LRHS NRog
* *romarovianum*	EBee
§ *rosenbachianum*	CArn CBro CHar EBee EBlw EMan
	EPar EPot EWTr GIBF LAma MLLN
	MWgw NCat NRog SPer WDav
- 'Akbulak'	EBee LRHS WCot
- 'Album'	EBee ECha ECho EPar EPot EVFa
	LAma MLLN NRog WCot WDav
§ - 'Michael Hoog'	EBee LAma LRHS WCot
- 'Purple King'	EBee LRHS
- 'Shing'	LRHS
roseum	CArn CMea CPom EBee ECtt EMon
	ERos LAma NRog WFTG WPer
§ - var. *bulbiferum*	CPou WCot
- 'Grandiflorum'	see *A. roseum* var. *bulbiferum*
§ *rotundum* subsp. *jajlae*	EBee LLWP WPer
rubens	CPom
sarawschanicum	EBee LRHS
'Chinoro'	
sativum	CArn CPLG EEls EOHP MHer
	NBlu SIde WJek WSel WWye
- 'Asher'	IIve
- 'Benjamin'	IIve
- 'Chengdou' **new**	IIve
- 'Chesnok Red' **new**	IIve
- 'Dan'	IIve
- 'Ephraim'	IIve
- 'Gad'	IIve
- 'Germinadour' **new**	IIve
- golden	GPoy IIve
- 'Issachar'	IIve
- 'Judah'	IIve
- 'Korean Red'	IIve
- 'Levi'	IIve
- 'Loicano' **new**	IIve
- 'Manasseh'	IIve
- Mexican	IIve
- 'Naphtali'	IIve
- var. *ophioscorodon*	EBee GPoy IIve ILis LAma
- 'Printanor'	CBod
- 'Reuben'	IIve
- 'Simeon'	IIve
- 'Tarne' **new**	IIve
- 'Thermidrome'	CBod
- 'Tokyo' **new**	IIve
- 'Zebulon'	IIve
saxatile	EBee
schmitzii	EMon
schoenoprasum	More than 30 suppliers
- 'Black Isle Blush'	GPoy MHer
- 'Corsican White'	EMon SUsu
- fine-leaved	ELau IHMH IIve WHHs
- 'Forescate'	CBod CM&M CPrp CSpe ECha
	EFou ELau EWes GBar GCal LRHS
	MLLN MRav MWgw SPet SSpe
	WBca WCHb WCot WFlm
- medium-leaved	ELau NPri
- 'Pink Perfection'	GPoy MHer
- 'Polycross' **new**	WHHs
- 'Polyphant'	CBre EBee WCHb WRha WWpP
- *roseum*	NCot
- var. *sibiricum*	GBar GPoy MBri SDix WSel WShi
- 'Silver Chimes'	CAvo CMil ELau MBri SHDw
	WWpP
- 'Wallington White'	GBar MBro
- white	CArn CMea CSWP ECha ELau
	IHMH LEdu LPhx MBro MHer
	MSte NBir NCot SIde SSvw WBea
	WCHb WCot WEas WHer WRha
	WWpP WWye
schubertii	More than 30 suppliers

	scorodoprasum	CAgr GIBF WCHb
	- subsp. *jajlae*	see *A. rotundum* subsp. *jajlae*
	senescens	CArn CBro EBee ECGP EPar ERos
		ESis GIBF MRav NChi NJOw
		SRms SSpe SSvw WBea
	- var. *calcareum*	IHMH
§	- subsp. *montanum*	CBro CSpe ECha ECho EGoo EPot
		LEdu NMen SDix SIng WAbe WMoo
§	- - var. *glaucum*	CArn CLyd CMea CPBP CPrp CStr
		EBee EBre ECha EMan EMar EPar
		EPla ESis GEdr LEdu SAga SIng
		WCot WHer WPer WWye
	- subsp. *senescens*	EMon MLLN SUsu
	sibthorpianum	see *A. paniculatum*
	siculum	see *Nectaroscordum siculum*
	sieheanum	EBee
§	*sikkimense*	CHea CMea CPlt EBee EMan ERos
		GDra GIBF GKir MBro NMen NSla
		NWCA SBla SSvw WBea WPer
	sinkiangense	EBee
	songpanicum new	EBee LAma
	sphaerocephalon	More than 30 suppliers
	- 'Hair' new	CFwr LAma
	splendens	CPom
	stellatum	LRHS WFTG WPrP
	stellerianum	WPer
	- var. *kurilense*	CLyd CNic
§	*stipitatum*	CPom EBee EChP EMon GIBF
		LAma LRHS NRog WCot
	- 'Album'	CArn CBro EBee EMon EPot
		LAma LRHS NRog
	- 'Glory of Pamir'	EMan LRHS
	stracheyi	WCot
	strictum Schrad.	see *A. lineare*
	strictum Ledeb.	see *A. szovitsii*
	suaveolens new	GIBF
	subhirsutum	CLyd EBee
	subulosum new	EBee
	subvillosum	WCot
	'Summer Beauty' new	WCot
§	*szovitsii*	EBee
	tanguticum	GKir WCot
	thunbergii ♀ H4	EBee GCrs NBir
	- 'Nanum'	EPot WCot
	- 'Ozawa'	EHyt NMen SBla SIng WCot
	tibeticum	see *A. sikkimense*
*	*tournefortii*	EBee ECho
	tricoccum	GIBF
	triquetrum	CAgr CAvo EBee EBlw ELan EPfP
		EPot GGar GIBF IBlr ILis LAma
		MBow NBir NRog NSti SYvo
		WCHb WCot WCru WHer WMoo
		WPer WPnP WShi WWin
	tuberosum	More than 30 suppliers
	- purple/mauve	ELau GWCH WMoo
	- variegated (v)	ELau
	tubiflorum new	EBee
	turcomanicum new	EBee
	turkestanicum	GIBF
§	*unifolium* ♀ H4	More than 30 suppliers
	ursinum	CArn CAvo CKin GDea GKir
		GPoy LAma MBow MUlv NGHP
		NMir NRog WCHb WHen WShi
		WWye
	'Valerie Finnis'	SAga SBla
	victorialis	GCal GIBF
	- 'Kemerovo'	EBee
	vineale	CArn EBee WHer
	violaceum	see *A. carinatum*
	virgunculae	EHyt SBla SCnR
	wallichii	CLyd CPou EBee EMon GBuc
		LAma NBir WCot WLin WTin
	- ACE 2458	WCot

	- CC&McK 1025	WCot
	- plum	GEdr
	'World Cup' new	LRHS
	zaprjagajevii	EBee LEdu
	zebdanense	ERos LAma LRHS MNrw

Allocasuarina (Casuarinaceae)

	campestris new	SPlb
§	*littoralis*	CCtw
	monilifera	ECou
	nana	CTrC
§	*verticillata*	CTrC

Alnus ✿ (Betulaceae)

	B&SWJ 5414 new	WPGP
	cordata ♀ H4	More than 30 suppliers
	crispa	see *A. viridis* subsp. *crispa*
	firma	CDul CMCN IArd
	formosana	GIBF
	fruticosa	see *A. viridis* subsp. *fruticosa*
	glutinosa	CBcs CCVT CDoC CDul CKin
		CLnd CSBt CSam EBee ECrN
		ENot EPfP GKir LBuc LHyr
		LPan MGos NBee NRog NWea
		SHBN SHFr SPer WDin WMou
		WOrn WStI
	- 'Aurea'	CDul CEnd CLnd CTho ECrN
		LRHS MBlu MDun SSpi
	- var. *barbata*	GIBF
	- 'Imperialis' ♀ H4	CDoC CDul CEnd CLnd CTho
		EBee ENot EPfP GKir LPan LRHS
		MAsh MBri MDun NBee NPSl
		SPer SSpi WDin WMoo
	- f. *incisa*	ELan
	- 'Laciniata'	CDoC CDul CTho ECrN MBlu
		MHFa WFar WMoo
	hirsuta	CMCN GKir
	- var. *sibirica*	GIBF
	x *hybrida* new	GIBF
	incana	CDoC CDul CKin CLnd CMCN
		CWib EBee ECrN ENot GKir LBuc
		MBar MGos NRog NWea SHBN
		SKee WDin WMoo
	- 'Aurea'	CBcs CDul CEnd CLnd COtt
		CTho EBee ECrN ELan ENot EPfP
		EPla GKir LPan LRHS MBar MBlu
		MBri MGos MHFa NRog SHBN
		SPer SSpi WDin WOrn
	- 'Laciniata'	CDul CLnd CTho EBee ENot
		MHFa MRav WDin WFar
	- 'Pendula'	CLnd
	japonica	CLnd
	- var. *arguta* new	GIBF
	lanata	CMCN
	nepalensis	WCwm
	nitida	CFil CMCN IArd IDee WCwm
	oregana	see *A. rubra*
	orientalis	GIBF
§	*rubra*	CAgr CCVT CDoC CDul CLnd
		CMCN CTho EBee ECrN ELan
		ENot NWea SKee WDin WMou
	- 'Pinnatifida'	see *A. rubra* f. *pinnatisecta*
§	- f. *pinnatisecta*	CLnd CMCN CTho
§	*rugosa*	CMCN
	serrulata	see *A. rugosa*
	sinuata	see *A. viridis* subsp. *sinuata*
	x *spaethii*	CDoC CDul CTho SRPl
	subcordata	CLnd
	viridis	CAgr CMCN ECrN NWea
	- subsp. *crispa*	GIBF
	- - var. *mollis*	CAgr CMCN
	- subsp. *fruticosa* new	GIBF
§	- subsp. *sinuata*	CAgr CMCN NWea

Alocasia ✿ *(Araceae)*

x **amazonica** ♀ H1	ERea LRHS MBri MNew
- 'Polly'	MNew
'Aquino'	MNew
'Black Velvet'	MNew
'Crinkles'	MNew
cucullata	MNew WMul
culionensis	MNew
cuprea	MNew
'Elaine'	MNew
gageana	MNew WMul
'Green Shield'	MNew
'Green Velvet'	MNew
guttata var. **imperialis**	MNew
'Hilo Beauty'	MNew
lancifolia	MNew
longiloba	MNew
macrorrhiza	EAmu LEur MNew WMul
- 'Lutea'	MNew WMul
- 'Variegata' (v) ♀ H1	MNew
maximiliana	MNew
micholitziana	MNew
'Mindanao'	MNew
nigra	see *A. plumbea* 'Nigra'
odora	MNew WMul
plumbea	MNew
§ - 'Nigra'	MNew WMul
portei	MNew
'Portora'	MNew WMul
sanderiana 'Nobilis'	MNew
x **sedenii**	MNew
'Tigrina Superba'	MNew
§ 'Uhinkii'	WMul
villeneuvei	WMul
watsoniana	MNew
wentii	MNew
wenzelii	WMul
whinkii	see *A.* 'Uhinkii'
'White Knight'	MNew
zebrina	MNew
- 'Reticulata'	MNew

Aloe *(Aloaceae)*

aculeata	CTrF
ammophila	EPem
arborescens	CAbb CHEx CTrC CTrF EOas
	MBro SChr SPar SSte
- blue-leaved	CTrF
- early-flowering	CTrF
- 'Frutescens'	CTrF
- late-flowering	CTrF
- yellow-flowered **new**	EOas
arborescens x **ferox**	CTrF
aristata ♀ H1	CHEx CHal CTrF EOas MBri SAPC
	SArc SChr SPar SPet SSte WHer
barbadensis	see *A. vera*
barberae	CTrC
boylei	CFir
branddraaiensis new	WCot
brevifolia ♀ H1	CRoM CTbh EOas SArc
broomii	EOas EPem SChr
- **tarkahensis**	CTrF
- **camperi**	CTrF
- 'Maculata'	CTrC CTrF MBri SChr
candelabrum	CTrF SMrm
ciliaris	EMan EOas ERea SChr WCot
* - var. **robusta**	CTrF
- var. **tidmarshii**	CTrF
claviflora	CTrF
comosa	CTrF
cooperi	CAbb
cremnophila	CTrF

dawei	CTrF
dichotoma	CAbb GBin
dumetorum new	EPem
ecklonis	CTrC EOas SChr SPlb WCot
erinacea	EOas
excelsa	SChr
ferox	CBrP CTrC CTrF EOas EPem MSal
	SChr SPar
fosteri	CTrC EOas
gariepensis	EPem
globuligemma	CTrF WCot
grandidentata	CTrF
greatheadii var. **davyana**	CCtw EOas
grisea	CTrF
humilis	EPem
juvenna	CTrF EPem
lineata var. **muirii**	CTrF
littoralis new	EPem
marlothii	CTrF EOas WCot
mawii	CTrF
mitriformis	CTrF EOas MPRe NPri SChr SEND
mutabilis	CHEx CTrC CTrF EOas
parvibracteata	CTrF
plicatilis	CAbb CTrC EOas
pluridens	CTrF
pratensis	CFir CTrC EOas SChr SPlb
- glaucous-leaved **new**	EOas
prinslooi new	EPem
reitzii	CTrC EOas
rupestris	CTrF
saponaria	CHEx CRoM CTrC EOas
spectabilis new	EOas
striata	CTrF
striatula	CAbb CBrP CFil CHEx CTCD
	CTrC CTrF EOas EPla IBlr SAPC
	SArc SChr WPGP
- var. **caesia**	IBlr
succotrina	CTrF
variegata (v) ♀ H1	CTrF WEas
§ **vera** ♀ H1	CArn CDoC COld ELau EOHP
	EOas EPem ERea ESlt GPoy IFro
	ILis MPRe MSal NPer NPri SIde
	SPar SSte WCot WHHs WHer
- grey	CTrF
'Walmsley's Blue'	MBri
wickensii	EPem

Alonsoa *(Scrophulariaceae)*

'Bright Spark' **new**	CSpe
meridionalis	LRav NJOw
'Pink Beauty'	CSpe CWCL NBur
'Snowflake' **new**	LRav
unilabiata	CSpe
warscewiczii	CHll ELan ERea LRHS NDov SHFr
- pale	see *A. warscewiczii* 'Peachy-keen'
§ - 'Peachy-keen'	CSpe EMan LRHS NDov SPet

Alopecurus *(Poaceae)*

alpinus	EHoe EMan EPPr LRHS NBur
- subsp. **glaucus**	CBrm CSLe EHoe
lanatus	NBea
pratensis	CKin NOrc
§ - 'Aureovariegatus' (v)	CBcs CBrm EBee EGra EHoe ENot
	EPPr EPla EWsh GCal GKir GMaP
	GSki MBar MBri MMoz MPRe MSte
	NBid NFor NHol NLon SLin SPar
	SPer WFar WLeb WMoo WPnP
- 'Aureus'	EBee EBlw EChP ECha EGle EGra
	GBin LRHS MRav MWhi NBro
	NGdn NSti SDes SMad SPlb WFar
	WLin WPer WRHF WWin
- 'No Overtaking' (v)	EMan EMon EPPr WWpP

Alophia (Iridaceae)

drummondii	ERos
lahue	see *Herbertia lahue*

Aloysia (Verbenaceae)

chamaedrifolia	CPle
citriodora	see *A. triphylla*
§ **triphylla** ♀ H2	More than 30 suppliers

Alpinia (Zingiberaceae)

chinensis new	EBee LEur
formosana	WMul
§ **hainanensis**	LEur
japonica	EBee LEdu LEur MSal
katsumadai	see *A. hainanensis*
officinarum	CArn
speciosa	see *A. zerumbet*
§ **vittata** (v)	MOak
§ **zerumbet**	EAmu LEur MOak MPRe NPal
- '**Variegata**' (v)	EAmu EBot MOak MPRe WMul

Alsobia see *Episcia*

Alstroemeria ✿ (Alstroemeriaceae)

'Aimi'	CBcs COtt EBee LRHS MBri NCat SBai SPer WFar WViv
'Angelina' **new**	SBai SVil
'Apollo' ♀ H4	COtt GKir LRHS MBNS MBri MGrG SBai SPer WLRN WViv
aurantiaca	see *A. aurea*
§ **aurea**	CTri EBee EMar EPfP EWoo GGar IKee MDun MRav MWrn NCat NLar NMGW NSti SMrm SRms WCot
- 'Apricot' **new**	GCal
- 'Cally Fire'	GCal
- 'Dover Orange'	CPrp EBee EChP EMan EPfP LRHS SCoo
- 'Lutea'	CTri EChP EMar ENot EWTr EWll LRHS NEgg SPer SPlb
- 'Orange King'	EBee EPfP ETub EWll LRHS MTed NEgg NFla NLar SDeJ WCom WCot
'Blushing **Bride**'	CBcs MBNS MBri SBai SVil
brasiliensis	CLAP GCal LPio MDKP SSpi WCot WSHC
Butterfly **hybrids**	SWal
'Charm'	LRHS NCat WFar
'Coronet' ♀ H4	COtt LRHS MBNS SPer WViv
I 'Crusader Lily' **new**	EMui
'Dayspring **Delight**' (v)	CBos CDes CLAP WCot
Diana, **Princess** of Wales = '**Stablaco**'PBR	EMui
diluta	WCot
- subsp. **chrysantha** F&W 8700	WCot
Doctor **Salter's hybrids**	ECGP EFou MNrw SRms SWal
'Eternal **Love**' **new**	COtt LIck
'Evening **Song**'	LRHS MBNS MBri SBai WViv
aff. **exserens**	WCot
'Firefly'	LBuc LRHS SPer WViv
'Fortune'	LRHS
'Frances' (v) **new**	LHop
'Freedom' **new**	EBee
'Friendship' ♀ H4	CBcs LBuc SBai SWal WCot WViv
'Fury' **new**	EBee
garaventae	WCot
gayana	MDKP WCot
'Golden **Delight**'	COtt LIck MBri SPla SVil WViv
haemantha	CLAP MDKP
Hawera **Seedlings**	CDes EBee SMrm
hookeri	ECho GCal MTho SCnR SIgm
- subsp. **cummingiana**	WCot
- subsp. **hookeri**	CFil

huemulina	MDKP
'Inca Blaze' **new**	WViv
'Inca Dream'	WViv
'Inca Ice'	WViv
'Inca Moonlight'	WViv
'Inca Tropic'	WViv
kingii	see *A. versicolor*
leporina new	WCot
- F&W 9550	MDKP
ligtu hybrids	More than 30 suppliers
- variegated (v)	CRDP
- var. **ligtu**	LPhx
'Lilac Wonder' **new**	NBhm
'Little Eleanor'PBR	COtt GKir LRHS SBai WCot WFar WViv
'Little Miss Charlotte'	COtt LRHS WFar WViv
'Little Miss Christina' **new**	SBai SVil WViv
'Little Miss Gloria' **new**	SBai SVil
Little Miss Isabel	SBai WViv
'Little Miss Lucy'	COtt
'Little Miss Matilda'	COtt LRHS SBai WViv
'Little Miss Olivia' **new**	SBai
'Little Miss Rosanna'	COtt LRHS SBai WViv
'Little Miss Roselind' **new**	SBai SVil WViv
'Little Miss Sophie' **new**	SBai SVil WViv
'Little Miss Tara' **new**	SBai WViv
'Little Miss Veronica' **new**	SVil WViv
'Lucinda' **new**	MBri SBai SVil
magnifica	MDKP
- subsp. **maxima**	WCot
'Marina'	LRHS MBNS SPer WViv
'Marissa'	LRHS WViv
'Mars'	LRHS SWal
Meyer hybrids	MTho
'Orange Gem' ♀ H4	COtt LRHS MBNS NCat WFar WViv
'Orange Glory' ♀ H4	CBcs COtt EBee IArd LRHS MBNS MBri SBai SMrm SPla WCot WFar WViv
'Oriana' **new**	SBai SVil
pallida	CBro CFil SIgm
- JCA 2.028.500	WCot
patagonica	EHyt WCot
- P&W 6226	ETow
- 'Maxi' **new**	WCot
§ **paupercula**	CSev
pelegrina	ECho MTho SIgm WCot
- 'Alba'	ELan SIgm WCot
- var. **humilis**	WCot
- 'Rosea'	ELan
'Perfect Love'	COtt EBee LIck
philipii new	WCot
'Phoenix' **new**	SVil
'Pink Perfection'	LRHS MGrG NLar
'Polka' **new**	SBai SVil
presliana	EBee
- RB 94103	WCot
- subsp. **australis**	CPou SIgm
- - JCA 12590	SSpi
- subsp. **presliana**	SBla
Princess Angela = 'Staprilan'PBR	COtt LBuc MBNS
Princess Astrid = 'Stabopink'PBR	EMui
Princess Beatrix = 'Stadoran'	EMui
Princess Caroline = 'Stakaros'	EMui
Princess Charlotte = 'Staprizsa'PBR	EMui LBuc
Princess Daniela = 'Stapridani'PBR	CBcs LBuc LIck MMil

Princess Ella	NLar	
= 'Staprirange'PBR		
Princess Freckles	EMui	
Princess Frederika	EMui	
= 'Stabronza'		
Princess Grace	EMui	
= 'Starodo'PBR		
Princess Ileana	EMui	
= 'Stalvir'		
'Princess Ivana' **new**	EMui NLar	
Princess Juliana	EMui	
= 'Staterpa'		
Princess Leyla	CBcs LBuc MBNS WCot	
= 'Stapriley'PBR		
'Princess Margaret'	EBee SPla	
Princess Marie-Louise	EMui	
= 'Zelanon'		
Princess Marilene	COtt LBuc MBNS	
= 'Staprilene'PBR		
Princess Monica	COtt EMui SPla	
= 'Staprimon'PBR		
Princess Morana	COtt EMui	
= 'Staprirana'PBR		
Princess Oxana	LIck MMil	
= 'Staprioxa'PBR		
'Princess Paola'	CBcs COtt EBcc MBNS SPla	
Princess Sarah	EMui MMil	
= 'Stalicamp'		
Princess Sissi	COtt EMui	
= 'Staprisis'PBR		
Princess Sophia	EMui	
= 'Stajello'PBR		
Princess Stephanie	CBcs EBee EMui NLar SPla	
= 'Stapirag'		
Princess Susana	EMui MMil NLar	
= 'Staprisusa'PBR		
Princess VictoriaPBR	see A. 'Victoria'	
Princess Zavina	CFir COtt EMui LIck MBNS MMil	
= 'Staprivina'PBR	NLar	
pseudospathulata	CDes WCot	
RB 94010		
§	*psittacina*	CBro CFil CHad CHar CRDP CScv EBee EHrv ELan EPPr EPar ERos EWoo GCal LAst LHop MHer MStc MTis SIgm SMrm SSpi SWal WCot WFar WPGP WSHC WViv WWpP
- 'Mona Lisa' **new**	EWll	
- 'Royal Star' (v)	CFwr CLAP CRDP EBee EChP ELan EMan EMar EMon ENot EPPr EVFa LBuc LPio LRHS MGrG NMRc SIgm SSpi WCom WCot WFar WHil WRus WViv
- variegated (v)	see A. psittacina 'Royal Star'	
pulchella Sims	see A. psittacina	
pulchra	CFil LPio MDKP SBla SIgm WCot	
JCA 2.029.410		
'Purple Rain' **new**	CBcs SBai SVil WAbe	
pygmaea	EHyt MTho SCnR	
Queen Elizabeth	EMui	
The Queen Mother		
= 'Stamoti'PBR		
'Red Beauty' (v)	EBee GKir LRHS MBNS MBri NBir SBai SPer SPlb SVil WCot WViv
'Red Coat' **new**	EBee	
'Red Elf'	EFou GKir LRHS MBNS MBri SBai WFar WViv
'Regina'PBR	see A. 'Victoria'	
revoluta	CFil	
- F&W 8722	WCot	
schizanthoides **new**	MDKP	
'Selina'	EBee LRHS MBNS MTed SPer SVil WFar WViv
'Short Purple'	WCot WPGP	

'Solent Candy'	GKir WFar	
'Solent Crest'	WFar	
'Solent Dawn'	LRHS WFar	
'Solent Pride'	WFar	
'Solent Wings'	WFar	
'Spitfire' **new**	SBai	
'Spring Delight' (v)	EMan WCot	
'Sunstar'	LRHS	
'Sweet Laura'PBR	EBee WCot	
'Tessa'	LBuc LIck LRHS WViv	
'Verona'	LRHS	
§	*versicolor*	GCrs MDKP SBla WCot
- BC&W 4624	GBin	
- F&W 8721	SIgm	
§	'Victoria'PBR	EMui
violacea	see A. *paupercula*	
werdermannii F&W 869	WCot	
- F&W 9589	SIgm	
- var. *flavicans*	MDKP	
F&W 956289 **new**		
- var. *werdermannii*	MDKP	
F&W 9585 **new**		
'White Apollo'	EBee LIck SPla WCot	
'Yellow Friendship' ♀ H4	COtt GKir LRHS MBNS NLar SBai SPer SPlb WFar WLRN WViv
'Yellow Queen'	WFar	

Althaea (Malvaceae)

armeniaca	EBee EMan EMon GBuc LPio WCot	
cannabina	CBri CFis CRDP EChP EMon GBri GCal LPio MBro MEHN MFir SOkh WAul WEas WFTG WHal WHoo WOld WWhi
- MESE 510	EBee	
officinalis	CAgr CArn CKin CPrp CScv ELan EMon EWTr GBar GMac GPoy ILis ITer MChe MHcr MMil MPkx MSal SBHF SIde WHHs WPer WWye
- *alba*	EChP NLar WCom WHer	
§	- 'Romney Marsh'	EBee EWTr EWll GCal MRav SMad WSHC
'Parkallee' **new**	EMon	
rosea	see Alcea rosea	
rugosostellulata	see Alcea rugosa	

Alyogyne (Malvaceae)

'Elle Marie' **new**	SOWG	
hakeifolia	CSpe ECou ERea	
§	*huegelii*	EMan LRHS MOak WCot
- 'Santa Cruz'	CBcs CPLG CSpe FOrc EReu MStc SBrw SOWG WOld

Alyssoides (Brassicaceae)

utriculata	WCot WPer	
- 'Tinkerbells' **new**	MPWC	

Alyssum (Brassicaceae)

alyssoides **new**	CNat	
argenteum hort.	see A. murale	
idaeum	LRHS	
markgrafii	CLyd WCom	
montanum	CArn ECha MWat NBlu SPlb SRms WCom WMoo
§	- 'Berggold'	CBcs EPfP LHrt LPVe LRHS
- Mountain Gold	see A. montanum 'Berggold'	
§	*murale*	IHMH
oschtenicum	WLin	
oxycarpum	EHyt NMen SBla WAbe	
pyrenaicum	NWCA	
repens subsp.	GIBF	
repens **new**		
saxatile	see Aurinia saxatilis	
- 'Plena' (d) **new**	GEdr	

	serpyllifolium	CLyd EHyt MOne NWCA
	sinuatum	see *Aurinia sinuata*
	spinosum	CMea MBro WAbe WFar WLin
§	– 'Roseum' ♀ H4	CNic ECha EDAr EHyt ELan EPot ESis GDra GMaP ITim LBee LRHS MWat NMen SBla WAbe WCot WPat WPer WWin
	– 'Strawberries and Cream'	WAbe
	wulfenianum	NMen NRya

Amana see *Tulipa*

x *Amarcrinum* (*Amaryllidaceae*)
	memoria-corsii	NGar
	– 'Howardii'	EBee EMan LPio LRHS WCot

x *Amarine* (*Amaryllidaceae*)
	tubergenii	CAvo LPio
	– 'Zwanenburg'	EBee EMan WCot

x *Amarygia* (*Amaryllidaceae*)
§	*parkeri* 'Alba'	CAvo EBee ECho EMan LPio SSpi WCot

Amaryllis (*Amaryllidaceae*)
§	*belladonna* ♀ H2-3	CBcs CBro CFil CStu EMan EPar ETub LAma LBow LRHS MBri NRog SChr SDeJ SPer SSpi WCot WGer
	– 'Bloemfontein'	CAvo
	– 'Johannesburg'	CAvo LRHS WCot
	– 'Major'	CAvo
	– 'Parkeri Alba'	see x *Amarygia parkeri* 'Alba'
	– 'Purpurea'	EBee ETub WCot
	– white	SSpi WCot
	– 'Windhoek'	CAvo

Amelanchier ✿ (*Rosaceae*)
	alnifolia	CAgr CDul CPle CTho EPla WBcn
	– 'Obelisk'PBR	EBee SKee WWeb
	– pink-fruited	NLar
§	– var. *pumila*	CPMA CPle CTho GBin GSki LHop MSte NHol SSta WDin WNor
	– 'Smokey'	CDul
*	*alpina*	EHyt
	arborea	CPle CTho EGFP WNor
	bartramiana	CTho SSta
	– 'Eskimo'	SMad
	canadensis	More than 30 suppliers
	x *grandiflora* 'Autumn Brilliance'	CEnd GKir LRHS NHol
	– 'Ballerina' ♀ H4	More than 30 suppliers
	– 'Cole's Select' **new**	SReu
	– 'Robin Hill'	CBcs GKir LPan LRHS MAsh MBlu MGos SKee SLim SMad WFar
	– 'Rubescens'	CDul CEnd LRHS
	'La Paloma'	MBri NLar SMad
	laevis	CBcs CDul EPfP SKee SPer
	– 'Princess Diana'	NLar SMad
	– 'R.J. Hilton'	GKir
	– 'Snow Cloud'	MBri
	– 'Snowflakes'	CEnd CWSG GKir LRHS MBri MDun NPro SKee SLim
	lamarckii ♀ H4	More than 30 suppliers
	pumila	see *A. alnifolia* var. *pumila*
	rotundifolia 'Edelweiss'	CEnd CPMA GKir MBlu MBri MGos
	– 'Helvetia'	CEnd GKir LRHS MAsh MBri WEas
	spicata	CPle ECrN GIBF

x *Amelasorbus* (*Rosaceae*)
	jackii	MBlu

Amicia (*Papilionaceae*)
	zygomeris	CAbb CBot CHEx CHll CMdw CPle CPom CSpe EBee EMan EWes GBuc GCal SMad SMrm SUsu WSHC WWye

Ammi (*Apiaceae*)
	majus	EMan MSal WCot WEas
	visnaga	GPoy LPio MSal

Ammobium (*Asteraceae*)
	calyceroides **new**	EMan WCot

Ammocharis (*Amaryllidaceae*)
	coranica	WCot

Ammophila (*Poaceae*)
	arenaria	GQui

Amomum (*Zingiberaceae*)
	dealbatum	CKob EBot LEur
	subulatum	CKob EBot LEur

Amomyrtus (*Myrtaceae*)
§	*luma*	CDoC CTbh CTrC CTrG CTri CTrw EPfP IDee ISea SArc WBod WJek WPic

Amorpha (*Papilionaceae*)
	canescens	CAgr CBcs CPle EMan GKir NSti SEND WBVN
	fruticosa	CAgr CBcs CFil CPle ECre EWTr LEdu MBlu MNrw SBrw SLon SPlb

Amorphophallus (*Araceae*)
	albus **new**	LEur
	bulbifer	CKob EAmu LAma LEur LRHS WMul
	dunnii **new**	EBee LEur
	kerrii	EBee
	konjac	CHEx CKob ITer LEur SSpi
	rivierei	EBee GCal LEur NBlo WMul XBlo
	stipitatus	EBee SSpi
	yunnanensis	LEur

Ampelocalamus (*Poaceae*)
	scandens	CFil EPla

Ampelodesmos (*Poaceae*)
	mauritanicus	CBrm CHar COIW EBee ECha EFou EHoe EMan LEdu LHrt LPhx LRav MCCP NGdn NOGN SEND SMad SPlb WLRN

Ampelopsis (*Vitaceae*)
	aconitifolia	CPIN SBra
	arborea	CPIN
	bodinieri	CPIN
	brevipedunculata	see *A. glandulosa* var. *brevipedunculata*
	chaffanjonii	CPIN SMur
§	*glandulosa* var. *brevipedunculata*	CBcs CRHN LHop MGrG SCoo SGar SLim SPer SPet WDin WFar
	– var. *brevipedunculata* f. *citrulloides* B&SWJ 1173	WCru
§	– – 'Elegans' (v)	More than 30 suppliers
	– – 'Tricolor'	see *A. glandulosa* var. *brevipedunculata* 'Elegans'
	– var. *hancei* B&SWJ 3855	WCru
*	– var. *maximowiczii*	CPIN

henryana   see *Parthenocissus henryana*
megalophylla   CBcs CBot CFil CHEx CPlN EBee
ELan EPfP EShb LRHS MBlu SPar
SPer WBcn WCru WFar WNor
WOVN WPGP
orientalis   CPlN
sempervirens hort.   see *Cissus striata*
thunbergii   CPlN
tricuspidata 'Veitchii'   see *Parthenocissus tricuspidata*
'Veitchii'

Amphicome see *Incarvillea*

Amsonia (*Apocynaceae*)

ciliata   CFee CFir EBee ECGN LPhx WCot
WFar WPer
hubrichtii   EBee EGle EMan MSPs SIgm SMac
SMad WHil
illustris   EBee EFou EMan LRHS MSte
WPer WTin
jonesii   EBee SIgm
§ *orientalis*   More than 30 suppliers
tabernaemontana   CFir CLyd EBee ECGN ECha EGle
ELan EMan EWTr GBuc GEil LRHS
MNrw NDov NPPs SAga SIgm SMac
SMad SMrm SOkh SRms WAul
WCot WFar WOld WPer WPnP
- var. *salicifolia*   EBee EChP EGle EOrc GKir GSki
LPhx LRHS MCAu MSte NCat WFTG

Amygdalus see *Prunus*

Anacamptis (*Orchidaceae*)
pyramidalis   CHdy EFEx WHer

Anacyclus (*Asteraceae*)
pyrethrum   GPoy
- var. *depressus*   EBre ECtt ELan EMNN EMlt EPfP
ESis GKir GMaP GTou LRHS MSte
NFor NLap NVic NWCA SBla SIng
SPet SPlb WCFE WFar WHoo WPer
WWin
- - 'Garden Gnome'   MPWC NPri SRms

Anadenanthera (*Mimosaceae*)
colubrina   MGol

Anagallis (*Primulaceae*)
arvensis   MHer MSal WHbs
foemina   MSal
linifolia   see *A. monellii* subsp. *linifolia*
§ *monellii* ♀ H4   CNic ECtt SAga SBla WCom WWin
§ - subsp. *linifolia*   EHyt
- 'Sunrise'   CPBP SBla SUsu WCot WWol
'Skylover'   EMan SMrm SPet WCot WWol
tenella   SIng
- 'Studland'   EDAr EMlt EPot NJOw NMen
NWCA SBla WAbe

Ananas (*Bromeliaceae*)
comosus   LRHS
- var. *variegatus* (v)   MBri SMur

Anaphalis (*Asteraceae*)
CC 3725   WCot
CC 3726   ITer
alpicola   EPot NMen
margaritacea   COIW CSBt ECha ECtt EWTr GBin
GGar GMaP ITer MBri MLLN NBid
NBro NOak SMer SPar SRms WFar
WMoo
§ - var. *cinnamomea*   EMon WEas
§ - 'Neuschnee'   CTri EBee GKir LBBr MWgw

NArg NGdn NHol NMir NPri SPla
WBea WPer
- New Snow   see *A. margaritacea* 'Neuschnee'
§ - var. *yedoensis* ♀ H4   CBre CTri EBee ECot EFou EGle
MWat SBri SDix WBrE
§ *nepalensis* var.   EBee ELan EMon MWat NMRc NSti
monocephala
nubigena   see *A. nepalensis* var.
monocephala
sinica 'Moon's   WCot
Silver' **new**
triplinervis ♀ H4   More than 30 suppliers
- CC 1620   WCot
§ - 'Sommerschnee' ♀ H4   CSLe EBee EBre EChP ECha ECot
ECtt EFou EGle EPfP ERou LRHS
MBri MCLN MTis NFor NLon
SAga SChu SDes SPer WBea WElm
WMnd WPer WWal
- Summer Snow   see *A. triplinervis*
'Sommerschnee'

Anchusa (*Boraginaceae*)
angustissima   see *A. leptophylla* subsp. *incana*
§ *azurea*   CPLG GKir IGor MGol MWrn
NOrc WHil WPer WWeb
- 'Blue Angel'   EMar GKir IBal LRHS NJOw WWeb
- 'Dropmore'   COIW CTri EBee EPfP LAst LRHS
MAnH MEHN MPWC NLon NOrc
NPer SRms SSth WBry WPer WWeb
- 'Feltham Pride'   CSBt CSam ECtt GKir GMaP
MAnH NLon NPri WFar WHil
WHoo WPGP WPer WWhi
- 'Little John'   COtt ECot ELan FRou NFla 3Aga
SRms WTcl
- 'Loddon Royalist' ♀ H4   More than 30 suppliers
- 'Opal'   EBee ECGP ECot EMan EPfP ERou
LRHS MAnH MCAu MNFA MWat
NDov SChu SMrm SPla WLRN
- 'Royal Blue'   LRHS
barrelieri   MLLN
caespitosa hort.   see *A. leptophylla* subsp. *incana*
capensis   LAst
cespitosa Lamarck   ECho EHyt ELan EWes SBla SIng
italica   see *A. azurea*
laxiflora   see *Borago pygmaea*
leptophylla   MDKP
F&W 9550 **new**
§ - subsp. *incana*   CRDP EDif EMFP ITim LRHS MSph
myosotidiflora   see *Brunnera macrophylla*
officinalis   CArn LRHS MGol MSal WHHs WHil
sempervirens   see *Pentaglottis sempervirens*
undulata   SIgm

Ancrumia (*Alliaceae*)
cuspidata F&W 8233   WCot

Andrachne (*Euphorbiaceae*)
colchica   EMan WCot

Andromeda (*Ericaceae*)
glaucophylla   MBar SBrw WDin
polifolia   CMHG EMil GCrs GKir SBrw
WDin WFar
- 'Alba'   EBee ELan GDra GEdr GKir LRHS
MAsh MBar MBro MRav NHar
NHol NRya SBod SBrw SPar SPer
SPlb WFar WPat WWin
- 'Blue Ice'   ELan EPfP GKir LRHS MAsh SPer
SSpi WAbe WPat
- 'Compacta' ♀ H4   CDoC CWib EBee EHoe EMil EPot
GCrs GGar GKir LRHS MBar MBri
MGos NHar NHol NMen SPar
SPer SRms WPat WSHC WWin

- 'Compacta Alba' ♀ H4   SPar
- 'Grandiflora'   ELan GKir ITim LRHS MAsh MBri
                   MGos SBod SPer
- 'Hayachine'   EPot
- 'Kirigamine'   GKir LRHS MAsh MBri MGos NHol
                  WPat
- 'Macrophylla' ♀ H4   EPot GDra GEdr ITim MBro NDlv
                        NHar NHol WAbe WPat
- 'Nana'   EPfP EPot GKir LRHS MAsh NMen
            SPer STre WStI WWeb
- 'Nikko'   GBuc IKee ITim MGos NHol WPat

Andropogon (Poaceae)

gerardii   CBrm CKno EBee EBre ECGN
                EHoe EHul EMan EMon EPPr EPla
                LPhx MAnH MWhi SDes WDyG
                WPer WWpP
hallii hybrid   EPPr
ischaemum   see *Bothriochloa ischaemum*
saccharoides   EBee
scoparius   see *Schizachyrium scoparium*
virginicus   CBrm LPhx

Androsace (Primulaceae)

akbaitalensis new   EHyt
albana   ITim NWCA
alpina   SPlb
axillaris ACE 1060   EHyt
baltistanica   CGra EHyt
barbulata   WLin
carnea   CPBP MNrw NHar NMen SIng
               WWin
- *alba*   LRHS NHar NRya NWCA WLin
- subsp. *brigantiaca*   GCrs GDra GTou ITim MBro
                          NHar NSla WAbe WHoo
- var. *halleri*   see *A. carnea* subsp. *rosea*
- subsp. *laggeri* ♀ H4   ECho GCrs GTou LTwo NHar NSla
                            NWCA SIng WAbe WPat
§ - subsp. *rosea* ♀ H4   CPBP
carnea x **pyrenaica**   EPot ITim NHar NMen SOkd
chaixii   ITim
chamaejasme   ECho
ciliata   EPot GTou ITim
cylindrica   CGra CPBP EPot GTou ITim LRHS
                  NHar NMen WFar
- 'Val d'Ossue'   EPot
cylindrica x **hirtella**   CGra EHyt EPot GTou ITim LRHS
                                 NHar WAbe
delavayi   WAbe
foliosa   EHyt
geraniifolia   CPLG EBee ECha LHop WCru
globifera   CGra CPBP EHyt EPot GKev ITim
                 NMen WAbe
hausmannii   GTou ITim
hedraeantha   CLyd EPot ITim MWat NMen
                   NRya NWCA SIng WAbe WLin
x **heeri** pink   CGra
- white   SBla
himalaica   CGra CNic CPBP EHyt EPot SBla
hirtella   ETow GTou ITim NMen
idahoensis   CGra
jacquemontii   see *A. villosa* var. *jacquemontii*
* **kochii tauricola**   ITim
§ **lactea**   CNic GCrs GTou ITim WAbe
§ **laevigata**   CGra CNic EHyt NMen WAbe WLin
- var. *ciliolata*   GTou NWCA SIng
- 'Gothenburg'   WPat
lanuginosa ♀ H4   CLyd CMea CPBP CPlt EHyt EPot
                       GCrs GEdr MBro MWat NMen
                       NWCA SBla SDys SIng SRms
                       WAbe WWin
- compact   EPot
- 'Wisley Variety'   SIgm

limprichtii   see *A. sarmentosa* var. *watkinsii*
x **marpensis**   EPot
mathildae   EHyt GTou ITim NMen NWCA
                 WAbe WLin
microphylla   see *A. mucronifolia* G.Watt
§ **mollis**   CPBP SIgm SIng
§ **montana**   CGra NWCA
mucronifolia hort.   see *A. sempervivoides*
§ **mucronifolia** G.Watt   EHyt EPot GTou
- CHP&W 296   NWCA
mucronifolia x   EHyt EPot WOBN
   sempervivoides
muscoidea   EPot WAbe
- C&R 188   GTou
- SEP 132   EHyt
- 'Breviscapa'   EPot
- f. *longiscapa*   CGra ITim NWCA
- Schacht's form new   CGra EHyt GCrs SBla SIgm
§ **nivalis**   EHyt
x **pedemontana**   ITim
primuloides   see *A. studiosorum*
pubescens   CGra ITim LRHS LTwo NMen
pyrenaica   CGra EHyt GTou ITim LRHS
                 NMen NWCA SIng WAbe
rigida   WLin
- KGB 168   EPot
robusta   EHyt GCrs
* - subsp. *purpurea*   SIgm WAbe
rotundifolia   GTou SBla WCru
sarmentosa misapplied   see *A. studiosorum*
sarmentosa Wall.   EDAr EHyt ELan GTou ITim LBee
                        MBro MWat NMen SRms WCom
                        WHoo WTel
- CC 407   LRHS
- CC 2627   WOBN
- from Namche, Nepal   WAbe
- 'Chumbyi'   see *A. studiosorum* 'Chumbyi'
- 'Salmon's Variety'   see *A. studiosorum* 'Salmon's
                        Variety'
- 'Sherriffii'   CFee EPot GEdr MOne NHar
                  NLAp SIgm SRms WLin WWin
§ - var. *watkinsii*   EPot NHar NMen
- var. *yunnanensis*   see *A. studiosorum*
   misapplied
- var. *yunnanensis*   see *A. mollis*
   Knuth
selago new   WAbe
§ **sempervivoides** ♀ H4   CLyd ECha EDAr EHyt ELan EPot
                             GDra GKev LBee LHop LRHS
                             MBro NDlv NHar NHol NLAp
                             NMen NWCA SBla SIgm SIng
                             SRms WHoo WLin WPat WWin
- dark   ITim
- 'Greystone'   EPot
- 'Susan Joan' (v)   CPBP EHyt WAbe
septentrionalis   CBrm ECho NJOw
   'Stardust'
sericea   EHyt WLin
strigillosa   WAbe
§ **studiosorum** ♀ H4   EPot NLAp
- 'Brilliant'   CNic
- 'Chumbyi'   EHol ETow LTwo MBro MOne NHol
               NWCA SBla SIng SRms WOBN WPat
- 'Doksa'   EHyt EPot GCrs NMen SOkd WAbe
- 'Salmon's Variety'   CMea CTri ECho NRya SIgm WAbe
tapete   EHyt WAbe
- ACE 1725   EPot
vandellii   CGra CPBP EHyt EPot GTou ITim
                 WAbe WLin
villosa   ITim
- var. *arachnoidea*   EHyt WLin
- - 'Superba'   NMen
- var. *congesta*   CGra EHyt

§	- var. *jacquemontii*	EHyt ETow NMen NWCA SBla SIgm WLin
	- - lilac	CPBP EPot
	- - pink	EPot NLAp WAbe
	- subsp. *taurica*	CLyd EHyt
	vitaliana	see *Vitaliana primuliflora*
	watkinsii	see *A. sarmentosa* var. *watkinsii*
	yargongensis ACE 1722	EPot

Andryala (Asteraceae)
agardhii	WPat
lanata	see *Hieracium lanatum*

Anemanthele see *Stipa*

Anemarrhena (Anthericaceae)
asphodeloides	EBee MSal

Anemone ✿ (Ranunculaceae)
	B&SWJ 1452	WCru
	aconitifolia new	CSpe EMon
	altaica	GAbr ITim MSal SRms
	amurensis new	EBee
	apennina ♀ H4	CBos CLAP ECha EPar SCro WTin
	- var. *albiflora*	CDes CFwr CLAP CRDP EBee ECha EPot ERos GMac LRHS MSte WCot WPGP WPnP
	- double	CBos
	- 'Petrovac' CE&H 538	EBee LRHS WCot
	baicalensis	NSti
	baldensis	ECho GAbr GKir LBee LRHS NBur NMen NOak NWCA SRms WCom WViv
	barbulata	EChP EMan LPhx NLar
	blanda ♀ H4	CBri EBre EOrc GKir ITim LAma MBri NBlu NChi NDov NRog SChu WBea WCom WFar WPer WShi
	- blue	CAvo CBri CBro CMea CPLG CTri ELan EPot EPot GAbr GKir ITim LAma LRHS MBri NLon SMrm SRms WFar
	- 'Blue Shades'	CFwr ECho EMar ETub GEdr IGor LPhx LRHS WBrE WHil WPGP
	- 'Charmer'	EPar EPot MBNS MNrw NMen
	- 'Ingramii' CE&H 626	EMan EPar LAma NRog WCot
	- 'Pink Star'	CBro EPot LAma LRHS MBNS NBir NRog
	- 'Radar' ♀ H4	CBro CLAP CMea ECho EPar EPot LAma MNrw NBir NMen NRog SVal WLin
	- var. *rosea* ♀ H4	CAvo CFwr CNic ECho ELan EPfP LAma MLLN WFar WPer
	- 'Violet Star'	CFwr EMar EPot LRHS NLon WCot WFTG WLin
	- 'White Splendour' ♀ H4	More than 30 suppliers
	canadensis	CHar CNic CSpe EBee EBre ECGP GKir MBrN MNrw MSte NBur NWoo WCot WLin WRos
	caroliniana	CLyd EBre EMFP EPla EPot ESis GBuc GCrs GKir LRHS NOak WCru
	caucasica	SBla SCnR
	coronaria	CTri LAma LHop NRog WFar
	De Caen Group	
§	- - 'Die Braut'	GBri NRog WFar WRHF
	- - 'Mister Fokker'	ETub LAma NRog SBri WFar
	- - The Bride	see *A. coronaria* (De Caen Group) 'Die Braut'
	- - 'The Governor'	NRog WFar WRHF
	- 'Jerusalem'	WFar
	- (Mona Lisa Group) 'Sylphide'	NBir NRog WFar

	- Saint Bridgid Group (d)	LAma MBri NRog SDeJ WFar
	- - 'Lord Lieutenant' (d)	EMan GBri NBir NBur NRog WCom WFar
	- - 'Mount Everest' (d)	EMan NBir
	- - 'The Admiral' (d)	ETub NBir NRog WFar
	- Saint Piran Group	SDeJ
	crinita	EBee
	cylindrica	CFir CMHG EBee EBlw EChP GAbr MDKP MNrw
	davidii B&SWJ 7508 new	WCru
	decapetala	GCal
	demissa	EBee EMan GAbr GBuc GKev NRya
	dichotoma	EBee
	drummondii	CCge CHar CLyd EBee EBre EMan GKir GSki LRHS MBrN NBur NChi WWeb
	elongata B&SWJ 2975	WCru
	eranthoides	CDes EBee EPot
	fasciculata	see *A. narcissiflora*
	flaccida	CBro CLAP CRDP EBee EPot GMac LPhx LRHS MSte WCot WCru WFar
	x *fulgens*	ECha SAga SIgm SVal
	- 'Annulata Grandiflora'	ECGP
	- 'Multipetala'	ETub NRog
	- Saint Bavo Group	CBro ECGP
	globosa	see *A. multifida*
	'Guernica'	ECho GBuc MOne SRot
	'Hatakeyama Double' (d) new	GCal
	'Hatakeyama Single' new	GCal
	hepatica	see *Hepatica nobilis*
§	*hortensis*	CMil LPhx SBla
	- JCA 161 003	IDac
	- subsp. *heldreichii*	SAga SCnR
§	*hupehensis*	CBos CBot EBee EWll GKir LRHS NOrc SVal WFar
	- f. *alba*	CDes CMil EBee WPGP
§	- 'Bowles' Pink' ♀ H4	CMil CRDP CStr EBee EGle EPPr MBro MWat NPPs WCom WCru WHoo WMaN WPGP
	- 'Crispa'	see *A.* x *hybrida* 'Lady Gilmour'
	- 'Eugenie'	CMil CStr EBee EChP EMan GSki LRHS MBNS NBir
	- 'Hadspen Abundance' ♀ H4	More than 30 suppliers
§	- var. *japonica*	CBos CPou GCal NCiC NFor WEas
	- - B&SWJ 4886	WCru
	- - 'Bodnant Burgundy'	CPen CPrp EBee EChP ECtt EGle EMan IPot LRHS MBri MCAu MCCP MWgw SDes WHil WPnP
§	- - 'Bressingham Glow'	CMHG EBre EChP ECtt EGle ELan EPfP ERou ETub GKir GSki LHop LRHS MCAu MCLN MMil MNrw NBir NHol NOrc NSti NVic SCro SHBN SPer SWat WAbb WFar WMnd WWal
§	- - 'Pamina' ♀ H4	More than 30 suppliers
	- - Prince Henry	see *A. hupehensis* var. *japonica* 'Prinz Heinrich'
§	- - 'Prinz Heinrich' ♀ H4	More than 30 suppliers
§	- - 'Rotkäppchen'	EBee EBlw EMan EWTr MRav NBur NSti WAul WRHF
	- 'Praecox'	EBee EBlw EHrv EPfP GBri GSki LRHS MBNS MBri MWgw NBir NGdn NHol NPri NSti SCro SPar WAbb WCru WHal WMnd WPnP WWal WWin
	- 'September Charm'	see *A.* x *hybrida* 'September Charm'

	- 'Splendens'	CMHG COlW CPLG EBee EMan ENot LAst LHop LRHS LSyl NCiC NHol SDes SPer WAbb WBro WElm WFar WHal WLin
	- 'Superba'	EBee EBlw GKir WKif
§	x **hybrida**	CAvo EBlw EPar MBro MWgw NChi NOak SChu SGar WBod WCru WFar WMoo
	- 'Alba' hort. (UK)	see *A.* x *hybrida* 'Honorine Jobert'
	- 'Andrea Atkinson'	CPrp EChP EMan EPfP GMac GSki LAst LGro LPVe LRHS MBri MBro MCLN MNFA NHol NPSI NSti SChu SDes SMrm SPla WCot WCra WFar WHil WHoo WLRN WMnd WMoo
	- 'Bowles' Pink'	see *A. hupehensis* 'Bowles' Pink'
	- 'Bressingham Glow'	see *A. hupehensis* var. *japonica* 'Bressingham Glow'
	- 'Burganetty' **new**	CFwr
	- 'Elegans' ♀ H4	EFou MDKP MRav SDes SWat WCru WHoo
§	- 'Géante des Blanches'	CBos CHar CMil CStr EBee ECtt GKir GMac LRHS MAnH MBro MSph NDov NPPs SMrm WFar WHoo
§	- 'Honorine Jobert' ♀ H4	More than 30 suppliers
§	- 'Königin Charlotte' ♀ H4	More than 30 suppliers
	- 'Kriemhilde'	GCal GMac
	- 'Lady Gilmour'	CElw CRDP CSpe EBee EChP ECtt EGle EHol EHrv EMan GCal GKir GMaP LRHS MAnH MCCP MRav MTis NBir NChi NEgg SAga SOkh SPar WBro WCot WCru WFar WHil WPnP
	- 'Lady Gilmour' misapplied	see *A.* x *hybrida* 'Margarete'
	- 'Loreley'	CM&M CPrp EBee EChP EMan IPot LPVe MBNS MCLN MSte MWat MWgw NPSI NSti SMrm WElm WHil WWpP
	- 'Luise Uhink'	CHor CPou LRHS MDKP NBir NHol SSpi WEas
§	- 'Margarete'	More than 30 suppliers
	- 'Max Vogel'	EBee EMan ERou LPhx MCAu MDKP NCat WBcn WHil
	- 'Monterosa'	see *A.* x *hybrida* 'Margarete'
	- 'Pamina'	see *A. hupehensis* var. *japonica* 'Pamina'
	- Prince Henry	see *A. hupehensis* var. *japonica* 'Prinz Heinrich'
	- 'Prinz Heinrich'	see *A. hupehensis* var. *japonica* 'Prinz Heinrich'
	- 'Profusion'	LBuc LRHS MLan SHBN
	- Queen Charlotte	see *A.* x *hybrida* 'Königin Charlotte'
	- 'Richard Ahrens'	CDoC EBlw EChP EGle ERou GBuc GKir GMaP LHop LPhx LRHS MNFA NDov NHol NOrc SAga SCro SMrm SPla SWat WBro WCru WFar WHil WLin WMnd WPnP WWal
	- 'Robustissima'	CSpe EBee EBlw EChP ECtt EFou EGra ENot EPfP ERou LRHS MBri MRav MSte MWgw NBir NBlu NHol NPri NSti SDes SHBN SPar SPer SPla SWat WAbb WAul WFar WMnd
	- 'Rosenschale'	CBos EBee EGle GCal MBri WCru WFar
	- 'Rotkäppchen'	see *A. hupehensis* var. *japonica* 'Rotkäppchen'
§	- 'September Charm' ♀ H4	More than 30 suppliers
	- 'Serenade'	EBee EBlw ECtt EFou EGle EMan

		ENot EPfP ERou LPVe LRHS MBri MCAu NBir NHol NPSI SDes SHBN SVil WAul WCot WFar WHil WMoo
	- 'Terry's Pink' **new**	WCot
	- Tourbillon	see *A.* x *hybrida* 'Whirlwind'
§	- 'Whirlwind'	More than 30 suppliers
	- 'White Queen'	see *A.* x *hybrida* 'Géante des Blanches'
	- Wirbelwind	see *A.* x *hybrida* 'Whirlwind'
	japonica	see *A.* x *hybrida*, *A. hupehensis*
	x **lesseri**	More than 30 suppliers
	leveillei	CMil CRDP EBee EHrv ELan EPPr GIBF GMac GSki LPhx LRHS MHar MLLN MTis NGdn NSti SIgm SSpi SUsu WAbe WCom WCru WRus WSHC WSan
§	x **lipsiensis**	CAvo CBro CDes CRDP CStu EBee ECha EGle EHyt EPar ERos ETow GMac ITim LPhx MRav MTho NGar NMen SIgm SUsu WCot WCru WFar WHal WHil WLin WPGP
	- 'Pallida' ♀ H4	CHad CPlt CRDP ECho ERos GCrs GKev MNFA NPar SMrm WCot
	lyallii	EPPr GBuc
N	**magellanica** hort.	see *A. multifida*
§	**multifida**	More than 30 suppliers
	- JCA 2050.5	SBla
	- 'Major'	CFir CLyd CRDP LAst LPhx LRHS MBNS MBro NLon NPro NWCA SAga SBla SMad WCFE WCom WHil WMoo WPnP
	- pink	GBuc WSan
*	- 'Rubra'	CHar CPLG EHrv EWll LAst LPhx LRHS MBNS MNrw NBir NDlv NMen NWCA SMad WHil WWeb
	- white	EBre
	multifida misapplied red	see *A.* x *lesseri*
§	**narcissiflora**	EBee ECGP GKir NChi SVal WCom
§	- subsp. **biarmiensis**	WCot
	- **citrina**	GKir SBla
	nemorosa ♀ H4	CAvo CBro CElw CFwr CKin CPLG EBot EMar EPar EPfP EPot ETub GKir GSki ITim LAma LSyl MBow MSal NHar NHol SDes SIng SRms SSpi WBrE WFar WShi WWeb
N	- 'Alba Plena' (d)	CBro CHea CNic CSWP EBee EBlw ECha EPPr EPot ERos GBuc GGar GMac IMGH LRHS MTho NMGW NMen SIng SUsu WAbb WCot WCru WEas WFar WHil WLin WPnP
	- 'Allenii' ♀ H4	More than 30 suppliers
	- 'Amy Doncaster'	SCro
	- 'Atrocaerulea'	EPar GBuc GMac IBlr NHol WCru
	- 'Bill Baker's Pink'	CLAP
	- 'Blue Beauty'	CLAP EGle EPot ERos GBuc IBlr MNFA MNrw NMen SSpi WCru
	- 'Blue Bonnet'	CElw CStu ECho GBuc ITim MNrw WCot
	- 'Blue Eyes' (d)	CBos CDes CLAP CRDP EGle GCrs IBlr MAvo MSte SBla SIgm WCot WCru WPGP
	- 'Blue Queen'	EPot
	- 'Bowles' Purple'	CBos CDes CStu EBee EPPr EPar ETow GMaP GMac IBlr ITim MAvo MNrw NGar NHar NRya SIgm SIng WBor WCot WCru WFar WIvy WPGP
	- 'Bracteata'	EHrv ERos ITim NDov
	- 'Bracteata Pleniflora' (d)	EBee ECha EGle GBuc GMaP IBlr LHop MAvo MBro MNFA NBir NGar WBor WCot WCru WFTG WFar

- 'Buckland'	CBos CDes EHrv IBlr WCru
- 'Cedric's Pink'	CBos EPPr ERos IBlr ITim WCru
- 'Dee Day'	CLAP EPPr GBuc ITim MNrw
	NGar SMrm WCru
- 'Flore Pleno' (d)	CBos CDes EBee EBre EHyt EOrc
	EPar GKir GMaP MBro NBir NGar
	NMen SPar WMaN WPGP
- 'Glenroy Blush'	MWrn
- 'Green Fingers'	ECho EPot GBuc GMaP ITim LPhx
	MNrw NGby NPar SCnR WCru
	WIvy
- 'Hannah Gubbay'	CLAP CRDP EBee EGle EPar GBuc
	IBlr MSte SSpi
- 'Hilda'	CLAP EGle EPar EPot ERos ETow
	GBuc MAvo MNFA MNrw MWrn
	NDlv NGar NMen NRya SSpi WCru
- 'Jack Brownless' **new**	IBlr
- 'Kentish Pink' **new**	GCrs
- 'Knightshayes Vestal'	EMan GMac MAvo MRav WCot
(d)	WCru WIvy
- 'Lady Doneraile'	CDes CLAP EBee ECha ETow
	GBuc NBir WCru WFar
- 'Leeds' Variety'	CRDP EGle GCrs GMac ITim
	LPhx MTho NHar NHol SBla
	SMrm WCot
§ - 'Lismore Blue' **new**	EPot
§ - 'Lismore Pink'	EHrv
- 'Lychette'	CAvo EBee ECha EGle EPar EPot
	GBuc IBlr ITim LPhx NDov NSla
	NWCA WCru
- 'Merlin' **new**	WCot
- 'Monstrosa'	EBee EPar EPot WCot
- 'New Pink'	CLAP IBlr
- 'Parlez Vous'	CMil EGle EPPr MNrw NGar
	SMrm WCru
- 'Pentre Pink'	IBlr MTho WCru WIvy
- pink	CPlt LPhx WCru
- 'Robinsoniana' ♀ H4	More than 30 suppliers
- 'Rosea'	CAvo EPot GMac MNFA SMrm
	WCru
- 'Royal Blue'	CAvo CDes CLAP CMil CNic CRDP
	EBee ECha EPPr EPar EPot ETow
	GBuc GEdr GMaP GMac LAma
	MAvo MNFA NDov NGar NHol
	NMen SBla WCru WFar WPnP WTin
- 'Tinney's Blush'	SSpi
- 'Tomas'	GMac
- 'Vestal' (d) ♀ H4	More than 30 suppliers
- 'Virescens' ♀ H4	CAvo CDes CStu EChP FCha EGle
	EHrv EPPr ERos EVFa GCrs GEdr
	MAvo MNFA MWrn NGar NPar
	SIng WIvy WLin WPGP
- 'Viridiflora'	CRDP EBee GBuc GMac LHop
	LPhx MRav MTed MTho NBir NSti
	SSpi WCot WCru WFar
- 'Westwell Pink'	CDes MSte SIgm WCot
- 'Wilks' Giant'	EBee ITim WCot WCru
- 'Wilks' White'	CBos CLAP EGle EPar EPot LBuc
	WCru
- 'Wyatt's Pink'	CBos CLAP LPhx WCru WPnP WTin
- 'Yerda Ramusem'	ECho
nemorosa x	see *A.* x *lipsiensis*
ranunculoides	
obtusiloba	CRDP GBuc GCrs GDra GTou
	IMGH LEur MTho NHar SBla SRms
- CLD 1549	GEdr
- *alba*	CRDP GDra LEur NHar SBla
- yellow	GBuc LEur SBla
palmata	EPot SCnR SSpi WCru
parviflora	CHea
patens	see *Pulsatilla patens*
pavonina	ECha ERos MAsh MTho SBla
	SCnR SIgm SVal

- 'Chapeau de	SBla
Napoléon' **new**	
- 'Grecian Sunset' **new**	MAsh
- var. *ocellata*	IDac
poilanei HWJ 631 **new**	WCru
polyanthes	EBee EBre GKir GTou LRHS
aff. **polyanthes** ex ACE	SIgm
prattii new	EBee
protracta new	EBee
pseudoaltaica	NGar WCru
pulsatilla	see *Pulsatilla vulgaris*
raddeana	EBee
ranunculoides ♀ H4	More than 30 suppliers
- 'Frank Waley' **new**	WCot
* - *laciniata*	GBuc GMaP MSte NGar
- 'Pleniflora' (d)	CHea CLAP CMil CRDP ECha
	EHrv EPar EPot MRav NGar
	WCom WCot WFar WIvy
- subsp. *wockeana*	EBee
richardsonii	CPla
riparia	see *A. virginiana* var. *alba*
rivularis	More than 30 suppliers
- CLD 573	CDes WLin
rossii new	EBee
rupicola	GMac NBir NWCA SRot
x **seemannii**	see *A.* x *lipsiensis*
sibirica new	EBee
smithiana new	EBee
stellata	see *A. hortensis*
sulphurea	see *Pulsatilla alpina* subsp.
	apiifolia
sylvestris	More than 30 suppliers
§ - 'Elise Fellmann' (d)	CDes CLAP CRDP EBee EMan
	LPhx SHar WCot
- 'Flore Pleno'	see *A. sylvestris* 'Elise Fellmann'
- 'Macrantha'	CDes CLAP CPen CPrp CRDP
	EBee EChP EMan EPfP GMac LAst
	SMrm SSpi WCot WPGP
tetrasepala	CDes EBee WPGP
§ **tomentosa**	CMGP EBee EBlw FCha EMan GDra
	GGar GSki LRHS SCro SDix SRms
	SWat WFar WGwG WRha WWal
- 'Albadura'	EBee GSki
- 'Robustissima'	see *Anemone* x *hybrida*
	'Robustissima'
trifolia	CBos CRDP EBee ECha EHyt
	EMan EPPr EPot ERos GMac NGar
	NMen SCnR SRms SUsu WCot
- pink	CDes CLAP MSte
- 'Semiplena' (d)	CDes WCot
trullifolia	CRDP ETow GCrs GDra GMac
	ITim NHar SBla WCot
- *alba*	GDra GGar GTou
- blue	GTou
- *coelestina* **new**	EBee
vernalis	see *Pulsatilla vernalis*
virginiana	CBri CCge CFir MDKP MSte MTed
	NBid NBir NChi WCot WFar
§ - var. *alba*	EBee ITim NSti SHar WBVN
vitifolia hort.	see *A. tomentosa*
vitifolia DC.	WCru
B&SWJ 2320	
- CC 3230	MDCh
- from Phulchowki,	SSpi
Nepal **new**	

Anemonella (Ranunculaceae)

thalictroides	CFir CGra CLAP CRDP EChP
	EFEx EHyt EMan EPar EPot GEdr
	GGar GSki ITim LAma LEur NGar
	NHar NMen NPPs NRya SBla SDes
	SMrm WAbe WCru WFar WLin
- 'Alba Plena' (d)	NHar

	- 'Amelia'	GEdr NPar SOkd
	- 'Betty Blake' (d)	CRDP NHar
	- 'Cameo'	EFEx
	- 'Double Green' (d)	EFEx
	- 'Flore Pleno' **new**	NLar
	- 'Full Double White'	EFEx
	- 'Green Hurricane'	EFEx
	- f. *rosea*	CElw CLAP CPom CRDP EPar
		EPot GBuc LEur NLar
	- - double pink (d)	NHar SBla
	- - 'Oscar Schoaff' (d)	NHar WAbe
	- semi-double pink (d)	CRDP
	- semi-double white (d)	CLAP CRDP EPar ETow SBla WCot
	- 'Snowflakes' (d) **new**	NPar

Anemonopsis (*Ranunculaceae*)

	macrophylla	CBro CPlt CRDP EMan ETow GCal
		LEur LPhx LRHS MNrw MTed
		MTho NLar SBla SSpi WCru WSan

Anemopaegma (*Bignoniaceae*)

	chamberlaynii	CPlN

Anemopsis (*Saururaceae*)

	californica	CRDP EMan EOHP WCru

Anethum (*Apiaceae*)

	graveolens	CArn GPoy LRHS MBow MChe
		MHer SIde WCer WPer WSel WWye
	- 'Bouquet' **new**	NPri
	- 'Dukat'	CSev ELau MChe
	- 'Fern Leaved'	CBod CPrp EOHP WHHs WJek

angelica see *Angelica archangelica*

Angelica (*Apiaceae*)

	PC&H 129	WBry
	acutiloba	EBee SBla SDix SIgm WCot
	- JCA via P. Kelaidis	IDac
	archangelica	More than 30 suppliers
	- 'Corinne Tremaine' (v)	CBos EMan EVFa GBri NEgg NGHP
		NSti SPer WBry WCHb WCot
	arguta	EBee WCot
	atropurpurea	EMan EMar EVFa EWll EWsh ITer
		LEdu MCAu MFir MHer MLLN
		MNrw NBur NGHP NLar SWat
		WCHb WFar WHil WJek
	dahurica	CArn EBee IIve
	decursiva **new**	LPio
	- B&SWJ 5746	WCru
	florentii	EBee GIBF
	gigas	More than 30 suppliers
	- B&SWJ 4170	WCru
	- 'Gold Leaf' **new**	EBee
	grayi	EBee
*	*hispanica*	CArn CBri CSpe EBee EChP EPyc
		EWll GAbr GBar LPhx MAvo MCCP
		MHer MLLN NBir NChi NGHP
		SMad WBry WCHb WCru WHHs
	lineariloba	WCot
	NNS 99-23 **new**	
	montana	see *A. sylvestris*
	pachycarpa	CBct CRDP EBee EChP EFou
		EGoo EMan EOHP LPio NChi
		SIgm SWat WAul WFar WJek
		WWye
	pubescens	WCru
	B&SWJ 5593 **new**	
	- var. *matsumurae*	WCru
	B&SWJ 6387	
	razulii	EBee
	sachalinensis	EBee GIBF
	saxatilis	EBee GIBF

	sinensis	EBee EVFa GPoy IIve WCHb
	'Summer Delight' **new**	EMan EVFa MDKP MWrn SPoG
§	*sylvestris*	CAgr CArn CKin GBar NSco
		WCHb WHer
*	- 'Purpurea'	CSpe EBee EWes GKir SBla
		WPGP
	- 'Vicar's Mead'	IBlr LPhx NChi
	taiwaniana	EBee EBre LPhx SWat WOut
	ursina	EBee GIBF

Angelonia (*Scrophulariaceae*)

	gardneri	NBlu
*	'Mandiana Bicolour' **new**	NPri
	'Stella Gem'	LRHS MOak SMrm SPoG

Anigozanthos (*Haemodoraceae*)

	flavidus	CBcs CTrC EBee ECre EOHP MBri
		SPlb WCot
	- pink **new**	WWeb
	- red	WWeb
	- yellow	WBrE WWeb
	manglesii ♀ H1	CHEx GGar SGar SPlb WBrE

Anisodontea (*Malvaceae*)

§	*capensis*	CBcs EBee ELan EMan ERea GKir
		LAst MAsh MBNS NBir SChu SLim
		SMrm SOWG SRms SVen
	- 'Tara's Pink'	LHop LPhx MAsh SAga SCro
		SMrm
	elegans	CSpe SAga
	huegelii	see *Alyogyne huegelii*
	x *hypomadara* hort.	see *A. capensis*
§	x *hypomadara*	CMHG CSev ECtt NPer SRms WPer
	(Sprague) Bates	
	malvastroides	CSev
	scabrosa	CChe CWib

Anisotome (*Apiaceae*)

	sp. **new**	NSti
	imbricata	GDra

Annona (*Annonaceae*)

	cherimola (F)	CTrG NBlo SSte XBlo
	muricata (F)	NBlo XBlo
	reticulata (F)	WMul
	squamosa (F)	NBlo XBlo

Anoda (*Malvaceae*)

	cristata 'Opal Cup'	EMon

Anoiganthus see *Cyrtanthus*

Anomalesia see *Gladiolus*

Anomatheca (*Iridaceae*)

	cruenta	see *A. laxa*
	grandiflora	CHll ERos
§	*laxa* ♀ H2-3	CMHG CPLG CStu ECha ELan EMan
		EPfP EPot ERos LBow MNrw MTho
		NLAp NMen NPPs SDix SRms SSpi
		STes SYvo WAbe WCom WCot WCru
		WFar WPat WPer WWeb WWin
	- var. *alba* ♀ H2-3	CNic CSpe CStu ELan ERos MTho
		NMen SSpi WAbe WCom WCot
		WOBN WWeb
	- *alba-maculata*	LRHS NPPs
	- blue	ERos WAbe
	- 'Joan Evans'	CElw CNic ECtt ELan EPot ERos
		LTwo NMen SRms WAbe WCot
		WHrl WOBN
	- red spot	CPLG EDif LHop
	viridis	CPLG CPou CStu EBee ERos
		LBow LRHS WCot

anise see *Pimpinella anisum*

Anopterus (Escalloniaceae)
glandulosus	IBlr WCru

Anredera (Basellaceae)
§ *cordifolia*	CPlN CRHN ECho IIve LEdu LRHS

Antennaria (Asteraceae)
aprica	see *A. parvifolia*
dioica	CTri GPoy MBro MHer NBlu NFla NLon SPlb SRms WFar WWye
- 'Alba'	EDAr EHoe GAbr
- 'Alex Duguid'	CPlt EHyt GCrs GMaP LBee LRHS SAga SBla WCom
- 'Aprica'	see *A. parvifolia*
§ - var. *hyperborea*	LGro
- 'Minima'	ECho EPot GDra MWat NBro NHar NMen SIng
- 'Nyewoods Variety'	EPot GDra NLAp
- red	SIng
- var. *rosea*	see *A. rosea*
* - 'Rubra'	CTri ECha EDAr GDra MHer NLAp NMen NPri SBla WHen WTel
- *tomentosa*	see *A. dioica* var. *hyperborea*
'Joy'	SBla
macrophylla hort.	see *A. microphylla*
§ *microphylla*	EDAr EHoe EMNN ESis LGro MBar NFla NHol WBea WEas WPat WPer
§ *parvifolia*	CLyd CNic CTri ESis GDra MBar NEgg NPri SRms WBea WMoo WPer
- var. *rosea*	see *A. microphylla*
plantaginifolia	EBee
'Red Wonder'	CMea
§ *rosea* ♀ H4	ECho GKir MHer NLAp NMen NVic SPlb

Anthemis ✿ (Asteraceae)
from Turkey	LLWP
§ *aizoon*	see *Achillea ageratifolia* subsp. *aizoon*
§ 'Beauty of Grallagh'	CMea ECtt FFou GCal GMac NDov NGdn SDix WCot WWpP
'Cally Cream' **new**	EFou GCal
'Cally White' **new**	EFou GCal
carpatica	NBro
- 'Karpatenschnee'	EWTr GKir
cretica	SMrm
- subsp. *columnae* MESF 377 **new**	WAbe
§ - subsp. *cretica*	CLyd
- N3 754	NWCA
frutescens	see *Argyranthemum frutescens*
§ 'Grallagh Gold'	EBee ECha ECtt EMon EOrc EWes GKir LDai LHop LPhx LRHS MBri MWat NDov NPer SAga SCro WBea WFar WTel WViv
'Grallagh Gold' misapplied (orange-yellow)	see *A.* 'Beauty of Grallagh'
§ *marschalliana*	EBee ECha EDAr EPot IHMH LBee MSte ECha EDAr EPot IHMH LBee MSte NDov NOak SMrm WPer
montana	see *A. cretica* subsp. *cretica*
nobilis	see *Chamaemelum nobile*
punctata	CSLe
- subsp. *cupaniana* ♀ H3-4	More than 30 suppliers
- - 'Nana'	EMon GKir NPer SHar
rudolphiana	see *A. marschalliana*
sancti-johannis	EBee ECoo EGle EGoo ERou IGor LDai MBct MBri MWgw NArg

---

	NPer SPer SRms SWal WBea WBry WFar WMnd WPer WRHF WWpP
Susanna Mitchell = 'Blomit'	CHar CHea EBee EBre EChP ECtt EMan EPfP EWTr EWll GKir GMaP GMac LRHS MMil MNrw MSph NCat SCro WCom WWeb WWhi
'Tetworth'	CStr EBee ECha EHrv ELan EMan EMon GBuc GMac LRHS MMil MSte NGdn SChu SMad WCot WFar WPer WViv WWpP
tinctoria	CArn EBee ECha ELan ELau EMon GKir GMac GPoy LRHS MBow MChe MHer NFor NLon NPer SPet WBea WJek WWeb WWye
- 'Alba'	COIW EMan GKir LPhx LRHS MHer NChi SChu SHar SSth WHen WLRN WPer WWpP
* - 'Compacta'	EFou EWes LPhx SAsh SMrm
- dwarf	EBee GMac SBla SBri SUsu WCot WFar WWpP
- 'E.C. Buxton'	More than 30 suppliers
- 'Eva'	EMon LRHS NCat NDov NLar WEas WWhi
- from Judea **new**	EMon
- 'Golden Rays' **new**	NPro
- 'Grallagh Gold'	see *A.* 'Grallagh Gold'
- 'Kelwayi'	More than 30 suppliers
- 'Lemon Maid'	EFou SChu SCro SMrm SUsu
- 'Pride of Grallagh'	see *A.* 'Beauty of Grallagh'
- 'Sauce Béarnaise'	CBri EMon
- 'Sauce Hollandaise'	More than 30 suppliers
- 'Wargrave Variety'	More than 30 suppliers
triumfettii	NPer
tuberculata	EMan LRHS NChi SBla SIng

Anthericum (Anthericaceae)
algeriense	see *A. liliago* var. *major*
* *fistulosum*	EBee GSki
liliago	CBro CFil CRDP EBee EBre ELan ERos EWTr GCal GDra GMaP GSki LHop MLLN MSte SPer WAul WPGP WPer
§ - var. *major* ♀ H4	CAvo CDes ECha EHrv EPla GDra IBlr LPhx NLAp SSpi
ramosum	CAvo CDes EBee ECGN EChP ECha ELan EMan EPot EROS EWes GDra GSki LPhx LRHS MBrN MBro MLLN NBid NBir NWCA SHel SIng SMrm WPer
- *plumosum*	see *Trichopetalum plumosum*
undulatum **new**	EROS

Antholyza (Iridaceae)
coccinea	see *Crocosmia paniculata*
crocosmioides	see *Crocosmia latifolia*
paniculata	see *Crocosmia paniculata*

Anthoxanthum (Poaceae)
odoratum	CArn CBig CKin ELau GBar GIBF GPoy NNor WWye

Anthriscus (Apiaceae)
cerefolium	CArn CBod CPrp CSev EOHP GPoy ILis MBow MChe MDun MHer NPri WHHs WHbs WJek WLHH WPer WSel WWye
sylvestris	CArn WShi
- 'Broadleas Blush'	CNat
- 'Hullavington' (v)	CNat
- 'Moonlit Night'	EHoe
- 'Ravenswing'	More than 30 suppliers

Anthurium (*Araceae*)
amazonicum   MBri
andraeanum ♀ H1   MBri
scherzerianum ♀ H1   MBri

Anthyllis (*Papilionaceae*)
barba-jovis   CSpe EMan
hermanniae'   see *A. hermanniae* 'Minor'
  Compacta'
§ - 'Minor'   EPot NSla SBla WAbe WLin
montana   SBla
- subsp. **atropurpurea**   LRHS
- 'Rubra' ♀ H4   EChP ECho EDAr EGle EMan EPot
    LTwo MHer NFor NMen WWin
vulneraria   CFee CKin GTou MChe MMir
    NSco SSpi WHer
- var. **coccinea**   CHar CMil CSpe EMan GGar LPhx
    MBro MCCP MLLN MNrw MSte
    MTho NSla NWCA SGar WAbe
    WCom WFar WHil

Antigonon (*Polygonaceae*)
leptopus   CPlN SOWG

Añu see *Tropaeolum tuberosum*

Antirrhinum (*Scrophulariaceae*)
asarina   see *Asarina procumbens*
barrellieri   EMon
braun-blanquetii   CHal EBee EMan ERou MCAu
    MLLN MOne MSPs STes
glutinosum   see *A. hispanicum* subsp.
    hispanicum
graniticum new   EBee LRav
§ **hispanicum**   CNic EBee NBir SBla
- 'Avalanche'   CHal ECtt EMan MLan NLon SPet
    WWol
- subsp. **hispanicum**   CMdw CSpe
§ - - **roseum**   CMea CSpe EDAr EMan SPet WKif
majus 'Black Prince'   CHad CSpe EMan LHop SAga
    WEas
- subsp. **majus**   EWll
- 'Taff's White' (v)   LRHS
molle   CBri CPom CSpe EBee ECtt EHyt
    EOrc GCal MSte MTho NBir NPer
    NWCA SAga SIng SRot SUsu
- pink   CBri CSWP EOrc GCal MSte
    MTho SAga
'Night and Day' new   CSpe
'Powys Pride' (v)   EWll
pulverulentum   EVFa LHop LPhx MArl NPPs SAga
    WKif
sempervirens   EBee EMan ESis SBla WHil WWeb
siculum   EBee

Aphanes (*Rosaceae*)
§ **arvensis**   MSal WWye

Aphelandra (*Acanthaceae*)
squarrosa   CHal LRHS MBri

Aphyllanthes (*Aphyllanthaceae*)
monspeliensis   CFee ECho SBla

Apios (*Papilionaceae*)
§ **americana**   CPlN EBee EChP EMan EMon
    EOrc GBin LEdu MCCP NBir NChi
    NSti WCot WCru WSHC WWhi
tuberosa   see *A. americana*

Apium (*Apiaceae*)
graveolens   CArn CBgR CBod CPrp ELau

            EOHP GPoy IIve MBow MHer
            MSal SIde WBri WJek
- (Secalinum Group)   MHer NGHP
  'Par-cel'
x **Petroselinum**   see *A. graveolens* Secalinum Group

apple see *Malus domestica*

Apocynum (*Apocynaceae*)
cannabinum   CArn GPoy IIve MSal WWye

Aponogeton (*Aponogetonaceae*)
distachyos   CBen CRow CWat EHon ELan
    EMFW EPfP LMdh LPBA MSta
    NBlu NPer SAWi SCoo SLon SWat
    WFar WMAq WWeb WWpP

apricot see *Prunus armeniaca*

Aptenia (*Aizoaceae*)
cordifolia ♀ H1-2   CSev EOHP NPer SChr SEND SPet
    SSte SVen WRos
- 'Variegata' (v)   MRav

Aquilegia ✿ (*Ranunculaceae*)
from Baboquivari Mts,   LCTD
  Arizona
akitensis hort.   see *A. flabellata* , *A. flabellata* var.
    pumila
'Alaska' (State Series)   LCTD LEur
* **alba variegata** (v)   WEas
alpina   CBot CMea ECtt EDAr ELau EPfP
    EWTr GKir GTou LSyl MCAu MHer
    MLan MWgw MWod NFor NPPs
    SDes SPer SPet SRPl SRms SSth WFar
    WHen WMoo WPer WStl WWin
- 'Alba'   MWgw NLon NOak
- 'Carl Ziepke'   EBee
- 'Hensol Harebell'   see *A.* 'Hensol Harebell'
amaliae   see *A. ottonis* subsp. *amaliae*
* **anemoniflora**   EPyc NEgg
'Apple Blossom' new   MAnH SPoG
§ **atrata**   CPou EBee EMan EWTr GSki LEur
    MDKP MSPs NOak WLin WPer
atrovinosa   EBee EHyt
aurea misapplied   see *A. vulgaris* golden-leaved
aurea Janka   EBee
'Ballerina'   EBee NPPs WHer
barnebyi   CMea
bernardii   NJOw NOak
bertolonii ♀ H4   CFee EHyt EMNN GCrs GKev GTou
    LBee LHop LRHS MBro NMen
    NOak SBla SRms WHoo WPat
Biedermeier Group   EMil GKir LPVe LRHS MBNS NCot
    NNor NOrc SDes SWal WPer WWpP
'Blue Berry'   CMHG EBee MBro WPat
'Blue Jay' (Songbird   CFai EMar LEur MAvo NPri SPer
  Series)
'Blue Star' (Star Series)   EBee ECtt LEur LRHS NPSI WHil
    WPer
'Bluebird' (Songbird   LCTD LEur
  Series)
brevicalcarata   EBee
buergeriana   EBee LEur MAvo MDKP NChi
    STes WPer
- 'Calimero'   MAnH NChi NGby WHil
- var. **oxysepala**   see *A. oxysepala*
'Bunting' (Songbird   EMar EWll LEur
  Series)
'Burnished Rose' new   CPla
'Cameo Rose'(Cameo   NBir
  Series) new
canadensis ♀ H4   CMHG CSpe EBee EDAr EFWa

	ELan GSki LEur MHer NBid NBir
	NBro NOak SGar SMac SRms SWal
	WCru WPer
- 'Corbett'	GBuc LCTD WHil
- 'Little Lanterns' **new**	CFwr
- 'Nana'	LCTD
'Cardinal' (Songbird	CFai EMar LEur SPer SSvw
Series)	
caucasica	EBee MDHE
§ *chaplinei*	CBot EBee NBir SIgm WEas
chrysantha	CHea EBee EBre ECGN EWTr
	GBin GCrs LEur LHrt MLLN NHar
	NOak SRms WBrE WCot WCru
	WEas WLin WPer
- var. *chaplinei*	see *A. chaplinei*
- dwarf	LCTD
- 'Flore Pleno' (d)	EBee
- 'Yellow Queen'	CHea CSpe EBee EPfP GMaP LAst
	LEur MAvo MDKP SOkh SSvw WHil
clematiflora	see *A. vulgaris* var. *stellata*
coerulea ♀ H4	EFWa EWTr GBin GCrs LCTD
	LEur NCat SIgm SRms WEas WLin
- 'Mrs Nicholls'	EPar MBri
- var. *ochroleuca*	EBee WLin
- 'Rose Queen' **new**	MDKP
'Colorado' (State Series)	CFai EMar LEur
'Crimson Star'	CHea CPen EBee EBre ENot EPfP
	GKir LEur SPer WMoo WWeb
'Debutante' **new**	MDKP
desertorum	EBee LCTD SMac WAbe
discolor	CStu EPot GEdr GSki GTou LHop
	LRHS LTwo NMen SIng WPat
'Dorothy'	LCTD LHop LRHS
'Double Chocolate'	LRHS
Double Rubies (d)	EGoo EMan WCom WCot
double white	CFee
'Dove' (Songbird Series)	CFai EWll LCTD LEur MHer SPer
	SWat WCra
I 'Dragonfly'	CBcs EPfP MBri NMir NOak WFar
ecalcarata	see *Semiaquilegia ecalcarata*
einseleana	GSki
elegantula	EBee GCrs LCTD
eximia	EBee LCTD SBla WLin
'Firecracker'	LEur
'Firewheel'	see *A. vulgaris* var. *stellata*
	'Firewheel'
§ *flabellata* ♀ H4	EBlw GDea GDra MBro WPat WPer
- from Rebun-to,	CStu
Japan **new**	
§ - f. *alba*	ELan SBla SRms WEas
- 'Blue Angel'	CBcs EDAr GDra NCot WPer
- 'Blue Jewel' (Jewel	SPla
Series)	
- Cameo Series	CWib EWll MAvo SIng WCra WFar
	WGor WHil WRos
- - 'Cameo Blue'	LPVe
- - 'Cameo Pink and	MHer
White'	
- Jewel Series	CSpe ECho EMMN NBlu WHil
	WPer
- 'Ministar'	CHor CM&M ECho EDAr EMlt EPfP
	ESis GKir GSki LRHS MBNS MBro
	MHer NOak NVic SPar SRot SSpe
	WFar WHil WHoo WPer WWin
- 'Nana Alba'	see *A. flabellata* var. *pumila* f. *alba*
- 'Pink Jewel' (Jewel	CMHG SPla
Series)	
§ - var. *pumila* ♀ H4	ECha EHyt GDra GTou LHop LPVe
	MAnH NOak SBla SIng SRms WCom
	WCru WFar WLin WPat WPer
§ - - f. *alba* ♀ H4	CBot ECha GDra GEdr LBee LHop
	LRHS MBNS MSte SIng SRms WHil
	WWin

- - f. *kurilensis*	GDra MSte
- - 'Silver Edge' (v)	CElw CPla GBri MNrw WCom
* - 'White Angel'	WPer
- 'White Jewel'	SPla
(Jewel Series) **new**	
flavescens	EBee WPer
- var. *miniana*	IDac LTwo
formosa	CBot EBee LCTD NChi NPri
	NWCA SBri WCru WPer WViv
- NNS 93-43	IDac
- var. *formosa*	LEur
- var. *truncata*	CRDP GBuc MLLN WCru
- var. *wawawensis*	IDac
RMRP 950136	
§ *fragrans*	CPou EBee ECGN EHyt EMan
	GBin GEdr LSyl MBro MCLN
	MTho NOak NSti NWCA SBla
	STes WCra WHoo WMaN WRha
- white	LEur
glandulosa	CMHG EBee GDrg MAvo SSte
	WEas WLin
glauca	see *A. fragrans*
'Goldfinch' (Songbird	CBot CFai EMar LEur NBir SPer
Series)	
grata	EBee
Harbutt's hybrids	ERou
§ 'Hensol Harebell' ♀ H4	CPou CSWP EBee MBow MBro
	MCLN MFir SHar SRms WHoo
hirsutissima	see *A. viscosa* subsp. *hirsutissima*
'Ice Blue'	SMHy
'Irish Elegance'	EGoo WRha
japonica	see *A. flabellata* var. *pumila*
jonesii	ITim WLin WPat
- x *saximontana*	ITim
'Kansas'	LCTD LEur
karelinii	EWTr LEur MWrn SRob STes
kitaibelii	EBcc
'Koralle'	GBin WFar WHil
'Kristall'	EBee EPri ERou LAst LEur NOak
	SSvw STes WHil
Langdon's Rainbow	MDKP
hybrids	
laramiensis	CGra CPBP MDKP
* 'Lavender and White'	see *A.* 'Nuthatch'
(Songbird Series)	
longissima ♀ H4	CHar CMea GBri GBuc LCTD
	MAvo MHer MLLN SBla SSte STes
	WCot WEas
- from Texas **new**	LCTD
'Louisiana' (State Series)	LCTD
'Lovebird'	LEur
'Magpie'	see *A. vulgaris* 'William Guiness'
'Maxi'	MDKP WHil
McKana Group	CWCL EBre ELan EMlt ENot EPfP
	GMaP LAst LHop LPVe LRHS
	MBow MWgw NBlu NFor NGdn
	NLon NOak NVic SGar SPer SPlb
	SRms SWal WPer WViv
'Mellow Yellow'	CPla ECGP ECoo EMan GBuc
	MAnH MBNS SIgm STes WBea
	WMoo WPer WPnP WViv
micrantha	EBee
'Milk and Honey'	CBre EBee EGoo EMan LPhx
	SPoG SSte WCot
'Mobius'	LEur
moorcroftiana	EBee
Mrs Scott-Elliot hybrids	COlW CSBt EBee EHol EMan IGor
	LEur LHop LIck MLan NHol SPer
	WFar WViv
Music Series ♀ H4	CHor NOak SMrm SRms
nigricans	see *A. atrata*
§ 'Nuthatch' (Songbird	CFai EMar LEur
Series)	

*	– – 'Woodside Blue'	EBlw ECtt
*	– – 'Woodside Pink'	EBlw
	– 'Strawberry Ice Cream' (d)	EBee EGoo EMan GBri NBro NBur
	– 'Talia's Red'	GDrg
	– 'The Bride'	EBee
	– variegated foliage	see *A. vulgaris* Vervaeneana Group
§	– Vervaeneana Group (v)	More than 30 suppliers
	– – 'Graeme Iddon' (v)	EBee GBuc MLLN NMGW SAga
	– – 'Woodside'	see *A. vulgaris* Vervaeneana Group
	– – 'Woodside Blue' (v)	COIW EGoo SRob
	– – 'Woodside White' (v)	MLwd NBir SPar
	– 'Warwick'	WCot
	– 'Westfaeld'	MTed MWrn NOak
	– 'White Spurless'	see *A. vulgaris* var. *stellata* white
§	– 'William Guiness'	More than 30 suppliers
	– 'William Guiness Doubles' (d)	MCCP
	– Winky Series	SMac SWal
	– – 'Winky Purple and White' **new**	WHil WWeb
	– – 'Winky Blue and White'	LAst WHil WWeb
	– – 'Winky Red and White'	LAst WHil WWeb
	'White Star' (Star Series)	CHea EBee EPfP ERou MTis NPSI SPer WHil WPer
	yabeana	CHar CMil CPLG EBee MAnH MSPs MWrn STes
	'Yellow Star' (Star Series)	LEur WRHF

Aquilegia × *Semiaquilegia* (Ranunculaceae)

	– Cally hybrids **now**	GCal
	– hybrid blue **new**	NPPs WCru

Arabis (Brassicaceae)

	albida	see *A. alpina* subsp. *caucasica*
	alpina	SPlb
§	– subsp. *caucasica*	CStu NBlu WFar
	– – 'Corfe Castle'	ECtt
	– – 'Douler Angevine' (v)	GMaP LIck NPri NPro
§	– – 'Flore Pleno' (d) ♀ H4	CTCP CTri CWCL ECha ECtt ELan EOrc GAbr GMaP LGro MFir MHer MTho SBod SIng SRms SScr WCom WEas WFTG WFar WWin
	– – 'Pink Pearl'	WFar
	– – 'Pinkie'	EMNN
	– – 'Rosea'	MRav NBir NBlu SRms WFar WMoo
	– – 'Schneehaube' ♀ H4	ECtt EMNN EPfP EShb GKir MBar MHer NJOw NMir NOrc SRms WLRN WMoo WPer
	– – 'Snowcap'	see *A. alpina* subsp. *caucasica* 'Schneehaube'
	– – 'Snowdrop'	MRav NPri WFar
	– – 'Variegata' (v)	ECha ECtt EHoe ELan EPot GMaP LBee MBri MHer MTho NFor NLon SRms WCom WEas WFar WWin
	androsacea	GTou SRms WLRN WPat
	× *arendsii* 'Compinkie'	ECtt MBow NPri SPlb SRms WLRN WRHF
	– 'Rosabella' (v)	GKir LRIIS MBNS
	blepharophylla	MWat SPet WCot
§	– 'Frühlingszauber' ♀ H4	CBcs GDra GKir IHMH LPVe MOne NBlu NPri SRms WBVN WFar
	– Spring Charm	see *A. blepharophylla* 'Frühlingszauber'
	bryoides	EPot GTou LRHS NMen
	caerulea **new**	CBrm
	carduchorum	NMen
	caucasica	see *A. alpina* subsp. *caucasica*
§	*collina*	GDra

	ferdinandi-coburgi	EPot GKir WEas
	– 'Aureovariegata' (v)	CTri ECtt EDAr EHoe GKir LGro NLon SPet
	– 'Old Gold'	ECtt EDAr EMlt EPfP EPot ESis GDra GKir LBee MBar MHer MRav NEgg NHar NHol NLAp NVic SBla SRms WCom WFar WHoo WMoo WPat WRHF WWin
	– 'Variegata'	see *A. procurrens* 'Variegata'
	glabra	WPer
	× *kellereri*	NMen
	parishii **new**	GKev
	'Pink Snow'	GKir
	procurrens	NLAp
§	– 'Variegata' (v) ♀ H4	ECha ECtt ELan EMlt EPot EWes GDra GKir GTou LBee MBar MHdf MHer MTho MWat NFor NHar NJOw NWCA SBla SHFr SPlb SRms WCom WFar WTel
§	*scabra*	CNat
§	*soyeri* subsp. *coriacea*	NDlv
	stricta	see *A. scabra*
	× *sturii*	ETow

Arachniodes (Dryopteridaceae)

	aristata	LEur
	simplicior	LEur WCot WRic

Aralia ❀ (Araliaceae)

	armata B&SWJ 3137	WCru
	cachemirica	CDes CHad FBee EWes GCal GIBF MTed MBid NLar SDix SSpi WHoo WPGP WTin
	californica	GCal GPoy MSal MSte NLar SIgm WCru
	chinensis hort.	see *A. elata*
	chinensis L.	CAgr CSam MBNS MSal SPer
	continentalis	EBee EPPr GCal WCru
	cordata	CHEx EWes GCal LEdu MSal NLar
	– B&SWJ 5511	WCru
	decaisneana	WCru
	B&SWJ 3588	
§	*elata* ♀ H4	More than 30 suppliers
	– B&SWJ 5480	WCru
	– 'Albomarginata'	see *A. elata* 'Variegata'
	– 'Aureovariegata' (v)	CBcs CDoC ENot EPfP ICrw LNet NMoo WDin WPat
	– 'Golden Umbrella' (v) **new**	NLar
	– 'Silver Umbrella'	EPfP MGos NLar
	– 'Variegata' (v) ♀ H4	CBcs CBot CDoC CDul ENot EPfP ICrw LNet LRHS MBlu NMoo NPSI NPal SHBN SMad WDin WGer WPat
	foliolosa	WCru
	B&SWJ 8360 **new**	
	racemosa	CBrm EBee GCal GPoy LEdu MLLN MNrw MSal MSte MWgw NLar SRms WFar WHal WPnP WWye
	sieboldii	see *Fatsia japonica*
	spinosa	CHEx CTrC IArd MBlu WHer
	vietnamensis	WCru
	HWJ 755 **new**	

Araucaria (Araucariaceae)

§	*araucana*	More than 30 suppliers
	excelsa hort.	see *A. heterophylla*
§	*heterophylla* ♀ H1	LCon LRHS MBri WNor
	imbricata	see *A. araucana*

Araujia (Asclepiadaceae)

	angustifolia	CPIN
	graveolens	CPIN

sericifera CBcs CHEx CMHG CMac CPIN
CRHN CTrG EMil ERea GQui SBra
SGar SSpi WBor WSHC

Arbutus ✿ *(Ericaceae)*

andrachne CBrm CDul
x **andrachnoides** CAbP CBcs CDul CFil CMHG CPMA
  ♀ H4 ELan EPfP GKir LNet MAsh SAPC
SArc SBrw SHBN SMad SPar SPer
SReu SSpi SSta WHCG WPGP WPat
glandulosa see *Arctostaphylos glandulosa*
'Marina' CAbP CDoC CDul CEnd CFil
CPMA EBee ELan EPfP GKir ISea
LRHS MAsh MBlu MBro SMad SPer
SReu SSpi SSta WFar WPGP WPat
menziesii ♀ H3 CFil CMCN ECrN EPfP LNet SLon
SMad SPer SSpi WFar
unedo ♀ H4 More than 30 suppliers
- 'Atlantic' EBee EMil IArd MBri SLim WGer
WPat
- 'Compacta' CDoC EBee EBre GKir LRHS
MAsh MGos SHBN WDin
- 'Elfin King' ELan SBrw SSpi SSta
- 'Quercifolia' EPfP SReu SSpi SSta WPat
- f. *rubra* ♀ H4 More than 30 suppliers

Archontophoenix *(Arecaceae)*

alexandrae CRoM LPal
cunninghamiana CBrP CRoM CTrC LPal
  ♀ H1

Arctanthemum *(Asteraceae)*

§ **arcticum** CKno ECha EFou EMFP
- 'Roseum' EBee EFou
- 'Schwefelglanz' EBee EFou

Arcterica see *Pieris*

Arctium *(Asteraceae)*

lappa CAgr CArn CKin GBar GPoy IIve
MChe MHer MSal NCWG SIde
WHer
minus CKin MSal NSco
- 'Plus' WAlt
tomentosum IIve

Arctostaphylos *(Ericaceae)*

§ x **coloradensis** GKir
§ **glandulosa** SArc
x *media* 'Wood's Red' GEil GKir MBar MGos SBrw WFar
myrtifolia MBar
nevadensis see *Arenaria tetraquetra* subsp.
amabilis
stanfordiana C&H 105 GGGa
uva-ursi CArn CTri GPoy MBar NBlu
NMen SBod SBrw SHBN SPer SSta
WBod WDin
- 'Massachusetts' EWTr GKir GQui MAsh SMur
SReu SSta
- 'Radiant' **new** WWeb
- 'Snowcap' MAsh WWes
- 'Vancouver Jade' CDoC CEnd EBee GKir LRHS
MAsh MBar MGos NHol SBrw
SPer SPoG SReu SSta

Arctotis *(Asteraceae)*

fastuosa **new** MOak
- var. *alba* 'Zulu Prince' MOak
x **hybrida** 'African LRHS
Sunrise'
- 'Apricot' CHEx CTbh LRHS SAga SMrm
- 'Bacchus' SMrm
- 'China Rose' CTbh SAga SMrm

- cream SAga
- 'Flame' ♀ H1+3 CBrm CPlt CSpe LAst LRHS MBNS
MLan MOak MSte SAga SMrm
SPar WEas
- 'Killerton Red' CHad NPPs
* - 'Mahogany' ♀ H1+3 CTbh EShb MBNS SAga SPar SUsu
- 'Midday Sun' LRHS
- 'Red Devil' CHEx CSpe CTbh LAst LRHS
MBNS SAga SMrm
- white CHEx LRHS
- 'Wine' CBrm LAst LRHS MBNS MSte
SAga SMrm
'Prostrate Raspberry' CSpe SAga

Ardisia *(Myrsinaceae)*

crenata LRHS MBri SMur
japonica B&SWJ 3809 WCru
- 'Miyo-nishiki' (v) **new** WCot
maclurei B&SWJ 3772 LRHS

Areca *(Arecaceae)*

catechu MBri
concinna LPal
vestiaria LPal

Arecastrum see *Syagrus*

Arenaria *(Caryophyllaceae)*

acerosa var. *glabra* WLin
alfacarensis see *A. lithops*
balearica LBee LRHS NRya SIng SPlb SRms
bertolonii LRHS
festucoides CPBP GDra GTou
hookeri WLin
ledebouriana EHyt MWat WAbe
§ **lithops** CLyd
montana ♀ H4 More than 30 suppliers
- 'Avalanche' **new** MWrn
norvegica GKir
pinifolia see *Minuartia circassica*
procera subsp. *glabra* NMen
pulvinata see *A. lithops*
purpurascens CPBP ECho EDAr EHyt EMNN
ESis NSla NWCA SBla SRms SRot
NHol WPat
- 'Elliott's Variety'
tetraquetra EGle GCrs GDra WAbe
§ - subsp. *amabilis* CPBP EHyt EPot ITim LRHS MBar
NJOw NMen NSla NWCA SIng
SReu SSta
tmolea NMen
verna see *Minuartia verna*

Arenga *(Arecaceae)*

engleri CBrP CRoM LPal
pinnata **new** CRoM

Argemone *(Papaveraceae)*

grandiflora ELan
mexicana ELan WHer
pleiacantha **new** LRav

Argyranthemum ✿ *(Asteraceae)*

'Anastasia' LIck MOak WPnn
'Apricot Surprise' see *A.* 'Peach Cheeks'
'Blanche' (Courtyard IHMH
Series) **new**
§ 'Blizzard' (d) EPri LIck LRHS WPnn
'Bofinger' LIck
Boston yellow daisy see *A. callichrysum*
broussonetii LIck
'Butterfly' ♀ H1+3 LIck MBNS WGor WPnn WWol
§ **callichrysum** LIck
- 'Penny' LIck

– 'Prado'	LIck
'Camilla Ponticella'	LIck
canariense hort.	see *A. frutescens* subsp. *canariae*
'Champagne'	LIck
'Cheek's Peach'	see *A.* 'Peach Cheeks'
* *compactum*	LIck
'Comtesse de Chambord'	LIck SPet
'Cornish Gold' ♀ H1+3	CBcs LIck LRHS MBNS MSte SPar
	SPoG
coronopifolium	LIck
'Donington Hero'	LIck WPnn
♀ H1+3	
double cream (d)	LIck
double white (d)	LIck
double yellow (d)	WPnn
'Edelweiss' (d)	LIck LRHS WHen
'Flamingo'	see *Rhodanthemum gayanum*
§ *foeniculaceum* hort.	CSLe CTri EHol ELan LIck LRHS
	WHen WKif
§ *foeniculaceum* (Willd.)	CHal GMac
Webb & Sch.Bip.	
– pink	see *A.* 'Petite Pink'
§ – 'Royal Haze' ♀ H1+3	GMac LIck LRHS MOak NPer
'Frosty'	LIck MBNS
§ *frutescens*	CHEx ECtt LIck LRHS WEas
* – 'Album Plenum' (d)	SEND
§ – subsp. *canariae*	CHal LIck
♀ H1+3	
– 'Lemon Delight'	CHal LIck
– subsp. *succulentum*	LIck
'Margaret Lynch'	
– 'Sugar and Ice' PBR	LIck SPoG
– 'Sugar Button' PBR (d)	CBcs LIck WWeb
♀ H1+3	
– 'Summer Pink' PBR	LIck WGor
'Fuji Sundance'	LIck
'George'	LIck
'Gill's Pink'	CElw ECtt GMac LIck MFir WPnn
'Golden Treasure'	LIck
gracile 'Chelsea Girl'	CHal ECtt EHol LIck LRHS MLan
♀ H1+3	MSte SYvo WPnn
'Harvest Snow'	LIck MBNS
'Hopleys Double	LIck
Cream' (d)	
§ 'Jamaica Primrose'	CBot CFox LIck MHar MMil SPar
♀ H1+3	SPoG SRms WBod WEas WHen
	WPnn
'Jamaica Snowstorm'	see *A.* 'Snow Storm'
'Julieanne'	CBcs LAst MBNS
'Lemon Chiffon'	LIck
'Lemon Meringue' (d)	ECtt LIck
'Lemon Soufflé'	LIck
lemsii	LIck
§ 'Levada Cream' ♀ H1+3	LIck
'Lilliput'	LIck
§ *maderense* ♀ H1+3	CHal CSam IBlr LIck LRHS MSte
	SUsu
– pale	LIck
'Mary Cheek' (d) ♀ H1+3	LIck LRHS MOak SPet WPnn
'Mary Wootton' (d)	CElw ECtt LIck MSte
mawii	see *Rhodanthemum gayanum*
'Mike's Pink'	LIck
'Mini-snowflake'	see *A.* 'Blizzard'
§ 'Mrs F. Sander' (d)	ECtt LIck
'Nevada Cream'	see *Argyranthemum* 'Levada
	Cream'
ochroleucum	see *A. maderense*
'Patches Pink'	LIck
§ 'Peach Cheeks' (d)	CHal LIck LRHS MSte SPet
§ 'Petite Pink' ♀ H1+3	CElw CHal ECtt EPri LAst LIck
	MSte SEND WEas WHen
'Pink Australian' (d)	LIck
'Pink Break'	CHal LIck

I	'Pink Dahlia'	LIck
	'Pink Delight'	see *A.* 'Petite Pink'
	'Pink Pixie'	LIck
	'Powder Puff' (d)	ECtt LIck LRHS MRav WPnn
	prostrate double pink	LIck
§	'Qinta White' (d) ♀ H1+3	GMac LIck MOak WPnn
	'Rising Sun'	GMac LIck
	'Rosa Dwarf'	LIck
	'Royal Haze'	see *A. foeniculaceum*
		(Willd.) Webb & Sch.Bip. 'Royal
		Haze'
	'Royal Yellow'	LIck
	'Saimi'	LIck
	'Saute'	LIck
	'Silver Leaf'	LIck
	'Silver Queen'	see *A. foeniculaceum* hort.
	single pink	LIck
§	'Snow Storm' ♀ H1+3	CFox GMac LAst LIck MOak WPnn
	'Snowflake' (d)	ECtt LRHS MSte WHen
	'Snowflake' misapplied	see *A.* 'Mrs F. Sander'
	'Starlight'	LIck
	'Sugar Baby' PBR	LIck LRHS SMrm WWeb
	'Sugar Lace'	CBcs LIck
	'Summer Angel' PBR (d)	LIck
	'Summer Eyes'	LIck
	'Summer Melody' PBR (d)	CSpe LIck WLow WPnn WWeb
	'Summer Stars Pink' (d)	LIck
	'Sweety'	LIck WPnn WWol
	'Tenerife'	LIck MSte
	'Tony Holmes'	LIck
	'Vancouver' (d) ♀ H1+3	CBot CElw CWCL LAst LIck
		MOak NGdn SChu SPet SRms
		WEas WHen WPnn WWol
*	'Vera'	LIck
	'Wellwood Park'	LIck
	'Weymouth Pink'	LIck
	'Weymouth Surprise'	LIck
	'White Spider'	ELan LIck
	'White Star' **new**	WWol
	'Whitcknights' ♀ H1+3	LIck
	'Yellow Australian' (d)	LIck LRHS

Argyreia (Convolvulaceae)

nervosa	CPlN MGol

Argyrocytisus see *Cytisus*

Arisaema (Araceae)

ACE 2130	NGar
CC 382	WCot
amurense	CFil CFir CHEx CLAP CStu FRee
	GCal GDra GIBF IfFer LAma LEur
	MLLN NHar WCot WFar WPGP
– B&SWJ 947	WCru
– dark-flowered **new**	WWst
– green-flowered **new**	WWst
– subsp. *robustum*	WCru
B&SWJ 1186	
– subsp. *serratum*	WCru
B&SWJ 711	
angustatum	LAma
var. *amurense*	
– var. *peninsulae*	EBee LEur
– – B&SWJ 841	LAma WCru
* – – f. *variegatum* (v)	WCru
B&SWJ 4321	
– var. *serratum*	LAma
aridum **new**	EBee
asperatum **new**	EBec LAma
auriculatum	LAma
bathycoleum	EBee LAma
biauriculatum **new**	EBee
brevipes	EBee LAma

candidissimum ♀ H4 More than 30 suppliers
- green   EBee LAma
- white   EBee LAma LEur WCot
ciliatum   CBro CDes CFil CRDP CStu EBee
                   ITer LAma LEur MNrw NHar NLar
                   SBla SSpi WCot
- CT 369   SCnR
- GG 93167   WCot
- var. *liubaense*   EBee EBot WCru WWst
- - CT 369   WCot
- - GG 97091   WCot
clavatum new   EBee LAma
concinnum   CFir CStu EBee EMar EPot GGar
                   LAma LEur NLar WCot WCru
                   WPnP WViv
consanguineum   CBro CDes CFil CHEx CMea
                   CRow EBee EBot ITer LAma LEur
                   NWoo SSpi WPGP
- B&SWJ 071   WCru
- CLD 1519   GKir NHar
- GG 92112   WCot
- GG 97083   WCot
- 'J. Balis'   WCot
costatum   CFil CHEx EBee GBuc ITer LAma
                   LEur LRHS WCot WCru WPGP
decipiens new   EBee
dilatatum   EBee LAma LEur WCru
dracontium   CLAP EBee EBot ITer LAma NGar
                   NLar WCru
du-bois-reymondiae EBee LAma LEur WCru
elephas   EBee GKir LAma WCru
engleri   EBee ITer LEur
erubescens   EBee EPot ERos LAma LEur NLar
exappendiculatum   CDes CFil EPar WCru WPGP
fargesii   CLAP EBee EBot EPot ITer LAma
                   LEur WCru WWst
flavum   CBro CDes CFil CLAP CMea CStu
                   EBee EHyt EPot GCal GGar GIBF
                   GKir ITer LAma LRHS NGar
                   NMen SSpi WCot WCru WPGP
- CC 1782   WCot WCra
- subsp. *abbreviatum* WCot
- - GG 84193   WWst
- tall   CLAP ITer
- subsp. *tibeticum*   LEur
formosanum   EBee ITer LAma
- B&SWJ 280   WCru
- B&SWJ 390   CPou
- GG 95166   WCot
- var. *bicolorifolium* WCru
   B&SWJ 3528
- f. *stenophyllum*   WCru
   B&SWJ 1477
franchetianum   EBee ITer LAma LEur
fraternum CC 465   WCot
galeatum   CFir EBee LAma LEur WCru WViv
§ *griffithii*   EBee EPar EPot GEdr GGar LAma
                   LRHS NGar SSpi WCru WOBN
                   WPnP WViv
- var. *pradhanii*   EBee
handelii   EBee LEur
hatizyoense new   WWst
helleborifolium   see *A. tortuosum*
heterophyllum   EBee LAma LEur
- B&SWJ 2028   WCru
ilanense B&SWJ 3030 WCru
inkiangense   EBee LAma LEur
inkiangense   EBee
   maculatum new
intermedium   EBee EMar EPot ITer LAma MNrw
                   NGar
- CC 3102   WCot
- GG 96283   WCot

- var. *biflagellatum*   ITer
- - HWJCM 161   WCru
iyoanum   WCru
jacquemontii   CBro CFil CLAP EBee ECho EHyt
                   EPot GBuc GCrs GEdr GGar GKir
                   ITer LAma LRHS NLar WCru
- B&SWJ 2719   WCru
- GG 94120   WCot
japonicum   see *A. serratum*
jinshajiangense new LAma
kelung-insulare   WCru
   B&SWJ 256
kiushianum   CFil EBee EFEx LAma SOkd WCru
lichiangense new   LAma
lingyunense   EBee LAma WCru
lobatum   EBee LAma LEur WCru WWst
maximowiczii   WCru
multisectum new   EBee
negishii new   WCru WWst
§ *nepenthoides*   CBro CFir EBee EMar EPar GEdr
                   ITer LAma WViv
- B&SWJ 2614b   WCru
ochraceum   see *A. nepenthoides*
omeiense new   LAma
onoticum   EBee LAma
ovale   CLAP
penicillatum   EBee
polyphyllum   WCru
   B&SWJ 3904
propinquum   EBee EHyt GKir LAma WCru WViv
purpureogaleatum   EBee LAma
rhizomatum   EBee LAma LEur WCru
rhombiforme   EBee LAma
ringens hort.   see *A. robustum*
ringens (Thunberg)   CDes EFEx GIBF ITer LAma WPGP
   Schott
- f. *praecox*   EBee
- - B&SWJ 1515   WCru
- f. *sieboldii* B&SWJ 551 WCru
§ *robustum*   CFil CStu EBee ITer LRHS WPGP
saxatile   EBee LAma
sazensoo   WCru
§ *serratum*   CDes CFil EBee GIBF ITer LAma
                   SBla WCru
- AGSJ 249   WWst
- B&SWJ 5894   WCru
shihmienense new   EBee
§ *sikokianum*   CBro CDes CFil EBee EBot EFEx
                   ETub GIBF GKev LAma LRHS
                   WCru WPGP WViv
- *henryanum* new   EBee
- var. *serratum*   EBee
- variegated (v)   WCru
speciosum   CHEx EBee EBot EMar EPar
                   EPot GGar ITer LAma LEur
                   NGar SSpi WCot WCru WFar
                   WPnP WViv
- B&SWJ 2403   WCru
- CC 3100   WCot
- var. *mirabile*   WCru
   B&SWJ 2712
* - var. *sikkimense*   LAma
taiwanense   CFil SSpi WCot
- B&SWJ 269   WCru
- B&SWJ 356   CPou
- var.   WCru
   brevipedunculatum
   B&SWJ 1859
- f. *cinereum*   WCru
   B&SWJ 19121
- silver leaf   WCot
tashiroi   WCru
ternatipartitum   WCot WCru

thunbergii	EFEx WCot WViv	
- subsp. *autumnale* B&SWJ 1425	WCru	
- subsp. *thunbergii*	WCru	
- - variegated (v)	WCru	
- subsp. *urashima*	CLAP EBee EFEx GIBF ITer LAma WCru WWst	
§ *tortuosum*	CBro CDes CFil CLAP EBee EBot EHyt EMar EPar EPot ERos GIBF GKir ITer LAma LEur MNrw NLar SBla WCot WCru WPnP	
- CC 1452	CPou	
- CC 3211	WCot	
- GG 892230	WCot	
- GG 97148	WCot	
- high altitude B&SWJ 2386	WCru	
- low altitude B&SWJ 2298	WCru	
tosaense GG 91224	WCru	
triphyllum	CFil CHEx CLAP CPom EBee EBot EPar EPot GGar ITer LAma LEdu LRHS MSal NGar SMad SSpi WAul WCru WPGP	
- var. *atrorubens*	WPGP	
§ *utile*	EBee ITer LAma WViv	
- CC 3101	WCot	
- HWJCM 161	WCru	
verrucosum	see *A. griffithii*	
- var. *utile*	see *A. utile*	
wardii	EBee	
yamatense	WCru	
- subsp. *sugimotoi*	EBee GIBF ITer LAma WCru	
yunnanense	EBee ITer LAma LEur	

Arisarum ✿ (*Araceae*)

proboscideum	More than 30 suppliers	
- MS 958	EMar	
vulgare	CRDP SIgm	
* - f. *maculatum*	LEur	
- subsp. *simorrhinum*	EBla LEur WCot	
- - SF 296	LEur	
subsp. *vulgare*	LEur WCot	

Aristea (*Iridaceae*)

S&SH 88	SAga	
capitata **new**	CPne	
confusa	SWat	
ecklonii	CFil CHEx CPLG CPou CTrC EDif GGar GSki IGor SDes SSpi SWat WCot WWin	
ensifolia	CMdw WSHC	
grandis	WCot	
§ *major*	CCtw CFir CPne CTrC EMan GGar GSki WHil	
- pink	CDes	
spiralis	SWat	
thyrsiflora	see *A. major*	

Aristida (*Poaceae*)

purpurea	CBrm	

Aristolochia ✿ (*Aristolochiaceae*)

CC 962 **new**	CPLG	
baetica	CArn CPLG CPiN SSpi WCru	
californica	CPiN	
chrysops	CPiN	
clematitis	CArn EBee EChP GPoy MSal NCWG WCot WCru WWye	
contorta	CBcs SSpi	
debilis	CPiN LEur	
delavayii **new**	CHEx	
durior	see *A. macrophylla*	

elegans	see *A. littoralis*	
fimbriata	CPLG CPiN	
gigantea	CPiN SMur	
grandiflora	CPiN	
griffithii B&SWJ 2118	WCru	
heterophylla B&SWJ 3109	WCru	
kaempferi	CPiN	
- B&SWJ 293	WCru	
§ *labiata*	CPiN	
lindneri	CPLG	
§ *littoralis* ♀ H1	CPLG CPiN SMur SOWG	
§ *macrophylla*	CBcs CBot CHEx CPiN CRHN EBee ENot EPla GKir IDee NBlu NPal SHBN SLim SPer WCru WDin	
mandschurica **new**	GIBF	
manshuriensis	CPiN	
- B&SWJ 962	WCru	
paucinervis	WCru	
- AB&S 4393	WCot	
pearceii **new**	CPla	
ringens Link & Otto	see *A. labiata*	
ringens Vahl.	CPiN	
rotunda	CPiN WCot	
sempervirens	CPiN SSpi WSHC	
sipho	see *A. macrophylla*	
tagala	CPiN WMul	
tomentosa	CPiN WCru	
trilobata	CPiN	
watsonii	CPiN	
zollingeriana B&SWJ 7030 **new**	WCru	

Aristotelia (*Elaeocarpaceae*)

§ *chilensis*	WPic	
- 'Variegata' (v)	CBcs CWlb EBee LAst SLim SPlb WEas WLRN	
fruticosa	CPnc	
- (f)	ECou	
- (m)	ECou	
macqui	see *A. chilensis*	
serrata	ECou	
- (f) **new**	ECou	
- (m) **new**	ECou	

Armeria (*Plumbaginaceae*)

§ *alliacea*	CSpe ECha EPPr MHdf MWgw	
- f. *leucantha*	MWod SRms WMoo	
§ *alpina*	MWat	
Bees' hybrids	EWTr SRms WAnl WMoo	
'Bees' Ruby'	MBri WPer	
caespitosa	see *A. juniperifolia*	
euscadiensis	CSpe ESis	
formosa hybrids	CTri ELan EMan MWgw NBlu NMir	
§ *girardii*	EPot	
Joystick Series	EWTr GGar NArg NPPs	
- 'Joystick Lilac Shades'	IGor	
- 'Joystick Red' **new**	SBri	
§ *juniperifolia* ♀ H4	CLyd EBre ECtt EDAr ELan EMNN EPfP ESis LBee LRHS MHer MTho NMen NVic NWCA SIng SRms WWin	
- 'Alba'	CMea EDAr ELan EPfP MHer NHar NMen NPri SRms WAbe	
- 'Beechwood'	LBee LRHS NHol SBla	
- 'Bevan's Variety' ♀ H4	EBre ECha ECtt ELan EPfP EPot GCrs GKir LRHS MNrw MWat NHar NLAp NMen NPri NRya SBla SDes SRms SRot WAbe	
- dark	EWes GDra SBla WAbe	
- rose	EPot	
- spiny dwarf	EPot	
juniperifolia x *maritima*	SIng	

§ **maritima** CArn CKin EBre EMlt EPfP GKir
LRHS MBar MHdf NArg NBlu NFor
SPar SPet SWal WBea WFar WMoo
- 'Alba' More than 30 suppliers
- subsp. **alpina** see *A. alpina*
- 'Bloodstone' CTri ECot ELan MWat
- 'Corsica' CMea CTri ECha EPot MBNS
MHer NBir NPPs NRya SMer
- Düsseldorf Pride see *A. maritima* 'Düsseldorfer Stolz'
§ - 'Düsseldorfer Stolz' CPBP EBre ECha ECtt EDAr ELan
EPfP GDra GGar GKir LRHS MBri
NHar NMen NPri NPro WBea
WPat WWye
- 'Glory of Holland' EPot
- 'Laucheana' CBod WHoo WMoo
I - 'Rubrifolia' **new** CPlt CSpe EPPr WCot
- 'Ruby Glow' CTri LBuc
- 'Splendens' CBcs COlW EMNN EMil EMlt
ENot EPfP GDra GGar GWCH
LAst MBow MHer MLan MWgw
NBlu NHar NMir NRya NVic SWal
WFar WPer WWin
- 'Vindictive' ♀ H4 CMea CTri EDAr EPfP GKir LGro
'Nifty Thrifty' (v) CBod CLyd CMea EBee EDAr
EWes LRHS NPri NSla SCoo SRot
WCom WHen WMoo WPat WWeb
'Ornament' ECtt LRav NJOw WCra WFar WHen
plantaginea see *A. alliacea*
pseudarmeria EBee ELan MBct MLan MNrw
- 'Drumstick Red' **new** WPer
- 'Drumstick White' **new** WPer
setacea see *A. girardii*
tweedyi CLyd GTou WCom
vulgaris see *A. maritima*
welwitschii SRms
'Westacre Beauty' **new** EWes

Armoracia (Brassicaceae)

§ **rusticana** CArn CBod CHid COld CPrp CSev
ELau GAbr GPoy ILis MBri MHer
MSal NGHP NPri SIde WCer WHHs
WHer WJek WLHH WSel WWye
- 'Variegata' (v) CBod EBee ELau EMan EMar
EMon GBar ITer LHop LRHS
MAvo NSti SMad SPla WBar WCHb
WCot WHal WLRN WPnP WSel

Arnica (Asteraceae)

angustifolia EBee SRms
subsp. **alpina**
- subsp. **iljinii** EBee NBir
chamissonis Lessing EBee ELau GBar MNrw MSal WJek
WPer WWye
chionopappa EBee
frigida EBee IIve
lessingii EBee MDCh
longifolia EBee
montana CArn EOHP GBar GDra GPoy
GTou MChe MHer MLan NSti
SRms SWat WHHs WPer WWye
- yellow MLan
nevadensis EBee
sachalinensis EBee

Arnoglossum (Asteraceae)

§ **plantagineum new** EBee

Aronia (Rosaceae)

arbutifolia CBcs CPle EPfP EPla GBin MBlu
MWhi NBlu SHBN SLdr SLon WDin
- 'Erecta' CDul EBee ELan EPfP LAst LHop
MBNS MBlu MBri SLPl SMac SPoG
SRms SSpi WBor WFar

melanocarpa CBcs CMCN CMHG ELan EPfP
EWTr GKir LEdu LPan LRHS
MAsh MBar MBlu MRav SSpi
WCwm WDin WFar WHCG
- 'Autumn Magic' CDoC CFai CPMA EBee EPfP LAst
LRHS MBlu MBri NLar NPSI SBrw
SPer WRHF
- 'Brilliant' WWes
- var. **elata** EPla
- 'Red Viking' NPSI
- 'Viking' EBee ECrN ENot EPfP GEil LBuc
MAsh MRav WDin WLRN WWes
× **prunifolia** CAgr CBcs CDoC CMHG CPLG
EWTr GKir LEdu WHCG
- 'Brilliant' CDoC COtt EBee SPer SRPl WBcn

Arrhenatherum (Poaceae)

elatius SPer
subsp. **bulbosum**
- - 'Variegatum' (v) CElw CFwr EChP EGra EHoe ELan
EMon EPla EPot GBin LAst LEdu
IJus LRHS MBrN MBri MMoz MWgw
MWhi NBid NGdn NHol NOrc NSti
SDes SHFr WFar WMoo WPer WPnP

Artemisia ❀ (Asteraceae)

§ **abrotanum** ♀ H4 More than 30 suppliers
* - 'Variegata' (v) WWeb
absinthium CArn CPrp CSLe CSev EEls ELau
GPoy MBar MBow MChe MHer
MLLN MWgw NFor NSti SIde SPer
SWat WCer WGwG WHHs WHbs
WPer WWye
- 'Corinne Tremaine' (v) WHer
- 'Creeping Silver' IIve
- 'Lambrook Giant' EEls
- 'Lambrook Mist' CSLe CSev EBee EChP EEls ELan
♀ H3-4 EMan EPPr EPfP GBri GCal LRHS
MMil MRav NCiC NDov NSti SWat
WLRN WMnd
- 'Lambrook Silver' ♀ H4 More than 30 suppliers
- 'Silver Ghost' EEls
afra CArn EBee EEls EMan GBar IFro
§ **alba** CSWP CSev EEls EMan EMon
EOHP GBar GPoy ILis MHer NBur
NSti SIde SMad WCer WPer WRha
§ - 'Canescens' ♀ H4 More than 30 suppliers
annua CArn EEls MGol MSal SIde WJek
WWye
anomala EEls
arborescens CArn CMHG CTri ECha EEls EWTr
NSti SDix SDry SPer WDin WHer
- 'Brass Band' see *A.* 'Powis Castle'
- 'Faith Raven' CArn EBee EEls ERou GBuc NLar
NLon SRPl WHer WRus
- 'Little Mice' **new** EBee EFou
- 'Porquerolles' CSLe EEls
arctica EEls GIBF
- **saxicola new** EBee
argyi EEls
armeniaca EEls WWin
§ **armeniaca** EEls WWin
assoana see *A. caucasica*
atrata EEls
barrelieri EEls
brachyloba CFis CSLe MLLN WCHb
californica EEls
campestris EBlw EEls MChe MHer WCer
subsp. **borealis** WRha WSel
- - var. **borealis** WCot
NNS 96-19 **new**
- subsp. **campestris** EEls
- subsp. **maritima** EEls
- - Welsh form EEls

	camphorata	see *A. alba*
	cana	see *Seriphidium canum*
	canariensis	see *A. thuscula*
	canescens hort.	see *A. alba* 'Canescens'
	canescens Willd.	see *A. armeniaca*
	capillaris	EBee EEls MSal
§	*caucasica* ♀H3-4	CPBP CSLe EBee EBre EDAr EEls EMlt EWes GKir LGro LPhx MBrN SBla SMHy SRms SRot WCHb WEas WPer WViv
	- *caucasica*	EEls ESis WFar
	chamaemelifolia	CArn EBee EEls GBar IGor MHer WPer WWye
	cretacea	see *Seriphidium nutans*
	discolor Dougl. ex Besser	see *A. michauxiana*
	douglasiana	EEls
	- 'Valerie Finnis'	see *A. ludoviciana* 'Valerie Finnis'
	dracunculus	More than 30 suppliers
	- *dracunculoides*	CArn EEls GBar NPri
	ferganensis	see *Seriphidium ferganense*
	filifolia	EBee EEls
	fragrans Willd.	see *Seriphidium fragrans*
	frigida ♀H3-4	EBee EEls GBar ILis WHCG
	genipi	EEls ESis MSal
	glacialis	FCha EEls ITim
	gmelinii	EBee EEls GBar GIBF IIve
	gnaphalodes	see *A. ludoviciana*
	gorgonum	EEls
	gracilis	see *A. scoparia*
N	*granatensis* hort.	MSte
	herba-alba	EEls
	'Huntington'	CHad EEls
	kawakamii B&SWJ 088	EEls WCru
	kitadakensis	EEls
	- 'Guizhou'	see *A. lactiflora* Guizhou Group
	laciniata	EEls
	lactiflora ♀H4	CPrp FCha ECtt EEls EFou ELan ELan EMon EPar ERou EWTr GBar IHoc MRav NFor NGdn NLon NOrc NSti SDix SHel SMrm SPer SRms WFTG WFar WMoo WViv WWpP
	- dark	see *A. lactiflora* Guizhou Group
	- 'Elfenbein' **new**	LHop
§	- Guizhou Group	More than 30 suppliers
	- 'Jim Russell'	CElw EBee EWes LPhx NDov
	- *purpurea*	see *A. lactiflora* Guizhou Group
	- 'Variegata'	see *A. vulgaris* 'Variegata'
	lagocephala	EEls EMan WCot
	lagopus	EBee GIBF
	lanata Willd. non Lam.	see *A. caucasica*
	laxa	see *A. umbelliformis*
	leucophylla **new**	EBee
§	*ludoviciana*	CSLe EBee EBlw EEls ELan ELau ERou GBar GMac MBrN MRav MWat NBid NLon NOak NOrc SGar SRms WWin WWpP
N	- var. *latifolia*	see *A. ludoviciana* subsp. *ludoviciana* var. *latiloba*
	- subsp. *ludoviciana* var. *incompta*	ECha EEls EGle EMan EVFa MRav SUsu WCot WHer
§	- - var. *latiloba*	CHor EEls EHoc GBuc GMac LHop LRHS MBro MRav NBro NOak NSti SPar WCom WCot WCra WEas WHoo WPcr WWpP
	- subsp. *mexicana* var. *albula*	EEls WFar
	- 'Silver Queen' ♀H4	More than 30 suppliers
N	- 'Valerie Finnis' ♀H4	More than 30 suppliers
	manshurica	EBee EMan WCot
	maritima	see *Seriphidium maritimum*
§	*michauxiana*	EBee EEls NBur WHer
	molinieri	EEls
	mutellina	see *A. umbelliformis*

	niitakayamensis	EEls GBar
	nitida	EEls
	norvegica	EEls
	nutans	see *Seriphidium nutans*
	'Okra' **new**	MMil
	palmeri hort.	see *A. ludoviciana*
	pamirica	EEls
	aff. *parviflora* CLD 1531	EEls EMon
	pedemontana	see *A. caucasica*
	pontica	More than 30 suppliers
	'Powis Castle' ♀H3	More than 30 suppliers
	princeps	EEls
	procera Willd.	see *A. abrotanum*
	purshiana	see *A. ludoviciana*
	pycnocephala 'David's Choice'	EEls SMad
	ramosa	EEls
	'Rosenschleier'	CBre EBee EFou EMon EVFa LPhx WFTG WPGP
	rutifolia	EEls
	schmidtiana ♀H4	CFis EBlw ECha ECot EEls EFou EMan GKir MNrw MOne MWat NOrc SRms
	- 'Nana' ♀H4	More than 30 suppliers
§	- *scoparia*	EEls
	selengensis	EEls
	splendens hort.	see *A. alba* 'Canescens'
	splendens Willd.	ELan LPhx NSti WEas
	stelleriana	ECha EEls GGar GMaP MCAu MHer MTho MWgw NBro NFor NLon NSti SPet WAul WEas WPcr
N	- 'Boughton Silver'	More than 30 suppliers
N	- 'Mori'	see *A. stelleriana* 'Boughton Silver'
	- 'Nana'	ECha EEls EMan SBla
	- 'Prostata'	see *A. stelleriana* 'Boughton Silver'
	- 'Silver Brocade'	see *A. stelleriana* 'Boughton Silver'
	taurica	EEls
§	*thuscula*	EEls
	tilesii	EBec GIBF
	tridentata	see *Seriphidium tridentatum*
§	*umbelliformis*	EEls NBur
	vallesiaca	see *Seriphidium vallesiacum*
	verlotiorum	EEls GBar
	vulgaris	CAgr CArn CPrp EEls ELau GBar GPoy GWCH MChe MHer WHbs WHer WJek WLHH WWye
	- 'Byrne's Variegated' (v)	EGle EMar
	- 'Cragg-Barber Eye' (v)	EBee EEls MGrG NBid NPro SAga WAlt WBar WBry WCHb WCot WHcr WRha
	- 'Crispa'	ELau EMon
	- 'Obelisk'	EEls EFou
	- Oriental Limelight = 'Janlim' (v)	CFox CHea CSpe EBee ECtt EDAr EEls EFou EWll ITer LHop LRHS MBri MCCP MMil MTis NPri SHar SMrm SPar WFar WGwG WHer WJek WLow
	- 'Peddar's Gold' (v)	EWes
§	- 'Variegata' (v)	CBre EBee EEls GBar GLil NBir NPro NSti SMad WAlt WBea WCHb WCot WFar WHer WHil WJek WPer WRha
	- 'Woolaston' (v)	EMan WAlt WCot
	x *wurzellii*	EEls

Arthropodium (Anthericaceae)

candidum	CBot CDes CRow CStu ECha ECou GEdr ITim MBrN NWCA SHBN SRot WFar WHal WPer WRos

	- *maculatum*	GEdr SPlb
	- *purpureum*	CBcs CBrm CDoC CPLG EBee EChP EMan GBri GCal GGar LRHS MGGn MHdf MLan NEgg NJOw NLAp SDes WCot WFar WHrl WPGP WPat
*	*carlesii*	CDes CRHN
	cirratum	CAbb CHEx CTrC ECou ERea MLan SYvo WMul WSHC
	- 'Matapouri Bay'	CBcs CDes CDoC CHEx EBee EMan EMil WCot WPGP
	milleflorum	NWCA NWoo WCot

artichoke, globe see *Cynara cardunculus* Scolymus Group

artichoke, Jerusalem see *Helianthus tuberosus*

Arthrostylidium (Poaceae)

	naibuense **new**	CFil

Arum ✿ (Araceae)

	alpinum	CFil WPGP
	'Chameleon'	CAvo CDes CHad CLAP EBee EFou EMon LEur MAvo MMil MNrw NBir NCat SIgm SMad SPer WCot WFar WHal WViv
§	*concinnatum*	CFil CStu EBee EMar EMon EPot GIBF ITer LAma LEur SChr SSpi WPGP
	cornutum	see *Sauromatum venosum*
	creticum	CArn CBct CBot CBro CFir EBee EBot EChP ECha EHyt EMar EPar ETow IBlr ITer MAvo MMil MNrw MRav MTho SCnR SDix SSpi WHil WPGP
	- MS 696	MNrw
	- FCC form	CLAP SBla WCot
	- white	MNrw
	- yellow	NBir NPar WFar WIvy
	- x *italicum* **new**	LEur MAvo MDKP
	cyrenaicum	CDes CStu EBee EHyt ITer MNrw WCot
	- NS 21	LEur
§	*dioscoridis*	CDes CStu EBee EWes MTho NLar NRog WCot WPGP
	- JCA 195.197	WCot
	- MS&CL 524	ITer
	- W 5658	LEur
	- var. *cyprium*	EBee LEur
§	- var. *dioscoridis*	LEur WCot
	- - JCA 195.200	EMon
	- - JCA 195200	EMon
	- var. *liepoldtii*	see *A. dioscoridis* var. *dioscoridis*
	- var. *philistaeum* **new**	WWst
	- var. *smithii*	see *A. dioscoridis* var. *dioscoridis*
	dracunculus	see *Dracunculus vulgaris*
	elongatum RS 274/87	WCot
	hygrophilum	EMon
	idaeum	CLAP SSpi
	italicum	CFwr CLAP CTri EBee EHyt EWTr LAma MBri MTho NGdn NLar NRog SBod SEND SWat WAbe WCot WFar WPnP WShi WStI
	- subsp. *albispathum*	CBct CDes CFil CHid CStu EBee EMon LAma LEur MTed NRog WCot WPGP
	- black spotted	EHyt LEur WFar
	- 'Cyclops' EAF 7701	CHid CLAP MNrw WCot
	- 'Green Marble'	CBct SBla WFar
	- subsp. *italicum*	EPla
	- - 'Bill Baker'	EMon LEur

§	- - 'Marmoratum' ♀ H4	More than 30 suppliers
	- - 'Sparkler'	WCot
	- - 'Spotted Jack'	MNrw WCot
	- - 'Tiny'	EMon GCal LEur NLar
§	- - 'White Winter'	ECGP EMon GBuc WRus
	- 'Nancy Lindsay'	EMar EMon WPrP
	- subsp. *neglectum*	SChr
	- 'Miss Janay Hall' (v)	WCot
	- 'Pictum'	see *A. italicum* subsp. *italicum* 'Marmoratum'
	jacquemontii **new**	WWst
	korolkowii	NRog
	maculatum	CArn EBlw EPar EPot GPoy LAma LSyl MBow MHer MRav MSal NCWG WHer WShi WWye
	- 'Painted Lady' (v)	NCat WCot
	- 'Pleddel'	MRav NCat WCot
*	- 'Variegatum' (v)	GPoy
	nickelii	see *A. concinnatum*
§	*nigrum*	LEur WCot
	- CE&H 524	LEur
	orientale	EHyt EPot ETow LEur
	- subsp. *amoenum*	MNrw
	- subsp. *sintenisii*	WWst
	palaestinum	EMon
	petteri hort.	see *A. nigrum*
	pictum	CAvo CDes CLAP EBee LAma LEur LRHS NRog WCot WIvy
	- 'Taff's Form'	see *A. italicum* subsp. *italicum* 'White Winter'
	purpureospathum	CDes EHyt ITer LEur WCot
§	*rupicola* var. *rupicola*	WWst
	- var. *virescens*	EBee WCot
*	*sintenisii*	EBee WCot
	'Streaked Spectre'	EMon

Aruncus ✿ (Rosaceae)

	AGSJ 214	NHol
	aethusifolius ♀ H4	More than 30 suppliers
	- 'Little Gem'	WCru
	B&SWJ 4475	
	asiaticus	EBee
	dioicus	CTri CWib ECGP EChP EGle EMil EPfP EWTr GGar GKir GSki LHop LRHS MCAu NBlu NChi NGdn NPri NVic SPet SPlb SRPl SSpe WFar WHoo WLow WPnP WWpP
§	- (m) ♀ H4	CDoC CHor CRow CSBt EBre ECha ELan ENot EPla GSki LIck MBNS MRav MWgw NBro NFor NHol NSti SMad SPar SPer SRms SSpi SWat WFar WMoo WPer
	- var. *acuminatus*	EBee
	- Child of Two Worlds	see *A. dioicus* 'Zweiweltenkind'
	- 'Glasnevin'	CRow CSev ECha ECtt EMan MBri MRav NHol WFar
	- var. *kamtschaticus*	EChP EWes NHol
	- - AGSJ 238	NHol
	- 'Kneiffii'	More than 30 suppliers
§	- 'Zweiweltenkind'	CBrm EBee EHrv GCal GSki MBro WPer
	'Horatio' **new**	EBee EMon LPhx
	'Johannisfest' **new**	EMon
	plumosus	see *A. dioicus*
*	*sinensis*	EWll WFar
	sylvestris	see *A. dioicus*
	'Woldemar Meier' **new**	EMon

Arundinaria ✿ (Poaceae)

	amabilis	see *Pseudosasa amabilis*
	anceps	see *Yushania anceps*
	angustifolia	see *Pleioblastus chino* f. *angustifolius*

auricoma	see *Pleioblastus auricomus*
chino	see *Pleioblastus chino*
disticha	see *Pleioblastus pygmaeus* var. *distichus*
falconeri	see *Himalayacalamus falconeri*
fargesii	see *Bashania fargesii*
fastuosa	see *Semiarundinaria fastuosa*
fortunei	see *Pleioblastus variegatus*
funghomii	see *Schizostachyum funghomii*
§ **gigantea**	SDry WJun
- subsp. **tecta**	CBcs MGos
hindsii	see *Pleioblastus hindsii* hort.
hookeriana hort.	see *Himalayacalamus falconeri* 'Damarapa'
- Munro	see *Himalayacalamus hookerianus*
humilis	see *Pleioblastus humilis*
japonica	see *Pseudosasa japonica*
jaunsarensis	see *Yushania anceps*
maling	see *Yushania maling*
marmorea	see *Chimonobambusa marmorea*
murieliae	see *Fargesia murieliae*
nitida	see *Fargesia nitida*
oedogonata	see *Clavinodum oedogonatum*
palmata	see *Sasa palmata*
pumila	see *Pleioblastus humilis* var. *pumilus*
pygmaea	see *Pleioblastus pygmaeus*
quadrangularis	see *Chimonobambusa quadrangularis*
simonii	see *Pleioblastus simonii*
spathiflora	see *Thamnocalamus spathiflorus*
tessellata	see *Thamnocalamus tessellatus*
vagans	see *Sasaella ramosa*
variegata	see *Pleioblastus variegatus*
veitchii	see *Sasa veitchii*
viridistriata	see *Pleioblastus auricomus*
'Wang Tsai'	see *Bambusa multiplex* 'Fernleaf'

Arundo (*Poaceae*)

donax	More than 30 suppliers
- 'Golden Chain'	EMan EVFa
- 'Macrophylla'	CBig CFil CRow EPla LEdu LPJP WPGP
- 'Variegata'	see *A. donax* var *versicolor*
§ - var. **versicolor** (v)	More than 30 suppliers
- yellow variegated (v)	CKno CRDP SPar
formosana new	CKno CRez EPPr SApp
pliniana	CMCo CRow LEdu

Asarina (*Scrophulariaceae*)

antirrhiniflora	see *Maurandella antirrhiniflora*
barclayana	see *Maurandya barclayana*
erubescens	see *Lophospermum erubescens*
hispanica	see *Antirrhinum hispanicum*
lophantha	see *Lophospermum erubescens*
lophospermum	see *Lophospermum erubescens*
§ **procumbens**	CBri EBee EMan GDra GKir GTou MPEx MTho NCWG NFor SHFr SIng SRms SSpi WAbe WCru WFar WGwG WHer WPer WWin
- 'Alba'	SRms
- 'Iberian Trail'	EWTr
scandens	see *Lophospermum scandens*
'Victoria Falls'	see *Maurandya* 'Victoria Falls'

Asarum ✿ (*Aristolochiaceae*)

albomaculatum B&SWJ 1726	WCru
arifolium	CLAP EBee EHrv EPar LEur
* **campaniforme**	EBee LAma LEur WCru

canadense	CArn EBee EChP EMar EPot GGar GPoy GSki LRHS MSal NLar WCru
caudatum	CAvo CDes CLAP CRow EBee EHyt EMan EPPr LEur MTed NBro NLar NSti NWCA SRms WCot WCru WFar
- white	SSpi
caudigerum	EBee LAma LEur
- B&SWJ 1517	WCru
caulescens	CLAP EBee LAma LEur WCru
- B&SWJ 5886	WCru
chinense	EBee LEur WCru
debile	EBee LAma WCru
delavayi	EBee LAma LEur WCru
epigynum B&SWJ 3443	WCru
- 'Silver Web' B&SWJ 3442	WCru
europaeum	More than 30 suppliers
fauriei	WCru
forbesii	EBee LEur WCru
geophilum new	EBee
hartwegii	CDes CLAP EBee EHyt EMan EMar EPar ERos GBuc SSpi WCot WCru WPGP
heterotropoides new	EBee
- var. **mandshuricum** new	LEur
hexalobum	WCot
hypogynum B&SWJ 3628	WCru
infrapurpureum	WCot
- B&SWJ 1994	WCru
kumageanum	WCot
lemmonii	EMan LEdu WCru
leptophyllum B&SWJ 1985	WCru
longirhizomatosum	EBee WCru
macranthum	WCot
- B&SWJ 1691	WCru
maculatum	WCot
- B&SWJ 1114	WCru
magnificum	EBee LAma LEur WCru
maximum	EBee EMar EPot LAma LEur WCot WCru
minamitanianum	WCru
pulchellum	FBee EHrv EMan EPar WCot WCru
shuttleworthii	CLAP EBee NLar WCru
sieboldii	WCru
splendens	CBos CDes CFwr CStu EBee EHoc EHrv EMan EPPr EPot LAma LEur LHop MCCP NGdn NSti SBla SMrm SSpi WAul WCot WCru WHer WPGP
taipingshanianum B&SWJ 1688	WCru
virginicum	EBee
wulingense new	EBee LEur WCru

Asclepias (*Asclepiadaceae*)

'Cinderella'	CSev EBee LBuc SGar SIgm WWin
curassavica	CHal CSev LRHS SHFr SSte WMul
§ **fascicularis**	SIgm
fasciculata	see *A. fascicularis*
fruticosa	see *Gomphocarpus fruticosus*
incarnata	CAgr CPom CSev EBee ELan ERou GKir MRav MTis SPer SSte SWal WAul WOld WPer
- 'Alba'	EChP ELan EMon
- 'Ice Ballet'	CPLG CSev EBee EMan ERou LBuc LHop LRHS MUlv MWrn NDov SAga SIgm SSte SWat WElm WLin WMnd WMoo WRHF WWin
- 'Iceberg' new	EBee
- 'Soulmate'	CFai EBee EChP EPfP EWll LRHS LRav MLLN NJOw WMoo

	- 'White Superior'	EBee
	physocarpa	see *Gomphocarpus physocarpus*
	purpurascens	CArn SSte
	speciosa	EBee NLar
	sullivantii	EBee EMan SSte
	syriaca	CArn EBee LRHS MSte SHFr SSte WWin
	tuberosa	CArn CBcs CHad COIW EBee ELau EMan GKir GPoy LHop LRHS MHer MMHG MNrw MRav MSal NDov SPet SSpi SSte WCot WMnd WWin
	- Gay Butterflies Group	EBee MLan NLar SMrm
	- 'Hello Yellow'	LRHS SSte
	verticillata	SIgm SSte

Asimina (Annonaceae)

	triloba	IArd IDee MBlu NLar SBrw WNor

Askidiosperma (Restionaceae)

	chartaceum	CTrC
	esterhuyseniae	WNor
	paniculatum	CTrC

Asparagus (Asparagaceae)

	asparagoides ♀ H1	ERea EShb SEND
§	- 'Myrtifolius'	CHal SYvo
	cochinchinensis	ELau WCru
	B&SWJ 3425	
	crassicladus new	EShb
	densiflorus	EShb
	'Mazeppa' new	
	- 'Myersii' ♀ H1	CHal ERea SRms
	- Sprengeri Group ♀ H1	CHal LRHS MBri
	falcatus	MBri SEND
	officinalis	ERea IIve SEND WFar
	- 'Atlas'	EMui
	- 'Backlim' ♀ H4	EMui
	- 'Butler'	SDea
	- 'Cito' (m)	SDea WWeb
	- 'Dariana'	SDea
	- 'Franklim'	EMui WFar
	- 'Gijnlim' ♀ H4 new	EMui
	- 'Purple Jacq Ma'	EMui
	plumosus	see *A. setaceus*
	pseudoscaber	SMad
	'Spitzenschleier'	
	retrofractus	CFil WPGP
	scandens	EShb
	schoberioides	EBee
	- B&SWJ 871	WCru
§	*setaceus* ♀ H1	CHal LRHS MBri
	- 'Pyramidalis' ♀ H1	MBri
	suaveolens new	EShb

Asperula (Rubiaceae)

§	*arcadiensis* ♀ H3	CLyd EHyt EPot NWCA SBla SIng
	aristata subsp. *scabra*	EBee ECha ELan EMan EMar EMon
	- subsp. *thessala*	see *A. sintenisii*
	boissieri	SOkd
	cyanchica	MSal
	daphneola	CNic ECho EHyt EWes SBla SIng
	gussonei	CLyd CMea CStu EMNN EPot ESis GAbr LRHS MBro MWat NLAp NMen NWCA SBla WAbe WLin WPat
	lilaciflora var. *caespitosa*	see *A. lilaciflora* subsp. *lilaciflora*
§	- subsp. *lilaciflora*	CLyd CPBP EDAr EHol EPot ESis NMen SIng WWin
	nitida	ECho
	- subsp. *puberula*	see *A. sintenisii*
	odorata	see *Galium odoratum*
	orientalis	WPGP

§	*sintenisii* ♀ H2-3	CLyd EPot LBee LRHS MBro NMen NWCA SBla SIng WAbe WHoo
	suberosa hort.	see *A. arcadiensis*
	suberosa Sibth. & Sm.	ECho WAbe
	taurina subsp. *caucasica*	CPLG EMon MBro NLar NSti WCHb
	tinctoria	CArn EOHP GBar GPoy MChe MHer MSal SRms WCHb WSel

Asphodeline (Asphodelaceae)

	liburnica	CBro EBee ECGN EChP ECha ELan EMan EMar ERos ERou GSki MBro MCAu MRav MWgw SAga SEND SPar SSpi WCot WFar WGwG WPer
§	*lutea*	More than 30 suppliers
§	- 'Gelbkerze'	LRHS MNrw MPWC WBVN WPrP
	- Yellow Candle	see *A. lutea* 'Gelbkerze'
	rigidifolia	EBee
	taurica	EChP ECho EMan SMrm SVal WPer
	- JJ 96-100	WCot

Asphodelus (Asphodelaceae)

	acaulis	EHyt EWoo SCnR SIgm SOkd WAbe WCot
§	*aestivus*	CDes EBee ECha GAbr GSki NBur SMad SSvw SWat WPer
	albus	CArn CBot CBri CPLG CSpe EBee ECGN ECha EPPr GIBF GSki LPhx NBid SPlb SRms WPer
	cerasiferus	see *A. ramosus*
	fistulosus	CMea ECGN MHar NBir WPer WPrP WWin
	lusitanicus	see *A. ramosus*
	luteus	see *Asphodeline lutea*
	microcarpus	see *A. aestivus*
	morisianus new	EBee
§	*ramosus*	EBee ECGN ECGP EGoo EMan GSki MNrw MTho SIgm SMrm WBVN WCot WPer

Aspidistra (Convallariaceae)

	attenuata	CKob
	- B&SWJ 377	WCru
	caespitosa	IBlr LEur WCot
	'Jade Ribbons'	
	'China Moon' (v) new	WCot
	'China Star' new	WCot
	'China Sun' new	WCot
	daibuensis	CKob
	elatior ♀ H1	CBct CHEx CHal EBak IBlr LRHS MBri NPal NRog SAPC SArc SMad SPar WCot
	- 'Akebono' (v)	WCot
	- 'Asahi' (v) new	WCot
	- 'Hoshi-zora' (v) new	WCot
	- 'Milky Way' (v)	CBct CKob EBee EMan IBlr IFro LEur MHdf MSPs SDes SEND SMur WCot WViv
	- 'Okame' (v) new	WCot
	- 'Variegata' (v) ♀ H1	CBct CHEx CHal EMon IBlr IFro MHdf MTho NBir SMad SPar WCot
	linearifolia	WCot
	'Leopard' new	
	longiloba new	EBee LEur
	lurida	EBee IBlr LEur
	- 'Irish Mist' (v)	IBlr
	minutiflora new	EBee LEur

Asplenium ✿ (Aspleniaceae)

	adiantum-nigrum	EFer LRHS SRms
	bulbiferum ♀ H1-2	CHEx CTrC ESlt NMar SMur

	canariense	NMar
§	*ceterach*	CNat SMad SRms WHer
	dareoides	GDra SOkd SRot WAbe WCot
	marinum	EFer
	nidus ♀ H1	LRHS MBri
	platyneuron	EBee
	ruta-muraria	EFer SRms
§	*scolopendrium* ♀ H4	More than 30 suppliers
	- 'Angustatum'	CLAP CMil EBee GBin LRHS MAvo MMoz MTed NHar NHol NVic SMac WCru WPnP
	- 'Capitatum'	MDun
*	- 'Circinatum'	CRow WPGP
	- 'Conglomeratum'	SRms
	- 'Cornutoabruptum'	NMar
	- Crispum Group	CLAP CRDP CRow CSBt EBee EBre ECha EFer ELan MWgw NHar NHol SRms WFib WPGP
	- 'Crispum Bolton's Nobile' ♀ H4	NBro WFib WPGP
	- Crispum Cristatum Group	CLAP
	- Crispum Fimbriatum Group	GQui
	- Cristatum Group	CElw CFwr CHEx CLAP CPrp CRDP CRow EBee ELan EMar EPfP EWTr LRHS MBri MRav MWgw NDlv NHar NHol NMar SNut SPer SPla SRms SWat WFib WRic
	- 'Cristatum' **new**	EBlw
	- Fimbriatum Group	CLAP WRic
	- 'Furcatum'	CLAP EBee
*	- 'Kaye's Lacerated' ♀ H4	CLAP CRow EFer EGol ELan NHol NMar SChu
	- Laceratum Group	SRms
	Marginatum Group	NMar SWat WPGP
	- 'Irregulare'	CRDP NHar NHol SChu SRms WFib
	- 'Muricatum'	CLAP CRDP ELan GBin NMar SChu WFib
	- 'Ramocristatum'	CRow NMar
	- Ramomarginatum Group	CLAP ELan SRms WFar WRic
	- 'Sagittatocristatum'	WPGP
	- Undulatum Group	CLAP CPLG EBce EGol NBir NHar NMar NSti SPar SPla SRms SSpi SWat WCFE WPnP WRic
	- Undulatum Cristatum Group	MBri NDlv
	septentrionale	SRms
	trichomanes ♀ H4	More than 30 suppliers
	- 'Bipinnatum'	WRic
	- Cristatum Group	SRms
	- Grandiceps Group	EFer
	- Incisum Group	CLAP EBee EFer NHol NMar NOrc SMad
	- subsp. *pachyrachis*	NMar
	viride	SRms

Astartea (Myrtaceae)

	fascicularis	CPLG CTrC LRHS SOWG

Astelia (Asteliaceae)

	banksii	CBos CDoC CSpe CTrC IBal LEdu LPio WAbe WDyG
§	*chathamica* ♀ H3	More than 30 suppliers
	- 'Silver Spear'	see *A. chathamica*
	cunninghamii	see *A. solandri*
	fragrans	ECou IBlr LEdu SMrm WCot WDyG
	graminea	IBlr
	grandis	CHEx CTrC IBlr LEdu
	nervosa	CAbb CFil CTrC EBee IBlr LEdu MGrG SAPC SArc WCot WPGP
	- 'Bronze Giant' **new**	IBlr

	- 'Westland'	CBcs CDoC CPrp CTrC EBee IBlr MPRe
	nivicola	IBlr
	- 'Red Gem'	CBos IBlr LEdu
	petriei	IBlr
§	*solandri*	CHEx IBlr LEdu
	trinervia	IBlr

Aster ✿ (Asteraceae)

	ACE 425	WOBN
	acris	see *A. sedifolius*
	adscendens NNS 98-72	WCot
§	*albescens*	CPle ISea
	x *alpellus* hort. 'Triumph'	see *Aster* 'Triumph'
	alpigenus var. *alpigenus* **new**	CPBP
	- var. *haydenii*	NBid WCot
	alpinus ♀ H4	EBre EMNN EPfP GKir LHrt MNrw MPWC MWgw NJOw NLon SPet SRms WFar WPer WStl WWin
	- var. *albus*	EMil EPfP GDra WPer WWeb
	- Dark Beauty	see *A. alpinus* 'Dunkle Schöne'
	- var. *dolomiticus*	NSla
§	- 'Dunkle Schöne'	CBrm GKir NOak SRms WCra WPer WWeb
	- 'Goliath'	ECho GAbr SPlb WWeb
	- 'Happy End'	CM&M EMil IHMH LHrt NOak SRms WCot WWeb
	- 'Pinkie'	CBrm ESis ITim MSPs MWrn WWeb
	- 'Trimix'	EMlt ESis LPVe NArg NBir SRms WFar
	- violet	WPer
	- 'White Beauty'	NLon WRms
*	- 'Wolfii'	SRms
	amelloides	see *Felicia amelloides*
	amellus	ITim MHer NFor NLon WMoo
	- 'Blue King'	CHar EWsh LRHS MCAu MLLN
	- 'Breslau'	EBee
	- 'Brilliant'	EBee EBlw EChP ECtt EFou EGle EMan GMac LRHS MLLN MMil MRav MWat SPer WOld WWin
	- 'Butzemann'	GMac
	- 'Doktor Otto Petschek'	EBee WFar WViv
	- 'Fourncett Flourish'	EFou
	- 'Framfieldii' ♀ H4	EBee WFar WOld
	- 'Jacqueline'	CHar CMil EGle EPPr MBri SChu
	Genebrier' ♀ H4	SCro WCot WIvy
	- 'Joseph Lakin'	EBee WFar
	- 'King George' ♀ H4	CDoC CMHG EBee EBlw ERee ECtt EFou EGle EHrv ELan EPfP ERou GKir GMaP LRHS MBri MCAu MCLN MMil MRav MWat SChu SPer SPla SRms SWat WCot WFar WMnd WOld
	- 'Kobold'	LRHS WFar
	- 'Lac de Genève'	EBee LRHS MRav SUsu WCot WFar WOld
	- 'Lady Hindlip'	WEas WFar
	- 'Moerheim Gem'	EFou WEas
	- 'Nocturne'	EGle ERou WCot WOld
	- 'Peach Blossom'	EBee WCot
	- 'Pink Pearl'	WFar
	- Pink Zenith	see *A. amellus* 'Rosa Erfüllung'
§	- 'Rosa Erfüllung' Foerster 1964	CDoC EBee ECtt EFou ELan EPfP ERou GKir GMaP LHop LHrt MLLN MRav NFor SChu SCro SPer SPla SSpe WCot WEas WHoo WMnd WOld WPer
	- 'Rotfeuer'	EFou
	- 'Rudolph Goethe'	CBri CHar EBee EBlw EGle EGra EMil EPyc LRHS MLLN MMil

MRav MWhi NVic SHBN STes
WEas WFar WMoo WOld WWye

- 'September Glow' EFou EGle
- 'Sonia' ECha EGle SDes WCra WFar
- 'Sonora' EBee ECGP EGle ERou GMac
  LHop LPhx MAnH MCLN MSte
  NChi NDov SAga WKif WOld
- 'Sternkugel' WOld
- 'Ultramarine' WFar
- 'Vanity' GBuc WOld
§ - 'Veilchenkönigin' More than 30 suppliers
  Foerster ♀ H4
N - Violet Queen see *A. amellus* 'Veilchenkönigin'
- 'Weltfriede' WOld
'Anja's Choice' EBee EMon LPhx MAnH NDov WOld
asper see *A. bakerianus*
asperulus LPhx SBla
§ *asteroides* WLin
§ *bakerianus* EBee NOak WFar WPer
§ *capensis* 'Variegatus' see *Felicia amelloides* variegated
§ *carolinianus* WOld
chilensis EBee
ciliolatus 'Bigwig' **new** EBee
'Climax' EBee GBuc GCal LPhx MRav NSti
  SAga SMrm WOld
coelestis see *Felicia amelloides*
coloradoensis CGra CPBP NSla
concolor **new** EBee
'Connecticut Snow see *A. ericoides* f. *prostratus*
  Flurry' 'Snow Flurry'
'Coombe Fishacre' ♀ H4 COIW EBee EChP EMan EPPr
  ERou GCal LHrt LPhx LRHS
  MGrG MMil MOne MRav MSte
  SAga SHel SPla SSvw SUsu WCom
  WCot WEas WFTG WFar WMnd
  WOld WViv WWye
cordifolius WFar
- 'Aldebaran' EPPr LPhx
- 'Chieftain' ♀ H4 LPhx MNrw MTed SAga WIvy WOld
- 'Elegans' CStr EBee EFou MBri NSti WCot
  WIvy WMoo WOld
- 'Ideal' EBee EFou WOld WPer
- 'Little Carlow' see *A.* 'Little Carlow' (*cordifolius*
  hybrid)
- 'Little Dorrit' see *A.* 'Little Dorrit' (*cordifolius*
  hybrid)
- 'Photograph' see *A.* 'Photograph'
- 'Silver Queen' EBee WOld
- 'Silver Spray' CElw CPrp EFou EMan ERou
  GMaP GMac LPhx MLLN MNFA
  MWat NBro WOld WPer
- 'Sweet Lavender' ERou WOld
  ♀ H4
corymbosus see *A. divaricatus*
'Cotswold Gem' **new** WCot
§ 'Dark Pink Star' WOld
'Deep Pink Star' see *A.* 'Dark Pink Star'
delavayi EBee SUsu
diffusus see *A. lateriflorus*
diplostephioides EChP NLar
§ *divaricatus* More than 30 suppliers
- Raiche form **new** WCot
drummondii **new** EBee
N *dumosus* SHel WPer
eatonii EBee
ericoides CSam EShb LHrt NPPs WFar
  WMoo WWin
- 'Blue Star' ♀ H4 CPrp EBee EFou GBuc LPVe LRHS
  MCAu MLLN MSte NSti SChu SHel
  SPer WCot WOld
- 'Brimstone' ♀ H4 EPPr MRav WOld
- 'Cinderella' CHor COIW GBuc GMac MNFA
  NSti WOld

- 'Cirylle' EFou SMHy SMrm
- 'Constance' WOld
- 'Enchantress' ERou
- 'Erlkönig' CPrp EBee EChP EFou EMan EPPr
  GAbr LAst LRHS MCAu MMil MNFA
  MSte MWgw SChu SPla SWat
  WMnd WOld WPer WWin
- 'Esther' CHea EBee ECha EFou EGle ELan
  EMan EOrc EPri ERou MSte SDix
  WOld
- 'Golden Spray' ♀ H4 EBee EFou GMaP MBow MTed
  MWgw NSti SHel WFar WLRN WOld
- 'Herbstmyrte' EBee GBuc MLLN
- 'Hon. Vicary Gibbs' see *A.* 'Hon. Vicary Gibbs'
  (*ericoides* hybrid)
- 'Maidenhood' WOld
- 'Monte Cassino' see *A. pilosus* var. *pringlei* 'Monte
  Cassino'
- 'Pink Cloud' ♀ H4 CHor COIW EBee ECGN EFou
  EGle EGra EMar EPfP ERou GKir
  LAst LRHS MCAu MHer MRav
  MSte MWgw SChu SHel SPer SPla
  SWat WCot WFar WIvy WOld
  WPer WWin
- f. *prostratus* EMon EOrc EPot LRHS MWgw
  WFar
§ - - 'Snow Flurry' ♀ H4 CBre CSam EBee ECha ECtt EFou
  EGle EMan LPVe MCAu MLLN
  MNrw SDes SGar SPla SUsu WBor
  WCom WCot WEas WOld WRus
- 'Rosy Veil' GMac MNFA NBir NGdn WCot
  WOld
- 'Ruth McConnell' NSti
- 'Schneegitter' MLLN MSte WFar
- 'Sulphurea' MWat
- 'White Heather' CPrp EBee GMac MNFA WCot
  WIvy WOld WRHF
- 'Yvette Richardson' MSte SMHy WOld
falcatus **new** WCot
'Fanny's Fall' see *A. oblongifolius* 'Fanny's'
farreri NBro SSpi
- 'Blue Moon' WCom
§ *flaccidus* EBee GKir LRHS MGrG WCot
- McB 1029 WCot
foliaceus EBee
x *frikartii* EBee EBlw EBre EFou EGle ELan
  EPar EPfP ERou LAst MBro MRav
  SAga SChu SHBN SRms WEas
  WMnd WOld WPer WWin
- 'Eiger' WOld
- 'Flora's Delight' EBre EFou EMan GKir MGrG
  MRav SPer WOld
- 'Jungfrau' CFis EBee GMaP MMil MRav NLar
  SDes WAul WOld
N - 'Mönch' ♀ H4 More than 30 suppliers
- Wonder of Stafa see *A.* x *frikartii* 'Wunder von Stäfa'
§ - 'Wunder von Stäfa' CEnd CMGP EBee ECtt ELan EMan
  ♀ H4 EPfP GBuc GKir GMaP LHop LRHS
  MAvo MBNS MCAu MRav NBlu
  NLar SChu SDes SLon WLRN WMnd
  WOld WPGP WPnP WTel WViv
'Graham Dorrity' **new** MNes
'Herfstweelde' CMil CWCL EBee EFou EMon
  GBuc LPhx LRHS MSte SMrm
  SUsu WFar WOld
x *herveyi* EBee EMan EMon LPhx LRHS
  MSph SAga WOld
himalaicus EBee GDra GTou MWrn SRms
- CC&McK 145 NWCA
- ex CC 2815 MDCh
'Hittlemaar' WCot
§ 'Hon. Vicary Gibbs' EBee GMac MNFA MSte WOld
  (*ericoides* hybrid)

	hybridus luteus	see X *Solidaster luteus*
	ibericus	EBee
§	'Kylie' ♀ H4	CMGP EBee EMon GBuc LRHS
		MSte WCot WFar WOld WTin
	laevis	GKir MSte NLar
	– 'Arcturus'	CFir EBee LRHS MFir MHFa MHar
		MLLN MMil NMRc NSti SSvw
		WCot WFar
	– 'Blauhügel'	GCal
	– 'Calliope'	CHad CSam EBee ECha EMan GCal
		GMac LPhx LPio MAnH MAvo
		MBri MBro MMil NOak SAga SCro
		SMad SMrm WCom WEas WFar
		WHoo WIvy WKif WOld
	– var. ***geyeri***	MNrw
	lanceolatus Kuntze	see *Pyrrocoma lanceolata*
	lanceolatus Willd.	WCot
	– 'Edwin Beckett'	CBre EMan GMac MNFA WOld
§	***lateriflorus***	MNes MWat WMaN WOld WPer
	– 'Bleke Bet'	WCot WOld
	– 'Buck's Fizz'	ELan LHrt NLar SHar WOld WPrP
	– 'Datschii'	WFar
	– 'Delight'	GKir MLLN
	– 'Horizontalis' ♀ H4	More than 30 suppliers
	– 'Jan'	WOld
	– 'Lady in Black'	More than 30 suppliers
	– 'Lovely'	EBee EMan LRHS MBow MBro
		MLLN NOak WOld
	– 'Prince'	More than 30 suppliers
	laterifolius	see *A. ericoides* f. *prostratus*
	'Snow Flurry'	'Snow Flurry'
§	***linariifolius***	EBee
§	***linosyris***	CBgR EBee MSte NLar NSti SPer
		WHer WOld
	– 'Goldilocks'	see *A. linosyris*
§	'Little Carlow'	More than 30 suppliers
	(*cordifolius* hybrid) ♀ H4	
§	'Little Dorrit'	MAvo MLLN NBro NOak WLRN
	(*cordifolius* hybrid)	WOld
	maackii	EBee
	macrophyllus	CFee CPou EBee EBlw ELan EMon
		LRHS SPer WOld
	– 'Albus'	EMon EPPr WFar WIvy WOld
	– 'Twilight'	CMea EBee EBlw EChP ECha
		EFou EGle EMan EOrc EPla GCal
		LLWP MCAu MLLN MNFA MSte
		NDov NSti SDix SSpe WCot WIvy
		WMnd WOld WRHF
	'Midget'	NNor
	mongolicus	see *Kalimeris mongolica*
	natalensis	see *Felicia rosulata*
	'Natasha' **new**	WWeb
	novae-angliae	ELau WMoo WOld
	– 'Andenken an	More than 30 suppliers
	Alma Potschke'	
	– 'Andenken an	EMon NGby
	Paul Gerbe'	
	– 'Annabelle de Chazal'	WOld
	– Autumn Snow	see *A. novae-angliae*
		'Herbstschnee'
	– 'Barr's Blue'	CAbx EFou LRHS MAvo MBNS
		MSte MTed MWat NFla NSti WFar
		WMoo WOld
	– 'Barr's Pink'	CBre CBri EChP EFou EMon
		MCAu MRav MWat NFla SEND
		SHel WFar WHrl WOld WPer
*	– 'Barr's Purple' **new**	WOld
	– 'Barr's Violet'	EGle EPPr MSPs NFor NLon SHel
		SRms WCot WHoo WHrl WOld
		WPer WTin
	– 'Bishop Colenso'	EFou
	– 'Christopher Harbutt'	EGle ERou NPro WOld
	– 'Crimson Beauty'	CAbx CBri EMon EPPr MAvo
		MNFA MWat WOld
	– 'Evensong'	WOld
	– 'Harrington's Pink'	More than 30 suppliers
	♀ H4	
	– 'Helen Picton' **new**	WOld
§	– 'Herbstschnee'	CPrp CSBt EBre EChP EFou EHrv
		EMon ERou GMac MCAu MRav
		MSte MWat NFor NSti SChu SHel
		SPer SPet SSpe WFar WMnd
		WMoo WOld WPer WWye
	– 'John Davies'	WOld
	– 'Lou Williams'	WOld
	– 'Lye End Beauty'	CPou EGle EMon EOrc LRHS
		MAvo MFir MRav MSte MWat
		NFor NLon SChu WCom WCot
		WHoo WMoo WOld
	– 'Marina Wolkonsky'	WCot
	new	
	– 'Millenium Star'	WOld
	– 'Mrs S.T.Wright'	EFou EGle EMon ERou GMac
		MAnH MBrN MNFA MSte WFar
		WFoF WOld
*	– 'Mrs S.W.Stern'	WOld
	– 'Pink Parfait'	EFou GMac WCot WOld
	– 'Pink Victor'	CTri EPPr NLar SEND SHel
	– 'Primrose Upward'	WCot
	– 'Purple Cloud'	EMon ERou GMac LHop LRHS
		MHer MNFA MWat MWgw WCom
		WFoF WOld
I	– 'Purple Dome'	CPrp CSBt EBee EBre EFou EGle
		ELan EMon EWsh GMac LPhx LRHS
		MBro MCAu MNrw NSti SFND
		SMrm SSpe SSvw SUsu WCot WFar
		WHoo WMnd WMoo WOld WPnP
	– 'Quinton Menzies'	WCom WOld
*	– Red Cloud	CBri EFou SMrm WOld
	– 'Rosa Sieger'	CBre CPlt EBee EBre EFou EGle
		EMon GMac SChu SHel SUsu
		WOld WViv
	– 'Rose Williams'	WOld
	– 'Rubinschatz'	WOld
	– 'Rudelsburg'	EMon LBuc
	– 'Sayer's Croft'	EFou EGle EMon LRHS MWat
		WCot WHoo WOld WTin
	– September Ruby	see *A. novae-angliae*
		'Septemberrubin'
§	– 'Septemberrubin'	CBri CMea EBee ECtt EGle EMon
		ERou EWsh LHop MAnH MRav
		MSte NSti SChu SUsu WEas WFar
		WHoo WMoo WOld WPnP WWin
	– 'Treasure'	CBre EFou EMon WFar WMoo
		WOld
	– 'Violetta'	CAbx CMea CStr EBee EFou EGle
		EMon LPhx LRHS MAvo MSte
		MTed SHel WOld WWye
	– 'Wow'	EFou SMrm
N	***novi-belgii***	GWCH NSco WHer WMoo
	– 'Ada Ballard'	ENot ERou LRHS SPer SPet WLRN
		WOld WWye
	– 'Albanian'	WOld
	– 'Alderman Vokes'	ERou WOld
	– 'Alex Norman'	ERou WOld
	– 'Algar's Pride'	ERou LHrt LPhx NBro WOld
	– 'Alice Haslam'	CM&M EChP ECtt EFou GBri
		GKir LRHS MWgw NOrc NPri
		SSpe STes WLRN WOld WPer
	– 'Alpenglow'	WOld
	– 'Anita Ballard'	WOld
	– 'Anita Webb'	ERou GBri NBir NOak WOld
	– 'Anneke'	EPfP SHel WWeb
	– 'Apollo'	LCaP NPri
	– 'Apple Blossom'	SHel WOld

- 'Arctic'	ERou WOld
- 'Audrey'	CMGP CRez ECtt EFou ERou GKir GMaP LRHS MLLN MWgw NBro NOrc SChu SPla STes WBar WOld WTel
- 'Autumn Beauty'	WOld
- 'Autumn Days'	WOld
- 'Autumn Glory'	CSam ERou WOld
- 'Autumn Rose'	CHea WOld
- 'Baby Climax'	WOld
- 'Beauty of Colwall'	WOld
- 'Beechwood Challenger'	ERou MOne WOld
- 'Beechwood Charm'	WOld
- 'Beechwood Rival'	MAvo
- 'Beechwood Supreme'	ERou WOld
- 'Bewunderung'	NBro WOld
- 'Blandie'	CHea CTri EFou ERou MSte MWat MWgw NBro SHel WLRN WOld WTel
- 'Blauglut'	EFou NBro NCat WOld
- 'Blue Baby'	WPer WWye
- 'Blue Bouquet'	ERou SRms WBro WOld
- 'Blue Boy'	WOld
- 'Blue Danube'	CABx CMdw WOld
- 'Blue Eyes'	CElw ERou LPhx NOak SAga WOld WWye
- 'Blue Gown'	ERou GCal WOld
- 'Blue Lagoon'	LPVe LRHS MBow MBri WOld WWeb
- 'Blue Patrol'	ERou NOak WOld
- 'Blue Radiance'	WOld
- 'Blue Whirl'	ERou NBro WOld
- 'Bonanza'	WOld WTel
- 'Boningale Blue'	WOld
- 'Boningale White'	ERou WOld
- 'Bridesmaid'	WOld
- 'Brightest and Best'	WOld
- 'Caborn Pink'	LLWP
- 'Cameo'	WOld
- 'Cantab'	WOld
- 'Cantonese Queen' (v)	EMon
- 'Carlingcott'	ERou MOne NOak WOld
- 'Carnival'	CM&M EFou ERou MMHG NOrc SHel SPer SSpe WOld WTel
- 'Cecily'	NBro WOld
- 'Charles Wilson'	WOld
- 'Chatterbox'	CPrp LRHS MRav MWat NLar SChu SRms WOld
- 'Chelwood'	EBee WOld
- 'Chequers'	CBrm CM&M EBee ECot ERou MSte WLRN WOld
- 'Christina'	see A. novi-belgii 'Kristina'
- 'Christine Soanes'	EFou WOld
- 'Cliff Lewis'	ERou NBro WOld
- 'Climax Albus'	see A. 'White Climax'
- 'Cloudy Blue'	WOld
- 'Colonel F.R. Durham'	ERou
- 'Coombe Delight'	ERou
- 'Coombe Gladys'	ERou WOld
- 'Coombe Joy'	ERou NOak WLRN WOld
- 'Coombe Margaret'	WOld
- 'Coombe Pink'	ERou
- 'Coombe Queen'	WOld
- 'Coombe Radiance'	ERou MSte WOld
- 'Coombe Ronald'	ERou MWat WOld
- 'Coombe Rosemary'	ECtt ERou LRHS NLar NOak WOld WRHF WTel
- 'Coombe Violet'	LPhx MWat WOld
- 'Countess of Dudley'	WOld WPer
- 'Court Herald'	WOld
- 'Crimson Brocade'	ENot EPfP ERou LRHS MRav MWat SPar SPer WOld

- 'Dandy'	EBee ECot ELan EMar LRHS NBir NGdn SChu WOld
- 'Daniela'	WOld
- 'Daphne Anne'	WOld
- 'Dauerblau'	WOld
- 'Davey's True Blue'	CTri EFou ERou MSte WLRN WOld
- 'David Murray'	WOld
- 'Dazzler'	WOld
- 'Destiny'	WOld
- 'Diana'	CNic ERou MOne NBro WOld WViv
- 'Diana Watts'	ERou WOld
- 'Dietgard'	WOld
- 'Dolly'	NBir WOld
- 'Dusky Maid'	MBri SHel WOld
- 'Elizabeth'	WOld
- 'Elizabeth Bright'	WOld
- 'Elizabeth Hutton'	WOld
- 'Elsie Dale'	EBee WOld
- 'Elta'	WOld
- 'Erica'	CElw MWat WOld
- 'Ernest Ballard'	ERou WOld
- 'Eva'	WOld
- 'Eventide'	CBcs CElw ENot ERou NOak SPer WLRN WMoo WOld WRHF
- 'F.M. Simpson'	ERou WElm
- 'Fair Lady'	ERou MWat WOld
- 'Faith'	WOld
- 'Farnecombe Lilac'	EBee
new	
- 'Farrington'	WOld
- 'Fellowship'	CBcs CDes CFir CMGP EBee EFou ENot ERou LPhx MAnH MAvo MSte MWat SAga SPer SRms WCot WOld WTel
- 'Fontaine'	WOld
- 'Fran'	MFir
- 'Freda Ballard'	EBee EPPr ERou LRHS MWat WLRN WOld
- 'Freya'	WOld
- 'Fuldatal'	EFou WOld
- 'Gayborder Blue'	WOld
- 'Gayborder Royal'	CFir ERou MOne WOld
- 'Glory of Colwall'	WOld
- 'Goliath'	WOld
- 'Grey Lady'	WOld
- 'Guardsman'	ERou GKir LRHS MHFa WOld
- 'Gulliver'	WOld
- 'Gurney Slade'	CStr ERou GKir LRHS WOld
- 'Guy Ballard'	ERou
- 'Harrison's Blue'	ERou LPhx SAga WOld WPer
- 'Heinz Richard'	CM&M COlW EBee ECha EFou LRHS MSte NBir NGdn SChu SPet WLRN WOld WWpP
- 'Helen'	WOld
- 'Helen Ballard'	CHea CPlt CRez CStr ERou WOld
- 'Herbstpurzel'	EBee MOne
- 'Hilda Ballard'	ERou WOld
- 'Ilse Brensell'	MOne MSte WOld
- 'Irene'	WOld
- 'Isabel Allen'	WOld
- 'Janet Watts'	ERou NBro WOld
- 'Jean'	MWat SHel WOld
- 'Jean Gyte'	WOld
- 'Jenny'	More than 30 suppliers
- 'Jollity'	WOld
- 'Julia'	WOld
- 'Karminkuppel'	WOld
- 'King of the Belgians'	WOld
- 'King's College'	GKir LRHS WOld
- 'Kristina'	COlW EBre ECha EFou ERou GKir LRHS MGrG MOne MRav SPet SSpe WCot WOld WTel

§

- 'Lady Evelyn Drummond' — WOld
- 'Lady Frances' — WOld
- 'Lady in Blue' — COIW CSBt CSpe EBee EChP ECtt ELan ENot EPfP GKir LRHS MBNS MWat MWgw NMir NVic SPer SPet SRms SSpe STes SWat WFar WMoo WOld WPer WTel WWin
- 'Lady Paget' — WOld
- 'Lassie' — CHea ERou LLWP MWat SBri WCot WOld
- 'Lavender Dream' — WOld
- 'Lawrence Chiswell' — LPhx SHel WOld
- 'Lilac Time' — WOld
- 'Lisa Dawn' — NCat WOld
- 'Little Boy Blue' — CBcs ERou SHBN WOld
- 'Little Man in Blue' — WOld
- 'Little Pink Beauty' — COIW CPrp EBee ECtt EFou ELan ERou GKir LHop LRHS MBNS MRav NMir NVic SHel SPer SRPl SSpe STes WMoo WOld WTel WViv WWin
- 'Little Pink Lady' — ERou SAga WOld
- 'Little Pink Pyramid' — SRms
- 'Little Red Boy' — CBcs ERou WOld
- 'Little Treasure' — WOld
- 'Lucy' — WOld
- 'Madge Cato' — NOak WOld
- 'Malvern Castle' — ERou
- 'Mammoth' — WOld
- 'Margaret Rose' — NCiC NOrc WLRN WOld
- 'Margery Bennett' — ERou GBri NOak WOld
- 'Marie Ballard' — CBcs CHea CSBt CSam CWib ENot EPfP ERou GKir GMaP MAnH MFir MWat NBro NLon NOrc SHRN SHel SPar SPer SRms STes SWat WEas WOld WPer WTMC WTel WWpP
- 'Marie's Pretty Please' — NCat WOld
- 'Marjorie' — WOld
- 'Marjory Ballard' — WOld
- 'Martonie' — WOld WPer
- 'Mary Ann Neil' — WOld
- 'Mary Deane' — MSte WOld WPer
- 'Mauve Magic' — WOld
- 'Melbourne Belle' — NOak WOld
- 'Melbourne Magnet' — CHea ERou MOne WOld
- 'Michael Watts' — ERou WOld
- 'Mistress Quickly' — CRez ERou GBri MAvo MBri NOak WOld
- 'Mittelmeer' — EFou
- 'Mount Everest' — ERou WOld WPer
- 'Mrs Leo Hunter' — NOak WOld
- 'Nesthäkchen' — ECho
- 'Nobilis' — WOld
- 'Norman's Jubilee' — CPrp ERou NBir WOld
- 'Nursteed Charm' — WOld
- 'Oktoberschneekuppel' — ERou LRHS MBri NBro
- 'Orlando' — ERou WCot WOld
- 'Pamela' — ERou WOld
- 'Patricia Ballard' — CElw CPrp CSBt EBee ERou GKir MWat NBro NLon SPar SPer SSpe WBVN WFar WLRN WOld WPer WTel
- 'Peace' — WOld
- 'Percy Thrower' — ERou WLRN WOld
- 'Peter Chiswell' — MBri WOld
- 'Peter Harrison' — GMaP GMac NBir NBro WOld WPer
- 'Peter Pan' — EBee LCaP WOld
- 'Picture' — WOld
- 'Pink Gown' — WOld
- 'Pink Lace' — ERou MBNS MLLN WOld WPer

- 'Pink Pyramid' — WOld
- 'Plenty' — ERou LRHS MBri MHFa WOld
- 'Porzellan' — CElw CM&M CMGP COIW EMar WCot
- 'Pride of Colwall' — ERou MOne MWat
- 'Priory Blush' — CHea CRez ERou NOak WLRN WOld WWeb
- 'Professor Anton Kippenberg' — CSBt EBee EFou EPfP ERou GKir GMaP LRHS MHer MRav NBro SHel SPer WMoo WOld WTel
- 'Prosperity' — ERou GKir NMRc NOak WOld
* - 'Prunella' — ERou WOld
- 'Purple Dome' — ECha WOld
- 'Queen Mary' — ERou WOld
- 'Queen of Colwall' — WOld
- 'Ralph Picton' — WOld
- 'Raspberry Ripple' — ECot EMar ERou EWes NCiC WLRN WOld
- 'Red Robin' — MWat
- 'Red Sunset' — CBcs ERou SRms WOld
- 'Rembrandt' — EBee GKir LBuc
- 'Remembrance' — GKir LRHS WOld
- 'Reverend Vincent Dale' — WOld
- 'Richness' — ERou LPhx NOak SAga SHel WOld
- 'Robin Adair' — WOld
- 'Roland Smith' — WOld
- 'Rose Bonnet' — CSBt EFou ENot MWat SHBN SPlb WLRN
- 'Rose Bouquet' — WOld
- 'Rosebud' — WOld
- 'Rosemarie Sallmann' — MOne
- 'Rosenwichtel' — EBee EFou EMar LPVe MCLN NLar zur Linden WLRN WOld
- 'Royal Blue' — MAvo
- 'Royal Ruby' — ECtt WOld
- 'Royal Velvet' — ENot ERou WOld
- 'Rozika' — WOld
- 'Rufus' — ERou NOak WOld
- 'Sailor Boy' — EFou ERou WLRN WOld
- 'Saint Egwyn' — WOld
- 'Sam Banham' — ERou NBro
- 'Sandford White Swan' — ERou GKir LRHS MBri WPer
- 'Sarah Ballard' — ERou MWat WOld
§ - 'Schneekissen' — CPrp EBee ECtt EGoo EPfP EPla GMaP MHer MWgw NPri SEND SPer STes WHrl WLRN WOld
- 'Schöne von Dietlikon' — CKno EFou NOak WLRN WOld
- 'Schoolgirl' — ERou GKir LRHS WOld
- 'Sheena' — ERou LRHS MBri WOld
§ - 'Silberteppich' — GMac
- Silver Carpet — see A. novi-belgii 'Silberteppich'
- Snow Cushion — see A. novi-belgii 'Schneekissen'
- 'Snowdrift' — WOld
- 'Snowsprite' — CBcs CSBt EBee EPfP MBow MWat NBro NOrc NPro SWat WOld
- 'Sonata' — ERou GMaP NLon NOak SPer WCra WOld
- 'Sophia' — ERou NOak WOld
- 'Starlight' — ENot ERou LPVe MBNS MBri WFar WMoo WOld WRHF
- 'Steinebrück' — WOld
- 'Sterling Silver' — ERou NOak WOld
- 'Storm Clouds' — EFou
- 'Strahlenmeer' zur Linden — EFou
- 'Sunset' — EBee WOld
- 'Susan' — WOld
- 'Sweet Briar' — CElw WOld
- 'Tapestry' — WOld
- 'Terry's Pride' — WOld
- 'The Archbishop' — MAvo WOld
- 'The Bishop' — ERou WOld

	- 'The Cardinal'	ERou WOld
	- 'The Choristers'	WOld
	- 'The Dean'	ERou WOld
§	- 'The Rector'	WOld
	- 'The Sexton'	ERou WOld
	- 'Thundercloud'	LPhx WOld
	- 'Timsbury'	WOld
	- 'Tony'	WOld
	- 'Tovarich'	GMac WOld
	- 'Trudi Ann'	NBir WOld
	- 'Twinkle'	NBro WOld WTin
	- 'Victor'	MOne WOld
	- 'Vignem'	NSti
	- 'Violet Lady'	ERou WOld
	- 'Waterperry'	MWat
	- 'Weisses Wunder'	EFou WOld
	- 'White Ladies'	EBee ECtt EFou ERou GMaP LLWP MWat NOrc SPer WLRN WTel
	- 'White Swan'	CPou EPPr LPhx NOak WOld
	- 'White Wings'	MBri WOld
	- 'Winston S. Churchill'	CM&M COlW CTri ELan ENot EPfP ERou GMaP LRHS MWat NLon NOrc SHBN SHel SPer SPlb SSpe WBro WOld WPnP WTel
	oblongifolius	WOld
	- 'Fanny's'	EBee EMan MMil WCot WFar WOld
	'Ochtendgloren' (*pringlei* hybrid) ♀ H4	EBre EFou EGle EMon EPPr GBuc GKir GMac LPhx LRHS MAnH MAvo MBri MMil MNrw MSte NSti SAga SMad SMrm WCot WFar WMaN WOld WWye
	Octoberlight	see *A.* 'Oktoberlicht'
§	'Oktoberlicht'	EMon LPhx SAga WOld
	oolentangiensis new	EBee EMan EPPr
	pappei	see *Felicia amoena*
	'Pearl Star'	GMac WOld
	petiolatus	see *Felicia petiolata*
§	'Photograph' ♀ H4	CStr GCal MSte MTed MWat SMrm WFar WOld
§	*pilosus* var. *demotus* ♀ H4	EChP ECha EMon EWes MLLN MRav MSte SBri SCro SHel WFar WOld WTin
§	- var. *pringlei* 'Monte Cassino' ♀ H4	CHea CHid CPrp CSBt EBre EChP ECha EFou EGle EPfP ERou LHop LPhx LRHS MAnH MBNS MBri MLLN MWat MWgw NDov SAga SPer SUsu WFar WMaN WMnd WOld WRus WViv
I	- *pringlei* 'Phoebe'	WCot WOld
	- - 'Pink Cushion'	WCot
	'Pink Cassino'	WRus
	'Pink Star'	CMea CStr EBee EFou EMan GKir GMac LPhx LRHS MBri MRav MWgw NPri NSti WCot WFar WHoo WOld
	'Plowden's Pink'	WOld
	'Poollicht'	EFou
§	*ptarmicoides*	CFee CM&M EMon MBrN MLLN WCot WFTG WOld WPer
	puniceus var. *elliottii*	IFro
	purdomii	see *A. flaccidus*
	pyrenaeus 'Lutetia'	CHea EBee EChP ECha EFou EMan EOrc EPPr GCal LRHS MAnH MMil MNFA MSte MWgw NLar SBla WCot WFar WOld
	radula	EBee EMan EMon GCal LRHS NLar NSti SUsu WCot WOld
	'Ringdove' (*ericoides* hybrid) ♀ H4	EBee EFou EPfP ERou GMac LRHS MMil MNFA MNrw MTis MWat MWgw NSti NVic WCot WLRN WOld
	'Rosa Star'	SHel WOld

	rotundifolius 'Variegatus'	see *Felicia amelloides* variegated
	rugulosus 'Asrugo' new	EBee
	x *salignus*	WOld
	- Scottish form new	WOld
*	*sativus atrocaeruleus*	CFwr
§	*scaber*	CKno EBee LHop WPGP
	scandens	see *A. carolinianus*
	schreberi	CHea WCot WOld
§	*sedifolius*	CHea ELan EMan EPPr MGrG MSte MWat NBid SBla SChu SDix SPla SRms WBea WEas WFar WOld WPer
	- 'Nanus'	CElw EBee EFou EOrc ERou LRHS MBri MLLN MSte NBir NLar NSti SPer WCot WFar WOld
	- 'Snow Flurries'	see *A. ericoides* f. *prostratus* 'Snow Flurry'
	'Serendipity' new	WCot
	sericeus	EBee
	shreberi	MLLN
§	*sibiricus*	WOld
	'Snow Flurry'	see *A. ericoides* f. *prostratus* 'Snow Flurry'
	'Snow Star'	WOld
	souliei	WCot
	- B&SWJ 7655	WCru
	spathulifolius	NBir
	spectabilis	WOld
	stracheyi	GDea GEil
	subcaeruleus	see *A. tongolensis*
	subspicatus	WPer
	'Sunhelene'	WViv
	Sunplum = 'Danasplum'	WViv
	'Sunqueen'	WViv
	'Sunsky'	WViv
	tataricus	EBee ECha WOld
	- 'Jindai'	WCot WFar
	thomsonii 'Nanus'	CBos CSam EBee EBre EFou EGle EOrc GMaP LPhx NBid SMrm SPer WCot WFar WOld WSHC
	tibeticus	see *A. flaccidus*
§	*tongolensis*	EPfP GKir MSPs SRms WCot WFar WWeb WWin
	- 'Berggarten'	CHar EBre GKir GMac MBri MMil SUsu WFar WWeb
	- 'Dunkleviolette'	GBuc NBro SRms
	- 'Lavender Star'	EFou GBuc SRms
	- 'Leuchtenburg'	ERou
	- 'Napsbury'	CDes ECha ERou GKir LRHS MAvo WPGP
	- 'Wartburgstern'	EBee EChP EPfP GKir LRHS MAvo MBri MMil NGdn NPri SPla WFar WLRN WMnd WPer
	tradescantii hort.	see *A. pilosus* var. *demotus*
	tradescantii L.	EFou ELan EMan MBNS MFir MWgw NOak NSti SCou SHel SMad WCot WEas WOld
§	*trinervius* subsp. *ageratoides* new	CPou
	- subsp. *ageratoides* 'Asran'	CFwr EBee SSvw WFar
	- var. *harae*	WOld
	tripolium	WHer
§	'Triumph' new	WCot
	turbinellus hort. ♀ H4	CPlt ECGN EChP EFou EMan EMon GBuc GMac LPhx LRHS MBNS MBro MNFA MSte NDov SChu SDix SMHy SMrm WCot WFTG WFar WHer WHoo WMoo WOld WWeb
	turbinellus Lindl. new	EPPr
	- hybrid	CAbx CMea NPPs
	umbellatus	CBre EMon EPPr MCAu NSti SRms WCot WOld WTin

vimineus Lamarck   see *A. lateriflorus*
vimineus 'Ptarmicoides'   see *A. ptarmicoides*
§   'White Climax'   MSte MTed WCot WOld
     'Yvonne'   CBre EBee

Asteranthera (Gesneriaceae)

ovata   CDoC CFil CPlN GGGa GGar LAst
          SSpi WAbe WBod WCot WCru
          WGwG WSHC WWal

Asteriscus (Asteraceae)

maritimus   see *Pallenis maritima*

Asteromoea (Asteraceae)

mongolica   see *Kalimeris mongolica*
pinnatifida   see *Kalimeris pinnatifida*

Asteropyrum (Ranunculaceae)

cavaleriei   EBee LEur WCru

Astilbe ✿ (Saxifragaceae)

'America'   CMHG ECtt LBuc
'Aphrodite'   CMCo CPlt EBee EBlw EChP ENot
  (*simplicifolia* hybrid)   LAst MDKP NHol NMir NPro
          SChu SPla SSpi WBrE WGor
x *arendsii*   MBro MHer SDes SMac SPet
          WMoo WPer
- 'Amethyst'   CHor CMGP CMHG CSBt EBee
          EMan GSki LRHS MCAu MRav
          NPSI SBod SPer WAul WFar WHoo
          WMoo
- 'Anita Pfeifer'   CMHG GKir LBuc LRHS NLon
          WFar WPnP
- 'Bella' **new**   WWeb
- 'Bergkristall'   CMHG EMil
§ - 'Brautschleier' ♀ ᴴ⁴   CMHG CMac CPrp CTri EChP
          ECtt EFou ENot EPfP MOne NPSI
          NPri WHil WPnP
- 'Bressingham Beauty'   CDoC CMHG CPrp CWCL EBre
          EHon ELan EMFW ENot EPar EPfP
          EPla GKir GMaP LSyl MCLN MRav
          MWrn NHol NPro NSti SPer SSpe
          WTar WMoo WWpP
- Bridal Veil   see *A.* x *arendsii* 'Brautschleier'
- 'Bumalda'   CFir CMCo COtt ENot ETub
          GMaP GSki LRHS NDlv NPro SPlb
          SSpi WAul WFar WMoo WWeb
- 'Cattleya'   CMHG EBce EFou LCaP NHol
          WFar WMoo
- 'Cattleya Dunkel'   CMHG WFar
- 'Ceres'   CMHG NHol
- 'Darwin's Favourite'   NPri
§ - 'Diamant'   CHor CMHG CSBt EBee LAst
          LRHS MBri MWrn NGdn NHol
          SDes WFar
- Diamond   see *A.* x *arendsii* 'Diamant'
- 'Drayton Glory'   see *A.* x *rosea* 'Peach Blossom'
- Elizabeth Bloom   EBee EMan GSki LRHS MCLN SVil
  = 'Eliblo'ᴾᴮᴿ   WFar
§ - 'Ellie'   see *A.* x *arendsii* 'Ellie van Veen'
§ - 'Ellie van Veen'   CFai CM&M CMHG EMan EPGN
          GBin MBri MCLN NHol NPSI
          NPro SVil
- 'Erica'   CHor CMHG CTri EBee EWll GKir
          LRHS MBri MCAu MRav SDes
          WFar WMoo
- 'Fanal' ♀ ᴴ⁴   More than 30 suppliers
§ - 'Federsee'   CBcs CMGP CMHG CWCL EBee
          EFou ELan EMil ENot LRHS SPer
          WFar WLRN
§ - 'Feuer'   CMCo CMHG CPrp CSam EBee
          EBlw ELan EPfP MTis NHol NPro
          NVic SPar SPer SPla

- Fire   see *A.* x *arendsii* 'Feuer'
- 'Flamingo'ᴾᴮᴿ   MBri
- 'Gertrud Brix'   CBcs EBee EPar NBir NGdn NPro
          SBod
- 'Gladstone'   see *A.* 'W.E. Gladstone' (*japonica*
          hybrid)
- 'Gloria'   CMHG CTri LPBA LRHS WFar
§ - 'Gloria Purpurea'   CHor CMHG EBlw GKir LRHS
          MDun NHol WMoo
- Glow   see *A.* x *arendsii* 'Glut'
§ - 'Glut'   CMHG GKir LRHS NHol SRms
          WFar
- 'Granat'   CDoC CHor CM&M CMHG CMac
          EBee EMFW MCLN SPar WLRN
          WMoo WWin
- 'Grande' **new**   MWrn
- 'Grete Püngel'   GKir LBuc MLLN WFar
- 'Harmony'   CMHG
- Hyacinth   see *A.* x *arendsii* 'Hyazinth'
§ - 'Hyazinth'   CDoC CFai CMHG CPLG CPrp
          EBee EMFW EMan GSki LRHS
          NGdn NHol WWal
- 'Irrlicht'   CBcs CMHG EBee EHon ELan
          EMFW EPfP EPla EWTr GKir
          LHop LPBA LRHS NHol SDes SPer
          SWat WWpP
- 'Kvele'   CMHG GKir SOkh WFar WMoo
          WViv
§ - 'Lachskönigin'   CMHG
- 'Lilli Goos'   CMHG
- 'Mars'   CMHG
- 'Moerheim's Glory'   CM&M LAst
- 'Mont Blanc'   CMHG
- 'Obergärtner Jürgens'   CM&M EBee EChP EMan EPGN
          GBin WLow
- 'Paul Gaarder'   CMHG
- Pink Pearl   see *A.* x *arendsii* 'Rosa Perle'
- 'Queen of Holland'   see *A.* 'Queen of Holland'
          (*japonica* hybrid)
- Red Light   see *A.* x *arendsii* 'Rotlicht'
§ - 'Rosa Perle'   CMHG NHol
§ - 'Rotlicht'   CMHG CPlt ECot GKir LRHS NLar
          NPro NSti WFar WGor
- Salmon Queen   see *A.* x *arendsii* 'Lachskönigin'
- 'Snowdrift'   CMHG CSBt EBre EPGN EPla
          GKir GSki LRHS MBNS NFor NLon
          NOak NOrc NPro SDes SWat WFar
          WHil
- 'Solferino'   CMHG
- 'Spartan'   see *A.* x *arendsii* 'Rotlicht'
- 'Spinell'   EBee WPnP
- 'Venus'   CHar CSBt CSam EBee ECha ECtt
          EFou EGra EMFW EPla EWTr
          GGar GKir GMaP MCLN MSte
          NHol NOrc NVic SDes SPer SSpe
          SWat WFar WMoo
- 'Walküre'   CMHG
- 'Washington'   see *A.* 'Washington' (*japonica*
          hybrid)
§ - 'Weisse Gloria'   CMHG EBee ECha EPar EWTr
          LPBA MRav NHol NMGW NSti
          SBod SPar WMoo
- White Gloria   see *A.* x *arendsii* 'Weisse Gloria'
- 'White Queen'   NHol NWoo
- 'William Reeves'   CMHG MFir NHol
- 'Zuster Theresa'   CMHG EBee GKir LRHS WFar
astilboides   CMHG NHol
'Atrorosea'   NCot SRms
  (*simplicifolia* hybrid)
'Avalanche'   EPGN GKir NHol SPar
'Betsy Cuperus'   CMHG CMil LBuc MRav MSte
  (*thunbergii* hybrid)
biternata   EMon

	'Bonn' (*japonica* hybrid)	CBcs EPar LPBA NBlu SCoo SDes SRms
	'Bremen' (*japonica* hybrid)	CMHG LPBA
§	'Bronce Elegans' (*simplicifolia* hybrid) ♀ H4	More than 30 suppliers
*	**bumalda** 'Bronze Pygmy'	COIW EWTr NHol SPla STes
	'Carnea' (*simplicifolia* hybrid)	CMHG LBuc
	'Catherine Deneuve'	see *A.* x *arendsii* 'Federsee'
	'Cherry Ripe'	see *A.* x *arendsii* 'Feuer'
	chinensis	CMCo CMHG GDea GKir GSki IBlr LRHS MHer MPEx WLin WWeb
	- var. **davidii**	CMHG GSki
	- 'Finale'	EMFW GLil NHol NPro SPer SRms WEas WFar WLin
	- 'Frankentroll'	CMHG
	- from Russia	GCal
	- 'Intermezzo'	CFwr EBee GMaP
§	- var. **pumila** ♀ H4	More than 30 suppliers
	- - 'Serenade'	GSki LBuc LRHS MBri NGdn WFar
	- 'Purple Glory'	CMHG GKir
	- 'Purpurkerze'	CPen EBee EChP GMaP MBNS MBri MNrw NBro
	- 'Spätsommer'	CMHG
	- var. **taquetii**	EChP MDCh NSti SRms
	- - Purple Lance	see *A. chinensis* var. *taquetii* 'Purpurlanze'
§	- - 'Purpurlanze'	CMHG EBee EFou EGra EMan EPPr GKir GMaP LBBr LLWP LPhx MBri MCAu MRav NBir NCat NChi NGdn NPro SPar WCot WFar WMoo WWin
§	- - 'Superba' ♀ H4	CM&M CMHG CRow ECha ENot EPfP GGar IHMH MCCP MLLN MNrw MSte NBro NHol SChu SDix SPer SRms WEas WFar WMoo WOld WPGP
	- subsp. **taquetii** var. **superba** 'Rowden Sunstar'	CRow
	- 'Veronica Klose'	CMHG GKir MCAu NLar NPro SMrm
	- 'Vision in Red' **new**	MBri MCLN NPro
	- 'Visions'	CFai CMHG EBee EChP EMan ENot LRHS MBNS MBri MSte NGdn NPSI NPro WCot WFar
	- white	WCot
	Cologne	see *A.* 'Köln' (*japonica* hybrid)
	'Crimson Feather'	see *A.* x *arendsii* 'Gloria Purpurea'
	x **crispa**	IBlr WFar
	- 'Gnom'	NHar
	- 'Lilliput'	CLAP CMGP GKir LRHS MAvo NHar NLar NPro
§	- 'Perkeo' ♀ H4	COtt CRow EBee EBre ECha EPfP GDra GGar GMaP GSki IMGH LHop LRHS MDun MRav MSte NBir NCot NHar NLar NMen NOak SPar SRms SSpi WAul WCot WFar WMoo
	- 'Peter Pan'	see *A.* x *crispa* 'Perkeo'
	- 'Snow Queen'	LRHS NBir NHar NMen NPro WFar
	'Darwin's Dream'	LRHS MBri NPri
	'Deutschland' (*japonica* hybrid)	More than 30 suppliers
	'Dunkellachs' (*simplicifolia* hybrid)	CM&M MBri NHol NPro WFar WLin
	'Düsseldorf' (*japonica* hybrid)	CMHG EPar LRHS MBri SPer WRus
	'Dutch Treat' (*japonica* hybrid) (v)	CMea
	'Eden's Odysseus'	EBee EChP EFou EMan MOne
	'Elegans' (*simplicifolia* hybrid) **new**	CMHG
	'Elizabeth' (*japonica* hybrid) **new**	CMHG
	'Etna' (*japonica* hybrid)	CBcs CMHG EBee EGra GBri GSki LBBr LBuc MWrn NPro SDes SRms WPnP WRus
	'Europa' (*japonica* hybrid)	CM&M CMHG CMac CSBt EBee ECtt EMFW EPGN LBBr LHop LPBA MRav NOak SPla SSpe WFar WHil
	'Fata Morgana' (x *arendsii* hybrid) **new**	CMHG
§	**glaberrima**	EPar GCal NMen
	- var. **saxatilis** ♀ H4	CLyd CRow EHyt ETow IFro IMGH NOak NSla NWoo SAga WAbe WHal
	- **saxosa**	see *A.* 'Saxosa'
*	- - **minor**	NJOw
	- **grandis**	CMHG WHer
	'Hennie Graafland' (*simplicifolia* hybrid)	CBcs CMCo CMHG COtt CPen EChP EFou EMan EMil GKir MBNS NLar WLin
	'Holden Clough' (*japonica* hybrid)	NHol
	'Inshriach Pink' (*simplicifolia* hybrid)	CMHG EBee EFou EHoe ELan GCrs GDra GKir GLil LRHS MBri MCLN NBir NCot NHar NHol NMen NOak SAga WCot WFar WHal
	japonica var. **terrestris**	see *A. glaberrima*
	'Jo Ophorst' (*davidii* hybrid)	CMHG EBee EMan GSki LPBA MRav NGdn SPer WLRN WWal
	'Koblenz' (*japonica* hybrid)	CMHG
§	'Köln' (*japonica* hybrid)	CMHG EBee EMil LPBA SMrm WFar WGwG
	koreana	WCot
	'Koster'	LPBA
	'Kriemhilde'	CMHG
	'Lady Digby'	LPBA
	'Lollipop'	MBri
	longicarpa B&SWJ 6711	WCru
	'Maggie Daley'	EBee EPGN MBri NBro NPro WMoo
	'Mainz' (*japonica* hybrid)	CMHG EBee ELan EMil
	microphylla	CMHG NHol
	- pink	CMHG NHol
	'Moerheimii' (*thunbergii* hybrid)	CMHG
	'Montgomery' (*japonica* hybrid)	CMHG EChP LRHS MBri MRav NGdn NHol WBVN
	Ostrich Plume	see *A.* 'Straussenfeder' (*thunbergii* hybrid)
	'Peaches and Cream'	EBee GKir LRHS MRav NBro NLar WAul WPnP
	'Peter Barrow' (*glaberrima* hybrid)	SIng SRms
	'Pink Lightening' (*simplicifolia* hybrid) **new**	MBNS
	'Poschka' **new**	CFir
I	'Poschka Alba' **new**	CFir
	'Professor van der Wielen' (*thunbergii* hybrid)	CMHG CMil EGle EMan EMon GCal GGar LAst MCAu MSte SDix SPer SRms SSpi WFar WHoo
	pumila	see *A. chinensis* var. *pumila*
*	'Queen'	LPBA
§	'Queen of Holland' (*japonica* hybrid)	EBee
	'Radius' **new**	SVil
*	'Red Admiral'	NFor NLon
	'Red Sentinel' (*japonica* hybrid)	CBcs CFai CM&M EChP EMan EMil EPGN EPar GMaP LAst

MOne MTis NBro NHar NHol
NOrc SDes SMrm SPar SVil WFar

'Rheinland' *(japonica* CMHG EPGN EPfP IHMH LPBA
hybrid) ♀ H4   MBro MCAu MTis NArg NPri SDes
STes WEas WFar WHoo WPnP

rivularis   CMHG WCot

§ x ***rosea*** 'Peach Blossom'   CBcs CM&M CMHG EBee EChP
EMan EPGN EPar EWTr MBro MGrG
NArg NBir NHol NSti SHel SRPl
WFar WHoo WLow WMoo WWpP

- 'Queen Alexandra'   WFar
'Rosea' *(simplicifolia*   CHar NHol WFar
hybrid)
Rosemary Bloom   NHol
= 'Rosblo'
'Salmonea' *(simplicifolia*   CMHG
hybrid) **new**

§ 'Saxosa'   GGar SPla
* 'Showstar'   LRHS SDes SMac
simplicifolia ♀ H4   CRow GKir NHar NMen SSpi WFar
- 'Alba'   CMHG NHol NPro
- Bronze Elegance   see A. 'Bronze Elegans'
(simplicifolia hybrid)
- 'Darwin's Snow Sprite'   CLAP CMac CRez ECho GKir
LRHS MBri MSte NHol NLar NPri
NPro WFar WLin
- 'Jacqueline'   ECho EFou LBuc NHol NLar WFar
* - 'Nana Alba'   NPro
- 'Praecox'   NHar
- 'Praecox Alba'   CMCo EBee EChP ENot NHol
SMac SVil
simplicifolia   GDra NHar
x ***glaberrima***
'Sprite' *(simplicifolia*   More than 30 suppliers
hybrid) ♀ H4
§ 'Straussenfeder'   CM&M CMGP CMHG CTri EBee
(thunbergii hybrid)   EFou EMan EPfP FPla GCal GMaP
♀ H4   LAst LHop LRHS NHol SSpi WFTG
WLRN WMoo WPnP
'Sugar Plum'   LAst SVil
(simplicifolia hybrid)
'Superba'   see *A. chinensis* var. *taquetii*
'Superba'
* ***sylvestris*** **new**   ETub
thunbergii var.   WCru
terrestris B&SWJ
6125 **new**
'Touch of Pink'   MWrn
(simplicifolia hybrid)
new
'Vesuvius' *(japonica*   CBcs GKir LSyl MGrG NBlu NSti
hybrid)
§ 'W.E. Gladstone'   CMea EBee GSki LBBr MSte NBlu
(japonica hybrid)   NCtC NGby NHol WGor WWeb
WWpP
'Walter Bitner' **new**   SVil
§ 'Washington'   EPGN LAst WHil
(japonica hybrid)
'White Wings'
(simplicifolia
hybrid) **new**   NPro
'Willie Buchanan'
(simplicifolia hybrid)   More than 30 suppliers

Astilboides (Saxifragaceae)
§ ***tabularis***   More than 30 suppliers

Astragalus (Papilionaceae)
adsurgens **new**   GKev
arnotianus JCA 9128   CPBP
barrii **new**   CGra
canadensis   GKir
chrysochlorus **new**   CGra

cicer   NWCA
glycyphyllos   CAgr CArn EBee EChP IIve MSal
WWye
lusitanicus **new**   LRav
membranaceus   CArn ELau IIve MSal
sinicus **new**   WHer
utahensis   EHyt

Astrantia ❀ (Apiaceae)
bavarica   CCge CElw EBee EBlw EMan
EMar GCal MAvo MDKP MGGn
MTed SMrm WCot WOut
§ 'Buckland'   More than 30 suppliers
carniolica   EBlw EMon MGGn
- *major*   see A. *major*
- var. *rubra*   see A. *major* 'Rubra'
- 'Variegata'   see A. *major* 'Sunningdale
Variegata'
'Hadspen Blood'   More than 30 suppliers
helleborifolia hort.   see A. *maxima*
§ ***major***   More than 30 suppliers
* - *alba*   CMHG CRow EBee EBlw ECGN
ECha EGle EHrv EMon GSki
LLWP MRav MWrn NBir NCat
NGdn NPer WMnd
- 'Berendien Stam'   CCge EBlw EMon MAvo
- subsp. *biebersteinii*   CCge EBlw EMon NBir
- 'Buckland'   see A. 'Buckland'
- 'Celtic Star' **new**   CFai EBla EBlw ELan EMan LHop
MEHN MSph NCot NGdn NOak
SPla WAbe WCot
- 'Claret'   More than 30 suppliers
- Cliff's form **new**   MTed
- 'Compton Lane'   WCom
- 'Dulcie Scott' **new**   WOut
- 'Elmblut'   EBlw EMon
- 'Gill Richardson'   EFou
- Gwen's form **new**   MTed
- 'Hans Stam'   CCge
- 'Hillview Red'   CCge CElw EBee EBlw SHel
- subsp. *involucrata*   EBlw EHrv LRHS MBro MGGn
MTis NHol SCro SWat WFar
- - 'Barrister'   CBct CSam EBee EBlw GBuc SSpi
WFar WPGP
- - 'Canneman'   CBct CCge EBee EBlw EMon
EWes LPhx MAvo MBct NSti SCro
SMrm SOkh WCot
- - 'Margery Fish'   see A. *major* subsp. *involucrata*
'Shaggy'
- - 'Moira Reid'   EBee EBlw GBri NCot SHar WRus
- - 'Orlando'   EBlw
§ - - 'Shaggy' ♀ H4   More than 30 suppliers
- 'Lars'   More than 30 suppliers
- 'Lars' seedlings   GCal
- 'Maureen'   NOak
- 'Primadonna'   CBct CCge CHea CSam EBee
EBlw EChP EHrv EMan ERou
GSki MDNS MTis MWrn NArg
NHol NLar SCro SIgm SPlb SWal
WFar WMnd WMoo WPer WPnP
WViv WWeb
- 'Prockter'   WCra
- 'Roma' PBR   CBct CCge CHad COtt EBee EFou
EHrv EMan EMon LPhx MBri
MCAu MTed MWrn NBhm NCot
SUsu WAul WWeb
- var. *rosea*   More than 30 suppliers
- 'Rosensinfonie'   EBee EBlw GMaP GSki MBct
MSPs MWrn NBro NOak WFar
WMnd WMoo WViv
§ - 'Rubra'   More than 30 suppliers
- 'Ruby Cloud'   CBri CCge CHea CHid EBee
ECGN EChP EHrv EMan MCAu

	MNrw MSPs MWrn NSti SVil
	WCra WFoF WHil
– 'Ruby Wedding'	More than 30 suppliers
– 'Starburst'	EBee NCot WFar
– 'Sue Barnes' (v) **new**	EMon
§ – 'Sunningdale Variegated' (v) ♀ H4	More than 30 suppliers
– 'Titoki Point'	CBos EBlw WCot
– 'Variegata'	see *A. major* 'Sunningdale Variegated'
§ *maxima* ♀ H4	More than 30 suppliers
– 'Mark Fenwick'	NBir
* – *rosea*	NBir NGdn SDes SPet
minor	CPrp SSpi WCru
'Rainbow'	NLar WWeb
rubra	see *A. major* 'Rubra'
'Snow Star'	EHrv GBin MBri MWrn NSti
'Warren Hills' **new**	MWrn

Asyneuma (*Campanulaceae*)

canescens	ELan EMan MLLN WWin
limonifolium	SOkd
prenanthoides	EBee ELan MLwd
pulvinatum	CPBP EHyt

Asystasia (*Acanthaceae*)

bella	see *Mackaya bella*
§ *gangetica*	CSev
violacea	see *A. gangetica*

Athamanta (*Apiaceae*)

cretensis	LPhx
macedonica subsp. *arachnoidea*	EBee
– – JCA 224105	IDac
turbith	SIgm
– subsp. *haynaldii*	EBee ITer
vestina	CBos LPhx
– JCA 224300	SIgm SSpi

Athanasia (*Asteraceae*)

§ *parviflora*	GGar SPlb

Atherosperma (*Monimiaceae*)

moschatum	CBcs CPne WSHC

Athrotaxis (*Cupressaceae*)

cupressoides	CDul CKen MBar WCwm
laxifolia	CDoC CKen LCon MBar WCwm
selaginoides	CDoC CTrG EPot WCwm

Athyrium ✿ (*Woodsiaceae*)

'Branford Beauty' **new**	WRic
'Branford Rambler' **new**	WRic
drepanopterum	WRic
filix-femina ♀ H4	More than 30 suppliers
– var. *angustatum* 'Lady in Red' **new**	WRic
– 'Clarissimum'	WIvy WRic
* – *congestum cristatum*	CLAP WFib
– 'Corymbiferum'	GQui NHar NMar SRms
– 'Crispum Grandiceps Kaye'	SRms
– Cristatum Group	CLAP EBee EBlw EFer ELan EMon MMoz NHol SBla SWat WFib WRic
§ – Cruciatum Group	CBos CFwr CLAP CRDP CRow EBee EGol ELan EMar EMon EPfP MMoz MWgw NHar NHol NOGN NVic SLon SPer SRms WCru WFib WRic
– 'Fieldii'	CLAP CRow EFer NHar NHol SChu SRms WFib
– 'Frizelliae' ♀ H4	More than 30 suppliers
– 'Frizelliae Capitatum'	CLAP CRow NMar WFib WPGP
– 'Frizelliae Cristatum'	SRms
– 'Grandiceps'	EBee NHar NMar SRms
– 'Minutissimum'	CBos CFil CLAP CPlt CRDP EBee ECha EGol EHon ELan EMon LPBA MMoz NMar SBla WPGP
– 'Percristatum'	EMon
– Plumosum Group	CFil CLAP GBri GQui NMar WFib
– 'Plumosum Axminster'	CFil CRDP
– 'Plumosum Cristatum'	NMar
– 'Plumosum Percristatum'	GQui
– Ramocristatum Group	NMar
– 'Red Stern'	MMoz
– 'Rotstiel'	CLAP EBee WFar
– 'Setigerum Cristatum'	NMar
– 'Vernoniae' ♀ H4	CLAP ELan EMon LEur MWgw WRic
– 'Vernoniae Cristatum'	CLAP GBin NHol NMar SPer WFib
– Victoriae Group	see *A. filix-femina* Cruciatum Group
'Ghost' **new**	WRic
goeringianum 'Pictum'	see *A. niponicum* var. *pictum*
niponicum	SLdr
– f. *metallicum*	see *A. niponicum* var. *pictum*
§ – var. *pictum* ♀ H3	More than 30 suppliers
* – – 'Cristatoflabellatum'	CBos CLAP ELan EMon
– – 'Silver Falls' **new**	EFou
– – 'Ursula's Red' **new**	EFou MAvo
– – 'Wildwood Twist' **new**	MAvo
otophorum ♀ H4	CRDP EMon LEur NHol NMar NVic SChu SRms WPGP WRic
– var. *okanum*	CElw CFil CFwr CLAP CMHG CMil CPrp EBee EFer ELan EWTr GBin GCal LEur MAvo MBri NBlu NHar NHol SApp SNut SPar SRot WCru
'Rostiel' **new**	CFwr
vidalii	CLAP EBee MBri WRic

Atractylodes (*Asteraceae*)

japonica	EFEx
macrocephala	EFEx

Atragene see *Clematis*

Atriplex (*Chenopodiaceae*)

canescens	WDin
cinerea **new**	GGar
halimus	CBcs CBot CSLe ECha EHoe ENot IDee LRHS MBlu MBri MRav NLar SLon SPer SWat WCot WDin WHer WKif WPGP WTel
hortensis	MChe SPar
– gold-leaved	WCot WLHH
– var. *rubra*	CArn CHad CRDP CSpe EGra ELan EOHP MChe MHer NChi NDov SIde SUsu WCHb WCot WEas WHer WJek WKif WWpP WWye
portulacoides	see *Halimione portulacoides*

Atropa (*Solanaceae*)

bella-donna	CArn GBar GPoy IIve MGol MSal WWye
– var. *lutea*	IIve MSal
mandragora	see *Mandragora officinarum*

Atropanthe (*Solanaceae*)

§ *sinensis*	MSal

Aubrieta ✿ (*Brassicaceae*)

'Alba'	see *A.* 'Fiona'
albomarginata	see *A.* 'Argenteovariegata'

'Alix Brett' CMea CPBP EBre EDAr ELan LRHS NPer
'April Joy' ECho ECot ELan
§ 'Argenteovariegata' (v) CSpe ELan SBla SIgm SPar SRms
♀ H4 WWeb
'Astolat' (v) ECtt NLon SBla SRms WEas WPat
'Aureovariegata' (v) CMea EBre ECtt EDAr EGle ELan
♀ H4 GKir IHMH LRHS MHer NPer
NWCA SBla SIng WAbe WFar
'Belisha Beacon' ECho ECtt EMNN MBri
Bengal hybrids WGor
'Blaumeise' IHMH
§ 'Blue Beauty' CFai
'Blue Cascade' ECho ECtt EPfP GKir LPVe SPar
SPlb WGor
'Blue Emperor' MAvo
'Blue Midnight' EDAr
* 'Blue Mist' ECho EDAr
'Blue Sky' EDAr
§ 'Bob Saunders' (d) CMea EBre ECtt
'Bonfire' ECho
'Bressingham Pink' (d) CMea EBre ECho ECtt ELan LRHS
♀ H4
'Bressingham Red' EBre LRHS
campbellii new ECho
canescens subsp. WLin
cilicica new
Cascade Series MWgw NBlu WFar
'Claret Cascade' SPar
deltoidea 'Nana CLyd CMea EPot MTho WGor
Variegata' (v)
- Variegata Group (v) ECtt EPot GKir LHop LRHS MTho
NSla SIng WFar WLin WPat
'Doctor Mules' ♀ H4 EBre ECho EDAr GKir LRHS SIng
SRms WPat
'Doctor Mules CSpe EDAr EMlt LAst LGro MHer
Variegata' (v) NEgg NPri SIng
'Dream' SIng
'Elsa Lancaster' EHyt EMNN EPot
'Fiona' EDAr SIng
§ 'Frühlingszauber' GKir SRms WGor
glabrescens WAbe
MESE 536 new
'Gloriosa' CFai SIng
'Godstone' ECho
'Golden Carpet' SIng
'Golden King' see *A.* 'Aureovariegata'
* 'Graca' NPri
'Greencourt Purple' ECho EDAr ELan EMNN MWat
♀ H4 SIng WWin
'Gurgedyke' ECho ELan SIng SRms
'Hamburger Stadtpark' CWes ECho EDAr
'Harknoll Red' EPot
'Hartswood' SIng
Hemswell Purity ECho ECtt LRHS
= 'Snow Maiden' PBR
'Hendersonii' SRms
'J.S. Baker' SRms
'Joan Allen' EDAr
'Joy' (d) ECho EMNN SIng
'Leichtlinii' ECho NJOw WRHF
'Lemon and Lime' LRHS
'Lilac Cascade' ECho
'Little Gem' ECho
'Lodge Crave' SIng
macedonica EPot
'Maurice Prichard' EMNN LRHS
'Mrs Lloyd Edwards' ECho
'Mrs Rodewald' ♀ H4 ECho EDAr EMNN SRms
'Novalis Blue' SRms
'Oakington Lavender' ECho EDAr ELan
parviflora CStu
'Pike's Variegated' (v) ECho

pinardii EHyt
'Purple Cascade' CWib ECtt EMNN EPfP LRHS
NBlu NPro SCoo SPar SPlb SRms
WFar WGor
'Purple Charm' SRms
'Purple Emperor' SIng
'Red Carpet' EBre ELan EMNN EPot LGro LRHS
MAvo SIng SRms WWin
'Red Carpet CMea
Variegated' (v)
'Red Cascade' ♀ H4 CTri ECtt EMNN EPfP GKir NBlu
SCoo SPar SPlb
'Red Dyke' SIng
'Riverslea' SIng
'Rosanna Miles' SIng
'Rose Queen' CMea CPBP LBee LRHS SMrm
Royal Series MWgw
- 'Royal Blue' ECho LRHS MHer WMoo
- 'Royal Red' ESis MHer NPri SRms WFar WGor
WMoo
- 'Royal Violet' ECho LRHS MHer WPer
'Schofield's Double' see *A.* 'Bob Saunders'
'Silberrand' ECha ECtt EDAr NSla
'Somerfield Silver' SIng
'Somerford Lime' WPat WWeb
Spring Charm see *A.* 'Frühlingszauber'
= 'Frühlingszauber'
'Swan Red' (v) EPot
thessala CPBP
'Toby Saunders' ECho
'Triumphante' ECho FWll LRHS
'Wanda' ECho ELan SIng
'Whitewell Gem' SRms

Aucuba ✿ (Aucubaceae)

japonica (f) CCVT CDul EBee EWTr GKir
SMer
- (m) CBcs CHEx SReu
- 'Crassifolia' (m) CHig MRav SAPC SArc
- 'Crotonifolia' (f/v) More than 30 suppliers
♀ H4
- 'Dentata' CHEx WCru WWes
- 'Fructu Albo' (f/v) SPer
- 'Gold Dust' (f/v) LRHS
- 'Golden King' (m/v) CBcs CDoC CHEx CMac CTrw
♀ H4 CWib EBee ENot EPfP GKir LNet
LRHS MAsh MGos MWat SLim
SPln WFar WWeb
- 'Golden Spangles' (f/v) CBcs CDoC EBee ECot EPla
- 'Goldstrike' (v) EBee EHoc LNet WGer
- 'Lance Leaf' (m) SLon WCru
- f. *longifolia* ♀ H4 CHig CMac SAPC SArc SDix
WCru WStI
- - 'Salicifolia' (f) CHEx EBee ENot EPla LRHS MRav
SLon SMad SPer WBcn WCru
WDin WGer WPGP
- 'Maculata' hort. see *A. japonica* 'Variegata'
- 'Marmorata' EPla LRHS
- 'Nana Rotundifolia' (f) EPla WStl
- 'Pepperpot' (v) new CHEx MAsh
- 'Picturata' (m/v) CBcs CDul CHEx CMac CSBt
ENot EPfP EPla EVFa LRHS MRav
SAga SHBN SLim SPer WCFE WFar
- 'Rozannie' (f/m) ♀ H4 CBcs CDoC CSBt EBee ELan ENot
EPfP EPla EWTr GKir LRHS MAsh
MBlu MBri MGos MLan MRav
MWat NBee SLim SMad SPer SPla
SReu WDin WFar WStl
- 'Speckles' GSki
- 'Sulphurea Marginata' CBcs CDoC CMac EPla EVFa SPer
(f/v) WBcn WBod WGwG
§ - 'Variegata' (f/v) More than 30 suppliers
- Windsor form EPla LRHS MBri WWes

Aurinia (Brassicaceae)

§	**corymbosa**	LTwo
§	**saxatilis** ♀ H4	CAgr EBre GDra GKir MBar MWat
		NBlu SIng SPet SPlb WFar WRHF
		WTel
	– 'Citrina' ♀ H4	CHal ECha ECtt GMaP MWat
		SRms WCom
	– 'Compacta'	CTri EBre ECtt MBro NFla NLon
		WHoo
	– 'Dudley Nevill'	ECho EHol LRHS MWat SBla
	– 'Dudley Nevill	EBre ECha EWes LBee MHer NBir
	Variegated' (v)	SBla
	– 'Flore Pleno' (d)	EHol WCot
	– Gold Ball	see *A. saxatilis* 'Goldkugel'
	– 'Gold Dust'	ECtt LGro MOne SRms
	– 'Golden Queen'	ECtt MHer
§	– 'Goldkugel'	EMNN GKir IHMH LRHS SRms
	– 'Silver Queen'	WEas
	– 'Variegata' (v)	NPri SIng
	sinuata 'Pebbles' **new**	LRav

Austrocedrus (Cupressaceae)

§	**chilensis**	CKen CPne CTho

Austromyrtus (Myrtaceae)

§	**dulcis new**	ECou

Avena (Poaceae)

	candida	see *Helictotrichon sempervirens*
	sativa	SWal
	sterilis	SWal

Avenula see *Helictotrichon*

Averrhoa (Oxalidaceae)

	carambola (F)	NBlo XBlo

avocado see *Persea*

Ayapana see *Eupatorium*

Azalea see *Rhododendron*

Azara ✿ (Flacourtiaceae)

	from Chile	CPLG
	alpina	CFil
	– G&P 5015	WPGP
	dentata	CBcs CFil CHll CMac CPle EBee
		ERea GKir IDee LAst SBrw WPGP
		WSHC
	– 'Variegata' (v)	CWib ERea
*	**integerrima**	GQui
	integrifolia	CFil CRez IKee SBrw SLon WPGP
	– 'Variegata' (v)	CFil SBrw
	lanceolata	CBcs CFil CMCN CPLG CTri GKir
		ISea LAst LEdu NSti SBrw SPer
		WGer WPGP WPic
	– G 3502	WPGP
	microphylla ♀ H3	CBcs CChe CDul CFil CLnd
		CMCN CMHG CPle CSBt EPfP
		EPla GKir ISea LAst NSti SArc
		SBra SBrw SDry SPar SPer SSpi
		WBod WFar WPGP WSHC WTel
	– 'Variegata' (v)	CBcs CDoC CFil CMac CPle CSBt
		CWib EBee EHoe EPfP EVFa GQui
		ISea LAst MLan SBrw SSpi STre
		WCru WFar WGer WPGP WSHC
N	**paraguayensis**	GGar GKir ISea
	petiolaris	CFai CFil CPle EPfP GKir SBrw
		WGer WPic
	– G&P 5026	WPGP
	serrata ♀ H3	CDul CFil CMCN CPle CSBt CTbh

		CTrC CWib EPfP EPla GGar GKir
		IDee ISea SBrw SDix SPar SPer
		SRms SSta WBod WBor WCru
		WDin WFar WGer WHar WLRN
		WPGP WTel
	– 'Patagonica'	ISea
	uruguayensis	CFil CPLG EBee

Azolla (Azollaceae)

	caroliniana Willd.	see *A. filiculoides*
	caroliniana auct.	see *A. mexicana*
	non Willdenow	
§	**filiculoides**	CRow CWat EHon LPBA MSta
		NPer SCoo SWat WStI
§	**mexicana**	WWeb

Azorella (Apiaceae)

	compacta	SPlb
	filamentosa	ECou
	glebaria hort.	see *A. trifurcata*
	glebaria A.Gray	see *Bolax gummifera*
	gummifera	see *Bolax gummifera*
§	**trifurcata**	CPar CTri ECtt EPot GAbr GDra
		GEdr GKir GTou IHMH NLAp
		NWCA SBla SDys SIgm SIng WAbe
		WPer
	– 'Nana'	CNic GGar MBro MTho MWat
		NMen SDys WPat

Azorina (Campanulaceae)

§	**vidalii**	CBot CSpe EBee ERea ITer SAPC
		SAga SArc SVen
	– 'Rosea'	CKob

B

Babiana (Iridaceae)

	ACE 1	LRHS
	ambigua	CStu EGrW
	angustifolia	EGrW
	'Blue Gem'	LBow
	disticha	see *B. plicata*
	dregei	EGrW WCot
	ecklonii	WCot
	framesii new	CStu
	hybrids	EGrW LBow
	nana	CStu EGrW WCot
	odorata	WCot
	patula	LBow
§	**plicata**	SYvo WCot
	pulchra	EPot LBow
	pygmaea	WCot
	rubrocyanea	WCot
	sambucina new	CStu WCot
	sinuata	EGrW WCot
	striata	EMui
	stricta ♀ H1-2	EGrW LBow WCot
	– 'Purple Star'	ECho
	– 'Tubergen's Blue'	LBow
	thunbergii new	EGrW
	truncata	CStu EGrW WCot
	tubulosa	EGrW WCot
	vanzyliae	CStu EGrW WCot
	villosa	EGrW WCot
	'Zwanenburg's Glory'	WCot

Baccharis (Asteraceae)

	genistelloides	SMad WCot
	halimifolia	CBcs CPle CTrC GQui LRav

- 'Twin Peaks'	SDry
patagonica	GEil GGar LEdu LPhx SAPC SAga SArc SScr WKif
'Sea Foam'	EMan MGGn SBod SMad

Bacopa (Scrophulariaceae)

caroliniana	EBee EMan EOHP
'Snowflake'	see *Sutera cordata* 'Snowflake'

Baeckea (Myrtaceae)

densifolia **new**	ECou
virgata	CTrC ECou SBrw SPlb

Baillonia (Verbenaceae)

juncea	WSHC

Balbisia (Geraniaceae)

peduncularis	WFoF

Baldellia (Alismataceae)

ranunculoides	CRow EMFW EMan WMAq
- f. *repens*	CRDP EMan LHop

Ballota ❀ (Lamiaceae)

acetabulosa ♀ H3-4	EBee ECha EFou EGoo FMan EWes MGGn MWgw SDix SPar WCom WCot WWeb
'All Hallows Green'	CFee EBee EBlw EFou EGoo EMan EPfP GBuc GKir LAst LHop LRHS MWgw NGdn NSti SBla SChu SRPl
hirsuta	MGGn
nigra	CArn CPLG EBee GWCH MChe MGGn MHer MSal WHHs WMoo WWye
§ - 'Archer's Variegated' (v)	EBee EChP ECoo EGle EMan ERou EWes MBNS MGGn WCot WRus WSan
- 'Intakes White'	MGGn MInt
- 'Variegata'	see *B. nigra* 'Archer's Variegated'
- 'Zanzibar' (v)	EMon MGGn
pseudodictamnus ♀ H3-4	More than 30 suppliers
- 'Candia'	MGGn MSph SBla
- from Crete	ECha

Balsamita see *Tanacetum*

Balsamorhiza (Asteraceae)

sagittata	ECho

Bambusa ❀ (Poaceae)

glaucescens	see *B. multiplex*
gracilis	see *Drepanostachyum falcatum*
gracillima	COtt EPla
§ *multiplex*	EFul GKir LJus
- 'Alphonse Karr'	CDDB CFil COtt EBee GKir LJus LPal MMoz NMoo SDry
* - 'Elegans'	NMoo
§ - 'Fernleaf'	CHFx COtt EFul EPVP LJus SDry
- 'Golden Goddess'	NMoo
- 'Wang Tsai'	see *B. multiplex* 'Fernleaf'
textilis	WJun
ventricosa	NMoo SDry

banana see *Musa*

Banisteriopsis (Malpighiaceae)

caapi	MGol

Banksia (Proteaceae)

burdettii	SOWG
canei	CTrC SPlb

coccinea	SOWG
ericifolia	CTrC SOWG
grandis	CCtw CTrC SOWG
integrifolia	CBcs CCtw CTrC GQui
marginata	CTrC ECou SPlb
- mauve-flowered **new**	SOWG
media	CTrC SPlb
menziesii	CTrC
oblongifolia	SPlb
occidentalis	CCtw CTrC
paludosa	SPlb
robur	CTrC
serrata	CCtw SOWG
serratifolia	CPla
speciosa	CCtw CTrC SPlb
spinulosa var. *collina*	CCtw
- pink	SOWG
violacea	SPlb

Baptisia (Papilionaceae)

australis ♀ H4	More than 30 suppliers
- 'Caspian Blue' **new**	SPla
- 'Exaltata'	ELan GBuc LHop LRHS
- var. *minor*	LPVe LPhx
§ *bracteata*	SIgm
§ *lactea*	CMdw CPle EBee MGGn NBir SMac
leucantha	see *B. lactea*
leucophaea	see *B. bracteata*
pendula	EMan MCAu SIgm
'Purple Smoke' **new**	WCot
tinctoria	MSal

Barbarea (Brassicaceae)

praecox	see *B. verna*
rupicola	WPer
§ *verna*	CArn GPoy MHer WHer WWye
vulgaris 'Variegata' (v)	CArn CBrm CHal EBee EHoe ELan EMan EMon LDai MCAu MDun MWgw NBid NBro NCWG NOak NSti SWal WCHb WCot WMoo

Barleria (Acanthaceae)

repens	SOWG
suberecta	see *Dicliptera suberecta*

Barosma see *Agathosma*

Bartlettina see *Eupatorium*

Bashunia (Poaceae)

faheri Og 94053 **now**	EPla
§ *fargesii*	CDoC EPla ERod GKir MRav MWht SEND WJun
I *qingchengshanensis*	CFil EPla

basil see *Ocimum basilicum*

Bassia (Chenopodiaceae)

scoparia	MSal
- f. *trichophylla*	LPVe SPar

Basutica (Thymelaeaceae)

aff. *aberrans* JJ&JH 940178	NWCA

Bauera (Cunoniaceae)

rubioides var. *alba* **new**	ECou
- 'Candy Stripe' **new**	SOWG
- pink	ECou SOWG
- 'Ruby Glow' **new**	SOWG
sessiliflora	SOWG

Bauhinia (*Caesalpiniaceae*)
	alba	see *B. variegata*
	corymbosa	CPlN LRHS SOWG
	galpinii	CPlN SOWG SPlb
	monandra	SOWG WMul
	natalensis	SPlb
	tomentosa **new**	EShb
	vahlii	CPlN
§	variegata (v)	MGol WMul
	yunnanensis	SOWG

Baumea see *Machaerina*

bay see *Laurus nobilis*

Beaucarnea (*Agavaceae*)
stricta	EOas

Beaufortia (*Myrtaceae*)
micrantha	SOWG
orbifolia	SOWG
sparsa	CTrC SOWG
squarrosa **new**	SPlb

Beaumontia (*Apocynaceae*)
grandiflora	CPlN LRHS SOWG

Beauverdia see *Leucocoryne*

Beccariophoenix (*Arecaceae*)
madagascariensis	LPal

Beckmannia (*Poaceae*)
eruciformis	WRos

Bedfordia (*Asteraceae*)
salicina	ECou

Beesia (*Ranunculaceae*)
calthifolia **new**	EBee WCru
- DJHC 98447	CDes

Begonia ✿ (*Begoniaceae*)
	from Ruwenzori, Uganda	GCal
	'Abel Carrière'	CHal ER&R NShi WDib
	acerifolia	see *B. vitifolia*
	acetosa	ER&R
	acida	ER&R
	aconitifolia	ER&R
	acutifolia	ER&R NShi
	'Aladdin'	ER&R
	albopicta (C)	CHal EBak ER&R LRHS
	- 'Rosea'	CHal WDib
	alice-clarkiae	ER&R
	'Allan Langdon' (T)	CBla
	'Alleryi' (C)	ER&R NShi
	alnifolia	ER&R
	'Alto Scharff' ♀ H1	ER&R NShi
	'Alzasco' (C)	ER&R
	'Amigo Pink' (C) **new**	ER&R
	'Amigo Variegated' (v) **new**	ER&R
	ampla	ER&R
	'Amy' (T)	CBla
	angularis	see *B. stipulacea*
	'Anita Roseanna' (C)	ER&R
	'Ann Anderson' (C)	ER&R NShi
	'Anna Christine' (C)	ER&R
	'Anniversary' (T)	CBla
§	annulata	ER&R
	'Apollo' (T)	CBla
	'Apricot Delight' (T)	CBla
	'Aquarius'	ER&R

	'Arabian Sunset' (C)	ER&R
	'Argentea' (R)	EBak MBri
x	argenteoguttata (C)	CHal ER&R
	'Aries'	ER&R
	'Art Monday' **new**	NShi
	'Arthur Mallet'	ER&R
	'Aruba'	ER&R
	'Autumn Glow' (T)	ER&R
	'Avalanche' (T)	ER&R
	'Aya' (C)	WDib
	'Baby Perfection'	NShi WDib
	'Bahamas'	ER&R
	'Bantam Delight'	ER&R NShi
	'Barbara Ann' (C)	ER&R
	'Barbara Hamilton' (C) **new**	ER&R
	'Barbara Parker'	ER&R
	'Barclay Griffiths'	ER&R
	'Beatrice Haddrell'	CHal ER&R WDib
*	benichoma	WDib
	'Benitochiba' (R)	ER&R
	'Bernat Klein' (T)	CBla
	'Bess'	ER&R
	'Bessie Buxton'	ER&R NShi
	'Bethlehem Star'	ER&R WDib
§	'Bettina Rothschild' (R)	CHal ER&R NShi WDib
	'Beverly Jean'	ER&R
	'Big Mac' **new**	ER&R
	'Billie Langdon' (T)	CBla
	'Bill's Beauty'	ER&R
	'Bishop's Irish Eyes' **new**	NShi
	'Black Knight'	CHal NShi
	'Black Raspberry' (R)	ER&R NShi
	'Black Jack' (C)	ER&R
	'Blanc de Neige'	ER&R
	'Blue Vein' **new**	ER&R
	'Bokit'	ER&R WDib
	'Bonaire'	CHal
	'Boomer' (C)	ER&R
	'Botato' **new**	NShi
	'Bouton de Rose' (T)	NRog SDeJ
	bowerae	CHal ER&R LRHS
§	- var. nigramarga	ER&R
	'Boy Friend'	ER&R NShi
	bracteosa	ER&R
	brevirimosa	ER&R
	'Brown Twist'	WDib
	'Bunchii'	ER&R
	'Burgundy Velvet'	ER&R NShi WDib
	'Burle Marx' ♀ H1	CHal ER&R NShi WDib
	'Bush Baby'	CHal
	'Buttermilk' (C)	CBla
	'Calico Kew'	ER&R
	'Calla Queen' (S)	ER&R
	'Camelliiflora' (T)	NRog
	'Can-can' (R)	see *B.* 'Herzog von Sagan'
	'Can-can' (T)	CBla NShi
	'Carol Mac'	ER&R
	'Carol Wilkins of Ballarat' (T)	CBla
	'Carolina Moon' (R)	ER&R NShi
	carolineifolia	WDib
	carrieae	ER&R NShi
x	carrierei	see *B.* Semperflorens Cultorum Group
	'Cathedral'	ER&R NShi WDib
	'Cat's Paw'	SYvo
	'Chantilly Lace'	CHal ER&R
	chapaensis HWJ 642	WCru
	'Charles Chevalier'	ER&R
	'Charles Jaros'	ER&R
	'Charm' (S)	CHal ER&R WDib

'Cherry Jubiles' **new** NShi
'Chesson' **new** ER&R
'Chocolate Box' ER&R
'Chocolate Chip' ER&R
'Christine' **new** WWeb
'Christmas Candy' ER&R WDib
'Christy White' **new** NShi
'Chumash' ER&R NShi
'Clara' (R) MBri
'Cleopatra' ♀ H1 CHal ER&R MRav NShi WDib
'Clifton' ER&R
coccinea (C) ER&R WDib
compta see *B. stipulacea*
'Comte de Lesseps' (C) NShi WDib
conchifolia var. ER&R NShi
  rubrimacula
'Concord' ER&R
'Connee Boswell' ER&R WDib
convolvulacea ER&R
cooperi ER&R
'Coppelia' (T) CBla
'Cora Anne' ER&R
'Cora Miller' (R) ER&R
x *corallina* EBak
§ - 'Lucerna' (C) CHal EBak ER&R
  - 'Lucerna Amazon' (C) CHal IBlr
'Corbeille de Feu' CHal ER&R
'Cosie' **new** NShi
'Cowardly Lion' (R) ER&R NShi
'Cracklin' Rosie' (C) ER&R
crassicaulis ER&R
'Crestabruchii' ER&R
'Crimson Cascade' CBla
'Crystal Brook' **new** ER&R
* 'Crystal Cascade' CBla
cubensis ER&R
cucullata CHal ER&R
'Curly Fireflush' (R) ER&R
  new
'Curly Locks' (S) CHal
'Dale's Delight' (C) ER&R
'Dancin' Fred' ER&R
'Dancing Girl' ER&R
'Dannebo' MBri
'D'Artagnan' ER&R NShi
'David Blais' **new** NShi
'Dawnal Meyer' (C) ER&R WDib
'De Elegans' ER&R WDib
'Decker's Select' ER&R
decora ER&R
deliciosa ER&R
'Delray Silver' **new** NShi
'Dewdrop' (R) ER&R WDib
diadema ER&R
'Di-anna' (C) ER&R
dichotoma ER&R NShi
dichroa (C) ER&R
'Di-erna' ER&R
dietrichiana Irmsch. ER&R
'Digswelliana' ER&R
dipetala ER&R
discolor see *B. grandis* subsp. *evansiana*
domingensis ER&R
'Don Miller' ER&R
'Doublet Pink' ER&R
'Doublet Red' ER&R
'Doublet White' ER&R
'Douglas Nisbet' (C) ER&R
  new
'Dragon Wing' **new** NShi
dregei (T) ♀ H1 ER&R
  - var. *macbethii* NShi
  new

'Druryi' ER&R
'Dwarf Houghtonii' ER&R
* 'Ebony' (C) CHal ER&R NShi
echinosepala ER&R NShi
  - x *sanguinea* NShi
I 'Edinburgh Brevirimosa' ER&R
edmundoi ER&R
egregia ER&R
'Elaine' ER&R
'Elaine Ayres' (C) ER&R
§ 'Elaine Wilkerson' ER&R NShi
'Elaine's Baby' see *B.* 'Elaine Wilkerson'
'Elda' ER&R
'Elda Haring' (R) ER&R
'Elizabeth Hayden' ER&R
'Elsie M. Frey' ER&R
'Emerald Giant' (R) ER&R NShi WDib
'Emerald Isle' NShi
'Emma Watson' CHal ER&R
'Enchantment' ER&R
'Enech' ER&R
'English Knight' ER&R
'English Lace' ER&R
epipsila ER&R
x *erythrophylla* **new** NShi
  - 'Bunchii' ER&R
§ - 'Helix' CHal ER&R
'Essie Hunt' ER&R
'Esther Albertine' (C) CHal ER&R
  ♀ H1
'Eureka' (T) CBla
'Evening Star' ER&R
'Exotica' ER&R
'Fairy' ER&R NShi
'Fairylight' (T) CBla
feastii 'Helix' see *B.* x *erythrophylla* 'Helix'
fernando-costae ER&R
'Festiva' (T) CBla
§ 'Feuerkönigin' (S) ER&R
'Filigree' ER&R NShi
'Fire Flush' see *B.* 'Bertha Rothschild'
'Firedance' (T) CBla
'Fireworks' (R) ER&R WDib
'Five and Dime' ER&R
'Flamboyant' (T) ER&R
Flaming Queen see *B.* 'Feuerkönigin'
'Flamingo' ER&R NShi
'Flamingo Queen' ER&R
'Flo'Belle Moseley' (C) CHal ER&R WDib
'Florence Carrell' ER&R
'Florence Rita' (C) ER&R NShi
foliosa CHal ER&R WDib
  - var. *amplifolia* CHal ER&R NShi
§ - var. *miniata* 'Rosea' CDoC CHal LRHS
formosana B&SWJ WCru
  7041 **new**
'Freckles' (R) **new** ER&R
'Fred Bedson' ER&R NShi
friburgensis ER&R
'Friendship' **new** ER&R
'Frosty' (T) WDib
'Frosty Fairyland' ER&R
'Frosty Knight' ER&R NShi
'Fuchsifoliosa' ER&R
fuchsioides ♀ H1 CDoC EBak ER&R LIck MArl
  MOak SDix SYvo WDib
  - red **new** MOak WFar
  - 'Rosea' see *B. foliosa* var. *miniata*
  'Rosea'
'Full Moon' (T) CBla
'Fuscomaculata' ER&R
'Gay Star' **new** NShi
gehrtii ER&R

geranioides	ER&R	'Ivanhoe' (T)	CBla
glabra	ER&R	'Ivy Ever'	ER&R
glandulosa	ER&R	'Jade' **new**	NShi
glaucophylla	see *B. radicans*	'Jean Blair' (T)	CBla
'Glen Daniels' **new**	NShi	'Jelly Roll Morton'	ER&R
'Gloire de Sceaux'	ER&R	'Joe Hayden'	CHal ER&R
goegoensis	ER&R	'John Tonkin' (C)	ER&R
'Gold Cascade'	CBla	*johnstonii*	ER&R
'Gold Doubloon' (T)	CBla	'Joy Porter' **new**	NShi
'Goldilocks' (T)	CBla	'Jubilee Mine'	ER&R
'Good 'n' Plenty'	ER&R	'Jumbo Jeans'	ER&R
'Granada'	ER&R NShi	'Jumbo Jet' (C)	ER&R
§ *grandis* subsp.	CDoC CFwr CHEx CHal CTrC	'Kagaribi' (C)	ER&R
evansiana	CWCL EBee ELan EMan ER&R	*kellermanii* (C)	ER&R NShi
	GCal LEdu MLLN MOak MSte	'Kenlav-Ran' **new**	NShi
	MTho NCiC SDix SMad SMrm	'Kentwood' (C)	ER&R
	SSpi WCot WCru WFar WHen	*kenworthyae*	ER&R
– – B&SWJ 5702	WCru	*kingiana*	WDib
– subsp. *evansiana*	CDoC CHal EBee EMon ER&R	'Kit Jeans'	ER&R
var. *alba* hort.	GCal MOak MSte MTho SMad	'Kit Jeans Mounger'	ER&R
	SSpi WCot WPGP	'Kookaburra' (T)	CBla
– – 'Claret Jug'	CKno EMan WCot WPGP	'Krakatoa'	CBla
– 'Maria'	EBee WCot	'Kyoto' **new**	NShi
– 'Sapporo'	GCal MSte	'La Paloma' (C)	WDib
– 'Simsii'	WFar	'Lady Carol'	CHal
'Great Beverly'	ER&R	'Lady Clare'	ER&R
'Green Gold' (R)	NShi WDib	* 'Lady France'	ER&R MBri
'Green Lace' **new**	ER&R NShi	'Lady Rowena' (T)	CBla
'Grey Feather'	ER&R NShi	'Lady Snow'	CHal
griffithii	see *B. annulata*	'Lana' (C)	ER&R
'Gustav Lind' (S)	CHal ER&R	'Lancelot' (T)	CBla
'Guy Savard' (C)	NShi WDib	*langeana* **new**	NShi
'Gypsy Maiden' (T)	CBla	'Laurie's Love' (C)	ER&R
haageana	see *B. scharffii*	'Lawrence H. Fewkes'	ER&R
handelii	ER&R	*leathermaniae* (C)	ER&R
* 'Happy Heart'	ER&R	'Legia'	ER&R
* 'Harry's Beard'	ER&R NShi	'Lenore Olivier' (C)	ER&R
'Hastor'	ER&R	'Leopard'	ER&R MBri NShi
hatacoa	ER&R	'Lexington'	ER&R
– silver	CHal ER&R NShi	'Libor' (C)	ER&R
– spotted	ER&R	'Lillian' **new**	NShi
'Hazel's Front Porch' (C)	ER&R	'Lime Swirl'	ER&R
'Helen Lewis'	ER&R NShi	*limmingheana*	see *B. radicans*
'Helen Teupel' (R)	ER&R WDib	'Linda Dawn' (C)	ER&R
'Her Majesty' (R)	ER&R	'Linda Harley'	ER&R
heracleifolia var.	ER&R	'Linda Myatt'	ER&R
longipila		*lindeniana*	ER&R NShi
– var. *nigricans*	NShi	*listada* ♀ H1	CHal ER&R MBri WDib
– 'Wisley' **new**	NShi	'Lithuania'	ER&R
§ 'Herzog von Sagan' (T)	ER&R	'Little Brother	CHal ER&R NShi WDib
x *hiemalis* 'Elatior'	LRHS	Montgomery' ♀ H1	
hispida var.	ER&R	'Little Darling'	ER&R NShi
cucullifera		'Little Iodine'	NShi
'Holmes Chapel'	ER&R NShi	'Lois Burks' (C)	CHal ER&R WDib
homonyma (T)	ER&R	'Loma Alta'	ER&R
'Honeysuckle' (C)	ER&R	'Looking Glass' (C)	ER&R NShi WDib
'Hottentot' **new**	NShi	'Lospe-tu'	ER&R
hydrocotylifolia	ER&R	'Lou Anne'	CBla
hypolipara	ER&R	'Lubbergei' (C)	ER&R
(Illumination Series)	WWol	'Lucerna'	see *B.* x *corallina* 'Lucerna'
'Illumination Apricot'		'Lulu Bower' (C)	ER&R
– 'Illumination Rose'	SCoo WWol	*luxurians*	ER&R
– 'Illumination Salmon	SCoo	– 'Ziesenhenne'	ER&R
Pink' ♀ H2-3 **new**		*lyman-smithii*	ER&R
– 'Illumination White'	WWol	'Mabel Corwin'	ER&R NShi
imperialis	ER&R NShi	*macdougallii* var.	CHal NShi WDib
– x 'Bokit' **new**	NShi	*purpurea*	
incarnata (C)	ER&R	*macduffieana* **new**	NShi
– 'Metallica'	see *B. metallica*	*macrocarpa*	ER&R
'Ingramii'	ER&R	'Mac's Gold'	ER&R
'Interlaken' (C)	ER&R	*maculata* ♀ H1	ER&R
'Irene Nuss' (C) ♀ H1	ER&R NShi	– 'Wightii' (C)	CHal CSpe ER&R WDib
'Iron Stone' **new**	NShi	'Mad Hatter'	ER&R NShi

'Madame Butterfly' (C)	ER&R	
'Magic Carpet'	ER&R	
'Magic Lace'	ER&R NShi	
'Majesty' (T)	CBla	
manicata	ER&R WDib	
'Maphil'	MBri	
'Mardi Gras' (T)	CBla	
'Margaritae'	ER&R NShi	
'Marmaduke' ♀ H1	CHal WDib	
'Marmorata' (T)	LRHS NRog	
'Martha Floro' (C)	ER&R	
'Martin Johnson' (R)	ER&R NShi WDib	
'Martin's Mystery'	ER&R NShi	
masoniana ♀ H1	CHal ER&R ERea MOak NShi	
	WDib	
I 'Matador' (T)	CBla	
'Maurice Amey'	ER&R	
'Maverick'	ER&R	
maxima	ER&R	
mazae	ER&R	
'Medora' (C)	ER&R NShi	
'Melissa' (T)	CBla	
'Merry Christmas'	ER&R	
(R) ♀ H1		
metachroa	ER&R	
§ *metallica* ♀ H1	CHal ER&R	
meyeri-johannis	GCal	
'Midnight' **new**	NShi	
'Midnight Sun'	ER&R NShi	
'Midnight Twister'	ER&R	
'Mikado' (R)	ER&R	
minor	ER&R	
'Mirage' ♀ H1	ER&R NShi	
'Miss Priss' **new**	NShi	
mollicaulis	ER&R	
'Moon Maid'	ER&R	
* 'Moulin Rouge'	CBla	
'Mr Steve' (T)	CBla	
'Mrs Hashimoto' (C)	ER&R NShi	
'Mrs Shinkle' **new**	NShi	
multinervia	ER&R	
'Munchkin' ♀ H1	CHal ER&R WDib	
* 'Mystic'	ER&R	
'Mystique'	ER&R NShi	
'Nancy Cummings' **new**	ER&R	
natalensis (T)	ER&R	
'Nell Gwynne' (T)	CBla	
'Nelly Bly'	ER&R	
nelumbifolia	ER&R	
nigramarga	see *B. bowerae* var. *nigramarga*	
nigritarum **new**		
'Nokomis' (C)	ER&R NShi	
'Norah Bedson'	ER&R	
'Northern Lights' (S)	ER&R NShi	
obscura	ER&R	
'Obsession'	ER&R	
odorata	ER&R	
- var. *rosea*	NShi	
'Odorata Alba'	ER&R	
olbia	ER&R	
'Old Gold' (T)	ER&R	
'Oliver Twist'	ER&R	
'Ophelia' (T)	CBla	
'Orange Cascade' (T)	CBla	
'Orange Dainty'	ER&R	
'Orange Pinafore (C)'	ER&R	
new		
'Orange Rubra' (C) ♀ H1	CHal ER&R NShi	
'Orococo' **new**	NShi	
'Orpha C. Fox' (C)	ER&R	
'Orrell' (C)	ER&R	
'Othello'	ER&R	
'Otto Forster'	ER&R	

oxyphylla	ER&R	
paleata **new**	ER&R NShi	
palmata	CMdw GCal	
- from China	NShi	
- var. *palmata*	WCru	
B&SWJ 7175		
'Palomar Prince'	ER&R	
'Panasoffkee'	ER&R NShi	
'Pantaloon'	NShi	
'Panther'	ER&R	
'Papillon' (T)	ER&R	
paranaensis **new**	ER&R NShi	
* 'Parilis'	ER&R	
partita	ER&R	
'Passing Storm'	ER&R	
'Patricia Ogdon'	ER&R	
'Paul Harley'	ER&R	
'Paul Henry' **new**	NShi	
'Paul-bee'	ER&R	
paulensis	ER&R	
'Peach Parfait' (C)	ER&R	
pearcei	ER&R NShi	
'Pearl Ripple'	ER&R NShi	
'Pearls' (C)	ER&R	
'Peggy Stevens' (C)	ER&R	
peltata	ER&R	
* 'Penelope Jane'	ER&R	
'Persephone' (T)	CBla	
'Persian Brocade'	ER&R	
'Phil Corwin' **new**	NShi	
'Piccolo'	ER&R	
'Pickobeth' (C)	ER&R	
'Picotee' (T)	NRog	
'Pinafore' (C) ♀ H1	ER&R	
'Pink Basket' **new**	NShi	
'Pink Champagne' (R)	CBla NShi WDib	
'Pink Frosted' **new**	NShi	
'Pink Jade' **new**	NShi	
'Pink Nacre'	CHal ER&R NShi	
'Pink Parade' (C)	ER&R NShi	
'Pink Parfan' **new**	NShi	
'Pink Shasta' **new**	NShi	
'Pink Slate' **new**	NShi	
'Pink Spot Lucerne' (C)	ER&R NShi SYvo	
'Pink Taffeta' **new**	ER&R	
plagioneura	ER&R	
platanifolia var.	ER&R	
acuminatissima		
new		
'Plum Rose' **new**	ER&R	
polyantha	ER&R	
polygonoides	ER&R	
popenoei	ER&R	
'Posy Wahl' **new**	NShi	
'Potpourri'	ER&R	
'Président Carnot' (C)	ER&R SYvo	
'Pretty Rose' **new**	ER&R	
'Preussen'	ER&R NShi	
'Primrose' (T)	CBla	
'Princess of	ER&R	
Hanover' (R)		
prismatocarpa	ER&R	
procumbens	see *B. radicans*	
pustulata 'Argentea'	ER&R NShi	
'Queen Mother' (R)	ER&R NShi	
'Queen Olympus'	ER&R WDib	
'Quinebaug'	ER&R	
§ *radicans* ♀ H1	CHal ER&R LRHS MBri NShi	
'Raquel Wood'	ER&R	
'Raspberry Swirl' (R)	CHal ER&R WDib	
♀ H1		
ravenii	WCot	
- B&SWJ 1954	WCru	

	– from China	NShi
	'Raymond George Nelson' ♀ H1	CHal ER&R NShi
	'Razzmatazz' (R)	NShi WDib
	'Red Berry' (R)	ER&R NShi
	'Red Planet'	ER&R NShi WDib
	'Red Reign'	ER&R NShi
	'Red Robin' (R)	NShi WDib
	'Red Spider'	ER&R NShi
	'Red Wing' **new**	NShi
	'Regal Minuet' (R)	WDib
	'Regalia'	ER&R
	'Reine des Neiges' (R)	NShi
	rex	LRHS MBri MRav
	'Richard Robinson'	ER&R
	'Richmondensis'	ER&R
	'Ricinifolia'	ER&R
	'Ricky Minter' ♀ H1	ER&R NShi
	'Rip van Winkle'	ER&R
	'Robert Blais' **new**	NShi
	'Robin' (R)	ER&R
	'Robin's Red' (C)	ER&R
	'Roi de Roses' (R)	ER&R
	roxburghii	ER&R NShi
	'Roy Hartley' (T)	CBla
	'Royal Lustre'	ER&R
	'Royalty' (T)	CBla
	'Rubacon'	ER&R
	rubro-setulosa	ER&R NShi
	'Saber Dance' (R)	ER&R NShi
	'Sachsen'	ER&R
	salicifolia (C)	ER&R
	sanguinea	ER&R NShi
	'Scarlet Pimpernel' (T)	CBla
	'Scarlett O'Hara' (T)	CBla ER&R
	'Sceptre' (T)	CBla
	scharffiana	ER&R
§	*scharffii*	CHal EBak ER&R SDix
	'Scherzo'	CHal ER&R WDib
	'Scottish Star' **new**	NShi
	'Sea Coral' (T)	CBla
	'Sea Serpent' **new**	NShi
	semperflorens hort.	see *B.* Semperflorens Cultorum Group
§	Semperflorens Cultorum Group	MBri
	– double (d)	CHal
	'Serlis'	ER&R
	serratipetala	CHal EBak ER&R MBri NShi WDib
*	*sheperdii*	CHal WDib
	'Shiloh' (R)	ER&R
	'Shoppy' **new**	NShi
	'Sierra Mist'	ER&R
	'Silver Cloud' (R)	ER&R NShi WDib
*	'Silver Dawn'	ER&R NShi
	'Silver Jewell'	NShi WDib
	'Silver Lace' **new**	NShi
	'Silver Mist' (C)	ER&R
	'Silver Points'	ER&R
	'Silver Queen' (R) ♀ H1 **new**	NShi
	'Silver Sweet' (R)	ER&R NShi
	'Silver Wings'	ER&R NShi
	'Sinbad' (C)	ER&R
	sinensis	WCot
*	'Sir Charles'	ER&R
	'Sir John Falstaff'	ER&R NShi
	Skeezar Group	ER&R
	– 'Brown Lake'	ER&R
	'Snowcap' (S) ♀ H1	ER&R NShi WDib
	socotrana	ER&R
	solananthera ♀ H1	CHal ER&R WDib
	solimutata **new**	NShi

	sonderiana	ERea
	'Sophie Cecile' (C) ♀ H1	CHal ER&R NShi
	'Sophie's Jenny' **new**	NShi
	'Speculata' (R)	ER&R
	'Spellbound'	ER&R WDib
	'Spindrift'	ER&R NShi
	'Spotches'	ER&R
	'Stained Glass' (R)	WDib
§	*stipulacea*	CHal ER&R NShi
	subvillosa (S)	ER&R
	'Sugar Candy' (T)	CBla
	'Sun God' **new**	NShi
	'Superba Azella' **new**	NShi
	sutherlandii ♀ H1	CAvo CHEx CHal EBak EOHP ER&R ERea ERos LRHS MOak NBir NPer SDix SYvo WCot WCru WDib WEas WFar WHer
	– 'Papaya'	CSpe
	'Swan Song'	ER&R
	'Sweet Dreams' (T)	CBla
	'Sweet Magic'	CHal ER&R
	'Sweet Majic' **new**	NShi
	'Swirly Top' (C)	ER&R
	'Sylvan Triumph' (C)	ER&R
	'Tahiti' (T)	CBla
	'Tapestry' (R)	ER&R NShi
*	*taya*	WDib
	'Tea Rose'	ER&R NShi
	'Tequest' **new**	NShi
	teuscheri (C)	ER&R
	'Texastar'	ER&R NShi WDib
	'The Wiz'	ER&R
	thelmae	ER&R
	'Think Pink' **new**	NShi
	'Thumotec' **new**	ER&R
	'Thunderclap'	CHal ER&R
	'Thurstonii' ♀ H1	CHal ER&R NShi
	'Tiger Paws' ♀ H1	CHal ER&R MBri MOak NShi
	'Tingley Mallet' (C)	ER&R
	'Tiny Bright' (R)	ER&R NShi
	'Tiny Gem'	ER&R
	'Tom Ment' (C)	ER&R
	'Tom Ment II' (C)	ER&R
	'Tondelayo' (R)	ER&R NShi
	'Tornado' **new**	NShi
*	'Tribute'	ER&R
	tripartita (T)	ER&R WDib
	'Twilight' **new**	ER&R NShi
	'Two Face'	ER&R WDib
	ulmifolia	ER&R
	undulata (C)	CHal ER&R NShi
	'Universe'	ER&R
	'Venetian Red' **new**	NShi
	venosa	CHal ER&R NShi
	'Venus'	CHal ER&R
	'Vera Wyatt' **new**	NShi
	x *verschaffeltii*	ERea
	versicolor **new**	ER&R
	'Vesuvius'	NShi WDib
	'Viaudii'	ER&R
	'Viau-Scharff'	ER&R
§	*vitifolia*	ER&R
	'Wally's World' **new**	NShi
	'Weltoniensis'	ER&R
	'Weltoniensis Alba' (T)	ER&R
*	'White Cascade'	ER&R
	'Witch Craft' (R)	ER&R NShi
	'Withlacoochee'	ER&R WDib
	wollnyi	ER&R
	'Wood Nymph' (R)	ER&R NShi
	'Yellow Sweety' (T)	CBla
	'Zuensis'	ER&R

'Zulu' (T)   CBla

Belamcanda (Iridaceae)

chinensis	CArn CBro EBee EChP ECha EMan GEdr GPoy LRHS MAvo MLLN MSal SMac SPlb SYvo WBrE WCFE WCru WLun WPer WWye
- 'Hello Yellow'	GBuc MSte

Bellevalia (Hyacinthaceae)

dubia	WCot
forniculata	EHyt GTou
gracilis	WCot
hyacinthoides new	CStu WCot
longipes new	WCot
longistyla	WCot
§ paradoxa	CHar CPLG CPom EChP EHrv EHyt EMan EPar EPyc ERos GCal LTwo MAvo MSPs NRog WCot
pycnantha hort.	see B. paradoxa
romana	CNic ERos MTho NRog WCot WHil
tabriziana	ERos

Bellis (Asteraceae)

perennis	CKin NBlu NSco
- 'Alba Plena' (d)	ECho ELan
- 'Alice'	SUsu
- 'Dresden China'	ELan GAbr MTho NBlu SIng WAlt WCot WOut
- Hen and Chickens	see B. perennis 'Prolifera'
- 'Hullavington' new	CNat
- 'Jocelyn Castle' (d)	WAlt
- 'Lower Minety' (v)	CNat
- 'Maxiskirt'	WAlt
- 'Miniskirt'	WAlt
- 'Miss Mason'	GAbr WBro WRus
- 'Orkney Broccoli'	WAlt
- 'Orkney Cauliflower'	WAlt
- 'Parkinson's Great White'	GAbr
§ - 'Prolifera'	WAlt WHer
- 'Robert'	GAbr
- 'Rusher Rose'	EPfP
- 'Single Blue'	see B. rotundifolia 'Caerulescens'
- 'Tasso Strawberries & Cream' new	WRHF
- 'Upper Scagry'	CNat WAlt
§ rotundifolia	CElw CNic ELan GAbr NBir NBro
'Caerulescens'	NMGW WOut

Bellium (Asteraceae)

bellidioides	GEdr
* crassifolium canescens	CRDP WPer
minutum	ESis MTho

Beloperone see Justicia

Bensoniella (Saxifragaceae)

oregona	EBee EMon

Berberidopsis (Flacourtiaceae)

beckleri	CFil
corallina	More than 30 suppliers

Berberis ✿ (Berberidaceae)

ACE 2237	EPot
aetnensis new	GIBF
aggregata	EPla GKir MNrw NBir SPer SRms WDin
amurensis	IIve
- 'Flamboyant'	WBcn
- var. latifolia B&SWJ 4353	WCru
x antoniana	ESis LRHS MBri WBcn
aquifolium	see Mahonia aquifolium
- 'Fascicularis'	see Mahonia x wagneri 'Pinnacle'
N aristata	CAgr CArn CMCN SMrm
asiatica new	GPoy
atrocarpa	CPle
bealei	see Mahonia japonica Bealei Group
bergmanniae	SLPl
'Blenheim'	WFar
'Boughton Red'	MBri
brevipedunculata Bean	see B. prattii
x bristolensis	EPla MBri SLon SPla SRms
buxifolia	CPle MRav SDes WCFE
- 'Nana' hort.	see B. buxifolia 'Pygmaea'
N - 'Pygmaea'	CAbP CSBt CTri CWib EBee EMil ENot GGar GKir LRHS MAsh MBNS MBar MBri MRav NHol SLim SMer SPer STre WCom WDin WFar WStI
calliantha	CPle WBcn WFar
candidula	CSBt EBee EBre ENot EPfP GKir LAst MBar MGos MRav NFor NHol SLon SPer WDin WGwG WStI
- 'Jytte'	see B. 'Jytte'
x carminea 'Barbarossa'	SPer WDin
- 'Buccaneer'	ENot EPfP GKir
- 'Pirate King'	EBee ENot LRHS MBri MRav SPer WPat
chrysosphaera	WFar
§ concinna	IMGH
CC 3302	CPLG
cooperi new	GIBF
coxii	GGar WCwm
darwinii ♥ H4	More than 30 suppliers
dictyophylla ♥ H4	CFil CPMA CPle EPfP EPla MGos NLar NSti SLon SPer SSpi WCwm WDin WGer WPGP WPat WSHC
dulcis 'Nana'	see B. buxifolia 'Pygmaea'
empetrifolia	CPle NLon
erythroclada	see B. concinna
'Fireball'	CMac
franchetiana var. macrobotrys new	GIBF
francisci-ferdinandii	SMad
x frikartii 'Amstelveen' ♥ H4	CDoC CMac CSBt CSam EBee EBre ELan ENot EPfP GKir LAst MBNS MRav SDes WDin WFar
- 'Telstar'	CSBt EBee ENot LAst LBuc MBri MRav NPro SDes WStI
gagnepainii hort.	see B. gagnepainii var. lanceifolia
gagnepainii C.K. Schneid.	CMac GKir MRav NLon SLPl SPar WBVN WGwG WTel
- 'Fernspray'	EPfP EPla GKir LRHS MBri MRav SBod SRms WBod
§ - var. lanceifolia	CBcs CTri ENot EPla GKir MBar MDun MGos MWhi NHol NWea WDin WFar WLRN WWal
- 'Purpurea'	see B. x interposita 'Wallich's Purple'
'Georgei' ♥ H4	CMHG CWib EPfP GKir LRHS SMur SSpi WBcn
gilgiana	CPLG
glaucocarpa	EPfP EPla NHol
'Goldilocks'	CAbP CFil CPMA EPfP GKir LAst LRHS MBlu MBri SPoG SSpi WBcn WGer
gyalaica	GIBF

hookeri	GKir	
- var. *latifolia*	see *B. manipurana*	
x *hybridogagnepainii*	ELan SPer	
'Chenaultii'		
hypokerina	CMac	
insignis	WFar	
- subsp. *insignis*	WCru	
var. *insignis*		
B&SWJ 2432		
§ x *interposita*	CDoC EBee ENot EPfP MBar MDun	
'Wallich's Purple'	MRav NHol SPer WDin WLRN WStI	
jamesiana	CMac SLon WCFE	
julianae ♀ H4	CBcs CSBt EBee ELan ENot EPfP	
	EWTr GKir LAst MBar MGos	
	MRav NBee NLon NWea SHBN	
	SHFr SLPl SPer WDin WFar WHCG	
	WHar WSHC WTel	
- 'Mary Poppins'	LRHS MBri WSPU	
§ 'Jytte'	EBee MRav MWhi WDin	
kawakamii	CPle SLPl	
knightii	see *B. manipurana*	
koehneana	CPle	
koreana	CFil CMCN EPfP EPla GIBF WCom	
	WPGP	
- 'Red Tears'	LRHS	
lecomtei **new**	GIBF	
lempergiana	CMCN	
lepidifolia	GBin	
linearifolia	CMac WPat	
- 'Orange King'	CBcs CDoC CMac EBee ELan ENot	
	EPfP GKir LRHS MAsh MGos NBee	
	NHol SHBN SIgm SPer SSta WDin	
	WFar WHar WPat WStI WWeb	
'Little Favourite'	see *B. thunbergii* 'Atropurpurea	
	Nana'	
x *lologensis*	MGos NHol WDin	
- 'Apricot Queen' ♀ H4	CBcs CMac EPfP GKir LRHS MAsh	
	MGos NBea NBee NEgg SHBN	
	SPer WDin WStI	
- 'Mystery Fire'	CDoC COtt GKir LRHS MAsh	
	MBar MBlu MBri MGos NBlu NEgg	
	NHol SCoo WDin WFar WHar	
- 'Stapehill'	ELan EPfP GKir LRHS MAsh MBri	
	SSpi WBcn	
lycium	CAgr WHCr	
- CC 1729	CPLG	
macrosepala var.	WCru	
macrosepala		
B&SWJ 2124		
§ *manipurana*	ENot	
x *media* Park Jewel	see *B.* x *media* 'Parkjuweel'	
§ - 'Parkjuweel'	CBcs EBee ENot EPfP GKir IArd	
	MHFa MRav WDin WFar	
§ - 'Red Jewel' ♀ H4	CChe CDoC CMac EBee EBre	
	EPfP LRHS MBri MGos MWat	
	NBee NHol NPro SPer WBod	
	WDin WFar WGwG WMoo WWal	
montana	WPat	
morrisonensis	CFil WCom WPGP	
morrisonicola **new**	GIBF	
aff. *nepalensis* **new**	GIBF	
nummularia	GIBF	
x *ottawensis*	MWhi WStI	
- 'Auricoma'	EBee LRHS MAsh MBri MRav	
- f. *purpurea*	CWib EBee GKir MBri MGos SBod	
	WDin WHar	
§ - - 'Superba' ♀ H4	More than 30 suppliers	
§ - 'Silver Miles' (v)	EHoe EPfP LNet LRHS MBri	
	MCCP MRav NBee NHol SPoG	
	WBVN WFar WPat	
§ *panlanensis*	EBee ENot MBar MRav SLon WWes	
patagonica	NLon	
poiretii	NBhm	

§ *polyantha* hort.	see *B. prattii*	
§ *prattii*	CMHG CPle MBri MWat	
pruinosa	CFil	
'Red Tears'	CPMA CSam MBlu MBri MGos	
	MLan SPer WGwG WHCG	
'Rubrostilla'	GKir NLon	
x *rubrostilla* 'Cherry	CMac	
Ripe'		
- 'Wisley'	EPfP LRHS	
sanguinea hort.	see *B. panlanensis*	
sargentiana	CPle NFor NLon SLPl	
sherriffii	WCwm	
sieboldii	WPat	
x *stenophylla* ♀ H4	More than 30 suppliers	
- 'Autumnalis'	SDes	
- 'Claret Cascade'	EBee EPfP GKir LRHS MAsh MBri	
	MGos NHol SPer WBod WDin	
	WFar WGwG	
- 'Corallina'	WBcn	
- 'Corallina Compacta'	CFee CLyd ELan EPfP EPot ESis	
♀ H4	GKir LHop LRHS MAsh MBro NHol	
	NRya SChu SIng SPer SRms WPat	
- 'Cornish Cream'	see *B.* x *stenophylla* 'Lemon	
	Queen'	
- 'Crawley Gem'	CMHG ESis LRHS MBar MBri MGos	
	NHol WDin WFar WLRN WStI	
- Cream Showers	see *B.* x *stenophylla* 'Lemon	
	Queen'	
- 'Etna'	ELan LRHS MAsh	
- 'Irwinii'	CMHG CMac CSBt CTri GKir LAst	
	MBar MGos NHol SDes SLon SPer	
	WDin WFar WTel	
N - 'Lemon Queen'	SMer SPer WTel	
- 'Nana'	SRms	
- 'Pink Pearl' (v)	CMHG LBuc LRHS MGos	
temolaica ♀ H4	CFil CPMA ENot EPfP GKir ISea	
	LRHS NEgg SPer SSpi SSta WDin	
	WPat	
- SF 95186	ISea	
thunbergii ♀ H4	CDoC CSBt ENot GBin GKir LBuc	
	MRav NWea SMer SPer SPlb WBod	
	WDin WFar WStI	
- f. *atropurpurea*	CBcs CPle CTri EBee EBre ENot	
	EPfP EWTr GKir LAst LBuc MBar	
	MGos MWat NBee NBlu NFor	
	NWea SGar SPer WBod WDin	
	WFar WMoo WStI WWin	
§ - 'Atropurpurea Nana'	More than 30 suppliers	
♀ H4		
- 'Atropurpurea Superba'	see *B.* x *ottawensis* f. *purpurea*	
	'Superba'	
- 'Aurea'	More than 30 suppliers	
- 'Bagatelle' ♀ H4	CDoC COtt EBee EBre ECtt ELan	
	EMil ENot EPfP EPot ESis GKir IArd	
	LHop LRHS MAsh MBar MBri MGos	
	MRav MTis NBee SLim SPar SPer	
	WCFE WCom WDin WPat WWeb	
- Bonanza Gold	CAbP CBcs CDoC COtt EBee	
= 'Bogozam' PBR	ELan ENot EPfP LRHS MAsh MRav	
	NLar SMur WDin WWeb	
- 'Carmen'	LRHS MGos	
- 'Carpetbagger'	WHar	
- 'Crimson Pygmy'	see *B. thunbergii* 'Atropurpurea	
	Nana'	
- 'Dart's Purple'	LRHS MAsh MBri WFar	
- 'Dart's Red Lady'	CPLG CSBt CWib EBee EBre ECtt	
	ELan ENot EPfP ESis GKir LRHS	
	MAsh MBri MRav NPro SLim SPar	
	SPer SPla WDin WFar WPat	
- 'Erecta'	CMac EBee ENot EPfP ESis LRHS	
	MBar MGos MRav SDes SPer	
	WBod WCFE WDin	
- 'Golden Ring' ♀ H4	More than 30 suppliers	

	– 'Golden Torch' **new**	MBri WWeb
	– 'Green Carpet'	EBre ENot GKir LHop LRHS MBar MRav
	– 'Green Mantle'	see *B. thunbergii* 'Kelleriis'
	– 'Green Marble'	see *B. thunbergii* 'Kelleriis'
	– 'Harlequin' (v)	More than 30 suppliers
	– 'Helmond Pillar'	More than 30 suppliers
§	– 'Kelleriis'	CDoC CSev EPfP GKir MBar NPro SLon SPoG SRms WDin WFar WStI
	– 'Kobold'	EBee ENot EPfP ESis GKir LHop LRHS MAsh MBar MBri MGos MRav NHol SLim SPer SPla WFar WLRN WStI
	– 'Pink Queen' (v)	EBee ENot EPfP LAst MAsh MGos MHFa MRav SPar WDin WHar WPat
	– 'Pow-wow'	CBcs MBri MGos MMil NLar WBcn
	– 'Red Chief' ♀ H4	CBcs CMHG EBee EBre ECtt EGra ELan ENot EPfP GKir LRHS MGos MRav MWat SDes SLim SLon SPer SPla SRPl WDin WFar WHCG WHar WPat WStI WTel WWeb
	– 'Red King'	EBee MRav WDin
	– 'Red Pillar'	CChe CDoC CPle EBee EBre EHoe ELan GKir LRHS MAsh MBar MBri MGos MWat NDlv NHol SHBN SPla WDin WFar WGwG WPat WStI
	– 'Red Rocket'	EMil
	– 'Rose Glow' (v) ♀ H4	More than 30 suppliers
	– 'Silver Beauty' (v)	CMHG EBee ELan LRHS MGos WDin
	– 'Silver Carpet' **new**	NLar
	– 'Silver Mile'	see *B. x ottawensis* 'Silver Miles'
	– 'Somerset'	CMac
*	– 'Tricolor' (v)	CMac EHoe NHol WFar WPat WSHC
	tischleri var. ***abbreviata* new**	GIBF
	tsangpoensis	SLPl
	valdiviana	CFil EPfP EPla IArd SMad SSpi WPGP
	veitchii	SLPl
	verruculosa ♀ H4	CBcs EBee ENot EPfP GKir LAst MBar MGos MRav NFor NHol NLon NWea SGar SPer SRms WCFE WDin WFar WGwG WWal
	virescens B&SWJ 2646D **new**	WCru
	vulgaris	CArn CNat GPoy IIve
	– 'Wiltshire Wonder' (v)	CNat
	wardii	CPle
	wilsoniae	CAgr CBcs CFil CPle EBee EBre ENot EPfP EPla EWTr GFil MBar MWhi NLon NWea SHBN SPer WCFE WDin WFar
	– ACE 1847	EPot
	– ACE 2462	EHyt
	– L 650	WPGP
	– blue	GKir LRHS MBri NPro WBcn WFar WGer
	– 'Graciella'	EPla LRHS MBri NPro
	– var. *guhtzunica*	EPla EWes

Berchemia (*Rhamnaceae*)

racemosa	CPlN WSHC
scandens	CPlN

bergamot see *Citrus bergamia*

Bergenia ✿ (*Saxifragaceae*)

'Abendglocken'	ECGP ECha ECtt EGle EPfP GKir LGro LRHS MBri MWat MWgw NGdn NHol NSti SChu SWat WEas WFar

§	'Abendglut'	More than 30 suppliers
	'Admiral'	CBct ECha SDes
*	*agavifolia*	CBct
	'Autumn Magic' **new**	SPoG
	'Baby Doll'	COtt EBre ECha EGle EPla EWTr GKir GSki LHop LRHS MRav MSte NBir NEgg NOrc NPer NPro NSti SDes SMrm SPar SPla WCot WFar WMnd WRus WViv
	'Bach'	SSpi
§	'Ballawley' ♀ H4	CFir ECha ENot IBlr MRav NVic SSpi SWat WCot
	'Ballawley Guardsman'	EHrv ERou MTed
N	Ballawley hybrids	EPar GKir LGro NSti SDix SPer SWat WCot
	'Bartók'	SSpi
	beesiana	see *B. purpurascens*
	'Beethoven'	CBct CDes CLAP CPlt EBee ECha EGle EPla EVFa IGor MRav MTed NBir NPar SSpi SWat WCot WPGP WViv
	Bell Tower	see *B.* 'Glockenturm'
	'Bizet'	MTed SSpi
	'Brahms'	SSpi
	'Bressingham Bountiful'	CBct GKir SDes SPer WCot
	'Bressingham Ruby' PBR	CKno EBee EBre ECGP ECha GKir LRHS MRav MTed NBir SDes SHBN SWat WCot WPGP
	'Bressingham Salmon'	CHar EBee EGle ELan ENot EPfP ERou GMaP GSki LRHS MBri MRav NLar SDes SHBN SPer WCot WMnd WWeb
	'Bressingham White' ♀ H4	More than 30 suppliers
	'Britten'	CMac LPio SSpi
	ciliata	CDes CFee CHEx CKno CLAP CMGP CMil EBee EChP EPfP GCal LEdu MRav MSte NBir NHol NLar SBla SDix SPer SSpi SUsu WCot WEas WKif WPGP WPer
	– f. *ligulata*	CHEx CLAP EBee ECha LEdu MWgw NBid NBir NSti SSpi WCot
	– – B&SWJ 2693	WCru
	– – CC 3616	ITer WCot
	– – ex CC 2049	MDCh
	– 'Wilton'	WCot
	ciliata x *crassifolia*	see *B.* x *schmidtii*
	'Claire Maxine'	GCal
	cordifolia	More than 30 suppliers
	– 'Flore Pleno' **new**	EBee
	– 'Purpurea' ♀ H4	CBcs CDoC EBee ECha ELan ENot EPfP GKir GSki LBuc LGro LRHS MCLN MHFa MRav NBir SDes SDix SHBN SPar SPer SPla SRms SWat WPnP
	– 'Redstart'	NOak
	– 'Tubby Andrews' (v)	CRDP EGle GBri MLLN NEgg NLar NPro WHil
	– 'Winterglut'	GMaP IBal LPVe WHil WWeb
	crassifolia	EMan EPla SRms
	– DF 90028	EMon
	– 'Autumn Red'	EBee ECha
	– 'Orbicularis'	see *B.* x *schmidtii*
	– var. *pacifica*	CFil EBee GIBF
*	*cyanea*	WCot
	'David'	EMon EWes MTed
	delavayi	see *B. purpurascens* var. *delavayi*
	'Delbees'	see *B.* 'Ballawley'
	'Eden's Dark Margin'	EBee EFou EMan SSpe WAbe
	'Eden's Magic Carpet' **new**	CFir
	'Eden's Magic Giant'	EBee EChP EMan
	emeiensis	CDes EBee

	– hybrid	MWat
	'Eric Smith'	CBct CLAP EBee ECha EPar GCal MTed WCot
	'Eroica'	CBct CSpe EBee EChP ECha ELan EMan EMon GBin MBri MCAu NSti SDes SWat WMnd
	'Evening Glow'	see *B.* 'Abendglut'
§	'Glockenturm'	GCal
	'Herbstblute' **new**	EBee EMon
	'Jo Watanabe'	ECha
	'Lambrook'	see *B.* 'Margery Fish'
§	'Margery Fish'	SPer
	milesii	see *B. stracheyi*
§	'Morgenröte' ♀ H4	CBcs CMGP EBee ECha EMil EPfP GKir LRHS MRav NHol NSti SDes SHBN SPar SPer SRms SWat WCFE WCot
	'Morning Light' **new**	NPro
	Morning Red	see *B.* 'Morgenröte'
	'Mozart'	CLAP
	'Mrs Crawford'	CBct ECha
	'Oeschberg'	EMon MCAu
	'Overture'	MCAu WCot WFar
	'Perfect'	EBee WMnd WWeb
	'Pinneberg' **new**	EBee
	'Profusion'	SDes SPer
	'Pugsley's Pink'	ECha LPio SHBN
§	*purpurascens* ♀ H4	CBrm CMac ECha EWTr GDra GKir GMaP GSki NFla SDix SPar SPer SSpi WCot WWin
	– ACE 2175	WCot
	– CC 3285	WCot
	– SDR 1629	GKev
	– 'Ballawley'	see *B.* 'Ballawley'
§	– var. *delavayi* ♀ H4	SRms WPnP
	– – CLD 1366	WPer
	aff. *purpurascens* ACE 2175	WCot
	'Purpurglocken'	GCal
	'Rosette'	LPio
	'Rosi Klose'	EBee EChP ECha EMon EWes GAbr GBin GCal MBri MRav SBla WCot WViv
	'Rotblum'	EBee ECtt EPla GBin GMaP GSki GWCH LAst MDun NBir NGdn NOrc NPri NVic SDes WFar WPer WRHF WWeb
§	x *schmidtii* ♀ H4	CMac EBee ENot EWll NBir NFla SDes SDix WCot
	'Schneekissen'	EBee EGle LAst MCAu MRav SWat WElm WLRN
§	'Schneekönigin'	ECha LPio MRav WGer
§	'Silberlicht' ♀ H4	More than 30 suppliers
	Silverlight	see *B.* 'Silberlicht'
	Snow Queen	see *B.* 'Schneekönigin'
	'Snowblush'	SSpi
§	*stracheyi*	CBct EBee ECha EGle EGoo GDra MGrG NBid SDix WEas
	– CC 3760	CPLG
	– Alba Group	CRDP ECha EPfP GCal MSte WSHC
	'Sunningdale'	CBcs CMGP EBee ECha ELan EMan EPar EPfP EWTr GKir GMaP GSki LRHS MCAu MLLN MRav NBir SChu SDes SPar SPer SRPl SSpi SWat WMnd
	Winter Fairy Tales	see *B.* 'Wintermärchen'
§	'Wintermärchen'	CM&M CMGP EBee ECha ELan EMan ENot EPfP GKir GSki LRHS MRav MSte MWgw NOrc NSti SDes SWat WCot WMnd WRus
	'Winterzauber'	EBee MTed

Bergeranthus (Aizoaceae)

glenensis	EDAr
multiceps	SChr

Berkheya (Asteraceae)

macrocephala	WCot
multijuga	SMac
purpurea	CPom GGar SIgm WCot WRos

Berlandiera (Asteraceae)

lyrata	CFwr CPLG EBee EMan GCal WCot

Berneuxia (Diapensiaceae)

thibetica	EBee IBlr

Berula (Apiaceae)

erecta	EHon EMFW NPer WWpP

Berzelia (Bruniaceae)

galpini **new**	SPlb
lanuginosa	CTrC

Beschorneria (Agavaceae)

septentrionalis	CFil EBee EMan EOas WCot
tubiflora	CFil CHEx EBee EOas LEdu WPGP
yuccoides ♀ H3	CAbb CBcs CFil CHEx CPne CTCP CTrC EBee EBot EOas EPla IBlr LEdu MSte SAPC SArc SChr SIgm SLim SMad SPar WMul
– 'Quicksilver'	CDoC CFil CKno CTbh EBee ICrw MDun MSte SSpi WCot WPat

Bessera (Alliaceae)

elegans	CFir EBee EMan ETub LRHS WCot

Besseya (Scrophulariaceae)

wyomingensis	EBee

Beta (Chenopodiaceae)

trigyna	EMon WCot
vulgaris	WHer
– 'Bull's Blood'	CSpe EMan WCot WJek
– subsp. *cicla* var.	WJek
flavescens	
'Rhubarb Chard' ♀ H3	

Betonica see *Stachys*

Betula ✿ (Betulaceae)

	alba L.	see *B. pendula*, *B. pubescens*
	albosinensis misapplied	see *B. utilis*
	albosinensis ♀ H4	CBcs CCVT CDul CMCN EBee EPfP GIBF GKir MHFa NWea SPer WDin WFar WNor WOrn
	– 'Bowling Green'	CTho
	– 'China Ruby'	GKir LRHS MBri
	– 'Chinese Garden'	CTho
	– clone F	CTho
	– 'K.Ashburner'	CTho
	– 'Kansu'	GKir
	– var. *septentrionalis* ♀ H4	CDoC CDul CEnd CLnd CTho CWib EBee ECrN ENot EPfP GBin GKir IMGH LNet LRHS MAsh MBlu MBri SCoo SKee SLim SPer SSpi SSta WCwm WMoo
	– – 'Purdom' **new**	CLnd CPMA
§	*alleghaniensis*	CDul CLnd CMCN GKir SPoG WDin
	alnoides	GIBF WNor
	apoiensis	GIBF SBir SSta WNor
I	– 'Mount Apoi' **new**	SSpi
	austrosinensis	WNor

	borealis	see *B. pumila*
§	x **caerulea**	CDul CLnd CTho
	caerulea-grandis	see *B.* x *caerulea*
	chichibuensis	EPla GIBF SBir WHer
	chinensis	CMCN GIBF WNor
	'Conyngham'	CTho MBlu
	costata misapplied	see *B. ermanii* 'Grayswood Hill'
	costata Trautv.	CDul CLnd CTho ELan EPfP WDin WOrn
*	- 'Fincham Cream'	EPfP ERea GKir
	dahurica	CMCN IArd LRHS WNor
	- B&SWJ 4247	WHCr
	- 'Maurice Foster'	CTho
	divaricata <u>new</u>	GIBF
	ermanii	More than 30 suppliers
	- from Hokkaido, Japan	CSam
	- 'Blush'	see *B. ermanii* 'Grayswood Hill'
§	- 'Grayswood Hill' ♀ H4	CEnd CLnd CMHG CPMA CTho EBee GKir LPan LRHS MBri MGos SMad SPer SPoG SSpi SSta
	- 'Hakkoda Orange'	CTho GKir MBlu MBri
*	- 'Pendula'	GKir
	- 'Polar Bear'	CPMA GKir
	- var. **subcordata**	CSam
	ermanii ussuriensis <u>new</u>	GIBF
	'Fetisowii'	CDul CLnd CTho ECrN GKir IMGH LPan LRHS MAsh MBlu SKee SLim SSta WHCr
	fontinalis	see *B. occidentalis*
	fruticosa	see *B. humilis*
	glandulifera	see *B. pumila*
	globispica	EGFP GIBF WCwm WNor
	grossa	CDul CLnd CMCN GIBF
	'Haywood'	WHCr
	'Hergest'	CUtt EPfP GKir MBri MGos SKee WHCr
§	**humilis**	CLnd CMCN GIBF GQui WDin
	insignis <u>new</u>	GIBF
	'Inverleith'	see *B. utilis* var. *jacquemontii* 'Inverleith'
	jacquemontii	see *B. utilis* var. *jacquemontii*
	kamtschatica	see *B. humilis*
§	**kenaica**	CTho
	lenta	CLnd CMCN EPfP WDin
	- subsp. **uber**	CMCN
	luminifera	CPMA
	lutea	see *B. alleghaniensis*
	mandshurica <u>new</u>	GIBF IArd
§	- var. **japonica**	CBcs CDoC ECrN EWTr EWes GIBF GKir NPal SBir WNor
	- **kamchatcana** <u>new</u>	GIBF
	- - 'Whitespire Senior'	CDul LRHS
	maximowicziana	CBcs CDoC CLnd CMCN CTho EPfP EWTr GIBF LHop MDun NWea SSta WDin WNor WRHF
	medwedewii	CDul CLnd CMCN CTho EBee EPfP EPla GIBF NWea SBir SSta WPGP
	- 'Gold Bark'	MBlu
	megrelica	see *B. medwedewii*
§	**michauxii**	MBro NHol
	x **minor**	GIBF
	nana	ELan EMil ESis GIBF MBar MWhi NHol NSla SIng SRms SSta STre WDin WPer
	- subsp. **exilis** <u>new</u>	GIBF
	- 'Glengarry'	EPot GBin LBee NLAp
	- var. **michauxii**	see *B. michauxii*
§	**neoalaskana**	WNor
	nigra	CBcs CDoC CDul CEnd CLnd CMCN CMHG CSBt CTho EBec ECrN ENot GIBF GKir LPan LRHS
		MAsh MHFa NEgg NWea SSta WDin WGer WMou WNor WOrn
	- 'Heritage' ♀ H4	CDoC CDul CEnd CLnd CMCN CTho EBee ECrN ENot GKir LPan LRHS MBlu MBri MRav SLim SSpi SSta WDin WFar WMoo
	- Wakehurst form	EPfP GKir LRHS MBri SPer
§	**occidentalis**	MAsh
§	**ovalifolia**	GIBF
	papyrifera	More than 30 suppliers
	- var. **commutata**	WDin
	- subsp. **humilis**	see *B. neoalaskana*
	- var. **kenaica**	see *B. kenaica*
	- 'Occidentalis'	see *B. occidentalis*
	- 'Saint George'	CTho
	- 'Vancouver'	CTho MBlu
§	**pendula** ♀ H4	More than 30 suppliers
	- var. **aurea** <u>new</u>	GIBF
	- 'Bangor'	GKir MBri
*	- 'Boeugh's Variety'	CEnd CLnd
	- f. **crispa**	see *B. pendula* 'Laciniata'
N	- 'Dalecarlica' hort.	see *B. pendula* 'Laciniata'
	- 'Dalecarlica'	CCVT CSBt ECrN MHFa MRav SKee SLim WFar WHCr
	- 'Fastigiata'	CDoC CDul CLnd CSBt CTho EBee ECrN ELan ENot LPan MGos MHFa SLim SPer WDin WMoo WOrn
	- var. **fontqueri** <u>new</u>	GIBF
*	- 'Golden Beauty'	CDoC CDul LRHS MBlu MGos WDin
	- 'Gracilis'	CTho EMil
§	- 'Laciniata' ♀ H4	CBcs CDoC CDul CEnd CLnd CMCN CTho CWib EBee FNot EPfP GKir LPan LRHS MAsh MBri MGos MRav NBea NBee NWea SHBN SPer SSpi SSta WDin WMou WWeb WWes
	- 'Purpurea'	CCVT CDul CEnd CLnd CSBt CTho CWib EBee EBre ECrN ELan ENot LPan LRHS MGos MHFa NBea NBee SHBN SPer SSpi WDin WMoo WOrn
	- 'Silver Cascade' <u>new</u>	MGos
	- 'Silver Grace' <u>new</u>	ENot
	- 'Tristis' ♀ H4	More than 30 suppliers
	- 'Youngii'	More than 30 suppliers
	platyphylla	CMCN NWea
	- var. **japonica**	see *B. mandshurica* var. *japonica*
	- var. **kamtschatica**	see *B. mandshurica* var. *japonica*
	- subsp. **platyphylla** <u>new</u>	GIBF
	potaninii	GIBF
§	**pubescens**	CCVT CDul CKin CLnd ECrN GKir GTre LNet MHFa NBee NWea SLPl WDin WFar WMou
	- 'Arnold Brembo'	CTho
§	- var. **glabrata**	GIBF
§	**pumila**	GIBF WCwm
	raddeana	GIBF SBir WNor
	- 'Hugh McAllister'	CTho
	resinifera Britton	see *B. neoalaskana*
	schmidtii	GIBF IArd MBlu
	szechuanica	CLnd WDin
	- 'Liuba White'	CTho
	tianschanica	GIBF MDun WNor
	'Trost's Dwarf'	CBcs ECrN GQui MGos SPer WDin
	uber	see *B. lenta* subsp. *uber*
§	**utilis**	CLnd CMCN CMHG CSBt CTho EBee ECrN EMil ENot GKir LNet LRHS MAsh MBar MRav NBee NWea SPer SSta WDin WNor
	- BL&M 100	CTho
	- F 19505	CTho
	- McB 1257	CTho

	– Sch 2168	MBri
	– 'Fascination'	CDul CPMA EMil GKir LNet LRHS
		MBri SKee SLim SSpi
*	– 'Fastigiata' **new**	CPMA
	– 'Forrest's Blush'	CDul GKir LRHS MBri
N	– var. *jacquemontii*	More than 30 suppliers
	– – 'Doorenbos' ♀ H4	CLnd CPMA GKir LPan MBlu
		MGos NEgg SBrw SKee SSta WDin
		WOrn WPGP
	– – 'Grayswood Ghost'	CEnd CLnd CMHG CTho ECrN
	♀ H4	ENot EPfP GKir LPan MBri SBrw
		SHBN SMad SRPl SSpi SSta
§	– – 'Inverleith'	CEnd EBee GKir LRHS MBri SKee
		SLim SSpi WFar WOrn
	– – 'Jermyns' ♀ H4	CBcs CDul CEnd CLnd CMHG
		CTho ECot EPfP GKir LNet MBlu
		SBrw SKee SPer SRPl SSpi SSta
	– – 'Silver Shadow'	CLnd CPMA CTho EPfP GKir
	♀ H4	LNet MBlu MBri NWea SBrw SKee
		SMad SPer SSpi SSta
	– – 'Snowqueen'	CDul CEnd CLnd COtt CPMA
		CSBt CWSG EMui EPfP GKir
		IMGH LBuc LRHS MAsh MBri
		MDun MGos MLan SCoo SKee
		SLim WHCr WOrn
	– – variegated (v) **new**	CDul
	– 'Knightshayes'	CTho
	– 'Moonbeam'	CLnd CPMA GKir SSpi
	– var. *occidentalis*	CTho
	'Kyelang'	
	– 'Polar Bear'	GKir SBrw
	– var. *prattii*	CEnd CTho GKir MDun
	– 'Ramdana River'	CTho MBlu
	– 'Schilling'	CEnd GKir LRHS
	– 'Silver Queen'	SSpi
	– 'Thyangboche	MDun
	Monastery'	
	– 'Trinity College'	CLnd CPMA GKir SRPl SSpi
	– 'Wakehurst Place	CPMA GKir SSpi
	Chocolate'	
	verrucosa	see *B. pendula*

Biarum ✿ (*Araceae*)

	davisii	CLAP EHyt GCrs LAma
	– subsp. *marmarisense*	EPot
	dispar	WCot
	ditschianum	WCot
	ochridense	WCot
	spruneri S&L 229	SSpi
	tenuifolium	CLAP CStu ECho SSpi WCot
	– AB&S 4356	GCrs
	– var. *abbreviatum*	EPot

Bidens (*Asteraceae*)

	CD&R 1515	CLAP
§	*atrosanguinea*	see *Cosmos atrosanguineus*
	aurea	CFox CMil CStr ECtt EMon EPPr
		EVFa EWes GCal LIck LRHS
		MAnH MGrG MNrw MOak NPPs
		SAga SBla SGar SMrm SPet STes
		WBor WFar WOld WWye
	– cream	MAnH MNrw MSte
	– 'Hannay's Lemon Drop'	CHea CMdw CMea CSev CSpe
		CStr EBee GBri MAnH MDKP
		MHar MNrw MSte STes SUsu
	ferulifolia ♀ H1+3	ECtt NPPs NPer NPri SChu SMrm
		SPet WWol
	– 'Peters Goldteppich'	SMrm
	PBR	
	heterophylla hort.	SCoo
	– Ortega	see *B. aurea*
	humilis	see *B. triplinervia* var.
		macrantha

	integrifolia	EChP ECtt SMad
	ostruthioides	MOak
	tripartita	SHDw
§	*triplinervia* var.	LHop
	macrantha	

Biebersteinia (*Geraniaceae*)

odora **new**	EBee

Bignonia (*Bignoniaceae*)

capreolata	CPIN SBra SPer SSta WCru WSHC
– 'Tangerine Beauty' **new**	SSpi
lindleyana	see *Clytostoma calystegioides*
unguis-cati	see *Macfadyena unguis-cati*

Bilderdykia see *Fallopia*

Billardiera (*Pittosporaceae*)

bicolor	CPIN
cymosa	SOWG
longiflora ♀ H3	More than 30 suppliers
– 'Cherry Berry'	CPIN EBee ECou ELan EREa IArd
	LRHS MAsh MCCP SBra SBrw
	SLim SMur SPer SPoG WSHC
– *fructu-albo*	CBcs CPIN CPle EBee ELan EWes
	LRHS MAsh SBrw SLim SPer
– red berried	CPle
scandens	ECou

Billbergia (*Bromeliaceae*)

	x *gireaudiana* ♀ H1	SSte
	nutans	CHEx CHal EBak EGra EOHP
		EOas EShb ESlt GBin IBlr IDee
		LRHS MBri SAPC SArc SPar SRms
		SSte SVen WGwG WHer
*	– 'Variegata' (v)	ESlt WCot
I	*pyramidalis*	SSte
	'Variegata' (v)	
	'Santa Barbara' (v)	SSte
	x *windii* ♀ H1	CHEx CHal EBak ESlt SRms

Bismarckia (*Arecaceae*)

nobilis	EAmu LPal

Bistorta see *Persicaria*

Bixa (*Bixaceae*)

orellana	ELau

Blachia (*Euphorbiaceae*)

sp. **new**	EBee

blackberry see *Rubus fruticosus*

blackcurrant see *Ribes nigrum*

Blastus (*Melastomataceae*)

dunnianus **new**	EBee

Blechnum (*Blechnaceae*)

	alpinum	see *B. penna-marina* subsp.
		alpinum
	capense	CTrC EBot
	cartilagineum	CFil CRDP
N	*chilense* ♀ H3	CFil CHEx CRow EPfP GGar IBlr
		LEur NMar NVic SAPC SArc SChu
		SDix SSpi WAbe WCru WPGP WRic
	discolor	CTrC EBot LPal LPan
	gibbum	LRHS MBri
§	*glandulosum*	NMar
	magellanicum	see *B. chilense*
	misapplied	
	minus	NMar WRic

	- x *wattsii*	WRic
	moorei	NMar
	novae-zelandiae	WRic
	nudum	CFil CRDP EAmu EPfP MCCP
		NMoo WRic
	occidentale nanum	see *B. glandulosum*
	penna-marina ♀ H4	CBro CFil EBee EFer EHyt EMon
		EPar GAbr GGar LEdu LEur MBri
		NHar NMar NRya NVic NWCA
		SChu SDix SIng SRms SSpi WEas
		WMoo WPGP WRic WWye
§	- subsp. *alpinum*	CFil CLAP NMar WAbe WPGP
	- 'Cristatum'	CFil EFer GDra GGar NHar SRms
		WAbe WPGP
	punctulatum	WRic
	spicant ♀ H4	More than 30 suppliers
	- 'Cristatum'	WRic
	- Serratum Group	CFil
	tabulare misapplied	see *B. chilense*
N	*tabulare* (Thunb.)	WRic
	Kuhn ♀ H1	
	wattsii	WRic

Blepharocalyx (Myrtaceae)

	cruckshanksii	CPLG LRHS WGer
	- 'Heaven Scent'	LAst

Blephilia (Lamiaceae)

	ciliata	EBee IFro IIve MSal
	hirsuta	EBee

Bletilla ✿ (Orchidaceae)

	Brigantes g.	CHdy EPot LEur
*	- 'Moonlight'	LEur
	Coritani g.	LAma LEur WCot
	formosana	EPot LAma LEur
*	- *alba*	CHdy
	hyacinthina	see *B. striata*
	ochracea	LAma LEur WCot
	Penway Dragon g.	CHdy
*	**Penway Imperial g.**	CHdy EPot
	Penway Paris g.	CHdy EMan EPot
	Penway Princess g.	EPot LEur
	Penway Rainbow g.	EPot LEur
*	**Penway Rose g.**	LEur
	Penway Starshine g.	CHdy LEur
	Penway Sunset g.	LEur
§	*striata*	CBct CDes EBre ERea ERos ETub
		GKir GSki IBlr ITer LAma LEdu
		MRav MSal NHol NRog SBla SChr
		WCot WFar WPGP
	- *alba*	see *B. striata* var. *japonica* f.
		gebina
	- 'Albostriata'	CBct CDes EBee ELan EMan IBlr
		LAma LEur NRog WCot WOBN
	- var. *japonica*	EPot LEur
§	- - f *gebina*	CDes CHdy EBee GSki IBlr LAma
		LEur LRHS NRog SBla SChr SSpi
		WCot WFar WViv
	- - - variegated (v)	CHdy LEur
	szetschuanica	LAma LEur
	'Yokohama'	CHdy EPot LAma LEur

Bloomeria (Alliaceae)

	crocea var. *aurea*	LRHS WCot
	- var. *montana*	WCot
	NNS 98-84	

blueberry see *Vaccinium corymbosum*

Bocconia (Papaveraceae)

	cordata	see *Macleaya cordata*
	microcarpa	see *Macleaya microcarpa*

Boehmeria (Urticaceae)

	nivea	MSal

Boenninghausenia (Rutaceae)

	albiflora	EBee EMan SMac WCot
	- B&SWJ 1479	CRDP WCru
	japonica B&SWJ 4876	WCru

Boesenbergia (Zingiberaceae)

	longiflora	CKob LEur

Bolax (Apiaceae)

	glebaria	see *Azorella trifurcata*
§	*gummifer*	EPot SBla WAbe

Bolboschoenus (Cyperaceae)

	caldwellii <u>new</u>	EPPr
§	*maritimus*	CBrm LPBA WFar

Boltonia (Asteraceae)

	asteroides	CFee CSam EHrv EMon GMac
		LRHS MCAu NBro NGdn NSti
		SPer SWat WDyG WRHF
	- var. *latisquama*	EPPr GMaP MBrN MNFA MRav
		MSte MWat SMad SSvw WCot
		WFar WHal
	- - 'Nana'	CBre EBee ECGN EGoo EMan
		LRHS MLLN MRav MWgw NBid
		NBro NChi WBVN WMoo WPer
	- 'Pink Beauty'	CBre EMon
	- var. *recognita*	EMon LRHS
	- 'Snowbank'	ELan EMan EWTr
	decurrens	EBee
	incisa	see *Kalimeris incisa*

Bomarea (Alstroemeriaceae)

	JCA 13987	IDac
	RCB/Eq X-2	WCot
	from Mexico	SSpi
	caldasii ♀ H1	CFil CHEx CPIN CPne CRHN
		CTCP ERea SIgm SOWG SSpi
		WBor WPGP WSHC WTrc
	edulis	ERea
	hirtella	CFil CHEx CPIN CRHN EBee SSpi
		WCot WHil
	isopetala	CFil SSpi
	- JCA 13866	IDac
	kalbreyeri	WCot
	multiflora	CFil CPIN
	- JCA 13761	SSpi
	ovata	FRea
	patacocensis	IDac WCot
	JCA 13987	
	salsilla <u>new</u>	SIgm
	sasilla	CFil WCot WSHC

Bonatea (Orchidaceae)

	speciosa <u>new</u>	WCot

Bongardia (Berberidaceae)

	chrysogonum	CAvo EHyt LRHS NRog WCot

borage see *Borago officinalis*

Borago (Boraginaceae)

	alba	EOHP MChe WBry WCHb
	laxiflora	see *B. pygmaea*
	officinalis	CArn CBod CPrp CSev EChP
		EDAr ELau GKir GPoy LRHS
		MBow MBri MChe MHer NPPs
		NPri NVic SPar WCot WHHs
		WHer WPer WSel WWye

	– 'Alba'	CBre CPrp CSev EChP ELau EMon
		ILis MBow MHer NBid NBlu SPar
		WCHb WHHs WHer WJek WLHH
		WPer WRha WSel WWpP
*	– 'Bill Archer' (v)	CNat
	– 'Variegata' (v)	EMon
§	*pygmaea*	CArn CCge CHid CPLG CSev
		CSpe EChP ELan EMan EMon
		EOHP GBar GEil LHop MAnH
		MFir MHar MHer MTho NLar
		NMRc NSti STes SWat WCHb
		WHHs WOld WWin WWpP WWye

Borinda (Poaceae)

	SSNY 2 **new**	WPGP
	albocerea	CFil EPla ERod

Boronia (Rutaceae)

	citriodora **new**	SOWG
	denticulata **new**	ECou
	'Heaven Scent'	CBcs
	heterophylla	CBcs CPLG CSWP ECou SBrw
		SOWG
	– white-flowered **new**	ECou
	keysii **new**	ECou
	megastigma	CBcs ECou
	– 'Brown Meg'	CBcs
	mollis	SOWG
	pinnata	ECou SOWG
	serrulata	ECou

Bothriochloa (Poaceae)

	barbinodies **new**	CKno
§	*bladhii*	EPPr
	caucasica	see *B. bladhii*
§	*ischaemum*	CBig CBrm EHoe EPPr EWes LEdu
		MCCP WPrP

Botryostege see *Elliottia*

Bougainvillea (Nyctaginaceae)

	'Ailsa Lambe'	see *B.* (Spectoperuviana Group)
		'Mary Palmer'
	'Alabama Sunset'	CWDa
	'Alexandra'	MBri
	'Amethyst'	MBri
	'Apple Blossom'	see *B.* 'Elizabeth Doxey'
	'Asia'	ERea
	'Audrey Grey'	see *B.* 'Elizabeth Doxey'
	'Aussie Gold'	see *B.* 'Carson's Gold'
	'Barbara Karst'	CWDa ERea
	'Begum Sikander'	CWDa
	'Betty Lavers'	ERea
§	'Blondie'	CWDa
	'Bridal Bouquet'	see *B.* x *buttiana* 'Cherry Blossom'
	'Brilliance'	CWDa ERea LRHS
	'Brilliant' misapplied	see *B.* x *buttiana* 'Raspberry Ice'
	x *buttiana* 'Afterglow'	CWDa
	– 'Audrey Grey'	see *B.* 'Elizabeth Doxey'
§	– 'Cherry Blossom' (d)	CWDa ERea
	– 'Daphne Mason'	ERea
§	– 'Enid Lancaster'	ERea LRHS
	– 'Golden Glow'	see *B.* x *buttiana* 'Enid Lancaster'
§	– 'Golden McLean'	CWDa
§	– 'Jamaica Red'	ERea
	– 'Killie Campbell' ♀ H1	ERea MBri
	– 'Lady Mary Baring'	see *B.* 'Lady Mary Baring'
§	– 'Louise Wathen'	CWDa ESlt
§	– 'Mahara' (d)	CWDa ERea SOWG SPar
	– 'Mahara Double Red'	see *B.* x *buttiana* 'Mahara'
	– 'Mahara Off-white'	see *B.* x *buttiana* 'Cherry Blossom'
	– 'Mahara Pink'	see *B.* 'Los Banos Beauty'
§	– 'Mardi Gras' (v)	CWDa ERea

§	– 'Mrs Butt' ♀ H1	CWDa ERea SPar
§	– 'Mrs McLean'	ERea
§	– 'Poultonii'	ERea
§	– 'Poulton's Special'	ERea
	♀ H1	
§	– 'Rainbow Gold'	ERea
§	– 'Raspberry Ice' (v)	ERea LRHS SOWG
§	– 'Rosenka'	CWDa ERea
§	– 'Roseville's Delight' (d)	ERea LRHS SOWG
§	– 'Scarlet Glory'	ERea
§	– Texas Dawn =	ERea
	'Monas'	
	'California Gold'	see *B.* x *buttiana* 'Enid Lancaster'
	Camarillo Fiesta	CWDa ERea SOWG
	= 'Monle'	
	(*spectabilis* hybrid)	
	'Captain Caisy'	CWDa ERea
§	'Carson's Gold' (d)	CWDa ERea
	'Cherry Blossom'	see *B.* x *buttiana* 'Cherry Blossom'
	'Chiang Mai Beauty'	ERea
	'Chitra'	ERea
	'Coconut Ice' (v)	CWDa SOWG
	'Crimson Lake'	see *B.* x *buttiana* 'Mrs Butt'
	misapplied	
	'Dauphine'	see *B.* 'Los Banos Beauty'
	'David Lemmer'	CWDa ERea
	'Delicate'	see *B.* 'Blondie'
	'Dixie'	ERea
	'Donya'	CWDa ERea
	'Double Yellow'	see *B.* 'Carson's Gold'
	'Durban'	see *B. glabra* 'Jane Snook'
§	'Elizabeth Angus'	CWDa ERea
§	'Elizabeth Doxey'	ERea
	'Elizabeth' (*spectabilis*	ERea
	hybrid)	
*	'Elsbet'	CWDa
	'Enchantment'	see *B.* (Spectoperuviana Group)
		'Mary Palmer's Enchantment'
	'Fair Lady'	see *B.* 'Blondie'
	'Flamingo Pink'	see *B.* 'Chiang Mai Beauty'
	'Floribunda'	CWDa ERea
	'Gillian Greensmith'	ERea
	glabra ♀ H1	CPIN ERea LRHS MBri SPar WMul
	– 'Doctor David Barry'	CWDa ERea
	– 'Elizabeth Angus'	see *B.* 'Elizabeth Angus'
§	– 'Harrissii' (v)	CWDa ERea LRHS
§	– 'Jane Snook'	CWDa ERea
	– 'Jennifer Fernie'	see *B.* 'Jennifer Fernie'
§	– 'Magnifica'	ERea
§	– 'Pride of Singapore'	ERea
§	– 'Sanderiana'	ERea LPan
§	– 'Sanderiana Variegata'	SVen
	(v)	
	'Gladys Hepburn'	ERea
	'Gloucester Royal'	CWDa
	'Glowing Flame' (v)	CWDa ERea
	'Golden Doubloon'	see *B.* x *buttiana* 'Roseville's
		Delight'
	'Golden Glow'	see *B.* x *buttiana* 'Enid Lancaster'
	'Golden MacLean'	see *B.* x *buttiana* 'Golden McLean'
	'Golden Tango'	CWDa ERea
	'Harrissii'	see *B. glabra* 'Harrissii'
	'Hawaiian Scarlet'	see *B.* 'San Diego Red'
	'Hugh Evans'	see *B.* 'Blondie'
	'Indian Flame'	see *B.* 'Partha'
	'Isabel Greensmith'	CWDa ERea
	'Jamaica Orange'	CWDa ERea
	'Jamaica Red'	see *B.* x *buttiana* 'Jamaica Red'
	'James Walker'	ERea
	'Jane Snook'	see *B. glabra* 'Jane Snook'
§	'Jennifer Fernie'	ERea
	'Juanita Hatten'	CWDa ERea
	'Kauai Royal'	see *B.* 'Elizabeth Angus'

'Klong Fire' see *B.* x *buttiana* 'Mahara'
§ 'La Jolla' ERea
§ 'Lady Mary Baring' ERea LRHS SOWG
'Lavender Girl' CWDa ERea
'Lemmer's Special' see *B.* 'Partha'
'Limberlost Beauty' see *B.* x *buttiana* 'Cherry Blossom'
'Little Caroline' CWDa SOWG
'Lord Willingdon' see *B.* 'Pixie'
    misapplied
§ 'Los Banos Beauty' (d) CWDa ERea
'Magnifica' see *B. glabra* 'Magnifica'
'Mahara Double Red' see *B.* x *buttiana* 'Mahara'
'Mahara Off-white' see *B.* x *buttiana* 'Cherry Blossom'
'Mahara Orange' see *B.* x *buttiana* 'Roseville's
    Delight'
'Mahara Pink' see *B.* 'Los Banos Beauty'
'Mahara White' see *B.* x *buttiana* 'Cherry Blossom'
'Manila Magic Red' see *B.* x *buttiana* 'Mahara'
'Mardi Gras' see *B.* x *buttiana* 'Mardi Gras'
'Mary Palmer's see *B.* (Spectoperuviana Group)
    Enchantment' 'Mary Palmer's Enchantment'
'Meriol Fitzpatrick' ERea
* 'Michael Lemmer' CWDa
'Mini-Thai' see *B.* 'Pixie'
'Mischief' CWDa
§ 'Miss Manila' CWDa ERea
'Mrs Butt' see *B.* x *buttiana* 'Mrs Butt'
'Mrs Helen McLean' see *B.* x *buttiana* 'Mrs McLean'
'Mrs McLean' see *B.* x *buttiana* 'Mrs McLean'
Natalii Group CWDa ERea
'Nina Mitton' CWDa ERea
'Orange Glow' see *B.* Camarillo Fiesta = 'Monle'
'Orange King' see *B.* x *buttiana* 'Louise Wathen'
'Orange Stripe' (v) ERea
'Pagoda Pink' see *B.* 'Los Banos Beauty'
§ 'Partha' CWDa
'Penelope' see *B.* (Spectoperuviana Group)
    'Mary Palmer's Enchantment'
pink ESlt
'Pink Champagne' see *B.* 'Los Banos Beauty'
'Pink Clusters' CWDa ERea
§ 'Pixie' ERea
'Poultonii' see *B.* x *buttiana* 'Poultonii'
'Poultonii Special' see *B.* x *buttiana* 'Poulton's
    Special'
'Pride of Singapore' see *B. glabra* 'Pride of Singapore'
'Princess Mahara' see *B.* x *buttiana* 'Mahara'
'Purple Robe' CWDa ERea
'Rainbow Gold' see *B.* x *buttiana* 'Rainbow Gold'
'Raspberry Ice' (v) see *B.* x *buttiana* 'Raspberry Ice'
'Ratana Orange' ERea
'Ratana Red' ERea
'Red Diamond' ERea
'Red Fantasy' (v) ERea
'Red Glory' CWDa ERea
'Reggae Gold' (v) CWDa ERea
'Robyn's Glory' see *B.* x *buttiana* Texas Dawn =
    'Monas'
'Rosenka' see *B.* x *buttiana* 'Rosenka'
'Royal Purple' CWDa ERea
'Rubyana' CWDa ERea LRHS SOWG
§ 'San Diego Red' ERea ESlt SOWG
'Sanderiana' see *B. glabra* 'Sanderiana'
'Scarlet Glory' see *B.* x *buttiana* 'Scarlet Glory'
Scarlett O'Hara see *B.* 'San Diego Red'
'Singapore Pink' see *B. glabra* 'Doctor David Barry'
'Singapore White' CWDa ERea
'Smartipants' see *B.* 'Pixie'
'Snow Cap' see *B.* (Spectoperuviana Group)
    'Mary Palmer'
spectabilis 'Wallflower' CWDa
§ Spectoperuviana ERea
    Group (v)

§ – 'Mary Palmer' CWDa LRHS
§ – 'Mary Palmer's CWDa ERea
    Enchantment'
§ – 'Mrs H.C. Buck' CWDa ERea
'Summer Snow' CWDa
Surprise see *B.* (Spectoperuviana Group)
    'Mary Palmer'
'Tango' see *B.* 'Miss Manila'
* 'Tango Supreme' CWDa
§ 'Temple Fire' ERea SOWG
'Thai Gold' see *B.* x *buttiana* 'Roseville's
    Delight'
* 'Tom Thumb' CWDa
'Tropical Bouquet' CWDa
'Tropical Rainbow' see *B.* x *buttiana* 'Raspberry Ice'
* 'Turkish Delight' CWDa EPfP ESlt
'Variegata' (*glabra*) see *B. glabra* 'Harrissii' , *B. glabra*
    'Sanderiana Variegata'
'Vera Blakeman' CWDa ERea ESlt LRHS
'Wac Campbell' (d) CWDa SOWG
'Weeping Beauty' ERea
* 'White Cascade' CWDa ERea

Boussingaultia (Basellaceae)
baselloides Hook. see *Anredera cordifolia*

Bouteloua (Poaceae)
curtipendula CBig CBrm EBee EChP EMan
    EMon EPPr LEdu LRav MHdf
    NHol SRGP WPrP
§ *gracilis* CBig CBrm CFwr CKno CTrC
    EBre EChP EMon ENot EPPr
    EWsh MBNS MCCP MHdf MLLN
    MMoz MWgw MWud NBea NHol
    NJOw NSti SDcs SMrm SUsu SWal
    WLRN WPGP WPer
hirsuta EPPr

Bouvardia (Rubiaceae)
longiflora ERea LRHS SOWG

Bowenia (Boweniaceae)
serrulata CBrP
spectabilis CRoM NRog

Bowiea (Hyacinthaceae)
volubilis CHal CPIN

Bowkeria (Scrophulariaceae)
citrina CPle

Boykinia (Saxifragaceae)
aconitifolia EBee EBre GBuc GTou MLLN
    MPEx MRav NLar NRya SMad SSpi
    STes WCru WMoo
elata see *B. occidentalis*
heucheriformis see *B. jamesii*
§ *jamesii* CGra EDAr NJOw NWCA
major WCru
§ *occidentalis* EBee GGar WCru WMoo WPat
rotundifolia EBee GBuc SLon WCru WMoo WPnP
– JLS 86269LACA EMon
tellimoides see *Peltoboykinia tellimoides*

boysenberry see *Rubus* Boysenberry

Brachychilum see Hedychium

Brachychiton (Sterculiaceae)
bidwillii EShb

Brachyglottis ✿ (Asteraceae)
§ *bidwillii* CBcs CDoC SDry WCru

	- 'Basil Fox'	WAbe
§	*buchananii*	GEil SDry WSHC
	- 'Silver Shadow'	GGar GKir
§	*compacta*	ECou EPfP GKir LRHS MAsh NPro SDry SPer WEas
	- x *monroi*	ECou LRHS
	'County Park' **new**	ECou
	'Drysdale'	EBee EPfP GGar GKir LRHS MAsh MBri MRav NPri SDry SLon SPar SPoG
§	(Dunedin Group) 'Moira Reid' (v)	CHEx CPLG EGoo GGar SDry
	- 'Sunshine' ♀ H4	More than 30 suppliers
	'Frosty'	ECou
	greyi misapplied	see B. (Dunedin Group) 'Sunshine'
§	*greyi* (Hook. f.) B. Nord.	CTrG EBee EPfP ISea MBar MWhi NLon
§	*hectoris*	CHEx
§	*huntii*	CHEx CPLG SPer
	laxifolia misapplied	see B. (Dunedin Group) 'Sunshine'
§	'Leonard Cockayne'	SLim
§	*monroi* ♀ H4	CChe CSBt CWib EBee ECou EGoo EHoe EHol ELan EOHP EPfP GGar GKir LAst LHop MBar MLLN MRav NLon SBrw SLon SMer SPar SPer WBrE WDin WEas
	- 'Clarence'	ECou
	repanda	CBcs CHEx CPle CTrC CTrG SBrw
	- 'Purpurea'	CHEx
	- var. *rangiora*	LEdu
	repanda x *greyi*	CDoC CHEx CPle SAPC SArc
§	*rotundifolia*	CDoC CHEx CPle EPfP GGar WCru WEas
	'Silver Waves'	ECou
§	*spedenii*	GGar GTou
	'Sunshine Variegated'	see B. (Dunedin Group) 'Moira Reid'

Brachypodium (Poaceae)

	pinnatum	EHoe
	sylvaticum	CBig CBod CKin EHul

Brachyscome (Asteraceae)

	'Blue Mist'	SPet
	curvicarpa **new**	ECou
	formosa **new**	ECou
	melanocarpa	WCom
	'Mini Yellow' **new**	NPri
	multifida	MBri NPri
	nivalis var. *alpina*	see B. tadgellii
	'Pink Mist'	SPet WWol
	rigidula	ECou GKev MDHE
	'Strawberry Mousse'	SPet
§	*tadgellii*	GDra IMGH MTPN

Brachysema (Papilionaceae)

	celsianum **new**	SOWG

Brachystachyum (Poaceae)

	densiflorum	EPla SDry

Bracteantha see

Brahea (Arecaceae)

	aculeata	CBrP
	armata	CAbb CBrP CDoC CRoM CTrC EAmu EPVP EPfP LPal LPan MPRe NPal SAPC SArc SChr SPar SPer
	edulis	CBrP CRoM EAmu EPVP LPal MPRe

Brassaia see *Schefflera*

Brassica (Brassicaceae)

	japonica	see B. juncea var. crispifolia
§	*juncea* var. *crispifolia*	CArn WJek
	oleracea	WHer
*	- *botrytis aparagoides*	CAgr
*	*rapa* var. *japonica*	WJek
*	- var. *purpurea*	WJek

Breynia (Euphorbiaceae)

	nivosa 'Rosea Picta' (v)	ESlt

Brickellia (Asteraceae)

	eupatorioides	IIve
	grandiflora **new**	EBee

x *Brigandra* (Gesneriaceae)

	calliantha 'Tinney's Rose'	ETow

Briggsia (Gesneriaceae)

	aurantiaca	EHyt SOkd

Brillantaisia (Acanthaceae)

	subulugurica **new**	GFai

Brimeura (Hyacinthaceae)

§	*amethystina*	CAvo ERos ETub GDra LRHS MBow WCot
	- 'Alba'	CAvo ERos LPhx LRHS MBow NMen NRog
§	*fastigiata*	ERos

Briza (Poaceae)

	maxima	COlW CRDP EChP EFWa EGoo EHoe EPla LHop LHrt LIck NGdn NSti SSth SWal WHal WHer WRos WWye
	media	More than 30 suppliers
	- 'Limouzi'	CElw CKno EBee EFou EGle EHoe EMan EMon EPPr GCal LPhx LRHS MAvo MSph NSti SApp SDys SHel SMrm SOkh SSth WDyG WFTG WPGP WWpP
	minor	EGoo SWal WRos
	subaristata	WHal WWpP
	triloba	CPen EChP EHoe EMan EPPr EWes EWsh GBin NOGN SBod SMac SRGP SWal WHal WMoo WRos WWpP
	- RB 94154	EBee

Brodiaea (Alliaceae)

§	*californica*	CNic EBee ECho ERos ETub NMen
	- var. *leptandra*	WCot
	capitata	see *Dichelostemma capitatum*
	coronaria NNS 97-37 **new**	WCot
	'Corrina'	see *Triteleia* 'Corrina'
	elegans	ERos WCot
	ida-maia	see *Dichelostemma ida-maia*
	jolonensis	ERos
	laxa	see *Triteleia laxa*
§	*minor*	WCot
	peduncularis	see *Triteleia peduncularis*
	stellaris	EHyt WCot

terrestris subsp. | WCot
kernensis
NNS 98-88

Bromus (Poaceae)

inermis 'Skinner's | CBrm CFwr CWCL EBee EHoe
Gold' (v) | EHul EMan EPPr EVFa EWes EWsh
| LPhx MMoz NGdn
morrisonensis | EMan
ramosus | EHoe

Broussonetia (Moraceae)

kazinoki | WDin
papyrifera | CBcs CFil CMCN ELan IDee LEdu
| LPan SLon SPer WDin WPGP

Bruckenthalia see *Erica*

Brugmansia (Solanaceae)

§ *arborea* | CArn CHEx MGol SRms
aurea | CHEx LRHS
x *candida* | EBak ERea SSte
- 'Blush' | ERea
- 'Culebra' **new** | MGol
* - 'Ecuador Pink' | EPfP ERea
§ - 'Grand Marnier' ♀ H1 | CBot CHEx CMdw ECot ELan EPfP
| ERea ESlt LRHS SOWG SPar SVen
§ - 'Knightii' (d) ♀ H1 | CHEx CHal EBak ELan EPfP ERea
| ESlt LRHS MOak SOWG SPar
- 'Plena' | see *B.* x *candida* 'Knightii'
- 'Primrose' | ERea
§ - 'Variegata' (v) | CKob ERea MOak
§ x *insignis* pink | CHEx EPfP
'La Fleur Lilas' | see *Datura stramonium* var.
| *tatula* 'La Fleur Lilas'
meteloides | see *Datura inoxia*
* pink | LIck WFar WWol
rosei | see *B. sanguinea* subsp.
| *sanguinea* 'Flava'
§ *sanguinea* | CHEx EBak EShb MGol MOak
| MSal SOWG SPar SSte SVen WHer
- 'Red' **new** | CHEx
- 'Rosea' | see *B.* x *insignis* pink
§ - subsp. *sanguinea* | CHEx
'Flava'
§ *suaveolens* ♀ H1 | CHEx ELan ERea IDee MGol
| NPal
- *rosea* | see *B.* x *insignis* pink
- 'Variegata' (v) | CKob ERea
'Variegata Sunset' | see *B.* x *candida* 'Variegata'
versicolor hort. | see *B. arborea*
§ *versicolor* Lagerh. | ERea SOWG
yellow | LIck WFar WWol
* 'Yellow Trumpet' | EPfP

Brunfelsia (Solanaceae)

calycina | see *B. pauciflora*
jamaicensis | CSpe SOWG
latifolia | ESlt
§ *pauciflora* ♀ H1 | ELan LRHS MBri
- 'Floribunda' | SOWG
- 'Macrantha' | SOWG

Brunia (Bruniaceae)

albiflora | CTrC SPlb

Brunnera (Boraginaceae)

§ *macrophylla* ♀ H4 | More than 30 suppliers
- 'Alba' | see *B. macrophylla* 'Betty
| Bowring'
- Aluminium Spot | More than 30 suppliers
= 'Langtrees'
§ - 'Betty Bowring' | CDes CLAP CPlt CRDP CRow

| | ECha EGle EPPr EVFa GBuc LPhx
| | MBri MHar MTed NBhm NLar
| | SBla SMHy SUsu WCot WFar WHal
| | WPGP WPnP
§ - 'Dawson's White' (v) | More than 30 suppliers
- 'Gordano Gold' (v) | EHoe EMon EVFa WHal
- 'Hadspen Cream' (v) | More than 30 suppliers
♀ H4
- 'Jack Frost' **new** | CDes EBla ELan EMan EVFa LHop
| MSph NBir NGdn SPla SPoG
| WAbe WTMC
- 'Langford Hewitt' (v) | CLAP WCom
- 'Marley's White' **new** | EBee
- 'Variegata' | see *B. macrophylla* 'Dawson's
| White'
sibirica **new** | EMon

Brunonia (Goodeniaceae)

australis | SPlb

Brunsvigia (Amaryllidaceae)

radulosa | WCot
rosea 'Minor' | see *Amaryllis belladonna*

Bryonia (Cucurbitaceae)

dioica | GPoy MSal

Bryophyllum see *Kalanchoe*

Buchloe (Poaceae)

dactyloides | CBig

Buddleja ✿ (Buddlejaceae)

B&SWJ 3853 | WCru
from Philippines
agathosma | CBot CFil CPle EFpt SLon WEas
| WPGP WSHC
albiflora | CPle SLon WLav
alternifolia ♀ H4 | More than 30 suppliers
- 'Argentea' | CBot CDoC CPle EBee ELan ENot
| EPfP MBNS MBro MRav NLar NSti
| SHBN SPer SPla SSpi WCot WHCG
| WLav WPat WSHC
asiatica ♀ H2 | CBot CBrm CPlN CPle ERea EShb
| ESlt SLon WCom
- B&SWJ 7214 | WCru
auriculata | CAbb CBcs CBot CDoC CFil
| CMCN CWib EHol EPfP ERea
| GQui LAst NSti SDix SLon SOWG
| WCFF WCru WHCG WLav WPGP
| WPat
australis | CPle SLon
* 'Blue Trerice' | CPLG
* 'Butterfly Ball' | SLon WBVN WBcn WPer
caryopteridifolia | EBee EFpt EHol SLon
colvilei | CAbb CDoC CFil CPle CSBt CTrw
| EPfP GKir LAst WBor WCot
- B&SWJ 2121 | WCru
- 'Kewensis' | CBot CFil CPLG CRHN CSam EBee
| NSti SBra SLon SVen WBod WCom
| WCru WCwm WLav WPGP WSHC
cordata | SLon
coriacea | CPle SLon
§ *crispa* | CBcs CBot CDoC CPle ECha ELan
| EPfP GEil LRHS NSti SAga SBra
| SDry SHBN SOWG SPer SSpi SSta
| WCot WEas WFar WHCG WKif
| WPGP WSHC
- L 1544 | CFil
crotonoides | SLon
amplexicaulis
curviflora f. | SSte
venenifera **new**

– – B&SWJ 6036	WCru	
davidii	CArn CKin GWCH LHrt MBro NWea SGar SHFr STre WDin	
– Adonis Blue = 'Adokeep' **new**	ENot WWeb	
– 'African Queen'	CPLG SPer SRGP SRPl	
– var. **alba**	CNic SHBN	
– 'Autumn Beauty'	CPle	
– 'Black Knight' ♀ H4	More than 30 suppliers	
– 'Blue Horizon'	SEND SLon WCot WLav WMoo WRHF	
– 'Border Beauty'	CMac GKir SPla	
§ – 'Charming'	WMoo WSHC	
– 'Dartmoor' ♀ H4	CDoC CMHG CRow CSBt CSam CTrG EBee EBre ECtt ELan ENot EPfP LRHS MAsh MMil NPer SDix SHBN SMer SMrm SPer SPla SPlb SSta WCFE WEas WFar WHCG WSHC	
– 'Dart's Ornamental White'	ENot MRav	
– 'Dart's Papillon Blue'	EFpt SLPl	
– 'Dubonnet'	SLon WLav	
– 'Empire Blue' ♀ H4	CBcs CDoC CSBt CWib EBee ECtt ENot EPfP EWTr GKir LRHS MRav MWat NBee NPer NWea SPer SPlb SRGP WBod WDin WFar WStl WTel WWeb	
– 'Fascinating'	CTri WLav	
– 'Flaming Violet'	SLon WLav	
– from Beijing, China	SLon	
– 'Glasnevin Blue'	SDix SPer WLav	
– 'Gonglepod'	SLon	
– 'Harlequin' (v)	More than 30 suppliers	
– 'Ile de France'	CBcs CWib GKir MGos NWea SRms WLav	
– Masquerade = 'Notbud' PBR (v)	EBee EFpt ENot MBri MGos SLon WGor WLRN WStl WWes	
– Nanho Blue	see B. davidii 'Nanho Petite Indigo'	
§ – 'Nanho Petite Indigo' ♀ H4	CBcs CMHG CSBt EBee EBre ECtt ELan ENot EPfP GKir LBuc LRHS MAsh MBar MGos NFor SBod SHBN SLim SPla SRGP WBod WDin WFar WHar WMoo WSHC	
§ – 'Nanho Petite Purple' ♀ H4	CDoC CHar CMHG CTri EBee EGoo ELan ENot EPfP GKir LRHS MAsh MBar MRav NBlu SLim SLon SPer SPla SPlb SRGP WHar WSHC	
– Nanho Purple	see B. davidii 'Nanho Petite Purple'	
– var. **nanhoensis**	CPle MWhi SEND SIde SIgm SPer WHCG WLav	
– – **alba**	CChe ELan EPfP GKir MBar SPer SRPl SRms WFar WWeb	
– – blue	GKir SLon SPer SRPl	
– – purple	CPLG	
– Operette = 'Courtabud' **new**	MBri	
– 'Orchid Beauty'	MBNS NPro WBod WLav	
– 'Peace'	CChe CDoC CSBt EBee ENot EPfP NPer SPer WLav	
– Peacock = 'Peakeep' **new**	ENot WWeb	
– 'Pink Beauty'	GKir SHBN WHCG	
– 'Pink Charming'	see B. davidii 'Charming'	
– 'Pink Pearl'	SLon WLav	
– 'Pixie Blue'	NBlu SRGP WWeb	
– 'Pixie Red'	EBee NBlu NPri SLon WWeb	
– 'Pixie White'	MBNS SRGP WLav	
– Purple Emperor = 'Pyrkeep' **new**	ENot WWeb	
– 'Purple Friend' **new**	WLav	

– 'Royal Purple'	GKir SLim	
– 'Royal Red' ♀ H4	More than 30 suppliers	
– 'Salicifolia'	GEil	
– 'Santana' (v)	LHop LRHS SPar	
– 'Summer Beauty'	CWib EBee EMil ENot GKir LRHS MGos NPro WBcn WLav	
– 'Variegata' (v)	LRHS SMrm WLav	
– 'White Ball'	CFwr LRHS MBNS SLon	
– 'White Bouquet'	CSBt EBee EPfP GKir LAst LRHS MHer MWat NWea SBod SEND SMer SPer SReu SWal WLRN WLav WTel	
– 'White Butterfly'	LRHS SLon	
– 'White Cloud'	EPar GQui SGar SRms WGwG	
– 'White Harlequin' (v)	CRow EBee SLon WBcn WCFE WCot WEas	
– 'White Profusion' ♀ H4	CBcs CSam EBee ECtt ELan EPfP LRHS MBar MGos MRav NBee NBlu NFor NLon NWea SHBN SLim WBod WCFE WDin WEas WFar WHCG WHar WMoo WStl WWin	
– 'White Wings'	EFpt SLon WLav	
§ **delavayi**	CPLG CPle EREa WCru	
fallowiana misapplied	see B. 'West Hill'	
fallowiana Balf. f.	CBcs CPle IFro LRHS NFor NLon SPla WLav	
– ACE 2481	LRHS	
– CLD 1109	CFil WPGP	
– var. **alba** ♀ H3	CBot CDoC ELan ENot EPfP GEil LRHS MRav SLon SPer SPla SRPl SSta WCru WEas WFar WPGP WSHC WWeb	
farreri	CBot CPle MSte SOWG WBod	
forrestii	CBot CHEx CPle WCru	
globosa ♀ H4	More than 30 suppliers	
– 'Cally Orange' **new**	GCal	
glomerata **new**	EShb	
heliophila	see B. delavayi	
indica	CPLG CPle EFpt SLon	
japonica	CPLG CPle IFro	
x **lewisiana** 'Margaret Pike'	CBot SLon SOWG	
limitanea	SLon	
lindleyana	More than 30 suppliers	
'Lochinch' ♀ H3-4	More than 30 suppliers	
loricata	CBot CFil CPle CStr EFpt EREa EVFa GQui SGar SIgm SLon SOWG SPlb SSpi SVen WCFE WCot WLav WPGP	
macrostachya	CFil CPle	
– SBEC 360	NCWG	
§ **madagascariensis** ♀ H1	CPle CRHN SOWG WCot	
myriantha	GQui	
* – f. **fragrans** **new**	WCot	
nappii	EFpt SLon	
nicodemia	see B. madagascariensis	
nivea	CBot CMCN CPLG IFro SOWG SSte WLav	
– B&SWJ 2679	WCru	
– pink	SLon	
– var. **yunnanensis**	CPle MSte WCFE	
aff. **nivea** L 860	WPGP	
officinalis ♀ H2	CBot CPLG CPle CRHN EHol EREa	
paniculata	SLon	
parvifolia MPF 148	WLav WPGP	
pichinchensis	EFpt	
x **pikei**	SDys	
§ – 'Hever'	CHal CPle GQui	
– 'Pink Delight' ♀ H4	More than 30 suppliers	
saligna	CPle SLon	
'Salmon Spheres'	SSte	

salviifolia CAbb CBot CFil CPLG CRHN
CSWP CSam CTbh CTrG EBee
ELan GEil GGar GQui IFro LAst
NSti SDry SIgm SPer SWal WCom
WHer WLRN WLav
- white CRHN EFpt
stenostachya CPLG CPle GEil
sterniana see *B. crispa*
tibetica see *B. crispa*
tubiflora CBot EREa SLon SOWG WLav
venenifera B&SWJ 895 WCru
§ 'West Hill' SLon WLav
x **weyeriana** CRHN CSam ECtt EOrc EPar EPfP
GEil MNrw MTis MWat NBir SGar
SPar SPlb SSte WBea WBrE WDin
WFar WHCG WLav WMoo WSHC
WTel
- 'Flight's Fancy' (v) EWes WWeb
- 'Golden Glow' (v) CChe CSBt CTri EPfP NFor NLon
SHel SLon WBrE WLav WStI
WWeb WWin
- 'Lady de Ramsey' SEND WPer
- 'Moonlight' CPLG CPle CRow EFpt IFro SDes
WLav WSel
- 'Sungold' ♀ H4 CBrm CPle CWib EBee ELan EPfP
GKir LHrt MAnH MBlu MCCP
MGos MLLN MRav NBlu SLon SPer
SRGP WBod WCot WHar WLav
* - 'Variegata' (v) CPMA

Buglossoides (Boraginaceae)

§ **purpurocaerulea** CKin CMHG EBee ECha EFIs ELan
EMan EMar EMon EWTr LHop
LPVe LRHS MBro MSal MSte
MWhi SAga WCom WFar WRHF
WWin WWye

Bulbine (Asphodelaceae)

abyssinica new EBee
caulescens see *B. frutescens*
§ **frutescens** CPLG EMan EOas WCot WPrP
WWin
- yellow EOas
semibarbata CPLG MWhi NBro WPer

Bulbinella (Asphodelaceae)

angustifolia ECho EMan GDra WCot
cauda-felis WCot
eburnifolia WCot
elata WCot
floribunda IBlr
gibbsii var. ECho
  balanifera new
hookeri CRDP ECou EMan GCrs GDra
GGar ITim NDlv NHar SYvo WCot
WLin WPer
latifolia new EBee

Bulbinopsis see *Bulbine*

Bulbocodium (Colchicaceae)

vernum EPot ERos ETub GCrs LAma LPhx
MBri NRog NWCA WBor
- white-flowered new ECho

bullace see *Prunus insititia*

Bunium (Apiaceae)

bulbocastanum CAgr LEdu

Buphthalmum (Asteraceae)

§ **salicifolium** CSam CSev EBee ELan EPfP GKir
GMaP LHrt MBri MGrG NBid NBro

NGdn NNor NOrc SRms SWat
WCot WFar WLin WPer WWpP
- 'Alpengold' ECha GKir SIgm
- 'Dora' EMan WCot WWal
- 'Sunwheel' EFou EWll LRHS NPri
speciosum see *Telekia speciosa*

Bupleurum (Apiaceae)

angulosum CDes CFil CLyd CMil CPom CRDP
EBee SBla SIgm SMrm SSpi WCru
WFar WMaN WPGP
- copper see *B. longifolium*
benoistii SIgm
falcatum CLyd ECGP EChP ECha EPPr
MBro MLLN MRav MSal NDov
SBri SChu WAul WBWf WFar
fruticosum CBos CBot CFil CPle EPPr EPfP
MRav SChu SDes SDix SIgm SPar
SRPl SSpi WCot WCru WDin WEas
WFoF WKif WPat WSHC WStI
* **griffithii** MSal
§ **longifolium** CElw CFcc CMea CRDP CSpe
EBee EChP EGle GBin GGar
MAvo NChi SMrm WWhi
- short bronze WCru
- subsp. **aureum** NGby
longiradiatum WCru
  B&SWJ 729
multinerve NCat NChi
ranunculoides CLyd CPLG EBee NChi SIgm
rotundifolium MSal NDov WTGP
- 'Copper' new NDov
salicifolium CFil SIgm
spinosum SIgm SMad WCru
stellatum GGar LRHS
tenue B&SWJ 2073 WCru
- var. **humile** WCru
  B&SWJ 6470

Bursaria (Pittosporaceae)

spinosa CPLG ECou GQui SBrw

Butia (Arecaceae)

capitata CAbb CBrP CHEx CRoM CTrC
EAmu EGln EPVP LEdu LPJP LPal
LPan NPal SAPC SArc SChr SPar
WMul
eriospatha new CRoM
yatay CRoM LPal

Butomus (Butomaceae)

umbellatus ♀ H4 CBen CTwr CRow CWat ECha
ECoo ECtt EHon EMFW ENot
EPfP LMdh LPBA MCCP MSta
NBlu NPer SLon SWat WFar
WMAq WShi WWpP
- 'Rosenrot' CRow
- 'Schneeweisschen' CRow

butternut see *Juglans cinerea*

Buxus ✿ (Buxaceae)

aurea 'Marginata' see *B. sempervirens* 'Marginata'
balearica ♀ H4 CFil EPla SDry SLan SLon WPGP
WPic WSHC
bodinieri EPla SLan
- 'David's Gold' WEas WPen WSHC
glomerata SLan
'Green Gem' EPla LEar NHol SLan
'Green Mountain' SLan
'Green Velvet' EPfP LPan NHol SLan STop WWeb
harlandii hort. EPla LEar SIng SLan SRiv
- 'Richard' SLan STre

	henryi	SLan
	japonica 'Nana'	see *B. microphylla*
	leonii	SLan
	macowanii	SLan
	macrophylla	see *B. sinica* var. *insularis* 'Winter
	'Asiatic Winter'	Gem'
§	**microphylla**	CSWP GDra LPan MHer NHol
		NWea SIng SLan STre
§	– 'Compacta'	CFil SLan SRiv WCot WPat
	– 'Curly Locks'	EPla MHer NHol SLan
	– 'Faulkner'	EBee EMil ENot EPfP EPla LEar
		LHop LPan LRHS MBNS MBlu
		MBri MRav NHol SLan SRiv STop
		WBcn WLRN WWeb
	– 'Grace Hendrick	SLan
	Phillips'	
	– 'Green Jade'	SLan
	– 'Green Pillow'	NHol SLan SRiv
	– 'Helen Whiting'	SLan
	– var. **insularis**	see *B. sinica* var. *insularis*
	– var. **japonica**	SLan
	– – 'Gold Dust'	SLan
	– – 'Morris Dwarf'	SLan
	– – 'Morris Midget'	IArd NHol SLan
	– – 'National'	MHer SLan WPGP
	– – f. **yakushima**	SLan
	– 'John Baldwin'	SLan SRiv STop WBcn
	– var. **koreana**	see *B. sinica* var. *insularis*
	– var. **riparia**	see *B. riparia*
	– var. **sinica**	see *B. sinica*
	– 'Winter Gem'	see *B. sinica* var. *insularis* 'Winter
		Gem'
	'Newport Blue'	see *B. sempervirens* 'Newport
		Blue'
	papillosa new	SLan
§	**riparia**	EPla SLan
	rugulosa var.	SLan
	intermedia	
	sempervirens ♀ H4	More than 30 suppliers
§	– 'Angustifolia'	MHer NHol SLan SMad
	– 'Arborescens'	LPan
	– 'Argentea'	see *B. sempervirens*
		'Argentevariegata'
§	– 'Argenteovariegata' (v)	EPfP GKir MRav NHol SLan WBcn
		WFar WSHC
	– 'Aurea'	see *B. sempervirens*
		'Aureovariegata'
	– 'Aurea Maculata'	see *B. sempervirens*
		'Aureovariegata'
	– 'Aurea Marginata'	see *B. sempervirens* 'Marginata'
	– 'Aurea Pendula' (v)	EPla SLan SLon WBcn WWye
§	– 'Aureovariegata' (v)	More than 30 suppliers
	– 'Bentley Blue'	MBNS NHol
	– 'Blauer Heinz'	EMil LEar LRHS MBri MHer MTed
		SLan SRiv STop
§	– 'Blue Cone'	CHar GBin LEar
	– 'Blue Spire'	see *B. sempervirens* 'Blue Cone'
	– clipped ball	CWib EPfP LEar LPan NBlu
	– clipped pyramid	CWib EPfP LEar LPan NBlu
§	– 'Elegantissima' (v)	More than 30 suppliers
	♀ H4	
	– 'Gold Tip'	see *B. sempervirens* 'Notata'
	– 'Golden Frimley' (v)	LHop
§	– 'Graham Blandy'	LEar MHer NHol SLan SRiv STop
		WBcn
	– 'Greenpeace'	see *B. sempervirens* 'Graham
		Blandy'
	– 'Handsworthiensis'	EBee EMil LEar SEND SLan SPer
		STop
	– 'Handsworthii'	CTri NWea SRms
	– subsp. **hyrcana**	SLan
	– 'Ickworth Giant'	SLan STop
	– 'Inverewe'	SLan

	– 'Japonica Aurea'	see *B. sempervirens* 'Latifolia
		Maculata'
	– 'Kensington Gardens'	SLan
	– 'Kingsville'	see *B. microphylla* 'Compacta'
	– 'Kingsville Dwarf'	see *B. microphylla* 'Compacta'
	– 'Lace'	NHol NSti SLan
§	– 'Langley Beauty'	SLan WBcn
	– 'Langley Pendula'	see *B. sempervirens* 'Langley
		Beauty'
	– 'Latifolia Macrophylla'	SLan SLon
§	– 'Latifolia Maculata'	CAbP CChe CDoC CWib EBee
	(v) ♀ H4	EPfP EPla EWTr LEar LRHS NHol
		NPer SLan SRiv STop STre WJek
*	– 'Latifolia Pendula'	NHol SLan
	– 'Longifolia'	see *B. sempervirens* 'Angustifolia'
§	– 'Marginata' (v)	ECtt EPla GBar GKir LHop MHer
		MRav NHol NSti SHBN SHFr SLan
		SLon SRPl WBrE WHar WStI
	– 'Memorial'	LPhx MHer NHol SLan SMHy
		STop
	– 'Myosotidifolia'	CFil CMHG EPla NPro SLan SRiv
		WPGP
	– 'Myrtifolia'	CBot EPla MHer NHol SLan SLon
§	– 'Newport Blue'	MTed
§	– 'Notata' (v)	CBcs CSBt CSWP EBee GKir
		MAsh SBrw SPar SPlb WWal
	– 'Parasol'	MHer SLan
	– 'Pendula'	CMHG GKir SLan SLon WCom
	– 'Prostrata'	NHol NWea SLan WBcn
	– 'Pyramidalis'	GAbr NBee SLan SRPl
	– 'Rosmarinifolia'	MRav SLan
	– 'Rotundifolia'	CLnd EBee LPan MHer SBrw SIde
		SLan STop WDin WLRN
	– 'Salicifolia Elata'	SLan
	– 'Silver Beauty' (v)	CBcs EMil MGos
	– 'Silver Variegated'	see *B. sempervirens*
		'Elegantissima'
	– 'Suffruticosa' ♀ H4	More than 30 suppliers
I	– 'Suffruticosa Blue'	NHol SVil
	– 'Suffruticosa	CBcs EBee EOHP SRms
	Variegata' (v)	
	– 'Vardar Valley'	NPro SLan SRiv STop
*	– 'Variegata' (v)	CPLG LRHS SLon
	– 'Waterfall'	SLan WBcn
§	**sinica**	SLan
§	– var. **insularis**	EPla SLan
	– – 'Filigree'	EPla NHol SLan
	– – 'Justin Brouwers'	CSev MHer SLan SRiv STop
	– – 'Pincushion'	SLan
	– – 'Tide Hill'	SLan SRiv STop WBcn
§	– – 'Winter Gem'	EBee ENot LEar MHer MRav NHol
		SLPl SLan
	wallichiana	CFil EPla SLan WPGP

C

Cacalia (Asteraceae)

	atriplicifolia	IIve
	delphiniifolia	WCru
	B&SWJ 5789	
	firma B&SWJ 4650	WCru
§	**hastata**	EBee
	kiusiana B&SWJ 5911	WCru
	plantaginea	see *Arnoglossum plantagineum*
	suaveolens new	EBee

Caesalpinia (Caesalpiniaceae)

	gilliesii	CBot EBee MTPN SOWG SPlb
	pulcherrima	MGol SPlb

Caiophora (*Loasaceae*)
§   *lateritia*   WCot

Caladium (*Araceae*)

'Aaron' (v)	MOak
§ *bicolor* (v)	MBri
– 'June Bride'	MOak
– 'Mrs Arno Nehrling' (v)	MOak
– 'Postman Joyner'	MOak
– 'Rosebud' (v)	MOak
'Blaze'	MOak
'Candidum' (v)	MOak
'Candidum Junior' (v)	MOak
'Carolyn Whorton' (v)	MOak
'Fannie Munson' (v)	MOak
'Festivia' (v)	MOak
'Fire Chief'	MOak
'Flash Rouge'	MOak
'Florida Cardinal'	MOak
'Florida Elise'	MOak
'Freida Hemple'	MOak
'Galaxy' **new**	MOak
'Gingerland' (v)	MOak
x *hortulanum*	see *C. bicolor*
'Irene Dank'	MOak
'John Peed' (v)	MOak
'Kathleen'	MOak
'Lord Derby'	MOak
'Miss Muffet'	MOak
'Mrs F.M. Joyner' (v) **new**	MOak
'Mrs W.B. Haldeman' (v) **new**	MOak
'Pink Beauty'	MOak
'Pink Cloud' (v)	MOak
'Pink Gem' (v)	MOak
'Poecile Anglais' **new**	MOak
'Red Frill' **new**	MOak
'Rosalie' (v)	MOak
* 'Scarlet Pimpernell' **new**	MOak
'Symphonie Rose'	MOak
'Thomas Tomlinson' (v)	MOak
'White Christmas' (v)	MOak
'White Queen' (v)	MOak
'White Wing' (v)	MOak

Calamagrostis (*Poaceae*)

x *acutiflora*	ECGN
N – 'Karl Foerster'	More than 30 suppliers
– 'Overdam' (v)	More than 30 suppliers
– 'Stricta'	FPPr EWsh GKir LPhx
argentea	see *Stipa calamagrostis*
§ *arundinacea*	More than 30 suppliers
§ *brachytricha*	More than 30 suppliers
emodensis	CFwr CKno CMil CPen EBee EPla LPan MMoz SWal WPGP
§ *epigejos*	CBig CNat EMan EPPr GBin LHrt LPhx NHol NOGN SRGP SWal WRos WWpP
– CLD 1325	EPla
splendens	see *Stipa calamagrostis*
varia	CSam EHoe

Calamintha (*Lamiaceae*)

alpina	see *Acinos alpinus*
clinopodium	see *Clinopodium vulgare*
cretica	CLyd WPer WWye
* 'Fritz Kuhn'	EMan
§ *grandiflora*	More than 30 suppliers
– 'Elfin Purple' **new**	SPoG
– 'Variegata' (v)	CRow EBee ELan EMan EOHP ERou MAnH MGrG MMil NSti SCro

	STes WCHb WCom WCra WFar WHHs WHoo WMaN WRus WWeb
megalantha	EMon
§ *nepeta*	CArn CTri ECha LAst LPhx LRHS MBow MCAu MFir MGrG MHer MMil MSte NBir NBro NDov NWCA SBla SPar SPlb SWat WFar WHHs WHal WMoo WPer WWin WWye
– subsp. *glandulosa*	EBee WMoo
– – ACL 1050/90	LRHS WHoo
– – 'White Cloud'	CHea CSpe EBre ECGN EFou EHrv ERou EWTr GBar GBuc LLWP LPhx MBro MCAu MRav MSte NBir NDov WMoo WRus WWeb WWye
– 'Gottfried Kuehn'	MRav
§ – subsp. *nepeta*	CPrp CSev EFou ELan EMon EPfP ERou EWTr GBar LHop MBri MHer MRav MTho MWgw NOak NSti SHel SPer SRPl SUsu WCHb WCom WEas WFar WRus WSHC
– – 'Blue Cloud'	CHea CHor ECGN EChP ECha EFou EHrv ILis LPhx MCAu MWgw MWrn NBir NDov NGar SAga SBla SOkh SWat WCHb WRus WWeb WWye
nepetoides	see *C. nepeta* subsp. *nepeta*
§ *officinalis* misapplied	see *C. sylvatica* subsp. *ascendens*
* *prenanthoides*	STes
§ *sylvatica*	CPom NLar WJek
– HH&K 163	GBri
– subsp. *ascendens*	EBee IIve MLLN MWrn NCat WMoo WPrP
I – 'Menthe'	EBee
vulgaris	see *Clinopodium vulgare*

calamondin see x *Citrofortunella microcarpa*

Calamovilfa (*Poaceae*)
   longifolia   EBee

Calandrinia (*Portulacaceae*)

discolor	LRHS
grandiflora	MLLN WWin
* *ranunculina* **new**	CPBP
sericea	CPBP
sibirica	see *Claytonia sibirica*
umbellata	EMlt NLAp NWCA SBla WPer WWin
* – *amarantha*	EDAr
– 'Ruby Tuesday'	NPri

Calanthe (*Orchidaceae*)

amamiana	EFEx
arisanenesis	EFEx
aristulifera	EFEx LAma
bicolor	see *C. discolor* var. *flava*
biloba	LAma
caudatilabella	EFEx
chloroleuca	LAma
discolor	EFEx LAma WCot
§ – var. *flava*	CLAP LAma
hamata	EFEx
japonica	EFEx
Kozu g.	WCot
mannii	EFEx LAma
nipponica	EFEx LAma WCot
reflexa	EFEx LAma WCot
§ *sieboldii*	EFEx LAma
striata	see *C. sieboldii*
tokunoshimensis	EFEx
tricarinata	EFEx LAma WCot

Calathea (Marantaceae)

crocata ♀ H1	LRHS MBri
'Gemengd'	CHal
'Greystar'	MBri
louisae 'Maui Queen'	MBri
§ *majestica* ♀ H1	LRHS
makoyana ♀ H1	MBri
metallica	MBri
ornata	see *C. majestica*
picturata 'Argentea'	MBri
♀ H1	
roseopicta ♀ H1	LRHS MBri
veitchiana	MBri
warscewiczii	MBri
'Wavestar'	MBri
zebrina ♀ H1	MBri

Calceolaria (Scrophulariaceae)

acutifolia	see *C. polyrhiza*
alba	CPla EMan WHil
arachnoidea	NWCA NWoo
x *banksii*	EBee MFir WCom WCot
bicolor	WCot
§ *biflora*	CLyd EDAr EHol EHyt GDra GTou
	MBow MHer WLin
- 'Goldcap'	WWeb
- 'Goldcrest Amber'	WPer WWeb
'Camden Hero'	MOak
chelidonioides	GGar MTho
x *clibranii*	MOak
crenatiflora	NWoo
falklandica	CNic GDea NLAp SRms WHer
	WPer WWin
fothergillii	MOne NArg
glandulosa subsp.	WCot
alicahuensis	
F&W 9603 **new**	
'Goldcrest'	EPfP SRms
§ *integrifolia* ♀ H3	CBcs CPLG CSBt EBee ELan
	LRav MFir NRog SChu SEND
	SGar SIng SPar SPer SRms WAbe
	WOld
- var. *angustifolia*	MOak SDry
- bronze	SPer WAbe
'John Innes'	ECho ESis LRHS WCot WRha
	WWeb
'Kentish Hero'	CBcs CElw CHal EBee MOak MSte
	NPer SChu WCom WCot
lanigera	LRav
mexicana	CPLG SHFr
plantaginea	see *C. biflora*
§ *polyrhiza*	ECho EHyt NRya
rugosa	see *C. integrifolia*
Sunset Series **new**	NBlu
tenella	CStu ECtt EDAr ELan EPot NLAp
	NMen NWCA WAbe
uniflora var. *darwinii*	ECho EHyt GEdr GTou NMen
'Walter Shrimpton'	ECho EDAr EPot EWes SIng

Calea (Asteraceae)

zacatechichi	MGol

Calendula (Asteraceae)

arvensis **new**	MSal
meuselii	CFee
officinalis	CArn EDAr ELau GPoy GWCH
	MChe MHer MSal SIde WHHs
	WHbs WHer WJek WLHH WSel
	WWye
- 'Fiesta Gitana' ♀ H4	CBod CPrp WJek
- 'Prolifera'	WHer
- 'Variegata' (v)	MSal

Calla (Araceae)

aethiopica	see *Zantedeschia aethiopica*
palustris	CBen CRow CWat EHon EMFW
	EPfP LPBA MCCP MSta NCot
	NPer SBHF SLon SWat WFar
	WMAq WWeb WWpP

Calliandra (Mimosaceae)

* *emarginata minima*	LRHS SOWG
haematocephala **new**	SOWG

Callianthemum (Ranunculaceae)

anemonoides	GCrs GDra NHar NMen SBla WAbe
angustifolium	NMen
coriandrifolium	SBla
kernerianum	GCrs NMen

Callicarpa (Verbenaceae)

americana	WBcn
- var. *lactea*	CMCN
bodinieri	NBir WFar
- var. *giraldii*	CBrm GBin GIBF MRav SMac
	WBod WDin WWeb
- - 'Profusion' ♀ H4	More than 30 suppliers
cathayana	NLar
dichotoma	CPle CTrG EPfP GIBF LRHS MNes
	WBcn WBod WCru WFar WOTO
	WSHC WWin
- f. *albifructa*	GIBF
- 'Issai'	NLar WBcn
- 'Shirobana' **new**	WBcn
japonica	CPle IIve WWes
- 'Leucocarpa'	CBcs CMac EBee ELan EPfP GEil
	LRHS NLar NVic SPer WBcn WFar
kwangtungensis	CMCN
mollis	EBee WPGP
* *trichotoma*	GEil

Callirhoe (Malvaceae)

involucrata	CPLG EBee EMan NBur NWCA
	SMad WWeb
triangulata	EMan

Callisia (Commelinaceae)

elegans ♀ H1	CHal
§ *navicularis*	CHal
repens	CHal MBri

Callistemon ✿ (Myrtaceae)

'Burgundy' **new**	SOWG
'Burning Bush'	CBcs SOWG
chisholmii	SOWG
citrinus	CHll CSBt EBee ECot ECou ERom
	GGar GSki ITim SMer SOWG SPar
	SPer SPlb SSte SUsu WBrE WCru
	WDin WHar WWal WWin
- 'Albus'	see *C.* 'White Anzac'
- 'Angela' **new**	SOWG
- 'Canberra'	SOWG
- 'Firebrand'	CDoC LRHS MAsh SMur SOWG
- 'Horse Paddock'	SOWG
- 'Mauve Mist'	CTrC LRHS MAsh SBrw SOWG
- 'Reeve's Pink'	SOWG
- 'Splendens' ♀ H3	CBcs CBrm CDoC CHEx CMac
	CWib EBee EBre ELan EPfP GQui
	IArd MGos NPal SBra SBrw SDry
	SHBN SHFr SOWG SPar SPer SReu
	SSta WBod WFar WStl
comboynensis	SOWG
'Coochy Coochy	SOWG
Station' **new**	
* 'Country Park'	SBrw

'Dawson River Weeper'	SOWG
flavescens	SOWG
flavovirens	SOWG
formosus **new**	SOWG
glaucus	see *C. speciosus*
'Hannah's Child' **new**	SOWG
'Happy Valley' **new**	SOWG
'Injune'	SOWG
'Kings Park Special'	EHol LRHS SOWG
laevis hort.	see *C. rugulosus*
linearis ♀ H3	CMac CSBt CTrC CTri EBee ECou ELan EPfP EPla LRHS MHer SBrw SLim SLon SOWG SPar SPlb SRms SSpi WNor
macropunctatus	SOWG SPlb
pachyphyllus	ECou SOWG
- var. *viridis*	SOWG SSte
pallidus	CBrm CMHG CMac CPLG CWib EBee ECou ELan EPfP IDee ITim LRHS NNEX SBrw SMur SOWG SPer SPlb SSta SSte
paludosus	see *C. sieberi* DC.
pearsonii	SOWG
- prostrate **new**	SOWG
'Perth Pink'	CBcs CDoC CTrC ELan SBrw SOWG SPoG SSte
phoeniceus	ECou SOWG
- 'Pink Ice' **new**	SOWG
pinifolius	SOWG SPar SPlb SSte
- green-flowered	SOWG
- red-flowered	SOWG
- 'Sockeye'	SBrw SOWG
'Pink Champagne' **new**	SOWG
§ *pityoides*	CPLG CTrC ECou SOWG WBod
- from Brown's Swamp, Australia	ECou
polandii	SOWG
- dwarf **new**	SOWG
'Purple Splendour' **new**	SOWG
'Red Clusters'	CBcs CDoC CTrC EBee ELan ERea LAst MDun NPer SBrw SMur SOWG SPar WPat
rigidus	More than 30 suppliers
§ *rugulosus*	CBcs EBee IArd LRHS SBrw SOWG
salignus ♀ H3	CBcs CDoC CSBt CTrC CTri EBee EPfP GSki ISea LEur MHer SBrw SFND SHFr SLim SOWG SPar SPer SYvo WDin WSHC
- 'Ruber'	CTrC
sieberi misapplied	see *C. pityoides*
§ *sieberi* DC.	CBcs CDoC CMHG CTrC ECou EPfP GGar GSki LHop NBir NNEX SOWG SPlb SSpi WFar
§ *speciosus*	CPLG CTrC ECou EBee SMur SOWG SPar SPer WLRN
subulatus	CDoC CTrC EBee ECou MCCP NHol NLar NNEX SAPC SArc SBrw SOWG SPlb
- 'Crimson Tail' **new**	MDun
teretifolius	SOWG
viminalis	CTrC SGar SOWG SPlb
- 'Captain Cook'	ECou ERea EShb LAst LRHS SBrw SLim SOWG
- 'Hannah Ray'	NPer SBrw SOWG SPar
- 'Harkness'	SOWG
- 'Hen Camp Creek'	SBrw
- 'Little John'	CBcs CWSG EBee IArd LRHS SBrw SLim SOWG SPar SPoG
- 'Malawi Giant'	SOWG
'Violaceus'	LRav
viridiflorus	CBcs CTrC ECou GQui LEur MCCP SBrw SOWG SPar SWal WBod WCru
- 'County Park Dwarf'	ECou
- 'Sunshine'	ECou
§ 'White Anzac'	LRHS SOWG SSte

Callitriche (Callitrichaceae)

autumnalis	see *C. hermaphroditica*
§ *hermaphroditica*	EMFW WMAq WWpP
§ *palustris*	ECoo EHon LMdh
verna	see *C. palustris*

Calluna ✿ (Ericaceae)

vulgaris	GWCH LRHS
- 'Aberdeen'	EHea
- 'Adrie'	EHea
- 'Alba Argentea'	EHea
- 'Alba Aurea'	EHea MBar
- 'Alba Carlton'	EHea
- 'Alba Dumosa'	EHea
- 'Alba Elata'	CNCN EHea MBar
- 'Alba Elegans'	EHea
- 'Alba Elongata'	see *C. vulgaris* 'Mair's Variety'
- 'Alba Erecta'	EHea
- 'Alba Jae'	EHea MBar
- 'Alba Minor'	EHea
- 'Alba Multiflora'	EHea
- 'Alba Pilosa'	EHea
§ - 'Alba Plena' (d)	CMac EHea LRHS MBar WStI
- 'Alba Praecox'	EHea
- 'Alba Pumila'	EHea MBar
§ - 'Alba Rigida'	EHea LRHS MBar
- 'Alec Martin' (d)	EHea
- 'Alex Warwick'	EHea
- 'Alexandra' PBR ♀ H4	EHea LRHS NHol SCoo
- 'Alice Knight' **new**	EHea
- 'Alicia' PBR ♀ H4	EHea LRHS
- 'Alieke'	EHea
- 'Alison Yates'	EHea MBar
- 'Allegretto'	EHea
- 'Allegro' ♀ H4	EDAr EHea EPfP LRHS MBar MOke NHol WStI
- 'Alportii'	CMac EHea GKir MBar MOke WStI
- 'Alportii Praecox'	CNCN EHea LRHS MBar
- 'Alys Sutcliffe'	EHea
- 'Amanda Wain'	EHea
- 'Amethyst' PBR	EHea NHol
- 'Amilto'	CNCN EHea NHol
- 'Andrew Proudley'	EHea MBar
- 'Anette' PBR ♀ H4	EHea LRHS NHol SCoo
- 'Angela Wain'	EHea
- 'Anna'	EHea
- 'Annabel' (d)	EHea
- 'Anne Dobbin'	EHea
- 'Anneke'	EHea
- 'Annemarie' (d) ♀ H4	CBcs CMac CNCN EBre EHea EPfP LRHS MGos NBlu NHol SCoo
- 'Anne's Zwerg'	EHea
- 'Anthony Davis' ♀ H4	CNCN EHea GKir MBar MOke NHol
- 'Anthony Wain'	EHea
- 'Anton'	EHea
- 'Antrujo Gold'	EHea
- 'Apollo'	EHea
- 'Applecross' (d)	CNCN EHea
- 'Arabella' PBR	EHea LRHS NHol
- 'Argentea'	EHea MBar
- 'Ariadne'	EHea
- 'Arina'	CNCN EHea LRHS MBri MOke
- 'Arran Gold'	CNCN EHea MBar
- 'Ashgarth Amber'	EHea
- 'Ashgarth Amethyst'	EHea
- 'Ashgarth Shell Pink'	EHea
- 'Asterix'	EHea
- 'Atalanta'	EHea
- 'Atholl Gold'	CMac EHea

- 'August Beauty' — CNCN EHea MOke
- 'Aurea' — EHea LRHS
- 'Autumn Glow' — EHea
- 'Baby Ben' — EHea
- 'Baby Wicklow' — EHea
- 'Barbara Fleur' — EHea
- 'Barja' — EHea
- 'Barnett Anley' — CNCN EHea
- 'Battle of Arnhem' — CNCN EHea MBar
- 'Bayport' **new** — EHea
- 'Beechwood Crimson' — CNCN EHea
- 'Ben Nevis' — EHea
- 'Beoley Crimson' — CNCN EHea LRHS MBar MGos NBlu
- 'Beoley Crimson Variegated' (v) — EHea
- 'Beoley Gold' ♀ H4 — CNCN CTri EBre EHea EPfP GKir LRHS MBar MBri MGos MOke NHol WStI
- 'Beoley Silver' — CNCN EHea MBar NBlu
- 'Bernadette' — EHea
- 'Betty Baum' — EHea
- 'Bispingen' — EHea
- 'Blazeaway' — CMac CNCN CTri EHea EPfP GKir LRHS MBar MBri NHol WStI
- 'Blueness' — EHea
- 'Bognie' — CNCN EHea
- 'Bonfire Brilliance' — CNCN EHea MBar
- 'Bonne's Darkness' **new** — EHea
- 'Bonsaï' — EHea
- 'Boreray' — CNCN EHea
- 'Boskoop' — CMac CNCN EBre EHea LRHS MBar MBri NHol
- 'Bradford' — EHea
- 'Braemar' — CNCN EHea
- 'Braeriach' — EHea
- 'Branchy Anne' — EHea
- 'Bray Head' — CNCN EHea MBar
- 'Brita Elisabeth' (d) — EHea
- 'Bronze Beauty' — EHea
- 'Bud Lyle' — EHea
- 'Bunsall' — CNCN EHea
- 'Buxton Snowdrift' — EHea
- 'C.W. Nix' — EHea MBar
- 'Caerketton White' — EHea
- 'Caleb Threlkeld' — EHea NHol
- 'Calf of Man' — EHea
- 'Californian Midge' — EHea LRHS MBar NHol
- 'Carl Röders' (d) — EHea
- 'Carmen' — EHea
- 'Carngold' — EHea
- 'Carole Chapman' — EHea MBar
- 'Carolyn' — EHea
- 'Cassa' — EHea
- 'Catherine Anne' — EHea LRHS
- 'Celtic Gold' — EHea
- 'Charles Chapman' — EHea
- 'Chernobyl' (d) — EHea
- 'Chindit' — EHea
- 'Christina' — EHea
- 'Cilcennin Common' — EHea
- 'Clare Carpet' — EHea
- 'Coby' — EHea
- 'Coccinea' — CMac EHea MBar
- 'Colette' — EHea
- 'Con Brio' — CBcs CNCN EHea LRHS
- 'Copper Glow' — EHea
- 'Coral Island' — EHea MBar MGos
- 'Corbett's Red' — EHea
- 'Corrie's White' — EHea
- 'Cottswood Gold' — EHea
- 'County Wicklow' — CBcs CNCN CTri EBre EHea EPfP

- (d) ♀ H4 — GKir LRHS MBar MBri MGos MOke NBlu NHol
- 'Craig Rossie' — EHea
- 'Crail Orange' — EHea
- 'Cramond' (d) — CNCN EHea LRHS MBar
- 'Cream Steving' — EHea
- 'Crimson Glory' — EHea LRHS MBar NBlu NDlv WStI
- 'Crimson Sunset' — CNCN EHea WStI
- 'Crinkly Tuft' **new** — EHea
- 'Crowborough Beacon' — EHea
- 'Cuprea' — CNCN EHea EPfP LRHS MBar MBri MOke NBlu NHol WStI
- 'Dainty Bess' — EHea LRHS MBar NHol WStI
- 'Dark Beauty' PBR (d) ♀ H4 — CNCN EBre EDAr EHea EPfP GKir LRHS MBar MGos NBlu NDlv NHol WStI
- 'Dark Star' (d) ♀ H4 — CBcs CMac CNCN EBre EHea EPfP LRHS MBar MGos MOke NBlu NHol SCoo
- 'Darkness' ♀ H4 — CBcs CNCN CTri EHea EPfP GKir LRHS MBar MBri MGos MOke NBlu NHol SCoo WStI
- 'Darleyensis' — EHea
- 'Dart's Amethyst' — EHea
- 'Dart's Beauty' — EHea
- 'Dart's Brilliant' — EHea
- 'Dart's Flamboyant' — EHea
- 'Dart's Gold' — EHea MBar
- 'Dart's Hedgehog' — EHea
- 'Dart's Parakeet' — EHea
- 'Dart's Parrot' — EHea
- 'Dart's Silver Rocket' — EHea
- 'Dart's Squirrel' — EHea
- 'David Eason' — CNCN EHea
- 'David Hagenaars' — EHea
- 'David Hutton' — EHea MBar
- 'David Platt' (d) — EHea
- 'Denny Pratt' — EHea
- 'Desiree' — EHea
- 'Devon' (d) — EHea
- 'Diana' — EHea
- 'Dickson's Blazes' — EHea
- 'Dirry' — CNCN EHea
- 'Doctor Murray's White' — see *C. vulgaris* 'Mullardoch'
- 'Doris Rushworth' — EHea
- 'Drum-ra' — EHea MBar SRms
- 'Dunnet Lime' — EHea SPlb
- 'Dunnydeer' — EHea
- 'Dunwood' — EHea MBar
- 'Durford Wood' — EHea
- 'Dwingeloo Delight' **new** — EHea
- 'E.F. Brown' — EHea
- 'E. Hoare' — EHea MBar
- 'Easter-bonfire' — CNCN EHea NHol
- 'Eckart Miessner' — EHea
- 'Edith Godbolt' — EHea
- 'Elaine' — EHea
- 'Elegant Pearl' — EHea MBar
- 'Elegantissima' — CBcs EHea MOke
- 'Elegantissima Walter Ingwersen' — see *C. vulgaris* 'Walter Ingwersen'
- 'Elkstone White' — CNCN EHea MBar
- 'Ellen' — EHea
- 'Ellie Barbour' — EHea
- 'Elly' — EHea
- 'Else Frye' (d) — EHea
- 'Elsie Purnell' (d) ♀ H4 — CNCN EHea EPfP LRHS MBar MGos MOke NHol SPlb WStI
- 'Emerald Jock' — EHea
- 'Emma Louise Tuke' — EHea
- 'Eric Easton' — EHea

§ indicates section marks as shown.

- 'Eskdale Gold'	EHea
- 'Fairy'	CMac EHea MOke
- 'Falling Star'	EHea
- 'Feuerwerk'	EHea
§ - 'Finale'	EHea MBar
- 'Findling'	EHea
- 'Fire King'	EHea MBar
- 'Fire Star'	EHea
- 'Firebreak'	EHea MBar
- 'Firefly' ♀ H4	CBrm CMac CNCN EBre EDAr
	EHea EPfP GKir LRHS MBar MBri
	MOke NBlu WStI
- 'Flamingo'	CBcs CNCN EBre EHea LRHS
	MBar MBri MOke NHol
- 'Flatling'	EHea NHol
- 'Flore Pleno' (d)	EHea MBar
- 'Floriferous'	EHea
- 'Florrie Spicer'	EHea
- 'Fokko' (d)	EHea
- 'Fort Bragg' new	EHea
- 'Fortyniner Gold'	EHea
- 'Foxhollow Wanderer'	CNCN EHea MBar MOke
- 'Foxii'	EHea
- 'Foxii Floribunda'	EHea LRHS MBar
- 'Foxii Lett's Form'	see C. vulgaris 'Velvet Dome',
	'Mousehole'
- 'Foxii Nana'	CNCN EHea LRHS MBar NDlv NHol
- 'Foya'	EHea
- 'Fraser's Old Gold' new	EHea
- 'Fred J. Chapple'	CNCN EHea GKir LRHS MBar
	MBri MOke WStI
- 'Fréjus'	EHea
- 'French Grey'	CNCN EHea
- 'Fritz Kircher' PBR	EHea NHol
- 'Gaia' new	EHea
- 'Gerda'	EHea LRHS
- 'Ginkel's Glorie'	EHea
- 'Glasa'	EHea
- 'Glen Mashie'	EHea
- 'Glencoe' (d)	EHea LRHS MBar MBri MOke NBlu
- 'Glendoick Silver'	EHea
- 'Glenfiddich'	EHea MDar
- 'Glenlivet'	EHea MBar
- 'Glenmorangie'	EHea MBar
- 'Gloucester Boy' new	EHea
- 'Gnome Pink'	EHea
- 'Gold Charm'	EHea
- 'Gold Finch'	EHea
- 'Gold Flame'	EHea LRHS MBar
- Gold Hamilton	see C. vulgaris 'Chernobyl'
- 'Gold Haze' ♀ H4	CBcs CMac CNCN EBre EHea
	EPfP GKir LRHS MBar MBri MOke
	NBlu NHol SCoo WStI
- 'Gold Knight'	EHea EPfP LRHS MBar
- 'Gold Kup'	EHea MBar
- 'Gold Mist'	EHea LRHS NBlu NDlv
- 'Gold Spronk'	EHea
- 'Goldcarmen'	EHea
- 'Golden Blazeaway'	EHea
- 'Golden Carpet'	CNCN EHea LRHS MBar MBri
	MGos MOke NBlu NDlv NHol WStI
- 'Golden Dew'	EHea
- 'Golden Dream' (d)	EHea
- 'Golden Feather'	CNCN EHea LRHS MBar MGos
- 'Golden Fleece'	CNCN EHea
- 'Golden Max'	EHea
- 'Golden Rivulet'	EHea LRHS MBar
- 'Golden Turret'	CNCN EHea LRHS
- 'Golden Wonder' (d)	EHea
- 'Goldsworth Crimson'	EHea
- 'Goldsworth Crimson Variegated' (v)	CNCN EHea MBar
- 'Goscote Wine' new	EHea
- 'Grasmeriensis'	EHea MBar
- 'Great Comp'	MBar
- 'Green Cardinal'	MBar
- 'Grey Carpet'	CNCN EHea LRHS MBar
- 'Grijsje'	EHea
- 'Grizabella'	EHea
- 'Grizzly'	EHea
- 'Grönsinka'	EHea
- 'Grouse'	EHea
- 'Guinea Gold'	CNCN EHea LRHS MBar MBri NBlu
§ - 'H.E. Beale' (d)	CNCN CTri EBre EHea EPfP GKir
	LRHS MBar MBri MGos MOke
	NBlu NHol
- 'Hamlet Green'	CNCN EHea MBar
- 'Hammondii'	CNCN EHea GKir WStI
- 'Hammondii Aureifolia'	CNCN EHea LRHS MBar MBri
	MOke
- 'Hammondii Rubrifolia'	EHea LRHS MBar MBri MOke
- 'Harlekin'	EHea
- 'Harry Gibbon' (d)	EHea
- 'Harten's Findling'	EHea
- 'Hatje's Herbstfeuer' (d)	EHea
- 'Hayesensis'	EHea
- 'Heidberg'	EHea
- 'Heidepracht'	EHea
- 'Heidesinfonie'	EHea
- 'Heideteppich'	EHea
- 'Heidezwerg'	EHea
- 'Heike' (d) new	EHea
- 'Herbert Mitchell'	EHea
- 'Hester'	EHea
- 'Hetty'	EHea
- 'Hibernica'	EHea MBar
- 'Hiemalis'	EHea MBar
- 'Hiemalis Southcote'	see C. vulgaris 'Durford Wood'
- 'Highland Cream'	CNCN GKir
- Highland Cream	see C. vulgaris 'Punch's Dessert'
- 'Highland Rose'	CNCN EHea LRHS SPlb
- 'Highland Spring'	EHea
- 'Hilda Turberfield'	EHea
- 'Hillbrook Limelight'	EHea
- 'Hillbrook Orange'	EHea MBar
- 'Hillbrook Sparkler'	EHea
- 'Hinton White'	EHea
- f. hirsuta	GKir
- 'Hirsuta Albiflora'	EHea
- 'Hirsuta Typica'	CNCN EHea
- 'Hollandia'	EHea
- 'Holstein'	EHea
- 'Hookstone'	EHea MBar
- 'Hoyerhagen'	EHea
§ - 'Hugh Nicholson'	CNCN EHea
- 'Humpty Dumpty'	EHea NHol
- 'Hypnoides'	EHea
- 'Ide's Double' (d)	EHea
- 'Inchcolm'	EHea
- 'Inchkeith' new	EHea
- 'Inekc'	CNCN EHea MBar
- 'Inge' new	EHea
- 'Ingrid Bouter' (d)	EHea
- 'Inshriach Bronze'	CNCN EHea MBar
- 'Iris van Leyen'	CNCN EHea LRHS
- 'Islay Mist'	EHea
- 'Isle of Hirta'	CNCN EHea MBar NHol
- 'Isobel Frye'	EHea MBar
- 'Isobel Hughes' (d)	EHea MBar
- 'J.H. Hamilton' (d) ♀ H4	CNCN CTri EHea GKir LRHS MBar MBri MGos NHol SRms WStI
- 'Jan'	EHea
- 'Jan Dekker'	CNCN EHea LRHS NHol
- 'Janice Chapman'	EHea MBar
- 'Japanese White'	EHea

- 'Jenny'	EHea
- 'Jill'	EHea
- 'Jimmy Dyce' (d)	EHea
- 'Joan Sparkes' (d)	CNCN EHea LRHS MBar WStI
- 'Jochen'	EHea
- 'Johan Slegers'	EHea
John Denver	see *C. vulgaris* 'Marleen Select'
- 'John F. Letts'	EHea LRHS MBar MGos SRms WStI
- 'Johnson's Variety'	CBcs CNCN EHea MBar
- 'Jos' Lemon'	EHea
- 'Jos' Whitie' **new**	EHea
- 'Josefine'	EHea
- 'Joseph's Coat'	EHea
- 'Joy Vanstone' ♀ H4	CMac CNCN EHea GKir LRHS MBar MBri MGos MOke NHol
- 'Julia'	EHea
- 'Julie Ann Platt'	EHea
- 'Juno'	EHea
- 'Kaiser' **new**	EHea
- 'Karin Blum'	EHea
- 'Kermit'	EHea
- 'Kerstin' ♀ H4	CBcs EHea LRHS MBar NBlu NHol SPlb
- 'Kinlochruel' (d) ♀ H4	CMac CNCN CPLG EHea EPfP GKir LRHS MBar MBri MGos MOke NBlu NHol SRms
- 'Kir Royal'	EHea
- 'Kirby White'	CNCN EHea LRHS MBar MBri NBlu NDlv NHol
- 'Kirsty Anderson'	EHea LRHS MOke
- 'Kit Hill'	EHea MBar
- 'Kontrast' **new**	EHea
- 'Kuphaldtii'	EHea MBar
- 'Kuppendorf'	EHea
- 'Kynance'	CNCN EHea MBar
- 'Lady Maithe'	EHea
- 'Lambstails'	EHea MBar
- 'L'Ancresse'	EHea
- 'Larissa'PBR **new**	EHea
- 'Late Crimson Gold'	EHea
- 'Lemon Gem'	EHea
- 'Lemon Queen'	EHea
- 'Leslie Slinger'	EHea LRHS MBar
- 'Lewis Lilac'	EHea
- 'Liebestraum'	EHea
- 'Lilac Elegance'	EHea
- 'Lime Glade'	CNCN EHea
- 'Lime Gold'	EHea
- 'Little John' **new**	EHea
- 'Llanbedrog Pride' (d)	EHea MBar
- 'Loch Turret'	EHea MBar MBri MOke
- 'Loch-na-Seil'	EHea MBar
- 'London Pride'	EHea
- 'Long White'	CNCN EHea MBar
- 'Loni'	EHea
- 'Lüneberg Heath'	EHea
- 'Lyle's Late White'	CNCN EHea
- 'Lyle's Surprise'	EHea MBar
- 'Lyndon Proudley'	EHea
- 'Macdonald of Glencoe'	EHea
§ - 'Mair's Variety' ♀ H4	EHea LRHS MBar
- 'Mallard'	EHea
- 'Manitoba'	EHea
- 'Marianne' **new**	EHea
- 'Marie'	EHea
- 'Marion Blum'	EHea MBar
- 'Marleen'	CNCN EHea MBar NHol
- 'Marleen Select' **new**	EHea
- 'Marlies'	EHea NHol
- 'Martha Hermann'	EHea
- 'Martine Langenberg' **new**	EHea

- 'Masquerade'	EHea MBar
- 'Matita'	EHea
- 'Mauvelyn'	EHea
- 'Mazurka'	EHea
- 'Melanie'	EHea LRHS MBar NBlu NHol
- 'Mick Jamieson' (d)	EHea
- 'Mies'	EHea
- 'Minima'	EHea MBar
- 'Minima Smith's Variety'	EHea MBar
- 'Miniöxabäck'	EHea
- 'Minty'	EHea
- 'Mirelle'	CNCN EHea
- 'Miss Muffet'	EHea NHol
- 'Molecule'	EHea MBar
- 'Monika' (d)	EHea
- 'Moon Glow'	EHea
- 'Mountain Snow'	EHea
§ - 'Mousehole'	CNCN EHea LRHS MBar MOke NHol
- 'Mousehole Compact'	see *C. vulgaris* 'Mousehole'
- 'Mrs Alf'	EHea
- 'Mrs E. Wilson' (d)	EHea
- 'Mrs Neil Collins'	EHea
- 'Mrs Pat'	CNCN EHea LRHS MBar MOke NHol
- 'Mrs Pinxteren'	EHea
- 'Mrs Ronald Gray'	CNCN EHea MBar
- 'Mullach Mor'	EHea
§ - 'Mullardoch'	EHea MBar
- 'Mullion' ♀ H4	EHea MBar MOke NBlu
- 'Multicolor'	CNCN EHea GKir LRHS MBar MOke NBlu NDlv NHol SRms
- 'Murielle Dobson'	EHea MBar
§ - 'My Dream' (d) ♀ H4	CNCN EHea EPfP LRHS MBar NHol SCoo
- 'Nana'	EHea
- 'Nana Compacta'	CNCN EHea ESis LRHS MBar MOke SRms
- 'Natasja'	EHea
- 'Naturpark'	EHea MBar
- 'Nico'	EHea
- Nordlicht	see *C. vulgaris* 'Skone'
- 'October White'	CNCN EHea
- 'Odette'	EHea
- 'Oiseval'	EHea
- 'Old Rose'	EHea
- 'Olive Turner'	EHea
- 'Olympic Gold'	EHea
- 'Orange and Gold'	EHea LRHS
- 'Orange Carpet'	EHea
- 'Orange Max'	EHea
- 'Orange Queen'	CNCN EHea LRHS MBar
- 'Öxabäck'	EHea MBar
- 'Oxshott Common'	CNCN EHea GQui MBar
- 'Pallida'	EHea
- 'Parsons' Gold'	EHea
- 'Parsons' Grey Selected'	EHea
- 'Pastell' (d)	EHea
- 'Pat's Gold'	EHea
- 'Peace'	EHea
- 'Pearl Drop'	EHea MBar
- 'Peggy' **new**	EHea
- 'Penhale'	EHea
- 'Penny Bun'	EHea
- 'Pennyacre Gold'	EHea
- 'Pennyacre Lemon'	EHea
- 'Pepper and Salt'	see *C. vulgaris* 'Hugh Nicholson'
- 'Perestrojka'	EHea NHol
- 'Peter Sparkes' (d) ♀ H4	CMac CNCN EHea EPfP LRHS MBar MBri MGos MOke NBlu NHol SRms
- 'Petra'	EHea
- 'Pewter Plate'	EHea MBar

- 'Pink Beale'   see *C. vulgaris* 'H.E. Beale'
- 'Pink Dream' (d)   EHea
- 'Pink Gown'   EHea
- 'Pink Spreader' **new**   EHea
- 'Pink Tips'   EHea
- 'Plantarium'   EHea
- 'Platt's Surprise' (d)   EHea
- 'Polly'   EHea
- 'Poolster' **new**   EHea
- 'Porth Wen White'   EHea
- 'Prizewinner'   EHea
- 'Prostrata   EHea
  Flagelliformis'
- 'Prostrate Orange'   CNCN EHea MBar
- 'Punch's Dessert'   EHea
- 'Pygmaea'   EHea MBar
- 'Pyramidalis'   EHea LRHS
- 'Pyrenaica'   EHea MBar
- 'R.A. McEwan'   EHea
- 'Radnor' (d) ♀ H4   CBcs CNCN EHea LRHS MBar
                          MGos MOke
- 'Radnor Gold' (d)   EHea MBar
- 'Raket' **new**   EHea
- 'Ralph Purnell'   CNCN EHea MBar
- 'Ralph Purnell Select'   EHea
- 'Ralph's Pearl'   EHea
- 'Ralph's Red'   EHea
- 'Randall's Crimson'   EHea
- 'Rannoch'   EHea
- 'Red Carpet'   CNCN EHea LRHS MBar MOke
- 'Red Favorit' (d)   CBcs EHea LRHS
- 'Red Fred'   EHea MGos NHol SCoo
- 'Red Haze'   CBrm CMac CNCN EHea EPfP
                          LRHS MBar MOke NHol WStI
- 'Red Max'   EHea
- 'Red Pimpernel'   CNCN EHea EPfP MBar
- 'Red Rug'   EHea
- 'Red Star' (d)   CNCN EHea LRHS MBar MOke
                          NHol
- 'Red Wings'   EHea
- 'Redbud'   EHea
- 'Redgauntlet' **new**   EHea
- 'Reini'   EHea NHol
- 'Rica'   EHea
- 'Richard Cooper'   EHea MBar
- 'Rieanne'   EHea
- 'Rigida Prostrata'   see *C. vulgaris* 'Alba Rigida'
- 'Rivington'   EHea
- 'Robber Knight'   EHea
- 'Robert Chapman'   CBrm CMac CNCN EBre EHea
  ♀ H4   GKir LRHS MBar MBri MGos
                          MOke NBlu NHol
- 'Rock Spray'   EHea
- 'Roland Haagen' ♀ H4   EHea MBar MOke
- 'Roma'   EHea LRHS MBar
- 'Romina'   CNCN EHea NHol
- 'Ronas Hill'   CNCN EHea
- 'Roodkapje'   EHea
- 'Rosalind'   CNCN EPfP LRHS MBar MOke NHol
- 'Rosalind, Crastock   EHea
  Heath'
- 'Rosalind,   EHea LRHS
  Underwood's'
- 'Ross Hutton'   EHea
- 'Roswitha'   EHea
- 'Roter Oktober'   EHea
- 'Rotfuchs'   EHea
- 'Ruby Slinger'   CNCN EHea LRHS MBar
- 'Rusty Triumph'   EHea
- 'Ruth Sparkes' (d)   CMac CNCN EHea LRHS MBar
                          MOke NHol
- 'Sabrina' (d)   EHea
- 'Saima'   EHea

- 'Saint Nick'   EHea MBar
- 'Salland'   EHea
- 'Sally Anne Proudley'   CNCN EHea MBar
- 'Salmon Leap'   EHea GKir MBar NHol
- 'Sam Hewitt'   EHea
- 'Sampford Sunset'   CSam EHea
- 'Sandhammaren'   EHea
- 'Sandwood Bay'   EHea
- 'Sandy'PBR **new**   EHea
- 'Sarah Platt' (d)   EHea
- 'Saskia'   EHea
- 'Scaynes Hill'   EHea
- 'Scholje's Rubin' (d)   EHea
  new
- 'Schurig's Sensation'   CNCN EHea LRHS MBar MBri
  (d)   MOke
- 'Schurig's Wonder'   EHea
  (d) **new**
- 'Scotch Mist'   EHea
- 'Sedloňov'   EHea
- 'Sellingsloh'   EHea
- 'September Pink'   EHea
- 'Serlei'   EDAr EHea LRHS MBar MOke
- 'Serlei Aurea' ♀ H4   CNCN EHea LRHS MBar
- 'Serlei Grandiflora'   EHea MBar
- 'Serlei Purpurea'   EHea
- 'Serlei Rubra'   EHea
- 'Sesam'   EHea
- 'Sesse'   EHea
- 'Shirley'   CMac EHea MBar
- 'Silberspargel'   EHea
- 'Silver Cloud'   CNCN EHea MBar
- 'Silver Fox'   EHea
- 'Silver King'   CNCN EHea LRHS MBar
- 'Silver Knight'   CNCN EBte EDAr EHea EPfP GKir
                          LRHS MBar MBri MGos MOke
                          NHol SPlb WStI
- 'Silver Queen' ♀ H4   CNCN EBre EHea GKir LRHS
                          MBar MBri MOke NHol SRms
- 'Silver Rose' ♀ H4   CNCN EHea LRHS MBar
- 'Silver Sandra'   EHea
- 'Silver Spire'   CNCN EHea MBar
- 'Silver Stream'   EHea LRHS MBar
- 'Simone' **new**   EHea
- 'Sir Anthony Hopkins'   EHea
- 'Sir John Charrington'   CBcs CNCN EBre EHea EPfP GKir
  ♀ H4   LRHS MBar MBri MGos MOke
                          NBlu NHol WStI
- 'Sirsson'   EHea MBar MBri
- 'Sister Anne' ♀ H4   CNCN EBre EHea EPfP LRHS MBri
                          MGos MOke NBlu NDlv NHol SRms
- 'Skipper'   EHea MBar
- 'Skone' (v)   EHea
- 'Snowball'   see *C. vulgaris* 'My Dream'
- 'Snowflake'   EHea
- 'Soay'   EHea MBar
- 'Sonja' (d)   EHea
- 'Sonning' (d)   EHea
- 'Sonny Boy'   EHea
- 'Sophia' (d) **new**   EHea
- 'Sparkling Stars' **new**   EHea
- 'Spicata'   EHea
- 'Spicata Aurea'   CNCN EHea MBar
- 'Spicata Nana'   EHea
- 'Spider'   EHea
- 'Spitfire'   CNCN EHea LRHS MBar NHol WStI
- 'Spook'   EHea
- 'Spring Cream' ♀ H4   CBcs CNCN EBre EHea GKir
                          LRHS MBar MBri MGos MOke
                          NHol WStI
- 'Spring Glow'   CMac CNCN EHea LRHS MBar
                          MBri MOke
- 'Spring Torch'   CBcs CNCN EBre EHea GKir

		LRHS MBar MBri MGos MOke
		NHol SCoo WStl
	- 'Springbank'	EHea MBar
	- 'Stag's Horn'	EHea
I	- 'Startler'	EHea
	- 'Stefanie'	EHea
	- 'Stranger'	EHea
	- 'Strawberry Delight' (d)	EDAr EHea EPfP NHol
	- 'Summer Elegance'	EHea
	- 'Summer Orange'	CNCN EHea LRHS MBar NHol
	- 'Summer White' (d) **new**	EHea
	- 'Sunningdale'	see *C. vulgaris* 'Finale'
	- 'Sunrise'	CNCN EHea LRHS MBar MGos MOke NHol WStl
	- 'Sunset' ♀ H4	CBrm CNCN EBre EHea LRHS MBar NHol SRms WStl
	- 'Sunset Glow'	EHea
	- 'Talisker'	EHea
	- 'Tenella'	EHea
	- 'Tenuis'	EHea MBar
	- 'Terrick's Orange'	EHea
	- 'The Pygmy'	EHea
	- 'Tib' (d) ♀ H4	CMac EHea LRHS MBar MBri MGos MOke NBlu NDlv SRms WStl
	- 'Tijdens Copper'	EHea
	- 'Tino'	EHea
	- 'Tom Thumb'	EHea MBar
	- 'Tomentosa Alba'	EHea
	- 'Tom's Fancy'	EHea
	- 'Torogay'	EHea
	- 'Torulosa'	EHea
	- 'Tremans'	EHea
	- 'Tricolorifolia'	CNCN EHea GKir LRHS NHol
	- 'Underwoodii'	EHea LRHS MBar NBlu
	- 'Unity' **new**	EHea
	- 'Valorian'	EHea
	- 'Van Beek' **new**	EHea
§	- 'Velvet Dome'	EHea LRHS MBar
	- 'Velvet Fascination' ♀ H4	CBcs CNCN EHea EPfP GKir LRHS MBar MGos NHol
	- 'Violet Bamford'	EHea
	- 'Visser's Fancy'	EHea
§	- 'Walter Ingwersen'	EHea
	- 'Waquoit Brightness'	EHea GKir
	- 'Westerlee Gold'	EHea
	- 'Westerlee Green'	EHea
	- 'Westphalia'	EHea
	- 'White Bouquet'	see *C. vulgaris* 'Alba Plena'
	- 'White Carpet'	EHea
	- 'White Coral' (d)	EHea MGos
	- 'White Gown'	EHea
	- 'White Lawn' ♀ H4	CNCN EHea LRHS MBar MGos NBlu NDlv NHol SRms
	- 'White Mite'	EHea LRHS MBar
	- 'White Pearl' (d)	EHea
	- 'White Princess'	see *C. vulgaris* 'White Queen'
§	- 'White Queen'	EHea MBar
	- 'White Star' (d)	EHea LRHS
	- 'Whiteness'	CNCN EHea
	- 'Wickwar Flame' ♀ H4	CBcs CBrm CMac CNCN EBre EHea EPfP LRHS MBar MBri MGos MOke NBlu NHol WStl
	- 'Wilma'	EHea
	- 'Wingates Gem'	EHea
	- 'Wingates Gold'	EHea
	- 'Winter Chocolate'	CNCN EHea GKir LRHS MBar MBri MGos MOke NBlu NDlv NHol WStl
	- 'Winter Fire'	EHea
	- 'Winter Red'	EHea
	- 'Wollmers Weisse' (d)	EHea

- 'Wood Close'	EHea
- 'Yellow Basket'	EHea
- 'Yellow Dome'	CNCN
- 'Yellow Globe' **new**	EHea
- 'Yellow One'	EHea
- 'Yellow Queen'	EHea
- 'Yvette's Silver'	EHea
- 'Yvonne Clare'	EHea

Calocedrus (*Cupressaceae*)

§	decurrens ♀ H4	CAgr CBcs CDoC CDul CMac CTho CTri EBre EHul ENot EOrn EPfP GKir LCon LPan MBar MBlu MBri MGos NWea SLim SPer WEve
	- 'Aureovariegata' (v)	CDoC CKen EHul LCon LLin LPan LRHS MAsh MBar MBlu MBri NLar SLim
	- 'Berrima Gold'	CDoC CKen EPfP GKir LRHS MAsh MGos SLim
§	- 'Depressa'	CKen
	- 'Intricata'	CKen
	- 'Nana'	see *C. decurrens* 'Depressa'
	- 'Pillar'	CKen MBri
	macrolepis **new**	EMon ISea

Calocephalus (*Asteraceae*)

brownii	see *Leucophyta brownii*

Calochortus (*Liliaceae*)

albus	EPot WCot
- var. rubellus	ECho EPot LAma WCot
amabilis	EPot WCot
amoenus	WCot
argillosus	EPot
barbatus	EHyt EPot NWCA WCot
catalinae	EPot
clavatus	EPot
- var. avius	EPot
invenustus	EPot
leichtlinii	EPot
luteus	EPot GCrs LAma WLin
- 'Golden Orb' PBR	CBro EChP ECho ETub GCrs LRHS WCot WHil
monophyllus	EPot
obispoensis	EPot
palmeri	EPot
plummerae	EPot
- JA 94-104	EHyt
splendens	LAma
- 'Violet Queen'	CBro WHil
striatus JA 93-21	EHyt
superbus	CBro CPen EChP ECho EHyt EPot LRHS WLin
tolmiei	EHyt EPot
- JCA 1.178.020	WCot
- NNS 99-81	WCot
umpquaensis	EHyt
uniflorus	EHyt EPot GCrs WCot
venustus	CBro EChP EHyt EPot GCrs LAma LRHS WCot WHil WLin
vestae	EHyt EPot WCot

Calomeria (*Asteraceae*)

§ amaranthoides	WJek

Calonyction see *Ipomoea*

Calopogon (*Orchidaceae*)

tuberosus	SSpi

Calopsis (*Restionaceae*)

paniculata	CTrC IArd

Caloscordum (Alliaceae)
§   **neriniflorum**   EBur EHyt WAbe WCot

Calothamnus (Myrtaceae)
blepharospermus   SOWG
gilesii   CTrC SOWG
homolophyllus   SOWG
quadrifidus   SOWG
- yellow-flowered **new**   SOWG
rupestris   SOWG
sanguineus   SOWG
validus   SOWG SPlb

Caltha ✿ (Ranunculaceae)
'Auenwald'   CLAP CRDP CRow SSpi
'Honeydew'   CLAP CRDP CRow GBuc NCat
introloba   SWat
laeta   see *C. palustris* var. *palustris*
leptosepala   CLAP CRow EBee NWCA
§   - subsp. **howellii**   GKev
natans   CRow EBee
palustris ♀ [114]   More than 30 suppliers
- var. **alba**   More than 30 suppliers
- **barthei new**   CFir EBee SSpi WCot
- 'Flore Pleno' (d)   CBen CPrp CRow EBre ECha
  ♀ [114]   EGle EHon ELan GGar GKir
                                   LPBA LSyl MBri MSta NChi NFor
                                   NGdn NHar NPer NSti SDes SPer
                                   SPlb SWat WAul WCot WGwG
                                   WWeb
- var. **himalensis**   EBee ETow ITim WCot WWpP
- 'Marilyn'   CLAP CRDP GBuc NCat
- 'Multiplex' (d)   COtt EBee GBuc WLin
§   - var. **palustris**   CBen CBre CRDP CRow ECha
                                   EHon ELan EMFW EMon EPar
                                   GGar LPBA MSta SLon SMad SSpi
                                   SWat WCra WFar WMAq
- - 'Plena' (d)   COlW CRow CSam CWat ENot
                                   EPfP GDea LRHS WElm WFar
                                   WMAq
- var. **polypetala**   NPer WHil
- var. **radicans**   CRow GCrs SSpi
- - 'Flore Pleno' (d)   CRow
- 'Semiplena' (d)   EMon
- 'Stagnalis'   CRow
- Trotter's form **new**   GBuc
- 'Tyermannii'   CRow
- 'Yellow Giant' **new**   SLon
N   **polypetala** hort.   see *C. palustris* var. *palustris*
N   **polypetala** Hochst.   CLAP CWat EBee EWll
sagittata   CLAP CRow
- JLA 2.198.200   SSpi
scaposa   EBee
'Susan'   CRow

Calycanthus (Calycanthaceae)
fertilis   see *C. floridus* var. *glaucus*
- 'Purpureus'   see *C. floridus* var. *glaucus*
                                   'Purpureus'
floridus   CAgr CArn CBcs CFil CFwr
                                   CMCN CPMA CPle CTho
                                   EBee ELan EPfP LAst LEdu
                                   LRHS MBNS MBlu MDun
                                   MWhi SBrw SPer WBod
                                   WDin WLRN WWin
§   - var. **glaucus**   CFil CPLG CPle EPfP LBuc MGos
                                   NBlu WSHC
§   - - 'Purpureus'   CPMA MBlu NEgg NLar WBcn
- var. **laevigatus**   see *C. floridus* var. *glaucus*
occidentalis   CAgr CArn CBcs CFil CMCN CPle
                                   CWib EMil MBlu SBrw SIgm SSpi
                                   WBVN

Calydorea (Iridaceae)
speciosa   see *C. xiphioides*
§   **xiphioides**   EWes

Calystegia (Convolvulaceae)
affinis   CPIN
collina subsp. **venusta**   WCot
§   **hederacea** 'Flore   CFwr CPIN EBee EChP ECha ELan
  Pleno' (d)   EMon EOrc EPar LHop MCCP
                                   MTho NLar NSti SMad WCot WFar
                                   WHer WWin
japonica 'Flore Pleno'   see *C. hederacea* 'Flore Pleno'
macrostegia subsp.   WCot
  cyclostegia
silvatica 'Incarnata'   EBee EMon EOrc EWes

Calytrix (Myrtaceae)
§   **alpestris**   SOWG
longiflora yellow-   SOWG
  flowered **new**
sullivanii   SOWG
tetragona   SPlb
- compact, pink   SOWG

Camassia ✿ (Hyacinthaceae)
biflora   EBee
- F&W 8669   WCot
cusickii   More than 30 suppliers
- 'Zwanenburg'   EBee LRHS WDav
esculenta   see *C. quamash*
fraseri   see *C. scilloides*
leichtlinii hort.   see *C. leichtlinii* subsp. *suksdorfii*
N   - 'Alba' hort   see *C. leichtlinii* subsp. *leichtlinii*
*   - 'Alba Plena'   NDir
- 'Blauwe Donau'   see *C. leichtlinii* subsp. *suksdorfii*
                                   'Blauwe Donau'
- Blue Danube   see *C. leichtlinii* subsp. *suksdorfii*
                                   'Blauwe Donau'
- 'Electra'   ECha LPio
§   - subsp. **leichtlinii**   More than 30 suppliers
  ♀ [114]
N   - 'Plena' (d)   ECha WCom
- 'Semiplena' (d)   CAvo CBro CDes CFai CFwr CLAP
                                   CMea CMil CRDP EBee EMan EMon
                                   EPar EPot GEdr NMen SAga SYvo
                                   WAul WCot WDav WFTG WPnP
§   - subsp. **suksdorfii**   CAvo CBri CSam EBot EPPr EPar
                                   GBuc LRHS MSph NChi SCro
                                   SYvo WAul
§   - - 'Blauwe Donau'   LAma LRHS WDav
§   - - Caerulea Group   More than 30 suppliers
§   **quamash**   More than 30 suppliers
- 'Blue Melody' (v)   CBro CFwr CMea CRDP CStu
                                   EBee EBlw EMan EMar EMon EPPr
                                   EPot GBuc LBBr LRHS MBNS MNrw
                                   NMen WCot WFTG WHil WPnP
- 'Orion'   CBro CLAP CMea CPLG EBee EMon
                                   GBuc GMac MAvo WAul WCot
§   **scilloides**   CPLG EBee MBri WCot

Camellia ✿ (Theaceae)
'Auburn White'   see *C. japonica* 'Mrs Bertha A.
                                   Harms'
'Barbara Clark'   CTrG MGos SCog WCwm WWeb
  (*saluenensis*
  x *reticulata*)
'Barbara Hillier'   CDoC
  x *japonica* 'Juno'
'Bertha Harms Blush'   see *C. japonica* 'Mrs Bertha A.
                                   Harms'
'Black Lace' (*reticulata*   CDoC CTrh MAsh MBri SCam
  x *williamsii*) ♀ [114]   SCog SPer WGwG WLRN WWeb

	'Bonnie Marie' (hybrid)	CWib SCam SCog
	'Charles Cobb'	see *C. japonica* 'Mrs Charles Cobb'
	'Cinnamon Cindy' (hybrid)	SCog
	'Contessa Lavinia Maggi'	see *C. japonica* 'Lavinia Maggi'
*	'Cornish Clay'	ISea
	'Cornish Snow' (*cuspidata* x *saluenensis*) ♀ H4	CBcs CDoC COtt CSam CTrh CWib EPfP ISea LHyd SBrw SCam SCog SHBN SPer SReu SSpi SSta WFar WPGP
	'Cornish Spring' (*japonica* x *cuspidata*) ♀ H4	CBcs CDoC COtt CTrh EPfP LHyd SCog WBcn WLRN
	'Corsica'	SHBN
	'Czar'	see *C. japonica* 'The Czar'
	'Dainty Dale' (hybrid)	SCam
	'Delia Williams'	see *C.* x *williamsii* 'Citation'
	'Doctor Clifford Parks' (*reticulata* x *japonica*) ♀ H2	SCog
	'Donckelaeri'	see *C. japonica* 'Masayoshi'
	'El Dorado' (*pitardii* x *japonica*)	CTrG CTrh SPer
	'Extravaganza' (*japonica* hybrid)	CBcs CTrh IArd SBod WBcn
	'Felice Harris' (*sasanqua* x *reticulata*)	SCog
	'Fire 'n' Ice' **new**	SCog
	'Forty-niner' (*reticulata* x *japonica*)	CBcs CDoC SCog
	'Fragrant Pink' (*rusticana* x *lutchuensis*)	CTrh WBcn
	'Francie L' (*saluenensis* x *reticulata*) ♀ H3-4	CDoC CTrh EPfP SCam SCog SSta
	'Frau Minna Seidel'	see *C. japonica* 'Otome'
	'Freedom Bell' (hybrid) ♀ H4	CCtw CDoC CTrG CTrh GGGa ISea LHyd MAsh MBri SBrw SCog WBcn
	'Gay Baby' (hybrid)	MGos SCog
	grijsii	CTrh
	hiemalis 'Chansonette'	SCam
§	- 'Dazzler'	CDoC CWib LHyd SCog
	- 'Kanjirô'	CTrh
	- 'Shôwa-no-sakae'	SCog
§	- 'Sparkling Burgundy' ♀ H3	CBcs LHyd SBrw SCog
	'Hooker' (hybrid)	CDoC
	'Ice Follies' **new**	SCog
	'Imbricata Rubra'	see *C. japonica* 'Imbricata'
	'Innovation' (x *williamsii* x *reticulata*)	CBcs CWib WWeb
	'Inspiration' (*reticulata* x *saluenensis*) ♀ H4	CBcs CDoC CMHG CMac CTrG CTrh CWSG EPfP GGGa GKir ISea LHyd MBri NBlu SBod SBrw SCam SCog SHBN SPar SSpi WBod
	japonica 'Aaron's Ruby'	CBcs CDoC COtt
	- 'Ada Pieper'	CTrh
	- 'Adelina Patti' ♀ H4	CBcs CCtw CTrh LHyd SCog WCwm
	- 'Adolphe Audusson' ♀ H4	More than 30 suppliers
	- 'Adolphe Audusson Special'	CBcs
§	- 'Akashigata' ♀ H4	CHEx CTrG CTrw CWib ENot EPfP MWat SBrw SCam SCog SReu SSta WBod WCwm WWeb
§	- 'Akebono'	CTrw
	- 'Alba Plena' ♀ H4	CDoC CTrh CWSG ENot LHyd LNet SBod SBrw SCog SPer WFar
	- 'Alba Simplex'	CBcs CMac ELan EPfP LNet SBod SCam SCog SHBN SMer SPer SSpi SSta WLRN WStI
	- 'Alexander Hunter' ♀ H4	LHyd SBod WWeb
§	- 'Althaeiflora'	CBcs CDoC SCam SCog
	- 'Anemoniflora'	CBcs CDoC CTrG ELan SBrw SCam SPer WBod WFar
	- 'Angel'	CBcs SCam SCog
	- 'Angela Cocchi'	WBod
	- 'Ann Sothern'	CTrh
	- 'Annette Gehry' **new**	CBcs
	- 'Annie Wylam' ♀ H4	CTrh LHyd SCog
§	- 'Apollo'	CBcs CSam CTrG CTrh EPfP MAsh MGos NBlu SCam SHBN WBcn WBod
§	- 'Apple Blossom' ♀ H4	CBcs CMac ELan
	- 'Arajishii'	see *C. rusticana* 'Arajishii'
*	- 'Augustine Supreme'	CMac
	- 'Australis' ♀ H4	CTrh
	- 'Ave Maria' ♀ H4	CTrh
	- 'Ballet Dancer' ♀ H4	CDoC MGos SCam WBcn WGwG
	- 'Baron Gomer'	see *C. japonica* 'Comte de Gomer'
	- 'Benten' (v)	CTrG CTrw
	- 'Berenice Boddy' ♀ H4	CBcs CTrh SCam
	- 'Berenice Perfection'	LHyd LRHS
	- 'Betty Foy Sanders'	CTrh
	- 'Betty Sheffield'	CDoC COtt CTrG CWib MGos SCog SHBN WFar
	- 'Betty Sheffield Pink'	CTrG
	- 'Betty Sheffield Supreme'	CBcs SCog
	- 'Black Tie'	CBrm CDoC SCog
	- 'Blackburnia'	see *C. japonica* 'Althaeiflora'
	- 'Blaze of Glory'	CTrh SCog WBcn
§	- 'Blood of China'	CBcs CDoC CWSG LRHS SBod SCam SCog SPer WBod WCwm
	- 'Bob Hope' ♀ H4	CBcs CDoC CTrh LHyd LRHS MAsh MGos SCog
	- 'Bob's Tinsie' ♀ H4	CDoC CTbh CTrw EPfP GBin ISea LRHS MBri SCam
§	- 'Bokuhan' ♀ H4	CCtw CRDP EPfP SCog
	- 'Brushfield's Yellow' ♀ H4	CBcs CDoC CMHG COtt ECle EPfP GKir IArd IMGH LHyd MGos SCam SCog SPer SSta
	- 'Bush Hill Beauty'	see *C. japonica* 'Lady de Saumarez'
§	- 'C.M. Hovey' ♀ H4	CMHG CMac CTrh EPfP MAsh MNes SHBN WBcn WBod WGwG WWeb
	- 'C.M. Wilson'	CMac SCog
N	- 'Campbellii'	WBod
	- 'Campsii Alba'	LRHS SMer WStI
	- 'Can Can'	CBcs CTrG SCam SCog
	- 'Canon Boscawen'	CTrG
	- 'Cara Mia'	CBcs WBod
	- 'Carter's Sunburst' ♀ H4	CBcs CDoC CTrh EPfP SCog
	- 'Chandleri Elegans'	see *C. japonica* 'Elegans'
	- 'Charlotte de Rothschild'	CTrh CTri MBri
	- 'Cheryll Lynn'	CTrh
	- 'Christmas Beauty'	SCam WBod
	- 'Cinderella'	CDoC SCam SCog
	- 'Clarise Carleton'	CTrh LHyd
§	- 'Coccinea'	LRHS
	- 'Colonel Firey'	see *C. japonica* 'C.M. Hovey'
	- 'Commander Mulroy' ♀ H4	CTrh WBcn
	- 'Compton's Brow'	see *C. japonica* 'Gauntlettii'
§	- 'Comte de Gomer'	ELan EPfP LRHS SCam SSta WBcn
	- 'Conspicua'	CBcs
§	- 'Coquettii' ♀ H4	CBcs CDoC CWib MAsh SCam WBod WWeb
	- 'Countess of Orkney'	WBcn
	- 'Dahlohnega'	CTrh
	- 'Daikagura'	CBcs
	- 'Dainty'	CBcs WBcn

– 'Daitairin'	see *C. japonica* 'Dewatairin'
– 'Dear Jenny'	CBcs CTrG SCog
– 'Debbie'	CDoC EHol WGwG
– 'Debutante'	CBcs CMac CTrh LHyd LRHS MAsh MBri SCam SHBN WBcn WBod
– 'Deep Secret'	CDoC
– 'Desire' ♀ H4	CBcs CDoC CMHG CTrh MDun SCog WWeb
– 'Devonia'	CBcs EPfP LHyd LRHS
§ – 'Dewatairin'	CMac SCam
– 'Dixie Knight'	CDoC LRHS MGos SCam SSta
– 'Dobreei'	CMac NBlu WWal
– 'Doctor Burnside'	CBcs CMHG CTrh SCog
– 'Doctor Tinsley' ♀ H4	CDoC CTrh LRHS SCam WBcn WWeb
– 'Dona Herzilia de Freitas Magalhaes'	WBcn
– 'Dona Jane Andresson'	SCam
– 'Donckelaeri'	see *C. japonica* 'Masayoshi'
– 'Donnan's Dream'	CTrh
– 'Drama Girl' ♀ H2	CBcs CDoC CTrw SBod SCam SCog WBod
– 'Dream Time' **new**	CBcs
– 'Duc de Bretagne'	ISea
– 'Duchesse Decazes'	CBcs MBri
– 'Edelweiss'	SCog
– 'Effendee'	see *C. sasanqua* 'Rosea Plena'
– 'Eleanor Hagood'	CBcs WBcn
§ – 'Elegans' ♀ H4	CBcs CDoC CMac CTrG ENot EPfP LRHS MAsh MWat NBlu SBod SBrw SCam SCog SHBN SPar SPer SReu SSta WBcn
– 'Elegans Champagne'	CTrh WBcn
'Elegans Splendour'	WBcn
'Elegant Beauty'	see *C. × williamsii* 'Elegant Beauty'
– 'Elisabeth'	WFar
– 'Elizabeth Dowd'	CBcs
– 'Elizabeth Hawkins'	CTrh LHyd NBlu WLRN
– 'Ella Drayton'	SCog
– 'Emmett Barnes'	SCam
– 'Emmett Pfingstl' (v)	WBcn
– 'Emperor of Russia'	CDoC LRHS WBod
– 'Erin Farmer'	CBcs
– 'Eximia'	WBod
– 'Fashionata'	SCam
– 'Feast Perfection'	CDoC
– 'Finlandia Variegated'	SCam SCog
– 'Fire Dance'	CTrh
– 'Flame'	CBcs WBod
– 'Flashlight'	EPfP
§ – 'Fleur Dipater'	SCam
– 'Flowerwood'	SCog
– 'Forest Green'	ELan LRHS MAsh SCog
– 'Fortune Teller'	CDoC
– 'Fred Sander'	CBcs CDoC CWSG SCam
– 'Frosty Morn'	CBcs
– 'Furo-an'	MAsh
§ – 'Gauntlettii'	CBcs
– 'Geisha Girl'	SCam
– 'Général Lamoricière'	WWeb
– 'Giardino Franchetti'	CMHG
– 'Giuditta Rosani'	CDoC
– 'Glen 40'	see *C. japonica* 'Coquettii'
– 'Gloire de Nantes' ♀ H4	CBcs MNes NBlu SCam SCog WBcn WBod
– 'Gold Tone'	SCam
* – 'Golden Wedding'	LRHS
– 'Grace Bunton'	CBcs SCam SCog
– 'Granada'	SCog
– 'Grand Prix' ♀ H4	CDoC CTrh CTrw LRHS SCam
– 'Grand Slam' ♀ H2	CBcs CDoC CMac CTrh EPfP LRHS MAsh SCam WBcn
– 'Grandiflora Alba' **new**	CBcs
– 'Great Eastern'	CDoC
– 'Guest of Honor'	CBcs CDoC
– 'Guilio Nuccio' ♀ H4	CBcs CDoC CTrG IArd LRHS MGos SCam SCog SPer WBod
– 'Gus Menard'	SCam
§ – 'Hagoromo' ♀ H4	ELan ENot EPfP LRHS SBrw SCam SHBN SPer WBcn WBod WFar
– 'Hakurakuten' ♀ H4	CDoC CTrh CWib IArd ISea SBod SCog
– 'Hanafuki'	CDoC SCog
– 'Hanatachibana'	WBcn
– 'Hatsuzakura'	see *C. japonica* 'Dewatairin'
– 'Hawaii'	CBcs CTrh LRHS SCam SCog
– 'High Hat'	CBcs SCog
– 'Hinomaru'	CMac LRHS
– 'Holly Bright'	CTrh
§ – 'Imbricata'	CWib ENot MAsh MGos SCog
– 'Italiana Vera'	MAsh
– 'J.J.Whitfield'	CMac
– 'Jack Jones Scented'	CMHG
– 'Janet Waterhouse'	CBcs SCog
§ – 'Japonica Variegata' (v)	CMHG WBcn
– 'Jean Clere'	CTrG MGos SCog WBcn
– 'Joseph Pfingstl' ♀ H4	CDoC SCam WWeb
– 'Joshua E.Youtz'	LRHS SCam
– 'Jovey Carlyon' (hybrid)	CDoC WWeb
– 'Joy Sander'	see *C. japonica* 'Apple Blossom'
§ – 'Julia Drayton'	LRHS
– 'Julia France'	CBcs
– 'Juno'	CBcs
– 'Jupiter' ♀ H4	CBcs CDoC CMac CTrh CTrw EPfP ISea LHyd LNet MAsh MGos SCog SHBN WBVN WBod
– 'Just Sue'	CDoC
§ – 'K. Sawada'	SCam SCog
– 'Kenny'	CBcs WBod
– 'Kewpie Doll'	CDoC CTrh SCog
– 'Kick-off'	CBcs CTrh WBcn
– 'Kimberley'	CBcs CDoC EPfP SCog WBcn WBod WLRN
– 'King's Ransom'	CDoC CMac MAsh
§ – 'Kingyo-tsubaki'	SSta WBod
– 'Kitty Berry'	CTrh
– 'Kokinran'	SCam
§ – 'Konronkoku' ♀ H4	CCtw CDoC SCog WBcn WBod
– 'Kouron jura'	see *C. japonica* 'Konronkoku'
– 'Kramer's Beauty'	SCog
– 'Kramer's Supreme'	CBrm CDoC CTrG CWSG CWib LNet MGos NBlu SBod SBrw SCam SCog WFar WLRN
§ – 'Kumasaka'	WBod
– 'La Graciola'	see *C. japonica* 'Odoratissima'
– 'Lady Campbell'	SCam
– 'Lady Clare'	see *C. japonica* 'Akashigata'
§ – 'Lady de Saumarez'	CDoC LNet
– 'Lady Loch'	CTrh CWib MGos SCog
– 'Lady Mackinnon'	MAsh
– 'Lady Marion'	see *C. japonica* 'Kumasaka'
– 'Lady McCulloch'	SCam
– 'Lady Vansittart'	CBcs CBrm CDoC CSam CTrG EBee ELan ENot EPfP ISea LHyd LNet LRHS SBrw SCog SPer WBcn WBod WWeb
§ – 'Lady Vansittart Pink'	MGos SCam SHBN
§ – 'Lady Vansittart Red'	see *C. japonica* 'Lady Vansittart Pink'
– 'Lady Vansittart Shell'	see *C. japonica* 'Yours Truly'
§ – 'Lavinia Maggi' ♀ H4	CDoC CTrG CTrh ELan EPfP LHyd LPan LRHS MAsh MBri MGos SBod SBrw SCam SCog SHBN SMer SPer SReu SRms SSta WWeb

	– 'Lemon Drop'	CTrh
	– 'Lily Pons' ♀ H4	CTrh WBcn
	– 'Lipstick'	CTrh
	– 'Little Bit'	CBcs CDoC CTrh SCam
	– 'Little Bo Peep'	CTrh
	– 'Lotus'	see *C. japonica* 'Gauntlettii'
	– 'Lovelight' ♀ H4	CTrh ISea SCog
	– 'Lulu Belle'	SCog
	– 'Ma Belle'	CMHG
	– 'Mabel Blackwell'	SCam
	– 'Madame de Strekaloff'	CMac
	– 'Madame Lebois'	CBcs
	– 'Madame Martin Cachet'	CMHG SCog
	– 'Madge Miller'	LRHS
	– 'Magnoliiflora'	see *C. japonica* 'Hagoromo'
	– 'Magnoliiflora Alba'	see *C. japonica* 'Miyakodori'
	– 'Maiden's Blush'	CMac SCog WLRN
	– 'Margaret Davis'	CDoC CTrG EBee ECle EPfP IMGH LHyd MAsh MGos SCam WWeb
	– 'Margaret Davis Picotee' ♀ H4	CBcs CFwr CMHG CTrh CTrw MGos SCog SPer SSta WBcn
	– 'Margaret Rose'	SCam
	– 'Margaret Short'	WWeb
	– 'Margherita Coleoni'	CBcs SHBN
	– 'Marguérite Gouillon'	ISea
	– 'Marian Mitchell'	SCam
	– 'Mariana'	SCam
	– 'Mariann'	CTrh
	– 'Marie Bracey'	CBcs
	– 'Marinka'	CBcs
	– 'Marjorie Magnificent'	CDoC LRHS MAsh WWeb
	– 'Maroon and Gold'	WBcn
	– 'Mars' ♀ H4	CDoC MWat SBrw SCam WWeb
	– 'Mary Costa'	CBcs CTrh
	– 'Mary J. Wheeler'	CTrw
§	– 'Masayoshi' ♀ H4	CMac CTrG LHyd LNet
§	– 'Mathotiana'	LRHS
	– 'Mathotiana Alba' ♀ H4	CBcs CDoC CMac EPfP LRHS NBlu SCam SPer
	– 'Mathotiana Purple King'	see *C. japonica* 'Julia Drayton'
§	– 'Mathotiana Rosea' ♀ H4	CBcs CMac LNet SBrw SHBN SPer WBod
	– 'Mathotiana Supreme'	CDoC SCam
	– 'Matterhorn'	CTrh LRHS MAsh WBcn
	– 'Mattie Cole'	CDoC LHyd
	– 'Mercury' ♀ H4	CBcs CDoC CMac COtt CTrG CWSG GGGa MWat SCog SHBN SPer WBod
	– 'Mercury Variegated'	CMHG
	– 'Midnight'	CBcs CDoC CMHG MAsh WWeb
	– 'Midnight Magic'	CTrh
	– 'Midnight Serenade'	CCtw CTrh
	– 'Midsummer's Day'	CBcs
§	– 'Mikenjaku'	CDoC CTrG ENot LNet LRHS MAsh SCam WBod
	– 'Miriam Stevenson'	SCam
	– 'Miss Charleston'	CBcs LHyd SCog
	– 'Miss Universe'	CTrh
	– 'Mississippi Beauty'	CTrh
§	– 'Miyakodori'	EPfP LRHS
	– 'Monsieur Faucillon'	CBcs
	– 'Monte Carlo'	CDoC SCam
	– 'Morning Glow'	WBod
	– 'Moshe Dayan'	MAsh NBlu SMer WWeb
	– 'Moshio'	CDoC
§	– 'Mrs Bertha A. Harms'	SCam SCog
§	– 'Mrs Charles Cobb'	LPan
	– 'Mrs D.W. Davis'	CBcs CTrw EPfP SCam SCog
	– 'Mrs Sander'	see *C. japonica* 'Gauntlettii'
	– 'Mrs William Thompson'	NBlu

I	– 'Mutabilis'	WBcn
	– 'Nagasaki'	see *C. japonica* 'Mikenjaku'
	– 'Nigra'	see *C. japonica* 'Konronkoku'
	– 'Nobilissima'	CBcs CDoC CMac CTrG CTrh CTri ENot EPfP ISea LRHS MAsh MBri MWat SBrw SCam SCog SHBN SPar SPer WBcn WBod WFar WWeb
	– 'Nuccio's Cameo'	CDoC CTrh LHyd MAsh WWeb
	– 'Nuccio's Gem' ♀ H4	CDoC ELan LHyd LRHS SCam SCog SSta
	– 'Nuccio's Jewel' ♀ H4	CDoC COtt CTrh CWSG IMGH LHyd LRHS MGos SCog SPer WBcn WWeb
	– 'Nuccio's Pearl'	CBcs SCog WBcn WBod WWeb
§	– 'Odoratissima'	CTrG
	– 'Onetia Holland'	CBcs CDoC CTrw SCam
§	– 'O-niji'	SBrw
§	– 'Optima **new**'	SCog
	– 'Optima Rosea'	CBcs CTrG EBee ENot WBcn
§	– 'Otome'	NBlu WBod
	– 'Paolina Maggi'	CDoC SCog
	– 'Patricia Ann'	CTrh
	– 'Paul's Apollo'	see *C. japonica* 'Apollo'
	– 'Peachblossom'	see *C. japonica* 'Fleur Dipater'
	– 'Pink Champagne'	SBod WBod
	– 'Pink Clouds'	CBcs SCog
	– 'Pink Perfection'	see *C. japonica* 'Otome'
	– 'Pink Star'	WBod
	– 'Pope Pius IX'	see *C. japonica* 'Prince Eugène Napoléon'
	– 'Preston Rose'	CDoC WBcn
§	– 'Primavera'	CTrh
§	– 'Prince Eugène Napoléon'	CDoC
	– 'Princess Baciocchi'	CBcs SCam
	– 'Princess du Mahe'	CMac
	– 'Professor Sargent'	WCwm
	– 'Purple Emperor'	see *C. japonica* 'Julia Drayton'
	– 'R.L. Wheeler' ♀ H4	CBcs CDoC CTrw LHyd SCam SCog WBod WWeb
	– 'Rafia'	CDoC SCam
	– 'Rainbow'	see *C. japonica* 'O-niji'
	– 'Red Candles'	MNes
	– 'Red Dandy'	CDoC SCam SCog
	– 'Reg Ragland'	SCam
	– 'Roger Hall'	ISea SCog WCwm WOTO
	– 'Rôgetsu'	CBcs SCam
	– 'Roman Soldier'	CBcs
	– 'Rose Dawn'	WBod
	– 'Rosularis'	SCam SCog
	– 'Rubescens Major' ♀ H4	CBcs ISea LHyd SBrw WWeb
	– 'Ruddigore'	CTrh LRHS
	– 'Saint André'	CMac
	– 'San Dimas' ♀ H4	CDoC CTrh SCam SCog SSta WBcn
	– 'Saturnia'	CDoC COtt WWeb
	– 'Sawada's Dream'	ISea SCog
	– 'Scented Red'	CCtw SCog
	– 'Scentsation' ♀ H4	CDoC CMHG COtt SCog
	– 'Sea Foam'	LHyd SCam
	– 'Sea Gull'	CTrh
	– 'Seiji'	CMac
	– 'Shin-akebono'	see *C. japonica* 'Akebono'
§	– 'Shiragiku'	SPer WBod
	– 'Shiro Chan'	SCam WBcn
	– 'Shirobotan'	CTrG GQui SCam SCog
	– 'Shiro-daikagura'	see *C. rusticana* 'Shiro-daikagura'
	– 'Silver Anniversary'	CBcs CDoC CMHG CTrG CTrh ELan GQui LHyd LRHS MGos SCam SCog SPer SReu SSta WWeb
	– 'Silver Moon'	see *C. japonica* 'K. Sawada'
	– 'Simeon'	CDoC SCam
	– 'Sleigh Ride' **new**	WBcn

	- 'Smiling Beauty'	WBod
	- 'Snow Goose'	CDoC
	- 'Southern Charm'	WWeb
	- 'Souvenir de Bahuaud-Litou' ♀ H4	CBcs SCam SCog WBod
	- 'Spencer's Pink'	CBcs CTrw
	- 'Splendens Carlyon'	MAsh WWeb
	- 'Spring Formal'	CTrh
	- 'Spring Frill' **new**	SCog
	- 'Strawberry Blonde'	CDoC SCog
	- 'Sweetheart'	SCog
	- 'Sylva' ♀ H4	SSpi
	- 'Sylvia'	CMac LRHS WBod
	- 'Tammia'	COtt EPfP
	- 'Tarô'an'	CDoC
	- 'Teresa Ragland'	CDoC SCam
	- 'Teringa'	CDoC
§	- 'The Czar'	CBcs CTrw ISea WBod
	- 'The Mikado'	CDoC SCog
	- 'Tick Tock Blush'	SCam
	- 'Tickled Pink'	CDoC SCam
	- 'Tiffany'	CBcs CDoC CWib LHyd LNet LRHS SCam SHBN
	- 'Tinker Toy'	CTrh
	- 'Tom Thumb' ♀ H4	CMHG CTrh SRms
	- 'Tomorrow'	CBcs CDoC CTrw LRHS SCog
	- 'Tomorrow Park Hill'	SCog
§	- 'Tomorrow Variegated'	SCam
	- 'Tomorrow's Dawn'	CBcs
	- 'Touchdown'	SCam
	- 'Tregye'	CBcs
	- 'Trewithen White'	CSam
§	- 'Tricolor' ♀ H4	CBcs CDoC CMHG CMac CTrh ENot EPfP MAsh NBlu SBrw SCam SCog SHBN SPer WBod WBrE WFar WGwG WPnP WWeb
	- 'Tricolor Red'	see C. japonica 'Lady de Saumarez'
	- 'Twilight'	LRHS
	- 'Victor Emmanuel'	see C. japonica 'Blood of China'
	- 'Ville de Nantes'	CBcs CDoC SSta WBcn WBod
	- 'Ville de Nantes Red'	WBcn
	- 'Virginia Carlyon'	CBcs CCtw CDoC CWib
	- 'Vittorio Emanuele II'	CDoC CTrh
	- 'Warrior'	CDoC COtt CWib SCog
	- 'White Giant'	CDoC
	- 'White Nun'	SCog
	- 'White Swan'	CMac COtt
	- 'Wilamina' ♀ H4	CTrh
	- 'William Bartlett'	CTrh
	- 'William Honey'	CTrh
	- 'Wisley White'	see C. japonica 'Hakurakuten'
§	- 'Yours Truly'	CBcs CMac CTrh LHyd LRHS SBrw SCam WBcn
	- 'Yukimi-guruma'	WBod
§	- 'Yukishiro'	CTrw
	'John Tooby' **new**	COtt WWeb
	'Jury's Yellow'	see C. x williamsii 'Jury's Yellow'
	'Lavender Queen'	see C. sasanqua 'Lavender Queen'
	'Leonard Messel' (reticulata x williamsii) ♀ H4	CBcs CDoC CMHG CTrG CTrh ENot EPfP GGGa LHyd MGos NBlu SBrw SCam SCog SHBN SPer SReu WCwm WStI
	lutchuensis	CTrh
	'Madame Victor de Bisschop'	see C. japonica 'Le Lys'
§	maliflora (d)	CBcs
	'Nicky Crisp' (japonica x pitardii)	WCwm
	'Nijinski' (reticulata hybrid)	CDoC ISea
	oleifera	CSam CTrh CWib SCam SCog

	'Paradise Little Liane' PBR	CBcs
	'Pink Icicle' (hybrid)	MNes
	'Pink Spangles'	see C. japonica 'Mathotiana Rosea'
	'Polar Ice' (oleifera hybrid)	CDoC SCog
	'Polyanna' (hybrid)	CDoC SCog
	'Portuense'	see C. japonica 'Japonica Variegata'
	'Quintessence' (japonica x lutchuensis)	SCog
	reticulata 'Arch of Triumph'	CTrG
	- 'Mary Williams'	CBcs
	- 'Nuccio's Ruby'	LHyd
	- 'William Hertrich'	CBcs
	'Royalty' (japonica x reticulata) ♀ H3	CBcs CTrG
§	rusticana 'Arajishi'	CBcs CDoC CMac COtt SBrw SCam SCog SCoo WBod WLRN WWal
§	- 'Shiro-daikagura'	WBod
	saluenensis 'Exbury Trumpet'	CCtw
	- 'Trewithen Red'	CTrw WBod
	saluenensis x japonica	see C. x williamsii
	'Salutation' (reticulata x saluenensis)	CBcs ISea SCam
	sasanqua	CSam ISea LPan
	- 'Ben'	SCog
	- 'Bettie Patricia'	SCog
	- 'Cleopatra'	LPan
	- 'Cotton Candy'	SCog
	- 'Crimson King' ♀ H3	GQui SBrw SCam SCog SHBN WBcn
	- 'Dazzler'	see C. hiemalis 'Dazzler'
	- 'Flamingo'	see C. sasanqua 'Fukuzutsumi'
	- 'Flore Pleno'	see C. maliflora
	- 'Fuji-no-mine'	CTrh
§	- 'Fukuzutsumi'	CBrm COtt CTrG SBrw SCam SCog WCwm
	- 'Gay Sue'	CTrh SCam
	- 'Hugh Evans' ♀ H3	CBcs CDoC COtt CTrh LHyd SBrw SCam SCog SSta WBod
	- 'Jean May' ♀ H3	CDoC LHyd SBrw SCam SCog SSta WBcn WBod
	- 'Kenkyô'	SCam SSta
§	- 'Lavender Queen'	SCam
*	- 'Little Liane'	SCog
	- 'Lucinda'	SCog
	- 'Maiden's Blush' **new**	WFar
	- 'Mignonne'	CTrh
	- 'Mine-no-yuki'	SCog
	- 'Narumigata'	CBcs CDoC CMac CTrw ECle ENot EPfP LHyd MAsh SBrw SCam SCog SSta WBod WPnP WSHC
	- 'Navajo'	CTrh
	- 'Nyewoods'	CMac
	- 'Papaver'	SCam SCog
	- 'Paradise Blush'	CBcs SCog
	- 'Paradise Glow'	CBcs SCog
	- 'Paradise Hilda'	SCog
	- 'Paradise Pearl'	CBcs SCog
	- 'Paradise Petite' PBR	SCog
	- 'Paradise Venessa' PBR	CBcs SCog
	- 'Peach Blossom'	CBcs
	- 'Plantation Pink'	SBrw SCog SPer
	- 'Rainbow'	CBrm CTrG CTrh ISea SCam SCog SPer SSta WBod WFar
	- 'Rosea'	SCam SSta
§	- 'Rosea Plena'	CBcs CMac CTrw SCog
	- 'Sasanqua Rubra'	CMac
	- 'Sasanqua Variegata' (v)	SCam SSta

I	- 'Shishigashira'	CTrh SCam
	- 'Snowflake'	SCam SSta
	- 'Sparkling Burgundy'	see *C. hiemalis* 'Sparkling Burgundy'
	- 'Winter's Snowman'	SCam SCog
	'Scented Sun'	CTrh
	'Scentuous' (*japonica* x *lutchuensis*)	SCog WBcn
	'Sea Shell' **new**	WWeb
	'Shiro-wabisuke' (Wabisuke)	CDoC
	'Show Girl' (*sasanqua* x *reticulata*)	CDoC CTrh LHyd SBod SCog WBcn WBod
§	'Shôwa-wabisuke' (Wabisuke)	CTrh WBcn
§	*sinensis*	EShb GPoy
	'Snow Flurry' (*oleifera* hybrid)	CDoC SCog
	'Splendens'	see *C. japonica* 'Coccinea'
	'Spring Festival' (*cuspidata* hybrid) ♀ H4	CDoC CHig CMHG MGos
	'Spring Mist' (*japonica* x *lutchuensis*)	CMHG CTrh
	'Strawberry Parfait'	SPer
	'Swan Lake' (hybrid)	CTrG ISea
	'Tarôkaja' (Wabisuke)	SCam
	thea	see *C. sinensis*
	'Tinsie'	see *C. japonica* 'Bokuhan'
	'Tiny Princess' (*japonica* x *fraterna*)	CBcs
	'Tom Knudsen' (*reticulata* x *japonica*) ♀ H3	CTrh
	'Tomorrow Supreme'	see *C. japonica* 'Tomorrow Variegated'
	transnokoensis	CTrh
	'Tricolor Sieboldii'	see *C. japonica* 'Tricolor'
	'Tristrem Carlyon' (*reticulata* hybrid) ♀ H4	CBcs CCtw CDoC CTrG MAsh
	tsaii	CPLG
	'Usu-ôtome'	see *C. japonica* 'Otome'
	x *vernalis* 'Hiryû'	SCog
	x *williamsii*	More than 30 suppliers
	'Anticipation' ♀ H4	
	- 'Anticipation Variegated'	SCog
	- 'Ballet Queen'	CBcs CDoC MGos SCam WFar
	- 'Ballet Queen Variegated'	SCog SSta
	- 'Bartley Number Five'	CMac
	- 'Beatrice Michael'	CBcs CMac
	- 'Bow Bells'	CDoC CMac CTrh GKir LAst LHyd LRHS SCog
	- 'Bowen Bryant' ♀ H4	CTrh CTrw GGGa SCog
	- 'Bridal Gown'	LHyd
	- 'Brigadoon' ♀ H4	CDoC CMHG CTrG CTrh CTrw EPfP GGGa GKir LHyd LRHS MBri MGos SCog WWal
	- 'Burncoose'	CBcs
	- 'Burncoose Apple Blossom'	CBcs
	- 'C.F. Coates'	MNes SSta
	- 'Caerhays'	CBcs
	- 'Carnation'	MAsh WWeb
	- 'Celebration'	CBcs
	- 'Charlean'	CDoC SCam
	- 'Charles Colbert'	WBcn
	- 'Charles Michael'	CBcs
	- 'China Clay' ♀ H4	CDoC CTrG LHyd LRHS SBod SCog WBcn WBod WWal
§	- 'Citation'	CBcs CMac CTrw
	- 'Clarrie Fawcett'	CDoC
	- 'Contribution'	CTrh
	- 'Crinkles'	NBlu
	- 'Daintiness' ♀ H4	CDoC LRHS MBri
	- 'Dark Nite'	CMHG
	- 'Debbie' ♀ H4	More than 30 suppliers
	- 'Debbie's Carnation'	CMHG
	- 'Donation' ♀ H4	More than 30 suppliers
	- 'Dream Boat'	CBcs LHyd
	- 'E.G. Waterhouse'	CBcs CDoC CMHG CTrG CTrh CTri CTrw EPfP GKir LAst LHyd MAsh NBlu SBod SCam SCog SSta WBcn WBod WCwm WWeb
	- 'E.T.R. Carlyon' ♀ H4	CBcs CCtw EBee EPfP LHyd LRHS MAsh SCog WWeb
§	- 'Elegant Beauty' ♀ H4	CBcs CDoC CTrG CTrh CTrw CWSG SBod SBrw SCam SCog WCwm
	- 'Elizabeth Anderson'	CTrh
	- 'Ellamine'	CBcs
	- 'Elsie Jury' ♀ H3	CBcs CDoC CMac CTrG CTrw CWSG GKir GQui LHyd LRHS MGos NBlu SBod SCam SCog SPer WBcn WBod WGwG WWal
	- 'Francis Hanger'	CBcs CDoC CTrh LHyd SCam SCog SSpi WGwG WWal
	- 'Galaxie' ♀ H4	CBcs ISea
	- 'Garden Glory'	CTrh
	- 'George Blandford' ♀ H4	CBcs CMHG CMac
	- 'Glenn's Orbit' ♀ H4	CBcs CTrw SCam WBcn
	- 'Golden Spangles' (v)	CBcs CDoC CFwr CMac CTrG CTrh ELan EPfP GKir LHyd LRHS MGos MNes SBrw SCam SPar SReu SSta WBcn
	- 'Gwavas'	CBcs CWib SCog
	- 'Hilo'	CTrw
	- 'Hiraethlyn'	CBcs LHyd WBod
	- 'Hope'	LHyd
	- 'J.C. Williams' ♀ H4	CBcs CMac CSam CTrw CWSG ENot EPfP ISea LHyd SBrw SCog SPer SSpi WBod
	- 'Jean Claris'	CDoC
	- 'Jenefer Carlyon'	CCtw CDoC CWib
	- 'Jill Totty'	CTrh
	- 'Joan Trehane' ♀ H4	CTrw
	- 'Joe Nuccio' **new**	CTrh
	- 'Julia Hamiter' ♀ H4	CBcs CTrw
§	- 'Jury's Yellow' ♀ H4	CBcs CDoC CFwr CTbh CTrG CTrh CTri CTrw ECle ELan EPfP GKir GQui LHyd LRHS MAsh MBri MGos NBlu SCog SHBN SPer SSta WBcn WFar WWeb
	- 'Laura Boscawen'	CTrG CTrh
	- 'Les Jury' ♀ H4	LHyd SCog SPer
	- 'Margaret Waterhouse'	CDoC COtt SCam SCog
	- 'Mary Christian' ♀ H4	COtt EPfP LHyd
	- 'Mary Jobson'	CBcs CDoC
	- 'Mary Phoebe Taylor' ♀ H4	CBcs CDoC CTrG CTrw CWSG SCog SHBN
	- 'Mirage'	CTrh
	- 'Moira Reid' **new**	CDoC
	- 'Monica Dance'	CBcs
	- 'Muskoka' ♀ H4	CBcs CTrh ISea WCwm
	- 'New Venture'	CBcs
	- 'November Pink'	CBcs EHol GKir SCog
	- 'Phillippa Forward'	CMac WBod
	- 'Rendezvous'	CDoC SCam
	- 'Rose Court'	WBod
	- 'Rose Parade'	LHyd
	- 'Rosemary Williams'	CBcs CTrw
	- 'Rosie Anderson'	LRHS
	- 'Ruby Bells'	CMHG

- 'Ruby Wedding'	CBrm CTrh ECle GQui LHyd
	MAsh SCog SPer WBcn WWeb
- 'Saint Ewe' ♀ H4	CBcs CDoC CTrG CTrh CTri
	CTrw CWib EPfP LHyd MBri
	MGos NBlu SBrw SCam SCog
	SHBN SMer SPer WBod
- 'Sayonara'	SCog
- 'Senorita' ♀ H4	CDoC CTrh LHyd SCam SCog
- 'Taylor's Perfection'	CTrw
- 'The Duchess of	CCtw CDoC
Cornwall'	
- 'Tiptoe'	CTrh NBlu
- 'Water Lily' ♀ H4	CBcs CDoC CTrh CTrw EPfP
	MGos SCam WBcn WBod
- 'Wilber Foss' ♀ H4	CTrh CTrw LHyd SCam SCog
- 'William Carlyon'	CWSG
- 'Wood Nymph'	SBrw
- 'Yesterday'	SCog SMur
'Winter's Charm'	SCog
(oleifera x sasanqua)	
'Winter's Dream'	SCog
(biemalis x oleifera)	SCog
'Winter's Fire' (hybrid)	MNes SCog
'Winter's Interlude'	SCog
(oleifera x sinensis)	
'Winter's Joy' new	SCog
'Winter's Toughie'	CDoC SCog
(C.? oleifera x sasanqua)	
'Winton' (cuspidata x	CBcs CDoC SCam
suluenensis)	
'Wirlinga Belle' new	SCog
'Yoimachi' (fraterna x	CTrh
sasanqua) new	
'Yukihaki'	see C. japonica 'Yukishiro'

Camissonia (Onagraceae)

chieranthifolia	WPer

Campanula ❀ (Campanulaceae)

abietina	see C. patula subsp. abietina
alaskana	see C. rotundifolia var. alaskana
§ alliariifolia	More than 30 suppliers
- 'Ivory Bells'	see C. alliariifolia
allionii	see C. alpestris
§ alpestris	ECho GTou NBur NMen SIgm
alpina	MDCh NBur
ardonensis	NSla SOkd
argyrotricha	NBur
arvatica	CLyd EPot ETow LRHS MBro
	MDKP NHar NHol WAbe WPat
- 'Alba'	CGra CLyd WAbe WLin WPat
- x cochleariifolia	WBea
aucheri	see C. saxifraga subsp. aucheri
autraniana	NWCA
'Avalon'	SAsh
§ 'Balchiniana' (v)	WEas
barbata	CNic EBee ELan EPot GDra GTou
	LHop MAnH MLwd MWod WMoo
	WPer WWeb
- var. alba	GAbr NBur
beauverdiana	EHyt WCom
bellidifolia	MWrn NBir NSla
§ betulifolia ♀ H4	CGra CSam EHyt GDra ITim
	MAnH MBro NBur NHar NLon
	NMGW SIng
- JCA 252.005	SBla
- x troegerae	ITim MWrn
'Birch Hybrid' ♀ H4	CMHG ECtt EDAr ELan EMNN
	EPfP ESis GDra GKir LBee LRHS
	NHar SCro SIng WCom WCra
	WFar WTel
bononiensis	EBee MSph SRms
'Bumblebee'	CGra

'Burghaltii' ♀ H4	CBot CElw CHar CMil EBee EBlw
	EBre ECGP ECha EHrv ELan EMon
	GMac LRHS MBro MGrG MSte
	NCot SAga SBla SOkh SSpi WCot
	WFar WPGP WPer WWhi WWin
calaminthifolia	EBur
cana CC 3732 new	GKev
§ carnica	EBee ECho EVFa MSte
carpatha	SBla
carpatica ♀ H4	CWCL EBee ECho GDra ITim
	MBar MBri MDKP NBlu NBro
	NGdn NLon SPlb SRms SWat
	WWin
- f. alba	LPVe NFor NGdn SPlb SWat
- - 'Bressingham White'	EBre GKir SBla
§ - - 'Weisse Clips'	COkL ECtt EDAr ELan EMNN
	ENot EPfP ESis GDra GKir GTou
	LAst LHop MDun NBlu NGdn
	SDes SPar SPer SPla SRms WFar
	WPat WPer WWeb
§ - 'Blaue Clips'	ECtt EDAr ELan EMNN EMlt ENot
	EPar EPfP ESis GDra GKir GTou
	LAst MBNS MDun NGdn SDes
	SPar SPer SPla SRms WFar WGwG
	WPat WPer WWeb
- blue	MRav
* - 'Blue and White	LPVe
Uniform'	
- Blue Clips	see C. carpatica 'Blaue Clips'
- 'Blue Moonlight'	EBre EBur GKir LRHS SMer
- 'Caerulea'	CBcs
- 'Chewton Joy'	CLyd CTri EBre GKir LRHS WTel
- 'Ditton Blue'	GDra GMaP
- dwarf	EPot SSct
- 'Karpatenkrone'	EBee
Foerster	
- 'Kathy'	GBuc SAsh
- 'Kobaltglocke' new	EBee
- 'Maureen Haddon'	EBre GKir LRHS NWCA
- 'Suzie'	SBla
- var. turbinata	EHyt GDra MTho NSla SRms
	WPer
- - f. alba 'Hannah'	EBre GDra LRHS
- - 'Georg Arends'	CLyd CNic SAsh
- - 'Isabel'	EBee LRHS
- - 'Jewel'	LRHS
- - 'Karl Foerster'	EBee EBre GBuc GKir LRHS
	MTho SBla SMer WHoo
- - 'Pallida'	GDra
- - 'Wheatley Violet'	LRHS SBla
- White Clips	see C. carpatica f. alba 'Weisse
	Clips'
§ cashmeriana	EBur ETow NBur
- SEP 386	EHyt
cephallenica	see C. garganica subsp.
	cephallenica
§ chamissonis	NBur NSla SBla WCom WPat
§ - 'Major'	CPBP EDAr EMNN EPot EWes
	LBee MBro NBur NMGW SAga
- 'Oyobeni'	NHar WLin
§ - 'Superba' ♀ H4	FBur EGle ELan MTho NBur
	NMen NSla
choruhensis	CGra NBur WLin
§ cochleariifolia ♀ H4	CSpe CTri EDAr ELan EMNN EMlt
	EPfP ESis GDra GKir GTou MBro
	MDun MFir MTho MWat NHar
	NLAp SPet SSvw WFar WHoo
	WPer WTel WWhi WWin
- var. alba	CNic CSpe EDAr EMNN EMlt
	LRHS MBro MHer MWat NChi
	NHar NLAp NMen NRya SBla
	SRms WAbe WHoo WPer
- - 'Bavaria White'	ITim LPVe NHar

– – double white (d)	CRDP WPat
– – 'White Baby' (Baby Series)	EPfP GAbr NBlu NPri SDes
– 'Bavaria Blue'	ECho ITim LPVe NHar
– 'Blue Baby' (Baby Series)	ECho ECtt EPfP MHer NBlu NPro SDes
– 'Blue Tit'	GBuc
– 'Blue Wonder'	COtt EPot
– 'Cambridge Blue'	EBre LRHS NBur WAbe
– 'Elizabeth Oliver' (d)	More than 30 suppliers
– 'Flore Pleno' (d)	ECtt
– 'Miss Willmott'	CLyd EBur MTho NBir
– 'Oakington Blue'	LRHS SBla
– var. *pallida* 'Miranda'	LRHS WIvy
– – 'Silver Chimes'	ITim
– 'R.B. Loder' (d)	EMlt
– 'Tubby'	CLyd CNic CPlt CRDP ECho ITim LRHS MHer MTho SRms
– 'Warleyensis'	see *C.* x *haylodgensis* 'Warley White'
collina	CTri EBee GSki NHar NPri SIgm WCFE WPer
'Covadonga'	CMea CNic CPBP EMlt LHop LRHS LTwo
'Crystal' **new**	MAvo
dasyantha	see *C. chamissonis*
'E.K.Toogood'	CElw CPBP EBee ECtt EMNN MDHE MWat NBro NHar NHol NLAp NVic SBla SCro SMac SMrm SRms WWpP
elatines	NOak
'Elizabeth'	see *C. takesimana* 'Elizabeth'
eriocarpa	see *C. latifolia* 'Eriocarpa'
§ 'Faichem Lilac'	CHar EBee ECoo ECtt MAnH MWrn NChi NCot NLar NPro STes WBar WElm WPer
fenestrellata	GKev ITim MTho NBro SRms WAbe
finitima	see *C. betulifolia*
foliosa	MSPs WPer
formanekiana ♀ H2-3	EBee EBur EChP ECoo ELan EMan EPyc MAnH MBrn MLLN MWrn NBur WCom WFTG
– MP 77-98	IDac
fragilis	EBur ECho EHyt SOkd WPer
– subsp. *cavolinii*	EHyt
– 'Hirsuta'	ECho
'G.F.Wilson' ♀ H4	EBur ECho EMlt WRHF
garganica ♀ H4	EPfP ESis GAbr GSki MDKP MRav NBlu NFla NFor NHar NLAp NLon SIng SPet WFar WMaN WMoo WPer
– 'Aurea'	see *C. garganica* 'Dickson's Gold'
– 'Blue Diamond'	EDAr ELan EMNN LHop SBla SCro WAbe WLRN
§ – subsp. *cephallenica*	CElw NBro NJOw
§ – 'Dickson's Gold'	More than 30 suppliers
– 'Major'	ECho GDra IHMH LAst WRHF
– 'W.H. Paine' ♀ H4	CLyd EBre ECho EDAr LRHS MDKP NMen NSla SIng WHoo
§ 'Glandore'	NCat NMen NPro
glomerata	CBot CBri CKin CPLG EDAr GKir GTou LPVe MBNS MBow MBrN MFir MLwd NBid NBlu NBro NLan NMir NRya SOkh SPet STes SWal WBea WEas WFar WGwG WWin WWye
– var. *acaulis*	CPrp EBee EMNN EMan EMlt EPfP ERou GKir LRHS MBNS MHer MWhi MWrn NArg NOak NWCA SCro SPla WFar WHil WPer WWeb WWin
– var. *alba*	More than 30 suppliers
§ – – 'Alba Nana'	EVFa

§ – – 'Schneekrone'	CBri EBre ECha EFou EPfP ERou EWTr MGrG NLon NOak WBea WFar
– 'Caroline'	CPBP EBee EBre EChP EGle EMon ERou EVFa LRHS MAvo MCAu MCLN MRav MUlv NSti SCro SDes SOkh SUsu WAul WHal WHil WMaN WWeb
* – 'Compacta Alba' **new**	GKev
– Crown of Snow	see *C. glomerata* var. *alba* 'Schneekrone'
– var. *dahurica*	EWTr LPVe MHer MOne NBur NLar NOak WBea WHil WPer
– 'Joan Elliott'	CCge EBee EChP ECha EMan GBuc LRHS MRav MWat NGdn SPet
– 'Nana Alba'	see *C. glomerata* var. *alba* 'Alba Nana'
– 'Superba' ♀ H4	More than 30 suppliers
– 'White Barn'	ECha NOak
grossekii	CBri EBee EBre EHrv MWrn
'Hallii'	ESis LRHS MBro NWCA WPat
Hannay's form **new**	CHar
x *haylodgensis* sensu stricto hort.	see *C.* x *haylodgensis* 'Plena'
§ – 'Marion Fisher' (d)	CGra EDAr MBro NHar WAbe WCot WHoo
§ – 'Plena' (d)	ELan EPot LAst LBee LHop LRHS MBro NBro NHar NLAp NWCA SBla SRms WAbe WBVN WCot WEas WHoo WKif
§ – 'Warley White' (d)	CNic EBur ELan
– 'Yvonne'	COlW EDAr SDes WFar WPer WWol
'Hemswell Starlight'	CLyd NPro
hercegovina	EHyt
– 'Nana'	CPBP SBla WAbe
herminii	EHyt
– MP 94-56	IDac
'Hilltop Snow'	CGra CPBP
'Hillview Hose in Hose' **new**	WHil
hypopolia	EPfP
§ *incurva*	CBri CPou CSpe EBur EChP EMan GAbr ITim MAnH MLwd MNrw MTho MWrn NCot NOak NRya SBri SMrm STes WAbe WBea WPer
– *alba*	WPer
– 'Blue Ice'	WWin
x *innesii*	see *C.* 'John Innes'
isophylla ♀ H2	ECho MBri SIng SPet
– 'Alba' ♀ H2	ECho SIng SYvo
– 'Flore Pleno' (d)	EBur
– 'Mayi' ♀ H2	CSpe
– 'Mayi' misapplied	see *C.* 'Balchiniana'
– 'Variegata'	see *C.* 'Balchiniana'
jaubertiana	CGra EHyt
'Joe Elliott' ♀ H2-3	ECho EWes LRHS NSla
§ 'John Innes'	CLyd
kemulariae	ESis NBur SRms WCom WPer
– *alba*	IDac ITim
'Kent Belle' ♀ H4	More than 30 suppliers
'Kent Blue' **new**	CBri
lactiflora	More than 30 suppliers
– *alba*	see *C. lactiflora* white
N – 'Alba' ♀ H4	EChP EGle EMil ERou GKir GMac MTed STes
– 'Blue Avalanche'	EBee SMrm
– 'Blue Cross'	COtt ECoo EFou GKir GMac LRHS MAnH WHrl WTel
– 'Kirsty' **new**	NCat
– 'Loddon Anna' ♀ H4	More than 30 suppliers
– 'Pouffe'	EBee EChP ECha EGle ELan EMan EPfP GKir GMac LPVe LRHS MAnH MBct MGrG MRav MWrn

		NBro NGdn NSti SCro SPer SPet SPla SWat WFar WWin
	- 'Prichard's Variety' ♀ H4	More than 30 suppliers
	- 'Senior'	EBee EFou LPio WAul
	- 'Superba' ♀ H4	EBee GKir MTed WCot
	- 'Violet'	EBee SDes SWat WPer
§	- white	CBot EBee ECha EFou GAbr LAst MAnH MBro NBir NBur NCot NFla SChu SPer WHoo WPer
	- 'White Pouffe'	EBre EChP EGle ELan EOrc EPfP EWTr GKir GMaP GSki LRHS MAnH MBri MRav NChi NLar SMer SOkh SPer SPla STes SWat WFar WLin
	lanata	MAnH SVen
	lasiocarpa	CPBP EBur LRHS WFar
§	latifolia	CAgr CArn CKin CSev EBot EChP ECha GAbr GGar LRHS MCAu MCLN MHdf MWgw NBid NChi NFor NMir NOrc NVic SBla SMer SPer WCer WCra WFar WLin WMoo
*	- 'Amethyst'	EBee MGGn
	- 'Brantwood'	CBri CFwr EBre EChP EGle EMar ERou GMac MAnH MFir MRav MWat MWrn NChi NOak NPro SMer SSpe WCot WWin
§	- 'Buckland' **new**	SBla
§	- 'Eriocarpa'	MLwd MWrn NBur
	- 'Gloaming'	GKir LRHS NBur
	- var. **macrantha**	CFwr COIW CSBt EBlw EBre EFou EPfP ERou GLil LHop LPVe LRHS MHer MNrw MSte MWrn NSti SDes SPer SSvw WBea WCot WMoo WPer WRus WWeb WWye
	- - alba	CM&M CMil EBee ECha ECtt EHrv EMan EPri ERou GMaP LHop LPhx LRHS MAnH MCAu MRav MSte SPla STes WCot WMoo WPer
	- 'Roger Wood'	MWgw
	white	EDrc GAbr MAnH MCLN MSte MTis MWrn NGdn SBla SPer SSpi WEas WRus
	- 'White Ladies'	NBur
	- 'Witte Wieven'	CFwr
§	latiloba	CBre CElw CMHG GKir LGro MFir NChi NWoo SAga WEas WFar WHoo WWin
	- 'Alba' ♀ H4	CBre CHar CPlt EFou EGle ELan EPPr FPfP GCal GMac MAnH MDKP NChi NGdn SGar SHel WEas WMaN
	- 'Hidcote Amethyst' ♀ H4	More than 30 suppliers
	- 'Highcliffe Variety' ♀ H4	CHea CMGP EBee EBlw EChP EGle EMan EPfP GBuc MAnH MMHG MRav MTis NDov NSti SPer SPla SSpe SSpi WCot WEas WKif WLRN WMnd
*	- 'Highdown'	MLLN WFar
	- 'Percy Piper' ♀ H4	CSam CStr ELan GBri GBuc GKir GMac LRHS MBri NBro NFor NLon WFar WOut
	- 'Splash'	CFee EBee MAvo MGrG MTed MWrn WCot
	ledebouriana MP 81-98	IDac
	linifolia	see C. carnica
	'Lynchmere'	ETow
	makaschvilii	CHar CPla EChP EDif EMan EVFa GIBF GMac ITim MAnH MAvo MLwd MSph MTis MWrn NBur NChi NLar SAga SBod WCHb WCom WPer
	'Marion Fisher'	see C. x haylodgensis 'Marion Fisher'
	medium	EBot NBlu
§	- 'Calycanthema'	ERou WMnd
	- 'Cup and Saucer'	see C. medium 'Calycanthema'
	- white	EBot
	'Mist Maiden'	CLyd CMHG EPot ETow LRHS WFar
	mollis var. gibraltarica	NBur
	muralis	see C. portenschlagiana
	'Mystery'	EBee EGle EMan MBNS MBri NLar
	'Mystery in Blue' **new**	EMan EPfP ERou MBNS NCot NLar
	nitida	see C. persicifolia var. planiflora
	- var. planiflora	see C. persicifolia var. planiflora
	'Norman Grove'	CLyd EGle EPot LBee
	oblongifolioides	CFwr
	ochroleuca	CRDP EBee EFou EWTr GCal GDea LRHS MAnH MWrn NBur SPoG STes SWat WCFE WHal WHrl WMoo WWeb
	- 'White Bells' **new**	WHHs
	odontosepala **new**	CElw EMon
	olympica hort.	see C. rotundifolia 'Olympica'
	ossetica	see Symphyandra ossetica
	pallida subsp. tibetica	see C. cashmeriana
	parryi	IDac
	parviflora Lam.	see C. sibirica
	patula	NLar
§	- subsp. abietina	MAnH MWrn STes
	'Paul Furse'	LRHS MBri MDKP MFir NLar NSti SHar STes WWin
	pelviformis	MNrw
	persicifolia	More than 30 suppliers
	- 'Alba'	More than 30 suppliers
§	- 'Alba Coronata' (d)	CFir CStr EBre EMon GAbr GBri LRHS MBro MTis NBir WEas WFar
	- 'Alba Plena'	see C. persicifolia 'Alba Coronata'
	- 'Bennett's Blue' (d)	EBee EOrc LPio
	- 'Best China'	MAvo
	- blue	EMan EOrc LAst MBow MRav SPlb WEas WFar
	- 'Blue Bloomers' (d)	CElw CHar CMil EBee EBre EChP EGle EMon EVFa EWes GBri GMac MAvo MRav MSph WCot WHal WPnP
	- blue cup-in-cup (d)	MDKP WFar WLin WWin
	- 'Boule de Neige' (d)	CHea CM&M EBee EGle MAvo NMGW NOak WCom WEas
	'Caerulea Coronata'	see C. persicifolia 'Coronata'
*	- 'Cacrulea Plena' (d)	MBNS
	- 'Carillon'	GBri
§	- 'Chettle Charm' PBR ♀ H4	More than 30 suppliers
	- 'Coronata' (d)	EBre GMac MRav SGar WBrE
	- 'Cristine'	MDKP
	- cup and saucer blue (d)	WHil
N	- cup and saucer white (d)	CLyd ELan WHil WPer
	- double blue (d)	EGle NBro WEas
	- double white (d)	ELan NChi WMoo
	- 'Fleur de Neige' (d) ♀ H4	CSam ECtt LRHS MBro MLLN MSph NOak WAul WCot WHoo
	- 'Flore Pleno' (d)	NBir
	- 'Frances' (d)	CLAP EGle EMon GBri MAvo WMaN WPnP
	- 'Frank Lawley' (d)	LRHS
	- 'Gawen'	see C. persicifolia 'Hampstead White'
	- 'George Chiswell' PBR	see C. persicifolia 'Chettle Charm'
	- 'Grandiflora Alba'	GBuc MAnH SMrm
	- 'Grandiflora Caerulea'	NLar
§	- 'Hampstead White' (d)	More than 30 suppliers
	- 'Hetty'	see C. persicifolia 'Hampstead White'

	- Irish double white (d)	EMon MAvo
	- 'Kelly's Gold' **new**	NBhm NGdn NSti
	- 'La Belle' **new**	CFai WRus
	- 'Moerheimii' (d)	CHea EOrc EPar ERou MBri MDKP NBir NDov STes WHil WIvy WLin WMaN WWin
	- var. *nitida*	see *C. persicifolia* var. *planiflora*
	- 'Peach Bells'	MBNS NOak
	- 'Perry's Boy Blue'	NPer
	- 'Pike's Supremo'	see *C.* 'Pike's Supremo'
§	- var. *planiflora*	CPBP CSpe EBee EHyt ETow GDra GTou MWrn NHar SBla WAbe
§	- - f. *alba*	CSpe WAbe WWin
	- 'Pride of Exmouth' (d)	CCge CHar CHea CSam EBee EChP EHrv ELan EMan EMon GBuc LAst LLWP LRHS MArl MAvo MBri MBro NLon NOak WCot WKif
	- 'Rearsby Belle' (d)	MDKP
	- subsp. *sessiliflora*	see *C. latiloba*
	- 'Snowdrift'	SRms
	- 'Telham Beauty' misapplied	More than 30 suppliers
	- 'Tinpenny Blue'	WTin
	- 'White Bell' **new**	MWrn
N	- 'White Cup and Saucer' (d)	CElw WFar WWye
	- 'White Queen' (d)	NBur WEas WMnd
	- 'Wortham Belle' (d)	CSev EBee EChP EGle EMan EPri GBri GBuc GSki LAst LHop LRHS MAvo MCAu MCLN MRav MTis MUlv NCat NCiC NSti SPer SPla SRms SWat WCra WHil WLRN WRus WViv
	petrophila	CLyd EHyt
§	'Pike's Supremo' (d)	NBir
	pilosa	see *C. chamissonis*
	piperi 'Townsend Ridge'	CGra
§	*planiflora*	see *C. persicifolia* var. *planiflora*
§	*portenschlagiana* ♀ H4	CAgr CElw COlW CTri ELan ENot EPfP LGro LHop MBow MHer MRav MWat NBro NDlv NRya NVic SBla SCro SDes SDix SIng SPer SRms WAbe WCru WEas WFar WMoo WWin
	- 'Lieselotte'	CElw GBuc GMaP MDHE
	- 'Major'	GMaP WFar
	- 'Resholdt's Variety'	CMea CSam EBre EDAr EFou EMlt EPfP ITim LBee LHop LRHS NCat WPer
	poscharskyana	More than 30 suppliers
	- 'Blauranke'	EBee EWes MDHE WCom
	- 'Blue Gown'	EGle GMaP GMac MAnH WTel
	- 'Blue Waterfall'	EBre LRHS MAnH WWpP
	- 'E.H. Frost'	CBre CRez EBee ECtt EDAr EGle EMNN EPPr EPfP ESis EWTr GMac LAst LHop MAnH MWat NBro NCat NHol NRya SAga SCro SRms WBea WFar WPer WTel WWpP
	- 'Glandore'	see *C.* 'Glandore'
	- 'Lilacina'	CElw EPPr NDov SCro SHel
	- 'Lisduggan Variety'	CElw EBre EBur EDAr EGle EPPr ESis EWes GKir MWat NBro NCat SBla SWat WBea WCot WFar WMoo WPer WWin
	- 'Schneeranke' **new**	SCro
	- 'Stella' ♀ H4	EBee EBre ECha EGle EMNN ENot EPPr ESis LRHS MAnH MRav NBro NCat NJOw NVic SChu SDix SIng WCom WFar WWpP
	- variegated (v)	EHoe IBlr WCot
	- white	ELan MDKP WFar
*	*potaninii*	EGra
	prenanthoides	see *Asyneuma prenanthoides*
	primulifolia	CRez EBee EBlw ECoo ECtt ELan EMan IFro LRHS MAnH MMil MNrw MSte MTis MWrn SAga SBod SCro SMac STes WCHb WCom WMoo WPer WPnP WSan WWin
	- 'Blue Oasis'	CFwr NJOw WWeb
	- 'Blue Spires'	LRHS
	x *pseudoraineri*	EBur EDAr EHyt EWes NMen
	'Puff of Smoke' **new**	WCot
	pulla	CLyd CNic CPlt CRDP EBee EBur ECtt EDAr EHyt ELan EMNN EPot ESis MBro MTho NHar NLAp NMGW NRya SBla SIng WCru WFar WPat WPer
	- *alba*	CNic CRDP EBur ECtt EDAr EHyt EMNN EPot LBee LRHS MBro NHar NLAp NMGW SBla WCru WPat
	x *pulloides*	CLyd EBee EDAr
	punctata	More than 30 suppliers
	- f. *albiflora*	GDea GKir LEur LHop LRHS MAnH MBro MLLN MOne NChi WBro WFar WHil WWin
	- - 'Nana Alba'	CBri CMil EBee LRHS MWrn NBur WCot WMoo
	- 'Alina's Double' (d) **new**	MAvo WCot
I	- 'Beetroot'	CBri CDes CFwr CKno EBee EChP EMon GBri LHop MAnH MSph MWrn NChi WPGP
	- 'Bowl of Cherries' **new**	SHar
	- 'Cherry Bells'	CBgR EFou MAnH MAvo SHar WCot
	- var. *hondoensis*	CHar EBee EPPr IGor MBrN MNrw MWrn NSti SAga WBea WCot WMoo WWpP
	- - 'Bossy Boots'	EFou
	- hose-in-hose (d)	SSte WFar
	- 'Hot Lips' **new**	CFwr
	- var. *microdonta*	EBre
	- - B&SWJ 5553	WCru
	- 'Millennium'	MAvo WCot WFar
	- 'Milly'	CBri CDes EBee EMon MWrn
*	- 'Nana'	EChP
	- 'Pantaloons' (d) **new**	SHar
	- 'Pink Chimes' **new**	NBhm
	- 'Pink Eclipse'	WFar
	- 'Reifrock' zur Linden	EFou SMrm
	- 'Rosea'	LPio MBri SRms WFar WHil WSan
	- f. *rubriflora*	More than 30 suppliers
	- - 'Wine 'n' Rubies'	CElw CStr EFWa EHrv EMan MAvo MDKP MWrn SHar SUsu WCot
	- var. *takesimana*	see *C. takesimana*
	- 'Wedding Bells'	EFou MAnH NLar NSti SMrm WCot
	- white hose-in-hose (d)	CRDP MAnH MAvo SAga WCot WFar
	pusilla	see *C. cochleariifolia*
	pyramidalis	CBot CMGP CSpe EBee EBot EPfP GIBF GWCH LIck MBNS MHer MLwd MRav NOrc SDes SPlb STes WOut WPer
	- *alba*	CMGP CSpe EBee EWTr GWCH LPio SPlb WBrE WPer
	raddeana	CElw CLyd CRDP MBro NLar WFar WLin
	raineri ♀ H4	CPBP EPot LRHS MBro NMen NOak NWCA SBla WAbe
	- 'Nettleton Gold'	EPot
§	*rapunculoides*	CBrm EBee EGoo GAbr SWat WBea WHer WPer
§	- 'Afterglow'	MAvo WCot WFar
	- 'Alba'	CStr EMon MAvo WBar
	rapunculus	ILis MWgw
	recurva	see *C. incurva*

reiseri	MLwd
rhomboidalis L. **new**	MWrn
- Gorter	see *C. rapunculoides*
rigidipila	EBee
'Rosanna's Rainbow' (v)	WBar
rotundifolia	CArn CKin EPfP GWCH MBow MBro MHer MPWC NBid NLan NMir NSti SIde SPlb SWal WBea WElm WJek WPer
§ - var. **alaskana**	NWCA
- var. **alba**	CPBP MAnH WHoo
- 'Jotunheimen'	CPBP EHyt
§ - 'Olympica'	EBee EBur EMan EPfP GAbr IGor MBNS NPri WCot WFar WHoo WLow
- 'Superba'	SCro
rupestris	CPBP EBur LTwo
'Samantha'	EBee LAst SHar WCot WWol
'Sarastro'	CDes CHar CLAP CMil EBee EFou EGle EMon EPPr GBuc LPhx MAnH MAvo MBrN MHar NLar SAga SCro SOkh SUsu WCot WCru WFar WLin WPGP WPnP
sarmatica	CBri EBee ECoo EMan EMon EVFa GBuc MAnH MBrN MSte MWhi MWrn NBid NOak NPPs SMrm SRms STes WCHb WMaN WMoo WPer WPic
sartorii	EBur EMan ITim MWrn NMen STes WPer WWin
saxifraga	EBur IDac ITim NBur NMen SIgm WLin
§ - subsp. **aucheri**	EBur EPot GEdr ITim NBur NSla WAbe
scabrella	CGra EHyt
scouleri	NWCA
shetleri	CGra CPBP EHyt NWCA
§ **sibirica**	EMan NBur WGwG WPer
- white	NLar
siegizmundii	GMac NBur
'Smokey Blue' **new**	WCot
'Sojourner' **new**	CGra
speciosa	EBee MAnH MWhi STes
'Stansfieldii'	CPBP EBur EPot NMen SIng WPat
'Summer Pearl' **new**	LAst
'Swannables'	see *C. punctata* x *Symphyandra ossetica*, 'Swannables'
§ **takesimana**	More than 30 suppliers
* - **alba**	EBee GKir LPio MAnH MDKP MWrn SMad WCot WMoo WOut
- 'Beautiful Truth'	NBhm NSti SHar WCot WCru
- dark	GKir
§ - 'Elizabeth'	More than 30 suppliers
teucrioides	EHyt NWCA
thyrsoides	CBri EBee EMan EVFa EWll GDra GTou NBur NWCA WHal WPer
- subsp. **carniolica**	GDra SGar
'Timsbury Perfection' **new**	CGra
tommasiniana ♀H4	EHyt LRHS NBur SAsh
topaliana	WLin
trachelium	CBri CKin EBee EChP ECoo EPPr EPfP MAnH MBNS MBow MNrw MRav MWrn NLan SCou SGar WCot WFar WHer WPer
- var. **alba**	EBee EChP EWTr MAnH MCAu MFir MLwd MMHG MNrw NPar SCou SMac STes WBrE WCom WCot WFar WMaN WMoo WPer WWhi
- 'Alba Flore Pleno' (d)	CDes CFir CHar CHea CStr EMlt EMon LPhx LPio MAnH SBla SMac WBro WCot WFar WSan
- 'Bernice' (d)	More than 30 suppliers
- 'Faichem Lilac'	see *C.* 'Faichem Lilac'
- lilac-blue	NOrc WHHs
tridentata	ETow WPer
troegerae	LRHS NBur SBla
'Tymonsii'	CPBP EBur ECho EHyt ESis LRHS NBir
'Van-Houttei'	CElw CHar CMil CPlt CStr EBee GCal LPhx MSte SAga WCot WFar WPGP WPer
versicolor	EBee MAnH
- G&K 3347	EMon
vidalii	see *Azorina vidalii*
waldsteiniana	CPBP EPot LBee LRHS LTwo NBur WFar
'Warley White'	see *C.* x *haylodgensis* 'Warley White'
'Warleyensis'	see *C.* x *haylodgensis* 'Warley White'
witasekiana	EBee
x **wockei** 'Puck'	EBee EBur ECtt EHyt EMlt EPot LRHS MBro NHar NWCA WAbe WPat
zoysii	EHyt LRHS SBla

Campanula x *Symphyandra* (Campanulaceae)

§ *C.* **punctata** x *S. ossetica*, 'Swannables'	CPou EGle EMan GMac MAnH MWrn NCat NChi WCot

Campanumoea see *Codonopsis*

Campsis (Bignoniaceae)

* **atrosanguinea**	LRHS
grandiflora	CArn CBcs CPIN CSPN EBee EBre ELan ENot EPfP GSki IMGH LRHS MGos SPer WCFE
radicans	CArn CBcs CBot CDul CMac CPIN CRHN CSBt CWib EBee ELan EPfP GKir GQui LAst LPan LRHS MGrG MHer MWat NBlu SHBN SLon SPer SPlb WBrE WDin WWeb
- 'Atrosanguinea'	CPIN
- 'Flamenco'	CBcs CDoC CPIN EBee ELan GQui GSki LAst LRHS MAsh SBra SCoo SLim SPar WBro WCot WCru
§ - f. **flava** ♀H4	CDoC CFwr CPIN EBee ELan ENot EPfP IMGH LHop LRHS MAsh MBri MCCP MGos MWat MWgw NBlu NIlol NPal NSti SBra SLim SPar SPer SPet SSta WCot WSHC WWeb
- 'Indian Summer'	CBcs EBee MBlu MGos SLim WWeb
- 'Yellow Trumpet'	see *C. radicans* f. *flava*
x **tagliabuana** 'Madame Galen' ♀H4	More than 30 suppliers

Camptosorus see *Asplenium*

Campylandra see *Tupistra*

Campylotropis (Papilionaceae)

macrocarpa	WCot

Canarina (Campanulaceae)

canariensis ♀H1	CPIN EShb

Candollea see *Hibbertia*

Canna ✿ (Cannaceae)

'Adam's Orange'	CHEx MOak

'Aida' (Grand Opera Series)　MOak
'Alberich' **new**　CSam
altensteinii　MOak NBlo XBlo
'Ambassador'　CHEx EBee LAma MOak SPar
'America'　CHid EBee LAma WCot
'Angel Pink'　MOak
'Annaeei'　EAmu MOak
'Anthony and Cleopatra' (v) **new**　WCot
'Apricot Dream' **new**　MOak
'Apricot Ice'　MOak
'Aranyálom'　LAma
'Argentina'　MOak
'Aristote' **new**　MOak
'Assaut'　EBot LPio MOak SAPC SArc
'Australia'　MOak WCot
'Black Knight'　CPrp CSpe EAmu EBee EBot EChP GBuc IPot LAma LPVe LPio MBNS MOak SPar SPet SWal WHil
'Bonfire' **new**　CHEx
'Bonnezeaux'　MOak
brasiliensis　CHll NBlo WCot XBlo
– 'Rosea'　WMul
'Brighton Orange' **new**　MOak
'Brillant'　LAma LPVe MBNS MOak SPar
'Canary'　NBlo XBlo
'Centenaire de Rozain-Boucharlat'　MOak
'Centurion'　LAma
'Cerise Davenport'　CFir MOak
'Champigny' **new**　MOak
'Champion'　CHEx MOak
'Cherry Red' Schmid　MOak SPar
'Chinese Coral' Schmid　CHEx LAma MOak
§ 'City of Portland'　EBee LAma MBri MOak SChr SPar
'Cleopatra'　EAmu LAma LPVe MCCP MOak MUlv SPar SPet WGwG WHil WWeb
coccinea　MOak
§ 'Colibri' **new**　EBee LAma
'Confetti'　see *C.* 'Colibri'
'Creamy White'　CHEx
'Crimson Beauty'　LAma MOak
Crozy hybrids　LRav
'Délibáb'　CSam EBee EChP IPot LAma LPVe MBNS MOak SPar SPet
'Di Bartolo'　LPio MOak
'Durban' (v)　CFil CHEx CHll CKob CSpe CTrC EBee EBlw EMan EOrc EWes LHop LPJP MOak NBlo SCoo SDix SPar WCot WHal WMul XBlo
edulis　MOak
– green-leaved **new**　IIve
– 'Newlyn Green'　CHEx
– purple-leaved **new**　IIve
x *ehemanii*　CHEx CKob LPio SVen WMul
'Ember' **new**　NBlo XBlo
'Emblème'　MOak
'En Avant'　CHEx EBot LAma MOak SPar SPlb
'Endeavour'　CFil CHEx EBot LPJP MOak MSta WMAq WMul WPGP
'Erebus'　LPio MOak MSta SDix SPar SVen WMAq
'Étoile du Feu'　MOak NBlo XBlo
'Evening Star'　LAma
'Extase'　MOak
'Fatamorgana'　LAma
'Felix Ragout'　LAma SPar
* 'Felix Roux' **new**　MOak
Firebird　see *C.* 'Oiseau de Feu'
'Flame'　NBlo XBlo
'Flameché' **new**　MOak
'Florence Vaughan'　MOak SPar

'Fournaise'　MOak
'General Eisenhower'　MOak
x *generalis* hybrids　SHGC
glauca　EBot MOak SDix
'Gnom'　MOak
* 'Gold Ader'　LAma
'Gold Dream'　LAma LPVe
'Golden Girl' **new**　MOak SPar
'Golden Inferno' **new**　NBlo XBlo
'Golden Lucifer'　CSpe LAma LPVe MBri MRav SPar
'Grand Duc'　MOak
'Grande' **new**　CFir MOak
'Harvest Yellow' **new**　MOak
'Heinrich Seidel'　CHEx MOak
'Hercule'　MOak
'Horn'　MOak
§ *indica*　CBcs CSev EBot EFul IFro LPio MGol MOak SAPC SArc SPlb SYvo
– 'Purpurea'　CFil EBee EBlw ECha EOrc LEdu LPio MOak SDix SPar SVen WCot WDyG WMul WPGP
'Inferno' **new**　NBlo XBlo
'Ingeborg'　EBee LAma LPVe MOak SPar
'Intrigue'　MOak
iridiflora misapplied　see *C.* x *ehemanii*
iridiflora Ruiz & Pav.　CSev EBee MOak NBlo SAPC SArc SChr SDix SPar WPGP XBlo
'Jivago'　MOak
'Kansas City' (v)　EBee WCot
'King Haakon'　MOak
I 'King Humbert' (blood-red)　CBcs CHEx EBot LAma MCCP MGol SYvo WCot
King Humbert (orange-red)　see *C.* 'Roi Humbert'
'King Midas'　see *C.* 'Richard Wallace'
'Königin Charlotte'　MOak SPar
'La Bohème' (Grand Opera Series)　EBee LAma
'La Gloire'　MOak
'Lafayette'　MOak
'L'Aiglon' **new**　MOak
'Lesotho Lill'　CHll CMdw
'Libération'　MOak
'Liberté'　MOak
'Louis Cayeux'　MOak SDix
'Louis Coutin'　CPrp CSam EBot EChP ETub LAma LPVe LPio MBNS MOak SPar WHil
'Lucifer'　CBcs CSpe EAmu EBee EBot ETub LAma LPVe LRHS MLan MOak NPer SPar SPet SYvo WBrE WHil WWeb
lutea　CHEx NBlo XBlo
'Madame Angèle Martin'　MOak NBlo XBlo
'Madame Paul Casaneuve'　MOak
'Madeira' (Island Series)　MOak
'Malawiensis Variegata'　see *C.* 'Striata'
'Marvel'　LAma
'Meyerbeer'　MOak SPar
'Mrs Oklahoma'　LAma LPVe MOak
* *musifolia*　CHEx CKob EAmu EBot LPJP LPio MOak NBlo SDix SPar WCot WDyG WMul XBlo
'Mystique'　MOak SDix
'North Star Landscape Red'　MOak
§ 'Oiseau de Feu'　LAma MBri MOak SPar
'Oiseau d'Or'　MOak
'Orange Blush' **new**　MOak
'Orange Futurity' **new**　MOak
'Orange Perfection'　CFir CHEx CSam LAma MOak
'Orchid'　see *C.* 'City of Portland'
'Panache'　CFil CHEx MOak WCot WDyG
'Peach Blush' **new**　MOak

'Perkeo' | EBee EPyc LAma LPVe MOak SPar SPet
'Petit Poucet' | MOak
'Picadore' | MOak
'Picasso' | CBcs CHEx CPrp CSam CSut EAmu EBee LAma MBNS MLan MOak NBlo SPar SPet SWal SYvo XBlo
'Pink Futurity' (Futurity Series) **new** | MOak SPar
'Pink Sunburst' (v) | CKob CSpe MOak SPar WCot
'Pink Sunrise' **new** | MOak
'Plantagenet' | MOak
'President' | CSut EBee ECho LAma LPVe LPio MBri MOak SPar SPet WBrE
'Pretoria' | see C. 'Striata'
'Primrose Yellow' | MOak SPar
'Prince Charmant' **new** | MOak
'Princess Di' **new** | MOak
'Professor Lorentz' | CFil MOak NBlo WPGP XBlo
'Puck' | MOak
'Ra' | MOak MSta WMAq
'Red Futurity' (Futurity Series) **new** | MOak SPar
'Red Wine' **new** | MOak
§ 'Richard Wallace' | CSam EBee EBot LAma LPio MOak NBlo SAPC SArc SPar SPlb SVen SYvo WCot XBlo
'Robert Kemp' | LAma
§ 'Roi Humbert' | CPrp CSam EBee MOak SPar SVen
'Roi Soleil' | CFil CHEx LAma MOak WPGP
'Roitelet' | CHEx
'Rose Futurity' (Futurity Series) **new** | MOak
'Rosemond Coles' | CBcs CHEx CPrp CSam EBot EPfP LAma MLan MOak SPar SWal SYvo MOak
'Saladin' | MOak
'Salmon Pink' | CHEx MOak SPar
'Sémaphore' | MOak
'Singapore Girl' | MOak SPar
'Soudan' | MOak
speciosa | NBlo XBlo
'Stadt Fellbach' **new** | MOak SPar
'Strasbourg' | CSam LAma MOak NPer SPar WPGP
§ 'Striata' (v) | CFil CHEx CKob CSev CSpe EBee EBlw EMan EOrc LPJP LPio MOak MSta NBlo NPSI SPar SPet SYvo WCot WDyG WHal WMul XBlo
'Striped Beauty' (v) | CTrC MOak SHGC SVen
'Stuttgart' (v) | CSpe EAmu EBee EPfP MOak WCot
'Südfunk' | EAmu SPar
'Sunny Delight' **new** | MOak
'Tafraout' | MOak
'Talisman' | MOak
'Taney' | MOak MSta WMAq
'Tango' | MOak SChr
'Taroudant' | MOak SPar
'Tashkent Red' | CHad
'Tchad' **new** | MOak
'Tirol' | IPot LPVe MOak
'Tricarinata' **new** | CHEx
'Tropical Rose' | EAmu LRHS SRms WMul
Tropicanna = 'Phasion'[PBR] (v) | COtt EBee LRHS MOak NPer
'Vainqueur' | MOak
* 'Variegata' (v) | LAma LRHS WCot
'Verdi' | CSpe LAma MOak SPar WWeb
warscewiczii | MOak NBlo SPar SYvo WMul XBlo
'Wine 'n' Roses' **new** | MOak
'Woodbridge Pink' **new** | NBlo XBlo
'Wyoming' | CBcs CHEx CSam CSut EBee EBot LAma LPVe LPio MBNS

'Yellow Futurity' (Futurity Series) **new** | MCCP MOak NBlo NVic SPar SWal SYvo WCot WMul WWeb XBlo
 | MOak
'Yellow Humbert' | CSev LAma LPVe MOak

Cannomois (Restionaceae)
virgata new | WAbe

Cantua (Polemoniaceae)
buxifolia | CAbb CBcs CFee CFil CPLG CPle CPne GQui LRHS SIgm SOWG

Cape gooseberry see Physalis

Capsicum (Solanaceae)
annuum | MBri

Caragana (Papilionaceae)
arborescens | CDul EPfP GKir MBar MWhi NBee NWea SEND SPlb WBVN WDin WStI
 - 'Lorbergii' | CEnd CLnd EPfP GBin GKir MBlu SKee SPer WFoF
 - 'Pendula' | CWib EBee ELan ENot EPfP GKir LRHS MBar MBlu NBee NBlu NEgg NPri SCoo SLim SPer WDin WStI
 - 'Walker' | CBcs CDul COtt CWib EBee EBre ELan EMil ENot EPfP GKir LPan LRHS MAsh MBar MBlu MBri MGos SLim SPer WOrn WStI
aurantiaca | MBar
frutex 'Globosa' | NBlu SPer
jubata | EBee NLar
microphylla | WNor

carambola see Averrhoa carambola

caraway see Carum carvi

Cardamine ✿ (Brassicaceae)
alba | WEas
asarifolia hort. | see Pachyphragma macrophyllum
bulbifera | CLAP CPom CRDP EPPr IBlr LEdu NGar NRya NWoo WBri WCru
californica | EBee EMan EPar NGar NRya WCru
diphylla | CLAP EBee EPar MLLN NLar WCot WCru WFar
 - 'Eco Cut Leaf' **new** | WCru
enneaphylla | IBlr NCat NGby SSpi SVal WCru
glanduligera | CElw EBee EGle EPPr LEdu SMrm WCru
 - MDM 94010 | NGar
 - MDM 94011 | NGar
§ **heptaphylla** | CLAP ELan EPar IBlr MBri MRav NGar NHol SSpi SWat WBri WCru WHoo
 - Guincho form | CDcs CFir IBlr
 - white | CPlt
§ **kitaibelii** | CLAP ECha EPar IBlr NGar SSpi WCru
laciniata | EBee NLar SSpi SVal SWat WCru
latifolia Vahl | see C. raphanifolia
lineariloba **new** | IBlr
macrophylla | CLAP NGar SDys SSpi SWat WCot WCru WFar WIvy
§ **microphylla** | CLAP EHyt GCrs WCot WCru
pachystigma | WCot
  NNS 98-149 **new** |
pentaphylla ♥[H4] | EBre ECha EGle ELan EMar EPPr EPar EPla ERos EWTr GBuc GCrs GGar GKir GMaP MBri MRav NBir NDov NGar SSpi SVal WCot WCru

	- bright pink	CLAP WCot
	pratensis	CArn CKin CRow EBre EMFW
		EWTr MBow MGas MHer NLan
		NMir NOrc SIde SWat WFar WHHs
		WHbs WHer WMoo WShi WWye
	- 'Edith' (d)	CDes CLAP EBee EPPr GBuc
		MNrw NChi WPrP
	- 'Flore Pleno' (d)	CBre CFee CRow CSpe EBee
		ECha EMan GAbr GKir IFro LRHS
		MHer MNrw MTho NBid NBir
		NBro NLar SBla SUsu SWat WAlt
		WCot WEas WFar WHoo WOut
	- 'Improperly Dressed'	CNat
	- 'William' (d)	CMea EPPr GBuc MNrw NLar
		WMoo WPnP WPrP
	quinquefolia	CDes CLAP CMea CPlt EBee
		EGle EHrv EMan EMar EPPr EPar
		GBuc NCat NDov SBla SCro SDys
		SUsu WCot WCru WFar WPGP
		WRha WWye
§	*raphanifolia*	CBre CDes CRow EBee ECha
		EMan EOrc EPPr GAbr GBuc GCal
		GGar IBlr LEdu MFir MRav NBro
		NCat NVic SSpi SWat WBor WCru
		WPGP WPnP
	trifolia	More than 30 suppliers
*	- *digitata*	MTho
	urbaniana new	EBee
	waldsteinii	CElw CPlt ECho EGle EHrv EPPr
		MBro SCnR SSpi WCru WHoo
		WTin WWhi
	yezoensis new	IBlr NGar
	- B&SWJ 4659	WCru

Cardiandra (Hydrangeaceae)

alternifolia	WCru
B&SWJ 5845	
- B&SWJ 6354	WCru
formosana B&SWJ 2005 WCru	

cardoon see *Cynara cardunculus*

Cardiocrinum (Liliaceae)

cathayanum	EBee
cordatum	NMen
- B&SWJ 4841	WCru
- var. *glehnii*	CLAP GEdr SSpi
- - B&SWJ 4758	WCru
- red-veined	CLAP GEdr SSpi
giganteum	CBcs CBct CBot CBro CFil CHEx
	CPne EBee EBot EPar GBuc GEdr
	GGar GKir IBlr LAma MBri MDun
	SMad SPer SSpi WCru WHer WMul
	WPGP
- B&SWJ 2419	WCru
- var. *yunnanense*	CFil CLAP CPom EPfP GBuc GEdr
	GGGa IBlr NBid SSpi WCru WPGP

Carduus (Asteraceae)

benedictus	see *Cnicus benedictus*

Carex (Cyperaceae)

from Uganda	GBin GCal GGar LEdu MMoz SApp
from Nanking new	SApp
acuta new	CBig
acutiformis	GKir
alba	EPPr EVFa
albida	EBee EHul EMan EPla GKir LHrt
	LRHS SDes SWal
albula	MHdf MMoz WHoo
annectans var.	EPPr
xanthocarpa new	
appressa	EBee SApp

	arenaria	EPPr NNor
	atrata	CCol EBre EHoe EMon EPPr EPla
		ESis GKir LHrt LRHS WDyG
		WHrl
	aurea	EBee GDea GKir GSki NHol
	baccans	EPPr EPla GCal MAnH MWod
		NOak WDyG
	bebbii	EPPr
	berggrenii	More than 30 suppliers
	- narrow-leaved	ITim
	bicknellii new	EPPr
	boottiana	EWes
	brevior	EPPr
	brunnea	EHoe EPPr EWes WDyG
	- 'Variegata' (v)	CBrm EBee EHoe EVFa EWsh
		MMoz NGdn SDes WCot WRus
	buchananii ♀ H4	More than 30 suppliers
	- 'Viridis'	EBee EHoe ELan EMan EPla LRHS
		MMoz WDyG WHer
	bushii	EPPr
	caryophyllea	CElw EBee EChP EGoo EHoe
	'The Beatles'	EPPr EPla ESis GGar MMoz NBir
		NBro NHol
	chathamica	CRez EBee EMan MMoz NSti
		SApp SMac
	'China Blue'	CRez MMoz SApp
	comans	COIW CTrC EBee EBlw EFul EHoe
		ELan EMar EMon EPPr EPar GCal
		GKir GOrn GSki IBlr LRHS
		MWgw NBro NHol NOak NRya
		SDes SHel
	- bronze	More than 30 suppliers
	- 'Copper Green' new	EFou
	- 'Dancing Flame' new	CWCL EBee GBin MCCP WLeb
	- 'Frosted Curls'	More than 30 suppliers
	- 'Kupferflamme'	EFou
	- 'Small Red'	see *C. comans* 'Taranaki'
	- 'Taranaki'	CCol CWCL EBee EBre EMan
		GKir MBNS MLwd MMoz NGdn
		NHol SWal
	comosa	EPPr
§	*conica*	GKir MBri
	- 'Hime-kan-suge'	see *C. conica* 'Snowline'
	- 'Kiku-satura'	NHol
§	- 'Snowline' (v)	More than 30 suppliers
	coriacea from Dunedin,	EPPr
	New Zealand new	
	crinata	MNrw
	crinita	EPPr
	cristatella new	EBee EPPr
	crus-corvi	EBee EPPr
	dallii	EBee ECou EPPr EWes MMoz
	davisii	EPPr
	demissa	EBee EHoe EPPr WWye
	depauperata	EHoe EMon WWye
	digitata	WWye
	dipsacea	More than 30 suppliers
	dissita	CTrC LEdu
	disticha	GDea
	divulsa	GDea
	- subsp. *leersii*	EPPr
	dolichostachya	CBod CMil CRez EBee EGle EMan
	'Kaga-nishiki' (v)	EMon EPPr EVFa LEdu LRHS MMoz
		NCat SAga SApp WCot WLin
	duthiei KEKE 494 new	WPGP
	echinata new	GIBF
	elata new	EPPr
§	- 'Aurea' (v) ♀ H4	More than 30 suppliers
	- 'Bowles' Golden'	see *C. elata* 'Aurea'
	- 'Knightshayes' ♀ H4	CKno EMan GBin MMoz WCot
	'Evergold'	see *C. oshimensis* 'Evergold'
	fascicularis new	EPPr GGar
	ferruginea	GBin

firma 'Variegata' (v)	CMea ECtt EGle EHyt EPar EPot MAsh MDHE MTho MWat NHar NMen NWCA SChu SIng WAbe WCot	
§ *flacca*	CBig EHoe EMan EPPr EWsh GBin GDea GKir NPro SWal WPnP	
- 'Bias' (v)	CKin CNat EMan EMon EPPr EPla GKir LRHS MMoz	
§ - subsp. *flacca*	EBee EWes MMoz MTed NHol WPGP WWye	
flagellifera	More than 30 suppliers	
- 'Auburn Cascade' **new**	EBee GCal	
- 'Coca Cola' **new**	GCal	
- 'Rapunzel'	EBee EPPr MMoz WPGP	
flava	EBee EHoe EPPr GDea	
fortunei	see *C. morrowii*	
fraseri	see *Cymophyllus fraserianus*	
fraserianus	see *Cymophyllus fraserianus*	
glauca Scopoli	see *C. flacca* subsp. *flacca*	
glauca Bosc. ex Boott	CBig EBee EPla SApp	
granularis	EPPr	
grayi	CBig CKno CRDP EBee EBlw EHoe EMar EMon EPPr EPla GCal GKir LBuc LEdu LRHS MAnH MBlu MTho NOak WCot WPer WWye	
§ *hachijoensis*	EMon EPPr LAst LRHS WFar	
- 'Evergold'	see *C. oshimensis* 'Evergold'	
'Happy Wanderer'	SLPl	
hirsutella **new**	EPPr	
hirta	CKin EPPr	
hispida	CBig EPPr NOak SRGP WMoo WRus	
hordeistichos	EBee EPPr	
hystricina	CBrm EPPr	
§ 'Ice Dance' (v)	EBee EFou EPPr EVFa GGar MAvo MMoz SApp SIsu WCot WPrP WRus WWpP	
intumescens	EBee	
kaloides	EBee EHoe EMan EMon LRHS MAvo	
'Kan-suge'	see *C. morrowii*	
longebracteata **new**	GGar	
lupulina	CBrm EPPr	
lurida	CBod CEbD EBee EHoe EPGN EPPr GBin GGar MAvo MBNS MCCP	
macloviana	EPPr	
macrocephala	EPPr	
maorica	LEdu	
* *marylandica*	EBre	
'Milk Chocolate' (v)	CHar CMil GCal NPPs NPro WLeb	
* *mimosa* **new**	EPPr	
molesta **new**	EPPr	
montana	EPPr GKir	
morrowii hort.	see *C. oshimensis*, *C. hachijoensis*	
§ *morrowii* Boott	IBlr MWhi	
- 'Evergold'	see *C. oshimensis* 'Evergold'	
- 'Fisher's Form' (v)	CFil CHar CKno EFou EGle EHoe EPPr EPla EWsh GKir LHop LRHS MAvo MMoz MRav NGdn NHar NHol NMir SApp SDes SPar WBro WCot WPGP WPer WRus WWye	
- 'Gilt' (v)	EMon EPPr LRHS MAvo	
- 'Ice Dance'	see *C.* 'Ice Dance'	
- 'Nana Variegata' (v)	CTri NBir NWoo WPGP	
- var. *temnolepis* 'Silk Tassel'	EPPr EVFa WCot	
N - 'Variegata' (v)	More than 30 suppliers	
muhlenbergii **new**	EPPr	
multifida **new**	EPPr	
muricata	CKin GDea	
- subsp. *muricata* **new**	EPPr	
muskingumensis	More than 30 suppliers	
- 'Ice Fountains' (v)	EPPr	
- 'Little Midge'	EBee EFou EMan EPPr GKir	
- 'Oehme' (v)	CHar CWCL EBee EBre EFou EMan	

	EMon EPPr EPla EPyc GBin GCal MAvo MTed NBid WCot WDyG	
- 'Silberstreif' (v)	EMon EPPr	
- 'Wachtposten'	GCal MFir	
'Mystery' **new**	GGar	
nigra	CBrm CKin EHon EPPr GSki WWpP	
§ - 'On-line' (v)	EMon EPPr EWsh GBin LRHS MMoz SApp WCot	
- 'Variegata'	see *C. nigra* 'On-line'	
normalis	EPPr	
obnupta	CBrm EBee EPPr	
ornithopoda	EGle	
- 'Aurea'	see *C. ornithopoda* 'Variegata'	
§ - 'Variegata' (v)	CBrm CSam EBre ECtt EHoe EHul EPPr EPar EPla ESis EWsh MBrN MBro MMoz MWhi NBro NGdn NHar NHol SAga SApp SPar WCot WFar WMoo WRus WWye	
§ *oshimensis*	EDAr IBlr WCot	
§ - 'Evergold' (v) ♀ H4	More than 30 suppliers	
- 'Variegata' (v)	EBlw NBir	
otrubae	CKin	
ovalis	CKin WRos	
pallescens	EPPr GBin WWye	
- 'Wood's Edge' (v)	CNat EPPr	
panicea	CBri CKno CWCL EHoe EPPr EPla MMoz SApp SMac SRGP WFar WWpP	
paniculata	CBig	
pauciflora	EPPr GKir	
pendula	More than 30 suppliers	
- 'Cool Jazz' (v)	EVFa WAlt	
- 'Moonraker' (v)	CBot CFil CNat CWCL EHoe EMan EPPr EPla EVFa LEdu MAnH MAvo SApp WHal WLcb	
petriei	CWCL CWSG ECha ECoo EPPr EPot EWes EWsh GBuc GGar GOrn LAst LLWP MAvo MBNS MMoz NVic SGar SPar SWal WCot WFar WHoo WPer	
phyllocephala	EHoe EPla WCot WDyG WRos	
- 'Sparkler' (v)	More than 30 suppliers	
pilulifera 'Tinney's Princess' (v)	EBee EMan EPot GDra GKir LRHS NHol WCot	
plantaginea	CFil CFwr EBee EHoe EMar EMon EPPr EPla GBin NBea SApp SDes WCot WDyG WFar WHil WMoo WPGP	
platyphylla	WWye	
pruirea **new**	EPPr	
projecta	EPPr	
§ *pseudocyperus*	CElw CKin ECGN EHoe EHon EPPr EPla GBin GDea GIBF GKir MAnH MBow MMoz MNrw MSta NBlu NGdn NPer SCou SRGP SRms SWal WFar WLeb WPer WPnP WWpP WWye	
pulicaris	CKin	
remota	CBig CKin EPPr GBin GKir LBuc WWye	
riparia	EMFW EPPr LPBA MBow MWhi NHol NPer SLon SWal WFar WRos WShi WWeb	
- 'Bob's Variegated' (v) **new**	WCot	
- 'Bowles' Golden'	see *C. elata* 'Aurea'	
- 'Variegata' (v)	More than 30 suppliers	
* *saxatilis* 'Variegata' (v)	EHoe EMan	
scoparia	EPPr	
secta	CTrC EBee ECou EHoe EPPr GOrn MNrw SYvo WDyG WMoo WRos	
- from Dunedin, New Zealand **new**	EPPr	

– var. *tenuiculmis*	see *C. tenuiculmis*
shortiana **new**	EPPr
siderosticha	CFil EPla WHrl WPGP WPer
– 'Elaine West' (v) **new**	WCot
– 'Kisokaido' (v)	EMan EMon EPPr WCot
– 'Old Barn' **new**	EPPr
– 'Shima-nishiki' (v)	CBcs CMil EBee EBlw EGle EHoe
	EMan EMar EMon EPPr EPla EVFa
	GBin GEil LAst LHrt MAvo MCCP
	MMoz NCot NPro SPar SPoG
	WBor WCot
– 'Variegata' (v)	More than 30 suppliers
'Silver Sceptre' (v)	More than 30 suppliers
solandri	CTrC EBee EChP EWsh LEdu
	MAvo MWrn SHel SRGP WWpP
spissa	GKir MNrw
sprengelii	EPPr
stenocephala **new**	CHEx
sterilis **new**	EPPr
stipata	EPPr
stricta Gooden	see *C. elata*
– 'Bowles' Golden'	see *C. elata* 'Aurea'
stricta Lamarck	EPPr EPla WDyG
– 'Sue Ward' **new**	SApp
sylvatica	CKin EBee ECGN MBrN WWye
'Taranaki' **new**	EPPr
tenuiculmis	CBod CBrm CWCL EBee EChP
	EHoe EMan EMon EPPr EWsh GBin
	GGar GWCH LPVe LRHS MAvo
	MHFa MWhi NHol SWal WTin
tereticaulis	GGar
testacea	More than 30 suppliers
'- 'Old Gold'	CKno EBee EPPr EWes MAnH MCCP
	SMac SMer SPlb WBrE WFar WPnP
texensis	EPPr MMoz
trifida	CHEx CTrC EBee EHoe EPPr EPla
	EWsh GCal GGar LHrt LRHS
	MAnH MMoz MNrw MWhi NSti
	SRGP SWal WCot WDyG WFar
	WHal WMnd WWye
– 'Chatham Blue'	CMHG EChP EVFa LBuc
tuckermanii	EPPr
typhina **new**	EPPr
umbrosa **new**	CBig
– subsp. *sabynensis*	EMon EPPr
'Thinny Thin' (v)	
uncifolia	ECou
utriculata	EPPr
virgata	CTrC
vulpina	CBig CKin EPPr
vulpinoidea **new**	EPPr

Carica (Caricaceae)

goudotiana **new**	CKob
x *heilbornii* **new**	CKob
papaya (F)	MGol WHer
pubescens	CKob
quercifolia **new**	CKob

Carissa (Apocynaceae)

grandiflora	see *C. macrocarpa*
§ *macrocarpa* (F)	CSpe ERea EShb ESlt MWya

Carlina (Asteraceae)

acanthifolia	CArn NSla SIgm
– subsp. *cyanara*	NWCA
JJA 274.101	
acaulis	CM&M EGoo ELan EPfP GAbr
	NPri NWCA SPlb WFar WJek
	WPer
– subsp. *acaulis*	GPoy
– bronze	EGoo EMan EWll GCal LPhx MAvo
– var. *caulescens*	see *C. acaulis* subsp. *simplex*

§ – subsp. *simplex*	EBee EChP ECha EMan GBuc GKir
	GMaP LRHS MBri MCAu SMad
	SPer WFar WJek WPer WWeb
– – bronze	EBee NChi NSla
vulgaris	CKin WPer WWeb
– 'Silver Star'	EGoo EMan

Carmichaelia (Papilionaceae)

'Abundance'	ECou
'Angie'	ECou
angustata 'Buller'	ECou
appressa	ECou
– 'Ellesmere'	ECou
§ *arborea*	ECou
– 'Grand'	ECou
astonii	ECou
– 'Ben More'	ECou
– 'Chalk Ridge'	ECou
australis	ECou WBod
– 'Bright Eyes'	ECou
– 'Cunningham'	ECou
– Flagelliformis Group	ECou
– 'Mahurangi'	ECou
– Ovata Group	ECou
– 'Solander'	ECou
'Charm'	ECou
'Clifford Bay'	ECou
corrugata	ECou
'Culverden'	ECou
curta	ECou
enysii	EHyt SBrw
exsul	ECou
fieldii 'Westhaven'	ECou
flagelliformis 'Roro'	ECou
glabrata	CHEx CPLG CPle
'Hay and Honey'	ECou
juncea Nigrans Group	ECou
kirkii	ECou
'Lilac Haze'	ECou
monroi	ECou
– 'Rangitata'	ECou
– 'Tekapo'	ECou
nana	ECou
– 'Desert Road'	ECou
– 'Pringle'	ECou
– 'Waitaki'	ECou
nigrans 'Wanaka'	ECou
odorata	ECou
– Angustata Group	ECou
– 'Green Dwarf'	ECou
– 'Lakeside'	ECou
– 'Riverside'	ECou
ovata 'Calf Creek'	ECou
'Parson's Tiny'	ECou
petriei	ECou SMad
– 'Aviemore'	ECou
– 'Lindis'	ECou
– 'Pukaki'	ECou
– Virgata Group	ECou
'Porter's Pass'	ECou
'Spangle'	ECou
'Tangle'	ECou
uniflora	ECou
– 'Bealey'	ECou
'Weka'	ECou
williamsii	ECou
'Yellow Eyes'	ECou

x *Carmispartium* (Papilionaceae)

astens	see x *C. hutchinsii*
§ *hutchinsii*	ECou
– 'Butterfly'	ECou
– 'County Park'	ECou

- 'Delight'	ECou
- 'Pink Beauty'	ECou
- 'Wingletye'	ECou

Carpenteria (Hydrangeaceae)

californica ♀ H3	More than 30 suppliers
- 'Bodnant'	LRHS SPoG WGer WPGP
- 'Elizabeth'	CAbP CPMA EPfP GKir LRHS
	MAsh MBri SMur SPer SSpi SSta
- 'Eskimo'	SSpi
- 'Ladhams' Variety'	CBcs CPMA ENot EPfP MRav SBra
	SSpi SSta WPGP

Carpesium (Asteraceae)

| abrotanoides **new** | EBee |

Carpinus ✿ (Corylaceae)

B&SWJ 6275 **new**	WPGP
betulus ♀ H4	More than 30 suppliers
- 'Columnaris'	CLnd CTho GKir LRHS MBri
* - 'Columnaris Nana'	CMCN
§ - 'Fastigiata' ♀ H4	More than 30 suppliers
- 'Frans Fontaine'	CDul CMCN CTho EBee ENot
	GKir IMGH MBlu MHFa SCoo
	SLim SPer SSta
- 'Horizontalis'	CMCN
- 'Incisa'	CDul
- 'Pendula'	CDul CEnd CLnd CTho EBee GKir
	WDin
- 'Purpurea'	CDul ENot GKir
- 'Pyramidalis'	see C. betulus 'Fastigiata'
- 'Quercifolia'	CDul
caroliniana	CLnd CMCN WNor
cordata	CMCN SBir WCwm WDin
eerosana	CLnd CMCN CTho WDin WNor
fangiana	CEnd CLnd GKir
fargesii	see C. viminea
henryana	SBir WDin WNor
japonica ♀ H4	CDul CEnd CMCN EPfP GKir
	LBuc MBlu SMad WDin
laxiflora	SMad WNor
- var. macrostachya	see C. viminea
orientalis	CMCN WNor
polyneura	CMCN SBir WNor
* schisiensis	CMCN GKir
tschonoskii	CMCN
turczaninowii ♀ H4	CDul CMCN CMHG CTho GKir
	NPal NWea SBir STre WDin WNor
	WOTO
§ viminea	CDul CEnd CMCN EPfP GKir SBir
	SSpi WNor

Carpobrotus (Aizoaceae)

§ edulis	CAgr CHEx CTrC SAPC SArc SChu
	SEND SPar WHer
rossii **new**	GGar

Carthamus (Asteraceae)

| tinctorius | MChe MSal |

Carum (Apiaceae)

carvi	CArn CBod CPrp GPoy GWCH
	MChe MHer NPri NVic SIde
	WHHs WHer WJek WLHH WPer
	WSel WWye
copticum	MSal
petroselinum	see Petroselinum crispum
roxburgianum **new**	WHHs

Carya ✿ (Juglandaceae)

aquatica	CTho
cordiformis	CBcs CMCN CTho EPfP MBlu
floridana	CBcs CMCN

	glabra	CMCN
N	illinoinensis (F)	CBcs CMCN
	laciniosa (F)	CBcs CTho EPfP SSpi
	- 'Henry' (F)	CAgr
	- 'Keystone' seedlings	CAgr
	(F) **new**	
	myristiciformis	CMCN EGFP
	ovata (F)	CAgr CBcs CLnd CMCN CTho
		EPfP MBlu SSpi WDin WWes
	pallida	CBcs CMCN

Caryophyllus see Syzygium

Caryopteris ✿ (Verbenaceae)

x clandonensis	CSBt CTrw EBee ECtt ELan ENot
	MWat NBir WBod WCFE WDin
	WFar WHCG WHar WSHC WStI
	WTel WWin WWye
- 'Arthur Simmonds'	CSam CTri EBee ECha EPfP GKir
♀ H4	LHop MAsh SPer WGor
- 'Blue Danube' **new**	LAst
- 'Dark Night'	CHar EBee LRHS MBri WBcn
- 'Ferndown'	CDoC CWib EBee EBre EPfP
	EWTr GKir LRHS MGos SPer SPla
	SReu SRms SSpi WWeb
- 'First Choice' ♀ H4	CAbP ELan EPfP GKir LRHS MAsh
	MWat SChu SMad SMrm SMur
	SPer WBcn WRus
- Grand Bleu =	ENot
'Inoveris' PBR **new**	
- 'Heavenly Blue'	More than 30 suppliers
- 'Kew Blue'	More than 30 suppliers
- 'Longwood Blue'	CAbP EPfP GCal LRHS WBcn
- 'Pershore'	MTis
- 'Worcester Gold' ♀ H4	More than 30 suppliers
divaricata	EBee EMon
- 'Electrum'	EMon
- 'Jade Shades'	CDes EMan EMon
- variegated (v)	EMan
§ incana	CPle EBee EBre ELan EPfP MWhi
	SLon SPer SPoG WCot WOTO
	WSHC
- 'Alba' **new**	WCot
- 'Blue Cascade'	ENot MRav NSti
- weeping	CFwr CPle ELan GBuc GCal MBro
	MSte SAdn WLeb WPat
mastacanthus	see C. incana

Caryota (Arecaceae)

'Himalaya'	CRoM LPal
mitis ♀ H1	EAmu LPal
obtusa	LPal
ochlandra	EAmu LPal
urens	LPal

Cassandra see Chamaedaphne

Cassia (Caesalpiniaceae)

corymbosa Lam.	see Senna corymbosa
marilandica	see Senna marilandica
obtusifolia	see Senna obtusifolia

Cassinia (Asteraceae)

aculeata	GGar
leptophylla	CPLG SPer
- subsp. fulvida	CBcs ECou EHoe GGar GKir
	GTou MBar SPer WBcn
- subsp. vauvilliersii	CDoC GEil GGar NLon SBrw
	SPer
- - CC 570	NWCA
- - var. albida	CBcs EGoo EPfP LRHS SPer WBcn
	WCwm
- - 'Silberschmelze'	SOWG

N	*retorta*	CDoC ECou
	'Ward Silver'	CBot CRez ECou EHoe EMan
		EWes GSki SPar

Cassinia x *Helichrysum* (Asteraceae)

*	hybrid	WKif WSHC

Cassiope ✿ (Ericaceae)

*	'Askival'	ITim
	'Askival Arctic Fox'	GCrs
	'Askival Freebird'	see *C.* Freebird Group
	'Askival Snowbird'	EPot GCrs ITim
	'Askival Snow-wreath'	see *C.* Snow-wreath Group
	'Askival Stormbird'	GCrs ITim
	'Badenoch'	ECho EPot GCrs GDra GKir ITim
		NDlv NHar NLAp WAbe
	'Bearsden'	CMHG GDra MBar NDlv NHar WPat
	'Edinburgh' ♀ H4	CMHG EPfP GAbr GCrs GDra
		GEdr GKev GKir ITim MBar NDlv
		NHar NHol NMen WPat
	fastigiata	ITim
§	Freebird Group	GCrs ITim
	'George Taylor'	GGGa
*	*inermis*	NMen
	'Kathleen Dryden'	GDra
	lycopodioides ♀ H4	EPot GCrs GDra GTou ITim MBar
		NHar NHol
	- 'Beatrice Lilley'	EPot GAbr GEdr GKir GTou ITim
		LTwo MBar NDlv NHar NHol
		SRms WAbe WPat
	- var. *crista-pilosa*	GKir
	- 'Jim Lever'	GCrs ITim WAbe
	- *minima*	GEdr
	- 'Rokujō'	GCrs GDra GKir ITim NHol NMen
	'Medusa'	GDra GTou ITim NHol WPat
	mertensiana	ECho GDra MBar NDlv NMen SRms
	- var. *californica*	GDra GKir ITim
	- var. *gracilis*	CMHG GDra GEdr GKir NHar NHol
	- - dwarf	EPot
	'Muirhead' ♀ H4	CMHG EPot GDra GEdr GKir
		GTou ITim MBar MDun NDlv
		NHar NHol NLAp NMen SRms
		WAbe WPat
	'Randle Cooke' ♀ H4	CMHG EPot GCrs GDra GEdr
		GKir GTou MBar MBro MDun
		NDlv NHar NHol NLAp SRms
		WAbe WPat
	selaginoides	GAbr GDra
	- LS&E 13284	GCrs ITim WAbe
§	Snow-wreath Group	GCrs ITim
§	*stelleriana*	GCrs
	tetragona	GDra GKir GTou MBar SRms
	- var. *saximontana*	ITim NHol
	wardii	GGGa GKir
	- x *fastigiata*	GCrs GGGa ITim
	Askival strain	

Castanea ✿ (Fagaceae)

	dentata	CBcs
	'Layeroka' (F)	CAgr
	'Maridonne' (F) **new**	CAgr
	'Marigoule' (F) **new**	CAgr
*	'Marigoule'	SKee
	'Marlhac' (F) **new**	CAgr
	mollissima	CMCN ISea
	x *neglecta*	CTho ESim
	'Précoce Migoule' (F)	CAgr
	new	
	pumila	CAgr
	'Rousse de Nay' (F) **new**	CAgr
§	*sativa* ♀ H4	More than 30 suppliers
	- 'Albomarginata'	CDoC CDul CEnd CTho EBee
	(v) ♀ H4	EPfP IMGH LRHS MBlu MBri

		MGos NBea NBee SKee SLim
		SMad SPer WDin WWes
	- 'Anny's Red'	MBlu
	- 'Anny's Summer Red'	CDul
	- 'Argenteovariegata'	see *C. sativa* 'Albomarginata'
	- 'Aspleniifolia'	CBcs CDul MBlu WPGP
	- 'Aureomarginata'	see *C. sativa* 'Variegata'
*	- 'Doré de Lyon'	CAgr
	- 'Laguépie' (F) **new**	CAgr
	- 'Marron de Lyon' (F)	CEnd CTho EMui EPfP MBlu
		MCoo NWea SKee
	- 'Pyramidalis' **new**	WDin
	- 'Thompson' (F)	ESim
§	- 'Variegata' (v)	CBcs CLnd CMCN COtt CPMA
		ELan EMil EPfP LPan LRHS MAsh
		SCoo SKee WPGP
	- 'Vincent van Gogh'	SMad
	seguinii	LEdu LRHS
	'Vignols' (F) **new**	CAgr

Casuarina (Casuarinaceae)

	cunninghamiana	CTrC ECou
	glauca	CTrC
	littoralis	see *Allocasuarina littoralis*
	stricta	see *Allocasuarina verticillata*

Catalpa ✿ (Bignoniaceae)

	bignonioides ♀ H4	More than 30 suppliers
	- 'Aurea' ♀ H4	More than 30 suppliers
	- 'Nana'	SKee
	- 'Purpurea'	see *C.* x *erubescens* 'Purpurea'
	- 'Variegata' (v)	EPfP LNet LRHS MBro MRav NHol
		SLim SPer SSta WPat
	bungei	CLnd CTho LPan NPal WNor
	- 'Purpurea'	ELan
	x *erubescens*	CHEx
§	- 'Purpurea' ♀ H4	More than 30 suppliers
	fargesii	CFil CLnd
	- f. *duclouxii*	CFil CTho WPGP
	ovata	CMCN CPle CTho
	speciosa	CBcs CLnd CMCN CPle CTho
		EPfP LPan LRHS SPer
	- 'Pulverulenta' (v)	CBcs CDoC CDul CEnd CMCN
		LRHS SPer WStI

Catananche (Asteraceae)

	caerulea	More than 30 suppliers
	- 'Alba'	EBee EBla EBot EChP ECha EFou
		EPar EPfP ERou GKir LIck LRHS
		NBid NBir NPri SPer SUsu WHHs
		WMoo WPer WWhi
	- 'Amor White' **new**	MPWC
	- 'Bicolor'	CM&M CSev EMan LRHS MHer
		MNrw MSac STes SWal WElm
		WFar WHer WHoo WMoo WWal
	- 'Major' ♀ H4	EBee EChP LRHS SRms WEas
	caespitosa	SBla

Catha (Celastraceae)

	edulis	MGol WJek

Catharanthus (Apocynaceae)

	roseus ♀ H1	GPoy MBri
	- Ocellatus Group	MBri

Caulophyllum (Berberidaceae)

	thalictroides	CArn CLAP CRDP EBee GBuc GEdr
		LEur LRHS MSal NLar WCot WCru
	- subsp. *robustum*	EBee LEur NLar WCru

Cautleya ✿ (Zingiberaceae)

	new	EMan
§	*gracilis*	CBct CKob EBee IBlr LEur WMul

– CC 1751	WCot
– CC 3606	CPLG
lutea	see *C. gracilis*
spicata	CBct CHEx CKob CPLG EBee IBlr ITim LPio MTed
– B&SWJ 2103	WCru
– CC 3676	ITer
– 'Robusta'	CAvo CHEx CPLG CRDP EBee EMan GCal IBlr LRav SBla SCro SMad WCru WPGP

Ceanothus ✿ (*Rhamnaceae*)

'A.T.Johnson'	EBee ECrN ENot LCaP MAsh MWya SHBN SLim SPar SPer SRPl SRms
americanus	CArn
arboreus	SAPC SArc
– 'Owlswood Blue'	LRHS
– 'Trewithen Blue' ♀ H3	CBcs CChe CMac CSBt CTrw CWSG CWib EBee EBre ELan EPfP EWTr GKir IMGH ISea LHop LRHS MGos MRav NBea SLim SLon SPar SPer WFar WFoF WKif WSHC WStI WWeb
'Autumnal Blue' ♀ H3	More than 30 suppliers
'Basil Fox'	LRHS WBcn
'Blue Buttons'	LRHS
* 'Blue Carpet'	CWSG
'Blue Cushion'	CBcs CDoC CPMA CWSG EBee ECtt LAst LHop LPVe LRHS MGos MRav
'Blue Jeans'	EBee IArd LHop LRHS WLeb
* 'Blue Moon'	LRHS
'Blue Mound' ♀ H3	CBrm CDoC CHar CSBt CTrw CWSG EBee EBre EMil ENot EPfP GKir LPVe LRHS MGos MRav MWgw NFor NHol NLon NPri SLim SPer SPla SReu SSpi WBod WDin WSHC WWeb
'Blue Sapphire' **new**	EMil NPro SPer
'Burkwoodii' ♀ H3	CBcs CBrm CDoC CMac CSBt CTri CWSG EBee EBre ENot EPfP GKir LRHS MAsh MBri MDun MGos MHdf MRav NBea NHol NLon SHBN SPer SRPl SReu WFar
'Cascade' ♀ H3	CBcs CWSG EBee ENot GKir LAst LRHS MBri MGos MWat MWgw NBea NLon SLon SPer SPla SPlb SRPl WBod WHCG WStI
'Comtesse de Paris'	see *C.* x *delileanus* 'Comtesse de Paris'
'Concha' ♀ H3	More than 30 suppliers
§ **cuneatus** var. **rigidus**	CPle EHol LRHS SDry SRms
– – 'Snowball'	EBee ELan EPfP LRHS MGos WBcn
cyaneus	CPle
'Cynthia Postan'	CAbP CKno CMHG CPle CSBt CWSG EBee EBre EPfP IArd ISea LRHS MBri MBri MRav MWat WPat
'Dark Star' ♀ H3	CBcs CBrm CChe CDoC CMHG CPMA CSPN CTbh CWSG EBee EPfP EWll LRHS MBro MWgw NPro SMad SOWG SPar SPla SReu SSta WPat
'Delight'	CBcs ELan EPfP EPla LRHS MGos MRav NBea SPer WAbe WBod WDin WFar
x **delileanus**	CBcs
§ – 'Comtesse de Paris'	EBee
– 'Gloire de Versailles' ♀ H4	CBcs CBot CChe CDoC CMac CSBt CSam CWSG CWib EBee ELan ENot EPfP EWTr LRHS MAsh MBri MGos MRav NBee SHBN SPar SPer WBod WCFE WDin WFar WGwG WSHC WWin

– 'Henri Desfossé'	CPle EBee ELan IMGH LRHS MHdf MRav SOWG SPer WDin WKif
– 'Topaze' ♀ H4	CBcs CRez CWSG EBee ELan EMil EPfP LRHS MRav SLon SOWG WDin WHar WKif
dentatus hort.	see *C.* x *lobbianus*
dentatus Torr & A.Gray	ENot MAsh MGos SPer
– var. **floribundus**	CSBt EBee ELan LRHS SDix
* – 'Superbus'	EBee
'Diamond Heights'	see *C. griseus* var. *horizontalis* 'Diamond Heights'
divergens	EBee
'Edinburgh' ♀ H3	EBee EPfP MGos NBlu WBod
'Eleanor Taylor'	EBee
'Fallen Skies'	CAbP LRHS
foliosus	CPle
– var. **austromontanus**	CTrw SPar
'Frosty Blue'	LRHS
'Gentian Plume'	LRHS SMad
gloriosus	CFai EBee EWes LRHS SDry
– 'Anchor Bay'	COtt EBee ELan EPfP IArd LRHS SDes SLon SOWG WCot WWeb
– 'Emily Brown'	CBcs CSPN EBee NLar
§ **griseus** var. **horizontalis**	EBee LRHS MAsh NPri SPer WFar
'Diamond Heights' (v)	
– var. **horizontalis** 'Hurricane Point'	WFar
– – 'Silver Surprise' PBR (v)	CBcs CFai CSPN EBee ELan ENot MHFa NPri SHBN SLim SPer SPoG WWeb
– – 'Yankee Point'	CBcs CChe CDoC CMac CSBt EBee EMil ENot GGar GKir LPVe LRHS MBri MGos MRav NBlu SHBN SLim SPer SPlb WBod WDin WFar
impressus	CBcs CMHG CSBt CTri EBee ENot EPfP LRHS MAsh MRav SPar SPer SPla WCFE WCom WEas WFar WStI WWeb
N 'Italian Skies' ♀ H3	CBcs CChe CDoC CMHG CMac CSBt CWSG EBee EMil EPfP LAst LPVe LRHS MBri MDun MGos MRav NBlu NPri SLim SLon SPar SPer SPlb SRPl WBod WDin WFar WCmC WWeb
'Joyce Coulter'	CBcs EBee ISea
'Julia Phelps'	CMHG EBee WEas WLRN
'Ken Taylor'	LRHS
§ x **lobbianus**	CBcs CBrm CSBt CTri EHol LAst MRav WDin
– 'Russellianus'	CAbP EBee LCaP MGos MWya SHBN
x **pallidus**	CFai WBcn
– 'Golden Elan'	WBcn
– 'Marie Simon'	CBcs CBot CBrm CChe CPle CWib EBee ELan EMil EPfP GEil LHop LRHS MBri MDun NFor NLon SPar SPer SRms SSta WBod WCFE WDin WFar WGwG WKif WSHC WWeb
– 'Perle Rose'	CBcs CMac CPle EBee EPfP LRHS SHBN SOWG SPer WKif WSHC
papillosus	EBee
– var. **roweanus**	CPle WEas
'Pin Cushion'	CDoC CWSG CWib EBee EPfP LRHS MRav WBcn WPat WRHF
'Point Millerton'	see *C. thyrsiflorus* 'Millerton Point'
prostratus	CSBt MAsh SDry SHBN SMad WAbe WWin
'Puget Blue' ♀ H4	More than 30 suppliers
purpureus	LBuc LCaP WWeb
'Ray Hartman'	WBcn
repens	see *C. thyrsiflorus* var. *repens*
rigidus	see *C. cuneatus* var. *rigidus*

'Sierra Blue'	EBee
'Snow Flurries'	CBcs CSBt CWib EBee EMil EPfP LAst MGos MWat SRPl WAbe WFar WGwG
'Snow Showers' **new**	NBlu
'Southmead' ♀ H3	CDoC CTri EBee ECtt EMil EPfP EWTr GBuc LRHS MAsh MBri MGos NBlu NPri WBrE WDin WHCG
thyrsiflorus	CBcs CMac CTri CWSG CWib EBee EPfP LRHS MAsh MBri NHol SGar SHBN SPer SRms WDin WFar WHar WTel
– 'Borne Again' (v)	WBcn WWpP
§ – 'Millerton Point'	CChe CWSG EBee EMil EPfP LAst LRHS MBlu NLar SLim WWeb WWpP
§ – var. *repens* ♀ H3	More than 30 suppliers
– 'Skylark' ♀ H3	CDoC CMHG CPle CTbh EBee ELan ENot EPfP GKir LAst LHop LNet LPVe LRHS MAsh MBri MGos NBee NPri NPro SAga SDix SLim SReu SSta WFar WPat WWeb
'Tilden Park'	LRHS
x *veitchianus*	CMac CSBt EBee ELan ENot LAst LRHS MAsh MBar NHol SPar SPer SSta WWeb
velutinus	MSal
'Victoria'	EBee LBuc
'White Cascade'	CSBt EBee EHol LRHS
Zanzibar = 'Pershore Zanzibar'PBR (v)	CSPN CWSG EBee EHoe ENot EPfP LAst LRHS MCCP MGos MTis MWat MWgw MWya NEgg NPri SHBN SPer WOVN WWeb

Cedrela (Meliaceae)

sinensis	see *Toona sinensis*

Cedronella (Lamiaceae)

§ *canariensis*	CArn CBod CSev CTCP EShb GBar GGar GPoy IFro IIve ILis MBow MChe MHer MSal NCWG SIde SOWG SWat WCer WHHs WHer WPer WSel WWye
mexicana	see *Agastache mexicana*
triphylla	see *C. canariensis*

Cedrus (Pinaceae)

atlantica	CDul CSBt CTho ECrN EHul GKir LCon MBar NWea WEve WMou WPGP
– 'Aurea'	CDoC CMac LCon LLin LPan MBar MGos SCoo SSta WDin WHar
– 'Fastigiata'	CDoC CMac EHul LCon MAsh MBar MBri MGos SCoo SLim WEve
– Glauca Group ♀ H4	More than 30 suppliers
– – 'Silberspitz'	CKen
– 'Glauca Fastigiata'	CKen ECho LPan
– 'Glauca Pendula'	CDoC CKen EHul EOrn EPfP GKir IMGH LCon LNet LPan LRHS MBar MBlu MBri MGos NBee NBlu NPSI NWea SKee SLim SMad SSta WDin
– 'Pendula'	CDul CMac ECho GBin MAsh WOrn
brevifolia	ECho GKir LCon LLin LPan MBar MBri MGos NLar WEve
– 'Epstein'	LCon MBar
– 'Hillier Compact'	CKen
– 'Kenwith'	CKen
deodara ♀ H4	More than 30 suppliers
– 'Albospica' (v)	LCon LLin
– 'Argentea'	MBar MGos
– 'Aurea' ♀ H4	CDoC CDul CSBt CTho EHul EOrn EPfP GKir IMGH LBee LCon LLin

	LPan LRHS MAsh MBar MBri MGos SLim SPar WDin WEve WOrn
– 'Blue Dwarf'	CKen LCon LLin MAsh
* – 'Blue Mountain Broom'	CKen
– 'Blue Triumph'	LPan WEve
– 'Cream Puff'	CSli ECho LCon LLin MAsh MBar MGos
– 'Feelin' Blue'	CDoC CKen COtt CSli EBre EHul ENot EPla GKir IMGH LBee LCon LLin LPan LRHS MAsh MBar MBri MGos MLan NBlu NHol SCoo SLim SPar WStI WWeb
– 'Gold Cone'	MGos
– 'Gold Mound'	CKen CSBt LCon MAsh WEve
– 'Golden Horizon'	CDoC CKen CSBt EBre EHul EOrn GKir IMGH LBee LCon LLin LPan LRHS MAsh MBar MBri MGos NBee NBlu SHBN SLim SPer WDin WEve WWeb
– 'Karl Fuchs'	CDoC EBre GKir LPan LRHS MAsh MBri NBlu SCoo SMad WGor WMou
– 'Kashmir'	CSli
– 'Kelly Gold'	CDoC GKir MBri
– 'Klondyke'	LCon MAsh
– 'Mountain Beauty'	CKen
– 'Nana'	CKen
– 'Nivea'	CKen
– 'Pendula'	CDoC EHul LCon LPan MBar MGos MWat NPSI WDin WGor WStI
– 'Polar Winter'	SMad
– 'Pygmy'	CKen
– 'Raywood's Prostrate'	CKen
– 'Robusta'	WEve
– 'Roman Candle'	CSli ECho EOrn SHBN WEve
– 'Scott'	CKen
– 'Silver Mist'	CKen
– 'Silver Spring'	MGos NLar
* 'Home Park'	CKen
libani ♀ H4	More than 30 suppliers
– 'Comte de Dijon'	EHul LCon LLin SLim SPoG
– Nana Group	CKen ECho LCon MAsh
– 'Sargentii'	CDoC CKen EHul EOrn IMGH LCon LLin LRHS MAsh MBar MBri MGos SLim SSta WEve
– 'Taurus'	MBar

Celastrus (Celastraceae)

angulatus	CPIN GIBF WPGP
orbiculatus	CAgr CBcs CDoC CFwr CMac CPIN EBee GBin GEil LRHS MRav NSti SLon SRPl SReu SSta WFar WSHC
– 'Diana' (f)	NBea SSta
– 'Hercules' (m)	NBea
– Hermaphrodite Group ♀ H4	CBrm CSam EPla GSki MCCP SBra SDix SPer SSpi
– var. *papillosus* B&SWJ 591	WCru
– var. *punctatus* B&SWJ 1931	WCru
rosthorniana **new**	GIBF
scandens	CMac CPIN EBee ELan ENot IMGH SMur SPlb WDin

Celmisia ♣ (Asteraceae)

Timpany hybrids **new**	ITim
adamsii	IBlr
allanii	IBlr
alpina	IBlr SOkd
– large-leaved	IBlr
angustifolia	GCrs IBlr
– silver-leaved	IBlr

	argentea	EPot GCrs GGar GTou IBlr ITim
		NDlv NHar NLAp WAbe
	armstrongii	ECho IBlr
	asteliifolia	IBlr
	Ballyrogan hybrids	IBlr
	bellidioides	EPot EWes GCrs GDra GEdr IBlr
		NEgg NHar NLAp NMen WAbe
	bonplandii	IBlr
	brevifolia	IBlr
	coriacea misapplied	see *C. semicordata*
	coriacea Raoul	see *C. mackaui*
	coriacea (G. Forst.)	GCal IBlr MDun NFor NHar WEas
	Hook. f.	
	- 'Harry Bryce'	IBlr
	costiniana	IBlr
	dallii	IBlr
	'David Shackleton'	IBlr
	densiflora	GCrs IBlr SOkd
	- silver-leaved	IBlr
	discolor	IBlr
	durietzii	IBlr
	glandulosa	IBlr
	gracilenta	GCrs IBlr ITim NMen NSla SOkd
		SRot
	- CC 563	NWCA
	graminifolia	IBlr
	haastii	IBlr
	hectorii	GCrs IBlr ITim SOkd
	holosericea	IBlr
	hookeri	EPot GCal IBlr ITim
	inaccessa	IBlr
	incana	EPot GCrs IBlr ITim SOkd
	Inshriach hybrids	IBlr
	insignis	IBlr
	Jury hybrids	IBlr WCot
	latifolia	IBlr
	- large-leaved	IBlr
	longifolia	SSpi
	- large-leaved	IBlr
	- small-leaved	IBlr
§	*mackaui*	GGar IBlr
	markii **new**	IBlr
	monroi	EPot IBlr
	morganii	IBlr
	prorepens	IBlr
	pugioniformis	IBlr SOkd
	rumulosa	EPot GDra GEdr GGar ITim
	- var. *tuberculata*	GCrs GTou IBlr NSla
	saxifraga	IBlr ITim WAbe
§	*semicordata*	EPot IBlr ITim NSla WHil
	- subsp. *aurigans*	EPot IBlr
	- 'David Shackleton'	see *C.* 'David Shackleton'
	- subsp. *stricta*	EPot GCrs IBlr
	sericophylla	IBlr
	- large-leaved	IBlr
	sessiliflora	EPot GTou IBlr ITim
	- 'Mount Potts'	GDra IBlr
	spectabilis	IBlr MDun NEgg WCot
	- subsp. *magnifica*	IBlr
	- subsp. *spectabilis*	IBlr
	var. *angustifolia*	
	spedenii **new**	IBlr
	tomentella	IBlr
	traversii	IBlr WWeb
	verbascifolia	IBlr SOkd
	viscosa	IBlr
§	*walkeri*	GCrs GGar GTou IBlr
	webbiana	see *C. walkeri*

Celosia (*Amaranthaceae*)

argentea var. *cristata*	MBri
- var. *cristata*	MBri
Plumosa Group	

Celsia see *Verbascum*

x Celsioverbascum see *Verbascum*

Celtis (*Ulmaceae*)

australis	CAgr CBcs CDul CTho EGFP GKir
	LPan LRHS
bungeana	CMCN IDee
julianae	WCwm WNor
laevigata	CMCN
occidentalis	CPLG CTho ELan LRHS WBVN
- var. *pumila*	WNor
sinensis	CMCN EGFP WNor
trinervia **new**	GIBF

Cenolophium (*Apiaceae*)

denudatum	CDes EBee ECha SIgm WPGP

Centaurea ✿ (*Asteraceae*)

	DS&T 89061T	EBee
	HH&K 271	NBid
	achtarovii	SOkd
	aegialophila DC 150	MDCh
	alba	EBee NCot
	alpestris **new**	ECho NLar
	argentea	CBot
	atropurpurea	NLar SGar
	bella	More than 30 suppliers
	benoistii	CDes CHad CPlt EBee ECGN
		EMan LPhx MRav SIgm WPGP
		WRus
	'Blue Dreams'	EMon LPVe LRHS MGrG MLLN
		SCro SUsu
	candidissima hort.	see *C. cineraria*
	'Caramia'	SSvw SUsu
	'Carina' **new**	EBee
	cheiranthifolia	CDes CElw ECha EMon GCal
		MBct NBir WFar
§	- var. *purpurascens*	EBlw EMon LRHS MAvo
§	*cineraria*	EMan MOak SRms WCot WEas
	cyanus	CArn GWCH MBow MHer NArg
		SYvo WBWf WFar WJek
	cynaroides	see *Leuzea centauroides*
	dealbata	CBot COIW EBee EBlw EPfP
		GAbr LAst LRHS MBro MFir MHdf
		MHer NArg NBro NMir NOak
		NOrc SCro SDes SPer WCot WFar
		WMoo WPer WWeb WWin WWpP
	- 'Steenbergii'	CElw CHor CM&M CRDP EBre
		EChP EGle ELan EKou EWTr GCal
		GKir LRHS NBid NBlu NMGW
		NOak NPer NSti SMer SPer SSpe
		WAbb WCom WCot WFar WHoo
		WMnd
	declinata	NLon
	fischeri Willd.	EMon
	glastifolia	EBee EMon GCal MLLN WCot WPGP
	gymnocarpa	see *C. cineraria*
	'Hoar Frost'	CDes EMon
	hypoleuca	More than 30 suppliers
	'John Coutts'	
	jacea	EMan MBow NBid SSvw WCot
	kotschyana	CDes EBee NBid
	macrocephala	More than 30 suppliers
	marschalliana	NBid
	montana	More than 30 suppliers
	- 'Alba'	More than 30 suppliers
	- 'Carnea'	CElw CPom EBee EChP ECha EGle
		EMon GMaP IKee LLWP LPhx
		MAnH MAvo NChi NCot SCro STes
		SUsu WFTG WFar WRus WWin
	- 'Coerulea' **new**	IHMH

- 'Gold Bullion'	EBee EBlw ECGP EGle EMon EPPr EVFa EWes LDai MAvo MBri MCCP MCLN NBir NSti SMad SSvw SUsu SVil WBcn WCot WPGP WWeb
- 'Grandiflora'	EBee GGar MBri
- 'Horwood Gold'	LHop
- 'Joyce'	EMon
- 'Lady Flora Hastings'	CBot CBre CDes CElw CSam CSpe EBee GMac LPhx MAvo MTed NPPs SCro
- 'Ochroleuca'	EGle EGoo EMon MLLN WBcn
- 'Parham'	CElw CMGP CPou CPrp CSev EBee EBlw EMan ERou GCal LHop LLWP LRHS MCLN MRav NSti SChu SHel SPer SPla SPlb SWat WLRN WMnd
- 'Purple Prose'	EMon WBcn
- 'Purpurea'	CDes EBee MRav
- 'Rosea'	see *C. montana* 'Carnea'
* - *violacea*	IBlr MGrG
- 'Violetta'	CPom CPou NBir WFar
nervosa	see *C. uniflora* subsp. *nervosa*
nigra	CArn CKin COld EBee EMan LAst MOne NLan NMir NNor NPPs NSco SRob WMoo
- var. *alba*	CArn CBre CPou
- subsp. *rivularis*	EBlw ECha NBid
orientalis	CPLG CPou CRez CSam EChP LPhx NBro NLar SBla SIgm WPer
pannonica subsp. *pannonica*	CPom
- - HH&K 259	CStr
phrygia	EBee EMan GAbr GBuc MNrw NBid NLar WPer WRos
- subsp. *pseudophrygia*	CSam NBid
pulcherrima	ECha EGle EMan EMon NOak WPer
'Pulchra Major'	see *Leuzea centauroides*
pullata **new**	EBee
rhapontica	see *Leuzea rhapontica*
rigidifolia	EGle
rothrockii	WSan
rupestris	CPou LPhx SAga SBla SGar WBar WWin
ruthenica	CHea CPom EMan LPhx MCAu MSte NLar SIgm SPer WCot WHil
* - 'Alba'	MSte
salonitana	EMon
scabiosa	CArn CKin ECoo GWCH MBow MChe MHer MWhi NBid NLan WPer
- f. *albiflora*	CNat EBlw EMan EMon LAst LRHS WCot
- 'Nell Hill'	CNat
simplicicaulis	CNic CPlt CRDP EBee EGle EMan GBri MBro MFir MTho NMen SBla SIgm SRms SRot WCom WCot WEas WHoo WPGP WPer
stenolepis subsp. *razgradensis*	CMil
- - HH&K 297	CMil
thracica	EBee LPhx SAga SCro WCot
§ *triumfettii* subsp. *cana* 'Rosea'	CRDP NJOw SBla WWin
- subsp. *stricta*	CDes CSLe EBee EMon GBuc MSte NMGW SCro WPGP
§ *uniflora* subsp. *nervosa*	GGar MGas MHar NBid NBro WBea WPer

Centaurium (Gentianaceae)

§ *confertum*	WBVN
erythraea	CArn EMlt GPoy MChe MHer MSal WHHs WWye
scilloides	LRHS MTho NMen NWCA WWin

Centella (Apiaceae)

§ *asiatica*	CArn EBee EOHP ILis MGol MSal WJek

Centradenia (Melastomataceae)

floribunda	SYvo
inaequilateralis	CHal ECtt EMan LPVe MBri MOak
'Cascade'	NPri SHFr SPet WLRN

Centranthus (Valerianaceae)

§ *ruber*	More than 30 suppliers
§ - 'Albus'	More than 30 suppliers
- 'Atrococcineus'	ECha EMan SPer WHil WPer
- var. *coccineus*	CBcs EBee EChP EGoo ELan ENot EPfP GAbr GKir LIck LPhx LRHS MCAu MRav MWgw NBlu NDov SDes SEND SMrm SPar SPla SRPl WCot WFar
- mauve	LPhx NDov
- 'Roseus'	WMoo
- 'Ruby Red'	EWTr
- 'Snowcloud'	CSev EWTr MBow NPri
'White Cloud'	WJek

Cephalanthera (Orchidaceae)

falcata	EFEx
longibracteata	EFEx

Cephalanthus (Rubiaceae)

occidentalis	CDul CPLG CPle ECre EMil GEil IFro LRav MBNS MBlu MGos MTis NBlu SBrw SPer SSta

Cephalaria (Dipsacaceae)

from Nepal 2800m	CFox CSam
§ *alpina*	EBee ECha EDAr EHrv EMan EMlt GKir LAst LRHS MHer MNrw NLar SOkh SRms SWat WCot WFar WPer
- 'Nana'	CMil NMen NWCA
ambrosioides	MLLN
- MESE 503	EBee
dipsacoides	CFee CNat EBee ECha LPhx MWrn NLar
flava	EBre GKir
galpiniana subsp. *simplicior*	CCtw EBee
§ *gigantea*	More than 30 suppliers
* *graeca*	EBee
leucantha	CHea EBee ECGN EMan EMar GBuc MLLN NLar STes WElm
litvinovii	CElw
natalensis	EBee
tatarica	see *C. gigantea*
tchihatchewii	MLLN

Cephalotaxus (Cephalotaxaceae)

fortunei	CDoC CDul SLon
- 'Prostrate Spreader'	EHul
harringtonii	ECho LEdu LLin MRav SMur
- 'Fastigiata'	CDoC CKen EHul ENot EOrn GKir IArd IDee LCon LRHS MAsh MBar MBlu MBri SLim WDin WGer
- 'Gimborn's Pillow'	MBar
- 'Korean Gold'	CKen
- 'Prostrata'	MBar

Cephalotus (Cephalotaceae)

follicularis	EEls GTro SHmp

Cerastium (Caryophyllaceae)

alpinum	CMea SRms
- var. *lanatum*	ECho ETow EWes WPer

arvense NDlv
candidissimum EWes
tomentosum CHal EFer EPfP GKir GWCH LGro
MHer MPWC NBlu NDlv NFor
NJOw NPri SPer SPet SPlb WCer
WFar WLRN WPer
- var. *columnae* EBre ECha ECho EHoe EPfP EWes
SDes WCot
- 'Silberteppich' EGoo LPVe

Ceratonia (Caesalpiniaceae)
siliqua CAgr CFil CTCP LEdu MSal WHHs

Ceratophyllum (Ceratophyllaceae)
demersum CBen CRow EHon EMFW LMdh
SLon SWat WMAq WWpP

Ceratostigma ✿ (Plumbaginaceae)
abyssinicum CFwr ELan
'Autumn Blue' **new** EPfP
griffithii CBcs CBot CChe CDoC CFwr CHll
CPle CSBt CTrC CWSG EBee EBre
ECtt ELan EPfP EWTr LRHS MCCP
MRav SPar SPcr SPla WBod WBrE
WDin WOld WSHC WStI WWeb
- SF 149/150 ISea
- 'Album' MRav
minus CPLG
§ *plumbaginoides* ♀ H3-4 More than 30 suppliers
willmottianum ♀ H3-4 More than 30 suppliers
- Desert Skies CFwr EBee ELan EPfP GBuc IArd
= 'Palmgold'PBR LHop LRHS MAsh SCoo SHGC
SMad SPer SSta
- Forest Blue CAbP CDoC CFwr CSBt CWSG
= 'Lice'PBR EBee ELan ENot EPfP EVFa GKir
IArd LHop LRHS MAsh MRav NPri
NPro SCoo SMer SMrm SPar SPcr
SPla SRcu WPat WWeb

Cercidiphyllum ✿ (Cercidiphyllaceae)
japonicum ♀ H4 More than 30 suppliers
- 'Amazing Grace' **new** CTho
- 'Heronswood Globe' MBlu NLar
- f. *pendulum* ♀ H4 CBcs CDul CEnd CFil CMCN EPfP
GKir LBuc LRHS MAsh MBlu NBea
NLar SKee SLim SMad SPer SRPl
SSpi WDin WOrn WPGP WWes
- Red Fox see *C. japonicum* 'Rotfuchs'
§ - 'Rotfuchs' CBcs CEnd CMCN CPMA CTho
EBee EPfP GKir LRHS MAsh MBlu
MGos NLar SMad SSpi WGer
WPGP WPat
- 'Ruby' CPMA
I - 'Strawberry' MBlu NLar
magnificum CEnd CFil CMCN EPfP MBlu NLar
SSpi
- Og 95.111 CDoC
- Og 95.114 WCru
- Og 95.144 CFil EPla WPGP
- f. *pendulum* CPMA

Cercis (Caesalpiniaceae)
canadensis CAgr CBcs CBrm CHEx CLnd
CMCN CTri EMil EPfP EWTr GIBF
MCCP MGos NHol SPer WHCG
WNor WPat
- 'Forest Pansy' ♀ H4 More than 30 suppliers
§ - var. *occidentalis* CAgr LRav SOWG
- 'Royal White' EPfP MBlu NLar
- 'Rubye Atkinson' NLar
chinensis LRHS MCCP NLar NPSI SSta WDin
WOTO

- 'Avondale' CBcs CEnd CPMA CWib EBee
EMil EWes LNet LRHS MAsh MBlu
MGos NLar
griffithii NLar
occidentalis see *C. canadensis* var.
occidentalis
reniformis 'Oklahoma' CBcs CPMA EBee MBlu NLar
- 'Texas White' CBcs CPMA
siliquastrum ♀ H4 More than 30 suppliers
- f. *albida* CBot CTho EPfP LPan LRHS SPar
- 'Bodnant' EPfP NLar
- 'Rubra' WPat
yunnanensis NLar

Cerinthe (Boraginaceae)
glabra EMan MWgw SPlb WHil WWye
'Golden Bouquet' NPSI
major WEas WSan
- 'Kiwi Blue' CHll CSpe MDKP MWrn
- 'Purpurascens' More than 30 suppliers
- 'Yellow Gem' CPla
minor subsp. LIck
auriculata **new**
retorta **new** CSpe

Ceropegia (Asclepiadaceae)
barklyi CHal
linearis subsp. CHal IBlr MBri SRms
woodii ♀ H1
sandersonii ♀ H1 SSte

Ceroxylon (Arecaceae)
alpinum LPJP LPal
ventricosum LPal

Cestrum (Solanaceae)
aurantiacum CPle ERea IDee
auriculatum SOWG
x *cultum* CPle
- 'Cretan Purple' CHll ERea
§ *elegans* CHEx CHal CPLG CSev LRHS
MOak SOWG WCot WDin WMul
fasciculatum CBcs CPle GQui SIgm SMad SOWG
'Newellii' ♀ H2 CAbb CBcs CHEx CMHG CPLG
CSev CWib EBak ELan EPfP ERea
GQui MBlu NPSI SBrw SGar SIgm
SOWG WBor WSHC
nocturnum CBcs CDoC CHal CPle EBak ELan
ERea ESlt LRHS SOWG SYvo WMul
parqui ♀ H3 CAbb CHEx CMHG CPLG CPle
EBcc ECha ELan EPfP ERea EShb
MOak SBrw SDix SGar SLon SMad
SMrm SOWG SSte SVen SYvo WCot
WKif WOld WPat WPen WPic WSHC
psittacinum CPLG
purpureum see *C. elegans*
roseum CPLG CSev
- 'Ilnacullin' CPLG CTCP ERea IDee
* *splendens* SOWG
violaceum misapplied see *Iochroma cyaneum* 'Trebah'

Ceterach (Aspleniaceae)
officinarum see *Asplenium ceterach*

Chaenomeles (Rosaceae)
cathayensis CTho EPfP EPla WBcn WHer
§ *japonica* CCVT ENot MBar NEgg NFor
WDin WFar WOTO
- 'Orange Beauty' WFar
- 'Sargentii' CBcs CMac MHdf NEgg
'John Pilger' EBee NHol NPro
lagenaria see *C. speciosa*
'Madame Butterfly' **new** COtt GKir WWeb

	maulei	see *C. japonica*
	sinensis	see *Pseudocydonia sinensis*
§	*speciosa*	CSam ISea MBar NFor NWea WNor
	- 'Apple Blossom'	see *C. speciosa* 'Moerloosei'
	- 'Aurora'	LRHS
	- 'Brilliant'	EPfP
	- 'Contorta'	WCot
	- 'Falconnet Charlet' (d)	MRav WLRN
	- 'Geisha Girl' ♀ H4	CBcs CChe CDoC CEnd CHar CMac CSBt CWSG EBee EBre ECtt ENot EPfP GKir LAst LHop LRHS MAsh MCCP MGos MRav NHol SHBN SLim SPar SPer SPla SRms WFar WWeb
	- 'Grayshott Salmon'	EBee MCCP NCiC NHol NPro WFar WLeb
§	- 'Moerloosei' ♀ H4	CDoC CPMA CSBt CSam EBee ELan ENot EPfP GKir IMGH LAst LRHS MAsh MBri MRav MWat NSti SHBN SLim SPer SPla SSta WDin WGwG WMoo
	- 'Nivalis'	More than 30 suppliers
	- 'Port Eliot'	WBcn WWeb
	- 'Rosea Plena' (d)	WBcn
	- 'Rubra Grandiflora'	WBrE
	- 'Simonii' (d)	CBcs EBee EHol ENot EPfP LRHS MGos MRav NWea SPer WFar WPat
	- 'Snow'	CChe CSBt EBee MRav MWat NPro SRms WLRN WRHF WStI
	- 'Umbilicata'	ENot SPer SRms WWes
	- 'Winter Snow' **new**	ENot
	- 'Yukigoten'	LRHS WBcn
	x *superba*	NFor
	- 'Boule de Feu'	CTri CWib ECtt GKir
	- 'Cameo' (d)	CBot CChe EPfP LAst LRHS MBri NPri SLPl WLRN WWeb
	- 'Coral Sea'	NFor NLon
	- 'Crimson and Gold' ♀ H4	More than 30 suppliers
	- 'Elly Mossel'	CBcs CMac CSBt GKir NBlu SMer WFar WLRN
	- 'Ernst Finken'	EBee
	- 'Etna'	GKir WPat
	- 'Fire Dance'	CMac EBee ECtt EGra ENot IMGH MRav NBee NHol SPer SPoG WLRN WPat WRHF
	- 'Hollandia'	MGos
	- 'Issai White'	LRHS
	- 'Jet Trail'	CBcs CSBt EBee ELan ENot EPfP LAst LRHS MGos MRav NBlu NPro WFar WPat
	- 'Knap Hill Scarlet' ♀ H4	CBrm CDoC EBee EBre ECot ENot EPfP GKir LRHS MRav NHol SEND SLim SPer SRms WBod WDin WFar WStI
	- 'Lemon and Lime'	EBee ELan ENot EPfP GKir MGos MRav NSti SPer WBcn
	- 'Nicoline' ♀ H4	CBcs CDoC EBee ENot EPfP GKir LRHS MBri MRav MWat NEgg NLon NPri SBra WDin WFar WStI
	- 'Ohio Red'	WBod
	- 'Pink Lady' ♀ H4	More than 30 suppliers
	- 'Red Trail'	EBee ENot MRav
	- 'Rowallane' ♀ H4	EBee ELan ENot EPfP IMGH MRav SHBN SPer WLRN
	- 'Salmon Horizon'	EWTr WBcn
	- 'Texas Scarlet'	GKir WBcn
	- 'Tortuosa'	SPoG
	- 'Vermilion'	MBNS

Chaenorhinum (Scrophulariaceae)

| § | *origanifolium* | CElw EBee ESis LIck NBlu NWCA SPlb WPat WWin |

| | - 'Blue Dream' | CSpe CWes ECtt EMan MAvo MBri MNrw MWrn NBlu NBur NLap NPri SDes SPet WCot WElm WFar WPer WWal WWeb |

Chaerophyllum (Apiaceae)

| | *hirsutum* | CRow ELan |
| | - 'Roseum' | More than 30 suppliers |

Chamaecyparis ✿ (Cupressaceae)

	formosensis	CKen
	funebris	see *Cupressus funebris*
	lawsoniana	CDul EHul MBar NWea WDin WEve WMou
	- 'Albospica' (v)	ECho EHul GKir MBar SBod WFar
	- 'Albospica Nana'	see *C. lawsoniana* 'Nana Albospica'
	- 'Albovariegata' (v)	ECho EHul EOrn LBee LRHS MBar
	- 'Allumii Aurea'	see *C. lawsoniana* 'Alumigold'
	- 'Allumii Magnificent'	CBcs MAsh
§	- 'Alumigold'	CDoC CSBt CSli CWib GKir LCon MAsh MBar MGos SBod SMer SPer WDin WStI WWeb
	- 'Alumii'	CMac CSBt CTri EHul ENot GKir MAsh MBar MGos NWea SPer WStI WWeb
	- 'Argentea'	see *C. lawsoniana* 'Argenteovariegata'
§	- 'Argenteovariegata' (v)	CDoC CMac CSBt ECho GKir LCon SLim
	- 'Aurea'	CDul
	- 'Aurea Compacta'	ECho
	- 'Aurea Densa' ♀ H4	CKen CMac CNic CSBt CSli CTri EHul EOrn GKir MAsh MBar MGos SBod SPoG STre WGor
	- 'Aureovariegata' (v)	MBar WBcn
§	- 'Barabits' Globe'	MBar
	- 'Barry's Gold'	EOrn
	- 'Beacon Silver'	WBcn
§	- 'Bleu Nantais'	CBrm CKen CMac CSBt EHul EOrn GKir LBee LCon LLin LRHS MAsh MBar MBro MGos MWat SBod SHBN SLim WCFE WEve
	- 'Blom'	CKen EHul MBri
	- 'Blue Gem'	NHol
§	- 'Blue Gown'	EHul LBee MBar MGos SRms
§	- 'Blue Jacket'	MBar NWea
	- 'Blue Nantais'	see *C. lawsoniana* 'Bleu Nantais'
	- 'Blue Surprise'	CKen CSBt EHoe EHul EOrn LLin MBar MBro SAga WFar
	- 'Brégéon'	CKen
	- 'Broomhill Gold'	CBrm CDoC CMac CSBt CSli EBre EHul ENot GKir LCon LLin LRHS MAsh MBar MBri MGos MWat NHol SBod SLim SPer SPla WCFE WDin WStI WWeb
*	- 'Burkwood's Blue'	MBar
	- 'Caudata'	CKen MBar WBcn
	- 'Chantry Gold'	CKen ECho EHul GKir
§	- 'Chilworth Silver' ♀ H4	CSBt CTri EBre EHul EOrn EPot GKir LBee LRHS MAsh MBar MBri MGos SBod SHBN SLim SPer SRms WDin WFar WStI
	- 'Chingii'	EHul MAsh
	- 'Columnaris'	CBcs CDoC CMac EBre ENot EPfP GKir LBee LRHS MBar MBri MGos MOke NBlu NWea SHBN SLim WCFE WFar
	- 'Columnaris Aurea'	see *C. lawsoniana* 'Golden Spire'
N	- 'Columnaris Glauca'	CSBt CWib EBre EHul EOrn GKir LCon LPan MAsh MGos MWat SBod SPer WDin WFar WStI WTel
	- 'Crawford's Compact'	CMac

	- 'Cream Crackers'	ECho EHul
	- 'Cream Glow'	CKen SLim WGor
	- 'Croftway'	EHul
	- 'Dik's Weeping'	CDoC GKir SMad
	- 'Dorset Gold'	CMac
	- 'Duncanii'	EHul
	- 'Dutch Gold'	EHul GKir MAsh
	- 'Dwarf Blue'	see *C. lawsoniana* 'Pick's Dwarf Blue'
	- 'Eclipse'	CKen
N	- 'Elegantissima'	CKen CMac
	- 'Ellwoodii' ♀ H4	CChe CMac CSBt CWib EBre EHul ENot EPfP GKir LCon LLin LRHS MAsh MBar MGos MWat NBlu NEgg NWea SBod SLim SMer SPer WCFE WDin WFar WMoo WTel WWeb
	- 'Ellwood's Empire'	EHul LRHS MBri WEve
	- 'Ellwood's Gold' ♀ H4	More than 30 suppliers
	- 'Ellwood's Gold Pillar'	CSBt ECho EHul ENot EOrn GKir LBee MAsh MBri MGos NHol SCoo SLim SPla WLRN WPat
§	- 'Ellwood's Nymph'	CKen EOrn MAsh MBar SHBN SLim SPoG WGor
	- Ellwood's Pillar = 'Flolar'	CChe CDoC CKen CMac CSBt CSli EBre EHul EOrn EPfP GKir IMGH LBee LCon LLin LRHS MAsh MBar MBri MGos MWat NHol SBod SLim SPla WBrE WCFE WDin WFar WStI
	- 'Ellwood's Pygmy'	CMac ECho GKir MBar NHol
	- 'Ellwood's Silver'	MAsh WFar
	- 'Ellwood's Silver Threads'	CMac GKir
*	- 'Ellwood's Treasure'	ECho ENot
	- 'Ellwood's Variegata'	see *C. lawsoniana* 'Ellwood's White'
§	- 'Ellwood's White' (v)	CKen CMac CSBt CSli EHul EOrn EPfP LRHS MBar MBri NBlu SHBN WFar WMoo
I	- 'Emerald'	CKen MBar MBri NHol
	- 'Emerald Spire'	CMac MAsh NHol
	- 'Empire'	WFar
	- 'Erecta Argenteovariegata' (v)	WEve
	- 'Erecta Aurea'	ECho EHul LBee LRHS MAsh NBee
	- 'Erecta Filiformis'	MBar
§	- 'Erecta Viridis'	CMac CTrG GKir MBar NEgg NWea WCFE WDin WFar WStI
	- 'Ericoides'	EHul GKir
	- 'Erika'	MBar
	- 'Filiformis Compacta'	EHul
	- 'Fleckellwood'	CSli CWib ECho EHul MAsh MBar MGos SAga SMer WEve WLRN WStI
	- 'Fletcheri' ♀ H4	CBcs CMac CSBt CWib EHul ENot GKir LBee LCon LRHS MAsh MBar MGos NWea SBod SHBN SMer SPer SPla WDin WFar WOrn WStI
	- 'Fletcheri Aurea'	see *C. lawsoniana* 'Yellow Transparent'
	- 'Fletcher's White'	ECho EHul LRHS MBar MBri WBcn
	- 'Forsteckensis'	CDoC CKen CSli EHul EOrn GKir LLin MBar MGos MOne NWea SLim SRms WFar WGor
	- 'Fraseri'	MBar NWea WDin
	- 'Gimbornii' ♀ H4	CDoC CMac EBre EHul EOrn GKir LBee LCon MAsh MBar MBri SBod SLim SRms WCFE
	- 'Glauca'	CDul
	- 'Glauca Spek'	see *C. lawsoniana* 'Spek'
	- 'Globosa'	MGos
	- 'Globus'	see *C. lawsoniana* 'Barabits' Globe'
	- 'Gnome'	CDoC CMac EHul EOrn ESis GEdr LLin MBar MGos NHol SBod SCoo SLim

	- 'Gold Flake'	MBar MBri MGos
	- 'Gold Splash'	MBar
	- 'Golden King'	MBar
§	- 'Golden Pot'	CBrm CDoC CKen CMac CSBt CSli CWib EHul EOrn GKir LBee LRHS MBar MGos MOke MWat NBlu SMer WDin
§	- 'Golden Queen'	EHul
§	- 'Golden Showers'	EHul
	- 'Golden Spire'	LRHS MBar MBri MGos
	- 'Golden Triumph'	EHul
	- 'Golden Wonder'	CMac CSli EHul LBee LCon LRHS MAsh MBar MGos NBee NWea SRms WDin WEve WFar WStI
	- 'Grant's Gold'	EHul
	- 'Grayswood Feather'	CDoC CSBt ECho EHul GKir LBee LCon LRHS MAsh MBar MBri MGos SLim SMer
	- 'Grayswood Gold'	EHul EOrn LBee LRHS MAsh MBar MGos WEve
	- 'Grayswood Pillar' ♀ H4	CMac ECho EHul EOrn GKir LCon LRHS MBar MGos
*	- 'Grayswood Spire'	CMac
	- 'Green Globe'	CDoC CKen CSBt CSli EBre EHul EOrn GKir LBee LCon LLin LRHS MAsh MBar MBri SAga SBod WDin WEve
§	- 'Green Hedger' ♀ H4	CMac CSBt CTri EHul ENot GKir LBuc MBar SBod SRms WFar
§	- 'Green Pillar'	CBrm CSBt CWib LBee LCon LRHS MBar MGos SHBN SPoG
	- 'Green Spire'	see *C. lawsoniana* 'Green Pillar'
	- 'Greycone'	CKen LRHS
	- 'Hillieri'	MBar NBee
	- 'Hogger's Blue Gown'	see *C. lawsoniana* 'Blue Gown'
	- 'Howarth's Gold'	GKir LRHS MBri
	- 'Imbricata Pendula'	CKen IDee LCon
	- 'Intertexta'	EHul LCon WBcn WCwm
	- 'Ivonne'	EHul MGos NBlu WOrn
	- 'Jackman's Green Hedger'	see *C. lawsoniana* 'Green Hedger'
	- 'Jackman's Variety'	see *C. lawsoniana* 'Green Pillar'
	- 'Kelleriis Gold'	EHul MBar
	- 'Kilmacurragh' ♀ H4	CMac ENot GKir LLin MAsh MBar MGos NWea WOrn
	- 'Kilworth Column'	LLin MGos SPoG
	- 'Kingswood'	LRHS MBri
	- 'Knowefieldensis'	CMac EHul LLin WBcn
	- 'Lane' hort.	see *C. lawsoniana* 'Lanei Aurea'
	- 'Lanei'	CSBt CWib MAsh WDin
§	- 'Lanei Aurea' ♀ H4	CMac CSli ECho EHul ENot EPfP GKir LCon MBar MGos NWea WFar WOrn
	- 'Lemon Pillar'	WBcn WDin WOrn
	- 'Lemon Queen'	CSBt ECho EHul LBee LRHS WEve WGor
	- 'Limelight'	EHul MGos
	- 'Little Spire' ♀ H4	CDoC CMHG EBre EOrn GKir LBee LCon LLin LRHS MAsh MBar MBri MGos SLim WEve WGor
	- 'Lombartsii'	EHul WBcn WFar
	- 'Lutea' ♀ H4	CMac EHul MGos SBod
§	- 'Lutea Nana' ♀ H4	CKen CMac ECho EHul MAsh MBar MBro MGos MOne NLar WLRN
§	- 'Lutea Smithii'	MBar
	- 'Luteocompacta'	LBee LRHS MGos SHBN
	- 'Lycopodioides'	EHul MBar WBcn
*	- 'MacPenny's Gold'	CMac
	- 'Milford Blue Jacket'	see *C. lawsoniana* 'Blue Jacket'
§	- 'Minima'	MBar SRms WCFE
	- 'Minima Argentea'	see *C. lawsoniana* 'Nana Argentea'
	- 'Minima Aurea' ♀ H4	More than 30 suppliers

	– 'Minima Densa'	see *C. lawsoniana* 'Minima'
	– 'Minima Glauca' ♀ H4	CMac CSBt CSli EBre EHul ENot EPfP GKir LCon LRHS MAsh MBar MBri MGos MOke NEgg NHol NWea SBod SHBN SLim SPer SPla WDin WEve WFar WWeb
	– 'Moonlight'	MBar MGos
	– 'Nana'	MBar
§	– 'Nana Albospica' (v)	EHul EOrn EPfP GKir LBee LCon LRHS MAsh MBar MGos NPro SCoo SLim WFar WGor WStI
§	– 'Nana Argentea'	CKen CMac ECho EHul EOrn EPfP WGor
	– 'Nana Lutea'	see *C. lawsoniana* 'Lutea Nana'
	– 'Nidiformis'	EHul LBee LRHS MBar NWea SRms
	– 'Nyewoods'	see *C. lawsoniana* 'Chilworth Silver'
	– 'Nymph'	see *C. lawsoniana* 'Ellwood's Nymph'
§	– 'Pelt's Blue' ♀ H4	CDoC CKen CSBt CSli EHul LBee LCon LRHS MBar MBri MGos NBee SCoo SHBN SLim WDin WFar WLRN WOrn
	– 'Pembury Blue' ♀ H4	More than 30 suppliers
	– 'Pendula'	LLin MBar
§	– 'Pick's Dwarf Blue'	EHul MBar MBri NBlu NHol WGor
	– Pot of Gold	see *C. lawsoniana* 'Golden Pot'
	– 'Pottenii'	CMac CSBt CSli EHul GKir LBee LCon LRHS MAsh MBar MGos NWea SBod SHBN SMer SPer WDin WEve WFar WOrn WStI
	– 'Pygmaea Argentea' (v) ♀ H4	CKen CMac EBre EHul EOrn EPfP GEdr GKir LBee LCon LLin LRHS MAsh MBar MBri MGos NBee SBod SLim WCFE WDin WEve
	– 'Pygmy'	CNic CSli ECho EHul MBar SLim WLRN
	– 'Rijnhof'	EHul LBee LLin WBcn
	– 'Rogersii'	EOrn MBar SRms WFar
	– 'Romana'	ENot MAsh MBri NBlu
	– 'Royal Gold'	CSli ECho EHul EOrn
	– 'Silver Queen' (v)	CKen LCon MBar NWea WBcn
	– 'Silver Threads' (v)	CMac CSBt CSli EBre EHul ENot EOrn GKir LBee LRHS MAsh MBar MBri MGos MWat SBod SLim WStI
	– 'Silver Tip' (v)	EHul SCoo SLim
	– 'Slocock'	SHBN
	– 'Smithii'	see *C. lawsoniana* 'Lutea Smithii'
	– 'Snow Flurry' (v)	EHul
	– 'Snow White'PBR (v)	CDoC CSBt EBre EHul ENot GKir LBee LCon LLin LRHS MAsh MBar MBri MGos SLim SPla WGor WWeb
	– 'Somerset'	CMac MBar
§	– 'Spek'	CBcs MBar
	– 'Springtime'PBR	CDoC ECho EHul EOrn LCon LRHS MAsh MBri SCoo SLim WGor WWeb
	– 'Stardust' ♀ H4	CDoC CMac CSBt CSli CWib EHul ENot GKir LCon LPan LRHS MAsh MBar MBri MGos NBee NBlu SBod SHBN SLim SMer SPer WDin WOrn
	– 'Stewartii'	CDul CMac CTri ENot MBar MGos NBee NBlu NWea SBod SHBN SMer SPer WStI
	– 'Stilton Cheese'	MBar
*	– 'Summer Cream'	EHul
	– 'Summer Snow' (v)	CBcs CDoC CDul CMac CSBt EHoe EHul ENot EPfP GKir LBee LLin LRHS MAsh MBar MBri MBro MGos SBod SLim SPla SRms WCFE WEve WFar WStI WWeb
	– 'Sunkist'	CKen WFar
	– 'Sylvia's Gold'	EOrn
	– 'Tamariscifolia'	CDoC ECho EHul LCon MBar SBod SPoG WCFE WDin WFar WLRN WStI
	– 'Tharandtensis Caesia'	EOrn MBar WFar
	– 'Tilford'	EHul
	– 'Treasure' (v)	CKen CSli EBre EHoe EHul EOrn EPfP LBee LCon LRHS MAsh MBar MBri NHol SLim WEve
	– 'Triomf van Boskoop'	MBar
	– 'Van Pelt's Blue'	see *C. lawsoniana* 'Pelt's Blue'
	– 'Versicolor' (v)	MBar
	– 'Waterfall' **new**	SMad
	– 'Westermannii' (v)	CMac EHul LCon LLin SBod SCoo SLim WBcn
	– 'White Spot' (v)	CDoC CSli EBre EHul GKir LBee LRHS MBar MBri MGos NBlu SLim WStI
	– 'Winston Churchill'	CSBt MBar MGos NWea SBod
	– 'Wisselii' ♀ H4	CDoC CKen CMac CTrG EHul ENot GKir LBee LCon LLin LRHS MAsh MBar NBlu NWea SBod SRms WDin WFar
	– 'Wisselii Nana'	CKen EHul
	– 'Wissel's Saguaro'	CDoC CKen LCon LRHS MAsh NLar
	– 'Witzeliana'	CDoC CSBt ECho EOrn LRHS MBar MBri MGos SCoo WGer WGor WOrn
	– 'Wyevale Silver'	MBar
	– 'Yellow Cascade'	ECho
	– 'Yellow Queen'	see *C. lawsoniana* 'Golden Queen'
	– 'Yellow Success'	see *C. lawsoniana* 'Golden Queen'
§	– 'Yellow Transparent'	CDoC CMac CSBt CSli LCon MBar SBod SHBN SLim SPoG
	– 'Yvonne'	ECho GKir LLin LRHS MAsh MBar MBri SCoo SLim SPla
	leylandii	see X *Cupressocyparis leylandii*
	nootkatensis	CDul MBar
	– 'Aurea'	GKir WDin WEve
	– 'Aureovariegata' (v)	EHul SLim WBcn
	– 'Compacta'	CTri MBar
	– 'Glauca'	CTho LCon MBar
	– 'Gracilis'	EHul
	– 'Green Arrow' **new**	CKen SLim
	– 'Jubilee'	SCoo SLim SMad
	– 'Lutea'	CMHG CMac CTri LCon MBar NWea SLim
	– 'Nidifera'	MBar WCwm
	– 'Pendula' ♀ H4	CDoC CTho EBre ENot EOrn GKir LCon LLin LPan LRHS MAsh MBar MBri MGos NBee NBlu NWea SLim SMad SPer WCFE WCwm WDin WMou WOrn
	– 'Strict Weeper' **new**	CKen
	– 'Variegata' (v)	EVFa MBar SLim WBcn
	obtusa 'Albospica' (v)	ECho EHul
	– 'Albovariegata' (v)	CKen
	– 'Arneson's Compact' **new**	CKen
	– 'Aurea'	CDoC
	– 'Aureovariegata'	see *C. obtusa* 'Opaal'
	– 'Aurora'	CKen EOrn LCon MAsh
*	– 'Autumn Gold'	MBar
	– 'Bambi'	CKen EOrn MGos
	– 'Barkenny'	CKen
	– 'Bartley'	CKen EPot
	– 'Bassett'	CKen
	– 'Bess'	CKen
	– 'Brigitt' **new**	CKen
	– 'Buttonball' **new**	CKen
	– 'Caespitosa'	CKen EPot
	– 'Chabo-yadori'	CDoC EHul EOrn LCon LLin MBar MGos NHol SLim WFar WStI
	– 'Chilworth'	CDoC LCon MBar MGos NLar

	– 'Chima-anihiba'	CKen
	– 'Chirimen'	CKen NLar
	– 'Clarke's Seedling'	MGos NLar
	– 'Confucius'	EHul NHol
	– 'Contorta'	EOrn EPot LCon MBar
	– 'Cooper's Gem'	EPot
§	– 'Coralliformis'	CMac ECho EOrn LCon LLin
		MBar NHol SMur WBcn
§	– 'Crippsii' ♀ H4	CBcs CDoC CKen CMHG CMac
		ECho EHul EOrn GBin LCon LLin
		MAsh MBar MGos NHol SBod
		SLim SPoG
	– 'Crippsii Aurea'	see C. obtusa 'Crippsii'
	– 'Dainty Doll'	CKen EOrn
	– 'Densa'	see C. obtusa 'Nana Densa'
	– 'Draht'	CDoC MBar WBcn
	– 'Elf'	CKen
	– 'Ellie B'	CKen EOrn
	– 'Ericoides'	CKen ECho EOrn
	– 'Erika'	ECho EOrn WBcn
	– 'Fernspray Gold'	CDoC CKen CMac CSli CTri EHul
		EOrn GKir LCon LLin MAsh MBar
		NHol SBod SLim SPer WWeb
	– 'Flabelliformis'	CKen
	– 'Gimborn Beauty'	MGos
	– 'Gnome' **new**	CKen
	– 'Gold Fern' **new**	CKen
	– 'Golden Fairy'	CKen EOrn
	– 'Golden Filament' (v)	CKen
	– 'Golden Nymph'	CKen CSli EOrn MGos
	– 'Golden Sprite'	CKen EBre MGos
	– 'Goldilocks'	ECho EHul WBcn
	– 'Gracilis Aurea'	CKen
	– 'Graciosa'	see C. obtusa 'Loenik'
	– 'Green Diamond'	CKen
	– 'Hage'	CKen EOrn LCon
	– 'Hypnoides Nana'	CKen EOrn
	– 'Intermedia'	CKen EOrn EPot MGos
	– 'Ivan's Column'	CKen
	– 'Junior' **new**	CKen
	– 'Juniperoides'	CKen EOrn
	– 'Juniperoides Compacta'	CKen EPot
	– 'Kamarachiba'	CKen LCon LLin SLim WBcn
	– 'Kanaamihiba'	MBar NLar
	– 'Konijn'	EHul EOrn WLRN
	– 'Kosteri'	CDoC CKen CMac EBre EHul EOrn
		LBee LCon LLin MAsh MBar MGos
		NDlv SHBN SIng SLim WEve WStI
	– 'Leprechaun'	NLar
	– 'Little Markey'	CKen EOrn
§	– 'Loenik'	ECho EOrn MBar NHol WBcn
	– 'Lycopodioides'	ECho EOrn
	– 'Lycopodioides Aurea'	SLim
	– 'Marian'	CKen
§	– 'Mariesii' (v)	CKen CSli EHul EOrn LCon MAsh
		SHBN
	– 'Minima'	CKen MGos SCoo SMer
	– 'Nana' ♀ H4	CKen CMac ECho LBee LCon
		LRHS MBar MGos NHol
	– 'Nana Albospica'	ECho
	– 'Nana Aurea' ♀ H4	CDoC CMac EBre EHul EOrn EPfP
		GKir MAsh MBar MGos NBee NHol
		NPro SHBN SMer WBrE WFar WStI
	– 'Nana Compacta'	EOrn LCon MAsh NHol
§	– 'Nana Densa'	CKen CMac NLar
	– 'Nana Gracilis' ♀ H4	More than 30 suppliers
I	– 'Nana Gracilis Aurea'	EHul SMur WEve
I	– 'Nana Lutea'	CDoC CKen CSBt EBre EHul EOrn
		EPfP GKir LBee LCon LLin LRHS
		MAsh MBar MBri MGos NDlv
		NHol SBod SLim SPla WGer
	– 'Nana Rigida'	see C. obtusa 'Rigid Dwarf'

	– 'Nana Variegata'	see C. obtusa 'Mariesii'
§	– 'Opaal' (v)	MBar WBcn
	– 'Pygmaea'	CSBt EBre EHul ENot EOrn LCon
		LLin MBar MGos SBod SLim SPoG
	– 'Pygmaea Aurescens'	MBar SIng
	– 'Repens'	EOrn WBcn
§	– 'Rigid Dwarf'	CKen EHul EOrn IMGH LBee
		LCon LRHS MBar SCoo WEve
		WLRN
*	– 'Saint Andrew'	CKen
	– 'Snowflake' (v)	CDoC CKen EOrn MAsh MGos
		WBcn WGor
	– 'Snowkist' (v)	CKen
	– 'Spiralis'	CKen MBar
	– 'Stoneham'	CKen LCon MBar
	– 'Tempelhof'	CKen CSBt EHul EOrn GKir LCon
		LLin LRHS MAsh MBar MGos
		NDlv SBod SCoo SLim WEve
		WStI
	– 'Tetragona Aurea'	CBcs CBrm CMac ECho EGra
		EHul EOrn IMGH LLin MBar
		MGos MOne SLim SPoG WEve
	– 'Tonia' (v)	CDoC CKen EHul EOrn MAsh
		MBri NHol SCoo SLim WEve WGor
		WLRN
	– 'Topsie' **new**	CKen
	– 'Torulosa'	see C. obtusa 'Coralliformis'
	– 'Tsatsumi Gold'	CKen
	– 'Verdon'	CKen
	– 'Wissel'	CKen EOrn
	– 'Wyckoff'	CKen
	– 'Yellowtip' (v)	CKen EHul LCon MBar MGos
		WBcn
	pisifera 'Aurea Nana' misapplied	see C. pisifera 'Strathmore'
	– 'Avenue'	EHul LCon LLin
	– 'Baby Blue'	CKen EPfP LCon SCoo SLim
	– 'Blue Globe'	CKen EOrn
	– 'Boulevard' ♀ H4	More than 30 suppliers
	– 'Compacta'	ECho EOrn NDlv
	– 'Compacta Variegata' (v)	ECho EHul EOrn MAsh MBar NDlv
	– 'Curly Tops'	CDoC CKen ECho GKir LCon
		MGos MOne SLim WBcn WGor
	– 'Devon Cream'	LBee LRHS MAsh MBar NHol
	– 'Filifera'	CMac CSBt EBre GKir MBar SCoo
		SLim SLon WFar
	– 'Filifera Aurea' ♀ H4	CKen CMac CSBt CWib EBre
		EHul EOrn GKir LBee LCon LLin
		LRHS MAsh MBar MBri NWea
		SBod SRms WCFE WDin WEve
		WFar
	– 'Filifera Aureovariegata' (v)	CMac EBre EHul LLin MBar SLim
	– 'Filifera Nana'	CDoC EBre EHul EOrn GKir
		MBar MBri MOne NDlv STre
		WDin WFar
	– 'Filifera Sungold'	see C. pisifera 'Sungold'
	– 'Futiri-tsukomo'	CKen
*	– 'Gold Cascade'	MGos
	– 'Gold Cushion'	CKen
	– 'Gold Dust'	see C. pisifera 'Plumosa Aurea'
	– 'Gold Spangle'	EHul EOrn MBar MGos SBod
		WFar
	– 'Golden Mop' ♀ H4	CKen ECho EHul MAsh NDlv
	– 'Hime-himuro'	CKen
	– 'Hime-sawara'	CKen EOrn
	– 'Margaret' **new**	CKen
	– 'Nana'	CKen EBre EHul ENot EPfP LLin
		MAsh MBar MWat NDlv NHol
		SBod SMer WFar
I	– 'Nana Albovariegata' (v)	CDoC ECho EOrn LLin LRHS
		MBar MBri NPro

§	- 'Nana Aureovariegata' (v)	CDoC CMac CSBt EHul IMGH LBee LCon LLin LRHS MAsh MBar MBri NDlv NHol SLim SPoG WFar
I	- 'Nana Compacta'	CMac SRms
	- 'Nana Variegata' (v)	ECho LBee LRHS MAsh MBar SLim SPer WFar
I	- 'Parslorii'	CKen
	- 'Pici'	CKen
	- 'Plumosa'	SRms
	- 'Plumosa Albopicta' (v)	ECho MBar
§	- 'Plumosa Aurea'	CKen EHul GKir MAsh MBar NWea WDin WFar
	- 'Plumosa Aurea Compacta'	CKen CMac NDlv
I	- 'Plumosa Aurea Compacta Variegata' (v)	CMac
	- 'Plumosa Aurea Nana'	ENot MAsh MBar MGos NDlv SMer
I	- 'Plumosa Aurea Nana Compacta'	CMac
	- 'Plumosa Aurescens'	CMac
§	- 'Plumosa Compressa'	CDoC CKen ECho EHul EOrn ESis LBee LCon MAsh MBar MGos NDlv SLim SPoG WGor
	- 'Plumosa Densa'	see C. pisifera 'Plumosa Compressa'
	- 'Plumosa Flavescens'	EHul LRHS MBar NDlv
I	- 'Plumosa Juniperoides'	CKen EHul EOrn LLin MBar NDlv SLim WGor
	- 'Plumosa Purple Dome'	see C. pisifera 'Purple Dome'
I	- 'Plumosa Pygmaea'	ECho MGos NDlv SBla WGor
§	- 'Plumosa Rogersii'	EHul EOrn LRHS MBar MGos SBod WGor
§	- 'Purple Dome'	CSli ECho EHul EOrn MBar WLRN
	- 'Rogersii'	see C. pisifera 'Plumosa Rogersii'
	- 'Silver and Gold' (v)	EHul MBar
	- 'Silver Lode' (v)	CKen EOrn
	- 'Snow' (v)	CKen CMac EOrn MBar SMer
	- 'Snowflake'	CKen EHul
	- 'Spaan's Cannon Ball'	CKen
§	- 'Squarrosa'	MBar NWea WDin WFar
§	- 'Squarrosa Dumosa'	CKen CSli EHul MBar
	- 'Squarrosa Intermedia'	EHul MBar MGos
I	- 'Squarrosa Lombarts'	CMac CSBt CSli EBre ECho EHul EOrn LBee LCon MBar
	- 'Squarrosa Lutea'	CKen MAsh MBar NPro
	- 'Squarrosa Sulphurea'	CSBt CSli EBre EGra EHul EOrn EPfP LBee LCon LRHS MAsh MBar SLim SPla WDin WFar
	- 'Squarrosa Veitchii'	see C. pisifera 'Squarrosa'
§	- 'Strathmore'	CKen EHul LLin MBar NHol WDin
§	- 'Sungold'	CDoC CKen CSBt CTri CWib EGra EHul ENot LCon LLin LRHS MAsh MBar MBri NBlu NDlv NWea SBod SLim SPla WEve
	- 'Tama-himuro'	CKen MGos WBcn
*	- 'Tsukibeni'	WBcn
	- 'White Beauty' (v)	CKen
*	- 'White Brocade'	CMac
	- 'White Pygmy'	EOrn EPot
	thyoides 'Andelyensis'	CDoC CMac CSBt ECho EHul ENot EOrn GKir LLin MBar NDlv SCoo SPoG
	- 'Andelyensis Nana'	CKen
	- 'Aurea'	EHul MBar WBcn
	- 'Conica'	CKen CSli MAsh
	- 'Ericoides' ♀ H4	CDoC CKen CMac CSli CTri EHul ENot EOrn GKir LBee LCon LLin MAsh MBar MWat SBod WDin WFar

§	- 'Glauca'	EOrn
	- 'Kewensis'	see C. thyoides 'Glauca'
	- 'Little Jamie'	CKen
	- 'Red Star'	see C. thyoides 'Rubicon'
§	- 'Rubicon'	CKen CMac CSBt CSli EBre EHul EOrn EPfP ESis LBee LCon LLin LRHS MAsh MBar MGos NDlv SLim SPla WEve WGer
	- 'Schumaker's Blue Dwarf'	WBcn
	- 'Top Point'	CDoC CKen EOrn LBee LCon MAsh MBri SCoo SLim WEve
	- 'Variegata' (v)	CDoC ECho EHul MBar
	- 'Winter Wonder' **new**	EHul

Chamaecytisus (Papilionaceae)

§	albus	GKir GQui WDin WStI
	austriacus	GEil
§	hirsutus	CFil WCot WLin WPGP WWeb
	- subsp. hirsutissimus	WCot
	prolifer	CPLG
§	purpureus	EBre ELan EPfP GKir MBar MBri MGos MRav NBlu NWea SHBN SPer SRPl WBod WDin WFar WPat WWeb
	- f. albus	EPfP MBar SHBN SPer WBcn
	- 'Atropurpureus' ♀ H4	ENot LAst NHol SPer WTel
	- 'Incarnatus'	see C. purpureus 'Atropurpureus'
§	supinus	MNrw SRms

Chamaedaphne (Ericaceae)

§	calyculata	CBcs GEil LRHS SPer WSHC
	- 'Nana'	CMHG MBar MGos NBlu NLar

Chamaedorea (Arecaceae)

	cataractarum	CBrP
	elegans ♀ H1	EPVP LPal MBri
	erumpens	see C. seifrizii
	linearis	LPal
	metallica hort.	see C. microspadix
	metallica Cook ♀ H1	LPal
§	microspadix	CRoM CTrC EPVP LPJP LPal
	radicalis	CBrP CRoM EAmu EPVP LPJP LPal
§	seifrizii ♀ H1	LPal

Chamaelirium (Melanthiaceae)

	luteum	EBee

Chamaemelum (Asteraceae)

§	nobile	CArn CPrp CSev EDAr ELau GBar GDea GKir GMac GPoy MBar MBow MBri MHer NBlu NDov NGdn SGar SPlb SRms SWal WHHs WJek WPer WSel WWye
	- dwarf	GBar
	- dwarf, double-flowered (d)	CPrp GBar
	- 'Flore Pleno' (d)	More than 30 suppliers
	- 'Treneague'	More than 30 suppliers

Chamaenerion see Epilobium

Chamaepericlymenum see Cornus

Chamaerops (Arecaceae)

	excelsa hort.	see Trachycarpus fortunei
	excelsa Thunb.	see Rhapis excelsa
	humilis ♀ H3	More than 30 suppliers
§	- var. argentea	CBrP CTrC EAmu EPVP LPJP LPal NPal SPar WMul
	- var. cerifera	see C. humilis var. argentea

Chamaespartium see *Genista*

Chamaesphacos (*Lamiaceae*)
ilicifolius **new**	CDes

Chambeyronia (*Arecaceae*)
macrocarpa	CBrP LPal

Chamelaucium (*Myrtaceae*)
axillare	SOWG
uncinatum	ESlt LRHS SOWG

Chamerion see *Epilobium*

Chasmanthe (*Iridaceae*)
aethiopica	CPou GGar LBow SYvo
bicolor	CPou WCot
floribunda	CTrF ERea LBow LRHS WCot
- var. *duckittii*	EBee ECho LRHS WCot
* grandiflora **new**	CPLG

Chasmanthium (*Poaceae*)
§ latifolium	More than 30 suppliers

Cheilanthes (*Adiantaceae*)
argentea	WRic
distans	SRms
hirta	WRic
lanosa	SRms WRic
lindheimeri	WCot
sinuata **new**	WRic
tomentosa	SRms WRic

Cheiranthus see *Erysimum*

Cheiridopsis (*Aizoaceae*)
derenbergiana **new**	EMan WCot

Chelidonium (*Papaveraceae*)
japonicum	see *Hylomecon japonica*
majus	CArn CKin CRow ELau GPoy MChe MGas MGol MHer MSal NCWG WCHb WHer WShi WWye
- 'Flore Pleno' (d)	CBre CRow ECoo MGol MGrG NBid NBro NSti WCHb WCot WHer
- var. *laciniatum*	CPLG EMon GBar NBid NSti WCHb
- 'Laciniatum Flore Pleno' (d)	CRow EMar IBlr MMHG WCot

Chelone (*Scrophulariaceae*)
barbata	see *Penstemon barbatus*
§ glabra	More than 30 suppliers
lyonii	EBee LEdu NLar SHFr WMoo WShi
obliqua	More than 30 suppliers
- var. *alba*	see *C. glabra*
- 'Forncett Poppet'	EFou
- 'Ieniemienie' **new**	EMon
- rosea	CHar EBee LRHS WHHs

Chelonopsis (*Lamiaceae*)
moschata	CDes EBee ECha EMan MHar WMoo WPGP
yagiharana **new**	WCot

Chenopodium (*Chenopodiaceae*)
album	WHHs
ambrosioides	WJek
bonus-henricus	CAgr CArn CPrp GBar GPoy
	GWCH ILis LRHS MChe MHer SIde WCHb WHer WSel WWye
botrys	MSal
giganteum **new**	WJek
- 'Magentaspreen' **new**	ECoo

cherimoya see *Annona cherimola*

chervil see *Anthriscus cerefolium*

cherry, duke see *Prunus* x *gondouinii*

cherry, sour or Morello see *Prunus cerasus*

cherry, sweet see *Prunus avium*

chestnut, sweet see *Castanea sativa*

Chiastophyllum (*Crassulaceae*)
§ oppositifolium ♀ H4	More than 30 suppliers
- 'Frosted Jade'	see *C. oppositifolium* 'Jim's Pride'
§ - 'Jim's Pride' (v)	More than 30 suppliers
simplicifolium	see *C. oppositifolium*

Chiliotrichum (*Asteraceae*)
diffusum	CPle GDra GEil GGar GKir GSki ISea SMad
- 'Siska'	EBee IArd WCot WWes

Chimaphila (*Ericaceae*)
maculata	EBee SSpi

Chimonanthus (*Calycanthaceae*)
fragrans	see *C. praecox*
§ praecox	More than 30 suppliers
* - 'Fragrance'	ERea
- 'Grandiflorus' ♀ H4	CEnd ENot WPat
- var. *luteus* ♀ H4	CEnd CPMA ENot EPfP SPer
- 'Mangetsu'	SSta
- 'Trenython'	CEnd SSta

Chimonobambusa (*Poaceae*)
fulcata	see *Drepanostachyum falcatum*
hookeriana hort.	see *Himalayacalamus falconeri* 'Damarapa'
macrophylla f. intermedia	EPla SDry
§ marmorea	CAbb CDDB CFil EPla ERod LJus LPal MMoz NMoo SDry WDyG WJun WPGP
- 'Variegata' (v)	CFil EFul EPla ERod LJus MTed SDry SLPl WJun WPGP
§ quadrangularis	CBcs CDDB CDoC CFil CHEx EFul EPfP EPla ERod LJus MMoz MTed NMoo SDry WJun WPGP
- f. *nagaminea* (v)	EPla
- 'Svow' (v)	EPla SDry
§ tumidissinoda	CAbb CDDB EPla ERod MHdf MMoz SDry WDyG WJun WPGP

chinese chives see *Allium tuberosum*

Chiogenes see *Gaultheria*

Chionanthus (*Oleaceae*)
retusus	CMCN EPfP IDee SBrw SSpi WDin
virginicus	CBcs CDoC CDul CEnd CFil CMCN CPMA EBee ELan EPfP EWTr GKir IDee IMGH LRHS MBlu MBri SBrw SMad SPer SSpi SSta WDin WHCG WOrn WPGP WPat

Chionochloa (*Poaceae*)

conspicua	CAbb CElw CFil CKno CMil EBee EChP ELan EMan EWsh GIBF GSki LEdu LPhx MAvo MCCP MFir MNrw MWhi MWrn NBir NOGN SApp WHer WLRN WPGP WWye
- subsp. **conspicua**	WCot
- subsp. **cunninghamii**	CPLG
- 'Rubra'	see *C. rubra*
flavescens	CKno EBee EHoe GSki SVen
flavicans	CKno CTrC EChP EMan EWsh MLLN SMad
rigida	LEdu
§ **rubra**	More than 30 suppliers
- subsp. **cuprea**	EGle

Chionodoxa ✿ (*Hyacinthaceae*)

cretica	see *C. nana*
§ **forbesii**	CBro CNic EPar EPot ETub GDra LRHS NBlu NLon SRms WHer WPer WPnP WShi
- 'Alba'	ECho EPar ETub LAma NRog
- 'Blue Giant'	EPot LRHS
- 'Rosea'	EPar LAma NRog
- Siehei Group	see *C. siehei*
gigantea	see *C. luciliae* Gigantea Group
luciliae hort.	see *C. forbesii*
luciliae Boissier ♀ H4	CAvo CBro EPar EPfP EPot LAma MBri NRog
- 'Alba'	CBro CFwr ECho LPhx LRHS WBry WFTG
§ - Gigantea Group	ECho ELan EPar EPot LAma NEgg NJOw NRog
- - 'Alba'	EPar EPot GCrs MBNS
§ **nana**	EHyt
'Pink Giant'	CAvo CBro EPar EPfP EPot ETub EWTr LAma LRHS NEgg WCra WHil
sardensis ♀ H4	CBro ECho EPar EPot LAma LRHS MBNS NEgg NRog WPer WShi
§ **siehei** ♀ H4	CBro
'Valentine Day' **new**	EPot

Chionographis (*Melanthiaceae*)

japonica	EFEx WCru

Chionohebe (*Scrophulariaceae*)

armstrongii	EPot ITim
§ **densifolia**	EPot GCrs GDra GMaP ITim NWCA
pulvinaris	GCrs ITim NHar NSla

Chirita (*Gesneriaceae*)

'Aiko'	WDib
'Chastity'	WDib
'Diane Marie'	WDib
heterotricha new	WDib
'Keiko' **new**	WDib
linearifolia	WDib
'New York' **new**	WDib
sinensis ♀ H1	CHal WDib
- 'Hisako'	WDib
tamiana	WDib

Chironia (*Gentianaceae*)

baccifera	SPlb

x *Chitalpa* (*Bignoniaceae*)

tashkentensis	CEnd CMCN EPfP MBlu NLar SMad SRPl WPGP
- 'Summer Bells'	CDoC SRPl

chives see *Allium schoenoprasum*

Chlidanthus (*Amaryllidaceae*)

fragrans	CFwr CStu ECho NRog WCot

Chloranthus (*Chloranthaceae*)

fortunei	EBee LEur SBla WCru
henryi new	EBee
japonicus	EBee SSpi WCru
multistachys	EBee
oldhamii B&SWJ 2019	EBee WCru
serratus	EBee WCru

Chloris (*Poaceae*)

from Turkey	WRos
distichophylla	see *Eustachys distichophylla*
virgata	CWCL EPPr

Chlorophytum (*Anthericaceae*)

comosum	SEND
- 'Mandanum' (v)	CHal
- 'Variegatum' (v) ♀ H1+3	CHal LRHS MBri SRms
- 'Vittatum' (v) ♀ H1+3	CHEx SRms
intermedium B&SWJ 6447 **new**	WCru
krookianum	WCot
macrophyllum new	EShb
§ **majus**	WCot
nepalense B&SWJ 2393	WCru

Choisya (*Rutaceae*)

arizonica new	SIgm
'Aztec Pearl' ♀ H4	More than 30 suppliers
dumosa	LHop
- var. **arizonica**	SDry SLon
- var. **mollis**	SLon
Goldfingers = 'Limo' PBR	CABP EBee EHan ELan ENot EPfP LRHS MAsh MBri MGos NPri NPro SCoo SHGC SLon SPer SSta WWeb
ternata ♀ H4	More than 30 suppliers
- 'Brica' PBR	see *C. ternata* Sundance = 'Lich'
- Moonshine = 'Walcho' PBR	LRHS
- Moonsleeper PBR	see *C. ternata* Sundance = 'Lich'
§ - Sundance = 'Lich' PBR ♀ H3	More than 30 suppliers

Chondropetalum (*Restionaceae*)

mucronatum	CAbb CTrC
tectorum	CAbb CBcs CBig CFir CKno CPen CTrC ENot IArd IDac LEdu SApp WHal WMul WNor

Chondrosum (*Poaceae*)

gracile	see *Bouteloua gracilis*

Chonemorpha (*Apocynaceae*)

fragrans	CPIN

Chordospartium (*Papilionaceae*)

muritai	ECou
- 'Huia Gilpen'	ECou
- 'Ron Feron'	ECou
- 'Wayne Nichols'	ECou
stevensonii	CPle ECou EPfP SMad WBVN
- 'Duncan'	ECou
- 'Kiwi'	ECou
- 'Miller'	ECou

Chorizema (*Papilionaceae*)

cordatum ♀ H1	ECou

diversifolium	ERea
ilicifolium	CAbb CBcs CPlN CSPN ERea GQui SBra

Chronanthus see *Cytisus*

Chrysalidocarpus (Arecaceae)
lutescens	see *Dypsis lutescens*

Chrysanthemopsis see *Rhodanthemum*

Chrysanthemum ✿ (Asteraceae)
'Albert Broadhurst' (24b)	NHal
'Albert's Yellow' (29Rub)	MMil
'Alec Bedsar' (25a) **new**	WWol
'Allouise' (25b) ♀ H3	NHal
alpinum	see *Leucanthemopsis alpina*
'Amber Chessington' (25a)	NHal
'Amber Gigantic' (1)	WIvo
'Amber Matlock' (24b)	NHal
'Anastasia' (28)	CHid ECtt EPPr GMac LHop MMil MNrw MRav NSti SChu SRms WCot WFar WIvy WPer WRHF WWin
'Anastasia White' (28)	WCot WIvy
'Anne' (29K)	SAga
'Anne, Lady Brocket'	GBuc MNrw WCot
'Annie Lea' (25b)	NHal
'Apollo' (29K)	EFou EWll WCom
'Apricot' (29Rub)	CPrp EBee EBre EChP EFou EPPr GKir MNrw MRav
'Apricot Chessington' (25a)	NHal
'Apricot Courtier' (24a)	NHal
'Apricot Enbee Wedding' (29d)	see *C.* 'Bronze Enbee Wedding'
'Apricot Harry Gee' (1)	WIvo
arcticum L.	see *Arctanthemum arcticum*
argenteum	see *Tanacetum argenteum*
'Arona Gran' (25b)	NHal
'Autumn Days' (25b)	NHal
'Babs' (28)	MMil
'Balcombe Perfection' (5a)	NHal WWol
balsamita	see *Tanacetum balsamita*
Barbara = 'Yobarbara'PBR (22)	EPfP NBlu NHal WWol
'Beacon' (5a) ♀ H2	NHal
'Beppie' (29e)	WWol
'Beppie Bronze' (29)	WWol
'Beppie Dark' (29)	WWol
'Beppie Purple' (29)	WWol
'Beppie Yellow' (29)	WWol
'Bernadette Wade' (23a)	NHal
'Bill Wade' (25a)	NHal
* 'Billy Bell' (25a)	WWol
'Brautstrauss'	FFou
Bravo = 'Yobra'PBR (22c) ♀ H3	EPfP NHal
* 'Breitner's Supreme'	MNrw
'Brennpunkt'	EFou WMnd
'Bright Eye' (28)	WPer
'Brightness' (29K)	SChu SUsu
'Bronze Beauty' (25b)	WFar
'Bronze Carlene Welby' (15b)	WWol
'Bronze Cassandra' (5b) ♀ H2	NHal
§ 'Bronze Dee Gem' (29c)	NHal
§ 'Bronze Elegance' (28b)	CM&M CSam EBee EMon MLLN NBir NGdn NPPs NSti SPla SRms WEas WIvy WMnd

§ 'Bronze Enbee Wedding' (29d) ♀ H3	NHal
'Bronze John Wingfield' (14b)	NHal
'Bronze Margaret' (29c) ♀ H3	NHal
'Bronze Matlock' (24b)	NHal
'Bronze Max Riley' (23b) ♀ H3	NHal
'Bronze Mayford Perfection' (5a) ♀ H2	NHal WWol
'Bronze Mei-kyo'	see *C.* 'Bronze Elegance'
'Bronze Pamela'	see *C.* 'Pamela'
'Bronze William Florentine' (15a)	NHal
'Bruera' (24b)	NHal
'Bryan Kirk' (4b)	WWol
'Buff Peter Rowe' (23b)	NHal
'Carlene Welby' (25b)	NHal
'Carmine Blush' (29Rub)	EBee EFou MNrw WCot
'Caroline Barclay' (14b)	WWol
I 'Cassandra' (5b)	WWol
'Cawthorne' (29d) **new**	WWol
'Cherry Chessington' (25a)	NHal
'Cherry Margaret' (29c)	NHal
'Chessington' (25a)	NHal
'Chestnut Talbot Parade' (29c) ♀ H3	NHal
'Christopher Lawson' (24b)	NHal
cinerariifolium	see *Tanacetum cinerariifolium*
'Citrus' (29K)	EFou
'Clapham Delight' (23a)	NHal
'Clara Curtis' (29Rub)	CSam EBee EChP ECha EFou FLan EPfP GKir GMac LRHS MCAu MRav MTis NBir NPer NSti SChu SPer SPla SRPl SRms STes WAul WCot WEas WFar WPer WRus WWin WWol
'Clare Dobson' (25b)	WWol
clusii	see *Tanacetum corymbosum* subsp. *clusii*
coccineum	see *Tanacetum coccineum*
'Cornetto' (25b)	NHal
'Corngold' (5b)	NHal
corymbosum	see *Tanacetum corymbosum*
'Cossack' (2)	WWol
'Cottage Apricot'	CHca EBee EWoo GMac LHop MBNS MNrw NPPs SMrm WEas WRHF
'Cottage Pink'	see *C.* 'Emperor of China'
'Cottage Yellow'	MSte WCot WHoo
'Courtier' (24a)	NHal
'Cream Duke of Kent' (1)	WIvo
'Cream Margaret' (29c) ♀ H3	NHal
'Cream Patricia Millar' (14b)	NHal
'Cream Talbot Parade' (29c)	NHal
'Crimson Gala'	WWol
Dana = 'Yodana' (25b) ♀ H3	NHal
'Dark Red Mayford Perfection' (4b) ♀ H2	WWol
'Darren Pugh' (3b) **new**	WWol
'David McNamara' (3b)	WWol
Debonair = 'Yodebo'PBR (22c) ♀ H3	EPfP NBlu NHal
'Dee Gem' (29c) ♀ H3	NHal
'Delta Orange' (29)	WWol
* 'Delta Pink' (29)	WWol

*	'Delta White' (29)	WWol
	'Delta Yellow' (29)	WWol
§	'Doctor Tom Parr' (28)	ELan EMon IGor LHop
	'Doreen Statham' (4b)	NHal
	'Dorothy Stone' (25b)	NHal
	'Dorridge Beauty' (24a)	WWol
	'Dorridge Crystal' (24a)	NHal WWol
	'Dorridge Vulcan' (23b)	WWol
	'Duchess of Edinburgh' (18b)	CPrp CSam EBee EBre EChP ECtt ELan EMon GKir GMac LRHS MBri MRav MTis WRHF
	'Duke of Kent' (1)	NHal WIvo
	'Ed Hodgson' (25a)	NHal
	'Edelgard'	WMaN
	'Edelweiss' (29K)	EFou GMac
	'Egret' (23b)	NHal
	'Elaine Johnson' (3b)	NHal
	'Elegance' (9c)	WWol
	'Elegance Yellow' (9e)	WWol
	'Elizabeth Burton' (5a)	WWol
	'Elizabeth Lawson' (5b)	NHal
	'Elizabeth Shoesmith' (1)	NHal
	'Ellen' (29c)	WWol
*	'Emma Jane' (25a)	WWol
§	'Emperor of China' (29Rub)	CElw CSam EBee ECha EFou GCal IGor LPhx LRHS MNrw MRav MSte SChu SSvw WFar WHoo WMnd WRus
	'Enbee Wedding' (29d) ♀ H3	NHal
	'Ermine' (23a)	NHal
*	'Evesham Vale' (24b)	WWol
	'Fairway' (15a)	NHal
	'Fieldfare' (22)	NHal
	'Firecracker'PBR (22)	WWol
	'Fitton's Reward' (1)	NHal WIvo
	foeniculaceum hort.	see *Argyranthemum foeniculaceum* hort.
	foeniculaceum (Willd.) Desf.	see *Argyranthemum foeniculaceum* (Willd.) Webb & Sch.Bip.
	'Frances Jeavons'	EBee
	'Fred Shoesmith' (5a)	WWol
	frutescens	see *Argyranthemum frutescens*
	'Gambit' (24a)	NHal
	'Geof Brady' (5a) new	WWol
	'George Griffiths' (24b) ♀ H3	NHal
	'Gerry Tull' (29d)	NHal
	'Gigantic' (1)	NHal WIvo
	'Gingernut' (25b)	NHal
	'Gladys' (24b)	EBee ELan EWoo
	'Gladys Emerson' (3b) new	NHal
	'Gold John Wingfield' (14b)	NHal
	'Gold Margaret'	see *C.* 'Golden Margaret'
	'Golden Cassandra' (5b) ♀ H2	NHal
	'Golden Courtier' (24a)	NHal
	'Golden Gigantic' (1)	NHal WIvo
§	'Golden Margaret' (29c) ♀ H3	NHal
	'Golden Mayford Perfection' (5a) ♀ H2	NHal WWol
	'Golden Pamela' (29c)	NHal
	'Golden Plover' (22)	NHal
	'Golden Seal' (7b)	GBuc
	'Goldengreenheart' (29Rub)	EFou WCot
	'Goodlife Sombrero' (29a) ♀ H3	NHal
	'Grace Fraser' (15b)	WWol

	'Grace Wade' (25b) new	WWol
§	*grandiflorum*	SRms
	'Green Boy' (10b)	WWol
*	'Green Envy' (10b)	WWol
	'Green Nightingale' (10)	WWol
	'Green Satin' (5b)	WWol
	Grenadine = 'Yogrena' (22c) ♀ H3	NHal
	'Hanenburg'	NHal WWol
*	'Happy Days' (15b)	WWol
	haradjanii	see *Tanacetum haradjanii*
	'Harold Lawson' (5a)	NHal
	'Harry Gee' (1)	WIvo WWol
	'Harry Woolman' (3b)	NHal
	'Hazy Days' (25b)	NHal
	'Heather James' (3b)	NHal
	'Heide' (29c) ♀ H3	NHal
	'Helen Gravestock' (4a) new	WWol
	'Herbstrubin'	IGor
	'Hesketh Knight' (5b)	NHal
	'Honey Enbee Wedding' (29d)	NHal
	hosmariense	see *Rhodanthemum hosmariense*
	'Impressario'	WWol
	'Innocence' (29Rub)	CSam EBee ELan EMon GMac IGor LPhx MNrw MRav NGdn NSti SAga SPla
*	'Iris Morris' (4b)	WWol
	'Ivor Mace' (1)	WIvo
	'Ja Dank'	WWol
	'Jan Horton' (3b)	WWol
	'Janice'PBR (7a)	NBlu
	'Jante Wells' (28)	EMon WEas WTel
	'Jessie Cooper'	see *C.* 'Mrs Jessie Cooper'
	'Jessie Habgood' (1)	WIvo
	'John Harrison' (25b)	NHal
	'John Hughes' (3b)	NHal
	'John Wingfield' (14b)	NHal
	'Joyce Frieda' (23b) new	WWol
	'Julia' (28)	EFou GMac
	Julia = 'Yojulia'	CHea
	'Julie Lagravère' (28)	EFou EMon GBuc WWhi
	'Kay Woolman' (13b)	NHal WWol
	'Kimberley Marie' (15b)	NHal
	'Kota Kinabalu' (1)	WIvo
	x *koreanum*	see *C. grandiflorum*
	'Lady in Pink' (29Rub)	GBuc
	'Lakelanders' (3b)	NHal
	'Lameet' (29)	WWol
	'Lancashire Fold' (1)	WIvo
	'Lancashire Lad' (1)	WIvo
	'Laser' (24b)	WWol
	'Laureate'	WWol
	'Le Bonheur Red' new	WWol
	'Leading Lady' (25b)	WWol
	Legend = 'Yoleg' (22)	NHal
	'Lemon Margaret' (29c) ♀ H3	NHal
	leucanthemum	see *Leucanthemum vulgare*
	'Lilac Chessington' (25a)	NHal
	Linda = 'Lindayo'PBR (22c)	NBlu
	'Lindie' (28)	EFou
	'Lizzie Dear' (25b) new	NHal
	'Long Island Beauty' (6b) ♀ H2	WTel
	'Lord Barnard' (3b)	WWol
	'Lorna Wood' (13b)	NHal
	'Louise Park' (24a)	NHal
	'Lucy' (29a)	NHal
	'Lucy Simpson' (29K)	MMil
	'Lundy' (2)	NHal

'Luv Purple'   WWol
'Lynn Johnson' (15a)   NHal
Lynn = 'Yolynn'PBR   NHal
   (22c) ♀ H3
macrophyllum   see *Tanacetum macrophyllum*
'Malcolm Perkins' (25a)   NHal
'Mancetta Comet' (29a)   NHal
'Mandarin' (5b)   EFou
maresii   see *Rhodanthemum*
                                hosmariense
'Margaret' (29c) ♀ H3   NHal
'Mark Woolman' (1)   NHal WIvo
'Mary Stoker' (29Rub)   CElw CPrp CSam EBee EChP ECha
                                ECtt EFou ELan EMon GBri GMac
                                LRHS MBri MBro MCAu MNrw
                                MRav MTis NSti SPer STes SUsu WAul
                                WEas WFar WHoo WMaN WRus
'Matador' (14a)   WWol
'Matlock' (24b)   NHal
mawii   see *Rhodanthemum gayanum*
'Max Riley' (23b) ♀ H3 NHal
maximum hort.   see *Leucanthemum* x *superbum*
maximum Ramond   see *Leucanthemum maximum*
                                (Ramond) DC
'Maxine Johnson' (25b)   NHal
'May Shoesmith' (5a)   NHal
   ♀ H2
'Mayford Perfection'   NHal WWol
   (5a) ♀ H2
'Megan Woolman' (3b)   WWol
'Mei-kyo' (28b)   CHar CM&M CMea EBee EMon
                                IGor MLLN MRav MWgw SPla
                                SRms WEas WFar
'Membury' (24b)   NHal
'Michelle Preston' (13b)   NHal
'Migoli'   WWol
'Minstreel Bronze' (9)   WWol
'Minstreel Dark' (9)   WWol
'Moonlight' (29d/K)   MRav
§ 'Mrs Jessie Cooper'   ELan GMac MNrw MSte NBir
   (29Rub)   SChu WCom WCot WHoo WHrl
'Mrs Jessie Cooper No.1'   MSph
'Music' (23b)   NHal
'Myss Goldie' (29c)   NHal
naktongense   see *C. zawadskii* var. *latilobum*
'Nancy Perry' (19Rub)   CSam ELan EMon MRav SChu
§ *nankingense*   EMon WFar
'Nantyderry Sunshine'   CSam CSpe EBee EFou LRHS
   (28b) ♀ H4   MNrw MWgw SMrm SPla WCot
                                WEas WMnd WPer WRha
'Netherall Moonlight'   EBee
   new
Nicole = 'Yonicole'PBR   NHal WWol
   (22c) ♀ H3
nipponicum   see *Nipponanthemum nipponicum*
'Orange Allouise' (25b)   NHal WWol
'Orange Enbee   NHal
   Wedding' (29d)
pacificum   see *Ajania pacifica*
§ 'Pamela' (29c)   NHal
'Pandion'   WWol
'Parkfield Tigger' (29c)   NHal
parthenium   see *Tanacetum parthenium*
'Pascal Dark' (29)   WWol
'Pat Davison' (25b)   NHal
'Patricia Millar' (14b)   NHal
'Paul Boissier' (30Rub)   CElw EFou ELan LPhx NSti WHoo
                                WMnd
'Payton Dale' (29c) ♀ H3 NHal
'Payton Glow' (29c)   NBir
'Peach Allouise' (25b)   NHal
   ♀ H3
'Peach Courtier' (24a)   NHal

'Peach Enbee Wedding' NHal
   (29d) ♀ H3
'Peach John Wingfield'   NHal
   (14b)
'Pearl Celebration' (24a)   NHal
'Peggy Anne' (1)   WIvo
'Pennine Bullion'   WWol
I 'Pennine Coconut' (29)   WWol
'Pennine Dart' (29d)   NHal
'Pennine Drift'   WWol
'Pennine Gift' (29c)   NHal
'Pennine Ginger' (29c)   NHal
   ♀ H3
'Pennine Goal' (29c)   WWol
   ♀ H3
'Pennine Grant'   WWol
'Pennine Jane'   WWol
'Pennine Marie' (29a)   NHal
   ♀ H3
'Pennine Oriel' (29a)   NHal
   ♀ H3
'Pennine Pageant' (29d)   NHal
'Pennine Passion' (29c)   WWol
'Pennine Perfecta' (29d)   WWol
'Pennine Point'   WWol
'Pennine Polo' (29d)   NHal WWol
   ♀ H3
'Pennine Port'   WWol
'Pennine Ranger' (29d)   NHal
'Pennine Romeo' (19c)   NHal
'Pennine Splash' (29d)   NHal
'Pennine Sunlight' (19d)   WWol
'Pennine Swan' (29c)   NHal
'Pennine Toy'   WWol
'Pennine Volcano'   WWol
'Perry's Peach'   MNrw NDov NPer SUsu
'Peter Rowe' (23b)   NHal
'Peter Sare' (29d)   EBre GMac
'Peterkin'   CHea EBre ECtt EMon GMac
                                MNrw MWgw
'Phil Houghton' (1)   WIvo WWol
'Pink Duke' (1)   NHal
'Pink Duke of Kent' (1)   WIvo
'Pink Ice' (5b)   WRha
'Pink John Wingfield'   NHal
   (14b)
'Pink Marvellous' (29f)   WWol
'Pink Progression'   GMac MWgw NBir
'Polar Gem' (3a)   NHal
'Polaris' (9c)   WFTG
* 'Pompon Bronze' (28)   WWol
* 'Pompon Pink' (28)   WWol
* 'Pompon Purple' (28)   WWol
* 'Pompon Yellow' (28)   WWol
praeteritum   see *Tanacetum praeteritum*
'Primrose Allouise'   NHal
   (24b) ♀ H3
'Primrose Chessington' NHal
   (25a)
'Primrose Courtier'   see *C.* 'Yellow Courtier'
'Primrose Dorothy   NHal
   Stone' (25b)
'Primrose Dorridge   NHal
   Crystal' (24a)
'Primrose Enbee   NHal
   Wedding' (29d) ♀ H3
'Primrose Ermine' (23a) NHal
'Primrose Jessie   WIvo
   Habgood' (1)
'Primrose John   NHal
   Hughes' (3b)
'Primrose Mayford   NHal
   Perfection' (5a) ♀ H2

'Primrose West NHal
Bromwich' (14a)
'Prince Bishop' (25a) NHal
'Promise' (25a) NHal
'Purleigh White' (28b) EFou GMac NSti SPla WCot WRha
'Purple Glow' (5a) NHal
'Purple Margaret' (29c) NHal
'Rachel Fairweather' (3a) NHal
Radiant Lynn = 'Radiant NHal
Yolynn'PBR (22c)
'Ralph Lambert' (1) WIvo
Raquel = WWol
'Yoraquel'PBR (22c)
'Red Balcombe NHal WWol
Perfection' (5a)
'Red Bella' (29c) NBir
'Red Pamela' (29c) NHal
'Red Pennine Gift' (29c) NHal
'Red Regal Mist' (25b) WWol
new
'Red Shirley Model' (3a) NHal
'Regal Mist' (25b) WWol
'Revert'PBR WWol
'Riley's Dynasty' (14a) NHal
'Rio'PBR (22d) WWol
'Rita May' (2) **new** NHal
'Rita McMahon' NHal
(29d) **new**
Robin = 'Yorobi'PBR NHal
(22c)
'Romantika' CHea GMac
'Romany' (2) CElw WEas
'Rose Enbee NHal
Wedding' (29d)
'Rose Mayford NHal WWol
Perfection' (5a) ♀ H2
'Rosette' (29c) EFou
roseum see *Tanacetum coccineum*
'Royal Command' EBee EMon MNrw
(29Rub)
'Rubaiyat' WWol
rubellum see *C. zawadskii*
'Ruby Enbee Wedding' NHal
(29d) ♀ H3
'Ruby Mound' (29c/K) EFou LPhx LRHS WEas
'Rumpelstilzchen' CMdw CMea EBee MNrw WPer
'Russet Gown' EBee
'Saint James' (25b) **new** WWol
'Salmon Allouise' (25b) NHal
'Salmon Chessington' NHal
(25a)
'Salmon Enbee Wedding' NHal
(29d) ♀ H3
'Salmon Lilac Prince' (1) WIvo
'Sam Vinter' (5a) NHal
'Sarah Louise' (25b) **new** NHal
'Sarah's Yellow' CSam
Shelley = 'Yoshelley' WWol
(22b)
'Shirley Primrose' (1) WIvo
'Silver Gigantic' (1) WIvo
Soft Lynn = 'Soft NHal
Yolynn'PBR (22c)
'Sonnenschein' LHop WHen
'Sophie Elizabeth' (24a) NHal
'Southway Shiraz'(29d) NHal
new
'Southway Snoopy' NHal
(29d)
'Southway Sonar' (29d) NHal
'Southway Spree' (29d) NHal
'Southway Sting' (29d) NHal
'Southway Stomp' (29d) NHal

'Southway Strontium' NHal
(29d)
'Spartan Fire' WWol
'Spartan Glory' (25b) WWol
'Spartan Leo' (29c) WWol
'Spartan Linnet' WWol
'Spartan Moon' (25b) WWol
'Spartan Seagull' WWol
'Spartan Sunrise' (29c) WWol
'Spartan Torch' WWol
* 'Spoons' SCro
'Stella' (29c) EFou
'Stockton' (3b) NHal
'Sunbeam' (28) EBre EFou
Sundoro = 'Yosun'PBR NHal
(22d)
Sunny Linda = WWol
'Sunny Lindayo' (22c)
'Sunny Tripoli'PBR WWol
'Sutton White' (25a) WWol
'Talbot Bolero' (29c) NHal
'Talbot Parade' (29c) NHal
♀ H3
'Talbot Ultra' (29f) NHal
'Tap Dance' (22d) **new** WWol
'Tapestry Rose' (29K) CMea EBee EMon IGor MMil
MNrw NPPs
Target = 'Yotarget' (22) NHal
'Thoroughbred' (24a) NHal WWol
'Tinseltown' WWol
'Toledo' (25a) WWol
'Tom Parr' see *C.* 'Doctor Tom Parr'
'Tom Snowball' (3b) NHal
'Tracy Waller' (24b) NHal
'Trapeze' WWol
'Trina Bell' (25b) NHal
Triumph = 'Yotri' (22) NHal
uliginosum see *Leucanthemella serotina*
'Universiade' (25a) NHal
'Vagabond Prince' CSam MBro WHoo
'Venice' (24b) NHal
'Venus' (29K) MBro
'Virginia' (29K) WWol
'Vreneli' EFou
'Wedding Day' (29K) CElw GBuc MMil MNrw WHoo
WMaN WRus
'Wedding Sunshine' LRHS MMil
(29K)
welwitschii see *Xanthophthalmum segetum*
'West Bromwich' (14a) NHal
§ *weyrichii* EBre ECtt MHer MTho NMGW
NWCA SBla SRms WGwG
'Whitby' (5b) NHal
'White Allouise' (25b) NHal
♀ H3
'White Beppie' (29e) WWol
'White Bouquet' (28) WWol
'White Cassandra' (5b) NHal
'White Enbee Wedding' NHal
(29d)
'White Gloss' (29K) LRHS
'White Lancashire WIvo
Fold' (1)
'White Lilac Prince' (1) WIvo
'White Margaret' (29c) NHal
♀ H3
'White Marvellous' (29f) WWol
'White Skylark' (22) NHal
'White Tower' MNrw
'Wilder Charms' EFou
'William Florentine' NHal
(15a)
'Windermere' (24a) NHal

'Wine Carlene Welby' NHal
(25b)
'Winnie Bramley' (23a) WWol
'Winning's Red' (29Rub) LHop SMad WWin
'Woolman's Century' (1) WWol
'Woolman's Prince' (3a) WWol
'Woolman's Star' (3a) NHal
'Woolman's Venture' (4b) NHal
'Yellow Allouise' (25b) NHal
§ 'Yellow Courtier' (24a) NHal
'Yellow Dorothy Stone' NHal
(25b)
'Yellow Duke of Kent' (1) WIvo
'Yellow Egret' (23b) NHal
'Yellow Ellen' (29c) NHal
'Yellow Fred Shoesmith' WWol
(5a)
'Yellow Gingernut' (25b) NHal
'Yellow Hazy Days' (25b) NHal
'Yellow Heide' (29c) NHal
♀ H3
'Yellow John Hughes' NHal
(3b) ♀ H2
'Yellow John Wingfield' NHal
(14b)
'Yellow Margaret' (29c) NHal
♀ H3
'Yellow May Shoesmith' NHal
(5a)
'Yellow Mayford NHal WWol
Perfection' (5a) ♀ H2
'Yellow Megan WWol
Woolman' (3b)
'Yellow Pennine Oriel' NHal
(29a) ♀ H4
'Yellow Phil Houghton' WIvo WWol
(1)
'Yellow Plover' (22) NHal
'Yellow Ralph Lambert' WIvo
(1)
'Yellow Rio' (22d) ♀ H3 WWol
'Yellow Talbot Parade' NHal
(29c)
'Yellow Whitby' (5b) NHal
§ *yezoense* ♀ H4 EBee ELan EMon IDac MNrw WEas
- 'Roseum' EBee MNrw NSti WPGP
§ *zawadskii* GKir WFar
§ - var. *latilobum* EBcc

Chrysocoma (Asteraceae)
ciliata JJH 9401633 NWCA
coma-aurea NWCA

Chrysogonum (Asteraceae)
australe EBcc
virginianum CHal CMea CRDP EBee ECha
EMan EMar EWes LRHS MAvo
MRav SPer SPet WFar

Chrysolepis (Fagaceae)
sempervirens **new** WCot

Chrysopogon (Poaceae)
gryllus CBig EBee EMon WPGP

Chrysopsis (Asteraceae)
mariana EMon WOld
villosa see *Heterotheca villosa*

Chrysosplenium (Saxifragaceae)
davidianum CBre CPLG EBee ECha EMan EPPr
EPar EPot NBir NDov SScr WBor
WCot WCru WGer WPrP WTMC

- SBEC 231 NHol NWoo
macrophyllum **new** EBee
oppositifolium EBee EMNN WHer WShi

Chrysothemis (Gesneriaceae)
pulchella ♀ H1 CHal

Chusquea ✿ (Poaceae)
coronalis CFil WJun
culeou ♀ H4 More than 30 suppliers
- 'Breviglumis' see *C. culeou* 'Tenuis'
§ - 'Tenuis' EPla ERod LJus SDry WJun WNor
cumingii WJun
gigantea EPla
macrostachya CFil
montana CFil EPla WPGP
pittieri WJun
quila CFil MMoz SDry WPGP
ramosissima CFil SDry
sulcata WJun
uliginosa WJun
valdiviensis WJun

Cicerbita (Asteraceae)
B&SWJ 5162 WCru
§ *alpina* MSph NBid NCWG NLar SPlb WSan
bourgaei IKee
macrorhiza WCot WCru
B&SWJ 2970
plumieri CStr EMan WCot WFar

Cichorium (Asteraceae)
intybus CKin CPrp EBre EChP ECoo ELau
EWTr GMaP GMac LHop MBow
MChe MRav NBlu NMir SIde SPer
SPlb WCHb WHHs WHer WJek
WMoo WWin WWye
- f. *album* CPou CPrp CRDP EBee EChP
ECha ECoo EGle EMan EMar
EMon EPfP LHop LRHS MBow
MCAu MRav NDov NGdn NStl
SRPl SWat WCHb
- 'Roseum' CHad CPrp CRDP CSpe EBee
ECGP EChP ECha ECoo ECot
EGle ELan EMan EMar EMon EPfP
GBri LHop LRHS MBow MCAu
MRav NDov NGdn SPer SWat
WCHb WWal WWin
spinosum SOkd

Cimicifuga see Actaea
americana see *Actaea podocarpa*
foetida see *Actaea cimicifuga*
ramosa see *Actaea simplex* 'Prichard's
Giant'
rubifolia see *Actaea cordifolia*

Cineraria (Asteraceae)
maritima see *Senecio cineraria*

Cinnamomum (Lauraceae)
camphora CBcs CFil CHEx CTrG ERea LPan
japonicum CFil WPGP
verum NBlo XBlo

Cionura (Asclepiadaceae)
§ *erecta* CPlN
oreophila CPlN GCal WSHC

Circaea (Onagraceae)
lutetiana MSal NSco WHer WShi
- 'Caveat Emptor' (v) CHid EMan EMon ITer WCot
WHer WHil WWeb

Cirsium (Asteraceae)

*	**atroroseum**	SWat
	diacantha	see *Ptilostemon diacantha*
	eriophorum	WBWf
	falconeri	NBur
	helenioides	see *C. heterophyllum*
§	**heterophyllum**	CDes EBee EMan EMon NBur
		NLar SHar WCot WPGP
	japonicum	SGar
	- 'Early Pink Beauty' **new**	MSPs
	- 'Early Rose Beauty'	MSPs NVic WHil
*	- 'Pink Beauty'	GKir MAnH WHil
	- 'Rose Beauty'	ELan LRHS MAnH MBri NBlu NBro
	oleraceum	LEdu NLar
	purpuratum	EMan WCot WPGP
	- JCA 4.192.500	CDes
	rivulare	More than 30 suppliers
	'Atropurpureum'	
	vulgare	CKin GGar
	- 'Silk Cushion'	WAlt
	- variegated (v)	WAlt
	- white	WAlt

Cissus (Vitaceae)

	adenopoda	CPiN
	antarctica ♀ H1	CTrC LRHS MBri
	discolor	CHal
	pedata B&SWJ 2371	WCru
	rhombifolia ♀ H1	MBri
	- 'Ellen Danica' ♀ H1	CHal LRHS
§	**striata**	CBcs CDoC CHEx CPiN CTrC
		EBee EMan EMil EPla IMGH LRHS
		MPRe SBra SLim WCot WCru
		WSHC WWeb

Cistus ✿ (Cistaceae)

	x **aguilarii**	CChe CPLG CSBt CSam CTri EBee
		EPfP EWTr SIgm WGer WSHC
	- 'Maculatus' ♀ H3	CBcs CBot CDoC CHar EBee EBre
		ELan EPfP GEil GGar GKir LPhx
		LRHS MBri MWgw SDry SDys
		SLPl SLdr SPar SPer SPla WAbe
		WBrE WCFE WGer WHCG WKif
		WWeb WWin
	albidus	CArn CFil EGoo MLLN SDry
		SMrm SSpi WHer
	algarvensis	see *Halimium ocymoides*
	'Ann Baker'	SLPl
	'Anne Palmer'	see *C.* x *fernandesiae* 'Anne Palmer'
	x **argenteus** 'Blushing Peggy Sammons'	LPhx MAsh MBri WAbe
	- Golden Treasure	CDoC EBee EPfP LAst MCCP
	= 'Nepond' (v)	MGos MRav MWat SLim SMur SPar
§	- 'Peggy Sammons' ♀ H3	More than 30 suppliers
	- 'Silver Ghost'	CDoC EBee SCoo SPar
N	- 'Silver Pink'	More than 30 suppliers
	atriplicifolius	see *Halimium atriplicifolium*
	'Barnsley Pink'	see *C.* 'Grayswood Pink'
	'Blanche'	see *C. ladanifer* 'Blanche'
	x **bornetianus** 'Jester'	CSBt EBee SPar
	'Candy Stripe' (v)	GBri NPro
	x **canescens** f. **albus**	CWib MBri NSti SBri SIgm WEas
		WGer WHCG
	'Chelsea Pink'	see *C.* 'Grayswood Pink'
§	**clusii**	CHar MAsh
	x **corbariensis**	see *C.* x *hybridus*
	creticus	LAst SGar SPoG
	- subsp. **creticus**	CFil CMHG CTrC EBee EGoo ELan
		ENot EPfP GEil LRHS MSte SPar
		SPer WAbe WBcn WGer WWin

*	- - **lasithii**	WAbe
	- subsp. **incanus**	CTrC EWTr LPhx MNrw WHCG
§	x **crispatus**	MBri NPPs NSti SHBN SIgm WAbe
	'Warley Rose'	WWeb
	crispus hort.	see *C.* x *pulverulentus*
§	**crispus** L.	EGoo GEil NFor SIgm WAbe WEas
		WGer
	- 'Prostratus'	see *C. crispus* L.
	- 'Sunset'	see *C.* x *pulverulentus* 'Sunset'
§	x **cyprius** ♀ H4	CArn CSBt CSpe CTrC EBee ECtt
		ELan ENot EPfP LHop MGos MRav
		MWat MWgw NSti SDix SEND
		SHBN SLPl SRms WBod WBrE WDin
		WFar WGer WPnn WWeb WWpP
	- f. **albiflorus**	MSte WBcn
	- var. **ellipticus** 'Elma' ♀ H3	CMHG EBee ELan EPfP EVFa LPhx
		LRHS MAsh MWgw SDry SIgm
		SPer SPla WAbe WEas WGer WHCG
§	x **dansereaui**	CHar CMHG CSam EOrc MRav
		MSte NSti WFar WWpP
	- 'Albiflorus'	see *C.* x *dansereaui* 'Portmeirion'
	- 'Decumbens' ♀ H4	CBcs CMHG CTrC EBee EBre
		ELan EPfP ESis MAsh MBNS MBri
		MDun MRav MWgw NFor NLon
		SArc SHBN SIgm SMer SPar SPer
		SPla WAbe WBod WDin WGer
		WHCG WStI WWeb
	- 'Jenkyn Place'	EBee MBri SLPl SUsu
	- 'Little Gem'	LPhx LRHS
§	- 'Portmeirion'	MBri WAbe WFar
§	x **fernandesiae**	EPfP SIgm WAbe WFar
	'Anne Palmer'	
§	x **florentinus** hort.	see x *Halimiocistus* 'Ingwersenii'
§	x **florentinus** Lam.	CAbP CHar SChu
	- 'Fontfroide'	WWeb
	formosus	see *H. lasianthum* subsp. *formosum*
§	'Grayswood Pink' ♀ H4	More than 30 suppliers
	x **heterocalyx**	CFai CPlt EBee LPhx MSte SIgm
	'Chelsea Bonnet'	SLim SRPl WBrE WPen WWeb
	hirsutus Lam. 1786	see *C. inflatus*
	- var. **psilosepalus**	see *C. inflatus*
	x **hybridus**	More than 30 suppliers
	incanus	see *C. creticus* subsp. *incanus*
§	**inflatus**	GDra NWoo SDry SEND WAbe
		WBod WHar WHer
	ingwerseniana	see x *Halimiocistus* 'Ingwersenii'
	'Jessamy Beauty'	SLPl SVen
	'Jessamy Bride'	SLPl
	'Jessamy Charm'	LPhx
	'John Hardy'	EBee
	ladanifer hort.	see *C.* x *cyprius*
	ladanifer L. ♀ H3	CDoC CFil CTri ECha ELan EPfP
		EWTr IMGH LRHS MRav NFor
		NLon SChu SGar SPar SPer SPla
		WBod WEas WFar WHar WLin
		WSHC WTel WWye
	- var. **albiflorus**	CBcs SSpi
§	- 'Blanche'	LRHS SIgm WKif
§	- 'Paladin'	WAbe
	- Palhinhae Group	see *C. ladanifer* var. *sulcatus*
	- 'Pat'	ELan EPfP LRHS MAsh
§	- var. **sulcatus**	CHar LPhx LRHS MSte SDry WAbe
		WFar
	lasianthus	see *Halimium lasianthum*
	laurifolius ♀ H4	CDoC CFil CHar EBee ENot EPfP
		LPio MGos MNrw NBee NBir
		SLPl SLon SPar SPer WCot WHar
		WWal
§	x **laxus** 'Snow White'	CAbP CDoC EBee EPfP LHop LPhx
		LRHS MDun MSte MWgw NLon
		NPer NPro NSti SChu SLPl SLim
		SLon SPer SSpi SUsu WKif WLeb

x *ledon*	SLPl WWeb	
libanotis	CHar CSam MAsh NFor NLon	
x *longifolius*	see *C.* x *nigricans*	
x *loretii* hort.	see *C.* x *dansereaui*	
x *loretii* Rouy & Fouc.	see *C.* x *stenophyllus*	
x *lusitanicus* Maund.	see *C.* x *dansereaui*	
'Merrist Wood Cream'	see x *Halimiocistus wintonensis* 'Merrist Wood Cream'	
monspeliensis	CAbP ENot EPfP EWTr LPio LRHS SPer SSpi WFar	
- CMBS 62	WPGP	
§ x *nigricans*	MAsh SLPl SRPl WCot	
x *oblongifolius* 'Barr Common'	LRHS	
x *obtusifolius* hort.	see *C.* x *nigricans*	
x *obtusifolius* Sweet	EPfP EWes MAsh WEas	
ochreatus	see *C. symphytifolius* subsp. *leucophyllus*	
ocymoides	see *Halimium ocymoides*	
osbeckiifolius	SIgm	
'Paladin'	see *C. ladanifer* 'Paladin'	
palhinhae	see *C. ladanifer* var. *sulcatus*	
parviflorus hort.	see *C.* 'Grayswood Pink'	
parviflorus Lam.	CBot LPhx NSti SChu WSHC	
'Peggy Sammons'	see *C.* x *argenteus* 'Peggy Sammons'	
x *platysepalus*	LPhx	
populifolius	CBrd CMHG CWib ECha SPer WAbe WHer	
- var. *lasiocalyx*	see *C. populifolius* subsp. *major*	
§ - subsp. *major* ♀H3	CPle EPfP LPhx SMrm	
- *prilosepalus*	see *C. inflatus*	
§ x *pulverulentus*	CPLG CTri ECha EPfP MMHG MWgw SChu WDin WLRN WSHC	
§ 'Sunset' ♀H3	More than 30 suppliers	
- 'Warley Rose'	see *C.* x *crispatus* 'Warley Rose'	
§ x *purpureus* ♀H3	More than 30 suppliers	
- 'Alan Fradd'	CBcs EBee ENot EPfP LHop LRHS MAsh MDun MGos MGrG MTis MWgw SCoo SEND SLim SMrm SPar SPla SWal WGer WGwG WWal	
- var. *argenteus* f. *stictus*	EBee WAbe	
- 'Betty Taudevin'	see *C.* x *purpureus*	
rosmarinifolius	see *C. clusii*	
'Ruby Cluster' **new**	WLeb	
sahucii	see x *Halimiocistus sahucii*	
salviifolius	CArn CPle EMil ISea LRHS NSla SSpi WAbe WHCG WLRN WWeb	
- 'Avalanche'	EBee GEil MRav NPro WAbe	
- 'Prostratus'	ELan ESis LPhx LRHS NPro SRPl WHCG WWeb	
- x *monspeliensis*	see *C.* x *florentinus*	
'Silver Pink' misapplied	see *C.* 'Grayswood Pink'	
§ x *skanbergii* ♀H3	CBcs CHar CSBt CSLe CSpe CWib EBee ELan ENot EPfP IMGH LHop LRHS MAsh MGos MRav MWat MWgw NBir SDix SHBN SIgm SPar SPcr WCom WEas WFar WWal WWin	
§ 'Snow Fire' ♀H4	CDoC CSBt EBee LPhx LRHS MAsh MBri SIgm SLPl SSpi SUsu WAbe WGer WWeb	
§ x *stenophyllus*	LPhx SPer WKif	
symphytifolius	CSLe WPGP	
§ - subsp. *leucophyllus*	CFil	
- - MSF 98.019	WPGP	
tomentosus	see *Helianthemum nummularium* subsp. *tomentosum*	
x *verguinii*	EBee LHop LPhx LRHS SIgm	
- f. *albiflorus*	WAbe	
- var. *albiflorus* misapplied	see *C.* x *dansereaui* 'Portmeirion'	
villosus	see *C. creticus* subsp. *creticus*	
wintonensis	see x *Halimiocistus wintonensis*	

Citharexylum (Verbenaceae)

spicatum	CPLG CPle

x *Citrofortunella* (Rutaceae)

§ *floridana*	CGOG	
- 'Eustis' (F)	ERea SCit	
- 'Lakeland' (F)	ERea	
lemonquat (F)	SCit	
limequat	see x *C. floridana*	
§ *microcarpa* (F) ♀H1	CDoC CGOG EMui EPfP ERea MBri SCit WBVN WOTO	
§ - 'Tiger' (v/F) ♀H1	EPfP ERea ESlt SCit	
- 'Variegata'	see x *C. microcarpa* 'Tiger'	
mitis	see x *C. microcarpa*	
procimequat (F)	SCit	
reticulata (F)	SCit	
swinglei 'Tavares' (F)	ERea	

citron see *Citrus medica*

x *Citroncirus* (Rutaceae)

'Swingle' (F)	SCit
webberi 'Benton' (F)	SCit
- 'Carrizo'	SCit
- 'Rusk'	SCit

Citrus ✿ (Rutaceae)

amblycarpa Djeruk lime (F)	ERea	
aurantiifolia (F)	SCit	
- Indian lime (F)	ERea	
aurantium (F)	SCit	
- 'Aber's Narrowleaf' (F)	SCit	
- 'Bigaradier Apepu'	SCit	
- 'Bittersweet' (F)	SCit	
- 'Bouquet de Fleurs'	CGOG ERea SCit	
- 'Bouquetier de Nice à Fleurs Doubles' (d)	SCit	
- 'Gou-tou Cheng' (F)	SCit	
- var. *myrtifolia* 'Chinotto' (F)	CGOG ERea SCit	
- 'Sauvage' (F)	SCit	
- 'Seville' (F)	CGOG ERea	
- 'Smooth Flat Seville' (F)	SCit	
- 'Willowleaf' (F)	SCit SPer	
bergamia bergamot	CGOG ERea	
- 'Fantastico'	SCit	
calamondin	see x *Citrofortunella microcarpa*	
deliciosa	see *C.* x *nobilis*	
ichangensis (F)	SCit	
jambhiri 'Milam'	SCit	
- red rough lemon (F)	SCit	
- rough lemon (F)	SCit	
- Schaub rough lemon (F)	SCit	
japonica	see *Fortunella japonica*	
kinokuni	SCit	
kumquat	see *Fortunella margarita*	
'La Valette'	CDoC EPfP ERea ESlt	
latifolia (F/S)	CGOG CWSG EPfP ERea ESlt SPer	
limettoides (F)	CArn SCit	
limon (F)	CGOG LPan	
- 'Eureka Variegated' (F/v)	SCit	
- 'Fino' (F)	CGOG EPfP SCit	
§ - 'Garey's Eureka' (F)	CDoC CWSG EPfP ERea	
- 'Imperial' (F)	ERea	
- 'Lemonade' (F)	ERea SCit	
- 'Lisbon' (F)	ERea	
- 'Quatre Saisons'	see *C. limon* 'Garey's Eureka'	
- 'Toscana'	EPfP ERea	
- 'Variegata' (F/v) ♀H1	ERea SPer	
- 'Verna' (F)	CGOG SCit	

- 'Villa Franca' (F)	ERea
- 'Yen Ben' (F)	SCit
x *limonia* 'Rangpur' (F)	ERea
macrophylla	SCit
madurensis	see *Fortunella japonica*
maxima (F)	ERea SCit
medica (F)	SCit
- 'Cidro Digitado'	see *C. medica* var. *digitata*
§ - var. *digitata* (F)	CGOG ERea ESlt SCit
- 'Ethrog' (F)	ERea ESlt SCit
- var. *sarcodactylis*	see *C. medica* var. *digitata*
x *meyeri* 'Meyer'	CBcs CDoC CPLG CWSG EPfP
(F) ♀ H1	ERea ESlt GTwe LRHS SCit SPer
microcarpa	see x *Citrofortunella microcarpa*
Philippine lime	
mitis	see x *Citrofortunella microcarpa*
natsudaidai	SCit
§ x *nobilis* (F)	LPan
- 'Blida' (F)	ERea SCit
- 'Ellendale' (F)	EPfP SCit
- 'Murcott' (F)	EPfP ERea SCit
- Ortanique Group (F)	CGOG EPfP ESlt SCit
- 'Silver Hill Owari' (F)	ERea
- Tangor Group (F)	ERea
x *paradisi* (F)	LPan
- 'Foster' (F)	ERea
- 'Golden Special' (F)	ERea
- 'Marsh' (F)	CGOG
- 'Navel' (F)	EPfP SCit
- 'Red Blush' (F/S)	CGOG
- 'Star Ruby' (F/S)	CGOG ERea ESlt SCit
- 'Wheeny' (F)	SCit
pennivesiculata (F)	SCit
'Ponderosa' (F)	CGOG ERea SCit
reshni Cleopatra	SCit
mandarin (F)	
reticulata (F)	SArc
- 'Arrufatina' (F/S)	CGOG
- 'Dancy' (F)	SCit
- 'Fina' (F/S)	SCit
- 'Hernandina' (F)	CGOG SCit
- Mandarin Group (F)	CDoC
- - 'Clementine' (F)	CDoC ERea
- - 'De Nules' (F/S)	CGOG ESlt SCit
- - 'Encore' (F)	ERea
- - 'Fortune' (F)	CGOG ESlt SCit
- - 'Tomatera' (F)	CGOG
- 'Marisol' (F/S)	CGOG SCit
- 'Nour' (F)	CGOG SCit
- 'Nova'	see *C.* x *tangelo* 'Nova'
- 'Orogrande'	CGOG
- Satsuma Group	see *C. unshiu*
- 'Suntina'	see *C.* x *tangelo* 'Nova'
sinensis (F)	ERea LPan SAPC SArc
- 'Egg' (F)	ERea
- 'Embiguo' (F)	ERea
- 'Harwood Late' (F)	ERea
- 'Jaffa'	see *C. sinensis* 'Shamouti'
- 'Lane Late' (F)	CGOG EPfP SCit
- 'Malta Blood' (F)	ERea ESlt
- 'Moro Blood' (F)	ERea SCit
- 'Navelate' (F)	CGOG SCit
- 'Navelina' (F/S)	CDoC CGOG ERea ESlt SCit
- 'Newhall' (F)	CGOG SCit
- 'Parson Brown' (F)	ERea
- 'Prata' (F)	ERea
- 'Ruby' (F)	ERea
- 'Saint Michael' (F)	ERea
- 'Salustiana' (F/S)	CGOG SCit
- 'Sanguinelli' (F)	CGOG ERea SCit
§ - 'Shamouti' (F)	ERea
- 'Succari' (F)	SCit
- 'Tarocco' (F)	SCit

- 'Thomson' (F)	ERea
- 'Valencia' (F)	ECot ERea
- 'Valencia Late' (F)	CGOG ERea ESlt SCit
- 'Washington' (F/S)	CGOG ERea GTwe SCit
tachibana	SCit
x *tangelo* 'Minneola' (F)	CGOG SCit
- 'Nocatee' (F)	SCit
§ - 'Nova' (F/S)	CGOG SCit
- 'Orlando' (F)	SCit
- 'Samson' (F)	SCit
- 'Seminole' (F)	ERea
- 'Ugli' (F)	SCit
§ *unshiu* (F)	ERea SPer
- 'Clausellina' (F/S)	CGOG ERea ESlt
- 'Hashimoto' (F/S)	CGOG SCit
- 'Okitsu' (F/S)	CGOG SCit
- 'Owari' (F/S)	CGOG SCit
volkameriana	ERea SCit

Cladium (*Cyperaceae*)

rubiginosum	WCot
variegated (v) **new**	

Cladothamnus see *Elliottia*

Cladrastis (*Papilionaceae*)

kentukea	CArn CBcs CDul CLnd CMCN
	CTho ELan EPfP MBlu NHol NLar
	SHBN SPer SSpi WBod WDin WNor
- 'Rosea'	CMCN IArd
§ *lutea*	see *C. kentukea*
sinensis	CFil CMCN EPfP MBlu SSpi WPGP

Clarkia (*Onagraceae*)

* *repens*	CSpe

Clavinodum (*Poaceae*)

§ *oedogonatum*	EPla SDry WJun

Claytonia (*Portulacaceae*)

alsinoides	see *C. sibirica*
australasica	see *Neopaxia australasica*
caroliniana	EBee LAma NLar NRog
§ *megarhiza* var. *nivalis*	ETow GDra MAsh NWCA
§ *nevadensis*	EMar
parvifolia	see *Naiocrene parvifolia*
§ *perfoliata*	CArn CPLG GPoy ILis WCHb WHer
§ *sibirica*	CAgr CArn CElw CNic CRow
	CSpe ECoo EEls EMan NBid NLAp
	WHen WRHF WWye
- 'Alba'	CElw NBid
virginica	EBee EPot LAma NRog WFar WMoo

Clematis ✿ (*Ranunculaceae*)

B&SWJ 599	WCru
CC 2713	CPLG
RCB TQ-H-7	WCot
'Abundance' (Vt) ♀ H4	CDoC CElw CFRD CPev CRHN
	CSPN EBee EOrc ERob ESCh ETho
	GMac LRHS MAsh MBri MCad
	NBea NPri NTay SBra SDix SHBN
	SPer SPet WSHC WTel WTre WWeb
addisonii	CBcs CSPN ERob ESCh ETho
	MWhi NBrk NHaw WTre
aethusifolia	CPIN CSPN ERob
afoliata	CBcs CPev CSPN CStu ECou ERob
	ESCh ETho WTre
afoliata x *forsteri* (Fo)	ECou
'Aino' (Vt)	ERob
'Akaishi' (P)	ERob ESCh ETho MCad NBrk NTay
akebioides	CPIN EBee LRHS MAsh MCad
	NBrk SBra SHBN SLim WCru
- SDR 1744	GKev

	'Akemi' (L)	ERob ESCh MCad NTay
	Alabast = 'Poulala'PBR	CSPN EBee EMil ERob ESCh ETho
	(Fl) ♀ H4	MBNS MCad NTay SBra SCoo
		SLim WTre
	'Alba Luxurians'(Vt)	More than 30 suppliers
	♀ H4	
	'Albatross' **new**	EHan ERob ESCh
	'Albiflora'	CSPN ECtt ESCh ETho NSti WTre
I	'Albina Plena' (A/d)	ESCh NBrk SLim WTre
	'Aleksandrit' (P)	ERob
	'Alice Fisk' (P)	CSPN EBee ERob ESCh ETho
		MAsh MCad NBea NBrk NHaw
		NTay SBra SHBN WGor WTre
	'Alionushka' (D) ♀ H4	CElw CHad CRHN EBee EBre
		EHan ELan EOrc EPfP ERob ESCh
		ETho LRHS MBri MCad MGos
		MWgw NBea NBrk NTay SBra
		SLim SMur SPer SPet SPla WSHC
		WTre WWeb
	'Allanah' (J)	CFRD CRHN EBee EPfP ERob
		ESCh ETho GKir LAst MAsh MGos
		NBea NHaw NTay SBra SCoo SLim
		WStI WTre WWeb
§	*alpina* (A) ♀ H4	CMac COlW CPev ECtt EPfP GDra
		GKir GSki MBar MCad MWhi
		NEgg NPer SHBN SLim SPlb WCot
		WFar
	- 'Albiflora'	see *C. alpina* subsp. *sibirica*
	- 'Burford White' (A)	CSPN EBee EOrc EPfP ERob ESCh
		MCad NBrk NTay WTre
	- 'Columbine' (A)	CFRD CPev CWSG EBee ENot ETho
		LBuc MAsh MBar MCad MWgw
		NBea SCoo SDix SLim WTre WWeb
	- 'Columbine White'	see *C. alpina* 'White Columbine'
	- 'Constance' (A) ♀ H4	CElw CFRD CSPN EBee ENot
		EOrc EPfP ERob ESCh ETho LRHS
		NBrk NSti NTay SBra SPer SPet
		SRms WPGP WTre WWeb
	- 'Foxy' (A) ♀ H4	CFRD EPfP ERob ESCh NBrk NTay
		SLim SLon WTre
	- 'Frances Rivis' (A) ♀ H4	More than 30 suppliers
	- 'Frankie' (A) ♀ H4	CDoC CSPN EBee EBre ELan ENot
		ERob ESCh ETho LRHS NTay SBra
		SLim SPer WTre WWeb
	- 'Jacqueline du Pré'	CElw CFRD CHad CPev CSPN
	(A) ♀ H4	EBee EHan EOrc EPfP ERob ESCh
		ETho GMac MAsh MCad MGos
		NBea NTay SBra WTre
	- 'Jan Lindmark' (A)	see *C. macropetala* 'Jan Lindmark'
	- 'Mary Whistler' **new**	ESCh
	- 'Odorata' (A)	CSPN ERob ESCh LBuc MGos
		NBea
§	- 'Pamela Jackman' (A)	CDoC CFRD CSPN CWSG EBee
		EHan ELan ESCh EWTr GKir LAst
		LRHS MAsh MCad MGos MWgw
		NBea NHol NSti NTay SBra SDix
		SLim SPer WTre
	- 'Pink Flamingo'	CElw CMHG CSPN EBee EBre ECtt
	(A) ♀ H4	ELan ENot EPfP ERob ESCh ETho
		LRHS MBri NEgg NPri NSti NTay
		SLim SMur SPet SRkn WTre WWeb
	- 'Rosy Pagoda' (A)	EBee ELan EOrc EPfP ERob ESCh
		LRHS MCad NBea NBir NHaw
		WTel WTre
	- 'Ruby' (A)	CFRD CMHG CPev CSPN CWSG
		EBee ELan EPfP ESCh ETho LRHS
		MCad MGos MWgw NBea NEgg
		NHol NSti SBra SChu SDix SHBN
		SLim SPer SPet SReu WTMC WTel
		WTre WWeb
§	- subsp. *sibirica* (A)	CPev ERob NTay SPla
§	- - 'Riga' (A)	ERob ESCh NTay WTre
§	- - 'White Moth' (A)	CElw CFRD CSPN CWSG EBee ELan

		EPfP ESCh ETho EWTr LRHS MAsh
		MGos NBrk NHol NTay SBra SLim
		SPer SPet SPla SRms WTel WTre
	- 'Tage Lundell'	see *C.* 'Tage Lundell'
	- 'Violet Purple' (A)	ERob ESCh
§	- 'White Columbine'	EPfP ERob ESCh ETho LAst NBea
	(A) ♀ H4	NSti WTre
	- 'Willy' (A)	CElw CPev CSPN EBee EBre ELan
		EPfP ESCh ETho GKir LRHS MBar
		MBri MCad MGos NBea NHol
		NPri NSti NTay SBra SDix SLim
		SPer SPet SPla WCru WTre
	'Alpinist' (L)	ERob
	'Amelia Joan' (Ta)	ERob
	'Ametistina' (A)	ERob
	'André Devillers'	see *C.* 'Directeur André Devillers'
I	'Andromeda' (Fl)	CSPN ERob ESCh ETho NBrk
		NHaw NTay SBra WTre
	'Anita' (Ta)	EBee EHan EMil ERob ESCh ETho
		MCad NHaw SBra SLim WTre
	'Anna' (P)	ERob ESCh MCad NTay
	'Anna German' (L)	ERob ESCh
	Anna Louise =	CSPN EBee ERob ESCh ETho
	'Evithree'PBR	LRHS MBri MCad NTay SBra SCoo
	(P) ♀ H4	SLim WTre WWeb
	'Annabel' (P)	CSPN ERob ESCh MAsh MCad
	'Annamieke' (Ta)	ERob ESCh MGos NTay SBra WTre
	'Annie Treasure'	ERob WTre
	'Anniversary'	EBee EHan ENot ERob ESCh NBrk
	'Anouchka' (L)	EBre
	anshunensis	see *C. clarkeana*
	'Anti'	ESCh
	'Aoife' (Fo)	ETho
	'Aotearoa'	ERob ESCh
	'Aphrodite' **new**	ERob WTre
	apiifolia	CPev ERob ESCh MWhi NTay
	- B&SWJ 4838	WCru
	'Arabella' (D) ♀ H4	CElw CFRD CHad CPev CPou
		CSPN EBee EPfP ERob ESCh ETho
		LAst LRHS MAsh MBri MCAu
		MCad MGrG NBea NBrk NPri
		NTay SBra SMur SPer SPet WCru
		WFar WTre WWeb
	Arctic Queen =	CSPN EBee EBre EHan ENot ESCh
	'Evitwo'PBR (Fl)	ETho GKir LRHS MAsh MBNS
	♀ H4	MCad NBea NPri NTay SLim SPer
		WLRN WTre WWeb WWcs
	armandii	More than 30 suppliers
	- 'Apple Blossom' ♀ H4	More than 30 suppliers
	- var. *biondiana*	ERob MNes SBla WTre
	- 'Bowl of Beauty'	ERob ESCh MCad MGos SPer
	- 'Little White	SPoG
	Charm' **new**	
	- 'Meyeniana'	CSPN ERob MCad SPer
§	- 'Snowdrift'	CBcs CPev CSBt CSPN CSam CWSG
		ELan EPfP ERob ESCh EWTr LRHS
		MCad MGos MLan NSti NTay SLim
		SPar SPer SReu SRms WTre WWeb
	- Treasure's form	WTre
	x *aromatica*	CSPN EBee EOrc EPfP ERob ESCh
		ETho GMac LAst LRHS MBri
		MCad MWgw NBea NSti NTay
		SBra WTre WWeb
§	'Asagasumi' (L)	ERob ESCh LBuc MCad NBrk
	'Asao' (P)	CElw CFRD CRHN EBee EBre
		ELan ERob ESCh ETho LAst LRHS
		MAsh MCad NBea NTay SBra
		SLim SPer SPet WTre WWeb
	'Ascotiensis' (J)	CPev CRHN CSPN EBee EBre
		EPfP ESCh ETho LRHS MAsh
		MCad MWgw NBea NPri NTay
		SBra SDix SLim SPer WTre WWeb
§	'Aureolin' (Ta)	CSPN CWSG EBee EBre ENot EPfP

	ERob GKir LRHS MBar MGos NBrk NHol SBra SLim WPGP WTre	
australis	ERob ITim NHaw	
'Bagatelle' (P)	ESCh MCad	
'Bałtyk' (P)	CSPN ERob ESCh NTay	
'Barbara Dibley' (P)	CPev CTri CWSG EBee ERob ESCh LRHS MAsh MBNS MCad NBea NTay SBod SBra SDix SLim WBar WTre	
'Barbara Jackman' (P)	CPev CRHN EBee ECtt ENot ERob ETho GKir LRHS MAsh MBar MCad MWgw NBea NBlu NTay SBra SLim SPer SPet WFar WFoF WStI WTre WWeb	
'Barbara Wheeler' **new**	ERob	
barbellata (A)	EHyt ERob	
- 'Pruinina'	see 'Pruinina'	
'Basil Bartlett'	ECou ERob ESCh	
'Beata' (L)	ESCh MCad	
'Beauty of Richmond' (L)	CWSG ERob ESCh MCad NBea SDix WTre	
'Beauty of Worcester' (Fl/L)	CPev CSPN CWSG EBee EBre ELan EPfP ESCh ETho GKir LAst LRHS MAsh MBar MCad NBea NBlu NEgg NHaw NTay SBra SDix SLim SPer SPet WFar WTre WWeb	
'Bees' Jubilee' (P)	More than 30 suppliers	
'Bella' (J)	ERob ESCh ETho NTay	
'Belle Nantaise' (L)	CElw CPev EBee EBre EPfP ERob ESCh LRHS MCad NBea NTay SPet WTre	
'Belle of Woking' (Fl/P)	CElw CPev CRHN CSPN CWSG EBee EBre ECtt EHan ELan ENot EPfP ERob ETho LRHS MBar MCad NBea NTay SBra SDix SHBN SLim SPer SPet WTre WWeb	
'Bessie Watkinson'	ERob ESCh MAsh	
§ 'Beth Currie' (P)	CSPN EBee ERob ESCh	
'Betina' (A)	CSPN ERob ESCh LBuc MAsh MCad WTre	
'Betty Corning' (VtxT) ♀ H4	CHad CSPN EBee EBre EMil EOrc EPfP ERob ESCh ETho GMac LRHS MBri MCad NBea NBrk NTay SBra SLon WSHC WTMC WTel WTre	
'Betty Risdon' (P)	ERob ESCh ETho MAsh NBea NBrk	
'Big Bird' (A/d)	ERob ESCh LBuc	
§ 'Bill MacKenzie' (Ta) ♀ H4	More than 30 suppliers	
'Black Madonna' (P)	ERob	
'Black Prince' (Vt)	CRHN ELan EPfP ERob ESCh ETho NBrk NTay WTre	
'Black Tea' **new**	ERob	
§ 'Błekitny Anioł' (J/Vt) ♀ H4	CFRD CRHN CSPN EBee EHan ERob ESCh ETho LRHS MAsh MCad MGrG NBea NBrk NPri NTay SBra SCoo SLim SPar SPet WTre	
Blue Angel	see *C.* 'Błekitny Anioł'	
'Blue Belle' (Vt)	CElw CFRD CPou CRHN CSam EBee ELan ERob LRHS MBri MCad NBea NBrk NSti NTay SBra SLim SPet WTre WWeb	
'Blue Bird' (A/d)	CBcs CPIN CWSG EBee ECtt GDea MBri MCad MWgw NBea SBra SLim SPer SPet WTre	
'Blue Boy' (D)	see *Clematis* x *eriostemon* 'Blue Boy' (D)	
'Blue Boy' (L/P)	see *C.* 'Elsa Späth'	
'Blue Dancer' (A)	CAbP CElw EBee EOrc EPfP ERob ESCh ETho GKir MWat NBea NBrk NTay SPet WTre WWeb WWes	
'Blue Eclipse'	CSPN ERob WTre	
'Blue Eyes'	CSPN EBee ERob ESCh NHaw	
'Blue Gem' (L)	ERob ESCh MCad NTay SBra SLim	
'Blue Japan' (I)	NBrk	
'Blue Light'[PBR] (L/d)	CSPN EHan ELan ENot ERob ESCh ETho LBuc MCad MGos NBrk NTay SBra WTre	
Blue Moon = 'Evirin'[PBR]	EBee EBre ENot ESCh ETho LAst LRHS MBNS NBea NPri NTay SBra SCoo WWeb	
Blue Rain	see *Clematis* 'Sinij Dozhdj'	
'Blue Ravine' (P)	EBee EPfP ERob ESCh ETho MCad NTay SBra SCoo WTre	
'Blue Stream' (A) **new**	ESCh	
x *bonstedtii* (H)	ESCh	
§ - 'Campanile'	CFRD CPev EBee ERob ESCh MCad NBea NBir NBrk NTay SDix	
- 'Crépuscule' (H)	ERob ESCh GCal NBrk NTay SMrm SRms WCot WTre WWeb	
'Boskoop Beauty' (PxL)	ERob ESCh MCad NBrk	
'Bracebridge Star' (L/P)	ECtt ERob ESCh	
brachiata	ESCh SBra	
brachyura	ERob	
'Bravo' (Ta)	ERob NTay WTre	
brevicaudata	GIBF	
'Brocade' (Vt) **new**	ERob	
'Broughton Bride' (A)	ERob	
§ 'Brunette' (A)	CSPN EPfP ERob ESCh ETho MCad MGos NBrk NTay SBra WTre	
buchananiana Finet & Gagnep.	see *C. rehderiana*	
buchananiana DC.	ERob ITim	
'Budapest' (I)	ERob ESCh LBuc NHaw SBra WTre	
'Burford Bell'	ERob WTre	
* 'Burford Princess'	ERob	
'Burford Variety' (Ta)	ERob ESCh MCad NBea NTay WTre	
'Burma Star' (P)	CElw CFRD CPev EHan ERob ESCh ETho MCad NBea NBrk NHaw NTay SBra SPet WTre	
'C.W. Dowman' (P)	ERob ETho	
'Caddick's Cascade'	MCad	
'Caerulea Luxurians'	ERob ESCh WTre	
calycina	see *C. cirrhosa*	
campaniflora	CBot CElw CFRD CNic CPev CSPN EBee EHyt EOrc EPla ERob ESCh ETho MAsh MCad MWhi NBea NBrk NWCA SBra SDix SGar SLim SPer WPGP WTre	
- 'Lisboa'	ERob ESCh NBrk SBra WSHC	
'Campanile'	see *Clematis* x *bonstedtii* 'Campanile'	
I 'Campanulina Plena' (A/d)	ERob	
'Candle Glow'	CSPN	
'Candy Stripe'	EBee ERob ESCh GKir NTay SLim	
'Capitaine Thuilleaux'	see *C.* 'Souvenir du Capitaine Thuilleaux'	
'Cardinal Wyszynski'	see *C.* 'Kardynał Wyszyński'	
'Carmen Rose' (A)	ERob	
'Carmencita' (Vt)	CSPN EBee ERob ESCh ETho NBrk NHaw NTay SBra SLim WTre WWeb	
'Carnaby' (L)	CDoC CRHN CSPN CWSG EBee EBre ENot EPfP ERob ESCh ETho LAst LRHS MBar MBri MCad MGos NBea NBlu NTay SBra SLim SPar SPet WPGP WTre WWeb	
'Carnival Queen'	CSPN CWSG ERob ESCh MAsh NBrk NTay	
'Caroline' (J)	CHad CPev CSPN EBee ERob ESCh ETho LBuc MCad NBea NBrk NHaw NTay SBra WTre	
'Caroline Lloyd' (Vt)	ERob	
§ x *cartmanii* hort.	CSPN EHan ERob ESCh LBuc	
'Avalanche'[PBR] (Fo) ♀ H3	LRHS MAsh NPri SBla SLim SPer	
- 'Blaaval'[PBR]	see *C.* x *cartmanii* 'Avalanche'	
- 'Joe' (Fo)	More than 30 suppliers	

- 'Snow Valley' (Fo) — MAsh
- 'White Abundance' (Fo) — MAsh
'Celebration'PBR — MCad
'Centre Attraction' — MCad
'Chalcedony' (FlxL) — CPev CSPN ERob ESch ETho MCad MGos NBrk NTay SBra WTre
'Charissima' (P) — CBcs CElw CPev CSPN CSam EBee EHan ERob ESch ETho NTay SBra SCoo SPet WTre
chiisanensis — CBcs CSPN ERob MCad SBra WCwm WHrl WTre
- B&SWJ 4560 — WCru
- 'Lemon Bells' (A) — LRHS WWeb
- 'Love Child' — CBcs CSPN ERob ESch ETho LBuc NTay SCoo SLim SPer WTre
chinensis hort. — see *C. terniflora*
chinensis Retz — ERob
'Christian Steven' (J) — CSPN ERob ESch
chrysantha var. *paucidentata* — see *C. hilariae*
chrysocoma hort. — see *C. montana* var. *sericea*
N *chrysocoma* Franchet — CPev EPfP ERob EWTr MAsh MBNS MBar NHol SBra SDix WCru
- ACE 1093 — CPou
- B&L 12237 — NBea
- hybrid — ERob NTay
'Cicciolina' (Vt) — ERob
§ *cirrhosa* — CBot CPev CTri ELan ESch LRHS MAsh MCad MGos MWhi NTay SArc WTre
- var. *balearica* — More than 30 suppliers
- 'Freckles' ♀H3 — More than 30 suppliers
- 'Jingle Bells' — CElw EBee EHan EPfP ERob ESch ETho LRHS MCad NBea NHaw NTay SBra SCoo SLim WFar WTre WWeb
- 'Lansdowne Gem'**new** — CSPN LBuc MBlu
- 'Ourika Valley' — ERob
- subsp. *semitriloba* — ERob ESch
- 'Wisley Cream' ♀H3 — More than 30 suppliers
§ 'Citra' (A) — ERob ESch NBea NBrk NTay
§ *clarkeana* **new** — ETho
coactilis — ERob
'Colette Deville' (J) — EPfP ERob ESch MCad NTay
columbiana — EHyt ERob
§ - var. *tenuiloba* — ESch SAga SOkd
- - 'Ylva' — EHyt WAbe
'Columella' (A) — ERob
'Comtesse de Bouchaud' (J) ♀H4 — More than 30 suppliers
connata — CPIN EPfP ERob ESch NBrk SBra
- CC&McK 37 — NWCA
- HWJCM 132 — WCru
'Corona' (PxL) — CFRD CPev CSPN EBee ELan ERob LAst LRHS MAsh MBar MCad NBea NBlu NHaw NTay SBra SLim SPet WTre WWeb
'Corry' (Ta) — ERob ESch MCad NBrk
'Cotton Candy' — ERob
'Countess of Lovelace' (P) — CFRD CSPN CWSG EBee EBre EHan EPfP ERob ESch ETho LRHS MAsh MBar MBri MCad MGos NBea NTay SBra SDix SLim SPer SPet WTre
County Park Group (Fo) — ECou
- 'Fairy' (Fo/f) — ECou ESch
- 'Fragrant Joy' (Fo/m) — ECou
§ - 'Pixie' (Fo/m) — CSPN CStu CWib EBee ECou ENot EPfP ESch ETho LRHS MGos NHaw NTay SBra SCoo WStI WTre WWeb
'Cragside' **new** — ETho
crassifolia B&SWJ 6700 — WCru

'Crimson King' (L) — ERob ESch MAsh MCad NTay SBod WGor
§ *crispa* — CFRD CPou CSPN EHyt ERob ESch ETho MCad MWhi NBea WSHC WTre
§ - 'Cylindrica' — ERob NBrk
- 'Rosea' — see *C. crispa* 'Cylindrica'
Crystal Fountain = 'Fairy Blue'**new** — ESch ETho LRHS MAsh NPri WWeb
cunninghamii — see *C. parviflora*
'Cyanea' (A) — EBee ERob ESch NTay WTre
x *cylindrica* — CSPN ESch NBrk NTay WTre
'Daniel Deronda' (P) ♀H4 — CPev CSPN CWSG EBee EBre ECtt ELan ENot ERob ESch ETho EWTr GKir LAst LRHS MCad NBea NTay SBod SBra SDix SLim SPar SPer SPet WTre WWeb
'Dark Secret' — CSPN ERob ESch WWeb
'Dawn' (L/P) — CPev CSPN EBee ERob ESch ETho LRHS MAsh MCad NBea NTay SBra SLim SPer SPet WGwG WTre
'Débutante' — ESch ETho
delavayi SDR 1850 **new** — GKev
'Denny's Double' (d) — CSPN CWSG ERob ESch ETho MAsh MCad NBrk NRib NTay WTre
denticulata — WTre
'Diana' — ERob ESch
dioscoreifolia — see *C. terniflora*
§ 'Directeur André Devillers' (P) — ERob ESch MCad
'Docteur Le Bêle' — ERob NBrk NTay
'Doctor Ruppel' (P) — More than 30 suppliers
'Doggy' (Vt) — ERob
'Dominika' (J) — CSPN ERob ESch ETho NHaw NTay SBra WTre
'Dorath' — ERob ESch WTre
'Dorota' (J) — ERob
'Dorothy Tolver' (P) — ERob ESch ETho WTre
'Dorothy Walton' (J) — CRIIN CSPN EBee ERob ESch ETho MAsh MCad NBrk NHaw NTay SBra SCoo SLim WTre WWeb
douglasii — see *C. hirsutissima*
'Duchess of Albany' (T) — More than 30 suppliers
'Duchess of Edinburgh' (Fl) — More than 30 suppliers
'Duchess of Sutherland'(Vt/d) — CPev CRHN EBcc ERob ESch LRHS MAsh MCad NBea NHaw NTay SBra SDix SPet WTre
'Dulcie' **now** — NHaw
x *durandii* (D) ♀H4 — More than 30 suppliers
'Early Sensation' (Fo) — CBcs CFRD COtt CSPN CWSG CWib ECtt ELan ENot EOrc EPfP ESch ETho LAst LRHS MAsh MBlu MCad MGos NBea NPal NSti NTay SBra SCoo SLim WCot WFoF WTre WWeb
'Edith' (L) ♀H4 — EBee EBre ECtt EPfP ERob ESch ETho LRHS MAsh MCad NBea NBrk NTay SBra SLim WGor WGwG WTre
'Edomurasaki' (L) — EBee ERob ESch ETho NBrk NTay WTre
'Edouard Desfossé' (P) — EBee ERob ESch NTay SBra WTre
'Edward Prichard' (H) — CFRD CSPN ERob ESch ETho MAsh NBea NBrk NHaw SBra SDix WTre
'Eetika' (Vt) — ERob ESch
'Ekstra' (J) — ERob ESch ETho NBrk
'Eleanor' — ECou ESch
'Eleanor of Guildford' (P) — EHan ENot ERob ESch
'Elf' — CPev

'Elfin' (v)	ECou
§ 'Elsa Späth' (L/P)	More than 30 suppliers
'Elvan' (Vt)	CFRD CPev CRHN EBee ERob
	ESCh MCad NBea NBrk NHaw
	NTay SPet WTre
'Emerald Stars' **new**	ESCh
'Emilia Plater' (Vt)	CRHN CSPN ERob ESCh ETho
	MBri MCad NBea NBrk NTay SBra
	WBcn WTre
'Emogi' **new**	ESCh
'Empress of India' (P)	EBre ERob ESCh ETho WTre
'Entel' (J)	ERob NBrk WTre
§ x *eriostemon* (D)	CFRD EBee EOrc EPfP ESCh GEil
	GKir LRHS MAsh MBNS MCad
	MSte NHaw NHol SBra SDix
	SGar SPer SPet WCot WTre WWeb
§ - 'Blue Boy' (D)	CFRD CSPN EPfP ERob ESCh
	ETho MAsh MBri MCad MGos
	NBrk NHaw NTay SBra WTre
§ - 'Hendersonii' (D)	More than 30 suppliers
§ - 'Lauren' (D)	ERob WTre
§ - 'Olgae' (D)	CFRD CPev CSPN EBee EHan
	ESCh ETho MCad MDKP NBea
	NBrk NTay SBra SDix SLim WTre
'Ernest Markham'	More than 30 suppliers
(J/Vt) ♀ H4	
'Etoile de Malicorne' (P)	EBee ERob ESCh LRHS MCad
	NBea WGor WTre
'Etoile de Paris' (P)	EBee ERob ESCh ETho MWgw
	NTay SBra WTre
'Etoile Nacrée'	ERob ESCh
'Etoile Rose' (T)	CPev CSPN CTri EBee EBre ELan
	ENot EOrc EPfP ERob ESCh ETho
	GKir LAst LRHS MCad MWgw NBea
	NTay SBra SDix SLim SMur SPer
	WFar WPGP WSHC WTre WWeb
'Etoile Violette' (Vt) ♀ H4	More than 30 suppliers
'Europa'	ERob
'Eva'	ERob NBrk
Evening Star =	ERob ESCh NTay SBra SLim
'Evista'PBR	
'Eximia' (A/d)	ERob ESCh
'Fair Rosamond' (L/P)	CPev EBee EPfP ERob ESCh LRHS
	MAsh MCad NBea NHaw NTay
	SBra SCoo SDix SLim WTre
'Fairy Queen' (L)	ERob ESCh ETho MCad SBra
fargesii	see *C. potaninii*
x *fargesioides*	see *C.* 'Paul Farges'
fasciculiflora	CBot CMHG CPIN CRHN CSPN
	ERob ESCh LRHS SLon SSpi
- L 657	CFil SAga WCru WPGP
fauriei (A)	ERob
finetiana hort.	see *C. paniculata* J.G. Gmel.
'Firefly'	ERob ESCh NTay
'Fireworks' (P)	COtt CSPN EBee EBre ECtt ENot
	EPfP ESCh ETho LAst LRHS MBri
	MCad MGos NBea NBlu NPri NTay
	SBra SLim WFoF WGor WTre WWeb
'Flamingo' (L)	CWSG ERob MCad
flammula	More than 30 suppliers
- var. *flavescens*	ERob
- 'Ithaca' (v)	ERob
- 'Rubra Marginata'	see *C.* x *triternata*
	'Rubromarginata'
§ 'Floralia' (A/d)	CSPN EBee ELan EOrc ESCh LRHS
	NBea NBrk NTay SCoo SLim
florida	CSPN ERob ESCh ETho
- 'Bicolor'	see *C. florida* var. *sieboldiana*
- var. *flore-pleno* (d)	CPev CPIN CSPN EBee EBre ELan
	EOrc EPfP ESCh ETho GMac LAst
	LRHS MAsh MCad NBea NRib
	NTay SBod SBra SHBN SMad SPer
	SPla WTre

- var. *sieboldiana* (d)	More than 30 suppliers
foetida	CBcs CSPN ESCh
forrestii	see *C. napaulensis*
§ *forsteri*	CBcs CSPN EBee EOrc ERob ESCh
	ETho GSki IDee MCad NBrk SBra
	WPGP WSHC
- x *indivisa*	WCru
'Foxtrot' (Vt)	CRHN ERob ESCh NBrk WTre
'Frau Mikiko' (P)	ERob
'Fryderyk Chopin' (P)	CSPN ERob ESCh ETho NHaw WTre
'Fuji-musume' (L) ♀ H4	CSPN EBee EHan ERob ESCh
	ETho MCad NBrk NHaw NTay
	SBra SLim WTre
'Fujinami' (L)	ERob
fusca hort.	see *C. japonica*
fusca Turcz.	ERob MAsh MWhi WTre
- B&SWJ 4229	WCru
- var. *coreana*	WCru WTre
f. *umbrosa*	
B&SWJ 700	
§ - subsp. *fusca*	ESCh ETho GIBF
- var. *kamtschatica*	see *C. fusca* subsp. *fusca*
§ - var. *violacea*	see *C. ianthina*
fusijamana	ERob
'G. Steffner' (A)	ERob ESCh NBrk
'Gabriëlle' (P)	CSPN ERob ESCh LBuc MCad
	NHaw SLim WTre
'Gekkyuuden' **new**	ERob
'Gemini'	ENot ERob ESCh
'General Sikorski' (L)	CBcs CElw CMHG CMac CSPN
	CSam CWSG EBee EBre ECtt ELan
	EPfP ESCh ETho LAst LRHS MBri
	MCad MGos NBea NTay SBra SDix
	SLim SPar SPer SPet WTre WWeb
gentianoides	ERob WAbe WCot
'Georg' (A/d)	ERob WTre
'Georg Ots' (J)	ERob ESCh
'Gillian Blades' (P) ♀ H4	CFRD CRHN CSPN EBee EBre EHan
	ELan ENot EPfP ERob ESCh ETho
	LAst LRHS MCad NBea NBrk NPri
	NTay SBra SLim SPet WTre WWeb
'Gipsy Queen' (J) ♀ H4	More than 30 suppliers
'Gladys Picard' (P)	ERob ESCh MCad NTay SLim WTre
glauca hort.	see *C. intricata*
'Glynderek' (L)	ERob ESCh MAsh MCad NTay
	SBra WTre
'Golden Harvest' (Ta)	ERob ESCh MAsh NHol SBra WTre
Golden Tiara	CSPN EHan ENot ERob ESCh ETho
= 'Kugotia'PBR	LRHS MCad MGos NBea NBrk NPal
(Ta) ♀ H4	NPri NTay SPer WCot WTre WWeb
'Gornoye Ozero'	ERob ESCh
gouriana	ERob ESCh
- subsp. *lishanensis*	WCru
B&SWJ 292	
'Grace' (Ta)	CElw CSPN ERob ESCh ETho
	NBrk NHaw WTre
gracilifolia	ERob ESCh WTre
- var. *dissectifolia*	ERob
'Grandiflora Sanguinea'	ERob SLim
(Vt)	
'Grandiflora Sanguinea'	see *C.* 'Södertälje'
Johnson	
grata hort.	see *C.* x *jouiniana*
grata Wall.	CPev ERob NBrk
- B&SWJ 6774	WCru
'Gravetye Beauty' (T)	More than 30 suppliers
'Green Velvet' (Fo)	CPIN ECou
grewiiflora B&SWJ 2956	WCru
'Guernsey Cream' (P)	CFRD CSPN CSam CWSG EBee
	EBre EHan EMil ESCh ETho LAst
	LRHS MAsh MBri MCad NBea
	NPri NTay SBra SDix SLim SPet
	WFar WLRN WTre WWeb WWes

'Guiding Star' (L)	ERob MCad NHaw NTay SBra
'H.F.Young' (L/P)	More than 30 suppliers
'Hagley Hybrid' (J)	More than 30 suppliers
'Hainton Ruby' (P)	ERob ESch
'Haku-ôkan' (L)	CPev CSPN EBee EBre EHan EPfP
	ERob ESCh ETho LRHS MAsh
	MCad NBea NTay SBra SLim SPet
	WTre WWeb
'Hakuree' **new**	ETho
'Hanaguruma' (P)	CSPN EBee ERob ESCh ETho MCad
	NBea NBrk NHaw NTay WTre
'Hanajima' (I)	EHyt ERob ESCh ETho NBrk
'Hanna' (Vt)	ERob ESCh ETho
'Harmony' (d)	ERob ESCh
'Haruyama'	ESCh MCad
Havering hybrids (Fo)	ECou
'Helen Cropper' (P)	ERob ESCh ETho MAsh MCad NBrk
'Helios' (Ta)	CFRD CSPN EBee ENot EPfP
	ERob ESCh ETho MAsh MCad
	MGos MWgw NBea NBrk NTay
	SBra WCot WTre
'Helsingborg' (A) ♀ H4	CBcs CSPN EBee ECtt ELan ENot
	EPfP ERob ESCh LRHS
	MAsh MCad NBea NHol NPri NSti
	NTay SBra SLim SPet SPla WTel
	WTre WWeb WWes
hendersonii Stand.	see *C. x eriostemon*
hendersonii Koch	see *C. x eriostemon* 'Hendersonii'
'Hendersonii Rubra' (D)	CSPN
henryi	ENot MWgw
– B&SWJ 3402	WCru
henryi (P) ♀ H4	More than 30 suppliers
henryi var. *morii*	WCru
B&SWJ 1668	
heracleifolia (H)	CBcs CBot CPou EChP ECtt EHol
	EPyc ESCh GKir Göki MCad NLar
	NWCA WMoo WTre
– Alan Bloom[PBR]	see *C. tubulosa* Alan Bloom =
	'Alblo'
– 'Blue Dwarf' **new**	ETho
I	– 'Cassandra' (H)	EBee EFou ESCh ETho NBrk
– 'China Purple' (H)	CFai EBee ERob MCAu NLar SSpi
	WAul WBor WCot WHil
– var. *davidiana*	see *C. tubulosa*
– dwarf **new**	EHyt
– 'New Love'[PBR] (H)	CSPN EGle EHan ENot ERob ESCh
	ETho LBuc MBlu MGos NHaw
	NSti WHil
– 'Roundway	CBot LHop NHaw
Bluebird' (H)	
'Herbert Johnson' (P)	CPev ESCh ETho MAsh NBrk SBra
hexapetala hort.	see *C. recta* subsp. *recta* var.
	lasiosepala
hexapetala DC.	see *C. forsteri*
'Hikarugenji' (P)	CSPN ERob ESCh MCad NBrk
	NHaw NTay
§	*hilariae* (Ta)	ERob ESCh NTay
§	*hirsutissima*	EHyt WLin
– var. *hirsutissima* **new**	EBee
– var. *scottii*	ERob
'Honora' (P)	CSPN ERob ESCh MCad NTay WTre
'Horn of Plenty' (L/P)	EBee EHan ERob ESCh LRHS
	MCad NBea NBrk NHaw NTay
	SBra SLim WTre
'Huldine' (Vt) ♀ H4	More than 30 suppliers
'Huvi' (J)	ERob ESCh
§	'Hybrida Sieboldii' (L)	CRHN EBee ERob ESCh ETho
	MAsh MCad NBea NBlu NBrk
	NTay SBra SLim WTre
'Hythe Egret'	EHyt LTwo
'Hågelby White' (Vt)	ERob ESCh
ianthina	EHyt EPfP ERob ESCh SBra WPGP
	WSHC WTre

– var. *kuripoensis*	ERob ETho
'Ice Maiden'	ESCh
'Ideal' (L)	ERob ESCh
'Ilka' (P)	ERob ESCh
'Imperial' (P/d)	ERob ESCh ETho NBrk
indivisa	see *C. paniculata* J.G. Gmel.
'Inglewood' (P)	ERob NTay
Inspiration = 'Zoin'	CSPN EHan ERob ESCh ETho LBuc
	MCad NBrk NTay SBra WTre WWhi
integrifolia	More than 30 suppliers
– 'Alba'	CBot CElw CFRD CSPN ECtt
	EHan LAst LRHS NBea NHaw
	NTay SLim SPer WSHC
§	– var. *albiflora*	CBcs CHad EBee ESCh ETho
	GBuc MCad MDKP NBea NBir
	NBrk SBra SPet WCru WTre
– 'Amy'	ERob ESCh
*	– 'Finnis Form'	SChu
– 'Floris V'	EBee ERob ESCh NBrk
– 'Hendersonii' Koch	see *C. x eriostemon* 'Hendersonii'
I	– 'Hendersonii' hort.	ERob ETho GKir LRHS MSte NTay
	SPet WTre
– subsp. *integrifolia*	ERob
var. *latifolia*	
– 'Olgae'	see *Clematis* x *eriostemon* 'Olgae'
– 'Pangbourne Pink'	CFRD CHad CSPN EBee EHan
♀ H4	EOrc EPfP ERob ESCh ETho GBuc
	GDea LRHS MCad NBea NBrk
	NHaw NTay SBra SLim WCru WTre
– 'Pastel Blue'	CPev ERob ESCh ETho MCad NBea
– 'Pastel Pink'	CPev ERob ESCh ETho MCad WTre
– 'Rosea' ♀ H4	CBcs CBot CHar CM&M CPev
	CSPN EBee EHan EPfP ERob ESCh
	ETho EWTr LAst LHop LRHS MBri
	MCad MTho NBea NBrk NChl
	NPal NTay SLim WCom WSHC
	WTre WWeb
– 'Tapestry'	CPev ERob MCad SBra WTre
– white	see *C. integrifolia* var. *albiflora*
§	*intricata*	CBcs CFRD CSPN ECre EPfP
	ERob IArd
– 'Harry Smith'	ERob ESCh
'Iola Fair' (P)	CSPN ERob ESCh ETho NTay
'Ishobel' (P)	ERob ESCh MCad NBrk
'Ivan Olsson' (PxL)	CFRD CSPN ERob ESCh ETho
'Izumi' **new**	ESCh
'Jackmanii' ♀ H4	CBcs CMHG CMac CTri EBee
	EBre ENot EPfP ERob ESCh ETho
	GKir LRHS MCad NBea NBlu
	NEgg NWea SBod SBra SLim SPar
	SPer SPet WEar WTel WTre WWeb
'Jackmanii Alba' (J)	CPev EBee EBre ELan EPfP ERob
	ESCh ETho LAst LRHS MAsh MBar
	MCad NBea NBlu NBrk NTay SLim
	SPer SPet WStI WTre WWeb
'Jackmanii Rubra' (J)	CPev ERob ESCh MAsh MCad
	NBea SCoo SLim WLRN WTre
N	'Jackmanii Superba' (J)	More than 30 suppliers
'James Mason' (P)	CMHG CPev CSPN EBee EHan
	ESCh ETho MCad NBea NTay
	SBra SCoo SPet WTre
§	'Jan Paweł II' (J)	CMHG CMac CWSG EBee EBre
	ECtt ELan EPfP ESCh ETho GKir
	LRHS MCad NBea NTay SBra SLim
	SPar SPer SPet WTre WWeb
Jānis Rupléns no. 1	ERob
§	*japonica*	CPev CSPN ERob ESCh NBrk
	NHaw NTay SBra WTre
– B&SWJ 5017	WCru
'Jasper'	ERob ESCh WTre
'Jennifer Valentine'	MCad
'Jenny Caddick' (Vt)	CFRD CSPN ERob ESCh ETho
	MCad NHaw NTay WTre

'Jim Hollis' (Fl) ERob ESCh MAsh WTre
'Joan Baker' (Vt) ERob
'Joan Gray' (d) ERob ESCh
'Joan Picton' (P) CWSG EBee ESCh MAsh NBea
  NBrk NRib NTay SBra WTre
'John Gould Veitch' (Fl) ERob ESCh
'John Gudmundsson' (L) ERob ESCh
'John Huxtable' (J) CDoC CPev CRHN EBee EPfP
  ♀ H4 ERob ESCh ETho LRHS MCad
  NBea NBrk NHaw NTay SBra SDix
  SLim WGor WTre WWeb
John Paul II see C. 'Jan Pawel II'
'John Treasure' WTre
'John Warren' (L) CWSG EBee ERob ESCh ETho
  EWTr LRHS MCad NBea NTay
  SBod SBra SCoo SLim SPer WTre
'Jorma' (J) ERob
Josephine = COtt CSPN EHan ENot EOrc ESCh
  'Evijohill'PBR ♀ H4 ETho GKir LAst LRHS MAsh MBNS
  MCad NPri NTay SBra SCoo SPer WWeb
§ x *jouiniana* EBee ERob ESCh GBuc MAsh MBlu
  MCad MWya NHol SPer WGwG
  WSHC WTre
- 'Chance' ESCh
- 'Côte d'Azur' (H) EBee EHan EOrc ERob ESCh GCal
  MAvo MCad MTed NBrk NLar WTre
- 'Praecox' ♀ H4 More than 30 suppliers
'Jubileinyi 70' ERob ESCh MWgw
'June Pyne' **new** ESCh ETho LRHS NPri
'Juuli' (I) ERob ESCh ETho NBrk
'Kaaru' (Vt) CFRD CSPN ERob ESCh ETho WTre
'Kacper' (L) CFRD CSPN ESCh ETho MCad
  NBrk NTay WTre
'Kaiu' (T x Vt) ERob ESCh
§ 'Kakio' (P) CDoC CElw CFRD EBee ERob
  ESCh ETho GKir LAst MAsh MCad
  MGos NBea NBlu NTay SBra SLim
  SPer SPet WLRN WTre WWeb
'Kalina' (P) ERob ESCh NBrk NHaw
'Kamilla' ERob ESCh
'Kardynal Wyszynski' (J) CFRD CRHN EBee ERob ESCh ETho
  MAsh MCad MGos NBea NBlu NBrk
  NTay SBra SCoo SLim WTre
'Kasmu' (Vt) ERob ESCh WTre
'Kasugayama' (L) ERob MCad WTre
'Katharina' ERob ESCh
'Katherine' MCad
'Kathleen Dunford' (Fl) CFRD EBee EHan ERob ESCh LAst
  LRHS MAsh MCad NBea NHaw
  NTay SCoo SLim SPet WTre WWeb
'Kathleen Wheeler' (P) CPev EBee ERob ESCh ETho MAsh
  MCad NBea NTay SCoo SDix SLim
  WTre
'Keith Richardson' (P) CPev ERob ESCh MAsh MCad
  NBea NBrk NTay WTre
'Ken Donson' (L) ♀ H4 CElw CFRD CSam EBee EPfP ERob
  ESCh ETho MCad NBrk NTay SBod
  SPet
'Kermesina' (Vt) ♀ H4 More than 30 suppliers
'Ketu' ERob
'Kiev' (Vt) ERob
'King Edward VII' (L) EBee EPfP ERob ESCh ETho LRHS
  NBea NBrk NTay SBra WGor WStI
  WTre WWeb
'King George V' (L) ERob ESCh NBrk
'Kinokawa' (P) ERob
'Kiri Te Kanawa' CPev CSPN EHan EPfP ERob ESCh
  ETho LAst MAsh MCad NBea NBrk
  NHaw NTay SBra SCoo SLim WTre
kirilovii ERob
'Kirimäe' (P) ERob ESCh
'Kjell' ERob ESCh
'Klaara' (P) ERob

'Kommerei' (Vt) ERob ETho WTre
'Königskind' (P) CFRD CSPN ERob ESCh ETho
  MCad NBrk NTay WTre
'Königskind Rosa' (P) ERob ESCh WTre
koreana ERob MAsh NBea NHol WTre
- 'Brunette' see C. 'Brunette'
- *citra* see C. 'Citra'
- f. *lutea* CElw CFRD EHyt ESCh MCad NBrk
- 'Shiva' see *Clematis* 'Shiva'
- 'Simplicity' see *Clematis* 'Simplicity'
'Kosmiczeskaja CSPN ERob ESCh NBrk NTay
  Melodija' (J)
'Kotkas' (J/L) ERob
'Kuba' (P) ERob NBrk
'Küllus' ERob ESCh ETho NTay
ladakhiana (Ta) CFRD CPev CSPN EBee EPfP
  ESCh ETho GQui MCad NBea
  NBir NHaw NTay SBra WCru
'Lady Betty Balfour' CFRD CPev CSPN CWSG EBee
  (J/Vt) EBre ERob ESCh ETho GKir LRHS
  MBNS MBri MCad MHdf NTay
  SBra SDix SLim SPar SPet WFar
  WTre WWal WWeb
'Lady Caroline Nevill' (L) CPev CRHN EBee ERob ESCh
  ETho MCad NBea NTay WTre
'Lady Katherine' (d) ERob
'Lady Londesborough' CFRD CPev ELan ERob ESCh ETho
  (P) LRHS MAsh MCad NBea NBrk
  NHaw NTay SDix SLim WLRN WTre
'Lady Northcliffe' (L) CPev CSPN CTri CWSG EHan
  EPfP ERob ESCh ETho ISea LRHS
  MAsh MCad NBea NTay SBra SDix
  SLim WTre
'Ladybird Johnson' (T) CFRD CPev EBee ERob ESCh
  ETho GMac MCad NBrk NTay
  SBra SLim WSHC WTre
'Lanuginosa Candida' (L) ESCh MCad WTre
lasiandra ERob NHaw
- B&SWJ 6775 WCru
- white ERob
lasiantha EHyt ESCh
'Last Dance' (Ta) ERob ESCh
'Lasting Love' **new** ESCh
'Lasurstern' (P) ♀ H4 More than 30 suppliers
'Laura' (L) ERob ESCh MCad NBrk NHaw WTre
'Laura Denny' (P) ESCh MCad NBrk
'Lavender Lace' ERob ESCh MAsh MCad
'Lawsoniana' (L) CElw CFRD CWSG EBee ESCh
  LAst MAsh MBar MCad NBea
  NBlu NBrk NTay SLim SPet WTre
'Lemon Chiffon' (P) CSPN EBee ERob ESCh ETho
  MCad NBea NBrk NTay SBra SLim
Liberation = 'Evifive'PBR EBee ERob ESCh ETho LAst LRHS
  MAsh NTay SBra SCoo SLim WTre
  WWeb
§ *ligusticifolia* ERob ESCh GSki NHaw
'Liisu' (J) ESCh
'Lilacina Floribunda' (L) CBcs CFRD EBee ESCh LRHS
  MBNS MBar MCad NBea NBrk
  NHaw NTay SBra SLim WTre
'Lilactime' (P) ERob ESCh NBea
'Lincoln Star' (P) CPev CRHN EBee EBre EHan EPfP
  ERob ESCh GKir LAst LRHS MBar
  MCad NBea NBrk NPri NTay SBra
  SDix SLim SPer SPet WTre WWeb
'Lincolnshire Lady' (A) NTay
'Little Bas' CSPN ERob ESCh NBrk
'Little Butterfly' (Vt) **new** ERob ESCh
'Little Nell' (Vt) CElw CPev CRHN CSPN EBee
  EBre ELan EOrc ERob ESCh ETho
  GKir LRHS MCad NBea NBrk
  NHol NTay SBod SBra SDix SLim
  SPer SPet WSHC WTre WWeb

'Lord Herschell'	CElw CPev ERob ESCh ETho	
'Lord Nevill' (P)	CMHG CPev CRHN CWSG EBre	
	ERob ESCh ETho LRHS MAsh MCad	
	NBea NBlu NTay SBra SDix WTre	
'Louise Rowe' (Fl)	CFRD EBee EBre ELan ERob ESCh	
	ETho LRHS MAsh MCad MGos	
	NBea NTay SBra SLim SPet WTre	
	WWeb	
loureiriana	WCru	
HWJ 663 **new**		
'Love Jewelry' **new**	ETho	
'Lucey' (J)	ESCh NBrk NTay	
'Lucie' (P)	MCad NBea WTre	
'Lunar Lass' (Fo)	CRez EBee ECho EHyt EPfP ESCh	
	ETho GGar ITim LBee NHar NSla	
	WAbe WPGP WTre	
'Lunar Lass' x	ECou EPot	
foetida (Fo)		
I 'Lunar Lass Variegata'	ECho	
(Fo/v)		
'Luther Burbank' (J)	CFRD ERob ESCh ETho MCad	
	NBea NTay WTre	
'Macrantha'	ERob	
macropetala (A/d)	More than 30 suppliers	
- 'Alborosea' (A/d)	EBee ERob ESCh GMac NTay	
- 'Ballerina' (A/d)	MCad	
- 'Ballet Skirt' (A/d)	ERob ESCh ETho LBuc LRHS	
	MCad MGos NHaw SLim WTre	
- 'Blue Lagoon'	see *C. macropetala* 'Lagoon'	
§ - 'Chili' (A)	ERob NBrk NTay	
- 'Floralia'	see *C.* 'Floralia'	
- 'Harry Smith'	see *C. macropetala* 'Chili'	
§ - 'Jan Lindmark' (A/d)	EBee EOrc ERob ESCh ETho LRHS	
	MAsh MCad MGos NBea NBir	
	NHol NSti NTay SBra SLim WCru	
	WTre WWeb	
§ - 'Lagoon' (A/d) ♀ H4	CSPN ERob ETho LRHS MAsh	
	NBea NBrk NSti SBra SCoo SLim	
	SMur WCru WTre	
- 'Maidwell Hall'	CDoC CSPN CWSG EBcc EBre	
hort. (A/d)	EPfP ERob ESCh ETho EWTr	
	LRHS MCad MGos NBea NBrk	
	NHol SBra SHBN SPer WCru	
	WPGP WSHC WTel WTre	
- 'Markham's Pink'	More than 30 suppliers	
(A/d) ♀ H4		
- 'Pauline' (A/d)	CWSG EBee ERob ESCh ETho	
	LRHS MBri NBea NBrk NTay SBra	
	SLim WTMC WTre	
- 'Pearl Rose' (A/d)	CWSG ERob ESCh	
- 'Purple Spider' (A/d)	CBcs CElw CFRD CSPN EBee	
	EOrc ERob ESCh ETho GKir LBuc	
	NBea NTay SBra SLim SPet WTre	
- 'Snowbird' (A/d)	CPev CSPN ERob ESCh MAsh	
	MWgw NHol SBra WTre	
- 'Wesselton' (A/d)	CSPN ERob ESCh ETho MAsh MCad	
	NBrk NHaw NHol NTay WTre	
- 'White Lady' (A/d)	EPfP ERob ESCh GKir NTay SBra	
	SDix WTre	
- 'White Moth'	see *C. alpina* subsp. *sibirica*	
	'White Moth'	
- 'White Swan'	see *C.* 'White Swan'	
- 'White Wings' (A/d)	CBcs ERob ESCh ETho LAst	
'Madame Baron	CFRD CMHG CPev EBee EBre	
Veillard' (J)	ECtt ESCh LAst LRHS MAsh MBar	
	MCad MWgw NBrk NTay SBra	
	SDix SLim SRPl WTre WWeb	
'Madame Edouard	CDoC CPev CRHN CSPN EBee	
André' (J)	EPfP ERob ESCh ETho LRHS MCad	
	NBea NTay SBra SDix SLim WTre	
'Madame Grangé'	CPev CRHN CSPN EBee EPfP ESCh	
(J) ♀ H4	ETho LRHS MCad NBea NBrk NHaw	
	NTay SBra SDix SLim SPet WTre	

'Madame Julia Correvon'	More than 30 suppliers	
(Vt) ♀ H4		
'Madame le Coultre'	see *C.* 'Marie Boisselot'	
'Madame van Houtte' (L)	ERob ESCh MCad	
'Magnus Johnson' (A)	ERob	
'Majojo' (Fo)	CStu ESCh WTre	
'Mammut' (P)	ERob ESCh	
§ *mandschurica*	EBee ERob ETho GCal GSki NLar	
	SBra	
- B&SWJ 1060	WCru	
marata (Fo)	GCrs WCot	
'Marcel Moser' (P)	CPev ERob ESCh MAsh MCad	
	NBrk NTay SDix	
'Margaret Hunt' (J)	CMHG CSPN EBee ELan ERob ESCh	
	ETho LRHS MAsh MCad NBea NBrk	
	NHaw NTay SBra SPla WTre	
'Margaret Wood' (P)	ERob ESCh MCad NTay	
'Margot Koster' (Vt)	CDoC CElw CFRD CRHN CSam	
	EBee EBre EPfP ESCh ETho LRHS	
	MAsh MBri MCad NBea NHaw	
	NTay SBra SLim SPet WSHC WTre	
§ 'Marie Boisselot'	More than 30 suppliers	
(L) ♀ H4		
'Marie Louise Jensen' (J)	ESCh MCad NTay SBra WTre	
marmoraria	CPBP EHyt ESCh GBin GCrs ITim	
(Fo) ♀ H2-3	LHop LRHS NHar NSla SBla SIng	
	WAbe WFar	
- hybrid (Fo)	ITim LBee NHar	
- x *cartmanii* hort.	MGos NHar	
'Joe' (Fo)		
- x *petriei* (Fo/f)	ITim	
'Marmori'	ERob ESCh ETho	
'Mary Claire' (d)	ERob ESCh	
§ 'Maskarad' (Vt)	CSPN EBee EBre ERob ESCh NBrk	
	SBra WLRN WTre WWeb	
'Masquarade' (Vt)	see *C.* 'Maskarad' (Vt)	
'Masquerade' (P)	ETho LRHS MBri NTay SCoo SMur	
'Matka Siedliska' (Fl)	CFRD CSPN ERob ESCh ETho NTay	
§ 'Matka Teresa'	ERob MCad	
'Matka Urszula	ERob ETho	
Ledóchowska' (P)		
'Maureen' (L)	CPev CSPN CWSG ESCh ETho	
	MAsh MCad NBea	
mauritiana	ERob	
maximowicziana	see *C. terniflora*	
'Meeli' (J)	MCad NBrk	
'Meloodia' (J)	WTre	
'Memm' (A/d)	ERob	
'Mercury' **new**	NHaw	
'Mia' (P/d)	ERob	
'Michelle' (I)	ERob	
microphylla	ECou MCad	
'Miikla' (J)	ERob	
'Mikelite' (P)	ERob ESCh ETho	
'Miniseelik' (J)	CFRD ERob ESCh NBrk	
'Minister' (P)	CFRD ESCh ETho MCad NBrk	
'Minuet' (Vt) ♀ H4	CElw CHad CRHN CSPN EBee	
	EBrc EPfP ERob ESCh ETho GKir	
	LRHS MCad NBea NHol NTay	
	SBra SLim SPer SPla WSHC WTel	
	WTre WWeb	
'Miriam Markham' (J)	CPev ERob ESCh MCad NBea	
	NBrk NHaw SBra WTre	
'Miss Bateman' (P) ♀ H4	More than 30 suppliers	
'Miss Crawshay' (P)	CPev EBee ERob ESCh MCad	
	NBea NHaw NTay SLim WTre	
N *montana*	CBcs CPev CSBt EBee ECtt FNot	
	ESCh EWTr GKir MBar MCad	
	MGos MWat NBea NBlu NEgg	
	NHol SBod SBra SDix SHBN SLim	
	SPet SSta WFar WGwG WTre WWeb	
- B&SWJ 6930	WCru	
- *alba*	see *C. montana*	

- 'Alexander'	CDoC CPou CWSG EBee ERob ESCh LRHS MBNS MCad MGos NTay SRPl WBrE WCru
- 'Brookfield Clove' **new**	ERob
- 'East Malling'	ERob ESCh
- 'Elten'	CSPN ERob ESCh
- 'Fragrant Spring'	CSPN EBee ECtt ERob ESCh ETho MCad MGos NBlu NHaw NTay SBra SLim WBcn WTre WWeb
- 'Gothenburg'	EPfP ERob ESCh NBea NTay SBra WTre
- f. **grandiflora** ♀ H4	More than 30 suppliers
§ - 'Hidcote'	ERob ESCh SBra WTre
- 'Jacqui' (d)	ERob ESCh ETho LRHS SBra SCoo SLim
- 'Jenny Keay' (d)	ERob ESCh LBuc SBra
- 'Lilacina'	ESCh MAsh SBra WPen WTre
- 'Mrs Margaret Jones' (d)	EBee ERob ESCh NBrk NTay SBra WTre
- 'New Dawn'	CSPN ERob ESCh MCad NBlu NTay SBra WTre
- 'Odorata'	CDoC EBee EPfP ERob ETho GSki MCad MGos NTay SCoo SLim WGor
* - 'Olga'	ERob ESCh
- 'Peveril'	CPev CSPN ERob ESCh ETho MCad NBrk SBra WTre
- 'Pleniflora' (d)	CFRD ESCh MCad MGos NHaw SBra WTre
- 'Rubens Superba'	see C. montana var. rubens 'Superba'
- var. **rubens**	More than 30 suppliers
- - 'Broughton Star' (d) ♀ H4	More than 30 suppliers
- - 'Continuity'	ERob ETho MCad NTay SBra SDix SLim SPla WSHC WTre
- - 'Elizabeth' ♀ H4	More than 30 suppliers
- - 'Freda' ♀ H4	More than 30 suppliers
- - 'Marjorie' (d)	More than 30 suppliers
- - 'Mayleen' ♀ H4	CElw CHad CPou CSBt CWSG EBee EBre ENot ERob ESCh ETho LRHS MBri MCad MGos NBea NBlu NPri NTay SAga SBra SHBN SLim SPar SPer SPet WFar WPen WTre WWeb
- - 'Odorata'	ESCh SLim WTre WWeb
- - 'Picton's Variety'	CDoC CPev CTri EBee EHan ERob ESCh ETho MAsh MBri MCad NBea NHaw NHol NTay SBra SHBN SRms WTre
- - 'Pink Perfection'	CDoC CElw CWSG EBee EBre ECtt ELan EPfP ERob ESCh LAst LRHS MCad NBea NBlu NBrk NHol NTay SBra SLim SPer SPet WFar WGwG WStI WTre WWeb
§ - - 'Superba'	CMHG CWSG EBee ECtt ESCh GKir SHBN SLim SPar
- - 'Tetrarose' ♀ H4	More than 30 suppliers
- - 'Vera'	CFRD CSPN EBee ERob ESCh ETho LRHS MCad NBea NBir NBrk NTay SBra SCoo SLim SPla WCru WStI WTre
- - 'Warwickshire Rose'	CElw CFRD CSPN CWSG ECtt EHan ERob ESCh ETho GKir MAsh MCad NBea NBrk NHaw NHol NPro NTay SBra WCot WPGP WPen WSHC WTre WWeb WWhi
§ - var. **sericea**	CBot CElw CFRD CPev CTri CWSG EBee ECtt ERob ESCh GKir LRHS MAsh MCad MWgw NBea NBrk NPro NTay SBra SLim SLon SRms WCru WFoF WWeb
- 'Spooneri'	see C. montana var. sericea
- 'Sunrise' (d) **new**	COtt CSPN EHan EOrc ESCh WWeb

- 'Unity'	ESCh
- 'Veitch's Form'	CBot
- var. **wilsonii**	CElw CFwr CPev CSPN CSam EBee EBre ECtt ELan EPfP ERob ESCh ETho EWTr GGar LAst LRHS MBar MCad MWat NBea NTay SBra SDix SPer WBod WBrE WTre
- - 'Hergest'	ESCh
'Monte Cassino' (J)	CFRD CSPN ERob ESCh ETho MAsh MCad NBrk NTay SPet WTre
'Moonbeam' (Fo)	CFRD EBre ECou EHyt EOrc EPot ESCh GEdr GKir ISea ITim MGos NBrk NSla NTay SBra SLon SMrm SPer WCot
§ 'Moonlight' (P)	CPev CSPN EBee ERob ESCh LAst MAsh MCad NBrk NTay SBra WTre
'Moonman' (Fo)	ETho SIng
Morning Cloud	see C. 'Yukikomachi'
Mother Theresa	see C. 'Matka Teresa'
'Mrs Bush' (L)	ERob ESCh LRHS MCad NBea WTre WWes
'Mrs Cholmondeley' (L) ♀ H4	More than 30 suppliers
'Mrs George Jackman' (P) ♀ H4	CPev CSPN EBee ERob ESCh ETho MAsh MBri MCad NBea NBlu NBrk NTay SBra SLim SPar SPla WStI WTre
'Mrs Hope' (L)	CPev ERob ESCh MCad NBea NBrk NTay SBra WTre
'Mrs James Mason'	CPev EBee ERob ESCh ETho MAsh MCad NBea NHaw NTay SBra SLim WTre
'Mrs N. Thompson' (P)	More than 30 suppliers
'Mrs P.B. Truax' (P)	CMHG EBee EHan ERob ESCh ETho LRHS MAsh MCad NBea NTay SBra SCoo SDix SLim WLRN WTre
'Mrs. P.T. James' **new**	ERob
'Mrs Robert Brydon'	CPen EBee EPfP ERob ETho GEil IPot MCad MUlv NBrk NHol NTay SCoo SLim WCot WTre
'Mrs Spencer Castle' (Vt)	CPev CSPN ERob ESCh MAsh MCad NBea NTay SBra WTre
'Mrs T. Lundell' (Vt)	CFRD CSPN ERob ESCh ETho MCad NBea NBrk NTay WTre
'Multi Blue'	More than 30 suppliers
'My Angel' PBR (Ta)	CSPN EBee ELan ENot ESCh MBri MCad MGos NHaw NPri NTay SPer WTre
'Myôjô' (P)	CSPN EBee ERob ESCh LRHS MCad SBra SLim WTre
'Myôkô' (L)	SLim
'Nadezhda' (P)	CFRD ERob ESCh ETho NTay
§ **napaulensis**	CBcs CFRD CPev CPlN CSPN EBee EOrc ERob ESCh LEur LRHS MCad NBea NTay SBra SLim WCru WLRN WSHC WTre
'Natacha' (P)	ERob ESCh NBea NBrk NHaw SBra SLim SPet WTre
'Negritjanka' (J)	CSPN ERob ESCh LBuc MBri NBrk NHaw NTay WTre
'Negus' (J)	ERob ESCh
'Nelly Moser' (L/P) ♀ H4	More than 30 suppliers
Nettleton seedlings	EPot
New Zealand hybrids (Fo)	ECou
'Nikolai Rubtsov'	CSPN ERob ESCh NTay WTre
'Niobe' (J) ♀ H4	More than 30 suppliers
'Norfolk Queen'	ESCh
'North Star'	see C. 'Põhjanael'
'Nuit de Chine'	ERob ESCh MCad NBrk
obscura	ERob
occidentalis var. **dissecta**	EHyt
ochotensis (A)	CSPN ERob SDys

	ochroleuca	CRDP
	'Odoriba' **new**	ETho
I	'Ola Howells' (A/d)	ERob ESCh
	'Olimpiada-80' (L)	ERob ESCh NTay
	'Opaline'	see *C.* 'Asagasumi'
	orientalis hort.	see *C. tibetana* subsp. *vernayi*
	orientalis L. (Ta)	EPfP ESCh GSki IMGH LRHS
		MCad NHol SBod SBra SReu
	- 'Bill MacKenzie'	see *C.* 'Bill MacKenzie'
	- 'Orange Peel'	see *C. tibetana* subsp. *vernayi*
		'Orange Peel'
	- var. *orientalis* (Ta)	CStr ERob ETho
*	- 'Rubromarginata' (Ta)	CPev
	- 'Sherriffii'	see *C. tibetana* subsp. *vernayi*
	- var. *tenuifolia* (Ta)	ERob ESCh
	- var. *tenuiloba*	see *C. columbiana* var. *tenuiloba*
	'Otto Fröbel' (L)	CSPN ERob ESCh ETho MCad
		NBrk NTay
	'Paala'	ERob
	'Paddington' (P)	ERob ETho
	'Pagoda' (PxVt) ♀ H4	CDoC CElw CFRD CPev CRHN
		EBee EHan EOrc EPfP ESCh ETho
		GMac LAst LRHS MAsh MBri
		MCad NBea NHol NPal NTay SBra
		SLim SPla SRms WSHC WTre
	'Päkapikk' (Vt)	ERob
	'Pamela'	CSPN ERob ESCh LBuc NTay WTre
	'Pamela Jackman'	see *C. alpina* 'Pamela Jackman'
	'Pamiat Serdtsa' (I)	ERob ESCh ETho NTay
	paniculata J.G. Gmel.	CPev CSPN EBee GGar LRHS SBra
		WPGP W3IIC
	paniculata Thunb.	see *C. terniflora*
	- var. *lobata*	MGrG WTre
	'Paola' (d)	ESCh MCad
	'Parasol'	CSPN ERob ESCh MAsh NBrk NTay
§	*parviflora*	ERob
	- x *forsteri*	ESCh WTre
	parviloba var.	WCru
	bartletii B&SWJ	
	6788 **new**	
	'Pastel Princess'	ERob ETho MCad NHaw NTay
	'Pat Coleman' (P)	ESCh ETho
	patens	NBea
	- from China	ERob ESCh
	- from Japan	ERob ESCh
	- 'Nagoya' **new**	ESCh
	Patricia Ann Fretwell	CPev CSPN ERob LRHS MAsh
	= 'Pafar' PBR	MCad NBea
§	'Paul Farges' ♀ H4	CBcs CFRD CSPN EBee EOrc
		ERob ETho MAsh MBlu MBri
		MCad NBrk NHol NSti NTay SBra
		SLim WTel WTre
	'Pendragon'	ERob ESCh
	'Pennell's Purity' (L)	ERob ESCh ETho MCad
	'Percy Picton' (P)	MAsh
	'Perle d'Azur' (J)	More than 30 suppliers
	'Perrin's Pride' (Vt)	CFRD EBee ERob ESCh LRHS MCad
		NBrk NTay SBra SCoo WTre WWeb
	'Peter Pan' (P)	ERob
	peterae	ERob
	- var. *trichocarpa*	ERob
	Petit Faucon =	CElw EBee EBre ECtt EHan ENot
	'Evisix' PBR ♀ H4	EPfP ERob ETho GMac LAst LRHS
		MAsh MBNS MBri MCad NBea NPri
		NTay SBra SLim SPer SRkn WPGP
		WTre WWeb
	petriei (Fo)	EBee ECou EMan ETow LPio NHar
	- 'Princess' (Fo/f)	ECou
	- 'Steepdown' (F)	ECou
	- x *foetida* (Fo)	ECou
	'Peveril Peach'	CPev ESCh
	'Peveril Pearl' (P)	CPev ERob ESCh ETho MCad
		NTay WWeb

	'Peveril Pendant'	CPev
I	'Phoenix' (P)	ESCh
	pierotii	ERob
	'Piilu' (P)	CFRD CSPN EHan ELan ERob ESCh
		ETho LBuc LRHS MCad NBrk
		NHaw NPri NTay SBra SCoo SLim
		WTre
	'Pink Champagne'	see *C.* 'Kakio'
	'Pink Fantasy' (J)	CFRD CPev CRHN CSPN CTri
		CWSG EBee EBre ERob ESCh ETho
		LRHS MAsh MBar MCad NBea
		NBrk NTay SBra SLim SPar WTre
		WWeb
	'Pink Pearl' (P)	ESCh MCad NBrk
	'Pirko' (Vt)	ERob ESCh
	Pistachio =	COtt CSPN EHan EOrc ESCh ETho
	'Evirida' PBR (Fl)	LBuc MBNS NTay SLim WWhi
§	*pitcheri*	CPev CPIN ERob ESCh NBrk NTay
	'Pixie'	see *C.* (County Park Group) 'Pixie'
	'Põhjanael' (J)	CSPN CWSG EBee ERob ESCh
		MCad NBea NBrk SCoo SLim WTre
		ESCh
	'Pointy' (A) **new**	ESCh
	'Polish Spirit' (Vt) ♀ H4	More than 30 suppliers
§	*potaninii*	CCge CRHN CSPN ELan GIBF
		MCad MWhi WSHC WTMC
§	- var. *potaninii*	CPev EHyt EPfP ERob MCad NBea
		NTay SDix WTre
	- var. *souliei*	see *C. potaninii* var. *potaninii*
	- 'Summer Snow'	see *C.* 'Paul Farges'
	'Prairie River' (A)	ERob WTre
	'Pribaltika' (J)	ERob WTre
	'Primrose Star' (d)	CDoC COtt CSPN EHan EOrc ERob
		ESCh ETho LAst LBuc LRHS MCad
		NBrk SBra SCoo SPer WTre WWeb
	'Prince Charles' (J) ♀ H1	CElw CHad CPou CRHN CSPN
		CTri EBee EBre ELan EPfP ESCh
		ETho LRHS MCad NBea NBir
		NTay SBra SDix SLim SPar SPer
		SPet WSHC WTre WWeb
	'Prince Philip' (P)	ERob ESCh NBrk NTay SBra
§	'Princess Diana' (T) ♀ H4	CBcs CElw CFRD CHad CPev CRHN
		CSPN CWSG EBee EHan ELan ERob
		ESCh ETho LBuc MBlu MCad MGos
		MWat NBea NBrk NHaw NPri NTay
		SBra SLim SPet SRkn WTre WWeb
§	'Princess of Wales' (L)	EPfP ERob LRHS MAsh MBNS
		MCad SBra WSHC WTre
	'Prins Hendrik' (L/P)	ERob ESCh MCad WGor WTre
	'Propertius' (A)	CFRD ERob ESCh ETho NBrk
	'Protcus' (Fl)	CPev CSPN EBee EBre EHan ELan
		EPfP ESCh ETho GKir LAst LRHS
		MBNS MCad NBea NTay SBra
		SDix SLim SPer SPet WTre WWeb
§	'Pruinina' (A)	CSPN ERob NTay WTre
	'Pulmapäev' (L)	ERob ESCh
	'Purple Haze'	CRHN
	quadribracteolata	ECou
	- 'Nancy's Lookout'	ECou
	'Queen Alexandra' (P)	ERob ESCh MCad
	'Radostj' (J)	ERob
	'Ragamuffin' (d)	EBee ENot ERob ESCh
	'Rahvarinne'	ERob ESCh
	'Ramona'	see *C.* 'Hybrida Sieboldii'
	ranunculoides	WCru
	CD&R 2345	
	recta	CFRD CFee CHad CPev CSPN
		EChP ECtt EPfP ERob ETho GKir
		GSki LRHS MBro MCad MLLN
		MNrw MWhi NBea NLar NWCA
		SPer WHil WPer WTre WWye
	- 'Grandiflora'	GKir
	- 'Peveril'	CFRD CPev ERob ESCh ETho
		GDea NBrk WTre

	- 'Purpurea'	More than 30 suppliers
§	- subsp. *recta* var. *lasiosepala*	CSPN ERob
*	- 'Velvet Night'	CSpe EBee EChP EMan ERob ESCh ETho LAst LHop MBri MLLN MTis NHol SMrm WCom WCot WSHC WTre
	'Red Ballon' (Ta)	ERob ESCh LBuc
	'Red Cooler'	ERob ESCh NBrk NHaw
	'Red Pearl' (P)	ERob ESCh ETho
§	*rehderiana* ♀ H4	More than 30 suppliers
	- CC 3601	CPLG
	'Reiman' (L/J)	ERob
	reticulata	ERob
	'Rhapsody' (P) ♀ H4	CFRD CPev CSPN EBee EPfP ERob ETho LRHS MAsh MBri MCad NBrk NHaw NTay SBra SCoo WBar WTre WWeb
	'Richard Pennell' (P) ♀ H4	CPev EBee EHan ERob ESCh ETho LRHS MAsh MBri MCad NBea NBrk NPri NTay SBra SCoo SDix SLim WTre
	'Ristimägi' (J)	ERob
	'Rodomax' (A)	ERob ESCh
	'Roko' (J)	ERob
	'Roko-Kolla' (J)	CSPN ERob ESCh ETho NBea NBrk SBra WWes
	'Romantika' (J)	CFRD CSPN EBee EHan ELan ERob ESCh ETho MAsh NBea NHaw NTay SBra SLim SPer WTre
	'Roogoja' (L)	ERob ESCh
	'Rooguchi' (I)	CFRD ERob ESCh ETho LRHS NBrk
	'Rose Supreme'	MCad
	'Rosy O'Grady' (A) ♀ H4	EBee ELan EOrc ESCh MAsh MBar MCad MGos NBea NHol NSti SLim SPer WTre WWeb
	'Rouge Cardinal' (J)	More than 30 suppliers
	'Royal Velours' (Vt) ♀ H4	CDoC CElw CHad CPev CRHN CSPN EBee EBre ELan EPfP ERob ESCh ETho GKir LRHS MCad MWgw NBea NHol NSti SBra SDix SHBN SLim SPer SPet WFar WTre
	Royal Velvet = 'Evifour' PBR	CSPN EBee ESCh ETho LAst MBri MCad NTay SBra SCoo SLim WTre WWeb
	'Royalty' (LxP) ♀ H4	CElw CFRD CSPN EBee EBre ELan EPfP ERob ESCh LRHS MAsh MCad NBea NBir NPri NTay SBra SDix SLim SPer SPet WTre WWeb
	'Ruby Glow' (L)	EBee EPfP ERob ESCh MCad NTay SCoo WLRN WTre WWeb
	'Rüütel' (J)	CFRD ERob ESCh ETho MCad NBrk NHaw NTay SBra SCoo SLim WTre
	'Saalomon' (J)	ERob
	'Sakala' (P)	ERob ESCh
	'Sally Cadge' (P)	ERob ESCh MAsh MCad
	'Samantha Denny' (P)	CSPN ERob ESCh NBrk NHaw NRib NTay WTre
	'Sander' (H)	CSPN ERob ESCh ETho WTre
	'Sandra Denny' **new**	ESCh
	'Satsukibare' (P)	ERob ESCh MCad NBrk WTre
I	'Saturn' (Vt)	ECle ERob ESCh MCad NBea SPla WTre
	'Saturn' (P)	SCoo
	'Scartho Gem' (P)	CPev EBee EPfP ERob ESCh MCad NBea NPri NTay SCoo WTre WWeb
	'Schneeglanz' (P)	MCad
	'Sealand Gem' (L)	CFRD CPev EBee ERob ESCh ETho LAst MAsh MCad NBea NBlu NHaw NTay SBra SCoo SLim WTre WWeb
	'Semu' (J)	CSPN ERob ESCh ETho
	'Serenata' (J)	ERob MCad NBea NTay
	serratifolia (Ta)	CElw CFRD CPev EHyt ERob
	'Sheila Thacker' (P)	ESCh ETho MCad MLLN MWhi NTay SDix WTre
	'Sherriffii' (Ta)	ERob ESCh
	'Shirakihane'	NBrk
	'Shirayukihime' (L)	CSPN ESCh
§	'Shiva'	ERob MAsh
	'Shorty' (Ta)	ERob ESCh
	'Sho-un' (L)	EBee EHan ERob ESCh ETho NTay SBra
	'Shropshire Blue'	ERob WTre
	'Sialia' (A/d)	ERob ESCh NTay
	sibirica	see *C. alpina* subsp. *sibirica*
	'Signe' (Vt)	ERob ESCh ETho MCad WTre
	'Siirus' (L)	ERob
	'Silmakivi' (L/J)	ERob ESCh
	'Silver Lining'	MCad
	'Silver Moon' (L)	CSPN EBee EHan ERob ESCh ETho MAsh MCad NBea NTay SBra WTre WWeb
§	'Simplicity'	CSPN ERob ESCh MAsh WWeb
	simsii Britt. & A. Br.	see *C. pitcheri*
	simsii Sweet	see *C. crispa*
	'Sinee Plamia' (J)	ERob ESCh NHaw
§	'Sinij Dozhdj' (D)	CSPN ERob ESCh LBuc MBri NBrk WTre
	'Sir Garnet Wolseley' (P)	ERob ESCh MAsh NBrk NTay SDix WTre
	'Sir Trevor Lawrence' (T)	CFRD CPev CSPN EBee EBre ERob ESCh ETho LAst LRHS MAsh MCad NBea NHaw NHol NPal NSti NTay SBra SDix SLim SPer WPGP WTre
	'Sizaia Ptitsa' (I) **new**	ERob
	'Snow Queen' (P)	CElw CFRD CSPN EBee EBre EHan EPfP ESCh ETho LRHS MBri MCad NBea NTay SBra SPet WTel WTre WWeb
	'Snowdrift'	see *C.* 'Paul Farges', *C. armandii* 'Snowdrift'
§	'Södertälje' (Vt)	CFRD CRHN EBee EBre ERob ESCh ETho MCad NBea NTay SBra WLRN WSHC WTre
	'Solveig' (P)	ERob
	songarica	ESCh LRHS MAsh MCad NBrk NHol NTay SBra WHil WSHC
	- var. *songarica*	ERob
	- 'Sundance'	CSPN ERob ESCh WTre
	'Souvenir de J.L. Delbard' (P)	ERob ESCh NBrk NTay SBra
§	'Souvenir du Capitaine Thuilleaux' (P)	CPev EBee ESCh GKir LAst MAsh MCad MGos NBea NBlu NTay SBra SLim SPer WTre WWeb
	'Special Occasion' (P)	CSPN EBee ERob ESCh ETho LBuc MBNS NBea NHaw NPri NTay SBra SCoo SLim WTre
	spooneri	see *C. montana* var. *sericea*
	- 'Rosea'	see *C.* x *vedrariensis* 'Rosea'
	'Sputnik' (J)	CSPN ERob ESCh NBrk NTay
	stans	CHea CMdw CPou EOrc EPfP ERob ESCh ETho GSki IFro ITer LRHS MWhi NLar SIng WTre
	- 'Rusalka'	ERob
	'Star Fish' (L)	ERob ESCh NHaw
	'Star of India' (P/J)	CFRD CPev EBee EBre EPfP ERob ESCh ETho LRHS MCad NBea NTay SBra SDix SLim SPer WTre WWeb
	'Stasik' (J)	ERob ESCh
	'Strawberry Roan' (P)	ESCh NTay
	Sugar Candy = 'Evione' PBR (P)	EBee EBre EMil ERob ESCh LAst MBri NPri NTay SBra SLim WTre WWeb WWes
	Summer Snow	see *C.* 'Paul Farges'
	'Sunset' (J) ♀ H4	EBee EHan EOrc ERob ESCh ETho

	LRHS MAsh MBri MCad NBea NPri NTay SBra SMur WLRN WTre WWeb
'Susan Allsop' (L)	CPev ERob ESCh WTre
'Sylvia Denny' (Fl)	CWSG EBee EBre ELan ERob ESCh ETho GKir LAst LRHS MAsh MBar MCad NBea NBrk NRib NTay SBra SLim SPer WTre WWeb
'Sympathia' (L)	ERob ESCh MCad NHaw NTay SGar WTre
'Syrena' (J)	ESCh NHaw
* *szuyuanensis* B&SWJ 6791	WCru
§ 'Tage Lundell' (A)	CElw CFRD CRHN CSPN ERob ETho GDea MAsh MCad NBea NBrk NTay SPet WCru WTre
'Tango' (T)	CElw CFRD CRHN ERob ESCh MCad NBrk NTay SBra SPet WTre
tangutica	More than 30 suppliers
- SDR 1848	GKev
- 'Aureolin'	see *C.* 'Aureolin'
- 'Bill MacKenzie'	see *C.* 'Bill MacKenzie'
- 'Gravetye Variety'	ERob ESCh MWgw WTre
- 'Lambton Park' ♀ H4	EBee EPfP ERob ESCh ETho LRHS MCad NBea NBrk NTay WTre WWpP
- 'Radar Love'	GMaP WGwG
'Tartu' (L)	CSPN ERob ESCh
tashiroi	ERob ESCh
- B&SWJ 1423	WCru
'Tateshina' (P)	MCad
'Teksa' (J)	ERob ESCh
'Tentel' (J)	ERob
tenuiloba	see *C. columbiana* var. *tenuiloba*
§ *terniflora*	CFRD CPev CPIN EBee EHol EPfP ESCh ETho LRHS MAsh MCad NBea NBrk NHaw NSti NTay SBra SLim SPer WCru
- var. *mandshurica*	see *C. mandshurica*
- var. *robusta*	see *C. terniflora* var. *terniflora*
§ - var. *terniflora*	ERob ESCh
'Teruko' **new**	ERob
'Teshio' (Fl)	CSPN ERob ESCh ETho LBuc MCad NBrk NHaw SBra SLim WTre
texensis	ETho MAsh MCad SPar
- 'Red Five'	CPev
- 'The Princess of Wales'	see *C.* 'Princess Diana'
'The Bride' (J)	CSPN EBee ERob ESCh ETho LBuc MCad NBea NBrk NHaw NTay SBra SLim WTre
'The Comet'	ERob
'The First Lady'	CSPN ERob ESCh ETho LBuc MCad NTay SLim WTre
'The President' (P) ♀ H4	More than 30 suppliers
'The Princess of Wales' (L)	see *C.* 'Princess of Wales' (L)
'The Princess of Wales' (T)	see *C.* 'Princess Diana' (T)
'The Vagabond' (P)	CFRD CSPN CWSG EBee ELan ERob ETho MCad NBea NBrk NHaw NTay SBra WLRN WTre
'The Velvet' **new**	ERob
'Theydon Belle' **new**	ESCh
thunbergii hort.	see *C. terniflora*
'Thyrislund'	CSPN ESCh
Tibetan mix	CSPN ERob ESCh MAsh
§ *tibetana*	CPev ETho MBar MCad MNrw NHaw NTay SCoo SLim SPer SSpi WSHC
- SDR 1737	GKev
§ - subsp. *vernayi*	CMHG EBee EHyt EPfP ERob GKir MCad MSte NLon NSti SBra SCoo SPer WCru WWin
- - CC&McK 193	NWCA
- - var. *laciniifolia*	ERob ESCh MAsh NHol WTre
- - LS&E 13342	see *C. tibetana* subsp. *vernayi* 'Orange Peel'
§ - - 'Orange Peel' LS&E 13342	CBcs CDoC CPev EBee EHan ENot EPfP ERob ESCh GKir LAst LBuc LRHS MCad NBrk NHol SBra SDix SGar SLim WTre
Timpany NZ hybrids	ITim
'Tinkerbell'	see *Clematis* 'Shiva'
'Titania' (PxL)	EPfP ERob ESCh NBrk
'Toki'	ETho
tongluensis HWJCM 076	WCru
'Treasure Trove'	CFRD CSPN ESCh LBuc MAsh SPer WTre
'Trianon' (P)	ERob NBrk
'Triiibu' **new**	ESCh
'Trikatrei' **new**	ESCh NBrk
'Trine' (Vt)	ERob
§ x *triternata* 'Rubromarginata' ♀ H4	More than 30 suppliers
'Tsuzuki' (P)	CSPN ERob ESCh ETho NBea NTay
tubulosa	CFRD CPev CPle CSPN ESCh ETho NHol
§ - Alan Bloom = 'Alblo' PBR (H)	EBre GKir LRHS
- 'Alba'	ERob
- 'Wyevale' (H) ♀ H4	More than 30 suppliers
'Tuczka' (J)	ERob
'Twilight' (J)	CSPN EBee ESCh ETho MAsh MCad NBea NTay SBra SCoo SLim WTre WWeb
'Ulrique' (P)	EBee ERob
uncinata B&SWJ 1893	CPev ERob SDix
	WCru
- var. *ovatifolia*	ERob
urophylla	ERob
'Valge Daam' (L)	ERob ESCh ETho MCad NHaw NTay SCoo SLim
'Vanessa' (J)	CRHN ERob ESCh ETho MAsh NBrk
'Vanilla Cream'	ECou
x *vedrariensis*	MCad NBrk
- 'Dovedale'	CPev ESCh
- 'Hidcote'	see *C. montana* 'Hidcote'
- 'Highdown'	ERob MCad NBrk SBra WTre
§ - 'Rosea'	CTrw ERob ESCh MCad NBrk
veitchiana	ERob
'Velutinea Purpurea' (J)	ERob
'Venosa Violacea' (Vt) ♀ H4	CElw CFRD CRHN CSPN EBee EHan ELan EOrc EPfP ERob ESCh ETho LAst LRHS MAsh MCad NBea NHol NPri NSti SBra SDix SPer SPet SPla WFar WSHC WTre WWeb
vernayi	see *C. tibetana* subsp. *vernayi*
'Veronica's Choice' (L)	CPev CRHN CSPN EBee EHan ELan EOrc ERob ESCh ETho LRHS MBri MCad MGos NBea NHaw NTay SBra WTre
versicolor	ERob ESCh
verticillaris	see *C. occidentalis*
'Vetke' (J)	ERob
N 'Victoria' (J) ♀ H4	CPev CSPN EBee EBre ERob ESCh ETho LAst LRHS MAsh MCad MWgw NBea NBlu NPri NTay SBra SDix SLim SPet WTre WWeb
'Ville de Lyon' (Vt)	More than 30 suppliers
Vino = 'Poulvo' PBR (J)	EBee ERob ESCh LRHS MAsh MBri MCad NBea NTay SBra SCoo WTre WWeb
I 'Viola' (J)	CFRD CSPN ECle ERob ESCh ETho MAsh MCad NBea NBrk NHaw NTay WBcn WTre

'Violet Charm' (L) — CWSG EBee ENot ERob ESCh ETho MAsh NBrk NTay SBra SCoo WTre
'Violet Elizabeth' (P) — ESCh MAsh MCad NBrk SBra WTre
'Violetta' (P) — ERob
viorna — CPIN EHyt ERob ESCh NBea WSHC
virginiana hort. — see *C. vitalba*
virginiana Hook. — see *C. ligusticifolia*
§ *vitalba* — CArn CPev ERob ESCh ETho EWTr MAsh MBar MCad MHer NHaw NTay WHer WTre
viticella ♀ H4 — CPev CWib ERob ESCh ETho EWTr MBNS MCad NBea NBlu NHaw SBra SDix WSHC WStI WTel WTre
 – 'Brocade' — CFRD CPev CSPN ETho
I – 'Danae' — ERob WTre
 – 'Mary Rose' (d) — CPev ERob ESCh ETho LAst MCad NBrk NHaw SBra WTre
 – 'Purpurea Plena Elegans' (d) ♀ H4 — More than 30 suppliers
 – 'Rosea' (Vt) — ERob
'Viticella Rubra' (Vt) — EWTr LBuc MAsh NBrk
Vivienne — see *C.* 'Beth Currie'
'Vivienne Lawson' — ERob ESCh MAsh NTay WTre
'Voluceau' (Vt) — CPou CRHN EBee ELan ERob ESCh LAst MCad NBea NTay SBra SLim SPer WStI WTre WWeb
'Vostok' (J) — ERob ESCh NBrk NTay
'Vyvyan Pennell' (Fl/P) — More than 30 suppliers
'W.E. Gladstone' (L) — CPev EBee ERob ESCh ETho EWTr GKir LRHS MAsh MCad NBea NTay SBra SDix WTre
'W.S. Callick' (P) — CFRD ERob ESCh MCad NTay WTre
'Wada's Primrose' (P) — More than 30 suppliers
'Walenburg' (Vt) — ERob ESCh NBrk SBra
'Walter Pennell' (Fl/P) — CPev CWSG EBee ESCh ETho MAsh MCad NBea NTay SBra SCoo SLim WGor WTre
'Warszawska Nike' (J) ♀ H4 — CElw CFRD CRHN EBee EHan ELan EPfP ERob ESCh ETho EWTr LAst MAsh MBri MCad MGos NBea NBlu NBrk NTay SBra SCoo SPer SPet WStI WTre WWeb
'Waterperry Star' (Ta) — ERob
'Western Virgin' — ERob ESCh NTay WTre
'Westerplatte' (P) — CSPN EHan ERob ESCh ETho LAst LBuc LRHS MAsh MCad NBea NBrk NHaw NTay SCoo WTre
§ 'White Swan' (A) — CSPN EBee EPfP ERob ESCh ETho LRHS MBri MCad MGos NBea NHol NPri NSti SLim SPer SPla WFoF WPGP WTre
'White Tokyo' (A) — MGos
'Wilhelmina Tull' (L) — CSPN ERob ESCh MAsh MCad NBrk WTre
'Will Goodwin' (L) ♀ H4 — CBcs EBee EBre ELan EPfP ERob ESCh ETho GMac LAst LRHS MAsh MBri MCad NBea NBrk NPri SBra SLim WStI WTre
'William Kennett' (L) — CMHG CPev CWSG EBee EHan ELan EPfP ESCh ETho LAst LRHS MAsh MBNS MBar MBri MCad MGos NBea NBlu NTay SBod SBra SDix SLim SPer SPet WTre WWeb
'Wolga' (P) — MCad
'Xerxes' — see *C.* 'Elsa Späth'
'Yatsuhashi' **new** — ERob
'Yellow Pinnochio' **new** — WWeb
'Yellow Queen' — see *C.* 'Moonlight'
'Yorkshire Pride' — ERob MCad
§ 'Yukikomachi' (LxJ) — CSPN ERob ESCh ETho MCad NBrk WTre
'Yuki-no-yosooi' **new** — ERob
'Yukiokoshi' (Fl) — ERob ESCh

yunnanensis — ERob
'Yvette Houry' (L) — ERob ESCh MCad NHaw NTay WTre
'Zingaro' (Vt) — ERob
'Zolotoi Jubilei' (J) — ERob ESCh

Clematopsis see *Clematis*

Clementsia see *Rhodiola*

Clerodendrum (Verbenaceae)

bungei — More than 30 suppliers
 – 'Herfstleu' — MGos
§ *chinense* var. *chinense* (d) ♀ H1 — ERea
 – 'Pleniflorum' — see *C. chinense* var. *chinense*
fragrans var. *pleniflorum* — see *C. chinense* var. *chinense*
mutabilis — WCru
 B&SWJ 6651 **new**
myricoides — CHll CKob CPlN CSpe ELan EPfP
 'Ugandense' ♀ H1 — ERea ESlt SOWG WMul
philippinum — see *C. chinense* var. *chinense*
x *speciosum* — CPIN SOWG
splendens ♀ H1 — SOWG
thomsoniae ♀ H1 — CPIN ELan LRHS MBri SOWG
trichotomum — More than 30 suppliers
 – 'Carnival' (v) — CFil ELan EPfP EWes GKir IArd LRHS MBri NLar SBrw SLim SMad SMur SPer SSta WCom
 – var. *fargesii* ♀ H4 — CAbb CBcs CBrm CDul CHEx CPMA CWSG EBee ELan EPfP EWTr GKir IArd LHop MBNS MBlu MGos MRav NPal SHBN SIgm SPer SRPl SSpi WBod WCot WEas WPat
 – 'Hopleys' (v) **new** — LHop
 – white calyx — WCru
 B&SWJ 4896 **new**

Clethra (Clethraceae)

B&SWJ 5416 **new** — WPGP
acuminata — EPfP NLar
alnifolia — CBcs CBrm CDul CEnd CMHG CPLG CSBt CTrG CWib EPfP EWTr GKir IDee MBar SBrw SMur SPer SRPl SRms SSpi WBod WCFE WDin WFar WPic WWin
 – 'Fingle Dwarf' — SReu SSta
 – 'Hummingbird' — CEnd EBee ELan EPfP GEil GKir LRHS MAsh MBlu SBrw SMur SSpi WFar
 – 'Paniculata' ♀ H4 — CDoC CFwr SMac SPoG
 – 'Pink Spire' — CBcs CDoC CFwr EBee EPfP EWTr MRav NBlu SBrw SCoo SMac WBor WDin WFar WLRN WOrn WStI
 – 'Rosea' — CBot CDul CTri GKir IMGH MBar MBlu MGos SHBN SPer WFar WSHC
* – 'Ruby Spice' — CEnd CMHG CPLG EBee EMil ENot EPfP GEil GKir IMGH LRHS MAsh MBlu MBri NBee SBrw SMur SPer SSpi WBVN WBcn
 – 'September Beauty' — NLar
arborea — CBcs CFil CHEx CMHG CPLG CPle
barbinervis ♀ H4 — CBcs CFai CMCN CPLG EPfP IDee IMGH MBlu NLar SBrw SPer WBVN WBod WDin WFar WSHC
delavayi — CDoC EPfP GGGa GQui
 – C&H 7067 — GGGa
fargesii — CPLG EPfP MGos
monostachya — GGGa
tomentosa — WWes
 – 'Cottondale' **new** — SSpi

Cleyera (Theaceae)

fortunei	see *C. japonica* 'Fortunei'
– 'Variegata'	see *C. japonica* 'Fortunei'
§ *japonica* 'Fortunei' (v)	CDoC CFil CHal CMac CWib SBrw WFar
– var. *japonica*	CFil EMil WPGP
– var. *wallichii*	CFil EBee WPGP

Clianthus (Papilionaceae)

maximus	ECou
§ *puniceus* ♀ H2	More than 30 suppliers
§ – 'Albus' ♀ H2	CBcs CBot CHEx CHll CPLG CTrw CWib EBee EMil ERea LAst LRHS MLan SBrw SDry SLon SOWG SPer SVen
– 'Flamingo'	see *C. puniceus* 'Roseus'
– 'Kaka King'	CBcs
– 'Red Admiral'	see *C. puniceus*
– 'Red Cardinal'	see *C. puniceus*
§ – 'Roseus'	CPLG EMil ERea LRHS MTPN SBrw SPer
– 'White Heron'	see *C. puniceus* 'Albus'

Clinopodium (Lamiaceae)

acinos	see *Acinos arvensis*
ascendens	see *Calamintha sylvatica* subsp. *ascendens*
calamintha	see *Calamintha nepeta*
georgianum new	SSpi
grandiflorum	see *Calamintha grandiflora*
§ *vulgare*	CArn CKln ECou GBar MGas MHer NMir NSco SIde WHer

Clintonia (Convallariaceae)

andrewsiana	CBro GDra GGGa LEur NMen SSpi WCru
borealis	CBro EBee SCnR WCru
udensis	WCru
umbellulata	EBee NLar WCru
uniflora	CBro GDra

Clitoria (Papilionaceae)

mariana	CPIN

Clivia ✿ (Amaryllidaceae)

caulescens	ERea
x *cyrtanthiflora*	ERea
gardenii	ERea
miniata ♀ H1	CBcs CHal LRHS MLan SMur SRms SYvo WCot
– 'Aurea' ♀ H1	CSpe
– var. *citrina* ♀ H1	ECho
– – 'New Dawn'	ERea
– hybrids	ERea LAma MBri NPal SEND
– 'Striata' (v)	ERea
nobilis ♀ H1	ERea IBlr

Clytostoma (Bignoniaceae)

§ *calystegioides*	CPIN CRHN ERea

Cneorum (Cneoraceae)

tricoccon	CKob SSpi

Cnicus (Asteraceae)

§ *benedictus*	CArn GPoy MHer MSal SIde WHer WWye

Cobaea (Cobaeaceae)

pringlei	ERea
scandens ♀ H3	CFox CPIN CSpe SGar SMur SPar WPen
– f. *alba* ♀ H3	SMur WPen

---

cobnut see *Corylus avellana*

Coccothrinax (Arecaceae)

crinita	LPal

Cocculus (Menispermaceae)

carolinus	CPIN
§ *orbiculatus*	EMon
– B&SWJ 535	WCru
trilobus	see *C. orbiculatus*

Cochlearia (Brassicaceae)

armoracia	see *Armoracia rusticana*
glastifolia	MSal
officinalis	MHer MSal WHer

Cocos (Arecaceae)

plumosa	see *Syagrus romanzoffiana*
weddelliana	see *Lytocaryum weddellianum*

Codiaeum ✿ (Euphorbiaceae)

variegatum var.	
pictum 'Excellent' (v)	LRHS
– – 'Petra' (v)	LRHS MBri

Codonanthe (Gesneriaceae)

gracilis	EBak WDib
'Paula'	WDib

x *Codonatanthus* (Gesneriaceae)

'Sunset'	WDib
'Tambourine'	WDib

Codonopsis ✿ (Campanulaceae)

ACE 1626	EPot WCot
CC 3350	WCot
from Chollipo, Korea	LEur
affinis HWJCM 70	LEur WCru
bhutanica	CHid EBcc EHyt ITim
bulleyana	EBee NLar WSan
cardiophylla	GCal GDra NLar NPPs WLin
celebica	WCru
B&SWJ 8296 new	
clematidea	More than 30 suppliers
– 'Lilac Eyes' new	SPoG
convolvulacea hort.	see *C. grey-wilsonii*
convolvulacea Kurz	CPIN GBuc MTho NHar NSla WCru WHoo WPGP
– ex J&JA 4220705	LEur NWCA
– 'Alba'	see *C. grey-wilsonii* 'Himal Snow'
– Forrest's form	see *C. forrestii* Diels
dicentrifolia	EMan
– HWJCM 267	WCru
forrestii hort.	see *C. grey-wilsonii*
§ *forrestii* Diels	EHyt ITim NHar WCru
§ *grey-wilsonii* ♀ H4	CBro CLAP GCrs ITim SBla
§ – 'Himal Snow'	CLAP EHyt GCrs GEdr IMGH ITim NHar SBla
handeliana	see *C. tubulosa*
§ *javanica* B&SWJ 380	WCru
kawakamii	CPLG EPot
– B&SWJ 1592	WCru
§ *lanceolata*	CPIN CRDP EBee EHyt EPot ITer ITim LEur MCCP NChi NLar
– B&SWJ 562	WCru
lancifolia B&SWJ 3835	LEur WCru
meleagris misapplied	see *C. meleagris* hybrid
meleagris Diels	WCru
§ – hybrid	EBee

	mollis	EBee EChP GSki MLwd NLar WCru
	nepalensis Grey-Wilson	see *C. grey-wilsonii*
	obtusa	EBee NChi WCot
	ovata	CBot CFir CHid CLyd EBee EPri GBuc GDra MTho NBro NChi SBla SChr SIgm SRms WCru WEas
§	*pilosula*	EBee EHyt GPoy ITer LEur MLLN MNrw MSal MTho WCot WCru
	rotundifolia	CPlN ITim LEur
	– CC 1770	WCot
§	– var. *angustifolia*	CPLG LEur MDKP
	silvestris	see *C. pilosula*
	subsimplex	CLyd
	tangshen misapplied	see *C. rotundifolia* var. *angustifolia*
	tangshen Oliver	CArn CPlN GBuc MCCP MNrw MSal MTho NChi SHFr
	thalictrifolia MECC 93	WCru
§	*tubulosa*	CPlN EMan
	ussuriensis	see *C. lanceolata*
	vinciflora	EHyt IDac LEur SBla WCru
	– white **new**	GKev
	viridiflora	LEur

Coffea (Rubiaceae)

arabica	LRHS

coffee see *Coffea*

Coix (Poaceae)

lacryma-jobi	CBrm CFwr MSal

Colchicum ✿ (Colchicaceae)

	agrippinum ♀ H4	CAvo CBro CFee EHyt EPar EPot GCrs GKev LAma MGrG MRav NBir NMGW NRog NRya WTin
	'Antares'	LAma NBir
	atropurpureum	CBro EPot GEdr LAma
	– Drake's form	EPot
	'Attlee'	LAma
	'Autumn Herald'	LAma
N	'Autumn Queen'	CBro LAma
§	*autumnale*	CArn CAvo CBro CFee EPot GPoy ITim LAma LRHS MLwd NMGW NMen NRya WFar WShi
*	– 'Albopilosum'	NBir
	– 'Alboplenum'	CBro CSWP EPot ETub LAma NMGW
	– 'Album'	CAvo CBro CSWP EHyt EPar EPot ETub GEdr LAma LRHS NBir NMGW WHoo WPnP WShi WTin
	– 'Atropurpureum'	CAvo
	– var. *major*	see *C. byzantinum*
	– var. *minor*	see *C. autumnale*
	– 'Nancy Lindsay' ♀ H4	CBro ECho EPot NMGW
§	– 'Pleniflorum' (d)	CBro EPar EPot LAma
*	– *roseum* **new**	GAbr
	– 'Roseum Plenum'	see *C. autumnale* 'Pleniflorum'
	baytopiorum	EHyt EPot GEdr
§	*bivonae*	CBro ECha LAma
I	'Blom's Hybrid' **new**	WTin
§	*boissieri*	EHyt ERos SSpi
	– MFF 2192	WCot
	bornmuelleri hort.	see *C. speciosum* var. *bornmuelleri* hort.
	bornmuelleri Freyn	CBro EPar EPot LAma
	bowlesianum	see *C. bivonae*
§	*byzantinum* ♀ H4	CBro ECho EPar EPot LAma LRHS MBri NBir NRog
	– *album*	see *C. byzantinum* 'Innocence'
	– 'Innocence'	CBro EPot

	cilicicum	CBro EPot ETub GAbr LAma LRHS
	– 'Purpureum'	LAma
	'Conquest'	see *C.* 'Glory of Heemstede'
	corsicum	EPar ERos LAma NMen
	'Daendels'	LAma
	'Dick Trotter'	GKir LAma
	'Disraeli'	CBro
	doerfleri	see *C. hungaricum*
	'E.A. Bowles'	LAma LRHS
§	*giganteum*	EPot ETub GEdr LAma
§	'Glory of Heemstede'	ECha LAma
	hierosolymitanum	LAma
§	*hungaricum*	CBro EPot LAma SCnR
	illyricum	see *C. giganteum*
	kotschyi	LAma
	laetum hort.	see *C. parnassicum*
	'Lilac Wonder'	CBro ECha EHyt EPot LAma LRHS MBri NMGW NRog WCot WHoo
	lingulatum	NRog WTin
§	*longiflorum*	LAma
	lusitanicum	LAma
	luteum	EHyt LAma NRog
	macrophyllum	LAma
	micranthum	LAma
	neapolitanum	see *C. longiflorum*
	'Oktoberfest'	EPot
§	*parnassicum*	CBro CLAP ECha EHyt
	'Pink Goblet' ♀ H4	CBro EHyt EPot LAma
	polyphyllum	LAma
	'Prinses Astrid'	LAma NMGW
	procurrens	see *C. boissieri*
	'Rosy Dawn' ♀ H4	CBro ECha EPot LAma
	sibthorpii	see *C. bivonae*
	speciosum ♀ H4	CAvo CBro EBre EHyt EPot LAma LRHS NBir WCot
	– 'Album' ♀ H4	CAvo CBro CFee ECha ECho EHyt EPar EPot LAma LRHS MBri NBir NMGW WCot
	– 'Atrorubens'	CAvo ECha GDra LAma LRHS
I	– var. *bornmuelleri* hort.	GEdr
	– var. *illyricum*	see *C. giganteum*
	– 'Maximum'	LAma
	tenorei ♀ H4	EPot LAma NBir WCot
	'The Giant'	CBro EPot ETub GKev LAma LRHS NMGW NRog SChr
	troodii	ERos
	variegatum	CBro LAma
	'Violet Queen'	CBro EPot GAbr LAma LRHS
	'Waterlily' (d) ♀ H4	CAvo CBro CLyd EBre EPar EPot ETub GAbr LAma LRHS MBri NBir NMGW NRog WCot WHoo WPnP
	'William Dykes'	LAma
	'Zephyr'	LAma

Coleonema (Rutaceae)

album	CTrC SBrw WPat
pulchrum	CHEx CSpe NSti WCot
'Sunset Gold'	CSpe CTrC

Coleus see *Solenostemon*

Colletia (Rhamnaceae)

	armata	see *C. hystrix*
	cruciata	see *C. paradoxa*
§	*hystrix*	CBcs CHEx CTri GBin GGar SAPC SArc SLon SMad SOWG SPar
	– 'Rosea'	CAbb CPle
§	*paradoxa*	CBcs CHEx CPle CWib LPJP SAPC SArc SIgm SMad
	spinosissima	CPle

Collinsonia (Lamiaceae)
canadensis   CArn EBee ELan EMan MSal WWye

Collomia (Polemoniaceae)
debilis   EHyt NMen NWCA
- var. **larsenii**   see C. larsenii
§ **larsenii**   GTou

Colobanthus (Caryophyllaceae)
CC 465   NWCA
canaliculatus   EPot

Colocasia (Araceae)
affinis var. **jeningsii**   EAmu LEur MOak WMul
antiquorum   see C. esculenta
§ **esculenta** ♀ H1   CHEx EAmu LEur MOak WMul
* - var. **aquatilis**   LEur
- 'Black Magic'   EAmu WMul
- 'Elephant Ears' **new**   MOak
- 'Fontanesii'   EAmu LEur WMul
- 'Illustris'   WMul
- 'Nigrescens'   EAmu WMul

Colquhounia (Lamiaceae)
coccinea   CArn CHEx CHal CTrC MRav
SIgm WCom WCru WHer WPGP
WSHC WWye
§ - var. **vestita**   CBcs CFai CFil CFwr CPle CPom
CWib EBee EPfP IMGH MSte SBra
SEND WPGP
- - B&SWJ 7222   WCru

Columnea (Gesneriaceae)
'Aladdin's Lamp'   CHal WDib
'Apollo'   WDib
x **banksii** ♀ H1   CHal WDib
- variegated (v) **new**   WCot
'Bold Venture'   WDib
§ 'Broget Stavanger' (v)   WDib
'Chanticleer' ♀ H1   CHal MBri WDib
I 'Firedragon'   WDib
'Gavin Brown'   WDib
gloriosa   EBak
hirta ♀ H1   MBri WDib
- 'Variegata'   see C. 'Light Prince'
'Inferno'   WDib
'Katsura'   MBri WDib
I 'Kewensis Variegata'   MBri
(v) ♀ H1
§ 'Light Prince' (v)   WDib
'Merkur'   WDib
microphylla   MBri
'Variegata'
I 'Midnight Lantern'   WDib
'Rising Sun'   WDib
'Robin'   WDib
schiedeana   CHal MBri WDib
'Stavanger' ♀ H1   CHal EBak WDib
'Stavanger Variegated'   see C. 'Broget Stavanger'
Yellow Dragon Group   CHal

Colutea (Papilionaceae)
arborescens   CArn CBcs EBee EBre GKir LHop
LRHS MBlu MGos MSal NWea
SBrw SHBN SPar SPer WDin WHer
WWin
§ **buhsei**   SLPl SOWG
istria   GEil
x **media**   CHad MBlu MNrw
- 'Copper Beauty'   CBcs GEil MGos SPer WPat
orientalis   CBcs CPle GEil LAst
persica hort.   see C. buhsei

Comarum see Potentilla

Combretum (Combretaceae)
paniculatum   CPIN

Commelina (Commelinaceae)
coelestis   see C. tuberosa Coelestis Group
communis   EMan
dianthifolia   GBuc GCal GCrs GKir MTho
NMen NWCA SYvo WCom WPer
- 'Sapphirino'   EMon
tuberosa   CAvo CBct ELan EPfP ERos EWTr
GBuc MLan MSte NSti WWeb
- 'Alba'   EBee ELan MLLN MSte WPer
- 'Axminster Lilac'   WPer
- Coelestis Group   CFwr EBee EChP ECha EMan
ETub GEil IGor MLLN SRms SYvo
WCom WFar WPGP WPer WWin
- - 'Hopleys   EMan
Variegated' (v)
virginica L.   IBlr

Commiphora (Burseraceae)
opobalsamum   LEdu

Comptonia (Myricaceae)
peregrina   CMac NLar WCru

Conandron (Gesneriaceae)
ramondioides **new**   EHyt

Conicosia (Aizoaceae)
pugioniformis   CTrf

Coniogramme (Adiantaceae)
intermedia   NMar

Conioselinum (Apiaceae)
morrisonense   WCru
B&SWJ 173
schugnanicum   EBee

Conium (Apiaceae)
maculatum   CArn MGol MSal

Conopodium (Apiaceae)
majus   WShi

Conradina (Lamiaceae)
verticillata   WPat

Consolida (Ranunculaceae)
§ **ajacis**   MSal
ambigua   see C. ajacis
regalis   ECoo

Convallaria ✿ (Convallariaceae)
japonica   see Ophiopogon jaburan
keiskei   CLAP
majalis ♀ H4   More than 30 suppliers
§ - 'Albostriata' (v)   CBct CFil CFwr CLAP CRDP
CRow EBee ECha ELan EMan
EMon EPar EPfP EVFa LEur MRav
MTho NBir SOkh WCHb WCot
WCru WEas WHer WPGP
- 'Berlin Giant'   EBee NRya WCot
- 'Dorien'   CBre CFir CFwr EBee EChP LEur
- 'Flore Pleno' (d)   EBee EPar LEur WCot
- 'Fortin's Giant'   CAvo CBct CBro CLAP CMea
CRDP CRow EBee EPar EPla LEur
MRav SIng SMad WCot WPGP WSel
- 'Gerard Debureaux' (v)   see C. majalis 'Green Tapestry'

– 'Golden Slippers' **new**	NPar
§ – 'Green Tapestry' (v)	CRow EMon EVFa
– 'Haldon Grange' (v)	CBct EMon
– 'Hardwick Hall' (v)	CAvo CLAP CRDP CRow ECha EHoe EPar EPla EPot EVFa LEur MGrG MTed NPar WBro WCot WSan
– 'Hofheim' (v)	CRow WTMC
– 'Prolificans'	CAvo CBro CFir CLAP CRDP CRow EBee EMon EPar ERos LEur MRav NGar SIng SMad
– var. *rosea*	More than 30 suppliers
– 'Variegata' (v)	CBro CHar EPar EPla ERou GCrs SChu SMac SMad WHil WSel
– 'Vic Pawlowski's Gold' (v)	CBos CPLG CRow SBla WCHb
montana	EBee LRHS
transcaucasica	EBee

Convolvulus (Convolvulaceae)

althaeoides	CBot CHad CPle EChP LPhx LRHS MNes MNrw MTho SBla SHFr SMad WAbb WCru WEas WHal WPGP WWeb WWin
§ – subsp. *tenuissimus*	CSWP CSpe EBee EMan EWes LHop MBri MHer WCFE WCot
§ *boissieri*	CFir EMan NWCA SBla WAbe
cantabricus	CHll EChP
chilensis	EMan
cneorum ♀ H3	More than 30 suppliers
elegantissimus	see *C. althaeoides* subsp. *tenuissimus*
incanus	WCru
lineatus	ECho EHyt EMan EPot ESis LRHS MBro MTho NMen NWCA SMrm SRot
mauritanicus	see *C. sabatius*
nitidus	see *C. boissieri*
§ *sabatius* ♀ H3	CElw CHEx CHad CHal CSam ECha ECtt ELan EPfP EPot ERea LHop LHrt LRHS MHdf MLan MOak NBlu NMen SAga SBla SDix SIng SPar SPet SYvo WCFE WEas WWin WWol
– 'Compton Lane'	WCom
– dark	CMHG CSpe ELan EMan LIck LLWP MOak MSte SMrm SUsu

x *Cooperanthes* see *Zephyranthes*

Cooperia see *Zephyranthes*

Copernicia (Arecaceae)

alba	CRoM LPal

Coprosma ✿ (Rubiaceae)

acerosa 'Hawera'	CTrC
– 'Live Wire' (f)	ECou
areolata (m)	ECou
atropurpurea (f)	ECou NWCA
– (m)	ECou
'Autumn Orange' (f) **new**	ECou
'Autumn Prince' (m) **new**	ECou
baueri	see *C. repens*
'Beatson's Gold' (f/v)	CBcs CBot CChe EMil EPfP ERea CPLG CTrG EBee EMil EPfP ERea GEil GGar GQui SAga SBrw SPar STre WDin WHen WSHC WStl
'Blue Pearls' (f)	ECou
'Brunette' (f)	ECou
§ *brunnea*	CTrC ECou
– 'Blue Beauty' (f)	ECou
– 'Violet Fleck' (f)	ECou
'Bruno' (m)	ECou
cheesemanii (f)	ECou
– 'Hanmer Red' (f)	ECou
– 'Mack' (m)	ECou
– 'Red Mack' (f)	ECou
'Chocolate Soldier' (m)	ECou
'Coppershine'	CBcs CHEx CPLG CTrC ERea MOak
crassifolia x *repens* (m)	ECou
x *cunninghamii* (f)	ECou
– x *macrocarpa* (m)	ECou
'Cutie' (f)	ECou
depressa	ECou
– 'Orange Spread' (f)	ECou
'Evening Glow' (v)	CDoC COtt LHop LRHS MAsh WWeb
'Green Girl' (f)	ECou
'Hinerua' (f)	ECou
'Indigo Lustre' (f)	ECou
'Jewel' (f)	ECou
'Karo Red' (v)	CDoC COtt LRHS MAsh WWeb
x *kirkii* 'Kirkii' (f)	ECou ERea MNes STre
– 'Kirkii Variegata' (f/v)	CBcs CBot CDoC CTrC EBee ECou ERea GEil GQui IFro LHop MOak SBrw SOWG SPar STre WBrE WSHC WStl
'Kiwi' (m) **new**	ECou
'Kiwi-gold' (m/v)	ECou ERea
'Lemon Drops' (f)	ECou
linariifolia (m)	ECou
lucida (f)	ECou
– 'Mount White' (m) **new**	ECou
– 'Wanaka' (f) **new**	ECou
macrocarpa (f)	ECou
– (m)	ECou
'Middlemore'	CDoC
nitida (f)	ECou
parviflora (m)	CTrC ECou
– purple fruit (f)	ECou
– red fruit (f)	ECou
– white fruit (f)	ECou
'Pearl Drops' (f)	ECou
'Pearl's Sister' (f)	ECou
'Pearly Queen' (f)	ECou
petriei	ECou
– 'Don' (m)	ECou
– 'Lyn' (f)	ECou
'Pink Surprise' **new**	WWeb
'Pride'	CDoC CTrC
propinqua	SDry
– (f)	ECou
– (m)	ECou
– var. *latiuscula* (f)	ECou
– – (m)	ECou
'Prostrata' (m)	ECou
pseudocuneata (m)	ECou
'Rainbow Surprise' (v)	COtt LRHS MAsh SVen WWeb
§ *repens*	CDoC CPLG
§ – (f)	CHEx ECou
– (m)	CBcs ECou SEND
– 'Apricot Flush' (f)	ECou
– 'County Park Purple' (f)	ECou ERea
– 'Exotica' (f/v)	ECou
– 'Marble King' (m/v)	ECou
– 'Marble Queen' (m/v) ♀ H1-2	CHll ECou WCot WFar WLRN
– 'Orangeade' (f)	ECou
– 'Painter's Palette' (m)	CBcs ECou WDin
– 'Picturata' (m/v) ♀ H1-2	ECou ERea EShb
– 'Pink Splendour' (m/v)	CBcs CDoC ECou ERea LHop WDin
– 'Rangatiri' (f)	ECou
– 'Silver Queen' (m/v)	ECou SVen
– 'Variegata' (m/v)	CDoC CHEx ECou
rigida	ECou
– 'Ann' (f) **new**	ECou

- 'Tan' (m) **new** — ECou
robusta — CTrC ECou SDry
- 'Cullen's Point' (f) — ECou
- 'Sally Blunt' (f) — ECou
- 'Steepdown' (f) — ECou
- 'Tim Blunt' (m) — ECou
* - 'Variegata' (m/v) — ECou
- 'William' (m) — ECou
- 'Woodside' (f) — ECou
rotundifolia — ECou
'Roy's Red' (m) — ECou
rugosa (f) — ECou
I 'Snowberry' (f) — ECou
'Taiko' — CTrC
tenuifolia (m) — ECou
'Translucent Gold' (f) — ECou
'Violet Drops' (f) — ECou
virescens (f) — ECou
'Walter Brockie' — CHal CHll CTrC SVen
'White Lady' (f) — ECou
'Winter Bronze' (f) — ECou

Coptis (Ranunculaceae)

japonica var. *major* — WCru
new
quinquefolia — WCru
   B&SWJ 1677
trifolia **new** — GBin

x *Coralia* (Papilionaceae)

'County Park' — ECou
'Essex' — ECou
'Havering' — ECou

Corallospartium (Papilionaceae)

crassicaule — ECou
- 'Jack Sprat' **new** — ECou
- var. *racemosum* — ECou

Cordyline (Agavaceae)

australis ♀ H3 — More than 30 suppliers
- 'Albertii' (v) ♀ H3 — CBcs CWSG GQui LHop LNet
   MBri MCCP NMoo NPri SAPC
   SArc SPar SPoG WCot
* - 'Atropurpurea' — CBcs CDoC GKir SPar WDin WFar
- 'Black Tower' — CBcs CDoC ELan LRHS MGos
- 'Coffee Cream' — CSBt CWSG EAmu EBee EGln
   ELan EPVP EPfP LRHS MBlu MLan
   SLim SPar WDin WFar WGer
- 'Krakatoa' **new** — ENot
- 'Pink Stripe' (v) — CBcs CDoC COtt CSBt CTrC EBee
   ELan EPVP EPfP ISea LRHS MCCP
   MLan NPri SAga SLim SNew SPar
   SPla WCot WFar WPat
- 'Purple Heart' **new** — WPat
- 'Purple Tower' — CBcs CDoC COtt CTrC CWSG EAmu
   EBee EBlw EChP EMil ENot EPfP
   LRHS MCCP MPRe NCot NHol SLim
   SMad SNew SPar SWal WCot WPat
- Purpurea Group — CBcs CBot CChe CHEx CHar
   CMHG CSBt CTrC CWSG EBee EBot
   EBre ENot ERea EWTr GQui ISca
   LAst LRHS MGos NBlu SEND SHBN
   SPar SPer SPlb WFar WGer WStI
- 'Red Robin' — LRav
- 'Red Sensation' **new** — GKir LRHS MAsh
- 'Red Star' — More than 30 suppliers
- 'Sundance' ♀ H3 — More than 30 suppliers
- 'Torbay Dazzler' — More than 30 suppliers
   (v) ♀ H3
- 'Torbay Green' — ENot
- 'Torbay Red' ♀ H3 — CAbb CBcs CBrm CDoC CMHG
   COtt CWSG EBee ELan EPVP EPfP

LHop LPan LRHS MAsh MBlu MBri
MWgw SPar SPla WFar WPat WWeb
- 'Torbay Sunset' — CDoC COtt ELan LRHS WPat
- 'Variegata' (v) — CBot
'Autumn' — CTrC WFar
banksii — CRoM CTrC LEdu
- 'Purpurea' — LPVe
'Dark Star' — CDoC LAst MCCP
'Emerald Isle' — CTrC
fruticosa 'Atom' — MBri
- 'Baby Ti' (v) — MBri
- 'Calypso Queen' — MBri
- 'Kiwi' — MBri
- 'New Guinea Black' — CAbb EChP ELan LAst NCot WCot
- 'Orange Prince' — MBri
- 'Red Edge' ♀ H1 — MBri
- 'Yellow King' — MBri
'Green Goddess' — CBcs CTrC MPRe
§ *indivisa* — CBrP EBak ITim LEdu LPan LRHS
   MBow MBri NGdn SPar SPlb SWal
   WGer WMul WPGP
- 'Perkeo' **new** — EBee
kaspar — CAbb CHEx CRoM LEdu SAPC
   SArc
- bronze — CRoM CTrC LEdu
parryi 'Purpurea' — NPal
pumilio — CMea CTrC LEdu
'Red Fountain' PBR — EBee ENot
§ *stricta* — CHEx MBri
terminalis — see C. fruticosa

Coreopsis ✿ (Asteraceae)

auriculata — see C. auriculata 'Schnittgold'
   Cutting Gold
§ - 'Schnittgold' — SDes WFar WPer
'Baby Gold' — EBee EPfP MBNS NBlu NFla NNor
   WFar WWeb
Baby Sun — see C. 'Sonnenkind'
'Goldfink' — EBre GKir GSki LRHS MBrN MRav
   SRms
grandiflora — SRPl SWat
- 'Astolat' — CMGP CStr EMon MNrw
- 'Badengold' — CBcs EBee EMil MLwd SDes
- 'Bernwode' **new** — EMan
I - 'Calypso' (v) — EBee EWcs LRHS SCoo WWeb
- 'Domino' — EBee LHop NOak
- 'Early Sunrise' — CBrm CSBt CSam EBee ECtt ERou
   GMaP LPVe LRHS MHer MWrn
   NMir NPer SAga SDes SGar SMer
   SPet SWal WFar WGwG WHen
   WHoo WMnd WPer
- Flying Saucers — EBee GDii GKir LRHS SCoo WWeb
   = 'Walcoreop'
- 'Kelvin Harbutt' — CStr EMan ERou
- 'Mayfield Giant' — CSBt EBee EFou EMan ERou LRHS
   MNrw MWat NPri SChu SMer
   SRms SWat WMnd
lanceolata — EFou GDea NStI SMac
- 'Baby Gold' **new** — EBee
- 'Sterntaler' — CFir EBee EFou EMil EPar ERou
   GKir LPVe LRHS NOrc NPri NVic
   WMoo WPer
latifolia — EBee
maximiliani — see Helianthus maximiliani
pubescens — EBee
pulchra — EBee
rosea — NLar SRPl WFar
- 'American Dream' — More than 30 suppliers
- f. *leucantha* — CStr
- 'Sweet Dreams' **new** — EBre
§ 'Sonnenkind' — EBee ECtt EMil EPar GMaP IHMH
   LRHS MHer NBro WPer
Sun Child — see C. 'Sonnenkind'

'Sunburst'	COtt EBee LRHS NOak WMnd WPer WWpP
'Sunray'	CBcs CDoC COlW CSBt EBee ECtt EMlt EPar GKir LPVe LRHS MBri MNrw MWrn NGdn NOak NOrc SDes SMac SPlb SRms WFar WMnd WMoo WPer WWal WWeb WWye
'Tequila Sunrise' (v)	CFwr EBee EMan MBNS WCot
tinctoria	MSal WHer
– var. *atkinsoniana*	WPer
tripteris	CMea CPou EBee EMan EMon LPhx SAga SSvw WMoo
– 'Pierre Bennerup' <u>**new**</u>	EMon
verticillata	CMea CTri EBee ECha EHrv ENot EPfP LRHS MBrN MBro MDun MFir MHer MWat NPPs NPer SDes SDix SRPl SRms SWat WAbe WFar WHal
– 'Golden Gain'	CMGP CTri EBee EBre ECtt EFou EMan EPla GBri GKir GSki LHop LRHS MArl MLLN MMil NGdn NHol WMnd WWal
– 'Golden Shower'	see *C. verticillata* 'Grandiflora'
§ – 'Grandiflora' ♀ H4	More than 30 suppliers
– 'Moonbeam'	More than 30 suppliers
– 'Zagreb' ♀ H4	More than 30 suppliers

coriander see *Coriandrum sativum*

Coriandrum (Apiaceae)

sativum	CArn CSev EOHP GPoy ILis LRHS MChe MHer NBlu NVic SIde WHHs WHer WLHH WPer WWye
– 'Leisure'	CBod CPrp CSev MBow NPri
– 'Moroccan'	WHHs
– 'Santo'	ELau WJek

Coriaria ✿ (Coriariaceae)

arborea	WCru
intermedia B&SWJ 019	WCru
japonica	WCot WCru
– B&SWJ 2833	WCru
kingiana	ECou WCru
§ *microphylla*	GEil WCru
myrtifolia	CFil GCal GSki WCot WCru WFar
napalensis	GCal WCru
pteridoides	WCru
ruscifolia	LEdu WCru
– HCM 98178	WCru
sarmentosa	GCal WCru
terminalis	CElw CTrG CWib EBee EMan
var. *xanthocarpa*	EPfP GBuc GCal GEil SSpi WCot WCru WGwG WPGP
thymifolia	see *C. microphylla*

Cornus ✿ (Cornaceae)

alba	CCVT CDoC CKin CLnd CWib ENot GKir MHer MRav NWea SRms WDin WMou WStI
* – 'Albovariegata' (v)	ENot
– 'Argenteovariegata'	see *C. alba* 'Variegata'
– 'Aurea' ♀ H4	More than 30 suppliers
– 'Elegantissima' (v) ♀ H4	More than 30 suppliers
– 'Gouchaultii' (v)	CBcs EBee EPfP GKir IKee LCaP LPan MBar NBlu NPri SPar SPer SRms WDin
– 'Hessei'	GKir LRHS MRav
– 'Hessei' misapplied	see *C. sanguinea* 'Compressa'
– Ivory Halo = 'Bailhalo'PBR	EBee EBre ENot EPfP GKir LRHS MBri MGos MRav NMoo NPri SPer WGer
– 'Kesselringii'	CAbP CBcs CDoC CDul EBee EBre EHoe EMil ENot EPfP EPla

	EWTr GEil GKir LBuc LRHS MBar MBri MRav NWea SMad SPer SPla WBod WDin WFar
– 'Red Gnome' <u>**new**</u>	WPat
– 'Siberian Pearls'	CBcs EBee ELan MBlu MGos NEgg NMoo SSta
§ – 'Sibirica' ♀ H4	More than 30 suppliers
– 'Sibirica Variegata' (v)	CDoC CMac EBee EBre EPfP EPla GEil GKir LPan LRHS MAsh MBlu MBri MGos NBee NEgg NPri SHBN SLim SPar SPer SSpi SSta WFar
– 'Spaethii' (v) ♀ H4	More than 30 suppliers
§ – 'Variegata' (v)	CBcs LAst SPer WWal WWin
– 'Westonbirt'	see *C. alba* 'Sibirica'
alternifolia	CMCN CMHG COtt ELan EWTr GIBF GKir MDun SBrw SSpi WPat
§ – 'Argentea' (v) ♀ H4	More than 30 suppliers
– 'Variegata'	see *C. alternifolia* 'Argentea'
amomum	CBcs NHol WBcn WWpP
angustata	CTho SPer SSpi
§ 'Ascona'	CPMA ELan EPfP LNet LRHS MBlu MBri NLar SBrw SKee SPer SSpi SSta WPat
Aurora = 'Rutban'	CPMA NLar
baileyi	see *C. sericea* 'Baileyi'
* *benthamii* <u>**new**</u>	WPat
§ *canadensis* ♀ H4	More than 30 suppliers
candidissima	see *C. racemosa*
capitata	CBcs CDoC CMac CPne CTbh CTrG CTri EPfP GIBF IDee LRHS SEND SSpi WCwm WFar WGer WPGP
– ACE 2033	WAbe
– JN 468	GGar
– subsp. *emeiensis*	SSpi
Celestial = 'Rutdan'	CPMA
Constellation = 'Rutcan'	CPMA IArd
controversa	CBcs CDul CFee CMCN CTho CWSG ELan EMil EPfP EWTr LPan MBar MBlu MDun NDlv NPSI NWea SBrw SHBN SLPl SPer SReu SSpi SSta WDin WHar WOrn WPGP
I – 'Marginata Nord' <u>**new**</u>	NLar
– 'Pagoda'	MBlu NBhm SSpi
– 'Variegata' (v) ♀ H4	More than 30 suppliers
– 'Variegata' Frans type (v)	CBcs CBot CEnd CPMA EBre ELan EMil ERom LNet LPan MBlu MBri SHBN SPer SReu SSta WDin WHCG WPat
'Eddie's White Wonder' ♀ H4	More than 30 suppliers
florida	CDul CLnd CMCN CTho ELan EPfP GIBF ISea LRHS MBar NBlu SBrw SKee SPer SRPl SReu WLRN WNor WPat
– 'Alba Plena' (d)	CPMA MAsh
– 'Apple Blossom'	CMac CPMA ECho
– 'Cherokee Brave'	CBcs CPMA CWib LRHS NLar SSpi SSta
– 'Cherokee Chief' ♀ H4	CAbP CBcs CEnd CPMA CWib ECho EPfP IArd IMGH LPan LRHS MGos NBee NLar NPSI SKee SLim SPer WDin WOrn WPat
– 'Cherokee Daybreak' (v)	CBcs CWib
– 'Cherokee Princess'	CPMA EPfP GKir LPan LRHS MAsh SMur SSpi SSta
– 'Cherokee Sunset' (v) <u>**new**</u>	NLar
– 'Clear Moon'	LPan
– 'Cloud Nine'	CBcs CDoC CPMA EMil LAst MGos SLdr SLim SSpi WOrn WPat
– 'Daybreak' (v)	CEnd CPMA CWib LPan MGos SPer WPat

	- 'First Lady'	CBcs CPMA ECho LPan SSpi
	- 'G.H. Ford' (v)	CPMA
	- 'Golden Nugget'	CPMA
	- 'Junior Miss'	CBcs CPMA
	- 'Junior Miss Variegated' (v)	CPMA
	- 'Moonglow'	CPMA
	- 'Pendula'	CPMA
	- 'Purple Glory'	CPMA
	- 'Rainbow' (v)	CAbP COtt CPMA CWib EPfP GKir LPan LRHS MAsh MBri MGos NBee NEgg NPSI SKee SPer SPla SSta WDin WPat
	- 'Red Giant'	CAbP CPMA ELan EPfP LRHS SMur SPer SSpi SSta
	- 'Royal Red'	CBcs CPMA
	- f. *rubra*	CBcs CSBt CWib EPfP LAst LPan LRHS MGos NEgg SBrw SPer SSta WGer WNor WPat
	- 'Spring Song'	CMac CPMA ECho LRHS MBri
	- 'Stoke's Pink'	CEnd COtt CPMA ECho GKir
	- 'Sunset' (v)	CEnd CPMA CWib MGos SPer WPat
	- 'Sweetwater'	CBcs CPMA
	- 'Tricolor'	see *C. florida* 'Welchii'
§	- 'Welchii' (v)	CEnd CPMA
	- 'White Cloud'	CPMA
	'Greenlight'	WWeb
	hemsleyi	CNat EPla
	hessei misapplied	see *C. sanguinea* 'Compressa'
	hongkongensis	CBcs
	'Kelsey Dwarf'	see *C. sericea* 'Kelseyi'
	kousa	CBcs CDoC CDul CMCN CTbh CTho CWSG ECrN ELan EPfP ERom GKir ISea LNet LRHS MBar MLan MWat NFor NLon NPSI SBrw SHBN SPer WAbe WDin WFar WHCG WHar WStI
	- B&SWJ 5494	WCru
	- 'Autumn Rose'	EPfP
	- 'Beni-fuji'	CPMA
	- 'Boltinckx Beauty'	LRHS SSpi
	- 'Bonfire' (v)	CPMA
	- var. *chinensis* ♀H4	More than 30 suppliers
	- - 'Bodnant Form'	CEnd CPMA GKir
	- - 'China Girl'	CAbP CEnd COtt CPMA CWib ELan EPfP GKir LBuc LPan LRHS MAsh MBlu MBri MGos MWya SHBN SLim SPer SSpi SSta WDin WOrn WPGP WPat
	- - 'Greta's Gold' (v)	CPMA
	- - 'Milky Way'	CPMA NLar WBod
	- - 'Snowflake'	CPMA
	- - Spinners form	CPMA WPat
	- - 'White Dusted'	EPfP
	- - 'White Fountain'	LPan
	- - 'Wieting's Select'	CPMA
	- 'Doubloon'	CPMA
	- 'Ed Mezitt' **new**	CPMA
	- 'Elizabeth Lustgarten'	SSpi SSta
	- 'Gold Cup' (v)	CPMA
	- 'Gold Star' (v)	CAbP CBcs CEnd CMac COtt CPMA CTho CWib ELan EPfP LRHS MAsh MBri MGos NBee SHBN SKee SPer SPla SSpi SSta
	- 'John Slocock'	SSpi
	- 'Lustgarten Weeping'	LRHS NLar SSpi
	- 'Madame Butterfly'	CEnd CPMA LRHS SSpi
	- 'Moonbeam'	CPMA
	- 'National'	CPMA MGos
	- 'Nicole'	CDoC WDin
	- 'Radiant Rose'	CPMA MBlu
	- 'Rosea'	CPMA
	- 'Satomi' ♀H4	CBcs CDoC CDul CEnd COtt

		CPMA EBee ELan EPfP GKir LBuc LNet LPan LRHS MBlu MBri MGos NBea SKee SLdr SLim SPer SRPl SReu SSpi SSta WDin WPGP WPat
	- 'Schmetterling'	CPMA
	- 'Snowboy' (v)	CBcs CEnd CPMA LRHS NBee NEgg NLar SKee
	- 'Southern Cross'	CPMA
	- 'Summer Majesty'	CPMA
	- 'Sunsplash' (v)	CPMA CTho
	- 'Temple Jewel' (v)	LRHS MBri SSpi
	- 'Triple Crown'	CPMA
	- 'Tsukubanomine'	CPMA
	- 'Weaver's Weeping'	CPMA
	macrophylla	CMCN EPfP IArd SMad WCwm
	mas	More than 30 suppliers
	- 'Aurea' (v)	CAbP CPMA EBee ELan EPfP GKir LPan MAsh MBri MBro MCCP MRav SLim SPer SSpi WAbe WDin WPat
§	- 'Aureoelegantissima' (v)	CFil CPMA EBee LNet LRHS MBro NHol NLar SPer WFar WPGP WPat WSHC
	- 'Elegantissima'	see *C. mas* 'Aureoelegantissima'
	- 'Golden Glory' ♀H4	CBcs CPMA MBlu
	- 'Variegata' (v) ♀H4	CBcs CBot CDul CMCN CPMA CTho EBee EPfP GKir LNet LRHS MBlu MBro MGos NBee NEgg NPal SBrw SKee SSpi WDin WFar WPat
N	'Norman Hadden' ♀H4	CAbP CDoC CDul CEnd CMCN CMac CPMA CSBt CSam CTbh CTho EPfP GKir LAst LRHS MAsh MBro MRav SBrw SHBN SHFr SMad SPer SSpi SSta WAbe WDin WFar WPGP WPat
	nuttallii	CBcs CTho CWib ELan EPfP ISea IPan LRHS MDun NWea SBrw SHBN WDin WFar WNor
	- 'Ascona'	see *C.* 'Ascona'
	- 'Colrigo Giant'	CPMA SSpi
	- 'Gold Spot' (v)	CMac CPMA EPfP LPan LRHS MGos WPat
	- 'Monarch'	CPMA CTho NLar
	- 'North Star'	CPMA NLar
	- 'Portlemouth'	CEnd CPMA LRHS MBri SSpi WPat
	obliqua	CFil WPGP
§	*occidentalis*	EPla
	officinalis	CMCN EPfP LPan LRHS MBri NLar WCwm WDin
	'Ormonde'	CPMA ECho LRHS MBri SBrw SSpi
	paucinervis	GIDF
	'Pink Blush'	CPMA
	'Porlock' ♀H4	CPMA ENot EPfP LRHS WDin
	pubescens	see *C. occidentalis*
	pumila	CPMA NHol WDin
§	*racemosa*	WFar
	rugosa	WNor
	'Ruth Ellen'	CPMA
	sanguinea	CBcs CCVT CDul CKin CLnd CSam CTri EBre ENot EPfP LBuc LHyr MPEx MRav NFor NLon NWea SPer WDin WGwG WHar WMou
§	- 'Compressa'	EBee GEil MBro NHol NLar WWes MBri
	- 'Magic Flame' **new**	MBri
	- 'Midwinter Fire'	More than 30 suppliers
§	- 'Winter Beauty'	CDoC CDul CSBt CWib EBee EPfP MBlu MBro NBee SHBN WPat
§	*sericea*	CArn EPla MGos SMer
	- 'Baileyi'	IArd
§	- 'Flaviramea' ♀H4	More than 30 suppliers
	- 'Kelseyi'	CBcs CFwr CMac CSBt EBee ENot

	EPla ESis GKir MBNS MBar MRav NPri NPro SBod SLPl SMac SPer WLRN WWeb
- Kelsey's Gold = 'Rosco'	SLon WPat
- 'Sunshine'	CSpe
§ - 'White Gold' (v) ♀ H4	CDoC CPMA EBee EHoe ENot LNet LRHS MBri MGos MRav NPro SPer WBcn WDin WFar
Stellar Pink = 'Rutgan'	CPMA CWib
stolonifera	see *C. sericea*
suecica	GIBF
walteri	CMCN WCwm WFar

Corokia (Escalloniaceae)

buddlejoides	CDoC CMHG CPle CWib ECou GGar IKee SBrw SOWG SPer WBod WCru WFar
'Coppershine'	CBcs CMHG
cotoneaster	CAbP CHor CMac CSBt CTrw EBee ECou ELan EMan ENot EPfP EPot MGos SBrw SDry SIgm SLon SMad SMur SPar SPer WBod WBrE WCot WFar WOTO WPat WWes
- 'Ohau Scarlet'	ECou
- 'Ohau Yellow'	ECou
- 'Swale Stream'	ECou
- 'Wanaka'	ECou
macrocarpa	CDoC ECou ISea SDix WSHC
x *virgata*	CAbP CBcs CDoC CMHG CPLG CPle CTrC CTri EBee ECou ELan EPfP LRHS MBlu MCCP MWhi SAPC SAga SArc SBrw SMac SPar SPer WCom WStk WWal
- 'Bronze King'	CBrm CDoC CPLG CTrC EBee SBrw SPer
- 'Cheesemanii'	ECou GGar
- 'County Park Lemon'	ECou SOWG
- 'County Park Orange'	ECou
- 'County Park Purple'	ECou
- 'County Park Red'	ECou
- 'Frosted Chocolate'	CBcs CDoC CTrC EBee ECou EPfP MGos SBrw WBcn WDin
- 'Havering'	ECou
- 'Mangatangi' **new**	MGos
- 'Pink Delight'	CDoC ECou EPfP SBrw
- 'Red Wonder'	CBrm CMHG CTrC EBee ERea GGar LRHS SAga SBrw SDry SEND SOWG WCot WDin WStl
- 'Sunsplash' (v)	CBcs CDoC CTrC EBee ECou MGos SAga SBrw
- 'Virgata'	CChe CTrC ECou
- 'Yellow Wonder'	CBcs CMHG CTrC EBee ECot ECou EMan GEil GGar MGos WDin

Coronilla (Papilionaceae)

cappadocica	see *C. orientalis*
comosa	see *Hippocrepis comosa*
coronata	EBre
emerus	see *Hippocrepis emerus*
glauca	see *C. valentina* subsp. *glauca*
minima	ETow SBla
§ *orientalis*	NWCA WWin
valentina	CDoC CMac CRHN CSPN CSam EMil LHop SBra SDix
§ - subsp. *glauca* ♀ H3	CBot CFee CMac CPle CSBt CSam CTri CWib EBee ELan ENot EPfP ERea LRHS MWhi NMen SAga SGar SPar SPer SRms SVen WAbe WBod WHCG WPic
- - 'Citrina' ♀ H3	More than 30 suppliers
* - - 'Pygmaea'	NMen WCot

- - 'Variegata' (v)	More than 30 suppliers
§ *varia*	CAgr CStr EBee NLar

Correa (Rutaceae)

alba	CDoC CPLG CTrC ECou EPfP SMur
- 'Pinkie' ♀ H2	CPLG ECou LHop LRHS SDys SOWG
backhouseana ♀ H2	CAbb CBcs CDoC CPLG CPle CTrC CTrG CTri GCal GGar GQui LHop LRHS SAga SBrw SLon SOWG WBod WCot WPat WSHC
baeuerlenii	CMHG CPLG SOWG
decumbens	CPLG CPle CTrC ECou ESlt GSki SDys SMur SOWG
'Dusky Bells' ♀ H2	CDoC CHll CSWP CTrC ECou EPfP LHop MOak SBrw SOWG WCFE
'Dusky Maid'	CAbb CPLG WAbe
'Harrisii'	see *C. 'Mannii'*
'Ivory Bells'	ECou SDys
lawrenceana	CDoC CTrC GQui SBrw SEND WAbe WLRN
§ 'Mannii' ♀ H2	CBrm CHEx CPLG CSev CWib EBee ECou LRHS MNes SBrw SOWG WSHC
'Marian's Marvel' ♀ H2	CAbb CFwr CMHG CPLG ECou GQui LRHS SDys SOWG SVen WAbe WGwG WLRN
'Peachy Cream'	CDoC
'Poorinda Mary'	SOWG
pulchella ♀ H2	CDoC CPLG CTri GQui LRHS MNes SOWG
§ *reflexa* ♀ H2	CBcs CDoC CPLG CPle ECou SOWG WAbe WBor
- 'Federation Bell' **new**	SOWG
- var. *reflexa*	CPLG
- *virens*	CPLG WEas
- 'Yanakie'	CPle SOWG
speciosa	see *C. reflexa*
* *spectabilis*	CPLG
viridiflora	GQui

Cortaderia ✿ (Poaceae)

argentea	see *C. selloana*
§ *fulvida*	CAbb CBig EBee EBre EWes IBlr MNrw SMad SWal WDin WPrP
richardii hort.	see *C. fulvida*
§ *richardii* (Endl.)	CHEx CKno EBre EFou EHoe
Zotov ♀ H3-4	EPPr EPla EWes GGar IBlr NVic SAPC SArc SPar SRGP SWal WBea WCot WCru
§ *selloana*	CBcs CHEx CTri EBee EHul ENot EPfP GKir MBar MHdf MRav NBee NBir NBlu NFor SAPC SArc SPlb WMoo WStl
§ - 'Albolineata' (v)	CBrm CKno EBee EHoe EPla EVFa EWes EWsh LAst MCCP MWht SDes SEND SLim SMad SPar WLRN WLeb WMoo WPat
§ - 'Aureolineata' (v) ♀ H3	More than 30 suppliers
- 'Elegans'	CBig
- 'Gold Band'	see *C. selloana* 'Aureolineata'
- 'Golden Comet' **new**	EBee
- 'Monstrosa'	SMad
- 'Patagonia'	EHoe
- 'Pink Feather'	EPfP EWsh GKir NEgg SAdn SHBN SPar SRms WFar WLow WStl WWeb
- 'Pumila' ♀ H4	More than 30 suppliers
- 'Rendatleri'	CBcs CBig CDoC EBee ELan EPfP EWsh GKir LRHS MAsh SDes SLim SMad SPer WDin WLRN
- 'Rosea'	CBig EBee GSki LRHS MBar MGos NGdn WFar WMoo
- 'Silver Comet'	EBre EVFa GKir

	- Silver Feather	ENot WWeb
	= 'Notcort' **new**	
	- 'Silver Fountain'	ELan EPfP LRHS MAsh SPer
	- 'Silver Stripe'	see *C. selloana* 'Albolineata'
	- 'Sunningdale	More than 30 suppliers
	Silver' ♀ H3	
	- 'White Feather'	NGdn WFar WLow WWeb
	Toe Toe	see *C. richardii* (End.) Zotov

Cortusa (Primulaceae)

	brotheri	NWCA
	matthioli	EPfP GGar GKir GTou LBee
		MBow NMGW NMen NWCA
		SRms WFar WWhi
	- 'Alba'	ECGN GBuc NHar NLar NWCA
		SRms WFTG
	- subsp. **pekinensis**	CFir CLyd EMlt GBuc GDra LSyl
		NHar NLar NMen SRms
	- var. **yezoensis**	EHyt
	turkestanica	ECho

Corydalis (Papaveraceae)

	from Sichuan, China	NCot
	afghanica	GKir
	alexeenkoana	CLAP EHyt
	- subsp. **vittae**	see *C. vittae*
	x **allenii**	WWst
	alpestris new	EPot
	ambigua hort.	see *C. fumariifolia*
	angustifolia	GCrs
	- white **new**	WWst
	aquilegioides new	EBee
	'Blackberry Wine'	CHll EBee GBri
§	**blanda**	EHyt EPot
	subsp. **parnassica**	
	'Blue Panda'	see *C. flexuosa* 'Blue Panda'
	bracteata	EHyt GCrs
	- white	WWst
	bulbosa auct. non DC.	see *C. cava*
	bulbosa (L.) DC.	see *C. solida*
	buschii	CDes CElw CLAP EBee EHyt ERos
		GCrs GEdr NDov SBla SChu SCnR
		WAbe WPGP WWst
	cashmeriana	EBee EHyt GCrs GEdr GTou NHar
		NHol NLar SBla WAbc WIvy
	- 'Kailash'	FMon GBuc
	caucasica	EPot ERos GBuc GCrs GDra LAma
		NMen
	- var. **alba** misapplied	see *C. malkensis*
§	**cava**	CPLG EBee EChP ECho EMan
		EPot GGar LAma WFTG
	- **albiflora**	EPar EPot SBla
	- subsp.	NMen
	marschalliana	
	chaerophylla	IBlr
	- B&SWJ 2951	WCru
	cheilanthifolia	More than 30 suppliers
	darwasica	WWst
	davidii new	EBcc
I	**decipiens**	CFwr
	hort. ♀ H4 **new**	
	decipiens Schott,	see *C. solida* subsp. *incisa*
	Nyman & Kotschy	
§	**densiflora**	WWst
	'Early Bird' **new**	EWes
	elata	More than 30 suppliers
	- 'Blue Summit'	GKir SBla
	- x **flexuosa**	CLAP WCot
	flexuosa ♀ H4	CFee CMil CPLG CSpe ECGN
		EDAr EGle ELan EMar EPot MArl
		MBro MGrG MNrw MTho NCot
		NLAp SChu SGar SMac WAbe
		WCFE WFar WSHC WWin

	- CD&R 528	EHyt MBro MRav NHar NRya
		SAga WRHF
	- 'Balang Mist'	EBee EGle LHop MSph NCot SBla
		SMrm SOkh SUsu
	- 'Blue Dragon'	see *C. flexuosa* 'Purple Leaf'
§	- 'Blue Panda'	CElw EGle EPfP EWes GBuc
		GMaP IBlr ITim LPio LRHS NGar
		SBla SSpi WAbe
	- 'China Blue'	More than 30 suppliers
	CD&R 528c	
	- 'Nightshade'	CElw GBuc MAvo NBid NCot
		NDov NGar SWat WCot WCra
		WFar WIvy WPrP
I	- 'Norman's Seedling'	EBee EPPr NCot WCot WPGP
	- 'Père David'	More than 30 suppliers
	CD&R 528b	
	- 'Purple Leaf'	More than 30 suppliers
	CD&R 528a	
§	**fumariifolia**	EBee GDra LAma MTho NRog WLin
	glauca	see *C. sempervirens*
	glaucescens	EHyt
	gracilis	WWst
	haussknechtii	EHyt
	henrikii	EHyt
	heterocarpa	SScr
	integra	WCot WWst
	jingyuanensis new	EBee
	'Kingfisher' **new**	WAbe
	kusnetzovii	EHyt GCrs
	ledebouriana	WWst
	leucanthema	CDes
	DJHC 752 **new**	
	- 'Silver Sceptre' **new**	SSpi
	linstowiana	CPom EBee EDAr EHyt EMan EMon
		EPPr IBlr LPhx NCot NWCA WOBN
	- CD&R 605	CLAP
§	**lutea**	CBcs CPLG EBee EChP EDAr
		EMar GBuc IBlr LGro LHrt MBow
		MPWC MTis MWgw NPer NVic
		SEND SHFr SRms WCot WMoo
	maculata B&SWJ 4417	WCru
	magadanica	EHyt EPot GIBF
§	**malkensis** ♀ H4	EHyt EPot ETow GCrs NBir NHar
		SBla SCnR WCot WWst
	nobilis	CPom CSpe NEgg SHBN WCot
	nudicaulis	WWst
	ochotensis	NLar WCot
	- B&SWJ 3138	WCru
§	**ochroleuca**	CElw CRow EChP EMar EPot ESis
		EVFa GCrs MTho NCot NEgg
		WBro WFar WMoo
	ophiocarpa	COIW EHoe ELan EMan EMar GCal
		GIBF IBlr MAnH MBNS MLan MRav
		MWhi MWod NBur NCot STcs SWal
		WBea WCot WFoF WMoo WWpP
	oppositifolia	EHyt
	subsp. **oppositifolia**	
	ornata	EHyt GCrs WWst
	- white	WWst
	paczoskii	EHyt EPot ERos GBuc GCrs GKir
		LRHS NMen WAbe WOBN
	pallida B&SWJ 395	WCru
	parnassica	see *C. blanda* subsp. *parnassica*
	paschei	EHyt EPot GCrs
	popovii	MTho NCot
	pseudocristata new	EBee
	pseudofumaria alba	see *C. ochroleuca*
	pumila	EPot ETow GCrs
	repens new	EBee
	rosea	EPPr IBlr NCot
	ruksansii	WWst
§	**saxicola**	CSpe
	scandens	see *Dicentra scandens*

schanginii	EPot
- subsp. **ainii** ♀ H2	EHyt EPot
- subsp. **schanginii**	EHyt EPot
scouleri	EMFP NBir
seisumsiana	WWst
§ **sempervirens**	EMan WCru WPat WRos WSan WWin
- **alba**	ECho ELan WFoF
shearei new	EBee
smithiana	EDAr GKev WFar WTin
- ACE 154	EHyt EMar GBuc NCot WOBN
aff. **smithiana** CLD 385	EDAr
§ **solida**	More than 30 suppliers
- BM 8499	NHol
- M&T 4056	GDra
- pink and red shades	CFwr
- 'Apple Snow'	GCrs
- 'Harkov'	GCrs
§ - subsp. **incisa** ♀ H4	CMea EBee EHyt LRHS MNrw MTho WFTG WShi
- - 'Vermion Dawn' new	WWst
- 'Ivory'	EHyt
- 'Lilac Time'	EHyt
- 'Maxima'	GCrs
- Nettleton seedlings	EPot
- 'Punk Lips'	EHyt
- 'Rozula'	EHyt
- 'Smokey Blue'	EHyt
- 'Soft Pink'	EPot
§ - subsp. **solida**	CLAP EHyt EPot GCrs GDra NBir NHar NMen NRya WAbe WCot
- - 'Beth Evans'	CBro EHyt EPot LTwo NMen SCnR WCot WWst
- - 'Dieter Schacht' ♀ H4	GCrs LAma NPar WCot WWst
- - from Penza, Russia	GBuc GCrs SBla
- - 'George Baker' ♀ H4	CBro CMea CRDP EBee EHyt EPar EPot GCrs GEdr LAma LRHS LTwo MTho NGar NHar NMen SCnR SOkh SUsu WAbe WCom WCot WLin WWst
- - 'Highland Mist'	ETow GCrs NGar NHar
- - 'Lahovice'	GCrs WAbe WCot
- - 'Munich Sunrise'	EHyt NRya
- - 'Prasil Sunset'	EHyt SOkh WCot
- - 'Snowstorm'	EHyt
- - 'White Knight'	GCrs
- subsp. **subremota**	WWst
- 'White King'	WWst
'Spinners' new	LPhx
taliensis	GEdr
- ACE 2443	EPot NCot
tauricola	EHyt EPot
temulifolia new	EBee
thalictrifolia Franchet	see C. saxicola
tomentella	GEdr MWod
'Tory MP'	CDes CHid CKno CSam EBee WHoo WPGP
triternata ♀ H4	EPot
turtschaninovii	WWst
verticillaris	EHyt
§ **vittae**	EHyt
vivipara new	EBee
wendelboi	EHyt GCrs
- subsp. **congesta**	WWst
- - 'Abant Wine'	EPot
wilsonii	CBot EHyt ETow GEdr IBlr MTho SBla SIng WEas

Corylopsis ✿ (Hamamelidaceae)

from Chollipo, South Korea	LRHS SSpi
§ **glabrescens**	CEnd CPMA GIBF IMGH LRHS NLar SMur SPer WNor WWes

- var. **gotoana**	EPfP LRHS MAsh SMur SSpi SSta WBod
- - 'Chollipo' new	MAsh SSta
himalayana	NLar
multiflora	SSpi SSta
pauciflora ♀ H4	More than 30 suppliers
platypetala	see C. sinensis var. calvescens
- var. **laevis**	see C. sinensis var. calvescens
sinensis	GIBF SSta
§ - var. **calvescens**	CBcs CPMA CPne LRHS NLar
§ - - f. **veitchiana** ♀ H4	CPMA EPfP IArd LRHS NLar SBrw SMur WDin
- - - purple selection	CPMA
§ - var. **sinensis** ♀ H4	CDoC CMHG CPMA CWSG EPfP LAst SBrw SPer SRPl SReu WAbe WBod WDin WFar
- - 'Spring Purple'	CAbP CMac CPMA EPfP IArd LRHS NLar SBrw SPer SPla SPoG SSpi SSta WDin WPGP WPat
spicata	CBcs CPMA CSBt EBee GIBF LRHS MBlu MNes NBlu SBrw SLim SPer SRPl WBod
- 'Red Eye'	NLar
veitchiana	see C. sinensis var. calvescens f. veitchiana
willmottiae	see C. sinensis var. sinensis

Corylus ✿ (Corylaceae)

avellana (F)	CCVT CDoC CKin CLnd CSam CTri EBre ECrN EMui ENot EPfP ERea LBuc LHyr LRHS MBar MBri NBee NRog NWea SKee SPer WDin WHar WMou WStI
- 'Aurea'	CEnd CLnd COtt CSBt CTho EBee ECrN ELan ENot EPfP GKir LBuc LRHS MAsh MBlu MBri MGos NHol SKee SLim SPer SSta WDin WFar
- 'Bollwylle'	see C. maxima 'Halle'sche Riesennuss'
- 'Contorta'	More than 30 suppliers
- 'Cosford Cob' (F)	CDoC CSBt CTho CTri EMui ERea ESim GKir GTwe LBuc LRHS MBlu MBri MGos NRog SDea SKee SPer
- 'Fortin' (F)	ESim
§ - 'Fuscorubra' (F)	GKir SAga
§ - 'Heterophylla'	CEnd CTho EBee EPfP GKir WMou WWes
- 'Laciniata'	see C. avellana 'Heterophylla'
- 'Merveille de Bollwyller'	see C. maxima 'Halle'sche Riesennuss'
- 'Nottingham Prolific'	see C. avellana 'Pearson's Prolific'
§ - 'Pearson's Prolific' (F)	ERea ESim GTwe LBuc SDea
- 'Pendula'	MBlu
- 'Purpurea'	see C. avellana 'Fuscorubra'
- 'Webb's Prize Cob' (F)	ERea GTwe MBlu NRog SDea WMou
colurna ♀ H4	CDul CFil CLnd CMCN CTho EBee ECrN ENot EPfP GKir LHyr LPan MGos NBee NWea SKee SLPl SPer WDin WMou WOrn
x **colurnoides** 'Chinoka' (F)	ESim
- 'Laroka' (F)	ESim
maxima (F)	CDul CLnd ECrN EMui GTwe NWea SDea WDin
- 'Butler' (F)	ERea GTwe LRHS MBri SKee
- 'Ennis' (F)	ERea GTwe LRHS SDea SKee
- 'Fertile de Coutard'	see C. maxima 'White Filbert'
- 'Frizzled Filbert' (F)	ECrN EMil ERea
- 'Frühe van Frauendorf'	see C. maxima 'Red Filbert'
- 'Garibaldi' (F)	MBlu
- 'Grote Lambertsnoot'	see C. maxima 'Kentish Cob'
- 'Gunslebert' (F)	CSBt ERea GKir GTwe LRHS MBri SDea SKee

- Halle Giant | see *C. maxima* 'Halle'sche Riesennuss'
§ - 'Halle'sche Riesennuss' (F) | ERea GTwe SKee
§ - 'Kentish Cob' (F) | CDoC CSBt CTho CWSG EBre EMui EPfP ERea ESim GTwe LBuc LRHS MBlu MGos NBee NPri NRog SDea SFam SKee SPer SRms WHar WWeb
- 'Lambert's Filbert' | see *C. maxima* 'Kentish Cob'
- 'Longue d'Espagne' | see *C. maxima* 'Kentish Cob'
- 'Monsieur de Bouweller' | see *C. maxima* 'Halle'sche Riesennuss'
- 'Purple Filbert' | see *C. maxima* 'Purpurea'
§ - 'Purpurea' (F) ♀ H4 | More than 30 suppliers
§ - 'Red Filbert' (F) | CEnd CWSG ERea GKir GTwe IMGH LRHS MBlu MBri NRog SKee SLim
- 'Red Zellernut' | see *C. maxima* 'Red Filbert'
- 'Spanish White' | see *C. maxima* 'White Filbert'
§ - 'White Filbert' (F) | ERea GTwe NRog SKee WHar
- 'White Spanish Filbert' | see *C. maxima* 'White Filbert'
- 'Witpit Lambertsnoot' | see *C. maxima* 'White Filbert'
sieboldiana | CMCN
var. *mandshurica*
'Te Terra Red' | CMCN GKir MBlu SMad WMou

Corymbia see *Eucalyptus*

Corynephorus (*Poaceae*)
canescens | CBig CPen EBee EHoe EMan LPVe MCCP MLLN NBir NHol NWCA WWeb

Corynocarpus (*Corynocarpaceae*)
laevigatus | CHEx ECou MBri
I - 'Picturatus' | CHEx

costmary see *Tanacetum balsamita*

Cosmos (*Asteraceae*)
§ *atrosanguineus* | More than 30 suppliers

Costus (*Costaceae*)
amazonicus new | MOak
curvibracteatus | MOak
erythrophyllus | MOak
pictus | WMul
speciosus | CKob ELau MOak NRog WMul
stenophyllus new | MOak

Cotinus (*Anacardiaceae*)
americanus | see *C. obovatus*
§ *coggygria* ♀ H4 | More than 30 suppliers
- 'Foliis Purpureis' | see *C. coggygria* Rubrifolius Group
- Golden Spirit = 'Ancot' PBR | CAbP EBee EHan ELan EMan ENot EPfP GKir MGos MRav NPri NSti SCoo SLon SPar SPer WWeb
- 'Notcutt's Variety' | CMac EBre ELan ENot EPfP GKir MAsh MRav NSti WBod WWes
- 'Pink Champagne' | CPMA EPfP NLar
- Purpureus Group | ENot
- 'Red Beauty' | LRHS MBri
- 'Royal Purple' ♀ H4 | More than 30 suppliers
§ - Rubrifolius Group | CBcs EBee EPfP GKir LRHS NFor SChu SDix SPer WDin WHCG
- 'Velvet Cloak' | CAbP CPMA EBee ELan ENot EPfP GKir LRHS MAsh MGos MRav SLon SPar SPla WHCG
'Flame' ♀ H4 | CDul CPMA ELan EPfP LAst LRHS MAsh MGos MRav SLim SPla SSpi WPat
'Grace' | More than 30 suppliers
§ *obovatus* ♀ H4 | CMCN CMHG CPle CTho ELan

| | ENot EPfP IArd MRav NLar SHBN SPer SSpi SSta WWes |

Cotoneaster ✿ (*Rosaceae*)
CC&McK 465 new | NWCA
acuminatus | SRms WPGP
adpressus ♀ H4 | EPfP GDra GKir MGos MWgw NFor NHar NLon NWea
§ - 'Little Gem' | ECho LRHS SRms WLin
- var. *praecox* | see *C. nanshan*
- 'Tom Thumb' | see *C. adpressus* 'Little Gem'
affinis | SRms
albokermesinus | SRms
amoenus | SLPl SRms
- 'Fire Mountain' | LRHS NPro WFar
§ *apiculatus* | GKir MBar SRms
- 'Tom Thumb' new | NBlu
armenus | SRms
§ *ascendens* | SRms
assadii | SRms
assamensis | SRms
§ *astrophoros* | MBlu
atropurpureus
§ - 'Variegatus' (v) ♀ H4 | More than 30 suppliers
atuntzensis new | SRms
beimashanensis new | SRms
bisramianus | SRms
boisianus | SRms
bradyi | SRms
brickellii new | SRms
browiczii | SRms
§ *bullatus* ♀ H4 | CDul CLnd CTri ENot GKir MGos NFor NLon SEND SLon SRms WCwm WOrn WSHC WTel
- 'Bjuv' new | SRms
- 'Firebird' | see *C. ignescens*
- f. *floribundus* | see *C. bullatus*
- var. *macrophyllus* | see *C. rehderi*
- 'McLaren' new | SRms
bumthangensis new | SRms
buxifolius | ESis
- blue-leaved | see *C. lidjiangensis*
- f. *vellaeus* | see *C. astrophoros*
calocarpus | GIBF
camilli-schneideri | SRms
canescens | SRms
cardinalis new | SRms
cavei | SRms
chungtiensis new | SRms
cinerascens | SRms
cinnabarinus new | SRms
cinovskisii new | SRms
§ *cochleatus* | EBee EPot GDra GIBF GKir LAst MBar MGos NBee NLon NMen SReu SRms WEas WLin
§ *congestus* | CFee CSBt CWib EBee GKir IKee LRHS MBar MBro MGos MRav NFor NLon SPer SPlb WBod WDin WHar WWin
- 'Nanus' | CLyd CMHG CTri ELan EOrn LRHS MAsh MBro MOne NBid NFor NHol WPat
conspicuus | CBcs CSam SRms
- 'Decorus' ♀ H4 | CCVT CDoC CMHG CSBt CWSG EBee EHoI ENot EPfP GKir LRHS MBar MGos MRav MWhi NFor NHol NLon NWea SLim SPer SPlb SWal WDin WStI WTel WWes
- 'Flameburst' | LRHS SHBN
- prostrate new | SRms
- 'Red Alert' | SRms

	cooperi	SRms
	- 'Rumsey Gardens' **new**	SRms
*	'Coral' **new**	SCoo
	cornifolius **new**	SRms
	crispii	SRms
	- 'Ruby' **new**	SRms
	aff. *crispii*	SRms
	cuspidatus	SRms
	daliensis **new**	SRms
N	*dammeri* ♀ H4	More than 30 suppliers
§	- 'Major'	LBuc NBlu SPla SRms WCFE
§	- 'Mooncreeper'	CChe LRHS MBNS
	- 'Oakwood'	see *C. radicans* 'Eichholz'
	- var. *radicans* hort.	see *C. dammeri* 'Major'
	- var. *radicans* C.K.Schneid.	see *C. radicans*
	- 'Streib's Findling'	see *C.* 'Streib's Findling'
	dielsianus	GIBF NWea SPer SRms
	distichus var. *tongolensis*	see *C. splendens*
	divaricatus	ENot EPfP NWea SLon SRms WFar
	dojamensis **new**	SRms
	'Donald Lowndes'	see *C. integrifolius* 'Donald Lowndes'
	duthieanus 'Boer'	see *C. apiculatus*
	elatus **new**	SRms
	elegans	SRms
	ellipticus	SRms
	emeiensis **new**	SRms
	'Erlinda'	see *C.* x *suecicus* 'Erlinda'
	falconeri	SRms
	fastigiatus **new**	SRms
	flinckii	SRms
	floccosus	CSBt EBee GKir LRHS MBri NWea SPer SRms WLRN
	floridus	SRms
	forrestii	SRms
	franchetii	CBcs CChe CDul CSBt EBee EBre ECrN ELan EMil EPfP GIBF GKir LBuc LPan LRHS MGos MRav MWat MWgw NWea SLim SPer WCFE WDin WFar WGwG WHar WStI WTel WWeb
	- var. *sternianus*	see *C. sternianus*
	frigidus	EBee NWea SRms
N	- 'Cornubia' ♀ H4	More than 30 suppliers
	- 'Fructu Luteo'	GKir MBri WWes
	- 'Notcutt's Variety'	EBee ELan ENot MRav WWes
§	- 'Pershore Coral'	GKir MBri
	- 'Saint Monica'	MBlu
	froebelii	SRms
	gamblei	WCwm
	ganghobaensis	SRms
	glabratus	SLPl SRms
	glacialis	SRms
	glaucophyllus	SEND SRms
§	*glomerulatus*	MBar SRms
	gracia **new**	SRms
	gracilis	SRms
	granatensis **new**	SRms
	harrovianus	SLPl SRms
	hedegaardii yellow-fruited **new**	SRms
	henryanus	CDoC SRms
	- 'Anne Cornwallis'	WBcn
	'Herbstfeuer'	see *C. salicifolius* 'Herbstfeuer'
	'Highlight'	see *C. pluriflorus*
	hillieri	SRms
	hissaricus	SRms
§	*hjelmqvistii*	LBuc SRms
	- 'Robustus'	see *C. hjelmqvistii*
	- 'Rotundifolius'	see *C. hjelmqvistii*
	hodjingensis **new**	SRms
	horizontalis ♀ H4	More than 30 suppliers
	- 'Peitz' **new**	SRms
	- 'Variegatus'	see *C. atropurpureus* 'Variegatus'
	- var. *wilsonii*	see *C. ascendens*
	hualiensis	SRms
	humifusus	see *C. dammeri*
	hummelii	CPle SRms
	hunanensis **new**	SRms
	hupehensis	ECre EWTr
	'Hybridus Pendulus'	More than 30 suppliers
§	*hylmoei*	SLPl SRms
	hypocarpus **new**	SRms
	ignavus	SLPl SRms
	ignescens	LRHS
	ignotus	SRms
	incanus **new**	SRms
	induratus	MBri SLPl SRms
	insculptus	SRms
	insolitus	SRms
	integerrimus	SRms
	- Mac&W 5916 from China	GIBF
§	*integrifolius* ♀ H4	CMHG EPfP EPla GKir LRHS MBar MWhi NBlu NMen SRms STre WMoo
§	- 'Donald Lowndes'	SRPl
	kangdingensis **new**	SRms
	klotzii **new**	SRms
	kuanensis **new**	SRms
	lacteus ♀ H4	EBee ELan ENot EPfP EPla EWTr GKir LBuc LPan LRHS MGos MRav SEND SHBN SLon SPer SPla SRPl SRms WCFE WDin WFar
	- 'Golden Gate'	EVFa
	- 'Variegatus' (v)	CEnd
	lancasteri	SRms
	langei	SRms
	laxiflorus	SRms
	lesliei **new**	SRms
§	*lidjiangensis*	SRms WCot
§	*linearifolius*	CLyd EHol GKir LRHS MWht
	lomahunensis	SRms
	lucidus	SRms
	ludlowii	SRms
§	*mairei*	CSBt SRms
	marginatus	SRms
	marquandii	EPla SRms
§	*meiophyllus*	SRms
	meuslii	SRms
	microphyllus hort.	see *C. purpurascens*
	microphyllus Wall. ex Lindl.	ENot GIBF MBar MGos NFor NWea SDix SHBN SPer STre WDin WTel WWal
	- var. *cochleatus*	see *C. cochleatus*
	- 'Donard Gem'	see *C. astrophoros*
	- 'Ruby' **new**	SRms
	- 'Teulon Porter'	see *C. astrophoros*
	- var. *thymifolius* hort.	see *C. linearifolius*
	- var. *thymifolius* (Lindl.) Koehne	see *C. integrifolius*
	milkedandai	SRms
	miniatus	SRms
	mirabilis **new**	SRms
	moliensis Yu 14196 **new**	GIBF
	monopyrenus	SRms
	'Mooncreeper'	see *C. dammeri* 'Mooncreeper'
	morulus	SRms
	moupinensis	SRms
	mucronatus	SRms
	multiflorus	SRms
	'My Pet'	NLAp
§	*nanshan*	NWea SRms

	- 'Boer'	see *C. apiculatus*
	newryensis	SRms
	niger	GIBF
	nitens	SRms
	nitidifolius	see *C. glomerulatus*
	nohelii new	GIBF SRms
	notabilis new	SRms
	nummularioides	SRms
	nummularius	SRms
	obscurus	SRms
	obtusus	SRms
	omissus	GIBF SRms
	otto-schwarzii	SRms
	pannosus	SLPl SRms WFar
	- 'Speckles' new	SRms
	paradoxus	SRms
	parkeri	SRms
	pekinensis	SRms
	permutatus	see *C. pluriflorus*
	perpusillus	SRms WFar
	'Pershore Coral'	see *C. frigidus* 'Pershore Coral'
§	*pluriflorus*	SRms
	poluninii	SRms
	polycarpus new	SRms
	praecox 'Boer'	see *C. apiculatus*
§	*procumbens*	EBee MAsh SRms WDin
	- 'Queen of Carpets'	CDoC EBee EBre ECtt GKir LRHS MAsh MBNS MBri MGos MRav NHol SLim SRms WGwG
	- 'Seattle'	SRms
	- 'Streib's Findling'	see *C.* 'Streib's Findling'
	prostratus	SRms
	- 'Arnold Forster'	SRms
	przewalskii	SRms
	pseudoobscurus new	SRms
§	*purpurascens*	CSBt EBee MDun WFar WOTO
	pyrenaicus	see *C. congestus*
	qungbixiensis new	SRms
	racemiflorus	EHol
§	*radicans*	LRHS
§	- 'Eichholz'	EBee GKir IArd LRHS MGos WWeb
	rannensis	SRms
§	*rehderi*	SRms
	roseus	GIBF SRms
	'Rothschildianus'	see *C. salicifolius* 'Rothschildianus'
	rotundifolius	EBee SLon SRms
	'Royal Beauty'	see *C.* x *suecicus* 'Coral Beauty'
	rufus new	SRms
	rugosus	SRms
	salicifolius	CLnd EMil GKir NBcc NFor NLon SRms WDin WFar
	- Autumn Fire	see *C. salicifolius* 'Herbstfeuer'
§	- 'Avonbank'	CDoC CEnd EBee MAsh WLRN WWeb
	- 'Bruno Orangeade' new	SRms
	- 'Elstead'	MRav
	- 'Exburyensis'	CBcs CDoC CDul CSam EBee EBre EPfP GKir MAsh MBri MGos SHBN SPer WDin WFar WHCG WWeb WWin
	- 'Gnom'	EBee EPfP GKir LAst LRHS MAsh MBar MBlu MBri MGos MRav MWht NFor NLon SRms WDin WFar
§	- 'Herbstfeuer'	EHol GKir MGos MRav NFor SRms WDin WFar WRHF
	- 'Merriott Weeper'	CDoC
	- Park Carpet	see *C. salicifolius* 'Parkteppich'
§	- 'Parkteppich'	NWea
	- 'Pendulus'	see *C.* 'Hybridus Pendulus'
	- 'Red Flare'	SRPl
	- 'Repens'	CChe CDoC CWib EHol EPfP NLon NWea SPer SRms WDin WFar
§	- 'Rothschildianus' ♀ H4	CCVT CDoC CSBt CTri CWib EBee EBre ECrN ECtt EMil ENot EPfP GKir LRHS MAsh MBar MRav NBlu SAga SLim SMac SPla WJas WMoo
	- var. *rugosus* hort.	see *C. hylmoei*
	- 'Scarlet Leader'	LRHS MBri
	salwinensis	SLPl SRms
	sandakphuensis	SRms
	saxatilis	SRms
	scandinavicus	SRms
	schantungensis	SRms
	schubertii	SRms
	serotinus misapplied	see *C. meiophyllus*
	serotinus Hutchinson	CAbP EPla SLPl SRms
	shannanensis new	SRms
	shansiensis	LRHS MBri SRms
	sherriffii	SRms
	sikangensis	GBin SLon SRms
	simonsii ♀ H4	CChe CDoC CLnd EBee EBre ELan EPfP GKir LBuc LRHS MBar MGos NWea SRms WDin WFar WHar
§	*splendens*	GIBF WFar
	- 'Sabrina'	see *C. splendens*
	spongbergii	SRms
	staintonii	SRms
§	*sternianus* ♀ H4	EPfP GKir LRHS MBar MBri SLPl SRms
	– ACE 2200	EPot
	'Streib's Findling'	SRms
	subacutus	SRms
	subadpressus	SRms
§	x *suecicus* 'Coral Beauty'	More than 30 suppliers
§	- 'Erlinda' (v)	CEnd CWib EBee MBar MGos SRms
	- 'Ifor'	SLPl SRms
	- 'Juliette' (v)	MBar MGos NBlu SLim WWeb
	- 'Jürgl'	SRms
	- 'Skogholm'	CSBt CWSG CWib EBee GKir LRHS MBar MGos MWat NWea SPer SRms WDin WHar WStI WWin
	taoensis	SRms
	tardiflorus	SRms
	tauricus	SRms
	teijiashanensis new	SRms
	tengyuehensis	SRms
	thimphuensis new	SRms
✦	*thraciaensis*	SRms
	tomentosus	SRms
	trinervis	SRms
	- 'Bruno' new	SRms
	tripyrenus	SRms
	tsarongensis new	SRms
	turbinatus	SRms
	uzbezicus new	SRms
	'Valkenburg' new	SRms
	vandelaarii new	SRms
	veitchii	SRms
	verruculosus	SRms
	villosulus	EHol SRms
	vilmorinianus	SRms
	wardii hort.	see *C. mairei*
	wardii W.W. Sm.	GIBF NBee
	x *watereri*	CCVT CDul CLnd CSBt CWib LRHS MGos NWea WCFE WDin WJas WTel WWeb
	- 'Avonbank'	see *C. salicifolius* 'Avonbank'
	- 'Corina'	SRms
	- 'Cornubia'	see *C. frigidus* 'Cornubia'
	- 'Goscote'	MGos
	- 'John Waterer' ♀ H4	EPfP MGos WBod WFar
	- 'Pendulus'	see *C.* 'Hybridus Pendulus'
	- 'Pink Champagne'	CAbP GKir LRHS MBri SPer
	- 'Willeke' new	SRms

	yakuticus **new**	SRms
	yallungensis **new**	SRms
	yinchangensis	SRms
	yui **new**	SRms
	zabelii	GIBF SRms

Cotula (Asteraceae)

	C&H 452	NWCA
	atrata	see *Leptinella atrata*
	– var. *dendyi*	see *Leptinella dendyi*
	coronopifolia	CBen CSev CWat LPBA MSta NBlu
		NPer SBHF SWat WWpP
§	*hispida*	More than 30 suppliers
	lineariloba	ECha EWes LBee LRHS
	minor	see *Leptinella minor*
	perpusilla	see *Leptinella pusilla*
	'Platt's Black'	see *Leptinella squalida* 'Platt's Black'
	potentilloides	see *Leptinella potentillina*
	pyrethrifolia	see *Leptinella pyrethrifolia*
	rotundata	see *Leptinella rotundata*
	sericea	see *Leptinella albida*
	serrulata	see *Leptinella serrulata*
	squalida	see *Leptinella squalida*

Cotyledon (Crassulaceae)

	chrysantha	see *Rosularia chrysantha*
	gibbiflora	see *Echeveria gibbiflora* var. *metallica*
	var. *metallica*	
	oppositifolia	see *Chiastophyllum oppositifolium*
	orbiculata	CStu SDix SIgm
	– var. *oblonga*	EBee EMan SChr WCot WEas
	simplicifolia	see *Chiastophyllum oppositifolium*
	undulata	WEas

Cousinia (Asteraceae)

	alpina **new**	EBee

Coxella (Apiaceae)

	dieffenbachii	GCal WCot

Crambe (Brassicaceae)

	cordifolia ♀ H4	More than 30 suppliers
	maritima ♀ H4	More than 30 suppliers
	– 'Lilywhite'	ILis WCot WHer
	orientalis	WCot
	tatarica	CArn EMan NLar WPer

cranberry see *Vaccinium macrocarpon*, *V. oxycoccos*

Crassula (Crassulaceae)

	anomala	SChr
	arborescens	SRms STre
	argentea	see *C. ovata*
	coccinea	CHEx CTrC SPar WOld
	dejecta x *coccinea*	CTrC
	falcata ♀ H1	EShb IBlr MBri
§	*helmsii*	EHon EMFW IHMH WWpP
	justi-corderoyi	CHal
	lactea	CHal STre
§	*milfordiae*	GDra GKir MBar MOne MWat
		NBir NJOw NLAp WPer
	multicava **new**	GFai
	muscosa	STre
	obtusa	SRot
§	*ovata* ♀ H1	CHal EBak EPem MBri NPer SPar
		SVen SWal
	– 'Blue Bird'	EPem
	– 'Hummel's Sunset' (v) ♀ H1	CHal EPem SPar
*	– *minima* **new**	EPem

*	– *nana*	STre
	– 'Variegata' (v)	CHal EBak
	pellucida subsp. *marginalis*	CHal
*	– – 'Variegata' (v)	CHal
	peploides	SChr
	perforata	CHal
	– 'Variegata' (v)	CHal
	portulacea	see *C. ovata*
	recurva	see *C. helmsii*
	rupestris ♀ H1	MBri
§	*sarcocaulis*	CHEx CHal CStu CTri ELan EMlt
		EOas ESis GGar GTou ITim MTho
		NMen NVic NWCA SIgm SIng
		SPar SPlb SRms SRot SScr STre
		WAbe WEas WLow WPat WSHC
		WWin
	– *alba*	CHal EMlt SHFr STre WPer
	– 'Ken Aslet'	SPet STre
	schmidtii	CHal MBri
	sedifolia	see *C. milfordiae*
	sediformis	see *C. milfordiae*
	socialis	CHal WPat
	tetragona	SEND
	'Très Bon'	STre

Crataegus ✿ (Rosaceae)

	arnoldiana	CEnd CLnd CTho EPfP GKir
		MBri MCoo SEND SKee SLPl
		WOrn
	'Autumn Glory'	CEnd CLnd EBee EBre GKir LRHS
		MGos
	azarolus	CAgr LEdu
	champlainensis	CLnd CTho
	chlorosarca	GIBF
	chungtienensis	SSpi
	ACE 1624	
N	*coccinea*	NWea
	cordata	see *C. phaenopyrum*
	crus-galli hort.	see *C. persimilis* 'Prunifolia'
	crus-galli L.	CCVT CDoC CDul CLnd CTho
		ECrN EPfP GKir LBuc MHFa SPer
		WDin WJas WMou
	– var. *pyracanthifolia*	CLnd CTho
	douglasii **new**	GIBF
	x *durobrivensis*	CAgr CLnd CTho GKir
	ellwangeriana	CAgr CLnd ECrN GKir
	eriocarpa	CLnd
	flabellata	CEnd GIBF GKir SSpi
	gemmosa	CEnd CLnd CTho GKir
	greggiana	CLnd
	x *grignonensis*	CBcs CCVT CDul CLnd EBee EMil
		ENot MHFa SPer WJas
	jonesiae	EPfP
	laciniata	see *C. orientalis*
§	*laevigata*	NWea WMou
	– 'Coccinea Plena'	see *C. laevigata* 'Paul's Scarlet'
	– 'Crimson Cloud'	CDoC CEnd CLnd CWSG CWib
		EBee ECrN ELan EMui ENot EPfP
		GKir LRHS MAsh MBri MGos
		MWat NWea SCoo SKee SLim
		SLon SPer WJas WOrn
	– 'Flore Pleno'	see *C. laevigata* 'Plena'
	– 'Mutabilis'	CLnd CTho GKir SHBN
§	– 'Paul's Scarlet' (d) ♀ H4	More than 30 suppliers
	– 'Pink Corkscrew'	CTho GKir MBlu WPat WWes
§	– 'Plena' (d)	CBcs CDoC CDul CLnd CRez
		CSBt CTho CWib EBee EWTr
		GKir LAst LPan LRHS MBri MHFa
		MWat NWea SFam SHBN SKee
		SLim SPer WDin WOrn
	– 'Punicea'	GKir

- 'Rosea'	SKee
- 'Rosea Flore Pleno' (d) ♀ H4	More than 30 suppliers
x *lavalleei*	CCVT CLnd CTri EBee ECrN ENot EPfP GKir MHFa NWea SKee SPer SRPl WDin
- 'Carrierei' ♀ H4	CDoC CDul CSam CTho EPfP GKir LPan LRHS MAsh MBri NWea SCoo SKee SRPl
maximowiczii **new**	GIBF
x *media* 'Gireoudii' (v)	CDul CEnd CWib GKir LNet MBlu MGos WPat
mexicana	see *C. pubescens* f. *stipulacea*
mollis	CTho ECrN EPfP NWea
monogyna	CBcs CCVT CDoC CKin CLnd CSam EBre ECrN ELan ENot EPfP GKir GTre GWCH LBuc LHyr LRHS MBar MBri MGos MHFa NBee NBlu NWea SPer SRPl WDin WMou
§ - 'Biflora'	CDul CEnd CTho EBee ECrN MAsh MCoo MGos NWea SLim WPGP
- 'Compacta'	MBlu SMad
- 'Ferox'	CTho
- 'Flexuosa'	LNet
- 'Praecox'	see *C. monogyna* 'Biflora'
- 'Stricta'	CCVT CDul CLnd CSBt CTho EBee ECrN ENot GKir MHFa
- 'Variegata' (v)	CDul ECrN LNet WBcn
x *mordenensis* 'Toba' (d)	CDoC CDul CLnd CTho
neofluvialis **new**	GIBF
orientalis	CDul CEnd CLnd CMCN EBee ECrN EPfP GIBF GKir LRHS MAsh MBri MCoo NWea SIDN SKee SLPl SLim SPer SSpi WCFE WJas WMou
oxyacanthu	see *C. laevigata*
pedicellata	CDul CLnd CTho EPfP GKir SKee
§ *persimilis* 'Prunifolia' ♀ H4	More than 30 suppliers
- 'Prunifolia Splendens'	EWTr LPan
§ *phaenopyrum*	CDul CLnd CMCN CTho EPfP GIBF GKir SLPl SSpi WMou
pinnatifida	SMad
- var. *major*	CEnd EPfP GKir SMad
- 'Big Golden Star'	CTho ECrN ESim
prunifolia	see *C. persimilis* 'Prunifolia'
§ *pubescens* f. *stipulacea*	SSpi
punctata	SLPl
sanguinea	GIBF
schraderiana	CLnd CTho
succulenta var. *macracantha*	GKir
tanacetifolia	CLnd CTho GKir MBlu SPoG SSpi
uniflora	GIBF
viridis 'Winter King'	GKir MBlu
wattiana	CTho

x *Crataemespilus* (Rosaceae)

grandiflora	CDul CLnd CTho GKir

Craterostigma (Scrophulariaceae)

wilmsii **new**	SPlb

Cremanthodium (Asteraceae)

lineare **new**	EBee

Crenularia see *Aethionema*

Crepis (Asteraceae)

aurea	ECha GAbr IBlr NJOw NWCA WCom
incana ♀ H4	CFee CPla EBre ECha EGoo GBri

	GKir GSki LPhx LRHS MAvo MTho NBid NChi NSla NWCA SIng WAbe WHil WPat WWin
rubra	LPio LRHS

Crinitaria see *Aster*

Crinodendron (Elaeocarpaceae)

§ *hookerianum* ♀ H3	More than 30 suppliers
- 'Ada Hoffmann' **new**	NLar
patagua	CBcs CPLG CPle CSam CStu CWib EBee GGar GKir GQui IDee LRHS MLan SBrw SLon SPer SRPl WAbe WBod WFar WSHC

Crinum (Amaryllidaceae)

asiaticum var. *sinicum*	CDes EBee
§ *bulbispermum*	CFil CFir EBee ELan WCot
- 'Album'	EMan
§ *campanulatum*	EBee
capense	see *C. bulbispermum*
'Carolina Beauty' **new**	WCot
'Ellen Bosanquet'	CDes CFir EBee WCot WPGP
erubescens **new**	WCot
'Hanibal's Dwarf' **new**	WCot
macowanii **new**	WCot
moorei	CDes CFir EBee NBlo NRog SChr WPGP XBlo
- f. *album*	CAvo WMul
§ x *powellii* ♀ H3	More than 30 suppliers
- 'Album' ♀ H3	CAvo CBct CDes CHEx CPne CSpe CTca EBee ECha ELan EMan EWes LAma LBow LPio LRHS MRav NRog SSpi WCot WCru WFar WPGP WPic WViv
- 'Harlemense'	SSpi
- 'Longifolium'	see *C. bulbispermum*
- 'Roseum'	see *C.* x *powellii*
variabile **new**	EBee WCot
yemense	WCot

Criogenes see *Cypripedium*

Crithmum (Apiaceae)

maritimum	CArn EBee GPoy MSal NLar SIgm WBri WWye

Crocosmia ✿ (Iridaceae)

'African Glow' **new**	EBee
'Amberglow'	CFlw CFwr CWcs EBee EWoo IBlr LAst MBNS WFar WRus WWpP
'Anniversary'	CRDP SSpl
aurea hort.	see *C.* x *crocosmiiflora* 'George Davison'
aurea ambig.	NBir SPlb WHil
aurea Planchon	CPou SSpi
- JCA 3.100.000	WCot
- var. *aurea*	GCal IBlr
- var. *maculata*	IBlr
- var. *pauciflora*	IBlr
aurea x *paniculata* **new**	CBos
Bressingham Beacon = 'Blos'	EBre GGar GKir IBlr LRHS NHol WBea WRHF
'Bressingham Blaze'	CBre CMHG EBre GCal GKir IBlr LRHS NOak WCot WHil WWin
'Cadenza'	IBlr
'Carnival'	IBlr
'Cascade'	IBlr
'Chinatown'	IBlr
N 'Citronella' misapplied	see *C.* 'Honey Angels'
'Comet' Knutty	GBuc IBlr IBro MBri SIgm SSpi WHil WMaN WWhi

× _crocosmiiflora_ COlW EGra EPla IBlr LAst NLon NOrc SIng SPlb SRms SWat WCHb WCot WFar WMoo WRHF WShi WWpP WWye

- 'A.J. Hogan' IBal IBlr
- 'Apricot Queen' IBlr
- 'Baby Barnaby' CKno EBee IBlr MTed WPGP
- 'Babylon' CBos CBre CBro CFwr CPou CSpe CTca EBee GKir IBlr IBro MAvo MBNS MBri MTed NBir NGdn SSpi WAul WFar WHil WLin WMaN WPer WWhi
- 'Burford Bronze' IBlr
- 'Buttercup' CFwr EBee IBlr
- 'Canary Bird' CBro CPrp CRow CSam EBee GAbr GCal GMac IBlr LRHS NGdn
- 'Carmin Brillant' ♀ H3-4 CAvo CBos CBro CFwr CHar CMHG CRow CSam CTca EBre ECha GCal GGar GKir GMac IBlr IBro LAma LRHS MBri NHol NSti SCro SDys WCot WFar WHil WOld WPGP
- 'Challa' CFwr EBee
- 'Citronella' J.E. Fitt CBro CFwr CHar CSam CTri EBee ECGP EChP EHrv EPfP GKir MUlv NGdn NHol WHoo WRha
- 'Columbus' CFwr CM&M EBee EChP EFou GMac LHop LRHS SSpe SVil WAul WMnd
- 'Colwall' CPou IBlr
- 'Constance' CBre CBro CElw CFwr CSam CTca EBee EChP EPot GKir IBlr LRHS MBNS MBri MNrw NGdn WCHb WFar WHil WLin
- I 'Corona' IBlr
- 'Corten' IBlr
- § 'Croesus' CAbx EGra GBri IBlr MAvo MCLN MRav SCro WCot WHil
- 'Custard Cream' GKir IBlr IBro LRHS WCot WFar WHil
- 'D.H. Houghton' IBlr
- 'Debutante' CBos CMil IBlr MCLN WCot WMaN WRus WWhi
- 'Dusky Maiden' More than 30 suppliers
- § 'E.A. Bowles' CPou EBee GCal IBlr WCot
- 'Eastern Promise' CBre CMea EBee GKir IBlr SMrm SPlb WLin
- 'Elegans' CElw CStr ECtt IBlr
- § 'Emily McKenzie' More than 30 suppliers
- 'Etoile de Feu' IBlr
- 'Fantasie' CFwr EBee MBNS
- 'Firebrand' IBlr
- 'Flamethrower' IBlr
- § 'George Davison' Davison More than 30 suppliers
- § 'Gerbe d'Or' More than 30 suppliers
- § 'Gloria' IBlr
- § 'Golden Glory' CPrp CSam EBlw EHrv GKir GMaP IBlr NBir NChi NHol NPPs STes WBrE WCot WCra WFar WHil
- 'Golden Sheaf' GBri IBlr NGdn SDys SUsu WBea
- 'Goldfinch' IBlr IBro
- 'Hades' IBlr
- 'His Majesty' CBro CMil CPou CRDP CRow CSam CSpe EBee GKir IBlr IBro LRHS SAga SCro SDys SMad WFar WHil WMaN WPer WWhi
- § 'Jackanapes' More than 30 suppliers
- § 'James Cocy' J.E. Fitt More than 30 suppliers
- * 'Jesse van Dyke' IBlr
- § 'Jessie' CElw EBee GCal IBlr LRHS NPPs WCot WPer WWpP
- 'Kiatschou' EBee GMac IBlr LEur SDys
- 'Lady Hamilton' More than 30 suppliers
- 'Lady McKenzie' see C. × _crocosmiiflora_ 'Emily McKenzie'
- 'Lady Oxford' EBre EMan GCal IBlr IBro
- 'Lutea' EBre EGra IBlr
- 'Marjorie' LAma NHol WCot
- 'Mephistopheles' IBlr
- 'Météore' CFwr CTca EBee GGar LAst MBNS NOrc WWeb
- 'Morning Light' CBos CPen ECtt IBlr WCot
- § 'Mrs Geoffrey Howard' CBos CPlt CSam EBee GBri IBlr IBro MAvo SUsu WCot WCru WMaN WPGP WWhi
- 'Mrs Morrison' see C. × _crocosmiiflora_ 'Mrs Geoffrey Howard'
- 'Newry seedling' see C. × _crocosmiiflora_ 'Prometheus'
- 'Nimbus' CBos CRDP GBri IBlr MAvo WCot
- § 'Norwich Canary' More than 30 suppliers
- I 'Pepper' IBlr
- 'Polo' CFwr EBee
- 'Princess' see C. × _crocosmiiflora_ 'Red Knight'
- 'Princess Alexandra' IBlr WCHb
- 'Prolificans' IBlr
- § 'Prometheus' IBlr
- ♀ 'Queen Alexandra' J.E. Fitt CBos EChP ECha IBlr IBro LAma LHop SWat WHal WPer
- 'Queen Charlotte' IBlr
- 'Queen Mary II' CPar EMan IBlr WCot WHil
- 'Queen of Spain' CPrp EBre GKir IBlr IBro LRHS MBri MLLN SCro WHil WLin WViv
- 'Rayon d'Or' IBlr
- 'Red King' CFwr CHar CTca EBee EBla GGar IBlr LAst WWeb
- § 'Red Knight' CM&M IBlr IBro MAvo MTed WCot
- 'Rheingold' see C. × _crocosmiiflora_ 'Golden Glory'
- 'Rose Queen' IBlr
- 'Saracen' EBee EBlw EChP EMan GCal IBlr MAvo SIgm SMad SMrm SOkh SPla SSpi WCot WFar WPer
- 'Sir Matthew Wilson' EBre EGra GBri IBlr WCot
- 'Solfatare' ♀ H3 More than 30 suppliers
- 'Solfatare Coleton Fishacre' see C. × _crocosmiiflora_ 'Gerbe d'Or'
- 'Star of the East' ♀ H3 More than 30 suppliers
- § 'Sulphurea' CPou CRow CSam EBee EOrc GCal GGar GKir IBlr LAma NHol NPPs SDix SIng WAbe WCot WEas WHal WHil WPer WTin
- 'Sultan' CBro CElw CSpe EBee IBlr LPio WCot WFar WPGP
- 'Venus' CAbx CBre CFwr CPen CPou CTca EBee EBre EGra GBuc IBlr STes WFar WLin
- 'Vesuvius' W. Pfitzer CElw CSpe GCal GKir IBlr LRHS WFar
- 'Culzean Peach' GAbr GCal MAvo NBir NPPs SMrm WCot
- 'Darkleaf Apricot' see C. × _crocosmiiflora_ 'Gerbe d'Or'
- 'Eclatant' IBlr
- 'Eldorado' see C. × _crocosmiiflora_ 'E.A. Bowles'
- 'Emberglow' More than 30 suppliers
- 'Fandango' IBlr
- 'Festival Orange' MAvo
- * 'Feuerser' NHol
- 'Fire King' misapplied see C. × _crocosmiiflora_ 'Jackanapes'
- 'Fire Sprite' **new** IBlr
- 'Firebird' EBre GBuc IBlr IGor LRHS NHol SIgm SMer WBea WCot

'Fireglow' — IBlr WFar WPer
fucata — IBlr
- 'Jupiter' — see *C.* 'Jupiter'
- plicate leaf — IBlr
* 'Fusilade' — IBlr
'George Davison' hort. — see *C.* x *crocosmiiflora* 'Golden Glory', 'Sulphurea'
Golden Fleece Lemoine — see *C.* x *crocosmiiflora* 'Gerbe d'Or'
'Goldsprite' — IBlr
'Highlight' — IBlr
§ 'Honey Angels' — CBos CFwr CPrp EBee EChP EGle EHrv EMan GKir ITim LAst MAvo NBir NChi NHol NSti SCro STes SUsu WBod WBro WCot WCra WFar WHil WMoo WOld WPer
'Irish Dawn' — CTca
'Jennine' — WHil
Jenny Bloom — CM&M EBee EBre GBuc GKir
 = 'Blacro'PBR — GSki LRHS MNFA NBir
'John Boots' — CFwr CPen EBee EPot GBuc MAvo MBNS
§ 'Jupiter' — CBos CBre CHar CM&M CPou EBee EFou GMac IBlr LRHS NHol SApp SMrm WCot WFar WLin WOld
'Kiaora' — IBlr
'Lady Wilson' hort. — see *C.* x *crocosmiiflora* 'Norwich Canary'
'Lambrook Gold' — CAvo
'Lana de Savary' — GCal IBlr WCot
'Late Cornish' — see *C.* x *crocosmiiflora* 'Queen Alexandra'
'Late Lucifer' — CHEx SDix
§ *latifolia* — IBlr
- 'Castle Ward Late' — CAbx CBos CLAP CPou CRow EBee ECha EFou GCal GGar IBlr MNFA MStc WMoo
 'Vulcan' T.Smith — GKir IBlr MAvo
'Lord Nelson' — CBos
'Loweswater' — MAvo
'Lucifer' ♀ H4 — More than 30 suppliers
'Malahide Castle' — CRDP WCot
§ 'Mandarin' — IBlr
§ 'Marcotijn' — EBee EBre EChP EMan EWoo GCal IBlr IGor NChi NLon WGwG
'Mars' — CFwr CMil EBee EBla ECtt EWes GBuc GCal GGar GMac IBlr IBro LRHS MAnl MCAu NHol SCro SPlb WCHb WFar WOld WPGP WPer
§ *masoniorum* ♀ H3 — More than 30 suppliers
- Auricorn — IBlr
- 'Dixter Flame' — IBlr SDix
- 'Fern Hill' — IBlr
- 'Flamenco' — CHad GKir IBlr IBro LRHS MBri MTed
- 'Minotaur' — IBlr
- red — COlW IBlr
- 'Rowallane orange' — IBlr MAvo NHol
- 'Rowallane Yellow' — CBos EBre GBri GKir IBlr LRHS MAvo MBri NHol WCot WHil
 ♀ H3-4
mathewsiana — IBlr
aff. *mathewsiana* — IBlr
'Merryman' — GMac WRus
'Mistral' — CAbx CFwr CTca EBee GBuc IBlr LRHS MNrw WCot WFar WLin WMoo
'Mount Stewart' — see *C.* x *crocosmiiflora* 'Jessie'
'Mount Usher' — GCal IBlr
'Mr Bedford' — see *C.* x *crocosmiiflora* 'Croesus'
Old Hat — see *C.* 'Walberton Red'
'Orange Devil' — MBri
'Orange Lucifer' — EFou
'Orangeade' — CHar EBee EBre GBri IBlr WLin
§ *paniculata* — CBcs CElw CHEx CPLG CPou

EBla EChP ECtt EMar GAbr GGar IBlr LBow LRHS MNFA MNrw NHol NOrc SAPC SChu SIng SPar SPet WCot WHil WPen WPrP WShi
- brown/orange — IBlr
- 'Major' — CTri
- x *masoniorum* — IBlr
 'Shocking'
- red — EBre GKir IBlr
* - 'Ruby Velvet' — IBlr
aff. *paniculata* — ECtt IBlr
pearsei — IBlr
'Plaisir' — CFwr CTca EBee EPot IBlr MBNS MBri WFar
pottsii — CAvo CFee CRow EChP ECtt GBin GMac IBlr LEur LHop WFar
- CD&R 109 — CBre CLAP CPou
- 'Culzean Pink' — EBee EBre GBuc GKir IBlr WHil
- deep pink — IBlr IGor
- 'Grandiflora' — IBlr
- 'Lady Bangor' **new** — CBos
rosea — see *Tritonia disticha* subsp. *rubrolucens*
'Rowden Bronze' — see *C.* x *crocosmiiflora* 'Gerbe d'Or'
'Rowden Chrome' — see *C.* x *crocosmiiflora* 'George Davison'
'Rubygold' — IBlr
'Saturn' — see *C.* 'Jupiter'
'Scarlatti' — IBlr
'Severn Sunrise' ♀ H3-4 — More than 30 suppliers
'Short Red' — NCat
'Sonate' — NCat NGby NHol SPlb WPer
'Spitfire' — CBot CMil CRow CSam CTca EBlw EBre EChP ECha EGle EMar GAbr GBuc GKir GSki IBlr LHop LRHS MArl MRav NHol SChu SPla SWat WEas WFar WLRN
'Sunset' — GSki
'Sunzest' — WFar WLow
'Tangerine Queen' — CAbx CPlt EBre EGra IBlr WCot
* 'Tiger' — CElw IBlr
'Vic's Yellow' — SGar SMrm SSpc
* 'Voyager' — CFwr CTca GKir IBlr MBri NBlu NPPs WHil
I 'Vulcan' A.Bloom — CMdw EBre FWoo IBlr LRHS SAga WFar WHil
§ 'Walberton Red' — CFwr IBlr SApp SUsu
Walborton Yellow — CFwr SApp SSpi WCot
 = 'Walcroy'PBR
'Zeal Giant' — IBlr
'Zeal Tan' — CElw CPen EBee EChP ELan EMan IBlr NCat SMad WCot
Zeal unnamed — IBlr

Crocus ✿ (Iridaceae)

WM 9809 from Bosnia — MPhe
abantensis — CBro EPot ERos
adanensis — ERos
albiflorus — see *C. vernus* subsp. *albiflorus*
§ *ancyrensis* — CBro EPar EPot LAma NGar NRog WLin
- 'Golden Bunch' — ETub LPhx LRHS WShi
§ *angustifolius* ♀ H4 — CBro EBre EPot ERos ETub GIBF LAma NRog
- 'Minor' — EPot LAma
antalyensis — EPot
asturicus — see *C. serotinus* subsp. *salzmannii*
asumaniae — ECho EHyt EPot ERos
aureus — see *C. flavus* subsp. *flavus*
banaticus ♀ H4 — CBro EHyt EPot ERos GCrs GEdr LAma NGar NMGW WCot WWst

- *albus* ERos NGar
baytopiorum CAvo EPot ERos
biflorus LAma NRog
- WM 9908 MPhe
- subsp. *adamii* ERos LAma
- subsp. *alexandri* EPot ERos LAma LRHS NRog
§ - subsp. *biflorus* ERos LAma
§ - - 'Parkinsonii' ERos
- subsp. *crewei* ERos
- subsp. *isauricus* ERos
- subsp. *melantherus* ERos
- JCA 341.353 WCot
- 'Miss Vain' CAvo EPot LAma LRHS
- var. *parkinsonii* see *C. biflorus* subsp. *biflorus* 'Parkinsonii'
- subsp. *pulchricolor* LAma
- subsp. *tauri* WWst
- subsp. *weldenii* 'Albus' CMea EPot ERos LAma
- - 'Fairy' CBro CMea EPot ERos LAma LRHS
boryi CAvo EHyt
cambessedesii ERos SBla
§ *cancellatus* ERos LAma
   subsp. *cancellatus*
- var. *cilicicus* see *C. cancellatus* subsp. *cancellatus*
- subsp. *mazziaricus* CNic ERos
- subsp. *pamphylicus* ERos
candidus see *C. olivieri* subsp. *olivieri*
   var. *subflavus*
§ *cartwrightianus* ♀ H4 CAvo CBro EPot LAma
N - 'Albus' ♀ H4 EPot ERos
chrysanthus 'Advance' CBro EPar EPot LAma NRog
- 'Ard Schenk' EPot LAma LRHS
- 'Aubade' EPot
- 'Blue Bird' CBro EPar EPot LAma LRHS
- 'Blue Pearl' ♀ H4 CAvo CBro CMea EPar EPot LAma LPhx LRHS MBri NBir NRog WShi
- 'Blue Peter' LAma
- 'Brass Band' LAma LRHS
- 'Canary Bird' NFor NRog
- 'Cream Beauty' ♀ H4 CAvo CBro EBre EPar EPot ETub LAma LPhx LRHS MBri NBir NRog
- 'Dorothy' EPot LAma LRHS NRog
- 'E.A. Bowles' ♀ H4 ECho LAma
- 'E.P. Bowles' CBro EPot LAma LRHS MBri NRog
- 'Elegance' LAma LRHS
- 'Eye-catcher' EPot LAma LRHS
- var. *fuscotinctus* EPot LAma MBri NRog
- 'Gipsy Girl' CBro EPot LAma LRHS MBri NRog
- 'Goldilocks' EPot LAma LRHS
- 'Herald' LAma LRHS
- 'Ladykiller' ♀ H4 CAvo CBro EBre EPar EPot LAma LRHS MBri NRog
- 'Moonlight' CAvo EPot ETub LAma LRHS NRog
- 'Prins Claus' EPot LAma
- 'Prinses Beatrix' EPot LAma LRHS NRog
- 'Romance' CAvo EPot LAma LRHS
- 'Saturnus' EPot LAma NRog
- 'Skyline' CBro EPot LRHS
- 'Snow Bunting' ♀ H4 CAvo CBro EPar EPot LAma LPhx LRHS NBir NRog WShi
- 'Spring Pearl' CBro LAma LRHS
- 'Warley' NRog
- 'White Beauty' LAma
- 'White Triumphator' CBro EPot LAma NBir NRog
- 'Zenith' LAma
- 'Zwanenburg Bronze' ♀ H4 EBre EPar EPot LAma LRHS NRog
'Cloth of Gold' see *C. angustifolius*
clusii see *C. serotinus* subsp. *clusii*
corsicus ♀ H4 EPot ERos LAma
dalmaticus EPot LAma
- 'Petrovac' **new** WWst

danfordiae ERos ETow
'Dutch Yellow' see *C.* x *luteus* 'Golden Yellow'
etruscus ♀ H4 ERos
- 'Rosalind' EPot WLin
- 'Zwanenburg' EPot LAma NCel WCot
flavus see *C. flavus* subsp. *flavus*
§ - subsp. *flavus* ♀ H4 EPot GIBF LAma LRHS WCot WShi
fleischeri EPot ERos LAma NGar
gargaricus ERos
- subsp. *gargaricus* ERos
- subsp. *herbertii* WWst
'Golden Mammoth' see *C.* x *luteus* 'Golden Yellow'
goulimyi ♀ H4 CAvo CBro EPar EPot ERos LAma LRHS SIgm WCom WCot
- 'Albus' see *C. goulimyi* 'Mani White'
- var. *leucanthus* EHyt
§ - 'Mani White' ♀ H4 EHyt ERos
graveolens **new** EPot
'Haarlem Gem' LAma
§ *hadriaticus* ♀ H4 CAvo ERos LAma
- var. *chrysobelonicus* see *C. hadriaticus*
imperati ♀ H4 ERos
- subsp. *imperati* CAvo EPot LAma LRHS
   'De Jager'
- subsp. *suaveolens* ERos
x *jessoppiae* ERos WWst
karduchorum CBro EPot LAma NRog
korolkowii EPar EPot ERos GIBF LAma LPhx LRHS
- 'Kiss of Spring' EPot
- 'Unicoloratus' WWst
kosaninii EPot ERos
kotschyanus ♀ H4 CBri ECho EHyt EPar
- 'Albus' ECho EHyt LRHS
§ - subsp. *kotschyanus* CBro EPot LAma NCel NRog WCot
- var. *leucopharynx* ECha LRHS
laevigatus ♀ H4 LAma
- 'Fontenayi' CBro EHyt EPot ETub LAma LEdu WPnP
- from Crete EHyt
'Large Yellow' see *C.* x *luteus* 'Golden Yellow'
ligusticus EPar
longiflorus ♀ H4 CAvo CBro EPot ERos GEdr
§ x *luteus* 'Golden Yellow' EPot ETub LAma NCel
   ♀ H4
§ - 'Stellaris' EPot ERos
malyi ♀ H2-4 EHyt ERos GCrs
'Mammoth Yellow' see *C.* x *luteus* 'Golden Yellow'
mathewii JCA 347.910 WCot
medius ♀ H4 CBro ECha EPot ERos LAma NMGW NRog
michelsonii WWst
minimus CBro CMea EHyt EPot ERos LAma LRHS NGar WLin
niveus CAvo CBro EHyt EPot ERos GCrs LAma WCot
nudiflorus CAvo CBro EHyt ERos GCrs LAma NMen WCot
ochroleucus ♀ H4 CBro EBre EHyt EPot ERos LAma LRHS NRog
olivieri ERos LAma
- subsp. *balansae* CMea EPot
   'Zwanenburg'
§ - subsp. *olivieri* EHyt ERos LAma LRHS
pallasii subsp. *pallasii* ERos
pelistericus EHyt
pestalozzae EHyt ERos
- var. *caeruleus* ERos
pulchellus ♀ H4 ECho EPot ERos GCrs LAma MBow
'Purpureus' see *C. vernus* 'Purpureus Grandiflorus'
reticulatus subsp. WWst
   hittiticus **new**

- subsp. *reticulatus*	EPot
rujanensis	ERos
salzmannii	see *C. serotinus* subsp. *salzmannii*
sativus	CArn CAvo CBod CBro EHyt ELan EOHP EPar EPot ETub GPoy LAma LRHS MBri MSal NBir NGHP NRog
- var. *cartwrightianus*	see *C. cartwrightianus*
scepusiensis	see *C. vernus* subsp. *vernus* var. *scepusiensis*
§ *serotinus* subsp. *clusii*	CBro EPot LAma
§ - subsp. *salzmannii*	CBro EHyt EPar EPot ERos LAma LRHS
- - 'Erectophyllus'	EPot
sibiricus	see *C. sieberi*
§ *sieberi* ♀ H4	EPot ERos
§ - 'Albus' ♀ H4	CAvo CBro ECho EPot LAma LRHS WLin
- subsp. *atticus*	EPot LAma LRHS
- 'Bowles' White'	see *C. sieberi* 'Albus'
- 'Firefly'	CBro EPot LAma LRHS NRog
- 'Hubert Edelsten' ♀ H4	EPot ERos LAma
- subsp. *sublimis* 'Tricolor' ♀ H4	CAvo CBro ECho EPot ERos ETub LAma LRHS NMen
- 'Violet Queen'	CBro EPot LAma LRHS MBri NRog
speciosus ♀ H4	CAvo CBro EBre EPar EPot ETub LAma LRHS MBro NMGW NRog WCot WHoo WShi
- 'Aitchisonii'	CBro EPot LAma LRHS
- 'Albus' ♀ H4	CBro CMea EPar EPot LRHS
- 'Artabir'	CBro EPot LRHS
- 'Cassiope'	EPot LAma LRHS
- 'Conqueror'	CBro ETub LAma LRHS
- 'Oxonian'	EMon EPot LAma LRHS
x *stellaris*	see *C.* x *luteus* 'Stellaris'
susianus	see *C. angustifolius*
suterianus	see *C. olivieri* subsp. *olivieri*
tommasinianus ♀ H4	CAvo CBro CMea ECho EPar EPot ETub LAma MBri MRav NMGW SRms WShi
- f. *albus*	CBro EHyt EPot LAma LRHS WCom
- 'Barr's Purple'	EPot LAma LRHS
- 'Bobbo'	EHyt
- 'Eric Smith'	CAvo
- 'Lilac Beauty'	EPot LAma
- var. *pictus*	CAvo EPot ERos LAma WCom
- var. *roseus*	CBro CMea EPot ERos LAma LPhx NMGW WCom WCot
- 'Ruby Giant'	CAvo CBro CNic EHyt EPar EPot ETub LAma LRHS NCel NMGW NRog WCot WShi
- subsp. *tommasinianus* new	GIBF
- 'Whitewell Purple'	CAvo CBro ECho EPot ETub LAma LPhx LRHS MBri NCel NMGW NRog WCot
tournefortii ♀ H2-4	CBro ERos LAma WCot WWst
§ 'Vanguard'	CBro EPot ETub LAma LPhx NRog
veluchensis	EPot WCot
§ *vernus* subsp. *albiflorus*	EPot ERos LAma
- 'Enchantress'	EPot LAma
- 'Flower Record'	EPot NBir
- 'Graecus'	EPot ERos
- 'Grand Maître'	LAma NRog
- 'Haarlem Gem'	EPot
- 'Jeanne d'Arc'	CBro EPot ETub LAma LPhx NBir NCel NRog
- 'King of the Blues'	NCel NRog
- 'King of the Striped'	NCel
- 'Paulus Potter'	NRog
- 'Peter Pan'	NRog
- 'Pickwick'	EPot ETub LAma NBir NCel NRog

§ - 'Purpureus Grandiflorus'	CBro EPot LAma NCel NRog
- 'Queen of the Blues'	CBro EPot LPhx NCel NRog
- 'Remembrance'	EPot ETub LAma LPhx NBir NCel NRog
- 'Sky Blue'	NCel NRog
- 'Snowstorm'	LAma NCel
- 'Striped Beauty'	LAma NCel NRog
- 'Vanguard'	see *C.* 'Vanguard'
- subsp. *vernus*	see *C. vernus* 'Purpureus Grandiflorus' Grandiflorus'
§ - - Heuffelianus Group	EPot WWst
* - - *napolitanus*	ERos
- - 'Oradea' new	WWst
§ - - var. *scepusiensis*	EPot ERos
- 'Victor Hugo'	NRog
versicolor	EHyt
- 'Picturatus'	EBre EPot ERos ETub LAma LRHS WLin
'Yellow Mammoth'	see *C.* x *luteus* 'Golden Yellow'
'Zephyr' ♀ H4	CBro EPot ERos ETub LAma LRHS
zonatus	see *C. kotschyanus* subsp. *kotschyanus*

Croomia (Stemonaceae)

heterosepala new	WCru

Crowea (Rutaceae)

exalata x *saligna*	CPLG

Crucianella (Rubiaceae)

stylosa	see *Phuopsis stylosa*

Cruciata (Rubiaceae)

§ *laevipes*	CKin NMir

Cryptanthus (Bromeliaceae)

bivittatus ♀ H1	CHal
- 'Roseus Pictus'	CHal
bromelioides	MBri

Cryptogramma (Adiantaceae)

crispa	SRms WHer

Cryptomeria (Cupressaceae)

fortunei	see *C. japonica* var. *sinensis*
japonica ♀ H4	CDul CTho GKir ISea LCon MGGn NBea STre WNor
- Araucarioides Group	EHul LCon
- 'Bandai-sugi' ♀ H4	CDoC CKen CMac EHul EOrn LCon LLin MBar MGos MOne NDlV SLim STre WEve WGor WStI
- 'Barabits Gold'	CDoC MGos
- 'Compressa'	CDoC CKen CSli EHul EPfP LDee LCon LLin LRHS MAsh MBar MBri MGos MOne SLim WLRN
§ - 'Cristata'	CDoC CMac ECho EOrn ICrw LCon LLin MBar NPal WWeb
* - 'Cristata Compacta'	EOrn
- Elegans Group	CBcs CBrm CMac CSBt CTri EHul ELan ENot EOrn EPfP GDra GKir LCon LLin LNet LPan MBar MGos MWat SHBN SKee SLim SPer WDin WFar WWin
- 'Elegans Aurea'	CBcs CDoC CSli CTri EHul LCon LLin MAsh MBar MBri SPoG SRms STre WDin WEvc WStI
- 'Elegans Compacta' ♀ H4	CDoC CSli CWib EHul EOrn EVFa GBin IMGH LBee LCon LRHS MAsh MBNS MBar MBri SLim SPar SPoG WBVN WEve WWeb
- 'Elegans Nana'	LBee LRHS SLim SRms
- 'Elegans Viridis'	LBuc SCoo SLim SPer

	- 'Globosa'	EOrn SRms
	- 'Globosa Nana' ♀ H4	CBrm ECho EHul ERom LBee LCon LLin LPan LRHS MAsh MBar NDlv SHBN SLim WGor
	- 'Golden Promise'	EOrn MAsh SCoo SLim WGor
	- 'Jindai-sugi'	CMac MBar NDlv NLar WEve
	- 'Kilmacurragh'	CDoC CKen EHul MBar NWea SLim
	- 'Knaptonensis' (v)	CDoC LLin
	- 'Kohui Yatsubusa'	CKen ECho
*	- 'Konijn Yatsubusa'	CKen
	- 'Koshiji-yatsubusa'	EOrn LCon MBar MBri
	- 'Koshyi'	CKen
	- 'Little Champion'	CKen
	- 'Little Diamond'	CKen
	- 'Littleworth Dwarf'	see C. japonica 'Littleworth Gnom'
§	- 'Littleworth Gnom'	LCon LLin
	- 'Lobbii Nana' hort.	see C. japonica 'Nana'
§	- 'Mankichi-sugi'	NLar
	- 'Monstrosa'	MBar
	- 'Monstrosa Nana'	see C. japonica 'Mankichi-sugi'
§	- 'Nana'	CDoC CMac CTri EBre EGra EHul EOrn EPfP LCon LLin LRHS SCoo WLRN
	- 'Pipo'	CKen
	- 'Pygmaea'	LCon LLin MBar MGos SRms
	- 'Rasen-sugi'	COtt LBuc LCon LLin NPal SCoo SLim SMad
	- 'Sekkan-sugi'	CBcs CSli EBre EHul EOrn LBee LCon LLin LRHS MAsh MBar MBri MGos SCoo SLim SPar
	- 'Sekka-sugi'	see C. japonica 'Cristata'
§	- var. sinensis	CMCN NOGN WPGP
*	- - 'Vilmoriniana Compacta'	EOrn
§	- 'Spiralis'	CDoC CKen CMac EHul EOrn EPfP LBee LCon LLin LRHS MAsh MBar SCoo SLim SPer SPla SPoG WEve WFar
§	- 'Spiraliter Falcata'	CDoC LBuc MBar NLar
§	- 'Tansu'	CKen EHul EOrn LCon LLin MBar
	- 'Tenzan-sugi'	CKen LLin
	- 'Tilford Cream'	MAsh
	- 'Tilford Gold'	EGra EHul EOrn LLin MBar MGos NDlv NHol WBcn WEve
	- 'Vilmorin Gold'	CKen EOrn MBri
	- 'Vilmoriniana' ♀ H4	CDoC CKen CMHG CNic CSli CWib EBre EHul ENot EOrn EPfP EPot IMGH LBee LCon LLin LRHS MAsh MBar MGos NHol SAga SHBN SIng SLim SPer WDin WFar WWeb
	- 'Viminalis'	NHol
	- 'Winter Bronze'	CKen
	- 'Yatsubusa'	see C. japonica 'Tansu'
	- 'Yore-sugi'	see C. japonica 'Spiralis', 'Spiraliter Falcata'
	- 'Yoshino'	CKen
	sinensis	see C. japonica var. sinensis

Cryptotaenia (Apiaceae)

	canadensis	EBee MRav
	japonica	CAgr CPou MHer WHer WJek
	- f. atropurpurea	CFwr CHar CPla CSpe ECha ECoo EGle EHoe EMan EMar EMon GCal GGar ITer LDai LPVe LPhx LRHS MFir MNrw MWrn NSti SBla WCHb WCot WCru WEas WFar

Ctenanthe (Marantaceae)

§	amabilis ♀ H1	CHal
§	lubbersiana ♀ H1	CHal
§	oppenheimiana	LRHS

Cucubalus (Caryophyllaceae)

baccifer	EBee GIBF NLar

Cudrania see Maclura

cumin see Cuminum cyminum

Cuminum (Apiaceae)

cyminum	CArn SIde WHHs

Cunila (Lamiaceae)

origanoides	EOHP

Cunninghamia (Cupressaceae)

§	lanceolata	CBcs CDoC CDul CMCN IArd LCon LLin MBlu NNEX SCoo SLim SMad SPar SSta STre WEve WNor WPGP
§	- 'Bánó'	CMac MBro
	- 'Compacta'	see C. lanceolata 'Bánó'
	- 'Glauca'	SLim
	- 'Little Leo'	CKen
	sinensis	see C. lanceolata
	unicaniculata	see C. lanceolata

Cunonia (Cunoniaceae)

capensis	CTrC EShb

Cuphea (Lythraceae)

	caeciliae	CHal MOak WBor
	cyanaea	CMHG MLLN MOak SDix SIgm SOWG SSte
	glutinosa new	ITer
	hirtella	EBee LHop MOak SDys SOWG SSte
	hyssopifolia ♀ H1	CFee CHal CHll ESlt MBri MOak SOWG SPar SRms STre
	- 'Alba'	LIck MOak SOWG STre
	- 'Riverdene Gold'	CHal EMan
	- 'Rosea'	LIck
§	ignea ♀ H1	CHal ELan EShb MBri MLLN MOak SOWG SPar SRms
*	- 'Alba'	CRDP
	- 'Variegata' (v)	CHal MOak SOWG SPar
	llavea 'Georgia Scarlet'	LIck MOak NPri SSte
	- 'Tiny Mice'	see C. llavea 'Georgia Scarlet'
	macrophylla hort.	CHll MOak
	melvilla	ERea
	platycentra	see C. ignea
	procumbens new	SHFr
	viscosissima	SHFr

x Cupressocyparis ✿ (Cupressaceae)

§	leylandii ♀ H4	CBcs CChe CDoC CMac EBre EHul ENot GKir LBuc LCon LHyr LPan LRHS MAsh MBar MBri MGos NBlu NWea SLim SPer WDin WEve WHar WMou WStI
	- 'Castlewellan'	More than 30 suppliers
	- 'Galway Gold'	see x C. leylandii 'Castlewellan'
	- 'Gold Rider' ♀ H4	CDoC EHul LBee LCon LPan MAsh MBar MBri MGos NMoo SCoo SLim SPer WDin WEve WHar WWeb
§	- 'Harlequin' (v)	LCon MBar SLim WWeb
	- 'Herculea'	CDoC LCon LPan WWeb
	- 'Hyde Hall'	CTri EOrn EPla LBee
	- 'Naylor's Blue'	CMac SEND
	- 'New Ornament'	SMad
	- 'Olive's Green'	CDoC EHul LCon LPan SCoo
	- 'Robinson's Gold' ♀ H4	CMac EHul GQui LBee LCon MBar NWea SLim WEve WFar WHar WStI
	- 'Silver Dust' (v)	MBri NEgg SRms WFar
	- 'Variegata'	see x C. leylandii 'Harlequin'
	- 'Winter Sun'	WCFE

	notabilis	WCwm
	ovensii	EHul WCwm

Cupressus (*Cupressaceae*)

	arizonica	ECrN
	var. *arizonica*	
§	- - 'Arctic'	MBri
	- 'Conica Glauca'	LHyr MBar
	- var. *glabra* 'Aurea'	ECho EHul LCon LLin LPan MAsh MBar SLim SPar
	- - 'Blue Ice' ♀ H3	CBcs CDoC CDul CMHG CTho EHul EOrn LCon LLin LRHS MAsh MBar MBri MGos SCoo SLim SPer WEve WGer WLRN
	- - 'Blue Pyramid' **new**	WEve
	- - 'Compacta'	CKen
	- - 'Conica'	CKen NBlu SBod
I	- - 'Fastigiata'	CBcs CDoC EHul LCon LPan MBar
	- - 'Glauca'	ECho MBlu
*	- - 'Lutea'	EOrn
	- 'Pyramidalis' ♀ H3	CMac ECho EPfP LRHS MAsh SCoo SPar WCwm
I	- 'Sulfurca'	CKen MAsh
	cashmeriana ♀ H2	CBcs CTho ERea LCon LLin LPan NPal SLim WEve WNor
	duclouxiana	CMHG
	dupreziana	WCwm
§	*funebris*	CMCN
	glabra	see *C. arizonica* var. *glabra*
	goveniana	MBar
	- var. *abramsiana*	WCwm
	guadalupensis	CMHG
	lusitanica	NNEX WCwm
	- var. *benthamii*	WCwm
	'Knightiana'	
	- 'Brice's Weeping'	CKen
	- 'Glauca Pendula'	CKen EPfP LCon MAsh MBri WCwm WEve
	- 'Pygmy'	CKen
	macrocarpa	CDoC CSBt CTrC EHul SEND
	- 'Barnham Gold'	SBod SRms
	- 'Compacta'	CKen
	- 'Donard Gold'	CMac CSBt ECho EOrn MBar
	- 'Gold Spread'	CDoC ECho EHul EOrn LBee LCon LLin LRHS SCoo SLim SPoG WBcn WEve WGer
	- 'Goldcrest' ♀ H3	CBcs CDoC CMac CSBt CTrC EHul ENot EOrn LBee LCon LLin LPan LRHS MBar MBri MGos NBlu SBod SLim SPar SPer WCFE WDin WFar WStI WWeb
	- 'Golden Cone'	CKen CMac CSBt ECho LRHS
	- 'Golden Pillar' ♀ H3	CDoC CMac CTrC EHul EOrn LBee LCon LRHS MAsh MBar MBri MWat SLim SPer WDin WGer WLRN WWeb
	- 'Greenstead Magnificent'	LCon MAsh SCoo SLim
	- 'Horizontalis Aurea'	EHul MBar WBcn
	- 'Lohbrunner'	CKen
	- 'Lutea'	CDoC CMac CTrC ECho
	- 'Pygmaea'	CKen
	- 'Sulphur Cushion'	CKen
	- 'Wilma'	ECho EHul EOrn LBee LCon LRHS MAsh MGos SCoo SLim WBcn WStI WWeb
	- 'Woking'	CKen
	sempervirens	CBcs CMCN CTCP EHul ERom ISea LHyr LLin STop WEve WFar
	- 'Garda'	CDoC
	- 'Green Pencil'	CKen EPfP LRHS
	- 'Pyramidalis'	see *C. sempervirens* Stricta Group
	- var. *sempervirens*	see *C. sempervirens* Stricta Group
§	- Stricta Group ♀ H3	CArn CMCN CSWP EHul EPfP

		LCon LLin LPan SAPC SArc SCoo SPar WCFE
	- 'Swane's Gold'	CDoC CKen CMHG ECho EHul EOrn EPfP LBee LCon LLin MAsh SCoo SLim WEve
	- 'Totem Pole'	CDoC CKen CSBt CTho EHul EOrn EPfP LBee LCon LLin MAsh MGos SCoo SEND SLim SPoG WBcn WEve WGor
	torulosa	CDoC EGFP
	- CC 3687	CPLG

Curcuma (*Zingiberaceae*)

	amada	CKob LEur
	angustifolia	CKob LEur
	aromatica	CKob LEur
I	*aurantiaca* 'Rainbow Curcuma' **new**	MOak
	cordata 'Jewel of Thailand' **new**	MOak
	elata	CKob
	gracillima 'Chiang Mai Chocolate' **new**	MOak
	longa	CKob EBot GPoy LEur MSal
	ornata	CKob
	petiolata	WMul
	- 'Emperor' (v)	CKob
	- variegated (v)	WMul
	'Pink Wonder' **new**	ETub
	roscoeana 'Pride of Burma' **new**	MOak
	'Siam Diamond' **new**	MOak
	'Siam Ruby' **new**	MOak
	thorelii 'Chiang Mai Snow' **new**	MOak
	zedoaria	CKob GPoy LAma LEur LRHS WMul

Curtonus see *Crocosmia*

Cuscuta (*Convolvulaceae*)

	chinensis	MSal

Cussonia (*Araliaceae*)

	paniculata	CKob CPLG EOas SIgm WMul
	spicata	CKob WMul
	transvaalensis	CKob

custard apple see *Annona cherimola*, *A. reticulata*

Cyananthus (*Campanulaceae*)

	integer hort.	see *C. microphyllus*
	integer Wallich 'Sherriff's Variety'	GDra NHar WOBN
	lobatus ♀ H4	CPla ECho EHyt EMan GBuc NLAp NSla SBla SIng WLin WOBN
	- 'Albus'	EHyt EPot EWes NLAp SBla WAbc
	- dark	EWes GDra WAbe
	- giant	EPot GCrs GDra GTou SBla WAbe WCom
	- x *microphyllus*	EPot NWCA WAbe
	longiflorus	SBla
	macrocalyx	EHyt SBla
§	*microphyllus* ♀ H4	CPla EPot GDra GEdr GMaP NSla SBla WAbe
	sherriffii	EHyt GEdr WAbe
	spathulifolius	EHyt
	CLD 1492	

Cyanella (*Tecophilaeaceae*)

§	*hyacinthoides*	LBow
	orchidiformis	LBow

Cyanotis (*Commelinaceae*)
somaliensis ♀ H1	CHal

Cyathea (*Cyatheaceae*)
from New Guinea	WRic
arborea <u>new</u>	WRic
* **atrox**	WRic
australis	EAmu GQui LPal SPar WMul WRic
brownii	EAmu WMul WRic
celebica	WHer
cooperi	CBcs LJus WMul WRic
* - 'Brentwood'	WRic
cunninghamii	LRav WRic
dealbata	CAbb CBcs CBrP CTrC EAmu
	EBot GQui LJus LPal LPan MGos
	SPar WMul WRic
dregei	EAmu SPlb WMul WRic
incisoserrata	WMul WRic
kermadecensis	WHer WRic
lepifera	LPal
medullaris	CAbb CBcs CTrC EAmu EBot LJus
	LPan MGos WMul WRic
milnei	LPal
robusta	WRic
smithii	CTrC EAmu EBot LJus LPan WMul
	WRic
spinulosa	WRic
tomentosissima	WMul WRic

Cyathodes (*Epacridaceae*)
§ **colensoi**	EPot GCrs MBar MBri MGos NHar
	NHol NJOw NLar SLon SPer SSpi
	WBod WPat
empetrifolia	EPot
fasciculata	see *Leucopogon fasciculatus*
fraseri	see *Leucopogon fraseri*
juniperina	ECou SReu
§ **parviflora**	ECou
parvifolia	ECou

Cycas (*Cycadaceae*)
cairnsiana	CRoM
circinalis	CRoM LPal NRog
media	CRoM LPal NRog
panzihihuaensis	LPal
platyphylla	CRoM
revoluta ♀ H1	CAbb CBrP CDoC CHEx CRoM
	CTrC CWSG EAmu EBot EPVP EPfP
	LPal LRHS MBri MPRe NMoo NPal
	SAPC SArc SEND SPar WMul WNor
- x **taitungensis**	CBrP
§ **rumphii**	CBrP EAmu LPal LRHS NRog
siamensis	LPal SChr
taitungensis	CBrP CRoM
thouarsii	see *C. rumphii*
wadei <u>new</u>	NRog

Cyclamen ✿ (*Primulaceae*)
africanum	CBro CElm CLCN CStu EBee EBre
	EJWh EPot ITim LAma LRHS MAsh
	NMen STil WCom WCot WPat
balearicum	CBro CElm CLCN EBre EJWh EPot
	LAma LRHS MAsh STil WCot
cilicium ♀ H2-4	CBro CElm CLCN EBre ECtt EHyt
	EJWh EPot ERos GIBF ITim LAma
	LRHS MBri MS&S MTho NHol NMen
	SBla SDeJ SPar SSpi STil WCom WCot
	WFar WIvy WNor WPat
- f. *album*	CBro CElm CLCN CWoo EBre
	EHyt EJWh EPot GCrs ITim LAma
	LCTD LRHS MAsh STil WCot
- patterned leaf	NBir

§ **coum** ♀ H4	More than 30 suppliers
- from Turkey	ERos
- var. **abchasicum**	see *C. coum* subsp. *caucasicum*
- 'Broadleigh Silver'	CElm LCTD
§ - subsp. **caucasicum**	ERos ETow LAma SSpi STil
- subsp. **coum**	CBro
- - f. **albissimum**	LCTD
- - - 'George Bisson'	CElm
- - - 'Golan Heights'	CElm LCTD MAsh STil
- - 'Atkinsii'	CBro MBro
- - f. **coum**	SDeJ
'Crimson King'	
- - - 'Linnett Jewel'	LCTD
- - - 'Linnett Rose'	LCTD
- - - Nymans Group	LCTD MAsh SBla
- - Pewter Group	CBel ECGP ERos MAsh MTho
♀ H2-4	NGar NPar SSpi WCom WIvy
- - - - bicoloured	EJWh
- - - - 'Blush'	MAsh NGar STil
- - - - 'Maurice Dryden'	CAvo CBel CBro CPBP ECGP EHrv
	GBuc GCrs ITim LAma LCTD LRHS
	MAsh NGar SSpi STil WAbe WIvy
- - - - red	CLCN LAma LCTD WPat
- - - - 'Tilebarn	CBel EHrv EHyt MAsh NGar STil
Elizabeth'	
- - - - white	GBuc MAsh
- - - plain-leaved red	STil
- - - 'Roseum'	CElm CWCL ETub GBuc LAma
	SDeJ STil SUsu
- - Silver Group	CBro CElm CWoo EHrv LRHS
	MAvo MBro NSla SSpi WAbe
- - - - bicolor	LCTD
- - - - red	CAvo EBre EPot MTho NHar STil
	WHoo
- - - - 'Silver Star'	LCTD
- - - - 'Sterling Silver'	LCTD
- - magenta	CWCL MBro
- - f. **pallidum**	GCrs
- - - 'Album'	CAvo CBel CBot CElm EHyt EPot
	ERos ITim LAma MAsh NGar SDeJ
	SIng STil WAbe WCot WHoo
	WNor WPat
- - - 'Marbled Moon'	LCTD MAsh STil
- - dark pink	CAvo EDAr ITim WHoo
- - subsp. **elegans**	LCTD MAsh STil
- 'Elm Tree Special' <u>new</u>	CElm
- - marbled leaf	CWCL EDAr ITim WHoo
- - 'Meaden's Crimson'	EPot LCTD
* - **merymana**	CElm
- plain-leaved	CElm EPot ITim LCTD WAbe
- red	EDAr GKir
- scented	ITim
- 'Tilebarn Graham' <u>new</u>	EHyt
creticum	CBro CLCN EJWh LAma MAsh
	STil
- x **repandum**	see *C.* x *meiklei*
cyprium	CBro CElm CFwr CLCN EBre
	EHyt EJWh ETub LAma LRHS
	MAsh SBla STil WCot WIvy
- 'E.S.'	LCTD MAsh STil
europaeum	see *C. purpurascens*
fatrense	see *C. purpurascens* subsp.
	purpurascens from Fatra, Slovakia
graecum	CBro CElm CFil CLCN CStu CWoo
	EJWh EPot ESis LAma LRHS MAsh
	NMen SIgm SRot SSpi STil WCot
	WIvy
- MS 772	WCot
- f. *album*	CBro CElm EJWh EPot LAma
	LRHS MAsh STil
- subsp. **anatolicum**	STil
- subsp. **candicum**	MAsh
- subsp. **graecum**	STil

f. *graecum* 'Glyfada'	
§ *hederifolium* ♀ H4	More than 30 suppliers
- var. *confusum*	LCTD MAsh STil WCot
- var. *hederifolium*	More than 30 suppliers
f. *albiflorum*	
--- 'Bowles' Apollo	CLCN LCTD SIgm WCom
Group	
§ ---- 'Artemis'	STil WCot
---- 'White Bowles'	see *C. hederifolium* var.
Apollo'	*hederifolium* f. *albiflorum*
	(Bowles' Apollo Group) 'Artemis'
--- 'Linnett	LCTD
Longbow' **new**	
--- 'Linnett Stargazer'	LCTD
new	
--- 'Nettleton Silver'	see *C. hederifolium* var.
	hederifolium f. *albiflorum* 'White
	Cloud'
--- 'Perlenteppich'	EDAr GMaP LCTD
§ --- 'White Cloud'	CElm EHyt EPot ESis ITim LCTD
	MAsh STil WIvy
- f. *hederifolium*	CLAP CWCL ECGP ITim LCTD
Bowles' Apollo	MAsh SBla SSpi STil WCom
Group	
--- 'Daley Thompson'	LCTD
--- 'Fairy Longbow'	LCTD
new	
--- 'Fairy Rings'	CElm LCTD MAsh
--- 'Oliver Twist' **new**	LCTD
--- 'Rosenteppich'	EDAr EShb GBuc GMaP LCTD
	MAsh NHol
--- 'Ruby Glow'	CElm LCTD MAsh WCot WPat
--- 'Silver Cloud'	CBel CBro CLAP CLCN GBuc
	LCTD MAsh NBir SSpi STil WAbe
	WCot WIvy
'Silver Foil' **new**	LCTD
--- 'Silver Shield'	LCTD
- island scented	WCot
strain **new**	
- 'San Marino Silver'	LCTD
- scented	CBel CLCN STil
- silver-leaved	CElm ECGP EPot GCrs LCTD LHop
	LRHS MAsh NGar SBla SRot STil
hederifolium	ECho EHyt ITim
x *africanum*	
x *hildebrandii*	WIvy
ibericum	see *C. coum* subsp. *caucasicum*
intaminatum	CBel CBro CLCN CPBP CSWP
	CWoo EHyt EJWh ERos LAma
	LRHS MAsh NHol NMen SBla
	SChr STil WAbe WIvy WPat
- Linnett strain	LCTD
- patterned-leaved	CBel EJWh LCTD STil
- pink	NMen STil
- plain-leaved	CElm STil
latifolium	see *C. persicum*
libanoticum	CAvo CBel CBro CElm CLCN EBre
	EJWh ERos GCrs LAma LCTD
	LRHS MAsh NMen SBla STil
§ x *meiklei*	CBro CLCN
mirabile ♀ H2-3	CBel CBro CLCN EBre EJWh EPot
	GCrs LAma LRHS MAsh NMen
	STil WAbe WIvy
- 'Tilebarn Anne'	EHyt MAsh STil
- 'Tilebarn Jan'	STil
- 'Tilebarn Nicholas'	CElm EHyt MAsh STil WCot
neapolitanum	see *C. hederifolium*
orbiculatum	see *C. coum*
parviflorum	EJWh LAma MAsh NMen STil
peloponnesiacum	see *C. repandum* subsp.
	peloponnesiacum
§ *persicum*	CBro CElm CFil CLCN CPBP EJWh
	LAma LRHS MAsh NMen SChr STil

- CSE 90560	STil
- var. *persicum*	STil
f. *puniceum* from	
Lebanon	
--- 'Tilebarn	CElm STil
Karpathos'	
pseudibericum ♀ H2-3	CBel CBro CLCN EBre EHyt EJWh
	GCrs LAma LCTD LRHS MAsh
	SBla STil
- 'Roseum'	CLCN LCTD MAsh NMen STil
§ *purpurascens* ♀ H4	CBro CElm CFil CLCN CMea EBre
	EJWh LAma LRHS MAsh MBro
	MS&S NHol NMen SBla SSpi STil
	WHoo WIvy WPat
- f. *album*	SBla
- var. *fatrense*	see *C. purpurascens* subsp.
	purpurascens from Fatra, Slovakia
- 'Lake Garda'	CFil MAsh SSpi WPGP
§ - subsp. *purpurascens*	EHyt STil
from Fatra, Slovakia	
- silver-leaved	CElm LCTD
-- from Limone, Italy	SBla SSpi
repandum	CAvo CBro CElm CFil CLCN EBre
	EHrv EHyt EJWh EPot ERos LAma
	LCTD LRHS MAsh NMen SBla
	SSpi STil WCot WHer
- BS 961	WCot
- JCA 5157	SSpi
§ - subsp.	EHyt EJWh ERos MAsh WAbe
peloponnesiacum	
♀ H2-3	
I -- f. *albiflorum*	STil
§ - var.	CBel CBro CElm CLCN LCTD SSpi
peloponnesiacum	STil
-- var. *vividum*	STil
- 'Pelops' misapplied	see *C. repandum* subsp.
	peloponnesiacum var.
	peloponnesiacum
- subsp. *repandum*	CElm CLCN EJWh MAsh SBla STil
f. *album*	WCot
- subsp. *rhodense*	CLCN LAma LCTD MAsh SSpi
	STil
rohlfsianum	CBro CFil CLCN EJWh EPot LRHS
	MAsh STil
x *saundersii*	CLCN EJWh MAsh STil
trochopteranthum	CAvo CBro CElm CLCN EHyt
	EJWh GKir LAma LRHS MAsh
	NGar NRog STil
x *wellensiekii*	LCTD MAsh STil

Cydista (Bignoniaceae)

aequinoctialis	CPIN

Cydonia ✿ (Rosaceae)

japonica	see *Chaenomeles speciosa*
oblonga 'Agvambari'	SKee
(F) **new**	
- 'Champion' (F)	SKee WJas
- 'Ekmek' (F) **new**	SKee
- 'Isfahan'	SKee
- 'Krymsk' **new**	ESim
- 'Leskovac'	MGos WJas
- 'Ludovic'	WJas
- 'Lusitanica' (F)	GTwe NRog SKee WJas
- 'Meech's Prolific' (F)	CCVT CLnd CSam CTho EMui
	ERea GKir GTwe LRHS MBlu MGos
	MWat SDea SFam SKee SPer WWeb
- pear-shaped	ECrN ENot NRog
- Portugal	see *C. oblonga* 'Lusitanica'
- 'Sciboşa' (F)	SKee
- 'Shams'	SKee
- 'Sobu' (F) **new**	SKee
§ - 'Vranja' (F) ♀ H4	CCVT CDoC CEnd CLnd CMac

CSBt CTho EBee EMui EPfP ERea
GTwe LBuc LRHS MBri MGos
NRog SDea SFam SKee SPer WDin
WJas

Cymbalaria (Scrophulariaceae)
§ **aequitriloba** 'Alba'   GGar
§ **hepaticifolia**   EDAr LRHS WCru WPer
  - 'Alba'   CNic
§ **muralis**   CKin ECtt MAvo MBar MHer MWat
    NPri WBVN WBri WGor WHer
  - 'Albiflora'   see *C. muralis* 'Pallidior'
§   - 'Globosa Alba'   CHal EDAr EPot MDHE
  - 'Kenilworth White'   WGwG WMoo
  - 'Len's Favourite'   MGas
  - 'Nana Alba'   EMlt MDHE NPri NWCA WPer
§   - 'Pallidior'   CMea ESis MAvo MBar NHar NVic
    WWin
  - 'Rosea'   WFar
§ **pallida**   CMea LRHS NHar SBla SPlb WCru
    WFar WMoo WPer
§ **pilosa**   ECtt EMNN EMan

Cymbopogon (Poaceae)
citratus   CArn COld CSev GPoy LRav MChe
    MGol MSal NGHP NPri SHDw
    SIde WCHb WHHs WHer WJek
    WLHH
flexuosus   GWCH MHer MPEx WBri
martinii   CArn GPoy MSal
  - var. **motia**   MHer
nardus   CArn GPoy MSal

Cymophyllus (Cyperaceae)
fraserianus   EBee EHoe EPla GBin

Cymopterus (Apiaceae)
terebinthinus   SIgm

Cynanchum (Asclepiadaceae)
* **acuminatifolium**   GCal

Cynara (Asteraceae)
§ **baetica** subsp.   SIgm
    maroccana
§ **cardunculus** ♀ H3-4   More than 30 suppliers
  - ACL 380/78   SWat
*   - 'Cardy'   CBot EBee EChP EGoo EMan
    MLLN MSPs MWat MWrn SMrm
    SWat WWhi
  - dwarf   SDix WCot
*   - 'Florist Cardy'   COIW IGor NLar NPPs NPSI SRob
    WBry WWpP
§   - Scolymus Group   CAgr CBcs CHEx CKno EBee
    ENot EPfP EWes GCal GPoy IGor
    ILis LRHS MBri SMrm SPer WHer
    WHil WHoo WWeb
  - - 'Gigante di   WHer
    Romagna'
  - - 'Green Globe'   CBod CBot CPrp CSBt CSev EBee
    NPer NVic WBry
  - - 'Gros Camus   MAvo WBar WCot
    de Bretagne'
  - - 'Gros Vert de Lâon'   CSpe EBee EBlw ECha ELan
    NBhm SCro WCot
  - - 'Large Green'   NLar
  - - 'Purple Globe'   CArn CSBt WBry
  - - 'Violetto di Chioggia'   CSev WHer
  - 'Vert de Vaux en Velin'   LPio
hystrix   see *C. baetica* subsp.
    maroccana
scolymus   see *C. cardunculus* Scolymus
    Group

Cynodon (Poaceae)
aethiopicus   EHoe LPhx SMrm
dactylon new   MPEx

Cynoglossum (Boraginaceae)
amabile ♀ H4   WTMC
  - f. **roseum**   WPGP
    'Mystery Rose'
dioscoridis   CBot EChP NLar WPer WWin
grande   CFee SCro
nervosum   CArn CBot EBee EBre EChP ECtt
    EFou EMan EMil EPar EPfP EWTr
    LHop LRHS MRav MTis MWgw
    NChi NGdn NMRc SPer SWat
    WCHb WCot WTMC WWin
officinale   CArn MChe MHer MSal WCHb
    WCer WHer WWye
wallichii   CFee

Cynosurus (Poaceae)
cristatus   CKin

Cypella (Iridaceae)
aquatilis   MSta
§ **coelestis**   EBee EMan WCot
herbertii   CNic CPom EDif LAma
peruviana   EMan
plumbea   see *C. coelestis*

Cyperus (Cyperaceae)
§ **albostriatus**   CHal MBri
alternifolius hort.   see *C. involucratus*
  - 'Compactus'   see *C. involucratus* 'Nanus'
'Chira' new   EChP EPPr SRGP SWal
§ **cyperoides**   MBri
diffusus hort.   see *C. albostriatus*
§ **eragrostis**   More than 30 suppliers
esculentus   IBlr
fuscus   CElw EPPr MDKP NDov NSti
    WFar WHal WMoo
§ **giganteus**   CMCo
glaber   EMan EPGN MBar
haspan hort.   see *C. papyrus* 'Nanus'
§ **involucratus** ♀ H1   CBen CHEx CHal CWCL EBak
    EHon EMFW ERea EShb EWsh
    LMdh MBri MSta NBea SArc SSte
    SWal SWat SYvo WFar WMAq
    WMul WWeb WWpP WWye
  - 'Gracilis'   EBak MBri
§   - 'Nanus'   CMCo SWal
longus   CBen CFwr CHad CRow EBee
    EHoe EHon EMFW EMon EPPr
    LHrt LPBA MBar MSta NPer NSti
    SMad SWal SWat WFar WHal
    WMAq WWeb WWpP WWye
nanus   CHEx
papyrus ♀ H1   CHEx CHad CMCo CPLG EAmu
    ERea ESlt LMdh LPan MBri MSta
    SAPC SArc SLdr WHal WMul
  - 'Mexico'   see *C. giganteus*
§   - 'Nanus' ♀ H1   ERea ESlt LMdh LPal WMul
rotundus   CFwr EChP EPGN MCCP MFir
    SBHF SRGP SWal WWpP
sumula hort.   see *C. cyperoides*
ustulatus   EPPr MMoz
vegetus   see *C. eragrostis*

Cyphia (Campanulaceae)
phyteuma new   CDes

Cyphomandra (Solanaceae)
betacea (F)   CHEx LRav WMul

- 'Goldmine' (F)	ERea
- 'Oratia Red' (F)	ERea

Cyphostemma (Vitaceae)

juttae	CRoM

Cypripedium (Orchidaceae)

Aki g.	CHdy
calceolus	CHdy
debile	EFEx
Emil g.	CHdy XFro
§ *formosanum*	CHdy EFEx LAma SSpi
franchetii	CHdy
Gisela g.	CHdy GCrs XFro
- yellow **new**	GCrs XFro
guttatum	EFEx
- var. *yatabeanum*	see *C. yatabeanum*
henryi	EFEx LAma
himalaicum	EFEx
japonicum	EFEx LAma
- var. *formosanum*	see *C. formosanum*
Karl Heinz g.	CHdy
kentuckiense	CHdy
- x *reginae*	CHdy
macranthos	CHdy EFEx
- green-flowered	EFEx
- var. *hotei-atsumorianum*	EFEx
- var. *rebunense*	EFEx
- var. *speciosum*	EFEx
margaritaceum	EFEx
montanum	EFEx LAma
parviflorum	CHdy
§ - var. *pubescens*	CHdy LAma
Philipp g.	XFro
pubescens	see *C. parviflorum var. pubescens*
reginae	CHdy LAma SSpi
segawae	CHdy EFEx
tibeticum	CHdy EFEx
§ *yatabeanum*	EFEx

Cyrilla (Cyrillaceae)

parvifolia **new**	SSpi
racemiflora	WBcn

Cyrtanthus (Amaryllidaceae)

'Alaska'^{PBR}	CBro LRHS WCot
§ *brachyscyphus*	EBee EGrW MTIs SHFr WCot
breviflorus	CDes SIgm
contractus **new**	CDes
'Edwina' **new**	ECho
§ *elatus* ♀ H1	CBro CHal CSev CSpe CStu EBot
	ERea LAma LBow LRHS MCCP
	NCiC NRog SYvo WCot WHer
- 'Delicatus'	LBow
- pink **new**	CSpe
'Elizabeth' **new**	ECho
flanaganii	CDes
§ *luteus*	EBee
mackenii	CDes CPne EBee EGrW NRog WCot
- var. *cooperi*	EBee EGrW WCot
montanus	EBee EGrW WCot
* *ochroleucus*	WCot
'Stutterheim Variety'	
parviflorus	see *C. brachyscyphus*
* 'Pink Diamond'	CBro ETub LRHS
purpureus	see *C. elatus*
sanguineus	EBee ECho EGrW WCot
speciosus	see *C. elatus*

Cyrtomium (Dryopteridaceae)

§ *caryotideum*	GQui NMar WRic
§ *falcatum* ♀ H3	CFwr CHEx CHal CLAP CMHG

	CMil CRDP EBee EBlw ELan EPla
	GCal GMaP LEur MDun MWgw
	NHol NMar NOrc NSti SEND SPar
	SRms SRot WFar WPnP WRic
- 'Rochfordianum'	WFib
§ *fortunei* ♀ H4	CFil CFwr CHal CHid CLAP CTrC
	EBee EBlw EFer ENot EPfP GBin
	GGar LEur LPVe MDun MMoz
	NBid NDlv NHol SBla SChu SPar
	SRms WFib WRic WWeb
- var. *clivicola*	CFwr EBee LEur MAvo NDlv SPar
	SRot WHil WRic
macrophyllum	CFil CLAP NMar WCru WRic

Cystopteris ✿ (Woodsiaceae)

bulbifera	CLAP EFer GQui NMar
diaphana	WRic
dickieana	CLAP EMon EPot LEur NHar
	NMar NVic WCot WFib
fragilis	ECha EFer GQui LEur MAvo NBro
	NMar SBla SRms WRic
- 'Cristata'	CLAP
- var. *sempervirens*	WRic
montana	GCrs
tennesseensis	WRic

Cytisus (Papilionaceae)

albus hort.	see *C. multiflorus*
albus Hacq.	see *Chamaecytisus albus*
'Andreanus'	see *C. scoparius* f. *andreanus*
'Apricot Gem'	MBar MGos WBcn
ardoinoi ♀ H4	ECho GDra
battandieri ♀ H4	More than 30 suppliers
- 'Yellow Tail' ♀ H4	CEnd LRHS WPGP
x *beanii* ♀ H4	CPLG EBee ELan ENot FPfP GKir
	LRHS MAsh MBar NFor SLon SPer
	SRms WDin
'Boskoop Ruby' ♀ H4	CDoC CHar CSBt EBee EGra ENot
	EPfP GKir LAst LRHS NBlu NWoo
	SPer WLRN
'Burkwoodii' ♀ H4	CBcs CDoC CHar CSBt CWSG
	EBee ENot GKir LAst LRHS MRav
	MWhi SPoG WFar WStI
canariensis	see *Genista canariensis*
'Compact Crimson'	CDoC EBee EBre
'Cottage'	EPot IMGH WBod WLin
'Dainty'	EBee
'Dainty Maid'	CEnd
'Daisy Hill'	CSBt
§ *decumbens*	CLyd MAsh NHar WLin
'Donard Gem'	CDoC LAst WWeb
'Dorothy Walpole'	WFar
'Dukaat'	EBee GKir MAsh SHBN WBcn
'Firefly'	CBcs CSBt NBlu
'Fulgens'	CHar CSBt EPfP MAsh MBar NBlu
	SPer WLRN
'Golden Cascade'	CBcs CDoC ELan LRHS WLRN
'Golden Sunlight'	CSBt EBce ENot EPfP SHBN
	WStI
'Goldfinch'	CBcs CDoC CHar CSBt CWSG
	EBee ENot GKir MBri MRav MWat
	NBlu NPri
hirsutus	see *Chamaecytisus hirsutus*
'Hollandia' ♀ H4	CBcs CDoC CHar CWSG EBee
	EBre ENot EPfP EWTr GKir LRHS
	MBar MGos MPWC NPri SHBN
	SPer WDin WFar WStI WWin
x *kewensis* ♀ H4	CSBt CWSG EBee EBre ELan ENot
	EPfP EPot GKir LRHS MBar MBri
	MGos MRav SHBN SPer SReu
	SRms WDin WPat WWeb WWin
- 'Niki'	CDoC EBee EPfP LRHS MAsh
	MGos SHBN SPer SPoG WGer

'Killiney Red'   EBee ENot GKir MBri MRav SHBN
'Killiney Salmon'   CTri ENot MAsh MRav WFar
'La Coquette'   CDoC CMHG EBee EGra LRHS
                          MBar MWat SPlb
leiocarpus **new**   GEil
'Lena' ♀ H4   CDoC CHar EBee EBre EGra EPfP
                          GKir LAst LRHS MAsh MBar MBri
                          MGos MRav MTis NBlu NPri WFar
                          WStI WWeb
leucanthus   see *Chamaecytisus albus*
'Lord Lambourne'   MHdf
'Luna'   EBee LRHS NBlu
maderensis   see *Genista maderensis*
'Maria Burkwood'   EPfP NBlu SHBN
'Minstead'   CDoC EBee EBre ELan EPfP LAst
                          SPer SPoG
* 'Minstead Pink' **new** GEil
'Moonlight'   EWTr SPer
'Moyclare Pink'   CMHG
§ *multiflorus* ♀ H4   GKir LRav SRms
 - 'White Bouquet'   MBri
nigrescens   see *C. nigricans*
§ *nigricans*   CFil CPle EBee ENot SPer
                          WPGP
 - 'Cyni'   ELan EPfP GEil IArd LRHS MAsh
                          SPer SSpi
orientalis **new**   WCot
'Palette'   EBee LAst LRHS MBar NBlu SPer
'Porlock'   see *G.* 'Porlock'
x *praecox*   CSBt EWTr LAst MAsh MRav SPar
                          WFar WWeb
 - 'Albus'   CDoC CHar EBee EBre ELan ENot
                          EPfP EWTr GKir LAst LRHS MBar
                          MGos MRav MWat NBlu SEND
                          SHBN SPar SPer SRPl WBod WFar
                          WHCG WWeb
 - 'Allgold' ♀ H4   CBcs CChe CDoC CMHG CSBt
                          CWSG EBee EBre ENot EPfP GKir
                          LRHS MAsh MBar MBri MRav
                          SHBN SLon SPer SReu SRms
                          WBod WDin WFar WStI WWeb
 - 'Canary Bird'   see *C.* x *praecox* 'Goldspeer'
 - 'Frisia'   CBcs MBar NBlu
§ - 'Goldspeer'   CSBt EBee ENot SEND
 - 'Lilac Lady' **new**   LRHS
§ - 'Warminster' ♀ H4   EBee ENot EPfP GKir LAst LRHS
                          MAsh MBar MBri MGos MRav MWat
                          NBlu NWea SHBN SPar SPer SRms
'Princess'   LRHS MBri WBcn
procumbens   EHyt LHop NBid
purgans   NLon
purpureus   see *Chamaecytisus purpureus*
'Queen Mary'   WBcn
racemosus hort.   see *Genista* x *spachiana*
Red Favourite   see *C.* 'Roter Favorit'
'Red Wings'   GKir SPer WStI
§ 'Roter Favorit'   EPfP MBar WGor
scoparius   CAgr CArn CKin ENot GWCH
                          Ilve MCoo NWea SRms WDin
§ - f. *andreanus* ♀ H4   CDoC EBee EGra ENot EPfP GKir
                          MGos MRav NLon SPoG
 - - 'Splendens'   CBcs EWTr WStI
 - 'Cornish Cream'   EBee ECot EPfP GKir SPar SPer
                          WWeb
§ - subsp. *maritimus*   GEil GSki MBri MMHG MRav
                          NLon SLPl WGer
 - var. *prostratus*   see *C. scoparius* subsp. *maritimus*
 - 'Vanesse'   EBee ENot
x *spachianus*   see *Genista* x *spachiana*
supinus   see *Chamaecytisus supinus*
'Windlesham Ruby'   CDoC CPLG EBee ELan EPfP GKir
                          LAst LRHS MAsh MBar SHBN SPer
                          WDin WFar WWeb

'Zeelandia' ♀ H4   CBcs EBee ENot EPfP GKir LAst
                          LRHS MBar MRav MWat NBlu NPri
                          SEND SPer WFar WRHF WWeb

D

Daboecia ✿ (*Ericaceae*)

§   *cantabrica* f. *alba*   CMac CPLG MBar MBri MGos
                            MOke NHol WStI
 - 'Alba Globosa'   EHea EPfP MBar
* - 'Arielle'   EHea WBan
 - 'Atropurpurea'   CNCN CSBt EHea GKir MGos
                            MOke NHol WStI
 - subsp. *azorica*   EHea
    'Arthur P. Dome' **new**
 - 'Barbara Phillips'   EHea MBar
 - 'Bicolor' ♀ H4   CNCN EHea EPfP MGos MOke
 - 'Blueless'   EHea EPfP SDys
 - f. *blumii* 'Pink Blum' EHea
 - - 'White Blum'   EHea
 - 'Bubbles'   EHea
 - 'Celtic Star'   EHea WBan
 - 'Chaldon' **new**   EHea
 - 'Charles Nelson' (d)   EHea MBar MOke
 - 'Cherub'   EHea
 - 'Cinderella'   CNCN EHea MBar
 - 'Cleggan'   EHea
 - 'Covadonga'   EHea MBar
 - 'Creeping White'   EHea
 - 'Cupido'   CNCN EHea MGos
 - 'David Moss' ♀ H4   EHea MBar WBan
 - 'Donard Pink'   EHea MBar
 - 'Early Bride'   EHea
 - 'Eskdale Baron'   EHea
 - 'Eskdale Blea'   EHea
 - 'Eskdale Blonde'   EHea
 - 'Glamour'   EHea
 - 'Globosa Pink'   EHea
 - 'Harlequin'   EHea
 - 'Heather Yates'   EHea MOke
 - 'Heraut'   EHea
 - 'Hookstone Purple'   EHea MBar MGos MOke NHol
 - 'Lilac Osmond'   EHea MBar
 - 'Pink'   see *D. cantabrica* 'Donard Pink'
 - 'Pink Lady'   EHea MBar
 - 'Polifolia'   CNCN EHea MOke SRms
 - 'Porter's Variety'   EHea MBar MOke
 - 'Praegerae'   CMac CNCN CTri EHea GKir
                            MBar NHol
 - 'Purpurea'   EHea GKir MBar
 - 'Rainbow' (v)   CNCN EHea MBar
 - 'Rodeo'   EHea
 - 'Rosea'   EHea MBar
 - 'Rubra'   EHea
 - subsp. *scotica*   EHea MBar
    'Bearsden'
 - - 'Ben'   EHea
 - - 'Cora'   CNCN EHea MBar
 - - 'Goscote'   EHea MGos
 - - 'Jack Drake' ♀ H4   CNCN EHea MBar MBri MOke NDlv
 - - 'Red Imp'   EHea
 - - 'Robin'   EHea
 - - 'Silverwells' ♀ H4   CBcs CNCN EHea MBar MBri NDlv
 - - 'Tabramhill'   CNCN EHea MBar
 - - 'William Buchanan'   CMac CNCN EHea GKir MBar MBri
     ♀ H4   MGos MOke NDlv NHol NMen
 - - 'William Buchanan   CNCN EHea MBar MBri
     Gold' (v)
 - 'Snowdrift'   EHea MBar

- 'Waley's Red' ♀ H4   EHea GQui MBar SDys
- 'White Carpet'   EHea
- 'Wijnie'   EHea

Dacrycarpus (*Podocarpaceae*)
§   **dacrydioides**   ECou LEdu
- 'Dark Delight'   ECou

Dacrydium (*Podocarpaceae*)
bidwillii   see *Halocarpus bidwillii*
cupressinum   CAbb CDoC SMad
franklinii   see *Lagarostrobos franklinii*
laxifolium   see *Lepidothamnus laxifolius*

Dactylis (*Poaceae*)
glomerata   CBod EBee EGle EMan EMon ENot
'Variegata' (v)   EPPr EPla IBlr MBlu MCCP NBid
    NBro NGdn NHol NPPs NSti
    WFar

Dactylorhiza (*Orchidaceae*)
aristata   EBee EFEx
- f. **punctata**   EFEx
aristata x **fuchsii**   EFEx
x **braunii**   ECha IBlr
Calibra g. (*elata* (f)   CHdy
    x *majalis* (m))
§   **elata** ♀ H4   CDes CEnd CHdy CLAP EPar
    GCrs GMaP IBlr LAma LPhx MBri
    MDun SMHy SSpi
- 'Lydia'   CLAP GCrs
Estella g.   CHdy EPot LEur
    (*elata* x *foliosa*)
§   **foliosa** ♀ H4   CBro CDes CElw CFir CLAP
    CItow EBee ERos GCrs GKir IBlr
    LPhx LRHS MAvo MDun MTho
    NHar SBla WCot WFar WOld
foliosa x **saccifera**   CHdy EPot
§   **fuchsii**   CHdy EBee EPot ERos GBuc GCrs
    GKev MNrw NGar NHar NMen
    NRya SCnR SSpi SUsu WHer WShi
- 'Bressingham Bonus'   GCrs WTin
x **grandis**   CHdy
hybrids   WCra
incarnata   CFir CPrp EBee LAma SSpi
§   **maculata**   CHdy CHid CPrp EBee EChP
    EMan EPar EPot LAma LAst NGdn
    NHar NRog SPer WCra WFar
    WHer WPnP WShi
- 'Madam Butterfly'   CAvo CBro EPot GCrs LEur
- 'Strawberry Fields'   EPot
maderensis   see *D. foliosa*
Madonna g. (*majalis*   CHdy
    x *sambucina*)
§   **majalis**   CHdy CLAP CPrp EBee LAma SPer
    SSpi WFar
- subsp. **praetermissa**   see *D. praetermissa*
mascula   see *Orchis mascula*
§   **praetermissa**   CFir CHdy CLAP CPrp EBee EPot
    LEur SSpi WFar WShi
purpurella   CLAP CPrp EBee EPot NHar SSpi
    SUsu WCot WFar WSan WShi
saccifera   CHdy
sambucina   CHdy
'Tinney's Spotted'   CDes
traunsteineri   EBee

Dahlia ✿ (*Asteraceae*)
'A La Mode' (LD) **new**   CWGr
'Abba' (SD) **new**   CWGr
'Abingdon Ace' (SD)   CWGr
'Abridge Alex' (SD) **new**   CWGr
'Abridge Ben' (MinD)   CWGr

'Abridge Florist'   CWGr
    (SWL) **new**
'Abridge Fox' (MinD)   CWGr
'Abridge Natalie' (SWL)   CWGr
'Abridge Primrose'   CWGr
    (SWL) **new**
'Abridge Taffy' (MinD)   CWGr
'Adelaide Fontane' (LD)   CWGr
'Aimie' (MinD) **new**   CWGr
'Akita' (Misc)   CWGr WAba
'Alan Sparkes' (SWL) **new**   CWGr
'Albert Schweitzer'   CWGr
    (MS-c) **new**
'Alden Regal'   CWGr
    (MinC) **new**
'Alfred C' (GS-c)   CWGr
'Alfred Grille' (S-c)   CWGr LRHS
'Alice Ireland'   CWGr
    (MinD) **new**
'Aljo' (MS-c) **new**   CWGr
'All Triumph'   CWGr
    (MinS-c) **new**
'Allan Snowfire' (MS-c)   NHal
'Allan Sparkes' (SWL)   LAyl
    ♀ H3
'Alloway Cottage' (MD)   CWGr NHal
'Alltami Apollo' (GS-c)   CWGr
'Alltami Cherry' (SBa)   CWGr
'Alltami Classic' (MD)   CWGr NHal
'Alltami Corsair' (MS-c)   CWGr LAyl
'Alltami Cosmic' (LD)   CWGr
'Alltami Ruby' (MS-c)   CWGr
'Allyson' (MinBa) **new**   CWGr
'Almand's Climax'   CWGr WAba
    (GD) ♀ H3
'Almand's Supreme'   CWGr
    (GS-c) **new**
'Alpen Beauty' (Col) **new**   CWGr
'Alpen Fern' (Fim) **new**   CWGr
'Alpen Flame'   CWGr
    (MinC) **new**
'Alpen Mildred'   CWGr
    (SS-c) **new**
'Alpen Sun'   CWGr
    (MinS-c) **new**
'Alstergruss' (Col)   CWGr NPPs
'Alva's Doris' (SS-c) ♀ H3   CWGr LAyl
'Alva's Lilac' (SD) **new**   CWGr
'Alva's Supreme'   CWGr NHal WAba
    (GD) ♀ H3
'Amanda Jarvis'   CWGr
    (MinS-c) **new**
'Amanjanca'   CWGr
    (MinS-c) **new**
'Amaran Candyfloss'   CWGr
    (SD)
'Amaran Guard' (LD)   CWGr
'Amaran Pentire'   CWGr
    (SS-c) **new**
'Amaran Pico' (MD)   CWGr
'Amaran Relish' (LD)   CWGr
'Amaran Return'   CWGr
    (GD) **new**
'Amaran Royale' (MinD)   CWGr
'Amaran Troy'   CWGr
    (SWL) **new**
'Amazone' (D)   MBri
'Amber Banker' (MC)   CWGr
'Amber Festival' (SD)   CWGr NHal
'Amber Queen'   CWGr
    (Pom) **new**
'Amber Vale' (MinD) **new**   CWGr
'Amberglow' (MinBa)   CWGr LAyl

'Amberley Jean' (SD) CWGr
'Amberley Joan' CWGr
  (SD) **new**
'Amberley Nicola' (SD) CWGr
'Amberley Victoria' CWGr
  (MD)
'Ambition' (SS-c) **new** CWGr NHal
'Amelia's Surprise' CWGr
  (LD) **new**
'American Copper' (GD) CWGr
'Amethyst' (SD) **new** CWGr
'Amgard Coronet' CWGr WAba
  (MinD) **new**
'Amgard Delicate' (LD) CWGr
'Amgard Rosie' CWGr
  (SD) **new**
'Amira' (SBa) CWGr NHal WAba
'Amorangi Joy' (SC) **new** CWGr
'Amy Campbell' (MD) NHal
* 'Anaïs' CWGr
'Anata Patel' (MinD) **new** CWGr
* 'Anatol' (LD) CWGr
'Anchorite' (SD) CWGr
'Andrea Clark' (MD) **new** LBut NHal
'Andrew Lockwood' CWGr
  (Pom)
'Andrew Magson' CWGr NHal
  (SS-c) ♀ H3
'Andrew Mitchell' (MS-c) CWGr NHal WAba
* 'Andries Amber' (MinS-c) CWGr LBut
'Andries' Orange' CWGr LBut
  (MinS-c)
'Anglian Water' (MinD) CWGr NHal
'Angora' (SD/Fim) **new** CWGr
'Anja Doc' (MS-c) **new** CWGr
'Anniversary Ball' CWGr LAyl
  (MinBa)
'Apache' (MS-c/Fim) CWGr
  new
'Appenzell' (MS-c) CWGr
'Appetizer' (SS-c) CWGr
'Apple Blossom' (MC) CWGr
'Apricot Beauty' (MS-c) CWGr
'Apricot Honeymoon CWGr WAba
  Dress' (SD)
'Apricot Jewel' (SD) CWGr LAyl
'Apricot Parfait' CWGr
  (SS-c) **new**
'April Dawn' (MD) **new** CWGr
'Arab Queen' (GS-c) **new** CWGr
'Arabian Night' (SD) CElw CPen CSam CWGr EBee
                      EBlw EHrv EMan LRHS MNrw
                      MSte NCot NPPs NPSI SDeJ WAba
                      WCot WWeb
'Arc de Triomphe' CWGr
  (MD) **new**
'Arizona'PBR **new** CWGr
'Arlequin' (MD) **new** CWGr
'Arnhem' **new** CWGr
'Arranger's Delight' CWGr
  (SWL) **new**
'Arthur Godfrey' CWGr
  (GD) **new**
'Arthur Hankin' CWGr
  (SD) **new**
'Arthur's Delight' CWGr
  (GD) **new**
'Asahi Chohje' (Anem) CWGr
  ♀ H3 **new**
'Askwith George' CWGr
  (MinD) **new**
'Aspen' (MS-c) **new** CWGr
'Athalie' (SC) CWGr

'Athelston John' CWGr
  (SC) **new**
'Atilla' (SD) **new** CWGr
'Audacity' (MD) CWGr LAyl
'Audrey Grace' (SD) **new** CWGr
'Audrey R' (SWL) **new** CWGr
'Aurora's Kiss' (MinBa) CWGr LBut NHal
'Aurwen's Violet' (Pom) CWGr LAyl NHal
australis **new** CFil
'Autumn Choice' (MD) NHal
'Autumn Lustre' CWGr LAyl
  (SWL) ♀ H3
'Awaikoe' (Col) **new** CWGr
'B.J. Beauty' (MD) CWGr LAyl NHal WAba
'Baarn Born' (GD) **new** CWGr
'Babette' (S-c) LBut
'Baby Fonteneau' CWGr
  (SS-c) **new**
'Baby Royal' (SD) CHad CWGr
'Babylon' (GD) **new** CSut CWGr
'Bacchus' (MS-c) CWGr
'Bach' (MC) CWGr LRHS
'Balcombe (Purple)' CWGr
  (MinD) **new**
'Ballego's Glory' CWGr
  (MD) **new**
'Bambino' (Lil) **new** CWGr
'Banker' (MC) CWGr
'Bantling' (MinBa) **new** CWGr
'Barb' (LC) **new** CWGr
'Barbara Schell' (GD) CWGr
'Barbara's Pastelle' (MS-c) CWGr
'Barbarossa' (LD) CWGr
'Barbarry Ball' (SBa) CWGr
'Barbarry Banker' (MinD) CWGr LAyl
'Barbarry Bluebird' NHal
  (MinD)
'Barbarry Cadet' CWGr
  (MinD) **new**
'Barbarry Carousel' (SBa) CWGr WAba
'Barbarry Chevron' CWGr
  (MD) **new**
'Barbarry Chick' WAba
  (MinD) **new**
'Barbarry Choice' (SD) WAba
'Barbarry Clover' CWGr
  (SB) **new**
'Barbarry Cosmos' CWGr
  (SD) **new**
'Barbarry Dominion' CWGr
  (MinD)
'Barbarry Flag' (MinD) CWGr NHal WAba
'Barbarry Gem' CWGr
  (MinBa) **new**
'Barbarry Noble' CWGr
  (MinD) **new**
'Barbarry Olympic' CWGr
  (SBa) **new**
'Barbarry Oracle' (SD) CWGr WAba
'Barbarry Orange' (SD) WAba
'Barbarry Pimpernel' CWGr
  (SD) **new**
'Barbarry Pinky' (SD) CWGr
'Barbarry Red' CWGr
  (MinD) **new**
'Barbarry Riviera' CWGr
  (MinD) **new**
'Barbarry Ticket' (SD) WAba
'Barbarry Token' (SD) WAba
'Barbarry Triumph' CWGr
  (MinD) **new**
'Barbarry Trooper' **new** CWGr
'Barbetta' (MinD) **new** CWGr

'Camano Passion' (MS-c) **new** — CWGr
'Camano Poppet' (SBa) **new** — CWGr
'Camano Regal' (MS-c) **new** — CWGr
'Cameo' (WL) — CWGr LBut
'Campo's Billy M' (LS-c) **new** — CWGr
'Campo's Hush' (SSC) **new** — CWGr
'Campo's Philip M' (GD) **new** — CWGr
* 'Canary Fubuki' (MD) — CWGr
'Candy' (SD) **new** — CWGr
'Candy Cane' (MinBa) — CWGr
'Candy Cupid' (MinBa) ♀ H3 — CWGr LBut NHal WAba
'Candy Hamilton Lilian' (SD) **new** — CWGr
'Candy Keene' (LS-c) — CWGr NHal
'Caproz Jerry Garcia' (MD) **new** — CWGr
'Capulet' (SBa) **new** — CWGr
'Cara Tina' (Misc/O) **new** — CWGr
'Careless' (SD) **new** — CWGr
'Carolina Moon' (SD) — CWGr LAyl NHal
'Carrie' (MinD) **new** — CWGr
'Carstone Cobblers' (SBa) — CWGr WAba
'Carstone Ruby' (SD) — NHal
'Carstone Sunbeam' (SD) — CWGr
'Carstone Suntan' (MinC) — CWGr NHal
'Castle Drive' (MD) **new** — CWGr
'Catherine Ireland' (MinD) — CWGr
'Cerise Prefect' (MS-c) **new** — CWGr
'Cha Cha' (SS-c) **new** — CWGr
'Chanson D'Amour' (SD) **new** — CWGr
'Charles de Coster' (MD) **new** — CWGr
'Charles Dickens' (SBa) **new** — CWGr
'Charlie Kenwood' (MinD) — CWGr
'Charlie Two' (MD) — CWGr LAyl LBut NHal WAba
'Charlotte Bateson' (MinBa) — CWGr
'Chat Noir (Black Cat)' (MS-c) ♀ — CWGr
'Chee' (SWL) **new** — CWGr
'Cheerio' (SS-c) — CWGr
'Cheerleader' (GS-c) **new** — CWGr
'Cherida' (MinBa) — CWGr
'Cherokee Beauty' (GD) **new** — CWGr
'Cherokee Delight' (LD) **new** — CWGr
'Cherry Wine' (SD) — CWGr
'Cherrywood Millfield' (MS-c) **new** — CWGr
'Cherrywood Stoddard' (MD) **new** — CWGr
'Cherrywood Turnpike' (SD) **new** — CWGr
'Cherrywood Wilderness' (MD) **new** — CWGr
'Cherubino' (Col) **new** — CWGr
'Cherwell Goldcrest' (SS-c) — CWGr NHal WAba

'Cherwell Skylark' (SS-c) **new** — NHal
'Chessy' (Sin/Lil) — CWGr LAyl LRHS WAba
'Cheyenne' (SS-c) — CWGr
'Chic' (MinBa) **new** — CWGr
'Chilson's Pride' (SD) **new** — CWGr
'Chiltern Amber' (SD) — CWGr
'Chiltern Fantastic' (SC) **new** — CWGr
'Chiltern Herald' (MS-c) **new** — CWGr
'Chiltern Sylvia' (MinS-c) **new** — CWGr
'Chimacum Topaz' (MS-c) **new** — CWGr
'Chimborazo' (Col) — CWGr LAyl
'Chinese Lantern' (SD) — CWGr
'Chislehurst Charisma' (SD) **new** — CWGr
'Chloe's Keene' (LS-c) **new** — CWGr
'Chocolate Orange' **new** — WCot
'Chorus Girl' (MinD) — CWGr
'Christine' (SD) — CWGr
'Christmas Carol' (Col) — CWGr NHal
'Christmas Star' (Col) **new** — CWGr
'Christopher Nickerson' (MS-c) — CWGr
'Christopher Taylor' (SWL) — CWGr NHal WAba
I 'Cindy' (MinD) **new** — WAba
'Clair de Lune' (Col) ♀ H3 — CWGr NHal
'Claire Diane' (SD) **new** — CWGr
'Clara May' (MS-c/Fim) **new** — CWGr
'Clarence' (S-c) — CWGr
'Classic A.1' (MC) — CWGr LAyl
'Clint's Climax' (LD) — CWGr WAba
'Cloverdale' (SD) — CWGr
coccinea (B) — CElw CFil CPou CWGr EBee EMan EOrc GDrg MSte SChu WAba WCot
- x merckii (B) — EMan EWes
'Cocktail' (S-c) — CWGr
'Colac' (LD) **new** — CWGr
'Color Spectacle' (LSD) — CWGr
'Coltness Gem' (Sin/DwB) **new** — CWGr
'Comet' (Misc Anem) **new** — CWGr
'Como Polly' (LD) **new** — CWGr
I 'Concordia' (SD) **new** — CWGr
'Connie' (Dwf MinD) **new** — CWGr
'Connie Bartlam' (MD) — CWGr NHal
'Connoisseur's Choice' (MinBa) **new** — CWGr
'Conquistador' (GS-c) **new** — CWGr
'Constance Bateson' (SD) **new** — CWGr
'Constantine' (MD) **new** — CWGr
'Contraste' (Misc) **new** — CWGr
'Conway' (SS-c) **new** — CWGr
'Copper Queen' (MinD) — NHal
'Coral' (SD) **new** — CWGr
'Coral Jupiter' (GS-c) **new** — CWGr
* 'Coral Puff' — CWGr LRHS

'Coral Strand'(SWL) **new**   CWGr
'Coralee' (SD) **new**   CWGr
'Coralle' (MD) **new**   CWGr
'Cornel' (SBa)   CWGr LBut NHal WAba
'Cornish Minx'   CWGr
(Pom) **new**
'Corona' (SS-c/DwB)   CWGr
'Coronella' (MD) **new**   CWGr
'Corrie Vigor' (SS-c)   NHal
'Corrine' (SWL)   WAba
'Cortez Silver' (MD)   CWGr
'Cortez Sovereign'   CWGr
(SS-c) **new**
'Corton Bess' (SD)   CWGr
'Corton Olympic'   CWGr
(GD) **new**
'Corydon' (SWL) **new**   CWGr
'Cottesmore' (MD) **new**   CWGr
'Cottontail' (Col) **new**   CWGr
'Country Boy'   CWGr
(MS-c) **new**
'Coxwell Moonlight'   CWGr
(MS-c) **new**
'Crazy Legs' (MinD) **new** CWGr
'Cream Alva's' (GD) ♀ H3   CWGr
'Cream Beauty' (SWL)   CWGr
'Cream Delight' (SS-c)   CWGr
'Cream Elegans'   CWGr
(SS-c) **new**
'Cream Klankstad' (SC)   CWGr
'Cream Linda' (SD)   CWGr
'Cream Moonlight'   CWGr
(MS-c) **new**
'Cream Reliance'   CWGr
(SD) **new**
'Creve Coeur' (GD) **new**   CWGr
'Crichton Cherry'   CWGr
(MinD)
'Crichton Honey' (SBa)   CWGr
'Croesus' (GS-c) **new**   CWGr
'Crossfield Allegro'   CWGr
(SS-c) **new**
'Crossfield Ann'   CWGr
(MinD) **new**
'Crossfield Ebony'   CWGr
(Pom) **new**
'Crossfield Festival'   CWGr
(LD) **new**
'Croydon Ace' (GD) **new** CWGr
'Croydon Jumbo'   CWGr
(GD) **new**
'Croydon Snotop'   CWGr
(GD) **new**
'Croydon Superior'   CWGr
(GD) **new**
'Crushed Velvet'   CWGr
(MinD) **new**
'Cryfield Bryn' (SS-c)   CWGr NHal
'Cryfield Jane' (MinBa)   CWGr
'Cryfield Keene' (LS-c)   CWGr
'Cryfield Max' (SC)   CWGr
'Cryfield Rosie' (SBa)   CWGr
'Crystal Ann' (MS-c)   CWGr
'Curate' (Misc) **new**   CWGr
'Curiosity' (Col)   CWGr LAyl NHal
'Currant Cream'   CWGr
(SBa) **new**
'Cyclone' (MD) **new**   CWGr
'Cycloop' (SS-c) **new**   CWGr
'Cynthia Chalwin'   CWGr
(MinBa) **new**
'Cynthia Louise'   CWGr
(GD) **new**

'Czar Willo' (Pom) **new**   CWGr
'Czardas'   GCal
'D Day' (SD) **new**   CWGr
'Daddy's Choice' (SS-c)   CWGr
'Dad's Delight' (MinD)   CWGr
'Dahlstar White'   CWGr
(DwB/Sin) **new**
'Daleko Adonis' (GS-c)   CWGr
'Daleko Gold' (MD)   CWGr
'Daleko Jupiter' (GS-c)   CWGr NHal WAba
'Daleko National' (MD)   CWGr
'Daleko Olympic' (LD)   CWGr
'Daleko Tangerine' (MD)   CWGr
'Daleko Venus' (MS-c)   CWGr
'Dana' (MS-c) **new**   CWGr
'Dana Audrey' (MinC)   CWGr
'Dana Dream'   CWGr
(MinS-c) **new**
'Dana Frank' (Pom) **new**   CWGr
'Dana Iris' (SS-c)   CWGr
'Dana Rumba'   CWGr
(MinC) **new**
'Dana Sunset' (SC) **new**   CWGr
'Dancing Queen' (S-c)   CWGr
'Danjo Doc' (SD)   CWGr
'Danum Belle' (SD) **new**   CWGr
'Danum Cherry'   CWGr
(SD) **new**
'Danum Chippy'   CWGr
(SD) **new**
'Danum Cream' (MS-c)   CWGr
'Danum Fancy' (SD) **new**   CWGr
'Danum Gail' (LD) **new**   CWGr
'Danum Hero' (LD) **new**   CWGr
'Danum Julie' (SBa) **now**   CWGr
'Danum Mark'   CWGr
(MSC) **new**
'Danum Meteor' (GS-c)   CWGr WAba
'Danum Pinky' (MS-c)   CWGr
'Danum Rebel'   CWGr
(LS-c) **new**
'Danum Rhoda'   CWGr
(GD) **new**
'Danum Salmon'   CWGr
(MS-c) **new**
'Danum Steady'   CWGr
(SD) **new**
'Danum Torch'   CWGr
(Col) **new**
'Dark Delicious' **new**   WCot
'Dark Desire' (Sin/DwB)   CAvo
'Dark Splendour' (MC)   CWGr
'Dark Stranger'   CWGr
(MC) ♀ H3 **new**
'Darlington Diamond'   CWGr
(MS-c) **new**
'Darlington Jubilation'   CWGr
(SS-c) **new**
'Davar Hayley' (SC) **new**   CWGr
'Davenport Anita'   CWGr
(MinD)
'Davenport Honey'   CWGr WAba
(MinD)
'Davenport Lesley'   CWGr
(MinD)
'Davenport Sunlight'   CWGr NHal
(MS-c)
'Dave's Snip'   CWGr
(MinD) **new**
'David Digweed' (SD)   CWGr NHal
'David Howard'   CBcs CHad CMGP CSam CWGr
(MinD) ♀ H3   EBlw EBre EPfP ERou LAyl LRHS
MMil MSte NHal NPPs NVic SAga

	SChu SPar SPer SPla SUsu WAba WCot WWeb
'David Shaw' (MD) **new**	CWGr
'David's Choice' (MinD) **new**	CWGr
'Dawn Chorus' (MinD) **new**	CWGr
'Dawn Sky' (SD)	CWGr LAyl
'Daytona' (SD)	CWGr
'Deborah's Kiwi' (SC)	CWGr NHal
'Debra Anne Craven' (GS-c)	CWGr NHal
'Deep Delight' **new**	WCot
'Deepest Yellow' (MinBa)	CWGr
'Defile' (MD)	CWGr
'Denise Willow' (Pom)	CWGr WAba
'Dentelle de Venise' (MC) **new**	CWGr
'Deuil de Roi Albert' (MD) **new**	CWGr
'Deutschland' (MD) **new**	CWGr
'Devon Joy' (MinD) **new**	CWGr
'Diana Gregory' (Pom)	CWGr
'Dinah Shore' (LS-c) **new**	CWGr
'Director' (SD) **new**	CWGr
dissecta **new**	CFil
'Doc van Horn' (LS-c)	CWGr
'Doctor Anne Dyson' (SC) **new**	CWGr
'Doctor Arnett' (GS-c) **new**	CWGr
'Doctor Caroline Rabbitt' (SD)	CWGr
'Doctor John Grainger' (MinD)	CWGr
'Doktor Hans Ricken'(SD)	WAba
'Don's Delight' (Pom) **new**	CWGr
'Doris Bacon' (MinBa) **new**	CWGr
'Doris Day' (SC)	CWGr LBut NHal WAba
'Doris Knight' (SC)	CWGr LBut
'Doris Rollins' (SC) **new**	CWGr
'Dottie D' (SBa) **new**	CWGr
'Downham Royal' (MinBa)	CWGr
'Drummer Boy' (LD) **new**	CWGr
'Duet' (MD)	CSut CWGr LRHS
'Dusky Harmony' (SWL)	CWGr LBut
'Dutch Baby' (Pom)	CWGr WAba
'Dutch Boy' (LD) **new**	CWGr
'Dutch Triumph' (LWL) **new**	CWGr
'Earl Haig' (LD) **new**	CWGr
'Earl Marc' (SC)	CWGr LBut
'Early Bird' (SD)	CWGr
'East Anglian' (SD)	CWGr
'Easter Sunday' (Col)	CWGr
'Eastwood Moonlight' (MS-c)	CWGr NHal WAba
'Eastwood Star' (MS-c)	CWGr WAba
'Ebbw Vale Festival' (MinD) **new**	CWGr
'Edge of Gold' (GD)	CWGr
'Edgeway Joyce' (MinBa) **new**	CWGr
'Edinburgh' (SD)	CWGr WAba
'Edith Holmes' (SC) **new**	CWGr
'Edith Muellar' (Pom) **new**	CWGr
'Eileen Denny' (MS-c)	CWGr
'El Cid' (SD) **new**	CWGr
'El Paso' (SD)	CSut CWGr
'Eldon Wilson' (Misc/O) **new**	CWGr
'Elgico Leanne' (MC) **new**	CWGr
'Elizabeth Hammett' (MinD)	CWGr WAba
'Elizabeth Snowden' (Col) **new**	CWGr WAba
'Ella Britton' (MinD)	CPen EBee LRHS
'Ellen Huston' (Sin/DwB) ♀ H3	CWGr EBee LRHS MBri NHal SAga
'Elma E' (LD)	CWGr NHal WAba
'Elmbrook Chieftain' (GD)	CWGr
'Elmbrook Rebel' (GS-c)	CWGr
'Emma's Coronet' (MinD) **new**	CWGr
'Emmie Lou' (MD) **new**	CWGr
'Emory Paul' (LD)	CWGr
'Emperor' (MD) **new**	CWGr
'Enfield Salmon' (LD) **new**	CWGr
'Engadin' (MD) **new**	CWGr
'Enid Adams' (SD) **new**	CWGr
'Eric's Choice' (SD) **new**	CWGr
'Erife' (MD) **new**	CWGr
'Erik the Red' (Col) **new**	CWGr
'Ernie Pitt' (SD)	CWGr
'Esau' (GD) **new**	CWGr
'Esther'	MBri
'Eugina Huston' (GD) **new**	CWGr
'Eveline' (SD)	CWGr LRHS
'Evelyn Foster' (MD)	CWGr NHal
'Evelyn Rumbold' (GD)	CWGr
'Evening Lady' (MinD) **new**	CWGr
excelsa (B)	CHll
'Exotic Dwarf' (Sin/Lil)	CWGr NHal
'Explosion' (SS-c)	CWGr
'Extase' (MD)	CWGr LRHS
'Fabula' (Col) **new**	CWGr
'Facet' (Sin/Lil) **new**	WAba
'Fairway Pilot' (GD) **new**	CWGr
'Fairway Spur' (GD)	CWGr NHal
'Fairy Queen' (MinC) **new**	CWGr
'Falcon's Future' (MS-c) **new**	CWGr
'Fascination' (SWL/DwB) ♀ H3	CBgR CBos CHad LAyl NHal SChu
'Fashion Monger' (Col)	CWGr NHal
'Fatima' (MinD) **new**	CWGr
'Fermain' (MinD)	CWGr WAba
'Fern Irene' (MWL) **new**	CWGr
'Ferncliffe Fuego' (MC) **new**	CWGr
'Fernhill Champion' (MD)	CWGr
'Fernhill Suprise' (SD)	CWGr LBut
'Festivo' (Dwf Col) **new**	CWGr
'Feu Céleste' (Col)	CWGr
'Fidalgo Blacky' (MinD) **new**	CWGr
'Fidalgo Bounce' (SD) **new**	CWGr
'Fidalgo Climax' (LS-c/Fim)	CWGr
'Fidalgo Magic' (MD)	CWGr WAba
'Fidalgo Snowman' (GS-c) **new**	CWGr
'Fidalgo Splash' (MD) **new**	CWGr

* 'Fernhill Suprise' (SD)   CWGr LBut

'Fidalgo Supreme' (MD) CWGr LAyl
'Fiesta Dance' (SC) **new** CWGr
'Figurine' (SWL) ♀ H3 CWGr NHal WAba
'Fille du Diable' (LS-c) CWGr
'Finchcocks' CWGr LAyl
  (SWL) ♀ H3
'Fiona Stewart' (SBa) CWGr
* 'Fire Mountain' NHal
  (MinD/DwB)
'Firebird' (Sin) LRHS WAba
'Firebrand' (SC) **new** CWGr
'First Lady' (MD) **new** CWGr
'Flevohof' (MS-c) **new** CWGr
'Florence Vernon' CWGr
  (MinBa) **new**
'Flutterby' (SWL) CWGr
'Foreman's Jubilee' (GS-c) CWGr
'Formby Perfection' (MD) CWGr
'Formby Supreme' (MD) CWGr
'Forncett Furnace' (B) GCal
'Forrestal' (MS-c) **new** CWGr
'Frank Holmes' (Pom) CWGr WAba
'Frank Hornsey' (SD) CWGr
'Frank Lovell' (GS-c) CWGr WAba
'Franz Kafka' CWGr
  (MinBa) **new**
'Frau Louis Mayer' **new** CWGr
'Fred Burrows' (SD) **new** CWGr
'Fred Wallace' (SC) **new** CWGr
'Freelancer' (LC) **new** CWGr
'Freestyle' (SC) CWGr
'Freya's Thalia' LAyl
  (Sin/Lil) ♀ H3
'Friendship' (LC) **new** CWGr
'Frigoulet' CWGr
'Fringed Star' (MS-c) CWGr LRHS
'Frits' (MinBa) CWGr
'Funfair' (MD) **new** CWGr
'Funny Face' (Misc) CWGr WAba
'Fusion' (MD) CWGr
'G.F. Hemerik' (Sin) CWGr
'Gala Parade' (SD) CWGr NHal
'Gale Lane' (Pom) CWGr
'Gallery Art Deco'PBR CWGr WWol
  (SD) ♀ H3
'Gallery Art Fair'PBR WWol
  (MinD)
'Gallery Art Nouveau'PBR CWGr WWol
  (MinD) ♀ H3
'Gallery Leonardo'PBR CWGr WWol
  (SD) ♀ H3 **new**
'Gallery Monet'PBR CWGr WWol
  (SD) **new**
'Gallery Rembrandt'PBR CWGr
  (MinD) **new**
'Gallery Renoir'PBR WWol
  (SD) ♀ H3 **new**
'Gallery Vermeer'PBR CWGr
  (MinD) **new**
'Gamelan' (Dwf Ancm) CWGr
  new
'Garden Festival' (SWL) CWGr LAyl
'Garden Party' CWGr LAyl
  (MC/DwB) ♀ H3
'Garden Princess' CWGr
  (SC/DwB) **new**
'Garden Wonder' (SD) CWGr LRHS
'Gargtantuan' CWGr
  (GS-c) **new**
Gateshead Festival CWGr NHal
  = 'Peach Melba' (SD)
'Gay Mini' (MinD) CWGr
'Gay Princess' (SWL) CWGr LAyl

'Gay Triumph' CWGr
  (GS-c) **new**
'Geerling's Cupido' CWGr
  (SWL) **new**
§ 'Geerlings Indian NHal
  Summer' (MS-c) ♀ H3
'Geerling's Jewel' CWGr
  (SWL) **new**
'Geerling's Star' CWGr
  (MS-c) **new**
'Geerling's Yellow' CWGr
  (SS-c) **new**
'Gemma Darling' CWGr
  (GD) **new**
'Gemma's Place' CWGr
  (Pom) **new**
'Geneve' (MD) **new** CWGr
'Gentle Giant' (GD) **new** CWGr
'Geoffrey Kent' (MinD) LBut
  ♀ H3 **new**
'Gerald Grace' (LS-c) CWGr
'Gerlos' (MD) **new** CWGr
'Gerrie Hoek' (SWL) CWGr LBut LRHS
'Geum' (MC) **new** CWGr
'Gill's Pastelle' CWGr WAba
  (MS-c) **new**
'Gilt Edge' (MD) CWGr
'Gina Lombaert' (MS-c) CWGr LRHS WAba
* 'Ginger Willo' CWGr
'Giraffe' (Misc) CWGr
'Gitt's Perfection' CWGr
  (LD) **new**
'Gitty' (SBa) **new** CWGr
'Glad Huston' CWGr
  (Dwf SS-c) **new**
'Glenafton' (Pom) CWGr
'Glenbank Honeycomb' CWGr
  (Pom)
'Glenbank Paleface' CWGr
  (Pom) **new**
'Glenbank Twinkle' CWGr
  (MinC)
'Glengarry' (SC) **new** CWGr
'Glenplace' (pom) **new** CWGr
'Globular' (MinBa) **new** CWGr
'Gloria Romaine' (SD) CWGr
'Glorie van Heemstede' CWGr LAyl LBut LRHS NHal
  (SWL) ♀ H3
'Glorie van Naardwijk' CWGr
  (SD)
'Glory' (LD) **new** CWGr
'Glow Orange' CWGr
  (MinBa) **new**
'Go American' (GD) CWGr NHal
'Gold Ball' (MinBa) **new** CWGr
'Gold Crown' (LS-c) CSut
'Gold Standard' (LD) **new** CWGr
'Goldean' (GD) **new** CWGr
'Golden Ballade' CWGr
  (MD) **new**
'Golden Charmer' CWGr
  (SC) **new**
'Golden Emblem' (MD) CWGr SDeJ
'Golden Explosion' CWGr
  (LC) **new**
'Golden Fizz' (MinBa) CWGr
'Golden Heart' CWGr
  (MS-c) **new**
'Golden Impact' (MS-c) CWGr NHal
'Golden Leader' (SD) CWGr
'Golden Sceptre CWGr WAba
  (Saphire)'
  (MinD) **new**

'Hit Parade' (MS-c)   CWGr
'Hockley Maroon'   CWGr
   (SD) **new**
'Holland Festival' (GD)   CWGr
'Honey' (Anem/DwB)   CWGr LRHS WAba
'Honeymoon Dress' (SD)   CWGr NHal
'Hugh Mather' (MWL)   CWGr
'Hulin's Carnival'   CWGr
   (MinD) **new**
'Hy Fire' (MinBa) **new**   CWGr
'Ice Queen' (SWL)   CWGr
'Ida Gayer' (LD) **new**   CWGr
'I-Lyke-It' (SS-c) **new**   CWGr
'Imp'   see D. 'Harvest Imp'
imperialis (B)   CHEx CWGr EMon EWes GCal
                             LPio MOak WBVN WCot WHal
I - 'Alba' (B)   EMon
   - 'Tasmania' (B)   GCal
'Impression Flamenco'   CWGr LRHS
'Impression Fortuna'   CWGr
   (Dwf Col) **new**
'Inca Concord'   CWGr
   (MD) **new**
'Inca Dambuster' (GS-c)   CWGr NHal
'Inca Glamour' (LD) **new** CWGr
'Inca Matchless' (MD)   CWGr WAba
'Inca Metropolitan' (LD)   CWGr
'Inca Panorama'   CWGr
   (MD) **new**
'Inca Royale' (LD) **new**   CWGr
'Inca Vanguard'   CWGr
   (GD) **new**
'Inca Vulcan' (GS-c) **new** CWGr
'Indian Summer' (SC)   CWGr WAba
'Inflammation'   see D. 'Harvest Inflammation'
'Inglebrook Jill' (Col)   CWGr LAyl
'Ingol' (SS-c) **new**   CWGr
'Inland Dynasty' (GS-c)   CWGr
'Inn's Gerrie Hoek'   CWGr
   (MD) **new**
'Inskip' (SC) **new**   CWGr
'Invader' (SC)   CWGr
'Iola' (LD) **new**   CWGr
'Irene van der Zwet'   CWGr
   (Sin)
'Iris' (Pom)   CWGr WAba
'Irisel' (MS-c) **new**   CWGr
'Islander' (LD) **new**   CWGr
'Ivy Della' (SD) **new**   CWGr
'Jack O'Lantern'   CWGr
   (Col) **now**
'Jackie Magson'   CWGr WAba
   (SS-c) **new**
'Jackie's Baby'   WAba
   (MinD) **new**
'Jackie's Desire'   CWGr
   (SS-c) **now**
'Jacqueline Tivey' (SD)   CWGr
'Jaldec Jerry' (GS-c)   CWGr
'Jaldec John' (SD) **new**   CWGr
'Jaldec Joker' (SC)   CWGr
'Jaldec Jolly' (SC)   CWGr
'Jamaica' (MinWL) **new**   CWGr
'Jamie' (SS-c)   CWGr
'Jan Carden' **new**   CWGr
'Jan Lennon' (MS-c) **new** CWGr
'Jan van Schaffelaar' **new** CWGr
'Janal Amy' (GS-c)   NHal
'Jane Cowl' (LD) **new**   CWGr
'Jane Horton' (Col)   CWGr
'Janet Becket' (LC) **new** CWGr
'Janet Clarke' (Pom)   CWGr

'Janet Goddard' (SD)   CWGr
'Janet Jean' (SWL) **new**   CWGr
'Japanese Bishop'   CWGr
   (Misc) **new**
'Japanese Waterlily'   CWGr
   (SWL) **new**
'Jason' (SS-c)   WAba
'Jazzy' (Col) **new**   CWGr
'Je Maintiendrai'   CWGr
   (GD) **new**
'Jean Fairs' (MinWL)   CWGr LBut
'Jean Marie' (MD)   CWGr LRHS
'Jean McMillan' (SC)   NHal
'Jean Melville'   CWGr
   (MinD) **new**
'Jeanette Carter'   CWGr
   (MinD) ♀ H3
'Jeanne d'Arc' (GC)   CSut CWGr
'Jeannie Leroux'   CWGr
   (SS-c/Fim) **new**
'Jean's Carol' (Pom) **new** CWGr
'Jennie' (MC/Fim)   CWGr
'Jersey Beauty' (Ba)   CWGr
'Jescot Buttercup'   CWGr
   (SD) **new**
'Jescot India'   CWGr
   (MinD) **new**
'Jescot Jess' (MinD)   CWGr LBut
'Jescot Jim' (SD)   CWGr
'Jescot Julie' (O)   CWGr LAyl NPPs
'Jescot Lingold' (MinD)   CWGr WAba
'Jescot Nubia' (SS-c)   CWGr
'Jescot Redun'   CWGr
   (MinD) **new**
'Jessica' (S-c)   CWGr
'Jessie G' (SBa)   CWGr
'Jessie Ross' (MinD/DwB)   CWGr
'Jet' (SS-c) **new**   CWGr
'Jill Day' (SC)   CWGr LBut
'Jill Doc' (MD)   CWGr
'Jill's Blush' (MS-c)   CWGr
'Jill's Delight' (MD)   CWGr
'Jim Branigan' (LS-c)   CWGr NHal WAba
'Jo Anne' (MS-c)   CWGr
'Joan Beecham' (SWL)   CWGr
'Jocondo' (GD)   CWGr NHal
'Johann' (Pom)   CWGr NHal
'John Butterworth'   CWGr
   (GD) **new**
'John Prior' (SD)   CWGr
'John Street'   CWGr
   (SWL) ♀ H3
'John's Champion'   CWGr
   (MD) **new**
'Jomanda'   CWGr LBut NHal WAba
   (MinBa) ♀ H3
'Jorja' (MS-c)   CWGr NHal
'Jo's Choice' (MinD)   CWGr LBut
'Joy Donaldson'   CWGr
   (MC) **new**
'Joyce Green' (GS-c)   CWGr
'Joyce Margaret   CWGr
   Cunliffe' (SD) **new**
'Juanita' (MC) **new**   CWGr
'Judith' (SWL) **new**   CWGr
'Julie One'   CWGr
   (Misc Dbl O) **new**
'Julio' (MinBa) **new**   CWGr
'Jura' (SS-c) **new**   CWGr
'Just Jill' (MinD) **new**   CWGr
'Kaftan' (MD) **new**   CWGr
'Kaiser Wilhelm'   CWGr
   (SBa) **new**

'Kaiserwalzer' (Col) **new** CWGr
'Karenglen' (MinD) ♀ H3 CWGr LBut NHal WAba
'Kari Blue' (SWL) **new** CWGr
'Kari Quill' (SC) **new** CWGr
I 'Karma Fuchiana'   CWGr
   (SD) **new**
'Karras' (SS-c)   NHal
'Karras 150' (SS-c) **new** CWGr
'Kary Anne' **new**   CWGr
'Kasasagi' (Pom) **new** CWGr
'Kathleen's Alliance'   CWGr NHal
   (SC) ♀ H3
'Kathryn's Cupid'   CWGr WAba
   (MinBa) ♀ H3
'Kathy' (SC) **new**   CWGr
'Katie Dahl' (MinD)   CWGr NHal
'Katisha' (MinD)   CWGr
'Katja' (MinBa) **new**   CWGr
'Kay Helen' (Pom)   CWGr
'Keith's Choice' (MD)   CWGr NHal WAba
'Kelsea Carla' (SS-c)   CWGr NHal WAba
* 'Keltie Jimmy Flood'   NHal
   (MinBa)
'Keltie Peach' (MD)   NHal
'Kelvin Floodlight' (GD) CWGr
'Kenn Emerland' (MS-c) CSut CWGr
'Kenora Canada' (MS-c) CWGr WAba
'Kenora Challenger'(LS-c) CWGr NHal WAba
'Kenora Christmas'   CWGr
   (SBa) **new**
'Kenora Clyde'   CWGr
   (GS-c) **new**
'Kenora Fireball' (MinBa) CWGr NHal
'Kenora Frills' (MD) **new** CWGr
'Kenora Lisa' (MD) **new** CWGr
'Kenora Moonbeam'   CWGr
   (MD)
'Kenora Peace'   CWGr
   (MinBa) **new**
'Kenora Petite' (MinS-c) CWGr
'Kenora Sunburst' (LS-c) CWGr
'Kenora Sunset'   CWGr LAyl LBut NHal
   (MS-c) ♀ H3
'Kenora Superb' (LS-c)   CWGr NHal WAba
'Kenora Valentine'   CWGr LAyl NHal WAba
   (LD) ♀ H3
'Kenora Wildfire' (LD)   CWGr
'Ken's Coral' (SWL)   CWGr NHal
'Ken's Flame' (SWL) **new** CWGr
'Ken's Rarity' (SWL)   NHal
'Key West' (LD)   CWGr
'Kidd's Climax'   CWGr NHal WAba
   (GD) ♀ H3
'Kilmorie' (SS-c) **new**   NHal
'Kim Willo' (Pom) **new**   CWGr
'Kimberley B'   CWGr
   (MinD) **new**
'Kimi' (O)   CWGr
'Kim's Marc' (SC)   CWGr LBut
'Kingston' (MinD) **new**   CWGr
'Kismet' **new**   CWGr
'Kiss' **new**   CWGr
'Kit Kat' (LC) **new**   CWGr
'Kiwi Brother' (SS-c) **new** CWGr
'Kiwi Cousin' (SC) **new** CWGr
'Kiwi Gloria' (SC)   CWGr NHal WAba
'Kiwi Sister' (SS-c) **new** CWGr
'Klankstad Kerkrade' (SC) CWGr
'Klondike' (MS-c)   CWGr WAba
* 'Kogano Fubuki' (MD)   CWGr
'Kochelsee' (MinD)   CWGr
'Kotare Jackpot' (SS-c)   CWGr
'Kung Fu' (SD)   CWGr

I 'Kyoto' (SWL)   CWGr WAba
'L.A.T.E.' (MinBa)   CWGr NHal WAba
'La Cierva' (Col)   CWGr
'La Corbière' (MinBa)   CWGr
'La Gioconda' (Col)   CWGr
'Lady Jane' (SWL) **new**   CWGr
'Lady Kerkrade' (SC)   CWGr
'Lady Linda' (SD)   CWGr LBut NHal WAba
'Lady Orpah' (SD)   CWGr
'Lady Sunshine' (SS-c)   CWGr
'Lancastrian' (SC) **new**   CWGr
'L'Ancresse' (MinBa)   CWGr LAyl NHal WAba
'Larkford' (SD) **new**   CWGr
'Last Dance' (MD) **new**   CWGr
'Laura Marie' (MinBa)   CWGr
* 'Laura's Choice' (SD)   CWGr
'Laurence Fisher' (MS-c)   CWGr
'Lauren's Moonlight'   CWGr NHal WAba
   (MS-c)
'Lavendale' (MinD)   CWGr
'Lavender Athalie' (SC)   CWGr
'Lavender Freestyle'   CWGr
   (SC) **new**
'Lavender Leycett' (GD)   CWGr
'Lavender Line' (SC)   CWGr NHal
'Lavender Nunton   CWGr
   Harvest' (SD)
'Lavender Perfection'   CWGr
   (GD)
'Lavender Prince' **new**   CWGr
'Lavengro' (GD)   CWGr
'Le Batts Premier'   CWGr
   (SD) **new**
'Le Castel' (D)   CWGr
'Le Patineur' (MD) **new** CWGr
'Le Vonne Splinter' (GS-c) CWGr
'Leander' (GD) **new**   CWGr
'Lecta' (MC) **new**   CWGr
'Lemon' (Anem)   CWGr WAba
'Lemon Cane' (Misc)   CWGr WAba
'Lemon Elegans'   CWGr LBut NHal WAba
   (SS-c) ♀ H3
'Lemon Meringue'   CWGr
   (SD) **new**
* 'Lemon Puff' (Anem)   CWGr
'Lemon Zing' (MinBa)   NHal WAba
'Lenny' (Dwf MinD) **new** CWGr
'Lexington' (MinD) **new** CWGr
'Leycett' (GD)   CWGr
'Liberator' (GD)   CWGr
'Libretto' (Col) **new**   CWGr
* 'Life Force' (GD)   CWGr
'Life Size' (LD)   CWGr
'Light Music' (LC) **new**   CWGr
'Lilac Athalie' (SC)   CWGr
'Lilac Shadow' (S-c)   CWGr
§ 'Lilac Taratahi' (SC) ♀ H3 CWGr NHal
'Lilac Time' (MD)   CWGr LRHS SDeJ
'Lilac Willo' (Pom) **new** CWGr
'Lilianne Ballego' (MinD)   NHal
'Lillianne Ballego'   CWGr
   (Dwf MinD) **new**
'Linda's Chester' (SC)   CWGr LBut
'Linz' (Dwf SD) **new**   CWGr
'Lipoma' (MinBa)   CWGr
'Lisa' ᴾᴮᴿ **new**   CWGr
'Lismore Canary'   NHal
   (SWL) **new**
'Lismore Carol' (Pom)   CWGr NHal
'Lismore Chaffinch'   NHal
   (MinD)
'Lismore Moonlight'   CWGr LAyl NHal
   (Pom)

'Lismore Peggy' (Pom) CWGr
'Lismore Robin' (MinD) NHal
'Lismore Sunset' (Pom) CWGr NHal WAba
'Lismore Willie' CWGr LAyl LBut NHal WAba
  (SWL) ♀ H3
'Little Berliner CWGr
  (Berliner Kleene)'
  (Dwf MinD) **new**
'Little Dorrit' CWGr LBut
  (Sin/Lil) ♀ H3
'Little Glenfern' CWGr
  (MinC) **new**
'Little John' **new** CWGr
'Little Lamb' (MS-c) **new** CWGr
'Little Laura' (MinBa) CWGr
'Little Matthew' CWGr
  (Pom) **new**
'Little Reggie' (SS-c) **new** CWGr
'Little Robert' CWGr
  (MinD) **new**
'Little Sally' (Pom) CWGr NHal
'Little Scottie' (Pom) **new** CWGr
'Little Shona' CWGr
  (MinD) **new**
'Little Snowdrop' CWGr
  (Pom) **new**
'Little Tiger' CWGr
'Liverpool' **new** CWGr
'Liz' (MS-c) **new** CWGr
'Liza' (MinD) **new** CWGr
'Lloyd Huston' (GS-c) CWGr
'Lois Walcher' (LD) **new** CWGr
'Lollipop' (Pom) **new** CWGr
'Lombada' (Misc) **new** CWGr
'Long Island Lil' (SD) **new** CWGr
'Longwood Dainty' CWGr NHal
  (DwB)
'Loretta' (MinD) **new** CWGr
'Loud Applause' (SC) CWGr
'Louis V' (LS-c) **new** CWGr
'Louise Bailey' (MinD) CWGr
'Love's Dream' (SWL) CWGr
'Lucky Devil' (MD) **new** CWGr
'Lucky Number' CWGr
  (MD) **new**
'Ludwig Helfert' (S-c) CWGr LRHS NPPs
'Lupin Dixie' (SC) **new** CWGr
'Lutt Wichtan' CWGr
  (MinWL) **new**
'Lyn Mayo' (SD) **new** CWGr
'Lynda Windsor' (Sin) CRDP
'Lyndsey Murray' CWGr
  (MinD) **new**
'Lynn Clark' (SD) **new** WAba
'Mabel Ann' (GD) CWGr
'Madame Elisabeth CWGr
  Sawyer' (SS-c) **new**
'Madame Simone CWGr EBee
  Stappers' (WL)
'Madame Vera' (SD) LBut
'Madelaine Ann' (GD) CWGr
'Maelstrom' (SD) CWGr
'Mafolie' (GS-c) **new** CWGr
'Magenta Magic' NHal
  (Sin/DwB)
'Magic Moment' (MS-c) CWGr
'Magnificat' (MinD) CWGr
'Maisie' (SD) **new** CWGr
'Maisie Mooney' CWGr
  (GD) **new**
'Majestic Athalie' (SC) CWGr
'Majestic Kerkrade' (SC) CWGr
'Majjas Symbol' (MS-c) CWGr

'Malham Honey' CWGr
  (SD) **new**
'Malham Portia' CWGr
  (SWL) **new**
'Maltby Fanfare' CWGr
  (Col) **new**
'Maltby Whisper' (SC) LAyl NHal
'Mandy' (MinD) **new** CWGr
'Marble Ball' (SBa) **new** CWGr
'Margaret Ann' (MinD) CWGr LAyl LBut
'Margaret Brookes' CWGr
  (LD) **new**
* 'Margaret Haggo' (SWL) NHal
'Margareth' CWGr
  (MinD) **new**
'Margie' (SD) CWGr WAba
'Marie' (SD) **new** CWGr
'Marie Schnugg' (Misc) CWGr
'Mariner's Light' (SS-c) CWGr
'Mariposa' (Col) CWGr WAba
'Mark Damp' (LS-c) CWGr
'Mark Hardwick' (GD) CWGr NHal
'Mark Lockwood' (Pom) CWGr WAba
'Market Joy' (SD) **new** CWGr
'Marla Lu' (SS-c) **new** CWGr
'Marlene Joy' (MS-c/Fim) CWGr NHal WAba
'Maroen' PBR (Misc) **new** CWGr
'Mars' (Col) **new** CWGr
'Marshmello Sky' CWGr
  (Col) **new**
'Marta' (GD) **new** CWGr
'Martin's Red' (Pom) CWGr NHal
'Martin's Yellow' (Pom) CWGr NHal WAba
'Mary Eveline' (Col) LAyl NHal
'Mary Hammett' (MinD) WAba
'Mary Jennie' CWGr
  (MinS-c) **new**
'Mary Jo' (MinS-c) **new** CWGr
'Mary Layton' (Col) CWGr
'Mary Magson' CWGr
  (SS-c) **new**
'Mary Munns' (Pom) **new** CWGr
'Mary Partridge' CWGr
  (SWL) **new**
'Mary Pitt' (MinD) CWGr
'Mary Richards' CWGr
  (SD) **new**
'Mary's Jomanda' NHal
  (SBa) **new**
'Master David' CWGr
  (MinBa) **new**
'Master Michael' CWGr
  (Pom) **new**
'Match' (SS-c) CWGr
'Matilda Huston' (SS-c) CWGr NHal
'Matt Armour' CWGr
  (Sin) **new**
'Maureen Hardwick' CWGr
  (GD) **new**
'Maxine Bailey' (SD) CWGr
'Maya' (MinD) **new** CWGr
'Meiro' (SD) CWGr
'Melanie Jane' (MS-c) CWGr
'Melton' (MinD) CWGr
merckii (B) CHad CSpe CWGr EGoo EOrc
  EWes GCal GEil GMac LRHS MNrw
  MSte SChu SMad WAba WCom
  WWin

- *alba* (B) CFil CHad EBee MSte WPGP
- compact (B) CBos CFil EBee EMan WPGP
- 'Edith Edelman' (B) CFil
'Meredith's Marion CWGr
  Smith' (SD)

'Mermaid of Zennor' **new** CBos EBlw EMan NCot WAbe
'Merriwell Topic' (MD) CWGr
'Mi Wong' (Pom) CWGr NHal
'Miami' (SD) **new** CWGr
'Michael J' (MinD) **new** CWGr
'Michigan' (MinD) **new** CWGr
'Mick' (SC) **new** CWGr
'Mick's Peppermint' (MS-c) **new** CWGr
'Midas' (SD) **new** CWGr
'Midnight' (Pom) **new** CWGr
'Midnight Sun' (MinD) NHal
'Mies' (Sin) CWGr
'Minder' (GD) CWGr
'Mingus Alex' (MS-c/Fim) **new** CWGr
'Mingus Gregory' (LS-c) **new** CWGr
'Mingus Kyle D' (SD) **new** CWGr
'Mingus Nichole' (LD) **new** CWGr
'Mingus Tracy Lynn' (SS-c) **new** CWGr
'Mingus Whitney' (GS-c) **new** CWGr
'Mini' (Sin/Lil) CWGr LBut
'Mini Red' (MinC) **new** CWGr
'Minley Carol' (Pom) ♀ H3 CWGr LAyl NHal WAba
'Minley Iris' (Pom) CWGr
'Minley Linda' (Pom) CWGr
'Minley Sharron' (Pom) **new** CWGr
'Minnesota' (LD) **new** WAba
'Miramar' (SD) CWGr
'Miss Blanc' (SD) CWGr
'Miss Rose Fletcher' (SS-c) **new** CWGr
'Miss Swiss' (SD) CWGr
'Misterton' (MD) **new** CWGr
'Mistill Beauty' (SC) CWGr
'Mistill Delight' (MinD) CWGr
'Mistral' (MS-c/Fim) **new** CWGr
'Mom's Special' (GD) **new** CWGr
'Monk Marc' (SC) CWGr LBut
'Monkstown Diane' (SC) CWGr
'Monrovia' (Pom) **new** CWGr
'Montresor' (Dwf) **new** CWGr
'Moonfire' (Misc/DwB) ♀ H3 CFir CWGr EBee EBre EMan ENot ERou LAyl LRHS MBri MMil MSte NCot NGdn NHal NPPs SAga SPar SPer SUsu WAba WCot WHer WViv WWeb
'Moonglow' (LS-c) **new** CWGr
'Moor Place' (Pom) CWGr NHal WAba
'Moret' (SS-c) **new** CWGr
'Morley Lady' (SD) CWGr
'Morley Lass' (SS-c) CWGr
'Morning Dew' (SC) CWGr
'Motto' (LD) **new** CWGr
'Mount Noddy' (Sin) CWGr
'Mrs A Woods' (MD) **new** CWGr
'Mrs Black' (Pom) **new** CWGr
'Mrs Clement Andries' (MS-c) **new** CWGr
'Mrs H Brown' (Col) **new** CWGr
'Mrs McDonald Quill' (LD) CWGr NHal
'Mrs Silverston' (SD) CWGr

'Mummies Favourite' (SD) CWGr
'München' (MinD) **new** CWGr
'Murdoch' CBos CPen EBee EMan NCot WAba WCot
'Muriel Gladwell' (SS-c) **new** CWGr
'Murillo' CWGr MBri
'Murray May' (LD) **new** CWGr
'Murray Petite' (SS-c) **new** CWGr
'Musette' (MinD) **new** CWGr
'My Joy' (Pom) **new** CWGr
'My Love' (SS-c) CSut CWGr LRHS
'My Valentine' (SWL) **new** CWGr
'Mystery Day' (MD) **new** CSut CWGr
'Nancy H' (MinBa) **new** CWGr
'Nankyoko' **new** CWGr
'Nargold' (MS-c/Fim) CWGr LAyl
'Narooma Princess' (SWL) **new** CWGr
'Natal' (MinBa) **new** CWGr
'National Vulcan' (MinD) **new** CWGr
'Nationwide' (SD) CWGr WAba
'Neal Gillson' (MD) CWGr
'Nellie Birch' (MinBa) CWGr
'Nellie Geerlings' **new** CWGr
'Nenekazi' (MS-c/Fim) CWGr NHal
'Nepos' (SWL) CWGr LBut
'Nescio' (Pom) CWGr WAba
'Nettie' (MinBa) CWGr
'New Baby' (MinBa) CWGr LRHS
'New Dimension' (SS-c) **new** CWGr
'New Look' (LS-c) **new** CWGr
'Newchurch' (MinD) **new** CWGr
'Newsham Wonder' (SD) **new** CWGr
'Nicola' (SS-c) **new** CWGr
'Nicola Higgo' (MC/Fim) **new** CWGr
'Nicola Jane' (Pom) ♀ H3 NHal
'Nicolette' (MWL) CWGr
'Night Editor' (GD) CWGr
'Nijinsky' (SBa) CWGr
'Nina Chester' (SD) CWGr WAba
'Nita' **new** CWGr
'Nonette' (SWL) CWGr WAba
'Norbeck Dusky' (SS-c) **new** CWGr
'Noreen' (Pom) CWGr NHal
'Norman Lockwood' (Pom) **new** CWGr
'North Sea' (MD) **new** CWGr
'Northland Primrose' (SC) **new** CWGr
'Nuit D'Ete' (MS-c) **new** CWGr
'Nunton Form' (SD) **new** CWGr
'Nunton Harvest' (SD) CWGr
'Nutley Sunrise' (MC) **new** CWGr
'Nymphenburg' (SWL) **new** CWGr
'Oakwood Diamond' (SBa) CWGr LBut
'Old Boy' (SBa) **new** CWGr
'Old Gold' (SD) **new** CWGr
'Omo' (Sin/Lil) ♀ H3 CWGr LAyl LBut WAba
'Onesta' (SWL) **new** CWGr
'Only Love' (MS-c) **new** CWGr

'Onslow Michelle' (SD) CWGr
'Onslow Renown' CWGr
  (LS-c) **new**
'Opal' (SBa) **new** CWGr
'Optic Illusion' (SD) **new** CWGr
'Opus' (SD) **new** CWGr
'Orange Berger's CWGr
  Record' (MS-c) **new**
'Orange Cushion' CWGr
  (MinD) **new**
'Orange Fire' (MS-c) **new** CWGr
'Orange Jewel' CWGr
  (SWL) **new**
'Orange Keith's Choice' CWGr NHal
  (MD)
'Orange Mullett' CWGr
  (MinD/DwB)
'Orange Nugget' (MinBa) CWGr LRHS
I 'Orange Queen' (MC) CWGr
'Orange Sun' (LD) **new** CWGr
'Oranjestad' (SWL) **new** CWGr
'Orchid Lace' (MC) **new** CWGr
'Orel' (Col) **new** CWGr WAba
'Oreti Duke' (Pom) CWGr NHal
'Oreti Fiesta' (SD) **new** NHal
'Orfeo' (MC) CWGr
I 'Orion' (MD) CWGr
'Ornamental Rays' (SC) CWGr LBut
'Othello' (MS-c) **new** CWGr
'Pacific Argyle' (SD) NHal
'Pacific Revival' (Pom) CWGr NHal
'Paint Box' (MS-c) **new** CWGr
'Palomino' (MinD) **new** CWGr
'Pamela' (SD) CWGr
'Pari Taha Sunrise' CWGr
  (MS-c) **new**
'Park Feur' CWGr
  (Dwf MinD) **new**
'Park Princess' (SC/DwB) CWGr LRHS NHal SDeJ
'Paroa Gillian' (SC) **new** CWGr
I 'Paso Doble' (Ancm) CWGr LAyl
'Pat Mark' (LS-c) CWGr NHal
'Pat 'n Dee' (SD) **new** CWGr
'Pat Seed' (MD) CWGr
'Patricia' (Col) **new** NHal
'Paul Chester' (SC) CWGr
'Paul Critchley' (SC) **new** CWGr
'Paul Smith' (SBa) **new** CWGr
'Paul's Delight' (SD) CWGr
'Peace Pact' (SWL) CWGr WAba
'Peach Athalie' (SC) **new** CWGr
'Peach Cupid' CWGr LBut NHal WAba
  (MinBa) ♀ H3
'Peach Kokarde' CWGr
  (MinD) **new**
'Peachette' CWGr LBut
  (Misc/Lil) ♀ H3
'Pearl Hornsey' (SD) CWGr
'Pearl of Heemstede' CWGr LAyl NHal
  (SD) ♀ H3
'Pearl Sharowean' (MS-c) CWGr WAba
'Pembroke Pattie' CWGr
  (Pom) **new**
'Pennsclout' (GD) **new** CWGr
'Pennsgift' (GD) **new** CWGr
'Pensford Marion' (Pom) CWGr WAba
'Perfectos' (MC) **new** CWGr
'Periton' (MinBa) CWGr LAyl
I 'Peter' (LD) LRHS
'Peter Nelson' (SBa) **new** CWGr
'Peter' small semi-cactus CWGr
  (SS-c) **new**
'Petit Bôt' (SS-c) **new** CWGr

'Petit Byoux' **new** CWGr
'Philis Farmer' CWGr
  (SWL) **new**
I 'Phoenix' (MD) CWGr WAba
'Pianella' (SS-c) **new** CWGr
'Pim's Moonlight' CWGr
  (MS-c) **new**
'Pineapple Lollipop' CWGr
  (MinBa) **new**
'Pineholt Princess' CWGr
  (LD) **new**
'Pinelands Pam' (MS-c) CWGr NHal
'Pink Attraction' CWGr
  (MinD) **new**
'Pink Breckland Joy' CWGr
  (MD) **new**
'Pink Carol' (Pom) CWGr
  new
'Pink Frank Hornsey' CWGr
  (SD)
'Pink Giraffe' (O) CWGr
'Pink Honeymoon CWGr
  Dress' (SD)
'Pink Jupiter' (GS-c) CWGr NHal
'Pink Katisha' (MinD) CWGr
'Pink Kerkrade' (SC) CWGr
'Pink Leycett' (GD) CWGr
'Pink Loveliness' CWGr
  (SWL) **new**
'Pink Newby' CWGr
  (MinD) **new**
'Pink Pastelle' CWGr NHal WAba
  (MS-c) ♀ H3
'Pink Preference' CWGr
  (SS-c) **new**
'Pink Risca Miner' (SBa) CWGr
'Pink Robin Hood' CWGr
  (SBa) **new**
'Pink Sensation' (SC) CWGr LBut
'Pink Shirley Alliance' CWGr LAyl
  (SC)
'Pink Suffusion' (SD) WAba
'Pink Sylvia' (MinD) **new** CWGr
'Pink Symbol' (MS-c) CWGr
'Pink Worton Ann' CWGr
  (MinD)
'Piperoo' (MC) **new** CWGr
'Piper's Pink' (SS-c/DwB) CWGr LAyl
I 'Pippa' (MinWL) CWGr LBut
'Playa Blanca' CWGr LRHS
'Playboy' (GD) CWGr
'Plum Surprise' (Pom) CWGr
'Polar Sight' (GC) CWGr
'Polly Bergen' (MD) **new** CWGr
'Polly Peachum' CWGr
  (SD) **new**
'Polventon Supreme' CWGr
  (SBa)
'Polyand' (LD) CWGr
'Pontiac' (SC) CWGr LAyl
'Pop Willo' (Pom) CWGr
'Poppet' (MinD) **new** CWGr
I 'Poppet' (Pom) CWGr WAba
'Poppett' (MinC) **new** CWGr
'Popular Guest' CWGr
  (MS-c/Fim) **new**
'Porcelain' CWGr LBut NHal
  (SWL) ♀ H3
'Potgieter' (MinBa) CWGr
'Pot-Pourri' (MinD) **new** CWGr
'Prefect' (MS-c) CWGr
'Prefere' CWGr LRHS
'Preference' (SS-c) CWGr

'Preston Park'   CWGr LAyl NHal
   (Sin/DwB) ♀ H3
'Pretty Polly'   CWGr
   (SWL) **new**
Pride of Berlin   see *D.* 'Stolze von Berlin'
'Pride of Holland'   CWGr
   (LC) **new**
'Prime Minister'   CWGr
   (GD) **new**
'Primrose Accord'   CWGr
   (LS-c) **new**
'Primrose Diane' (SD)   CWGr NHal WAba
'Primrose Rustig' (MD)   CWGr
'Prince Valiant'   CWGr
   (SD) **new**
'Princess Beatrix' (LD)   CWGr
'Princess Marie Jose'   CWGr
   (Dwf Sin) **new**
'Prinzessin Irene Von   CWGr
   Preussen' (SD) **new**
'Pristine' (Pom) **new**   CWGr
'Procyon' (SD)   CSut CWGr LRHS
'Prom' (Pom) **new**   CWGr
'Promise' (MS-c/Fim)   CWGr
'Punky' (SD) **new**   CWGr
'Purbeck Lydia' (LS-c)   CWGr
'Purbeck Princess'   CWGr
   (MinD) **new**
'Purity (Dutch)'   CWGr
   (SS-c) **new**
'Purpinca'   CWGr WAba
   (Dwf Anem) **new**
'Purple Cottesmore'   CWGr
   (MWL) **new**
*   'Purple Doris Day' (SC)   CWGr
'Purple Gem'   CSut CWGr LRHS
'Purple Globe'   CWGr
   (SBa) **new**
'Purple Joy' (MD)   CWGr
'Purple R 'O' Schen'   CWGr
   new
'Purple Sensation'   CWGr
   (MD) **new**
'Purple Tai Hei Jo'   CWGr
   (GD) **new**
'Purpur Konig'   CWGr
   (Pom) **new**
'Pussycat' (SWL) **new**   CWGr
'Quel Diable' (LS-c)   CWGr
'Rachel's Place' (Pom)   CWGr
'Radfo' (SS-c)   CWGr WAba
'Radiance' (MC)   CWGr
'Raffles' (SD)   CWGr LAyl
I   'Ragged Robin' (Misc)   CAvo
'Raiser's Pride' (MC)   CWGr NHal WAba
'Raspberry Ripple'   CWGr
   (MS-c) **new**
'Rebecca Lynn' (MinD)   CWGr
'Red Admiral' (MinBa)   CWGr
'Red Alert' (LBa)   CWGr
'Red and White' (SD)   CWGr
'Red Arizona' **new**   CWGr
'Red Arrows' (SD) **new**   CWGr
'Red Balloon' (SBa)   CWGr NHal
'Red Beauty' (SD) **new**   CWGr
'Red Cap' (MinD) **new**   CWGr
'Red Carol' (Pom)   CWGr
'Red Diamond' (MD)   CWGr NHal
'Red Dwarf'   see *D.* 'Harvest Red Dwarf'
'Red Highlight' (LS-c)   CWGr
   new
'Red Kaiser Wilhelm'   CWGr
   (SBa) **new**

'Red Majorette'   CWGr
   (SS-c) **new**
'Red Pimpernel'   CWGr
   (SD) **new**
'Red Pygmy' (SS-c) **new**   CWGr
'Red Riding Hood'   CWGr
   (MinBa) **new**
'Red Schweitzer' (MinD)   CWGr
'Red Sensation' (MD)   CWGr
'Red Sunset' (MS-c) **new**   CWGr
'Red Triumph' (SD) **new**   CWGr
'Red Velvet' (SWL)   CWGr LAyl
'Red Warrior' (Pom) **new**   CWGr
'Reddy' (Dwf Lil) **new**   CWGr
I   'Reedley' (SWL)   CWGr LBut
'Reedly' (SD) **new**   CWGr
'Reese's Dream'   CWGr
   (GD) **new**
'Regal Boy' (SBa)   CWGr WAba
'Regal Choice' (MD) **new**   CWGr
'Regal Kerkrade' (SC)   CWGr
'Reginald Keene' (LS-c)   CWGr NHal
'Reliance' (SBa) **new**   CWGr
'Rembrandt (USA)'   CWGr
   (Dwf Sin) **new**
'Renato Tozio' (SD) **new**   CWGr
'Reputation' (LC) **new**   CWGr
'Requiem' (SD)   CBos CSut CWGr WAba
'Respectable' (GS-c) **new**   CWGr
'Reverend P. Holian'   CWGr
   (GS-c)
'Rheinfall' (SD) **new**   CWGr
'Rhonda' (Pom)   CWGr NHal
'Rhonda Suzanne' (Pom)   CWGr
'Richard Howells'   CWGr
   (MinD) **new**
'Richard Marc' (SC)   CWGr
'Riisa' (MinBa) **new**   CWGr WAba
'Rip City' (MS-c)   CWGr NPPs
'Risca Miner' (SBa) **new**   CWGr WAba
'Rita Easterbrook'   CWGr
   (LD) **new**
'Rita Hill' (Col) **new**   CWGr
'Roan' (MinD) **new**   CWGr
'Robann Royal'   CWGr
   (MinBa) **new**
'Robbie Huston' (LS-c)   CWGr
'Robert Too' (MinD) **new**   CWGr
I   'Roberta' (SD)   WAba
'Robin Hood' (SBa)   CWGr WAba
'Rockcliffe Gold'   CWGr
   (MS-c) **new**
'Rockliffe' (MinD)   WAba
'Rokesley Radiant'   CWGr
   (MinD) **new**
'Rokesly Mini' (MinC)   CWGr
'Rokewood Candy'   CWGr
   (MS-c) **new**
*   'Rokewood Opal' (SC)   CWGr NHal
'Romance' (MinS-c) **new**   CWGr
'Ron's Baby' (SD) **new**   CWGr
'Rood Kapte' (Misc) **new**   CWGr
'Rosalinde' (S-c)   CWGr
'Rose Cupid' (MinBa)   CWGr
'Rose Jupiter' (GS-c)   CWGr LRHS NHal
'Rose Tendre' (MS-c) **new**   CWGr
'Rosella' (MD)   CWGr LRHS
'Rosemary Webb'   CWGr
   (SD) **new**
'Rossendale Luke' (SD)   CWGr WAba
'Rosy Cloud' (MD) **new**   CWGr
'Rothesay Castle'   CWGr
   (MinD/DwB)

'Rothesay Herald'   CWGr
(SD/DwB)
'Rothesay Reveller' (MD)   CWGr
'Rothesay Robin' (SD)   CWGr WAba
'Rothesay Snowflake'   CWGr
(SWL) **new**
'Rothesay Superb'   CWGr
(MinBa) **new**
'Rotonde' (SC)   CWGr
'Rotterdam' (MS-c)   CWGr SDeJ
I   'Roxy'   CWGr EBee EBlw EMan EMil
   LRHS MBri NCot NGdn NPPs
   NVic WAba WCot WWeb
'Royal Blood' (Misc)   CAvo
'Royal Blush' (MinD)   CWGr
'Royal Visit' (SD) **new**   CWGr
'Royal Wedding'   CWGr
(LS-c) **new**
'Ruby Puff'   CWGr
(Dwf Anem) **new**
'Ruby Red' (MinBa) **new**   CWGr
'Ruby Wedding' (MinD)   CWGr
'Ruskin Belle' (MS-c)   CWGr
'Ruskin Charlotte' (MS-c)   CWGr NHal WAba
'Ruskin Delight'   CWGr
(SS-c) **new**
'Ruskin Diane' (SD)   CWGr LBut NHal WAba
'Ruskin Dynasty' (SD)   CWGr
'Ruskin Emil' (SS-c)   CWGr
'Ruskin Gypsy' (SBa) **new** CWGr
'Ruskin Impact' (SD) **new** WAba
'Ruskin Lilo' (SD)   WAba
*   'Ruskin Marigold' (SS-c)   CWGr LBut NHal
'Ruskin Myra' (SS-c) **now** NHal
'Ruskin Orient'   CWGr
(SS-c) **new**
'Ruskin Petite' (MinBa)   CWGr
*   'Ruskin Tangerine' (SBa)   CWGr
'Russell Turner' (SS-c)   CWGr
'Rustig' (MD)   CWGr WAba
'Rusty Hope' (MinD)   CWGr
'Rutland Gem'   CWGr
(MinD) **new**
'Rutland Water' (SD) **new** CWGr
'Ryedale King' (LD) **new** CWGr
'Ryedale Pinky' (SD) **new** CWGr
'Ryedale Prince'   CWGr
(GD) **new**
'Ryedale Queen'   CWGr
(MinD) **new**
'Ryedale Rebecca' (GS-c)   CWGr
'Safe Shot' (MD)   CWGr
'Sailor' (MS-c) **new**   CWGr
'Saint Croix' (GS-c)   CWGr
'Saladin' (Misc) **new**   CWGr
'Salmon Athalie' (SC)   CWGr
'Salmon Carpet'   CWGr
(MinD) **new**
'Salmon Hornsey'   CWGr
(SD) **new**
'Salmon Keene' (LS-c)   CWGr NHal WAba
'Salmon Kokarde' (MinD)   CWGr
'Salmon Rays' (SC) **new** CWGr
'Salmon Symbol' (MS-c)   WAba
'Sam Huston' (GD)   CWGr NHal WAba
'Samantha'   see D. 'Harvest Samantha'
'San Souci' **new**   CWGr
'Santa Claus' (SD) **new**   CWGr
'Sarabande' (MD) **new**   CWGr
'Sarah G' (LS-c) **new**   CWGr
'Sarah Jane' (LD) **new**   CWGr
'Sarah Louise' (SWL) **new** CWGr
'Sarum Aurora' **new**   CWGr

'Sarum Queen' (SD) **new** CWGr
'Sassy' (MinD) **new**   CWGr
'Satellite' (MS-c)   CWGr
'Saynomore' (SWL) **new** CWGr
'Scarborough Ace'   CWGr
(MD) **new**
'Scarlet Comet'   CWGr
(Misc) **new**
'Scarlet Kokarde' (MinD)   CWGr
'Scarlet Rotterdam'   CWGr WAba
(MS-c)
'Scarlet Star' (SC) **new**   CWGr
'Scaur Princess' (SD)   CWGr
'Scaur Swinton' (MD)   CWGr NHal
'Schlop Reinbek' **new**   CWGr
'Schweitzer's Kokarde'   CWGr
(MinD)
'Scottish Impact'   CWGr
(MinS-c) **new**
'Scott's Delight'   CWGr
(MD) **new**
'Scura' (Dwf Sin) **new**   CWGr
'Seattle' (SD)   LRHS
'Seikeman's Feuerball'   WAba
(MinD)
'Senior Ball' (SBa) **new**   CWGr
'Senzoe Brigitte'   CWGr
(MinD) **new**
'Senzoe Ursula' (SD)   CWGr
'September Morn'   CWGr
(SC) **new**
'Severin's Triumph'   CWGr
(MD) **new**
'Shandy' (SS-c)   CWGr LAyl NHal
'Shannon' (SD) **new**   CWGr
sherffii   CHad CHal CWGr EOrc GDrg
   GEil MCCP MNrw
– x *coccinea*   CHad
'Sherwood Monarch'   CWGr
(GS-c)
'Sherwood Standard'   CWGr NHal WAba
(MD)
'Sherwood Sunrise' (SD)   CWGr
'Sherwood Titan' (GD)   CWGr
'Sherwood's Peach'   CWGr
(GD) **new**
'Shiloh Noelle' (GD) **new** CWGr
'Shining Star' (MC) **new** CWGr
'Shirley' (SD) **new**   CWGr
'Shirley Alliance' (SC)   CWGr WAba
'Shirley Jane' (LD) **new**   CWGr
'Shooting Star' (LS-c)   CWGr
*   'Show and Tell'   CWGr
'Shy Princess' (MC)   CWGr
'Siedlerstolz' (LD) **new**   CWGr
'Siemen Doorenbos'   CWGr WAba
(Anem)
'Silver City' (LD)   CWGr NHal
'Silver Slipper' (SS-c)   CWGr
'Silver Years'   CWGr WCot
'Simon' (Dwf MinD) **new** CWGr
'Sir Alf Ramsey' (GD)   CWGr NHal WAba
'Sir Garth' (LD) **new**   CWGr
'Sisa' (SD) **new**   CWGr
'Skipley Spot' (SD) **new** CWGr
'Skipper Rock' (GD) **new** CWGr
'Sky High' (SD)   CWGr
'Small World'   CWGr LAyl NHal WAba
(Pom) ♀ H3
'Smokey'   CSut CWGr LRHS
'Smoky O' (MS-c) **new**   CWGr
'Smoots' (SC/Fim)   CWGr NHal
'Sneezy' (Sin)   CWGr LRHS

'Snip' (MinS-c)   CWGr WAba
'Snoho Barbara'   CWGr
  (MS-c) **new**
'Snoho Peggy' (SBa) **new**   CWGr
'Snoho Tammie'   CWGr
  (MinBa) **new**
'Snow Cap' (SS-c) **new**   CWGr
'Snow Fairy' (MinC) **new**   CWGr
'Snow White'   CWGr
  (Dwf Sin) **new**
'Snowflake' (SWL)   CWGr WAba
'Snowstorm' (MD)   CSut CWGr SDeJ
'Snowy' (MinBa) **new**   CWGr
'So Dainty' (MinS-c)   CWGr LAyl WAba
  ♀ H3
'Sondervig' (SD) **new**   CWGr
'Song of Olympia'   CWGr
  (SWL) **new**
'Sonia'   CWGr
'Sonia Henie' (SBa) **new**   CWGr
'Sorrento Fiesta'   WAba
  (SS-c) **new**
'Sorrento Girl' (SS-c) **new**   WAba
'Sorrento Style' (SD) **new**   WAba
'Souire De Crozon'   CWGr
  (SWL) **new**
'Souvenir D'Ete'   CWGr
  (MinD) **new**
'Spartacus' (LD)   CSut CWGr
'Spassmacher'   CWGr
  (MS-c) **new**
'Spectacular' (SD) **new**   CWGr
'Spencer' (SD)   CWGr
'Spennythorne King'   CWGr
  (SD) **new**
'Spikey Symbol'   CWGr
  (MS-c) **new**
'Star Child' (Misc) **new**   CWGr WAba
'Star Elite'   LRHS
'Star Spectacle'   CWGr
  (MS-c) **new**
'Starlight Keene'   CWGr
  (LS-c) **new**
'Starry Night'   CWGr
  (MinC) **new**
'Star's Elite' (MS-c) **new**   CWGr
'Star's Favourite'   CWGr
  (MS-c) **new**
'Star's Lady' (SS-c) **new**   CWGr
'Star's Surprise'   CWGr
  (MC) **new**
'Stefan Bergerhoff'   CWGr
  (Dwf D) **new**
'Stella J' (SWL) **new**   CWGr
'Stella's Delight'   CWGr
  (SD) **new**
'Stellyvonne'   CWGr
  (LS-c/Fim) **new**
'Stephanie' (SS-c) **new**   CWGr
'Stevie D' (SD) **new**   CWGr
§ 'Stolze von Berlin'   WAba
  (MinBa)
'Stoneleigh Cherry'   CWGr
  (Pom)
'Stoneleigh Joyce' (Pom)   CWGr
'Storm Warning'   CWGr
  (GD) **new**
* 'Stump Cross'   CWGr
'Stylemaster' (MC)   CWGr
'Sue Willo' (Pom)   CWGr
'Suffolk Fantasy'   CWGr
  (SWL) **new**
'Suffolk Punch' (MD)   CWGr LBut

'Suffolk Spectacular'   CWGr
  (MD)
'Suitzus Julie' (Lil) **new**   CWGr
'Summer Festival'   CWGr
  (SD) **new**
'Summer Night' (MC)   CHad CPlt CWGr ECGP
'Summer Night' (SC)   LAyl NHal
'Summer's End' **new**   CWGr
'Sunburst' (Col)
'Sungold' (MinBa) **new**   CWGr
'Sunlight' (SBa) **new**   CWGr
'Sunlight Pastelle'   CWGr
  (MS-c) **new**
* 'Sunny Boy' (MinBa)   CWGr LRHS WAba
'Sunray Glint' (MS-c)   CWGr WAba
'Sunray Silk' (MS-c) **new**   CWGr
'Sunset Pink' **new**   WWeb
I 'Sunshine' (Sin) **new**   LAyl
'Sunstruck' (MS-c) **new**   CWGr
'Super Rays' (MC) **new**   CWGr
'Super Trouper' (SD) **new**   CWGr
'Superfine' (SC)   CWGr WAba
'Sure Thing' (MC)   CWGr
'Surprise' (GS-c) **new**   CWGr
'Susan Willo' (Pom) **new**   CWGr
'Susannah York'   CWGr
  (SWL) **new**
'Suzette' (Dwf SD) **new**   CWGr
'Swallow Falls' (SD)   CWGr
'Swan Lake' (SD)   MBri
'Swanvale' (SD)   CWGr
'Sweet Content' (SD)   CWGr
'Sweet Miss'   CWGr
  (MinBa) **new**
'Sweet Sensation' (MS-c)   CWGr WAba
'Sweet Sixteen'   CWGr
  (SWL) **new**
'Sweetheart' (SD)   CBgR ETub LRHS WAba
'Sylvia's Desire' (SC)   CWGr NHal
'Symbol' (MS-c)   CWGr
'Sympathy' (SWL)   CWGr NHal WAba
'Syston Harlequin'   CWGr
  (SD) **new**
'Syston Sofia'   CWGr
  (MinBa) **new**
'Tahiti Sunrise' (MS-c)   CWGr
'Tally Ho' (Misc) ♀ H3   CWGr EBee EMan LRHS MBri
                                 WBry WCot
'Tango' (SD)   CWGr
'Tanjoh' (SS-c) **new**   CWGr
'Taratahi Lilac'   see D. 'Lilac Taratahi'
'Taratahi Ruby'   CWGr LBut NHal
  (SWL) ♀ H3
'Tartan' (MD) **new**   CWGr
'Teesbrooke Audrey'   LAyl NHal
  (Col)
'Temptress' (SC) **new**   CWGr
'Tender Moon' (SD)   CWGr
'Thames Valley'   CWGr
  (MD) **new**
'That's It!' (SD) **new**   CWGr
'The Baron' (SD) **new**   CWGr
'The Queen' (SS-c) **new**   CWGr
'Thelma Clements' (LD)   CWGr
'Theo Springers'   CWGr
  (SD) **new**
'Thika' (SD) **new**   CWGr
'Thomas A. Edison' (MD)   CWGr
'Thoresby Jewel'   CWGr
  (SD) **new**
'Tiara' (SD) **new**   CWGr
'Tiffany Lynn' (Misc) **new**   CWGr
'Tiger Eye' (MD) **new**   CWGr

'Tiger Tiv' (MD) CWGr
'Tina B' (SBa) **new** CWGr
'Tinker's White' (SD) CWGr
'Tiny Tot' see *D.* 'Harvest Tiny Tot'
'Tioga Spice' CWGr
  (MS-c/Fim) **new**
'Todd H' (SS-c) **new** CWGr
'Toga' (SWL) **new** CWGr
'Tohsuikyou' (Misc) **new** CWGr WAba
'Tommy Doc' (SS-c) CWGr NHal WAba
'Tommy Keith' CWGr
  (MinBa) **new**
'Tomo' (SD) LAyl NHal
'Top Affair' (MS-c) **new** CWGr
'Top Choice' (GS-c) CWGr SDeJ
* 'Topaz Puff' LRHS
* 'Toto' (DwB) CWGr NHal
'Townley Class' CWGr
  (SD) **new**
'Trampolene' (SS-c) **new** CWGr
I 'Tranquility' (Col) NHal
'Trelawny' (GD) CWGr WAba
'Trelyn Kiwi' (SC) **new** CWGr WAba
'Trendy' (SD) CWGr
'Trengrove Autumn' CWGr
  (MD) **new**
'Trengrove d'Or' CWGr
  (MD) **new**
'Trengrove Jill' (MD) CWGr LAyl
'Trengrove Summer' CWGr
  (MD)
'Trengrove Tauranga' CWGr
  (MD)
'Trengrove Terror' CWGr
  (GD) **new**
'Trevelyn Kiwi' (S-c) NHal
'Trevor' (Col) **new** CWGr
'Trinidad' (GS-c) **new** CWGr
'Tsuki Yorine Shisha' CWGr WAba
  (MC) **new**
'Tu Tu' (MS-c) **new** CWGr
'Tui Orange' (SS-c) CWGr NHal WAba
'Tui Ruth' (SS-c) **new** CWGr
'Tujays Lemondrop' NHal
  (SD) **new**
'Tula Rosa' (Pom) **new** CWGr
'Tutankhamun' CWGr
  (Pom) **new**
'Twiggy' (SWL) CWGr LRHS
'Twilight Time' (MD) CWGr LRHS
'Uchuu' (GD) **new** CWGr
'Union Jack' (Sin) CWGr WAba
'United' (SD) **new** CWGr
'Usugesho' (LD) **new** CWGr
'Utrect' (GD) **new** CWGr
'Vader Abraham' CWGr
  (MinD) **new**
'Val Saint Lambert' (MC) CWGr
'Valentine Lil' CWGr
  (SWL) **new**
'Valley Pop' (MinD) **new** CWGr
'Vanquisher' (LS-c) **new** CWGr
'Velda Inez' (MinD) **new** CWGr
'Vera's Elma' (LD) CWGr NHal
'Vesuvius' (MD) **new** CWGr
'Vicky Baum' (SBa) **new** CWGr
'Vicky Crutchfield' (SWL) CWGr LBut
'Vicky Jackson' (SWL) CWGr
'Victory Day' (LC) **new** CWGr
'Vidal Rhapsody' (MS-c) CWGr
'Vigor' (SWL) CWGr
'Vinovium' (MinBa) **new** CWGr
'Violet Davies' (MS-c) CWGr

'Vivex' (MinBa) **new** CWGr
'Volkskanzler' (Sin) **new** CWGr
'Vrouwe Jacoba' CWGr
  (SS-c) **new**
'Vulcan' (LS-c) **new** CWGr
'Walter Hardisty' (GD) CWGr
'Walter James' (SD) CWGr
'Wanborough Gem' CWGr
  (SBa) **new**
'Wanda's Capella' (GD) CWGr NHal WAba
'Wanda's Moonlight' CWGr
  (GD) **new**
'Wandy' (Pom) ♀ H3 CWGr WAba
'Warkton Willo' (Pom) CWGr
'Warmunda' CWGr LRHS
'Washington' **new** CWGr
'Waveney Pearl' CWGr
  (SWL) **new**
'Welcome Guest' (MS-c) CWGr WAba
'Welsh Beauty' (SBa) **new** CWGr
'Wendy' (MinBa) **new** CWGr
'Wendy Spencer' CWGr
  (MinD) **new**
'Wendy's Place' (Pom) CWGr
'Wennie' (Dwf) **new** CWGr
'Weston Aramac' (SS-c) CWGr
'Weston Forge' (SC) CWGr
'Weston Miss' CWGr
  (MinS-c) **new**
'Weston Nugget' (MinC) CWGr WAba
'Weston Princekin' CWGr
  (MinS-c) **new**
'Weston Spanish Dancer' CWGr LBut WAba
  (MinC) ♀ H3 **new**
'Whale's Rhonda' (Pom) CWGr WAba
'Wheel' (Col) **new** WAba
'Whiston Sunrise' CWGr
  (MS-c) **new**
'White Alva's' (GD) ♀ H3 CWGr NHal
'White Aster' (Pom) CWGr
'White Ballet' (SD) ♀ H3 CWGr LAyl LBut NHal
'White Charlie Two' NHal
  (MD) **new**
'White Hunter' (SD) **new** CWGr
'White Klankstad' (SC) CWGr
'White Knight' (MinD) NHal
'White Linda' (SD) CWGr NHal
'White Mathilda' CWGr
  (Dwf) **new**
'White Merriwell' CWGr
  (SD) **new**
'White Moonlight' (MS-c) CWGr LAyl LBut NHal WAba
'White Nettie' CWGr
  (MinBa) **new**
'White Pastelle' WAba
  (MS-c) **new**
'White Perfection' (LD) CSut CWGr
'White Polventon' (SBa) CWGr NHal
'White Rustig' (MD) CWGr
'White Star' CWGr LRHS NPPs
'White Swallow' (SS-c) NHal
'Wicky Woo' (SD) **new** CWGr
'Wildman' (GS-c) **new** CWGr
'Wildwood Marie' CWGr
  (SWL) **new**
'Wildwood Swirls' CWGr
  (SC) **new**
'Willemse Glory' CWGr
  (Misc Orch) **new**
'William 'B'' (GD) CWGr
'William John' (Pom) CWGr
'Williamsburg' CWGr
  (MS-c) **new**

'Willo's Borealis' (Pom) **new**	CWGr NHal
'Willo's Flecks' (Pom)	CWGr WAba
'Willo's Night' (Pom)	CWGr
'Willo's Surprise' (Pom)	CWGr NHal
'Willo's Violet' (Pom)	CWGr WAba
'Willowfield Matthew' (MinD) **new**	NHal
'Willowfield Mick' (LD)	CWGr NHal WAba
'Wine & Roses' (SWL) **new**	CWGr
'Winholme Diane' (SD) **new**	NHal
'Winkie Colonel' (GD)	CWGr NHal
'Winnie' (Pom) **new**	CWGr
'Winsome' (SWL) **new**	CWGr
'Winston Churchill' (MinD)	CWGr LBut
'Winter Dawn' (SWL)	CWGr
'Wise Guy' (GD) **new**	CWGr
'Wisemark' (MS-c) **new**	CWGr
'Wisk' (Pom) **new**	CWGr
'Wittem' (MD)	CWGr
'Wittemans Superba' (SS-c) ♀ H3	CWGr LAyl NHal
'Wolstad' **new**	CWGr
'Wootton Cupid' (MinBa) ♀ H3	CWGr LBut NHal WAba
'Wootton Impact' (MS-c) ♀ H3	LBut NHal
'Wootton Phebe' (SD) **new**	CWGr
'Wootton Tempest' (MS-c) **new**	CWGr
'Worton Bluestreak' (SS-c)	CWGr LBut
'Worton Revival' (MD) **new**	CWGr
'Worton Superb' (SD) **new**	CWGr
'Wundal Horizon' (LS-c) **new**	CWGr
'Yarra Falls' (LD) **new**	CWGr
'Yellow Abundance' (SD) **new**	CWGr
'Yellow Baby' (Pom) **new**	CWGr
'Yellow Bird' (Col) **new**	CWGr
'Yellow Frank Hornsey' (SD)	CWGr WAba
'Yellow Galator' (MC) **new**	CWGr
'Yellow Giraffe' (Misc) **new**	CWGr
'Yellow Hammer' (Sin/DwB) ♀ H3	CWGr LAyl NHal SChu SPla
'Yellow Linda's Chester' (SC)	CWGr
'Yellow Pages' (SD) **new**	CWGr
'Yellow Pet' (MinD) **new**	CWGr
'Yellow Show' (MD) **new**	CWGr
'Yellow Spiky' (MS-c)	CWGr
'Yellow Star' (MS-c)	CWGr
'Yellow Symbol' (MS-c)	CWGr LBut
'Yellow Twist' **new**	CHad
'Yelno Enchantment' (SWL)	CWGr LAyl
'Yelno Firelight' (SWL) **new**	CWGr
'Yelno Harmony' (SD) ♀ H3	CWGr LBut
'Yelno Little Glory' (MinWL) **new**	CWGr
'Yelno Velvena' (SWL)	LAyl

'York and Lancaster' (MD)	CWGr EMon IGor
'Yorkie' (MS-c)	CWGr WAba
'Yoro Kobi' (Bedder) **new**	NHal
'Young Bess' **new**	CWGr
'Yukino' (Col) **new**	CWGr
I 'Yvonne' (MWL)	CWGr WAba
'Zagato' (MinD) **new**	CWGr
* 'Zakuro Fubuki' (MD)	CWGr
'Zakuro-Hime' (SD) **new**	CWGr
'Zelda' (LD) **new**	CWGr
'Zest' (MD) **new**	CWGr
'Zing' (LS-c) **new**	CWGr
'Zorro' (GD) ♀ H3	CWGr NHal WAba
'Zurich' (SS-c) **new**	CWGr

Dais (Thymelaeaceae)

cotinifolia	CPle

Daiswa see *Paris*

Dalechampia (Euphorbiaceae)

dioscoreifolia	CPlN

Dampiera (Goodeniaceae)

diversifolia	CSpe ECou
lanceolata	ECou
teres	ECou

damson see *Prunus insititia*

Danae (Ruscaceae)

§ racemosa	CBcs CFil EBee EMon ENot EPfP EPla GCal IDee LRHS MRav SAPC SArc SBrw SDry SPar SPer SRms SSpi SSta WCot WDin WPGP

Danthonia (Poaceae)

californica	CBig

Daphne ✿ (Thymelaeaceae)

acutiloba	CPMA ERea NABC SAga SBrw
albowiana	CFil CPMA CPle EPot EWes SAga SBla SSpi WCru WPGP
'Allison Carver' (v)	CPMA
alpina	CPMA EHyt SBla
altaica	CPMA
arbuscula ♀ H4	CPMA EPot NMen SBla SIgm
- subsp. arbuscula f. albiflora	SBla
bholua	CAbP CHll CPMA CWSG ERea GEdr ICrw LHop LRHS MGos MPRe NABC SAga SBrw SLim SReu SSta WBod WCru
I - 'Alba'	CBcs CFil CPMA MGos NABC SBla SSta WCru WPGP
- 'Darjeeling'	CFil CPMA EPfP LRHS SBrw SSpi SSta WCru WPGP
- var. glacialis	WCru
- - 'Gurkha'	CPMA NABC SBla
- 'Glendoick'	EPfP GGGa
- 'Jacqueline Postill' ♀ H3	More than 30 suppliers
- 'Peter Smithers'	SBla SBrw SReu SSta
blagayana	CFil CPMA CWSG EPot GGGa GKir MDun NABC SBla SBrw SIgm SRms WCru WFar WPat
- 'Brenda Anderson' **new**	ITim
x burkwoodii ♀ H4	CBcs EBee ECho EPot GKir SAga SHBN SLon WBrE WDin WGwG
- 'Albert Burkwood'	CBcs CPMA EPot GEdr GLbr LTwo MDun NABC NLar NWea SPer WBrE WGwG WWeb

	- 'Astrid' (v)	CPMA CWib LHop LNet LRHS MGos MLan SAga SBrw SCoo SMrm SMur SSta WDin WStI WWes
	- Briggs Moonlight = 'Brimoon' (v)	LRHS SPer
§	- 'Carol Mackie' (v)	CPMA CWSG GAbr GGGa GKir LRHS LTwo MDun MGos MPRe NABC NLar SBla SIgm SPer SSta WWeb
	- 'G.K.Argles' (v) ♀ H4	CFil CPMA CWSG ERea GEdr GLbr LAst LRHS MAsh MDun MGos MHFa MLan MPRe NABC SPer SSta WBod WBrE WFar WPGP WPat WWeb WWes
	- 'Gold Strike' (v)	CPMA
	- 'Lavenirei'	CPMA
	- 'Somerset'	More than 30 suppliers
§	- 'Somerset Gold Edge' (v)	CPMA
§	- 'Somerset Variegated' (v)	LAst NABC SAga
I	- 'Variegata' (v)	SAga WPat
	- 'Variegata' broad cream edge	see D. x burkwoodii 'Somerset Variegated'
	- 'Variegata' broad gold edge	see D. x burkwoodii 'Somerset Gold Edge'
	- 'Variegata' narrow gold edge	see D. x burkwoodii 'Carol Mackie'
	caucasica	CPMA IDac SBla
	circassica new	SBla
	cneorum	CBcs CFil CPMA ENot EPfP EWTr LRHS MGos NBee NEgg NMen SBod SMur SSpi WDin WPat WStI WWin
	- f. alba	CPMA SBla
	- var. arbuscula x var. verlotii	CPMA
	- 'Blackthorn Triumph'	CPMA SBla
	- 'Eximia' ♀ H4	CPMA CWSG EMil EPot GAbr GEdr GKir GLbr LNet MDun MGos MPRe NABC SBla SHBN SIng SMrm SPer SRms SSpi WBod WGwG WPat
	- 'Grandiflora'	see D. x napolitana 'Maxima'
	- 'Lac des Gloriettes'	CPMA
	- 'Puszta'	CPMA SAga SIgm WCru
	- var. pygmaea	CPMA EPot SBla
	- - 'Alba'	CPMA EPot SBla
	- 'Rose Glow'	CPMA
	- 'Stasek'	CPMA SAga SBla
	- 'Variegata' (v)	CPMA ECho EPot GCrs LHop MGos MMil NABC NWCA SHBN SIng WAbe
	- 'Velký Kosíř'	CPMA
	collina	see D. sericea Collina Group
	feddei new	SBla
	'Fragrant Cloud' (aff. acutiloba) CD&R 626	CPMA SBla
	genkwa	LRHS SBla SBrw WCru
	giraldii	CPMA EHyt GCrs SIgm SSpi WCru
	x hendersonii	CPMA EPot
	- 'Appleblossom'	CPMA SBla
	- 'Aymon Correvon'	CPMA SBla
	- 'Blackthorn Rose'	SBla
	- 'Ernst Hauser'	CPMA EPot GLbr MPRe SBla SScr
	- 'Fritz Kummert'	CPMA SBla
	- 'Kath Dryden' new	SBla
	- 'Rosebud'	SBla
	x houtteana	CBot CPMA NABC NBir SSta
	x hybrida	CPMA ECho SBla
	japonica 'Striata'	see D. odora 'Aureomarginata'
	jasminea	CPMA ECho EHyt LTwo NMen SBla
	jezoensis	CPMA SBla SSta WCru
	juliae	CPMA SBla

	kosaninii	GKir
	laureola	CFil CPMA CSWP EPfP GCrs GPoy MBro MGos MSte NBir NPer SSta WCFE WPGP WWye
	- var. cantabrica	SChu
	- 'Margaret Mathew'	CPMA EPot
	- subsp. philippi	CBgR CPMA CSBt CTrC CWSG EPfP GEdr GKir LHop LRHS MAsh MBro NABC NDlv SBrw SChu SHBN SPer SSpi SSta WCru WFar WWeb
	'Leila Haines'	SBla
	'Leila Haines' x arbuscula	CPMA
	longilobata	CPle NABC
	- 'Peter Moore'	NABC
	x manteniana	MGos SBrw SSpi
	- 'Manten'	CPMA EPot GEdr GLbr MDun MNes MPRe SLon WPat
	x mauerbachii 'Perfume of Spring'	CPMA SBla
	'Meon'	see D. x napolitana 'Meon'
	mezereum	More than 30 suppliers
	- f. alba	CFil CPMA EPfP GDra GIBF GKir LAst LHop LRHS MBar MDun MGos MGrG MPRe SBla SBrw SHBN SIng SPar SPer SRms SSta WAbe WCru WPat WTin
	- - 'Bowles' Variety'	CBot CPMA EPot GDra SPer
	- 'Rosea'	SRms
	- var. rubra	CBcs CFil CPMA CSBt CWSG ELan EPfP GKir LNet MGos NDcc NBlu SBod SPer SReu SSta WAbe WCru WDin WOrn WStI
	- 'Variegata' (v)	LHop
	x napolitana ♀ H4	CPMA CWSG EBee ECho EMil EPot GEdr GLbr LNet MDun MGos MPRe NABC NLar SHBN SSta WBrE WPat
§	- 'Maxima'	MGos
§	- 'Meon'	CPMA MPRe NMen SBla WAbe
	odora	CPMA CPle CSBt ERea LRHS MGos MPRe NMen SBrw SChu SSta WDin WStI
§	- f. alba	CPMA ERea LRHS MGos
I	- 'Aureamarginata Alba' (v)	CPMA
§	- 'Aureomarginata' (v) ♀ H3-4	More than 30 suppliers
	- 'Clotted Cream'	CPMA
	- 'Geisha Girl' (v)	ERea SPer
	- var. leucantha	see D. odora f. alba
	- 'Marginata'	see D. odora 'Aureomarginata'
	- var. rubra	LRHS NABC SBrw
	- 'Sakiwaka'	CPMA
	- 'Walberton' (v)	LRHS WWeb
*	- 'Zuiko-nishiki'	WCru
	oleoides	CPMA GCrs LNet SBla
	papyracea	GGGa
	petraea	SBla
	- 'Alba'	see D. petraea 'Tremalzo'
	- 'Grandiflora'	EPot GCrs NMen SBla WAbe
§	- 'Tremalzo'	SBla
	pontica ♀ H4	CBcs CFil CPMA CPle EBee EHyt EPfP EPla GCrs GKir MBro SBrw SDix SPer SSpi WCru WPGP
	pseudomezereum	WCru
	retusa	see D. tangutica Retusa Group
	'Richard's Choice'	CPMA
	x rollsdorfii 'Arnold Cihlarz'	CPMA
	- 'Wilhelm Schacht'	CPMA SBla
	'Rosy Wave'	CPMA SAga SBla
	x schlyteri	CPMA SBla

§   ***sericea***   CPMA SBla SBrw SRms
§   – Collina Group   CPMA EPfP SBla SIgm SRms SSpi
        SSta WAbe WBod
    – – x ***petraea***   SSta
    – Hidcote form **new**   EPot
  x ***susannae***   SBla
      'Anton Fahndrich'
  – x ***collina*** **new**   NLar
  – 'Cheriton'   CPMA EPot SBla SSta WBcn
  – 'Tichborne'   CPMA SBla
  tangutica ♀ H4   More than 30 suppliers
  – SDR 1944   GKev
§   – Retusa Group ♀ H4   CPMA EHyt EOHP EPot
        GAbr GCrs GGGa GKir GMaP
        ITim LAst LHop MBri MGos
        NLAp NRya SBrw SHBN
        SIgm SPer SReu SRms SSpi
        SSta WCru
  x ***thauma***   NMen SBla
  x ***transatlantica***   SBla
      'Jim's Pride'
  x ***whiteorum***   CPMA EPot GKir GLbr NABC
        SBla
      'Beauworth'   SIgm SSta WAbe
  – 'Kilmeston'   CPMA GKir NABC NMen
  – 'Warnford'   CPMA

Daphniphyllum (Daphniphyllaceae)

  calycinum **new**   SSpi
  glaucescens   WCru
      B&SWJ 4058
§   ***himalaense*** subsp.   CBcs CDoC CFil CHEx CMCN
    macropodum   EBee EPfP EPla NLar SAPC SArc
        SBrw SDix SLPl SSpi WCru WFar
        WPGP
    – – B&SWJ 2898   WCru
    – – B&SWJ 581   WCru
    humile   see *D. himalaense* subsp.
        macropodum
    teijsmannii   WCru
      B&SWJ 3805

Darlingtonia (Sarraceniaceae)
  californica ♀ H1   CFil CSWC EEls EFEx GTro LHew
        SHmp

Darmera (Saxifragaceae)
§   ***peltata*** ♀ H4   More than 30 suppliers
  – 'Nana'   CCol CHEx EBee ECha GBuc
        GKir MBri MFir MTed MTis NLar
        SWat WAbe WCot WFar WPnP

Darwinia (Myrtaceae)
  collina   SOWG
  fascicularis   SOWG
  grandiflora   SOWG
  leyostyla **new**   SOWG
  oxylepis **new**   SOWG
  rhadinophylla   SOWG
  squarrosa   SOWG
  taxifolia **new**   SOWG

Dasylirion (Dracaenaceae)
§   ***acrotrichum***   SAPC SArc
  cedrosanum **new**   EOas
  glaucophyllum   EAmu EPVP MPRe
  gracile   see *D. acrotrichum*
  longissimum   CBrP CTrC EOas SChr
  texanum   CTrC EOas
  wheeleri ♀ H1   CAbb CBrP CRoM CTrC EOas
        SChr

date see *Phoenix dactylifera*

Datisca (Datiscaceae)
  cannabina   CArn EBee ECha EMan GCal LPhx
        SMad SMrm SPoG WCot WPGP WPic

Datura (Solanaceae)
  arborea   see *Brugmansia arborea*
  cornigera   see *Brugmansia arborea*
§   ***inoxia*** ♀ H3   EBak MGol MSal SVen SYvo
  – 'Evening Fragrance'   SPar
  metel   MGol
  – 'Belle Blanche' **new**   MGol
  – 'Cherub' (d)   GQui
  meteloides   see *D. inoxia*
  rosea   see *Brugmansia* x *insignis* pink
  rosei   see *Brugmansia sanguinea*
  sanguinea   see *Brugmansia sanguinea*
  stramonium   CArn MGol MSal SYvo WHer WWye
  – var. ***chalybaea***   MSal
  – var. ***inermis*** **new**   MSal
§   – var. ***tatula***   SPar
      'La Fleur Lilas'
  suaveolens   see *Brugmansia suaveolens*
  versicolor   see *Brugmansia versicolor*
        Lagerh.
  – 'Grand Marnier'   see *Brugmansia* x *candida*
        'Grand Marnier'

Daucus (Apiaceae)
  carota   CArn CKin EPPr IIve NSco WHer
  – 'Jane's Lace'   CNat

Davallia (Davalliaceae)
  canariensis ♀ H1   CFil
§   ***mariesii*** ♀ H3   CFil NMar SMad WCot
  – var. ***stenolepis***   NMar
  pyxidata   see *D. solida* var. *pyxidata*
§   ***solida*** var. ***pyxidata***   NMar
  tasmanii   CFil
  trichomanoides   NMar
  – f. ***barbata***   NMar
  – var. ***lorrainei***   NMar

Davidia (Cornaceae)
  involucrata ♀ H4   More than 30 suppliers
  – var.   CBcs CDoC ELan EPfP EWTr
    vilmoriniana ♀ H4   IMGH LNet LRHS MAsh MGos
        SPer SRPl WOrn

Daviesia (Papilionaceae)
  brevifolia   SPlb

Decaisnea (Lardizabalaceae)
  fargesii   CDoC CPLG CPle CPne CWib
        EBee EGFP ELan EPfP EPla EWTr
        GGGa ICrw MBlu MCCP MGos
        MWhi NPal SBrw SMad SPar SPer
        WBod WBor WDin WFar WGer
        WHer WPGP WPat
  insignis   WNor

Decodon (Lythraceae)
  verticillatus   EMon

Decumaria (Hydrangeaceae)
  barbara   CBcs CDoC CFil CFwr CMac
        CPIN CTrC EBee EMil EPfP GEil
        LRHS NSti SBra SHBN SLim SLon
        SSta WCru WFar WSHC
  sinensis   CPIN EPfP SBra SSpi WSHC

Degenia (Brassicaceae)
  velebitica   EHyt ETow

Deinanthe (Hydrangeaceae)

bifida	WCru
- B&SWJ 5012	WCru
caerulea	CDes CRDP EBee LEur SBla WCru WPGP

Delonix (Caesalpiniaceae)

regia	MGol NBlo SMur SOWG XBlo

Delosperma (Aizoaceae)

	LEG 037 **new**	CStu
§	**aberdeenense** ♀ H1	CHEx
*	**album**	CHEx
	ashtonii	CStu EDAr ETow SChr WPer
	'Basutoland'	see *D. nubigenum*
	cooperi	ECtt EDAr EOas ETow GEdr ITim NLAp SChr SIng SMad WBea WFar WPat WPer WWeb
	esterhuyseniae new	CStu
	floribundum	CTrC
	lineare	NBir
	lydenburgense	CHEx IBlr SChr
§	**nubigenum**	CHEx CHal CTrC ECtt EDAr ELan EMlt EPot GDra GEdr GGar ITim LRHS NJOw SIng WPer WRHF WWin
	sutherlandii	EDAr NLAp

Delphinium ✿ (Ranunculaceae)

'Abendleuchten'	LPhx
'Agnes Brookes'	ERou
'Alice Artindale' (d)	CDes CHad CPlt EBee IFro LPhx SAga SBla SMrm WPGP WSan
'Alie Duyvensteyn'	ERou
ambiguum	see *Consolida ajacis*
Amour' **new**	GLbr
'Ann Kenrick'	MWoo
'Ann Woodfield'	MWoo
'Anne Page'	ERou
anthriscifolium	EBee
Astolat Group	CBcs CBot COlW CSBt CWib EBee EBre ELan EPfP GKir LPVe LRHS MBri MRav MWat MWgw NBir NFor NLar NLon NPri SMer SPer WFar WHoo
'Augenweide'	EFou
Avon strain	MWoo
'Basil Clitheroe'	LPhx
beesianum ACE 1361	GBin
Belladonna Group	EShb SRPl
- 'Atlantis' ♀ H4	EBee EBre ECha EFou GBin LPhx LRHS MBri SBla SBod SMrm SWat
- 'Balaton' **new**	EFou
- 'Ballkleid'	EBee EFou
- 'Capri'	EBee EFou
- 'Casa Blanca'	CPlt EBee EFou LRHS MAnH NLar SIgm SMrm SWat WLRN WPer
- 'Cliveden Beauty'	EBee EPyc GBri LAst MAnH MRav MStc NLar NPri SIgm SWat WLRN WPer
- 'Kleine Nachtmusik'	EBee
- 'Moerheimii'	EBee EWTr LAst SBod SMrm
- 'Peace'	EBre LRHS
- 'Piccolo'	EBee EBre SMrm SWat
- 'Pink Sensation'	see *D.* x *ruysii* 'Pink Sensation'
- 'Völkerfrieden'	EBee EBre EFou GBin LRHS MBri MRav NPri NPro SBod WRus
x **bellamosum**	CBot CMGP EBee EFou LRHS MAnH MWgw NLar SWat WLRN WPer
'Berghimmel'	EBee EFou
'Beryl Burton'	CNMi ERou
Black Knight Group	More than 30 suppliers
'Blauwal'	EBee SWat

Blue Bird Group	CBcs COlW CSBt CTri ELan EPfP GAbr GKir LRHS MBri MBro MCAu MRav NFor NLar NLon NMir NPri NVic SMer SPer SPla WFar WHoo
'Blue Butterfly'	see *D. grandiflorum* 'Blue Butterfly'
'Blue Dawn' ♀ H4	CBla ERou
Blue Fountains Group	CSBt EMan EPfP GKir LPVe LRHS MBri NBee NOak SPer SRms WStI
Blue Jade Group	CBla ERou
'Blue Jay'	CBcs CTri EBre ENot EWTr LRHS MBow NBir NLar NPri SPer WLRN
'Blue Lagoon'	CBla
'Blue Mirror'	SRms
'Blue Nile' ♀ H4	CBla CNMi ERou MWoo
'Blue Oasis'	CNMi
'Blue Skies'	NLar
Blue Springs Group	NGdn NLar NOrc
'Blue Tit'	CBla CNMi ERou MWat
'Blue Triumphator'	EBee
'Bruce' ♀ H4	CPlt ERou MWoo WCFE
brunonianum	SBla
'Butterball'	CBla EWTr
Cameliard Group	CBcs CSBt EBre ECtt ELan EMan LRHS NLar NLon NPri SPer SRPl WLRN
'Can-can' ♀ H4	CNMi ERou
cardinale	EHrv
'Carl Topping'	ERou
cashmerianum	EBee ETow MTho
'Cassius' ♀ H4	CBla ERou MWoo
ceratophorum	EBee
'Chelsea Star'	CBla ERou
'Cher'	CNMi
'Cherry Blossom'	NLar
'Cherub' ♀ H4	CBla ERou MWoo
chinense	see *D. grandiflorum*
'Christel'	EBee ERou
'Circe'	ERou
'Clack's Choice'	ERou
'Claire' ♀ H4	MWoo
Clear Springs Series	LIck MPWC
'Clifford Lass'	MWoo
'Clifford Pink'	CBla MWoo
'Clifford Sky' ♀ H4	MWoo
Connecticut Yankees Group	MAnH NOak SIgm SRms
'Conspicuous' ♀ H4	CBla ERou MWoo
'Constance Rivett' ♀ H4	ERou
'Cream Cracker'	CNMi
'Cressida'	ERou
'Cristella'	ERou
'Crown Jewel'	CBla ERou WCFE
'Cupid'	CBla CPlt ERou
'Darling Sue'	CNMi
'David's Magnificent'	WEas
delavayi	GEil SBla WCot
- B&SWJ 7796	WCru
- CLD 895	EHyt
'Demavand'	CNMi
'Dolly Bird'	CBla ERou
'Dreaming Spires'	SRms
dwarf dark blue	LRHS
dwarf lavender	LRHS
dwarf pink	LRHS
dwarf sky blue	LRHS
'Eelkje' **new**	ERou
elatum	CArn GCal MAnH SRms SSth
'Elizabeth Cook' ♀ H4	CNMi
'Emily Hawkins' ♀ H4	CNMi ERou MWoo
'Eminence'	EBee
'Eva Gower'	ERou
'F.W. Smith'	EBee
'Fanfare'	CBla ERou

	'Father Thames'	ERou
	'Faust' ♀ H4	CBla ERou MWat MWoo WCot
	'Fenella' ♀ H4	CBla CNMi MWoo WCFE
	'Filique Arrow' **new**	CFir
	'Finsteraarhorn'	EBee EFou ERou LPhx WCot
	'Florestan'	CNMi
	'Frühschein' **new**	EFou
	Galahad Group	More than 30 suppliers
	'Garden Party'	CBla
	'Gemma'	MWoo
	'Gillian Dallas' ♀ H4	CBla CNMi ERou MWoo
	'Giotto' ♀ H4	CNMi
	'Gletscherwasser'	EFou LPhx
	'Gordon Forsyth'	CBla CNMi ERou MWoo
	'Gossamer'	CNMi
§	*grandiflorum*	ESis SMrm
§	– 'Blauer Zwerg'	EBee EPfP IBal WRus
§	– 'Blue Butterfly'	CBot CSpe EBee EBre EBur LRHS
		MWgw NCot NOrc SBla SCoo
		SPlb WPer WWeb WWin
	– Blue Dwarf	see *D. grandiflorum* 'Blauer Zwerg'
*	– 'Tom Pouce'	NGdn
	Guinevere Group	CBcs CSBt CWib EBre ECtt GAbr
		LPVe LRHS MBow MBri MRav MWat
		MWgw NBir NFor NLar NLon NPPs
		NPri SPar SPer SPla WFar WWeb
	'Guy Langdon'	CNMi ERou
	'Harlekijn'	EBee ERou
	'Harmony'	ERou
	'Heavenly Blue'	LPVe NLar
	Ivory Towers Group	ECtt
	'Jenny Agutter'	CNMi
	'Joyce Roffey'	ERou
	'Judy Knight'	MWat
	'Kennington Calypso' **new**	CNMi
	'Kestrel'	CNMi ERou
	King Arthur Group	CBcs CSBt ECtt EHol ELan ENot EPfP
		EWTr GAbr GKir IFro MBri MCAu
		MOne MRav MWat MWgw NLar
		NPri SMer SPar SPer WFar WHoo
	'Lady Guinevere'	EBee ERou
§	'Langdon's Royal Flush' ♀ H4	CBla MWoo
	'Lanzenträger' **new**	EFou
	'Leonora'	CNMi ERou
	likiangense	ETow
	'Lilian Bassett' ♀ H4	MWoo
	'Loch Leven' ♀ H4	CBla ERou MWoo
	'Lord Butler' ♀ H4	CBla WCot
	'Lorna'	ERou
	'Lucia Sahin' ♀ H4 **new**	CNMi
§	*luteum*	SIgm WIvy
	maackianum **new**	GCal
	Magic Fountains Series	CSam EBre GKir NPri SPlb WGor WHil
	– 'Magic Fountains Dark Blue'	NLar
	– 'Magic Fountains Deep Blue'	NLar
	– 'Magic Fountains Lavender' **new**	WWeb
	– 'Magic Fountains Lilac Rose'	NLar WWeb
	– 'Magic Fountains Pure White'	MPWC NLar WWeb
	– 'Magic Fountains Sky Blue'	LRHS
	'Margaret Farrand'	ERou
	menziesii	EChP ERos
	'Mèrel' **new**	EBee MBri
	'Michael Ayres' ♀ H4	CBla ERou MWoo
	'Micky'	EBee
	micropetalum	WCru
	CNDS 031 **new**	
	'Mighty Atom'	CBla CPlt ERou MWoo WCot
	'Min' ♀ H4	CNMi ERou MWoo
	'Molly Buchanan'	CBla ERou
	'Moonbeam'	CBla
	'Mother Teresa'	ERou
	'Mrs Newton Lees'	EBee ERou
	'Mrs T. Carlile'	ERou
	'Mystique'	CBla ERou
	'Ned Rose' **new**	ERou
	'Ned Wit' **new**	EBee
	New Century hybrids	CBcs EBre LRHS
	'Nicholas Woodfield'	MWoo
	'Nimrod'	CBla ERou
	'Nobility'	CBla ERou
	nudicaule	CBot EBee EDAr EPfP LPVe MBNS MHer SRot
	– var. *luteum*	see *D. luteum*
	'Olive Poppleton' ♀ H4	CBla MWoo
	'Oliver' ♀ H4	MWoo
*	*orfordii*	EBee
	'Our Deb' ♀ H4	CNMi MWoo
	'Ouvertüre'	EBee
	Pacific hybrids	CSam ENot EPfP GAbr GKir LPVe LRHS NBlu NLar NOak SRms
	'Pandora'	CBla
	'Parade' **new**	ERou
	'Parlemour' **new**	EBee
	'Patricia Johnson'	ERou
	Percival Group	LRHS NLar NLon WWeb
	'Pericles'	CBla
	'Perlmutterbaum'	LPhx
	'Petticoat'	EBee
	'Pink Ruffles'	CBla CNMi
	Princess Caroline = 'Odabar' PBR	CBcs
	'Pure White'	WWeb
	'Purity'	ERou
	'Purple Ruffles'	ERou
	'Purple Sky'	EBee
	'Purple Triumph'	ERou
	'Purple Velvet'	CBla
	pylzowii	EBee
	'Pyramus'	ERou
	'Rakker'	EBee ERou
	requienii	CBot CPom CStr MGol MTho MWgw NBir WCot WEas
	'Rona'	CNMi
	'Rosemary Brock' ♀ H4	ERou MWoo
	'Royal Flush'	see *D.* 'Langdon's Royal Flush'
	'Rubin'	LPhx
	'Ruby'	CBla
§	x *ruysii* 'Pink Sensation'	CBot CDes CPen EBee EMan EMon ERou EWTr GBri IPot NLar NPri NPro SBod SMrm STes WPGP WRus
	'Sabrina'	CBla
	'Samantha'	ERou
	'Schildknappe'	EBee LPhx SMrm
§	*semibarbatum*	CBot NPri SGar SIgm
	'Sentinel'	CNMi
	'Shimmer'	CBla ERou
	siamense B&SWJ 7278	WCru
	'Silver Jubilee'	ERou
	'Silver Moon'	ERou
	'Sir Harry Secombe'	CNMi
	'Skyline'	CBla ERou
	Snow White Group	NOak
	'Solomon'	ERou
	'Sommerabend'	LPhx
*	'Space Fantasy'	SBla
	'Special'	SWal
	'Spindrift' ♀ H4	CNMi

stapeliosmum WCru
  B&SWJ 2954
staphisagria CArn ECGP EOHP LHrt MGol MSal
'Strawberry Fair' CBla CNMi EBee ERou EWTr MWat
'Summer Haze' ERou
Summer Skies Group CBcs CSBt ECtt EMan EPfP EWTr
  LHop LRHS MBri MCAu MWat
  NBir NLar NLon NPri SMer SPer
  SRPl WBrE WFar WHoo
'Summerfield Ariane' MWoo
'Summerfield Diana' CNMi MWoo
'Summerfield CNMi MWoo
  Miranda' ♀ H4
'Summerfield Oberon' CNMi MWoo WCot
'Summerfield Viking' MWoo
'Sungleam' ♀ H4 CBla CFir CNMi CPlt EBee ERou
  EWTr MWat
'Sunkissed' ♀ H4 CNMi MWoo
sutchuenense B&SWJ WCru
  7867 **new**
tatsienense EHyt GDra MTho SRms WCru
  WHoo
- 'Album' EWes WCom
- 'Blue Ice' EHyt
tenii B&SWJ 7693 **new** WCru
'Tessa' ERou
'Thundercloud' ERou
'Tiddles' ♀ H4 CBla
'Titania' CBla
tricorne CLAP EBee
'Turkish Delight' CBla ERou
'Vanessa Mae' CNMi
'Venus Carmine' LRHS
'Vespers' CBla
vestitum GDea NBir
'Walton Beauty' MWoo
* 'Walton Benjamin' MWoo
'Walton Gemstone' ♀ H4 CBla CNMi MWat MWoo
'Watkin Samuel' ERou
'West End Blue'PBR EBee MBri WMnd
'White Ruffles' CBla
Woodfield strain **new** WHrl
'Yvonne' ERou
zalil see *D. semibarbatum*

Dendranthema ✿ (Asteraceae)
nankingense see *Chrysanthemum*
  nankingense
pacificum see *Ajania pacifica*

Dendriopoterium see Sanguisorba

Dendrobenthamia see Cornus

Dendromecon (Papaveraceae)
rigida CBcs CFil EPfP LHop LRHS SBrw
  SMad SMrm SMur SSpi WPGP

Dennstaedtia (Dennstaedtiaceae)
punctilobula **new** WRic

Dentaria see Cardamine
microphylla see *Cardamine microphylla*
pinnata see *Cardamine heptaphylla*
polyphylla see *Cardamine kitaibelii*

Deparia (Woodsiaceae)
pycnosora **new** WRic

Derris (Papilionaceae)
elliptica CPIN

Derwentia see Parahebe

Deschampsia (Poaceae)
cespitosa CBig CBrm CKin CNat COIW
  EBlw EPPr GDea GOrn ITim LBuc
  LHrt LPhx MBar MBrN MHar
  NArg NHol NNor NPPs SIng SWal
  SYvo WCFE WDin WGwG WMoo
  WPer WPnP WWpP
- subsp. *alpina* EMon EPPr LRHS
- Bronze Veil see *D. cespitosa* 'Bronzeschleier'
§ - 'Bronzeschleier' More than 30 suppliers
- 'Fairy's Joke' see *D. cespitosa* var. *vivipara*
- Gold Dust see *D. cespitosa* 'Goldstaub'
- Golden Dew see *D. cespitosa* 'Goldtau'
- Golden Pendant see *D. cespitosa* 'Goldgehänge'
- Golden Shower see *D. cespitosa* 'Goldgehänge'
- Golden Veil see *D. cespitosa* 'Goldschleier'
§ - 'Goldgehänge' ECtt EHoe EHul EMan EMon EPPr
  EPfP EPla NBir NHol NPro NSti SLPl
§ - 'Goldschleier' CBrm EBlw EBre ECGN ECGP
  EChP ECha EFou EHoe EMon EPPr
  EPla EWsh GKir GOrn LPhx LRHS
  MCLN NGdn NOak SApp SDes
  SPar SPet WCot WMoo WPGP
§ - 'Goldstaub' EFou EPPr WCot
§ - 'Goldtau' More than 30 suppliers
- 'Morning Dew' ECoo WFar
- 'Northern Lights' (v) CBrm CDes CKno CMHG CMil
  CPen EBee EBlw EFou ELan EMan
  ENot EPPr EPfP EVFa GBin LBuc
  LHop MAvo MBri SPer WLeb WWeb
- subsp. *paludosa* EMon EPPr
§ - var. *vivipara* CKno EBee EBlw EBre ECtt EHoe
  EMon EPPr EPla EWsh LRHS MMHG
  NBid NBro NHol NOGN NSti SRGP
  SWal WCom WTrP WHoo WWpP
- 'Willow Green' **new** EFou GCal
elongata **new** CBig
flexuosa CBig CBrm COIW CPen EHoe
  EMon EPPr EWsh GDea GIBF
  LRHS MBri MHar WEas WI in WPer
- 'Tatra Gold' More than 30 suppliers
holciformis CBig

Desfontainia (Loganiaceae)
§ *spinosa* ♀ H3 More than 30 suppliers
- 'Harold Comber' CMac MDun WBod WCru WDin
  WGer
- *hookeri* see *D. spinosa*

Desmanthus (Mimosaceae)
illinoensis EBee MGol MSal

Desmodium (Papilionaceae)
callianthum CDoC CMac EBee EPfP LRHS
  SBrw WSHC
canadense EBee EMan LPhx MSPs NLar WCot
§ *elegans* ♀ H4 CBcs CFil CPle EBee EPfP GMac
  IDee SSpi WCru WHer WPGP WSHC
glutinosum EBee
motorium see *Codariocalyx motorius*
podocarpum WSHC
praestans see *D. yunnanense*
tiliifolium see *D. elegans*
§ *yunnanense* CHEx CPle EPfP LRHS SBrw SSpi
  WSHC

Desmoschoenus (Cyperaceae)
spiralis CTrC

Deutzia ✿ (Hydrangeaceae)
calycosa CFil
- 'Dali' SBEC 417 SDys WPGP

chunii	see *D. ningpoensis*
compacta	CFil WBod WFar WPGP
- 'Lavender Time'	CPLG EWTr GSki MBNS MBro
	NSti WCFE
cordatula B&SWJ 6917	WCru
corymbosa	CDoC CFil
crenata 'Flore Pleno'	see *D. scabra* 'Plena'
- var. *nakaiana*	SIng WPat
- - 'Nikko'	CBcs CPBP EBee EHyt ESis EWTr
	EWes GEil GKir LRHS MBar MBro
	MGos MHer NJOw NPro SPlb WDin
	WHCG WKif WSHC WWeb WWin
§ - var. *pubescens*	CFil WPGP
x *elegantissima*	ENot ISea MRav SReu SRms
- 'Fasciculata'	EPfP SPer WLeb WWin
- 'Rosealind' ♀ H4	CBcs EBee EBre ECtt ENot EPfP
	LHop LRHS MBri MRav NBee
	NLon NSti SPer SReu SRms SSpi
	WBod WCom WKif WPGP WSHC
glabrata	WPGP
- B&SWJ 617	WCru
glomeruliflora	CFil EPla WPGP
gracilis	CDoC CHar CSBt EBee EPfP EWTr
	GEil GQui MBar MBro MRav MWat
	NBee SPar SPer WBod WDin WFar
	WGwG WMoo WStI WWal
- 'Carminea'	see *D.* x *rosea* 'Carminea'
§ - 'Marmorata' (v)	WCom WHCG
- 'Rosea'	see *D.* x *rosea*
- 'Variegata'	see *D. gracilis* 'Marmorata'
hookeriana	GGGa ISea WFar
x *hybrida* 'Contraste'	LBuc MBri SPer
- 'Joconde'	CPLG ECtt WFar WKif
- 'Magicien'	CBrm CDoC CHar CMHG CPLG
	CSBt CSam CWib EBee ENot EPfP
	EPla GQui MRav NHol SHBN
	SLon SPer WBod WCot WFar
	WHCG WHar WPGP WPat
- 'Mont Rose' ♀ H4	CBrm CDoC EBee EBre ELan ENot
	EPfP GKir IMGH LAst LBuc LRHS
	MAsh MBar MGos MRav NBee NLon
	SPer SReu WCFE WDin WFar WHCG
	WMoo WSHC WStI WWeb WWin
- 'Perle Rose'	CWSG
- 'Strawberry	CFai CFil CHar CPLG CSam EBee
Fields' ♀ H4	ELan EMil EPla GKir LAst LRHS MBar
	MBlu MBri MRav MTis NBee NPro
	SBod SLon WBod WKif WLRN WPGP
- 'Tourbillon Rouge'	GEil WDin
x *kalmiiflora*	CBcs CSBt CTri EBee EHol EPla
	GKir GQui LRHS MBar MBri
	MDun MGos MHFa MRav MWhi
	NFor SLPl SPer SRms WMoo
x *lemoinei*	CBot
longifolia	CFil CPLG CWib WPGP
- 'Veitchii' ♀ H4	CPle CSBt GEil GQui MRav SMrm
	WCFE
§ - 'Vilmoriniae'	MRav
x *magnifica*	CBcs CWib EHol ELan GEil GQui
	LRHS SRms WCom WDin WHCG
	WHar WWeb WWin
- 'Nancy'	EWTr
- 'Rubra'	see *Deutzia* x *hybrida*
	'Strawberry Fields'
x *maliflora* 'Boule	GEil
Rouge' **new**	
monbeigii	ENot WBcn WKif
§ *ningpoensis* ♀ H4	CBcs CFil EBee EPla EWTr NHol
	SPer SSta WBcn WPGP
parviflora	CPLG
'Pink Pompon'	see *D.* 'Rosea Plena'
pubescens	see *D. crenata* var. *pubescens*
pulchra	CFai CFil CHar CPLG CPom ECha

	EPfP GEil GKir NPro SLon SMac
	SMrm SPer SSpi WFar WHCG
	WPGP WWeb
- B&SWJ 3870	WCru
- B&SWJ 6908	WCru
§ x *rosea*	CPle CTrw CWSG CWib EBee
	ENot EPfP LAst LRHS MBar MHdf
	MWat NLon SHBN SMer SRms
	WFar WKif WStI WWin
- 'Campanulata'	CPLG ENot EPfP
§ - 'Carminea'	CChe CSBt EWTr MDun MRav
	SPer SPlb SRms SSta WCom WDin
	WFar WMoo
'Rosea Plena' (d)	CDoC CHar CPLG CSBt CWib
	EPfP GKir LRHS MDun MGos
	NBlu SLim SSta WBod WCFE
	WCom WFar WGwG WPat WWeb
rubens **new**	GEil
scabra	GKir NPro
§ - 'Candidissima' (d)	CMHG GQui MBri MRav SMer
	SPer WBod WCFE
- 'Codsall Pink'	MBri MRav
- 'Macrocephala' **new**	GEil
§ - 'Plena' (d)	CChe CWib EBee ECtt EGra ELan
	EPfP EWTr IMGH LRHS MDun
	MRav SHBN SPer WMoo WWal
- 'Pride of Rochester' (d)	CBcs CPLG CWib EBre EHol ENot
	MBar MDun MRav SLon WDin
	WHar WLRN
- 'Punctata' (v)	CFai EHoe EVFa SRms WFar
- 'Variegata' (v)	NPro SLim WPGP WSHC
setchuenensis	CFil EPfP GGGa GQui SSpi WHCG
	WSHC
- var.	CBcs CBot CDoC CFil EBee EPfP
corymbiflora ♀ H4	EPla GEil WBcn WCom WFar WKif
	WPGP
staminea	CFil WPGP
taiwanensis	CFil WPGP
- B&SWJ 6858	WCru
x *wellsii*	see *D. scabra* 'Candidissima'
x *wilsonii*	SRms

Dianella ✿ (*Phormiaceae*)

caerulea	CRez EBla ECou ELan GBuc IGor
	NBir SMrm
- var. *petasmatodes*	EBee EMan WCot
- 'Variegata'	see *D. tasmanica* 'Variegata'
intermedia	IBlr SMad WCot
nigra	CFil CPou ECou IFro LEdu WFar
	WHer
revoluta	ECou IBlr
tasmanica	More than 30 suppliers
§ - 'Variegata' (v)	CBcs CFir CFwr CRDP CSpe ECou
	EGra ELan EMan EPfP GQui IBlr LHop
	MSte SMad SPar WCot WCru WOld

Dianthus ✿ (*Caryophyllaceae*)

ACW 2116	CLyd LBee WPer
from DDR **new**	GDra
acicularis	EHyt
'Admiral Lord Anson' (b)	WKin
'Alan Titchmarsh' (p)	EWll LAco SBai
'Albatross' (p)	SChu
'Albus'	MGGn MWgw SYvo
'Aldridge Yellow' (b)	SAll
'Alice' (p)	EBee EMFP EPfP SAll SHay WKin
'Alice Forbes' (b)	SAll SHay
'Alice Lever' (p)	LAco MDHE WAbe
'Allegro' (pf) **new**	SBai
§ 'Allen's Huntsman' (p)	CBcs
'Alloway Star' (p)	EMFP WKin
'Allspice' (p)	CLyd MBro MRav SChu SSvw
	WEas WHoo WKin WWye

	Name	Nurseries
	'Allspice Sport' (p)	WKin
	Allwoodii Alpinus Group (p)	ECho LPVe NJOw NLAp SGar SRms
	'Allwood's Crimson' (pf)	SHay
	alpinus ♀ H4	CElw CLyd EMlt GKev GKir GTou ITim LBee LRHS MDHE NBlu NMen NWCA SPet SRms WCom WHen WPer
	– 'Albus'	CPBP EHyt LRHS WAbe
§	– 'Joan's Blood' ♀ H4	CLyd ECGP EPot ESis LHop MBro NHar NLAp NMen NWCA SBla WAbe WCom WHoo
	– 'Millstream Salmon'	CLyd EPot GCrs ITim
	'Alyson' (p)	SAll
*	'Amalfi' (pf)	SAll
	'Amarinth' (p)	MNrw
	amurensis	EBre GCal GDra LPhx LRHS SIgm SSvw WPer
	– 'Andrey'	GCal
	anatolicus	CElw CLyd CTri EGle LAco LBee LRHS MHer NDlv SSvw WAbe WCom WPer
	'Angelo' (b)	SAll
	'Annabelle' (p)	EBee EMFP EMil LAst LRHS SChu
	'Annette' (pf)	COIW EBee EDAr LRHS MBNS
	'Anniversay' (p)	CBcs SBai
	'Apricot Chace' (b)	SHay
	'Apricot Sue' (pf)	SHay
	'Arctic Star' (p)	CMea EBee EDAr MBNS
	arenarius	CMea CNic EMlt LPVe MHer NJOw SItcl SPlb SSvw SWal WPer
	'Arevalo' (pf)	SHay
	'Argus' (p)	SChu WKin
	'Arizona' (pt)	SAll
*	'Arlene' (b)	SAll
	armeria	CKin NEgg WHer WOut WPer
	arpadianus	MDHE NHol
	– var. *pumilus*	EHyt NWCA
	'Arthur' (p)	EMFP WKin
	'Arthur Leslie' (b)	SAll
§	x *arvernensis* (p) ♀ H4	ECha EPot GAbr MBro WAbe
	– 'Albus'	WAbe
	'Ashley' (p)	SAll
	'Audrey's Frilly'	SChu WKin
	'Aurora' (b)	SHay
	'Autumn Tints' (b)	SAll
	'Auvergne'	see *D.* x *arvernensis*
	'Avon Dasset'	EDAr LBuc
	'Baby Treasure' (p)	CLyd ECho NHol SRot
	'Badenia' (p)	CLyd LBee LRHS MDHE SChu SIgm
	'Bailey's Celebration' (p)	SBai
	'Bailey's Festival' (p)	SBai
	'Bailey's Starlight'	SBai
	barbatus	GWCH SSvw
	– *albus*	NPPs
	– 'New Era' **new**	NCat
	– Nigrescens Group (p,a) ♀ H4	CBre CHad CMea CSpe LPhx NPPs
I	– 'Sooty'	CBri EBee EChP ELan MWrn NDlv WBry WCom WHer
	'Barleyfield Rose' (p)	CLyd SBla WAbe
	'Bath's Pink'	GKir LRHS
§	'Bat's Double Red' (p)	EMFP SChu WKin
	'Beauty of Cambridge' (b)	SAll
	'Beauty of Healey' (p)	EMFP WKin
	'Becka Falls' (p)	SHay
	'Becky Robinson' (p) ♀ H4	SAll SHay
	'Belle of Bookham' (b)	SAll
	'Berlin Snow'	CLyd EPot ESis ITim LBee
	'Bet Gilroy' (b)	SHay
	'Betty Buckle' (p)	SChu
	'Betty Morton' (p) ♀ H4	COkL ECtt MSph SBla SSvw WKif WKin
	'Betty Tucker' (b)	SHay
	'Binsey Red' (p)	EMFP SSvw WKin
	Black and White Minstrels Group	CElw CLyd WKin
	Blakeney seedling (p)	WKin
	blandus	MDHE
*	'Blue Carpet'	WPer
	'Blue Hills' (p)	CLyd ECho ELan LBee MWat SChu
	'Blue Ice' (b)	SAll SHay
	'Blush'	see *D.* 'Souvenir de la Malmaison'
	'Bobby' (p)	SAll
	'Bobby Ames' (b)	SHay
	'Bombardier' (p)	EBre
	'Bookham Fancy' (b)	SAll SHay
	'Bookham Grand' (b)	SHay
	'Bookham Lad' (b)	SAll
	'Bookham Perfume' (b)	SHay
	'Bookham Sprite' (b)	SAll
	'Bourboule'	see *D.* 'La Bourboule'
	'Bovey Belle' (p) ♀ H4	CBcs EBre LRHS MBNS SBai SHay
	'Boydii' (p)	CLyd
	'Bransgore' (p)	CLyd
	'Bremen'	COkL
	'Bressingham Pink' (p)	ECtt
	brevicaulis	WLin
	'Brian Tumbler' (b)	SAll
	'Bridal Veil' (p)	EMFP SChu SSvw WKin
	'Brigadier' (p)	SRms WWin
	'Brilliance' (p)	MBow
	'Brilliant'	see *D. deltoides* 'Brilliant'
	'Brilliant Star' (p)	CPBP EDAr NBlu
	'Brimstone' (b)	SHay
	'Brympton Red' (p)	ECha EMFP EOrc MRav SBla SChu WCom WEas WKif WKin
	'Buckfast Abbey' (p)	CHll
§	'Caesar's Mantle' (p)	GAbr WKin
	caesius	see *D. gratianopolitanus*
	callizonus	ESis NWCA
	'Calypso Star' (p)	EBee ECtt EDAr GBuc MBNS NBlu
	'Camelford' (p)	SChu WKin
	'Camilla' (b)	CLyd EGoo EMFP WCom WKin
	'Can-can' (pf)	ECtt
	'Candy' (p)	see *D.* 'Sway Candy' (p)
	'Candy Clove' (b)	SAll SHay
	'Candy Spice' (p) **new**	CMea WWol
	'Carinda' (p)	SHay
	'Carlotta' (p)	SHay
	'Carmen' (b)	SHay
	'Carmine Letita Wyatt'PBR (p)	EMFP
	'Caroline Bone' (b)	SHay
	'Caroline Clove' (b)	SHay
	carthusianorum	CElw CHad IGor LPhx MSte NDov SAga SGar SSvw SWat WCom WEas WOut WPer
	caryophyllus	CArn GBar GWCH IIve MPEx WHHs
*	'Casper' (pf)	SAll
	'Casser's Pink' (p)	GBuc
	'Catherine Glover' (b)	SAll
*	'Catherine Tucker'	WEas
	'Catherine's Choice'	see *D.* 'Rhian's Choice'
	'Cecil Wyatt' (p)	EBee EMFP EPfP WMnd
§	'Cedric's Oldest' (p)	SChu WKin
	'Charcoal'	EBee WCot
	'Charity' (p)	GDra
	'Charles' (p)	SAll
	'Charles Edward' (p)	SAll SBai
	'Charles Musgrave'	see *D.* 'Musgrave's Pink'
	'Charlotte'	SAll SHay

	'Charm' (b)	SHay
	'Chastity' (p)	MBro SBla SChu WHoo WKin
	Cheddar pink	see *D. gratianopolitanus*
	'Cheerio' (pf) **new**	SBai
	'Cherry Clove' (b)	SAll
	'Cherry Moon'	LRHS
	'Cherry Pie' (p)	WWol
	'Cherryripe' (p)	SHay
	'Cheryl'	see *D.* 'Houndspool Cheryl'
	'Chetwyn Doris' (p) ♀ H4	SBai
	'Chianti' (pf)	NGdn
	'China Doll' (p) **new**	SBai
	chinensis (p,a)	WHer
	'Chocolate Chip' (p) **new**	EMFP
	'Christine Hough' (b)	SAll
	'Christopher' (p)	EBre LRHS SAll SHay
	'Circular Saw' (p)	SChu
	'Clare' (p)	SAll SHay
	'Claret Joy' (p) ♀ H4	CBcs COlW EBee EBre EDAr EMFP SBai WGwG
	'Clarinda' (p)	SAll
	'Clifford Pink'	WKin
	'Clunie' (b)	SAll SHay
§	'Cockenzie Pink' (p)	EMFP GAbr SAll WEas WKin
	'Constance' (p)	SAll
	'Constance Finnis'	see *D.* 'Fair Folly'
	'Consul' (b)	SAll
	'Conwy Silver'	WAbe
	'Conwy Star'	WAbe
	'Copperhead' (b)	SHay
	'Corleone' (pf) **new**	SBai
	'Coronation Ruby' (p) ♀ H4	CBcs SBai SHay
	'Coste Budde' (p)	CLyd WEas WKin
	'Cotton Chace' (b)	SHay
	'Cranborne Seedling' (p)	WKin
	'Cranmere Pool' (p) ♀ H4	CBcs CMea COlW EBre ECtt EDAr ELan EWTr LRHS MBNS MCAu SBai SHay SMrm WWol
	'Cream Sue' (pf)	SHay
	cretaceus	NWCA
	'Crimson Ace' (p)	SHay
	'Crimson Joy' (p)	EDAr
	'Crimson Tempo'PBR (pf)	SBai SHay WWol
	'Crimson Velvet' (b)	SHay
	crinitus	SHFr
	cruentus	LPhx MSte
	'Dad's Choice' (p)	CBcs SBai
	'Dad's Favourite' (p)	EHol EMFP EOrc SAll SChu SHay SRms SSvw WCom WEas WHoo WKin WWhi
	'Daily Mail' (p)	CBcs SBai SChu
	'Dainty Dame' (p) ♀ H4	COlW CSpe CTri EBee EDAr EMlt ESis GBuc GMaP LRHS MWgw NBlu NHol NJOw SAga SBla SChu SIng SRot WLRN
	'Damask Superb' (p)	WKin
	'Daphne' (p)	SAll
	'Dark Star' (p)	EMFP
	'Dark Tempo' (pf)	SHay
	'Darling' (b)	SAll
	'Dartington Laced'	WKin
	'David' (p)	COkL SAll SHay
	'Dawlish Charm' (p)	SBai
	'Dawlish Joy' (p)	EDAr EMFP WHil
	'Dawn' (b)	SAll SHay
	'Daydream' (pf) **new**	SBai WWol
	'Deep Purple' (pf)	SHay
	Delphi (pf)	SBai SHay WWol
	deltoides ♀ H4	CArn CSev ECha ELau EPfP GBar GWCH MDKP NBlu NSco NWCA SIng SPlb SRms WFar WJek WSel

	– 'Albus'	CNic ECGP ECha EPfP GBar IHMM MBar NPri SWat WCom WHrl WMoo WPer WRos WSel
	– 'Arctic Fire'	NGdn WMoo
	– 'Bright Eyes'	ECho
§	– 'Brilliant'	EWTr GTou LPVe MDKP MDun MPWC NBid NBlu NPri NVic SRms SWat WGor WHrl WWpP
	– 'Dark Eyes'	EWes
	– 'Erectus'	EPfP NLon
	– Flashing Light	see *D. deltoides* 'Leuchtfunk'
§	– 'Leuchtfunk'	COkL EBre ECtt EMNN EPfP GKir GTou LGro LRHS MHdf MOne NBlu NHar NMir WEas WFar WHen WPer WRos
	– 'Microchip'	MHdf NHar NJOw WFar
	– 'Nelli' (p)	WMoo
	– red	NBlu
	– 'Shrimp' **new**	MPWC
	'Denis' (p)	ELan SAll
	'Desert Song' (b)	SAll
	'Desmond'	WCom WRus
	'Devon Blush' (p)	EBre
	'Devon Charm' (p)	LRHS
	'Devon Cream'PBR (p)	EBee EBre EMFP LRHS WLRN WWol
	'Devon Dove'PBR (p) ♀ H4	CMea EBee EBre EGra EPfP
	'Devon General'PBR (p)	CTri EBee EBre ECtt EMFP LHop
	'Devon Glow'PBR (p) ♀ H4	EBee EBre EMFP EPfP LRHS WLRN
	'Devon Joy' (p)	LRHS
	'Devon Maid'PBR (p) ♀ H4	EBee EPfP
	'Devon Pearl'PBR (p)	EMFP LHop WWol
	'Devon Pride' (p) ♀ H4	EBre
	'Devon Velvet'PBR **new**	WHil
	'Devon Wizard'PBR (p) ♀ H4	EMFP LRHS NPri WLRN
	'Dewdrop' (p)	CMea CTri ECtt EDAr ESis LRHS MHer NBir NGdn NHar NPro SAll SChu WAbe WCom WFar WKin WPer
	'Diane' (p) ♀ H4	EBee EBre EDAr ELan EMFP SAll SHay SPla WMnd WPer WWal
*	'Diane Cape'	SAll
	'Dianne' (pf)	EDAr WHil
	'Diplomat' (b)	SAll
	'Doctor Archie Cameron' (b)	SHay
	Dona = 'Brecas' (pf)	LAst LRHS SAll SBai SHay
	'Donnet's Variety' **new**	WEas
	'Dora'	LRHS SChu
	'Doris' (p) ♀ H4	CBcs CMea COkL COlW CSLe EBre EDAr EGoo ELan EMFP EMlt ENot EPfP GKir LHop LRHS MCAu MRav MWat SAll SBai SHay SPlb SRms SSvw WMnd WTel WWin WWol
	'Doris Allwood' (pf)	CSBt SHay WMal
	'Doris Elite' (p)	SAll
	'Doris Majestic' (p)	SAll
	'Doris Ruby'	see *D.* 'Houndspool Ruby'
	'Doris Supreme' (p)	SAll SHay
	'Doris Wyatt' **new**	WHil
§	'Dubarry' (p)	CTri ECtt WGor WPer
	'Duchess of Westminster' (M)	WMal
	'Dusky' (p)	WKin
	'Dwarf Vienna'	COkL
	'E.J. Baldry' (b)	SHay
	'Earl of Essex' (p)	EHol EMFP SAll SHay SSvw WKin
	'Ebor II' (b)	SAll
	echiniformis	GKir
	'Edenside Scarlet' (b)	SHay

	'Edenside White' (b)	SAll
	'Edna' (p)	SAll
	'Eileen' (p)	SAll
	'Eileen Lever' (p)	CPBP EPot MDHE SBla WAbe EDAr
	'Elfin Star' (p)	EDAr
	'Elizabeth' (p)	CFee
	'Elizabeth Pink'	SMrm
	'Elizabethan' (p)	GMac SBla WKin
*	'Elizabethan Pink'	CCge CNic
	'Emile Paré' (p)	SChu WKin
	'Emperor'	see D. 'Bat's Double Red'
	'Enid Anderson' (p)	SChu WKin
	'Enid Burgoyne'	WKin
	erinaceus	CMea EHol EMNN EPot GCrs GDra GTou LRHS MOne NHar NJOw NWCA SRot WAbe WPer WWin
	- var. alpinus	CLyd EPot GKir NSla SIng
	'Erycina' (b)	SAll
	'Ethel Hurford'	WHoo WKin
	'Eudoxia' (b)	SAll
	'Eva Humphries' (b)	SAll SHay
	'Evening Star' (p)	CPBP EDAr MWgw
	'Excelsior' (p)	NFor NLon
	'Exquisite' (b)	SAll
§	'Fair Folly' (p)	SChu SSvw WEas WKin
	'Falcon'PBR (pf)	SBai WWol
	'Fanal' (p)	NBir WKin
*	'Fancy Magic' (pf)	SAll
	'Fancy Schubert' (pf) new	SBai
	'Farida' (pf) new	SBai
	'Farnham Rose' (p)	SChu
	'Fenbow Nutmeg Clove' (b)	SChu WKin
	ferrugineus	MDHE
	'Fettes Mount' (p)	CLyd EMon MWgw SChu WCot WKin
	'Feuerhexe' (p)	LRHS NPro
	'Fiery Cross' (b)	SAll SHay
	'Fimbriatus' (p)	WHoo WKin
	'Fingo Clove' (b)	SAll
	'Fiona' (p)	SAll
	'First Lady' (b)	SAll
	'Flame' (p)	SHay
	'Fleur' (p)	SAll
	'Forest Glow' (b)	SAll
	'Forest Sprite' (b)	SAll
	'Forest Treasure' (b)	SAll
	'Forest Violet' (b)	SAll
	'Fortuna' (p)	SAll
	'Fountain's Abbey' (p)	EMFP WIvy WKin
	'Fragrant Ann' (pf) ♀H1	SHay
*	fragrantissimus	LRHS
	'Frances Isabel' (p)	SAll
	'Frances Sellars' (b)	SHay
	'Frank's Frilly' (p)	WKin
	'Freckles' (p)	SHay
	'Freda' (p)	SAll
	freynii	CLyd EWes MDHE NDlv NLAp SBla
N	fringed pink	see D. superbus
	furcatus	NWCA
	'Fusilier' (p)	CMea EBee EBre ECtt EDAr EMFP GKir LHop LRHS MBar MHer MWgw NBlu NPri NWCA SAll SChu WAbe WFar WKin WPat
	'Galil' (pf)	SAll
	'Garland' (p)	CTri LRHS WGor
	'Garnet' (p)	COkL SChu
	'Gaydena' (b)	SAll
	giganteus	IBlr MNrw MSte WKin
	'Gingham Gown' (p)	NBir SBla
	'Gipsy Clove' (b)	SHay
	glacialis	GTou MDHE NHar
	- subsp. gelidus	NMen
	'Gloriosa' (p)	WKin
	'Gold Fleck'	EMlt LBee SChu SIng
	'Grandma Calvert' (p)	SAll
	graniticus	WPer
	'Gran's Favourite' (p) ♀H4	CBcs CMea CSBt EBee EBre ECtt EDAr EMFP EPfP LAst LRHS MCAu MWat NPri SBai SBla SChu SHay SPlb SRms WEas WKin WWol WWye
§	gratianopolitanus ♀H4	CArn CElw CSLe CTri EPot GTou LRHS MBow MHer MNrw MRav NBid NJOw NLAp NOak NWCA SPet SRms WAbe WKin WPer WWye
	- 'Albus'	CLyd EPot
	- 'Flore Pleno' (d)	EMFP MInt SSvw
	- from Cheddar	CLyd
	- 'Rosenfeder' (p)	WPer
	- 'Splendens' (p)	WPer
§	- 'Tiny Rubies' (p)	ECho WKin
	'Gravetye Gem' (b)	SRms
	'Gravetye Gem' (p)	WKin
	'Grenadier' (p)	ECho ELan
	'Gwendolen Read' (p)	SHay
	'Gypsy Star' (p)	CMea COlW ECho EDAr MBNS NBlu
	haematocalyx	CPBP MDHE NWCA WAbe WCom WPer
	- 'Alpinus'	see D. haematocalyx subsp. pindicola
§	- subsp. pindicola	CGra CLyd EMFP ITim MDHE NHol NMen WPat
	'Harlequin' (p)	ECtt EMFP WPer
	'Harmony' (b)	SAll SHay
	'Harry Oaks' (p)	WKin
	'Havana'PBR (pf)	SHay
	'Haytor'	see D. 'Haytor White'
	'Haytor Rock' (p) ♀H4	EBre EPfP SHay WHil
§	'Haytor White' (p) ♀H4	EBee EBre EDAr EMFP EPfP LAst LRHS NLon SBai SChu SHay SRms WEas WWhi WWol
I	'Heath' (b)	WKin
	'Heidi' (p)	EPfP
	'Helen' (p)	SAll SHay
	'Herbert's Pink' (p)	WKin
	'Hereford Butter Market'	EBee SChu WKin
	'Hidcote' (p)	CLyd COlW CTri ELan LRHS MWat NMen SBla WKin WLRN WWin
	'Hidcote Red'	ECho LBee LRHS
	'Highland Fraser' (p)	MBro SAll SChu SRms WEas WKif WWin
	Highland hybrids	MWgw
	'Highland Queen' (p)	WKin
*	'Hi-lite' (pf)	SAll
	'Hoo House' (p)	WKin
	'Hope' (p)	EMFP SChu WKin
	'Horsa' (b)	SHay
	'Hot Spice' (p) ♀H4 new	CMea EWll WHil WWol
§	'Houndspool Cheryl' (p) ♀H4	COkL CSBt CSam EBee EMFP EPfP LRHS SBai SRms
§	'Houndspool Ruby' (p) ♀H4	COlW CSam EMFP EPfP EWTr MBNS MCAu MWat SBai WEas
	'Huntsman'	see D. 'Allen's Huntsman'
	'Ian' (p)	CBcs SAll SBai SHay
	'Ibis' (b)	SHay
	'Icomb' (p)	CLyd MBro SRms WHoo WKin WPer
	'Imperial Clove' (b)	SHay
	'Impulse'PBR (pf)	SBai
	'Ina' (p)	SRms
	'Incas' (pf) ♀H1	SHay
	'Inchmery' (p)	EBre EMFP NFor SAll SChu SHay SSvw WEas WHoo WKin WWhi
	'India Star' (p)	EDAr NBlu
	'Indios' (pf) ♀H1	SBai SHay

	'Ine' (p)	COkL
	'Inglestone' (p)	CTri NHar NHol SBla WLin WPer
	'Inshriach Dazzler'	CLyd CMea CPBP EBre ECtt EDAr
	(p) ♀ H4	GCrs GDra GKir ITim LBee MHer
		NDlv NHar NPri SBla SIng SMrm
		SSvw WAbe WCom WKin
	'Inshriach Startler' (p)	CLyd CMea
	'Ipswich Pink' (p)	CBri LGro LPVe LRHS WBro
I	'Ivonne' (pf)	SHay
	'Ivonne Orange' (pf)	SBai SHay
	'James Michael	SHay
	Hayward' (b)	
	'James Portman' (p)	SBai
	'Jane Austen' (p)	SChu WKin WPer
	'Jane Coffey' (b)	SHay
	'Janet Walker' (p)	GMaP
	japonicus	CSpe
	'Jenny Wyatt' (p)	SHay
	'Jessica' (p)	SAll
	'Jessica Oliver' (p)	SBai
	'Joan Schofield' (p)	CLyd CMea EDAr EMlt SRot WAbe
	'Joan Siminson' (p)	WKin
	'Joan's Blood'	see *D. alpinus* 'Joan's Blood'
	'John Ball' (p)	EMFP WKin
	'John Grey' (p)	WKin
	'John Partridge' (p)	SBai
	'Joy' (p) ♀ H4	CBcs COIW EBee EBre ECtt EDAr
		EMFP EPfP LRHS SHay
	'Julian' (p)	SAll
	'June Hammond'	SHay
	'Kesteven Chambery' (p)	WPer
	'Kesteven Chamonix' (p)	WPer
	'Kesteven Kirkstead'	CSWP
	(p) ♀ H4	
	'King of the Blacks' (p,a)	ELan MRav
	kitaibelii	see *D. petraeus* subsp. *petraeus*
	'Kiwi Pretty' (p)	LAco
	knappii	ELan EPfP LAst MLLN MNrw NOak
		NVic SSvw WPer WWin WWye
	- 'Yellow Harmony' (p,a)	EWsh LRHS MBNS WFTG WHer
		WMnd
§	'La Bourboule' (p) ♀ H4	EDAr ELan EMNN EMlt EPot GKir
		LBee LRHS MBar MBro MWat NBlu
		NHol NMen NPri SBla SRms WFar
		WGwG WKin WLin WPat WWin
	'La Bourboule Albus' (p)	EDAr EMlt EPot SBla WFar WGor
		WWin
	'Laced Hero' (p)	IGor SChu WKin
	'Laced Joy' (p)	CElw EDAr EMFP SAll SChu SHay
	'Laced Monarch' (p)	CBcs COIW CSBt EBre ECtt EDAr
		LRHS MCAu SAll SBai SChu SPlb
		WKin WWol
	'Laced Mrs Sinkins' (p)	CBcs SBai
	'Laced Prudence'	see *D.* 'Prudence'
	'Laced Romeo' (p)	EMFP SAll SChu SHay WKin
	'Laced Treasure' (p)	SAll
	'Lady Granville' (p)	IGor SSvw WKin
	'Lady Salisbury' (p)	EMFP WKin
§	'Lady Wharncliffe' (p)	EMFP IGor WKin
	'L'Amour' (p)	SAll
	'Lancing Lady' (b)	SAll
	'Lancing Monarch' (b)	SAll SHay
	'Laura' (p)	SAll SHay
	'Lavastrom' **new**	SOkd
	'Lavender Clove' (b)	SAll
	'Lawley's Red' (p)	WKin
	'Leiden' (b)	SAll
	'Lemsii' (p) ♀ H4	ECtt EMFP NMen NVic WPer WWye
	'Leslie Rennison' (b)	SAll SHay
	'Letitia Wyatt' (p) ♀ H4	CMea COIW EDAr EMFP
	'Leuchtkugel'	ECho WLin
	'Liberty' (pf)	SBai SHay
	liboschitzianus	MDHE

	'Lightning' (pf)	SAll
	'Lionheart' (p)	EBre LRHS
	'Lipstick' (pf) **new**	SBai
	'Lisboa' (pf)	SHay
	'Little Gem' (pf)	WKin
	'Little Jock' (p)	EBre EDAr ELan EMNN EPot GKir
		LBee LRHS MBar MHer MRav NEgg
		NHar NHol SAll SBla SChu SMrm
		SPlb SRms WEas WFar WKin WWin
	'Little Miss Muffet' (p)	CHll
	'London Brocade' (p)	WKin
	'London Delight' (p)	EMFP SHay WKin
	'London Glow' (p)	SAll WKin
	'London Lovely' (p)	SAll SSvw WKin
	'London Poppet' (p)	SAll SSvw WKin
	'Loveliness' (p)	CBre
	lumnitzeri	EHyt EPot GCal LTwo MDHE WPer
	'Lustre' (b)	SAll SHay
	'Mab'	WKin
	'Mabel Appleby' (p)	SHel
	'Madame Dubarry'	see *D.* 'Dubarry'
	'Madonna' (pf)	SHay WKin
	'Malaga' (pf) **new**	SBai
	'Malaga' (pf) ♀ H1	SAll SHay
	'Mambo' PBR (pf) ♀ H4	SAll SBai SHay WWol
	'Mandy' (p)	SAll
	'Manningtree Pink'	see *D.* 'Cedric's Oldest'
	'Maria'	see *D.* 'Allen's Maria'
	'Marmion' (M)	WMal
	'Mars' (p)	ECtt ELan GAbr SAll SChu WAbe WFar
	'Marshmallow' (p) **new**	WWol
	'Marshwood Melody' (p)	SBai
	'Marshwood Mystery' (p)	LAco WKin
	'Mary Simister' (b)	SAll
*	'Mary's Gilliflower'	EMFP WKin
	'Matador' (b)	SHay
	'Maybole' (p)	SAll SHay
	'Maythorne' (p)	SRms
	'Mendip Hills' (b)	SAll SHay
	'Mendlesham Belle'	EMFP
	(p) ♀ H4	
	'Mendlesham Frilly' (p)	EMFP
	'Mendlesham Glow' (p)	EMFP
	'Mendlesham Maid'	EMFP
	(p) ♀ H4	
	Mendlesham Minx =	CLyd CMea EDAr EMFP
	'Russmin' PBR (p)	
	'Mendlesham Miss'	EMFP
	(p) **new**	
	'Mendlesham Moll' (p)	EMFP
	'Mendlesham Saint	EMFP
	Helen's' (p)	
	'Mendlesham Spice'	EMFP
	(p) **new**	
	'Mercury' (p)	SAll
	'Merlin' **new**	ENot
	'Merlin Clove' (b)	SHay
	'Messines Pink' (p)	SAll
	microlepis	EHyt ITim NMen NWCA WAbe
	- f. *albus*	NSla WAbe
*	- var. *degenii*	CPBP EPot
	- 'Leuchtkugel'	ECho EHyt ITim WAbe
	- var. *musalae*	CLyd CMea CPBP EHyt EPot LTwo
		MDHE NHar WAbe WLin
	'Miniver'	SHay
	'Miss Sinkins' (p)	EDAr GKir SPla
*	'Momoko' (p)	SAll
	'Monica Wyatt' (p) ♀ H4	EBee EBre EDAr EMFP GKir LRHS
		SBai SChu SHay
	monspessulanus	GDra NEgg NWCA WMoo WPer
	- MP 94-82	IDac
	'Montrose Pink'	see *D.* 'Cockenzie Pink'
	'Moortown Plume'	WKin

	'Moulin Rouge'	SChu WWol
	'Mountain Mist' (b) **new**	EFou
	'Mrs Clark'	see D. 'Nellie Clark'
	'Mrs Gumbly' (p)	WKin
	'Mrs Holt' (p)	EMFP
	'Mrs Jackson' (p)	CLyd
	'Mrs Macbride' (p)	WKin
	'Mrs N. Clark'	see D. 'Nellie Clark'
	'Mrs Perkins' (b)	SAll
	'Mrs Roxburgh'	CSam WKin
	'Mrs Sinkins' (p)	More than 30 suppliers
	'Murray's Laced Pink' (p)	WKin
N	'Musgrave's Pink' (p)	CNic CSam ECha MRav SAga SAll SBla SChu SSvw WEas WKin
	'Musgrave's White'	see D. 'Musgrave's Pink'
	myrtinervius	CLyd ECho EHyt GDra NWCA WPer
	- subsp. *caespitosus* MESE 433 **new**	WAbe
	'Mystery' (pf)	SAll
	'Nan Bailey' (p)	SBai
*	'Napoleon'	SAll
	'Napoleon III' (p)	WCom WKif
	nardiformis	WPer
	'Nautilus' (b)	SAll SHay
	neglectus	see D. pavonius
§	'Nellie Clark' (p)	CLyd SChu SRot
	'Nelson'PBR	SHay
	'Neon Star' (p) **new**	EMFP
	'New Tempo' (pf)	SBai SHay
	'Nichola Ann' (p) ♀H4	SAll
	'Night Star' (p)	NBlu SChu
	nitidus	CLyd NBir NWCA WPer
	nivalis	NWCA
	noeanus	see D. petraeus subsp. noeanus
	'Nonsuch' (p)	WKin
	'Northland' (pf)	SHay
	'Nyewoods Cream' (p)	CTri EBre EMFP EPot ESis GDra GKir LBee LRHS MBar MBro MHer MRav NHar NMen NPri SIng SRot WCom WPat WPer WRHF
§	'Oakington' (p)	CTri EBre EMNN LRHS MRav MWat NPri NWCA SChu WKin WTel
	'Oakington Rose'	see D. 'Oakington'
	'Oakwood Gillian Garforth' (p) ♀H4	SBai
	'Oakwood Romance' (p) ♀H4	NLon
	'Oakwood Splendour' (p) ♀H4	MBNS
*	'Odino'	SAll
	'Old Blush'	see D. 'Souvenir de la Malmaison'
	'Old Dutch Pink' (p)	SChu WKin
	'Old Fringed Pink' (p)	WKin
	'Old Fringed White' (p)	EMFP
	'Old Irish' (p)	WKin
	'Old Mother Hubbard' (p)	CFee CHll
	'Old Red Clove' (p)	WCot WEas
§	'Old Square Eyes' (p)	EBee EOrc MNrw SAga SAll SBla SChu SMrm WEas WKin
	'Old Velvet' (p)	GCal SChu WKin
	'Oliver' (p)	SAll
*	'Olivia' (pf)	SAll
*	'Omagio' (pf)	SAll
*	'Ondina' (pf)	SAll
	'Opera'	SAll SHay
*	'Orange Magic' (pf)	SAll
	'Orange Maid' (b)	SAll
	'Oscar' (p)	SAll
	'Osprey' (b)	SHay
	'Paddington' (p)	SChu WKin
	'Painted Beauty' (p)	EMFP NBir
	'Painted Lady' (p)	CLyd SAll SChu WKin
	'Paisley Gem' (p)	SChu SSvw WKif WKin
	'Patricia' (b)	SHay
	'Paul' (p)	EBre
	'Paul Hayward' (p)	SHay
§	*pavonius* ♀H4	CLyd EHyt EMlt EWes GTou NWCA SBla SIgm SIng WAbe WPer
	- *roysii*	see D. 'Roysii'
	'Pax' (pf)	SAll SBai SHay
	'Peach' (p)	SHay
	'Pearl'	SAll
	'Perfect Clove' (b)	SHay
§	*petraeus*	EWes NWCA
§	- subsp. *noeanus*	CLyd ESis WAbe WPat WPer
	- - *albus*	WLin
§	- subsp. *petraeus*	NOak WPer
	'Petticoat Lace' (b)	SHay
	'Phantom' (p)	SHay
	'Pheasant's Eye' (p)	EMFP SSvw WKin
	'Philip Archer' (b)	SHay
*	'Picton's Propeller' (p)	GBuc GDea
	'Pike's Pink' (p) ♀H4	COlW CSLe CSpe EBee EDAr ELan EMlt GDra LBee LHop LRHS MHer MRav NEgg NHol NLAp NMen SAll SBla SChu SRPl SRms SSvw WAbe WEas WGwG WKin WLin WTel WWin
	pindicola	see D. haematocalyx subsp. pindicola
	'Pink Bizarre' (b)	SHay
*	'Pink Dona' (pf)	SAll SBai SHay
	'Pink Jewel' (p)	CLyd CMea EDAr EMlt LBee LRHS MHer NMen SAll SChu SIng WEas WWeb
	'Pink Mrs Sinkins' (p)	EMFP MHer SAll SBai SChu WKin
	'Pink Pearl' (p)	EDAr SAll
	'Pink Slm' (pf)	SAll
	'Pixie' (b)	EPot
	'Pixie Star'PBR	EDAr
	plumarius	EWTr NMir SRms SSvw WGor WGwG WHHs WMoo WPer
	- 'Albiflorus'	WPer
I	- 'Snowdonia'	WBry
	- 'Spring Charm' **new**	LPVe
	pontederae	NDlv SSvw WPer
	'Portsdown Fancy' (b)	SHay
	'Prado' (pf) ♀H4	SAll SHay
	'Prado Rofit' (pf) **new**	SBai
	'Pretty'	LHop LRHS
	'Prince Charming' (p)	CLyd ELan EMNN EPot NMen NPri SIng SRms WPer
	'Princess Charming'	see D. gratianopolitanus 'Princess Charming'
	'Princess of Wales' (M)	WMal
	'Priory Pink' (p)	SAll
§	'Prudence' (p)	SAll WHoo WKin
	'Pudsey Prize' (p)	CLyd CPBP EHyt
	'Pummelchen' (p)	EPot ITim
	'Purple Jenny' (p)	SAll
	'Purple Pacal'PBR (pf)	SHay
	'Purple Rendez-vous' (pf)	SAll
	pygmaeus	LHop NBro SMac
*	- 'Pink Frills'	WBro
	'Queen of Hearts' (p)	CTri EBre LRHS NWCA SMrm WPer
§	'Queen of Henri' (p)	ECtt EDAr GEdr GMac LBee LRHS MHer SBla SChu SHar WBVN WFar WKin
	'Queen of Sheba' (p)	EMFP SChu SSvw WKin
	'Raggio di Sole' (p)	SAll SBai
	'Rainbow Loveliness' (p.a)	NBir SAll WHil
	'Ralph Gould' (p)	ECho
	'Raspberry Ripple' (p)	CWCL
	'Red and White' (p)	WKin
	'Red Dwarf'	EMFP

*	'Red Rimon' (pf)	SAll
	'Red Velvet'	CLyd LRHS SAsh
	'Reiko' (pf)	SAll
	'Reine de Henri'	see D. 'Queen of Henri'
	'Rendez-vous'[PBR] (pf)	SAll SBai
	'Renoir' (b)	SAll SHay
	repens	IIve
	'Revell's Lady Wharncliffe'	see D. 'Lady Wharncliffe'
	'Richard Gibbs' (p)	MOne
	'Rimon' (pf)	SAll
	'Rivendell' (p)	CPBP NHar NSla
	'Robert' (p)	SAll
	'Robert Baden-Powell' (b)	SHay
	'Roberta' (pf)	SAll
*	'Robin Ritchie'	WHoo WKin WWhi
	'Robin Thain' (b)	SAll SHay
§	'Roodkapje' (p)	WKin
	'Rose de Mai' (p)	CLyd CSam CSev EMFP SAll SChu SSvw WEas WHoo WKin
	'Rose Joy' (p) ♀ H4	EBee EDAr EMFP EPfP SHay
	'Rosealie' (p)	SHay
	'Royalty' (p)	SHay
§	'Roysii' (p)	NDlv WPer
	'Rubin' (pf)	WEas
	'Ruby'	see D. 'Houndspool Ruby'
	'Ruby Doris'	see D. 'Houndspool Ruby'
	'Russling Robin'	see D. 'Fair Maid of Kent'
	'Sahara' (pf)	SAll
	'Saint Edith' (p)	WKin
	'Saint Nicholas' (p)	EMFP SChu WKin
	'Saint Winifred'	SChu WKin
	Salamanca = 'Kosalamana' (pf)	SBai SHay
	'Sally Anne Hayward' (b)	SHay
	'Sam Barlow' (p)	COkL EGoo SAll SChu SHay WKin WWye
	'Santa Claus' (b)	SAll SHay
	'Santorini'	SHay
	'Scania' (pf)	SHay
	scardicus	EHyt
	'Scarlet Fragrance' (b)	SHay
	scopulorum perplexans	EPot ETow
	seguieri	MNrw SSvw WMoo WPer
	serotinus	EPot SIng
	Shiplake seedling (p)	WKin
	'Show Aristocrat' (p)	SAll
	'Show Portrait' (p)	NFor NLon
	simulans	CLyd EHyt
	'Sir Cedric Morris'	see D. 'Cedric's Oldest'
	'Sir David Scott' (p)	WKin
*	'Six Hills'	WCom WPat
	'Snowbird' (pf)	SAll
	'Snowfire'	SChu
	'Snowshill Manor' (p)	WPer
*	'Sofia' (pf)	SAll
	'Solar Chiaro' (pf) **new**	SBai
	'Solar Giallo Oro' (pf) **new**	SBai
	'Solomon' (p)	SSvw WKin
	'Solomon's Hat' (p)	WKin
	'Sops-in-wine' (p)	EBee ECha EMFP GBuc GCal GDea ITim MNrw SAll SChu SHay SMrm WKin WWhi
	'Southmead' (p)	ECho
§	'Souvenir de la Malmaison' (M)	WMal
	'Spangle' (b)	SAll
	'Spangled Star' (p)	EDAr MBNS
	'Spencer Bickham' (p)	EMFP EPot MNrw WKin
	'Spirit' (pf) **new**	SBai
	'Spring Beauty' (p)	LPVe NBir WHer

	'Spring Star' (p)	ECtt
	'Square Eyes'	see D. 'Old Square Eyes'
	squarrosus	EPot GKir NWCA
*	- *alpinus*	ECho ITim
	- 'Nanus'	ELan EWes LRHS
	'Squeeks' (p)	SChu
	'Stan Stroud' (b)	SHay
	'Starry Eyes' **new**	CMea
	sternbergii JJH 931078	NWCA
	'Storm' (pf)	WMal
	'Strathspey' (b)	SAll SHay
	'Strawberries and Cream' (p)	CBcs EBee EBre ECtt EDAr EMFP LHop LRHS NOrc SHay SPla WMnd WWol
*	*strictus* subsp. *pulchellus*	EHyt GCrs SOkd
§	*subacaulis*	NHar
	suendermannii	see D. petraeus
	'Sunray' (b)	SAll SHay
	'Sunstar' (b)	SAll SHay
§	*superbus*	EWTr LPhx MSal MTho WCom WKin WPer WWin WWye
	- 'Crimsonia'	WPer
	- var. *longicalycinus*	MNrw MSte WHer
I	- 'Primadonna'	WPer
*	- 'Rose'	WPer
	- 'Snowdonia'	WPer
	'Susan' (p)	SAll
	'Susannah' (p)	SAll
*	'Susan's Seedling' (p)	SAll
	'Swanlake' (p)	SHay
	'Sway Belle' (p)	CBcs SBai
	'Sway Delight' (p) **new**	SBai
	'Sway Gem' (p)	SBai
	'Sway Melody' (p)	CBcs SBai
	'Sway Pearl' (p)	CBcs SBai
	'Sway Ripple' (p)	CBcs SBai
	'Sway Sorbet' (p) **new**	SBai
	'Sway Sunset' (p)	CBcs SBai
	'Sweet Sue' (b)	SAll SHay
	'Sweetheart Abbey' (p)	EMFP GBuc IGor SChu SSvw WKin
	sylvestris	EPot SSvw
	- subsp. *tergestinus*	MDHE
	'Syston Beauty' (p)	WKin
	'Tamsin' (p) ♀ H4	SBla WKin
	'Tatra Blush'	GCal GMac
	'Tatra Bull's-eye' (p)	GCal
	'Tatra Fragrance'	GCal
	'Tatra Ghost'	GCal
	'Tayside Red' (M)	WMal
	'Tempo' (pf) ♀ H1	SBai SHay WWol
	'Terra'[PBR] (pf)	SHay
	'Terry Sutcliffe' (p)	WKin
	'Texas' (pf)	SAll
	the Bloodie pink	see D. 'Caesar's Mantle'
	'Theo' (pf)	SAll
	'Thomas' (p)	CSLe SAll SChu SMrm WEas
	'Thomas Lee' (b)	SAll
	'Thora' (M)	WMal
	'Tiny Rubies'	see D. gratianopolitanus 'Tiny Rubies'
	'Toledo' (p)	EMFP WKin
	'Treasure' (p)	SHay
	'Trevor' (p)	SAll
	'Tundra'[PBR] (p)	SBai
	turkestanicus	NBir
	'Tweedale Seedling'	GBuc
	Tyrolean trailing carnations	SAll
	'Unique' (p)	EMFP SChu SSvw WHoo WKin
	'Ursula Le Grove' (p)	EMFP IGor SChu SSvw WIvy WKin
	'Valda Wyatt' (p) ♀ H4	CBcs COIW EBee EDAr ELan EMFP EPfP GKir LRHS SAll SBai SChu SHay SPla WGwG WMnd

'Violet Clove' (b)	SHay
'Visa' (pf)	SAll
'W.A. Musgrave'	see *D.* 'Musgrave's Pink'
'W.H. Brooks' (b)	SAll
'Waithman Beauty' (p)	CTri ECtt GAbr MBar SAll WEas WKin WPer WWye
'Waithman's Jubilee' (p)	SRms WLin
'Warden Hybrid' (p)	CMea COlW CTri EBee ECtt EDAr EMNN EPfP ESis GEdr LRHS NBlu SBla WAbe WLRN WLin
'Weetwood Double' (p)	CFee WPer
'Welcome' (b)	SHay
weyrichii	CLyd ECho NMen WPer
'Whatfield Anona' (p)	CLyd ELan SAll
'Whatfield Beauty'	CLyd ECho ECtt EDAr ELan EMlt EPot LRHS SAll
'Whatfield Brilliant' (p)	CLyd GKir
'Whatfield Can-can' ♀ H4	CLyd CMea COkL CPBP EBee ECtt EDAr EMFP ESis GKir LRHS NBlu SAll WAbe
'Whatfield Cerise'	CLyd
'Whatfield Cream Lace'	NWCA
'Whatfield Cyclops'	CLyd CPBP EDAr EMlt LRHS SAll SChu WKin WLRN
'Whatfield Dawn'	CLyd ECho ELan SAll
'Whatfield Dorothy Mann' (p)	ECho ELan SAll
'Whatfield Fuchsia' (p)	CLyd SAll
'Whatfield Gem' (p)	CLyd COlW CPBP EBee EBre ECtt ELan EMFP ESis GCal GDra LRHS MRav MWgw NPri SAll WFar WKin WPer
'Whatfield Joy' (p)	CLyd ECtt EDAr ELan EMlt EPfP EPot ESis LBee LRHS MHer NMen NPri SAll
'Whatfield Magenta'	CLyd ELan EMlt EPot ESis GEdr GKir
(p) ♀ H4	LBee LRHS NWCA SAll SChu WEas
'Whatfield Mini' (p)	EDAr SAll SRms WPer
'Whatfield Miss' (p)	SAll
'Whatfield Misty Morn' (p)	CLyd ECho ELan
'Whatfield Peach' (p)	SAll
'Whatfield Pom Pom' (p)	CLyd
'Whatfield Pretty Lady' (p)	ECho ELan SAll
'Whatfield Rose' (p)	ECho EPot SAll
'Whatfield Ruby' (p)	CLyd EGle ELan GKir LRHS NWCA SAll WPer
'Whatfield Smokey Joe'	CLyd
'Whatfield Supergem'	CLyd ECho ECtt ELan EPot SAll
'Whatfield White' (p)	CLyd ECho ECtt ELan LRHS SAll SRms WGwG
'Whatfield White Moon' (p)	ECho
'Whatfield Wisp' (p)	CM&M CPBP CTri ELan ESis GEdr MRav NBir NMen NWCA WAbe WFar WLRN
'White Joy'PBR (p) ♀ H4	EDAr EMFP
'White Ladies' (p)	ELan ENot SAll WKin
'White Liberty'PBR (pf)	SHay
'White Lightning' (pf)	SAll
'Whitecliff' (b)	SAll SHay
'Whitehill' (p) ♀ H4	EPot MBro MHer NHol NMen NWCA NWoo WLin WPat WWin
'Whitesmith' (b) ♀ H4	SAll
'Whitford Belle' (p)	SBai
'Widecombe Fair' (p) ♀ H4	CMea COlW CSam EBre ECtt EDAr ELan LRHS MCAu NLon SAll SRms WWol
* 'Wild Velvet' (p)	WKin
'William Brownhill' (p)	EMFP SChu WKin
'Winsome' (p)	SHay

'Yorkshireman' (b)	SAll SHay
'Zebra' (b)	SAll SHay
zederbaueri	NWCA
'Zoe's Choice' (p) ♀ H4	COkL

Diapensia (*Diapensiaceae*)
lapponica var. *obovata*	WAbe

Diarrhena (*Poaceae*)
japonica	EPPr SRGP WDyG

Diascia ✿ (*Scrophulariaceae*)
anastrepta	EOrc WPer WWye
– HWEL 0219	NWCA
'Appleby Appleblossom'	EOrc GCal SChu WRHF WRus WWeb
'Appleby Apricot'	NDov NGdn
'Apricot' hort.	see *D. barberae* 'Hopleys Apricot'
* 'Aquarius'	SChu WPen
'Baby Bums' **new**	WWol
barberae	EBre ELan
– 'Belmore Beauty' (v)	EBre ECtt EMan EPyc EVFa EWes MHer NFla SChu WCom
– 'Blackthorn Apricot' ♀ H3-4	CBot CElw CFox CMHG ECha ECtt EDAr EHyt EPfP GBuc GKir GMac LRHS MBow MHer MOak MSte NBlu NHar NRya SBla SChu SMrm SPer SPlb WFar WPer WWin
– 'Crûg Variegated' (v)	EPot WCru WPat WPer
§ – 'Fisher's Flora' ♀ H3-4	NBro NDov NHar NMen WFar WWin
– 'Fisher's Flora' x 'Lilac Belle'	ECtt EDAr SCoo SHFr
§ – 'Hopleys Apricot'	EPfP LHop
§ – 'Ruby Field' ♀ H3-4	CBcs CFox CWCL ECha ECtt EDAr EHyt ELan EMNN EPfP GKir LAst LHop LRHS MDun NEgg NGdn NLAp NPPs SBla SGar SPar SPer SRms WCFE WFar
Blue Bonnet = 'Hecbon'	CElw ECtt EMan EPot GMac MDKP SChu SGar SMrm WFar
'Blush'	see *D. integerrima* 'Blush'
'Coldham'	EMan LHop SDys SGar
Coral Belle = 'Hecbel'PBR ♀ H3-4	CFwr CPBP CSpe EBcc ECtt EMan EOrc EPfP EPot EWes GMac LAst LHop LRHS MDun MSte MTis NCiC NFla NHar NLon SChu SIng SUsu WEas WFar WLRN WPer WWeb
cordata misapplied	see *D. barberae* 'Fisher's Flora'
cordifolia	see *D. barberae* 'Fisher's Flora'
'Dainty Duet'	SChu WPer
'Dark Eyes' ♀ H3-4	MSte SChu
Eclat = 'Heclat'PBR	WFar
elegans misapplied	see *D. fetcaniensis, D. vigilis*
elegans (Hiern) Hiern	see *D. capsularis*
'Elizabeth' ♀ H3-4	MMil NHar NLon
'Emma'	CMea CWCL LHop NHar NLon SChu SUsu
§ *felthamii*	see *D. fetcaniensis*
§ *fetcaniensis*	CMHG CSpe EBee EPfP GDea LHop SCro SIgm SPer WCFE WHal WPer WWin
– 'Daydream'	LRHS WLin WWeb
flanaganii misapplied	see *D. vigilis*
flanaganii	see *D. stachyoides*
'Frilly' ♀ H3-4	ECtt MSte SChu
I 'Hazel' **new**	SScr
'Hector Harrison'	see *D.* 'Salmon Supreme'
'Hector's Hardy' ♀ H3-4	GMaP MSte
Ice Cracker = 'Hecrack'	CElw CMea CSpe ECtt EHyt EMan EOrc EPot GMac LAst LHop MOak NFla NGdn SDes SIng WWol
§ *integerrima* ♀ H3-4	CSam CSpe ECha ELan EMan

		EOrc LLWP LPhx MFir SChu SGar
		SIgm SMrm SPla WCot
§	- 'Alba'	see *D. integerrima* 'Blush'
§	- 'Blush'	CElw CSam CSpe EGoo EMan GMac
		MSte NHar NPPs SAga SGar SMrm
	- 'Ivory Angel'	see *D. integerrima* 'Blush'
	integrifolia	see *D. integerrima*
	'Jack Elliott'	see *D. vigilis* 'Jack Elliott'
	'Jacqueline's Joy'	CMea EMan GMac MSte NFla
		NGdn NHar NPer SChu SMrm
		WBar WFar WRHF
	'Joyce's Choice' ♀ H3-4	CHar EOrc EPot EWes LPhx MSte
		NGdn SBri SUsu WFar WLRN
	'Kate'	LRHS NDov SChu SMrm
	'Katherine Sharman' (v)	CSpe ECtt EMan EWes LHop
		LRHS MBNS MDKP MHar NGdn
		SAga SUsu WCom WWol
	'Lady Valerie' ♀ H3-4	CElw EWes MSte NHar SMrm SPar
		WPer WWin
	'Lilac Belle' ♀ H3-4	CBcs CFox CFwr CSam ECtt EHyt
		ELan EPfP LAst LHop LRHS MBro
		MHar MHer MOak NGdn NHar
		NLon SBri SMrm SPar SPlb WFar
		WHoo WPer WWin
	'Lilac Dream'	WWin
	'Lilac Lace' (v)	NHar
	'Lilac Mist' ♀ H3-4	EVFa LPhx NDov NHar NLon NPer
		NWoo SChu SGar SPar SUsu WPen
	'Lilac Queen'	WEas
	lilacina	ESis WPer
	Little Dancer = 'Pendan'	LIck SGar SIng SMrm WGor
		WLow WWeb
	'Little Flamingo' **new**	LIck WWeb
	'Louise'	CSpe EOrc EPot GBuc NHar SMrm
	'Lucy'	EPot NHar
	'Lucy' x *mollis*	SChu SDys SUsu
	'Megavil'	EPot
	'Miro' **new**	WWol
	'Pale Face'	NHar SPar
	patens	CHll
	Pink Panther = 'Penther'	LIck WGor WWeb
	'Pink Queen'	ECtt GDra
*	'Pisces'	SChu
	purpurea	SScr
	Red Ace = 'Hecrace'PBR	CSpe EBee EOrc EPfP NPer
	Redstart = 'Hecstart'	EBee ECtt EPfP GMac LAst LHop
		MOak NCiC NFla NGdn NHar
		NPri SChu SGar SIng SPet SUsu
		WFar WLRN WWeb WWin WWol
	rigescens ♀ H3	More than 30 suppliers
§	- 'Anne Rennie'	CBri
	- pale	see *D. rigescens* 'Anne Rennie'
	- x *lilacina*	CElw SIgm
I	'Rosa' **new**	WWol
	'Ruby Field'	see *D. barberae* 'Ruby Field'
	'Rupert Lambert' ♀ H3-4	CElw CStr EMon EPot GBuc LLWP
		NDov NHar SBri SChu WPer
§	'Salmon Supreme'	CFwr EBee ECtt ELan LPhx NDov
		NGdn NHar NPer NPri SChu
		SRms WEas WFar WPer
	'Selina's Choice'	GBuc SChu
§	*stachyoides*	ELan LHop WPer
*	'Summer Delight' **new**	NBlu
	Sun Chimes Series **new**	NBlu
	'Super Salmon'	EPot
	Susan = 'Winsue'PBR	WFar
	Sydney Olympics = 'Hecsyd'	EMan NHar WPer
	tugelensis	WFar
	'Twinkle' ♀ H3-4	CPBP ECtt EDAr EPot EWes GCal
		GMac LAst NBir NGdn NHar NPer
		NPri SChu SGar SIng SMrm SPar
		SPet WEas WFar WPer WWeb WWin

*	'Twins Gully'	GCal MTed SMrm
*	*variegata* (v)	MBNS
§	*vigilis* ♀ H3	CBot CFee CMHG CSam EBre
		ECha EDAr EOrc EPfP EWTr GCal
		GMaP LPhx NBro NEgg NGdn
		NLon SAga SChu SDix SGar SIng
		SPer WCom WPer
§	- 'Jack Elliott'	CWCL MDun MWgw NDov SPla
		WCFE
	- - ex JE 8955	EBre LHop WLRN WPer
	'White Cloud'	SChu

Diascia x *Linaria* see *Nemesia caerulea*

Dicentra ✿ (*Papaveraceae*)

	'Adrian Bloom'	EBee EBlw EBre EChP ECtt EHrv
		EPla EWTr GSki LRHS MBNS
		MCLN NCat NOak NSti SCoo SDes
		SPar SPer WFar WMnd WMoo
	'Bacchanal' ♀ H4	More than 30 suppliers
	'Boothman's Variety'	see *D.* 'Stuart Boothman'
	'Bountiful'	CMHG EBee EMan EWTr GKir
		GMaP GSki LRHS MBro MLLN
		MRav NArg NFor NGdn NLon
		NSti SChu SPar SPer SPet SPla
		WMnd WRHF WWeb
	'Brownie'	GBuc MCLN NCat
	canadensis	EBee EPot GBuc MTho NSti SSpi
		WCot WCru WPnP
	'Catforth Filigree'	NCat
	'Coldham'	SMac WCru WTin
	cucullaria	More than 30 suppliers
	- 'Pittsburg'	CBos SSpi WCot
*	'Dark Stuart Boothman'	ECGN NOak
	eximia hort.	see *D. formosa*
	eximia (Ker Gawl.) Torr.	EBee MTho MWat SWat
	- 'Alba'	see *D. eximia* 'Snowdrift'
§	- 'Snowdrift'	CLAP CM&M CSpe EBee EChP
		ECtt EHrv ELan EMan EPfP EWTr
		GKir LRHS MBro MHer MRav
		MTho NGdn SDys SMrm SPar
		SRms SSpi WBar WCot WFar
		WHoo WMnd WMoo WPnP
§	*formosa*	More than 30 suppliers
§	- *alba*	CRow CTri ECha MCLN MWrn
		NBir NCot NFor NLon NOak NSti
		NVic SChu SDes SPer SPla SRPl
		SRms STes WCru WFar
*	- 'Aurora'	CBre CHid EBee EChP EMan EMar
		EWTr GBin GSki LRHS MBri
		MCCP MCLN MRav NHol SDes
		SPar WFar WMnd
	- dark	WMoo
	- 'Furse's Form'	NCat NOak WCot
	- golden-leaved	EVFa
	- subsp. *oregana*	CLAP CRow EPPr EPar GCal GKir
		NCat NChi NMen NOak SSpi
		WAbb WCru WWin
	- - 'Rosea'	EPPr NPar SSpi
	- 'Spring Gold' **new**	ECha
	'King of Hearts'	CSpe EBee EChP EMan EPPr EVFa
		GBin MBri MCLN NBro NCot NGdn
		NLar SOkh SPla WCot WCra WWol
	'Langtrees' ♀ H4	More than 30 suppliers
	'Luxuriant' ♀ H4	More than 30 suppliers
	macrantha	CBos CDes CFil CRow EBee ECha
		EPfP GBuc LAma LPhx MTho SBla
		SMad SSpi WCru WPGP
	macrocapnos	CBcs CFir CPlN CRow EBee EMan
		EPfP GBuc GQui LRHS MDKP MSPs
		MTho NABC NCot NSti SMrm WBor
		WBrE WCru WLRN WTre
	'Pearl Drops'	More than 30 suppliers

§ ***peregrina***   GTou SOkd
§ ***scandens***   CBrm CHar CMHG CMil CPiN
                                 CRHN CRow CSpe EBee EPfP GCal
                                 IFro MCCP MGrG MTho NLar SDix
                                 SGar SSpi WHil WSHC WViv WWhi
   – B&SWJ 2427   WCru
   – CC 3223   WRos
   – CC 3806   WCot
   – 'Shirley Clemo'   CPLG
   'Silversmith'   CFil
   Snowflakes = 'Fusd'   EBre EWes GKir LRHS MCCP
                                 MRav NMen WCer WViv
   spectabilis ♀ H4   More than 30 suppliers
   – 'Alba' ♀ H4   More than 30 suppliers
   – 'Gold Heart'PBR   CHad CPen EBee EHan EMan ENot
                                 EPfP GBri GKir NSti SPer WFar
   'Spring Morning'   CElw CMHG CMil CPLG CPrp
                                 CRow CSam EHrv EMon EPPr EPfP
                                 IBlr NSti SChu SSpi WEas WRHF
§ 'Stuart Boothman' ♀ H4   More than 30 suppliers
   thalictrifolia   see *D. scandens*

Dichelostemma (Alliaceae)

§ ***capitatum***   ETow
   – NNS 95-213   WCot
   congestum   CAvo CPen EBee EMan EPot ERos
                                 LRHS WCot
   – NNS 97-75   SIgm
§ ***ida-maia***   CAvo CBro CStu EBee EPot ETub
                                 LRHS WPrP
   – 'Pink Diamond'   CAvo CBro EBee EPot ETub
   pulchellum   see *D. capitatum*
   volubile NNS 95-220   WCot

Dichocarpum (Ranunculaceae)

   dalzielii new   EBee

Dichondra (Convolvulaceae)

   micrantha new   EShb

Dichotomanthes (Rosaceae)

   tristanticarpa   CFil

Dichroa (Hydrangeaceae)

   febrifuga   CAbb CBcs CDoC CEnd CFil CHll
                                 CKob CMil CPLG CWib EMan
                                 EWes GBri GQui LRHS SBrw SLon
                                 SOWG WCot WCru WOVN
                                 WPGP
   – B&SWJ 2367   WCru
   – pink   CHEx
   versicolor B&SWJ 6565   WCru

Dichromena see *Rhynchospora*

Dicksonia ✿ (Dicksoniaceae)

   antarctica ♀ H3   More than 30 suppliers
   fibrosa ♀ H3   CAbb CBcs CBrP CTrC EAmu
                                 EBee EBot EPVP LJus LPan NPSI
                                 SPar WMul WRic
   sellowiana   LPal WMul WRic
   squarrosa ♀ H2   CAbb CBcs CBrP CHEx CTrC EBee
                                 EBot EPVP ERea LJus LPan NMoo
                                 NPSI SAPC SArc SPar WMul WRic
   youngiae   WMul WRic

Dicliptera (Acanthaceae)

§ ***suberecta***   CBcs CHal CHll EHol EMan ERea
                                 LHop MOak SAga SIgm SOWG
                                 SRkn SUsu WDyG

Dicranostigma (Papaveraceae)

   lactucoides   WLin

Dictamnus ✿ (Rutaceae)

   albus   CArn CAvo CBcs EBlw EBre ECha
                                 EFou EHrv ELan EMon EPfP ERou
                                 GCal LHop LPhx LRHS MBri MCAu
                                 MRav NBlu NSti SChu SDes SPer
                                 WCom WCot WHoo WLin WWye
§ – var. ***purpureus*** ♀ H4   More than 30 suppliers
   caucasicus   EBee
   fraxinella   see *D. albus* var. *purpureus*

Dictyosperma (Arecaceae)

   album   CRoM LPal

Didymochlaena (Dryopteridaceae)

   lunulata   see *D. truncatula*
§ ***truncatula***   CHal MBri

Dieffenbachia (Araceae)

   'Camille' (v) ♀ H1   LRHS
   'Compacta' (v)   LRHS

Dierama ✿ (Iridaceae)

   CD&R 192   CRow
   from Lesotho   SUsu
   ambiguum   ECGN SHFr
   argyreum   CFil CPla EBee IBlr WSan
   – JCA 3.140.400   CMil
   'Ariel'   IBlr
   'Black Knight'   IBlr
   'Blush'   IBlr
   'Candy Stripe'   CPla CRow EWTr GBri GSki
                                 MCCP SMad STes
   cooperi   CPrp GBri IBlr
   – 'Edinburgh White'   LCTD
   'Donald Legacy'   GBri IBlr WHil
§ ***dracomontanum***   More than 30 suppliers
   – dwarf lilac   CM&M GCal
   – dwarf pale pink   CM&M GCal
   dubium   IBlr
   – x ***robustum***   EBee
   ensifolium   see *D. pendulum*
   erectum   CLAP EBee IBlr WCot
   floriferum   CBro IBlr
   galpinii   CLAP CPla GSki STes WHil
   grandiflorum   IBlr
   'Guinevere' new   CBgR CFai EHrv EMan EVFa NBir
                                 NCat NCot NSti SOkh SPla WAbe
                                 WCot WElm
   igneum   More than 30 suppliers
   – CD&R 278   CPou CRDP
   'Iris' new   IBlr
   jucundum   GBri GBuc MLLN
   'Knee high Lavender'   CSpe
   latifolium   ECGN EChP GSki IBlr MWrn
                                 SIgm SMad WCot WPrP WSan
   luteoalbidum   CDes CLAP CStu EBee WPGP
   'Mandarin'   IBlr
   medium   CFil CMil EBee GSki LPio SMrm SUsu
                                 SWat WAbe WCot WOBN WPGP
   'Merlin' new   CBgR CFai CSpe EBlw EChP EHrv
                                 EMan EVFa MSph NBir NCat NCot
                                 NSti SOkh SPla WAbe WCot WElm
   'Milkmaid'   IBlr
   mossii   EBee IBlr
   nixonianum new   IBlr
   'Pamina'   IBlr
   'Papagena'   IBlr
   'Papageno'   IBlr
   pauciflorum   More than 30 suppliers
   – CD&R 197   CPBP
   – JCA 3.143.500   SMad
§ ***pendulum***   More than 30 suppliers

'Pretty Flamingo'	IBlr
'Puck'	CDes GCal IBlr IGor MLLN
pulcherrimum	More than 30 suppliers
– var. *album*	CAbb CHar COlW EBee ECGN
	ECha ELan EVFa GBuc GDrg GSki
	LCTD LHop LPio MAnH MAvo
	MGrG MNrw MWrn SHar STes
	SUsu SWal WHrl WWhi
– 'Angel Gabriel'	WWpP
– 'Blackbird'	CM&M EBee EMan EPfP EPla GSki
	IBlr LPio MAnH MAvo MCCP MTis
	MWhi MWrn NLar NPPs NVic STes
	SUsu WBVN WPGP
– brick red **new**	WHil
– dwarf	GCal GSki LHop WWhi
– lilac	LHop
– 'Pearly Queen'	CRow
– 'Peregrine'	WPGP WRHF
– Slieve Donard hybrids	CFwr CSam EBre ECGN EChP
	EFou EMan GBri GCal ITim LHop
	LRHS MAnH MHer MTis MWrn
	STes WCot WHrl WPnP WRHF
	WSan
pumilum hort.	see *D. dracomontanum*
'Queen of the Night'	IBlr
reynoldsii	CAbb CMil CPla EBee EMan EVFa
	GCal GSki IBlr LCTD MAnH
	MCCP MWrn NPPs SPlb STes
	WCot WPrP
robustum	CFil CPou GBri IBlr WAbe WBVN
– SH 20	CPLG
'Sarastro'	IBlr
'September Charm'	IBlr
sertum	CBro
'Snowballs' **new**	CWCL
'Tamino'	IBlr
'Titania'	IBlr ITim
trichorhizum	CHar CLAP CPla EVFa GBri GSki
	IBlr LCTD MWrn STes WElm
	WHil
'Tubular Bells'	IBlr
'Violet Ice'	IBlr
'Westminster Chimes'	CDes IBlr

Diervilla ✿ (*Caprifoliaceae*)

lonicera	CHar SMac WFar
middendorffiana	see *Weigela middendorffiana*
rivularis	CPle
§ *sessilifolia*	CBcs CHar CPle CSpe EBee EPar
	EPfP IMGH MRav SGar SLon SPar
	WBod WCFE WCot WFar WRus
	WSHC WWin WWpP
– 'Butterfly'	GKir LRHS
x *splendens*	CMHG CPle CWib EBee EHoe
	ELan EPfP GEil LAst LHop LRHS
	MBNS MBar MRav MTis NHol SBrw
	SGar SLPl SPar SPer SSta WDin

Dietes (*Iridaceae*)

bicolor	CAbb CHEx EMan ERea LBow
	LEdu LPio
grandiflora	CAbb CArn CFee CFwr CPne
	EBee EDif EMan ERea ITer LEdu
	LPio LRHS SMrm WAbe WWye
* – 'Reen Lelie'	CMdw
§ *iridioides*	CNic CSWP CTCP EBee GBin
	LEdu LRHS MSte WPer

Digitalis ✿ (*Scrophulariaceae*)

ambigua	see *D. grandiflora*
apricot hybrids	see *D. purpurea* 'Sutton's Apricot'
'Callisto' **new**	LEur
cariensis	EBla WBry

ciliata	CFir EBee EChP ELan MLLN NOak
	SBla WBry WCom WCot
cream hybrids	EFou
davisiana	CBot CBri CPLG EBee EBla EChP
	GBuc MCAu MLwd MWod NLar
	NOak STes WCHb WMoo WPer
	WViv
dubia	CBot CSpe CWes EBee EBla EPfP
	EWTr MBri NBir NLar WAbe
	WCom
– 'Silver Anniversary' **new**	WWeb
– 'Elsie Kelsey' **new**	CFwr ITer MDKP
eriostachya	see *D. lutea*
ferruginea ♀ H4	More than 30 suppliers
– 'Gelber Herold'	CBel CBot CBri EMan EPfP ERou
	GMaP LPhx LRHS MSPs MSte
	NLar WGor WLin WWeb
– 'Gigantea'	CBot CPou EBee ECGN EChP
	EMan ERou GCal LRHS MBNS
	MTis NNor NPri NSti SSte SWat
– var. *schischkinii*	CDes EBee EBla EWTr GCal
	MCAu MLwd NLar
ferruginea x	EBlw
grandiflora	
'Flashing Spires'	see *D. lutea* 'Flashing Spires'
* *floribunda*	EBee
fontanesii	EBee EChP GBuc GMac MLwd
	NBur WLin
x *fulva*	MLLN NBir
'Glory of Roundway'	CBot CDes EBee LEur MHer SWat
	WBro WFar WPGP WSan
§ *grandiflora* ♀ H4	More than 30 suppliers
– MESE 359	EBee
– MESE 407	EBee
– 'Carillon'	EBee EChP EMan EMar LDai LPVe
	LPhx MBNS MSte NLar NPri NPro
	WBro WGor WHil WPer
– 'Temple Bells'	EBla ECoo EMar MWrn SAga SWat
	WBry WPer
heywoodii	see *D. purpurea* subsp.
	heywoodii
'John Innes Tetra'	CSam EChP ECoo LEur LRHS
	MBNS NChi SGar STes SWal SWat
	WBry WGor WPGP WPer WWin
kishinskyi	see *D. parviflora*
laevigata	CBot CBri CHad CSam CWCL
	EBee EBla ECGN EChP EDAr
	EMan ERou EWTr LHrt LPhx
	LRHS MLwd MSte NBro NSti SIgm
	SIng SSte WCHb WHer WPer
	WWeb
– subsp. *graeca*	CMdw EBee WGor
– subsp. *laevigata*	LEur
lamarckii hort.	see *D. lanata*
lamarckii Ivanina	EBee SIgm WPer
§ *lanata*	More than 30 suppliers
leucophaea	EGoo EMar
'Loxley Manor' **new**	WRHF
§ *lutea*	More than 30 suppliers
§ – subsp. *australis*	EBla LDai SHFr WBry
– Brickell's form	EVFa WRHF
§ – 'Flashing Spires' (v)	CPla EChP EMan EVFa EWTr GBri
	SSte WBar WBry WHer
– 'Yellow Medley'	WCot
x *media*	ECGN
x *mertonensis* ♀ H4	More than 30 suppliers
– 'Summer King'	ECtt WCot
micrantha	see *D. lutea* subsp. *australis*
'Molten Ore'	ESis
nervosa	EBla
obscura	CBot CFir EBee EBla EBlw EHrv
	EMan EPPr ERou GEil LAst LRHS
	MCAu MLwd NOak NPri SBla

		SIgm SSpi WCHb WCot WGor WHer WMnd WPer WWeb
§	*orientalis*	see *D. grandiflora*
	parviflora	More than 30 suppliers
	'Purple Dwarf' **new**	WWeb
	purpurea	CArn CKin EBlw EBre ECtt EDAr EFou ELau ENot EWTr GPoy LHrt MBow MHer NArg NFor NLan NMir NPri SIde SPlb WMoo WPer WWye
	- f. *albiflora*	More than 30 suppliers
	- - unspotted	EMar
*	- 'Campanulata Alba'	MHer
	- 'Chedglow' (v)	CNat WCHb
	- dwarf red	MBNS WGor
	- Excelsior Group	CBcs CBot CCge COlW CSBt CTri EBre EMan ENot EPfP ERou GMaP MBow MBri MWat NBlu NMir NVic SDes SMer SPer SRms WGor
	- - primrose	ERou SPer
	- - (Suttons; Unwins) ♀ H4	CBrm MRav
	- - white	ERou
	- Foxy Group	CBot CWib EHrv EMar GKir MBNS MPWC MRav SPet SRms WHen WPer WSan
	- - 'Foxy Apricot' **new**	NSti
	- - 'Foxy Primrose' **new**	MPWC
	- pink **new**	EMan NSti SPla SSpi
	- Giant Spotted Group	CBot COtt CSam EBlw EChP ECoo ECtt EHrv EPfP EVFa GKir LHop LRHS MWrn SCoo WHil WPer
	- - purple	CWCL
	- Glittering Prizes Group	LRHS SWat WBry
	- Gloxinioides Group	EBee EChP ELan ENot EPfP MBow SHFr WCot
	- - 'Isabellina'	CBot WPer
	- - 'The Shirley' ♀ H4	ECtt SGar WBry WGor
*	- *heptandra* **new**	CNat
§	- subsp. *heywoodii*	CBot CSam CSpe EBee ELan EMan ENot GBuc LEur LHrt NPPs WCHb WPer WWin
	- - 'Pink Champagne' **new**	SSvw
	- subsp. *mariana*	EBee
	- subsp. *nevadensis*	CBot
	- 'Pam's Choice'	CHad CSpe
	- peloric	WCHb
	- 'Primrose Carousel'	ECoo ERou MGGn MWrn SSvw WBry WGwG WHHs
	- 'Snow Thimbles' **new**	CFwr
§	- 'Sutton's Apricot' ♀ H4	More than 30 suppliers
*	- 'Sutton's Giant Primrose'	CBot EChP EMan EWTr EWll WBry
	- 'Tinkerbell' **new**	MDKP
	- 'Torpedo Cream' **new**	WHil
	- 'Torpedo Lilac Rose'	WHil
	'Saltwood Summer' **new**	COtt MBri WWeb
	sibirica	EBee EChP GBuc GMac IIve LPhx MLwd WCHb WPer
*	*spaniflora* **new**	EChP LPhx MCAu
*	*stewartii*	CHar EBee EChP ELan EMan EWes GIBF LDai MBNS MCAu MDKP MSPs NBur SBod SPoG WBry WLin WPrP
	thapsi	CBot CBri CHar EBla EBlw ECtt EDAr EMan EMlt MLLN MLwd MSPs NBur NPri SBod SMrm WCHb WFTG WPer
	- JCA 410.000	EBee
	trojana	EBee ECGN GBuc LRHS MLLN MWod SGar WPer WWin
*	*tuberosa*	CBri

viridiflora	EBee EBla EBlw ECtt EDAr EWTr LEur MBNS MDKP MHer MLwd MWhi NBro SGar WCHb WFar WHer WPer WWin

dill see *Anethum graveolens*

Dionaea (Droseraceae)

muscipula	CSWC LRHS NABC
- 'Royal Red'	CSWC

Dionysia (Primulaceae)

afghanica **new**	EHyt
'Annielle'	EHyt EPot
archibaldii	EHyt
aretioides ♀ H2	WOBN
- 'Gravetye'	ECho
- 'Paul Furse'	EHyt
- 'Phyllis Carter'	ECho
- 'Susan Hale'	EHyt
- 'Susan Tucker'	EHyt
aretioides × *freitagii*	EHyt
'Charlson Drew' **new**	EHyt
'Charlson Gem'	EHyt
'Charlson Jake'	EHyt
'Charlson Petite'	EHyt
'Charlson Stuart' **new**	EHyt
'Charlson Thomas'	EHyt
curviflora	EHyt EPot
- × *tapetodes*	EHyt WOBN
'Emmely'	EHyt
'Eric Watson'	EHyt
'Ewesley Epsilon'	EHyt
'Ewesley Gamma' **new**	EHyt
'Ewesley Iota'	EHyt
'Ewesley Kappa'	EHyt
'Ewesley Mu'	EHyt
'Ewesley Theta'	EHyt
'Francesca'	EHyt
freitagii **new**	EHyt
- × *viscidula* MK 91-1	EHyt
'Ina'	EHyt
involucrata white **new**	CGra
janthina	EHyt
lamingtonii	EHyt
- H 1909-1	EHyt
'Markus'	EHyt EPot
michauxii	EHyt
'Monika' MH 8809/1	EHyt EPot
'Nan Watson'	EHyt
'Nocturne' **new**	EHyt
'Rhapsodic' **new**	EHyt
'Schneeball'	EHyt
tapetodes 'Brimstone'	EHyt
- farinose	ECho
- 'Peter Edwards'	EHyt EPot
- 'Sulphur'	EHyt

Dioon (Zamiaceae)

edule ♀ H1	CBrP CRoM LPal
- var. *angustifolium*	CBrP
mejiae	CBrP LPal NRog
merolae	CBrP
rzedowskii	CBrP LPal
spinulosum	CBrP EAmu LPal NRog

Dioscorea (Dioscoreaceae)

	batatas	CPlN IIve LEdu MSal WCru
	japonica	ITer WBVN
*	- 'Variegata' (v)	ITer
	nipponica	EBee IIve MSal
	quinqueloba	WCru
	villosa	CArn MSal

Diosma (*Rutaceae*)

ericoides	LBuc SPar
- 'Pink Fountain'	CWSG
- 'Sunset Gold'	CWib LBuc SBrw SCoo

Diosphaera (*Campanulaceae*)

asperuloides	see *Trachelium asperuloides*

Diospyros (*Ebenaceae*)

duclouxii	CFil SSpi
kaki (F)	CBcs CLnd CMCN EPfP ERom
	SSpi WCot WDin
- 'Kostata' **new**	CGOG
- 'Rojo Brillante' **new**	CGOG
lotus	CAgr CFil CLnd CMCN CTho
	ECre LPan SSpi WFar WPGP
ramulosa **new**	SPlb
rhombifolia	CFil WPGP
virginiana (F)	CAgr CBcs CMCN CTho EPfP
	SSpi

Dipelta (*Caprifoliaceae*)

floribunda ♀ H4	CBot CBrm CFil CMCN CPMA
	EBee EMil EPfP GKir LRHS MBlu
	SBrw SLon SSpi WBod WPGP WTel
ventricosa	CFil CPMA CPle EPfP GKir LRHS
	MBlu SLon SSpi WFar WPGP
yunnanensis	CFil CPMA CTri EMil EPfP LRHS
	NLar SBrw SSpi SSta WPGP WWes

Diphylleia (*Berberidaceae*)

cymosa	CRDP EBee ECha EMan EPar LEur
	LPhx MSal SSpi WCot WCru
grayi	EBee WCru
sinensis	EBee LEur WCru

Dipidax see *Onixotis*

Diplacus see *Mimulus*

Dipladenia see *Mandevilla*

Diplarrhena (*Iridaceae*)

Helen Dillon's form	EMan SUsu
§ latifolia	CFil CHar EMan GGar LBee WAbe
	WCot
moraea	CBrm CDes CFil CHid CPLG EBee
	EGle EMan GAbr GCal GSki IBlr
	ILis ITim LPio LRHS SPar SSpi
	WAbe WBrE WCot WHal WLin
	WPGP WSHC WWin
- 'Slieve Donard'	CLAP CRDP
- West Coast form	see *D. latifolia*

Diplazium (*Woodsiaceae*)

caudatum	WRic

Diplolaena (*Rutaceae*)

dampieri	SOWG

Diplotaxis (*Brassicaceae*)

muralis	CArn WJek

Dipogon (*Papilionaceae*)

§ lignosus	CPIN

Dipsacus ✿ (*Dipsacaceae*)

asper	EBee
§ fullonum	CArn CKin GBar IKee LHrt MBow
	MChe MHer NBid NBro NMir NVic
	SIde SYvo WBea WCer WHer WWye
- subsp. *fullonum*	CPrp WJek

inermis	EBee ECha EMon GBar NBid WFar
	WHer
japonicus **new**	EBee MSal
laciniatus	WMoo
pilosus	CKin EBee
sativus	NCWG WHer
sylvestris	see *D. fullonum*

Dipteracanthus see *Ruellia*

Dipteronia (*Aceraceae*)

sinensis	CFil CMCN LRHS NLar SSpi WNor
	WPGP

Disanthus (*Hamamelidaceae*)

cercidifolius ♀ H4	CAbP EPfP GKir IMGH LRHS
	MAsh MBlu MGos NLar SPer SReu
	SSpi SSta WBod

Discaria (*Rhamnaceae*)

chacaye	CFil LEdu WPGP

Diselma (*Cupressaceae*)

archeri	CDoC CKen CNic LCon MBar SCoo

Disphyma (*Aizoaceae*)

crassifolium	SChr

Disporopsis (*Convallariaceae*)

B&SWJ 3891	EBee LEur WCru
from Philippines	
arisanensis	CDes LEdu LEur WFar
- B&SWJ 1490	EBee WCru WFar
* aspera	EBee LEur WCru
fuscopicta **new**	EBee EHrv EPPr LEur WCru WTin
longifolia B&SWJ 5284	WCru
§ pernyi	CBct CElw CHid CLAP CRDP
	EBee EBre EHrv EMon EPPr EPar
	EPla LEur LPhx MDun MGrG
	MSte NHar SCro SDes SOkd SSpi
	SUsu WCot WCru WFar WHal

Disporum (*Convallariaceae*)

bodinieri	CDes EBee LEur
cantoniense	CDes EBee LEur WCru
- B&L 12512	CLAP SBla
- B&SWJ 1424	WCru
- DJHC 98485	CDes
- var. *cantoniense* f.	EBee WCru
brunneum	
B&SWJ 5290	
- var. *kawakamii*	WCru
B&SWJ 350	
flavens	CBct CDes CFil CRDP CStu EBee
	EBre EMan EPPr EPar EPfP GKir
	LEur LPhx MDun SBla SOkh SSpi
	SUsu WFTG WFar WPGP WSHC
- B&SWJ 872	WCru
* flavum	SOkd
hookeri	EPar GKir NLar NMen WCot WCru
- var. *oreganum*	CBro GCrs GTou IBlr WCru
lanuginosum	CBro EBee GCrs WCot WCru
leucanthum **new**	SMHy
- B&SWJ 2389	WCru
lutescens	LEur WCru
maculatum	CLAP CRDP EPar LPhx SMac WCru
megalanthum	EBee LEur SSpi WCru
- CD&R 2412b	EPPr
nantauense B&SWJ 359	CBct EBee WCot WCru
sessile	EBee EWTr LEur WCru
I - 'Aureovariegatum' (v)	WCru
I - 'Robustum	EBee
Variegatum' **new**	

- 'Variegatum' (v)   More than 30 suppliers
- var. *yakushimense*   WCru
  shimadae B&SWJ 399   WCru
  smilacinum   EBee EPar LEur WCru
- B&SWJ 713   WCru
*   - 'Aureovariegatum' (v)   WCot WCru
- 'Choyo' **new**   WCru
- double **new**   WCru
- pink   WCru
  smithii   CFil CRDP CStu EBee EPar EPot
    ERos GBuc GCrs GKir ITim LEur
    NBir NGar NHar NLar NMen
    WCot WCru WPGP
  taiwanense B&SWJ 1513 LEur WCru
  uniflorum   WCru
- B&SWJ 651   LEur WCot WCru
  viridescens   EBee WCru
- B&SWJ 4598   WCru

Distictis (Bignoniaceae)
  buccinatoria   CPIN
  'Mrs Rivers'   CPIN

Distylium (Hamamelidaceae)
  myricoides   CFil CMCN EPfP WFar
  racemosum   CBcs CFil EBee EPfP GSki IDee
    LRHS MBlu SBrw SHBN SMur SReu
    SSta WBVN WBcn WFar WSHC

Diuranthera see *Chlorophytum*

Dizygotheca see *Schefflera*

Dobinea (Podoaceae)
  vulgaris B&SWJ 2577   WCru

Dodecatheon ✿ (Primulaceae)
  alpinum   EBee NHar NLAp NRya SRms WViv
- JCA 11744   SBla
- subsp. *majus* **new**   NSla
  amethystinum   see *D. pulchellum*
  'Aphrodite' **new**   CMGP
  austrofrigidum **new**   GKev
  clevelandii   ETow
- subsp. *insulare*   EBee LRHS NWCA
- subsp. *patulum*   LRHS
  conjugens   EBee
  cusickii   see *D. pulchellum* subsp. *cusickii*
  dentatum ♀ H4   CElw CPBP CPLG EPar GBuc
    LRHS MDKP MTho NMen WAbe
    WFar
- subsp. *ellisiae*   GCrs
- - M&PS 97/028   NMen
  frigidum   WAbe
§   *hendersonii* ♀ H4   CBro EBee EPar EPot GBuc GKir
    NSla SRms
  integrifolium   see *D. hendersonii*
§   *jeffreyi*   CFwr EBee EBlw GSki LRHS NDlv
    NHar NMen NWCA SBla WAbe
- 'Rotlicht'   NHar SRms WPer
*   x *lemoinei*   WAbe
§   *meadia* ♀ H4   More than 30 suppliers
- f. *album* ♀ H4   CBcs CBro CSWP CStu EBee EBlw
    EBot EChP EGle ELan EOrc EPar
    EPfP GSki LAma LHop LRHS
    MLLN MTho NHol NMen SPer
    SRms WFTG WLin WPnP WPrP
- 'Aphrodite' **new**   EChP
- from Cedar County   WAbe
*   - 'Goliath'   GSki
- membranaceous   WAbe
- Millard's clone   EPar
- 'Queen Victoria'   CFwr EBee GSki WBro WFar WPnP

  pauciflorum hort.   see *D. pulchellum*
  pauciflorum (Dur.)   see *D. meadia*
    E.Greene
  poeticum   ETow MDKP
§   *pulchellum* ♀ H4   CBro EBee EHyt EPar GCrs GDra
    GKev GSki LHop LRHS MNrw
    NHar NMen NRya NWCA SIng
§   - subsp. *cusickii*   LRHS NWCA SRms
- subsp. *pulchellum*   CFwr CMea EBee EBre GDra MBri
    'Red Wings'   WHoo
- *radicatum*   see *D. pulchellum*
- 'Sooke's Variety'   CStu SCnR WAbe
  radicatum   see *D. pulchellum*
  redolens   EBee EHyt WAbe
  tetrandrum   see *D. jeffreyi*

Dodonaea (Sapindaceae)
  viscosa   CArn CHEx CTrC ECou SPlb
- (f) **new**   ECou
- (m) **new**   ECou
- 'Picton' (f) **new**   ECou
- 'Purpurea'   CAbb CBcs CBrm CDoC CTrC
    ECou ERea EShb GBri
- 'Purpurea' (f) **new**   ECou
- 'Purpurea' (m) **new**   ECou
- 'Red Wings' (f) **new**   ECou

Doellingeria (Asteraceae)
  scabra   see *Aster scaber*

Dolichos (Papilionaceae)
  lignosus   see *Dipogon lignosus*

Dombeya (Sterculiaceae)
  burgessiae   LRHS SOWG

Dondia see *Hacquetia*

Doodia (Blechnaceae)
  aspera   GQui NMar
§   *caudata*   NMar WRic
  heterophylla   NMar
  media   GQui NMar WRic
  mollis   NMar
I   'Sonter's Linearis'   WRic
  squarrosa   see *D. caudata*

Doronicum ✿ (Asteraceae)
  austriacum   MCAu NBid WCot
  carpetanum   CSam
  caucasicum   see *D. orientale*
§   *columnae*   GDra NMen
  cordatum   see *D. columnae*
§   x *excelsum* 'Harpur   EBee ERou MCAu MCLN MRav
    Crewe'   NPer NVic WEas
  'Finesse'   EBee EPfP LAst LRHS NOak SRms
    WCot WMoo
§   'Frühlingspracht' (d)   CRDP GDra MInt SPer WEas
  glaciale **new**   NMen
  grandiflorum   EBee
  'Little Leo'   COIW EBee EMan ERou EShb
    LHop LRav MBri MHer NEgg
    NJOw NLar NPri SPet WAul
    WBVN WBrE WHil WPnP WWeb
  'Miss Mason' ♀ H4   LRHS MBNS MBri
§   *orientale*   CBri CPrp EChP EMar ENot EPfP
    LRHS MOne NBid NBlu NCiC
    NFla NJOw SDes STes SWat
    WWpP
- 'Goldcut'   LPVe NGdn
- 'Magnificum'   More than 30 suppliers
  pardalianches   CMea ECha GGar IHMH NSco
    WCot WRHF

- 'Goldstrauss' EBee
plantagineum see *D.* x *excelsum* 'Harpur Crewe'
'Excelsum'
'Riedels Goldkranz' LRHS MBct MBri MWhi
Spring Beauty see *D.* 'Frühlingspracht'

Doryanthes (*Doryanthaceae*)
excelsa CTrC

Dorycnium see *Lotus*

Doryopteris (*Adiantaceae*)
pedata MBri

Douglasia see *Androsace*
vitaliana see *Vitaliana primuliflora*

Dovyalis (*Flacourtiaceae*)
caffra (F) NBlo XBlo

Doxantha see *Macfadyena*

Draba (*Brassicaceae*)
acaulis EHyt
aizoides EBre ECha ELan EMlt GDra GKir
LRHS MHer MOne MWat SIng
SPlb SRms WWin
aizoon see *D. lasiocarpa*
bertolonii Boiss. see *D. loeseleurii*
bruniifolia CGra EBre EBur EWes LRHS
MTho NLAp NWCA
bryoides see *D. rigida* var. *bryoides*
compacta see *D. lasiocarpa* Compacta
Group
cretica NMen
cusickii CPBP
cuspidata CNic
dedeana ECho EHyt EWes WLin
densifolia EHyt
§ ***glabella*** NLAp
hispanica NMen
imbricata see *D. rigida* var. *imbricata*
§ ***incana*** MOne
§ ***lasiocarpa*** CPBP MPWC NArg NJOw
- Compacta Group CNic ECho NRya NWCA
lemmonii **new** CGra
§ ***loeseleurii*** MMHG SCro
longisiliqua ♀ H2 EHyt ETow NLAp SIng
- EMR 2551 EPot
mollissima EHyt EPot GTou NWCA
nivalis **new** SScr
oligosperma NWCA
- subsp. ***subsessilis*** WLin
ossetica EHyt WLin
paysonii var. ***treleasei*** WAbe WLin
polytricha CGra EHyt GTou WLin
repens see *D. sibirica*
rigida MOne MTho NRya
§ - var. ***bryoides*** EHyt NLAp NWCA SOkd WAbe
§ - var. ***imbricata*** EHyt
- - f. ***compacta*** EPot
rosularis CGra EHyt
sakuraii EDAr
scardica see *D. lasiocarpa*
§ ***sibirica*** CNic
ussuriensis WPer
ventosa GTou WAbe
yunnanensis WLin

Dracaena ✿ (*Dracaenaceae*)
congesta see *Cordyline stricta*
draco ♀ H1 CArn CTrC
fragrans MBri

- (Compacta Group) MBri
'Compacta Purpurea'
- - 'Compacta MBri
Variegata' (v)
- (Deremensis Group) LRHS MBri
'Lemon Lime'
(v) ♀ H1
- - 'Warneckei' MBri
(v) ♀ H1
- - 'Yellow Stripe' MBri
(v) ♀ H1
* - ***glauca*** MBri
- 'Janet Craig' MBri
- 'Massangeana' MBri
(v) ♀ H1
indivisa see *Cordyline indivisa*
marginata (v) ♀ H1 LRHS MBri
- 'Colorama' (v) MBri SMur
sanderiana (v) ♀ H1 LRHS MBri
* ***schrijveriana*** MBri
steudneri MBri
stricta see *Cordyline stricta*

Dracocephalum (*Lamiaceae*)
altaiense see *D. imberbe*
argunense CPBP CPlt CRDP EBee EPot GEdr
GKir LBee LPhx LRHS MBro MWrn
SAga SBla SCro SGar SRms SRot
SUsu WCru WOut WPat WPer WWin
* - 'Album' EBee SAga
- 'Fuji Blue' CFwr MWrn NLar
- 'Fuji White' **new** LPhx MWrn SIng WWeb
austriacum SSvw
botryoides CPBP EMan GSki MWrn NWCA
WPer
bullatum EBee
'Eminence Grise' **new** SUsu
forrestii EPot ESis NLAp SBla
grandiflorum CMea CRDP EChP ESis GDra
GEdr GSki LPhx LTwo NLar SAga
WFar WMoo WWeb
hemsleyanum EBee MBro WPat
heterophyllum EBee
§ ***imberbe*** MLLN WLin
isabellae GEil NLar WLin
moldavica SIde
nutans EBee MWrn NLar SLon
oblongifolium EBee
palmatum EBee IIve
peregrinum SGar
prattii see *Nepeta prattii*
rupestre CFwr EPPr MBri MBro
ruyschianum CFwr EMan GDra GEdr LPhx
LRHS MLLN MRav MWrn NFla
NLar NWCA WPat WWeb
sibiricum see *Nepeta sibirica*
tanguticum NLar
* ***tataricum*** **new** EBee
virginicum see *Physostegia virginiana*
wendelboi GEdr MLLN NBir NWCA WPat
WPer WWin

Dracophyllum (*Epacridaceae*)
pronum ITim
prostratum **new** GDra

Dracunculus (*Araceae*)
canariensis ITer LEur WCot
muscivorus see *Helicodiceros muscivorus*
§ ***vulgaris*** CHid CLAP CPom CTCP EBee
EBot EMon EPar EPot ETub ITer
LEdu LRHS MCCP MRav SDix
SEND SMad WCot WCru WPnP

- var. *creticus* JCA   WCot
  0.424.126

Draperia (Hydrophyllaceae)
systyla <u>new</u>   NWCA

Dregea (Asclepiadaceae)
§   *sinensis*   CBcs CBot CHEx CPIN CSam
     ELan EPfP ERea EWes GQui LRHS
     SBra SOWG WCot WCru WFar
     WPGP WSHC WWeb
- 'Variegata' (v)   WCot

Drepanocladus (Amblystegiaceae)
revolvens   EMFW

Drepanostachyum (Poaceae)
§   *falcatum*   CAbb CTrC LJus MGos WJun
   falconeri hort.   see *Himalayacalamus falconeri*
   hookerianum   see *Himalayacalamus
     hookerianum*
§   *khasianum*   CFil CPLG EBee WPGP
§   *microphyllum*   SDry WJun

Drimiopsis (Hyacinthaceae)
maculata   CStu WCot

Drimys (Winteraceae)
   aromatica   see *D. lanceolata*
   colorata   see *Pseudowintera colorata*
   granatensis   CFil WPGP
§   *lanceolata*   More than 30 suppliers
   - (f)   ECou GEil GGar SPer
   - (m)   CDoC ECou GGar
     L 1737   CFil
   - 'Mount Wellington'   GCal
*   *latifolia* <u>new</u>   CHEx
   winteri ♀ H4   More than 30 suppliers
   - var. *andina*   CFil EBee EPfP EPla GGGa SSpi
     WPGP
§   - var. *chilensis*   CFil CHEx CPLG EBee ISea MAsh
     SSpi WBod WCru WPGP
   - Latifolia Group   see *D. winteri* var. *chilensis*

Drosanthemum (Aizoaceae)
   floribundum   CHEx
   hispidum   CHEx EBre ECtt EDAr ELan EMlt
     EPfP EPot ITim LRHS MBro MTho
     NMen NWCA SIng WBea WPat

Drosera (Droseraceae)
   admirabilis   LHew
   aliciae   CSWC SHmp
   andersoniana   EFEx
   androsacea   LHew
   binata   GTro SHmp
§   - subsp. *dichotoma*   CSWC
   - 'Multifida'   GTro
   browniana   EFEx
   bulbigena   EFEx
   bulbosa subsp. *bulbosa* EFEx
   - subsp. *major*   EFEx
   callistos   LHew
   capensis   GTro LRHS NABC SHmp
   - 'Albino'   GTro
   dichotoma   see *D. binata* subsp. *dichotoma*
   dichrosepala   LHew
   erythrorhiza   EFEx
   - subsp. *collina*   EFEx
   - subsp. *erythrorhiza* EFEx LHew
   - subsp. *magna*   EFEx
   - subsp. *squamosa*   EFEx
   gigantea   EFEx

   graniticola   EFEx
   heterophylla   EFEx
   loureirii   EFEx
   macrantha   EFEx
   - subsp. *macrantha*   EFEx
   - subsp. *planchonii*   NEgg
   macrophylla subsp.   EFEx
     macrophylla
   marchantii subsp.   EFEx
     prophylla
   menziesii subsp.   EFEx
     basifolia
   - subsp. *menziesii*   EFEx
   - subsp. *thysanosepala* EFEx
   modesta   EFEx
   orbiculata   EFEx
   peltata   CSWC EFEx
   platypoda   EFEx
   ramellosa   EFEx
   rosulata   EFEx
   rotundifolia   SHmp
   salina   EFEx
   scorpioides   CSWC
   sewelliae   LHew
   slackii   LHew
   stelliflora   LHew
   stolonifera subsp.   EFEx
     compacta
   - subsp. *humilis*   EFEx
   - subsp. *porrecta*   EFEx
   - subsp. *rupicola*   EFEx
   - subsp. *stolonifera*   EFEx
   tubaestylus   EFEx
   zonaria   EFEx

Drosophyllum (Droseraceae)
   lusitanicum   LHew

Dryandra (Proteaceae)
   formosa   SPlb
   praemorsa   CTrC

Dryas (Rosaceae)
   drummondii   EPot SBla WAbe
*   - 'Grandiflora   NHar
     E.B. Anderson'
§   *integrifolia*   CMea CNic EPot GDra IMGH
     NHar NMGW NMen
   - 'Greenland Green'   WAbe
   octopetala ♀ H4   CLyd EDAr EPfP GDra GIBF GKir
     GTou IMGH LHop MWat NChi
     NFor NHar NLAp NLon NRya
     NVic SBla SIng SRms WAbe WCFE
     WCom WCot WHoo WWin
   - 'Harry Bush'   NHar
   - var. *lanata* <u>new</u>   GIBF
   - 'Minor' ♀ H4   CLyd EDAr LBee LRHS NMen
     NWCA NWoo WAbe
x *suendermannii* ♀ H4   CMHG EBre EHol EPfP EPot
     GKir GMaP GTou LRHS MBro
     MCCP NLAp NMen NWCA SMrm
     WAbe
   tenella Pursh   see *D. integrifolia*

Dryopteris ✿ (Dryopteridaceae)
   from Emei Shan, China   WPGP
   aemula   SRms
§   *affinis* ♀ H4   CFil CLAP CRow EBee EBlw ECha
     EFou EMon ENot EPar EPfP GGar
     LSyl MMoz MWgw NHol NMar
     NVic SDes SRms WFib WRic
§   - subsp. *borreri*   EFer MBri
   - subsp. *cambrensis*   EFer

	Name	Suppliers
	– 'Congesta'	CLAP EBee GKir SPar WFib
	– 'Congesta Cristata'	CLAP CPrp EBee EFer EPfP MBri MRav NHar NHol NSti SPla SRot
	– Crispa Group	CLAP CSBt EBlw ENot GBin LAst LRHS MMoz SMac SRPl
	– 'Crispa Barnes'	WPGP
§	– 'Crispa Gracilis' ♀ H4	CBos CLAP EFer ELan ENot EPot GBin MBir NBir WRic
§	– 'Cristata' ♀ H4	More than 30 suppliers
	– 'Cristata Angustata' ♀ H4	CFwr CLAP EFer ELan EMon GBin MMoz NDlv NHol NMar SRms WFib WPGP WRic
	– 'Cristata The King'	see D. affinis 'Cristata'
	– 'Grandiceps Askew'	EBee NMar WFib
*	– 'Insubrica'	EFer
*	– kerryensis	NVic
	– 'Pinderi'	CLAP CPLG CPrp EBee EFer EFou ELan GBin MBri NOrc SRms
	– Polydactyla Group	EBee GQui MDun MRav NMar
*	– 'Polydactyla Mapplebeck' ♀ H4	CLAP CRDP CRow NHol SRms
	– 'Revolvens'	EFer SRms
	atrata hort.	see D. cycadina
	X australis new	WRic
	austriaca hort.	see D. dilatata
	bissetiana	WRic
	blanfordii	CFil WPGP
	borreri	see D. affinis subsp. borreri
	carthusiana	CFil CLAP EBee EFer GBin NHar SRms WRic
	– 'Cristata'	NVic
	celsa new	WRic
	championii new	WRic
	clintoniana	CFil CFwr EBee LEur WPGP WRic
	X complexa 'Stablerae'	CLAP GQui NMar WFib WPGP WRic
	crassirhizoma	LEur
	cristata	CFwr EBee EFer EMar EMon EPfP LEur MLan WCru WRic
§	cycadina ♀ H4	More than 30 suppliers
	dickinsii	CMil EBee EMon WRic
§	dilatata ♀ H4	CKin EBee ECha EFer ELan EMon EPfP MGas MWgw NHol NMar SRms WFib WRic WWye
	– 'Crispa Whiteside' ♀ H4	CFil CFwr CLAP CPLG EBee EFer EMon MBri MWgw NHar NHol NLar SPlb SRms WFib WPGP WRic WWeb
	– 'Grandiceps'	CLAP CMHG CRDP CRow EFer EMon MBri NHar NHol SChu WFib WRic
	– 'Jimmy Dyce'	WRic
	– 'Lepidota Crispa Cristata'	CLAP LRHS
	– 'Lepidota Cristata' ♀ H4	CFwr CLAP CMHG CRDP EBee EFer ELan EMon GBin IMGH NBlu NHar NHol NMar NVic SRms WFib WRic
	– 'Lepidota Grandiceps'	CLAP NMar
*	– 'Recurvata'	CLAP WRic
	erythrosora ♀ H4	More than 30 suppliers
*	– 'Prolifera' ♀ H4	CFwr CLAP CRDP GCal MSte NBir NCiC NDlv NHar NHol NRib SPla WCot WFib WRic
	expansa	EMon
	filix-mas ♀ H4	CSBt EBee EBlw ECha EFou EMFW ENot EPfP GKir GMaP IIve LPBa LPVe LRHS MCLN MMoz MRav MWgw NHol SGar SMac SPar SPer SRPl SRms WShi WWye
	– 'Barnesii'	CLAP CMil EFer MSte NDlv NHar NMar SPlb WRic
	– 'Bollandiae'	WRic
*	– 'Corymbifera Crispa'	EFer
	– 'Crispa'	EBee EHon NHol WFib
	– 'Crispa Congesta'	see D. affinis 'Crispa Gracilis'
	– 'Crispa Cristata'	CLAP CPrp CRDP EBre EGol ELan EMon LHop MBri MCLN MDun MWgw NHol NMar NSti SApp SChu SCro SMer SRms SWat WFib WGor WRic WWye
	– 'Crispatissima'	NVic
	– 'Cristata' ♀ H4	CFil CKin CRow EBre EFer EHon ELan GKir MMoz NMar NOak NOrc SWat WFib WRic WWye
	– Cristata Group	EBee EBlw EFer NMar SPer WFib WRic
	– – 'Fred Jackson'	CLAP NHol WFib
*	– 'Cristata Grandiceps'	EFer
	– 'Cristata Jackson'	SPlb
	– 'Cristata Martindale'	CLAP CRDP CRow GQui NHol NMar SRms WFib WRic
	– 'Depauperata'	CFil CLAP CRDP SChu WFib WPGP
	– 'Euxinensis'	CLAP
	– 'Furcans'	CLAP
	– 'Grandiceps Wills' ♀ H4	CRow EMon NHol NMar SChu WFib WRic
	– 'Linearis'	CMHG CRow EBee EBlw EFer EHon ELan EMon MBri SRms
	– 'Linearis Congesta'	CFil WPGP
	– 'Linearis Cristata'	NMar WRic
	– 'Linearis Polydactyla'	CFwr CLAP CPrp EBee EFer GBin IMGH LBBr MBri MMoz NHar NHol NMar NVic SApp SLdr SMac SMad SPar STes WAbe
	– 'Multicristata'	NMar
	– Polydactyla Group	MRav NMar WFib
	– 'Polydactyla Dadds'	EBee MBri WFib
	– 'Rich Beauty'	CTrC
	formosana	EFer
	goldieana	CFwr CLAP CMHG EBee EFer GBin GGar GMaP NBir NHar NMar SSpi STes WFar WGwG WPnP WRic
	hirtipes	see D. cycadina
	hondoensis	CFil WRic
	lacera	NHar
	marginalis	CLAP EBee GBin MMoz NOGN WRic
	oreades	SRms
	pacifica new	WRic
	paleacea	CLAP
	polylepis new	WRic
	pseudofilix-mas new	WRic
	pseudomas	see D. affinis
	pycnopteroides new	WRic
	X remota	NVic SRms WRic
	sieboldii	CFil CFwr CLAP CTrC EBee EFer ELan EMon GCal IMGH LEur NBlu NDlv NHar NHol NOGN SApp SChu SMad SRms SSpi WCru WFib WPGP WRic WWye
	stewartii	NHar
	tokyoensis	CLAP GBin LEur NHar SHar WRic
	uniformis	CLAP ELan EMon
	– 'Cristata' new	WRic
	wallichiana ♀ H4	More than 30 suppliers

Duchesnea (Rosaceae)

	Name	Suppliers
	chrysantha	see D. indica
§	indica	CAgr CBgR CSWP EMan GAbr GDra IBlr IGor ITer MPEx MRav NHol SRms WBor WCer WMoo
§	– 'Harlequin' (v)	EMan GBar ITer MCCP MTho
*	– 'Snowflake' (v)	CRow EBee WMoo

- 'Variegata'   see *D. indica* 'Harlequin'

Dudleya (*Crassulaceae*)

cymosa	ETow SIgm
- JCA 11777	CNic
- subsp. **pumila**	NWCA
farinosa	CHEx
- NNS 93-240	IDac
paniculata NNS 98-221 **new**	NWCA
pulverulenta	SIgm
saxosa subsp. **aloides** NNS 99-141	WCot

Dugaldia (*Asteraceae*)

hoopsii	see *Hymenoxys hoopesii*

Dunalia (*Solanaceae*)

australis	see *Iochroma australe*
- blue	see *Iochroma australe* 'Bill Evans'
- white	see *Iochroma australe* 'Andean Snow'

Duranta (*Verbenaceae*)

§ **erecta**	LRHS
- 'Geisha Girl' **new**	ESlt
plumieri	see *D. erecta*
repens	see *D. erecta*

Dyckia (*Bromeliaceae*)

* 'Morris Hobbs' **new**	EMan WCot
remotiflora	SChr

Dymondia (*Asteraceae*)

margaretae	SBla WAbe

Dypsis (*Arecaceae*)

§ **decaryi**	CBrP EAmu LPal NBlo XBlo
decipiens	CBrP CRoM
§ **lutescens** ♀ H1	CRoM EPVP LPal LRHS MBri

Dysosma see *Podophyllum*

E

Ebenus (*Papilionaceae*)

cretica	ETow

Ecballium (*Cucurbitaceae*)

elaterium	LEdu MSal WHer

Eccremocarpus (*Bignoniaceae*)

scaber	CBcs CPlN CRHN CTrG EBee ELan EMil ENot EPfP GKir IDee LIck MBri MEHN MNrw NPer SBrw SGar SLim SPar SPer SRms SYvo WBrE
- apricot	EMar
- 'Aureus'	EPfP MAsh MWgw NLar SHFr
- 'Carmineus'	CBri EPfP GGar LPhx MAsh NChi NLar SGar WCot
- orange	MAsh MPEx MWgw
I - 'Roseus'	CBot MAsh

Echeveria ♣ (*Crassulaceae*)

affinis	MBri
agavoides ♀ H1	EOas MRav WBrE
* - 'Metallica'	MBri

* 'Black Prince'	EMan NPer SRot WCom WCot
derenbergii ♀ H1	CHEx
* 'Duchess of Nuremberg'	SRot
elegans ♀ H1	CHEx CHal EBee EOas MBri SAPC SPar WBrE
- x **elegans** var. **hernandonis new**	EBla
§ **gibbiflora** var. **metallica** ♀ H1	WEas
glauca Bak.	see *E. secunda* var. *glauca*
harmsii ♀ H1	CHal CSWP
'Imbricata'	CHEx
'Mahogany' **new**	MAvo SUsu
'Paul Bunyon'	CHal
peacockii	EBee EPfP NBlu NGdn SPet
'Perle d'Azur'	CHEx CTrC WCom WCot
'Perle von Nürnberg' ♀ H1	EPem
pulvinata ♀ H1	CHal
- 'Ruby'	SYvo
secunda	CAbb EMlt STre SWal
§ - var. **glauca** ♀ H1	CHEx EBee ELan NBir SArc STre SUsu WCom WWeb
- - 'Gigantea'	NPer
setosa ♀ H1	CHEx
'Warfield Wonder' ♀ H1	WEas

Echinacea ♣ (*Asteraceae*)

angustifolia	CArn CFwr EBee EHrv EMan EPPr EPfP GPoy LPio LRHS MBNS MCAu MHer MLLN MSal NSti WBor WBri WHer WMnd WSel WWye
- 'Mecklenburg Select'	EBee
atrorubens new	EBee EPPr
'Greenheart'	LPhx
laevigata	EBee
pallida	CBot CSam EBee EChP ELan EMan EMar EOrc EPPr GPoy GSki LPhx MAnH MBri MCAu MSal MWrn NChi NPri NSti SSvw WBro WCot WMoo WRus WSel WWeb
paradoxa	CPou CSam EHrv EMan EMar EPPr EWTr GSki LDai LPhx MCAu MSPs MSal NSti SDys WBea WBro WHil WWhi WWpP
§ **purpurea**	More than 30 suppliers
- 'Alba'	IHMH NBlu NDov
- 'Augustkönigin'	CBos CKno EBee EBlw EChP EMan EVFa GBin MSph MSte NBir NCat NDov NLar SAga SBla WCot
- Bressingham hybrids	EBee EBrc ELan EMar LRHS SChu SPet SPct SPla WFar
- dark-stemmed	EFou LPhx MAnH SAga
- 'Forncett Parasol' **new**	EFou
- 'Green Edge'	CFwr
- 'Kim's Knee High'	CFai CKno COtt EBre EChP EFou EGle EPfP EVFa GAbr GBin GKir LAst LHop MLLN MTis NBir NGdn NPSI SAga SDys SMad STes SUsu SWat WCot WLin WMaN WWhi
- 'Kim's Mop Head'	CFai CKno EBee EChP EMan EWes GBin LAst SAga WCot WWhi
- 'Leuchtstern'	EBee EBlw ECGN EShb GSki MAnH NBir NGdn MSm SWat WBea WPer
- 'Magnus'	More than 30 suppliers
- 'Maxima' **new**	WCot
- 'Pink Flamingo'	WWhi
- 'Robert Bloom'	EBee ECGN EHrv EMil LPhx MSph NPSI SVal SWat WCot WWhi
- 'Rubinglow'	CBos CMil EBee EChP EGle EMar EVFa MAnH MSph MSte NBir NCat NDov NLar SPoG WCot WLin WRus

	– 'Rubinstern'	CFwr CHar COtt CSam EBee EBlw EGle EHrv EMan EMar EPfP ERou EWll LPVe LRHS MAnH MBri MSPs MWrn NChi NPSI NSti SCro SMad WBea WCot WHil WMnd WSel WWeb WWhi
	– 'Verbesserter Leuchtstern'	NLar
	– 'White Lustre'	EBee EBre EChP ECha EPfP EVFa GSki LCaP MCAu SDes WCot WFar WMnd
	– 'White Swan'	More than 30 suppliers
	tennesseensis	CArn EBee IIve

Echinops (Asteraceae)

	RCB TQ-H-2 **new**	WCot
	albus	see *E.* 'Nivalis'
§	*bannaticus*	CSBt EBee GSki LLWP NBid SDes SMer WCot WFar WTel
*	– 'Albus'	EPfP EWll LAst LRHS NGdn NSti SPer SPoG
§	– 'Blue Globe'	CBre COIW EBee ECGN EChP EMan EPfP ERou EWTr GCal GSki LAst LPVe LRHS SCoo SDes SIgm SMad WBrE WCra WHil WLRN WLin WMnd WPer WWal WWeb
	– 'Taplow Blue' ♀ H4	CBcs CPrp CSev EBee EBre EFou ELan ERou GKir GSki LHop LPVe LRHS MBNS MCAu MCLN MRav MWat NPer SCro SDes SEND SMad SPar SPer SPla WFar WLRN WMnd WTel
	commutatus	see *E. exaltatus*
§	*exaltatus*	EBee MWgw NBir WCot
§	*maracandicus*	GCal WCot
§	'Nivalis'	CBre EBee ECha ELan ERou GCal SEND
	niveus	IFro
*	*perringii*	GCal
	ritro hort.	see *E. bannaticus*
§	*ritro* L. ♀ H4	More than 30 suppliers
	– 'Moonstone'	CRow
§	– subsp. *ruthenicus* ♀ H4	CKno CRDP EBee ECGP ELan EWTr GBuc IGor MHar SIgm WCot WPGP
	– 'Veitch's Blue'	More than 30 suppliers
	– 'Veitch's Blue' misapplied	see *E. ritro* L.
	sphaerocephalus	CPen ELan EMan EWTr IBlr NBid NBur SBla SIgm SMac SPlb WBea WPer WWpP
	– 'Arctic Glow'	More than 30 suppliers
	strigosus	EBee
	tienschanicum **new**	EChP GIBF MCAu
	tjanschanicus	EMan EWll WBVN
	tschimganicus	EBee

Echinopsis ✿ (Cactaceae)

	candicans **new**	EOas
	chamaecereus ♀ H1	CHEx EOas
	chilensis **new**	EOas

Echinospartum see *Genista*

Echium (Boraginaceae)

	albicans	EWll
	amoenum **new**	EBee
	boissieri	CTCP EAmu EGoo WHer
	brevirame **new**	CTCP
§	*candicans* ♀ H2-3	CAbb CCtw CFir CHEx CPLG CTCP CTbh CTrF EAmu EBee ECre ESlt IDee NBur SAPC SArc SRob SSte WCHb WCot WFar

	decaisnei **new**	CTCP
	fastuosum	see *E. candicans*
	giganteum **new**	CTCP
	italicum	LPhx NLar
	lusitanicum subsp. *polycaulon* **new**	CTCP
	nervosum	CTrC EBee
§	*pininana* ♀ H2-3	CAbb CCtw CHEx CTCP CTbh CTrC CTrF EBee EBot ECre ELan EWll IArd IDee ISea LPhx MLwd NBur NVic SAPC SArc SBod SChr SGar SMad SPar SSte WCHb WHer WWpP
	– 'Snow Tower' **new**	CPla ELan
	– x *wildpretii*	CTCP
	pinnifolium	see *E. pininana*
	rossicum **new**	GIBF
	russicum	CFir CPom CTCP EChP EGoo EWll ITim LPhx MSPs NLar SIgm SOkh SSte WAul WBVN WCHb WCot WHil WSan WWeb
	x *scilloniense*	CTCP SYvo
	strictum **new**	CTCP
	sventenii **new**	CTCP
	tuberculatum	EBee EChP LPhx NBur SBod
	virescens	CTCP
	vulgare	CArn CKin EBot ECGN EEls ELan EOHP MBow MChe MHer MSal NLar NMir SIde WBrE WCHb WHHs WHer WJek WWye
	– 'Devil's Blood' **new**	CTCP
	– Drake's form	MAnH SGar WElm
	webbii	CTCP
	wildpretii ♀ H2-3	CAbb CRez CTrC CTrF EWll
	– subsp. *wildpretii*	CTCP
	– subsp. *trichosiphon* **new**	CTCP

Eclipta (Asteraceae)

	alba	see *E. prostrata*
§	*prostrata*	MSal

Edgeworthia (Thymelaeaceae)

§	*chrysantha*	CBcs CPLG CPMA CWib EPfP ICrw LBuc LPan MNes WSHC
	– B&SWJ 1048	WCru
I	– 'Grandiflora'	CPMA NLar
	– 'Red Dragon'	CPMA NLar
	– f. *rubra* hort.	see *E. chrysantha* 'Red Dragon'
	papyrifera	see *E. chrysantha*

Edraianthus (Campanulaceae)

	croaticus	see *E. graminifolius*
	dalmaticus	ETow SBla
	– *albus*	EPot
	dinaricus	NSla
§	*graminifolius*	CPBP ECho ECtt NHar NLAp NMen WFar WPer WWin
	parnassicus	NMen
§	*pumilio* ♀ H4	CLyd EHyt EPot GEdr GKev LRHS NHar NMen NWCA SBla WAbe
§	*serpyllifolius*	NMen SScr
§	– 'Major'	EHyt NMen NSla SBla WAbe
	tenuifolius	CPBP

Ehretia (Boraginaceae)

	dicksonii	CFil CHEx WPGP

Ehrharta (Poaceae)

	thunbergii	EPPr

Eichhornia (*Pontederiaceae*)

crassipes	CWat EMFW LMdh LPBA MSta SCoo
- 'Major'	NPer

Elaeagnus ✿ (*Elaeagnaceae*)

angustifolia	CBot EBee ECrN EPfP EWTr LPan MBar MBlu MCoo MRav SHBN SPer SRPl SRms WDin WGer
- Caspica Group	see *E.* 'Quicksilver'
argentea	see *E. commutata*
§ **commutata**	CAgr CBot CMCN ECrN EHoe EPar IMGH LHop MBlu MTis MWgw MWhi NFor NLon SPer WDin WRus
x **ebbingei**	More than 30 suppliers
- 'Coastal Gold' (v)	CAbP CBcs CDoC CDul COtt EBee EMil ENot LBuc LRHS MAsh MBri MGos SLim SReu SRms WPat WStl WWes
- 'Gilt Edge' (v) ♀ H4	More than 30 suppliers
- Gold Splash = 'Lannou' (v)	CDoC CDul CWSG EBee ENot MAsh MBri WGer
- 'Limelight' (v)	More than 30 suppliers
- 'Salcombe Seedling'	LRHS MBri
* - 'Tricolor' (v)	CSBt
glabra	CAgr EPfP
- 'Reflexa'	see *E.* x *reflexa*
macrophylla	CSam EPfP NFor SDry SSpi
multiflora	CDul SPer WPGP
- 'Gigantea'	ELan
parvifolia	EBee ENot EPfP
pungens	ERom NBir
- 'Argenteovariegata'	see *E. pungens* 'Variegata'
- 'Aureovariegata'	see *E. pungens* 'Maculata'
= 'Dicksonii' (v)	CTrC CWib LNet LRHS SLon SPer SRms WBcn WFar
- 'Forest Gold' (v)	CAbP ELan EPfP LRHS MAsh
- 'Frederici' (v)	CBcs CDoC CMHG CMac CTrC EBee ELan EPfP EPla MAsh MBri MRav SDes SHBN SLim SPer WDin WHCG WPat WRHF
- 'Goldrim' (v) ♀ H4	COtt EBee EPfP LRHS MBri MGos SDes SHBN SLim WDin
§ - 'Maculata' (v)	More than 30 suppliers
§ - 'Variegata' (v)	CBcs CMac EBee LRHS MBri NBir SDes SHBN SPer SRPl WGer WHCG
§ 'Quicksilver' ♀ H4	More than 30 suppliers
§ x **reflexa**	CFil WBcn WHCG
x **submacrophylla**	see *Elaeagnus* x *ebbingei*
umbellata	CDul CPle EBee EPfP EWTr MBlu SMad SPer WHCG WMou WSHC

Elatostema (*Urticaceae*)

repens var. **pulchrum** ♀ H1	CHal MBri
- var. **repens**	CHal

elderberry see *Sambucus nigra*

Elegia (*Restionaceae*)

capensis	CAbb CBig CCtw CFee CFir CHEx CTrC GGar IArd ITer SPar SPlb WDyG WMul WNor
cuspidata	CBig CPLG CTrC LRav
equisetacea	CBig CFee WNor
filacea new	CTrC
fistulosa	CBig
grandis	CTrC
grandispicata	CBig
intermedia new	CTrC
persistens	CBig
racemosa	CTrC

Eleocharis (*Cyperaceae*)

acicularis	ELan EMFW IHMH WWpP
dulcis variegated (v)	CRow EPla
palustris	EMFW MSta
sphacelata new	GGar

Elephantopus (*Asteraceae*)

tomentosus	EBee

Elettaria (*Zingiberaceae*)

cardamomum	CArn EShb GPoy LEdu MBri MSal SHDw WJck WMul

Eleutherococcus (*Araliaceae*)

hypoleucus B&SWJ 5532	WCru
nikaianus B&SWJ 5027	WCru
pictus	see *Kalopanax septemlobus*
sciadophylloides B&SWJ 4728	WCru
senticosus	GIBF GPoy LEdu
- B&SWJ 4528	WCru
septemlobus	see *Kalopanax septemlobus*
§ **sieboldianus**	MRav WDin WFar
§ - 'Variegatus' (v)	CBot CFwr EBee EHoe ELan EPfP EVFa ICrw MBlu MGos MRav NPal WHer WSHC

Elingamita (*Myrsinaceae*)

johnsonii	ECou

Elisena (*Amaryllidaceae*)

longipetala	see *Hymenocallis longipetala*

Elliottia (*Ericaceae*)

bracteata	see *Tripetaleia bracteata*
pyroliflorus	SSta

Ellisiophyllum (*Scrophulariaceae*)

pinnatum	MGrG
- B&SWJ 197	WCru

Elodea (*Hydrocharitaceae*)

canadensis	CBen EHon EMFW WMAq
crispa	see *Lagarosiphon major*

Elsholtzia (*Lamiaceae*)

ciliata	CArn IIve MSal
fruticosa	CArn WWye
stauntonii	CArn CBcs CBot CFee EBee ECha ECre EMan EOHP EPri GPoy IMGH MHer SLPl WHil WMoo WWyc
- 'Alba'	CArn CBot LRav WWye

Elymus (*Poaceae*)

arenarius	see *Leymus arenarius*
californicus new	CBig
canadensis	CWCL EHoe EPPr EWsh WMoo
- f. **glaucifolius**	GCal MTed SLim WCot
cinereus from Washington State, USA	EPPr
farctus	EPPr
fibrosus new	EPPr
giganteus	see *Leymus racemosus*
glaucus hort.	see *E. hispidus*
glaucus new	EPPr
§ **hispidus**	More than 30 suppliers
N **magellanicus**	More than 30 suppliers
riparius new	EPPr
§ **scabrus**	SMrm
sibiricus	EPPr EWsh SWal
solandri new	GBin
- JCA 5.345.500	WPGP

tenuis	SMad	
villosus **new**	EPPr	
- var. *arkansanus*	EPPr NOGN WWpP	
virginicus	EPPr	

Elytrigia (Poaceae)

campestris **new**	EPPr

Embothrium ✿ (Proteaceae)

coccineum	CBrm CFil CHEx CPne CTrG EPfP ICrw IMGH LRHS MAsh MCCP SDry SPar SReu WBrE WNor WPGP WPat
- Lanceolatum Group	CBrm CDoC CEnd CPLG CSBt EBee ELan EPfP GGar GKir LRHS MDun MLan NPal SBrw SHBN SSpi SSta WDin WPat WPic
- - 'Inca Flame'	CDoC CDul COtt CPLG CPMA CSBt EPfP LRHS MDun NDlv SBrw SMur SSta WPat
- - 'Ñorquinco' ♀ H3	CBcs CDoC GGar LRHS SSpi WBod WCru WPat
- Longifolium Group	CBcs IBlr ISea SBrw
grandiflorum **new**	CFil

Emmenopterys (Rubiaceae)

henryi	CFai CFil CPle EBee EPfP SBrw SMad SSpi WPGP

Empetrum (Empetraceae)

luteum	MBar
nigrum	GPoy MBar
- 'Bernstein'	NHar NHol
- var. *japonicum*	GTou
- 'Lucia'	MGos
- 'Tore' (v)	NHar
rubrum	WWes

Encephalartos (Zamiaceae)

altensteinii	CBrP
cycadifolius	LPal
ghellinckii	LPal
kisambo	LPal
lebomboensis	CBrP
lehmannii	CBrP LPal
natalensis	CBrP LPal
senticosus	LPal
villosus	CBrP LPal

Endymion see *Hyacinthoides*

Engelmannia (Asteraceae)

pinnatifida	EBee

Enkianthus ✿ (Ericaceae)

campanulatus ♀ H4	More than 30 suppliers
- var. *campanulatus* f. *albiflorus*	LRHS MAsh SMur SSpi
- var. *palibinii*	EPfP GGGa GKir LRHS MAsh MGos NHol NLar SBrw SSpi SSta WBrE WNor
- 'Red Bells'	CDoC COtt EBee EPfP GKir LRHS MDun MGos NDlv SBrw SPer SSpi SSta
- var. *sikokianus*	GGGa LRHS MAsh MDun NLar SSpi
* - 'Variegatus' (v)	LRHS MAsh
- 'Wallaby'	NLar
cernuus	GKir
- f. *rubens* ♀ H4	EPfP GGGa LRHS MAsh NBea NEgg SSpi WDin WGer WNor WPic
chinensis	EPfP GGGa GKir LRHS MAsh NLar SSpi SSta WNor
deflexus	CFil LRHS MAsh SReu SSpi SStaWPGP

perulatus ♀ H4	CBrm CFil CRez EPfP GKir MBar SBrw SSpi SSta WWes	
sikokianus **new**	CAbP	

Ensete (Musaceae)

	glaucum	CKob EAmu EShb WMul
	- 'Vudu Vudu'	CKob
	superbum	CKob NBlo XBlo
§	*ventricosum* ♀ H1+3	CBot CDoC CHEx CKob CRoM EAmu ESlt LPal LPan MPRe NBlo SAPC SArc WKif WMul XBlo
§	- 'Maurelii'	CHEx CKob EAmu SAPC SArc WMul WPGP
	- 'Rubrum'	see *E. ventricosum* 'Maurelii'
	wilsonii **new**	NPal

Entelea (Tiliaceae)

arborescens	CHEx ECou

Eomecon (Papaveraceae)

chionantha	More than 30 suppliers

Epacris (Epacridaceae)

longiflora **new**	SOWG
microphylla	SOWG
paludosa	GCrs GGGa IMGH SReu
petrophila	GCrs GGGa WPat

Ephedra (Ephedraceae)

	distachya	GPoy NFor NLon WWye
	equisetina	MSal SMad
	fragilis	CTCP SDry
	gerardiana	IFro
	- KR 0853	EPla
	- var. *sikkimensis*	CStu EPla NLar SDry WOld WPer
§	*major*	SDry WHer
	minima	NWCA
	nebrodensis	see *E. major*
	nevadensis	CAgr GPoy MHer MSal
	sinica	MSal
	viridis	CArn ELau MSal

Epidendrum (Orchidaceae)

§	*ibaguense*	CHal

Epigaea (Ericaceae)

gaultherioides	GGGa
repens	GGGa

Epilobium (Onagraceae)

§	*angustifolium*	CKin GBar GWCH NSco SWat WHer
	- var. *album*	More than 30 suppliers
	- 'Isobel'	CSpe MLLN MRav NCWG WAbb WCom WCot
	- f. *leucanthum*	see *E. angustifolium* var. *album*
	- 'Stahl Rose'	CBot CHid CMea CStr EBee EMar EWes LPhx NCWG SMrm SSpi WFTG WPGP WSHC
	californicum hort.	see *Zauschneria californica*
	canum	see *Zauschneria californica* subsp. *cana*
§	*chlorifolium*	GEdr
	- var. *kaikourense*	see *E. chlorifolium*
	crassum	ESis GBuc NWoo WMoo WWin
§	*dodonaei*	EMan MLLN MTho NGar SMac WMoo WSHC WWin
	fleischeri	EDAr WSHC
	garrettii	see *Zauschneria californica* subsp. *garrettii*
	glabellum hort.	CHea CSpe ECtt EMan ESis GKir GMac LPhx LRHS MRav MWat NBir NPPs SAga SUsu WAbe WCom WCru WEas WWhi WWin
N		

hirsutum	CKin SWat
- **album**	NSti WAlt WGwG
- 'Caerphilly Castle' (d)	WAlt
- 'Pistils at Dawn'	WAlt
- **roseum**	WRha
- 'Spring Lime'	WAlt
- 'Well Creek' (v)	CHea CM&M EMan MLLN NBid WAlt WBar WCHb WCot WHil WHrl
microphyllum	see *Zauschneria californica* subsp. *cana*
obcordatum	CLyd NWCA
obscurum	IIve
- 'Mottisfont' (v)	WAlt
rosmarinifolium	see *E. dodonaei*
septentrionale	see *Zauschneria septentrionalis*
x **subhirsutum**	WAlt
tasmanicum	CLyd
villosum	see *Zauschneria californica* subsp. *mexicana*
wilsonii hort.	see *E. chlorifolium*

Epimedium ✿ (*Berberidaceae*)

from Yunnan, China **new**	LEur
acuminatum	CDes CElw CFil CLAP EBee EFEx EHyt GLil LEur LPio SChu SMac WAbe WPGP WRus
- L 575	CBos CRDP EHrv MSte SBla SSpi WAbe WPnP
- L 1962	SBla
- 'Galaxy' L 1962 **new**	SBla
'Akakage'	GLil
'Akebono'	CDes EBee GLil LEur NLar WPGP
alpinum	CFis CMGP CMac FBee EMon EPPr EPar GBuc GKir LEur NHol SMac SMer SPer WMoo
'Amanagowa'	CPMA LEur SBla
Asiatic hybrids	EBee LEur SChu WPnP
'Beni-chidori'	EBee GLil LEur WPGP
'Beni kujaku'	EBee GBuc GLil LEur WPGP
brachyrrhizum	EBee LEur
- CPC 940477	SBla
brevicornu	CPMA EBee LEur
- Og 88.010	SBla
- f. **rotundatum**	CDes
Og 02.010	LEur SBla
'Buckland Spider' **new**	SBla
campanulatum Og 93087	SBla
x **cantabrigiense**	CBro EBee ECtt EMan EOrc EPPr EPla EWTr GKir GLil LEur LRHS MRav MWgw NHol SDes SMac SPer
chlorandrum	CDes LEur
- Og 94.003	SBla
cremeum	see *E. grandiflorum* subsp. *koreanum*
davidii	CDes CPMA CPom CRDP EBee ECha GBri LEur MBro MSte SMac SSpi WAbe WFar WHal WHoo WPGP WRus
- EMR 4125	CElw CLAP EHrv LEur SBla
diphyllum	CBos CPrp EHrv LEur NDov SAga WBVN WHal
- dwarf white	GLil
dolichostemon	EBee EGle
- Og 81.010	LEur SBla
ecalcaratum	CDes CPMA EBee LEur WPGP
- Og 93.082	SBla
'Enchantress'	CDes CLAP EBee ECha EGle GBuc LEur SSpi WAbe WHal
epsteinii	CDes EBee
- CPC 940347	SBla
fangii	SSpi
fargesii	CDes EBee WPGP WRus

- Og 93.053	LEur
- Og 93.057	SBla
- 'Pink Constellation' Og 93.023	CPMA LEur SBla
flavum Og 92.036	LEur SBla
franchetii	LEur
- 'Brimstone Butterfly' Og 87.001	CDes CPMA LEur SBla SSpi WAbe
- 'Genpei'	GLil
§ **grandiflorum** ♀ H4	CBcs CElw CFis CPla CTri EBlw EHrv ELan EPar EPfP EPot GAbr GKir LEur MBro NBir NHar NMen SAga SBla SIng SMac SPer WCru WFar WHil WLin WPnP WRus
- 'Album'	CLAP EPot IMGH SPar
- var. **coelestre**	GLil LEur
- 'Crimson Beauty'	CFwr CLAP CPMA ECha EMan GBuc LEur LPhx MRav SAga SChu SUsu WCru WHal WHoo
- 'Crimson Queen'	CDes EBee WPGP
- 'Elfenkönigin'	EBee LEur WAbe
- 'Jennie Maillard' **new**	SUsu
- 'Koji'	EBee EGle LEur
§ - subsp. **koreanum**	CFil CLAP CPla CRDP EBee ECha EFEx GLil LPhx MBro NHar WAbe
- - 'La Rocaille'	LEur SBla
- lilac	CBos CPlt CRDP WFar
- 'Lilacinum'	LEur SBla
- 'Lilafee'	More than 30 suppliers
- 'Mount Kitadake'	EGle GLil LEur SSpi WAbe
- 'Nanum' ♀ H4	CDos CDes CLyd CPom CRDP EBee EHrv EHyt EPot ETow NHar NMen SBla SChu SMac SSpi WAbe WCru WPGP
l - 'Nanum Freya'	EBee
I - 'Nigrum'	LEur
- 'Pallidum'	CHid EBee
- pink	EHrv
- 'Purple Prince' **new**	SBla
- 'Queen Esta'	SBla
- 'Red Beauty' **new**	CLAP MSte WRHF
- 'Rose Queen' ♀ H4	More than 30 suppliers
§ - 'Roseum'	CHid CLAP EBee EBre GBri NMen EBee EBlw GBin GLil LEur NHol NLar WOVN
- 'Rubinkrone'	
- 'Saturn' **new**	SBla
- 'Shikinomai'	EBee EGle LEur WAbe
- 'Sirius'	SBla
- f. **violaceum**	CFir CFwr CLAP LEur SBla SChu SMac WAbe
- 'White Beauty'	EGle
- 'White Queen' ♀ H4	CFir CFwr CPMA CPlt CRDP EBee EChP EHrv LEur LPhx NOak SBla SMHy SSpi WAbe WRus
- 'Yellow Princess' **new**	SBla
higoense	EBee SIgm
ilicifolium Og 93020	SBla
'Kaguyahime'	CDes LEur SBla SMac WAbe
latisepalum	CDes CPMA EBee LEur SHar WPGP
leptorrhizum	CDes CLAP CPMA EBee EBlw EGle EMon GEil GLil LEur SMHy SWat WAbe WPGP
- Og Y 44	CRDP EHyt SAga SDys SSpi
'Little Shrimp'	CLyd CTri EBee EGle EPPr LEur MBro NLar WPat
macranthum	see *E. grandiflorum*
membranaceum	CPMA EBee LEur WAbe
- Og 93.047	SBla
myrianthum Og 940110 **new**	SBla
ogisui	CDes CPMA CPom EBee EGle EHyt WPGP
- Og 91.001	LEur SSpi WAbe

x	*omeiense*	LEur WBcn
	- 'Emei Shan' Og 82.001	CDes CPMA EBee LEur SBla WPGP
	- 'Stormcloud' Og 82.002	CDes CPMA LEur SBla SMac
	pauciflorum	CPMA LEur WHil
x	*perralchicum* ♀ H4	CBro CPMA EBee EMan EMon
		EPot GBuc GKev GKir GMaP
		NLon NPPs SIng SLPl SSpi WBVN
		WPGP WPnP WRus WSHC
	- 'Frohnleiten'	More than 30 suppliers
	- 'Wisley'	CElw CPMA CStu EHrv EWes LEur
		MBro MTed SBla
	perralderianum	CFil CHEx CKno CPom CSam
		CStu EBee EGle ELan EMan ENot
		EPar GKir LEur LGro MFir NHar
		SCro SRPl SRms SSpi WAbe WCru
		WHen WPGP WPnP WViv WWin
	- 'Weihenstephan'	MTed
	pinnatum	EBee GLil GMaP LEur MDun WHal
		WRha
§	- subsp. *colchicum*	More than 30 suppliers
	♀ H4	
	- - L 321	LEur SBla
	- - 'Black Sea'	CLAP EBee EHrv GLil IBlr LEur
		LHop NLar
	- *elegans*	see *E. pinnatum* subsp. *colchicum*
	platypetalum	CPMA EBee
	- Og 93.085	EGle LEur SBla
	- *album*	EBee
	pubescens	CPMA LEur SAga
	- Og 91.003	SBla WAbe
	pubigerum	CFwr CHid CPMA EBee ECha
		EGle EMan GKir GLil IMGH LEur
		MWgw NHar NHol NPPs NPri
		SDes WHil WLin
	rhizomatosum	LEur
	- Og 92.114	CPMA SBla
x	*rubrum* ♀ H4	More than 30 suppliers
	sagittatum	EBee EFEx GLil LEur
	'Sasaki'	GBuc
	sempervirens	LEur
	- 'Aurora'	NHol
x	*setosum*	CElw CFil EBee ECha EHrv LEur
		MSte SMac SSpi WAbe
	'Shiho'	EBee GLil LEur
	'Sohayaki'	EBee
	stellulatum 'Wudang	CDes EBee EHrv EHyt EWes LEur
	Star' L 1193	SMac WAbe WCot
	'Sunset'	GLil
	'Tama-no-genpei'	LEur
x	*versicolor*	CPLG LEur WMoo
	- 'Cupreum'	LEur SMac SSpi
	- 'Neosulphureum'	CBro CLAP CM&M CPLG EBee EMon
		EPPr LEur SAga SBla SSpi WViv
	- 'Sulphureum' ♀ H4	More than 30 suppliers
	- 'Versicolor'	CLAP EHrv LPhx NHar SAga
x	*warleyense*	More than 30 suppliers
	- 'Orangekönigin'	EBee EBre EGle EPar GBuc LEur
		LPio MCAu MMil NDov NHol
		NPPs NSti SAga SLPl SPla WAbe
		WHil WPnP
	wushanense	CPMA LEur
	- Og 93.019	SBla
	- 'Caramel' Og 92.009	CDes CPMA LEur SBla
x	*youngianum*	CBcs EGle LEur WCru
	- blush	LEur
	- 'Capella'	LEur
	- 'Lilacinum'	see *E.* x *youngianum* 'Roseum'
	- 'Merlin'	CBos CFir EBee ECha EHrv EHyt
		EMan EPPr LEur SBla SChu SOkh
		WAbe
	- 'Niveum' ♀ H4	More than 30 suppliers
§	- 'Roseum'	More than 30 suppliers
	- 'Tamabotan'	CDes GBuc GLil SBla

	- 'Typicum'	EBee EGle EHyt LEur WAbe
	- white	NMen
	- 'Yenomoto'	EBee LEur SBla

Epipactis (Orchidaceae)

	gigantea	CAvo CBct CBro CFil CHdy CMea
		CStu EBee ECha EHyt ELan EMan
		EPar EPot ERos GCrs GMaP IBlr
		LEur MTho NGar NHar NLAp
		NMen SBla WAbe WCru WFar
	- 'Serpentine Night'	IBlr
	helleborine	MWrn
*	**Lowland Legacy g.**	CHdy LEur
	'Edelstein'	
*	- 'Frankfurt'	CHdy LEur
	palustris	CHdy EBee EHyt SBla WHer
	'Renate'	CHdy LEur
	Sabine g. new	CHdy
*	- 'Frankfurt'	CHdy LEur NGar
	thunbergii	EFEx

Epiphyllum (Cactaceae)

	anguliger **new**	ERea
	crenatum **new**	ERea

Epipremnum (Araceae)

§	*aureum* ♀ H1	CHal EBak MBri
	- 'Marble Queen' (v)	CHal LRHS
§	*pinnatum*	LRHS MBri

Episcia (Gesneriaceae)

	'Country Kitten'	CHal
	cupreata	CHal
§	*dianthiflora*	CHal SRms WDib
	'Pink Panther'	CHal
*	'San Miguel'	CHal WDib

Equisetum ✿ (Equisetaceae)

	arvense	IIve MSal
	'Bandit'	CNat EMon SMad
x	*bowmanii*	CNat
*	*camtschatcense*	CDes CMCo ITer SMad
x	*dycei*	CNat
	fluviatile **new**	CNat
	hyemale	CBrm CFwr CMCo CMil CNat
		EBla EPfP EPla NBlu NPer SLon
		SPlb SSpi WDyG WFar WHal
		WMAq WMoo WPrP WWye
§	- var. *affine*	CNat ELan EMan EMon EPla LEur
		MBlu SMad WHal WOld
	- var. *robustum*	see *E. hyemale* var. *affine*
	palustre **new**	GWCH
	ramosissimum var.	EMFW LMdh MCCP WWpP
	japonicum	
	scirpoides	CKno CMCo CMil CNat CPen
		EFer EMFW EMon EPla LMdh
		MCCP NPer SBHF SLon SPar
		WMAq WPrP WWeb
	telmateia	CNat
	variegatum	NVic

Eragrostis (Poaceae)

	abyssinica	see *E. tef*
	airoides	CHar CWCL EBee EChP EMan
		EPPr EWsh ITer LPhx MAvo
		MGGn MWrn NPPs NPro SAsh
		SMad WCot WHrl WMoo WPGP
		WPnP WRos WWeb WWpP
	capensis	EPPr
	chloromelas	CKno CMHG EBee EMan EPPr
		LPhx WPGP
	curvula	More than 30 suppliers
	- S&SH 10	CRDP MSte WPGP

	- 'Totnes Burgundy'	CDes CElw CKno CWCL EBee EPPr MMoz WPGP
	elliottii **new**	CBrm
	gummiflua	CBig
	'Silver Needles'	see *Agrostis canina* 'Silver Needles'
	spectabilis	CBrm CFwr
§	*tef*	LIck NPPs
	trichodes	CBig CPen CWCL EMan EPPr GBin WPer

Eranthis (*Ranunculaceae*)

§	*hyemalis* ♀ H4	CBro CMea ELan EMon EPar EPfP EPot ETub GMaP LAma LRHS MBri MBro NRog WCot WFar WMaN WShi
§	- Cilicica Group	CBro EMon EPar EPot GEdr LAma MAvo MLwd NRog WCot WShi
	- 'Flore Pleno' (d)	EPot
	- 'Orange Glow'	EHyt
§	- Tubergenii Group	EPot
	- - 'Guinea Gold' ♀ H4	CBro EHyt GCrs SOkd WCom
	pinnatifida	EFEx GCrs WCru
	stellata	EBee WCru

Ercilla (*Phytolaccaceae*)

volubilis	CAbb CFee CPLG CPIN CRHN CSam EBee EHol SBrw SPer WCot WCru WPic WSHC

Eremaea (*Myrtaceae*)

beaufortioides	SOWG
pauciflora	SOWG

Eremophila (*Myoporaceae*)

glabra 'Burgundy' **new**	SOWG
maculata	CPLG ECou
- var. *brevifolia* **new**	SOWG
- pale pink-flowered **new**	SOWG
- 'Peaches and Cream' **new**	SOWG
'Yellow Trumpet' **new**	ECou

Eremurus (*Asphodelaceae*)

§	*aitchisonii*	EBee GIBF LAma NRog SIgm
	- Albus	WCot
	'Brimstone Beauty'	NRog
*	'Brutus'	EBee EBre ERou EVFa LAma MSte NFor
	bungei	see *E. stenophyllus* subsp. *stenophyllus*
	elwesii	see *E. aitchisonii*
	'Emmy Ro'	EBee LAma LRHS NCel NRog
	'Harmony'	NRog
	himalaicus	CBot CHar CSpe EBee ELan EMan EPar EPot ERou ETub EWTr GIBF LAma LRHS MHer MSte NCel NEgg NRog SMad SPer
	'Image'	NCel NRog
	x *isabellinus* 'Cleopatra'	More than 30 suppliers
	- 'Obelisk'	CMea CPen EBee ELan LAma LRHS NRog WCot
	- 'Pinokkio'	CM&M EBee EMan ETub LAma MHer NCel NLar NRog SPar WPGP WViv
	- Ruiter hybrids	CSWP EBee EBlw EChP ECot ELan EMan EMon EPar ETub LAma LAst LRHS MLLN MWgw NCel NGdn NRog SPar SSpe WAul WFar WViv
	- Shelford hybrids	CBcs CBro EBee EBlw ELan EMan EMon LAma LRHS MLLN MNrw NCel NOak SDeJ WFar

	- 'Tropical Dream'	CM&M EBee EChP LAst WViv
	'Jeanne-Claire' **new**	LAma NLar
	'Joanne' **new**	EBee LAma NLar
	lactiflorus	SIgm
	'Moneymaker'	EBee EBre ERou LAma LRHS NCel NRog SCou WViv
	'Oase'	CAvo CHar CM&M CPen EBee EBlw EBre EChP ELan EMan ERou EVFa EWTr LRHS NCel NLar NRog SPer WCot
	olgae	GIBF
	'Rexona'	EBee LAma NRog
	robustus ♀ H4	More than 30 suppliers
	- pink-flowered	NCel
	'Roford'	CM&M CPen EBee LAma LAst NCel NRog SPar
	'Romance'	CAvo CMea EBee LAma LRHS MSte NCel NRog WViv
	stenophyllus ♀ H4	CBro CM&M EPot LHop LRHS MGrG NGdn NMRc SMrm WCot WPGP WPrP WViv WWeb
§	- subsp. *stenophyllus*	CAvo CMea EBee EBlw EBre EMon EPar ERou ETub LAma MAnH MHer MLLN MNrw MRav NCel NEgg NFor NOak NPri NRog SPar SPer WFar
	'Yellow Giant' **new**	WCot

Erianthus see *Saccharum*

Erica ❀ (*Ericaceae*)

	x *afroeuropaea* **new**	EHea
	arborea	CNCN CTrG SAPC SLon SPar SPlb
§	- 'Albert's Gold' ♀ H4	CBcs CMac CNCN CPLG CSBt EBre EHea ELan EPfP GKir LRHS MAsh MBar MBri MOke NBlu SBod SBrw SPar SPer SPla WBan WWeb
	- var. *alpina* ♀ H4	CDoC CMac CNCN EBee EHea ENot EPfP GKir LRHS MBar SBod SBrw SPer SPoG
	- 'Arbora Gold'	see *E. arborea* 'Albert's Gold'
	- 'Arnold's Gold'	see *E. arborea* 'Albert's Gold'
	- 'Estrella Gold' ♀ H4	CDoC CMac CNCN CSBt EBre EHea ELan EPfP LRHS MAsh MBar MGos NBlu EBrw SPar SPer SPla WBan WStI
*	- 'Picos Pygmy'	EHea SDys
	- 'Spanish Lime'	SDys
	- 'Spring Smile'	EHea
	australis ♀ H4	CBcs LRHS MBar
	- 'Castellar Blush'	CNCN EHea SBrw
	- 'Holehird'	EHea
	- 'Mr Robert' ♀ H3	CNCN EHea EPfP LRHS MBar
	- 'Riverslea' ♀ H4	CNCN EHea LRHS MBar MOke SBod SBrw SPar SPer WBcn
	caffra	CTrC EHea SPlb
	canaliculata ♀ H3	CBcs CTrC EHea SBrw
	carnea	ELan
	- 'Accent'	EHea
	- 'Adrienne Duncan' ♀ H4	CNCN EHea GKir MBar MBri MGos MOke NDlv NHol WTel
	- 'Alan Coates'	CNCN EHea MBar
	- 'Alba'	EHea
	- 'Altadena'	CNCN EHea MBar
	- 'Amy Backhouse'	CMac
	- 'Amy Doncaster'	see *E. carnea* 'Treasure Trove'
	- 'Ann Sparkes' ♀ H4	CMac CNCN EBre EHea GKir LGro MBar MBri MGos MOke MWat NBlu NHol SPla
	- 'Atrorubra'	CNCN EHea MBar NHol
	- 'Aurea'	CMac CNCN EHea LGro MBar MBri MOke NDlv NHol

- 'Barry Sellers' — EHea LRHS NHol
- 'Bell's Extra Special' — EHea
- 'Beoley Pink' — CNCN EHea
- 'C.J. Backhouse' — EHea
- 'Carnea' — CNCN EHea MBar MOke NHol
- 'Catherine Kolster' — EHea
- 'Cecilia M. Beale' — CNCN EHea MBar NHol
- 'Challenger' ♀ H4 — CNCN EBre EHea EPfP MBar MBri MGos NHol SCoo SPla
- 'Christine Fletcher' — EHea
- 'Clare Wilkinson' — CNCN EHea
- 'David's Seedling' — EHea
- 'December Red' — CBcs CMac CNCN EBre EHea EPfP MBar MBri MOke MWat NHol SPla WBan
- 'Dommesmoen' — EHea
- 'Dwingeloo Pride' — EHea
- 'Early Red' — EHea
- 'Eileen Porter' — CMac CNCN EHea LPVe MBar WBcn
- 'Foxhollow' ♀ H4 — CMac CNCN EBre EHea EPfP GKir IArd LGro MBar MBri MGos MOke MWat NHol SPla WBan WTel
- 'Foxhollow Fairy' — CBcs CBrm CNCN EHea MBar SRms
- 'Gelber Findling' — EHea
- 'Golden Starlet' ♀ H4 — CMac CNCN EHea EPfP LGro MBar MGos NBlu NHol SPla WBan
- 'Gracilis' — EHea MBar NDlv NHol
- 'Hamburg' **new** — EHea
- 'Heathwood' — CNCN EHea MBar NHol SCoo SRms
- 'Hilletje' — CNCN EHea NHol
- 'Ice Princess' ♀ H4 — CNCN EHea EPfP NHol SCoo SPla WBan WBcn
- 'Isabell' ♀ H4 — CNCN EHea LRHS SCoo SPla WBan WBcn
- 'Jack Stitt' — EHea MBar
- 'James Backhouse' — CNCN CTri EHea NHol
- 'January Sun' — EHea NHol
- 'Jason Attwater' — EHea
- 'Jean' — CNCN EHea LRHS NHol
- 'Jennifer Anne' — CNCN EHea MBar
- 'John Kampa' — CNCN EHea MBar NHol
- 'John Pook' — EHea
- 'King George' — CMac CNCN CTri EHea GKir MBar MGos MWat NHol WTel
- 'Kramer's Rubin' — EHea
- 'Lake Garda' — EHea NHol
- 'Late Pink' — EHea
- 'Lesley Sparkes' — EHea MBar
- 'Little Peter' — EHea
- 'Lohse's Rubin' — EHea NBlu NDlv
- 'Lohse's Rubinschimmer' **new**
- 'Loughrigg' ♀ H4 — CMac CNCN CTri EHea GKir MBar MOke NHol SPla WStl WTel
- Madame Seedling — see *E. carnea* 'Weisse March Seedling'
- 'March Seedling' — CNCN EBre EHea MBar MBri MGos MOke NHol SPla WStl WTel
- 'Margery Frearson' — EHea
- 'Martin' — EHea
- 'Moonlight' — EHea
- 'Mrs Sam Doncaster' — CNCN EHea MBar
- 'Myretoun Ruby' ♀ H4 — CBcs CMac CNCN EBre EHea GKir LGro MBar MBri MGos MOke NDlv NHol SPla WTel
- 'Nathalie' ♀ H4 — CNCN EHea LRHS NHol SCoo WBan WBcn
- 'Netherfield Orange' — EHea
- 'Orient' — EHea
- 'Pallida' — EHea
- 'Pink Beauty' — see *E. carnea* 'Pink Pearl'
- 'Pink Cloud' — CNCN EHea
- 'Pink Mist' — EHea LRHS

§ - 'Pink Pearl' — CNCN EHea MBar
- 'Pink Spangles' ♀ H4 — CBcs CMac CNCN EBre EHea GKir MBar MBri MGos MOke NHol WTel
- 'Pirbright Rose' — CNCN EHea MGos
- 'Polden Pride' — EHea
- 'Porter's Red' — EHea LRHS MBar WBan
- 'Praecox Rubra' ♀ H4 — CBcs CNCN EHea GKir LGro MBar MGos MOke NHol
- 'Prince of Wales' — CNCN EHea NHol
- 'Queen Mary' — CNCN EHea
- 'Queen of Spain' — EHea MBri MOke
- 'R.B. Cooke' ♀ H4 — CBrm CNCN EHea EPfP MBar MBri SCoo SPla
- 'Red Rover' — EHea
- 'Robert Jan' — EHea
- 'Romance' — EHea
- 'Rosalie' ♀ H4 — CBcs CNCN EHea IArd LRHS NHol SCoo SPla WBan WBcn
- 'Rosalinde Schorn' — EHea NHol
- 'Rosantha' — EHea NHol
- 'Rosea' — EHea
- 'Rosy Gem' — CNCN EHea MBar
- 'Rosy Morn' — EHea
- 'Rotes Juwel' — EHea LRHS
- 'Rubinteppich' — CNCN EHea
- 'Rubra' — EHea GKir
- 'Ruby Glow' — CNCN EHea GKir MBar MOke NDlv NHol SPla WTel
- 'Scatterley' — EHea
- 'Schatzalp' — EHea
- 'Schneekuppe' — EHea NHol
- 'Schneesturm' — EHea
§ - 'Sherwood Creeping' — EHea MBar
- 'Sherwoodii' — see *E. carnea* 'Sherwood Creeping'
- 'Smart's Heath' — CNCN EHea NHol
- 'Sneznick' — EHea
- 'Snow Prince' — EHea
- 'Snow Queen' — CMac CNCN EHea MBar
- 'Snow White' **new** — EHea
- 'Spring Cottage Crimson' — EHea MBar
- 'Spring Day' — EHea
- 'Springwood Pink' — CBcs CBrm CNCN CTri EHea LGro MBar MBri MGos MOke MWat NHol WTel
- 'Springwood White' ♀ H4 — CBcs CBrm CNCN EBre EHea EPfP GKir LGro MBar MBri MGos MOke MWat NHol SPla WTel
- 'Startler' — EHea LRHS MBar NHol
- 'Sunshine Rambler' ♀ H4 — CNCN EHea MBar MGos NHol
- 'Thomas Kingscote' — CNCN EHea MBar
§ - 'Treasure Trove' — CMac EHea NHol
- 'Tybesta Gold' — CNCN EHea NHol
- 'Urville' — see *E. carnea* 'Vivellii'
- 'Viking' — CNCN EHea NHol
§ - 'Vivellii' ♀ H4 — CNCN CTri EBre EHea GKir MBar MBri MOke MWat NDlv NHol SPla WTel
- 'Vivellii Aurea' — EHea
- 'Walter Reisert' — CNCN EHea
- 'Wanda' — EHea MBar
- 'Weisse March Seedling' — EHea
- 'Wentwood Red' — EHea
- 'Westwood Yellow' ♀ H4 — CMac CNCN EBre EHea GKir LGro MBar MBri MGos NHol SPla
- Whisky — see *E. carnea* 'Bell's Extra Special'
- 'White Glow' — CMac
- 'Whitehall' — EHea LRHS NHol
- 'Winter Beauty' — CNCN EHea GKir MGos MOke NDlv NHol
- 'Winter Gold' — EHea

- 'Winter Melody'	EHea
- Winter Rubin	see *E. carnea* 'Kramer's Rubin'
- 'Winter Snow'	EHea SCoo
- 'Winter Sports'	EHea
- 'Winterfreude'	EHea NHol
- 'Wintersonne'	CBcs EHea LGro NHol
ciliaris alba	EHea
- 'Aurea'	CMac CNCN EHea MBar SRms
- 'Camla'	EHea MBar
- 'Corfe Castle'	CNCN EHea MBar
- 'David McClintock'	CNCN EHea GKir MBar
- 'Globosa'	EHea
- 'Maweana'	EHea
- 'Mrs C.H. Gill' ♀ H4	CMac CNCN EHea MGos
- 'Ram'	EHea
- 'Rotundiflora'	EHea
- 'Stapehill'	EHea
- 'Stoborough' ♀ H4	CNCN EHea MBar
- 'White Wings'	CNCN EHea
- 'Wych'	EHea
cinerea f. *alba*	CMac
- 'Alba Major'	CNCN EHea MBar
- 'Alba Minor' ♀ H4	CNCN EHea MBar MBri MHdf
	MOke NHol
- 'Alette'	EHea
- 'Alfred Bowerman'	EHea
- 'Alice Ann Davies'	EHea
- 'Angarrack'	EHea
- 'Anja Bakker' **new**	EHea
- 'Anja Blum'	EHea
- 'Anja Siegers'	EHea
- 'Ann Berry'	CNCN EHea MBar
- 'Apple Blossom'	EHea
- 'Apricot Charm'	CNCN EHea MBar
- 'Aquarel'	EHea
- 'Ashdown Forest'	EHea
- 'Ashgarth Garnet'	EHea MBar
- 'Atropurpurea'	CNCN EHea MBar NDlv
- 'Atrorubens'	EHea GKir MBar SRms
- 'Atrorubens, Daisy Hill'	EHea
- 'Atrosanguinea'	CNCN MBar
- 'Atrosanguinea Reuthe's Variety'	EHea
- 'Atrosanguinea Smith's Variety'	EHea
- 'Baylay's Variety'	EHea MBar
- 'Blossom Time'	EHea MBar
- 'Brick'	EHea
- 'Bucklebury Red'	EHea
- 'C.D. Eason' ♀ H4	CBcs CMac CNCN EHea EPfP GKir
	MBar MBri MGos MOke NHol
§ - 'C.G. Best' ♀ H4	CMac CNCN ECho EHea MBar
- 'Cairn Valley'	EHea
- 'Caldy Island'	EHea MBar
- 'Carnea'	EHea
- 'Carnea Underwood's Variety'	EHea
- 'Celebration'	EHea
- 'Cevennes'	CMac CNCN EHea MBar MOke
- 'Champs Hill'	EHea
- 'Cindy' ♀ H4	CNCN EHea MBar MOke NHol
- 'Coccinea'	CNCN EHea
- 'Colligan Bridge'	EHea MBar
- 'Constance'	EHea MBar
- 'Contrast'	EHea LRHS MBar
- 'Daphne Maginess'	CNCN
- 'Discovery'	EHea
- 'Doctor Small's Seedling'	EHea
- 'Domino'	CNCN EHea MBar MGos MOke
- 'Duncan Fraser'	CNCN EHea MBar
- 'Eden Valley' ♀ H4	CMac CNCN EHea GKir MBar
	MGos NHol SRms
- 'Eline' **new**	EHea
- 'England'	EHea
- 'Felthorpe'	EHea
- 'Fiddler's Gold' ♀ H4	CNCN EHea MBar MBri MOke
	NBlu NDlv NHol
- 'Flamingo'	EHea
- 'Foxhollow Mahogany'	EHea MBar
- 'Frances'	EHea
- 'Frankrijk' **new**	EHea
- 'Fred Corston'	EHea
- 'G. Osmond'	EHea MBar MOke
- 'Geke'	EHea
- 'Glasnevin Red'	EHea MBar
- 'Glencairn'	EHea MBar NHol
- 'Godrevy'	EHea
- 'Golden Charm'	CMac CNCN EHea NHol
- 'Golden Drop'	CNCN EHea GKir MBar MBri
	MOke NHol
- 'Golden Hue' ♀ H4	CMac CNCN EHea MBar MOke
	NDlv NHol
- 'Golden Sport'	EHea MGos
- 'Golden Tee'	EHea
- 'Graham Thomas'	see *E. cinerea* 'C.G. Best'
- 'Grandiflora'	EHea
- 'Guernsey Lime'	EHea MBar
- 'Guernsey Pink'	EHea
- 'Guernsey Plum'	EHea
- 'Guernsey Purple'	EHea
- 'Hardwick's Rose'	CNCN EHea MBar
- 'Harry Fulcher'	CNCN EHea MBri MGos MOke
- 'Heatherbank'	EHea
- 'Heathfield'	EHea
- 'Heidebrand'	EHea MBar
- 'Hermann Dijkhuizen'	EHea
- 'Honeymoon'	EHea MBar
- 'Hookstone Lavender'	EHea
- 'Hookstone White'	CNCN EHea MBar NDlv
♀ H4	
- 'Hutton's Seedling'	EHea
- 'Iberian Beauty'	EHea
- 'Jack London'	CNCN EHea
- 'Janet'	EHea MBar
- 'Jersey Wonder'	EHea
- 'Jim Hardy'	EHea
- 'Jiri'	EHea
- 'John Ardron'	EHea
- 'John Eason'	EHea
- 'Jos' Golden' **new**	EHea
- 'Jos' Honeymoon' **new**	EHea
- 'Joseph Murphy'	CNCN EHea MBar
- 'Joseph Rock'	EHea
- 'Josephine Ross'	EHea MBar
- 'Joyce Burfitt'	CNCN EHea
- 'Katinka'	CNCN EHea MBar NHol
- 'Kerry Cherry'	EHea
- 'Knap Hill Pink' ♀ H4	CNCN EHea MBar
- 'Lady Skelton'	EHea MBar
- 'Lavender Lady'	EHea
- 'Lilac Time'	EHea MBar
- 'Lilacina'	EHea MBar MOke
- 'Lime Soda' ♀ H4	CMac CNCN EHea MBri
- 'Lorna Anne Hutton'	EHea
- 'Maginess Pink'	CNCN
- 'Marina'	EHea
- 'Michael Hugo'	CNCN EHea
- 'Miss Waters'	EHea MBar
- 'Mrs Dill'	EHea MBar
- 'Mrs E.A. Mitchell'	CNCN EHea LRHS MOke SPlb
- 'Mrs Ford'	EHea MBar
- 'My Love'	CNCN EHea MBar MBri MOke
- 'Nell'	EHea MBar
- 'Nellie Dawson'	EHea
- 'Newick Lilac'	EHea MBar MOke

	– 'Next Best'	EHea MBar
	– 'Novar'	EHea
	– 'Old Rose'	EHea
	– 'P.S. Patrick' ♀ H4	CNCN EHea GKir MBar
	– 'Pallas'	EHea
	– 'Pallida'	EHea
	– 'Patricia Maginess'	CNCN
	– 'Peñaz'	EHea
	– 'Pentreath' ♀ H4	CNCN EHea MBar MBri MOke
	– 'Pink Foam'	EHea MBar
	– 'Pink Ice' ♀ H4	CMac CNCN EBre EHea EPfP GKir MBar MBri MGos MOke NDlv NHol
	– 'Plummer's Seedling'	EHea MBar
	– 'Promenade' **new**	EHea
	– 'Prostrate Lavender'	EHea
	– 'Providence'	EHea LRHS
	– 'Purple Beauty'	CNCN EHea MBar MGos MOke
	– 'Purple Robe'	EHea LRHS
	– 'Purple Spreader'	EHea
	– 'Purpurea'	EHea
	– 'Pygmaea'	EHea MBar
	– 'Red Pentreath'	EHea
	– 'Robert Michael'	EHea
	– 'Rock Pool'	EHea MBar NHol
	– 'Rock Ruth'	EHea
	– 'Romiley'	EHea MBar MBri MOke
	– 'Rose Queen'	EHea
	– 'Rosea'	EHea
*	– 'Rosea Splendens'	EHea
	– 'Rosy Chimes'	CNCN EHea MBar
	– 'Rozanne Waterer'	EHea
	– 'Ruby'	CMac CNCN EHea MBar
	– 'Sandpit Hill'	EHea MBar
	– 'Schizopetala'	CNCN EHea MBar
	– 'Screel' **new**	EHea
	– 'Sea Foam'	CNCN EHea MBar
	– 'Sherry'	CNCN EHea MBar
	– 'Smith's Lawn'	EHea
	– 'Snow Cream'	EHea MBar
	– 'Son of Cevennes'	MGos
	– 'Spicata'	EHea
	– 'Splendens'	CNCN EHea
	– 'Startler'	EHea MBri MOke
	– 'Stephen Davis' ♀ H4	CNCN EBre EHea GKir MBar MBri MOke NBlu NHol
	– 'Strawberry Bells'	EHea
	– 'Sue Lloyd'	EHea
	– 'Summer Gold'	CNCN EHea LRHS NDlv
	– 'Tilford'	EHea
	– 'Tom Waterer'	EHea MBar
	– 'Uschie Ziehmann'	EHea
	– 'Velvet Night' ♀ H4	CMac CNCN EHea GKir MBar MBri MOke NHol SRms
	– 'Victoria'	EHea MBar
	– 'Violacea'	EHea
	– 'Violetta'	CNCN EHea
	– 'Vivienne Patricia'	EHea MBar
	– 'W.G. Notley'	EHea
	– 'West End'	EHea
	– 'White Dale'	EHea MBar
	– 'Windlebrooke' ♀ H4	CNCN EHea MBar MGos NHol
	– 'Wine'	EHea
	– 'Yvonne'	EHea
	curviflora	EHea SPlb
	x darleyensis	WTel
	– 'Ada S. Collings'	CNCN EHea MBar
	– 'Alba'	see E. x *darleyensis* 'Silberschmelze'
	– 'Archie Graham'	EHea
	– 'Arthur Johnson' ♀ H4	CBcs CMac CNCN EBre EHea MBri MGos MOke NHol SRms
	– 'Aurélie Brégeon'	EHea

	– 'Cherry Stevens'	see E. x *darleyensis* 'Furzey'
§	– 'Darley Dale'	CBcs CMac CNCN EBre EHea EPfP MBar MBri MOke NHol SCoo
	– 'Dunreggan'	EHea
	– 'Dunwood Splendour'	MBar
	– 'Epe'	EHea
	– 'Erecta'	EHea
§	– 'Furzey' ♀ H4	CMac CNCN EHea GKir MBar MBri MGos MOke NDlv NHol SCoo SRms WTel
	– 'George Rendall'	CMac CNCN CTri EHea GKir NHol SCoo SPla
	– 'Ghost Hills' ♀ H4	CBcs CBrm CNCN EBre EHea MBar MOke NHol SCoo
	– 'J.W. Porter' ♀ H4	CBcs CNCN EHea EPfP MBar MOke NDlv SCoo SPla WTel
§	– 'Jack H. Brummage'	CMac CNCN CTri EBre EHea GKir IArd MBar MBri MGos MOke NHol SPla WTel
	– 'James Smith'	EHea MBar
	– 'Jenny Porter' ♀ H4	CMac CNCN EHea MBar MBri MOke WBan
	– 'Kramer's Rote' ♀ H4	CBrm CMac CNCN CTri EBre EHea EPfP GKir MBar MBri MGos MOke NBlu NDlv NHol SPla WBan
	– 'Margaret Porter'	CBcs CMac CNCN EHea SPla WTel
	– 'Mary Helen'	CBcs CBrm CNCN EHea EPfP LRHS MGos NHol SCoo WBan WBcn
	– Molten Silver	see E. x *darleyensis* 'Silberschmelze'
	– 'Mrs Parris' Red'	EHea
	– 'N.R. Webster'	CNCN EHea
	– 'Pink Perfection'	see E. x *darleyensis* 'Darley Dale'
§	– 'Silberschmelze'	CBcs CMac CNCN CTri EBre EHea EPfP GKir MBar MBri MGos MOke NBlu NDlv NHol WTel
	– 'Spring Surprise' PBR	EHea
	– 'W.G. Pine'	EHea
	– 'White Fairy' **new**	EHea
	– 'White Glow'	CNCN CTri EHea NHol
	– 'White Perfection' ♀ H4	CBcs CNCN EBre EHea EPfP IArd MBar MBri NHol SCoo SPla
	discolor	EHea
	erigena 'Alba'	CMac EHea MBar
	– 'Brian Proudley'	CNCN EHea MBar
	– 'Brightness'	CBcs CNCN EHea EPfP GKir MBar MBri MOke NDlv NHol SCoo WTel
	– 'Coccinea'	EHea
	– 'Ewan Jones'	CNCN EHea MBar
	– 'Glauca'	EHea
	– 'Golden Lady' ♀ H4	CMac CNCN EHea MBar MBri MGos MOke NBlu NHol SCoo
	– 'Hibernica'	EHea GKir
	– 'Hibernica Alba'	EHea MBar
	– 'Irish Dusk' ♀ H4	CNCN EBre EHea GKir MBar MBri MGos MOke NHol SCoo SRms
	– 'Irish Salmon'	CMac CNCN EHea MBar NDlv
	– 'Irish Silver'	MBar MBri
	– 'Maxima'	EHea
	– 'Mrs Parris' Lavender'	EHea
	– 'Mrs Parris' White'	EHea
	– 'Nana'	EHea
	– 'Nana Alba'	CNCN EHea MBar
	– 'Nana Compacta'	EHea
	– 'Rosea'	EHea MBar
	– 'Rosslare'	EHea
	– 'Rubra'	EHea NDlv
	– 'Superba'	CMac CNCN EHea MBar MGos MOke
	– 'Thing Nee'	EHea
	– 'W.T. Rackliff' ♀ H4	CBcs CNCN EBre EHea EPfP GKir

	- 'Charm'	EHea
	- 'Chittendenii'	EHea
	- 'Cornish Cream' ♀ H4	CNCN EHea EPfP MBar MHdf NHol
	- 'Cream'	CNCN EHea MOke
	- 'Diana Hornibrook'	CNCN EHea MBar MOke
	- 'Diana's Gold'	EHea
	- 'Fiddlestone'	CNCN EHea GKir MBar
	- 'French White'	CNCN EHea MBar
	- 'George Underwood'	EHea MBar
	- 'Golden Triumph'	EHea MBar NHol WBan
	- 'Grandiflora'	CNCN EHea MBar
	- 'Holden Pink'	CNCN EHea MOke
	- 'Hookstone Rosea'	EHea MBar
	- 'Ida M. Britten'	EHea MBar
	- 'J.C. Fletcher'	EHea
	- 'Kevernensis Alba' ♀ H4	EHea MBar
	- 'Leucantha'	EHea
	- 'Lilacina'	CMac CNCN EHea MBar
	- 'Lyonesse' ♀ H4	CMac CNCN EBre EHea MBar MBri MGos MOke NHol SRms
	- 'Miss Waterer'	EHea MBar
	- 'Mrs D.F. Maxwell' ♀ H4	CBcs CMac CNCN EBre EHea GKir MBar MBri MGos MOke NHol SRms WBan
	- 'Mrs Donaldson'	EHea
§	- 'Nana'	EHea MBar
	- 'Pallida'	CNCN EHea
	- 'Peach Blossom'	EHea MBar
	- 'Pyrenees Pink'	CMac CNCN EHea MBar MOke
	- 'Rosea'	EHea
	- 'Rubra'	CNCN EHea MBar
	- 'Saint Keverne'	CMac CNCN CTri EHea GKir IArd MBar MGos MOke NHol WBan
	- 'Summertime'	CNCN EHea MBar
	- 'Valerie Proudley' ♀ H4	CBcs CMac CNCN EBre EHea GKir MBar MBri MGos MOke MWat NBlu NHol SRms
	- 'Valerie Smith'	EHea
	- 'Viridiflora'	CNCN EHea MBar
	- 'White Giant'	EHea
	- 'White Lady'	EHea MBar
	- 'White Rocket'	CNCN EHea MBar
	- 'White Spire'	EHea
	- 'Yellow John'	CNCN EHea MBar NBlu WBan
	x *veitchii* 'Brockhill'	EHea SDys
	- 'Exeter' ♀ H3	CNCN CSBt EHea ELan EPfP LRHS MAsh MBar SBrw WBcn
	- 'Gold Tips' ♀ H4	CNCN CSBt EHea MAsh MBar MBri MGos SBrw
	- 'Pink Joy'	CNCN EHea MAsh MBri MOke SBrw
	ventricosa **new**	EHea
	verticillata	CTrC EHea
	x *watsonii* 'Cherry Turpin'	EHea
	- 'Dawn' ♀ H4	CNCN EHea MBar MBri
	- 'Dorothy Metheny'	EHea
	- 'Dorset Beauty'	EHea
§	- 'F.White'	EHea MBar
	- 'Gwen'	CNCN EHea MBar
	- 'H. Maxwell'	CNCN EHea
	- 'Mary'	EHea
	- 'Morning Mist'	EHea
	- 'Pink Pacific'	EHea
	- 'Rachel'	EHea
	- 'Truro'	EHea
	x *williamsii* 'Cow-y-Jack'	EHea
	- 'Croft Pascoe' **new**	EHea
	- 'David Coombe'	EHea
	- 'Gew Graze'	EHea
	- 'Gold Button'	EHea MBar
	- 'Gwavas'	CNCN EHea MBar
	- 'Jean Julian' **new**	EHea

	- 'Ken Wilson'	EHea SDys
	- 'Lizard Downs'	EHea
	- 'Marion Hughes' **new**	EHea
	- 'P.D. Williams' ♀ H4	CNCN EHea MBar

Erigeron ✿ (*Asteraceae*)

	from Bald Mountains	NWCA
	from Big Horns	WOBN
	acer	CKin WHer
	'Adria'	EBee EBre EChP GBuc LRHS NGdn SPer WMnd
§	*alpinus*	EHol GKir GTou LRHS MOne NPPs
	'Amity'	EBre GMac
	aurantiacus	EDAr EHol EPfP GMaP LPVe MAvo MHer MWgw MWrn NBro NJOw NOak NPPs SPet
§	*aureus*	NSla WAbe
	- NNS 96-87	NWCA
§	- 'Canary Bird' ♀ H4	EPfP GCrs NBir NHar NMen SIng SPer WAbe WLin WWeb
*	'Azure Beauty'	EPfP LRHS NFla NPro
	Azure Fairy	see *E.* 'Azurfee'
§	'Azurfee'	CSBt EBee ELan ENot EPfP ERou GKir GMaP LPVe MBNS MHer NBir NMir NOak SPer SPla SWal WHen WMoo WPer WWin
	Black Sea	see *E.* 'Schwarzes Meer'
	bloomeri var. *bloomeri* **new**	LTwo
	blue	WBar
	'Blue Beauty'	LRHS SRms
	'Charity'	ERou LRHS MRav SSpe WBrE
	chrysopsidis 'Grand Ridge'	CPBP EHyt EPfP LHop LRHS LTwo NWCA SBla
	compositus	ITim SRms WPer
§	- var. *discoideus*	EBur ESis GKir NMen SPlb WPer
	- 'Rocky'	ECho
	Darkest of All	see *E.* 'Dunkelste Aller'
	deep pink	CHEx
	'Dignity'	EBee EFou EGle ELan ERou MCLN MWat NBro SHel SPer SSpe SUsu WCot WFar WPGP
	'Dimity'	CMea ECha EDAr MBri WAbe WFar WWin
§	'Dunkelste Aller' ♀ H3	More than 30 suppliers
	'Felicity'	EBee ERou
	flettii	EBee WPer WWin
	'Foersters Liebling' ♀ H4	CMGP CStr EBee EGle ENot EPfP GKir GMac LAst LRHS MBri MCAu MNrw MWat NFla NGdn SBla SHel SPet WCot
	'Four Winds'	EBre ECtt EDAr ELan ESis EWes LHop LRHS MRav NGdn NJOw NMen WPer WWeb
	'Gaiety'	EBee EFou
	glaucus	CAgr COIW CSBt EBee EHol EMar EWll GMaP IHMH LHrt NCat NLon NVic SMad SMrm WBea WCot WFar WLRN WWeb
	- 'Albus'	LHop LRHS SMad WBea WPer
	- 'Elstead Pink'	CTri EBee EBre EChP SAga WEas WFar WWeb
	- pink	NCat
*	- 'Roger Raiche'	WCot
	- 'Roseus'	CBcs CHal ECha ERou NLon
	- 'Sea Breeze'	COIW NBlu NPri WWeb
	'Goat Rocks'	GCrs
	howellii	EBee
	hyssopifolius	WHil
§	*karvinskianus* ♀ H3	More than 30 suppliers
	leiomerus	EFou LBee LTwo NWCA
	linearis	NMen WAbe
	'Mrs F.H. Beale'	EFou SCro

	mucronatus	see *E. karvinskianus*
	'Nachthimmel'	EBee EMan NGdn SHel SPet
	nanus	NWCA WPer
	oreganus	EBre IIve
§	*peregrinus*	NOak
	philadelphicus	CElw IGor NBir NBro SUsu
	'Pink Beauty'	ECtt MPWC
	Pink Jewel	see *E.* 'Rosa Juwel'
	Pink Triumph	see *E.* 'Rosa Triumph'
	pinnatisectus	NWCA WPer
	'Profusion'	see *E. karvinskianus*
	'Prosperity'	EBee
	pyrenaicus hort.	see *E. alpinus*
	'Quakeress'	CElw CSam EBre EFou EMan GKir
		GMac LRHS MRav NBro SHel SMrm
		SSpe SUsu WCot WFar WRHF WTel
§	'Rosa Juwel'	CBri CSBt CTri EBee ECtt ENot EPfP
		GAbr GKir IBal LPVe LRHS MBNS
		MHer MTis NBir NFla NMir NOak
		SEND SPer SPla SRms SWal WHen
		WMnd WMoo WPer WWeb
§	'Rosa Triumph'	EBee EFou
	'Rosenballett'	EBre
	'Rotes Meer'	EBee ELan LRHS MBri MCLN
	rotundifolius	see *Bellis rotundifolia*
	'Caerulescens'	'Caerulescens'
	salsuginosus	see *E. peregrinus*
	(Richardson) A. Gray	
§	'Schneewittchen'	CMGP EBee EChP EFou ELan
		EMan EPfP LAst LHop MRav MWat
		MWgw NSti NVic SCro SPla SPoG
§	'Schwarzes Meer'	EBee ERou GKir LRHS NGdn SPer
		WCot WFar WTel
	scopulinus	CGra CNic CPBP EHyt ITim
		LRHS
	simplex	CPBP LRHS MWat NMen
	'Sincerity'	EFou
	'Snow Queen'	WFar
	Snow White	see *E.* 'Schneewittchen'
	'Sommerabend'	EBee
	'Sommerneuschnee'	ECha NPri WMnd
*	'Spanish Daisy'	LAst
	speciosus	EBee SMer
	- var. *macranthus*	SIgm
	'Strahlenmeer'	EBee LRHS MWgw WMnd
	trifidus	see *E. compositus* var. *discoideus*
	tweedyi	NBro
	uncialis var. *conjugans*	CGra
	uniflorus	LTwo
	vagus	LTwo WWln
	'Wayne Roderick'	SMac
	'White Quakeress'	CElw CMea EGle ERou GBuc
		MAnH MAvo NGar WCot WRHF
	'Wuppertal'	EBee EMan MRav NBro NGdn
		WMnd

Erinacea (Papilionaceae)
§	*anthyllis* ♀ H4	CPBP SIng SOkd
	pungens	see *E. anthyllis*

Erinus (Scrophulariaceae)
	alpinus ♀ H4	CMHG CMea EBot ECtt EMlt EPfP
		ESis GKir GTou MBro MPWC MWat
		NBlu NBro NFor NHol SPet SRms
		WCom WEas WFar WPer WWin
	- var. *albus*	CBot EMlt GDra GTou MBro NHol
		NLAp NMen NWCA SRms WAbe
		WCom WHoo WPer
	- 'Doktor Hähnle'	CNic EBre EDAr EMlt GKir LRHS
		NLAp NMen SGar SIng SRms
		WHoo WRHF
	- 'Mrs Charles Boyle'	MBro
	- 'Roseus'	NLAp

Eriobotrya (Rosaceae)
	deflexa	CFil CHEx
	japonica (F) ♀ H3	More than 30 suppliers

Eriocapitella see *Anemone*

Eriocephalus (Asteraceae)
	africanus	SPlb WJek

Eriogonum (Polygonaceae)
	brevicaule var. *nanum*	NWCA
	cespitosum	CGra WLin
	- subsp. *douglasii*	see *E. douglasii*
§	*douglasii*	WLin
	flavum	GEdr WPer
	jamesii	WPat
	kennedyi var.	WLin
	alpigenum	
	ovalifolium	WLin
	- var. *depressum*	CStu NWCA
	thymoides	CGra
	umbellatum	ECha EPot LRHS NLAp
	- var. *humistratum*	SBla WLin
	- var. *porteri*	NWCA
	- var. *subalpinum*	WAbe
	- var. *torreyanum*	CMea MBro NHol WPat
	- var. *umbellatum*	LBee
	wrightii	WLin

Eriophorum (Cyperaceae)
	angustifolium	CBen CBrm COIW CWat EGle
		EHoe EHon EMFW ENot EPPr
		FPla GOrn LPBA MCCP MMoz
		MSta SPlb SWal SWat WHer
		WMAq WPer WWLb WWpp
	latifolium	LPBA
	vaginatum	CRow EHoe SWal WWeb

Eriophyllum (Asteraceae)
	lanatum	CFis CHal EBee ECha EPfP EWTr
		MCAu MEHN MWat NArg NBid
		SAga SBla SCro WCom WRHF
		WWeb WWin
	- 'Bella'	NLar
*	- 'Pointe'	GSki
	nevinii **new**	EBee

Eriostemon (Rutaceae)
	'Cascade of Stars' **new**	SOWG

Eritrichium (Boraginaceae)
	- var. *pectinatum*	NEgg NSla

Erodium ✿ (Geraniaceae)
	absinthoides	LRHS MDHE
	- from Genoa	MDHE
	- var. *amanum*	see *E. amanum*
§	*acaule*	CBrm EMan GSki NCiC NMGW
	'Almodovar' **new**	MDHE
	alpinum	MDHE
§	*amanum*	CElw EBee LRHS MDHE WAbe
	'Ardwick Redeye'	CElw MDHE SRot
	balearicum	see *E. x variabile* 'Album'
§	'Bidderi'	MDHE NChi WAbe
	'Burnside Silver'	MDHE
	'Carla'	MDHE
	'Carmel'	MDHE
	'Caroline'	CElw MBro WHoo WTin
	carvifolium	CElw CMea EBee GKir LRHS MDHE
		NMGW NWCA WFar WLin WPnn
§	*castellanum*	CLyd EBee GCrs GKir NBro
		NMen NSti SBla SRms

	– 'Cupidon' **new**	MDHE
	– 'Dujardin' **new**	MDHE
	– 'La Féline'	MDHE
	'Catherine Bunuel'	MDHE
	celtibericum	MDHE
	– 'Javalambre' **new**	MDHE
	– 'Peñagolosa'	SIgm
	chamaedryoides	see *E. reichardii*
§	*cheilanthifolium*	EBee MDHE NFla SHBN
	– 'Bidderi'	see *E.* 'Bidderi'
	– 'David Crocker' **new**	EPot
	chrysanthum	More than 30 suppliers
	– pink	CSpe ECha LPhx NCot SMrm
		SRot SUsu
	– *sulphureum*	WPnn
	corsicum	CNic EBur EHyt ETow MDHE
		MTho NMen SRot WAbe
	– 'Album'	EHyt LTwo MDHE SIng WAbe
§	'County Park'	CLyd CMea CPlt EBee ECha ECou
		EDAr EMlt EWes MDHE MOne
		NMen NRya SBla SChu SHBN
		SRms WAul WCom WPnn
	crispum x *saxatile*	MDHE
	daucoides hort.	see *E. castellanum*
	'Eileen Emmett'	EPot MDHE
	'Elizabeth'	WPnn
§	*foetidum*	EGle ETow MDHE MTis MWat NMen
	– 'County Park'	see *E.* 'County Park'
	– 'Pallidum'	see *E.* 'Pallidum'
	– 'Roseum'	GCal MWat
	'Fran's Choice'	see *E.* 'Fran's Delight'
§	'Fran's Delight'	CElw CMea CSpe MBro MDHE
		WElm WHoo
	'Fripetta'	MDHE
	'Géant de Saint Cyr'	CElw EMan EMon WCot
N	*glandulosum* ♀ H4	CMea EBee EDAr EMlt EPfP GCal
		LBBr MBro MDHE MHer SBla
		SRms WCom WKif WPat
	– 'Emma'	CMea MDHE
	– 'Espiguette'	SIgm
	– 'Marie Poligné'	MDHE
	gruinum	ECoo WPat WPnn WSan WWpP
	guicciardii	EDAr MDHE
	guttatum misapplied	see *Erodium* 'Katherine Joy'
N	*guttatum*	EBee EMan ERou ETow EWTr LPio
		MBri MHer MWat NMen SAga SRms
		WCom WHal WPer WSHC WWeb
	x *hybridum* hort.	see *E.* 'Sara Francesca'
	x *hybridum* Sünderm.	EGle WAbe WHal
	hymenodes L'Hér.	see *E. trifolium*
	jahandiezianum	MDHE NWCA
	'Julie Ritchie'	CMea MDHE WHoo
	'Katherine Joy'	CNic EWes MDHE MOne NChi
		NDlv NLAp NRya SRot WAbe
	x *kolbianum*	MBro MDHE SMrm WAbe WHoo
		WPnn
	– 'Nadia'	MBri
	– 'Natasha'	CMHG CNic EPot EPri EWes GKir
		LBee LRHS MDHE MHer NChi
		NHol NMGW NMen SChu SHBN
		SMrm SWat WAbe WFar WKif WPnn
	'La Belette' **new**	MDHE
	'Las Meninas'	CPlt CRDP
	'Lilac Wonder'	MDHE
	x *lindavicum*	MDHE WPnn
	– 'Charter House'	LPio
	'Lograno Real' **new**	SIgm
	macradenum	see *E. glandulosum*
	manescaui	More than 30 suppliers
	'Maryla'	MDHE
	'Merstham Pink'	GMaP MDHE NChi NLar SBla WLin
	'Mesquita'	CMea
	'Nunwood Pink'	MDHE

§	'Pallidum'	CHal CSam
	'Parma' **new**	MDHE
	pelargoniiflorum	CBot CBri CRDP CSpe EBlw EVFa
		EWes GSki LHrt MAnH MHer
		MTho NBro NChi NDov NLar NPPs
		SMad SRms STes WEas WFar WKif
		WPGP WPer WPnn WWeb WWin
	'Pequenito'	MDHE
	'Peter Vernon' **new**	NWCA
	petraeum subsp.	see *E. cheilanthifolium*
	crispum misapplied	
	– subsp. *glandulosum*	see *E. glandulosum*
	– subsp. *petraeum*	MHer SBla
	'Phanie'	MDHE
	'Pickering Pink'	EPot MDHE NMen SRot SWat
	'Princesse Marion'	MDHE
*	'Purple Haze'	CSpe EBee LIck NPri SRot
	'Rachel'	see *E.* x *willkommianum* 'Rachel'
§	*reichardii*	CElw ECtt EMlt EWTr GMaP GSki
		LBee LRHS MDHE MHer MTho
		NFla NLAp NPPs SBla SPet SRms
		SWat WPnn WTel
	– albino	EPot
	– 'Album'	WHoo WLin
	– 'Bianca'	EChP MLLN SUsu
	– 'Pipsqueak'	MDHE
*	– 'Rubrum'	CElw MDHE
	'Robespierre'	MDHE
	'Robin' **new**	MDHE
	'Rock et Rocaille'	MDHE
	rodiei	MDHE
	– x *glandulosum*	MDHE
	romanum	see *E. acaule*
§	*rupestre*	CBot CMea ECho ECtt GMaP
		MDHE MOne NChi NDlv SAsh
		SBla SRot
	'Santamixa'	MDHE
§	'Sara Francesca'	MDHE
	'Sarck' **new**	MDHE
	sebaceum 'Polly'	NWCA
	'Sierra Celtica'	MDHE
	'Spanish Eyes'	ECha EHyt GKir MAvo MDHE
		NChi SAga SMrm SRot SScr WCot
	'Stephanie'	CFis CLyd EGle EWes GMaP LBee
		LPio LRHS MDHE NChi NHol
		SAsh SHBN SIgm SRot SWal
	supracanum	see *E. rupestre*
	'Tiny Kyni' **new**	MDHE
	tordylioides	EBee
	trichomanifolium hort.	see *E. cheilanthifolium*
	trichomanifolium	EWes LBee LRHS MHer NJOw
	L'Hér.	WPnn
§	*trifolium*	ELan EPfP NChi NCiC NMGW
		NSti SBri SIng SSpi WCru WHal
		WHoo WPnn
§	x *variabile*	CBrm ECtt EHyt MDHE
§	– 'Album'	CMHG EBee EDAr EMNN EPot
		GBuc LBee MBar MDHE MHer
		MTho NHar NHol NPri NWCA
		SBla SHBN SHFr SRms WAbe WEas
		WPat WPer WPnn WTel WWin
I	– 'Bishop's Form'	CMHG EBee ECtt EDAr EMNN EMlt
		EPot ESis LPio LRHS MBar MBro
		MDHE MHer NBro NHar NHol
		NMen NPri NWCA SBla SHBN SIng
		SRms WCom WHoo WPat WWeb
	– 'Derek'	CGra ECho
	– 'Flore Pleno' (d)	EBee ECtt EDAr ELan EMlt EOrc
		EWes MDHE MHer NJOw NMen
		SHBN SHFr SIng SRms SUsu WAbe
		WFar WPer WPnn
	– 'Red Rock'	EWes MDHE SIng
	– 'Roseum' ♀ H4	CBot ECho ECtt EDAr ELan EOrc

		GSki LRHS MDHE MHer NLAp
		NWCA SHBN SRms WAbe WFar
		WPer WWin
	'Veinina'	MDHE
I	'Westacre Seedling'	EWes
	'Whiteleaf'	MDHE
	x *willkommianum*	MDHE NFla
§	- 'Rachel'	MDHE

Erpetion see *Viola*

Eruca (Brassicaceae)

	vesicaria subsp. *sativa*	CArn CBod CSpe ELau GPoy MChe
		MHer MSal NBlu SIde WHHs WHer
		WJek WLHH WSel WWye

Eryngium ✿ (Apiaceae)

	- CD&R 1227	EBee EWes
	- CDPR 3076	CFil WPGP
	- PC&H 268	MAvo MSph NLar
	- RB 94054	MDCh MSph NChi NSti
§	*agavifolium*	More than 30 suppliers
	alpinum ♀ H4	More than 30 suppliers
	- 'Amethyst'	CRDP EBee EFou GBuc LPhx
		LRHS MBri MCLN MSte MTed
		NBro NLar SMrm WCot WWeb
	- 'Blue Star'	CBcs CBot CHar CSpe EBee EBlw
		ECGN EChP EHrv EPfP ERou
		GCal GSki LPhx MSte MWrn
		NHol NLon SSpi WHHs WHil
		WHoo WPer WTel WWeb
	- 'Holden Blue'	CPlt GMac
	- 'Slieve Donard'	see E. x *zabelii* 'Donard Variety'
	- 'Superbum'	CBot CRDP ECGN EHrv GBri
		GSki MNrw NDov NLar NLon
		SBla SMad SRms WSan WViv
	amethystinum	CBot ECGN ECha EGle EHrv EMan
		GSki LPhx MAnH MCAu MNrw
		SChu SIgm SMad WBea WLRN WPer
	biebersteinianum	see E. *caeruleum*
	bourgatii	More than 30 suppliers
	- Graham Stuart	More than 30 suppliers
	Thomas's selection	
	- 'Oxford Blue' ♀ H4	CMea CMil COlW CPom CRDP
		EHrv EPar GMac LPio MMil NLar
		SGar SSpi WCom WEas WOld
	- 'Picos Blue' PBR	EHrv LPhx MBro SMrm WCom
		WHoo WPGP WTin
	bromeliifolium hort.	see E. *agavifolium*
§	*caeruleum*	EBee GBuc MNrw NChi SIng
§	*campestre*	CBot EWll MDKP MHer NChi
		NGby NLar SIgm WFar WPer
	carlinae	LPhx
	caucasicum	see E. *caeruleum*
	creticum	EBee NBir NBro
	Delaroux	see E. *proteiflorum*
	dichotomum	EMon EPPr NChi
	ebracteatum	CHad EBee GCal LPhx LPio SIgm
		WCot
	- var. *poterioides*	LPhx SMad
§	*eburneum*	CBot CPom EBee EBre ECha ECoo
		EMon EPfP EWes GBuc LEdu LPio
		LRHS MAnH MGrG MWgw NBro
		NChi WCot WFar WPic
	foetidum	CArn
§	*giganteum* ♀ H4	More than 30 suppliers
	- 'Silver Ghost' ♀ H4	More than 30 suppliers
	glaciale	WAbe
	horridum	CFil CFwr EBee EBre EWTr EWes
		GAbr LEdu LPhx LRHS MAnH
		MCAu MFir MNrw MWod NBro
		NChi SAPC SArc SIgm WAul WFar
		WHer WWhi WWin

	- HCM 98048	WCru
	'Jos Eijking' PBR	EMan ENot GKir LRHS MRav
		NLar WBro
	maritimum	CArn CBot CPou CSpe GPoy
		LPhx MAvo MCAu MHer NLar
		SIgm SPlb WAbe WCot WFar WSel
	Miss Willmott's ghost	see E. *giganteum*
	monocephalum new	WPGP
	x *oliverianum* ♀ H4	CHad CMea CRDP CSam EBlw
		EFou EHrv ELan EMan ENot GBuc
		GMac LRHS MAvo MBro MCAu
		SDix SIgm SPer WCot
	palmatum new	EBee
§	*pandanifolium*	CFwr CHEx CHar CKno CMHG
		CRez CRoM CTCP CTrG EBee
		EBlw EMan EPfP EWes GCal IBlr
		MAnH MCAu MMil MWrn NSti
		SAPC SArc SMad SPer WBor WBrE
		WHil WPGP
	- purple	LPhx SDix
	paniculatum	CFil WPGP
	planum	More than 30 suppliers
	- 'Bethlehem' ♀ H4	EBee EMan GCal LRHS MBNS NBro
§	- 'Blauer Zwerg'	CMea EBee EFou LHop LRHS
		NFla SPla SWat WFar
	- 'Blaukappe'	CBot CFir CHar COlW EBee EBlw
		ECGP ERou EWTr GBri GMac LDai
		LPhx LRHS MCAu MWrn NChi
		NLar SDes SMad SMrm WBea
		WCom WFar WViv WWhi WWpP
	- Blue Dwarf	see E. *planum* 'Blauer Zwerg'
	- 'Blue Ribbon'	CRDP EBee EMan LAst LCaP
		LRHS MCAu SWat WHil
	- 'Blue Thimbles'	FFou
	- 'Flüela'	CM&M CPrp EBee EMan EWes
		GCal GMaP IPot LPVc LRHS MAvo
		MCAu MMHG MNFA MWgw NBro
		SPar SWat WGwG WHHs WWal
	- 'Seven Seas'	CFir CM&M EBee LHop LRHS
		MAvo MCAu MWgw NBro SChu
		SPar SPla SRPl SWat WCom WPer
	- 'Silverstone'	EBee GCal GMaP GSki LPVe LRHS
		MCAu NBro NPri NSti SDes
	- 'Tetra Petra'	EBee GBin LPio MCCP SRkn WPer
	- violet blue	GCal
§	*proteiflorum*	CRDP GCal LPhx LRHS MAvo
		SWat WCru
	serra	EBee EWes GBuc LDai
	spinalba	CBot GSki LPio NChi SIgm WPer
	tricuspidatum	EBee EBre LRHS WPer
	x *tripartitum* ♀ H4	More than 30 suppliers
✦	*umbellulatum*	EMon
	variifolium	More than 30 suppliers
	venustum	EBee LPhx LPio MAnH SIgm
	yuccifolium	CFil CHEx CTrC EBlw EBot EBre
		ECGN EChP ECoo ERou EWes
		GAbr GCal GKir LPio MAnH MBri
		SDes SDix SIgm SMad SPar WBrE
		WCot WFar
	x *zabelii*	CKno CPom CRDP EBee ELan
		ETow GCal GMac LPhx MAvo
		MFir NBir NDov SMrm WEas
		WPGP
	- 'Donard Variety'	CDes EBlw GCal IBlr LAst LRHS
		SWat
	- 'Forncett Ultra'	EFou WPGP
	- 'Jewel'	CMdw MAvo MNFA SUsu SWat
	- 'Violetta'	CPlt ELan GBuc IGor MBri MSte
		MTed NGby SWat WFar WHoo

Erysimum (Brassicaceae)

	from Madeira	CPLG
	alpinum hort.	see E. *bieraciifolium*

'Anne Marie' ELan SOkh
'Apricot Delight' **new** COtt WWeb
'Apricot Twist' CElw CFai CM&M CSBt CSpe
EBee EBlw EChP ECtt EMan GBri
LAst LDai MAsh MSph MTis NDov
NLar NPPs SAga SMrm SOkh SPar
SSvw WCot WLin WWhi
arkansanum see *E. helveticum*
§ *asperum* IFro
'Aunt May' SMrm
bicolor WCot
'Bowles' Mauve' ♀ H3 More than 30 suppliers
'Bowles'Yellow' ERou GBuc
'Bredon' ♀ H3 CFis CHar COlW EBee ECoo ELan
EMan EPfP GKir LRHS MAsh NPer
NPri SDes SUsu WHoo WKif
'Butterscotch' CFee CSam GKir WBry WEas
WHoo WWhi
'Butterscotch GBri
Variegated' (v)
capitatum CLyd NMen
cheiri CArn GWCH MBow MHer NSco
WHer
- 'Bloody Warrior' (d) CBot CElw ECtt ELan GBri GBuc
NPer WEas
- 'Deben' CBot
- 'Harpur Crewe' (d) CBot CElw CFee EBee ECha ELan
EPfP EPot ERou EShb GKir IFro
LRHS MMil MTho NLon NPer
SChu SMrm SRms SSvw WCom
WCot WHoo WPat WWin
- 'Jane's Derision' CNat
'Chelsea Jacket' EBee ECtt EHol EPfP ERou GBri
LDai MGrG MMil MRav MSph
MWgw NSti SUsu WEas
'Chequers' WPer
concinnum see *E. suffrutescens*
'Constant Cheer' CElw CPlt CSam CSpe EBee EChP
EGoo EPfP ERou GBuc LRHS
MEHN NFla NPer SWal WCom
WKif WMnd WPat WPer WRha
WRus WWeb WWhi
'Cotswold Gem' (v) CElw CFai COtt CSpe EBee EBlw
EChP EMan EPPr GBri LAst LDai
MAvo MSph NPPs NPer SAga SBri
SPoG WCFE WCot WLin WWeb
'Devon Gold' see *E.* 'Plant World Gold'
'Devon Sunset' EChP GBri MSte NDov SAga SChu
WHoo WSan
'Dorothy Elmhirst' see *E.* 'Mrs L.K. Elmhirst'
dwarf lemon WHoo
'Ellen Willmott' WBry
'Fragrant Sunshine' **new** WWeb
* *gelidum* var. *kotschyi* NWCA
* 'Gingernut' NPer
'Glowing Embers' SOkh
'Gold Flame' WCom
'Gold Shot' **new** WWeb
'Golden Gem' EBee ECtt IHMH NBlu NDlv NPro
WPer
'Golden Jubilee' ECho LIck SIng
grandiflorum MBow
§ *helveticum* ECoo EMlt GTou IFro MOne NPri
SRms
§ *hieraciifolium* CNic EHol NFla NLAp
'Jacob's Jacket' ECtt EWTr NPer SChu SPar WEas
WWin
'John Codrington' CBel CPlt GBri GBuc MHer MRav
NFla NGdn NPer SAga SChu
SHBN SUsu WKif
'Jubilee Gold' EBee EWll
'Julian Orchard' CElw CFis CSpe EBlw ECtt NCiC
SAga SChu SSth SUsu WRus

kotschyanum CGra CLyd CPBP ECtt EHyt ETow
LBee MDHE MOne NMen NWCA
SRms SScr WAbe WPat
'Lady Roborough' CFee GBuc
linifolium EBur ECoo EWTr SRms WGor
§ - 'Variegatum' (v) CArn CBrm EBee EBlw ECtt ELan
EOrc EPfP EPot ERou GGar LRHS
MAsh MHer NPer SAga SCro SDes
SMrm SPer SRot WCom WHoo
WPGP
'Miss Hopton' ETow WEas WLin
'Moonlight' CSam EPot GBuc LBee MHer
MTho NDov NFla NFor SAga SBla
SChu SRms WPer
§ 'Mrs L.K. Elmhirst' NPer SOkh WCot
* 'Multicolor' **new** MAsh
mutabile CFwr CHar CTri EBlw EGoo EOrc
MFir MGrG MRav NBir
- 'Variegatum' (v) WEas
nivale MWod
odoratum MBow
'Orange Flame' CMea EBee EPot LBee MBar MHer
NPer NWCA SIng SMrm SWal
WPer
'Parish's' CSpe EBee ECGP ECtt EPPr GBin
SChu SMrm
perofskianum WEas
Perry's hybrid NPer
'Perry's Peculiar' NPer
'Perry's Pumpkin' NPer
'Plant World Antique' WBry
§ 'Plant World Gold' CElw
'Plant World Lemon' CElw EPri MWrn WCom
'Primrose' WPer
§ *pulchellum* MWat
- 'Variegatum' (v) EBee WBrE
aff. *pulchellum* JJH NWCA
9309143
pumilum DC. see *E. helveticum*
rupestre see *E. pulchellum*
'Rushfield Surprise' CFai NLar
§ *scoparium* NMRc
'Sissinghurst Variegated' see *E. linifolium* 'Variegatum'
'Sprite' CLyd CMea CTri EDAr EPot IHMH
NPer SMrm
§ *suffrutescens* ESis NPer
'Sweet Sorbet' EBee MMil SMrm
'Valerie Finnis' WCom
N 'Variegatum' (v) CBcs SHBN WWin
'Walberton's Fragrant COtt LRHS MBri SCoo WWeb
Sunshine'
'Wenlock Beauty' CBel LDai MTho MTis NDov
NGdn NPPs SChu SRms WCot
WHoo WPer WWhi
wheeleri ECoo EWTr LHop MWrn NBur
NPer
witmannii SSth
'Yellow Bird' WMnd

Erythraea see *Centaurium*

Erythrina (Papilionaceae)

x *bidwillii* **new** SSpi
crista-galli CAbb CBcs CBot CFwr CHEx
CSpe EBee ELan ERea GQui ITer
LAst LHop LRHS SMur SOWG
SPlb SSpi WCot
- 'Compacta' SMad
flabelliformis **new** MGol
herbacea SSpi
- pink-flowered **new** SSpi
lysistemon SOWG
vespertilio SOWG

Erythronium ✿ (*Liliaceae*)

albidum	CLAP EBee EPot GBuc GKev LAma MBNS NMen NRog SSpi
americanum	CArn CLAP CRDP CWoo EBee EPot GBuc GCrs GEdr LAma MLLN MS&S NMen NRog SSpi WCru
'Beechpark'	IBlr
'Blush'	GBuc IBlr
californicum ♀ H4	CLAP CWoo EBee EBre GCrs MS&S NRog SCnR SIng WAbe WCru WWst
– J&JA 1.350.209	CWoo
– J&JA 13216	CLAP
– Plas Merdyn form	CRDP IBlr
§ – 'White Beauty' ♀ H4	More than 30 suppliers
caucasicum	CLAP NRog
citrinum	CWoo GBuc MPhe WLin
– J&JA 1.350.410	CWoo
– J&JA 13462	CLAP CWoo
'Citronella'	CBro CLAP EBee EBlw EChP EHrv ERos GBuc ITim LAma LRHS MMHG MS&S NDlv NHar NRog SSpi WAbe WCru WPnP
cliftonii hort.	see *E. multiscapoideum* Cliftonii Group
dens-canis ♀ H4	More than 30 suppliers
– from Slovenia	CLAP
– JCA 470.001	CLAP
– WM 9615 from E Slovenia	MPhe
– 'Charmer'	EPot WWst
– 'Frans Hals'	CLAP EPar EPot ERos GBuc GCrs GEdr GGar IMGH LAma MNFA MTho NMen NRog WAbe WCru
– 'Lilac Wonder'	EBee EHyt EPar EPot IMGH LAma LRHS MGrG MTho NRog WWst
* – 'Moerheimii' (d)	WWst
– var. **niveum**	ERos
* – – 'Plenum' (d)	WWst
– 'Old Aberdeen'	CLAP CRDP
– 'Pink Perfection'	EBee EPar EPot ERos GCrs GGar LAma LRHS NHar NRog WCru WOBN
– 'Purple King'	EBee EPot ERos GEdr IMGH LAma NHar NRog WCru
– 'Rose Queen'	CAvo CBro EBee EBlw EMar EPar EPot ERos ETub GBuc GCrs IMGH LAma LRHS MAvo MTho NHar NRog SSpi WLin
– 'Snowflake'	CAvo CLAP CMea CRDP EBee ECha EHyt EMar EPar EPot ERos GCrs GEdr GGar IMGH LAma MNFA NBir NHar NRog SSpi WAbe WCru
– 'White Splendour'	CBro ERos NEgg WWst
elegans	CNic EBee NMen SSpi WPGP
'Flash'	IBlr
§ **grandiflorum**	GBuc GCrs GKir NHar NMen
– J&JA 11394	CLAP
– M&PS 007	CLAP SSpi
– M&PS 025	WWst
– M&PS 96/024	NMen
– subsp. **chrysandrum**	see *E. grandiflorum*
helenae	CLAP CWoo IBlr WPGP
– J&JA 11678	WWst
hendersonii	CLAP CWoo LAma MPhe MS&S
– J&JA 1.351.301	CWoo
– J&JA 12945	CLAP CWoo SSpi
– JCA 11116	CLAP
howellii	CLAP GCrs MPhe SSpi WLin WPGP
– J&JA 13441	CLAP
japonicum	EBee EFEx LAma MPhe NMen NRog WCru
'Jeannine'	GBuc GEdr WCru
'Joanna'	CLAP CRDP LAma
'Kondo'	EBee EHyt EPot ERos GBuc GCrs GEdr GMaP LAma LRHS MAvo MBro MS&S MTho NBir NChi NHar NMen NRog WAbe WCru WHil WPnP
mesochoreum	IBlr
§ **multiscapoideum**	CLAP CWoo MPhe WCot WLin
– J&JA 135.2000	WOBN
– JCA 12700	SSpi
§ – Cliftonii Group	CLAP MPhe
– – J&JA 13525	CLAP SSpi
oregonum	CLAP CWoo ETow GBuc GDra MS&S WCru
– subsp. **leucandrum**	CLAP GCrs MPhe WLin
– – J&JA 13494	CWoo SSpi
'Pagoda' ♀ H4	More than 30 suppliers
purdyi	see *E. multiscapoideum*
revolutum ♀ H4	CBro CFir CLAP CMea CRDP CWoo EPot GBuc GCrs GDra GGar IBlr MS&S SBla SCnR SSpi WAbe WCru
– 'Guincho Splendour' **new**	IBlr
– Johnsonii Group	CNic CWoo NHar SSpi WAbe WCru
– 'Knightshayes Pink'	CLAP GBuc
– 'Pink Beauty'	WNor
– Plas Merdyn form	IBlr
– 'White Beauty'	see *E. californicum* 'White Beauty'
'Rippling Waters' **new**	IBlr
'Rosalind' **now**	IBlr
sibiricum	EBee GKev
– white	WWst
'Sundisc'	CRDP ECha EHyt MS&S MTho NRog WAbe
tuolumnense ♀ H4	CAvo CBro CLAP EBee EBre EHrv EMon EPar EPot ERos GBuc GCrs GDra GGar LAma MCCP MS&S NHar NMen NRog WAbe WCot WWst
– 'Spindlestone' **new**	WWst

Escallonia ✿ (*Escalloniaceae*)

'Alice'	CRsw EBee SLPl SPer
§ **alpina**	CRsw
'Apple Blossom' ♀ H4	More than 30 suppliers
'Bantry Bay'	CBcs
§ **bifida** ♀ H3	CDoC CPle CRsw WBcn WFar WSHC
'C.F. Ball'	CSBt CTri EBee EHol ELan GEil LBuc MGos NBlu NWea SEND SLim SRms WAbe WBod WDin WFar WMoo WStI WTel
'Cardinalis'	CRsw
'Compacta Coccinea'	CRsw
'Dart's Rosy Red'	NHol SLPl
'Donard Beauty'	CChe CRsw CSam EBee SRms WFar
'Donard Brilliance'	CRsw MGos
'Donard Gem'	CRsw
'Donard Radiance' ♀ H4	More than 30 suppliers
'Donard Rose'	CRsw
'Donard Scarlet'	CRsw
'Donard Seedling'	More than 30 suppliers
'Donard Star'	CDoC CRsw CSBt CWib EBee ENot EPfP LAst MGos MRav NWea SLPl WCFE WWeb
'Donard Surprise'	NFor NLon
'Donard White'	COkL CRsw
'E.G. Cheeseman' **new**	SVen
'Edinensis'	CMHG EBee ECtt EMil ENot EPfP MBar MRav NEgg SEND SLim WDin WFar WGer WMoo
'Erecta'	EPfP LAst
x **exoniensis**	SRms

fonkii	see *E. alpina*
'Glasnevin Hybrid'	CRsw
'Glory of Donard'	CRsw ENot
* *gracilis alba*	CRsw
'Gwendolyn Anley'	CMHG ESis SLPl SPer WFar
'Hopleys Gold'PBR	see *E. laevis* 'Gold Brian'
illinita	CPle CRsw WPGP
'Iveyi' ♀ H3	More than 30 suppliers
§ *laevis*	CDoC CRsw CTrw SDry WFar
§ - 'Gold Brian'PBR	CDul CMHG CRsw CSBt EBre
	EHoe ELan ENot EPfP LRHS MGos
	MWat SCoo SMer SPar SPer SWal
	WBod WFar WHar WStI
- 'Gold Ellen' (v)	CChe CRsw CTri CWSG EBee
	EBre EMil EPfP LRHS MBri MCCP
	MGos MRav SAga SCoo SEND
	SLim SPer SPla WCot WWeb
Lanarth no.1	CRsw
'Langleyensis' ♀ H4	CBcs CPLG CSBt CTri CWib MWat
	NEgg NLon NWea WDin WFar WHar
leucantha	CRsw WKif
mexicana	CBot WFar WPGP
x *mollis*	CRsw SPer
montevidensis	see *E. bifida*
'Newry'	CRsw SPer
organensis	see *E. laevis*
'Peach Blossom' ♀ H4	CChe CDoC CPle CRsw CSam
	CWib EBee ELan EMil ENot EPfP
	GKir LRHS MBNS MBri MGos
	NBlu NLon SHBN SLPl SLim SPer
	WFar WGwG WWal
'Pink Elf'	ECtt LRHS NHol NLon WLRN
'Pink Pearl'	CRsw
'Pride of Donard' ♀ H4	CBcs CDoC CRsw CSBt EBee EPfP
	GGar LRHS NBlu NPri SRms WBrE
pulverulenta	CRsw
punctata	see *E. rubra*
'Rebecca'	CRsw
'Red Dream'	CChe CFai CWSG EBee EBre
	LRHS MAsh MBri MGos NPro
	SCoo SRms WFar WGer WLRN
	WStI WWeb
'Red Elf'	CBrm CMHG EBee EBre ECtt
	ELan ENot EPfP GKir LHop LRHS
	MBar MGos MRav MTis MWat
	NHol NLon SGar SLPl SPer SPlb
	SRms WFar WHen WWeb
'Red Hedger'	CDoC CDul CSBt CTrG CWib
	LRHS MGos MTis SCoo WGwG
resinosa	CBcs CPle CRsw IFro SAPC SArc
	SVen
revoluta	CPle CRsw SDry WKif
rosea	CRsw
§ *rubra*	CRsw
- 'Crimson Spire' ♀ H4	CBcs CChe CDul COkL CSBt CTri
	CWSG CWib EBee EBre ENot
	EPfP GGar GKir LRHS MBNS
	MRav MWat SBod SHBN SLim
	SPer SPlb SRms WBod WHen
	WMoo WStI WWeb
- 'Ingramii'	CChe CMHG CRsw CSBt CWib
	NWea SHBN
§ - var. *macrantha*	CBcs CChe CDoC CDul CSBt
	CSam CWSG CWib EBee EPfP
	GGar GKir IArd LRHS MBri MHer
	NLon NWea SLim SMer SPar SPer
	WDin WFar WGer WGwG WMoo
	WStI WWal
- 'Pygmaea'	see *E. rubra* 'Woodside'
- var. *uniflora*	SDry
§ - 'Woodside'	EHol EPfP GEdr NHol SIng SRPl
	SRms WHCG
'Saint Keverne'	CRsw
'Silver Anniversary'	CBcs CRsw EPfP WBcn
'Slieve Donard'	CRsw EBee ENot EPfP MGos MRav
	NHol SLPl SLim SRPl SRms WFar
x *stricta* 'Harold Comber'	CRsw
tucumanensis	CPLG CPle CRsw
virgata	CRsw
viscosa	CRsw
'William Watson'	CRsw

Eschscholzia (Papaveraceae)

californica 'Jersey Cream'	CSpe

Eucalyptus ✿ (Myrtaceae)

acaciiformis	LRav
aggregata	LRav NNEX SAPC SArc SPer WCel
	WMul
amygdalina	GGar
approximans subsp. *approximans*	LRav WCel
archeri	CBrm CCVT CTho EPfP GKir
	GQui LPan NHol WBod WCel
	WOVN WPGP
baeuerlenii	LRav
barberi	LRav
§ *bridgesiana*	LRav MHer
caesia	SPlb
calycogona new	LRav
camaldulensis	NNEX SPlb
camphora	CTho LRav NNEX WCel
cinerea	CTrC GQui LRav SPlb WCel
citriodora	CPLG EOHP GQui MHer NNEX
	SGar SPlb SWal WCel WHHs
	WLRN WNor
cladocalyx new	NNEX
coccifera	CBrm CCVT CDoC CHEx CLnd
	CSBt CTho EBee ELan EPfP GKir
	LRHS MCCP MLan NBea NEgg
	NHol SEND SPar SPlb SSpi WBod
	WCel WDin WHer WNor WWeb
consideniana	NEgg
cordata	LRav NEgg WCel
cremulata	CTrC GQui LRav WCel
cypellocarpa	SPlb SVen
dalrympleana ♀ H3	CAbb CBcs CDoC CDul CMHG
	CTho EBee ELan ENot EPfP EWTr
	EWes GKir LPan LRHS MAsh
	MGos NBea NEgg NNEX SLim
	SPar SPer SRms WBod WBrE WCel
	WDin WPGP WWeb
- x *fraxinoides*	LRav
deanei	WCel
debeuzevillei	see *E. pauciflora* subsp. *debeuzevillei*
delegatensis	CMHG NNEX WCel
- subsp. *tasmaniensis* new	WNor
divaricata	see *E. gunnii divaricata*
dives	LRav
erythrocorys	SPlb
eximia	SPlb
* - *nana*	LRav NEgg WGwG
ficifolia	MGol
fraxinoides	LRav SPlb WCel
gamophylla	SPlb
glaucescens	CCVT CDoC CMHG CTho EPfP
	EWes GKir GQui LPan LRHS NEgg
	NHol NPri SAPC SArc SPer WCel
	WGer
globulus	CHEx ISea LRav MSal WCel WFar
goniocalyx	EPfP WCel
grandis	NNEX

§ *gregsoniana* CCVT CDoC LPan LRav NFor SPlb WBVN WCel

grossa **new** SVen

gunnii ♀ H3 More than 30 suppliers

- *divaricata* CCVT EPfP GQui LPan LRHS MBri NHol WCel WGer

johnstonii CAgr GGar ISea LRav SKee SPer

kitsoniana CBrm LRav WCel

kruseana SPlb

kybeanensis CBrm CCVT GQui LPan WBod WCel

lacrimans WCel

lehmannii SOWG

leucoxylon NNEX WCel

- subsp. *megalocarpa* SPlb

- 'Rosea' GGar

ligustrina LRav WCel

macarthurii WCel

macrocarpa SMur SPlb

macroryncha SPlb

mannifera subsp. LRav WCel
  elliptica

- subsp. *praecox* **new** LRav

mitchelliana WCel WDin

moorei WSHC

* - *nana* CTrC LRav MWat WHil WNor

neglecta EPfP LRav WCel

nicholii CBcs CBrm CCVT EPfP EWes GKir GQui LPan NHol SVen WBod WCel WGer WMul WOVN

niphophila see *E. pauciflora* subsp. *niphophila*

nitens CLnd GKir LPan LRav NEgg NNEX SAPC SArc SPlb WBod WCel

§ *nitida* CMHG WCel WNor

nova-anglica CMHG CTho

obliqua GGar

ovata GGar

parvifolia ♀ H4 CBcs CBrm CCVT CDoC CDul CLnd EPfP EShb EWTr GKir ISea LPan LRHS LRav MAsh NHol SDry SEND SPar WBod WCel WWeb

pauciflora CCVT CDoC CSBt CTho CTrC EBrc ELan EPfP NHol SEND SLim SPar SPer WBod WBrE WCel WNor

- subsp. *acerina* WCel

§ - subsp. *debeuzevillei* CBrm CCVT CDoC CLnd CMHG CTho EPfP EWTr EWes GKir GQui LPan LRHS MBlu SAPC SArc SPar WCel WMul WPGP

- subsp. *hedraia* WCel

- var. *nana* see *E. gregsoniana*

§ - subsp. *niphophila* More than 30 suppliers
  ♀ H4

- - 'Pendula' CCVT LPan LRHS WCel WPGP

perriniana CCVT CLnd CMHG CSBt EBee ECrN ELan ENot EPfP GKir LRHS NEgg NHol NNEX SDry SPer SPar SPlb WBod WCel WDin WFar WMul WNor WWeb

phoenicea SOWG

pulchella LRav

pulverulenta CBrm CSLe CTrC IMGH LRHS LRav SPlb WGer WHer

- 'Baby Blue' LRav WCel

regnans GGar ISea NEgg

risdonii GGar LRav WNor

rodwayi GGar LRav NEgg

rubida CMHG LRav NEgg WCel

scoparia LRav

sideroxylon SPlb

- 'Rosea' SPlb

simmondsii see *E. nitida*

spathulata **new** SVen

stellulata LRav NEgg WCel

stricta LRav

stuartiana see *E. bridgesiana*

sturgissiana LRav NEgg

subcrenulata CMHG CTho EPfP GKir GQui ISea LPan NHol WBod WCel

torquata SPlb

urnigera CCVT GKir LHop LRHS NNEX WCel WDin

vernicosa CCVT GGar WCel

- subsp. *johnstonii* CMHG WCel

viminalis CArn CHEx GGar LRav NEgg WCel WDin

youngiana ISea

Eucharidium see *Clarkia*

Eucharis (Amaryllidaceae)

§ *amazonica* ♀ H1 EBot LAma LRHS MLan NRog SDeJ

grandiflora hort. see *E. amazonica*

Eucodonia (Gesneriaceae)

'Adele' NMos WDib

andrieuxii NMos

- 'Naomi' NMos WDib

'Cornell Gem' see x *Achicodonia* 'Cornell Gem'

'Tintacoma' NMos

verticillata 'Frances' NMos

Eucomis (Hyacinthaceae)

hybrid SDix WHil

§ *autumnalis* ♀ H2-3 CAbb CAvo CBro CDes CHEx CPou CRHN CSWP CTca EBee EBot EPot GBin GSki LAma LPio LRHS MCCP MDun WHil WPGP

- subsp. CFil
  amaryllidifolia

- subsp. *autumnalis* CFil

- subsp. *clavata* CFil EBee

- 'White Dwarf' **new** EShb

bicolor ♀ H2-3 More than 30 suppliers

- 'Alba' CAvo EAmu EBee GSki LBow LPio LRHS

§ *comosa* CAvo CBrm CBro CHEx CHll CPLG CRHN CTca EBee EBot EChP GSki LAma LBow LEdu LRHS MDun NRog SVen SYvo WCru WEas WHil WLRN

'First Red' CPou

- purple leaved EBot SIgm

- 'Sparkling Burgundy' More than 30 suppliers

'John Treasure' **new** SMHy

montana CCrw CFil

pallidiflora ♀ H4 CFil CHEx EBee LEdu

pole-evansii CFil CFir CHEx CPLG EBee EBot EMar EOrc GBin GCal MMil NEgg NPSI SMrm WCru WHil WLRN

- bronze form CPne

- 'Burgundy' **new** CFee EBla

- 'Purpurea' **new** GCal

punctata see *E. comosa*

- 'Cornwood' CAvo

undulata see *E. autumnalis*

vandermerwei **new** EBee

zambesiaca EBee GBin GCal LBow LPio

'Zeal Bronze' CDoC CFil CMHG CStu EBee EPfP GCal LPio MCCP NSti WCru WPGP

Eucommia (Eucommiaceae)

ulmoides CBcs CFil CMCN CPle SMad

Eucryphia ✿ (*Eucryphiaceae*)

'Castlewellan'	ISea
cordifolia	CFil CMac CPne CTrw CWib ISea
	SPer WBod WDin WPGP
- Crarae hardy form	GGGa
- x **lucida**	CBcs CBrm CFai ELan ISea SPer
	WDin WPat
glutinosa ♀ H4	CBcs CDul CTho ELan EPfP GKir
	LHyd LRHS MBar MBri NBea NBir
	SBrw SHBN SPar SPer SSpi SSta
	WBod WDin WFar WNor WPat
- Plena Group (d)	WPat
x **hillieri**	CPne
- 'Winton'	CMHG ISea SSpi
x **intermedia**	CDul CSam CTrC CTrG CWSG
	ELan EPfP GGGa NPal NPri SBrw
	SHBN SPer SRms SSpi WDin WFar
	WPat
- 'Rostrevor' ♀ H3	CBcs CDul CMHG CPMA CSBt
	ELan EPfP GGar IArd ISea LHyd
	LRHS MAsh MDun MGos NRib
	SBrw SLon SPer SReu SSta WBod
	WPat WPic WSHC
lucida	CDoC CFil CTrC EBee ELan EPfP
	GGGa GGar GSki IArd ISea SBrw
	WBod WFar WNor WPGP
- 'Ballerina'	CPMA ISea LRHS SReu SSpi
	WFar
- 'Gilt Edge' (v)	CFil ISea WPGP
- 'Leatherwood	ISea SBrw
Cream' (v)	
- 'Pink Cloud'	CAbP CBcs CDoC CEnd CFil
	CPMA CWSG ELan EPfP ISea LPan
	LRHS MDun NPri SBrw SSpi SSta
	WFar WPGP
- 'Spring Glow' (v)	ISea
milliganii	CAbP CDoC CFil CMHG CPMA
	CTrC EBee EPfP GQui ISea LHop
	MBlu MDun NPal SBrw SHBN
	SRms SSpi WAbe WBod WGer
	WPGP WSHC
moorei	CBcs CFil ELan ISea SBrw SSpi WPGP
x **nymansensis**	CDul CFil CTrG EBre EMil NBee
	NEgg SAPC SArc SReu SRkn SRms
	SSpi WBrE WCru WFar WHCG·
	WStI
- 'George Graham'	GGGa ISea WBod
- 'Mount Usher'	ISea
- 'Nymansay' ♀ H3	More than 30 suppliers
N 'Penwith'	CDoC CPMA ISea SBrw SPer SSpi
	WBrE WDin WFar WGer

Eugenia (*Myrtaceae*)

myrtifolia	ERom STre

Eumorphia (*Asteraceae*)

sericea	CTrC NFor

Eunomia see *Aethionema*

Euodia (*Rutaceae*)

daniellii	see *Tetradium daniellii*
hupehensis	see *Tetradium daniellii*
	Hupehense Group

Euonymus (*Celastraceae*)

B&L 12543	EPla ESis EWes
alatus ♀ H4	More than 30 suppliers
- var. **apterus**	EPfP SHBN
- Chicago Fire	see *E. alatus* 'Timber Creek'
- 'Ciliodentatus'	see *E. alatus* 'Compactus'
§ - 'Compactus' ♀ H4	CDoC CEnd CPMA EBee EPfP ESis

	GKir LHop LNet LPan LRHS MAsh
	MBri MBro MGos MRav NEgg SLim
	SLon SPar SPer SPla SReu SSpi
	WCFE WDin WFar WPat WWeb
- 'Fire Ball'	EPfP
- 'Rudy Haag'	EPfP
- 'Select'	see *E. alatus* 'Fire Ball'
§ - 'Timber Creek'	EPfP
americanus	EPfP GIBF
- narrow-leaved	EPfP
atropurpureus	EPfP
bungeanus	CMCN EPfP EPla NLar
- 'Dart's Pride'	EPfP NLar
* - var. **mongolicus**	EPfP
- 'Pendulus'	EPfP
- var. **semipersistens**	CPMA
carnosus	EPfP NLar
cornutus var.	CFil CPMA EPfP MAsh NBhm
quinquecornutus	NLar WPGP WPat
'Den Haag'	EPfP
echinatus	EPfP EPla
- BL&M 306	SLon
europaeus	CArn CCVT CDoC CDul CKin
	CLnd CSam CWib EBre ECrN ELan
	EPfP EPla EWTr GIBF GKir LBuc
	LHyr LPan MHer NWea SRPl SRms
	SYvo WDin WHar WHer WMou
- f. **albus**	CBot CPMA EPfP
- 'Atropurpureus'	EPfP NLar
- 'Atrorubens'	CPMA
- 'Aucubifolius' (v)	CFil EPfP WBcn
* - 'Aureus'	CFox CNat
* - f. **bulgaricus**	EPfP
- 'Chrysophyllus'	CPMA EPfP
- 'Howard'	EPfP
- var. **intermedius**	EBee ENot EPfP MBlu NLar
	WWes
- 'Red Cascade' ♀ H4	More than 30 suppliers
- 'Scarlet Wonder'	EPfP NLar
- 'Thornhayes'	CTho
farreri	see *E. nanus*
fimbriatus	CBcs EPfP
fortunei	CDul
- Blondy =	CAbP CDoC CDul COtt CSBt CWSG
'Interbolwi'PBR (v)	CWib EBee EBre ELan EMil ENot
	EPfP GKir LRHS MAsh MBar MBri
	MGos NHol SCoo SLim SPar
	SPer WDin WGwG WWeb WWes
- 'Canadale Gold' (v)	CDoC COkL EBee ENot EPla ESis
	GEil LRHS MAsh MGos MWhi
	NBee NHol SPer WCFE WDin
- 'Coloratus'	EBee EHol ENot MBar SHBN SLon
	SPer WDin WGwG WWal
- 'Croftway'	SCro
- 'Dart's Blanket'	ELan ENot EPla MRav MWhi SLPl
	SSta WDin
- 'Emerald Cushion'	EBee ENot MRav SPer
- 'Emerald Gaiety' (v)	More than 30 suppliers
♀ H4	
- 'Emerald 'n' Gold' (v)	More than 30 suppliers
♀ H4	
- 'Emerald Surprise' (v)	EBee ENot LRHS MBri NHol NPro
♀ H4	
- 'Gold Spot'	see *E. fortunei* 'Sunspot'
- 'Gold Tip'	see *E. fortunei* Golden Prince
§ - 'Golden Pillar' (v)	EBee EHoe EHol EPla ESis NHol
	WCot WFar
§ - Golden Prince (v)	EBee ENot EPfP EPla LRHS MBar
	MRav NHol NPro SLim SPer WFar
	WGor WGwG WStI
- 'Harlequin' (v)	CBcs COtt CSBt CWSG EBee
	EHoe ELan EPfP LBuc LRHS MAsh
	MBar MGos MRav NPro SAga

		SHBN SIng SLim SMad SPar SPer
		SPla SRPl WCot WFar WWal
	- 'Highdown'	EMon
	- 'Kewensis'	CMHG EBee ENot EPfP GEdr LAst
		MBar MRav MWat SAPC SArc
		SBod SLon WCru WFar
	- 'Minimus'	CTri EPla ESis MGos NHol NPro
		SMrm WFar WPer
*	- 'Minimus Variegatus' (v)	ECho SPlb
	- 'Perrolino' **new**	WWeb
§	var. *radicans*	CPlN CRez
	- 'Sheridan Gold'	COkL CTri EBee ECtt EHoe EPla
		MRav NHol SHBN
	- 'Silver Gem'	see *E. fortunei* 'Variegatus'
	- 'Silver Pillar' (v)	EHoe EMlt ENot ESis LRHS MRav
		WFar
	- 'Silver Queen' (v)	More than 30 suppliers
	- 'Sunshine' (v)	CAbP ELan EPla LRHS MAsh NHol
		NPro
§	- 'Sunspot' (v)	CBcs CChe CMHG CWSG EBee
		EBre ECtt ELan ENot EPla IBal
		LRHS MBar MGos MRav NHol
		SLim SPar SPer SRPl SRms WBrE
		WDin WFar WHar WTel
	- 'Tustin' ♀ H4	EBee EPla MRav SLPl
§	- 'Variegatus' (v)	CMHG ENot MBar NFor NSti SPer
		SRms STre WCot WDin
	- var. *vegetus*	EPla SPer
	frigidus	EPfP
	grandiflorus	CPMA EPfP GIBF NLar WFar
	- 'Red Wine'	CPMA EBee EPfP SLim
	- f. *salicifolius*	EPfP
	hamiltonianus	CMCN GKir SSpi WFar
	- subsp. *hians*	see *E. hamiltonianus* subsp.
		sieboldianus
	- 'Indian Summer'	CPMA EBee EPfP LRHS MBlu NLar
	- *maackii*	GIBF
	- 'Miss Pinkie' **new**	GKir LRHS SCoo
	- 'Red Elf'	CPMA EPfP
§	- subsp. *sieboldianus*	CDul CMCN CPMA CTho EPfP
		GIBF GKir MRav SLPl WFar
	- - 'Calocarpus'	EPfP
	- - 'Coral Charm'	CPMA EPfP NLar SMur
	- - Semiexsertus Group	EPfP
*	- - var. *yedoensis* f.	EPfP
	koehneanus	
	- 'Snow'	EPfP
	- 'Winter Glory'	CPMA EPfP LRHS MBlu NLar WWes
	- var. *yedoensis*	see *E. hamiltonianus* subsp.
		sieboldianus
	hibarimiasake	see *E. japonicus* 'Hibarimisake'
	japonicus	CDoC CLnd CTrC EBee ENot EPfP
		LRHS MRav SAPC SArc SPer STop
		WDin
	- 'Albomarginatus'	CBcs CTri MBar NBlu SEND SRms
		STop WSHC
*	- 'Argenteus Compactus'	LPan
	- 'Aureopictus'	see *E. japonicus* 'Aureus'
	- 'Aureovariegatus'	see *E. japonicus* 'Ovatus Aureus'
§	- 'Aureus' (v)	CBcs CBrm CDoC CMHG CSBt
		CWib EBee ENot EPfP EPla LPan
		LRHS MRav MWat SHBN SHFr SLon
		SPer WDin WHar WTel WWeb
	- 'Bravo'	CDoC EBee EGra EHoe EMil EVFa
		LRHS MBri SPar SPer WDin
	- 'Chedju' (v)	WBcn
	- 'Chollipo' ♀ H4	ELan LRHS MAsh
*	- 'Compactus'	LPan WWeb
	- 'Duc d'Anjou' hort.	see *E. japonicus* 'Viridivariegatus'
	- 'Duc d'Anjou' Carrière	CBcs EBre EHoe ELan EPla EWes
	(v)	LHrt LPan MRav SDry SPar
	- 'Golden Maiden'	ELan EPfP LRHS MAsh SLim

	- 'Golden Pillar'	see *E. fortunei* 'Golden Pillar'
	- 'Grey Beauty' **new**	EBee
§	- 'Hibarimisake'	SBla
§	- 'Latifolius	EBee EHoe EHol EPfP EPla LRHS
	Albomarginatus'	MRav SPer SPoG WDin WWeb
	- 'Luna'	see *E. japonicus* 'Aureus'
	- 'Macrophyllus Albus'	see *E. japonicus* 'Latifolius
		Albomarginatus'
	- 'Maiden's Gold'	COtt CSBt EBee
	- 'Marieke'	see *E. japonicus* 'Ovatus Aureus'
§	- 'Microphyllus'	CDoC CMac EMil LCaP SAga STre
		WFar WGwG
§	- 'Microphyllus	CDoC CMHG CSBt CWSG EBee
	Albovariegatus' (v)	EMil EPfP EPla EVFa LRHS MBar
		MGos MRav SAga SBla SHBN SLim
		SLon SPla SRms WCot WDin WFar
		WHCG WPat WStI WWeb
§	- 'Microphyllus	CDoC CSLe EHyt EMil EPfP LPan
	Aureovariegatus' (v)	MWhi WCFE WPat
	- 'Microphyllus Aureus'	see *E. japonicus* 'Microphyllus
		Pulchellus'
§	- 'Microphyllus	CBcs CDoC CMHG CSBt CWSG
	Pulchellus' (v)	EBee ENot EPfP EPla LHop MBar
		MRav NDlv SPoG WDin WHCG
		WWcb
§	- 'Microphyllus	see *E. japonicus* 'Microphyllus
	Variegatus'	Albovariegatus'
§	- 'Ovatus Aureus'	CChe CDoC CMHG CSBt CTri
	(v) ♀ H4	CWSG EBee ENot EPfP ESis LPan
		LRHS MBar MGos MHFa MRav NBlu
		SLim SPar SPer SPlb SRPl SRms
		STop WCot WDin WPat WStI WTel
	- 'Président Gauthier' (v)	CDoC EBee EVFa LPan MGos SPar
		SPer WDin WGer WWcb
	- 'Pulchellus	see *E. japonicus* 'Microphyllus
	Aureovariegatus'	Aureovariegatus'
	- 'Robustus'	EPfP EPla
	- 'Royal Gold' **new**	WWeb
	- 'Silver King'	EBee
	- Silver Princess =	SHBN
	'Moness'	
	- 'Susan'	EGra EPla
§	- 'Viridivariegatus' (v)	EBee GEil LRHS MAsh
	kiautschovicus	EPfP EPla
	- 'Berry Hill'	EPfP
	latifolius	CMCN CPMA CTho EPfP WDin
	macropterus	EPfP EPla
	maximowiczianus	EPfP GIBF NLar
	morrisonensis	WCru
	B&SWJ 3700	
	myrianthus	CPMA EPfP NLar
§	*nanus*	CNlc CPMA CWib EHol EMon
		EPfP EPla ESis NHol NLar WSHC
	- var. *turkestanicus*	EPfP EPla ESis SLon SRms WFar
	obovatus	EPfP
	occidentalis	EPfP
	oresbius	CPMA EPfP WPGP
	oxyphyllus	CMCN CPMA EPfP GKir NLar
		WCru WDin WWes
	pauciflorus	EPfP
§	*pendulus*	CHEx
	phellomanus ♀ H4	CDul CEnd EBee EPfP GDra GIBF
		GKir LHop LNet LRHS MAsh
		MBar MBlu MBri NLar SHBN
		SMac SPar WDin WFar WPat
	- 'Silver Surprise' (v)	CPMA EPfP NLar
§	*planipes* ♀ H4	CDul CMHG CTho EBee ECrN
		ELan ENot EPfP EWTr GKir IMGH
		LHop LPan MBNS MBlu NBea
		NBlu NHol NSti NWea SHBN
		SLim SPer SSpi WNor WPGP
	radicans	see *E. fortunei* var. *radicans*
	'Rokojô'	CLyd MBro NWCA

rosmarinifolius	see *E. nanus*
sachalinensis hort.	see *E. planipes*
– from Ussuriland **new**	GIBF
sacrosanctus	EPfP
sanguineus	CPMA EPfP NLar SSpi
tanakae **new**	GIBF
tingens	CFil EPfP GIBF
vagans	EPfP EPla
– L 551	EPla SLon
velutinus	EPfP
verrucosus	CPMA CPle EPfP EPla NLar WWes
vidalii	EPfP
yedoensis	see *E. hamiltonianus* subsp. *sieboldianus*

Eupatorium (Asteraceae)

album	ERou NBid WPer
– 'Braunlaub'	EBee EChP EMan EMar EMon EWTr GKir LPio LRHS NGdn NSti SMrm SSpi WMnd
altissimum	CBot EMon EPar IIve MSal SRms
aromaticum	CRow CSev MLLN MRav MWgw NBro NSti SPer SWat WCHb WPer WWye
atrorubens	EBee EMan ERea GCal SYvo
cannabinum	CArn CKin EBee EHon ELan EMFW EMar GBar GGar GPoy MBNS MBow MHer MRav MSal MSta NBir NMir NPer NSti SRob SSpi SWat WCer WHHs WPer WWpP WWye
– 'Album'	EMon
– 'Flore Pleno' (d)	More than 30 suppliers
– 'Not Quite White'	WAlt
– 'Spraypaint'	CNat
capillifolium	LPio MLLN SAPC SAga SArc SDix SMrm WCot WPGP
– 'Elegant Feather'	CFwr CSpe EBee EMan EMar EWes LHop LPhx SLon SUsu
coelestinum	EBee EMan EWes LAst LBuc SMad WFar
* ***cyclophyllum***	EBee EBre EMan
* ***fistulosum***	MGol
* – 'Atropurpureum'	CKno WPer
* ***fortunei***	CArn EMon
* – 'Variegatum' (v)	CDes EBee EMan NDov WCot
hyssopifolium	EBee
§ ***ligustrinum*** ♀ H3	CBcs CDoC CPLG CPle CRHN CTbh CTri CWib EBee ECha ELan EMan GEil ISea LPhx LRHS SAga SBrw SDix SLim SMHy SMrm SPer WCHb WCot WFar WHCG WRus WSHC
lindleyanum **new**	EBee IIve
maculatum	see *E. purpureum* subsp. *maculatum*
'Massive White' **new**	GCal
micranthum	see *E. ligustrinum*
occidentale NNS 94-53	WCot
perfoliatum	CAgr CArn EBee GPoy MNrw MSal NLar WPer WWye
purpureum	More than 30 suppliers
– 'Album'	GKir LPhx
– 'Bartered Bride'	GKir
§ – subsp. ***maculatum***	CSam EBre ECGP EHrv EMon NGdn NLar NLon SSpi STes WFar WHil WOut WPer WWpP
– – 'Album'	EMFP EMon EWTr NSti
– – 'Atropurpureum' ♀ H4	More than 30 suppliers
– – 'Augustrubin'	EFou
– – 'Berggarten'	GCal
– – 'Gateway'	CRow EFou
– – 'Glutball'	EBee EVFa GCal SMad

– – 'Riesinschirm'	CKno EBee LPhx LRHS MSph MSte MTed SSvw SWat WElm
– 'Purple Bush'	CHad CKno EBee ECha LPhx SSvw SUsu
rugosum	CSam EBee EBre ELan EMar EOrc EPfP GBar GKir LPhx MAnH MFir MWgw NLar SDys SPer WCHb
– ***album***	see *E. album*
– 'Brunette'	EHrv
– 'Chocolate' ♀ H4	More than 30 suppliers
* 'Snowball'	SMrm
triplinerve	MSte
* ***variabile*** 'Variegatum' (v)	EMan EVFa EWes WCot WHil
weinmannianum	see *E. ligustrinum*

Euphorbia ❁ (*Euphorbiaceae*)

acanthothamnos	LPhx
altissima	MSte
amygdaloides	CKin CRow EBee ECtt GKir NBlu NWit SSpi WCer
– 'Brithembottom'	CSam
– 'Craigieburn'	CDes CSpe EBee EChP EGle EMan EVFa EWes GBri GCal MAvo NDov SUsu WCom WPGP
§ – 'Purpurea'	More than 30 suppliers
– 'Red Shank'	SBla
§ – var. ***robbiae*** ♀ H4	More than 30 suppliers
– – dwarf **new**	GCal
– – 'Pom Pom'	EMan WCot
– – 'Redbud'	EBee EPla EWes MTed
– – × ***characias***	WCot
– 'Rubra'	see *E. amygdaloides* 'Purpurea'
– 'Variegata' (v)	GBuc SHBN SMad WWeb
– 'Welsh Dragon'	WCot
– yellow-leaved **new**	WCot
balsamifera	EOas
barrelieri	NWit
baselicis **new**	CPla EMan MGol NPro SIgm SPoG
biglandulosa	see *E. rigida*
biumbellata	NWit
'Blue Haze'	SBla
brittingeri	NWit
– Baker's form	EPPr
* ***britzensis***	SPar
broteroi	WCot
* ***buschiana***	WLin
capitata	CLyd
capitulata	ELan EPot EWes MBro MTho NWit SMrm WWin
ceratocarpa	EBee EPPr EWes GBuc GMaP NWit SIgm SMad WCHb WCot WLun WSHC
characias	CBcs CBot CHEx COIW EBlw ECha ECtt EPfP GKir MBri MBro MDun NFor NHlc NOak NPer NPri NVic SPar SPer SRms SSpi WAul WCot WFar WHen WPer WWal
– 'Amber Eye'	IBlr
– Ballyrogan hybrids	IBlr
– 'Black Pearl'	CFwr CHid CMHG EBee EChP EMan EPfP EWTr GKir IArd IPot LAst MBNS MCCP MDun MSte NSti SDes SSpi WFar WOVN
– 'Blue Wonder'	CSpe EBee EBlw EFou EMan EPfP GBin GMaP LRHS MCCP MDun MSte SSpi WCot WGer WWeb
– subsp. ***characias***	CPrp EBee EHrv GAbr GMaP SPar WCru
– – 'Blue Hills'	ECtt EGle EMan GBin GBuc GCal IBlr MSph NWit SMrm WRus
– – 'Burrow Silver' (v)	CBot CFai CFir CFwr CRDP CSLe EBee ECtt EMan LAst MBNS

- - 'Green Mantle'	MCAu MCCP MLLN SCoo SDes SLim SPar SSpi SWat WCot WHil IBlr
- - 'H.E. Bates'	NBir
- - 'Humpty Dumpty'	CFwr CMdw COtt CPrp CSam EBlw EBre ECtt EHrv EPfP EWTr GCal GKir GMaP LRHS MCCP MRav NDov NPer NSti SDes SMrm SPer WCot WCra WFar WGer WLun WOVN WWhi
- - 'Perry's Winter Blusher'	ECtt NWit
- dwarf	SMrm
- 'Forescate'	CSWP EBee EBlw EGle EMil EPfP EWTr LRHS MGrG MRav MSte NGdn NWit SPar SRPl WFar WLun WMnd WRus
- 'Giant Green Turtle'	CMil
- 'Goldbrook'	CHad EBee EGle EMan LHop LRHS MRav NPSI SHBN SRPl SSpi
- 'Golden Wonder'	IBlr
- 'Portuguese Velvet' ♀ H4	More than 30 suppliers
- Silver Swan = 'Wilcott' (v) **new**	EHan ELan EMan ENot EPfP LBuc NSti WWeb
- 'Sombre Melody'	IBlr
- 'Spring Splendour'	EBee EWes MGrG NLar NWit
- 'Starbright'	EBee LBBr NWit
- 'Whistleberry Gold'	EGle
- 'Whistleberry Jade'	CFwr EGle NWit
- subsp. **wulfenii** ♀ H3-4	More than 30 suppliers
- - 'Bosahan' (v)	CBcs
- - 'Emmer Green' (v)	CSpe EBee ECGP ECtt EHrv EMan EWes GBri GCal MAvo MGrG NWit SBla SHBN SUsu SWat WCot WFoF WGer WRus
- - 'Jimmy Platt'	EGle EVFa MGrG SPar SRms SRob WBrE WCot WHrl
§ - - 'John Tomlinson' ♀ H3-4	CHar CHea EBee ECha EHrv EPla EVFa EWes GBin GMaP MBri MGrG SDes SMrm SUsu WCot WGer
- - Kew form	see *E. characias* subsp. *wulfenii* 'John Tomlinson'
- - 'Lambrook Gold' ♀ H3-4	CFwr CMHG CSam EBcc ECtt EGle ENot EPar EPfP EVFa LRHS MBri MGrG MRav MWat NPer SPar SSth SVal WCom WCot WGer WRus
- - 'Lambrook Gold' seed-raised	see *E. characias* subsp. *wulfenii* Margery Fish Group
- - 'Lambrook Yellow'	EMon EVFa EWsh GBuc LPio SMur SVal WLun
§ - - Margery Fish Group	EBee EFou EGle EMan LRHS MCLN MLLN NBir NCat NDov NPSI SMrm
- - 'Perry's Tangerine'	EWes NPer NWit
§ - - 'Purple and Gold'	CFwr CM&M CPou EBee EWes MGrG NDov SHBN WBrE WCot WLun
- - 'Purpurea'	see *E. characias* subsp. *wulfenii* 'Purple and Gold'
- - var. **sibthorpii**	ECGN SSth
- - 'Thelma's Giant' **new**	NWit
clavarioides var. **truncata**	WCot
cognata	NWit
- CC&McK 607	EWes
- CC&McK 724	EBee GBin
'Copton Ash' **new**	EBee EFou
corallioides	CBrm EBee EBre ECha EMan EPPr EWTr IBlr LRHS NPer NSti SHFr SIgm SPer SRms WBrE WCot WHer WPnP
§ **cornigera** ♀ H4	More than 30 suppliers
- CC 720	CPou
- 'Goldener Turm'	CFwr EBee GBin
corollata	WCot
cyparissias	CArn EChP ECha EDAr ELan GAbr GKir LHrt LRHS NBir NCWG NFor NGdn NLon NMen NSti NVic NWCA SPar SPer SRms WEas WFar WFoF WHal WMoo WPer WRus WWin
- clone 2	WCot
- 'Baby'	WFar
- 'Betten'	see *E.* x *gayeri* 'Betten'
- 'Bushman Boy'	GBri IBlr
- 'Clarice Howard'	see *E. cyparissias* 'Fens Ruby'
§ - 'Fens Ruby'	More than 30 suppliers
- 'Orange Man'	CFwr EBee EChP EFou EMon EPfP EWes GBin GBri IBlr LRHS MHer MWgw NBro NHol NSti SPla SWat WElm WFar
- 'Purpurea'	see *E. cyparissias* 'Fens Ruby'
- 'Red Devil'	CBre IBlr NCat NWit SChu
- 'Tall Boy'	EMar EMon EWes GBri IBlr LRHS
dendroides	SIgm
denticulata new	EBee
§ **donii**	EGle EWes IBlr MAvo NWit SDix SVal WPer
dulcis	CBre ECha ECtt EFou EPar NBro NCWG NOak NSti NWit SMac WEas WHen
- 'Chameleon'	More than 30 suppliers
I - 'Nana'	NHol
epithymoides	see *E. polychroma*
esula Baker's form	NWit
Excalibur = 'Froeup' PBR ♀ H4	CFwr CMil CTrC EBee EMan EVFa GBin GBuc LHop LRHS MBNS MBri MCCP NEgg SHBN SPar SSpi SVil WFar
fragifera	NWit
'Garblesham Enchanter'	EPPr
§ x **gayeri** 'Betten'	EMan GCal
glabriflora MESE 519 **new**	EBee
glauca	CFee WCot
'Golden Foam'	see *E. stricta*
griffithii	GKir NBro NCat SPar SSpi SWat WAbb WGer WTel
- 'Dixter' ♀ H4	More than 30 suppliers
- 'Dixter Flame'	NWit
- 'Fern Cottage'	CElw CRDP EFou EHrv EVFa EWes GAbr SMrm SUsu WHal
- 'Fireglow'	More than 30 suppliers
- 'King's Caple'	NWit
- 'Wickstead'	EBee WBrE WLun WViv
'Hale Bop' **new**	CFwr
hyberna	CFis GBri IBlr MLLN NMen NWit SChu SWat
jacquemontii	EMan LPio MNrw NChi NWit SBla SIgm
'Jade Dragon'	CSpe EFou MAvo
'Jessie' **new**	EBee
x **keysii**	MBri
lathyris	CBre CHEx CRow EBlw ELan EMar MDun MHer NBid NCWG NCat NLar NPer SRms WEas WHer WWye
longifolia hort.	see *E. cornigera*
longifolia D. Don	see *E. donii*
longifolia Lamarck	see *E. mellifera*
x **martini** ♀ H3	More than 30 suppliers
- dwarf **new**	GCal
- 'Red Dwarf'	CElw CMil CPlt EOrc MSph SPar
§ **mellifera** ♀ H3	More than 30 suppliers
milii ♀ H1	CHal EBak SVal

	- 'Koenigers Aalbäumle'	MBri
*	- 'Variegata' (v)	CHal
	- yellow-flowered	CHal ECtt
	myrsinites ♀ H4	More than 30 suppliers
	nereidum	EWes NWit
	nicaeensis	CDes CFil CKno EBee EMan EOrc
		GCal LHop LPhx NWit SBla SMrm
		SPar SPer SSpi WCot WPGP
	- subsp. *glareosa*	NWit SUsu
	oblongata	CFil EBee EBre EMan ERou EWes
		GBuc IBlr LRHS NWit SPar WCHb
	palustris ♀ H4	More than 30 suppliers
	- 'Walenburg's Glorie'	CMHG EBee EChP EWTr GBin
		LRHS MAvo MBri MCLN MNrw
		MRav NWit SMad SWat WCot WLun
	- 'Zauberflöte'	LHrt SRms WFar
	x *paradoxa*	NWit
	paralias	IIve NWit WHer
	pekinensis	MSal NWit
	pilosa 'Major'	see *E. polychroma* 'Major'
	pithyusa	CBot CBro CSpe EBee EChP ECha
		ECtt ELan EMan EVFa ITer MArl
		MLLN MRav NFla SBod SChu
		SHBN WCom WLun WRus WWeb
§	*polychroma* ♀ H4	More than 30 suppliers
§	- 'Candy'	CBot CMea CSam EBre ECha ECtt
		EHrv ELan EPfP ERou GBin GCal
		LRHS MBro MCCP MDun MTis
		NHar NHol NOak NSti SBla SDes
		SPar SPla WCom WCot WFar
		WHoo WMnd
	- 'Emerald Jade'	CKno EBee GBri IBlr NWit WPGP
§	- 'Lacy' (v)	CDoC CFwr CSpe EBee ECtt EGle
		EMan EWes MCCP MCLN MGrG
		MTis NBir NWit SDes SMad WCom
		WCot WHer WHil WLin WSan
§	- 'Major' ♀ H4	CMHG EBre ECha ELan EPPr GCal
		LPhx LPio MBri NCat SAga SPer
		WCom WCot WEas
	- 'Midas'	CFee EGle MNrw NLar NWit
		SMHy SMrm
	- 'Orange Flush'	WHoo
	- 'Purpurea'	see *E. polychroma* 'Candy'
*	- 'Senior'	EBee EMil GBin MCCP NLar WMnd
	- 'Sonnengold'	EWes GCal MBro SMad WSHC
	- 'Variegata'	see *E. polychroma* 'Lacy'
	portlandica	CNic MBri NWit SVen WHer
§	x *pseudovirgata*	EMan IBlr LHop NWit
	pugniformis	MBri
	pulcherrima	LRHS MBri
	'Purple Preference'	EPPr NWit
	Redwing =	EBee ELan EMan ENot EPfP LPan
	'Charam'PBR ♀ H4	LRHS MRav NSti SCoo SPer SSpi
		WGer WWeb
	reflexa	see *E. seguieriana* subsp.
		niciciana
§	*rigida*	CBot CBro CDes CFil CKno EBee
		EChP EGle EHrv EMan EMar EPfP
		EPyc EVFa EWes GCal LPhx MBro
		MLLN SBla SIgm SMrm SSpi WCot
		WHoo WPGP WSHC
	- 'Sardis'	NWit
	robbiae	see *E. amygdaloides* var. *robbiae*
	sarawschanica	EBee EMan GBin LPhx NWit WCot
	schillingii ♀ H4	More than 30 suppliers
	seguieriana	ECha EMan GBin NBir NLar WPer
§	- subsp. *niciciana*	CBot EChP EMan EMon MArl
		MBro MLLN MRav NBir NPPs
		NWit SBla SDix SMrm SUsu WCra
		WHoo WPGP WRus
	serrulata	see *E. stricta*
	sikkimensis ♀ H4	CBot CFee CFwr CMHG CSam
		CSpe CWCL EBre ECha EGra

		EMon MAvo SIgm SMrm SRms
		WCHb WCom WCru WEas WFar
		WLin WLun WWin WWye
	soongarica	MSte NWit
	spinosa	SIgm SMad
§	*stricta*	EMan GBri IBlr MCCP MFir WBWf
	stygiana	CFil LPhx MSte NWit SAga SSpi
		WSHC
	- 'Devil's Honey' **new**	NWit
	- x *mellifera* **new**	SIgm WPGP
*	*submammillaris*	MBri
	'Variegata' (v)	
	terracina	NWit WCot
	uralensis	see *E.* x *pseudovirgata*
	villosa	GBin MBro NWit
§	*virgata*	EMFP EWes NSti NWit WCHb
		WCot
	x *waldsteinii*	see *E. virgata*
	wallichii misapplied	see *E. donii*
	wallichii Kohli	see *E. cornigera*
	wallichii Hook. f.	CSam EBee EBre EMan GKir IBlr
		LRHS MBri NOrc SDes SMrm SPar
		WAbb WHil

Euptelea (*Eupteleaceae*)

	franchetii	see *E. pleiosperma*
§	*pleiosperma*	CMCN EPfP NLar SSpi
	polyandra	CFil EPfP WPGP

Eurya (*Theaceae*)

| | *japonica* | CFil CWib WPGP |
| | - 'Variegata' misapplied | see *Cleyera japonica* 'Fortunei' |

Euryops (*Asteraceae*)

	abrotanifolius	CTrC GGar WGer
§	*acraeus* ♀ H4	CBot CHea CPBP CPle EHyt ELan
		EPot EVFa GTou LBee LHop LRHS
		MDun MWat NFor NLAp NLon
		NMen NWCA SIng WAbe WCom
		WWin
	candollei	CTrC NWCA WAbe
§	*chrysanthemoides*	CBcs CDoC CHEx CSam EBee
		ERea GGar MMil MSte SVen WPer
	- 'Sonnenschein'	CHal EBee SPet
	decumbens	CNic NJOw NMen WLin
	evansii	see *E. acraeus*
	linearis	GGar SVen
	pectinatus ♀ H2	More than 30 suppliers
	tagetoides **new**	CPBP
	tysonii	CPle CTrC EWes GGar SPlb
		WCot
	virgineus	CBcs CHEx CTrC EBee GGar LRav
		SVen WGer

Euscaphis (*Staphyleaceae*)

| | *japonica* **new** | CPle |

Eustachys (*Poaceae*)

| § | *distichophylla* **new** | EPPr |

Eustoma (*Gentianaceae*)

| § | *grandiflorum* | LRHS MBri |
| | *russellianum* | see *E. grandiflorum* |

Eustrephus (*Philesiaceae*)

| | *latifolius* | ECou |

Euterpe (*Arecaceae*)

| | *edulis* | LPal |

Evolvulus (*Convolvulaceae*)

| | *convolvuloides* | ERea |
| § | *pilosus* 'Blue Daze' | ERea |

Ewartia (Asteraceae)
  planchonii ITim

Exacum (Gentianaceae)
  affine ♀ H1+3   LRHS MBri
  - 'Rococo'   MBri

Exochorda (Rosaceae)
  alberti   see *E. korolkowii*
  giraldii   CBrm CFwr CPle
  - var. **wilsonii**   CEnd CSam EBee EBre EPfP GEil
     GKir LHop LRHS MAsh MBNS
     MBlu SLim SSta
§   **korolkowii**   MAsh WBcn
  x **macrantha** 'The   More than 30 suppliers
     Bride' ♀ H4
  racemosa   EHol EPfP ISea LHop MGos NBlu
     SHBN SPer SRPl WDin WHCG
  serratifolia   EPfP NLar
  - 'Northern Pearls' **new**   CFai CPMA
  - 'Snow White'   CPMA EBee MBlu MDun

F

Fabiana (Solanaceae)
  imbricata   CAbP EBee EMil EPfP GGar GQui
     LRHS SBra SBrw SLon SPar SPer
     SPoG
  - 'Prostrata'   CTrC EPfP GCal IArd LRHS SBrw
     SDry SPer SSpi WAbe WWin
  - f. **violacea** ♀ H3   CBcs CFee CPLG CSBt CTri EBee
     EHol EMil EPfP EPla ESis GQui
     LAst LRHS MAsh MBar SBrw SPer
     WKif WSHC

Fagopyrum (Polygonaceae)
  cymosum   see *F. dibotrys*
§   **dibotrys**   EBee ECha ELan EPPr LEdu NSti

Fagus ✿ (Fagaceae)
§   **crenata**   CMCN WDin WNor
  - 'Mount Fuji'   SBir
  engleriana   CMCN
  grandifolia   CMCN LPan
  - subsp. **mexicana**   SBir
     new
  japonica   CMCN LRHS
  lucida   CMCN
  orientalis   CMCN CTho LRHS
  sieboldii   see *F. crenata*
  sylvatica ♀ H4   More than 30 suppliers
§   - 'Albomarginata' (v)   CDul CLnd CMCN
  - 'Albovariegata'   see *F. sylvatica* 'Albomarginata'
  - 'Ansorgei'   CDul CEnd CLnd CMCN GKir MBlu
  - 'Argenteomarmorata'   CDul
N   - Atropurpurea Group   More than 30 suppliers
  - - 'Swat Magret'   LPan
  - 'Aurea Pendula'   CEnd CMCN EPla MBlu SMad
  - 'Birr Zebra'   CEnd
  - 'Black Swan'   CDul CEnd CMCN LPan MBlu SBir
     SLim SMad WGor
  - 'Bornyensis'   CMCN SBir
  - 'Cochleata'   CMCN LRHS
  - 'Cockleshell'   CDul CMCN CTho LRHS
  - 'Comptoniifolia'   see *F. sylvatica* var. *heterophylla* 'Comptoniifolia'
  - 'Cristata'   CDul CMCN MBlu
N   - Cuprea Group   NWea

§   - 'Dawyck' ♀ H4   CBcs CDoC CDul CLnd CMCN
     COtt CSBt CSam CTho EBee EBre
     ECrN ELan EMil ENot EPfP GKir
     LHyr LPan MAsh MBar MGos MHFa
     MRav NWea SLim SPer WDin WOrn
  - 'Dawyck Gold' ♀ H4   CAbP CBcs CDoC CDul CEnd
     CLnd CMCN COtt CTho EBee
     ENot GKir LPan LRHS MAsh MBar
     MBlu MHFa MRav NBea NWea
     SBir SKee SLim SMad SPer SSpi
     WDin WFar WOrn
  - 'Dawyck Purple' ♀ H4   More than 30 suppliers
  - 'Fastigiata' misapplied   see *F. sylvatica* 'Dawyck'
  - 'Felderbach'   LRHS MBlu
  - 'Franken' (v)   MBlu
  - 'Frisio'   CEnd CMCN
  - 'Grandidentata'   CMCN LPan LRHS
  - 'Greenwood'   CDul CMCN MBlu
*   - 'Haaren'   CMCN
  - var. **heterophylla**   CLnd CSBt CTho ISea MHFa
     NWea WOrn
  - - 'Aspleniifolia' ♀ H4   CDoC CDul CEnd CMCN COtt EBee
     ELan EMil ENot EPfP GKir IMGH
     LPan MBar MBri MHFa SBir SCoo
     SMad SPer WDin WMou WNor
§   - - 'Comptoniifolia'   CMCN
  - - f. **laciniata**   CMCN GKir LRHS MBlu
  - - 'Horizontalis'   CMCN
  - - 'Interrupta'   SMad
  - - 'Luteovariegata' (v)   CEnd CMCN
  - - 'Mercedes'   CDul CMCN GKir MBlu
  - - 'Miltonensis'   CDul CMCN LPan LRHS
N   - 'Pendula' ♀ H4   CBcs CDoC CDul CEnd CLnd
     CMCN CSBt CTho EBee ECrN ELan
     ENot GKir ISea LPan MBar MHFa
     MRav NBlu NPSI NWea SBir SPer
     WDin WHar WMou WOrn WStI
  - 'Prince George of   CDul CEnd CMCN CTho LRHS
     Crete'
  - 'Purple Fountain'   CDoC CEnd CMCN COtt EBee
     ♀ H4   ELan EMil LPan LRHS MAsh MBar
     MBlu MGos MWhi NBee SKee
     SLim SPer SPoG
  - Purple-leaved Group   see *F. sylvatica* Atropurpurea Group
  - 'Purpurea Nana'   CMCN LRHS
  - 'Purpurea Pendula'   CDul CEnd CMCN CSBt CTho CTri
     CWib EBee ECrN ELan ENot EPfP
     LPan LRHS MBar MGos MHFa
     MWat NBee NBlu NWea SCoo SKee
     SLim SPer WDin WFar WHar WStI
§   - 'Purpurea Tricolor' (v)   CDoC CEnd CMCN GKir LPan LRHS
     MBar MGos MHFa NBea NBee NBlu
     SBir SCoo SHBN SLim SPer WDin
  - 'Quercifolia'   CDul CMCN
I   - 'Quercina'   CMCN LRHS
  - 'Red Obelisk'   see *F. sylvatica* 'Rohan Obelisk'
  - 'Remillyensis'   CMCN
  - 'Riversii' ♀ H4   More than 30 suppliers
  - 'Rohan Gold'   CDul CEnd CLnd CMCN EBee
     GKir LPan LRHS MBlu
  - 'Rohan Obelisk'   CEnd CMCN EBee ELan IArd LPan
     LRHS MBlu SBir WOrn
I   - 'Rohan Pyramidalis'   CDul CEnd CMCN LRHS
  - 'Rohan Trompenburg'   CMCN IArd LRHS MBlu
  - 'Rohan Weeping' **new**   MBlu
  - 'Rohanii'   CAbP CBcs CDoC CDul CEnd
     CLnd CMCN COtt CTho CTri
     EBee ELan EMil EPfP IMGH NBee
     SHBN SPer WDin WOrn
  - 'Roseomarginata'   see *F. sylvatica* 'Purpurea Tricolor'
  - 'Rotundifolia'   CDoC CTho LPan MBlu NWea
  - 'Silver Wood'   CMCN LRHS

	– 'Spaethiana'	CMCN LRHS
	– 'Striata'	CMCN SBir
	– f. *tortuosa*	SMad
	– 'Tortuosa Purpurea'	CMCN CTho
	– 'Tricolor' (v)	CBcs CDul CLnd CSBt CWib EBee ELan MAsh SKee SLim WDin
	– 'Tricolor' misapplied	see *F. sylvatica* 'Purpurea Tricolor'
	– 'Viridivariegata' (v)	CMCN
	– 'Zlatia'	CBcs CDoC CDul CLnd CMCN COtt CSBt CTho ELan EPfP GKir LPan LRHS MBar MGos MHFa NBee NWea SBir SHBN SKee SPer WDin WOrn WStI

Falkia (Convolvulaceae)

	repens	CFir WCot

Fallopia (Polygonaceae)

	aubertii	see *F. baldschuanica*
§	*baldschuanica*	More than 30 suppliers
	– Summer Sunshine = 'Acofal'	NEgg
x	*bohemica*	CHEx CRow EMon
	'Spectabilis' (v)	
§	*japonica*	CRow
§	– var. *compacta*	CRow NLar NPri WBea WFar WMoo
	– – 'Fuji Snow'	see *F. japonica* var. *compacta* 'Milk Boy'
	– – 'Midas'	IBlr
§	– – 'Milk Boy' (v)	CRow EMan EWes IBlr ITer SMad
	– – f. *rosea*	WWeb
	– – 'Variegata'	see *F. japonica* var. *compacta* 'Milk Boy'
	– 'Crimson Beauty'	CRow
§	*multiflora*	CArn EOHP IIve MSal
	– var. *hypoleuca* B&SWJ 120	WCot WCru
	sachalinensis	CHEx CRow EWes NLar

Farfugium (Asteraceae)

	formosana B&SWJ 7125 **new**	WCru
§	*japonicum*	CHEx MTho
	– B&SWJ 884	WCru
	– 'Argenteum' (v)	CFir CHEx WCot WFar WHal WHil WSan
	– 'Aureomaculatum' (v) ♀ H1	CAbb CFir CHEx CKob EBee EBre EChP EHoe EPfP MAvo MBNS MCCP MTho SMad SWat WCot WFar WHal WHer WHil WMul WPnP WSan
	– 'Crispatum'	CAbb CFir CHEx CHid CKob CRez EBee EChP EMan EWll LEdu MAvo MCCP MGrG SMad SPoG SWat WCot WFar WHil WPnP WTMC
	– var. *giganteum* **new**	WCot
*	– 'Kagami-jishi' **new**	WCot
	– 'Kinkan' (v)	WCot
I	– 'Nanum'	CHEx
	– 'Ryuto' **new**	WCot
	tussilagineum	see *F. japonicum*

Fargesia (Poaceae)

	angustissima **new**	EPla
	contracta	EPla
	denudata	CFil EPla
	– L 1575	MMoz WPGP
	dracocephala	CAbb CDoC CFil EBee EPfP EPla GBin GCal IJus MAvo MBrN MHdf MMoz MWht NBlu NGdn SDry SEND SLPl WCru WJun WNor WPGP
	ferox	CFil EPla
	frigida	EPla
	fungosa	CFil EPla WJun WPGP

§	*murielae* ♀ H4	More than 30 suppliers
	– 'Bimbo'	CFil CTrC EPfP GBin MWod WPGP
	– 'Grüne Hecke'	MWht
	– 'Harewood'	CWSG EBee GBin MCCP MMoz MWht WFar
	– 'Jumbo'	CAbb CTrC CWSG EAmu EBee EMil ENot EPfP EPla GBin GKir LPal LPan LRHS MAvo MBNS MCCP MMoz MTed MWht NGdn NPri SPar WJun WWeb
	– 'Kranich'	CFil
§	– 'Leda' (v)	SDry
	– 'Mae'	GBin
	– 'Novecento'	EBee ELan
	– 'Simba' ♀ H4	More than 30 suppliers
I	– 'Willow'	EBee MGos
	nitida	More than 30 suppliers
	– from Jiuzhaigou, China	CFil EPla
	– 'Anceps'	EPla MWht NPri
	– 'Eisenach'	CAbb CFil CTrC EBee EPla LRHS MMoz NGdn WCru
	– 'Nymphenburg' ♀ H3	CFwr CPMA EBee EBlw EPla GKir LRHS MMoz MWhi MWht MWod NPri WFar WMoo
	– 'Wakehurst'	EPla MWht
	robusta	CEnd EBee EFul EPfP EPla GBin LPal MBrN MMoz MWht NGdn NMoo SDry SLPl WJun WNor
	– 'Red Sheath'	CAbb CFil EPla ERod MHdf MMoz MWht WJun
	rufa	CAbb CDDB CFil EBee ENot EPVP EPfP EPla MAvo MBrN MCCP MMoz WJun WNor WPGP
	spathacea hort.	see *F. murielae*
	utilis	CAbb CDDB EBee EPla ERod IJus MAvo MHdf MMoz MWht SDry WJun WNor WPGP
	yulongshanensis	CFil EPla WPGP

Fascicularia (Bromeliaceae)

	andina	see *F. bicolor*
§	*bicolor*	CFil CFir CHEx CTbh CTrC EBak EGra EOas EWes GCal GGar IBlr ICrw NPer SAPC SArc SChr SMad SPar SSpi SSta WAbe WBor WCot WEas WFar WGer WOld WPic
	– subsp. *canaliculata*	CFil IBlr LEdu WCot WPGP
	kirchhoffiana	see *F. bicolor* subsp. *canaliculata*
	pitcairniifolia hort.	see *F. bicolor*

x *Fatshedera* (Araliaceae)

	lizei ♀ H3	CBcs CBot CDoC CHEx EBee EPfP EPla GKir GQui LRHS MGrG MPRe MWat NPal NRog SArc SBra SDix SDry SLon SMac SPar SPer SPla SPlb WCFE WDin WFar WWal WWeb
§	– 'Annemieke' (v) ♀ H3	CBot CHEx CSWP EPfP EPla EVFa EWes SBra SMac SMad SPar SPer
§	– 'Aurea' (v)	EHoe ELan EPfP LRHS SBra SDry SEND
	– 'Aureopicta'	see x *F. lizei* 'Aurea'
	– 'Lemon and Lime'	see x *F. lizei* 'Annemieke'
	– 'Maculata'	see x *F. lizei* 'Annemieke'
	– 'Pia'	CSWP
*	– 'Silver Prusca'	EPla
	– 'Variegata' (v) ♀ H3	CBcs ELan EPfP EVFa LAst LRHS MAsh MGrG MPRe SBra SDry SEND SMac SMer SPar SPer SPla WCot WDin WFar WWeb

Fatsia (Araliaceae)

§	*japonica* ♀ H4	More than 30 suppliers

	- 'Moseri'	CSam EChP GBin LAst MNrw MSte WCot
	- 'Murakumo Nishiki' (v) **new**	NPal
	- 'Variegata' (v) ♀ H3	CBcs CBot CHEx EBee LRHS MBri MGos NPal SArc SHBN
	papyrifera	see *Tetrapanax papyrifer*

Fauria see *Nephrophyllidium*

Feijoa see *Acca*

Felicia (Asteraceae)

§	*amelloides*	CHal ERea LRHS MLan SChu SGar SPlb
	- 'Astrid Thomas'	CSpe MOak
	- 'Read's Blue'	CHal CSpe LIck SPet WWol
	- 'Read's White'	CHal ERea MOak MSte SPet
§	- 'Santa Anita' ♀ H3	CHal CTri CWCL ECtt EOrc ERea LIck MOak SCro WEas
§	- variegated (v)	CHal ECtt ERea IHMH LIck MBNS MBri MOak MSte NPer NPri SHFr SPar SPet SUsu WEas
	- variegated, white-flowered (v)	LIck
§	*amoena*	CHal CTri CWib MOak SRms
	- 'Variegata' (v)	CTri CWCL SChu
	capensis	see *F. amelloides*
	- 'Variegata'	see *F. amelloides* variegated
	coelestis	see *F. amelloides*
	drakensbergensis	ETow
	erigeroides	CHal
	natalensis	see *F. rosulata*
	pappei	see *F. amoena*
§	*petiolata*	EBee EMan MOak NSti SGar SSpi WCot WWin
§	*rosulata*	EHyt EMon ESis GCrs GDra GEdr GGar GKir MHer MTho NBro NJOw NMen SRms SRot WCom WWin
	uliginosa	EDAr EWes GCrs GEdr GTou IHMH LRHS MTho WOBN

fennel see *Foeniculum vulgare*

fenugreek see *Trigonella foenum-graecum*

Ferraria (Iridaceae)

§	*crispa*	EBee LBow
	undulata	see *F. crispa*

Ferula (Apiaceae)

	assa foetida	CArn EBee MSal WCot WJek
	chiliantha	see *F. communis* subsp. *glauca*
§	*communis*	CArn CPom CRDP EBee ECha EFou EWTr GKir LEdu MAnH MFir NBid NChi NLar SDes SDix SMad SMrm WCot WHil WJek
	- 'Gigantea'	see *F. communis*
§	- subsp. *glauca*	CSpe EBee LPhx SDix SGar SIgm WPGP WSHC
	'Giant Bronze'	see *Foeniculum vulgare* 'Giant Bronze'
	tingitana	SIgm SMad
	- 'Cedric Morris'	EBee ECha LPhx SIgm SMad WCot

Ferulago (Apiaceae)

	sylvatica **new**	EBee

Festuca (Poaceae)

	amethystina	CBig CBrm CKno CWCL EHoe EMon ESis EWsh GBri IPot LHrt LRHS MBri MHdf MNrw MWhi
		NCiC NGdn NHol NOak SDes SPer SRGP SWal WMoo WPer WRos
	- 'Aprilgrün'	EHoe
	arundinacea	CKin
	'Banks Peninsula Blue'	CTrC LEdu MAvo WHrl
	californica	CBig
	curvula subsp. *crassifolia*	EPPr EPla EWsh NHol WDyG
	'Eisvogel'	EBee EMil
	elegans	EPPr
	erecta	EHoe EPPr
	eskia	CKno EBee EHoe EHul EPPr ESis GKir GOrn LRHS MWhi NEgg NHol SDes SHel SPer SPla SVil WDyG WPer
	filiformis	CKin EHoe EMon EPPr LRHS
	'Fromefield Blue'	CSLe EBee EChP EHul NPro SPar
§	*gautieri*	CBrm EBee ELan EPfP GBin GIBF LPVe MBar MBrN NGdn NOrc SDes SPar SPer WFoF
	- 'Pic Carlit'	EMon
	gigantea	CBig CKin GBin
	glacialis	EHoe
	glauca	More than 30 suppliers
I	- 'Auslese'	LPVe NGdn WBar WWeb
	- 'Azurit'	CCol EChP EHoe EMon EPPr EPla EVFa EWes EWsh NHol SDes WPrP
§	- 'Blaufuchs' ♀ H4	More than 30 suppliers
§	- 'Blauglut'	EBee EBre EHoe EHul EOrc EPGN EPfP EPla GKir GSki LRHS MWgw NHar NHol SDes SHel WCra WGer
	- Blue Fox	see *F. glauca* 'Blaufuchs'
	- Blue Glow	see *F. glauca* 'Blauglut'
	- 'Elijah Blue'	More than 30 suppliers
	- 'Golden Toupee'	More than 30 suppliers
	- 'Harz'	CBrm EBee EBre EHoe EHul EMil EPla GKir MBNS MBar NBea SDes WPnP
*	- *minima*	EPPr ESis WBcn WPGP
	- 'Pallens'	see *F. longifolia*
	- Sea Urchin	see *F. glauca* 'Seeigel'
§	- 'Seeigel'	EBre EGle EHoe EPPr GKir MAvo MBri MMoz NHol NPro NSti SDes SHel SPar SWal
	- 'Seven Seas'	see *F. valesiaca* 'Silbersee'
	- 'Silberreiher'	EPPr
	- 'Uchte'	CWCL EMil
*	*hogar*	EHoc
	idahoensis	CBig
§	*longifolia*	CKin EPPr
	muirei	EHoe EMon EPPr LRHS SWal WDyG
	novae-zelandiae	CCol CPen CTrC CWCL EPPr EWsh NNor
	ovina	CBrm EFWa EHoe NGdn NOrc WPer
	- subsp. *coxii*	EHoe
	- 'Söhrewald'	EPPr
*	- 'Tetra Gold'	GKir
	paniculata	EGle EHoe EMon EPla GOrn
	pulchella	CBig EBee EPPr
	punctoria	EBee ECha EHoe EVFa EWsh MRav NHar SIng WMoo
	rubra	CBig
	- var. *nankotaizanensis*	LPio
	- - B&SWJ 3190	EBee WCru
	scoparia	see *F. gautieri*
	tatrae	CBrm GBin WCot
	valesiaca	GOrn WFar WHil
	- var. *glaucantha*	CBig EGra EWll GWCH MBri NGdn WWeb
§	- 'Silbersee'	EBee ECha EHoe EPPr EPot ESis EWsh LRHS MBar MBri MNrw MSte NHol NOak SDes SIng SRms

		WCom WFar
- Silver Sea		see *F. valesiaca* 'Silbersee'
	violacea	EChP EMan EPPr MAvo SRGP
		SWal WRos WWpP
	vivipara	EGoo EHoe EMon EPPr LEdu
		LRHS NBid NHol WMaN WRos
*	'Willow Green'	CBod MSte SDes SLim SPar SPlb

Ficus ✿ (Moraceae)

	afghanistanica	ERea
	australis hort.	see *F. rubiginosa* 'Australis'
	benghalensis	MBri
	benjamina ♀ H1	CHal EBre LRHS MBri SRms
- 'Exotica'		CHal LRHS MBri
- 'Golden King'		LRHS MBri
- 'Starlight' (v) ♀ H1		LRHS MBri SMur
	capitola 'Long'	ERea
	carica (F)	CWSG LHyr LPan MBri SArc
- 'Abbey Slip' (F)		CHEx
- 'Adam' (F)		ERea
- 'Alma' (F)		ERea
- 'Angélique' (F)		ERea
- 'Beall' (F)		ERea
- 'Bellone' (F)		ERea
- 'Bifère' (F)		ERea
- 'Black Ischia' (F)		ERea
- 'Black Jack' (F)		ESim
- 'Black Mission' (F)		ERea
- 'Boule d'Or' (F)		ERea
- 'Bourjassotte Grise' (F)		ERea SDea
- 'Breva' (F)		CGOG
- 'Brown Turkey' (F) ♀ H3		More than 30 suppliers
- 'Brunswick' (F)		EBee ERea GBon GTwe LRHS
		MCCP MCoo SLim WCot
- 'Castle Kennedy' (F)		ERea GTwe
- 'Col de Dame Blanc' (F)		CGOG ERea
- 'Col de Dame Noir' (F) **new**		CGOG
- 'Conandria' (F)		ERea
- 'De Ley' (F) **new**		CGOG
§ - 'Desert King' (F)		ESim
- 'Figue d'Or' (F)		ERea
- 'Goutte d'Or' (F)		ERea SDea
- 'Grise de Saint Jean' (F)		ERea
- 'Grise Ronde' (F)		ERea
- 'Grosse Grise' (F)		ERea
- 'Kaape Bruin' (F)		ERea
- 'Kadota' (F)		ERea
- 'King'		see *F. carica* 'Desert King'
* - 'Laciniata' (F) **new**		SMad
- 'Lisa' (F)		ERea
- 'Longue d'Août' (F)		ERea
- 'Maellana Blanca' (F) **new**		CGOG
- 'Malcolm's Giant' (F)		ERea
- 'Malta' (F)		ERea GTwe
- 'Marseillaise' (F)		ERea GTwe SDea
- 'Napolitana' (F) **new**		CGOG
- 'Negro Largo' (F)		ERea
- 'Newlyn Harbour' (F)		CHEx
- 'Noir de Provence'		see *F. carica* 'Reculver'
- 'Osborn's Prolific' (F)		ERea
- 'Panachée' (F)		ERea
- 'Pastilière' (F)		ERea
- 'Peter's Honey' (F)		ERea
- 'Petite Grise' (F)		ERea
- 'Pied de Boeuf' (F)		ERea
- 'Pittaluse' (F)		ERea
- 'Précoce Ronde de Bordeaux' (F)		ERea
§ - 'Reculver' (F)		ERea
- 'Rouge de Bordeaux' (F)		ERea SDea

- 'Saint Johns' (F)	ERea
- 'San Pedro Miro' (F)	ERea SPar
- 'Snowden' (F)	ERea
- 'Sollies Pont' (F)	ERea
- 'Sugar 12' (F)	ERea
- 'Sultane' (F)	ERea
- 'Tena' (F)	ERea
- 'Troiano' (F)	ERea
- 'Trojano' (F)	ERea
- 'Verte d'Argenteuil' (F)	ERea
- 'Violette Dauphine' (F)	ERea
- 'Violette de Sollies' (F)	ERea
- 'Violette Sepor' (F)	ERea
- 'White Genoa'	see *F. carica* 'White Marseilles'
- 'White Ischia' (F)	ERea
§ - 'White Marseilles' (F)	CWib EHol EPfP ERea LRHS
	MCoo SDea SKee SPar
cyathistipula	MBri
deltoidea var. *diversifolia*	MBri
elastica	LRHS SEND
- 'Robusta'	MBri
foveolata Wallich	see *F. sarmentosa*
lyrata ♀ H1	MBri
microcarpa	STre
- 'Hawaii' (v)	CHal
pumila ♀ H1	CHEx CHal EBak LRHS MBri SAPC
	SArc
- 'Minima'	CFee
- 'Sonny' (v)	CHal MBri
- 'Variegata' (v)	CHEx CHal MBri
radicans 'Variegata'	see *F. sagittata* 'Variegata'
§ *rubiginosa* 'Australis'	MBri
- 'Variegata' (v) ♀ H1	CHal
§ *sagittata* 'Variegata' (v)	MBri
§ *sarmentosa*	MBri

fig see *Ficus carica*

filbert see *Corylus maxima*

Filipendula ✿ (Rosaceae)

alnifolia 'Variegata'	see *F. ulmaria* 'Variegata'
camtschatica	CFir CMCo CRow EBee ECoo ELan
	GDra GIBF MTed NBid NLar NMir
	NPSI SMac WFar WMoo WPGP
- 'Rosea'	IBlr LHop SMad
digitata 'Nana'	see *F. multijuga*
hexapetala	see *F. vulgaris*
'Kahome'	CMCo CRow EBee EChP EMan
	GBuc GGar GKir GMaP GMac
	IPot LAst LHop LPan LRHS MBro
	NBir NGdn NLar NMir NOrc NSti
	SPla SVil WFar WHoo WMoo WViv
kiraishiensis B&SWJ 1571	EBee WCru
§ *multijuga*	CRow EBee GCal GGar MBro
	WFar WHoo WMoo
palmata	ECha EFou GCal WFar WMoo
- 'Digitata Nana'	see *F. multijuga*
- dwarf	CLAP
- 'Elegantissima'	see *F. purpurea* 'Elegans'
- 'Nana'	see *F. multijuga*
- *purpurea*	see *F. purpurea*
- 'Rosea'	ERou IBlr NBir WCHb
- 'Rubra'	CTri GSki MRav NGdn WHHs
- *rufinervis* B&SWJ 941	WCru
§ *purpurea* ♀ H4	CKno CMea CRow EBee EBre
	EFou EPfP GGar LRHS MTis
	MWrn WCru WFar WMoo
- f. *albiflora*	LPhx NPri WMoo WPnP
- 'Elegans'	CHea CRow EBee ECGN EChP
	ECha EMan EMil GCal GGar LAst

		MSte NBid NCat NHol NPSI NSti
		SDes SSpe SWat WBro WFar WMoo
		WPnP
	- 'Pink Dreamland'	LPhx
*	- 'Plena' (d)	LCaP NLar
	'Queen of the Prairies'	see *F. rubra*
§	*rubra*	CRow GEil LAst LSyl NBid NWoo
		WBVN WFar WWpP
§	- 'Venusta' ♀ H4	More than 30 suppliers
	- 'Venusta Magnifica'	see *F. rubra* 'Venusta'
§	*ulmaria*	CAgr CArn CKin EBee EBot ECoo
		EHon ELau EWTr GBar GMaP
		GPoy LRHS MBow MChe MHer
		MTho NHol NLan NMir SIde SWat
		WFar WHHs WMoo WPer WShi
		WWpP WWye
	- 'Aurea'	More than 30 suppliers
	- 'Flore Pleno' (d)	CBre CMil CRDP CRow EBee
		EBlw GKir GSki LAst LRHS NBid
		NGdn NHol NSti SWat WCot
		WElm WFar WLRN WPnP
	- 'Rosea'	CRDP EBee IBlr
§	- 'Variegata' (v)	More than 30 suppliers
§	*vulgaris*	CArn CFee CKin CTri EBee ECtt
		GBar LAst LPBA MChe MSal MWgw
		NArg NBro NMir NOrc NPri SWat
		WBea WPer WWpP WWye
	- 'Alba' **new**	EBcc
	- 'Flore Pleno'	see *F. vulgaris* 'Multiplex'
	- 'Grandiflora'	EPPr WCot
§	- 'Multiplex' (d)	CRow CSpe EBee ECha EGle ELan
		EOrc ERou GKir GSki LRHS MHer
		MRav MTho NBid NBir NDov
		NHol NPri NRya SPer SRms WAul
		WCot WElm WFar WMoo WRus
		WWye
	- 'Plena'	see *F. vulgaris* 'Multiplex'
	- 'Rosea' **new**	EBcc

Fingerhuthia (Poaceae)

sesleriiformis	CWCL

Firmiana (Sterculiaceae)

simplex	CHEx IDee LPan

Fittonia (Acanthaceae)

albivenis Argyroneura	CHal LRHS
Group ♀ H1	
- Verschaffeltii Group	CHal
♀ H1	

Fitzroya (Cupressaceae)

cupressoides	CDoC CMac CTho IDee LCon
	MBar SCoo SLim SLon WCwm

Foeniculum (Apiaceae)

vulgare	CAgr CArn CPrp EChP ECha EEls
	ELan ELau GBar GMaP GPoy
	MBow MChe MHer MSal NBid
	NBlu NDov NPri SIde SPar SPer
	SPlb SWal WBrE WCer WHHs
	WPer WSel WWye
- 'Bronze'	see *F. vulgare* 'Purpureum'
- var. *dulce*	CSev SIde
§ - 'Giant Bronze'	ELan GKir LPhx WBrE WHen
§ - 'Purpureum'	More than 30 suppliers
- 'Smokey'	EFou IIve MRav

Fokienia (Cupressaceae)

hodginsii	SMad

Fontanesia (Oleaceae)

phillyreoides	CMCN

Fontinalis (Sphagnaceae)

antipyretica	WFar

Forestiera (Oleaceae)

	neomexicana	see *F. pubescens*
§	*pubescens*	CBcs CFil

Forsythia (Oleaceae)

	'Arnold Dwarf'	NLar SRms
N	'Beatrix Farrand'	CSBt CTri CWSG EBee ECtt GKir
		LRHS MGos MWat NFor NHol SPer
		SRms WLRN WMoo WRHF WTel
§	Boucle d'Or =	COtt ENot SLim
	'Courtacour'PBR	
	'Fiesta' (v)	CPle CSBt CWSG EBee EBre ENot
		EPfP GKir LAst LRHS MAsh MBar
		MBri MGos MRav MTis NLon
		NPro NWea SHBN SLim SPer
		WCot WDin WFar
	giraldiana	SRms WBcn WBod
	Gold CurlPBR	see *F.* Boucle d'Or = 'Courtacour'
	'Golden Bells'	EMil ENot LRHS MBri
	'Golden Nugget'	EBee EBre EPfP LRHS MAsh SLon
		SMer SPer WCFE
	'Golden Times' (v)	EBee EHoe EPla EWes LBuc LRHS
		MAsh MBri MGos NHol NPro SCoo
		SWal WBcn WBod WCot WDin
	'Golden Times Allgold'	WBcn
	x *intermedia* 'Arnold	MBlu WBod
	Giant'	
	- 'Densiflora'	NWea
	- 'Goldzauber'	NWea
	- 'Karl Sax'	GEil NWea WLRN
	- 'Lynwood' ♀ H4	CBcs CChe CDoC CSBt CWib EBee
		ELan ENot EPfP GKir ISea LAst
		LRHS MBar MBri MGos NBlu NFor
		NWea SLon SPer SRPl SReu SSta
		SWal WBod WDin WFar WTel
		WWeb
	- - LA 79	MLan SPoG
	- - variegated **new**	CWib
	'Minigold'	ECtt EPfP GEil LRHS MGos MWat
		NHol SRms WBVN WRHF WStI WTel
	- 'Spectabilis'	EWTr GKir LBuc MBar NWea SPer
		WDin WFar WTel WWal
	- 'Spectabilis	EVFa LRHS MBNS NPro SRPl WCot
	Variegated' (v)	
	- 'Spring Glory'	EBee ECtt ENot LPan LRHS MHcr
		NWea
	- 'Susan Gruninger' (v)	EVFa
	- 'Variegata' (v)	GEil NSti NWea SPer
	- Week-End =	CSBt CWSG EBee ENot EPfP LPan
	'Courtalyn'PBR ♀ H4	MGos NWea SLim SPlb WDin
	japonica var. *saxatilis*	GEil
	'Josefa' **new**	WBcn
	koreana 'Ilgwang' (v)	CPMA
	Marée d'Or =	COtt CSBt CWSG EBee ENot
		LRHS
	'Courtasol'PBR ♀ H4	MBri MGos MRav SPer WDin
		WLRN
	Mêlée d'Or =	EBee ENot LRHS SPer
	'Courtaneur'PBR	
	Melissa = 'Courtadic'	NWea
	'Northern Gold'	CBcs EPfP
	ovata	EMon
	- 'Tetragold'	CBcs CSBt EBee MBar NBee NWea
	'Paulina'	ESis NLar
*	*pumila*	EWes
	suspensa	CBcs CTri CWib EBee ENot EPfP
		IIve LRHS MBar MSal MWat NVic
		NWea SHBN SLon SPer WStI WTel
	- f. *atrocaulis*	CPle GGar NWea

	– 'Decipiens'	WBod
	– var. **fortunei**	WWal
	– 'Hewitt's Gold'	EMon
	– 'Nymans'	EBee EPfP GEil GKir MBri MRav NSti NWea SLPl WMoo
§	– 'Taff's Arnold' (v)	CFai CPMA EBee EVFa GEdr WBcn
	– 'Variegata'	see *F. suspensa* 'Taff's Arnold'
	'Tremonia'	NFor WGwG
	viridissima	NFor NWea
	– 'Bronxensis'	EBee EHyt EPot ESis GEdr NBir NWea SMad SRot WAbe
	– 'Weber's Bronx'	MBar NWea

Fortunella (Rutaceae)

	x **crassifolia** (F)	SCit
	– 'Meiwa' (F) ♀ H1	ERea
	'Fukushu' (F) ♀ H1	ERea ESlt SCit
	hindsii (F)	SCit
§	**japonica** (F)	SAPC SArc SCit
§	**margarita** (F)	CDoC CGOG LPan MBri SCit SPer
	– 'Nagami' (F)	ERea ESlt

Fothergilla (Hamamelidaceae)

	gardenii	CBcs CPMA EBre ELan EPfP EWTr GKir MAsh MBlu MBri SPer SSpi SSta WDin
	– 'Blue Mist'	CAbP CDoC CEnd CPMA CWSG ELan EPfP LRHS MAsh MBri MDun MGos SBrw SLim SPer SPla SReu SSpi SSta WDin WFar WPat
	'Huntsman'	SBrw SSta
	major ♀ H4	CBcs CEnd CPMA CWib EBee EBre ELan EPfP EWTr GKir LRHS MAsh MBri MGos MLan NBee NBlu SBrw SHBN SPer SReu SSpi WDin WFar WNor WPat WStl
	– Monticola Group	CDoC CPMA CSBt CWSG EBee ELan ENot EPfP IMGH LRHS MAsh MBar MBri MDun NDlv NPal SBrw SChu SHBN SLim SPer SRkn SSpi SSta WBrE WFar
	'Mount Airy'	CDoC CPMA EPfP IMGH SBrw

Fragaria (Rosaceae)

	from Taiwan	WHer
	alpina	see *F. vesca* 'Semperflorens'
	x **ananassa** (F)	NRog
	– 'Alice' (F)	CSut EMui NRog
	– 'Aromel' (F) ♀ H4	CSBt CWSG GTwe LRHS MBri SDea
	– 'Auchincruive Climax' (F)	EMui
	– 'Bogota'PBR (F)	GTwe LRHS
	– 'Bolero'PBR (F)	CSut EMui GTwe
	– 'Cambridge Favourite' (F) ♀ H4	CMac CSBt CWSG EMui GKir GTwe LRHS MBri NRog SDea WWeb
	– 'Cambridge Late Pine' (F)	CWSG EMui GTwe LRHS
	– 'Cambridge Rival' (F)	LRHS
	– 'Cambridge Sentry' (F)	EMui
	– 'Cambridge Vigour' (F)	CSBt CWSG GKir GTwe LRHS NBee SDea
	– 'Challenger' (F) **new**	EMui
	– 'Darselect'PBR (F)	EMui
	– 'Elsanta'PBR (F)	CTri CWSG EMui GKir GTwe IArd LRHS NRog SDea WWeb
	– 'Elvira'PBR (F)	EMui
*	– 'Emily' (F)	EMui GTwe LRHS
	– 'Eros'PBR (F)	CSBt EMui GTwe
	– 'Evita'PBR (F)	EMui
	– 'Florence'PBR (F)	EMui GTwe LRHS
	– 'Fraise des Bois'	see *F. vesca*
*	– 'Franny Karan' (F)	WGor
	– 'Gorella' (F)	LRHS

	– 'Hapil'PBR (F) ♀ H4	CSBt EMui GTwe LRHS NRog WLRN
	– 'Honeoye' (F) ♀ H4	CSBt EMui GTwe LRHS
	– 'Korona'PBR (F)	CSut EMui
	– 'Kouril' (F)	LRHS
	– 'Laura' (F)	EMui LRHS
	– 'Maraline' (F)	EMui
	– 'Marastil' (F)	EMui
	– 'Maxim' (F)	EMui
	– 'Pantagruella' (F)	LRHS
	– 'Pegasus'PBR (F) ♀ H4	EMui GTwe LRHS MAsh NRog
	– pink-flowered	CFee
	– 'Redgauntlet' (F)	GTwe LRHS NRog WWeb
	– 'Rhapsody'PBR (F) ♀ H4	EMui GTwe LRHS
	– 'Rosie' (F)	EMui
	– 'Royal Sovereign' (F)	CMac EMui GTwe LRHS WWeb
	– 'Serenata' (F)	NBur
	– 'Sophie'PBR (F)	LRHS
	– 'Symphony'PBR (F) ♀ H4	EMui NRog
	– 'Talisman' (F)	LRHS
	– 'Tamella' (F)	EMui GTwe LRHS
	– 'Tango' (F)	EMui
	– 'Temptation' (F) **new**	NPri
	– 'Totem' (F)	GTwe
§	– 'Variegata' (v)	CArn CMea CSev EBee EMan EPla GBar LBuc LDai LHop LRHS MCCP MHar MRav NEgg NHol NSti SIng SPer WBea WCom WMoo WRha
	– 'Viva Rosa' (F)	EMui MAsh MBNS SSte
	'Bowles' Double'	see *F. vesca* 'Multiplex'
	chiloensis (F)	CAgr EMon LEdu
	– 'Chaval'	CHid ECGP ECha EGoo EMon EPPr MRav MWgw NWoo WMoo
N	– 'Variegata' (v)	GCal LBuc WEas
	daltoniana	SIng
	indica	see *Duchesnea indica*
	'Lipstick'	EBee ENot NLar
	nubicola	GPoy
	Pink Panda = 'Frel'PBR (F)	CTri EBee EBre EChP ECtt EGra GKir LBuc LEdu LRHS MBri NGdn NHol NLar SHFr SIng SPer WEas WFar WLRN WMaN
	'Red Ruby'	EBee EBre ECGP EChP EMan GKir LRHS MCAu MLwd MNrw NGdn NLar SIng SPer WMoo
	'Variegata'	see *F x ananassa* 'Variegata'
§	**vesca** (F)	CAgr CArn CKin ECoo EPfP GPoy LPVe LRHS LSyl MBow MGas MHer NGHP NLon NMir NPri SIde SPet SPlb WHHs WJek WPer WShi WWye
	– 'Alexandra' (F)	CArn CBod CPrp ELau IHMH LPVe LRHS MBow MChe NVic SIde WCHb WHer
	– 'Flore Pleno'	see *F. vesca* 'Multiplex'
	– 'Fructu Albo' (F)	CAgr CBre CRow NLar WMoo WPer
	– 'Mara des Bois'PBR (F)	EMui GTwe
	– 'Monophylla' (F)	CRow EMon IGor LRHS NHol SIde WHer
§	– 'Multiplex' (d)	CFox CNat CRow CSev EMon MInt MRav NCWG NGHP NHol NLar WAlt WCHb WCom WHer WWye
§	– 'Muricata'	CFee CPou CRow GAbr IGor ITer LEdu WAlt WCer WCom WHer WWye
*	– 'Pineapple Crush'	WHer
	– 'Plymouth Strawberry'	see *F. vesca* 'Muricata'
	– 'Rügen' (F)	CHal IGor
§	– 'Semperflorens' (F)	ILis WAlt WHer WRHF
§	– 'Semperflorens Alba' (F)	WOut
N	– 'Variegata' (v)	EHoe EHrv EPar LAst NGHP SMac WHrl WPer WSel

virginiana	CAgr IIve

Francoa (*Saxifragaceae*)

appendiculata	CRez EBee EBla EMFP EMan EMar
	GMac LPio MGrG SGar SWal SYvo
	WFTG WHer WPic WPnP
Ballyrogan strain	IBlr MAvo
'Confetti'	CDes CKno EBee GMac LPhx
	MAnH MAvo MGrG WCot WPGP
'Purple Spike'	see *F. sonchifolia* Rogerson's form
§ **ramosa**	CMCo CPLG CTri EBee EChP
	EHrv EMan GAbr GBri GBuc IBlr
	LRHS MBct MLan MNrw MTis
	MWat NBro NRog SAga SDix STes
	WCom WCru WFar WMoo
* - 'Alba'	CSpe
§ **sonchifolia**	More than 30 suppliers
- 'Alba'	CPlt CRDP CSpe EBee MDKP
	SHar SMrm SUsu
- 'Dr. Tom Smith'	WCot
- 'Lynda Windsor' **new**	CRDP
- 'Molly Anderson'	MAvo
§ - Rogerson's form	More than 30 suppliers

Frangula see *Rhamnus*

Frankenia (*Frankeniaceae*)

laevis	CHal CTri SRms
thymifolia	CBrm CHal CMHG EPar EPot ESis
	LRHS MBar MHer MWat NLAp
	SPlb WFar WPer WTel WWin

Franklinia (*Theaceae*)

alatamaha	CBcs CTho EPfP LHyd SBrw SSpi
	WBor WFar WNor

Frasera (*Gentianaceae*)

albicaulis var.	GKev
columbiana new	
fastigiata new	GKev

Fraxinus ✿ (*Oleaceae*)

americana	CDul CMCN EGFP EPfP SKee
	WDin WLRN
- 'Autumn Purple'	CDul CEnd CTho ECrN EPfP GKir
	MAsh MBlu SKee
'Rosehill'	CTho
§ **angustifolia**	CLnd CMCN CTho EGFP
- 'Elegantissima'	CTho
- var. **lentiscifolia**	CTho
§ - 'Monophylla'	CLnd CTho
§ - subsp. **oxycarpa**	GIBF
- Raywood =	CBcs CCVT CDoC CDul CEnd
'Flame' ♀ H4	CLnd CTho CWib EBee ECrN
	ELan ENot EPfP EWTr GKir LRHS
	MBlu MGos NBee NWea SMad
	SPer WDin WFar WJas WOrn
* - 'Variegata' (v)	CPMA MGos
anomala	GIBF
bungeana	CMCN EGFP
chinensis	CDul CLnd CMCN CTho GIBF
- subsp. **rhynchophylla**	GIBF GKir
elonza	CLnd CTho
excelsior	CBcs CCVT CDoC CDul CKin
	CLnd CSBt CWib EBee ECrN ENot
	EPfP GKir GTre LBuc LHyr LPan
	MBar MGos MHFa NBee NWea
	SHBN SHFr SKee SPer WDin
	WMou WOrn WStI
- 'Allgold'	CEnd
- 'Althena'	MHFa
- 'Aurea Pendula'	CDul CEnd CMCN EBee LRHS
	MAsh MBlu SKee WGer

- 'Crispa'	NLar WCom
- f. **diversifolia**	CDul CLnd CTho WMou
- 'Geessink'	EBee ENot
- 'Jaspidea' ♀ H4	More than 30 suppliers
- 'Nana'	EMon WPat
- 'Pendula' ♀ H4	CCVT CDoC CDul CEnd CLnd CTho
	EBee ECrN ELan ENot EPfP GKir
	IMGH LPan LRHS MAsh MBlu MBri
	MHFa NBee NWea SHBN SKee SLim
	SPer WDin WJas WMou WOrn WStI
- 'R.E. Davey'	CDul CNat CTho
- variegated (v)	CDul ECrN
- 'Westhof's Glorie' ♀ H4	CCVT CDoC CLnd EBee ECrN
	ENot MHFa WDin WJas WOrn
griffithii	EGFP
holotricha	CTho
insularis var.	CFil CMCN WPGP
henryana	
§ **latifolia**	EGFP GIBF
longicuspis new	GIBF
mariesii	see *F. sieboldiana*
nigra	CFil CMCN
- 'Fallgold'	CEnd
ornus ♀ H4	CCVT CDul CLnd CMCN EBee
	ECrN ELan ENot EPfP EWTr GKir
	LRHS MBri MHFa NBee NWea
	SPer SSta WDin WFar
- 'Arie Peters'	CDul MHFa WStI
- 'Mecsek'	MBri
- 'Obelisk'	MBri MHFa
oxycarpa	see *F. angustifolia* subsp.
	oxycarpa
pennsylvanica	CDul CLnd CMCN GIBF
- 'Aucubifolia' (v)	CTho
- 'Summit'	CTho
- 'Variegata' (v)	CLnd CTho EBee GKir LPan LRHS
	MAsh MBri SSta
quadrangulata	NWea WDin
§ **sieboldiana**	CDoC CFil CPMA EBee EPfP GKir
	MBlu SSpi WPGP WPat
'Veltheimii'	see *F. angustifolia* 'Monophylla'
velutina	CDul CLnd CMCN CTho SLPl

Freesia (*Iridaceae*)

double, mixed (d)	NCel
elimensis	LBow
hybrids	NCel NRog
laxa	see *Anomatheca laxa*
leichtlinii	LBow
Royal Series	EMui
viridis	LBow
xanthospila	LBow

Fremontodendron (*Sterculiaceae*)

'California Glory' ♀ H3	More than 30 suppliers
californicum	CSBt CTri EBee ELan EMil MBri
	MLan MWhi NBlu SHBN SLim
	SOWG SPlb SRPl WBod WCFE
	WDin WNor WStI
'Ken Taylor'	LRHS
'Pacific Sunset'	CPMA EBee ENot EPfP LHop
	LRHS MRav SBra SBrw SMur SPer
'Tequila Sunrise' **new**	CPMA EBee ENot MRav

Freylinia (*Scrophulariaceae*)

tropica new	GFai

Fritillaria ✿ (*Liliaceae*)

acmopetala ♀ H4	CAvo CBro CPom EBlw EHyt EPar
	EPot ERos EWTr GBuc GCrs GDra
	GIBF ITim LAma LRHS MS&S
	MTho NMen NRog NWCA SSpi
	WCot WFTG WLin WPrP WSel

	Name	Suppliers
	- subsp. *wendelboi*	LAma WCot WDav
§	*affinis*	GCrs LAma MS&S NHar NMen SBla SSpi
§	- var. *gracilis*	LAma
	- 'Sunray'	GCrs SSpi
§	- var. *tristulis*	ERos NMen
	- 'Vancouver Island'	ECho EPot GCrs
	- 'Wayne Roderick'	EPot
*	*albidiflora*	LAma
	alburyana	EHyt EPot
	arabica	see *F. persica*
	aurea	CLAP GCrs MS&S NCel NMen
	- 'Golden Flag'	CAvo ETub GEdr LTwo NMen NWCA WDav WWst
	biflora	CLAP GCrs GIBF NCel
	- 'Martha Roderick'	CAvo CBro CMea EBre EPot GEdr LAma MS&S NCel SBla WWst
§	*bithynica*	CBro CLAP EHyt ITim LAma MS&S SCnR
	bucharica	CAvo CLAP EHyt EPot NMen
	- 'Nurek Giant'	WWst
	camschatcensis	CAvo CBro CRDP ECha EFEx EPar EPfP EPot ETub GCrs GDra GEdr GKir LAma LPhx MS&S MTho NBir NDov NHar NMen NRog NWCA SSpi WAbe WCru WLin
	- from Alaska	GCrs
*	- *alpina aurea*	GCrs
	- 'Aurea'	GBuc GEdr NMen
	- black	GBuc GKir
	- f. *flavescens*	EFEx LAma
	- green	WWst
	- *multiflora*	GDra
	carduchorum	see *F. minuta*
	carica	CAvo EHyt EPot MS&S NMen WCot
	- brown-flowered **new**	EPot
	caucasica	CLAP EHyt LAma NMen
	cirrhosa	GKir WWst
	- brown-flowered	GKir NMen
	- green-flowered	GKir NMen
	citrina	see *F. bithynica*
	conica	CAvo EHyt EPot GCrs NMen WCot
	crassifolia	GIBF LAma MS&S
	- subsp. *crassifolia*	CGra
§	- subsp. *kurdica*	EPot GCrs GEdr NMen SSpi WLin
	dagana **new**	WWst
	davidii	WWst
	davisii	CMea EHyt EPot ETub GEdr GKev LAma LPhx NLAp NMen SSpi WDav WFTG WPrP
	delphinensis	see *F. tubiformis*
	drenovskii	CLAP
	eduardii	WWst
	ehrhartii	EPot SBla
	elwesii	EHyt GCrs GEdr WCot
	ferganensis	see *F. walujewii*
	fleischeriana	WWst
	forbesii	EHyt GDra
	glauca	LAma MS&S NMen
*	- 'Golden Flag'	NMen
	- 'Goldilocks'	CMea EPot ETub GEdr LRHS NMen WDav
	graeca	CBro CHar CMea EPot EWTr GBuc GCrs GEdr MTho NMen WDav WLin
	- subsp. *graeca*	EHyt
	- subsp. *ionica*	see *F. thessala*
§	*grayana*	EPot MS&S NMen
	- tall	CLAP
	gussichiae	CLAP EHyt EPot GCrs MS&S NMen WWst
*	*halabulanica*	LAma
	hermonis from Jebel esh Sharqui Mtns, Lebanon	WWst
	- subsp. *amana*	CAvo CBro EHyt EPot GCrs GEdr ITim LAma LTwo NMen WCot WPrP
	- - 'Cambridge' ♀ H4 **new**	WCot
	hispanica	see *F. lusitanica*
	hupehensis	LAma
	imperialis	ECGP GIBF MBri NRog
	- 'Argenteovariegata' (v)	LAma
	- 'Aureomarginata' (v)	CMea EBee EPar LAma LRHS MBri NRog
	- 'Aurora'	CHar EBre EPar EPot ETub GAbr LAma LRHS MBNS MWat NCel NRog SPar WPnP
	- 'Crown upon Crown'	see *F. imperialis* 'Prolifera'
	- 'Lutea'	CAvo CHar CMea LRHS NCel NFor SPar WPnP
	- 'Lutea Maxima'	see *F. imperialis* 'Maxima Lutea'
	- 'Maxima'	see *F. imperialis* 'Rubra Maxima'
§	- 'Maxima Lutea' ♀ H4	CBro EBee EBre EPar EPfP EPot ETub LAma LRHS NCel NRog SYvo
§	- 'Prolifera'	EPar LAma LRHS
	- 'Rubra'	CAvo EBee EPar ETub LAma NBir NCel NRog SPar
§	- 'Rubra Maxima'	CBro CHar CMea EPfP EPot LAma LRHS NCel
	- 'Slagzwaard' **new**	EBee
	- 'Sulpherino'	EBee LAma LRHS
	- 'The Premier'	EBee EPar EPot LAma LRHS
	- 'William Rex'	EPot LAma
	involucrata	EHyt LAma MS&S
	ionica	see *F. thessala*
	japonica var. *koidzumiana*	EFEx
	karadaghensis	see *F. crassifolia* subsp. *kurdica*
I	*karelinii*	EPot WWst
	kotschyana	EPot GCrs NMen WWst
	lanceolata	see *F. affinis* var. *tristulis*
	latakiensis	WWst
§	*latifolia*	GEdr LAma
	- var. *nobilis*	see *F. latifolia*
	liliacea	LAma
§	*lusitanica*	CLAP LAma MS&S NMen SBla
	meleagris	More than 30 suppliers
	- 'Aphrodite'	EPot GBuc NBir NMen
	- var. *unicolor* subvar. *alba* ♀ H4	CAvo CBro CFwr CHar EPot GBri GBuc LAma LRHS MAvo MBri MBro MS&S NCel NRya WLin WPnP WShi
	meleagroides **new**	EPot
§	*messanensis*	EHyt GCrs LAma MS&S SBla WLin
	- subsp. *gracilis*	EHyt GCrs MS&S WLin WWst
	- subsp. *messanensis*	CBro
	michailovskyi ♀ H2	More than 30 suppliers
	micrantha	LAma
§	*minuta*	EPot GCrs GEdr MS&S NMen
	montana	EHyt GEdr MS&S NMen
	nigra hort.	see *F. pyrenaica*
	obliqua	WCot
	olivieri	CLAP GCrs
§	*orientalis*	WWst
§	*pallidiflora* ♀ H4	CBro CLAP EBee EHyt EPar EPot ERos ETub GEdr GIBF LAma LPhx MLLN MS&S MTho NBir NHar NMen NSla SSpi SYvo WCom WCru WFTG WPnP
§	*persica*	CBri CHar EBee EBlw EBot ECtt EHrv EPar EPot GIBF LAma LRHS MBri MLan MWgw MWrn NCel NMen WFTG WHil WSel

- 'Adiyaman' ♀ H4 — CAvo CBro EBee EBre ELan EMon ETub NRog SYvo WDav
phaeanthera — see *F. affinis* var. *gracilis*
pinardii — EHyt EPot GCrs NMen WWst
pluriflora — EPot NMen
pontica — CAvo CBro CFwr CLAP CMea EBlw EHyt EPar EPot ERos EWTr GBuc GCrs GDra GKir ITim LAma MLLN MS&S MTho NMen NSla SBla SIng SSpi WCru WLin
- Prasil form **new** — WWst
pudica — ETub GCrs LAma MS&S MTho NHar NMen SCnR WLin
* - 'Fragrant' — EPot GCrs NMen
- 'Richard Britten' — EHyt EPot GCrs NMen
puqiensis — LAma
purdyi — CLAP EPot GEdr GKir MS&S NMen WDav
§ *pyrenaica* ♀ H4 — CBro CLAP EHyt EPot ERos ETow GCrs GDra LAma MS&S NGar NHar NMen NSla SBla SChu SSpi WCom WCot WCru WLin WWst
- 'Cedric Morris' — LPhx
raddeana — CLAP ETub LAma
recurva — GIBF
- *coccinea* **new** — SSpi
- 'Sensational' — LAma
rhodocanakis — WCot
- subsp. *argolica* — WWst
roderickii — see *F. grayana*
roylei — MS&S
rubra major — see *F. imperialis* 'Rubra Maxima'
ruthenica — ERos MS&S NMen SBla
sibthorpiana — CBro NMen
sphaviotica — see *F. messanensis*
stenanthera — CBro EHyt EPot GCrs LAma WCot
stribrnyi — WWst
tachengensis — see *F. yuminensis*
tenella — see *F. orientalis*
§ *thessala* — FHyt GBuc MS&S MTho NMen WCot
thunbergii — CMea EHyt EPar EPot GCrs GEdr LPhx NMen WDav WWst
tortifolia — LAma
§ *tubiformis* — GCrs GEdr GKir NMen
tuntasia — NMen
§ *usuriensis* — LAma
§ *uva-vulpis* — CAvo CBri CBro CFwr CMea EChP ECtt EHyt EPar EPot FTub GBuc GEdr LAma LEdu LRHS MBow MNrw MTho NBir NCel NMen NWCA SSpi WCot WCru WHil WLin WPnP
verticillata — CAvo CBro CMea ECha EHrv EPar EPot ETub EWTr GCrs LAma MS&S MTho NHar NMen WCot WCru
§ *walujewii* — EPot LAma
§ *whittallii* — GCrs MS&S NMen
§ *yuminensis* — EPot LAma

Fuchsia ✿ (*Onagraceae*)

'A.M. Larwick' — CSil EBak EKMF
'A.W. Taylor' — EBak
'Aadenken Bert Pelgrims' **new** — WP&B
'Aalt Groothuis' — WP&B
'Aat van Wijk' (d) **new** — WP&B
'Abbé Farges' (d) — CLoc CSil EBak ECtt EKMF EPts MWhe NDlv SLBF SPet SWal WP&B
'Abbey Hill' — MWar
'Abigail' — EKMF WP&B
'Abinger Fayre' **new** — WP&B
'Abundance' — CSil
'Acclamation' (d) — SLBF WP&B

'Achievement' ♀ H4 — CLoc CSil EKMF LAco LCla MJac NDlv SPet
'Ada Perry' (d) — ECtt
'Adagio' (d) — CLoc
'Ada's Love' — EKMF
'Adinda' — LCla WP&B
'Admiration' — CSil EKMF
'Ailsa Garnett' — EBak
'Air Cadet Leah' **new** — EFpt
'Airedale' — MJac WP&B
'Aladna's Sanders' — WP&B
'Alan Ayckbourn' — WP&B
'Alan Hall' **new** — WP&B
'Alan Titchmarsh' (d) — CDoC EKMF EPts LCla SLBF
'Alaska' (d) — CLoc EBak EKMF WGwG WP&B
'Albertus Schwab' — LCla WP&B
'Albion' — WP&B
'Alde' — CSil
'Alf Thornley' (d) — CSil MWhe
'Alfie' (d) — CSil
'Alfred de Groot' **new** — WP&B
'Alfred Rambaud' (d) — CDoC CSil
'Algerine' — SLBF
'Alice Ashton' (d) — EBak EKMF
'Alice Doran' — CDoC EKMF LCla SLBF WP&B
'Alice Hoffman' (d) — CDoC CLoc COkL COlW CSBt
  ♀ H3-4 — CSil EBak EKMF EPts LCla LRHS LVER MBar MBri MGos MJac MWat MWhe SIng SPer SPet SPla SSea SWal WGwG WP&B WWeb
'Alice Mary' (d) — EBak EMan
'Alice Stringer' — ECtt
'Alice Travis' (d) — EBak
'Alipatti' — EKMF
'Alisha Jade' **new** — SLBF
'Alison Ewart' — CLoc EBak MJac MWhe SPet
'Alison Patricia' ♀ H3 — CSil EBak EKMF EMan LCla MJac MWar MWhe SLBF WP&B
'Alison Reynolds' (d) — LCla MWar
'Alison Ruth Griffin' (d) — MJac
'Alison Ryle' (d) — EBak
'Alison Sweetman' — CSil EKMF MJac MWhe
  ♀ H1+3
'Alison Woods' (d) **new** — MWar
'Allure' (d) — EPts
§ *alpestris* — CDoC CSil EBak EFpt EKMF LCla WGwG
'Alton Water' (d/v) — MWar
'Alwin' (d) — CSil MWhe
'Alyce Larson' (d) — EBak MJac WGwG
'Amanda Bridgland' (d) — EKMF
'Amanda Jones' — EKMF MWhe
'Amazing Maisie' (d) — SLBF WP&B
  new
'Amazing Mary' **new** — EFpt
'Ambassador' — EBak SPet
'Amelie Aubin' — CLoc EBak EKMF WP&B
'America' — EBak WP&B
'Amethyst Fire' (d) — CSil
'Amigo' — EBak
§ *ampliata* — CDoC EKMF LCla
'Amy Lou' **new** — SLBF WP&B
'Amy Lye' — CLoc CSil EBak EKMF WGwG
§ 'Andenken an Heinrich — CDoC CLoc EBak ECtt EKMF LCla
  Henkel' — MOak MWhe WP&B
'André Le Nostre' (d) — EBak
'Andreas Schwab' **new** — WP&B
andrei — EKMF LCla
'Andrew' — EBak EFpt EKMF
'Andrew Carnegie' (d) — CLoc
'Andrew George' — MJac
'Andrew Hadfield' — CSil EKMF MWar SLBF
I 'Andromeda' De Groot — CSil

'Andy Jordens' **new** WP&B
'Angela' EFpt
'Angela Leslie' (d) CLoc EBak EKMF
'Angela Rippon' MJac
'Angeline' (d) WLow
'Angel's Flight' (d) EBak
'Anita' (d) CLoc CSil EKMF EPts MJac MWar
MWhe NBlu SLBF SWal WGor
WLow WP&B
'Anjo' (v) SSea
'Ann Adams' (d) CSil MJac
'Ann Howard Tripp' CLoc CSil MBri MJac MWhe WP&B
'Ann Lee' (d) EBak
'Anna of Longleat' (d) EBak EMan SPet WP&B
'Anna Pauline' (d) **new** WP&B
'Annabel' (d) ♀ H3 CDoC CLoc CSil EBak EKMF
EMan EPts LCla LVER MBri MJac
MWar MWhe SLBF SPet SSea SWal
WGwG WLow
'Annabelle Stubbs' (d) WP&B
'Anneke de Keijzer' LCla WP&B
'Anneliese Hollmann'
new WP&B
'Annie Den Otter' **new** WP&B
'Annie Earle' EKMF
'Anniek Geerlings' **new** WP&B
'Anta Tamerus' **new** WP&B
'Anthea Day' (d) CLoc
'Anthony Heavens' SLBF WP&B
'Antigone' SLBF WP&B
'Anton Schreuder' (d) WP&B
new
'Aphrodite' (d) CLoc EBak
'Applause' (d) CLoc EBak ECtt EKMF EPts LVER
SPet
'Apple Blossom' EKMF WP&B
aprica hort. see *F.* x *bacillaris*
aprica Lundell see *F. microphylla* subsp. *aprica*
'Aquarius' MWhe WP&B
'Arabella' CSil MWhe
arborea see *F. arborescens*
§ *arborescens* CDoC CLoc CSil EBak ECre EKMF
EPts ERea EShb LCla LRHS SLBF
SYvo WGwG
- f. *parva* IFro
'Arcadia Gold' (d) ECtt MWhe WGwG
'Arcadia Lady' MJac
'Arcady' CLoc
'Arend Moerman' (d) EFpt WP&B
'Arendsnestje' **new** WP&B
'Ariel' CDoC CSil EFpt WCom
'Army Nurse' (d) ♀ H4 CDoC CLoc CSil EKMF LVER
MWhe NBir NDlv SLBF SPet SWal
'Art Deco' (d) WP&B
'Arthur Horning' **new** WP&B
'Ashley' CDoC LCla
'Ashley and Isobel' WP&B
'Ashtede' LCla
'Athela' EBak
'Atlantic Star' EKMF MJac WGwG
'Atlantis' (d) MJac
'Atomic Glow' (d) EBak
'Aubergine' see *F.* 'Gerharda's Aubergine'
'Audrey Booth' (d) MWar
'Audrey Hepburn' (d) EKMF
'Audrey Lamotte' **new** WP&B
'August Cools' **new** WP&B
'August Sibert' **new** WP&B
'Augustin Thierry' (d) MWhe
'Aunt Juliana' (d) EBak
'Auntie Bertha' (d) EPts
'Auntie Jinks' CSil EBak ECtt LCla MJac MWar
MWhe SPet WGwG WP&B

'Aurora Superba' CLoc CSil EBak EKMF SLBF
'Australia Fair' (d) EBak
§ *austromontana* EBak
'Autumnale' ♀ H1+3 CDoC CHEx CLoc CSil EBak ECtt
EKMF EMan EPts LCla LRHS LVER
MWhe NBlu NVic SLBF SMrm
SPet SPoG SSea
'Avalanche' (d) CLoc CSil EBak EKMF WP&B
'Avocet' CLoc EBak
'Avon Celebration' (d) CLoc
'Avon Gem' CLoc CSil
'Avon Glow' **new** CLoc
'Avon Gold' CLoc
ayavacensis EFpt EKMF LCla
'Azure Sky' (d) EKMF MJac
'Babette' (d) EKMF
'Baby Blue Eyes' CDoC CSil EKMF SLBF
'Baby Bright' CDoC CSil EPts LCla SLBF WP&B
'Baby Chang' CSil LCla MWhe
'Baby Girl' EKMF
'Baby Thumb' (d) CSil EPts
I 'Babyface' Felix WP&B
§ x *bacillaris* CAbb CDoC EBak EWes ITim
MBlu SLBF SRms WP&B
§ - 'Cottinghamii' CDoC CSil EKMF IKee WGwG WSHC
- 'Oosje' see *F.* 'Oosje'
§ - 'Reflexa' CTrC GQui SPar
'Bagworthy Water' CLoc WP&B
'Baker's Tri' EBak
'Bali Hi' WP&B
'Balkonkönigin' CLoc CSil EBak ECtt
'Ballet Girl' (d) ♀ H1+3 CLoc CSil EBak ECtt EKMF LCla
SLBF SPet
'Bambini' CSil EPts WGwG
'Banks Peninsula' EFpt GQui
'Barbara' CLoc CSil EBak EKMF EPts MJac
MWar MWhe SPet WEas WP&B
'Barbara Evans' MWar
'Barbara Pountain' (d) LVER
'Barbara Windsor' EPts MJac WP&B
'Barbara's Gem' (d) EFpt SLBF
'Baron de Ketteler' (d) CSil EKMF
'Baroness van Dedem' CSil EFpt
'Barry M. Cox' CSil WP&B
'Barry's Queen' CSil EBak EKMF SPet
'Bashful' (d) CSil EPts LCla LRHS NDlv SPet
'Beacon' CDoC CLoc CSil EBak EKMF
EMan EPts LCla MBri MJac MWhe
NDlv SPet SSea SWal WLow
WP&B WStl WTel WWeb
'Beacon Rosa' CLoc CSil EKMF EMan EPts LCla
MBri MHFa MJac MWar MWhe
NDlv SLBF SPet SWal WOld WP&B
'Beacon Superior' CSil
'Bealings' (d) CLoc CSil ECtt EMan MBri MJac
NBlu WP&B
'Beatrice Burtoft' EKMF
'Beau Nash' CLoc
'Beautiful Bobbie' (d) SLBF
'Beauty of Bath' (d) CLoc EBak
'Beauty of Clyffe Hall' CSil EBak EKMF
'Beauty of Exeter' (d) COtt CSil EBak EKMF
'Beauty of Prussia' (d) CDoC CLoc CSil ECtt
'Beauty of Swanley' EBak
'Beauty of Trowbridge' (d) CDoC LCla
'Becky' WP&B
'Becky Jane' CSil
'Bee Keesey' **new** WP&B
'Belijn' **new** WP&B
'Belinda Jane' **new** WP&B
'Bella Forbes' (d) ♀ H1+3 CLoc CSil EBak EKMF
'Bella Rosella' (d) CSil ECtt EFpt EKMF EPts MJac
SCoo SLBF WLow WP&B

'Belsay Beauty' (d) — MJac
'Belvoir Beauty' (d) — CLoc
'Belvoir Lakes' — ECtt
'Ben de Jong' — LCla MJac
'Ben Jammin' — CLoc CSil EPts LAst LCla MJac MWar WGor WP&B
I 'Béranger' Lemoine 1897 (d) — CSil EBak EKMF
'Berba's Coronation' (d) — EKMF WP&B
'Berba's Happiness' (d) — CSil
'Berba's Inge Mariel' (d) — ECtt
'Berba's Trio' — WP&B
'Bergnimf' — WGwG
'Berliner Kind' (d) — CSil EBak EKMF
'Bermuda' (d) — CSil
'Bernie's Big-un' (d) — MJac
'Bernisser Hardy' — CSil EKMF EPts
'Bert de Jong' **new** — WP&B
'Bertha Gadsby' — EKMF
'Beryl Shaffery' — WP&B
'Beth Robley' (d) — CSil
'Betsy Ross' (d) — EBak
'Betty Jean' (d) — MWar WP&B
'Betty Swennem' **new** — WP&B
'Betzi' **new** — SLBF
'Beverley' — CSil EBak EKMF EPts SPet
'Beverley Wilson' **new** — WP&B
'Bewitched' (d) — EBak
'Bicentennial' (d) — CLoc CSil EBak EKMF EPts LVER MJac MWar MWhe SPet SSea WLow WP&B
'Big Slim' — WP&B
'Bill Savage' — LCla
'Billy Green' ♀ H1+3 — CDoC CLoc CSil EBak ECtt EPts LCla LRHS MJac MWar MWhe SLBF SPet WHen
'Bishop's Bells' (d) — CSil
'Bittersweet' (d) — ECtt
'Black Beauty' (d) — CSil
'Black Prince' — CDoC CSil MWar
'Blackmore Vale' (d) **new** — WP&B
I 'Blanche Regina' (d) — MJac MWhe
'Bland's New Striped' — EBak EKMF EPts SLBF
'Blauer Engel' — WP&B
'Blaze Away' (d) — MBri MJac MWar
'Blood Donor' (d) — EKMF MJac
'Blowick' — EMan MBri MJac MWhe SPet SWal
'Blue Beauty' (d) — CSil EBak EKMF
'Blue Bush' — CSil EKMF MJac NDlv WP&B
'Blue Butterfly' (d) — EBak
'Blue Eyes' (d) — CDoC
'Blue Gown' (d) — CDoC CLoc CSil EBak EKMF LCla LRHS LVER MWhe NDlv SPet SWal WGwG WP&B
'Blue Ice' — CSil MWhe
'Blue Lace' (d) — CSil
'Blue Lake' (d) — CSil ECtt LVER
'Blue Mink' — EBak
'Blue Mirage' (d) — CSil EKMF LCla MWar WGwG
'Blue Mist' (d) — EBak
'Blue Pearl' (d) — EBak
'Blue Petticoat' (d) — CLoc
'Blue Pinwheel' — CSil EBak
'Blue Satin' (d) — COtt EFpt MWhe
'Blue Tit' — CSil
'Blue Veil' (d) — CLoc CSil EKMF LVER MJac MWar SCoo SLBF
'Blue Waves' (d) — CLoc CSBt CSil EBak MJac MWar MWhe SPet WGwG
'Blush o' Dawn' (d) — CLoc CSil EBak EKMF EPts LVER SPet WGwG WP&B
'Blythe' (d) — EPts SLBF
'Bobby Boy' (d) — EBak

'Bobby Dazzler' (d) — CSil ECtt EKMF
'Bobby Shaftoe' (d) — EBak MWhe
'Bobby Wingrove' — EBak
'Bobby's Girl' — EPts
'Bobolink' (d) — EBak
'Bob's Best' (d) — CSil EPts LVER MJac
'Boerhaave' — EBak
boliviana Britton — see *F. sanctae-rosae*
§ *boliviana* Carrière — CAbb CDoC CHEx CLoc CSil EBak EKMF LCla MOak SYvo WP&B
§ – var. *alba* ♀ H1+3 — CDoC CLoc CPne CSil EBak EKMF EPts LCla MOak MWhe
– var. *boliviana* — LRHS WGwG
– var. *luxurians* — see *F. boliviana* Carrière var. *alba*
– f. *puberulenta* — see *F. boliviana* Carrière
'Bon Accorde' — CLoc CSil EBak EKMF EPts LCla MJac SSea
'Bon Bon' (d) — CSil EBak
'Bonita' (d) — MJac WP&B
'Bonnie Lass' (d) — CSil EBak
'Bonny' (d) — CLoc EFpt
'Bootle Lady' — MWar
'Bora Bora' (d) — CSil EBak EKMF WP&B
'Borde Hill' (d) — EPts SLBF
'Bordeaux Belle' **new** — WP&B
'Border Princess' — EBak
'Border Queen' ♀ H3-4 — CBgR CDoC CLoc CSil EBak EKMF EMan EPts LCla MBNS MJac MWar SPet WP&B
'Border Raider' **new** — SLBF WP&B
'Border Reiver' — EBak
'Börnemann's Beste' — see *F.* 'Georg Börnemann'
'Bouffant' — CLoc
I 'Bountiful' Munkner (d) — CLoc CSil EKMF MWhe SPet
'Bouquet' (d) — CSil EKMF LCla
'Bow Bells' — CLoc MJac MWhe SPet
'Boy Marc' — LCla
'Braamt's Glorie' — WP&B
bracelinae **new** — EKMF
'Brandt's Five Hundred Club' — CLoc EBak SPet
'Brechtje' **new** — WP&B
'Breckland' — EBak
'Breeders' Delight' — CSil MBri
'Breeder's Dream' (d) — EBak
'Breevis Ambrax' **new** — WP&B
'Breevis Blauwtjc' **new** — WP&B
I 'Breevis Fuscus' **new** — WP&B
I 'Breevis Jordani' **new** — WP&B
'Breevis Karna' **new** — WP&B
'Breevis Lowi' **new** — WP&B
'Brenda' (d) — CLoc CSil EBak
'Brenda Pritchard' (d) — ECtt LVER
'Brenda White' — CLoc EPts
'Brentwood' (d) — EBak
brevilobis — CSil EFpt EKMF
'Brian C. Morrison' — LCla MWar WP&B
'Brian G. Soanes' — EBak
'Brian Hilton' **new** — MWar
'Brian Kimberley' — LCla MWar WP&B
'Bridal Veil' (d) — EBak
'Bridesmaid' (d) — CSil EBak SPet
'Brigadoon' (d) — CLoc EBak
'Brighton Belle' — CDoC CSil EWll LCla WGwG
I 'Brilliant' Bull — CDoC CLoc CSil EBak EKMF LCla MGos MWhe SWal
'Brilliant' ambig. **new** — NDlv
'Briony Caunt' — CSil EKMF
'British Jubilee' (d) — CSil EKMF
'Brodsworth' — CSil EKMF NDlv
'Bronze Banks Peninsula' — CSil EKMF
'Brookwood Belle' (d) — EPts LCla MJac SLBF SYvo
'Brookwood Dale' — MWhe

I

'Brookwood Joy' (d)	MJac
'Brookwood Lady'	MWhe
'Brutus' ♀ H4	CDoC CLoc CSil EBak EKMF EMan EPts LCla LRHS MAsh MHdf MWat MWhe NBlu NDlv SPet SWal WGwG WP&B WStI
'Bryan Breary'	LCla
'Buddha' (d)	EBak
'Bugle Boy'	EPts LCla MWar
'Bunny' (d)	CSil EBak SLBF
'Burton Brew'	MJac
'Buttercup'	CLoc EBak
'C.J. Howlett'	CSil EBak EKMF
'Caballero' (d)	EBak
'Caesar' (d)	EBak
'Caitlin Isabelle' **new**	WP&B
'Caledonia'	CSil EBak EKMF
'California' **new**	WP&B
'Cambridge Louie'	CSil EBak EFpt LCla MBri MWar MWhe SPet
campii	EKMF LCla
campos-portoi	CDoC CSil EKMF LCla
'Cancun' (d)	MJac
'Candlelight' (d)	CLoc CSil EBak
'Candy Bells' (d) **new**	SCoo
'Candy Stripe'	CLoc
canescens Munz	see *F. ampliata*
'Cannenburch Floriant'	WP&B
'Canny Bob'	MJac
'Canopy' (d) **new**	WP&B
'Capri' (d)	CSil EBak WP&B
'Cara Mia' (d)	CLoc CSil SPet
'Caradella' (d)	CLoc EKMF MJac
'Cardinal'	CLoc EKMF WP&B
'Cardinal Farges' (d)	CLoc CSil EKMF SLBF SPet SSea
'Carillon van Amsterdam'	MWhe SWal
'Carioca'	EBak
'Carisbrooke Castle' (d)	EKMF
'Carl Drude' (d)	CSil
'Carl Wallace' (d)	EKMF MJac
'Carla Johnston' ♀ H1+3	CLoc EKMF EPts LCla LVER MBri MJac MWar MWhe SSea
'Carmel Blue'	CDoC CLoc CSil EKMF LAst LCla MWar MWhe SPet WGor WGwG WLow
'Carmen' Lemoine (d)	CDoC CSil EKMF
'Carmine Bell'	CSil EKMF
'Carnea'	CSil
'Carnoustie' (d)	EBak
'Carol Grace' (d)	CLoc
'Carol Lynn Whittemore' (d)	SLBF WP&B
'Carol Nash' (d)	CLoc
'Carol Roe'	EKMF
'Carole Scott'	WP&B
'Caroline'	CLoc CSil EBak EFpt EPts MWhe WP&B
'Caroline's Joy' **new**	MJac MWhe NBlu
'Cascade'	CLoc CSil ECtt EKMF EMan EPts MBri MJac MWar MWhe NBlu SPet SSea WBVN WGwG WP&B
'Caspar Hauser' (d)	CSil SWal WP&B
'Catherine Bartlett'	EKMF
'Cathie MacDougall' (d)	EBak
'Cecil Glass'	EKMF
'Cecile' (d)	ECtt EKMF EPts LCla LVER MJac MWar MWhe SLBF WGwG WOld
'Celadore' (d)	CSil LVER MJac
'Celebration' (d)	CLoc CSil MWar
'Celia Smedley' ♀ H3	CDoC CLoc CSil EBak EKMF EPts LCla LVER MBri MJac MWar MWhe SLBF SPet WP&B
'Celine' **new**	WP&B
'Centerpiece' (d)	EBak
'Ceri'	CLoc
'Chameleon'	CDoC CSil EFpt SPet WGwG
'Champagne Celebration'	CLoc
'Chandleri'	EKMF SLBF
'Chang' ♀ H1+3	CDoC CLoc CSil EBak EKMF LCla LRHS MWar MWhe SLBF
'Chantry Park'	CDoC LCla
'Charles Edward'	CSil EKMF
Charlie Dimmock = 'Foncha' (d)	EFpt MWhe
'Charlie Gardiner'	EBak MWhe
'Charlie Girl' (d)	EBak
'Charlotte Clyne'	MJac
'Charming'	CDoC CLoc CSil EBak EKMF MJac MWar NDlv SPet
'Checkerboard' ♀ H3	CLoc CSil EBak ECtt EKMF EPts LCla LVER MJac MWar MWhe SLBF SPet SSea SWal WGwG
'Cheeky Chantelle' (d)	SLBF WP&B
'Cheers' (d)	EKMF MWar MWhe WP&B
'Chelsea Louise' **new**	EPts
'Chenois Godelieve' **new**	WP&B
'Cheryl'	EFpt MJac
'Chessboard'	CLoc CSil
'Chillerton Beauty' ♀ H3	CDoC CLoc CSil CTri ECtt EKMF LCla LRHS MJac MWhe SLBF SPer SPet WBod WGwG
'China Doll' (d)	EBak MWhe
'China Lantern'	CLoc CSil EBak
'Chris Nicholls'	CSil EKMF
'Christine Bamford'	CSil WP&B
cinerea	EKMF LCla
'Cinnabarina'	CLoc SLBF
* 'Cinnamon'	WP&B
'Cinpetio'	LCla WP&B
'Cinque Port Liberty' (d) **new**	SLBF WP&B
'Cinvulca'	LCla
'Circe' (d)	EBak EKMF
'Circus'	EBak
'Circus Spangles' (d)	CDoC COtt ECtt EKMF MWar WGwG
'Citation'	CLoc CSil EBak SSea
'City of Adelaide' (d)	CLoc MWhe
'City of Leicester'	CSil LCla SPet
'Claire de Lune'	EBak WP&B
'Claire Evans' (d)	CLoc
'Claire Oram'	CLoc SSea
'Clare Frisby' **new**	EKMF
'Claudia' (d)	MJac MWar
'Cliantha' (d)	LCla MJac MWar MWhe
'Clifford Gadsby' (d)	EBak
'Cliff's Hardy'	CSil EKMF LCla SPet
'Cliff's Own'	CSil WP&B
'Cliff's Unique' (d)	EPts MWar
'Clifton Beauty' (d)	MJac
'Clifton Charm'	CSil EKMF EPts MJac
'Clipper'	CSil
'Cloth of Gold'	CLoc EBak MJac MWhe SPet SSea
'Cloverdale Jewel' (d)	CSil EBak ECtt LCla MWhe SPet
'Cloverdale Joy'	EBak
'Cloverdale Pearl'	CSil EBak EKMF EMan ENot MJac MWhe SPet WP&B
'Coachman' ♀ H4	CLoc CSil EBak EKMF EMan EPts LCla MWar MWhe NBlu SLBF SPet WBVN WGwG
coccinea	CDoC CSil EKMF EPts LCla
x *colensoi*	CDoC CSil ECou EKMF LCla SHFr
* - var. *purpurascens* **new**	EFpt
'Collingwood' (d)	CLoc EBak
'Colne Fantasy' (v)	EFpt EKMF EPts

	'Colne Greybeard'	CSil
	'Come Dancing' (d)	CDoC CSil ECtt LCla SPet
I	'Comet' Tiret (d)	CLoc EBak SPet
	'Conchilla'	EBak
	'Connie' (d)	CSil EBak EKMF WP&B
	'Conspicua'	CSil EBak EKMF WP&B
	'Constance' (d)	CDoC CLoc CSil EKMF LCla MJac MWar MWhe NDlv SLBF SPet SWal
	'Constance Comer'	MJac
I	'Constellation' Schnabel (d)	CLoc EBak
	'Coombe Park'	MJac MWar
	'Copycat'	CSil
	'Coq Au Vin' (d) **new**	WP&B
	'Coquet Bell'	EBak
	'Coquet Dale' (d)	EBak
	'Coquet Gold' (d/v)	CSil ECtt
	'Coral Drop' **new**	WP&B
	'Coral Rose'	CSil
	'Coral Seas'	EBak
§	'Coralle'	CLoc EBak EKMF EMan EPts LCla MJac MWar MWhe SLBF
	'Corallina'	CDoC CLoc CSil EBak EHol EKMF LVER MWhe SPet SSea WFar WGwG
I	'Corallina Variegata' (v)	CSil
	cordifolia hort.	see *F. splendens*
	cordifolia Benth.	EBak EKMF MOak
	'Core'ngrato' (d)	CLoc EBak
	coriacifolia **new**	EKMF
	'Corneille' (d) **new**	WP&B
	'Cornelia Smith'	LCla WP&B
	'Corsair' (d)	CSil EBak EKMF
	corymbiflora misapplied	see *F. boliviana*
§	*corymbiflora* Ruíz & Pav.	CDoC EBak EKMF EPts
	- *alba*	see *F. boliviana* Carrière var. *alba*
	'Cosmopolitan' (d)	CSil EBak
	'Costa Brava'	CLoc EBak
	'Cotta 2000'	EKMF LCla
	'Cotta Bella' (d)	EKMF
	'Cotta Bright Star'	EFpt EKMF LCla MWar
	'Cotta Carousel'	EKMF LCla
	'Cotta Christmas Tree'	EKMF LCla
	'Cotta Fairy'	EKMF
	'Cotta Princess' (d)	EKMF
	'Cotta Vino'	EKMF SLBF WP&B
	'Cottinghamii'	see *F. x bacillaris* 'Cottinghamii'
	'Cotton Candy' (d)	CLoc ECtt EPts LCla MWhe
	'Countdown Carol' (d)	EPts
	'Countess of Aberdeen'	CLoc CSil EBak EKMF SLBF
	'Countess of Maritza' (d)	CLoc
	'County Park'	ECou EWes
	'Court Jester' (d)	CLoc EBak
	'Cover Girl' (d)	EBak EPts MWhe SPet
	'Coxeen'	EBak
	'Crackerjack'	CLoc EBak
	crassistipula	EKMF LCla
	'Crescendo' (d)	CLoc
	'Crinkley Bottom' (d)	EPts LCla LVER MJac SLBF SWal
	'Crinoline' (d)	EBak
	'Crosby Serendipity'	CLoc
	'Crosby Soroptimist'	CSil MWar MWhe
	'Cross Check'	EMan MBri MJac
	'Crystal Blue'	EBak
	'Cupid'	CSil EBak
	'Curly Q'	EBak SPet
	'Curtain Call' (d)	CLoc EBak
	x *cuzco*	EKMF LCla
	cylindracea misapplied	see *F. x bacillaris*
	cylindracea Lindl.	CSil EKMF LCla
	- (f)	EFpt
	'Cymon' (d)	MWhe

	'Cyndy Robyn'	WP&B
	cyrtandroides	CSil EKMF
	'Dainty'	EBak
	'Dainty Lady' (d)	EBak
	'Daisy Bell'	CLoc CSil EBak ECtt EKMF LCla MJac SPet SSea WGwG WP&B
	'Dalton'	EBak
	'Dana Samantha' **new**	EPts
	'Dancing Bloom'	EPts
	'Dancing Flame' (d) ♀ H1+3	CLoc CSil EKMF EMan EPts LCla LVER MBri MJac MWar MWhe SLBF SPet WGwG WLow WP&B
	'Daniel Austin' (d)	MJac
	'Danielle'	SLBF
	'Danielle Frijstein'	WP&B
	'Danielle Stoel' **new**	WP&B
	'Danielle's Dream' (d) **new**	SLBF WP&B
	'Danish Pastry'	SPet
	'Danny Boy' (d)	CLoc EBak EKMF MWhe WP&B
	'Danny Kaye' (d) **new**	WP&B
	'Daphne Arlene'	CSil
	'Dark Eyes' (d) ♀ H4	CLoc CSil EBak EKMF EMan LHrt LVER MBri MHFa MJac MWar MWhe SLBF SPet SSea WGwG WLow WP&B
	'Dark Lady'	MWhe
	'Dark Mystery' (d)	SLBF
	'Dark Night' (d)	CSil
	'Dark Secret' (d)	EBak
	'Dark Treasure' (d)	CDoC CSil EKMF
	'Dark Venus' **new**	WP&B
	'David'	CDoC CLoc CSil EKMF EOHP LCla MWhe NDlv SLBF WGor WGwG WP&B
	'David Alston' (d)	CLoc EBak
	'David Lockyer' (d)	CLoc
	'David Savage' (d)	LCla
	'Dawn'	EBak
	'Dawn Carless' (d)	WP&B
	'Dawn Fantasia' (v)	CLoc EKMF EPts SLBF WP&B
	'Dawn Sky' (d)	EBak
	'Dawn Star' (d)	CSil EFpt LVER MJac MWhe
	'Day by Day'	CSil
	'Day Star'	EBak
	'De Groot's Beauty' (d) **new**	WP&B
	'De Groot's Delight' **new**	WP&B
	'De Groot's Happiness' **new**	WP&B
	'De Groot's Knipoogje' **new**	WP&B
	'De Groot's Moonlight' **new**	WP&B
	'De Groot's Parade' **new**	WP&B
	'De Groot's Parel' **new**	WP&B
	'De Groot's Queen' **new**	WP&B
	'De Groot's Regenboog' **new**	WP&B
	'De Groot's Waterval' **new**	WP&B
	'De Pleiaden' **new**	WP&B
	'De Wissen' **new**	WP&B
	'Debby' (d)	EBak
	'Deben Petite'	CDoC CSil EWll
	'Deben Rose'	WGwG
	'Deborah Mitchell'	WGwG
	'Deborah Street'	CLoc
§	*decussata* Ruíz & Pav.	CDoC EBak EKMF LCla
	'Dee Copley' (d)	EBak
	'Dee Star' (d)	WP&B
	'Deep Purple' (d)	CDoC CLoc CSil ECtt EKMF MJac SCoo SLBF WLow WP&B
	'Delilah' (d)	MJac
	'Delta's Angelique' **new**	LCla SLBF WP&B
	'Delta's Bambi' **new**	WP&B

'Delta's Beauty' (d) **new** WP&B
'Delta's Bride' SLBF WP&B
'Delta's Delight' WP&B
'Delta's Dream' LCla WGwG WP&B
'Delta's Emperor' WP&B
'Delta's Fair' **new** WP&B
'Delta's Glorie' WP&B
'Delta's Groom' EFpt LCla
'Delta's K.O.' (d) LCla WP&B
'Delta's Matador' MJac WP&B
'Delta's Night' WP&B
'Delta's Paljas' WP&B
'Delta's Parade' (d) EPts LCla MWar WP&B
'Delta's Prelude' **new** WP&B
'Delta's Rien' WP&B
'Delta's Robijn' **new** WP&B
'Delta's Song' WP&B
'Delta's Symphonie' (d) WP&B
'Delta's Trick' WP&B
'Delta's Wonder' CSil WP&B
'Deltaschön' WP&B
'Demi van Roovert' **new** WP&B
§ *denticulata* CDoC CLoc CSil EBak EKMF LCla MOak SLBF WGwG

dependens see *F. corymbiflora* Ruiz & Pav.
'Derby Imp' WP&B
'Derby Star' CSil
'Desperate Daniel' EKMF EPts LCla
'Devonshire Dumpling' CDoC CLoc CSil EBak ECtt EKMF
(d) EMan EPts LVER MBri MJac MWar MWhe SLBF SPet WGwG WLow WP&B
'Diablo' (d) CSil EBak
'Diamond Celebration' EKMF LCla MWar WP&B
(d)
'Diana' (d) EBak
'Diana Brown' EKMF MWhe SSea
'Diana Wills' (d) MWhe
'Diana Wright' CSil EKMF LAco
'Die Schöne Wilhelmine' WP&B
'Dilly-Dilly' (d) ECtt
'Dimples' (d) CSil MBri
'Diny Hetterscheid' LCla
'Dipton Dainty' (d) CLoc CSil EBak LCla
'Dirk van Delen' MWhe WP&B
'Display' ♀ H4 CDoC CLoc CSil EBak EBee ECtt EKMF EMan EPts LCla LVER MBri MJac MWhe NDlv NPer SLBF SPet SSea WGwG WLow WStI
'Doc' CDoC CSil NDlv SPet
'Docteur Topinard' CLoc EBak EKMF
'Doctor' see *F.* 'The Doctor'
'Doctor Foster' ♀ H4 CDoC CLoc CSil CTri EBak EKMF ENot EPts NDlv WEas
'Doctor Olson' (d) CLoc EBak
'Doctor Robert' EPts MBri MJac MWhe
'Dodo' **new** WP&B
§ 'Dollar Princess' (d) CDoC CLoc CSil EBak ECtt EKMF
♀ H4 EMan EPts LCla MAsh MBri MJac MWar MWhe NDlv NPer SChu SLBF SPet SPlb SWal WFar WGwG WLow WStI WWeb
'Dolly Daydream' (d) EKMF
'Dominique' (d) EKMF
'Dominyana' EBak EKMF LCla
'Don Peralta' EBak
'Dopey' (d) CDoC CSil SPet
'Doreen Redfern' CLoc CSil MJac MWhe SPet
'Doris Coleman' (d) EMan
'Doris Joan' SLBF
'Dorothea Flower' CLoc CSil EBak EKMF
'Dorothy' CSil EFpt EKMF LCla SLBF SPet
'Dorothy Ann' **new** SLBF

'Dorothy Day' (d) CLoc
'Dorothy Hanley' (d) CSil EKMF EPts LAst MJac MWhe WGor WP&B
'Dorothy Shields' (d) LCla MJac
'Dorrian Brogdale' LCla
'Dorset Delight' (d) **new** WP&B
'Dove House' EKMF WP&B
'Dovercourt Pride' **new** EFpt
'Drake 400' (d) CLoc
'Drame' (d) CDoC CSil EBak EKMF LCla NDlv SPet SSea
'Drum Major' (d) EBak
'Du Barry' (d) EBak
'Duchess of Albany' CLoc CSil EBak
'Duchess of Cornwall' (d) CSil
'Duet' (d) CSil
I 'Duke of Wellington' CLoc
Haag (d)
'Dulcie Elizabeth' (d) EBak MJac SPet
'Dunrobin Bedder' CSil
'Dusky Beauty' CSil
'Dusky Rose' (d) CLoc CSil EBak MJac MWhe WGwG
'Dutch Kingsize' WP&B
'Dutch Mill' CLoc EBak
'Dutch Stefanie' **new** WP&B
'Dying Embers' **new** CLoc
'Dymph Worker van LCla
Groenland' **new**
'East Anglian' CLoc EBak
'Easter Bonnet' (d) CLoc
'Ebbtide' (d) CLoc EBak
'Echo' CLoc LRHS
'Ectors Nursery' **new** WP&B
'Ed Largarde' (d) EBak EKMF
'Edale' CSil EKMF
'Eden Lady' CLoc SPet
'Eden Princess' MJac MWhe
'Edith' Brown (d) CSil EFpt EKMF LCla SLBF
'Edith' ambig. **new** NDlv
'Edith Emery' (d) SPet
'Edna W. Smith' ECtt
'Edwin J. Goulding' LCla
'Eileen Raffill' EBak
'Eileen Saunders' CSil EBak
'Eileen Storey' EKMF WP&B
'Eisvogel' **new** WP&B
'El Camino' (d) WBVN
'El Cid' CLoc CSil EBak EKMF
'Elaine Ann' EPts MJac
'Eleanor Leytham' EBak EKMF LCla
'Eleanor Rawlins' CSil EBak EKMF
'Elf' CSil
'Elfin Glade' CLoc CSil EBak EKMF
'Elfrida' (d) CSil EKMF NDlv
'Elfriede Ott' CLoc EBak MWhe WP&B
'Eline Brantz' **new** WP&B
I 'Elizabeth' Whiteman EBak EKMF
'Elizabeth' Tiret (d) EFpt
'Elizabeth Broughton' EKMF
'Elizabeth Tompkins' (d) MJac
'Elizabeth Travis' (d) EBak
'Ellen Morgan' (d) EBak
'Elma' CSil LCla
'Elsa' (d) ECtt LRHS SPet
'Elsie Mitchell' (d) CSil MWhe SPet
'Elsie Vert' (d) WP&B
'Elsstar' EFpt WP&B
'Elysée' CSil EKMF
§ 'Emile de Wildeman' (d) CSil EBak EKMF LVER SPet
'Emily Austen' EKMF MJac
'Empress of Prussia' CDoC CLoc CSil EBak ECtt EKMF
♀ H4 EMan LRHS NDlv SLBF SPet SSea SWal WOld

'Enchanted' (d)	EBak MWar	
encliandra subsp. encliandra	EKMF LCla	
* – var. *gris*	LCla	
§ – subsp. *tetradactyla*	EFpt EKMF	
§ 'Enfant Prodigue' (d)	CDoC CLoc CSil EKMF SDix	
'English Rose' (d)	CSil	
'Enid Joyce'	SLBF	
'Enstone'	see *F. magellanica* var. *molinae* 'Enstone'	
'Eppsii'	CSil	
'Erecta'	MBNS NPri	
'Erica Julie' (d)	MWhe	
'Eric's Everest' (d)	EKMF WP&B	
'Eric's Hardy' (d)	CSil	
'Eric's Majestic' (d)	EKMF MJac	
'Erika Frohmann' (d)	WP&B	
'Erika Köth'	CSil LCla	
'Ernest Claes' **new**	WP&B	
'Ernest Rankin'	CSil	
'Ernie Bromley'	CSil SLBF	
'Errol' (d)	CLoc	
'Estelle Marie'	CLoc CSil EBak MBri MWar MWhc SLBF SPet SSea WP&B	
'Eternal Flame' (d)	CSil EBak EPts MBri MWhe	
'Ethel'	WP&B	
'Ethel Wilson'	CSil	
'Eureka Red' (d)	WGwG	
'Eurydice' (d)	CLoc	
'Eusebia' (d)	MJac	
'Eva Boerg'	CLoc CSil CTri EBak ECtt EKMF EMan LCla MBri MWar SPet SWal WGwG WKif WP&B	
'Eva Dawes' **new**	WP&B	
'Eva Dayes'	EKMF WP&B	
§ 'Evelyn Steele Little'	EBak	
'Evening Sky' (d)	EBak	
'Evensong'	CLoc CSil EBak EFpt MWhe	
I 'Excordi' **new**	WP&B	
excorticata	CBcs CDoC CHEx CSil CTrw EKMF LCla WPGP WPat WSHC	
'Exmoor Woods'	CSil	
'Fabian Franck'	CDoC LCla WP&B	
'Falklands' (d)	CSil EKMF	
'Falling Stars'	CLoc CSil EBak ECtt MWhe	
'Fan Dancer' (d)	EBak	
'Fancy Flute'	CSil	
'Fancy Free' (d)	MBri	
'Fancy Pants' (d)	CLoc EBak	
'Fanfare'	CDoC EBak EKMF EWll LCla WP&B	
'Fascination'	see *F.* 'Emile de Wildeman'	
'Fashion' (d)	EBak	
'Favourite'	EBak	
'Fenman'	EPts	
'Fergie' (d)	LCla	
'Festival' (d)	MWhe	
'Festival Lights'	SLBF	
'Festoon'	EBak	
'Fey' (d)	EKMF WP&B	
'Ffion'	EPts	
'Fiery Spider'	EBak	
'Fina Creten' **new**	WP&B	
'Finn'	EPts WP&B	
'Fiona'	CLoc CSil EBak SPet	
'Fiona Jane'	EKMF	
'Fire Mountain' (d)	CLoc CSil ECtt SSea	
Firecracker = 'John Ridding'PBR (v)	CHEx MJac SCoo WGwG WP&B	
'Firelite' (d)	EBak	
'First Love' (d)	WP&B	
'First Success'	EFpt EKMF LCla LHop WGwG	
'Flair' (d)	CLoc	

'Flame'	EBak	
'Flamenco Dancer' (d)	CLoc ECtt	
'Flash' ♀ H3-4	CDoC CLoc CSil CTri EBak EKMF EPts LCla MJac MWhe NDlv SLBF SPet WGwG WStI	
'Flashlight'	CSil NDlv WP&B	
'Flashlight Amélioré'	CSil	
'Flat Jack o' Lancashire' (d)	CSil ECtt EKMF	
'Flavia' (d)	EBak	
'Fleur de Picardie' **new**	WP&B	
'Flirt'	WP&B	
'Flirtation Waltz' (d)	CLoc CSil EBak EKMF EMan EPts LVER MJac MWhe SPet SSea	
'Flocon de Neige'	CSil EBak EKMF WP&B	
'Floral City' (d)	CLoc EBak	
'Florence Mary Abbott'	EMan WP&B	
'Florence Turner'	CSil EBak EKMF MWhe	
'Florentina' (d)	CLoc CSil EBak EKMF	
'Florrie's Gem' (d)	SLBF	
'Fluffy Frills' (d)	CSil	
'Flyaway' (d)	EBak	
'Flying Cloud' (d)	CLoc CSil EBak EKMF MBri	
'Flying Scotsman' (d)	CLoc CSil EBak EKMF EPts LVER MJac	
'Fohnhimmel' (d) **new**	WP&B	
'Folies Bergères' (d)	EBak	
'Foolke'	CSil EBak EPts	
'Forfar's Pride' (d)	CSil MWar	
'Forget-me-not'	CLoc CSil EBak EFpt EKMF	
'Fort Bragg' (d)	EBak	
'Forward Look'	MWhe	
'Fountains Abbey' (d)	EMan	
'Four Farthings' (d) **new**	EKMF	
'Foxgrove Wood' ♀ H3-4	CSil EBak EKMF EPts LCla SLBF	
'Foxy Lady' (d)	EKMF	
'Frances Haskins'	CSil MWhe	
'Francesca Reed' **new**	EFpt	
'Frank Lawrence' **new**	LCla	
'Frank Sanford' (d)	WP&B	
'Frank Saunders'	CSil LCla WP&B	
'Frank Unsworth' (d)	ECtt EKMF EPts MJac SPet	
'Frankie's Magnificent Seven' (d)	EPts	
'Frans Busschodts' **new**	WP&B	
'Frau Hilde Rademacher' (d)	CDoC CSil EBak EKMF EMan LVER SLBF SWal	
'Fred Hansford'	CSil	
'Fred Swales'	CSil LCla	
'Fred's First' (d)	CDoC CSil EKMF SWal	
'Freefall'	EBak	
'Freek van de Veen' **new**	WP&B	
'Friendly Fire' (d)	CLoc	
'Frosted Flame'	CLoc CSil EKMF LCla MJac MWar MWhe SPet SSea WP&B	
'Frozen Tears'	WP&B	
'Frühling' (d)	CSil EBak EKMF	
'Fuchsiade '88'	CLoc CSil EBak EKMF MWhe WP&B	
'Fuchsiarama '91'	WP&B	
'Fuji-San'	CDoC EPts LCla MWar WP&B	
'Fuksie Foetsie'	CDoC CSil EFpt WGwG	
fulgens ♀ H1+3	CDoC EKMF IFro LCla MOak MWhe SYvo	
– 'Gesneriana'	see *F.* 'Gesneriana'	
* – *goselli* **new**	WP&B	
* – var. *minuata*	EKMF	
– 'Rubra Grandiflora'	see *F.* 'Rubra Grandiflora'	
* – 'Variegata' (v)	CLoc CSil EKMF EPts LCla	
'Fuller's Pride' **new**	WP&B	
'Fulpila'	LCla WP&B	
'Für Elise' (d)	EBak	
furfuracea	EFpt EKMF	
'Gala' (d)	EBak	

'Garden News' (d) ♀ H3-4	CDoC CLoc CSil ECtt EKMF EPts LCla LRHS LVER MGos MJac MWar MWhe NDlv SLBF SPet SWal WFar WGwG WP&B
'Garden Week' (d)	MWhe WP&B
'Gartenmeister Bonstedt' ♀ H1+3	CDoC CLoc CSil EBak EKMF EPts LCla LRHS SPet SSea WEas WGwG WP&B
'Gay Anne' (d)	EKMF
'Gay Fandango' (d)	CLoc EBak ECtt LCla SPet
'Gay Future'	EKMF
'Gay Parasol' (d)	CLoc MJac
'Gay Paree' (d)	EBak
'Gay Senorita'	EBak
'Gay Spinner' (d)	CLoc
gehrigeri	EBak EKMF LCla
'Geisha Girl' (d)	CSil
'Gemma Fisher' (d)	EPts
'Général Charles de Gaulle'	LCla
'Général Monk' (d)	CDoC CSil EBak ECtt EFpt EKMF EMan EPts LVER MBri SWal WP&B
'Général Voyron'	CSil
'General Wavell' (d)	WGwG
'Genii' ♀ H4	More than 30 suppliers
'Geoffrey Smith' (d)	CSil ECtt EKMF
§ 'Georg Börnemann'	CLoc CSil EBak WGwG WP&B
'Georgana' (d)	MWhe
'George Barr'	EKMF LRHS
'George Bartlett' **new**	CLoc
'George Johnson'	CDoC SPet WGwG
'George Travis' (d)	EBak
'Georges Rumy' **new**	WP&B
'Gerald Drewitt'	CSil
§ 'Gerharda's Aubergine'	CLoc CSil EKMF SSea WP&B
'Gerharda's Kiekeboe'	EKMF
§ 'Gesneriana'	CLoc CSil EBak WGwG
'Ghislaine' (d)	WP&B
'Giant Pink Enchanted' (d)	CLoc EBak
'Gilda'	CSil MJac
'Gilt Edge' (v)	CLoc
'Gingham Girl' (d)	MJac WP&B
'Gipsy Princess' (d)	CLoc
'Girls Brigade'	EKMF
'Gitana' **new**	WP&B
'Gladiator' (d)	EBak EKMF LCla
'Gladys Lorimer'	EPts
'Gladys Miller'	CLoc
glazioviana	CDoC CSil EKMF LCla SLBF SWal WP&B
'Glitters'	EBak EKMF EPts
§ 'Globosa'	CAgr CSil EBak EKMF
'Gloria Johnson'	EKMF
'Glow'	CSil EBak EKMF
'Glowing Embers'	EBak
Glowing Lilac (d)	CSil ECtt EMan EPts
'Glyn Jones' (d)	EKMF
'Gold Brocade'	CSil SPet
'Gold Crest'	EBak
'Golden Anniversary' (d)	CLoc EBak EKMF EMan LVER MJac WP&B
'Golden Arrow'	CDoC LCla
'Golden Border Queen'	CLoc
'Golden Dawn'	CLoc EBak ECtt EFpt SPet
'Golden Eden Lady' (v)	MWhe
'Golden Feli Fey' (d) **new**	WP&B
'Golden Herald'	CSil SLBF SSea
'Golden La Campanella' (d/v)	CLoc ECtt MBri
'Golden Lena' (d/v)	CSil EMan
'Golden Margaret Roe' (v) **new**	CSil
'Golden Marinka' (v) ♀ H3	CLoc CSil EBak ECtt EKMF LRHS MBri SPet
'Golden Melody' (d)	CSil
'Golden Penny Askew' (v)	WP&B
'Golden Swingtime' (d)	CSil ECtt MBri MJac SPet SSea WGwG
'Golden Treasure' (v)	CLoc CSil ECtt EKMF MBri MHFa MWar
'Golden Vergeer' (v)	EKMF MWar SLBF
'Golden Wedding'	EKMF
'Goldsworth Beauty'	CSil LCla
'Golondrina'	CSil EBak WP&B
'Goody Goody'	CDoC EBak
'Gordon Boy' (d) **new**	CSil
'Gordon Thorley'	CSil EKMF MWhe
'Gordon's China Rose'	LCla
'Gorgeous Gemma' (d)	SLBF WP&B
'Gottingen'	CSil EBak EKMF LCla
'Governor 'Pat' Brown' (d)	EBak
'Grace Darling'	EBak MWhe
gracilis	see *F. magellanica* var. *gracilis*
'Graf Christian'	MWar
'Graf Witte'	CDoC CSil EKMF EPts NDlv SPet WGwG
'Grand Duchess'	LCla
'Grand Prix' (d)	EKMF
'Grandad Fred' (d)	EFpt SLBF
'Grandad Hobbs' (d)	LCla
'Grandma Hobbs'	LCla
'Grandma Sinton' (d)	CLoc CSil EMan MBri MJac MWhe
'Grandpa George' (d)	CSil LCla
'Grandpa Jack' (d)	SLBF WP&B
'Grayrigg'	CSil EKMF NDlv
'Great Ouse' (d)	EPts WP&B
'Great Scott' (d)	CLoc CSil
'Green 'n' Gold'	EBak
'Greenpeace'	EKMF LCla WP&B
'Greta'	WP&B
'Gretna Chase'	MBri MWhe
'Grey Lady' (d)	CSil
'Grobo '60' (d) **new**	WP&B
'Groene Boelvaar' (d)	WP&B
'Grumpy'	CDoC CSil EHol EPts LRHS MBri MLan MWhe SPet
'Gruss aus dem Bodethal'	CLoc EBak EKMF EPts WP&B
'Guinevere'	EBak
'Gustave Doré' (d)	CSil EBak EKMF
'Guy Dauphine' (d)	EBak
'Gwen Burralls' (d)	EKMF
'Gwen Dodge'	LCla WP&B
'H.G. Brown'	CSil EBak EKMF MWhe
'Halsall Beauty' (d)	MBri
'Halsall Belle' (d)	MBri
'Halsall Pride' (d)	MBri
'Hampshire Beauty' (d)	MJac
'Hampshire Blue'	CDoC CSil SSea
'Hampshire Pride'	WGwG
'Hampshire Prince' (d)	CSil LVER
'Hampshire Treasure' (d)	CSil
'Hanna' (d)	WP&B
'Hannah Gwen' (d)	EKMF
'Hannah Louise' (d)	EPts
'Hans Callaars' **new**	WP&B
'Happiness' (d)	CSil
'Happy'	CDoC CSil EPts LCla MWhe SPet WP&B
'Happy Anniversary' (s)	CLoc
'Happy Anniversary' (d/v)	EKMF
'Happy Fellow'	CDoC CLoc CSil EBak EKMF NDlv
'Happy Wedding Day' (d)	CDoC CLoc CSil ECtt EKMF EPts MJac MWhe SCoo WGwG WP&B
'Hapsburgh'	EBak
'Harlow Car'	EKMF WGwG

	'Harlow Perfection'	EKMF
I	'Harmony' Niederholzer	EBak
	'Harnser's Flight'	CSil LCla WP&B
	'Harrow Pride' (d)	CSil
	'Harry Cawood' (d) **new**	SLBF
	'Harry Dunnett'	EBak
	'Harry Gray' (d)	CLoc CSil EBak ECtt EMan EPts LCla MBri MJac MWar MWhe SPet SSea WGwG WP&B
	'Harry Taylor' (d)	EPts
	hartwegii	CDoC CSil EFpt EKMF LCla
	'Hathersage' (d)	EBak
	hatschbachii	CDoC CSil EKMF EPts LCla
	'Haute Cuisine' (d)	CLoc EMan LVER MWhe WP&B
	'Hawaiian Night' (d)	WP&B
	'Hawaiian Princess' (d)	ECtt
	'Hawaiian Sunset' (d)	SLBF WBVN WP&B
	'Hawkshead' ♀ H3-4	CDoC CLoc CSil ECha EKMF ELan EPfP EPts EVFa GCal GQui LCla LRHS MBri MGos MJac MWhe SChu SGar SLBF SMac SMrm SPet WBcn WCom WCot WP&B
I	'Hazel' (d)	MWhe WP&B
	'Heart Throb' (d)	EBak
	'Heavenly Hayley' (d)	SLBF WP&B
	'Hebe'	EBak MWhe
I	'Hedens Montana' **new**	WP&B
	'Heidi Ann' (d) ♀ H3	CDoC CLoc CSil EBak EKMF EMan EPts LCla MBri MWar MWhe NDlv SLBF SPet SSea SWal WGwG
§	'Heidi Weiss' (d)	CDoC CLoc CSil LCla MBri SPet WGwG
	'Heinrich Henkel'	see *F.'Andenken an Heinrich Henkel'*
	'Heirloom' (d)	ECtt EKMF
	'Helen Clare' (d)	CLoc EBak
	'Helen Nicholls' (d) **new**	EKMF
	'Hello Dolly'	CLoc
	'Hemsleyana'	see *F. microphylla* subsp. *hemsleyana*
	'Henkelly's Elegantie' **new**	WP&B
	'Henkelly's Stippelke' **new**	WP&B
	'Henkelly's Tipke' **new**	WP&B
	'Henning Becker'	WP&B
	'Henri Poincaré'	CDoC EBak EKMF
	'Herald' ♀ H4	CDoC CSil EBak EKMF NDlv SLBF SWal WGwG
	'Herbé de Jacques'	see *F.'Mr West'*
	'Heritage' (d)	CLoc CSil EBak EKMF
	'Herman de Graaff' (d)	EKMF WP&B
	'Hermiena'	CLoc CSil LCla MWar MWhe SLBF WGwG WP&B
	'Heron'	CSil EBak EKMF
	'Hessett Festival' (d)	CDoC CSil EBak MWhe
	'Heston Blue' (d)	EKMF
	'Hettenheuvel' **new**	WP&B
	'Hetty Blok' (d) **new**	WP&B
	'Hi Jinks' (d)	EBak
	hidalgensis	see *F. microphylla* subsp. *hidalgensis*
	'Hidcote Beauty'	CDoC CLoc CSil EBak EFpt MWhe SLBF SPet SSea WGwG
	'Hidden Treasure'	LCla MWar WP&B
	'Hier Ben Ik' **new**	WP&B
	'Highland Pipes'	CSil EKMF LCla
	'Hindu Belle'	EBak
	'Hinnerike'	CSil EPts LCla WP&B
	'Hiroshlge'	LCla
	hirtella **new**	WP&B
	'His Excellency' (d)	CSil EBak
	'Hobo' (d)	CSil MWar SLBF WP&B
	'Hobson's Choice' (d)	SLBF
	'Hokusai'	WP&B
	'Holly Hobit' **new**	NMRc
	'Holly's Beauty' (d)	CDoC EKMF EPts MWar WGwG WP&B
	'Hollywood Park' (d)	EBak
	'Hoornerveens Bloei' **new**	WP&B
	'Horatio'	CSil ECtt MJac
	'Hot Coals'	CBos CLoc CSil ECtt EKMF EPts LCla MJac MWar MWhe WP&B
	'Howlett's Hardy'	CDoC CLoc CSil EBak ECtt EKMF EPts LRHS MBri SWal
	'Hula Girl' (d)	CSil EBak EFpt EKMF MJac MWar MWhe SLBF SPet WP&B
	'Humboldt Holiday' (d)	EKMF
	'Huntsman' (d)	CDoC ECtt EKMF MWhe WGwG
	'Ian Brazewell' (d)	CLoc
	'Ian Leedham' (d)	EBak
	'Ice Cream Soda' (d)	EBak
	'Iceberg'	CSil EBak
	'Icecap'	EKMF MBri
	'Iced Champagne'	CLoc EBak MJac
	'Ichiban' (d)	CLoc WP&B
	'Icicle' (d)	WP&B
	'Ida' (d)	EBak EKMF
	'Igloo Maid' (d)	CLoc EBak EKMF MWhe SPet SSea WP&B
	'Impala' (d)	WP&B
	'Impudence'	CLoc CSil EBak SPet SSea
	'Impulse' (d)	CLoc EKMF SLBF
	'Indian Maid' (d)	EBak LVER WGwG WP&B
	'Insulinde'	CDoC CFee CSil EPts LCla MWar SLBF WP&B
	'Interlude' (d)	EBak
	'Iolanthe'	WP&B
	'Irene L. Peartree' (d)	LCla
	'Iris Amer' (d)	CLoc EBak
	'Irish Dawn'	MWar
	'Isabel Ryan'	CSil
	'Isis' Lemoine	CSil
	'Isle of Mull'	CSil SPet
	'Italiano' (d)	MJac
	'Ivy Grace'	CSil
	'Jaap Brummel' (d)	WP&B
	'Jack Acland'	ECtt
	'Jack Shahan' ♀ H3	CDoC CLoc CSil EBak EKMF EMan LCla MBri MJac MWar MWhe SPet SSea WGwG
	'Jack Stanway' (v)	CSil EFpt EPts MWar
	'Jack the Lad' **new**	EFpt
	'Jack Wilson'	CSil
	'Jackie Bull' (d)	EBak
	'Jackpot' (d)	EBak
	'Jackqueline'	CSil LCla WP&B
	'Jade's Gem' **new**	EFpt
	'Jam Roll' (d)	LVER
	'Jamboree' (d)	EBak
	'James Lye' (d)	EBak EKMF SWal
	'James Savage'	LCla
	'James Shurvell'	CSil
	'James Travis' (d)	CDoC CSil EBak EKMF LCla
	'Jan de Vos' **new**	WP&B
	'Jan van Erp' **new**	WP&B
	'Jane Humber' (d)	EKMF LCla MJac
	'Jane Lye'	EBak
	'Janet Williams' (d)	CSil
	'Janice Ann'	EKMF LCla MWar
	'Janice Perry's Gold' (v)	CLoc MJac WWeb
	'Janie' (d)	WWeb
	'Janna' **new**	WP&B
	'Jap Vantveer'	LCla
	'Jasper's Twister'	WP&B
	'Jaunty Jack'	SLBF

'Jean Baker'	CSil	
'Jean Campbell'	EBak	
'Jean Frisby'	CLoc	
'Jeane'	EKMF	
'Jennifer' **new**	EFpt	
'Jennifer Hampson' (d)	CSil	
'Jennifer Haslam'	LCla	
'Jennifer Lister' (d)	CSil EKMF	
'Jenny May'	EPts SLBF WP&B	
'Jenny Sorensen'	EKMF LCla MWar	
'Jess'	LCla SLBF	
'Jessica' **new**	EFpt	
'Jessica Reynolds' **new**	SLBF	
'Jessica's Dream' (d)	SLBF WP&B	
'Jessie Pearson'	WP&B	
'Jessimae'	SPet	
'Jester' Holmes (d)	CLoc CSil	
'Jet Fire' (d)	CSil EBak	
'Jiddles'	SLBF	
'Jill Harris' **new**	SLBF	
'Jill Whitworth'	CDoC	
'Jim Dodge' (d)	EPts LCla	
'Jim Muncaster'	EKMF	
jimenezii	EKMF LCla	
– hybrid	EKMF	
'Jimmy Carr' (d)	EKMF	
'Jingle Bells'	MWhe	
'Jinlye'	EKMF WP&B	
'Joan Barnes' (d)	CSil	
'Joan Cooper'	CLoc CSil EBak EKMF	
'Joan Gilbert' (d)	CSil	
'Joan Goy'	EKMF EPts MJac MWhe	
'Joan Knight'	CLoc	
'Joan Leach'	CSil	
'Joan Margaret' (d)	MJac	
'Joan Morris'	SLBF	
'Joan Pacey'	EBak EKMF	
'Joan Paxton' (d)	LCla	
'Joan Read' **new**	EFpt	
'Joan Smith'	CSil EBak	
'Jo-Anne Fisher' (d)	EPts	
'Joe Kusber' (d)	CSil EBak MJac WP&B	
'Joe Nicholls' (d)	EKMF	
'Joel'	CLoc SLBF	
'John E. Caunt'	CSil EKMF	
'John Grooms' (d)	CLoc MJac MWar	
'John Lockyer'	CLoc EBak	
'John Maynard Scales'	CDoC LCla MJac MWhe WP&B	
'John Shead' **new**	MWar	
'John Stephens'	SLBF	
'John Suckley' (d)	EBak	
'John Wright'	CSil	
'Johnny' (d)	CLoc SSea	
'Joke van Gosselaar'	WP&B	
'Jomam' ♀ H3	CLoc MWar WP&B	
'Jon Oram'	CLoc	
'Jopie' (d) **new**	WP&B	
'Joy Bielby'	EKMF	
'Joy Patmore'	CLoc CSil EBak EKMF EPts LCla MBri MWar MWhe SLBF SPet WP&B	
'Joyce Forward' **new**	WP&B	
'Joyce Hill'	SLBF	
'Joyce Maynard' (d)	MJac	
'Joyce Sinton'	EMan MBri	
'Joyce Storey'	EKMF	
'Joyce Wilson' (d)	EPts LCla	
'Jubie-Lin' (d)	WP&B	
'Jubilee Quest'	EKMF LCla MWar	
'Jules Daloges' (d)	EBak EKMF	
'Julia' (d)	CSil EFpt EKMF WP&B	
'Julie Ann'	MWar	
'Julie Marie' (d)	CSil MJac	
'Julie's Gem' **new**	EFpt	
'June Gardner'	EKMF	
'Jungle'	LCla WP&B	
I 'Juno' Kennett	EBak	
juntasensis	EKMF WP&B	
'Jupiter Seventy'	EBak	
'Just a Tad' (d) **new**	SLBF	
'Justin's Pride'	CDoC CSil EKMF	
'Kaboutertje'	EKMF	
'Kaleidoscope' (d)	CSil EBak	
'Karen Bielby'	EKMF	
'Karen Bradley'	MJac	
'Karen Isles'	LCla SLBF	
'Karen Louise' (d)	CLoc	
'Karin de Groot'	EKMF	
'Karin Siegers'	CSil	
'Karin van der Sande'	WP&B	
'Karl Hartness' **new**	EFpt	
'Kate Harriet' (d)	WGwG	
'Kate Wylie'	MWar	
'Kath van Hanegem'	CSil EFpt EPts WP&B	
'Kathleen Muncaster' (d)	EKMF WP&B	
'Kathleen Smith'	ECtt EKMF	
'Kathleen van Hanegan'	CLoc	
'Kathy Louise' (d)	EMan WP&B	
'Kathy's Pipes'	EKMF	
'Kathy's Prince'	ECtt EKMF WP&B	
'Kathy's Sparkler' (d)	EKMF	
'Katie Elizabeth Ann' (d)	MWar	
'Katie's Gem' **new**	EFpt	
'Katinka'	EPts LCla	
'Katjan'	EKMF SLBF	
'Katrientje' **new**	WP&B	
'Katrina' (d)	CLoc EBak	
'Katrina Thompsen'	CLoc EKMF EPts LCla MWar SLBF SSea WP&B	
'Katy James'	EKMF	
'Keepsake' (d)	CLoc EBak	
'Kegworth Supreme'	MJac	
'Kelly's Dream' (d)	SLBF WP&B	
'Ken Goldsmith'	EPts LCla SWal WP&B	
'Ken Jennings'	MJac	
'Ken Shelton' **new**	SLBF	
'Kenny Dalglish' (d)	CSil EKMF	
'Kernan Robson' (d)	CLoc EBak	
'Kerry Anne'	EPts	
'Kevin R. Peake' (d) **new**	MWar	
'Kevin Stals'	see F. 'Stals Kevin'	
'Keystone'	EBak	
'Khada'	MWhe	
'Kim Broekhof' **new**	WP&B	
'Kim Wright' (d)	MWhe	
'Kimberly' (d)	EBak	
'King of Bath' (d)	EBak	
'King of Hearts' (d)	EBak	
'King's Ransom' (d)	CLoc CSil EBak LRHS MWhe SPet	
'Kiss' (d) **new**	WP&B	
'Kiss 'n'Tell'	MJac MWhe	
'Kit Oxtoby' (d)	ECtt EKMF EMan LCla LVER MJac NBlu WP&B	
'Kiwi' (d)	EBak	
'Klassic'	SLBF	
'Knight Errant'	SSea	
'Knockout' (d)	CSil EKMF	
'Kolding Perle'	EKMF SPet	
'Königin der Frühe'	WGwG	
'Königin der Nacht' **new**	WP&B	
'Kon-Tiki' (d)	CLoc EKMF SPet	
'Koralle'	see F. 'Coralle'	
'Kwintet'	EBak LCla MJac SPet	
'La Bianca'	EBak	
'La Campanella' (d) ♀ H3	CDoC CLoc CSil EBak ECtt EKMF EMan EPts LCla MBri MJac MWar MWhe NVic SPet WGwG WP&B	

'La Fiesta' (d) EBak
'La France' (d) EBak EKMF
'La Neige' Lemoine (d) EBak EKMF
I 'La Neige' Tiret (d) WP&B
'La Porte' (d) CLoc
'La Rosita' (d) CSil EBak SLBF
I 'La Traviata' Blackwell (d) EBak
'La Violetta' (d) **new** MWhe
'Lace Petticoats' (d) EBak EKMF
'Lady Boothby' CHEx CSil EBak EKMF LRHS SLBF
SMrm SPet WP&B WWeb
'Lady Framlingham' (d) EPts
'Lady Heytesbury' EKMF MJac
'Lady in Grey' (d) EKMF MJac WP&B
'Lady Isobel Barnett' CDoC CLoc CSil EBak EKMF MBri
MJac MWar MWhe SPet WP&B
'Lady Kathleen Spence' CSil EBak MWhe SPet
'Lady Patricia EKMF EMan MWhe NBlu WGwG
Mountbatten'
'Lady Ramsey' EBak
'Lady Rebecca' (d) CLoc
'Lady Thumb' (d) ♀ H3 More than 30 suppliers
'Lady's Smock' EKMF
'Lakeland Princess' EBak
'Lakeside' EBak
'Laleham Lass' **new** EKMF
'Lambada' EFpt MJac MWhe WP&B
'Lancambe' **new** MWar
'Lancashire Lad' (d) MWar
'Lancashire Lass' MBri
'Lancelot' EBak WP&B
'Land van Beveren' MWar SLBF WP&B
'Lark' EPts WP&B
'L'Arlésienne' (d) CLoc
'Lassie' (d) CDoC CLoc EBak
I 'Laura' (Dutch) CLoc CSil EPts LCla MWar SLBF
I 'Laura' Martin (d) EKMF MWhe
'Laura Amanda' (d) EPts
'Lavaglut' **new** WP&B
'Lavender Kate' (d) CLoc EBak MJac
'Lavender Lace' MWhe
'Lavender Lady' CSil
Senior (d)
'Lazy Lady' (d) EBak
'Le Postier' **new** WP&B
'Lechlade Apache' LCla MWar
'Lechlade Chinaman' CDoC EKMF WGwG
'Lechlade Debutante' MWar
'Lechlade Fire-eater' LCla
'Lechlade Gordon' WGwG
'Lechlade Gorgon' CDoC CSil EKMF LCla WGwG
'Lechlade Magician' CDoC CSil EFpt EKMF LCla
WGwG WP&B
'Lechlade Maiden' CSil LCla
'Lechlade Martianess' LCla
'Lechlade Potentate' LCla
'Lechlade Rocket' WP&B
'Lechlade Violet' CSil EKMF WGwG
'Lee Anthony' CSil
'Leica' (d) EKMF MJac
'Leicestershire Silver' (d) MJac
'Len Bielby' CDoC LCla
'Lena' (d) ♀ H3 CDoC CLoc CSil EBak EFpt EKMF
EPts LVER MBri MJac MWhe NDlv
SPer SPet SSea SWal WEas WGwG
WP&B
'Lena Dalton' (d) CLoc EBak MWhe
'Leonhart von Fuchs' LCla
'Leonora' CDoC CLoc CSil EBak EKMF LCla
MBri MWhe SLBF SPet SWal
WGwG WP&B
'Lesley' LCla
'Leslie' **new** EFpt

'Lett's Delight' (d) EPts
'Letty Lye' EBak
'Leverhulme' see *F.* 'Leverkusen'
§ 'Leverkusen' CDoC CLoc CSil EBak LCla MJac
MWhe WGwG
'Li Kai Lin' CSil
I 'Liebesträume' EBak
Blackwell (d)
'Liebriez' (d) ♀ H3-4 CSil EBak EKMF EPts NDlv SPet SWal
'Lilac' CSil EBak
'Lilac Dainty' (d) CSil
'Lilac Lustre' (d) CLoc CSil EBak SPet
'Lilac Princess' MJac
'Lilac Queen' (d) EBak
'Lilian' EKMF WP&B
'Lillian Annetts' (d) CDoC EKMF LAst LCla MJac SLBF
WP&B
'Lillibet' (d) CLoc EBak WGwG
'Lillydale' (d) CSil
'Lilo Vogt' WGwG
'Lime Lite' (d) MJac
'Linda Goulding' EBak MWhe SSea
'Linda Grace' EKMF EPts MJac
'Lindisfarne' (d) CLoc EBak EKMF MJac MWar SPet
'L'Ingénue' WP&B
'Lionel' **new** CSil
'Lisa' (d) CDoC CSil EPts WP&B
'Lisa Jane' MWhe
'Lisa Rowe' (d) CSil
'Lisi' WP&B
'Little Baby' EKMF SLBF
'Little Beauty' CDoC CSil EKMF MWhe WP&B
'Little Brook Gem' **new** SLBF
'Little Cracker' **new** WWeb
'Little Gene' EBak
'Little Jewel' SPet
'Little Orphan Annie' LCla
'Little Ouse' (d) MWhe
'Little Witch' EKMF LCla SLBF
'Liz' (d) CSil EBak EFpt EKMF
'Lochinver' (d) CSil SYvo
'Locke's Marie-Lou' **new** WP&B
'Loeky' CLoc EBak SPet SSea
'Logan Garden' see *F. magellanica* 'Logan
Woods'
'Lolita' (d) EBak
'London 2000' **new** EFpt LCla
'Lonely Ballerina' (d) CLoc
'Long Distance' WP&B
'Long Wings' EKMF LCla
'Longfellow' **new** WP&B
'Lord Byron' CLoc EBak EKMF
'Lord Derby' CSil
'Lord Jim' LCla
'Lord Lonsdale' CSil EBak EPts LCla MWhe WP&B
'Lord Roberts' CLoc CSil
'Lorelei' EPts
'Lorna Fairclough' MJac
'Lorna Swinbank' CLoc
'Lottie Hobby' ♀ H1+3 CDoC CHEx CLoc CSil ECtt EKMF
EPfP EPts GEil LCla LRHS MAvo
MHar MOak MWhe SPet STes
WBod WCom WFoF WGwG WP&B
'Louise Emershaw' (d) CSil EBak MJac
'Louise Nicholls' EKMF
'Lovable' (d) EBak
'Lovable Rascal' (d) **new** SLBF
'Love in Bloom' (d) MWar
'Loveliness' CLoc CSil EBak EKMF MWhe
'Lovely Les' (d) **new** EFpt LCla
'Lovely Linda' SLBF
'Love's Reward' ♀ H1+3 CLoc CSil EKMF EPts LCla MJac
MWar MWhe SLBF WP&B

I	'Loxensis'	CDoC EBak EKMF LCla
	loxensis misapplied	see *F.* 'Speciosa', *F.* 'Loxensis'
	'Loxhore Calypso'	EKMF
	'Loxhore Chorale'	WP&B
	'Loxhore Fairy Dancer'	CSil
	'Loxhore Herald'	CSil
	'Loxhore Lullaby'	CSil
	'Loxhore Mazurka'	CSil WP&B
	'Loxhore Minuet'	CDoC CSil EFpt
	'Loxhore Operetta'	CSil
	'Loxhore Posthorn'	CSil LCla WP&B
	'Lubbertje Hop'	WP&B
	'Lucky Strike' (d)	CLoc CSil EBak
	'Lucy **new**	EFpt
	'Lucy Harris'	CSil
	'Lucy Locket'	MJac
	'Lunter's Trots' (d)	WP&B
	'Lustre'	EBak
§	**lycioides** Andrews	EBak EKMF
I	'Lycioides'	LCla
	'Lye's Elegance'	CSil EKMF
	'Lye's Excelsior'	EBak EFpt LCla
	'Lye's Own'	EBak SPet
	'Lye's Perfection'	EKMF
	'Lye's Unique' ♀ H1+3	CDoC CLoc CSil EBak EKMF EPts LCla MJac MWar MWhe SLBF SPet SYvo WP&B
	'Lynette' (d)	CLoc
	'Lynn Ellen' (d)	EBak
	'Lynne Marshall'	CSil
	'Mabel Greaves' (d)	CSil WP&B
	'Machu Picchu'	CLoc CSil EKMF EPts LCla MWar WP&B
	macrophylla	EKMF
	macrostigma	EKMF
	'Madame Aubin'	EKMF
	'Madame Butterfly' (d)	CLoc
	'Madame Cornélissen' (d) ♀ H3	CBgR CDoC CLoc CSBt CSil EBak EBee EKMF ENot EPts LHop LRHS LVER MBar MBri MGos MRav MWhe NDlv SPer SPet SPla SSea WCot WFar WGwG WP&B
	'Madame Eva Boye'	EBak EKMF
	'Madeleine Sweeney' (d)	MBri
	'Maes-y-Groes'	CSil EKMF
	magdalenae	EKMF
	magellanica	CDoC COld CWib EKMF EMil MWgw NFor NLon NPer NWea SGar SPer STes WFar WGwG WPnn WRha
	- 'Alba'	see *F.* magellanica var. molinae
I	- 'Alba Aureovariegata' (v)	CDoC EPfP LAst SPer WBcn WGwG
	- 'Alba Variegata' (v)	CSil WEas WMoo
	- 'Americana Elegans'	CDoC CSil
	- 'Comber'	CSil EFpt
	- var. **conica**	CDoC CSil EKMF
	- var. **discolor new**	CSil
	- 'Exmoor Gold' (v)	CSil WBcn
	- 'Fire Gold'	LRHS
	- 'Globosa'	see *F.* 'Globosa'
§	- var. **gracilis** ♀ H3	CDoC CHEx CLoc CSil EFpt EKMF LRHS MWhe WBod WPic WPnn
	- - 'Aurea'	CBot CDoC CMHG CSil EBee EFpt EHoe EKMF ELan ENot EPfP GQui LAst LCla LRHS MRav MWhe SAga SDix SLBF SPar SPer SPet SPla WCom WFar WGwG WHen WPnn WRus
§	- - 'Tricolor' (v)	CDoC CSLe CSil EFpt EHol EKMF EPts EWes LCla LRHS SLBF SPar SRms SSea WCFE WPnn WWpP
	- - 'Variegata' (v) ♀ H3	CMHG CSil EBak EBee ENot EPfP LCla LRHS MGos MRav SAga

		SChu SDix SIng SPar SPer SPet WCom WPnn
§	- 'Logan Woods'	CDoC CSil EKMF GCal SMrm WBcn
	- 'Longipedunculata'	CDoC CSil EKMF
	- var. **macrostema**	CSil EFpt EKMF
§	- var. **molinae**	More than 30 suppliers
§	- - 'Enstone' (v)	CSBt EKMF EPts WP&B
	- - 'Enstone Gold'	EKMF
	- - 'Golden Sharpitor' (v)	MDKP WCom WHen
	- - 'Mr Knight's Blush'	SAga
§	- - 'Sharpitor' (v)	CBcs CDoC CElw COIW CSLe CSil EBak ECha EKMF ELan EPfP EPts GGar IFro LRHS MAsh MBar MRav MWat NChi NPer SGar SPer WCom WEas WFar WKif WRus WSHC
	- var. **myrtifolia**	CDoC CSil GEil
*	- var. **prostrata**	CSil
	- var. **pumila**	CDoC CSil EFpt ETow EWes GCal GEil SAga SBla SIng SPer SRot
	- **purpurea**	WWeb
	- 'Riccartonii'	see *F.* 'Riccartonii'
§	- 'Thompsonii'	CDoC CSil ECGP EFpt EKMF GCal NDlv
§	- 'Versicolor' (v)	More than 30 suppliers
	'Magic Flute'	CLoc CSil EFpt MJac
	'Maharaja' (d)	EBak
	'Major Heaphy'	EBak EKMF MWhe
	'Malibu Mist' (d)	CSil EKMF LCla LVER WP&B
	'Mama Bleuss' (d)	EBak
	'Mancunian' (d)	CSil LCla MWar
I	'Mandarin' Schnabel	EBak
	'Mandi'	EWll LCla MWar
	'Mantilla'	CDoC CLoc CSil EBak EKMF LCla MJac MWhe
	'Maori Pipes'	CSil
	'Marcus Graham' (d)	CLoc EKMF LCla MWar MWhe SCoo WP&B
	'Marcus Hanton' (d)	LCla
	'Mardi Gras' (d)	EBak WGwG
	'Margaret' (d) ♀ H4	CDoC CLoc CSil CTri EBak EFpt EKMF ENot EPts ISea LCla LVER MHdf MWar MWhe NDlv SLBF SPet SSea SWal WGwG WStI
	'Margaret Brown' ♀ H4	CDoC CLoc CSil CTri EBak EKMF LCla MWhe NDlv SLBF SPet SWal WStI
	'Margaret Davidson' (d)	CLoc
	'Margaret Hazelwood'	EKMF
	'Margaret Pilkington'	MJac MWar SSea
	'Margaret Roe'	CDoC CSil EBak EKMF MJac SPet SWal WP&B
	'Margaret Rose'	MJac
	'Margaret Susan'	EBak
	'Margaret Tebbit'	MJac WGor
	'Margarite Dawson' (d)	CSil
	'Margery Blake'	CSil EBak EKMF
	'Maria Landy'	EKMF EMan LCla MJac MWar
	'Maria Merrills' (d)	EKMF EMan
	'Marilyn Olsen'	EPts LCla MWar
	'Marin Belle'	CSil
	'Marin Glow' ♀ H3	CLoc CSil EBak MWhe SLBF SPet
	'Marinka' ♀ H3	CLoc CSil EBak ECtt EFpt EKMF EMan LCla LVER MBri MJac MWar MWhe SLBF SPet SSea WGwG WP&B
	'Marion Hilton' **new**	MWar
	'Mark Kirby' (d)	EKMF WP&B
	'Marlea's Katrien' **new**	WP&B
	'Marlea's Vuurbol' (d)	MWar
	'Marles de Keijzer'	EFpt LCla
	'Martin's Choice'	WP&B
	'Martin's Cinderella'	WP&B
	'Martin's Inspiration' **new**	MWar

'Martin's Yellow Surprise' CLoc LCla SLBF
'Marton Smith'   MWhe
'Marty' (d)   EBak
'Mary' ♀ H1+3   CDoC CLoc CSil EFpt EKMF EPts
                        LCla LRHS MLan MWar MWhe
                        SLBF SSea WGwG WP&B
'Mary Ellen Guffey' (d) SLBF
'Mary Jones' (d)   EKMF
'Mary Lockyer' (d)   CLoc EBak
'Mary Poppins'   LCla WP&B
'Mary Shead' (d) **new** MWar
'Mary Thorne'   CSil EBak EKMF
'Mary Wright' (d)   MWhe
'Masquerade' (d)   EBak EMan
'Matador'   CSil
mathewsii   EKMF
'Maureen Ward'   EKMF
'Maurice Paul Ralph'   LCla
'Mauve Beauty' (d)   CSil EKMF NDlv
'Mauve Lace' (d)   CSil
'Max Jaffa'   CSil
'May Gibson'   MWar
'Mayblossom' (d)   ECtt SPet
'Mayfayre' (d)   CLoc
'Mayfield'   MWhe
'Meadowlark' (d)   EBak ECtt EFpt EKMF
'Meditation' (d)   CLoc CSil
'Melanie'   CDoC WP&B
'Melody'   CSil EBak MWhe SPet
'Melody Ann' (d)   EBak
'Melting Moments' (d)   EKMF MJac WP&B
'Mephisto'   CSil
'Mercurius'   CSil
'Merlin'   CSil EKMF LCla
'Merry Mary' (d)   CSil EBak EKMF
I 'Mexicali Rose' Machado CLoc
'Michael' (d)   CSil EFpt EPts
michoacanensis   see *F. microphylla* subsp. *aprica*
    misapplied
michoacanensis   WP&B
    Sésse & Moç
'Micky Goult' ♀ H1+3   CLoc EKMF EPts LCla MJac
                        MWhe SPet SSea WP&B
'Microchip'   CSil
microphylla   CBrd CDoC CElw CLoc CPLG
                        CSam CSil CWCL EBak GCal GGar
                        MLan MWhe SLon SSea STre
                        WCru WEas WGwG
§ - subsp. *aprica*   EKMF LCla
§ - subsp. *hemsleyana* CDoC CPLG CSil EFpt EKMF LCla
                        MWhe SWal WGwG
§ - subsp. *hidalgensis* CSil CTbh EKMF LCla SLBF
  - subsp. *microphylla* CSil EKMF
  - subsp. *quercetorum* CDoC CSil EKMF LCla
'Midas'   MBri
'Midnight Sun' (d)   CSil EBak EPts
'Mieke Meursing' ♀ H1+3 CDoC CLoc CSil EBak ECtt EKMF
                        MJac MWar MWhe SPet WP&B
'Miep Aalhuizen'   LCla WGwG WP&B
'Mike Oxtoby'   EKMF
'Mildred Wagg' **new** MWar
'Ming'   CLoc
'Miniature Jewels'   SLBF
'Minirose'   CSil EPts MWar MWhe
'Minnesota' (d)   EBak
'Mipan'   SLBF
'Mischief'   CSil
'Miss California' (d)   CLoc EBak ECtt EFpt MBri MWhe
'Miss Debbie' (d)   MJac
'Miss Great Britain'   CSil
'Miss Lye'   CSil EKMF
'Miss Muffett' (d)   CSil SIng
'Miss Vallejo' (d)   EBak

'Mission Bells'   CDoC CLoc CSil EBak EKMF EPts
                        LCla SPet WGwG
'Mistoque'   CSil
'Misty Blue' (d)   CSil
'Misty Haze' (d)   CSil LVER
'Moira Ann'   ECtt
'Molesworth' (d)   CSil EBak EKMF MJac MWhe SPet
'Mollie Beaulah' (d)   CSil ECtt EKMF
'Money Spinner'   CLoc EBak EFpt
'Monica Dare'   WP&B
'Monsieur Thibaut' ♀ H4 CSil EKMF ENot LCla SPet
'Monte Rosa' (d)   CLoc
'Monterey'   MWhe
'Montrose Village' (d) MWhe
'Monument' (d)   CSil
'Mood Indigo' (d)   CSil LVER WGwG WP&B
'Moon Glow'   MJac WP&B
'Moonbeam' (d)   CLoc CSil MWhe
'Moonlight Sonata'   CLoc EBak MJac SPet
'More Applause' (d)   CLoc EKMF LVER MWhe WP&B
'Morning Light' (d)   CLoc EBak SPet
'Morning Mist'   EBak
'Morning Star'   MBri
'Morrells' (d)   EBak
'Moth Blue' (d)   CSil EBak SPet
'Mountain Mist' (d)   EKMF
'Moyra' (d)   EKMF
'Mr A. Huggett'   CLoc CSil EKMF EPts LCla MWhe
                        SPet
'Mr P.D. Lee'   MWhe
'Mr W. Rundle'   EBak WP&B
§ 'Mr West' (v)   CSil EKMF SPet
'Mrs Churchill'   CLoc
'Mrs John D. Fredericks' CSil
'Mrs Lawrence Lyon' (d) EBak
'Mrs Lovell Swisher'   CDoC CSil EBak EPts LCla MJac
    ♀ H4   MWhe SPet
'Mrs Marshall'   CSil EBak SLBF SPet
'Mrs Popple' ♀ H3   More than 30 suppliers
'Mrs Victor Reiter'   CSil
'Mrs W. Castle'   CSil EKMF WGwG
'Mrs W.P. Wood' ♀ H3   CDoC CLoc CSil EKMF MBri SWal
                        WP&B
'Mrs W. Rundle'   CLoc CSil EBak EKMF LRHS
                        MWhe SLBF SPet WP&B
'Multa'   MJac SYvo
'Muriel' (d)   CLoc EBak ECtt EKMF MWhe
'My Fair Lady' (d)   CLoc CSil EBak SPet
'My Honey'   CSil
'My Mum'   LCla SLBF WP&B
'Nancy Darnley' (d)   EKMF
'Nancy Lou' (d)   CDoC CLoc EPts LCla LVER MJac
                        MWar MWhe SLBF SPet
'Nanny Ed' (d)   MBri
'Natasha Sinton' (d)   CLoc CSil ECtt EFpt EKMF EMan
                        LVER MBri MJac MWar MWhe
                        SLBF SPet WGwG
'Native Dancer' (d)   EBak
'Naughty Nicole' (d)   LCla SLBF WP&B
'Nautilus' (d)   EBak EKMF
'Navy Blue'   CSil
'Neapolitan' (d)   CDoC EPts MWhe SLBF
'Neil Clyne'   MWhe
'Nell Gwyn'   CLoc CSil EBak
'Nellie Nuttall' ♀ H3   CDoC CLoc CSil EBak EKMF EPts
                        MWar MWhe SLBF SPet SSea
'Neopolitan'   CLoc CSil WGwG
'Nettala'   CDoC WP&B
'Neue Welt'   CSil EBak EKMF
'New Fascination' (d)   EBak
'Nice 'n' Easy' (d)   LVER MBri MJac NBlu
'Nicki's Findling'   CSil EPts LCla WP&B
'Nicky Veerman'   WP&B

'Nicola'	CLoc EBak
'Nicola Jane' (d)	CDoC CSil EBak EKMF EPts LCla
	MBri MJac MWhe SLBF SPet SWal
	WP&B
'Nicolette'	MJac
'Nightingale' (d)	CLoc CSil EBak
§ *nigricans*	CDoC EKMF LCla
- x *gehrigeri*	EKMF
'Nina Wills'	EBak
'Niobe' (d)	EBak
'Niula'	EKMF LCla
'No Name' (d)	EBak
'Norfolk Ivor' (d)	WP&B
'Normandy Bell'	CSil EBak SPet
'North Cascades' (d)	WP&B
'Northern Dancer' (d)	EKMF SLBF WP&B
'Northumbrian Belle'	EBak WGwG
'Northway'	CLoc LCla MJac MWhe SPet
'Norvell Gillespie' (d)	EBak
'Novato'	EBak EPts
'Novella' (d)	EBak
'Noyo Star' (d)	CSil EFpt
'Nunthorpe Gem' (d)	CDoC CSil
obconica	CSil EKMF LCla WP&B
'Obcylin'	EKMF LCla SLBF
'Obergärtner Koch'	EKMF LCla
'Ocean Beach'	EPts
'Oddfellow' (d)	CSil
'Oetnang' (d)	CTri SCoo
'Old Somerset' (v)	LCla
'Olive Smith'	CSil EPts LCla MJac MWhe
'Olympia'	CSil EKMF MWhe
'Olympic Lass' (d)	EBak
'Onward'	CSil EKMF WP&B
§ 'Oosje'	CDoC CSil EFpt LCla
'Opalescent' (d)	CLoc
'Orange Crush'	CLoc CSil EBak MWar MWhe SPet
'Orange Crystal'	CSil EBak EKMF MJac MWhe SPet
'Orange Drops'	CLoc CSil EBak EKMF EPts MWhe
	SPet SYvo
'Orange Flare'	CLoc CSil EBak MWhe SLBF SSea
'Orange King' (d)	CLoc CSil EMan SSea WP&B
'Orange Mirage'	CLoc CSil EBak LVER MWhe SPet
'Orangeblossom'	CSil SLBF WP&B
'Oranje van Os'	MJac MWhe
'Orient Express'	CDoC CSil LCla MJac MWar
	MWhe SWal WGor WGwG
'Oriental Flame'	EKMF
'Oriental Sunrise'	MWhe
'Ornamental Pearl'	CLoc EBak SLBF
'Orwell' (d)	WP&B
'Other Fellow'	CSil EBak EKMF EPts LCla MJac
	MWhe SLBF SPet WP&B
'Oulton Empress' **new**	SLBF
'Oulton Red Imp' **new**	SLBF
'Oulton Travellers Rest' **new**	SLBF
'Our Darling'	MWhe
'Our Nan' (d)	MJac
'Our Ted'	WP&B
'Overbecks'	see *F. magellanica* var. *molinae*
	'Sharpitor'
'Overbecks Ruby'	GBuc
'P.J.B.' (d)	LCla
'Pabbe's Teudebel' (d)	WP&B
pachyrrhiza	EKMF
'Pacific Grove' Greene	see *F.* 'Evelyn Steele Little'
'Pacific Grove'	EBak
Niederholzer (d)	
'Pacific Queen' (d)	CLoc EBak
'Pacquesa' (d)	CDoC EBak EPts MWar MWhe SPet
'Padre Pio' (d)	MJac
'Pale Flame' (d)	MWhe
'Pallas' **new**	CSil

pallescens	EKMF LCla
'Pam Plack'	CSil EKMF LCla
'Pamela Knights' (d)	EBak
'Pam's People' **new**	LCla
'Pan'	EFpt LCla MWar WP&B
'Pan America' (d)	EBak
'Panache' (d)	LCla
'Pangea'	LCla
paniculata ♀ H1+3	CBot CDoC CEnd CRHN CTbh EBak
	EKMF EPts LCla SHFr SLBF WFoF
'Panique'	CSil
'Pantaloons' (d)	EBak
'Panylla Prince'	CDoC EPts LCla SLBF
'Papa Bleuss' (d)	CLoc EBak
'Papoose' (d)	CDoC CSil EBak EKMF LCla WP&B
'Partridge Lake'	MWar
'Party Frock'	CLoc CSil EBak LCla LVER SPet
parviflora hort.	see *F.* x *bacillaris*
§ *parviflora* Lindley	EBak
'Pastel'	EBak
'Pat Meara'	CLoc EBak
'Pathétique' (d)	CLoc
'Patience' (d)	CSil EBak MJac SWal
'Patio King'	EKMF
'Patio Princess' (d)	LAst LCla MBri MJac MWhe NBlu
	SSea WGor WLow
'Patricia' Wood	CSil EBak
'Patricia Ann' (d)	MWar
'Patricia Joan Yates'	WP&B
'Patty Evans' (d)	EBak
'Patty Sue' (d)	MBri MWar
'Paul Berry'	CSil EKMF WP&B
'Paul Cambon' (d)	EBak EKMF
'Paul Roe' (d)	MJac
'Paul Storey'	EKMF WP&B
'Paula Jane' (d)	CLoc LCla MBri MJac MWar
	MWhe SLBF WGor WLow WP&B
'Pauline Rawlins' (d)	CLoc EBak
'Paulus'	WP&B
'Peace' (d)	EBak
'Peachy' (d)	CDoC EKMF MJac SCoo WP&B
'Peachy Keen' (d)	EBak WP&B
'Peacock' (d)	CLoc
'Pearly Gates'	WP&B
'Pee Wee Rose'	CSil EBak EKMF
'Peggy Cole'	EPts
'Peggy King'	CDoC CSil EBak EKMF LCla
	MWhe SPet
'Peloria' (d)	CLoc EBak
'Pennine'	MBri MWar
'People's Princess'	MJac WP&B
'Peper Harow'	EBak
'Pepi' (d)	CLoc EBak SPet
'Peppermint Candy' (d)	EPts WGwG WP&B
'Peppermint Stick' (d)	CDoC CLoc CSil EBak EKMF
	EMan LCla LRHS LVER MBri MJac
	MWhe SPet SSea SWal
'Percy Graham'	SLBF
'Perky Pink' (d)	EBak EPts LCla MWhe SPet
'Perry Park'	EBak MBri MJac
'Perry's Jumbo'	NBir NPer
perscandens	CSil EKMF LCla WGwG
'Personality' (d)	EBak
'Peter Bellerby' **new**	EKMF
'Peter Bielby' (d)	EKMF LCla MWar
'Peter Crookes'	CSil LCla
'Peter James' (d)	CSil EKMF
'Peter Pan'	CSil EHol SPer
'Peter Sanderson'	MJac
petiolaris	CDoC EKMF LCla
'Petit Four'	WP&B
'Petit Point'	EFpt
'Petite' (d)	EBak

'Phaidra'	LCla	
'Pharaoh'	CLoc	
'Phénoménal' (d)	CSil EBak EKMF EPts LRHS WP&B	
'Phillip Taylor'	MJac	
'Phyllis' (d) ♀ H4	CDoC CLoc CSil EBak EFpt EKMF EPts LCla MHdf MJac MWhe NDlv SLBF SPet WGwG WP&B WTel	
'Phyrne' (d)	CSil EBak EKMF SWal WP&B	
'Piet G. Vergeer'	WP&B	
pilaloensis	EKMF	
x pilcopata	LCla	
'Pinch Me' (d)	CSil EBak EKMF LVER SPet SWal	
'Pink Aurora'	CLoc CSil	
'Pink Ballet Girl' (d)	CLoc EBak ECtt	
'Pink Bon Accorde'	CLoc WGwG WP&B	
'Pink Cloud'	CLoc EBak	
'Pink Cornet'	LCla	
'Pink Darling'	CLoc EBak MWhe	
'Pink Dessert'	EBak	
'Pink Domino' (d)	EKMF	
'Pink Fairy' (d)	CSil EBak SPet	
'Pink Fandango' (d)	CLoc	
'Pink Fantasia'	CDoC CLoc CSil EBak EKMF EPts LAst LCla MJac MWar MWhe SSea SWal WP&B	
'Pink Fireworks' **new**	EFpt	
'Pink Flamingo' (d)	CLoc EBak	
'Pink Galore' (d)	CLoc CSil EBak EKMF EMan LCla LVER MBri MJac MWhe SPet SSea WGwG WLow WP&B	
'Pink Goon' (d)	CDoC CSil EKMF LCla LRHS NDlv SLBF SWal	
'Pink Jade'	EBak WP&B	
'Pink la Campanella'	EMan MBri MWar MWhe NBlu WBVN WGor	
'Pink Lace' (d)	CSil SPet	
'Pink Lady' Ryle Atkinson	MWhe	
'Pink Marshmallow' (d) ♀ H1+3	CLoc CSil EBak EKMF EMan LCla LVER MJac MWar SLBF SPet SSea SWal WGwG WP&B	
'Pink Panther' (d)	EKMF MJac MWar WP&B	
'Pink Pearl' ambig.	SWal SYvo	
'Pink Pearl' Bright (d)	CSil EBak EKMF LVER	
'Pink Picotee'	LCla MJac	
'Pink Profusion'	EBak	
'Pink Quartet' (d)	CLoc EBak SPet	
'Pink Rain'	CSil EFpt EKMF EPts MJac WP&B	
'Pink Slippers'	CLoc	
'Pink Spangles'	EMan MBri SSea WGwG	
'Pink Surprise' (d)	MJac	
'Pink Temptation'	CLoc EBak	
'Pinkmost' (d)	ECtt EKMF	
'Pinto de Blue' (d)	EKMF LCla MWar WP&B	
'Pinwheel' (d)	CLoc EBak	
'Piper' (d)	CDoC CSil MWar	
'Piper's Vale'	LCla MJac SLBF WP&B	
'Pippa Rolt'	EKMF EPts WP&B	
'Pirbright'	EKMF	
'Pixie'	CDoC CLoc CSil EBak EKMF MJac NDlv SLBF SPet	
'Playford'	EBak	
'Plenty'	CSil EBak	
'Pole Star'	CSil	
'Polmont Pride'	EKMF	
'Pop Whitlock' (v)	EKMF SPet SSea	
'Popely Pride' (d)	WP&B	
'Popsie Girl'	LCla MWar SLBF	
'Port Arthur' (d)	CSil EBak	
'Postiljon'	CSil EBak SPet	
'Powder Puff' ambig.	ECtt MBri SPet	
'Powder Puff' Hodges (d)	CLoc CSil EFpt LVER	
I 'Powder Puff' Tabraham (d) **new**	CSil	

'Prelude' Blackwell	CLoc CSil	
I 'Prelude' Kennett (d)	EBak EKMF	
'President'	CDoC CSil EBak EKMF LCla	
'President B.W. Rawlins'	EBak	
§ 'President Elliot'	CSil EKMF MWhe	
'President George Bartlett' (d)	CSil EKMF EPts LAst MJac MWar SLBF WP&B	
'President Joan Morris' (d)	EKMF SLBF	
'President Leo Boullemier'	CSil EBak ECtt EKMF LCla MJac SPet WGwG WP&B	
'President Margaret Slater'	CDoC CLoc CSil EBak EMan MJac MWhe SPet	
'President Norman Hobbs'	EKMF MWar	
'President Roosevelt' (d)	CDoC ECtt	
'President Stanley Wilson'	EBak ECtt EPts SPet	
'Preston Guild' ♀ H1+3	CDoC CLoc CSil EBak EKMF LRHS MWar MWhe NPer SLBF SPet	
'Pride of the West'	CSil EBak EKMF	
'Prince of Orange'	CLoc CSil EBak EKMF	
'Prince of Peace' (d)	CSil	
'Princess Dollar'	see F. 'Dollar Princess'	
'Princess of Bath' (d)	CLoc	
'Princess Pamela' (d)	SLBF	
'Princessita'	CSil EBak ECtt EFpt EMan MJac MWar MWhe SPet	
procumbens	CDoC CHEx CLoc CPLG CSil CTrc EBak ECou EKMF EPts EShb GGar ITim LCla MWhe NWCA SHFr SIng SLBF SMad SSea SWal SYvo WGwG	
- 'Argentea'	see F. procumbens 'Wirral'	
- 'Variegata'	see F. procumbens 'Wirral'	
- 'Wirral' (v)	CDoC CLoc CSil EKMF GCal	
'Prodigy'	see F. 'Enfant Prodigue'	
'Profusion' ambig.	CDoC MWhe	
'Prosperity' (d) ♀ H3	CDoC CLoc CSil EBak EBee EKMF ENot EPts LCla LRHS LVER MJac MWar MWhe NDlv SPet SWal	
'Pumila'	CWib ECha EKMF ELan EPfP ITim SPet SWal	
'Purbeck Mist' (d)	EKMF	
'Purperklokje'	CDoC CSil EBak LCla WP&B	
'Purple Ann'	EKMF	
'Purple Emperor' (d)	CLoc	
'Purple Heart' (d)	CLoc CSil EBak	
'Purple Lace'	CSil	
'Purple Patch'	MBri	
'Purple Pride'	MBri	
'Purple Rain'	CLoc CSil EKMF WP&B	
'Purple Splendour' (d)	CDoC CSil	
'Pussy Cat'	CLoc CSil EBak LCla WP&B	
'Putney Pride'	EPts	
'Put's Folly'	EBak MJac	
putumayensis	CSil EBak EFpt	
'Quasar' (d)	CDoC CLoc CSil EKMF EPts LRHS LVER MJac MWhe SLBF SPet WBVN WGwG WP&B	
'Queen Mabs'	EBak	
'Queen Mary'	CLoc CSil EBak EKMF	
'Queen of Bath' (d)	EBak	
'Queen of Derby' (d)	LCla	
'Queen of Hearts' Kennett (d)	CSil	
'Queen Victoria' Smith (d)	EKMF	
'Queen's Park' (d)	EBak	
'Query'	CSil EBak EKMF SWal	
'R.A.F.' (d)	CLoc CSil EBak ECtt EKMF EPts LCla MWar SLBF SPet SSea WP&B	
'Rachel Craig' (d)	MWar	
'Rachel Sinton' (d)	EMan MBri MJac	
'Radcliffe Beauty'	MWhe	
'Radcliffe Bedder' (d)	CDoC CSil EKMF	
'Radings Karin'	CDoC WP&B	

'Radings Michelle'	CSil
'Ralph Oliver' (d)	WP&B
'Ralph's Delight' (d)	MJac WP&B
'Rambling Rose' (d)	CLoc CSil EBak ECtt EFpt MJac
'Rams Royal' (d)	CDoC LCla LVER MJac
'Rascal' (d)	MWar
I 'Raspberry' (d)	CLoc CSil EBak LCla MWhe
'Raspberry Red' **new**	EFpt
'Ratatouille' (d)	CSil EKMF
ravenii	CSil
'Ravensbarrow'	CSil WP&B
'Ravenslaw'	CSil EKMF
'Razzle Dazzle' (d)	EBak
'Reading Show' (d)	CSil EKMF EPts LCla SLBF
'Rebecca Williamson' (d)	MJac MWhe WP&B
'Rebeka Sinton'	CLoc EBak MBri MWar
'Red Ace' (d)	CSil
'Red Imp' (d)	CDoC CSil
'Red Jacket' (d)	EBak
'Red Rain'	WP&B
'Red Ribbons' (d)	EBak
'Red Rover'	MWar SLBF
'Red Rum' (d)	CSil SPet
'Red Shadows' (d)	CLoc CSil EBak MJac WGwG
'Red Spider'	CLoc CSil EBak EKMF EMan
	MHFa MWar MWhe SCoo SPet
	SSea WGor WGwG WP&B
'Red Sunlight'	EPts WP&B
'Red Wing'	CLoc
'Reflexa'	see *F.* x *bacillaris* 'Reflexa'
'Reg Gubler'	SLBF
'Regal'	CLoc
'Regal Robe' (d)	CSil
regia	CSil EFpt WP&B
- var. ***alpestris***	see *F. alpestris*
- subsp. ***regia***	CDoC CSil EKMF EPts LCla
- subsp. ***reitzii***	CDoC CSil EKMF LCla WGwG
- subsp. ***serrae***	CSil EKMF
'Remember Eric' **new**	EKMF
'Remembrance' (d)	CSil EFpt EKMF EPts LCla SSea
'Remus' (d)	CSil
'Requiem'	CLoc
'Reverend Doctor Brown' (d)	EBak
'Reverend Elliott'	see *F.* 'President Elliot'
I 'Rhapsody' Blackwell (d)	CLoc
'Rhombifolia'	CSil
'Rianne Foks'	WP&B
'Riant' (d)	WP&B
§ 'Riccartonii' ♀ H3	More than 30 suppliers
'Richard John Carrington'	CSil
'Ridestar' (d)	CLoc CSil EBak EMan MJac MWhe
'Ringwood Market' (d)	CSil ECtt EKMF EPts LCla MJac
	MWhe SPet
rivularis	WP&B
'Robbie'	EKMF WP&B
'Robbie's Reward' (d) **new**	SLBF
'Robert J. Pierce' **new**	MWar
'Robin Hood' (d)	CDoC CSil EKMF NDlv
'Rodeo'	WP&B
'Roger de Cooker' **new**	WP&B
'Rohees Alchita' **new**	WP&B
'Rohees Blaky' **new**	WP&B
'Rohees New Millenium' **new**	WP&B
'Rohees Nunki' **new**	WP&B
'Rohees Queen' **new**	WP&B
'Rolanda Bierinckx' **new**	WP&B
'Rolla' (d)	EBak EKMF
'Rolt's Bride' (d)	EKMF
'Rolt's Ruby' (d)	CSil EKMF EPts
'Roman City' (d)	CLoc
'Romany Rose'	CLoc
'Ron Chambers Love'	MWar
'Ron Ewart'	EKMF MWhe
'Ronald L. Lockerbie' (d)	CLoc
'Ron's Ruby'	MWhe WP&B
'Roos Breytenbach'	CDoC CSil EKMF LCla MJac WP&B
'Rosamunda'	CLoc
'Rose Aylett' (d)	EBak
'Rose Bradwardine' (d)	EBak
'Rose Churchill' (d)	LCla MBri MJac
'Rose Fantasia'	CDoC CLoc CSil EFpt EKMF EPts
	LCla MJac MWar MWhe SLBF SSea
	WLow WP&B
'Rose Marie' (d)	CLoc
'Rose of Castile'	CDoC CLoc CSil EBak EKMF LCla
	LRHS MJac MWhe
'Rose of Castile Improved' ♀ H4	CSil EBak EKMF LCla MJac MWar SPet WP&B
'Rose of Denmark'	CLoc CSil EBak MBri MJac MWar
	MWhe SPet SWal WGor WGwG
	WP&B
'Rose Reverie' (d)	EBak
'Rose Winston' (d)	MWhe WP&B
rosea hort.	see *F.* 'Globosa'
rosea Ruíz & Pav.	see *F. lycioides*
'Rosebud' (d)	EBak
'Rosecroft Beauty' (d)	CSil EBak MWhe
'Rosemarie Higham' **new**	MJac NBlu
'Rosemary Day'	CLoc
'Roslyn Lowe' (d)	CDoC
'Ross Lea' (d)	CSil
'Roswitha' **new**	SLBF
'Rosy Frills' (d)	CSil LCla MJac MWhe
'Rosy Morn' (d)	CLoc EBak
'Rosy Ruffles' (d)	EKMF
'Rough Silk'	CLoc CSil EBak
'Roy Walker' (d)	CLoc LVER MJac
'Royal Mosaic' (d)	CDoC MJac SWal WP&B
'Royal Orchid'	EBak
'Royal Purple' (d)	CSil EBak EKMF MBri WP&B
'Royal Touch' (d)	EBak
'Royal Velvet' (d) ♀ H3	CLoc CSil EBak EFpt EKMF EMan
	EPts LCla LVER MJac MWar MWhe
	SLBF SPet SWal WGwG WP&B
'Royal Wedding'	CSil LCla
§ 'Rubra Grandiflora'	EBak EKMF LCla SLBF
'Ruby Wedding' (d)	CSil EKMF SLBF WP&B
'Ruddigore'	WP&B
'Ruffles' (d)	EBak
§ 'Rufus' ♀ H3-4	CDoC CLoc CSil CTri EBak EHol
	EKMF EPts LCla LRHS MJac MWar
	MWhe NDlv SLBF SPet WGwG
'Rufus the Red'	see *F.* 'Rufus'
'Ruth'	CSil
'Ruth Brazewell' (d)	CLoc
'Ruth King' (d)	EBak ECtt WGwG
'Sailor'	EPts MJac
'Sally Bell' **new**	CSil
'Salmon Cascade'	CSil EBak ECtt EFpt EKMF EMan
	EPts LCla MJac MWhe SLBF SSea
	WP&B
'Salmon Glow'	MJac MWhe
'Sam's Song' (d)	MJac
'Samson' (d/v)	EBak
'San Diego' (d)	CSil
'San Francisco'	EBak
'San Leandro' (d)	EBak
'San Mateo' (d)	EBak
§ ***sanctae-rosae***	EBak EKMF EPts LCla
'Sandboy'	CSil EBak
'Sanguinea'	CSil EKMF
'Sanrina'	EKMF
'Santa Cruz' (d)	CSil EBak EKMF LCla MWhe NDlv
	SWal

'Santa Lucia' (d) — CLoc EBak
'Santa Monica' (d) — EBak
'Sapphire' (d) — CSil EBak EFpt
'Sara Helen' (d) — CLoc EBak
'Sarah Eliza' (d) — SCoo
'Sarah Greensmith' — EKMF
'Sarah Jane' (d) — CSil EBak
'Sarong' (d) — EBak
'Satellite' — CLoc EBak EKMF SPet WP&B
'Saturnus' — CSil EBak SPet WP&B
scabriuscula — CDoC EKMF LCla
scandens — see *F. decussata*
'Scarcity' — CDoC CSil EBak EKMF MWhe SPet SWal
'Scarlet Cascade' — EKMF LCla
'Schiller' ambig. — EKMF
'Schneckerl' (d) **new** — SLBF
'Schneeball' (d) — CSil EBak EKMF
'Schneewittchen' Hoech — CSil EKMF
'Schneewittchen' Klein — CSil EBak WP&B
'Schönbrunner Schuljubiläum' — EBak LCla
'Sea Shell' (d) — EBak
'Seaforth' — EBak EKMF
'Sealand Prince' — CDoC CSil ECtt EKMF LCla WP&B
'Seaside Stars' — LCla
'Seaside Swirls' — LCla
'Sebastopol' (d) — CLoc
serratifolia Hook. — see *F. austromontana*
serratifolia Ruíz & Pav. — see *F. denticulata*
sessilifolia — EKMF LCla
'Seventh Heaven' (d) — CLoc MJac WP&B
'Severn Queen' — CSil
'Shangri-La' (d) — EBak
'Shanley' — WP&B
'Sharon Allsop' (d) — MWhe WGwG
'Sharon Caunt' (d) — CSil EKMF
'Sharon Elle' — EKMF
'Sharpitor' — see *F. magellanica* var. *molinae* 'Sharpitor'
'Sheila Crooks' (d) — EBak EMan MJac MWhe WP&B
'Sheila Kirby' — MJac
'Sheila Mary' — EKMF
'Sheila's Love' **new** — MJac
'Shelford' — CDoC CLoc EBak EFpt EKMF EMan EPts LCla MJac MWar MWhe SLBF SSea WP&B
'Shell Pink' — CSil
'Shirley'PBR **new** — EFpt
'Shirley Halladay' (d) — EKMF LCla
'Shooting Star' (d) — EBak
'Shy Lady' (d) — MWhe SPet
'Sierra Blue' (d) — CLoc EBak EKMF
'Silver Anniversary' (d) — EKMF
'Silver Dawn' (d) — CSil EKMF EPts SLBF
'Silver Dollar' — MWhe WGwG
'Silver Pink' — CSil
'Silverdale' — CDoC CSil EKMF MWhe
'Simple Simon' — CSil
simplicicaulis — EBak EKMF LCla
'Sincerity' (d) — CLoc CSil
'Sinton's Standard' — MBri
'Sir Alfred Ramsey' — EBak MWhe
'Sir Matt Busby' (d) — EKMF EPts MJac MWar WP&B
'Siren' Baker (d) — EBak
'Sister Ann Haley' — EKMF EPts
'Sister Sister' (d) — SLBF WP&B
'Six Squadron' — EKMF
skutchiana — CPLG
'Sleepy' — CSil MBri SPet
'Sleigh Bells' — CLoc CSil EBak EKMF MWhe SPet WGwG
'Small Pipes' — EKMF LCla WP&B

'Smokey Mountain' (d) — MJac MWar
'Sneezy' — CSil EHol MWhe
'Snow Burner' (d) — CDoC MJac SWal WGwG
'Snow White' (d) — CSil SPet WGwG WP&B
'Snowbird' (d) **new** — SLBF
§ 'Snowcap' (d) ♀ H3-4 — CDoC CLoc CSil EBak EFpt EKMF EMan EPts GKir LCla LVER MAsh MBNS MBri MGos MJac MWar MWhe NDlv NPer SIng SLBF SPet SPla SSea WFar WGwG WLow WP&B WStI
'Snowdrift' Colville (d) — CLoc
'Snowdrift' Kennett (d) — EBak
'Snowfire' (d) — CLoc CSil ECtt EKMF MJac MWhe SCoo WGwG WP&B
'Snowflake' — EKMF
'Snowstorm' (d) — CSil ECtt SPet
'Snowy Summit' (d) — CSil WGwG
'So Big' (d) — EKMF
'Son of Thumb' ♀ H4 — CChe CDoC CLoc COkL CSil EKMF EMan EPts LAst MAsh MBar MBri MGos MJac MWhe NDlv SIng SLBF SPar SPet SSea WFar
'Sonata' (d) — CLoc EBak
'Sophie Louise' — EKMF EPts MWar WP&B
'Sophie Wilson' — SLBF
'Sophie's Surprise' — WP&B
'Sophisticated Lady' (d) — CLoc EBak ECtt EKMF EPts LVER MWar SPet
'Soroptimist International' — MWar
'South Gate' (d) — CLoc EBak EKMF EMan EPts MBri MJac MWar MWhe SPet WGwG WP&B
'South Lakeland' — CSil
'South Seas' (d) — EBak
'Southlanders' — EBak
'Southwell Minster' — EKMF
'Space Shuttle' — CLoc CSil EKMF LCla MWhe WP&B
'Sparky' — EPts LCla MWhe
§ 'Speciosa' — EBak EFpt EKMF LCla MWhe
'Spion Kop' (d) — CSil EBak EKMF MJac MWar MWhe SPet WGor
§ *splendens* ♀ H1+3 — CDoC CLoc CSil EBak EKMF EPts LCla NPer WGwG
– 'Karl Hartweg' — CDoC
'Sporty' — MJac
'Spring Bells' (d) — MWhe
'Squadron Leader' (d) — EBak EPts LVER
§ 'Stals Kevin' — LCla
'Stanley Cash' (d) — CLoc CSil EKMF LVER MWar SPet WP&B
'Star of Pink' (d) — MWhe
'Star Wars' **new** — MBri
'Stardust' — EBak LCla MJac MWhe
'Steeley' (d) — MWhe
'Stella Ann' — CSil EBak EPts LCla WP&B
'Stella Marina' (d) — CLoc EBak
'Stewart Taylor' — MJac
steyermarkii **new** — EKMF
'Straat Cook' — LCla
'Straat Magelhaen' — LCla
'Straat Malakka' — EPts LCla
'Strawberry Delight' (d) — CLoc EBak ECtt EKMF LVER MJac MWhe SPet
'Strawberry Mousse' (d) — LVER
'Strawberry Sundae' (d) — CLoc EBak
'Strawberry Supreme' (d) — CSil EKMF
'String of Pearls' — CLoc CSil EKMF LCla MJac SLBF SPet SSea
'Stuart Joe' — EKMF
'Sugar Blues' (d) — CDoC EBak
'Summerdaffodil' — CSil LCla SLBF WP&B

'Sunkissed' (d)	COtt EBak WGwG
'Sunlight Path'	LCla
'Sunningdale'	LCla
'Sunny'	COtt
'Sunny Smiles'	CSil EKMF SPet
'Sunray' (v)	CLoc EBak EKMF EPts LAst LRHS MAsh MBNS MWar MWhe NMRc NSti SPar SPla WP&B
'Sunset'	CLoc CSil EBak MWhe SPer
'Sunset Boulevard' (d)	CDoC
'Supersport' (d)	WP&B
'Superstar'	EPts WP&B
'Susan' (d)	COtt EFpt LCla WP&B
'Susan Ford' (d)	SPet WGwG
'Susan Green'	CSil EBak EKMF EMan MJac MWar MWhe SPet WGwG
'Susan McMaster'	CLoc
'Susan Olcese' (d)	EBak
'Susan Skeen'	MJac WP&B
'Susan Travis'	CLoc CSil EBak EKMF MWhe SPet
'Swanley Gem' ♀ H3	CLoc EBak EKMF MWhe SLBF SPet SSea WP&B
'Swanley Pendula'	CLoc
'Swanley Yellow'	EBak
'Sweet Leilani' (d)	CLoc EBak
'Sweet Sixteen' (d)	CLoc
I 'Sweetheart' van Wieringen	EBak
'Swingtime' (d) ♀ H3	CLoc CSil EBak EFpt EKMF EMan EPts LCla LVER MGos MJac MWar MWhe SLBF SPet WGwG WLow WP&B
'S'Wonderful' (d)	CLoc EBak
sylvatica Benth.	EKMF LCla
- Munz	see *F. nigricans*
'Sylvia Barker'	LCla MJac MWar
'Sylvy'	MWhe
'Symphony'	CLoc EBak
'Taco' LCla	WP&B
'Taddle'	EMan MJac SLBF SPet WGwG
'Taffeta Bow' (d)	CLoc CSil EKMF LVER
'Taffy' EBak	WP&B
'Tamworth'	CLoc EBak EFpt LCla MJac SSea
'Tangerine'	CLoc CSil EBak MWhe SSea
'Tantalising Tracy' (d)	SLBF WP&B
'Tanya'	CLoc EKMF SPet
'Tanya Bridger' (d)	EBak
'Tarra Valley'	LCla MWhe WP&B
'Tasty Tracey' **new**	EFpt
'Tausendschön' (d)	CLoc ECtt
'Ted Perry' (d)	CSil
'Ted's Tribute' **new**	EFpt
'Temptation' ambig.	ECtt SPet
'Temptation' Peterson	CLoc CSil EBak
'Tennessee Waltz' (d) ♀ H3	CLoc CSil EBak EFpt EKMF EMan EPts LCla LRHS LVER MJac MWar MWhe SChu SLBF SPer SPet SWal WEas WGwG WP&B
'Terri's Treasure' (d) **new**	SLBF
'Terry Tooke'	LCla
'Tessa Jane' **new**	CSil
tetradactyla misapplied	see *F.* x *bacillaris*
tetradactyla	see *F. encliandra* subsp. *tetradactyla*
'Texas Longhorn' (d)	CLoc CSil EBak EKMF WP&B
'Texas Star'	WP&B
'Thalia' ♀ H1+3	CDoC CLoc CSil EBak ECtt EFpt EKMF EPts LCla LHrt LRHS LVER MBri MJac MOak MWar MWhe SGar SLBF SPar SPet SPla SWal WBod WCom WEas WGwG WP&B
'Thamar'	CLoc CSil EPts MWar MWhe WP&B
'That's It' (d)	EBak WP&B
'The Aristocrat' (d)	CLoc EBak WGwG

'The Boys'	SLBF WP&B
§ 'The Doctor'	CLoc CSil EBak EKMF MWhe
'The Jester' (d)	EBak
'The Madame' (d)	EBak
'The Tarns'	CSil EBak EKMF NCiC
'Theresa Drew'	SLBF
'Therese Dupois'	CSil
'Théroigne de Méricourt'	EBak EKMF
'Thilco'	CSil EKMF
'Think Pink'	WGwG
'This England' (d)	CSil
'Thistle Hill' (d)	CSil EKMF
'Thompsonii'	see *F. magellanica* 'Thompsonii'
'Thornley's Hardy'	CSil EMan SPet WP&B
'Three Cheers'	CLoc EBak
'Three Counties'	EBak
'Thunderbird' (d)	CLoc EBak
thymifolia	ESis GQui LHop SHFr SIng SMrm WKif
- subsp. *minimiflora*	CSil EFpt EKMF LCla
- subsp. *thymifolia*	CDoC CSil EKMF LCla
'Tiara' (d)	EBak
'Tiffany' Reedstrom (d)	EBak
tillettiana	EKMF
'Tillingbourne' (d)	CSil EKMF LCla
'Tillmouth Lass'	EKMF
'Timlin Brened'	CSil EBak LCla MWhe
'Timothy Titus'	LCla SLBF WP&B
'Ting-a-ling'	CDoC CLoc CSil EBak EFpt EKMF LVER MWhe SLBF SPet SSea WP&B
'Tinker Bell' ambig.	CDoC NDlv
'Tinker Bell' Hodges	EBak
I 'Tinker Bell' Tabraham	CSil EKMF
'Tjinegara'	LCla
'Toby Bridger' (d)	CLoc EBak
'Tolling Bell'	CSil EBak MJac MWhe SPet WGwG
'Tom H. Oliver' (d)	EBak WP&B
'Tom Knights'	EBak MWhe SPet WGwG
'Tom Thorne'	EBak
'Tom Thumb' ♀ H3	More than 30 suppliers
'Tom West' misapplied	see *F.* 'Mr West'
'Tom West' Meillez (v)	CBrm CDoC CHEx CLoc CMHG COIW CSBt CSil EBak EKMF EPts LCla LHop LRHS LVER MAsh MJac MOak MWar MWhe NVic SAga SDix SLBF SMrm SPar SSea SWal WFar WGwG
'Tom Woods'	CDoC LCla MWhe
'Tony Porter' (d)	MJac
'Tony's Treat' (d)	EPts
'Toos'	WP&B
'Topaz' (d)	CLoc EBak
'Topper' (d)	EMan
'Torch' (d)	CLoc CSil EBak
'Torchlight'	CSil EPts LCla
'Torvill and Dean' (d)	CLoc CSil EKMF EPts LAst LRHS LVER MJac MWar MWhe SPet WGor
'Trabant'	WP&B
'Tracid' (d)	CLoc CSil
'Tracie Ann' (d)	EKMF
'Trail Blazer' (d)	CLoc CSil EBak MJac SPet
'Trailing Queen'	CSil EBak EKMF MJac WP&B
'Tranquility'	WP&B
'Trase' (d)	CDoC CSil CWib EBak EKMF EPts LVER SWal
'Traudchen Bonstedt'	CDoC CLoc CSil EBak EFpt EKMF EPts LCla MWhe SLBF SPet WP&B
'Traviata'	see *F.* 'La Traviata'
'Treasure' (d)	EBak
'Tresco'	CSil EFpt WBcn
'Treslong'	WP&B
'Tricolor'	see *F. magellanica* var. *gracilis* 'Tricolor'

'Tricolorii'	see *F. magellanica* var. *gracilis*
	'Tricolor'
'Trientje'	LCla
'Trio' (d)	CLoc
triphylla	EBak EKMF LCla LRHS
'Trisha'	EFpt WP&B
'Tristesse' (d)	CLoc EBak
'Troika' (d)	EBak EKMF
'Tropic Sunset' (d)	CSil MBri MWhe
'Tropicana' (d)	CLoc EBak
'Troubador' Waltz (d)	CLoc
'Troutbeck'	CSil
'Trudi Davro' **new**	MJac
'Trudy'	CSil EBak EKMF SPet SWal
'Truly Treena' (d)	SLBF
'Trumpeter' ambig.	CDoC
'Trumpeter' Fry **new**	EFpt
'Trumpeter' Reiter	CLoc CSil EBak EKMF EPts LCla
	MJac MWhe WP&B
'Tsjiep'	CDoC WP&B
'Tubular Bells' **new**	EKMF
'Tumbling Waters' (d)	LVER
'Tuonela' (d)	CLoc CSil EBak MWhe WP&B
'Tutti-frutti' (d)	CLoc
'Twinkletoes'	EPts
'Twinkling Stars'	CSil EKMF MJac WP&B
'Twinny'	EKMF EPts MWar SLBF
'Twirling Square	WP&B
Dancer' (d)	
'Twist of Fate' (d)	CSil EKMF
'Two Tiers' (d)	CSil EKMF WGwG
'U.F.O.'	CSil
'Ullswater' (d)	EBak LVER
'Ulrika' (d)	MWar
'Ultramar' (d)	EBak
'Uncle Charley' (d)	CDoC CLoc CSil EBak EKMF WEas
'Uncle Jinks'	SPet
'Uncle Steve' (d)	EBak
'University of Liverpool'	MJac
'Upward Look'	EBak EKMF SSea
'Valentine' (d)	EBak
'Valerie Ann' (d)	EBak SPet
'Valerie Hobbs' (d)	LCla
'Valerie Tooke' (d)	LCla
'Valiant'	EBak
'Vanessa' (d)	CLoc
'Vanessa Jackson'	CLoc MJac MWhe WGwG
'Vanity Fair' (d)	CLoc EBak WP&B
vargasiana	CDoC
'Variegated Brenda	EKMF
White' (v)	
'Variegated la	MWhe
Campanella' (d/v)	
'Variegated Lottie	CSil EFpt EKMF LCla
Hobby' (v)	
'Variegated Pink	EFpt
Fascination' **new**	
'Variegated Pixie' **new**	CSil
'Variegated Procumbens'	see *F. procumbens* 'Wirral'
'Variegated Snowcap' (d/v)	MWhe
'Variegated Superstar' (v)	MBri
'Variegated Swingtime' (v)	EBak
'Variegated Vivienne	MBri
Thompson' (d/v)	
'Variegated Waveney	MBri
Sunrise' (v)	
'Variegated White Joy' (v)	EKMF
'Veenlust'	LCla MJac WP&B
'Vendeta' **new**	LCla
'Venus Victrix'	CSil EBak EKMF MWhe SLBF
venusta	CDoC EBak EKMF LCla
'Versicolor'	see *F. magellanica* 'Versicolor'
'Vesuvio'	EKMF

'Victorian' (d)	CSil
'Victory' Reiter (d)	EBak
'Vielliebchen'	CDoC CSil
'Vienna Waltz' (d)	MJac
'Vincent van Gogh'	WP&B
'Violet Bassett-Burr' (d)	CLoc EBak
'Violet Gem' (d)	CLoc
'Violet Lace' (d)	CSil
'Violet Rosette' (d)	EBak
'Viva Ireland'	EBak ECtt
'Vivien Colville'	CLoc EKMF SSea
'Vivienne Davis'	LCla
'Vivienne Thompson' (d)	NBlu
'Vobeglo'	EKMF
'Vogue' (d)	EBak WP&B
'Voltaire'	CSil EBak EKMF
'Voodoo' (d)	CDoC CLoc CSil EBak EKMF
	EMan EPts LCla MWar SLBF SPet
	SSea SWal WGwG
vulcanica André	see *F. ampliata*
– Berry	CDoC EKMF LCla
– subsp. *hitchcockii*	EKMF
'Vyvian Miller'	MJac
'W.F.C. Kampioen'	WP&B
'W.P. Wood'	CSil
§ 'Wagtails White Pixie'	CSil EBak
'Waldfee'	CDoC CSil EKMF LCla MWhe
	WGwG
'Waldis Geisha' (d) **new**	SLBF
'Waldis Lydia' (d) **new**	SLBF
'Waldis Ovambo' **new**	SLBF
'Walsingham' (d)	CSil EBak
'Walton Jewel' **new**	EFpt
'Walz Bella'	LCla WP&B
'Walz Blauwkous' (d)	WP&B
'Walz Doedelzak'	LCla WP&B
'Walz Fanclub'	LCla WP&B
'Walz Fluit'	MJac WGor WP&B
'Walz Freule'	EKMF MJac
'Walz Gitaar'	WP&B
'Walz Gong'	WT&B
'Walz Harp'	LCla WP&B
'Walz Jubelteen'	CDoC CLoc CSil EKMF EMan EPts
	LCla MJac MWar MWhe SLBF SSea
	WOld WP&B
'Walz Kalebas'	WP&B
'Walz Kattesnoor'	WP&B
'Walz Lucifer'	LCla SLBF WP&B
'Walz Luit'	CDoC
'Walz Mandoline' (d)	MWar WP&B
'Walz Parasol'	WP&B
'Walz Polka'	LCla WP&B
'Walz Tamtam' (d)	WP&B
'Walz Triangel' (d)	CSil EKMF WP&B
'Walz Trommel' (d)	WP&B
'Walz Waterval'	WP&B
'Walz Wipneus'	WP&B
'Wapenveld 150'	LCla
'Wapenveld's Bloei'	CDoC LCla SLBF WP&B
'War Dance' (d)	MWhe
'War Paint' (d)	CLoc CSil EBak
'Water Nymph'	CLoc CSil SLBF SSea
'Wave of Life'	EKMF MWhe
'Waveney Gem'	CDoC CSil EBak EKMF EMan LCla
	MJac MWar SLBF SPet
'Waveney Sunrise'	CSil MJac MWar MWhe SPet
'Waveney Valley'	EBak MJac
'Waveney Waltz'	EBak EFpt MJac MWar
'Wee Lass'	CSil
'Welsh Dragon' (d)	CLoc EBak WGwG WP&B
'Wendy'	Catt see *F.* 'Snowcap'
'Wendy Atkinson' (d)	EKMF
'Wendy Harris' (d)	MJac

'Wendy Leedham' (d)	ECtt EKMF
'Wendy van Wanten'	EPts WP&B
'Wendy's Beauty' (d)	CLoc EPts MJac WP&B
'Wessex Hardy' **new**	CSil EKMF
'Westham'	LCla
'Westminster Chimes' (d)	CLoc CSil EFpt MWhe SPet
'Wharfedale'	CSil MJac
'Whirlaway' (d)	CLoc CSil EBak EKMF
'White Clove'	CDoC CSil LCla WGwG
'White Galore' (d)	EBak EKMF EMan LVER SPet
'White General Monk' (d)	CDoC CSil
'White Gold' (v)	EBak
'White Heidi Ann' (d)	CSil MWhe SSea WGwG
'White Joy'	EBak
'White King' (d)	CLoc CSil EBak EFpt EKMF EMan LVER MJac MWar MWhe SPet SWal WP&B
'White Lace'	CSil
'White Lady Patricia Mountbatten'	EMan
'White Loeky'	WP&B
'White Pixie' ♀ H3-4	CDoC CSil EKMF EPts LCla LVER MJac NDlv SPer SPet WP&B
'White Pixie Wagtail'	see F. 'Wagtails White Pixie'
'White Queen' Doyle	CSil EBak MWhe
'White Spider'	CLoc CSil EBak MWhe SPet SSea
'Whiteknights Amethyst'	CDoC CSil EKMF WBcn WGwG
'Whiteknights Blush'	CMdw CSil EVFa GCal GQui SMrm WBcn
'Whiteknights Cheeky'	CSil EBak LCla WGwG
'Whiteknights Gem' **new**	EFpt
'Whiteknights Green Glister'	CDoC CSil EKMF
'Whiteknights Pearl' ♀ H1+3	CDoC CSil ECha ECtt EKMF EPts LCla MHdf SLBF SPet WGwG
'Whiteknights Ruby'	CSil EKMF LCla WP&B
'Whitton Starburst'	LCla
'Wicked Queen' (d)	CSil
'Wigan Pier' (d)	LCla MWar SLBF
'Wight Magic' (d)	MJac
'Wild and Beautiful' (d)	EKMF SPet
'Wilf Langton'	MWar
'Wilfred C. Dodson'	WP&B
'Wilhelmina Schwab' **new**	LCla
'Will van Brakel' **new**	WP&B
'William Caunt'	EKMF
'William Jay' (d)	WP&B
'Willy Winky'	CSil
'Wilma Versloot'	WP&B
'Wilson's Colours'	EPts
'Wilson's Joy'	MJac WP&B
'Wilson's Pearls' (d)	LAco SLBF SPet WGwG
'Wilson's Sugar Pink'	EPts LCla MJac MWhe
'Win Oxtoby' (d)	EKMF
'Wine and Roses' (d)	EBak
'Wingrove's Mammoth' (d)	CSil
'Wings of Song' (d)	CSil EBak
'Winston Churchill' (d) ♀ H3	CLoc CSil EBak EFpt EKMF EMan EPts LCla LVER MBri MHFa MJac MWar MWhe NVic SPet SPlb SSea SWal WLow WP&B
'Winter's Touch'	EKMF
'Woodnook' (d)	CSil
'Woodside' (d)	CSil
wurdackii	CSil EKMF
'Ymkje'	LCla
'Yolanda Franck'	CDoC CSil
'Yuletide' (d)	CSil
'Yvonne Schwab'	LCla
'Zara'	CSil MWhe WP&B
'Zellertal' **new**	WP&B
'Zets Bravo'	WGwG
'Ziegfield Girl' (d)	EBak

'Zulu King'	CSil
'Zulu Queen'	WP&B
'Zwarte Dit'	WP&B
'Zwarte Snor' (d)	WP&B

Fumaria (Papaveraceae)

lutea	see *Corydalis lutea*
officinalis	MSal

Furcraea (Agavaceae)

bedinghausii	CFil EOas WMul WPGP
longaeva	CAbb CCtw CHEx CPne CTrC CTrF EAmu EBee EOas MOak SAPC SArc WPGP
selloa var. *marginata* (v)	CDoC CHEx

G

Gagea (Liliaceae)

lutea	EPot
pratensis	EPot

Gahnia (Cyperaceae)

filum **new**	GGar

Gaillardia (Asteraceae)

aristata hort.	see *G.* x *grandiflora*
- 'Maxima Aurea'	EMan MCAu
'Bijou' **new**	EBee NDlv
'Bremen'	EBee EPfP LRHS NNor NPri
'Burgunder'	More than 30 suppliers
'Dazzler' ♀ H4	CHar CSBt CWCL EBee ECtt ELan EMan ENot EPfP ERou GKir LRHS MAvo MBri MCAu NFor NLar NVic SPer WGor WPer WStI
'Dwarf Goblin' **new**	WWeb
§ 'Fackelschein'	SRms SWal WHer
Goblin	see *G.* 'Kobold'
§ 'Goldkobold'	ELan EPar ERou MHer
§ x *grandiflora*	MHdf SMac WWeb
- 'Aurea'	LRHS WWeb
- 'Aurea Plena' (d)	EBee
§ 'Kobold'	CBcs COlW CSBt CSam EBre ECtt ENot EPfP ERou GKir LPVe LRHS MBri MHer NBlu SCoo SMac SOkh SPer SPla SPlb SRms STes SWal WFar WLin WWin
'Mandarin'	EBre LRHS SRms
* new giant hybrids	WFar WMoo
'Tokajer'	EBee EPfP MCAu NLar
Torchlight	see *G.* 'Fackelschein'
'Wirral Flame'	EPar
Yellow Goblin	see *G.* 'Goldkobold'

Galactites (Asteraceae)

tomentosa	CRDP CSpe EHrv ELan EMan EMar LDai LHrt LRHS NBur NDov SGar WBea WCot WEas WHrl WWye
- white **new**	CPla

Galanthus ✿ (Amaryllidaceae)

G71	CAvo
WM 9809 from Croatia	MPhe
WM 9817 from Bosnia	MPhe
x *allenii*	CAvo CBro EMor
alpinus	CLAP LAma
'Anglesey Abbey'	EMor NGar
'Anne of Geierstein'	EMor
'Armine'	CAvo EMor

'Athenae'	CBro
'Atkinsii' ♀ H4	CAvo CBro CElw CLAP EMon
	EMor EOrc EPar EPot GDra LAma
	MBri MRav NBir NGar SChr
	WPGP WRus WShi WWye
'Augustus'	CAvo CBel CFee EHyt EMor ERos
	WIvy
'Barbara's Double' (d)	CAvo EMor NGar
'Benhall Beauty'	CAvo EMor
'Benton Magnet'	EMor
'Bertram Anderson'	EMor NGar
'Bitton'	CBro CLAP NGar WRus WTin
bortkewitschianus	CBro
'Brenda Troyle'	CBel CBro CLAP EPar EPot NGar
	WIvy WRus
byzantinus	see *G. plicatus* subsp. *byzantinus*
cabardensis	see *G. transcaucasicus*
caucasicus hort.	see *G. elwesii* var. *monostictus*
- var. *hiemalis*	see *G. elwesii* var. *monostictus*
	'Hiemalis'
caucasicus (Bak.) Grossh.	CAvo CBro ECha EHyt EMor
	LAma MTho NGar SIng
- 'Comet'	see *G. elwesii* 'Comet'
- 'Green Tips'	NGar
- 'John Tomlinson'	see *G. elwesii* 'John Tomlinson'
- late-flowering	LRHS
- 'Mrs McNamara'	see *G. elwesii* 'Mrs McNamara'
'Charmer Flore Pleno' (d)	CBro EMor
'Clare Blakeway-Phillips'	EMor NGar
'Colesbourne'	EMor
'Colossus'	CAvo
corcyrensis	see *G. reginae-olgae* subsp. *vernalis*
spring-flowering	
- winter-flowering	see *G. reginae-olgae* subsp. *reginae-*
	olgae Winter-flowering Group
'Cordelia' (d)	EMon EMor EPot
'Curly'	EMor
'David Shackleton'	EMor
'Desdemona'	CLAP EPot WCot WIvy
'Dionysus' (d)	CAvo CBro CLAP EHyt EMor EOrc
	EPot ERos MDri NBir NGar WRus
'Edinburgh Ketton'	EMor
§ *elwesii* ♀ H4	CAvo CBel CBro CFwr EBee ELan
	EMon EMor EOrc EPot ERos LAma
	LRHS MBri NBir NGar NMen NRog
	SRms WCot WIvy WShi
§ - 'Comet'	EMor NGar
- 'Fenstead End'	NGar
- 'Flore Pleno' (d)	CAvo
§ - 'John Tomlinson'	EMor
- 'Kyre Park' **new**	EMon
- 'Magnus'	CLAP
§ - var. *monostictus* ♀ H4	EMon
§ - - 'Hiemalis'	CBro ECha EMon EMor LAma
	WCot
§ - 'Mrs McNamara'	EMor
§ - 'Ransom's Dwarf'	EMor
- 'Selborne Green	EMon
Tips' **new**	
§ - 'Washfield Colesbourne'	EMor
- var. *whitallii*	CLAP
- 'Zwanenburg'	EMon NGar
'Falkland House'	EMor
'Fieldgate Superb'	EMor
* 'Finale'	ECha
fosteri	CAvo CBro EHyt LAma LRHS
- PD 256830	EMor
'Foxton'	EMor
'G.F. Handel'	LAma
'Galatea'	CLAP EMon EMor LRHS NGar WIvy
§ *gracilis*	CBro CLAP EMor EPar ERos MTho
	WIvy WRus
- 'Corkscrew'	EMor

- 'Highdown'	EHyt
graecus hort.	see *G. gracilis*
- Orph. ex Boiss.	see *G. elwesii*
'Grayling'	EMor
Greatorex double (d)	CLAP EMon SSvw
'H. Purcell'	LAma
'Heffalump'	EMor
'Hill Poë' (d)	CAvo CBel CBro EMor EPar GCrs
	NGar
'Hippolyta' (d)	CAvo CBro CElw CLAP ECha
	EMor EPar EPot WIvy
'Icicle'	EMor
ikariae	CElw EHyt EOrc EPar EPot ERos
	GKev LAma
- subsp. *ikariae*	EMor
Butt's form	
- Latifolius Group	see *G. platyphyllus*
'Imbolc'	EMor
'J. Haydn'	LAma
'Jacquenetta' (d)	CBro CLAP EMor EPot WPGP
'John Gray'	CBel CBro EMon EMor GCrs
	NGar
'Ketton'	CAvo CBro CElw EMor GCrs
	LRHS WIvy
'Kingston Double' (d)	CLAP
'Kite'	CBro EMor
'Lady Beatrix Stanley' (d)	CBro CLAP ECha EMon EMor
	EPar EPot ERos LAma LRHS MTho
	NGar NHar
§ *lagodechianus*	CAvo
latifolius	see *G. platyphyllus*
'Lavinia' (d)	CAvo CElw WRus
'Lime Tree'	CBel CLAP
'Little Dorrit'	EMor
lutescens	see *G. nivalis* 'Sandersii'
'Magnet' ♀ H4	CAvo CBel CBro CFee CLAP EMor
	EPot LAma NGar NHar WCot
	WPGP WRus
'Maidwell C'	EMor
'Maidwell L'	CAvo EMor
'Merlin'	CAvo CBel EMor EOrc IGor NGar
	NHar WIvy WRus
'Mighty Atom'	CBel CFee EMor
'Modern Art'	EMor
'Mrs Thompson'	EMor NGar WIvy
'Mrs Wrightson's	EMor
Double' (d)	
'Nerissa' (d)	EPot
nivalis ♀ H4	CBro CKin CNic ELan EMor EPar
	EPfP EPot ETub GDra LAma LRHS
	MBow MBri NGar NRog SHFr
	SRms WCot WFar WShi
- JRM 3139	EMor
- var. *angustifolius*	CBro
- 'Blonde Inge'	EMor
- 'Dreycot Greentip'	NGar
- 'Flavescens'	CBro
- 'Flore Pleno' (d) ♀ H4	CBro CFwr CStu EDrc EPar EPfP
	EPla EPot ETub GDra LAma LRHS
	NGar NMGW NRog NRya SRms
	WCot WFar WGwG WHen WShi
	WWye
- 'Greenish'	EMor
- 'Hambutt's Orchard'	EMor
- subsp. *imperati*	EHyt
- - 'Ginns'	CLAP EMor WRus
- 'Lady Elphinstone' (d)	CAvo CBro CRow EMor EPar EPot
	GCrs LAma MRav MTho NGar
	NHar
- 'Lutescens'	see *G. nivalis* 'Sandersii'
- 'Pewsey Vale' (d)	EMor
- Poculiformis Group	EMon NGar
- - 'Sandhill Gate' (d)	EMor NGar

– 'Pusey Green Tip' (d)	CAvo CBro CElw CLAP EMor EPar EPot GCrs NGar SIgm WPGP
– 'Rushmere Green'	EMor
§ – 'Sandersii'	CBro CRDP EMor EPot NGar SSpi
– 'Savill Gold'	EMor
– Scharlockii Group	CAvo CBel CBro EHyt EMon EMor EOrc LAma NGar NHar SBla
– 'Sibbertoft White'	EMor
– 'Tiny'	NGar
– 'Tiny Tim'	EPot NPar NRya
§ – 'Virescens'	CLAP EMor
– 'Viridapicis'	CAvo CBro CFwr ECha EHyt EMor EPar EPot LAma LRHS NGar NMen SIgm WCot WIvy WPGP WRus WShi
– 'Walrus' (d)	EMor NGar
– 'Warei'	EMor NGar
§ – 'Wonston Double'	EMor
'Ophelia' (d)	CAvo CBel CBro EMor EOrc EPar NGar NPar WRus
* 'Paradise Double'	EPar
* 'Paradise Giant'	EPar
'Peg Sharples'	EMor
§ *platyphyllus*	CBro EMor EOrc LAma NGar
plicatus ♀ H4	CFee EMon NGar SScr WShi
– 'Baxendale's Late'	EMor
– 'Bowles' Large'	ERos
§ – subsp. *byzantinus*	CAvo CBro EHyt EMor EOrc EPar ERos
– – LP 17	EMor
– – early-flowering	WIvy
– – 'Sophie North'	GCrs
– – 'Three Ships'	EMor
– – 'Trym'	EMor
– 'Colossus'	CBel
– 'Gerard Parker'	EMor
– large	EOrc
– 'Ron Ginns'	NGar
– 'Warham'	CAvo CBro EMor EOrc EPot NHar WPGP
– 'Wendy's Gold'	EMon EMor GCrs
'Primrose Warburg'	EMor
'Ransom's Dwarf'	see *G. elwesii* 'Ransom's Dwarf'
reginae-olgae	CBro EHyt EMor ERos LAma MRav NGar SIng SSpi WCom WCot
– WM 9901	MPhe
– WM 9908	MPhe
– subsp. *reginae-olgae* 'Cambridge'	EMor NGar
§ – – Winter-flowering Group	CBro EMor LAma
§ – subsp. *vernalis*	EMon EMor GCrs LRHS
– – AJM 75	EMor
rizehensis	CBro WIvy
'Robin Hood'	CFee EHyt EMor ERos GCrs NGar
'S. Arnott' ♀ H4	CAvo CBel CBro CElw CFwr CLAP ECha EMor EPar EPot LAma NBir NGar NHar NMen SBla SIgm WCom WPGP
'Sally Passmore'	CAvo
'Scharlockii'	see *G. nivalis* Scharlockii Group
'Shaggy' new	EHyt
'St Anne's'	WIvy
'Straffan'	CAvo CBel CBro EHyt EMor EOrc EPar EPot LAma LRHS NGar NHar WRus
'The Linns'	GCrs
'The Pearl'	EMor
'Three Leaves'	EMor
'Titania' (d)	CBro EMor NGar
§ *transcaucasicus*	EMon
'Trotter's Merlin'	EMor
'Tubby Merlin'	CAvo EMor

'Warley Belles'	NGar
'Warley Duo'	NGar
'Warley Longbow'	NGar
'Washfield Colesbourne'	see *G. elwesii* 'Washfield Colesbourne'
'Washfield Warham'	EMon LRHS
'Winifrede Mathias'	EMor
'Wonston Double'	see *G. nivalis* 'Wonston Double'
woronowii ♀ H4	CAvo CBel CBro CFwr CLAP EMon ETow LAma

Galax (Diapensiaceae)

aphylla	see *G. urceolata*
§ *urceolata*	CMac EBee IBlr SSpi

Galega (Papilionaceae)

bicolor	IBlr MLLN NBir SCro SPar SRms SSth STes SWat WFar
'Duchess of Bedford'	CFir CFwr MAvo NCat SWat
x *hartlandii*	IBlr MGGn MRav WHoo WWhi
– 'Alba' ♀ H4	CFwr EFou EGle EHrv EMar EMon EWes GBar GBri GCal IBlr LPhx MArl MAvo MBri NBro NDov SAga SMHy SOkh SWat WCom WCot WHoo WMaN WPer WWhi
– 'Lady Wilson' ♀ H4	CPlt CPom EBee ECtt EGle EMan EWes MArl MAvo MRav NDov WCom WCot WElm WFoF WHoo WPen
– 'Spring Light' (v) new	EMan EWes
'Her Majesty'	see *G.* 'His Majesty'
§ 'His Majesty'	EBee EGle EMan GBri MArl MAvo MBro MRav SAga SWat WBea WBry WCot WFar WHoo WMaN WPGP
officinalis	More than 30 suppliers
– 'Alba' ♀ H4	CBot CHad CMGP CMdw COIW CPom CPrp CStr EBee ECtt EGle ELan ELau EMan EPfP ITer MBrN MCLN MHer MWrn WBea WCHb WFar WHer WHrl WMoo WRus WWye
orientalis	CDes EBee GCal LPhx LRHS MArl MAvo MLLN MRav MWrn SMac SWat WAbb WCom WCot WMoo WPGP

Galeobdolon see *Lamium*

Galium (Rubiaceae)

aristatum	EMan MLLN NCat WCot
boreale	IIve
cruciata	see *Cruciata laevipes*
mollugo	CArn CKin MSal NSco WCHb
§ *odoratum*	More than 30 suppliers
palustre	CKin
saxatile	IIve
verum	CAgr CArn CKin CPLG GDea GPoy GWCH IIve MBow MChe MGas MHer MSal NLan NMir NSco SIde WCHb WHbs WHer

Galtonia (Hyacinthaceae)

§ *candicans* ♀ H4	More than 30 suppliers
princeps	CAvo CBri CBro CPLG EBee EBre ECha ERos ERou GBuc LPio SMac WBro
regalis	EBee GCal GEdr LPio WCot
viridiflora	CAvo CBcs CBot CBri CBro CFwr CHar EBre EChP ECha ELan ERos GCal GEdr GKir LAst LRHS MNrw NBid NWCA SAga SIgm WFar WLin

Gamolepis see *Steirodiscus*

Gardenia (Rubiaceae)

augusta	see *G. jasminoides*
florida L.	see *G. jasminoides*
globosa	see *Rothmannia globosa*
grandiflora	see *G. jasminoides*
jasminoides ♀ H1	EBak ELau EPfP LRHS MBri
thunbergia	EShb

garlic see *Allium sativum*

Garrya ✿ (Garryaceae)

elliptica	CBcs EBee EBre EMui ENot GKir ISea LPan LRHS MBri MGos NFor NHol NPSI NWea SPar SPet SPlb SRPl SReu WCru WFar WHar WPat WStl WWin
- (f)	MBro WPat
- (m)	CDoC CSBt EHol NBlu SLim WBod WFar WGwG
- 'James Roof' (m) ♀ H4	More than 30 suppliers
fremontii	NLar SMer WLRN
x *issaquahensis*	CAbP CDoC CPMA EBee ELan
'Glasnevin Wine'	EPfP IMGH LRHS MBlu MBri NHol NSti SMur SPer SSta WFar WWeb
- 'Pat Ballard' (m)	CPMA ELan EPfP LRHS NHol NLar SPar SPer WWeb
x *thuretii*	MGos WFar

Garuleum (Asteraceae)

woodii JCA 324000	CPBP

Gasteria ✿ (Aloaceae)

liliputana	EPem
* *multipluncata*	EPem
verrucosa	EPem

x *Gaulnettya* see *Gaultheria*

Gaultheria ✿ (Ericaceae)

SF 276	ISea
adenothrix	EPot
antipoda	SSta
cardiosepala new	GEdr
cumingiana B&SWJ 1542	WCru
cuneata ♀ H4	EPot GDra GEdr GKev LRHS MAsh MBar NDlv NLAp SSta
- 'Pinkie'	GKir LRHS
§ *eriophylla*	SReu
furiens	see *G. insana*
'Glenroy Maureen'	MCCP
glomerata var. *petraea*	SSta
hookeri	IBlr
§ *insana*	WPic
itoana	GEdr MBar NDlv NLAp
'Jingle Bells' new	MGos
miqueliana	MGos MMHG NLAp
mucronata	CMHG EBee EPfP MBar NWea WDin
- (m)	CDoC CTri CWSG ENot EPfP GKir LAst MAsh MBar MBri MGos MRav NBlu NHol SPer SPoG SRms WWeb
- RB 94095	GTou
- 'Alba' (f)	MAsh MBar MGos MRav SLon
- 'Bell's Seedling' (f/m) ♀ H4	CChe CDoC CTri CWSG EPfP GGar GKir LRHS MAsh MGos SHBN SPer SPoG SReu SSta WWeb
- 'Cherry Ripe' (f)	GKir SHBN
- 'Crimsonia' (f) ♀ H4	CBcs CChe EPfP GKir LRHS MAsh MBar MDun MGos SHBN SPer SReu SRms
- 'Indian Lake'	NHol
- 'Lilacina' (f)	MGos WGwG
- 'Lilian' (f)	CWSG ENot EPfP GKir GSki LAst SHBN WLRN
- Mother of Pearl	see *G. mucronata* 'Parelmoer'
- 'Mulberry Wine' (f) ♀ H4	EPfP GKir LRHS NHol SPoG
- 'October Red' (f)	NHol
§ - 'Parelmoer' (f)	CBcs CBrm ENot EPfP GKir LAst SPer SPoG
- 'Pink Pearl' (f) ♀ H4	MAsh SRms WLRN
- 'Rosalind' (f)	WWeb
- 'Rosea' (f)	MBar MGos
- 'Rosie' (f)	SBod
§ - 'Signaal' (f)	CBrm CDoC EBee ENot EPfP GKir GWCH LRHS MGos SPer WLRN
- Signal	see *G. mucronata* 'Signaal'
§ - 'Sneeuwwitje' (f)	CChe CWSG EBee ENot EPfP GKir GSki LRHS SHBN SPer
- Snow White	see *G. mucronata* 'Sneeuwwitje'
- 'Stag River' (f)	GDra MGos
- 'Thymifolia' (m)	CChe EPfP SHBN
- 'White Pearl' (f)	GKir WLRN
- 'Wintertime' (f) ♀ H4	CBrm MGos SRms WWeb
* *mucronifolia* new	NWCA
nummularioides	GDra GEdr NHol SReu
§ - var. *elliptica*	SSta
- 'Minuta'	see *G. nummularioides* var. *elliptica*
§ *parvula*	GCrs
'Pearls'	GCrs WAbe WOBN
phillyreifolia	CMHG SSta WPic
'Pink Champagne'	SSta
poeppigii	ITim
* - *racemosa*	SSta
procumbens ♀ H4	More than 30 suppliers
pumila	GCrs LEdu MBar MGos NHol NMen
- 'E.K. Balls'	NHol
pyroloides	GCrs
shallon	CBcs CDoC CSBt EBee ENot EWTr GBar GKir MBar MDun MGos SBrw SHBN SPer SRms WDin WFar
tasmanica	ECou GCrs GDra MBar WAbe
thymifolia	LAst SReu
willisiana	see *G. eriophylla*
x *wisleyensis*	LRHS MAsh MNes SKms SSta
- 'Pink Pixie'	CMHG EPfP GKir LRHS MAsh MBar MCCP MGos SBrw SIng SPer SSta
- 'Wisley Pearl'	CBcs CDoC GDra GGar GKir IBlr LAst MBar MGos NHar SBrw SPer SReu
yunnanensis	SReu

Gaura (Onagraceae)

lindheimeri ♀ H4	More than 30 suppliers
- compact pink new	WCot
- compact red new	CSpe
- 'Corrie's Gold' (v)	More than 30 suppliers
- 'Crimson Butterfly' new	COtt SPoG WWeb
- 'Jo Adela' (v)	EBee ELan EMan EPfP
- 'Madonna' new	CSpe EBee
- 'Passionate Pink' new	WWeb
- 'Pink Fountain' new	WWeb
- short	CSpe EMar SGar
- 'Siskiyou Pink'	More than 30 suppliers
- 'The Bride'	EBee EFou EMar LRHS MArl NGdn SCoo SMrm SPla STes SWal WHil
- 'Val's Pink' new	WHoo
- 'Whirling Butterflies'	CHar CKno CMGP CSpe EBee ECtt EMan EMil ENot EPfP IBal LAst LPio MLLN MTis NPri SAsh

	SBod SDes SIng SMad SMrm SPar SWat WMnd
- 'White Spray' **new**	WWeb
longiflora **new**	EShb

Gaussia (Arecaceae)

maya	LPal

Gaylussacia (Ericaceae)

brachycera	GGGa

Gazania (Asteraceae)

'Aztec' ♀ H1+3	CHal CWib LRHS SUsu
'Bicton Cream'	CHal
'Bicton Orange'	LRHS
'Blackberry Ripple'	COIW EBee LAst NCiC SAga SCoo
'Blaze of Fire'	LRHS
'Christopher'	CHal MOak MSte NCiC SAga SCoo
I 'Christopher Lloyd' **new**	LAst
'Circus'	LRHS
'Cookei' ♀ H1+3	CSpe MSte SAga WCot WEas
'Cornish Pixie'	CHal
cream	CHal NCiC
'Cream Beauty'	LRHS MSte
'Cream Dream'	LAst MOak
Daybreak Series	LPVe
- 'Daybreak Bronze'	MLan
'Dorothy' ♀ H1+3	LRHS MOak
double bronze	CHal
double yellow	see *G.* 'Yellow Buttons'
'Evening Sun'	LRHS
'Flash'	WEas
'Freddie'	SMrm
'Garden Sun'	MLan
Gazoo Series **new**	WWeb
* *grayi*	CHal
* 'Hazel'	LRHS MSte
(Kiss Series) 'Kiss Bronze Star'	LIck
I - 'Kiss Pomegranate' **new**	LIck
- 'Kiss Yellow'	LIck
linearis RMRP 95-0283	ETow
- 'Colorado Gold' **new**	CFir
'Magic'	LAst LRHS NPri SCoo WWol
'Michael' ♀ H1+3	LRHS
Mini Star Series	CBrm
'Northbourne' ♀ H1+3	GGar MSte
'Orange Beauty'	ELan LRHS
'Red Velvet'	CSpe MSte SAga
§ *rigens*	LRHS MBri
- 'Aureovariegata' (v)	SAga
- var. *uniflora* ♀ H1+3	MSte
- - 'Variegata' (v)	CBot
- 'Variegata' (v) ♀ H1+3	ELan LAst MOak
'Silver Beauty'	CBot LRHS
'Silverbrite'	CHal
splendens	see *G. rigens*
'Talent'	CHal
'Tiger'	LRHS
§ 'Yellow Buttons' (d)	LRHS

Geissorhiza (Iridaceae)

imbricata	CStu
secunda **new**	WCot

Gelasine (Iridaceae)

azurea	see *G. coerulea*
§ *coerulea*	CPLG EBee EMan WCot

Gelidocalamus (Poaceae)

fangianus	see *Drepanostachyum microphyllum*

Gelsemium (Loganiaceae)

rankinii	CPIN WCot
sempervirens ♀ H1-2	CArn CMCN CPIN ERea EShb IDee SOWG
- 'Flore Pleno' (d)	CPIN ERea
- 'Pride of Augusta'	CMCN

Genista (Papilionaceae)

aetnensis ♀ H4	CBcs CEnd CHEx CMCN CSBt EBee ECrN ELan ENot EPfP LRHS MBri MDun MLan MRav MWat SAPC SArc SDix SHBN SMad SPar SPer SRms SSpi SSta WDin WPGP WSHC
§ *canariensis*	CPLG CSBt CWib ERea WBrE
cinerea	WCFE
decumbens	see *Cytisus decumbens*
delphinensis	see *G. sagittalis* subsp. *delphinensis*
'Emerald Spreader'	see *G. pilosa* 'Yellow Spreader'
fragrans	see *G. canariensis*
hispanica	CBcs CSBt CTri EBee EBre ELan ENot EPfP GKir LRHS MBar MGos MWat SHBN SLim SPer SRms WAbe WCFE WDin WFar WGwG WHar WStI WTel WWeb
- 'Compacta'	ESis
humifusa	see *G. pulchella*
lydia ♀ H4	CBcs CChe CSBt CWSG EBee EBre ELan ENot EPfP GKir LAst LRHS MBar MGos MRav MWat NBee NHol SHBN SLim SPer SReu SRms SSta WBod WDin WFar WHar WWeb
maderensis **new**	WPic
monosperma	see *Retama monosperma*
pilosa	CTri ENot EPot ISea MBar MDun MWhi NHar NMen SPer WBVN WWin
- 'Goldilocks'	NHar
- 'Lemon Spreader'	see *G. pilosa* 'Yellow Spreader'
* - *major*	GDra NMen
- var. *minor*	GKir GTou IMGH NLon NMen WAbe
- 'Procumbens'	CMea GDra MDKP WPat
- 'Vancouver Gold'	CBcs CSBt EBee ELan ENot EPfP LRHS MAsh MGos MNrw MRav NHar NPro SRPl SRms WDin WFar WGor
§ - 'Yellow Spreader'	CBcs CMHG CSBt EHol GEdr IArd WBod WWeb
§ 'Porlock' ♀ H3	CBcs CDoC CSPN CWCL CWSG ELan MRav SEND SPar SPla WDin WStI WWeb
§ *pulchella*	CTri SBla
sagittalis	CPLG CTri EPfP GEil IKee LHop NBir NFor NLon NWoo SBla SLon SPer WBVN
§ - subsp. *delphinensis* ♀ H4	GDra NMen
- *minor*	see *G. sagittalis* subsp. *delphinensis*
§ x *spachiana* ♀ H1	CTri GEil
tenera 'Golden Shower'	SLPl
tinctoria	CAgr CArn CKin GBar GPoy GWCH ILis MChe MHer MSal NFor NLon SIde WHer WWye
- 'Flore Pleno' (d) ♀ H4	CLyd MGos NHar NMen NPro SRot WWeb
- 'Humifusa'	EPot GEdr NHar
- 'Moesiaca'	ITim
- var. *prostrata*	LBee

- 'Royal Gold' ♀ H4	CWSG CWib EBee ENot EPfP MGos MRav SHBN SPer SPlb WBod WWeb
villarsii	see *G. pulchella*

Gentiana

§ *acaulis* ♀ H4	More than 30 suppliers
- f. *alba*	WLin
- 'Alboviolacea' **new**	NHar
- Andorra form	GDra
- 'Belvedere'	NMen WAbe
- 'Coelestina'	EHyt EPot GCrs
- 'Dinarica'	see *G. dinarica*
- 'Krumrey'	EHyt EPot
- 'Max Frei'	GCrs
- *occidentalis*	see *G. occidentalis*
- 'Rannoch'	EPot NMen
- 'Trotter's Variety'	EPot
- 'Undulatifolia'	EPot WLin
- 'Velkokvensis'	EHyt
'Amethyst'	GCrs GDra NHar NLAp SIng WAbe WLin
angustifolia	GCrs
- Frei hybrid **new**	WLin
'Ann's Special'	GCrs GKir NHar
asclepiadea ♀ H4	More than 30 suppliers
- var. *alba*	CBot CFil CHea CLyd EBee GAbr GBuc GMac LRHS MBri MBro MDKP MTho NChi NHar SPer SRms WCom WCru WHoo
- 'Hoo House'	WHoo
- 'Knightshayes'	EBee NCat NLAp WCom WHoo
- pale blue	CFil WPGP
- 'Phyllis'	GBuc MBro WCom WHoo
- 'Pink Cascade'	SIgm
- 'Pink Swallow' **new**	WHil
- 'Rosea'	GAbr GBuc NMrw NChi NHar WHoo
- yellow-flowered **new**	ELan
atuntsiensis	GKev
SDR 1923 **new**	
'Barbara Lyle'	WAbe
bavarica var. *subacaulis*	SPlb
'Bellatrix Extra' **new**	NHar
bellidifolia	GTou
x *bernardii*	see *G.* × *stevenagensis* 'Bernardii'
bisetaea	SRms
'Blauer Diamant'	GCrs NHar
'Blauer Zwerg'	NHar
'Blue Flame'	GCrs GDra NHar WAbe
'Blue Heaven'	GDra
'Blue Sea'	NHar
'Blue Shell'	NHar
'Blue Silk'	EWes GCrs NHar NLAp SBla WAbe
burseri	NChi SSpi
§ - var. *villarsii*	EBee GIBF
N *cachemirica*	EBee GTou WPat
'Cairngorm'	CWCL EWes GCrs GEdr GKir NDlv NHar SUsu
calycosa NNS 96-109	NWCA
x *caroli*	NHar SBla WAbe
'Christine Jean'	GTou NDlv NHar SIng
clausa **new**	GIBF
clusii	EPot GCrs ITim NLAp WAbe
- *alba*	GCrs
* - *alboviolacea*	WLin
- subsp. *costei*	WAbe
- purple	CNic
coelestis CLD 1087	GCrs
'Compact Gem'	EPot GCrs NHar NLAp WAbe WOld
corymbifera	GCrs
crassicaulis	EBee

§ *cruciata*	EBee GTou MTho NLAp
- subsp. *phlogifolia*	GIBF
§ *dahurica*	EBee EPfP GCal LRHS NLAp SBla
'Dark Hedgehog'	GCrs GEdr
decumbens	CSam EPot GCal WLin
depressa	EPot MTho WAbe
'Devonhall'	GEdr
§ *dinarica*	CLyd EHyt MTho WAbe
Drake's strain	GDra GEdr GKir LRHS
'Dumpy'	CPBP EPot GEdr NHar WAbe WOBN WPat
'Dusk'	GDra NHar
'Elizabeth'	EWes GCrs GEdr MOne NDlv NHar WAbe
'Eugen's Bester' **new**	NHar
farreri	EWes GKir NSla WAbe
- Hybrids	GDra
'Fasta Highlands'	NBir
fetissowii	EBee
freyniana	SOkd
gelida	GAbr
Glamis strain	GCrs GEdr GMaP NDlv NHar
'Glen Isla'	EWes MOne NHar
'Glen Moy'	MOne
§ *gracilipes*	ECho GEdr LRHS MWat NLAp SPlb SRms
- 'Yuatensis'	see *G. wutaiensis*
grossheimii	GIBF WWin
x *hascombensis*	see *G. septemfida* var. *lagodechiana* 'Hascombensis'
'Henry'	WAbe
x *hexafarreri*	CWCL NHar
Inshriach hybrids	GDra GMaP MOne NHar NHol
'Inverleith' ♀ H4	CWCL EDAr EWes GEdr GKir IHMH MBri MBro MOne NHar NHol SPlb WGor WOld WPat
'John Aitken'	GCrs
'Juwel'	NHar
'Kirriemuir'	EWes GCrs NDlv
kochiana	see *G. acaulis*
kurroo	WPat
- var. *brevidens*	see *G. dahurica*
lagodechiana	see *G. septemfida* var. *lagodechiana*
linearis	EBee
lucerna	CWCL GCrs GEdr GKir NHar NLAp SUsu
lutea	EBee GCal GDra GIBF GKir GPoy NChi NHar NSla SDix SRms WAul WCot WHil WLin WWye
x *macaulayi* ♀ H4	CPla EDAr GCrs GEdr GKir MBri MBro NHol SIng SRms WHoo WOld
- 'Edinburgh' ♀ H4	GCrs GEdr
- 'Flata'	GCrs MBri NDlv NHar
- 'Kidbrooke Seedling'	CTri CWCL EDAr EWes GCrs GEdr GKir GMaP GTou MOne NHar NLAp NRya WAbe
- 'Kingfisher'	CPla CTri CWCL EDAr GDra GEdr GKir MOne NBir NFor NHar NLAp NMen SBla SBod SIng WAbe
§ - 'Praecox'	CWCL EDAr GCrs GEdr GKir GTou MBri NDlv NHar NLAp WOBN
§ - 'Wells's Variety'	GEdr MBri
makinoi	GCrs NWCA
- 'Royal Blue'	MMHG
'Margaret'	WAbe
'Maryfield'	GEdr
melandriifolia	WAbe
- ACE 2515	EPot
'Merlin'	GCrs
'Multiflora'	CWCL GCrs GEdr NLAp
* *nepaulensis*	GIBF
nipponica	EBee GIBF

§ *occidentalis*	EPot GCrs
Olga's pale	GCrs
olivieri	EHyt
orbicularis **new**	SOkd
oreodoxa	GCrs GTou
paradoxa	CLyd GAbr GCrs GEdr ITim NDlv NHar NSla SBla SIgm SOkd WAbe WLin WPat
– 'Blauer Herold'	GCal
phlogifolia	see *G. cruciata*
platypetala	GCrs SOkd
pneumonanthe	GIBF SPlb SSpi
prolata	GCrs ITim SOkd WAbe
– CC 2650	WOBN
przewalskii	CBrm GIBF WWin
punctata	EBee
purdomii	see *G. gracilipes*
purpurea	GCal GIBF
robusta	CRDP ELan GAbr
'Robyn Lyle'	WAbe
'Royal Highlander'	GEdr NHar
'Saphir Select'	GEdr
saxosa	CLyd CPBP CRDP CWCL GCrs GEdr GKir GTou ITim MTho NBir NHar NLAp NMen SIgm SIng WAbe WLin
scabra	WWye
– 'Ishusuki'	SBla
'Sensation'	GEdr NHar
'Sensation Extra' **new**	NHar
septemfida ♀ H4	EHyt ELan EMNN EPot GDra GEdr GKir LBee LHop LRHS MBri MBro MHer MTho MWat NBir NLAp NRya SBla SIng SPlb SRms WCom WHoo WLin WPat
– 'Alba'	NBir WPat
§ – var. *lagodechiana* ♀ H4	CSam CWes EDAr EHyt GAbr GCal LPVe NLAp NWCA SRms
– – 'Doeringiana'	ECho NMen
§ – – 'Hascombensis'	ECho
'Serenity'	GEdr NHar NLAp WAbe
serotina	EHyt
setigera	GKir
'Shot Silk'	CWCL EDAr EWes GEdr GMaP NHar NLAp SUsu WAbe WWin
'Silken Skies'	WAbe
sino-ornata ♀ H4	CPla CTri CWCL EDAr GCrs GDra GEdr GGar GKir LRHS MBri NHar NHol NLAp NMen SBla SIng SRms WAbe WCom WFar WOld
– 'Alba'	CPla GDra GKir NHar NLAp WFar WWin
– 'Angel's Wings'	CWCL EDAr GCrs GEdr GKir GTou MBri NHar
– 'Bellatrix' **new**	NHar
– 'Blautopf' **new**	NHar
– 'Brin Form'	SBod SIng SRms WAbe
– 'Downfield'	GCrs MOne NDlv NHar NHol NLAp
– 'Edith Sarah'	GCrs GEdr MBri MOne NHar NHol SBla SRms WPat WWin
– 'Elizabeth Brand' **new**	NHar
– 'Igel' **new**	NHar
– 'Mary Lyle'	GEdr MBri MOne MTho NHar WAbe
– 'Oha' **new**	NHar
– 'Praecox'	see *G.* x *macaulayi* 'Praecox'
– 'Starlight' **new**	NHar
– 'Trogg's Form'	EWes GCrs MOne NDlv NHar NRya
– 'Weisser Traum' **new**	NHar
– 'White Wings'	EWes GCrs LRHS NDlv NHar
– 'Woolgreaves'	NHar
x *stevenagensis* ♀ H4	CLyd CPla CTri LRHS MBri NHar SIng
§ – 'Bernardii'	EDAr GEdr MBri SIng WAbe
– dark	MBro NHar WAbe WPat
– 'Frank Barker'	MBri WAbe
stragulata	GCrs GKev NLAp WAbe
straminea	GAbr MDKP WCot
'Strathmore' ♀ H4	CTri CWCL EDAr EHyt EWes GAbr GCrs GEdr GKir LRHS MBri MOne NHar NHol NLAp NRya SIng SPlb WAbe WOld WWin
'Suendermannii'	EHyt
'Susan Jane'	GTou
ternifolia	EDAr GCrs GDra
– 'Cangshan' ex SBEC 1053	GEdr NHar NLAp WAbe
– 'Dali' ex SBEC 1053	GEdr MBri MOne NBir NHar
tibetica	CPla EBee GAbr GCal GIBF GPoy IIve MNrw NBid SOkd WEas WTin WWye
trichotoma	WAbe
triflora	CDes GBuc GCrs WFar WPGP
– 'Alba'	GBuc GKir
– var. *japonica*	GBuc GCal
– 'Royal Blue'	GCal WCot
Tweeddale strain	GCrs GEdr
veitchiorum	MBri
– hybrids	GDra
verna	CPBP CWCL EHyt EWes GKir ITim LHop LRHS MBro MOne MTho NLAp NMen NRya NSla SBla SIng WAbe WBWf WCom WPat
– 'Alba'	CPBP MBro NHar WAbe WPat
§ – subsp. *balcanica*	CLyd ELan GCrs GTou MBro MTho NHar SRms WAbe WHoo WPat
– subsp. *oschtenica*	WAbe
– slate blue	MBro NHar WPat
§ – subsp. *tergestina*	EDAr
'Violette'	GCrs GEdr
waltonii	ECho EWes
'Wealdensis' **new**	NHar
wellsii	see *G.* x *macaulayi* 'Wells's Variety'
§ *wutaiensis*	ECho GAbr
yakushimensis	GCrs

Gentianella (Gentianaceae)

quinquefolia	IIve

Gentianopsis (Gentianaceae)

grandis SDR 1538 **new**	GKev

Geranium (Geraniaceae)

from Pamirs, Tadzhikistan	EBee EOrc EPPr WPnP
from Sikkim	NWCA
aconitifolium misapplied	see *G. palmatum*
aconitifolium L'Hér.	see *G. rivulare*
'Alan Mayes' **new**	EPPr SCou
albanum	CElw CMCo COlW CSev EBee EChP EGra EMan EMar EOrc EPPr GSki LLWP MNrw MTis NCot NSti SCou SDix SRGP STes SWal WCru WMoo WPnP WTMC WWpP
albiflorum	CBri CCge CMCo EBee EChP EPPr IMGH LRHS MNFA MWhe NCat SCou SDys WCru WMoo WPnP
anemonifolium	see *G. palmatum*
'Ann Folkard' ♀ H4	More than 30 suppliers
'Anne Thomson'	More than 30 suppliers
antrorsum	SDys
argenteum	WCru
aristatum	CDes CFwr CPou EBee EChP EMan EMar EOrc EPPr EWes

	MLwd MNFA MNrw MRav MSph NBir NCot SCou SRGP STes WCra WCru WFTG WHil WMoo WPGP WPer WPnP WTMC WWpP
– NS 649	NWCA
armenum	see *G. psilostemon*
asphodeloides	More than 30 suppliers
§ – subsp. *asphodeloides*	CCge EMan EOrc EPPr NCot
white	SRGP WFar WHen WMoo WRus WWpP
– 'Catforth Sam'	NCat
– subsp. *crenophilum*	CElw EBee NCot WWpP
– 'Prince Regent'	CHid CStr EGle EMan EPPr LPio MNFA NCat SBri WCra
– 'Starlight'	SHel
atlanticum Hook. f.	see *G. malviflorum*
'Aussie Gem' **new**	CCge MSte
'Aya' **new**	LPio
'Baby Blue'	see *G. himalayense* 'Baby Blue'
'Bertie Crûg'	CHid CKno CPBP CSpe EBee EGle EHrv EMan EMlt EPPr GBin LTwo NBir SCoo SDes SIng SRms SRot SScr SWat WCru WHoo Wlvy WPat WPnP WWeb WWpP
biflorum	EBee
biuncinatum	IFro MLwd SCou WWin
'Black Beauty' **new**	EBee
'Black Ice'	GBuc SHel WCru
'Blue Cloud'	CBos CElw CMea CSpe EBee ECGP EGle EPPr LPhx MAvo MTed MTis NBir NChi NCot NMRc SCou SHel SMrm SRGP SUsu WOut WPnP WTMC WWpP
'Blue Pearl'	EBee EPPr MMil NBir NHaw NSti SCou SHel SRGP SUsu SVil WCra WPnP WWpP
§ 'Blue Sunrise'	CCge CFwr EBee EBre EMan GKir LPio LRHS MCCP MCLN MSte MWhe NHaw NLar SAga SCou SPla WCra WFar WPnP
'Bob's Blunder' **new**	WCot WCru
bohemicum	CCge EBee EMan GSki MLwd NCot NSti SRGP WCru WHcn WHer WPnP WWpP
– 'Orchid Blue'	CCge CFwr LRHS WFar
'Brookside'	More than 30 suppliers
brutium	WHen
brycei	MNrw
'Buckland Beauty'	CElw SSpi
'Buxton's Blue'	see *G. wallichianum* 'Buxton's Variety'
caeruleatum	EBee EMon EPPr SCou SHel SUsu
caffrum	CCge CMCo CPla EMan GBuc GSki MLwd MNrw NCot NPPs NWCA SRGP STes WBea WCru WEas WLin WOut WWpP
californicum	EPPr EWes GBuc WCru
– NNS 98-503	NWCA
canariense	CBod CCge CPla CSpe EBee EMan EMar EWes LDai LPhx LPio MLwd MWod SBod SCou SGar SPar SRGP WCru WPnP WWpP
candicans hort.	see *G. lambertii*
§ x *cantabrigiense*	More than 30 suppliers
– 'Berggarten'	EBee EPPr SHel SRGP WWpP
– 'Biokovo'	More than 30 suppliers
– 'Cambridge'	More than 30 suppliers
– 'Karmina'	CElw CMCo EBee EChP EGle EPPr EPla GKir IHMH MBro MLwd MNrw SCou WHoo WMoo WPnP WTMC WWpP
– 'Show Time'	CMCo SCro WHal
– 'St Ola'	More than 30 suppliers

– Westray = 'Bremwest'	CCge EBee EChP EPPr EVFa GAbr GBin GKir GLbr MCCP MSte NBlu NGdn NPro SCro SDes STes SVil WRus WWeb WWpP
cataractarum	CCge MNrw WCru
– subsp. *pitardii*	SRGP
'Chantilly'	CElw CHar CMCo CMil CSam EBee EBla EGra EMan EPPr GBuc MAvo MNrw NBir NCat NCot NPro SCou SCro SUsu WBea WCra WCru WMoo WPnP WTMC
'Chocolate Candy'PBR	CCge EBee LAst MWrn WFoF WWeb
* 'Chocolate Pot'	NArg
christensenianum **new**	NCat
– B&SWJ 8022	WCru
cinereum	ENot GKir MHdf
– 'Apple Blossom'	see *G. x lindavicum* 'Apple Blossom'
– 'Ballerina' ♀ H4	More than 30 suppliers
– 'Carol'PBR	CCge EBee EChP EMan EMar EPPr EVFa EWes GKir MAvo MCLN NGdn NSti SCou SLon SVil WElm WRus
– subsp. *cinereum* var. *cinereum*	CCge WBrE
– – – 'Album'	WCru
I – 'Heather'	CCge EBee EChP EMan EPPr LRHS MBri MCLN NGdn NSti SVil
– hybrids	WCru
– 'Janette'PBR	COtt EBee EBre GKir LBBr LRHS MBri MCLN
– 'Laurence Flatman'	More than 30 suppliers
'Purple Pillow' **new**	MBri
– subsp. *subcaulescens*	More than 30 suppliers
var. *subcaulescens* ♀ H4	
'Giuseppii'	CTbh EBre EChP ECtt EFou EPPr GKir GMaP LGro MCLN MNrw MRav MWhe NBro NCat NCot NHol SCou SRGP WBea WCra WFar WPnP WWeb
– – – 'Splendens' ♀ H4	CSpe EBre ECtt EDAr EFou EPPr EPfP GLbr LHop LRHS MBNS MDun MTis MWhe NLon NSla NSti SHBN SPar SPla SRGP SRms SWat WAul WCra WFar Wlvy WPat WPnP WWpP
– – – 'Violaceum'	EPPr
'Claridge Druce'	see *G. x oxonianum* 'Claridge Druce'
clarkei 'Kashmir Green' **new**	CFwr EBee NCat
'Kashmir Pink'	More than 30 suppliers
§ – 'Kashmir Purple'	More than 30 suppliers
§ – 'Kashmir White' ♀ H4	More than 30 suppliers
'Coffee Time'	SCro
collinum	EPPr GAbr GBuc LLWP MLwd MNrw NBir NCat NCot SCou SCro SHel SRGP SUsu WCru WHen WPnP WTMC WWpP
'Coombland White'	CBri CCge CElw CMCo EBee EBla EFou EOrc EPPr GMac IFro LPio MBri MBro MNrw NCot NPro NSti SCou SCro SDys SRGP SVil WCra WCru WHoo WMoo WPGP WPnP WWpP
Crûg strain	CHid CSpe EHrv EMan EPot GKir GSki LRHS MCCP MDun MLLN NBlu SDes SPar SRPl STes WCru WGwG
'Crûg's Dark Delight'	WCru
§ 'Cyril's Fancy'	EBee EPPr MAvo MNFA NCat SCro SHel SUsu WWpP
dahuricum	EBee WCru

dalmaticum ♀ H4 — More than 30 suppliers
- 'Album' — ECtt EDAr EHyt ELan EMlt EPPr EPot GKir MBro MHer MRav MTho MWhe NChi SCou SRGP SRms SRot WAbe WCra WCru WFar WHCG WPat WPnP WWin WPnP
- 'Bressingham Pink' — WPnP
- 'Bridal Bouquet' — GBri NMen SBla WHer
- x ***macrorrhizum*** — see *G.* x *cantabrigiense*
delavayi hort. — see *G. sinense*
delavayi Franch. — CBot CDes EBee WCru WPGP
'Dilys' — CBos CElw CStr EChP EGle EGra EPPr LLWP LPio MNrw NBir NCat NCot NGdn SBla SCou SHel SRGP SUsu WBea WCra WCru WFar WHal WHen WMoo WPGP WPnP WRus WWpP
dissectum — MSal SCou
'Distant Hills' — EBee EPPr NCot
'Diva' — CCge CElw CMCo CMil CSam EBee EBla EPPr MCLN MMil MNrw NCat NSti SCou SCro SHel SMrm SRGP SVil WCot WCra WCru WPnP WTMC WWpP
donianum HWJCM 311 — WCru
drakensbergense — CCge NCot SCou
'Dusky Crûg' — CElw MNrw NCat NPPs WCru
'Dusky Rose' — CFai CPen EMan EPfP GKir LRHS
'Elizabeth Ross' — CElw EPPr LRHS MAvo MNrw SMrm WCra WCru WMoo WOBN WRha WTMC WWhi
'Elizabeth Wood' — EMan SMrm WCra
'Elworthy Dusky' — CCge
'Emily' **new** — SRGP
endressii ♀ H4 — More than 30 suppliers
- 'Album' — see *Geranium* 'Mary Mottram'
- 'Beholder's Eye' — CCge EBee EPPr GAbr MSte NCot NSti
- 'Betty Catchpole' — EPPr NCat
- 'Castle Drogo' — ECtt EPPr NCat SRGP WBea WCra WTMC WWpP
- 'Prestbury White' — see *G.* x *oxonianum* 'Prestbury Blush'
- 'Priestling's Red' — CElw CMCo EGra EMar NCot SMrm
- 'Rose' — SDes WPer WPnP WWpP
- white-flowered **new** — SSpi
erianthum — CCge EMan GBuc GMac LLWP MSte MWhe NCat NLar NPPs SRGP STes WCru WElm WPnP
- 'Calm Sea' — CCge CDes EBee GBuc SUsu WCru WMoo WTMC
- 'Neptune' — EBee EPPr NCat SChu SCou SUsu WCra WCru
eriostemon Fischer — see *G. platyanthum*
'Espresso' **new** — CDes EBla EChP EHrv EMan EPPr MBri MSph NCat NCot NGdn SCou WAbe WTMC
'Eva' — NCat
§ ***farreri*** — CBot CCge CLyd EBee EGle EHyt ETow GBri GBuc GCal LHop LRHS MNrw NBir NLon SBla SIng WCru WEas
'Flamingo' — MTPN
fremontii — EBee
glaberrimum — WCru
goldmannii — SSpi
gracile — CElw EBee EChP EOrc EPla EVFa GBuc GMaP MBro MCLN MLwd MNrw NBir SCou SCro SRGP WCra WCru WHal WMoo WPGP WPnP WWpP
- 'Blanche' — CElw EBee EPPr NCat SCou

- 'Blush' — CElw CMCo EBee EMan EPPr NCat SDys WBea WWpP
grandiflorum — see *G. himalayense*
- var. ***alpinum*** — see *G. himalayense* 'Gravetye'
'Gwen Thompson' **new** — WOut
gymnocaulon — CCge CElw CMCo EBee EBla EMan EMar EPPr LRHS NCat NSti SCou SRGP STes WCru WElm WMnd WWpP
gymnocaulon x ***platypetalum*** **new** — EBee
'Harmony' — EPPr NCat
harveyi — CMea CPBP EBee EMan EWes GSki LGro LPhx MBro MNrw NWCA WCom WCra WCru WKif WPGP WPat WPnn
hayatanum — NCot WTMC
- B&SWJ 164 — CBod EBee EPPr SCou WCra WMoo WWpP
§ ***himalayense*** — More than 30 suppliers
- *alpinum* — see *G. himalayense* 'Gravetye'
§ - 'Baby Blue' — CBos CElw EBee EBla EFou EGle EPPr GBuc GCal GKir MAvo MBri MCLN MNrw NCat NCot NDov NSti SCou SCro WBea WCra WCru WHen WMoo WTMC WViv WWpP
- 'Birch Double' — see *G. himalayense* 'Plenum'
- 'Devil's Blue' — NCat SCro
- 'Frances Perry' — CCge SMur
§ - 'Gravetye' ♀ H4 — More than 30 suppliers
- 'Irish Blue' — More than 30 suppliers
- *meeboldii* — see *G. himalayense*
- 'Pale Irish Blue' — GCal
§ - 'Plenum' (d) — More than 30 suppliers
hispidissimum — CFee
ibericum misapplied — see *G.* x *magnificum*
ibericum — CCge CNic CSBt CTri IKee MHdf SRGP STes WFar WWpP
- 'Genyell' **new** — NCat
- subsp. ***ibericum*** — EBee EPPr
- subsp. ***jubatum*** — CElw EBee EBre EPPr GCal GKir LPhx MNrw NCot SCou SCro SRms WBea WCru WMoo WPnP WTMC WWpP
- subsp. ***jubatum*** x ***renardii*** — GCal
- var. ***platypetalum*** hort. — see *G.* x *magnificum*
- var. ***platypetalum*** Boissier — see *G. platypetalum* Fisch. & C.A.Mey.
incanum — CCge CSev ECoo EMan ETow EWes IFro MLwd MNrw NBir NPPs SMrm SRGP WAbe WCot WHal WLin
- var. ***multifidum*** — GGar SUsu WCru WFar
- white — SRGP
'Ivan' — CElw CMCo EBee EMan EPPr GBuc LPhx LRHS MAvo MBri NCat SCou SCro SIgm SRGP WCru WPGP WPnP WRus
'Jacqueline's Joy' — LPio
'Jean's Lilac' — NCot
'Johnson's Blue' ♀ H4 — More than 30 suppliers
'Joy' — More than 30 suppliers
'Kahlua' **new** — EBee ERou
§ 'Kashmir Blue' — CCge CHar EBee EBot EChP EPPr ERou EWsh GKir NCat NCot NMGW NSti SCro SHel WMoo
I 'Kashmir Lilac' — WHen
§ 'Kate' — CElw EBla EGle EPPr WCru WPnn
'Kate Folkard' — see *G.* 'Kate'
§ 'Khan' — CBos CMil EBla EPPr IFro MNrw

	NCat NCot SCou SDys SMHy SRGP WCra WCru WPnP WWpP
kishtvariense	CMCo EBee EBla EBre ECoo EMan EOrc EPPr GCal LPio LRHS MLwd MNrw MRav NCot NHol SSpi WCru WOVN WPGP WPnP WWhi
koraiense	CBod CCge EMan MLwd NSti WMoo WWpP
- B&SWJ 797	WCru
- B&SWJ 878	EBee SCou WCru
koreanum	CCge CFil CPla GBuc GKir LRHS MNFA NCot SSpi STes SUsu WBea WFar WMoo WPGP WTMC
- B&SWJ 602	SCou WCru
§ *kotschyi* var. *charlesii*	EBee
krameri	EMan NSti
- B&SWJ 1142	EBee NCat WCru
§ *lambertii*	CCge EWes GBuc LPio MNrw NBir NChi WTMC
- 'Swansdown'	CBos EChP EMan GBuc MNrw WCru
lanuginosum	EChP SRGP
libani	CDes EBee EBre EPPr GBuc GCal LLWP MTho MWhe NCot NSti SCou SCro WCot WCra WCru WEas WPGP WPnP WTMC WWpP
- x *peloponnesiacum* 'Libretto'	CBos CCge CDes CRDP CElw EBee NCat WCru
§ x *lindavicum* 'Apple Blossom'	CCge CLyd EDAr EPPr EPot GBuc GKir LBBr MBri MSte NMen NPPs SAsh SBla SRGP SRot WAbe WCom WCru WHCG WLin WWin
- 'Lissadell'	EPot SBla
linearilobum subsp. *transversale*	EPPr WCru WPnP
§ 'Little David'	EPPr SDys SRGP SUsu
'Little Devil'	see *G.* 'Little David'
'Little Gem'	CCge EBee EBre EFou EMan GKir LHop LRHS MAvo MRav MWhe NChi NCot NDov NPro SCro SUsu WCra WCru WFar WHoo
lucidum	EPPr MSal NCat NCot NSti NVic
'Lydia'	SRGP
§ *macrorrhizum*	More than 30 suppliers
- AL & JS 90179YU	CHid EPPr
- JJH 7003/95	EBee
- 'Album' ♀ H4	More than 30 suppliers
- 'Bevan's Variety'	More than 30 suppliers
- 'Bulgaria'	EPPr WTMC
- 'Czakor'	More than 30 suppliers
I - 'De Bilt' **new**	CFwr EBee
- 'Ingwersen's Variety' ♀ H4	More than 30 suppliers
- 'Lohfelden'	CDes CElw EGle EPPr GBuc MBro MNFA SDys SHel SRGP WCra WMoo WPnP WRHF WViv WWpP
- 'Mount Olympus'	see *G. macrorrhizum* 'White-Ness'
- 'Mount Olympus White'	see *G. macrorrhizum* 'White-Ness'
- 'Pindus'	CElw EBee EBre EPPr GAbr MBro MNFA NCat NCot NSti SCou SDys SHel SRGP SUsu WCru WFar WMoo WPnP WTMC WWpP
- 'Ridsko'	CElw CFee CMCo EBee EOrc EPPr GBuc GCal MNFA NBro NCat SCou SCro SHel SRGP WCru WHen WWpP
- *roseum*	see *G. macrorrhizum*
- 'Sandwijck' **new**	CFwr EPPr
- 'Snow Sprite'	CCge CPla GSki MCCP NCot NPro SPoG STes WHrl
- 'Spessart'	EBee EBre EChP ENot EPPr EPfP GKir NBee SCou SDes SRPl WCra
	WCru WFar WOVN WPnP WRHF WTMC WWpP
- 'Variegatum' (v)	More than 30 suppliers
- 'Velebit'	CBel CBri CCge EBee EPPr MSte SRGP WCru WMoo WTMC WWpP
§ - 'White-Ness'	CBel CBos CElw CLAP EBee EGoo EMon EPPr MWhi NCat NDov NGar NPro SHel SRGP SUsu WCot WCru WFar WHal WHen WMoo WPGP WRus
macrostylum	CDes CElw CPou EBee LHop MBro NCot WBVN WCot WCru WPGP WPer WPnP
- 'Leonidas'	see *G. tuberosum* 'Leonidas'
maculatum	CElw CRDP CSev ECha EFou EPfP GCal GPoy LRHS MBro MCAu MLwd MRav MSal NSti SCou SCro SMac SPar WCra WCru WHal WHen WHoo WPGP WPnP WWpP WWye
- f. *albiflorum*	CElw CRDP EGle EMan EMon EPPr GCal LPhx MBro MNrw NBid NSti SCou SRGP SSpi SUsu WCra WCru WMaN WMoo WPnP WTMC
- 'Beth Chatto'	More than 30 suppliers
- *purple*	EPPr SCro WWpP
- 'Shameface'	EBee EPPr MSte SDys SHel SOkh WPnP
- 'Vickie Lynn' **new**	CFwr
maderense ♀ H2	CAbb CElw CFwr CHEx CPla CPrp CSam CTbh CTrC CTrF EWes LHrt LPhx MNrw MWod NCot NPer SAPC SArc SBod SCou SDix SRGP WBrE WCru WPer WPnP WRos
§ x *magnificum* ♀ H4	More than 30 suppliers
- 'Peter Yeo'	CMHG EPPr NCat NSti
- 'Rosemoor'	CCge CFwr CHid CSpe EBee EChP EFou ELan EPfP IPot MSte NCot NSti WCra WMnd WWpP
magniflorum	IFro MRav NBid WBea WCru
'Maitre Hugo' **new**	NCat
§ *malviflorum*	CBro CElw CFwr CMHG EBre ECha EFou ELan EMar EPPr GKir LLWP LRHS MBow MBro MNrw MTho SCou SRms SSpi WAul WCot WCra WCru WFar WHoo WPnP
- pink C	Mil EBee SBla SCro WCru WMoo WPnP
- Spanish form	EPPr EWes
§ 'Mary Mottram'	CBos CMCo EBee EPPr MAvo MCLN MMil NBir NCat NCot NSti SCro SHel WCot WEas WPnP WWpP
maximowiczii	CCge CElw EBee
'Maxwelton'	NCat
'Meryl Ann' **new**	NCat
microphyllum	see *G. potentilloides*
molle	MSal
§ x *monacense*	CElw CMCo EBee EBlw EFWa EFou ELan EMar EPla EWsh GGar GKir GSki LRHS MWgw MWhe NSti SCou SCro SMac SSea SWat WBea WCru WHer WMnd WMoo WPnP WWpP
- var. *anglicum*	EBla EBre EChP ECtt EOrc EPPr GKir MBro MNFA MRav MWhe NSti SCou SCro WCra WMoo WPnP
- 'Breckland Fever' **new**	EPPr
- 'Claudine Dupont'	CElw EPPr NCat
- dark	CBri WMoo
- var. *monacense*	CElw WFar WHen

§ – 'Muldoon'   CHar CMHG CSam CSev EBlw
EBre EChP ECoo EPPr EPla GKir
GMaP GMac GSki MBow MRav
NBir NOak STes WFar WHCG
WHen WMoo WPer WPnP WPrP
moupinense new   EBee
'Mourning Widow'   see *G. phaeum* var. *phaeum*
multisectum   WCru WTMC
napuligerum hort.   see *G. farreri*
napuligerum Franch.   NSla
'Natalie'   MAvo NCat NCot
nepalense   CMCo EBee NCot SCou SHel
SRGP SRms WMoo WWpP
nervosum   CHar CMCo EBee EWsh MCCP
NPro NSti SCou STes WPnP
WTMC
'Nicola'   CCge CElw EBee EGle EPPr
MNFA NCat SAga SDys SUsu
WCra
'Nimbus'   More than 30 suppliers
nodosum   More than 30 suppliers
– dark   see *G. nodosum* 'Swish Purple'
– 'Julie's Velvet'   MSte MTed WCra WElm WHoo
WWhi WWpP
– pale   see *G. nodosum* 'Svelte Lilac'
– pink   WPrP
§ – 'Svelte Lilac'   CElw EBee EBla ECGP EGle EMan
EMon EPPr EPfP GCal MBro MSte
NCat NLon SCou SHel SRGP SWat
WBea WCot WCru WFar WMoo
WPnP WPrP WWpP
§ – 'Swish Purple'   CBos CElw CHar EBee EPPr
MNFA MSte NCiC SHel SIng SMac
SRGP SWat WCot WCru WFar
WHen WMoo WPGP WPnP
– 'Whiteleaf'   CBos CElw EBee EBla ECoo EGle
EPPr MBro NPro SAga SBla SUsu
SWat WBea WCra WCru WFar
WMoo WPnP WTMC
– 'Whiteleaf' seedling   EMan EMar SHel
'Nora Bremner'   SCro SUsu
'Nunwood Purple'   EPPr NCot WTMC
ocellatum   CBre CCge MLwd NCot
oreganum   CCge CElw CMCo ECGP EOrc
SCou SCro
§ **orientalitibeticum**   More than 30 suppliers
'Orion'   CCge CElw EBee EPPr MSte NCat
NGby STes
'Orkney Pink'   More than 30 suppliers
ornithopodon   IFro NCot
'Out of the Blue'   WOut
x **oxonianum**   EBre MHer NCot NPPs SCou
WCru WMoo
– 'A.T. Johnson' ♀ H4   More than 30 suppliers
– 'Breckland Brownie' **new**   CElw EPPr EVFa SRGP
– 'Breckland Sunset'   EBee EPPr SCou SHel SRGP WPnP
WTMC WWpP
– 'Bregover Pearl'   CBre CElw CMCo EBee EChP
EPPr MNFA NCat SCou SHel SRGP
WMoo WTMC
– 'Bressingham Delight'   CElw CMCo EBee EBre ECtt
EWsh GKir LRHS MCLN MWhe
NCot SCou SHel SRGP WCra
WPnP WTMC WWpP
– 'Buttercup'   EMan EPPr WWpP
I – 'Cally Seedling'   EBee EPPr EWes GCal NCot
§ – 'Claridge Druce'   More than 30 suppliers
– 'Coronet'   CCge EBee EPPr MNFA SHel
SRGP WBea WMoo
– 'Crûg Star'   CCge CElw
– 'David McClintock'   CCge CElw EBee EMan EPPr
MAvo MNFA MTed NSti SCou
SHel WFar WMoo WTMC WWpP

– 'Dawn Time'   SCro WPnP
– 'Dirk Gunst'   CElw
– 'Elsbeth Blush' **new**   EBee
– 'Elworthy Misty'   CElw EPPr
– 'Frank Lawley'   CElw CFis CMCo CPrp EBee EBla
EChP EPPr GBuc GMac LLWP
MNFA NBid NCWG NCat NCot
NPro NSti SCou SCro SHel SRGP
WBea WCra WMoo WPnP WTMC
WWpP
§ – 'Fran's Star'   EVFa WCru
– 'Hexham Pink'   CCge NCWG NCat NPro SCou
WTMC
– 'Hollywood'   CCge CElw CMCo EBee EChP
ELan EOrc EPPr GBuc GMac
LRHS MBri MSte MTho NCot
NPer SCro SMrm SSpe WBea
WBor WCra WFar WMoo WPnP
WTMC WWpP
– 'Julie Brennan'   CElw EBee EPPr GBin GCal GMac
MNFA NCat NGdn NSti SHel
SRGP WBea WCra WMoo WPnP
WWpP
– 'Kate Moss'   CFwr EPPr GKir MNFA NCWG
NSti WBar WCra WTMC WWpP
– 'Kingston'   see *G. versicolor* 'Kingston'
– 'Königshof' **new**   EPPr
– 'Lace Time'   CBre CElw CMCo CSev CWib EBee
EBla EPPr GMac MNFA MNrw
MWhe NCot NHol NOak NPPs
SCro WBea WMoo WPnP WTMC
– 'Lady Moore'   CElw CMCo CPrp EBee EPPr EPla
GBuc MBro MNrw MWhe NBro
NCot SCou SCro SRGP WBea
WBor WCra WHen WMoo WPnP
WTMC WWpP
– 'Lambrook Gillian'   CCge CElw CFis EBee EPPr MNFA
NCot SBri SCou SRGP WBea
WPnP WTMC WWpP
– 'Lasting Impression'   EPPr WWpP
– 'Miriam Rundle'   CElw EBee EFou EOrc EPPr MNFA
MNrw NCot SRGP WBea WCru
WMoo WPnP WTMC WWpP
– 'Moorland Jenny'   WMoo
– 'Mrs Charles Perrin'   CCge CPrp
– 'Old Rose'   CElw EBee EGle EPPr GCal GKir
LRHS MBri MNFA NCat NCot
NPro SCou SRGP WBea WCru
WMoo WPnP WTMC WWpP
– 'Pat Smallacombe'   CElw EPPr NCat NCot SRGP
WBea WCru WMoo WTMC
– 'Phoebe Noble'   More than 30 suppliers
– 'Phoebe's Blush'   EPPr GMac MNFA NCat SHel
WBea WTMC
– 'Pink Lace'   NCot
§ – 'Prestbury Blush'   CBre CElw CMCo EBee EGle EOrc
EPPr SCou WBea WCot WCru
WMoo WTMC WWin WWpP
– 'Prestbury White'   see *G.* x *oxonianum* 'Prestbury
Blush'
– 'Rebecca Moss'   More than 30 suppliers
– 'Red Sputnik'   EPPr WWpP
– 'Rose Clair'   More than 30 suppliers
I – 'Rosemary'   SCou WWpP
– 'Rosemary Verey'   SHel
– 'Rosenlicht'   CBos CElw CSev EBee EFou EMon
EPPr LRHS MCLN MRav NCat
NEgg NLar SChu SCou SHel SRGP
SRPl SSpi WBea WCra WCru WMnd
WMoo WPGP WPnP WWpP
– 'Sherwood'   More than 30 suppliers
– 'Southcombe Double' (d)   More than 30 suppliers
§ – 'Southcombe Star'   CMCo EOrc EPPr GAbr GCal IPot

	MFir MNFA NBro NGdn NLon NSti SHel SRGP WBea WCru WFar WHal WHen WMoo WPer WPnP WTMC
- 'Spring Fling' (v)	EPPr MAvo NSti WCot
- 'Stillingfleet'	see *G.* x *oxonianum* 'Stillingfleet Keira'
§ - 'Stillingfleet Keira'	NSti
- 'Summer Surprise'	CElw CFwr EBee EPPr EWes NCat SCou SCro SHel SRGP SUsu WPnP WTMC
- 'Susan'	EPPr EWes
- 'Susie White'	CElw EPPr MAvo NCWG
§ f. *thurstonianum*	More than 30 suppliers
- - 'Armitageae'	CElw EBee EPPr MNFA NCot SCou SHel SRGP WTMC WWpP
- 'Trevor's White'	EBee EGle MNFA MNrw NCat NCot WTMC WWpP
- 'Wageningen'	CBre CElw CMCo EBee EGle EMar GCal GKir GMac LPhx LRHS MAvo MMil NCat NCot NGdn NPro SAga SCou SRGP WBea WCra WCru WHal WHen WHer WMoo WTMC WWpP
- 'Walter's Gift'	More than 30 suppliers
- 'Wargrave Pink' ♀ H4	More than 30 suppliers
- 'Waystrode'	CMCo EBee EBla EPPr SCou SRGP WTMC WWpP
- 'Winscombe'	CElw CMCo EChP EFou GCal LGro LLWP LRHS MBow MBri MLwd MRav MTho MWgw NCat NCot NSti SCou SCro WBea WCru WGwG WHen WMnd WMoo WRus WWal WWpP
- x *sessiliflorum* subsp. *novae-zelandiae* 'Nigricans'	EHrv
'Pagoda'	CCge EOrc MNrw
§ *palmatum* ♀ H3	More than 30 suppliers
palustre	CBri CElw EBee EChP EMar EOrc EPPr LLWP MLwd MNFA MNrw NBro NCot NHol NSti SCou SRGP STes WCra WCru WFar WHen WMoo WPnP
papuanum	SBla WCru
'Pastel Clouds' **new**	EBee
'Patricia'	More than 30 suppliers
peloponnesiacum	CStr EBee EPPr GGar WCru WFar WPGP
- NS 660	CElw
'Persian Carpet'	ITer NCot NLar
'Peter Hale'	CMea
phaeum	More than 30 suppliers
- 'Album'	More than 30 suppliers
- 'Alec's Pink'	LLWP WOut
- 'All Saints'	CElw EBee EMon SUsu WPrP WTMC
- 'Aureum'	see *G. phaeum* 'Golden Spring'
- black	see *G. phaeum* var. *phaeum*
- 'Blue Shadow'	CElw EPPr WTMC WWpP
- 'Calligrapher'	CElw CMCo EBee EChP EGle EPPr SCou SHel SRGP SUsu WCra WMoo WTMC
- 'Charles Perrin'	CElw CHid EBee NCot STes
- 'Chocolate Chip' **new**	CFwr
- dark	CBri CElw SCou
- 'David Bromley'	EMon WPrP WTMC
§ - 'Golden Spring'	CElw EPPr NCat NChi NCot NPro
- 'Hannah Perry'	CBel CBri CElw CHad EBee EPPr LLWP WBea WBro
- var. *hungaricum*	EPPr NCat SCou WBea WCru WTMC WWpP
- 'Langthorns Blue'	CElw CMCo CMea CSev EBee ELan EPPr MLwd MNFA MNrw

	NCat NCot SCro SRGP WBar WCra WHen WPrP WTMC
§ - 'Lily Lovell'	More than 30 suppliers
- 'Little Boy'	CElw EMon EPPr NCat WTMC
- var. *lividum*	More than 30 suppliers
- - 'Joan Baker'	More than 30 suppliers
- - 'Majus'	CCge CElw ECtt EMon EPPr EPfP GKir LLWP LPhx MNFA MWgw NSti SCou SCro SWat WBea WFar WMoo WPnP WTMC
- 'Margaret Wilson' (v)	CBos CElw EBee EChP EMan EPPr EVFa NCot SCou SRGP SUsu WCot
- 'Mierhausen'	CElw
- 'Mourning Widow'	see *G. phaeum* var. *phaeum*
- 'Night Time'	EPPr LLWP MBro SCro WBea
- 'Our Pat' **new**	NCWG
§ - var. *phaeum*	CMil EChP EGle EPPr GBin GCal IBlr MWhe NCat NCot NDov SCou SCro SGar SPar SRGP SRms WBea WCra WCru WHen WMoo WPGP WWpP
* - 'Ploeger de Bilt' **new**	EPPr WTMC
- purple	EBee MDun
- 'Raven' **new**	CFwr
- red	MRav MTed
- 'Rose Air'	EBee EChP EGoo EPPr MNFA SRGP WCra WMoo WPnP WTMC WWpP
- 'Rose Madder'	CBel CBos CHad CM&M EBee EGle EPPr GBuc GCal LHop LLWP LPhx MBro MCLN MNFA MNrw MSte NCot SCou SHBN WMoo WPnP WWpP
- 'Samobor'	More than 30 suppliers
- 'Silver Fox'	WRha
- 'Small Grey'	WTMC
- 'Stillingfleet Ghost'	CElw EBee NCWG NCat NCot NSti SCou WTMC
- 'Taff's Jester' (v)	CElw EBee EWes NHol NSti SApp SCro SPar WCot WHer WTMC WWpP
- 'Variegatum' (v)	More than 30 suppliers
- 'Walküre' **new**	EPPr
- 'Zit Factory' **new**	WTMC
'Phillip Vapelle'	More than 30 suppliers
'Pink Delight'	CElw LPho WWpP
'Pink Spice' PBR	CCge ECtt MRav MWhe MWrn NHar WWeb
§ *platyanthum*	CCge EBee EChP EPPr GCal GKir MLwd MNrw MWod NCot SRGP WBVN WCru WHCG WHen WMoo WPer
- giant	SGar
- var. *reinii*	NCat
- - f. *onoei*	WCru
platypetalum misapplied	see *G.* x *magnificum*
platypetalum Franch.	see *G. sinense*
§ *platypetalum* Fisch. & C.A. Mey.	EBre EChP ENot EPPr GKir MAvo NBir NCat NSti SCou SRms SWat WCru WMoo WTMC
- 'Georgia Blue'	CFil EBee MSte SSpi WCru WFar WMoo WPGP
§ *pogonanthum*	CDes EOrc GBuc GCal IFro MNrw NBir NCot WCru WMoo
polyanthes	CMCo EBee GBuc GDra GTou MLwd MSph WPnP WTMC
- CC 2721	WOBN
- CC 3329	WRos
- HWJCM 276	WCru
§ *potentilloides*	CCge EBee GSki NBir NCWG SRGP
pratense	More than 30 suppliers

- CC&McK 442 — CMCo GTou
- 'Bittersweet' — EBee EChP EMon NCot WOut
- 'Cluden Sapphire' — CAbP CBod EBee EFou GKir LRHS MWhi NCot NHol NPro WCru WFar
- 'Flore Pleno' — see *G. pratense* 'Plenum Violaceum'
- 'Gay Hellyer' — EGle SCro
* - 'Himalayanum' — LGro NLar
- 'Janet's Special' **new** — WHoo
- Midnight Reiter strain — CBos CCol CSpe CWes EBee EMan GBin GBri LRHS MBNS MCLN MDun MSte MTis NChi SCoo SUsu WCot WCra WCru WFar WLin WPnP WWeb
- 'Misty Morn' (d) — NCat
- 'Mount Stewart' **new** — IBlr WCru
- 'Mrs Kendall Clark' ♀ H4 — More than 30 suppliers
- pale form — NPPs
§ - 'Plenum Caeruleum' (d) — More than 30 suppliers
- 'Plenum Purpureum' — see *G. pratense* 'Plenum Violaceum'
§ - 'Plenum Violaceum' (d) ♀ H4 — More than 30 suppliers
- subsp. *pratense* — More than 30 suppliers
 f. *albiflorum*
- - - 'Galactic' — CCge EBee EChP GKir MBro NBir SRGP WCra WCru WHen WMoo
- - - 'Plenum Album' (d) — CDes CElw CStr WCot
- - - 'Silver Queen' — CBre EBee EChP ECtt ELan EOrc EPPr MBro MNrw MWhe NBir NCot NMRc NPPs SCou SCro SRGP STes WBea WFar WHen WHoo WMoo WPnP WTMC WWpP
- - - 'Whimble White' — WWhi
- 'Purple Heron' — More than 30 suppliers
- 'Purple-haze' — CCge CPla ECoo GBuc GSki ITer MCCP NCot NLar NPPs STes WHrl WOut
- 'Rectum Album' — see *G. clarkei* 'Kashmir White'
§ - 'Rose Queen' — CBri EBee ELan EOrc MCAu MNrw MRav NBir NCWG NCat NHol NLar NSti SSpi STes WBea WCom WCra WCru WHen WPnP WTMC WWpP
- 'Roseum' — see *G. pratense* 'Rose Queen'
- 'Spinners' — see *G.* 'Spinners'
- 'Splish-splash' — More than 30 suppliers
- 'Stanton Mill' — NBid
- subsp. *stewartianum* — CElw MRav WPnP
- - 'Elizabeth Yeo' — CCge EBee EBla EPPr SCou SCro SUsu WCru WTMC WWpP
- 'Striatum' — More than 30 suppliers
- 'Striatum' pale — CBre
- Summer Skies = 'Gernic'PBR (d) — CCge CStr EBre EMan LRHS MWhe NLar SCou WCra WTMC
- 'Victor Reiter' — CBos CCge CElw CHar CSpe EBee EHrv ELan EPPr ITer LAst LPio MCLN MMHG NCat NCot NDov NGdn NPPs SAga SMrm SPar SRot WCot WCru WRus WWhi
- 'Victor Reiter Junior' — CSpe EBee EChP ECtt EFou EVFa LHop MCAu MEHN MSte MTis NBir NCat NPPs NSti SHar WCot WCra WPnP WWeb
- 'Wisley Blue' — CMCo EBee EPPr MSte SCou SCro SRGP WHal WMnd
- 'Yorkshire Queen' — CFwr EBee EPPr NCWG NCat NGdn SCou WCru
'Prelude' — CElw EBee GDea NBir NCat WBea WCra WTMC
'Priestley's Pink' — EBee

'Prima Donna' — NCat
procurrens — CBre CBri CElw CSev CSpe EBre ECha EPPr GCal GGar GKir IMGH LLWP LRHS MLLN MLwd NBid NGdn NSti SCou SPer WCru WFar WHCG WHen WMoo WPnP WRos WWin WWpP
§ *psilostemon* ♀ H4 — More than 30 suppliers
- 'Bressingham Flair' — More than 30 suppliers
- 'Gold Leaf' — WCot
- hybrid — CElw
pulchrum — CElw CMCo CSev CSpe ECre EMan EOrc EPPr LPio MCAu MNrw MWhi SGar SIgm SRGP SSpi STes SWal SWat WCot WCru WLin WPer WRos WWpP
punctatum hort. — see *G.* x *monacense* 'Muldoon'
- 'Variegatum' — see *G. phaeum* 'Variegatum'
pusillum — MSal
pylzowianum — CCge GDra GGar MBro MLwd MRav NBid NJOw NRya SBla SRGP WBea WCra WCru WFar WHal WHen WMoo WPnP WTel
pyrenaicum — CElw CKin CM&M CRDP CSev EBee GAbr MBow NCot NSti SCou WBea WHen WTMC WWpP
- f. *albiflorum* — CElw CPrp EBee EChP ESis GAbr GMac LLWP MHer MLwd MNrw MTho NBir NCot NSti SCou SCro SPar WBea WCra WHen WPer WWin WWpP
- 'Bill Wallis' — More than 30 suppliers
- 'Isparta' — CElw EBee EChP EPPr IFro LPio NCat NCot SRGP SUsu WCra
- 'Summer Sky' **new** — NCot SRGP WWpP
- 'Summer Snow' **new** — NCot SPoG
'Rambling Robin' — CCge EBee EMan EMar EPPr WCru WPGP WWpP
'Rays Pink' — CPla EBee
rectum — EBee EPPr NCot SCou WCru
- 'Album' — see *G. clarkei* 'Kashmir White'
'Red Admiral' — NCat NPro
'Red Dwarf' — CElw WMoo
reflexum — CHid CMCo CSev EBee EBla EChP EMan EPPr NCat NHol SCou SCro WFar WHCG WOut WPnP WTMC WWpP
refractoides — EBee
refractum **new** — EBee
regelii — CBos CElw CMCo CSam EBee EOrc EPPr GMac NCot SAga SChu WCra WCru WMoo WPnP WWpP
- CC 806 — CPou
renardii ♀ H4 — More than 30 suppliers
- blue — see *G. renardii* 'Whiteknights'
- 'Heidi Morris' **new** — SCro
- 'Tcschelda' — CFai CMil EBee EChP EFou EMan EMil LPio MCLN NCot SBod SDes SPar SPla SUsu SWat WCra WPnP WRus WViv WWpP
§ - 'Whiteknights' — CElw EGra GBuc MAvo MBro NBir NCot NDov NPro WBea WCru WEas WIvy WOut WWin
- 'Zetterlund' — CElw CMCo CSpe EBee EBre EGle EHrv EMar EPPr GKir LLWP MAvo MCAu MCLN MLLN NCot NSti SCou SUsu SWat WBea WCru WFar WHil WMoo WTMC
retrorsum — CCge
'Richard John' **new** — CCge
richardsonii — EBee EChP EMan EPPr GCal GMac MLwd MNrw NBir NCat NCot

	SCou SCro SRGP SRms WCra WCru WMoo WPnP WTMC WWpP
I 'Rise Top Lilac' **new**	EBee NCot
x **riversleaianum**	WCru
- 'Jean Armour'	EPPr WCru WTMC
- 'Mavis Simpson'	More than 30 suppliers
- 'Russell Prichard' ♀ H4	More than 30 suppliers
§ **rivulare**	CBri CCge CMCo EBee EMan GKir GSki MBro MNFA NCot NSti STes WBea WHCG WMnd WOut WPnP
- 'Album'	MBro
robertianum	CKin EEls EPPr GWCH MChe MHer SCou SRms WHbs WHen WWpP
§ - 'Album'	CBgR EPPr MHer NSti SCou SRms WAlt
- f. **bernettii**	see G. robertianum 'Album'
- 'Celtic White'	CBre CCge ECoo EMon EPPr GCal GSki MHer NCWG NCat SRGP WAlt WHen WPnP WWpP
- subsp. **celticum**	WAlt
robustum	CElw CHar EBee EOrc EPPr EPri GSki IFro MNrw MSph NBro NChi NCot SIgm SMad SRGP SScr STes WBea WCot WCra WCru WFar WHal WHer WLin WPGP WWin
- S&SH 14	WBea
- Hannays' form	CCge CMea CSpe
- 'Norman Warrington'	WHer
robustum x **incanum**	CCge CMea CSpe LAco MAnH MSph WCom WCru
'Rosie Crûg'	CCge CHid EBee EChP EMan EPPr MAvo MDun NLar NSti SAga SPla WCot WCru WWhi
roethornii	WCru
rotundifolium	SCou
Rozanne = 'Gerwat'PBR	CCge EBre GKir MWhe SCou WCra
rubescens	CCge CSpe EMar FPPr GGar MNrw NBir NBro NCat NCot NSti SRGP SUsu WCru WHal WOut WTMC WWye
rubifolium	CBod EBee EMan GGar MBri MCCP MLwd NHol SSpi WCru WTMC
ruprechtii	CElw CHar CRDP EBee EBre ECoo EMar GMac MLwd MNrw NCat NCot SRGP WBea WElm WPer WPnP WWin
'Salome'	More than 30 suppliers
'Sandra' **new**	SRGP
sanguineum	More than 30 suppliers
- Alan Bloom = 'Bloger'PBR	CMCo CCge EBre ECtt GKir LRHS MCLN SCou SIng SMer WCra WTMC
- 'Album' ♀ H4	More than 30 suppliers
- 'Alpenglow'	SHel SRGP
- 'Ankum's Pride'	More than 30 suppliers
- 'Aviemore'	EBee NCat SCou SHel
- 'Barnsley'	CElw EBee NPro SCou SHel WWpP
- 'Belle of Herterton'	CCge CMCo EPPr MSte NPro SCou SUsu WCru WTMC
- 'Bloody Graham'	EGle MWhe NCot NHaw SCou SHel WMoo
- 'Catforth Carnival'	NCat
- 'Cedric Morris'	CElw CFil EChP ECha EFou EGle EGra EPPr LPio MAvo MTho NBid SAga SCou SCro SHel SRGP SUsu WCru WHen WPnP WTMC WWpP
- 'Elliott's Variety'	SIng
- 'Elsbeth'	More than 30 suppliers
- 'Feu d'Automne'	NCat
- 'Fran's Star' (d)	see G. x oxonianum 'Fran's Star'
- 'Glenluce'	More than 30 suppliers
- 'Hampshire Purple'	see G. sanguineum 'New Hampshire'
- 'Holden'	CElw EPPr SCou SHel WCra
- 'Joanna'	SCou SHel
- 'John Elsley'	CElw CMCo EBre EChP ECtt EPPr GKir LLWP LRHS MMil MWhe NCot NGdn NLar SHel SRGP SSpe SSpi STes SWat WCra WMnd WPer WPnP WTMC WWpP
- 'Jubilee Pink'	CElw EBla EPPr GCal MBri SBla WCra WCru WTMC
- var. **lancastrense**	see G. sanguineum var. striatum
- 'Leeds Variety'	see G. sanguineum 'Rod Leeds'
- 'Max Frei'	More than 30 suppliers
- 'Minutum'	NCot SCou SUsu WPnP
- 'Nanum'	CMea EPar NHol NMen WCru WPnP WWpP
§ - 'New Hampshire'	EBee MCAu NBro NCot NLar
- 'Nyewood'	ECGP EMon EPPr IMGH MLLN SCou SEND SRGP WCra WCru
- 'Plenum'	EPPr
- var. **prostratum** (Cav.) Pers.	see G. sanguineum var. striatum
§ - 'Rod Leeds'	CBel EBee LPio NPro NSti SCou WHal WTMC
- 'Sara'	NSti WHen WPnP
- 'Shepherd's Warning' ♀ H4	CMea CSev EBre ECtt EDAr EPPr CMea CSev EBre ECtt EDAr EPPrGKir LRHS MBri MBro MLLN MRav MWhe NBir NLar SCou SRGP SVil SWat WBea WCra WCru WHCG WHoo WIvy WRus WTel
- 'Shepherd's Warning seedlings	GCal NCot
- 'South Nutfield'	SCou
§ - var. **striatum** ♀ H4	More than 30 suppliers
- - deep pink	SCro
- - 'Reginald Farrer'	GBuc NCat WCru
- - 'Splendens'	CElw CSev ECha ELan ENot EPPr LBee LHop MRav MWat NBid NChi NCot WCru WEas WWhi
- 'Vision'	CCge EBla LRHS NCot WPnP WWpP
- 'Westacre Poppet'	EWes
sanguineum x **swatense**	WMoo
'Sarah Louisa'	NPar
'Sea Fire'	CCge CElw CWCL EMar MNrw MTho SCro
'Sea Pink'	CElw MNrw MTho MWrn NHar WHal
'Sea Spray'	CCge EBre EFou EMar EPPr EWes GBuc GSki LPio MAvo MNrw MSte MTho MWrn NGdn SWat WCru WMnd WRus WTMC WWpP
'Sellindge Blue'	CElw
sessiliflorum	ECou EPar NHar
- subsp. **novae-zelandiae** green-leaved	SWat
- - 'Nigricans'	More than 30 suppliers
- - 'Nigricans' x **traversii** var. **elegans**	CBos CMHG CRDP NCat SRms SWat
§ - - 'Porter's Pass'	CMea EHoe EWes GBuc MBro MCCP MNrw NCWG NChi SPlb SWat WCra WCru WFar WHoo WPGP WPnP WTMC WWpP
- - red-leaved	see G. sessiliflorum subsp. novae-zelandiae 'Porter's Pass'
- 'Rubrum'	CCge GSki MWod
'Sheilagh Hannay'	CMdw CSpe CStr

shikokianum	EBee EChP GMac NLar SRGP WBea
- var. *kaimontanum*	EBee NCat WCru
- var. *quelpaertense*	CDes EBee NCat WHal WPGP
- - B&SWJ 1234	WCru
- var. *yoshiianum*	CElw EBee GBuc NCat WCru WMoo WPat WTMC
sibiricum	EBla
'Silver Cloak' **new**	MCCP
'Silver Shadow'	CCge SPer
§ *sinense*	CElw EBee GCal ITer NCot NLar NPPs NSti NWCA SIng SRGP STes WCru WHCG WHer WMaN WMnd WMoo WPGP WPer WPnP WTMC WWhi WWpP
'Sirak'	CElw CLAP EBla EChP EGle EPPr GBin GCal MAnH MAvo MBro MCLN MMil MNFA NCat NCot NSti SAga SCou SUsu WBea WCra WElm WFar WHoo WMoo WPGP WPnP WTMC
soboliferum	CBod EBee EBre ELan EMan EPPr GCal GMac LRHS MBri NBir NCot NDlv NSti SCou SCro SPla SRGP WAbe WCra WCru WHal WWpP
- Cally strain **new**	GCal MSte
solandieri **new**	CElw
'Southcombe Star'	see *G.* x *oxonianum* 'Southcombe Star'
§ 'Spinners'	More than 30 suppliers
'Stanhoe'	CCge CSpe ECtt GBin LRHS MWgw SHar WFar
'Stanhoe' purple-leaved	EVFa
stapfianum var. *roseum*	see *G. orientalitibeticum*
'Stephanie'	CDes EBee EPPr NCat NDov NPPs
'Strawberry Frost'	EBee EChP EMan MDun WCot
'Sue Crûg'	More than 30 suppliers
'Sugar Babe' PBR	CCge
'Summer Cloud'	EPPr SHel SRGP WHrl
suzukii	IFro
- B&SWJ 016	WCru
swatense	MLLN SWat WCru
sylvaticum	CM&M EWTr GKir MCAu MSal NBid NCWG SCou SRGP SSpi WHal WHen WMoo WOut WPer WShi WTMC
- f. *albiflorum*	CBel CBot CBre CCge CElw CMil EBee ELan EMar MBro MWhe NSti SSpi WCru WPGP WWin
- 'Album' ♀ H4	More than 30 suppliers
- 'Amy Doncaster'	More than 30 suppliers
- 'Angulatum'	CElw CPlt EBee EPPr LPhx MNFA WMoo
- 'Birch Lilac'	CElw CMCo EBee EChP EPPr EPfP GBuc GCal GKir LRHS MAvo NCat NPPs NSti WBea WCra WFar WMoo WPnP WTMC WWpP
- 'Blue Ice' **new**	EBee EPPr
- 'Heron' **new**	CCge
- 'Immaculée'	MRav NCat
- 'Kanzlersgrund'	CElw
- 'Lilac Time' **new**	EPPr
- 'Mayflower' ♀ H4	More than 30 suppliers
- 'Meran'	EBee EBre NCat
- f. *roseum*	CCge CMCo EBee GGar GKir NCat SCro
- - 'Baker's Pink'	More than 30 suppliers
- 'Silva'	CCol CElw EBee EMan EPPr MAvo MRav SCou SCro SWat WCru
- subsp. *sylvaticum* var. *wanneri*	CCge CMea EBee EPPr MRav SCro WCru WTMC WWpP
'Terre Franche'	EBee EFou GBin NCot NGby NLar NSti SSpi

§ *thunbergii*	CBri CMCo EBee EMar GGar GSki LAst LGro MBow MNrw MRav NBid NOak NSti WHen WPer WWpP
- dark	CSev
- 'Jester's Jacket' (v) **new**	CPla EMan EVFa ITer NPro SPoG WTMC
- pink	EPPr SCou SRGP WCru WTMC
- white	EPPr NCot SRGP WTMC
thurstonianum	see *G.* x *oxonianum* f. *thurstonianum*
'Tidmarsh' **new**	EBee
'Tinpenny Mauve'	WHoo
'Tiny Monster' **new**	CFwr
transbaicalicum	CCge EBee EMan EPPr LRHS MBow MNrw SCro SPar SRGP WPGP WPnP
traversii	CBot CCge CLyd CPBP EGle SMrm WRos
- 'Big White'	WPnP
- var. *elegans*	CFee CSpe EBee GEdr IGor LPhx MLwd MNrw NCot NPPs NWCA SRGP WCru WEas WHCG WHrl WKif WPGP WPnP
tuberosum	More than 30 suppliers
- var. *charlesii*	see *G. kotschyi* var. *charlesii*
§ - 'Leonidas'	CCol CFwr CPou LRHS WPnP
- subsp. *linearifolium*	WCru
- pink	EVFa WCru WHoo WPnP
'Vera May' **new**	SUsu
'Verguld Saffier'	see *G.* 'Blue Sunrise'
versicolor	More than 30 suppliers
- *album*	CCge CElw MGas MWhe WBea WPnP
§ - 'Kingston'	EPPr
- 'Knighton'	EBee
§ - 'Snow White'	EBee EChP EOrc EPPr MNrw NCot NDov NMGW SCou SHel SRGP WCra WCru WMoo WPnP WTMC WWpP
- 'The Bride'	CMea EBee EGra EMan EMar EPPr
- 'White Lady'	see *G. versicolor* 'Snow White'
'Victor Reiter'	see *G. pratense* 'Victor Reiter'
violareum	see *Pelargonium* 'Splendide'
viscosissimum	EBee EBla GCal GSki LRHS SBri SRGP STes WCra WMnd WPnP
- rose pink	NBir
wallichianum	CBod CCge CMCo CPou CStr EBee ECGP IFro LRHS NBir NChi NCot NSti SBla WAbe WBea WFar WHen WMoo WTMC
§ - 'Buxton's Variety' ♀ H4	More than 30 suppliers
- 'Chadwell's Pink'	CCge EBee
- pale blue **new**	CElw
- pink	EFou EMan EPPr GBuc GKir LPio MTed NCot WCru
- RBGE form **new**	EBee SUsu
- 'Rosie' **new**	SRGP
- 'Syabru'	CBri CCge CElw CHar CMea EBee EBla EMar EMil EVFa GBuc GSki MLwd MNrw NCot NLar SAga SSpi WFar WMoo
'Wednesday's Child'	WFar
'Welsh Guiness'	NCat WCru WTMC
'Whitehaven'	NCot
wilfordii hort.	see *G. thunbergii*
wilfordii Maxim.	CCge NCot
- variegated **new**	WCru
'Wisley Hybrid'	see *G.* 'Khan'
ulassovianum	More than 30 suppliers
- 'Blue Star'	CCge GKir MBri MRav NPro WCra WTMC WWpP
yesoense	EBee EBla EPPr GBin MDKP MLwd NBir NChi NCot NSti

	SWat WCru WFar WOut WPnP WPrP
- var. *nipponicum*	WCru
- white	EBee NWCA
yoshinoi	CMCo EBee EBla EMan EMar EWes GAbr GBuc GMac GSki LLWP MSte NCot NLar NPro NWCA SHel SRGP STes SWat WLin WMoo WTMC WWpP
yunnanense misapplied	see *G. pogonanthum*
yunnanense Franchet	EBee GGar MNrw WAbe

Gerbera (Asteraceae)

gossypina	EBee
nivea	EMan

Gesneria (Gesneriaceae)

cardinalis	see *Sinningia cardinalis*
x *cardosa*	see *Sinningia* x *cardosa*

Geum ✿ (Rosaceae)

	'Abendsonne'	CElw
	aleppicum	CFee EBee EPPr WBea WMoo
	alpinum	see *G. montanum*
	andicola	EBee
	'Apricot Beauty'	CFai EBee LPVe
	'Beech House Apricot'	CBre CElw CMdw CRDP CSev EBre ECtt GBri GKir LHop LPhx MAvo MBri MNrw NChi NDov SApp SMac WAbe WLin WPnP WTMC WWeb WWye
	'Bell Bank'	NDov NPPs WHil
	'Birkheads Cream'	NBir
	'Blazing Sunset' (d)	CElw EBee MDKP MSph MWrn NArg NDlv NPPs SBri SOkh WCot
N	'Borisii'	More than 30 suppliers
	'Borisii' x *montanum*	LHop
	bulgaricum	CBri CMea EBee GKir LRHS MAvo MBri MNrw MRav NBir NLar NPro NRya WPnP WPrP WTMC WTin
	calthifolium	EBee EBre EPPr GKir MCCP MLLN MOne MRav NBro WElm
	capense	NPro WCot
	- JJ&JH 9401271	EBee EWes
§	*chiloense*	EBee IIve NPPs SIng
	- P&W 6513	GBri MSte NWCA
	coccineum hort.	see *G. chiloense*
	coccineum ambig.	CPlt WRha
	coccineum	EBee
	Sibth. & Sm. MESE 374	
	'Coppertone'	CDes CElw CPla EBee ECha EHrv ELan EMan EMon GCal MAvo MBro MCLN MNrw MRav NBir NBro NCat NChi NCot NLon NRya SUsu WCom WHoo WMoo WPGP WTMC WWhi WWpP
	'Dingle Apricot'	EVFa MAvo MNrw MRav MTed MWgw NBir
	'Dolly North'	CHea EBee EFou ERou EVFa GAbr GBri GGar LRHS MAvo MBNS MBri MCAu MNrw NBro NCot SBri WAul WHal WPrP WTMC
I	'Elaine's Variety'	MAvo NCat
	elatum	EBee
I	'Farmer John Cross'	CBre CBri CDes CElw EBee ECtt MAvo MHar MNrw NCot SBri WCra WHal WPGP
	fauriei	EBee
	x *kamtschatica* **new**	
	'Feuermeer'	MSte NPro
	'Fire Opal' ♀ H4	CDes CPlt MNrw MSph NBir
	'Flames of Passion' **new**	GBin MBri MCAu NPro SUsu WAul WElm WHil

	'Georgeham'	CPla WWhi
	'Georgenburg'	More than 30 suppliers
	glaciale album **new**	EBee
	'Herterton Primrose' **new**	MAvo
*	*hybridum luteum*	NSti
	x *intermedium*	CBre CHor EBee EGle EMan EMon EPPr GBri LRHS MNrw NLar NPro SBri SChu SCro WFar WLRN WMoo WTMC WWin
	japonicum	EBee
	'Karlskaer'	CDes CElw EBee EChP ECtt EGle EWes GBin GCal LPVe LPio MAvo MHar MNrw SAga SBri SMrm SOkh SUsu WHil WMoo WPGP WPnP WViv
	'Lady Stratheden' ♀ H4	More than 30 suppliers
	'Lemon Drops'	CBri CElw EBee ECha ELan EMan EVFa GBri GMac MAvo MHar MNrw MRav MSte NChi NDov SBla SChu SOkh SWal WFar WHil WMoo WPGP WTMC WViv WWhi
	'Lionel Cox'	More than 30 suppliers
	macrophyllum	EBee EMan GBar MNrw NDlv WMoo
	magellanicum	EBee WCot
	- *perincisum* **new**	EBee
	'Mandarin'	CBos CFir CMdw GCal MAvo MTed WViv
	'Marika'	CBos CBre CHid CRow EBee MAvo MNrw SChu WCot WMoo
	'Marmalade'	CPlt EChP ECtt LPhx MAvo MHar MNrw NPPs SAga SDys SUsu WBea WCot WCra
§	*montanum* ♀ H4	EBre GKir GTou MBro NBid NBir NBro NDlv NRya SPet SRms WBea WMoo WPat WPer WWin
	- 'Maximum'	MNrw
	'Mrs J. Bradshaw' ♀ H4	More than 30 suppliers
	'Mrs W. Moore'	CDes EBee GBri MAvo MLLN MNrw NBir NCat NChi NCot NPPs NPro WCot WPGP WTMC
	'Nordek'	EBee EMan GMac MBri NCot SBri WWhi
*	'Orangeman'	MAvo MNrw
	parviflorum	LEdu MLLN MNrw NBro SBri
	'Paso Doble'	NCot NPro SBri WRHF WRos WSan
§	*pentapetalum*	GEdr MNrw WAbe
	- 'Flore Pleno' (d)	WAbe
	'Pink Frills' **new**	CElw
	'Present'	CDes EBee SBri WPGP
I	'Primrose' **new**	WTMC
	'Prince of Orange'	CElw IGor MNrw WFar WMoo WRha
	'Prinses Juliana'	More than 30 suppliers
	pyrenaicum	EBee MNrw NWCA
	quellyon	see *G. chiloense*
	'Red Wings'	CDrc CM&M EBee EFou EMan EMar ERou GCal MAvo MBNS MRav WCra WRus
	reptans	see *Sieversia reptans*
	x *rhaeticum*	EBee ETow MNrw WMoo WPic
	rhodopeum	EBee MNrw
	'Rijnstroom'	EBee ELan MTed NBro SBri SUsu WAul WCra
	rivale	More than 30 suppliers
	- 'Album'	More than 30 suppliers
	- apricot	WWin
	- 'Cream Drop'	NChi NWoo SBri
	- cream, from Tien Shan, China	CFee
*	- *islandicum*	EBee
	- lemon	CRDP EMan NPPs

- 'Leonard's Double' (d) — WElm WMoo WTMC
- 'Leonard's Variety' — More than 30 suppliers
- 'Marmalade' — MSph NChi
- 'Oxford Marmalade' — CElw SApp

roylei — EBee SBri

'Rubin' — CDes EBee EBlw EFou EPPr
MBNS MCAu MCLN MNrw NBro
NDov NGdn SChu SCro SPla SSpe
WAul WCot WTMC

'Sigiswang' — EFou GAbr GMac MAvo MFir
MNrw MSte NPro SBri SMrm

'Tangerine' — GGar MAvo MNrw MRav MWrn

x *tirolense* — EBee NCot

triflorum — CPBP EBee EBlw EChP EHrv
EMan EPla GKir GTou LPhx LPio
LRHS MAvo MBri MCCP MNrw
MRav MTis MWrn NLar SRot WFar
WHil WMoo WRus

- var. *campanulatum* — EDAr EHyt ETow GBri NChi NGar
NPro NRya

urbanum — CArn CKin ELau GBar GDea
GWCH MBow MChe MGas NLan
NSco SWat WHbs WHer WMoo
WPic

- 'Checkmate' (v) — EMon MWrn WBea WPrP
- from Patagonia — MDKP
'Werner Arends' — CBos CMHG EBee GCal LRHS
MAvo MBri MCLN MRav SBri
WCot WFar

Gevuina (Proteaceae)

avellana — CBcs CHEx CTrG CTrw IDee
SSpi

Gilia (Polemoniaceae)

aggregata — see *Ipomopsis aggregata*
californica — see *Leptodactylon californicum*

Gillenia (Rosaceae)

stipulata — CHea CPlt CRDP EGle EMon GCal
LPhx SMrm SVal WMaN

trifoliata ♀ H4 — More than 30 suppliers
- 'Pixie' — CFil EBee WPGP

Gingidia (Apiaceae)

montana — NWCA

Ginkgo ❀ (Ginkgoaceae)

biloba ♀ H4 — More than 30 suppliers
- 'Anny's Dwarf' **new** — MBlu
- 'Autumn Gold' (m) — CBcs CDoC CDul CEnd CMCN
EPfP LNet MBlu MBri MGos SKee
SMad WPGP
I - 'Barabits Nana' **new** — SMad
- 'Barabits Sztráda' — MBlu SMad
- 'Chotek' — MBlu
- 'Fairmount' (m) — CMCN MBlu
- 'Fastigiata' (m) — CMCN CWib MGos
- 'Hekt Leiden' — CMCN
- 'Horizontalis' — CMCN EPfP MBlu
- 'King of Dongting' (f) — CMCN GKir MBlu MBri WMou
- Pendula Group — CBcs CEnd CMCN CTho EPfP
LPan MBlu NPal
I - 'Prostrata' — CPMA
- 'Saratoga' (m) — CEnd CMCN CPMA CTho EMil
LCon LNet MBlu MGos WPGP
- 'Tit' — CMCN EPfP LCon LNet MGos
- 'Tremonia' — CDoC CMCN LCon LNet LRHS
MBlu MBri
- 'Tubifolia' — CMCN MBlu
- 'Umbrella' — CDul CMCN
- Variegata Group (v) — CMCN CPMA LNet MBlu

Gladiolus (Iridaceae)

acuminatus — EGrW
'Advantage'^PBR (L) — EGrW MSGs
alatus — EGrW
'Alba' (N) — CSut
'Alex Hall' (G) **new** — EGrW MSGs
'Alexandra' (P) — EGrW
'Allosius' (S) **new** — EGrW
'Amanda Mahy' (N) — CBro NRog
'Ambiance'^PBR (L) — EGrW MSGs
'Amsterdam' (G) — EGrW MSGs
'Anchorage' (L) — MSGs
'Andre Viette' — EBee EMan WCot
angustus — EGrW GCal WCot
'Anna Leorah' (L) — EGrW MSGs
antakiensis — CPou
'Antique Rose' (M) **new** — EGrW MSGs
'Applause' (L) — NRog
'Apricot Perfection' (P) — EGrW MSGs
'Arabella' (P) **new** — EGrW
* 'Arabian Night' — CSut
'Arctic Day' (M/E) **new** — EGrW
'Atom' (S/P) — CBro EBee WCot
atroviolaceus — WPGP
'Aubrey Lane' (M) — EGrW
'August Days' (L) — EGrW MSGs
aurantiacus — GCal
aureus — EGrW
'Baby Girl' **new** — MSGs
'Bandalero' **new** — MSGs
Barnard hybrids — EGrW
'Beau Rivage' (G) **new** — MSGs
'Beautiful Angel' **new** — MSGs
'Beauty of Holland'^PBR (L) — EGrW MSGs
'Bell Tower' (G) **new** — EGrW
'Ben Venuto' (L) **new** — EGrW
'Black Lash' (S) — MSGs
'Blackpool' (M) — NRog
blandus var. *carneus* — see *G. carneus*
'Blue Clouds' (L) **new** — EGrW
'Blue Conqueror' (L) — LRHS
'Blue Sky' (L) **new** — EGrW
'Blue Tit' (P) — EGrW
'Blueberry Wine' (L/E) **new** — EGrW MSGs
'Bombay' (G) — MSGs
'Bono's Memory' — LRHS
'Bradley W' **new** — MSGs
'Break of Dawn' **new** — NCel
'Bronze Tiger' (M/E) **new** — EGrW
'Brooke M' (S) **new** — EGrW
'Burgundy Queen' **new** — EGrW WCot
byzantinus — see *G. communis* subsp.
byzantinus
caeruleus — CPou EGrW
'Calimero' (M/E) **new** — EGrW
callianthus — CBri CSWP EBla EOrc EPyc SVen
WFar WWhi
'Calliope' (L/E) **new** — EGrW
'Cambourne' (Min) — NRog
'Candy Cane' (L) — EGrW
cardinalis — CAvo CDes CFil CMdw CMea
CPne CRDP EBee EBla EGrW
EMan GCal IBlr LPio SAga SIgm
SSpi WCot WPGP
carinatus — CDes EBee EGrW NRog
'Carine' (N) — EGrW
'Carla Gabor' (L) — EGrW
carmineus — EGrW LBow
§ *carneus* — CBro CPou EBee EGrW EMan
EPot GCal LRHS NRog
- 'Georgina' **new** — EGrW
'Carquirenne' (G) — EGrW MSGs

'Cartago' (L)	EGrW
'Carved Ivory' (M)	MSGs
caryophyllaceus	CPou EGrW
'CGS 75th Anniversary' (L) **new**	MSGs
'Cha Cha'^{PBR} (L) **new**	EGrW
'Charm' (N/Tub)	CAvo CBro EBla EGrW
'Charming Beauty' (Tub)	ECho NRog
'Charming Lady' (Tub)	ECho NCel
'Christabel'	LBow
'Christabel' (L)	EGrW ERos
'Chumba Wumba' **new**	MSGs
'Cindy' (B)	ECho
citrinus	see *G. trichonemifolius*
'Clarence's Choice' (L)	MSGs
'Columbine' (P)	NRog
x *colvillei*	IBlr
- 'Albus'	ETub WFTG
- 'The Bride' ♀ H3	CAvo CBro CHad CMil EBee EBla EBre EGrW EPyc GMac LAma NRog
'Comet' (N)	EGrW ETub MSph NRog WFTG
communis	LAma
§ - subsp. *byzantinus* ♀ H4	More than 30 suppliers
- subsp. *communis*	EBee
'Coral Dream' (L)	EGrW
'Côte d'Azur' (G)	EGrW MSGs
crassifolius	GBuc LPio
'Creme de Mint' (S)	MSGs
'Crimson Fire' (G)	EGrW
§ *dalenii*	CPou EGrW ERos GCal IBlr ITer LPio SSpi WCot
- yellow	EBee
'Dark Victory' (L) **new**	MSGs
'Daydreamer' (L) **new**	EGrW MSGs
'Doris Darling' (L) **new**	MSGs
'Drama' (L)	EGrW MSGs
'Dream Dust' **new**	MSGs
'Dream's End' (G) **new**	EGrW
'Dynamic' **new**	MSGs
'Early Little Lilac' (S) **new**	EGrW
'Ecstasy' (L) **new**	MSGs
'Edna' (S)	MSGs
'Egret' (L/E) **new**	EGrW
'El Diablo' (L/E) **new**	EGrW
'Elegance' (G) **new**	EGrW MSGs
'Elin' (M)	EGrW
elliotii **new**	EBee
'Elvira' (N)	EBee EBla ECho EGrW LAma NRog WPGP
'Emerald Green' **new**	MSGs
'Emerald Spring' (S)	EGrW WCot
'Emir' (S) **new**	MSGs
equitans	EGrW
'Esperanto' (M)	MSGs
'Essex' (P)	EGrW
'Esta Bonita' (G)	EGrW MSGs
'Estonia'^{PBR} (G)	EGrW
'Eunice Ann' **new**	MSGs
'Exactly' (S) **new**	MSGs
'Fair Lady' (Tub)	NRog
'Fashion Romance' **new**	MSGs
'Fidelio' (L)	LAma NCel
'Finishing Touch'^{PBR} (L) **new**	EGrW
'Fiona' **new**	MSGs
'Fireball II' (L) **new**	MSGs
'Firesprite' (Min) **new**	EGrW
'Flamenco' (L) **new**	MSGs
'Flamingo Dawn' (L/E) **new**	EGrW
'Flevo Amico' (S) **new**	EGrW
'Flevo Bambino' **new**	EGrW MSGs
'Flevo Candy' **new**	EGrW MSGs
'Flevo Clown' (S) **new**	EGrW
'Flevo Cosmic' (Min)	EGrW LPio MSGs WCot
'Flevo Eclipse' (G) **new**	EGrW
'Flevo Fire'^{PBR} (M)	EGrW
'Flevo Jive' (S) **new**	EGrW
'Flevo Junior' (S) **new**	EGrW
'Flevo Maitre' (L)	EGrW LPio MSGs
'Flevo Option' **new**	EGrW MSGs
'Flevo Party' **new**	EGrW MSGs
'Flevo Smile' (S) **new**	EGrW
'Flevo Souvenir'^{PBR} (L)	EGrW
'Florence C' (M)	EGrW MSGs
floribundus	EGrW LBow
'Flower's Sculpture' (L/E) **new**	EGrW
'Flowersong' (L)	LAma
'French Silk' (L) **new**	EGrW
'Friendship' (L)	LRHS
* *galpinii* **new**	EBee
x *gandavensis* **new**	EBee
garnieri	EGrW SSpi
geardii **new**	WCot
'General Patton' (G) **new**	MSGs
'Georgette' (B)	MSGs
'Gillian' (L)	LBow
'Gladiris' (L) **new**	MSGs
'Golden Sunset' (L) **new**	EGrW MSGs
'Goldfinch' (S) **new**	MSGs
'Good Luck' (N)	CBro
gracilis	EGrW
grandis	see *G. liliaceus*
'Green Star' (L)	MSGs
'Green With Envy' (L) **new**	MSGs
'Green Woodpecker' (M)	LAma LRHS NCel NRog
'Greyfriars' (P)	EGrW
'Guernsey Glory' (N)	EGrW NRog
§ *guthriei*	EGrW
'Gwendolyn' **new**	MSGs
'Halley' (N)	CBro ECho NCel
'Hastings' (P)	MSGs WCot
'Heidi' (S)	EGrW
'Henriette' (P) **new**	EGrW
'High Hopes' (S) **new**	EGrW
'High Style' (L)	EGrW
hirsutus **new**	EGrW
'Holland Pearl' (B)	CSut NRog
'Hunting Song' (N)	LAma NRog
'Huron Darkness' **new**	MSGs
'Huron Lady' **new**	MSGs
'Huron Silk' **new**	MSGs
huttonii	EGrW
hyalinus	EGrW WCot
'Ice Cap' (L)	EGrW
'Ice Follies' (L) **new**	MSGs
illyricus	CFil CNat CSam EGrW GBuc WPGP
- 'Mallorca'	EGrW
imbricatus	EBee EGrW ERos GBuc GCrs
'Impressive' (N)	NRog
§ *italicus*	EBee EGrW ELan LPhx LPio MBow
'Ivory Tower' (G)	EGrW
'Jackpot'	NCel
'Jeannie Rose' (S)	MSGs
'Jester' (L)	CSut
'Jim S' **new**	MSGs
'Julianna' (L) **new**	EGrW
'Jupiter' (B)	LRHS
§ *kotschyanus*	GCrs
'Krakatoa' (G) **new**	EGrW
'Kristin' (L)	EGrW MSGs
'Lady Eleanor' (P)	WCot
'Lady Godiva' (P/S)	NRog

'Lady in Red' (L) **new** — MSgs
'Lady Lucille' (M) — EGrW MSgs
'Lavender Flare' (S) — EGrW MSgs
'Lavender Masterpiece' (L) **new** — EGrW
'Leonore' (S) — CSut
lewisiae **new** — SSpi
'Liebelei' (B) — NCel
§ *liliaceus* — EGrW LBow
'Lime Green' (P) — LRHS
'Little Darling' (P/S) — MSgs
'Little Jude' (P) — EGrW MSgs WCot
'Little Wiggy' (P) — MSgs
'Lowland Queen' (L) — EGrW MSgs
'Margaret' (P) — EGrW
'Marj S' (L) **new** — EGrW MSgs
marlothii — EGrW
'Match Point' (L) **new** — MSgs
'Meersen' (L) — EGrW
'Mileesh' (L) — EGrW MSgs
'Mirella' (N) — EGrW MRav NRog
'Mondiale' (G) — EGrW MSgs
'Moon Kist' (S) **new** — EGrW
mortonius — EBee SIgm
'Mother Theresa' **new** — MSgs
'Mountain Meadow' (L) **new** — EGrW
'Mr Chris' (S) — EGrW MSgs
'Mr Fox' (S) **new** — MSgs
'Mrs Rowley' (P) — EGrW WCot
§ *murielae* ♀ H3 — CAvo CBro CFwr EBee EBot EGrW ETub LAma LBow NRog SDeJ STes WBea WHoo WOld WRHF WWeb
'Murieliae' — see *G. murielae*
'My Girl' (L) **new** — EGrW MSgs
'My Love' (L) — LAma
'Nancy' — LBow
natalensis — see *G. dalenii*
'Nathalie' (N) — EGrW ETub MSph WFTG
'New Wave'[PBR] **new** — MSgs
'Nicholas' (S) — MSgs
'Night Breeze' (L) **new** — MSgs
'Northern Messenger' (S) **new** — EGrW
'Nova Lux' (L) — LAma LRHS NCel NRog
'Nymph' (N) — CAvo EBla EChP EGrW ETub LAma MSph NRog WFTG
'Oasis'[PBR] (G) **new** — EGrW
'Obelisk' (P) — NRog
ochroleucus **new** — EGrW
'Of Singular Beauty' (L) **new** — EGrW MSgs
§ *oppositiflorus* — CPou EGrW SIgm
– subsp. *salmoneus* — see *G. oppositiflorus*
'Orchid Lace' (S/E) **new** — EGrW
orchidiflorus — CSWP EGrW LBow
'Orlando'[PBR] **new** — MSgs
'Oscar' (G) — LAma LRHS NRog
palustris — ERos
'Paparcio Ziedas' (L/E) **new** — EGrW
papilio — More than 30 suppliers
– 'David Hills' **new** — EGrW
§ – Purpureoaurautus Group — CBro CSam EBee EMan ERos GKir IBlr MFir SRms
– yellow-flowered **new** — SMad
pappei — CDes EBee EGrW WPGP
'Parade' (G) — EGrW
'Patricia' (L) **new** — MSgs
'Penelope' (P) **new** — EGrW
'Perth Pearl' **new** — MSgs
'Peter Pears' (L) — LAma LRHS NCel NRog
'Phenom' (G) **new** — EGrW

'Phyllis M' (L) — EGrW
'Picturesque' (P) — NRog
Pilbeam hybrids **new** — EGrW
'Pink Elf' (S) — MSgs
'Pink Lady' (L) — EGrW MSgs
'Pink Phantom' (L) **new** — EGrW
'Plum Tart' (L) — LRHS
'Pop Art' — LRHS NCel
'Praha' (L) — LAma NRog
'Pretty Woman' (L) — EGrW
primulinus — see *G. dalenii*
primulinus hybrids — SDeJ
'Prince Indigo' (L) **new** — MSgs
'Princess Margaret Rose' (Min) — LAma
'Prins Claus' (N) — CBro CSut EBee EBla EGrW LAma LRHS NRog
priorii — EGrW LBow
'Priscilla' (L) — LAma
'Pulchritude' (M) — EGrW MSgs
punctulatus — ERos
var. *punctulatus*
'Purple Prince' (M) — WCot
'Purple Velvet' (M) **new** — EGrW
purpureoauratus — see *G. papilio* Purpureoauratus Group
quadrangularis — SSpi
'Radinye' **new** — MSgs
'Rasmin' (L) **new** — MSgs
'Red Beauty' — LRHS MSgs
'Red Ruffles' **new** — MSgs
'Richmond' (B) — CSut NRog
'Robinetta' (*recurvus* hybrid) ♀ H3 — CBri CSut EBla EChP ECho EGrW EPfP LAma NCel NRog
rogersii **new** — EGrW
'Rose Elf' (S) — EGrW
'Route One' (L) **new** — EGrW
'Roxborough' (P) — EGrW
'Royal Canadian' (S) **new** — MSgs
'Royal Dutch' (L) — EGrW MSgs
'Royal Mounted' (Min) **new** — EGrW
'Sabu' — LRHS
saccatus — EGrW
'Sailor's Delight' (L) — EGrW MSgs
'Sally's Orange' (P) — EGrW
'Salmon Sorbet' **new** — EGrW
'San Remo'[PBR] (L) — EGrW MSgs
saundersii — CFil EGrW SIgm WPGP
'Scarlet Lady' (P) — EGrW
'Sceptre' (L) — MSgs
scullyi — EGrW LBow
segetum — see *G. italicus*
'Serafin' (Min) — LRHS NCel
sericeovillosus — EGrW
'Silver Shadow'[PBR] (S) — EGrW
'Sirael' (L/E) — EGrW
'Smokey Joe' (L) **new** — EGrW
'Souvenir' **new** — MSgs
splendens — CDes EGrW WCot
'Star Krajka' **new** — MSgs
stefaniae **new** — EGrW
'Stromboli' (L) — EGrW
'Sun Valley' **new** — MSgs
'Sunglo' **new** — MSgs
'Sunset Fire' (L) **new** — EGrW
'Sunsport' (M) **new** — EGrW
'Super High Brow' (G) **new** — EGrW MSgs
'Tantastic' (S) **new** — MSgs
tenellus — EGrW
'The Bride' — see *G. colvillei* 'The Bride'
'Three Musketeers' (M/E) **new** — EGrW

'Tickatoo' (P) **new** — EGrW
'Tiger Eyes' (S) **new** — MSGs
'Top O' the Marque' — EGrW
   (M/E) **new**
'Topaz' (L) — EGrW MSGs
'Torch' (L/E) **new** — EGrW
'Trader Horn' (G) — LAma NRog
§ *trichonemifolius* — EGrW LBow SSpi
tristis — CBro CElw CFil CPou CRow
ECha EGrW ELan EMan LBow
LPio NRog SAga SDix SSpi
SUsu WAbe WCot WHal WPGP
WPrP
- var. *aestivalis* — LBow
- var. *concolor* — EBee EGrW EMan ERos LBow
WCot WHer
'Tuscany' **new** — MSGs
undulatus — CSWP EGrW ERos LBow SSpi
WCot
'Victor Borge' (L) — NCel NRog
'Victoria' (M) — EGrW LRHS
'Video' (L) — EGrW
'Vienna' (L) — EGrW
'Violetta' (M) — CSut ECho EGrW EMan MSGs
virescens — EGrW LBow SSpi
'Visual Arts' (M) **new** — MSGs
watsonioides — CPou ERos SSpi
'White City' (P/S) — LRHS MSGs
'White Darling' **new** — MSGs
'White Friendship' (L) — LAma NRog
'White Prosperity' (L) — LRHS NCel

Glaucidium (Glaucidiaceae)

palmatum ♀ H4 — EBee EFEx EHyt ETow GCrs GDra
GIDF GKev NHar NSla WAbe
WCot WCru
- 'Album' — see *G. palmatum* var.
leucanthum
§ - var. *leucanthum* — CBri EFEx GCrs GDra

Glaucium (Papaveraceae)

§ *corniculatum* — CBot CHar EBre LPhx NPPs SEND
WCot WEas WMoo WWpP
flavum — CSpe ECha EMFP GKir LRHS
MHer MWgw SCro WCot WHer
WViv WWin
- *aurantiacum* — see *G. flavum* f. *fulvum*
§ - f. *fulvum* — ECha EMFP EMan LPio NDov
SChu SDix SMHy WHil
- orange — see *G. flavum* f. *fulvum*
- red — see *G. corniculatum*
grandiflorum — WWin
phoenicium — see *G. corniculatum*

Glaux (Primulaceae)

maritima — WPer

Glechoma (Lamiaceae)

hederacea — CAgr CArn CKin GBar GPoy Ilve
MHer NBro NMir WCer WHbs
WHer WWye
- 'Barry Yinger — CRow EBee WCot
   Variegated' (v)
- 'Little Crown' (v) — WAlt
- 'Rosea' — GBar WAlt
§ - 'Variegata' (v) — CHal IHMH ILis LRHS MBri MRav
NBlu SGar SPet

Gleditsia (Caesalpiniaceae)

caspica — IFro
japonica — EPfP
sinensis — SMad

triacanthos — CAgr CDul CWib ECrN ENot
LEdu LPan MHFa SPlb WNor
- 'Elegantissima' (v) — SPer
- 'Emerald Cascade' — CDul CEnd CLnd CPMA LRHS
- f. *inermis* — CAgr WNor
- 'Rubylace' — More than 30 suppliers
- 'Shademaster' — EBee ENot MRav
- 'Skyline' — LPan WGer
- 'Sunburst' ♀ H4 — More than 30 suppliers

Gleichenia (Gleicheniaceae)

microphylla — WRic

Globba (Zingiberaceae)

andersonii — CKob LEur
* *cathcartii* — CKob LEur
'Emerald Isle' — LRHS
marantina — LEur
winitii — LRHS
- 'Golden Dragon' **new** — MOak
- 'Mauve Dancing Girl' **new** — MOak
- 'Red Leaf' **new** — MOak
- 'Violett' **new** — MOak
- 'White Dragon' **new** — MOak

Globularia (Globulariaceae)

bellidifolia — see *G. meridionalis*
bisnagarica — GEdr WLin
cordifolia ♀ H4 — CBrm CNic CTri EDAr ETow
GEdr IMGH LBee LRHS MBro
MPWC MTho NHar NMen SAga
SBla SIng WFar WHoo WPat
- NS 696 — NWCA
incanescens — LBee LRHS WWin
§ *meridionalis* — CFee CLyd CPBP EWes MBro
MWat NHar NLAp NMen NWCA
SAga SBla SGar WPat
- 'Hort's Variety' — CStu CTri NMen WAbe
nana — see *G. repens*
nudicaulis — MBro NHar NLAp SBla
- 'Alba' — WIvy
§ *punctata* — LRHS NWCA SRms
pygmaea — see *G. meridionalis*
§ *repens* — CLyd CNic MBro MTho NMen WPat
spinosa — NMen
stygia — NMen
trichosantha — CFee EDAr GMaP NRya SMrm
SRms WCom WPer

Gloriosa (Colchicaceae)

lutea — see *G. superba* 'Lutea'
rothschildiana — see *G. superba* 'Rothschildiana'
§ *superba* ♀ H1 — LAma MBri NRog
§ - 'Lutea' — CHal LAma LBow LRHS NRog
§ - 'Rothschildiana' — CBcs CHal CPlN CRHN CStu
LAma LBow LEur LRHS SOWG
SRms SYvo

Glottiphyllum (Aizoaceae)

nelii 'Pygmaeum' **new** — GCrs

Gloxinia (Gesneriaceae)

'Chic' — NMos
'Medusa' — WDib
perennis — NMos
sylvatica — CHal WDib

Glumicalyx (Scrophulariaceae)

flanaganii — GBri GCrs GEdr NGar WAbe
- HWEL 0325 — NWCA
- LEG 021 — IDac
goseloides — ECre
montanus — CFee CTrC EBee EMan MAvo

Glyceria (*Poaceae*)

aquatica variegata	see *G. maxima* var. *variegata*
maxima	CBod EMFW NPer
§ - var. **variegata** (v)	More than 30 suppliers
spectabilis 'Variegata'	see *G. maxima* var. *variegata*

Glycyrrhiza (*Papilionaceae*)

echinata	CAgr CArn MSal NLar
§ **glabra**	CAgr CArn EBee ELau GWCH LPhx
	MHer MSal NLar WHer WJek WWye
- 'Poznan'	GPoy
glandulifera	see *G. glabra*
lepidota	EBee
uralensis	CArn EBee ELau GPoy MHer MSal
yunnanensis	LPhx

Gnaphalium (*Asteraceae*)

'Fairy Gold'	see *Helichrysum*
	thianschanicum 'Goldkind'

Godetia see *Clarkia*

Gomphocarpus (*Asclepiadaceae*)

§ **fruticosus**	SSte
§ **physocarpus**	CArn CPLG CTCP

Gomphostigma (*Buddlejaceae*)

virgatum	CDes CPle CPlt CRDP CSpe CTrC
	EBee EChP EMan EPPr LPio LRHS
	MGGn MGrG MLLN MSte NPSI SPlb
	SSvw WCot WHrl WSHC WWeb
- 'White Candy' **new**	EBee GBri

Gonatanthus (*Araceae*)

pumilus new	WAbe

Goniolimon (*Plumbaginaceae*)

incanum	EBee
§ - 'Blue Diamond'	CM&M WCot
§ **tataricum**	EMan LAst WRHF
§ - var. **angustifolium**	EBee MWgw NBlu SRms WCot WPer

Goodyera (*Orchidaceae*)

biflora	EFEx
hachijoensis	EFEx
var. **yakushimensis**	
pubescens	EBee EFEx LRHS WCru
schlechtendaliana	EFEx

gooseberry see *Ribes uva-crispa* var. *reclinatum*

Gordonia (*Theaceae*)

axillaris	CDoC CHEx CHll

Gossypium (*Malvaceae*)

herbaceum	MSal

granadilla see *Passiflora quadrangularis*

granadilla, purple see *Passiflora edulis*

granadilla, sweet see *Passiflora ligularis*

granadilla, yellow see *Passiflora laurifolia*

grape see *Vitis*

grapefruit see *Citrus* x *paradisi*

Graptopetalum (*Crassulaceae*)

bellum ♀ H1	SChr
§ **paraguayense**	CHal EOas SPar SVen

Gratiola (*Scrophulariaceae*)

officinalis	CArn EBee EHon EMan GDea MHer
	MSal WRHF WSel WWpP WWye

Greenovia (*Crassulaceae*)

aizoon	ETow
§ **aurea**	SIng

Grevillea ✿ (*Proteaceae*)

alpina	CFee CPLG CPle EBee GQui SMur
	SOWG
- 'Goldfields'	SOWG
- 'Olympic Flame'	CBcs CDoC CFwr CPLG CTrw
	CWib SLon SOWG
aquifolium new	SOWG
arenaria new	SOWG
- var. **canescens**	SOWG
aspleniifolia	SOWG
'Robyn Gordon'	
'Australflora Copper Crest'	see *G.* 'Copper Crest'
australis var. **brevifolia**	CPLG
banksii	CPLG
- 'Canberra Hybrid'	see *G.* 'Canberra Gem'
- var. **forsteri**	SOWG SPlb
barklyana	SOWG
baueri	SOWG
beadleana new	SOWG
bedggoodiana	SOWG
bipinnatifida	SOWG
'Bonnie Prince Charlie'	CPLG SOWG
'Bronze Rambler'	SOWG
§ 'Canberra Gem' ♀ H3-4	CDoC CHEx CPLG CPMA CPle
	CTrG CWSG EBee ECou LHop
	LRHS MBri MBro SDry SIgm
	SOWG SPar SPoG SSpi WBrE
	WCru WFar WGer WPat
'Clearview David'	ESlt LRHS SOWG
confertifolia	SOWG
§ 'Copper Crest'	SOWG
'Cranbrook Yellow'	CDoC CPLG SOWG
crithmifolia	CPLG SOWG
curviloba	CPLG
diffusa subsp. **evansiana**	SOWG
'Evelyn's Coronet' **new**	SOWG
'Fanfare' **new**	SOWG
gaudichaudii new	SOWG
'Honey Gem'	SOWG
johnsonii new	ESlt
juniperina	CPLG CTrC
- subsp. **amphitricha**	CPLG
- 'Molonglo'	CPLG
- f. **sulphurea**	CBcs CDoC CDul CFil CHll COtt
	CPLG CTrG CTrw EPfP GQui
	SIgm SOWG SPer WBod WPat
lanigera	CPLG
- 'Mount Tamboritha'	CPLG
- prostrate	SIgm SOWG
levis	SOWG
longistyla new	SPlb
'Mason's Hybrid'	SOWG
monticola	CPLG
'Moonlight'	SOWG
obtusifolia 'Gingin Gem'	SOWG
olivacea 'Apricot	SOWG
Glow' **new**	
'Orange Marmalade'	SOWG
paniculata new	SOWG SPlb
'Pink Lady' **new**	SOWG
'Pink Surprise' **new**	SOWG
'Poorinda Peter'	CPLG SOWG
robusta ♀ H1+3	CHal CTrC MGol SMur SOWG SPlb
'Robyn Gordon' **new**	ESlt

'Rondeau' **new**	ESlt
rosmarinifolia ♀ H3	More than 30 suppliers
– 'Desert Flame'	CPLG
– 'Jenkinsii'	CBcs CPLG
'Sandra Gordon'	SOWG
'Scarlet Sprite'	SOWG
§ × **semperflorens**	CBcs CDoC CPLG CRez CWib
	SOWG
sericea	SOWG
shiressii	SOWG
'Sid Reynolds'	CPLG
'Spider Man' **new**	ESlt
'Splendour'	SOWG
thelemanniana	CPLG ECou ESlt
– Spriggs' form **new**	SOWG
thyrsoides	CBcs CPLG SDry
tolminsis	see G. × semperflorens
tridentifera	CPLG
victoriae	SSpi
williamsonii	SIgm SOWG

Grewia (Tiliaceae)

flavicans new	SSte
lasiocarpa new	SSte
occidentalis	SSte
robusta	SSte

Greyia (Greyiaceae)

sutherlandii	CTrC SOWG SPlb

Grindelia (Asteraceae)

§ **camporum**	EBee EChP EMan GBar MSal SPlb
	WCot WPer
chiloensis	CAbb EBee NDov SDix SDry SIgm
	SMad WPat
oregana	EBee
robusta	see G. camporum
squarrosa	GBar
stricta	CArn

Griselinia (Griseliniaceae)

* 'Crinkles'	SDry SLon
littoralis ♀ H3	More than 30 suppliers
– 'Bantry Bay' (v)	CAbP CDoC CWSG EBee EHoe
	ELan GGar LRHS SAga SEND SLim
	SPar SPer WCru WFar
– 'Brodick Gold'	CPLG
– 'Dixon's Cream' (v)	CBcs CSBt EPfP GQui SAga SDry
	SLon WCru
– 'Green Jewel' (v)	CBcs CPMA CPne CWib EBee
	SDry SPla WLeb
– 'Luscombe's Gold'	CPne
– 'Variegata' (v) ♀ H3	More than 30 suppliers
scandens	CPle WSHC

guava, common see *Psidium guajava*

guava, purple or strawberry see *Psidium littorale*

Gueldenstaedtia (Papilionaceae)

himalaica B&SWJ 2631	WCru

Gunnera (Gunneraceae)

arenaria	GGar IBlr
chilensis	see G. tinctoria
dentata	CPla IBlr
flavida	CPla CRow EBee EMan GGar GSki
	IBlr
fulvida	IBlr
hamiltonii	CPla CRow CStu EBee ECha ECou
	EMan EPot GEil GGar IBlr NBir
	WHil

magellanica	More than 30 suppliers
– 'Osorno'	CDes EBee SSpi WPGP
manicata ♀ H3-4	More than 30 suppliers
monoica	CRow EBee GGar GSki IBlr
prorepens	CPla CStu EBee ECha EMan GSki
	IBlr LEdu NBir SSpi WWye
scabra	see G. tinctoria
§ **tinctoria**	CBen CFil CHEx CMHG CRow
	CTrC CTrG CWib EBlw EBot
	ECha EFWa EHon EPfP EPla GGar
	LHop NCot NGdn NOrc SDix
	SPar SSpi SWat WCru WLRN
	WPGP WStI WWpP
– 'Nana'	IBlr

Guzmania (Bromeliaceae)

'Claret'	see Neoregelia Claret Group
'Gran Prix'	MBri
* 'Surprise'	MBri
'Vulkan'	MBri

Gymnadenia (Orchidaceae)

conopsea	EFEx

Gymnocarpium (Woodsiaceae)

dryopteris ♀ H4	CLAP EFer EMar EMon EPar
	LEur LSyl MBri MMoz NMar
	NWCA SDix SRms WFib WNor
	WRic
– 'Plumosum' ♀ H4	CFil CFwr CLAP EMon GBin
	GQui LEur NHar NHol NMar
	NVic SChu SPoG WFib WHal
robertianum	EFer MWgw SRms

Gymnocladus (Caesulpiniaceae)

chinensis	WNor
dioica	CAgr CBcs CDul CFil CMCN
	CSam CTho EBee ELan EPfP MBlu
	MBri SMad SPer SSpi WDin WGer
	WNor WPGP

Gymnogramma see *Gymnopteris*

Gymnopteris (Adiantaceae)

vestita	EMon

Gymnospermium (Berberidaceae)

altaicum	GCrs

Gynandriris (Iridaceae)

sisyrinchium	EBee EMan NWCA

Gynerium (Poaceae)

argenteum	see Cortaderia selloana

Gynostemma (Cucurbitaceae)

pentaphyllum	WCru
B&SWJ 570 **new**	

Gynura (Asteraceae)

§ **aurantiaca** 'Purple	MBri
Passion' ♀ H1	
sarmentosa hort.	see G. aurantiaca 'Purple Passion'

Gypsophila (Caryophyllaceae)

acutifolia	ELan LPio
aretioides	EPot LRHS NMen NSla NWCA
	WRos
§ – 'Caucasica'	CPBP EBur EHyt EPot LTwo NDlv
	NHar SIng
– 'Compacta'	see G. aretioides 'Caucasica'
briquetiana	WPat
cerastioides	CTri ECtt EMNN EMan EWTr

	GAbr GTou LBee LHop LPVe LRHS MRav NDlv NLAp NLon NMen NWCA SPlb WAbe WAul WMoo WPer WPnn WWin
dubia	see *G. repens* 'Dubia'
fastigiata	EBee EMan WPer
(Festival Series) 'Festival'PBR	EBee EBre
- 'Festival Pink'	EBee GKir GMac LRHS SMrm WFar WViv
- 'Happy Festival'	LRHS WViv
- 'Royal Festival' **new**	WViv
- 'White Festival'PBR	WFar WViv
gracilescens	see *G. tenuifolia*
herniarioides	EBee
muralis 'Garden Bride'	LIck
- 'Gypsy Pink' (d)	LIck
nana	SIng
- 'Compacta'	CLyd
oldhamiana	EBee MLLN
pacifica	EBee ECtt GBuc IIve MWgw NBro NEgg NLar NOak WPer WRHF
§ *paniculata*	CTri EBee GKir GWCH MWgw NFor NMir SRms SWat WBod
- 'Bristol Fairy' (d) ♀H4	CBcs CSBt EBee EBre EFou ELan EMan ENot ERou GKir LRHS MBri MCAu MDun NBlu NOrc SDes WBrE
- 'Compacta Plena' (d)	EBee EChP EFou EGle ELan EPfP GCal GMaP GMac LHop MRav NLar SMrm SPer SPet SPla SRms SSpe WCom WLRN WPer
- double pink (d)	GKir
- double white (d)	GKir
- 'Fairy Perfect' **new**	EBee
- 'Flamingo' (d)	CBcs EBee ECha ECot EFou ERou LRHS MBri NLar SDes SPer
- 'Magic Gilboa'PBR	COtt
- 'Magic Golan'PBR	COtt
- 'Perfekta'	EBee SCoo SPer
§ - 'Schneeflocke' (d)	CKno EBee GKir MWat NPri NVic SRms WPer
- 'Snow White'	LPVe NOrc
- Snowflake	see *G. paniculata* 'Schneeflocke'
§ *petraea*	EPot WLin
repens ♀H4	ECtt EMil GKir GTou LBee LPVe MHer MOne MWat MWgw MWrn NJOw SPlb SWal WFar WPer
- 'Dorothy Teacher'	CLyd CMea ECtt EMNN SIng WEas WGor
§ - 'Dubia'	CLyd ECha ECtt EDAr EHol ELan EMNN EPot ESis MHer SIgm SRms WLin WPer WWin
- 'Fratensis'	ECtt ELan EMNN ESis ITim NMen
- Pink Beauty	see *G. repens* 'Rosa Schönheit'
§ - 'Rosa Schönheit'	EBee EBre ECha EPot LRHS SIgm SPer
- 'Rose Fountain'	WPat
- 'Rosea'	CWib ECtt EFou EMNN EMlt EPfP ESis GKir LPVe MWat MWrn NFor NOak NWCA SAga SBla SDes SPet SRPl SRms WBrE WCom WFar WHal WHoo
- white	CHor CM&M CWib EFou ELan EPfP ESis NFla NFor SDes SPet WPer
§ 'Rosenschleier' (d) ♀H4	EBee EBre EChP ECha EFou EGoo ELan ENot EPfP GKir MCAu MRav NDov SIgm SMrm SRms SUsu SWat WEas WHoo WMaN WOld
'Rosy Veil'	see *G.* 'Rosenschleier'

§ *tenuifolia*	CLyd CNic EPot ITim LBee MBro MWat NDlv NHol NMen SBla
transylvanica	see *G. petraea*
Veil of Roses	see *G.* 'Rosenschleier'

H

Habenaria (Orchidaceae)
radiata	see *Pecteilis radiata*

Haberlea (Gesneriaceae)
ferdinandi-coburgii	CLAP NWCA SIgm SIng
rhodopensis ♀H4	CElw CNic CStu EBee EHyt EPar GCrs GEdr MBro MSte MWat NGar NHar NMen NRya NSla NWCA SBla SIng SRms SSpi WAbe WPGP WPat
- 'Virginalis'	CElw CLAP GDra NHar NMen SBla SIng SOkd

Habranthus ✿ (Amaryllidaceae)
andersonii	see *H. tubispathus*
brachyandrus	CBro SRms
gracilifolius	CBro ERos SIng
martinezii	CBro EHyt
§ *robustus* ♀H1	CBro EBee EPot LAma LRHS NRog NWCA SIgm WCot
texanus	CBro ERos WAbe
§ *tubispathus* ♀H1	CBro CStu EBee ERos LBow NWCA SVen WCot WOBN WWin

Hacquetia (Apiaceae)
§ *epipactis* ♀H4	More than 30 suppliers
- 'Thor' (v)	CDes EMon SBla
- 'Variegata'	see *H. epipactis* 'Thor'

Haemanthus (Amaryllidaceae)
albiflos ♀H1	CAvo CHEx CHal CStu LAma SRms SYvo WCot
natalensis	see *Scadoxus puniceus*
pauciflorus **new**	WCot
sanguineus	NRog

Hakea (Proteaceae)
bucculenta	LRHS
§ *drupacea*	CTrC
epiglottis	CTrC ECou
lissocarpha	CTrC
§ *lissosperma*	CDoC CFil CHEx CTrC ECou EPla SPlb WPGP
microcarpa	SLon
nodosa	CTrC
§ *salicifolia*	CBcs LRHS SPlb
saligna	see *H. salicifolia*
sericea hort.	see *H. lissosperma*
suaveolens	see *H. drupacea*
teretifolia	CTrC

Hakonechloa (Poaceae)
macra	CFil CPla EBee EBlw EBre EHoe EMon EPPr EPar EPla LPhx MAvo MMoz MRav NOGN SApp SMad WCot WPGP
§ - 'Alboaurea' ♀H4	More than 30 suppliers
* - 'Albolineata'	CDes CKno EBlw EMon
- 'Aureola' ♀H4	More than 30 suppliers
- 'Beni-kaze' **new**	WCot
* - 'Mediopicta' (v) **new**	SApp
* - 'Mediovariegata' (v)	CFil EPPr EPla SAsh SSpi WPGP
- 'Variegata'	see *H. macra* 'Alboaurea'

Halenia (*Gentianaceae*)

elliptica	NLAp
– SDR 1843	GKev

Halesia (*Styracaceae*)

§ **carolina**	More than 30 suppliers
diptera	CMCN MBlu
– var. **magniflora**	MBlu
monticola	CBcs CDul CMCN COtt EBre ELan
	EPfP GGGa MAsh MBri NSti SPer
	SReu SSpi WFar WNor
– var. **vestita** ♀ H4	CAbP CDoC CPMA CTho EBee
	EPfP GKir IMGH LPan LRHS
	MAsh MBlu SBrw SHBN SPer SSpi
	WDin WFar WHCG WPat
– – f. **rosea**	CBcs EPfP MBlu SSta
tetraptera	see *H. carolina*

x *Halimiocistus* (*Cistaceae*)

algarvensis	see *Halimium ocymoides*
§ 'Ingwersenii'	CBcs CDoC EBee EWes MWhi
	SIng SPar SPer SRms WAbe WBod
	WCom WLin WPer
revolii hort.	see x *H. sahucii*
§ **sahucii** ♀ H4	CDoC EBee EBre ECha ELan
	EMlt EPfP EWTr MAsh MBNS
	MGrG MRav MWat MWgw
	NBlu SDys SGar SHBN SPer
	WCFE WDin WFar WKif WWeb
	WWin
– 'Ice Dancer' (v)	CDoC EBee MAsh MGrG NLon
	SPar SPer
'Susan'	see *Halimium* 'Susan'
§ **wintonensis** ♀ H3	CBcs CChe CDoC EBee EBre ELan
	EPfP LRHS MAsh MRav MWat
	SHBN SPer SPla SRms SSpi WHar
	WSHC WWal WWeb
§ – 'Merrist Wood Cream'	CBcs CDoC EBee EBre ELan ENot
♀ H3	EPfP GEil LAst LHop LRHS MAsh
	MWgw NBir NSti SChu SPar SPer
	SPla SSpi SSta SUsu WAbe WDin
	WPat WSHC WStI

Halimione (*Chenopodiaceae*)

§ **portulacoides**	EEls

Halimium ✿ (*Cistaceae*)

§ **atriplicifolium**	EWTr
§ **calycinum**	EBee ELan EPfP GEil LRHS MWgw
	SCoo SLim SPar SPer SSpi WAbe
	WBrE WDin WWeb
commutatum	see *H. calycinum*
formosum	see *H. lasianthum* subsp.
	formosum
N **halimifolium**	WBrE WSHC
§ **lasianthum** ♀ H3	CBcs CHar CPLG CWib EBee
	ELan ENot EPfP LAst LPhx LRHS
	MAsh MRav MTis SLim SPar WBod
	WBrE WEas WWin
– 'Concolor'	CWib EBee SDry WDin WWin
§ – subsp. **formosum**	CHar GEil WSHC
– – 'Sandling'	EGoo ELan EPfP LRHS MAsh
libanotis	see *H. calycinum*
§ **ocymoides** ♀ H3	CBcs CBrm CChe CDoC CWib
	EBee EGoo ELan EPfP LPhx
	LRHS MAsh MMHG MWat
	MWgw SLon SPer WBod WBrE
	WHar WWeb
x **pauanum**	EBee LPhx LRHS MAsh SUsu
x **santae**	LPhx
§ 'Susan' ♀ H3	CDoC EBee ELan EPfP LRHS
	MAsh MBro MGrG MMHG

	NLon SLim SPer SPla WAbe
	WSHC
§ **umbellatum**	LPhx LRHS SPer WDin WHCG
	WKif WPat
wintonense	see x *Halimiocistus wintonensis*

Halimodendron (*Papilionaceae*)

halodendron	EMil EPfP MBlu NBlu SPer WDin

Halleria (*Scrophulariaceae*)

lucida	CPLG
* **paniculata**	EHyt

Halocarpus (*Podocarpaceae*)

§ **bidwillii**	CDoC ECou

Haloragis (*Haloragaceae*)

erecta	CPle
– 'Rubra'	WCot WPer
– 'Wellington Bronze'	CPLG CSpe EBee ECoo ECtt EMan
	GGar GSki ITer LEdu MBNS
	MCCP MWrn NFor SBod SDys
	SMad SOkh WEas WElm WHer
	WLin WMoo WPnP WWpP

Hamamelis ✿ (*Hamamelidaceae*)

'Brevipetala'	CBcs CEnd GKir MBri NHol SBrw
	WWeb
'Danny'	SBrw
'Fireblaze'	SBrw
x **intermedia** 'Advent'	SBrw
– 'Alexander'	SBrw
– 'Allgold'	MBri
– 'Angelly'	MBlu MBri SBrw SSta
'Aphrodite'	EPfP MBlu MBri NDhm SRPl SSta
– 'Arnold Promise' ♀ H4	More than 30 suppliers
– 'Aurora'	MBri SBrw
– 'Barmstedt Gold' ♀ H4	EPfP GKir LRHS MAsh MBlu MBri
	MGos NHol SBrw SReu SSpi SSta
	WWeb
– 'Birgit'	SBrw
– 'Brandes'	SBrw
– 'Carmine Red'	MGos SBrw SPer WNor
– 'Copper Beauty'	see *H.* x *intermedia* 'Jelena'
– 'Diane' ♀ H4	More than 30 suppliers
– 'Doerak'	NLar SBrw
– 'Early Bird'	SBrw
§ – 'Feuerzauber'	CDul CMac GKir LBuc NBlu SBrw
	SPer WDin WOrn
– 'Tricsia'	SBrw
– 'Gimborn's Perfume'	SBrw
– 'Girard's Orange'	EPfP SBrw
– 'Glowing Embers'	SBrw
– 'Harry' **new**	MBri
– 'Hiltingbury'	LRHS MAsh SSpi
§ – 'Jelena' ♀ H4	More than 30 suppliers
– 'Limelight'	SBrw
– Magic Fire	see *H.* x *intermedia* 'Feuerzauber'
– 'Moonlight'	SBrw
– 'Nina'	SBrw WOrn
– 'Old Copper'	SBrw
– 'Orange Beauty'	CBcs CWib ENot EPfP MGos NLar
	SBrw
– 'Orange Encore'	SBrw
– 'Orange Peel'	EPfP MBri NLar
– 'Ostergold'	SBrw
– 'Pallida' ♀ H4	More than 30 suppliers
– 'Parasol'	SBrw
– 'Primavera'	CWSG EBee EPfP MLan NHol
	SBrw WWeb
– 'Ripe Corn'	EPfP MBri SBrw
– 'Robert' **new**	MBri
– 'Rubin' **new**	MBri

- 'Rubinstar'	SBrw
- 'Ruby Glow'	CBcs ECho GKir MGos NPri SPer SPoG WDin
- 'Sara'	SBrw
- 'Savill Starlight'	SBrw
- 'Strawberries and Cream'	EPfP NLar SBrw
- 'Sunburst'	EPfP MBri SBrw SSta
- 'Twilight'	SBrw
- 'Vesna'	EPfP LRHS MBlu MBri NLar SSta
§ - 'Westerstede'	COtt CWSG EBee ENot LBuc LPan LRHS MGos MRav NBlu NHol NWea SLim WDin WHar WWeb
- 'Wiero'	SBrw
japonica	WFar
- 'Arborea'	SBrw WNor
- compact	SBrw
- var. *obtusata*	SBrw
- 'Pendula'	SBrw
- 'Robin' **new**	NLar
- 'Rubra'	SBrw
- 'Sulphurea'	SBrw
- 'Zuccariniana'	CBcs SBrw
mollis ♀ H4	More than 30 suppliers
- 'Boskoop'	SBrw SSta
- 'Coombe Wood'	MBri
- 'Early Bright'	SBrw
- 'Gold Edge'	SBrw
- 'Jermyns Gold'	EPfP SBrw
- 'Princeton Gold'	SBrw
- 'Select'	see *H.* x *intermedia* 'Westerstede'
- 'Superba'	LRHS SBrw
- 'Wisley Supreme'	LRHS SSpi
'Rochester'	SBrw
vernalis	GIBF WDin
- 'Carnea'	SBrw
- 'Dora'	SBrw
- 'January Pride'	SBrw
- 'Lombart's Weeping'	NLar SBrw
- 'Orange Glow'	SBrw
- purple	MBlu NLar
- 'Purpurea'	SBrw
- 'Red Imp'	SBrw
- 'Sandra' ♀ H4	EPfP GIBF GKir LRHS MBri MGos SReu SSpi SSta
- 'Spring Magic'	SBrw
- 'Squib'	SBrw
virginiana	CBcs ECrN GIBF GPoy MDun WDin WFar

Haplocarpha (Asteraceae)

rueppellii	NBro NGar SRms SRot WPer

Haplopappus (Asteraceae)

acaulis	see *Stenotus acaulis*
brandegeei	see *Erigeron aureus*
coronopifolius	see *H. glutinosus*
diplopapus	EHyt
F&W 9331 **new**	
§ *glutinosus*	CMHG EBee ECha ECtt GEdr MMil MTho NWCA SAga SPlb SRms WCom
lanceolatus	see *Pyrrocoma lanceolata*
lyallii	see *Tonestus lyallii*
microcephalus	WPer
mucronatus	WLin
prunelloides	GEdr LBee
- - var. *mustersii* **new**	EBee
- - F&W 9384	WCot
pygmaeus	see *Tonestus pygmaeus*
rehderi	EBee WFar

Hardenbergia (Papilionaceae)

comptoniana ♀ H1	CPIN CSpe

- 'Rosea'	CSpe ERea
* *taridacea* **new**	CTrC
violacea ♀ H1	CAbb CPIN CRHN CSPN CSpe ELan EMil ERea ESlt GKir GQui LRHS SLim SMur SPer
§ - f. *alba* 'White Crystal'	EBee ERea ESlt
- 'Happy Wanderer'	EBee EMil ERea LRHS SOWG WWeb
- f. *rosea*	CBcs EBee ESlt SPer WWeb

Harpephyllum (Anacardiaceae)

caffrum (F)	NBlo XBlo

Harrimanella see *Cassiope*

Hastingsia (Hyacinthaceae)

alba	EBee GBuc
- NNS 98-310	WCot
- NNS 98-311	WCot

Haworthia ✿ (Aloaceae)

cymbiformis	EPem
var. *umbraticola* **new**	
fasciata **new**	EPem
reinwardtii ♀ H1	CHal
tortusa **new**	EPem

hazelnut see *Corylus*

Hebe ✿ (Scrophulariaceae)

albicans ♀ H4	CChe CNic CPLG EBee ECou ELan ENot EPfP ESis GKir GLbr LAst LRHS MBar MBri MGos MRav MWgw NBlu NLon SHBN SMer SPar SPer WBod WCom WFar WHCG WTel WWin
- 'Cobb'	ECou
- 'Cranleigh Gem'	ECou
* - 'Pink Elephant'	CAbP CDoC EPfP LAst LRHS MAsh SPar SPer WWeb
- prostrate	see *H. albicans* 'Snow Cover'
- 'Red Edge'	see *H.* 'Red Edge'
§ - 'Snow Cover'	EBee ECou EWes SPar
- 'Snow Drift'	see *H. albicans* 'Snow Cover'
- 'Snow Mound'	ECou
§ - 'Sussex Carpet'	ECou ESis
§ 'Alicia Amherst'	EHol SPer SRms SWal WLRN
allanii	see *H. amplexicaulis* f. *hirta*
'Amanda Cook' (v)	EHoe ESis MCCP NPer SDry
'Amethyst'	SPar
amplexicaulis	CNic
- clone 4	STre
- f. *hirta*	ESis GDra GEil NDlv NHol
§ 'Amy'	CTrC ESis MHer NBur NPer SHBN SPer WCom WSHC
x *andersonii*	COkL
- 'Argenteovariegata'	see *H.* x *andersonii* 'Variegata'
§ - 'Aurea' (v)	SDry
- 'Aureovariegata'	see *H.* x *andersonii* 'Aurea'
§ - 'Variegata' (v)	CSpe NBur NSti SDry SPar SRms WLRN
anomala hort.	see *H.* 'Imposter'
anomala (Armstr.) Cockayne	see *H. odora*
'Aoira'	see *H. recurva* 'Aoira'
§ *armstrongii*	CMHG ECou EHoe EOrn EPfP EPla GGar GKir MBar NFor NLon SPar WDin WPer
'Arthur'	ECou
'Autumn Beauty'	COkL WBrE
'Autumn Glory'	More than 30 suppliers
'Azurea'	see *H. venustula*

'Azurens'	see H. 'Maori Gem'
'Baby Blush'	CAbP ELan MAsh MBri WWeb
'Baby Marie'	CAbP CDoC CGra CLyd COtt
	EBee ECot ECou EHoe ELan EPfP
	ESis GKir LRHS MAsh MGos NBee
	NBlu NHol NLon NMen NPer
	SLim SPar SPla SRms WPer WWin
'Balfouriana'	WHCG
barkeri	ECou
'Beatrice'	ECou NDlv
'Beverley Hills'[PBR] **new**	LRHS MAsh
bishopiana	CFai EBee ECou ELan ESis EWTr
	LRHS MAsh SCoo
- 'Champagne'	see H. bishopiana
'Blue Clouds' ♀[H3]	ECou ESis LAst MBNS MWat NDlv
	SAga SPer SWal WCFE WRus
'Blue Star' **new**	LRHS SPoG
bollonsii	ECou GGar MSte SVen
'Boscawenii'	CTrG MGos
'Bowles'Variety'	see H. 'Bowles's Hybrid'
§ 'Bowles's Hybrid'	COkL CSBt EBee ECou LRHS
	MGos MRav NBee NFor NLon
	SRms WAbe
brachysiphon	CTrC ENot EPfP GWCH MGos
	MWhi SMer SPer SWal WDin WHCG
- 'White Gem'	see H. 'White Gem'
brevifolia	ECou
breviracemosa	ECou
* 'Brill Blue'	CLyd ELan NMen WWin
buchananii	EBee ECou ESis GDra GGar GKir
	GTou MBar MDHE MGos MHer
	MTho NBur NDlv NFor NLon
	NPer WPer
- 'Christchurch'	ECou
§ - 'Minor'	CLyd EPot ESis GCrs MBar NBir
	NDlv NHar NMen NWCA SIng
- 'Nana'	see H. buchananii 'Minor'
- 'Ohau'	ECou
§ - 'Sir George Fenwick'	MBro WHoo
buxifolia hort.	see H. odora
buxifolia (Benth.)	EBre ENot GGar GLbr NBlu NSti
Ckn. & Allan	NWea SPar SPer WDin WStI
- 'Champagne'	see H. bishopiana
N 'C.P.Raffill'	ECou
§ 'Caledonia' ♀[H3]	EBee ECou EPfP ESis GGar GLbr
	LRHS MAsh MBri MGos MSte
	MWhi NDlv NHol NLon NPer
	SPer SWal WCom WFar WPat
	WPer WWeb
'Candy'	ECou
§ *canterburiensis*	ECou GGar
N 'Carl Teschner'	see H. 'Youngii'
'Carnea'	SWal
'Carnea Variegata' (v)	ESis SBod SPer SWal
carnosula	EHoe ESis GEil GGar LRHS MBrN
	MGos NBir NFor NLon SPer
	WCom WPer
catarractae	see Parahebe catarractae
I 'Chalk's Buchananii'	CNic SBla WCom
* 'Charming White'	EBee EPfP LRHS SWal
chathamica	CNic ECou ESis GGar MHer
	MMHG NRya SDry
'Christabel'	EBee ECou ESis
§ 'Christensenii'	ECou
ciliolata x odora	GGar
'Clear Skies' **new**	WWeb
colensoi	ESis
- 'Glauca'	see H. 'Leonard Cockayne'
'Colwall'	CLyd ECho ESis WHen
corriganii	ECou
'County Park'	CLyd ECou ECtt ESis EWes MGos
	NHol NLon NMen SWal
'Cranleighensis'	MHer SPar

'Cupins'	see H. propinqua 'Cupins'
cupressoides	CFis CMHG CSBt ECou GKir
	MBar NBid NDlv NLon SEND SPar
	WDin WGwG
- 'Boughton Dome'	EBee ECha ECou EHoe EMNN
	EPfP ESis GTou MBro MGos
	MTho NLAp NMen SWal WAbe
	WCom WCot WEas WHoo WPer
	WSHC
- 'Golden Dome'	ESis
- 'Nana'	ECou
darwiniana	see H. glaucophylla
'David Hughes'	ENot
'Dazzler'[PBR] (v)	CAbP ELan LRHS MAsh MBNS
	SPer SPoG WWeb
* 'Deans Fya'	ESis
decumbens	CLyd CNic ECou ESis EWes GDra
	GGar NHol
'Diana'	ECou
dieffenbachii	GGar
* *diericifolia* **new**	ISea
diosmifolia	CAbP CBot CDoC CPle EBee
	ECou ESis SMrm WAbe
- 'Marie'	ECou ESis SWal
divaricata	ECou
- 'Marlborough'	ECou
- 'Nelson'	ECou
x *divergens*	NDlv
'Dorothy Peach'	see H. 'Watson's Pink'
'E.A. Bowles'	ECou
'E.B. Anderson'	see H. 'Caledonia'
'Early Blue'	CSpe NBir
'Edinensis'	CNic COkL EBee ECou GEil GKir
	WPer WSHC
'Edington'	CHal ECou LRHS SCoo SPer
	WCFE
elliptica	COkL ECou
- 'Anatoki'	ECou
- 'Charleston'	ECou
- 'Kapiti'	ECou
- 'Variegata'	see H. x franciscana 'Variegata'
'Emerald Dome'	WPer
'Emerald Gem'	see H. 'Emerald Green'
§ 'Emerald Green' ♀[H3]	More than 30 suppliers
epacridea	ESis EWes GDra GTou NDlv NHol
'Evcline'	see H. 'Gauntlettii'
evenosa	LRHS NDlv
'Eversley Seedling'	see H. 'Bowles's Hybrid'
'Fairfieldii'	CPLG EHol NMen SScr
'First Light' **new**	NPro SPoG
'Fragrant Jewel'	SEND
x *franciscana*	ECou LRHS
§ - 'Blue Gem'	COkL ENot ESis GGar GLbr LPVe
	LRHS MGos NBir NPer NWea SPer
	SPlb SRms WBod WGer WHar
- 'Purple Tips' misapplied	see H. speciosa 'Variegata'
- 'Tresco Magenta'	ECou
§ - 'Variegata' (v) ♀[H2]	CSBt EBee EBre ECou ELan ENot
	EPfP ESis GGar LRHS MAsh MBar
	MGos NCot NPer NSti SPar SPer
	WBod WHar WStI WWeb
- 'White Gem'	SRms
'Franjo'	ECou
§ 'Gauntlettii'	COkL CSBt EBee EHol ELan LRHS
	NBir NLon SPer WWeb
'Gibby'	ECou
N *glaucophylla*	ECou GLbr SBod
- 'Clarence'	ECou
'Glaucophylla	CNic CTri ECou ESis GLbr MHer
Variegata' (v)	MWgw NBir NDlv NSti SPer SWal
	WCom WKif WRus
'Glengarriff'	NHol
'Godefroyana'	see H. pinguifolia 'Godefroyana'

gracillima	SRPl
'Great Orme' ♀ H3	More than 30 suppliers
'Green Globe'	see *H.* 'Emerald Green'
'Greensleeves'	EBee ECou ESis GGar LRHS MBar
	MGos NDlv
'Gruninard's Seedling'	GGar
haastii	NFor NLon
'Hagley Park'	CSBt EHol EPfP ESis LRHS MMil
	SAga WHCG
§ 'Hartii'	MRav SPer
'Headfortii'	EBee
hectorii	ESis GTou
'Heidi'	ESis SWal
'Highdownensis'	COkL
'Hinderwell'	NPer
'Hinerua'	ECou GGar NNor
hookeriana	see *Parahebe hookeriana*
hulkeana ♀ H3	CBot CStr EOrc MHer MMil MTis
	NBir SIgm SPar SSpi WCom WEas
	WHCG WHoo WKif
§ 'Imposter'	CTrC SRms
'Inspiration'	EPfP MRav
insularis	ECou
'Jack's Surprise'	ECou
'James Platt'	ESis
'James Stirling'	see *H. ochracea* 'James Stirling'
'Jane Holden'	SBla WCom WSHC
'Janet'	COkL SGar
'Jannas Blue'	EPfP
'Jasper'	ECou ESis SWal
'Jenny' **new**	WOut
'Joan Lewis'	ECou ESis
'Joanna'	ECou
'Joyce Parker'	NDlv
'Judy'	ECou
'June Small'	CNic
'Karo Golden Esk'	ECou SPar
'Kirkii'	EBee EMil EPfP MWhi SPer SWal
'Knightshayes'	see *H.* 'Caledonia'
'La Séduisante'	see *H. speciosa* 'La Séduisante'
'Lady Ardilaun'	see *H.* 'Amy'
laevis	see *H. venustula*
laingii	CNic
latifolia	see *H.* x *franciscana* 'Blue Gem'
lavaudiana	ESis
'Lavender Spray'	see *H.* 'Hartii'
§ 'Leonard Cockayne'	MOne WSHC
'Lindsayi'	CLyd ECou NDlv NJOw
§ 'Loganioides'	CFai ESis GAbr GGar MHer NFor
	NLon WPer
'Lopen' (v)	ECou EVFa EWes
'Louise'	COkL SGar
lyallii	see *Parahebe lyallii*
lycopodioides	ESis EWes
- 'Aurea'	see *H. armstrongii*
§ 'Macewanii'	CMHG ECou NDlv
mackenii	see *H.* 'Emerald Green'
macrantha ♀ H3	EBee EPfP ESis GCrs GDra GGar
	ITim LPhx LRHS MAsh NFor
	NLon NMen SIng SPar SPer SRms
	WPat WWin
macrocarpa	ECou LRHS
- var. *latisepala*	ECou
§ 'Maori Gem'	CTrC EBee EWes SCoo SMrm SPar
	WCom
'Margery Fish'	see *H.* 'Primley Gem'
'Margret' PBR ♀ H4	COtt CSBt EBee EBre EMil EPfP
	GKir LAst LRHS MAsh MBNS
	MGos NMen SCoo SHBN SMrm
	SPer SRPl WStI WWeb WWhi
'Marie Antoinette'	WWeb
'Marjorie'	CSBt CTrC EBee ECtt ENot EPfP
	GLbr LRHS MGos MRav NDlv

	NFor NPer NWea SBod SPer SRPl
	WDin WRHF WTel
matthewsii	ECou
'Mauve Queen'	EHol
'Mauvena'	SPer
'McEwanii'	see *H.* 'Macewanii'
'McKean'	ECou ESis
'Megan'	ECou
'Mercury'	see *H. pimeleoides* 'Mercury'
'Midsummer Beauty' ♀ H3	EBre ECou ENot EPfP GGar GKir
	LRHS MGos MRav NBir NFor
	NLon SBod SHBN SPar SPer SPlb
	WDin WFar WGwG WStl WWeb
'Milmont Emerald'	see *H.* 'Emerald Green'
'Miss E. Fittall'	ECou
'Mist Maiden'	ESis
'Monica'	ECou GGar NDlv NHol
* 'Moppets Hardy'	SPer
'Mount Nimrod' **new**	GEil
§ 'Mrs Winder' ♀ H4	More than 30 suppliers
'Mystery'	ECou ELan SWal
'Mystery Red' **new**	MAsh
'Nantyderry'	CHal GBri MWgw
§ 'Neil's Choice' ♀ H4	ECou MSte
'Netta Dick'	ECou
'New Zealand'	SPar
'Nicola's Blush' ♀ H4	More than 30 suppliers
'Northumbria Beauty'	NLon
'Northumbria Gem'	NFor NLon
obtusata	ECou
ochracea	ECou MGos SPer SWal WBod
	WCom
§ - 'James Stirling' ♀ H4	More than 30 suppliers
'Oddity'	ECou
§ *odora*	EBee ECou EPfP ESis MRav MWhi
	WBrE WCFE
- 'New Zealand Gold'	CNic EBee ECou ESis GKir LRHS
	MBNS NDlv SEND SLon SPer SWal
	WStl
* - *patens*	MGos WHCG
- prostrate	ECou
- 'Stewart'	ECou
- 'Summer Frost'	CRez EBee MBNS NPri
- 'Wintergreen'	MRav
'Oratia Beauty' ♀ H4	MAsh MRav WLRN WWeb
'Orphan Annie' PBR (v)	EVFa MAsh MBri SCoo SPer
	WWeb
'Oswego'	ECou
'Otari Delight'	CMHG
parviflora hort.	see *H.* 'Bowles's Hybrid'
§ *parviflora* (Vahl)	GGar SWal
Cockayne & Allan	
- 'Holdsworth'	SDys
- 'Palmerston'	ECou
- var. *angustifolia*	see *H. stenophylla*
- var. *arborea*	see *H. parviflora* (Vahl) Cockayne
	& Allan
'Pascal' ♀ H4	COkL ECou ELan EPfP MAsh MBri
	MRav
pauciflora hort.	see *H.* 'Christensenii'
pauciramosa	ECou ESis SRms SWal
'Paula'	ECtt
'Pearl of Paradise' **new**	SPoG
perfoliata	see *Parahebe perfoliata*
'Perry's Rubyleaf'	NPer
'Petra's Pink'	ECou EOrc ESis LRHS MAsh SIgm
	SWal WWeb
'Pewter Dome' ♀ H4	CDoC CSBt EBee EBre ECou ECtt
	EHoe ENot EPfP EWTr MGos
	MRav NBee NDlv NFor SBod SDix
	SPar SPla SRms WAbe WBrE
	WCom WHen
'Pimeba'	NHol WCom

pimeleoides ECou MWhi
- 'Glauca' NLon NPer SWal
- 'Glaucocaerulea' ECou NDlv SPer WMoo
§ - 'Mercury' ECou
- 'Quicksilver' ♀ H4 CSBt CSLe EBee EBre ECou EHoe
  ELan ENot EPfP ESis GGar GKir
  LHop LRHS MBar MBri MGos
  MRav NBir NPPs NPer SPar SPer
  WBrE WCom WCot WEas WFar
  WGwG WWal
- 'Red Tip' CBcs
- var. *rupestris* ECou ESis
pinguifolia ECou NDlv SPlb WFar
§ - 'Godefroyana' SWal
- 'Hutt' ECou WGwG
- 'Mount Dobson' ECou NHol
- 'Pagei' ♀ H4 More than 30 suppliers
- 'Sutherlandii' CDoC ECou ESis GDra GEil GLbr
  LEdu LRHS MBar MWhi NBee
  NDlv SPar WFar
§ - 'Wardiensis' CMHG
'Pink Elephant' (v) ♀ H3 ELan ENot ESis EVFa LRHS SCoo
  SPla WWeb
'Pink Fantasy' EBee LRHS MRav
'Pink Goddess' CAbP MAsh WWeb
'Pink Paradise'PBR ELan EPfP LRHS NPri
'Pink Payne' see *H.* 'Gauntlettii'
'Pink Pixie' MBri SCoo WWeb
'Pink Wand' LPVe WGer
poppelwellii ITim
'Porlock Purple' see *Parahebe catarractae*
  'Delight'
§ 'Primley Gem' ESis LRHS WWeb
propinqua ESis MHer NLAp NMen SWal
§ - 'Cupius' CLyd ESis SWal
  'Minor' NDlv
'Prostrata' CNic CSBt NDlv
'Purple Emperor' see *H.* 'Neil's Choice'
'Purple Paradise'PBR EPfP MBri WWeb
'Purple Picture' ECou ECtt SDry
Purple Pixie = COtt MBri MGos SCoo WWeb
  'Mohawk'PBR
'Purple Queen' CPLG CSBt EBee ELan EPfP GGar
  GLbr MAsh SHFr SPla WWcb
Purple Shamrock = MAsh MBri SCoo SPer SPoG
  'Neprock' (v) WGwG WWeb
'Purple Tips' misapplied see *H. speciosa* 'Variegata'
'Rachel' **new** WWcb
rakaiensis ♀ H4 More than 30 suppliers
ramosissima EPot ESis GDra GTou WAbe
raoulii GBri NWCA WAbe WHoo
- var. *maccaskillii* ESis
- 'Mount Hutt' GTou
- var. *pentasepala* ESis
§ *recurva* CNic CTri EBee ECou ESis GAbr
  GGar GKir LAst LRHS MBri MTis
  NBee NFor NHol SHFr SPar SRms
  SWal WBod WBrE WCom WDin
  WPer
§ - 'Aoira' COkL ECou NDlv
- 'Boughton Silver' ♀ H3 ELan EPfP LRHS MAsh MBNS
  SDry
- 'White Torrent' ECou
§ 'Red Edge' ♀ H4 More than 30 suppliers
'Red Ruth' see *H.* 'Gauntlettii'
rigidula ECou ESis SWal
'Ritt' ESis
'Ronda' ECou
'Rosie'PBR MMHG NBee SCoo SPer WWeb
* 'Royal Blue' SWal
'Royal Purple' see *H.* 'Alicia Amherst'
salicifolia CChe CNic COkL ECou ELan
  ENot EPfP GAbr GGar LAst LGro

MRav SGar SHBN SPar SPer SPlb
  SRms WFar WHCG WTel
'Sapphire' ♀ H4 CDoC COkL ECou ESis EWTr GGar
  GKir MAsh MBNS MBar MGos
  NBlu SCoo SMrm SPar SPer SWal
  WGer
'Sarana' ECou
'Seksti' SWal
selaginoides hort. see *H.* 'Loganioides'
'Silver Dollar' (v) CAbP CFai CM&M CSBt EHoe
  ELan ENot EPfP EVFa MAsh
  MBNS MBri NPri SPar SPer SPoG
  WWeb
'Simon Delaux' CPLG CSBt ECou LRHS NCiC SPer
  WWeb
'Snow Mass' **new** GLbr
'Snow Wreath' (v) WCom
§ *speciosa* 'La Séduisante' CSBt ECou ENot GKir MRav
  SEND SGar WKif WOut WSHC
- 'Rangatira' ECou EWes
- 'Ruddigore' see *H. speciosa* 'La Séduisante'
§ - 'Variegata' (v) CHal IBlr NPer SDry WEas
'Spender's Seedling' hort. see *H. stenophylla*
'Spender's Seedling' EBee ECou EPfP LRHS NBee
  SEND SPer SRms STre
'Spring Glory' EBre LRHS
stenophylla ECou EShb EWes MTed SAPC
  SArc SDix SHFr SMac
stricta ECou
- var. *egmontiana* ECou
- var. *macroura* ECou SDry
subalpina CSBt EBee EBre ECou ESis MOne
  MTis
subsimilis GDra SBla
- var. *astonii* ESis
'Summer Blue' EBee WWcb
'Summer Snow' NBir
'Susan' ECou
'Sussex Carpet' see *H. albicans* 'Sussex Carpet'
'Sweet Kim' (v) COtt MAsh MBri WWeb
tetrasticha CNic
'Tina' ECou
'Tiny Tot' CLyd EHyt ESis MTho
'Tom Marshall' see *H. canterburiensis*
topiaria ♀ H4 CAbP CSBt EBee EBre ECou EMil
  EPfP ESis GFtl GGar GKir GLbr
  LHop MBrN MBri MTis MWgw
  NBee NFor NHol SAga SMrm SPar
  SPla WAbe WEas WStI
townsonii ECou SAga
traversii EBee ECou MSte SRms
- 'Mason' ECou
- 'Woodside' ECou
'Tricolor' see *H. speciosa* 'Variegata'
'Trixle' CNic ECou
tumida EPot SBla
urvilleana ECou
'Veitchii' see *H.* 'Alicia Amherst'
§ *venustula* ECou ESis GGar IArd MBri SMrm
  WPer
- 'Blue Skies' ECou
- 'Patricia Davics' ECou
vernicosa ♀ H3 CNic EBee ECou EPfP ESis GDra
  GLbr MBar MBri MGos MHer
  NBee NDlv NFor NHol NLon
  NPro SIgm SPar SPer SPlb SRot
  WAbe WCom WGwG WHCG
'Vikki' **new** SWal
'Vogue' COkL MAsh
'Waikiki' see *H.* 'Mrs Winder'
'Walter Buccleugh' ECou
'Wardiensis' see *H. pinguifolia* 'Wardiensis'
'Warleyensis' see *H.* 'Mrs Winder'

§	'Watson's Pink'	COkL ECou GGar SPer WKif
	'Whistleberry Sapphire'	SWal
	'White Diamond'	SPer
§	'White Gem' (*brachysiphon* hybrid) ♀ H4	ECou ESis EWTr MGos NBee NDlv NFor NPer SWal WBVN WStI
*	'White Grape'	CM&M
	'White Heather'	EBee ESis LRHS NBir SPar
	'Willcoxii'	see *H. buchananii* 'Sir George Fenwick'
	'Wingletye' ♀ H3	CWib EBee ECou EGoo ESis GDra GGar LRHS MBri MGos MWhi NDlv NNor SWal WAbe WCom WGwG WPer WTel
	'Winter Glow'	CLyd COtt
	'Wiri Charm'	CAbP CBcs CDoC COtt CSBt EBee ECle ENot EPfP ESis EVFa GLbr MLan MRav MTis SHBN SPar SVil WGer WGwG WOut
	'Wiri Cloud' ♀ H3	CAbP CSBt EBee EPfP ESis GGar MTis NBee NBlu WGwG
	'Wiri Dawn' ♀ H3	CAbP CBcs COtt CSBt EBee ELan EPfP ESis EVFa EWes MAsh MPWC MWgw SHBN SVil WHrl WLRN
	'Wiri Gem'	LRHS MRav
	'Wiri Image'	CBcs CDoC COtt CSBt CTrC EBee EVFa LRHS MRav SWal
	'Wiri Joy'	LRHS
	'Wiri Mist'	CBcs COtt EBee ESis GGar LRHS SPar SWal WBod WLRN
	'Wiri Prince'	EBee
	'Wiri Splash'	CDoC COtt CSBt CTrC LRHS SHBN SWal WGwG
	'Wiri Vision'	COtt CSBt ESis LRHS
§	'Youngii' ♀ H3-4	More than 30 suppliers

Hebenstretia (Scrophulariaceae)

	dura **new**	CPBP SScr

Hedera ✿ (Araliaceae)

	algeriensis	see *H. canariensis* hort.
	'Anita'	CHal
§	*azorica*	CWhi WFar WFib
	- 'Pico'	WFib
	- 'Variegata' (v)	WCot
§	*canariensis* hort.	CDoC CWhi SAPC SArc WFib
	- 'Algeriensis'	see *H. canariensis* hort.
	- 'Argyle Street'	WFib
	- var. *azorica*	see *H. azorica*
	- 'Cantabrian'	see *H. maroccana* 'Spanish Canary'
*	- 'Casablanca'	CWhi
*	- 'Etna'	CWhi
§	- 'Gloire de Marengo' (v) ♀ H3	More than 30 suppliers
	- 'Gloire de Marengo' arborescent (v)	SPer
	- 'Marginomaculata' ♀ H3	CDoC EBee EPfP LRHS MAsh NEgg SPar WCot WFib WWeb
	- 'Montgomery'	EBee WFib
	- 'Nevada'	see *H. hibernica* 'Nevada'
	- 'Ravensholst' ♀ H3	CMac NLon NSti WFib
	- 'Stauss'	WFib
	- 'Variegata'	see *H. canariensis* hort. 'Gloire de Marengo'
	chinensis	see *H. nepalensis* var. *sinensis*
§	*colchica* ♀ H4	ENot EPfP LRHS SPer WCFE WDin WFar WFib
	- 'Batumi'	MBNS
	- 'Dentata' ♀ H4	CWhi EPla MRav WCru WFib
	- 'Dentata Aurea'	see *H. colchica* 'Dentata Variegata'
	- 'Dentata Variegata' (v) ♀ H4	More than 30 suppliers

	- 'My Heart'	see *H. colchica*
	- 'Paddy's Pride'	see *H. colchica* 'Sulphur Heart'
§	- 'Sulphur Heart' (v) ♀ H4	More than 30 suppliers
	- 'Variegata'	see *H. colchica* 'Dentata Variegata'
	cristata	see *H. helix* 'Parsley Crested'
§	*cypria*	WCot WFib
	helix	CKin CTri CWhi MBar MGos NWea SHFr WDin WFib WHer
	- 'Abundance'	see *H. helix* 'California'
	- 'Adam' (v)	COkL CWhi CWib LAst MBri MTho WFib WRHF WWeb
I	- 'Ahorn'	CWhi WFib
	- 'Albany'	see *H. hibernica* 'Albany'
	- 'Alpha'	CWhi
	- 'Alte Brücke'	CWhi WFib
	- 'Alte Heidelberg'	CWhi WFib
	- 'Amberwaves'	CWhi WFib
I	- 'Ambrosia' (v)	CWhi WFib
	- 'Anchor'	CWhi
	- 'Angularis'	CWhi ECot
	- 'Angularis Aurea' ♀ H4	CWhi EBee EHoe EPfP MWht NBir NHol SHBN SLim WFib
	- 'Anita' **new**	GBin
§	- 'Anna Marie' (v)	CMac COkL CWhi EBee LRHS MBri WFib
	- 'Anne Borch'	see *H. helix* 'Anna Marie'
	- 'Annette'	see *H. helix* 'California'
	- 'Appaloosa'	WFib
	- 'Aran' misapplied	see *H. helix* 'Rutherford's Arran'
	- 'Arapahoe'	CWhi WFib
	- 'Arborescens'	CNat NPal WDin
	- 'Ardingly' (v)	CWhi MWhi WFib
	- 'Arran'	see *H. helix* 'Rutherford's Arran'
	- 'Asterisk'	CWhi WFib
	- 'Astin'	CWhi WFib
	- 'Atropurpurea'	CNat CWhi EPPr EPla GBin MBar WDin WFib
	- 'Aurea Densa'	see *H. helix* 'Aureovariegata'
§	- 'Aureovariegata' (v)	CMac CNic CWhi WFib
	- 'Avon' (v)	CWhi WFib
	- 'Baby Face'	CWhi
	- 'Baccifera'	CWhi WFib
	- 'Baden-Baden'	CWhi WFib
	- var. *baltica*	CWhi WFib
	- 'Barabits' Silver' (v)	EPla
	- 'Big Deal'	CWhi
	- 'Bill Archer'	CWhi EPla MHdf WFib
	- 'Bird's Foot'	see *H. helix* 'Pedata'
	- 'Blodwen' (v)	WFib
	- 'Bodil' (v)	CWhi SHFr WFib
	- 'Boskoop'	CWhi WFib
	- 'Bowles Ox Heart'	CWhi WFib
	- 'Bowles Shield'	CNic
	- 'Bredon'	WFib
	- 'Brigette'	see *H. helix* 'California'
	- 'Brightstone'	WFib
§	- 'Brokamp'	CWhi MWgw MWht SLPl WFib
	- 'Bruder Ingobert' (v)	CWhi WFib WHrl
	- 'Buttercup'	More than 30 suppliers
	- 'Buttercup' arborescent **new**	MAsh
	- 'Butterflies'	WFib
§	- 'Caecilia' (v) ♀ H4	CBcs CMac CWhi EBee ELan EPfP LRHS MAsh NPro NSti SPar SPer WCot WCru WFar WFib WLRN
N	- 'Caenwoodiana'	see *H. helix* 'Pedata'
	- 'Caenwoodiana Aurea'	CWhi WFib
	- 'Calico'	see *H. helix* 'Schäfer Three'
§	- 'California'	CWhi MBri NSti WFib
	- 'California Fan'	CWhi
	- 'California Gold' (v)	CWhi NPro WFib
	- 'Caristian'	WFib

- 'Carolina Crinkle'	CWhi EPla MWhi WFib
- 'Cascade'	WFib
- 'Cathedral Wall'	WFib
§ - 'Cavendishii' (v)	CWhi SRms WCru WFib WLRN
§ - 'Ceridwen' (v) ♀ H4	CRHN CWhi MBri SPlb WFib WWeb
- 'Chedglow Fasciated'	CNat WFar
- 'Cheltenham Blizzard' (v)	CNat
- 'Chester' (v)	CWhi MAsh MBri WFar WFib
- 'Chicago'	CWhi CWib WFib
- 'Chicago Variegated'	see *H. helix* 'Harald'
- 'Christian'	see *H. helix* 'Direktor Badke'
- 'Chrysanna'	WFib
- 'Chrysophylla'	CWhi EPla
- 'Cleeve'	MWht
- 'Clotted Cream'	see *H. helix* 'Caecilia'
- 'Cockle Shell'	CWhi EPot WFib
- 'Colin' **new**	GBin
- 'Congesta' ♀ H4	CWhi EPla GDra MTho SPar SRms
		STre WCot WFib
- 'Conglomerata'	CWhi ELan EPla MBar MBri MBro
		NBir NBlu NFor SPar SPer SRms
		WDin WFib WTel
- 'Conglomerata Erecta'	CSWP NLon SLon SRms WCFE
		WFib
- 'Corrugata'	WFib
- 'Crenata'	CWhi WFib
- 'Crispa'	MRav NFor NLon SPar
- 'Cristata'	see *H. helix* 'Parsley Crested'
- 'Cristata Melanie'	see *H. helix* 'Melanie'
- 'Curleylocks'	see *H. helix* 'Manda's Crested'
- 'Curley-Q'	see *H. helix* 'Dragon Claw'
- 'Curvaceous' (v)	CWhi WCot WFib
- 'Cuspidata Major'	see *H. hibernica* 'Cuspidata
		Major'
- 'Cuspidata Minor'	see *H. hibernica* 'Cuspidata
		Minor'
- 'Cyprus'	see *H. cypria*
- 'Dainty Bess' **new**	CWib
- 'Dead Again'	MHdf WCot
- 'Dealbata' (v)	CMac CWhi WFib
- 'Dean' (v)	WFib
- 'Deltoidea'	see *H. hibernica* 'Deltoidea'
- 'Denmark' (v)	WFib
- 'Denticulata'	CWhi WFib
- 'Diana'	CWhi
- 'Dicke von Stauss'	CWhi
§ - 'Direktor Badke'	CWhi WFib
- 'Discolor'	see *H. helix* 'Minor Marmorata'
- 'Dolly'	CWhi
- 'Domino' (v)	CWhi EPla EWes WFib
§ - 'Donerailensis'	CWhi GDra MBlu WFib WPer
- 'Don's Papillon'	CBgR CNat WAlt
- 'Dovers'	WFib
§ - 'Dragon Claw'	CWhi EPla WCru WFib
- 'Duckfoot' ♀ H4	CBgR CDoC CHal CSWP CWhi
		IKcc MTho MWhi NSti WFar WFib
		WOut
- 'Dunloe Gap'	see *H. hibernica* 'Dunloe Gap'
- 'Edison'	CWhi
- 'Elegance'	CWhi WFib
- 'Elfenbein' (v)	CWhi WFib
- 'Emerald Gem'	see *H. helix* 'Angularis'
- 'Emerald Globe'	CWhi WFib
- 'Emerald Jewel'	see *H. helix* 'Pittsburgh'
- 'Erecta' ♀ H4	CMac CWhi EMFP EPfP EPla GDra
		GEil MBar MGos MTho MWhi
		NBlu NGHP SMac SPar SPer SPlb
		WCot WDin WFar WFib WPat
		WWye
- 'Ester'	see *H. helix* 'Harald'
- 'Eugen Hahn' (v)	CWhi EPla WFib
§ - 'Eva' (v)	CMac CWhi MBri MGos NBir
		WDin WFib

- 'Evesham'	WFib
- 'Fallen Angel'	CWhi WFib
- 'Fan'	CWhi
- 'Fantasia' (v)	CWhi WFib
- 'Ferney'	WFib
- 'Filigran'	CWhi SMad WFib WHer
- 'Flamenco'	CWhi WFib
- 'Flava' (v)	CWhi
- 'Fleur de Lis'	CNat CWhi WFib
- 'Florida'	WFib
- 'Fluffy Ruffles'	CWhi EPla
* - 'Francis'	MBri
- 'Fringette'	see *H. helix* 'Manda Fringette'
- 'Frosty' (v)	CWhi
- 'Garland'	CWhi
- 'Gavotte'	CWhi EPPr MTho MWht WFib
- 'Gertrud Stauss' (v)	CWhi MBri WFib
- 'Glache' (v)	SHFr WFib
- 'Glacier' (v) ♀ H4	More than 30 suppliers
- 'Glacier Improved' (v)	NBea
- 'Glymii'	CWhi EPla SBra SLPl SPar WFib
		WTin
- 'Gold Harald'	see *H. helix* 'Goldchild'
- 'Gold Nugget'	CWhi
- 'Gold Ripple' **new**	EHoe
§ - 'Goldchild' (v) ♀ H3-4	CBcs CDoC COkL CSam CWhi
		EBee EBre ENot EPfP EPla LAst
		LRHS MAsh MBar MBri MGos
		MRav MTho MWhi NBir NHol
		SAga SHFr SPar SPer WDin WFib
		WTel
- 'Goldcraft' (v)	CWhi WFib
- 'Golden Ann'	see *H. helix* 'Ceridwen'
* - 'Golden Arrow'	ELan LRHS MAsh
- 'Golden Curl' (v)	EPfP
- 'Golden Ester'	see *H. helix* 'Ceridwen'
- 'Golden Gate' (v)	CWhi MBri
- 'Golden Gem'	NPro
- 'Golden Ingot' (v) ♀ H4	COkL CWhi ELan EPla MBar
		MGos MWhi WFib
- 'Golden Kolibri'	see *H. helix* 'Midas Touch'
- 'Golden Mathilde' (v)	CHal COkL EBee
- 'Golden Medal'	WFib
- 'Golden Snow' (v)	MBri
- 'Goldfinger'	see *H. helix* 'Goldstern'
- 'Goldheart'	see *H. helix* 'Oro di Bogliasco'
§ - 'Goldstern' (v)	CWhi EHoe MWhi SPar WFib
- 'Goldwolke' (v)	CWhi SLPl
- 'Gracilis'	see *H. hibernica* 'Gracilis'
- 'Green Feather'	CWhi EGoo ESis WFib
- 'Green Finger'	see *H. helix* 'Très Coupé'
§ - 'Green Ripple'	CBcs CMac CSBt CTri CWhi CWib
		EBee ENot GKir LRHS MAsh MBar
		MHFa MRav MWht NBro NCiC
		NLon NPro SEND SLim SPer SPlb
		WDin WFib WHen WLeb
- 'Green Spear'	see *H. helix* 'Spear Point'
- 'Hahn's Green Ripple'	see *H. helix* 'Green Ripple'
- 'Hamilton'	see *H. hibernica* 'Hamilton'
§ - 'Harald' (v)	CDoC CWhi CWib LAst MAsh
		MBri NSti SPar WDin WFib
- 'Harlequin' (v)	COkL WFib
- 'Harrison'	CWhi
* - 'Hazel' (v)	WFib
- 'Hebron'	CWhi
- 'Heise' (v)	CWhi WFib
- 'Heise Denmark' (v)	WFib
- 'Helvetica'	CWhi
- 'Helvig'	see *H. helix* 'White Knight'
- 'Henrietta'	CStr
- subsp. **hibernica**	see *H. hibernica*
- 'Hispanica'	see *H. maderensis* subsp. *iberica*
- 'Hite's Miniature'	see *H. helix* 'Merion Beauty'

- 'Holly'   see *H. helix* 'Parsley Crested'
- 'Hullavington'   CFox CNat
- 'Humpty Dumpty'   MBar
- 'Ideal'   see *H. helix* 'California'
- 'Imp'   see *H. helix* 'Brokamp'
- 'Ingelise'   see *H. helix* 'Sagittifolia Variegata'
- 'Ingrid'   see *H. helix* 'Harald'
- 'Innuendo'   WFib
- 'Irish Lace'   WFar
- 'Ivalace' ♀ H4   CBcs CNat CRHN CWhi EBee ECha EPfP EPla ESis MAsh MNrw MRav MWhi MWht NBid NSti SPar SRms WDin WFib WWeb
§ - 'Königers Auslese'   CRHN CWhi SLPl WFib
- 'Jack Frost' (v)   CWhi
- 'Jake'   CHal
- 'Jake's Gold'   WBcn
- 'Jane's Findling' (v)   CNat
- 'Jasper'   WFib
- 'Jersey Doris' (v)   CWhi
- 'Jerusalem'   see *H. helix* 'Schäfer Three'
- 'Jester's Gold'   ELan ENot EPfP EPla LRHS MBri MGos MRav NEgg SPar WWeb
- 'Jubilee' (v)   COkL CWhi WCFE WFar WFib
- 'Knülch'   CWhi EPla MWat WFib
- 'Kolibri' (v)   CDoC CHal CMac COkL CRHN CWhi EBee EBre EMil EPfP LAst MBar MBri MWht NPro SPar WFib WWeb
§ - 'Königers Auslese'   CRHN CWhi SLPl WFib
- 'Kurios'   CNat CWhi
- 'La Plata'   CWhi
§ - 'Lady Kay'   CWhi WFib
- 'Lalla Rookh'   CWhi MWgw WBcn WFib WHrl
- 'Lemon Swirl' (v)   CWhi WFib
- 'Leo Swicegood'   CSWP CWhi MWhi WFib
- 'Light Fingers'   EPla MAsh WFib WHrl
* - 'Lime Regis'   CWhi
- 'Limey'   CWhi
- 'Little Diamond' (v)   CDoC CTri CWhi EBee EHoe ELan EPfP EPla LHop LRHS MAsh MBar MBri MGos MWgw MWht SAga SHBN SLon SPar SRPl WDin WFib WHrl
- 'Little Gem'   CWhi WFib
- 'Little Luzii' (v)   WFib
- 'Little Picture'   CWhi WFib
- 'Little Witch'   CWhi EPla
- 'Liz'   see *H. helix* 'Eva'
- 'Liziz' (v)   WFib
- 'Lucy Kay'   see *H. helix* 'Lady Kay'
§ - 'Luzii' (v)   EHoe EPla MBar MGos NLon NSti SGar SHBN WFib
- 'Maculata'   see *H. helix* 'Minor Marmorata'
- 'Malvern'   WFib
§ - 'Manda Fringette'   CWhi MTho WFib
§ - 'Manda's Crested' ♀ H4   CSWP CWhi NCiC SPar WFib
- 'Manda's Fan'   WFib
- 'Maple Leaf' ♀ H4   CWhi WFib
- 'Maple Queen'   MBri
- 'Marginata' (v)   SRms
- 'Marginata Elegantissima'   see *H. helix* 'Tricolor'
- 'Marginata Major' (v)   CWhi
- 'Marginata Minor'   see *H. helix* 'Cavendishii'
- 'Marie-Luise'   WFib
- 'Marilyn' (v)   CWhi
- 'Marmorata'   see *H. helix* 'Luzii'
- 'Masquerade' (v)   WGor
- 'Mathilde'   CWhi LRHS MWht SGar WFib WWeb
- 'Meagheri'   see *H. helix* 'Green Feather'
§ - 'Melanie' ♀ H4   ECha EPla LRHS WCot WCru WFib WRHF
- 'Meon'   WFib

§ - 'Merion Beauty'   CWhi WFib
§ - 'Midas Touch' (v) ♀ H3-4   CChe COtt CWhi CWib EPfP MBri SPer WFib
- 'Midget'   CRow WFib
- 'Mini Ester' (v)   CWhi EPfP MBri
- 'Mini Heron'   MBri
- 'Mini Pittsburgh'   COkL
- 'Minima'   see *H. helix* 'Donerailensis'
§ - 'Minor Marmorata' (v) ♀ H4   CHal CWhi EBee EPla MTho WFib WSHC
- 'Mint Kolibri'   EHoe MBri WBcn
- 'Minty' (v)   CWhi EPla LRHS MWht
* - 'Minutissima'   EPla
- 'Miss Maroc'   see *H. helix* 'Manda Fringette'
- 'Misty' (v)   CWhi EPot WFib
- 'Mrs Pollock'   see *H. hibernica* 'Mrs Pollock'
- 'Mrs Ulin'   CWhi
- 'Needlepoint'   SIng
- 'Neilson'   CWhi WFib
- 'Neptune'   CWhi
- 'New Ripples'   CWhi MWht WFib
- 'Nigra'   CWhi
- 'Nigra Aurea' (v)   CWhi WFib
- 'Norfolk Lace'   EWes
- 'Northington Gold'   CWhi WBcn WFib
- 'Obovata'   CWhi SPar
- 'Olive Rose'   CWhi EPla MTho WCot WFib
N - 'Oro di Bogliasco' (v)   More than 30 suppliers
- 'Paper Doll' (v)   CWhi
§ - 'Parsley Crested' ♀ H4   CMac CSBt CWhi EBee EPfP EPla MAsh MBar NSti SGar SLim SPar SPer SRms WCru WFar WFib WMoo WRHF
N - 'Pedata'   CSWP CWhi EPfP WFib
- 'Pencil Point'   CWhi
- 'Pennsylvanian'   CWhi
- 'Perkeo'   CHal CWhi EGoo ESis SPar WFib
- 'Perle' (v)   CWhi NBir WFib
- 'Persian Carpet'   CWhi WFib
- 'Peter' (v)   CWhi WFib
* - 'Pin Oak'   EBee LBuc WCru
I - 'Pink 'n' Very Curly'   EPla WCom WCot
- 'Pirouette'   CWhi WFib
§ - 'Pittsburgh'   SPar WFib WWal
- 'Pixie'   CWhi WFib
- 'Plume d'Or'   CHal MTho WFib
§ - f. *poetarum*   CNat EPla MBlu WBcn WFib
- - 'Poetica Arborea'   ECha SDix
- 'Poetica'   see *H. helix* f. *poetarum*
- 'Preston Tiny'   NBir
- 'Professor Friedrich Tobler'   CNat CWhi EBee WFib
- 'Quatermas'   CWhi WFib
- 'Raleigh Delight' (v)   WCot
- 'Ralf'   CWhi WFib
- 'Rambler'   NBir
- 'Rauschgold' (v)   CWhi
- 'Ray's Supreme'   see *H. helix* 'Pittsburgh'
- 'Reef Shell' (v)   WFib
- 'Regency' (v)   CWhi
- subsp. *rhizomatifera*   WFib
- 'Ritterkreuz'   CWhi WFib
- 'Romanze' (v)   CWhi WFib
- 'Rüsche'   CWhi EGoo WFib
- 'Russell's Gold'   WFib
§ - 'Rutherford's Arran'   CWhi WFib
- 'Sagittifolia' Hibberd   see *H. hibernica* 'Sagittifolia'
- 'Sagittifolia' misapplied   see *H. helix* 'Königers Auslese'
§ - 'Sagittifolia Variegata' (v)   COkL CWhi EBee LRHS MAsh MBri NBea SPar SRms WFib WRHF
- 'Sally' (v)   CWhi WFib
- 'Salt and Pepper'   see *H. helix* 'Minor Marmorata'
§ - 'Schäfer Three' (v)   CWib WFib

	– 'Serenade' (v)	CWhi
	– 'Shamrock'	COkL CWhi EBee EPfP EPla MBri MWht WFib
	– 'Shannon'	CWhi
	– 'Silver Emblem' (v)	WFib
	– 'Silver Ferny'	EPot
	– 'Silver King' (v)	EBee MRav MWht NBir WFib
	– 'Silver Queen'	see *H. helix* 'Tricolor'
	– 'Sinclair Silverleaf'	WFib
	– 'Small Deal'	CWhi WFib
§	– 'Spear Point'	CWhi WFib
	– 'Spectre' (v)	CWhi MTho WFib WHer
	– 'Spetchley' ♀ H4	CHal CNic CSWP CWhi EPla ESis EWes GCal MBar MHdf MRav MTho MWhi NPer SMad WAlt WBcn WCFE WCot WFib WPat WPrP
	– 'Spinosa'	CWhi EPla
	– 'Spiriusa'	WFib
	– 'Staghorn'	CWhi
	– 'Stift Neuberg' (v)	WFib
	– 'Stuttgart'	CWhi WFib
	– 'Succinata'	WFib
	– 'Sunrise'	WFib
	– 'Suzanne'	see *H. nepalensis* var. *nepalensis* 'Suzanne'
	– 'Sylvanian'	WFib
	– 'Symmetry'	CWhi
	– 'Tango'	WFib
	– 'Telecurl'	CWhi WFib
	– 'Tenerife'	EPla WFib
	– 'Thorndale'	CWhi WFib
	– 'Tiger Eyes'	CWhi
	– 'Tony'	COkL
*	– 'Touch of Class'	CWhi
§	– 'Très Coupé'	CBcs CDoC CSWP CWhi EBee EGoo LRHS MAsh MTho SAPC SArc SPer WDin WFib WLeb
§	– 'Tricolor' (v)	CBcs CTri CWhi EPfP LRHS MAsh MGos MWht SBra SHBN SLim SMer WCFE WTel
	– 'Trinity' (v)	WFib
	– 'Tristram' (v)	CWhi WFib
	– 'Triton'	CWhi MBar MTho WFib
	– 'Troll'	CWhi WLeb
	– 'Trustee'	CWhi
	– 'Tussie Mussie' (v)	CWhi WFib
	– 'Ursula' (v)	CSWP WFib
	– 'Ustler'	CWhi
*	– 'Verity'	CWhi
	– 'Very Merry'	CBgR
I	– 'Victoria'	WWeb
	– 'Walthamensis'	CWhi WFib
	– 'White Heart' **new**	EBee
§	– 'White Knight' (v) ♀ H4	CWhi MBri WFib
	– 'White Kolibri'	MBri
	– 'White Mein Herz'	GBin
	– 'Whitehall'	WFib
	– 'Wichtel'	CWhi
	– 'William Kennedy' (v)	CWhi WFib
	– 'Woeneri'	CWhi MWht SLPl WFib
	– 'Yab Yum' (v) **new**	WBcn
	– 'Yellow Ripple'	COkL CWhi WBcn
	– 'Zebra' (v)	WFib
§	*hibernica* ♀ H4	CBcs CNat CSBt CWhi EBee ENot GKir LBuc LRHS MBar MRav NBea NBlu NFor NWea SBra SPer SRms WDin WFib WLeb WStI
§	– 'Albany'	CWhi WFib
	– 'Anna Marie'	see *H. helix* 'Anna Marie'
	– 'Aracena'	EPla SLPl
§	– 'Cuspidata Major'	CWhi WFib
§	– 'Cuspidata Minor'	CWhi WFib
§	– 'Deltoidea' ♀ H4	CWhi EPla MBri MHdf MWht WCot WFib
	– 'Digitata'	CWhi WFib
I	– 'Digitata Crûg Gold'	WCru
	– 'Dunloe Gap'	EPla
§	– 'Gracilis'	CWhi WFib
§	– 'Hamilton'	CWhi WFib
	– 'Helena' (v)	CWhi WFib
	– 'Helford River'	CWhi
*	– 'Lactimaculata'	CWhi
	– 'Lobata Major'	SRms
	– 'Maculata' (v)	EPla SLPl WBcn WSHC
	– 'Mrs Pollock' (v)	CWhi WFib
	– 'Nevada'	CWhi
	– 'Palmata'	CWhi WFib
	– 'Rona'	CWhi WFib
§	– 'Sagittifolia'	COkL CTri CWhi EPfP GBin LRHS MAsh MBar NLon SHFr SPar SRms WFar WFib WGwG
	– 'Sulphurea' (v)	CWhi WFib
	– 'Tess'	CWhi EPla WFib
	– 'Variegata' (v)	COkL CWhi MBar SLim
	maderensis	WFib
§	– subsp. *iberica*	WFib
	maroccana 'Morocco'	WFib
§	– 'Spanish Canary'	CWhi WFib
	nepalensis	WBcn WFib
§	– var. *nepalensis* 'Suzanne'	MBar WFib
§	– var. *sinensis*	CWhi WFib
	– – L 555	EPla
	pastuchovii	CWhi EVFa WBcn WFib
	– from Troödos, Cyprus	see *H. cypria*
*	– 'Volga'	CWhi
§	*rhombea*	CWhi WCot WFib
	– var. *formosana*	WFib
	– 'Japonica'	see *H. rhombea*
I	– f. *pedunculata* 'Maculata' **new**	CWib
	– var. *rhombea* 'Variegata' (v)	WFib

Hedychium ✿ (Zingiberaceae)

	B&SWJ 3110 **new**	WPGP
	B&SWJ 7155	WPGP
	'Anne Bishop'	CFil
	aurantiacum	EAmu EBee ETub LEdu WMul
	'Ayo'	LEur
	'Beni-oran'	LEur
	'Betty Ho'	LEur
	'Carnival'	LEur
	chrysoleucum	CAvo EBee LAma LEur LPio
	coccineum ♀ H1	CBcs CFil CKob LAma LRHS MNrw MOak WOld
	– var. *angustifolium*	LEur WMul
I	– – 'Peach'	LEur
	– var. *aurantiacum*	CBct CHEx LAma LEur
	– 'Orange Brush'	LEur
	– 'Tara' ♀ H3	CDoC CFil CHEx CKob EBee EPfP ERea LEdu LEur LPio MNrw MOak MSte SAPC SArc SChr SDix SSpi WCru WMul WPGP
	coronarium	CBct CHEx CKob EAmu EBee EBot LRHS MOak MSte SYvo WMul WRHF
	– 'Andromeda'	LEur WMul
	– var. *coronarium*	LEur
	– var. *flavescens*	see *H. flavescens*
	– gold spotted	CKob
	– var. *maximum*	CFir
	– 'Orange Spot'	EAmu
	– 'Daniel Weeks'	LEur
	– 'Dave Case'	CKob
	densiflorum	CAvo CBct CBrd CFil CHEx CHll

	CKob EAmu EBee EBot ECha EPla LEur MOak NPal SDix SSpi WCru WMul WPGP
- 'Assam Orange'	CBct CBrm CDoC CFil CHEx CKob CPlt CSam EBee GCal LEdu LEur LPio MNrw MOak MSte SChr SDix WCru WMul WPGP
- 'Stephen'	CBrd CFil CHEx CKob EBee LEur LPio MNrw MSte
'Doctor Moy'	CKob LEur
'Double Eagle'	CFil CKob LEur
'Elizabeth'	CFil LEur WMul
ellipticum	CKob EBee LAma LEdu LEur MOak NPal WCru WMul
'Filigree'	CFir CKob LEur
§ *flavescens*	CBct CFil CKob EAmu EBee LAma LEur LRHS MNrw MOak SChr WCru WMul WPGP
forrestii	CFil CKob EAmu EBee LEur LPJP LPio MNrw MOak MSte SAPC SArc SSpi WMul WPGP
gardnerianum ♀ H1	More than 30 suppliers
- B&SWJ 7155	WCru
- var. *pallidum*	CKob
'Giant Yellow'	LEur
'Gold Flame'	CFir CKob EBee LEur MNrw MOak WPGP
'Golden Butterfly'	LEur
'Golden Glow'	EBot LEur
gracile	CFil CKob LEur
Great Dixter hybrid	CKob
greenei	CBct CDoC CFil CFir CHEx CKob CSam EBee EBot LEdu LEur LPio LRHS MNrw MOak MPRe MSte NPal SArc SChr SDes SDix SYvo WBor WCot WCru WMul WPGP
griffithianum	EBee LEur
'Hardy Exotics 1'	CHEx
horsfieldii	CKob
§ 'Kinkaku'	CFil CKob LEur
'Lemon Beauty'	LEur
'Lemon Sherbet'	CFir CKob LEur
longicornutum	MSte
'Luna Moth'	CFil CKob EBee LEur WMul
'Maiko'	LEur
muluense	WMul
'Mutant'	LEur
'Orange Brush'	CKob
'Oto-himi'	LEur
'Pink Flame'	CKob
'Pink Sparks'	CKob LEur
'Pink V'	CFil CKob LEur
'Pradhan'	CFir CHEx EBee LEur WMul
x *raffillii*	CKob MNrw WCot
'Shamshiri'	see *H.* 'Kinkaku'
spicatum	CBrd CFil CFir CHEx CKob CMdw CPLG EBee EMan GPoy ITim LEur MNrw MSte SSpi WCFE WCot WCru WMul
- B&SWJ 2303	WCru WPGP
- CC 1705	CKob
- CC 3249	ITer WCot
- CC 3650	ITer
- PF 218	LEur
'Stepladder'	LEur
'Tangerine'	LEur
'Telstar 4'	CHEx
thyrsiforme	CFil CKob EBee LEur NPal WMul
'Tropic Bird'	LEur
'Twengwainran'	MOak
villosum	CKob EBee LAma WMul
- var. *tenuiflorum*	LEur
- var. *villosum*	LEur

'White Starburst'	LEur
yunnanense	CFil CHEx LEur MNrw WCru WMul WPGP

Hedysarum (Papilionaceae)

coronarium	CArn CBri CPle CSev CSpe CWCL EBee EChP EHrv ELan EMan EPfP LHop MAnH MBrN SGar SPar SPet SSpi SWal WCom
hedysaroides	EMan LPVe WCot
multijugum	CBcs EBee ICrw MBlu SPer WSHC
occidentale	EBee

Heimerliodendron see *Pisonia*

Heimia (Lythraceae)

myrtifolia **new**	GEil
salicifolia	CArn CPle GEil MBlu MGol MSal SGar WSHC WWye

Helenium (Asteraceae)

'Autumn Lollipop' **new**	SMac
autumnale	CMea CSam CTri EBee EBlw EChP LDai MBNS MSal NChi SMac SSvw SWal WBea WLin WMoo WRHF
- JLS 88007WI	CAbx
- 'All Gold'	WPer
- 'Praecox'	CSam
- 'Sunset Shades'	WElm
'Baudirektor Linne' ♀ H4	GKir SCro
* 'Biedermeier'	CRDP CSam CWCL EBee EFou
'Blütentisch' ♀ H4	CFwr CPrp CSam EBee EFou GMaP LBuc MAvo MNFA MWgw SUsu WHal WMnd WWpP
'Bressingham Gold'	CElw
'Bruno'	CFwr CHar CRDP CSam EBre EGle ELan ERou GKir LRHS MArl MMil SChu SOkh SPer
'Butterpat' ♀ H4	CHad EBee EFou EHrv ERou GKir GMaP LRHS MAvo MCLN MMil MRav NPPs NPri NSti SChu SPer WSan
'Chipperfield Orange'	CElw CHad CPlt EFou EMan ERou GBri LHop MArl MAvo MMil MRav NGdn NVic SRPl WHil WLRN
'Coppelia'	EBre EMan GKir MBro NFla NGdn SMrm WElm WHoo WOld WTel
Copper Spray	see *H.* 'Kupfersprudel'
'Crimson Beauty'	CMea CPlt CSam EBee EBre ELan EMan LRHS MLLN NBlu WLin
'Croftway Variety'	GKir SCro
Dark Beauty	see *H.* 'Dunkelpracht'
'Die Blonde'	EGle LPhx NDov SAga SCro WCot
§ 'Dunkelpracht'	More than 30 suppliers
'Feuersiegel' ♀ H4	CSam EBee LPhx NDov NPPs SAga SMrm WOld
flexuosum	EBee
'Gartensonne' ♀ H4	EFou LBuc
'Gay-go-round' **new**	CSam
Gold Fox	see *H.* 'Goldfuchs'
'Gold Intoxication'	see *H.* 'Goldrausch'
Golden Youth	see *H.* 'Goldene Jugend'
§ 'Goldene Jugend'	CElw CMea CSam ELan MRav SSpe WCot WEas WWpP
§ 'Goldfuchs'	CSam
§ 'Goldlackzwerg'	EBee EFou
§ 'Goldrausch'	CAbx CHar CSam EBee EFou MDKP MWat NCat SCro SDes WWpP
'Helena'	EFou

hoopesii	CPrp CSam EBre EHrv EPfP GDra GKir GMaP LHop LRHS MBNS MBow MNrw MRav MWrn NOak NPri NSti SDes SRms SYvo WFar WMnd WMoo WPer WViv WWal
'Indianersommer'	CSam EBee EChP EGle EHrv MAvo MOne NLar SDes SUsu WFar WHil
'July Sun'	NBir SSpe
'Kanaria'	CAbx CElw CPrp EBee EFou EMil ERou EWll MBri MNFA MRav WHil WMnd WOld WWpP
'Karneol'	CSam EFou LHop SOkh WWpP
'Kleiner Fuchs'	EBee EChP MRav SCro
'Königstiger'	CSam EBee EBre EFou MBri SMrm WWpP
'Kugelsonne'	EFou
§ 'Kupfersprudel'	EBre
'Kupferzwerg'	CAbx CSam CWCL LPhx NDov SCro SOkh
'Mahogany'	see *H.* 'Goldlackzwerg'
'Margot'	CSam EFou
'Mexican Hat' **new**	EFou
'Moerheim Beauty' ♥ H4	More than 30 suppliers
Pipsqueak = 'Blopip'	CSam CWCL EMan LRHS MCLN
'Potter's Wheel' **new**	CSam
puberulum **new**	MWrn
'Pumilum Magnificum'	CDes CPrp CSam EFou EGle EHol EPar EPfP LHop LRHS MBri MNFA MWat SCro SDes SPer WFar WTel
Red and Gold	see *H.* 'Rotgold'
'Ring of Fire' ♥ H4 **new**	CSam
'Riverton Beauty'	CSam CStr EBee ERou
'Riverton Gem'	CSam ECtt
§ 'Rotgold'	CDra CFwr CM&M CSam EBre ECGN ECtt ENot MHer MWrn NArg NChi NOak NPri SRms STes SWal WLRN WPer WWeb
'Rubinkuppel'	CSam LPhx NDov SChu SUsu
'Rubinzwerg' ♥ H4	CElw CFwr CPrp CSam EBee EChP EGle EMan GBin LHop LPhx MWgw SCro SDes SOkh SUsu WCot WRus
'Sahin's Early Flowerer' ♥ H4	More than 30 suppliers
'Septemberfuchs'	EBee EFou SCro
'Septembergold' **new**	CSam
'Sonnenwunder'	CSam ECha GKir
'Summer Circle' ♥ H4 **new**	CSam
'Sunshine'	WSan
'The Bishop'	More than 30 suppliers
'Waldtraut' ♥ H4	CM&M COlW CSam EBee EBlw ECot EFou EGle EHol EHrv ELan ERou GKir LEdu MRav MTis MWat MWgw NOak SCro SMad SPer WFar WSan WWpP
'Wesergold' ♥ H4	CSam EBee EFou MRav
'Wonnadonga'	EFou NCat
'Wyndley'	CBcs COlW CSam EBee EBlw EBre ECGN EFou EGle EHrv ERou GKir GMaP LRHS MCAu MMil MRav NSti SChu WEas WFar WLin WOld WViv WWpP
'Zimbelstern'	CAbx CElw CMil CSam EBee EBre GKir LPhx MRav NDov SAga SOkh WAul WFar

Heliamphora (Sarraceniaceae)

nutans	SHmp

Helianthella (Asteraceae)

§ *quinquenervis*	EBre EMan GCal NLar WFar

Helianthemum ✿ (Cistaceae)

'Alice Howarth'	CFul EWes MDHE SRms WPnn
alpestre serpyllifolium	see *H. nummularium* subsp. *glabrum*
'Amabile Plenum' (d)	CFul EPfP GAbr GCal GDra MBNS SDes SIgm WGwG
'Amber'	CFul GAbr
'Amy Baring' ♥ H4	CFul EBre EGle GAbr GDra GKir LRHS MOne NMen WCom WPer
'Annabel'	CFul COkL ECha EPfP GAbr GDra GKir IGor MWya NMGW SBla SChu SMer WCom WLin WPer WTel
apenninum	MDHE SRms WPer
'Apricot'	SBla SBod WBcn
'Apricot Blush'	WAbe
'Baby Buttercup'	CFul CLyd CMea GAbr MBro WPat
'Banwy Copper' **new**	WBVN
'Beech Park Red'	CFul ECtt LBee LRHS MBro MDHE MWat MWgw SAga SChu SIgm SWal WCer WHoo WKif
'Ben Afflick'	CFul COkL EMlt GKir LBee LRHS MBNS MDHE MHer SIgm SRms WCer WPnn
'Ben Alder'	CFul COkL GAbr MDHE MHer
'Ben Dearg'	CFul CMea COkL ECtt EMNN GAbr MDHE SRms
'Ben Fhada'	More than 30 suppliers
'Ben Heckla'	CFul COkL CSam CTca ECtt EMlt EPfP GAbr GKir LRHS MSte SBla SDes WPer WTel
'Ben Hope'	CFul COkL ECGP EMNN EPfP EWTr GAbr GDra NLon NPPs SDes SGar SRms WPer WWin
'Ben Ledi'	More than 30 suppliers
'Ben Lomond'	COkL GAbr GDra
'Ben Macdhui'	CFul COkL GAbr
'Ben More'	CBcs CFul COkL COlW ECtt EMNN GAbr GDra GKir GTou LRHS MHdf MWat NBir NLon NPri SBod SDes SGar WBrE WPat WWin
'Ben Nevis'	CFul COkL CTca CTri ECha GAbr GDra MDHE MHer SBla SRms WTel WWin
'Ben Vane'	CFul COkL COlW GAbr LRHS MDHE
'Bentley'	CFul
'Birch White'	CFul MDHE
'Boughton Double Primrose' (d)	CFul ELan EWes GKir GMaP GMac LRHS MBro SBla SChu SIgm SMer SUsu WEas WHoo WSHC
'Brilliant'	NBir
'Broughty Beacon'	CFul COkL GAbr GDra MDHE WGor
'Broughty Sunset'	CFul COkL CSam MBro MDHE NBir SIgm WHoo
'Bunbury'	CFul CMea CTca GAbr MBrN MDHE MWhi NBir
* 'Butter and Eggs'	SRms
'Butterball' (d)	MDHE
canum	SBla WPer
'Captivation'	CFul COkL EGoo GAbr
'Cerise Queen' (d)	CFul EBre ECha EWTr GAbr GKir LRHS SDix SIgm SRms WCom WPer
chamaecistus	see *H. nummularium*
'Cheviot'	CFul CMea ECha GAbr MBro MDHE NBir WEas WHoo WPer WSHC
'Chichester'	CFul
'Chocolate Blotch'	CFul COlW GAbr GKir LHop LRHS MHer NChi NHol NLon SChu SEND SIng WPer

	'Cornish Cream'	CFul EMlt EWes GAbr LBee LRHS
	croceum	LTwo
	cupreum	CFul GAbr
	'David'	EGoo
	double apricot (d)	GAbr
	double cream (d)	ECha MDHE WFar
	double pale pink (d)	SIgm
	double pale yellow (d)	NWoo
	double pink (d)	MWat NWoo WFar
	double primrose (d)	EMlt GAbr MDHE
	double red (d)	NChi
	'Elisabeth'	EGoo
	'Etna'	CFul
	'Fairy'	CFul GAbr LTwo MDHE NPro
§	'Fire Dragon' ♀ H4	CFul COkL CSam ECha EPfP GAbr
		GDra GKir LRHS MWhi NBir
		NWCA SBla SChu SIgm SRms
		WAbe WCom
	'Fireball'	see *H.* 'Mrs C.W. Earle'
	'Firegold'	WAbe
	'Flame'	COkL
	'Georgeham'	CFul CSam CTca ECtt EPfP EWTr
		GAbr GKir LBee LRHS MDHE
		NBir SBla SMer SRms WEas WGor
		WHoo WLin WPer
§	'Golden Queen'	CFul COkL ECtt EPfP GAbr
		LRHS MBNS MWhi SChu WPer
		WSan
	'Henfield Brilliant' ♀ H4	CFul COkL CPBP CSpe EBre EPfP
		GAbr GDra GKir GMac LAst LHop
		LRHS MBro NBir NHol NPPs NVic
		SBla SGar SIng SMad SMer SRms
		WEas WHoo WLin WPer WSHC
		WTel
	'Hidcote Apricot'	CFul GAbr MDHE SGar
	'Highdown'	GAbr SRms
	'Highdown Apricot'	ENot MDHE NPPs SDes
	'Honeymoon'	CFul MDHE SBla WLRN
	'John Lanyon'	MDHE
	'Jubilee' (d) ♀ H4	CFul COkL COIW CRez CSam
		CTca ECtt ELan EMNN EMlt
		ENot GAbr LAst NBid NBir
		NChi NFor NHol NLon SBla
		SDes SDix SIng SRms WAbe
		WEas WTel
I	'Jubilee Variegatum' (v)	CFul GAbr NLon
	'Karen's Silver'	WAbe
	'Kathleen Druce' (d)	CFul COkL ECtt EWes GAbr MWat
		WHoo WHrl
	'Lawrenson's Pink'	CTca MAvo WSan
	ledifolium	WPer
I	'Linton Rose'	NBir
	'Lucy Elizabeth'	CFul COkL GAbr
	lunulatum	CLyd CMea ECtt ESis LBee LRHS
		MBro NHol NMen SIgm WAbe
		WPat WWin
	'Magnificum'	EHol MDHE MWat
§	'Mrs C.W. Earle' (d) ♀ H4	CFul COkL COIW CTri ECtt ELan
		GAbr MBow MBrN MWya NPri
		SBla SDix SGar SIng SRms WAbe
		WHoo WPer WWin
	'Mrs Clay'	see *H.* 'Fire Dragon'
	'Mrs Croft'	SBla WPer
	'Mrs Hays'	GMac
	'Mrs Jenkinson'	WTel
	'Mrs Moules'	SRms
	mutabile	SPlb WPer
§	*nummularium*	CKin GPoy LPVe MBow MDHE
		MHer NMir NSco NWCA WPat
		WWye
§	- subsp. *glabrum*	CFul CNic EHyt GAbr MBro NHol
		NJOw NMGW NMen SIng WCom
		WPat WPer

	- subsp. *grandiflorum*	MWat
	'Variegatum' (v)	
*	- 'Lemon Queen'	WBcn
§	- subsp. *tomentosum*	CFul GAbr MWat
	oelandicum	NWCA
	- subsp. *alpestre*	CLyd ESis MBro NMen SRms WPer
	- subsp. *piloselloides*	CLyd WWin
	'Old Gold'	CFul EBre GAbr GKir LRHS SIgm
		SRms WAbe WPer WPnn WTel
	'Ovum Supreme'	CFul GAbr
	pilosum	SIgm
	'Pink Double'	EWTr
	'Pink Glow'	WPer
	'Praecox'	CFul CMea CTri GAbr LBee LRHS
		SIgm SMer SRms WHoo WPer WTel
	'Prima Donna'	CFul EWTr NBir
	'Prostrate Orange'	SRms
	'Raspberry Ripple'	CFul CHar EBre EGle EHyt ELan
		EPot GKir LRHS NChi NEgg
		NHol SDes SRms WAbe WHoo
		WPat WWin WWol
	'Razzle Dazzle' (v) **new**	LAst
	'Red Dragon'	GKir WAbe
	'Red Orient'	see *H.* 'Supreme'
	'Regenbogen' (d)	GCal
§	'Rhodanthe Carneum' ♀ H4	More than 30 suppliers
§	'Rosa Königin'	ECtt EMNN GAbr GKir MDHE
		MHer WAbe
	'Rose of Leeswood' (d)	CFul CMea CTca CTri GDra LBee
		LRHS MBro MHer NEgg NLon
		NRya SIgm SRms WEas WHoo
		WKif WSHC WWin
	Rose Queen	see *H.* 'Rosa Königin'
	'Roxburgh Gold'	SRms
	'Rushfield's White'	WBcn WRus
	'Saint John's College Yellow'	CFul COIW CSam GAbr LRHS WFar
	'Salmon Queen'	CElw CFul COkL ECtt EMNN
		GAbr GKir LBee LRHS NHol NPri
		SRms WHrl WPer WRHF WWin
	'Schnee' (d)	EGoo
	serpyllifolium	see *H. nummularium* subsp. *glabrum*
	'Shot Silk'	CFul COkL EWes MDHE SIng
	'Silvery Salmon' (v)	WAbe
	'Snow Queen'	see *H.* 'The Bride'
	'Southmead'	CFul COkL GAbr
	'Sterntaler'	CFul GAbr GDra MDHE SRms
	'Sudbury Gem'	CFul COkL COIW EBre ECha EHyt
		GAbr GKir LRHS NHol SIng SMer
		WPer WPnn WTel
	'Sulphureum Plenum' (d)	ECtt EPfP
	'Sunbeam'	CSam EMNN GAbr MDHE SRms
	'Sunburst'	CFul GAbr
§	'Supreme'	CFul ECGP ELan EPfP EWes LBee
		LRHS MWat SDix SIgm SRms WPer
	'Tangerine'	CFul GAbr
	'Terracotta' **new**	CRez
§	'The Bride' ♀ H4	CFul CMea EBre ECha EGle ELan
		EPfP GAbr GKir LHop LRHS MBro
		MHer MSte MWat MWgw SBla
		SChu SDix SRms WAbe WEas
		WHoo WLin WSHC
	'Tigrinum Plenum' (d)	CFul CPBP ESis EWes GDra LBee
		LRHS MDHE WWin
	'Tomato Red'	ECha NSla SMrm
	tomentosum	see *H. nummularium*
	umbellatum	see *Halimium umbellatum*
	'Venustum Plenum' (d)	WEas
	'Voltaire'	CFul ECtt EMNN EPfP GAbr
		MDHE MOne NPri SWal WWin
	'Watergate Rose'	CFul MWat NBir

'Welsh Flame'	WAbe
'Windermere'	SIgm
'Windmill Gold'	COkL
'Wisley Pink'	see *H.* 'Rhodanthe Carneum'
'Wisley Primrose' ♀ H4	More than 30 suppliers
'Wisley White'	CFul COkL CSam CTri ECha EGoo
	EPfP MBro NLon WCom WHoo
	WLin
'Wisley Yellow'	GKir
'Yellow Queen'	see *H.* 'Golden Queen'

Helianthus ✿ (*Asteraceae*)

angustifolius	CFwr WPer
atrorubens	CBri EBee EVFa LRHS MAvo MBri
	MRav WFar
'Capenoch Star' ♀ H4	CElw CPrp CRez CStr EBee ECha
	ECtt EFou EMan ERou GBuc IKee
	LRHS MArl MCLN MFir MLLN
	MRav NDov NLar SDix SMac
	SMrm WFar WLRN WOld WWpP
'Capenoch Supreme'	EBre EMan
cusickii	EBee
decapetalus	CStr MDKP NFla WCot WWye
- 'Maximus'	SRms
- Morning Sun	see *H.* 'Morgensonne'
divaricatus	EBee
x *doronicoides*	SRms
giganteus 'Sheila's	CBre CElw CFwr CStr GBri MAvo
Sunshine'	MSte WCot WOld
gracilentus new	EBee
grosseserratus	IIve LPhx WCot
'Gullick's Variety'	CBre CStr EBee EFou EPfP IBlr
	LLWP LPhx MAvo NBro NChi
	NPSI NSti SDes STes WOld
'Hazel's Gold' new	EBee
hirsutus new	EBee
x *kellermanii*	CStr EBee EFou EMon LPhx MTed
	MWgw NDov SAga SMad
§ x *laetiflorus*	EBee ELan EMan EMon NChi NLar
	NOrc
- 'Miss Mellish' new	WCot
* - 'Superbus'	IBlr NPSI
§ 'Lemon Queen'	More than 30 suppliers
'Limelight'	see *H.* 'Lemon Queen'
§ 'Loddon Gold' ♀ H4	EBre EFou ELan EMan EPfP ERou
	IBlr LPhx LRHS MAvo MRav MTis
	NVic SAga SMrm WBrE WCot
	WFar WMoo WTel WWye
'Low Down' new	EBee
§ *maximiliani*	EBee ECGN IIve LRHS MDKP
	MSte
microcephalus	EBee NPSI
mollis	EBee WCot WLin WPer
'Monarch' ♀ H4	CFwr CStr EBee EMan ERou LPhx
	MFir MWgw SAga SDix SMad SVal
	WCot WOld
'Morgensonne'	EHrv ERou MAvo MDKP MLLN
	WCot
x *multiflorus* 'Meteor'	CFwr EBee NChi
nuttallii	EBee
occidentalis	IBlr IIve LRHS WLin WPer
orgyalis	see *H. salicifolius*
quinquenervis	see *Helianthella*
	quinquenervis
rigidus (Cass.) Desf.	see *H. pauciflorus*
§ *salicifolius*	CFwr CRDP CSBt CStr EBee
	ECGN ECha EMan EMon EVFa
	EWTr LPhx LRHS MBri MSte
	MWat NSti SDix SMad SMrm SSpe
	SYvo WCot WFar WHrl WOld
	WWye
scaberrimus	see *H.* x *laetiflorus*
'Soleil d'Or'	EBee ECtt MCAu WOld

strumosus	IIve WCot
'Triomphe de Gand'	CRez CStr GBri LPhx MFir MRav
	MWat SSvw WFar WOld
tuberosus	EBee GPoy NRog WOld
- 'Dwarf Sunray'	IIve
- 'Fuseau'	IIve LEdu
- 'Garnet'	LEdu
- 'Sugarball'	LEdu

Helichrysum ✿ (*Asteraceae*)

from Drakensberg Mountains, CNic NWCA
South Africa

acutatum	GCal
alveolatum	see *H. splendidum*
ambiguum	CFis NOak SIgm WBcn WCom
angustifolium	see *H. italicum*
- from Crete	see *H. microphyllum* (Willd.)
	Cambess.
§ *arwae*	EHyt EPot WAbe
aureum var.	WLin
scopulosum new	
basalticum	CStu
bellidioides	ECha GGar LRHS SMer WCru
	WPer
bellum	NWCA
bracteatum	see *Xerochrysum bracteatum*
chionophilum	NWCA
'Coco'	see *Xerochrysum bracteatum*
	'Coco'
coralloides	see *Ozothamnus coralloides*
'County Park Silver'	see *Ozothamnus* 'County Park
	Silver'
'Dargan Hill Monarch'	see *Xerochrysum bracteatum*
	'Dargan Hill Monarch'
'Elmstead'	see *H. stoechas* 'White Barn'
fontanesii	SPar WHor
frigidum	CPBP EHyt EPot ITim LRHS WAbe
heldreichii	CPBP EPot SMrm
- NS 127	NWCA
hookeri	see *Ozothamnus hookeri*
hypoleucum	GGar
§ *italicum* ♀ H3	CArn CBod CSLe EChP ECha ELau
	EShb GPoy LGro MBar MBow
	MBri MHer MWgw NBid NChi
	SPar SPer SPet SRms WCer WDin
	WEas WGwG WHCG WHHs
	WWye
- 'Dartington'	CBod EOHP SIde WJek WSel
I - 'Glaucum' new	CWib
- 'Korma'	CAbP EBee ELan ENot EPfP MAsh
	MBNS MOak WJek WWeb
- subsp *microphyllum*	see *H. microphyllum* (Willd.)
	Cambess.
- 'Nanum'	see *H. microphyllum* (Willd.)
	Cambess.
§ - subsp. *serotinum*	CBrm CChe CHad EBee EGoo
	EPfP GEil GGar GPoy MAsh MRav
	SLim SMer SPar SPer SPla SRms
	STre SWal WDin WPer WSel WTel
	WWeb
lanatum	see *H. thianschanicum*
ledifolium	see *Ozothamnus ledifolius*
marginatum hort.	see *H. milfordiae*
marginatum DC.	CPBP
- JJ&JH 9401733	NWCA
microphyllum hort.	see *Plecostachys serpyllifolia*
microphyllum	see *Ozothamnus microphyllus*
Benth. & Hooker	
§ *microphyllum* (Willd.)	CFis ETow GBar NBlu NPri NWoo
	Cambess. SIde SIgm WJek WSel
§ *milfordiae* ♀ H2-3	EDAr EPot GEdr NHar NLAp
	NWCA SIng SRms WAbe WLin WPat
montanum	NWCA

orientale — EPot SMer
pagophilum — CPBP EHyt EPot ITim SIng WAbe WLin
  – JJ&JH 9401304 — NWCA
§ *petiolare* ♀ H2 — CFox CSLe EBak ECtt LPVe MOak MRav
  – 'Aureum' — see *H. petiolare* 'Limelight'
  – 'Goring Silver' ♀ H2-3 — CHal MOak NPri SPet
§ – 'Limelight' ♀ H2 — CFox CHal ECtt MOak MRav NPri SPet WWol
  – 'Roundabout' (v) — MOak
  – 'Variegatum' (v) ♀ H2 — CFox CHal ECtt MRav NPri SPet SPoG
petiolatum — see *H. petiolare*
plicatum — NWCA
plumeum — EPot ITim WAbe
populifolium — WHer
praecurrens — EHyt
rosmarinifolium — see *Ozothamnus rosmarinifolius*
'Ruby Cluster' — EBre
§ 'Schwefellicht' — CSLe EBee ECha EFou EGle EPfP ERou EVFa LRHS MBri NLon SChu SMer SPer SPet SRPl SWat WEas WSHC WWal
selago — see *Ozothamnus selago*
  – var. *tumidum* — NSla
serotinum — see *H. italicum* subsp. *serotinum*
serpyllifolium — see *Plecostachys serpyllifolia*
sessile — see *H. sessilioides*
§ *sessilioides* — EPot ITim NHar NLAp NWCA WAbe
§ *sibthorpii* — CSev LRHS NWCA WAbe
'Skynet' — see *Xerochrysum bracteatum* 'Skynet'
§ *splendidum* ♀ H3 — EBee EHoe EPfP GEil NBro NFor SLon SPer WBrE WCom WDin WPer
stoechas — CArn
§ – 'White Barn' — ECha LPio WEas
Sulphur Light — see *H.* 'Schwefellicht'
'Sussex Silver' — NPro
§ *thianschanicum* — ENot SRms
  – Golden Baby — see *H. thianschanicum* 'Goldkind'
§ – 'Goldkind' — EPfP GKir IHMH NBir NBlu NPri WMoo
thyrsoideum — see *Ozothamnus thyrsoideus*
trilineatum — see *H. splendidum*
aff. *trilineatum* — NWCA
  JJ&JH 9401783
tumidum — see *Ozothamnus selago* var. *tumidus*
virgineum — see *H. sibthorpii*
woodii — see *H. arwae*

Helicodiceros (Araceae)

§ *muscivorus* — CFir CHid EBee ITer WCot

Heliconia (Heliconiaceae)

bihai — WMul
bourgaeana — LPal
§ 'Bucky' — WMul
'Guyana' — see *H.* 'Bucky'
'Guyana Red' — see *H.* 'Bucky'
lingulata 'Fan' — LPal
orthotrica 'She' — WMul
* – 'Total Eclipse' — WMul
rostrata — LPal NBlo WMul XBlo
  – dwarf — WMul
stricta 'Cooper's Sharonii' — WMul
  – 'Dwarf Jamaican' — WMul

Helictotrichon (Poaceae)

pratense — EHoe EMon LRHS MAvo

§ *sempervirens* ♀ H4 — More than 30 suppliers
  – var. *pendulum* — EMon EPPr LRHS
  – 'Saphirsprudel' — CKno EBee EMon EPPr WCot WPGP

Heliophila (Brassicaceae)

carnosa — SPla
longifolia — CSpe

Heliopsis ❀ (Asteraceae)

helianthoides — CFwr CStr EMon
  – 'Limelight' — see *Helianthus* 'Lemon Queen'
  – var. *scabra* — EBee EPfP LPVe WMnd
  – – Ballerina — see *H. helianthoides* var. *scabra* 'Spitzentänzerin'
  – – 'Benzinggold' ♀ H4 — MRav SMrm
  – – Golden Plume — see *H. helianthoides* var. *scabra* 'Goldgefieder'
§ – – 'Goldgefieder' ♀ H4 — EBee EMan EPfP LRHS NFla WRHF WRus
  – – Goldgreenheart — see *H. helianthoides* var. *scabra* 'Goldgrünherz'
§ – – 'Goldgrünherz' — CFwr EBee EBre LRHS MBri WAul WRus
  – – 'Hohlspiegel' — EBee EBre ECha EMan MBri WLRN
  – – 'Incomparabilis' — MWgw
  – – 'Light of Loddon' ♀ H4 — MWat SVal
  – – 'Mars' **new** — MBri
§ – – 'Sommersonne' — CHar CM&M CSBt EBre ECtt EFou ERou GMaP MCAu MRav MWrn NArg NMir NPer SAga SPer SRms STes WFar WPer WWeb WWin WWpP
  – – 'Sonnenglut' ♀ H4 — MBri
§ – – 'Spitzentänzerin' ♀ H4 — CFwr EBee MBri
  – – Summer Sun — see *H. helianthoides* var. *scabra* 'Sommersonne'
  – – 'Venus' **new** — EBee MBri MCAu NGdn SSpe
Loraine Sunshine = 'Helhan'PBR (v) — EBre EMan LRHS
orientalis — EWTr

Heliotropium ❀ (Boraginaceae)

§ *amplexicaule* — EBee
anchusifolium — see *H. amplexicaule*
§ *arborescens* — CArn EPfP MOak
  – 'Chatsworth' ♀ H1 — CHad CPle CSev EHol EMan ERea MOak MSte SIde WFar WPen
  – 'Dame Alice de Hales' — CHal ERea MOak
  – 'Gatton Park' — ERea LRHS MOak MRav SMrm
  – 'Lord Roberts' — ERea MOak SYvo
  – 'Marine' — LIck SGar WGor
  – 'Netherhall White' — ERea
  – 'P.K. Lowther' — ERea MOak WEas
  – 'President Garfield' — MOak WFar
  – 'Princess Marina' ♀ H1 — CHal CSev EMan ERea LRHS MSte WEas
* – 'The Queen' — ERea
  – 'The Speaker' — MOak
  – 'White Lady' — CHal CSev EHol ERea MOak
peruvianum — see *H. arborescens*

Helipterum (Asteraceae)

anthemoides — see *Rhodanthe anthemoides*
'Paper Cascade'PBR — see *Rhodanthe anthemoides* 'Paper Cascade'

Helleborus ❀ (Ranunculaceae)

abschasicus **new** — EBee ITim MAsh
§ *argutifolius* ♀ H4 — More than 30 suppliers
  – from Italy — EHrv
  – 'Little 'Erbert' — MAsh
  – mottled-leaved — see *H. argutifolius* 'Pacific Frost'

§ - 'Pacific Frost' (v)	CAvo CHar CMil CPla EVFa MAsh MAvo NPro WCot
- 'Silver Lace'	CRDP CWCL ELan EPfP MAsh MAvo NBir SPer WPGP WWeb
atrorubens hort.	see *H. orientalis* Lam. subsp. *abchasicus* Early Purple Group
atrorubens Waldst. & Kit.	CBel CLCN CWib EBee NBlu WAbe WStI
- WM 9028 Slovenia	MPhe
- WM 9028	NRar
- WM 9319	NRar
- WM 9617 from Slovenia	SSth
- WM 9805 from Croatia	MPhe
- from Slovenia	GBuc
- - WM 9216	MPhe WCru
x *ballardiae*	LEur LRHS MPhe WAbe WFar
bocconei subsp. *bocconei*	see *H. multifidus* subsp. *bocconei*
Bradfield hybrids, double	EHrv
Bradfield hybrids, picotee **new**	EHrv
colchicus	see *H. orientalis* Lam. subsp. *abchasicus*
corsicus	see *H. argutifolius*
croaticus	CBel CLCN LBuc MAsh SSth
- WM 9313	MPhe
- WM 9416	MPhe
- from Croatia	GBuc
- - WM 9810	MPhe
cyclophyllus	EBee EMar EPfP GBuc GKir LRHS MAsh MPhe NDov NHol SPer SSpi WFar
- JCA 560.625	CLCN SSpi
dumetorum	CBel CLCN EBee GBuc MAsh NHol NLar NSla WCru WFar WPGP
- WM 9209 from Hungary	MPhe
- WM 9301 from Slovenia	MPhe
- WM 9627 from Croatia	MPhe
- WM 9920	MAsh
- WM 9924	MAsh
- WM 9926	MAsh
§ x *ericsmithii*	CRDP EBee EChP EHrv LHop LRHS MAsh SBla WAbe WFar WWeb
foetidus ♀H4	More than 30 suppliers
- 'Chedglow'	CNat
- 'Chedglow Variegated' (v)	CFox CNat
- 'Curio' (v)	CNat
- 'Gold Bullion'	CPla MCCP
- 'Green Giant'	CBel MAsh MTho WCru
- from Italy	GBin MAsh WCot WRus
- 'Miss Jekyll's Scented'	LBuc
- 'Ruth'	MAsh MPhe SSth
'Sienna'	LDuc MAsh
- 'Sopron'	EBee MAsh MPhe NLar WCru WLin
- Wester Flisk Group	More than 30 suppliers
N x *hybridus*	More than 30 suppliers
- 'Agnes Brook'	WFib
- Anderson's red hybrids	CLCN
- anemone-centred	CLAP EHrv LCTD NRar WFar
- 'Angela Tandy'	WFib
- 'Apple Blossom'	EBre EHrv WFar
- 'Apricot'	GBuc LCTD WFar
- apricot	CLCN EHrv SPla
- 'Aquarius'	CLCN
- Ashwood Garden hybrids	EHrv EPfP GKir LRHS MAsh MRav SCoo WWeb
- Ashwood Garden hybrids, anemone-centred	EPfP MAsh
- Ashwood Garden hybrids, double (d)	MAsh
- 'Baby Black'	ECot
- Ballard's Group	EBee EBre GKir LRHS MBri NRar WCot WCru WFar WPnP
- black	CBel CLCN CRDP EHrv EPPr GBuc GDra NRar WCru WFar
- 'Blowsy' seedlings	CLCN
- 'Blue Lady' **new**	EBee EPfP MBNS
- 'Blue Wisp'	LCTD
- blue-grey	CLCN EHrv GKir NPar
- Bradfield hybrids **new**	EHrv
- Bradfield hybrids, anemone-centred **new**	EHrv
- Bradfield Star Group **new**	EHrv
- 'Button'	LCTD
- Caborn hybrids **new**	LLWP
- 'Carlton Hall'	WFib
- 'Cheerful'	GKir LCTD NBir WCru
- 'Citron'	LCTD
- cream	CPMA MCCP NHol NPSI WFar
- 'David's Star' (d) **new**	WAbe
- 'Dawn'	LCTD
- deep red	GAbr GKir WFar WViv
- double (d)	CLAP LCTD NRar WFar
- Draco strain	CLCN
- 'Dusk'	LCTD WCru
- 'Elizabeth Coburn'	WFib
- Galaxy Group	NPar
- 'Garnet'	LCTD WFar
- 'Gertrude Raithby'	WFib
- 'Gladys Burrow'	WFib
- green	CLCN MBNS WCru WFar
- 'Greencups'	LCTD
- 'Gunther Jurgl'	LCTD
- 'Hades'	LCTD
- 'Hades' seedling	WCru
- Hadspen hybrids	CHad
- 'Harvington Pink'	GKir LRHS WBry
- 'Harvington Red'	GKir LRHS WBry
- 'Harvington Shades of the Night'	WBry
- 'Harvington Speckled'	GKir LRHS SPoG
- 'Harvington White'	GKir LRHS
- 'Harvington Yellow'	GKir LRHS
- 'Harvington Yellow Speckled' **new**	SPoG
- 'Helen Ballard'	LCTD
- Homelea hybrids, anemone-centred	CRDP
- Homelea hybrids, double (d)	CRDP
- 'Ian Raithby'	WFib
- 'Ingot'	LCTD
- ivory	CLCN CRDP WFar
- 'Joan Bridges'	LCTD
- 'John Raithby'	WFib
- Kaye's garden hybrids	EMar EPfP LBBr MHdf WMnd WWeb
- Kochii Group	ECha GKir WCru
- 'Lady Charlotte Bonham-Carter'	WFib
- 'Lady Macbeth' **new**	EWes
- 'Leo'	MTed
- 'Limelight'	ECha
- 'Little Black'	ECho ELan EWes
- 'Lynne'	LCTD
- 'Maia'	LCTD
- maroon	CRDP EBre NRar SPla WFar
- 'Mary Petit'	WFib
- 'Massive White'	NPar
- 'Maureen Key'	WFib
- 'Metallic Blue'	CFai EBee MBNS
- Midnight Sky Group	GKir
- 'Mystery'	WCru
- 'Orion'	LCTD

	– 'Pamina'	EHrv LCTD
	– Party Dress Group (d)	CRDP CWib EHrv MWrn NDov SBla WFar
	– 'Patchwork'	LCTD
	– 'Pebworth White'	WFib
	– 'Petsamo'	NRar
	– 'Philip Ballard'	LCTD SSth WCru
	– 'Philip Wilson'	LCTD
	– 'Picotee'	CRDP EHrv GBuc GKir LCTD MBro NDov NRar SPla SPoG WCru WFar WHoo
	– pink	CBel CLCN CPMA CRDP GAbr GBuc MBNS MBro MCCP NRar SPla WAbe WCru WFar WViv
	– plum	CLCN EHrv SSth WFar
	– 'Plum Stippled'	ECha
	– 'Pluto'	LCTD
	– primrose	CBel CRDP EBre GBuc GKir MBNS NHol NRar SPla WAbe WCru WFar
	– purple	CBel CLCN CPMA CRDP LBBr MBro NHol NPSI NRar SApp SMad SSth WAbe WBor WCru WFar
*	– 'Purpurascens'	MCCP
	– 'Queen of the Night'	CHid CRDP
	– red	NCot
	– 'Red Lady' **new**	MBNS
	– 'Red Mountain'	MBNS
I	– 'Rosa'	LCTD
I	– 'Rubens'	LCTD
	– 'Seamus O'Brien' **new**	MPhe
	– 'Shades of Night'	EHrv GKir LRHS
	– 'Sirius' seedlings	CLCN
	– slaty blue	CRDP EBre EHrv GBuc GKir NDov NRar SSth WCot WCru WFar
	– slaty purple	NDov NRar SAga WFar WHrl
	– smokey purple	WFar
	– 'Snow Queen'	EHrv
	– spotted	CAvo CLCN EBre GAbr GKir LBBr LRHS MCCP NHol SApp SBla WBry WCot WCru
	– spotted, cream	NBir SAga
	– spotted, green	CBel CRDP EBre SSth WFar
	– spotted, pink	CBel CRDP EBre NBir NDov NHol NRar SAga SPla WFar
	– spotted, primrose	SAga WFar
	– spotted, white	CBel CRDP EBre NBir NDov NRar SPla SSth WAbe WCot WCru WFar
	– 'Sunny'	LCTD WCru
	– 'Sunny' seedlings	CLCN
	– 'Sylvia'	LCTD
	– 'Titania'	LCTD
	– 'Tommie'	LCTD
	– 'Ushba'	LCTD
	– 'Ushba' seedlings	CLCN GCal MBro
	– 'Victoria Raithby'	WFib
	– white	CRDP EBre MBro NRar SAga WCFE WCot WCru WFar WViv
	– 'White Lady' **new**	EBee
	– 'White Lady Spotted' **new**	NCot
	– white-veined	WFar
	– 'William'	LCTD
	– yellow	NDov SSth WCot WCru WFar WHrl
	– 'Yellow Lady' **new**	EBee
	– Zodiac Group	CLCN ENot EOrc GBuc NPar SApp WWeb
	lividus ♀ H2-3	CAvo CBot CBro CHar CLCN EBre EHyt ELan EWes GKir LHop LRHS MAsh MPhe NBir NHar SBla SIgm SSth SWat WAbe WCru WFar WViv
	– Anne Watson strain **new**	NRar
	– subsp. ***corsicus***	see *H. argutifolius*
	Marion White Group	SBla

	multifidus	CLCN EBee EMar EPfP NBir NHol SPer WFar
§	– subsp. ***bocconei***	CBel EHrv LBuc MAsh WFar
	– – WM 9719 from Italy	MPhe
	– – WM 9901	MAsh
	– subsp. ***hercegovinus***	CBel EHrv LBuc SBla SIgm SSth WFar
	– – WM 0020	MPhe
	– subsp. ***istriacus***	CBro GBuc LBuc WFar
	– – WM 9322	MPhe
	– – WM 9324	MPhe
	– – WM 9815	MAsh
	– subsp. ***multifidus***	EHrv
	– – WM 9104	MPhe
	– – WM 9529	MPhe
	– – WM 9936	MAsh
	– – from Croatia	MAsh
	– – – WM 9748	MPhe
	– – – WM 9833	MPhe
	niger ♀ H4	More than 30 suppliers
	– Ashwood strain	MAsh
	– Blackthorn Group	EHrv GKir SBla
I	– 'Crûg Hybrid'	WCru
	– Harvington hybrids	COtt EHrv GKir LRHS MAsh
	– 'Louis Cobbett'	EHyt
§	– subsp. ***macranthus***	EBee WCot
	– ***major***	see *H. niger* subsp. *macranthus*
	– 'Nell Lewis' **new**	MAsh
	– 'Potter's Wheel'	CPMA CRDP EBee EBre ECot GBuc LRHS MRav SBla SPla SVil WCru WViv WWeb
	– 'Ras Buis' **new**	WMnd
	– Sunrise Group	CBel
	– – WM 9519	CLCN MPhe
	– Sunset Group WM 9113	GBuc MPhe
	– 'White Magic'	CBcs CPMA SBla SPar WCru
	x *nigercors* ♀ H4	CRDP EBre ENot ETow GKir LPio LRHS MAsh NPar SBla WAbe WWeb
	– 'Alabaster'	NBir
	x *nigristern*	see *H.* x *ericsmithii*
	odorus	CAvo CBel CLCN EBee EHrv MAsh MPhe SPer WFar
	– WM 9202	MPhe WCru
	– WM 9310	GBuc
	– WM 9415	MPhe
	– WM 9921	MAsh
	– from Hungary	LBuc
	– – WM 9088	MPhe
	– – WM 9728	MPhe
N	***orientalis*** hort.	see *H.* x *hybridus*
	orientalis Lam.	CBel EBlw MBro MNrw MPhe NBlu SSth
§	– subsp. ***abchasicus***	SRms WCru
§	– subsp. ***abchasicus*** Early Purple Group	CAvo CLCN CTri CWib GCal LPio LRHS MAsh NBee NSti SPer WCru WFar WMnd
	– subsp. ***guttatus***	GGar SPla SSpi WCru
	– ***olympicus***	see *H. orientalis* Lam. subsp. *orientalis*
§	– subsp. ***orientalis***	NHol
	purpurascens	CBel CLCN EBee EChP EHrv GBuc GKir GMaP LRHS MAsh MBNS MCAu NBir SBla SDes SIgm SSth WAbe WBrE WFar WLin WPnP
	– WM 9211 from Hungary	MPhe WCru
	– WM 9412	MPhe WCru
	– WM 9924	MAsh
	Snowdon strain	ENot LBuc WWeb
	x *sternii*	More than 30 suppliers
	– Ashwood strain	MAsh
	– Blackthorn Group ♀ H3-4	CPMA EBre EHrv EPfP GBuc GKir LRHS MBri MRav SBla SPar SSpi

	WAbe WCot WCru WFar WHoo WPGP WViv
- Blackthorn dwarf strain	CLCN EBee GBuc
- Boughton Group	MAsh WCru
- 'Boughton Beauty'	CAvo CHar EBee ECha EHrv EHyt ELan GBuc LEur LHop MTho WCot
- Bulmer's blush strain	EMan LRHS MAsh
- Cally strain	GCal
- dwarf	WFar
thibetanus	EBee EFEx EHrv GBuc LAma MAsh MNrw MPhe SBla SSpi WCru WViv
- red-flowered **new**	GKev
torquatus	CBel CBro CLCN EBee EHrv LBuc MAsh MPhe MTho NHol SPer SSth WFar WTin
- WM 9820 from Bosnia	MPhe
- WM 9925	MAsh
- Caborn hybrids	LLWP
- 'Dido' (d)	SBla WFar
- double-flowered hybrids (d)	CBos WFar
- double-flowered, from Montenegro (d)	WFar
- WM 9106 from Montenegro	GBuc MPhe WCru
- hybrids	CBel ECGP EHrv SBla WFar
- Party Dress Group	see *H.* x *hybridus* Party Dress Group
- semi-double (d)	CRDP WFar
- Wolverton hybrids	SBla WFar
vesicarius	EBee EHrv SSpi
viridis	EBee EBre ECha EHrv EMar EPfP GKir LRHS SPer SRms WBWf WCot WCru WFar WTin
- subsp. *occidentalis*	CAvo CBel CBro LBuc
- - WM 9401	MPhe
- - WM 9502 from Germany	MPhe
- subsp. *viridis*	LBuc SSth
- - WM 9723 from Italy	MPhe
'Winter Joy Bouquet'	EBre

Helonias (Liliaceae)

bullata **new**	EBee

Heloniopsis (Melanthiaceae)

acutifolia B&SWJ 218	WCru
japonica	see *H. orientalis*
kawanoi	SOkd
§ *orientalis*	CBro CLAP CPLG GBuc GEdr LRHS NGar SIng SOkd SSpi WCot WCru
- B&SWJ 956 from Korea	WCru
§ - var. *breviscapa*	CFil NGar WCru WPGP
§ - var. *kawanoi*	CRDP NGar WCru
- variegated (v) **new**	WCru
- var. *yakusimensis*	see *H. orientalis* var. *kawanoi*
umbellata B&SWJ 1839	WCru

Helwingia (Helwingiaceae)

* *asiatica* **new**	WPGP
chinensis	CPle SSpi
himalaica	CFil
japonica	CBot EFEx WFar

Helxine see *Soleirolia*

Hemerocallis ✿ (Hemerocallidaceae)

'Aabachee' **new**	CCol
'Adah'	SDay
'Addie Branch Smith'	EGol SDay
'Admiral's Braid' **new**	LSde
'Adoration'	SPer
'Aglow'	MTed

'Alan'	EBre EChP MNFA MRav SCro WFar
'Alan Adair' **new**	LSde
'Alaqua' **new**	CMil EGle MNrw WAbe
'Albany'	CCol
'Alec Allen'	SRos
'All American Baby' **new**	LSde
'All Fired Up' **new**	LSde
altissima	CHEx EMon EPla LPhx MNFA SDix
'Always Afternoon'	EBee EMar GBri MBNS MBri NLar SApp SDay WAul WHrl
'Amadeus'	SDay
'Amazon Amethyst'	MCAu
'Amber Classic' **new**	SApp
'Amber Star'	LPBA
'American Revolution'	CPar CSpe EBee ECtt EHrv EMan EWll LCaP MAvo MBNS MCAu MCCP MSte SApp SRos WCot WGer WMaN WPnP WTin WWhi
'Amersham'	EBee EGle GSki MNFA WLRN
'Angel Artistry'	SDay
'Angel Curls'	EGol
'Angel Unawares'	WTin
'Ann Kelley'	MSte SApp SDay
'Anna Warner'	MPWC
'Annie Welch'	CFai EBee ECGP ECle EPla MBNS MMil
'Antique Rose'	CKel SDay
'Anzac'	EBre ECha ECtt EHrv EPla ERou GKir GMac LRHS MAvo MBNS NGdn NHol NMGW NPri SAga SDes WFar WTMC
'Apache Uprising' **new**	SDay
'Apple Court Chablis' **new**	SApp
'Appolodorus'	SDay
'Apres Moi'	EMar LAst LPVe MBNS MCAu MLLN
'Apricot Beauty'	EBee EMar EWTr LBuc NPri
'Apricot Jade' **new**	LSde
'Apricotta'	WBro WCot WPnP
'Arctic Snow'	EBee EGle EMar EPfP ERou EWoo MLan NLar SDay SRos SUsu WAul
'Ariadne'	SBla
'Arriba'	MNFA NBro WLRN
'Arthur Moore'	SDay
'Artistic Gold'	WTin
'Artist's Brush'	LBuc
'Asiatic Pheasant'	CCol
'Aten'	LPVe MNFA NPri SDes WAul
'Atlanta Bouquet'	SRos
'Atlanta Full House'	SDay
'August Morn' **new**	LSde
aurantiaca	MWrn
'Autumn Lace' **new**	SCro
'Autumn Minaret'	CCol
'Autumn Red'	EBee EMar ERou MBNS NBir NCat NHaw NOak SDes WCot
'Ava Michelle'	SDay
'Avante Garde' **new**	LSde
'Awash With Color' **new**	LSde
'Awesome Blossom' **new**	ENot
'Aztec Furnace'	SApp
'Baby Darling'	SDay
'Baby Julia'	MTed
'Baby Moon Café'	CAbx
'Baby Talk'	CFir LRHS SVil
'Baja'	MNFA WFar
'Bailey Hay'	see *H.* 'Bali Hai'
'Bald Eagle'	EGle SChu
§ 'Bali Hai'	COIW EBee EMar LCaP LRHS MBNS NGdn SDes WHrl
'Ballerina Girl'	SRos
'Ballet Dancer'	CMdw ERou
'Bandolero' (d)	EBee

'Barbara Mitchell'	EBee SApp SDay WAul
'Barbaresco'	SApp
'Barbary Corsair'	SDay
'Baroni'	ECha
'Battle Hymn'	MCAu
'Bayou Ribbons'	MAvo MBNS
'Beat the Barons'	SRos
'Beautiful Edgings'	SRos
'Beauty Bright'	MCAu
'Beauty to Behold'	SApp SDay SRos
'Becky Lynn'	EBee WAul WHoo
'Bed of Roses'	MNFA
'Bedarra Island'	SDay
'Bejewelled'	EBee EGol EPla NMoo
'Bela Lugosi' **new**	LSde WCot
'Beloved Returns' ♀ H4	MCAu
'Benchmark'	SApp SRos
'Berlin Lemon' ♀ H4	MNFA
'Berlin Maize' **new**	SApp
'Berlin Oxblood'	MNFA
'Berlin Red' ♀ H4	CPrp EBee EGle EMar EPla LBuc
	MMil MNFA NGdn SChu
'Berlin Red Velvet' ♀ H4	MNFA
'Berlin Tallboy' **new**	SApp
'Berlin Yellow'	EFou
'Berliner Premiere'	MNFA
'Bernard Thompson'	MNFA SApp
'Bertie Ferris'	LBuc
'Bess Ross'	CMHG MCAu
'Bess Vestale'	ENot ERou MNFA MWat NHol
'Best of Friends'	GKir
'Bette Davis Eyes'	SRos
'Betty Woods' (d)	CRDP SRos
'Beverly Center' **new**	LSde
'Bibury'	SCro
'Big Bird'	CPar EChP EFou SHBN SHar
'Big Smile' **new**	IPot MBNS WHil
'Big Snowbird' **new**	SRos
'Big World'	MNFA
'Bill Norris'	SApp
'Bitsy'	EBee EGle EGol MOne MSte
	MTed SSpe WCot WMnd
'Black Ambrosia' **new**	LSde
'Black Emmanuella' **new**	EMar
'Black Eyed Stella'	CKel EBee ENot MBNS
'Black Knight'	SRms
'Black Magic'	CBro CHad CHar CMGP CPLG
	EBee EGol ELan EMar EPla ERou
	GMaP LRHS MBro MNFA MRav
	MWgw NBir NGdn NHol SChu
	SPer WHer WMoo
'Black Plush' **new**	SApp
'Black Prince'	EBee EWll MBNS SMrm WAul
	WRus WViv
'Black Taffeta'	CKel
'Blackberry Candy'	GBri MBri WAul
'Blaze of Fire'	SDes
'Blessing'	SRos
'Blonde Is Beautiful'	SDay SRos
'Blue Happiness' **new**	SDay
'Blue Sheen'	CCol CFir EBee ECtt EGle EGol
	EWoo LAst LRHS MBNS MCAu
	MCCP NGdn NPri WMoo WWeb
'Blueberry Candy'	WAul
'Blushing Belle'	CFai CMil EBee EChP EMar IBal
	LRHS MBNS MNFA WWin
'Bold One'	CAbx SRos
'Bold Tiger' **new**	LSde SDay
'Bonanza'	More than 30 suppliers
'Booger'	SRos
'Boulderbrook Serenity'	SDay
'Bourbon Kings'	CMHG EBee EGol EMar ERou
	MBNS SDay

'Bowl of Roses'	MCAu
'Brand New Lover'	SApp
'Brass Buckles'	see H. 'Puddin'
'Bridget'	ELan
'Bright Spangles'	SApp SDay SRos
'Brilliant Circle'	EFou SApp
'Broadway Dancer' **new**	LSde
'Brocaded Gown'	SDay SRos
'Brunette'	MHar SAga SApp
'Bruno Müller'	MNFA
'Bubbly'	SApp
'Buffy's Doll'	EBee MBNS SDay SRos
'Bumble Bee'	EMar GKir MBNS SApp
'Buried Treasure'	MNFA
'Burning Daylight' ♀ H4	CMGP EBre EHrv EMar EPfP EPla
	ERou GSki LRHS MNFA MNrw
	NFla NHol SDes SPer SRms WCot
	WFar WViv
'Butterpat'	EFou
'Buzz Bomb'	CRDP EBee EBre ECGP EGle EHrv
	EMar GSki LRHS MCAu MHar
	MNFA NGdn SChu SPer SRos
	WLRN WWal
'California Sunshine'	SRos
'Camden Gold Dollar'	EGol
'Cameroons'	SDay
'Canadian Border Patrol' **new**	CMGP EBee LSde
'Canadian Goose'	EFou
'Canary Feathers' **new**	SApp
'Canary Glow'	CTri EBre SDes SRos SSpe WFar
'Canary Wings'	CAbx -
'Candide'	SApp
'Cantique'	SApp
'Cap and Bells'	SApp
'Captive Audience'	SRos
'Caramea'	EMar LAst WFar WWal
'Carolipiecrust'	SApp
'Carrot' **new**	SDay
'Cartwheels' ♀ H4	EBre EGra EHrv EMFW EMar EPfP
	EPla EWTr GMaP LRHS MBNS
	MCAu MMil MNFA NBro SPer
	SRos WFar WMoo
'Casino Gold'	SRos
'Catherine Woodbery'	More than 30 suppliers
'Cathy's Sunset'	EBee EMar MBNS NGdn
'Cedar Waxwing'	CHea EGol SCro
'Celestial City' **new**	SDay
'Champagne Memory' **new**	SApp
'Chance Encounter' **new**	LSde
'Chantilly Lace'	CMHG NGdn
'Charbonier'	MNFA
'Charles Johnston'	CKel EChP SApp SDay SRos WAul
	WTMC
'Charlie Brown'	SDay
'Charlie Pierce Memorial'	SRos
'Chartreuse Magic'	EGol EPla NHol SChu SPer
'Cherry Cheeks'	EBre ECtt EGol ELan EPfP
	ERou GKir LRHS MBNS MBri
	MCAu MRav NHol NPPs SRos
	SVil WAul WCot WCra WFar
	WWeb
'Cherry Eyed Pumpkin' **new**	SRos
'Cherry Ice Cream' **new**	SApp
'Cherry Kiss'	SRos
'Cherry Smoke'	SApp
'Chic Bonnet'	SPer
'Chicago Apache'	COtt EChP EGle ENot EPfP LPan
	LRHS MBNS NBir SApp SDay SRos
	SUsu SVil
'Chicago Blackout'	CFir CMil COtt CSpe EBee EChP
	EGol EPfP MCAu NHol WAul

'Chicago Cattleya'	CFir EChP EFou EGle EGol EWoo LAst MRav SApp WAul
'Chicago Cherry'	WWpP
'Chicago Fire'	EBee EGol EPfP MBNS WWye
'Chicago Firecracker' **new**	CAbx
'Chicago Heirloom'	CFir COtt EChP EGle EGol MCAu SVil WAul
'Chicago Jewel'	CFir EBee EGle EGol NSti SCro WAul
'Chicago Knobby'	EMar LPan MBNS
'Chicago Knockout'	CFir COtt EGle EGol EPfP EWoo MCAu WAul
'Chicago Peach'	EChP EFou EMan IPot MCAu
'Chicago Petticoats'	EGol LRHS NHol WAul
'Chicago Picotee Lace'	EBee EChP EGle EGol EPfP GKir MCAu NGdn SApp WAul
'Chicago Picotee Memories'	EBee EGle SDay
'Chicago Picotee Queen'	EBre LRHS MNFA
'Chicago Princess'	EFou EGle EGol
'Chicago Rainbow'	EWoo IPot WAul
'Chicago Rosy'	EFou EGol
'Chicago Royal Crown'	LRHS MBri
'Chicago Royal Robe'	EBre EFou EGol EPla GKir LLWP MBNS MNFA MRav MSte NBid NVic SCro SPer SWal WCot WWhi WWin
'Chicago Silver'	CFir COtt EGle EGol IPot MCAu
'Chicago Sunrise'	EBee EGol EMar EPla GMaP IBlr LPVe LRHS MBNS MBri MNFA MSta NGdn NHol NMoo NOrc SApp SRos SUsu SVil WPer
'Chicago Violet'	MCAu
'Chief Sarcoxie' ♀ H4	MCAu SApp SRos
'Children's Festival'	More than 30 suppliers
'China Lake' **new**	LSde
'Chinese Autumn'	SApp SRos
'Chinese Cloisonne'	CKel
'Chinese Coral'	WBcn
'Chloe's Child'	SCro
'Chorus Line'	SDay SRos
'Christmas Carol' **new**	SApp
'Christmas Is'	EBee EFou EGol EMar MBNS MUlv SApp WAul
'Churchill Downs'	MNFA
'Ciao'	SApp
'Ciel d'Or' **new**	LSde
'Cindy's Eye' **new**	LSde
'Cinnamon Circle' **new**	LSde
citrina	EFou ELan EMon EWTr LRHS MNFA MSte MWgw NFla NGdn WTin
'Civil Rights'	SRos
'Classic Simplicity'	MCAu
'Classy Lassie'	MTed
'Claudine'	SApp
'Coming up Roses'	SRos
'Condilla' (d) **new**	SDay
'Contessa'	CBro EHon SCro WWpP
'Cookie Monster'	LRHS
'Cool It'	EBee EGle EMar LBBr LPio LRHS MBNS SDes
'Cool Jazz'	SRos
'Coral Cay' **new**	LSde
'Coral Dawn'	CKel
'Coral Mist'	CCol EFou MBNS WWeb
'Corky' ♀ H4	More than 30 suppliers
'Corryton Pink'	SApp
'Corsican Bandit'	CM&M
'Cosmic Hummingbird'	SDay
'Countess Zora'	CMHG
'Country Club'	EBee EChP EGle EGol EMan EWoo GMaP LAst LHop MCAu NHol WWpP

'Country Melody'	SDay
'Country Pride'	SApp
'Court Concubine'	CAbx
'Court Magician'	SDay SRos
'Coyote Moon' **new**	LSde
'Cranberry Baby'	EGle SDay SRos WHoo WTin
'Cream Drop'	CMGP CPrp EBre EChP ECtt EFou EGle EGol EMar GMaP LRHS MBri MRav MTis MWat NBro NCiC NOrc NSti SChu SDes SPer SSpe WAul WCot WCra WMoo WRus WTMC WTel
'Creative Edge' **new**	MBNS
'Crimson Icon'	MSte WTin
'Crimson Pirate'	CBre CCol EMil EPPr ERou GKir LRHS MBNS MCAu MLan MNFA NBir NHol NPri SDes SPlb
'Croesus'	NHol SCro SRms
'Croftway'	SCro
'Cupid's Bow'	EGol
'Cupid's Gold'	SRos
'Custard Candy'	MBNS NBir SApp SRos SUsu WAul
'Cynthia Mary'	EBee EGle MBNS MNFA
'Dad's Best White'	EMar SCro
'Daily Dollar'	GKir LRHS MBri NGdn SApp
'Dainty Pink'	EGol
'Dallas Spider Time' **new**	CAbx
'Dallas Star'	SApp
'Dan Tau'	CKel
'Dance Ballerina Dance'	SDay SRos
'Dancing Shiva'	SApp SDay
'Dancing Summerbird' **new**	SApp
'Daring Deception'	CKel MBNS WAul
'Dark Angel' **new**	SApp
'Dark Avenger' **new**	LSde
'Darrell'	SDay
'David Kirchhoff'	WAul
'Decatur Imp'	EGol
'Delicate Design'	SApp
'Delicate Treasure' **new**	LSde
'Delightsome'	SApp SDay SRos
'Demetrius'	MBri MNFA SApp
'Destined to see' **new**	WCot
'Devon Cream'	SChu
'Devonshire'	SApp SRos
'Dewberry Candy' **new**	LSde
'Diamond Dust'	EBee EChP EGle EMar EPla LPhx LRHS MBNS MTed NLar SChu SPer WLRN
'Dido'	CTri ERou GBuc MSte
'Diva Assoluta' **new**	SApp
'Divertissment'	CAbx SApp
'Dominic'	SApp SRos
'Dorethe Louise'	CRDP SDay SRos
'Dorothy McDade'	COlW EGol ENot SApp
'Double Coffee' (d)	SApp
'Double Cream' (d) **new**	WCot
'Double Cutie' (d)	CCol EBee EFou MBNS NLar SChu SDay WAul
'Double Daffodil' (d)	MCAu
'Double Delicious' (d)	WCot
'Double Dream' (d) **new**	EMar
'Double Firecracker' (d)	CBcs EMar MBNS WCot
'Double Oh' (d)	MTed
'Double Oh Seven' (d)	SApp
'Double Pompom' (d)	MCAu
'Double River Wye' (d)	CFir EBee EChP EGol EMar EMil IPot LPan MBNS MBro MNrw MTed NPri SCro SHBN SHar SRos WCot WHoo WMnd WTin WWye
'Dragon King'	LSde
'Dragon Mouth' **new**	EGol
'Dragon's Eye'	SDay

'Dragon's Orb' — CKel
'Dream Legacy' — MBri WAul
'Dublin Elaine' (d) **new** — LSde
§ 'Dubloon' — CMGP COIW ENot ERou GAbr GBuc NHol
dumortieri — CAvo CBot CBro CHea CMHG CSam EBre ECGN ECha EFou EGol EGra EHrv EMar EOrc EPla GGar MLwd MNrw MRav MWat NBir NHol NSti NVic SPer SSpe WCot WWin WWpP
'Dutch Beauty' — EMar EPla WFar WTMC
'Dutch Gold' — CFai MNrw NBro
'Dynasty Pink' **new** — SApp
'Easy Ned' — SDay
'Ed Murray' — MCAu MNFA SRos WAul
'Edelweiss' — EWTr SDay WBcn
'Edge of Darkness' **new** — EBee EChP EGle MBNS
'Edna Spalding' — SRos
'Eenie Allegro' — CBro CCol EChP EGle EGol EMan MBNS SOkh SPer SPla WHil WMnd
'Eenie Fanfare' — COtt CSpe EGle EGol GKir IBal LRHS MBNS MNFA WAul WCra
'Eenie Gold' — LRHS
'Eenie Weenie' — CBro CFee EBla ECtt EGle EGol EPla ERos GKir IBal LRHS MBNS MBri NBur SAga SApp SChu SHBN SPer SRms WPer WTMC WWye
'Eenie Weenie Non-stop' — ECha EPPr
'Egyptian Ibis' — MBNS
'Eighth Day' **new** — LSde
'El Desperado' **new** — MBNS MCAu SUsu WCot WHil
'El Glorioso' — CAbx
'Elaine Strutt' — EGol MBNS MNFA SApp SDay SRos WCot
'Eleanor Marcotte' **new** — SDay
'Elegant Candy' — CCol CKel CPen ENot LBuc MBNS
'Elegant Greeting' — CCol EBee LBuc MBNS NOak
'Elizabeth Ann Hudson' — MNFA
'Elizabeth Elaine' **new** — LSde
'Elizabeth Salter' — EBee MBNS MCAu MCLN SRos SUsu
'Elizabeth Yancey' **new** — EGol
'Emperor Butterfly' — SApp
'Enchanted Elf' **new** — LSde
'English Toffee' — SApp
'Erin Prairie' — SApp
'Esther Walker' — WBcn
'Eternal Blessing' — SRos
'Etruscan Tomb' **new** — LSde
'Evelyn Claar' — EChP SCro SDes
'Evening Bell' **new** — SApp
'Ever So Ruffled' **new** — SRos
exaltata **new** — GIBF
'Eye of Newt' **new** — LSde
'Fairest Love' — EMar MBNS
'Fairy Charm' — SApp
'Fairy Summerbird' — SApp
'Fairy Tale Pink' — SApp SDay SRos
'Faith Nabor' — CAbx SRos
'Fall Guy' **new** — SApp
'Fan Club' **new** — LSde
'Fan Dancer' — EGol
'Farmer's Daughter' **new** — SApp
'Fashion Model' — SApp WPer
'Fellow' **new** — CCol
'Femme Osage' — SRos
'Fiery Chariot' **new** — LSde
'Final Touch' — WCot
'Finlandia' — MNFA
'Fire Dance' — SCro
'Firestorm' **new** — SApp

'Flamboyant Show' — EBee LBuc
'Flames of Fantasy' — MTed SRos
'Flaming Sword' — CMGP EBee GBuc LRHS NHol NPPs
flava — see *H. lilioasphodelus*
'Fleeting Fancy' — SRos
'Fly Catcher' — SRos
'Flying Carpet' **new** — LSde
'Forever Red' **new** — LSde
forrestii — EBee
– 'Perry's Variety' — CCol EMon
'Forsyth Tangerine Ruffles' **new** — LSde
'Forty Second Street' **new** — CFir MBNS MBri
'Fragrant Bouquet' **new** — SRos
'Fragrant Pastel Cheer' — SDay
'Frances Fay' — SRos WAul
'Frank Gladney' — SApp SRos
'Frans Hals' — EBre EChP EMar ENot EPfP EPla ERou GKir LLWP LRHS MBri MNrw MRav NPri SEND SPer SPla SRos WAul WFar WHoo WMnd WPer WPnP WTMC WWye
'French Porcelain' — SDay
'Friar's Lantern' **new** — LSde
* 'Frilled Soft Orange' **new** — NCat
'Fritz Schroer' **new** — CAbx
'Fuchsia Fashion' **new** — SApp
'Full Moon Magic' **new** — LSde
fulva — EGra IBlr LRHS MHar MWgw NBir NLon SHBN SRms WPnP WWin WWpP
N – 'Flore Pleno' (d) — CAvo CFee CHar CMHG EChP ECtt EGol EHon ELan EPfP IBlr LHop MCAu MCLN MFir MRav NBir NBro NGdn NSti SHBN SPer SRms SWat WEas WMoo WWin
N – 'Green Kwanso' (d) — CHar CPLG CRow CSWP EBlw ECha ECtt EPla IBlr MCLN MHer MMHG NVic SMad SPla WAul WFar WPnP WRha WWpP
– 'Kwanso Variegata' (d/v) — CBot CRow EBee EChP EGle ELan EPPr EVFa IBlr LHop MRav MTed MTho NBir SBla SDes WBcn WCot WFar WHer WHil
– var. *littorea* — SSpi
– var. *rosea* — SMHy
'Gadsden Goliath' — CAbx
'Garden Plants' — SRos
'Gay Rapture' — SPer
'Gemini' — SRos
'General Francis Marion' **new** — LSde
'Gentle Country Breeze' — SRos
'Gentle Shepherd' — More than 30 suppliers
'George Cunningham' — CMGP CSev ECtt EGle EGol EHrv ELan EPla ERou MCAu MNFA MRav NBir SChu SRos SUsu WFar
'Georgette Belden' — MBri
'Georgia Cream' (d) **new** — MBNS
'Giant Moon' — CMHG EBre ELan EPla EPri ERou LRHS MBri SChu WFar
'Gingerbread Man' — CRDP
'Glomunda' — SApp
'Glowing Gold' — ENot MCAu
'Gold Crest' — MNFA
'Gold Imperial' — EWll
'Golden Bell' — NGdn NHol
'Golden Chimes' ♀ H4 — More than 30 suppliers
'Golden Dewdrop' — LSde
'Golden Ginkgo' — LRHS MBri MNFA SApp
'Golden Nugget' **new** — MBNS
'Golden Orchid' — see *H.* 'Dubloon'

'Golden Peace'	SRos
'Golden Prize'	EBre EFou EPla NGdn NPri SDay
	SRos WCot WFar
'Golden Scroll'	SDay SRos
'Golden Zebra' **new**	EBee ENot NSti
'Golliwog'	SApp
'Good Looking' **new**	EGol
'Graceful Eye'	SApp
'Grand Masterpiece'	CM&M CSpe EBee EChP IPot NGdn
'Grape Magic'	EGol WTin
'Grape Velvet'	CHar CPar CSpe EGle EGol MAvo
	MBNS MCAu MCCP MCLN NSti
	SApp SHar WAul WMnd WWye
'Great Goodness	LSde
Gracious' **new**	
'Great Northern' **new**	SApp
'Green Drop'	WFar
'Green Eyed Giant'	MNFA
'Green Flutter' ♀ H4	CSev EBee EChP EWTr LPhx LPio
	LRHS MBNS MCLN MNFA NBir
	NGdn SApp SAsh SRos SVil
'Green Glitter'	MNFA
'Green Gold'	CMHG MNFA
'Green Morning Glow' **new**	LSde
'Green Puff'	NBir SDay
'Green Spider'	CAbx SApp
'Green-Eyed Lizard' **new**	SApp
'Grumbly'	EBee ELan WPnP
'Guardian Angel'	WTin
'Gussie Harris'	CAbx
'Gusto'	MCAu
'Halo Light'	MNFA
'Happy Bandit' **new**	LSde
'Happy Returns'	CHid CMGP COtt ECha EGol
	ELan EMar EWoo IFro LAst MBNS
	MBri MCAu MHar NBlu NGdn
	SApp SDay SRos SSpe WAul
'Harmonic	LSde
Convergence' **new**	
'Hawaiian Punch'	EGol
'Hawaiian Purple' **now**	EGol
'Hazel Monette'	EGol
'Heavenly Treasure'	MTed SRos
'Heidi Edelweiss'	CPLG EBee
'Heirloom Lace'	MCAu WBcn WFar
'Helle Berlinerin' ♀ H4	EFou MNFA
'Helter Skelter'	CAbx
'Hercules'	NFla
'Here Comes Sallyann' **new**	LSde
'Hey There'	SDay SRos
'High Energy'	SApp
'High Tor'	GCal GQui SHar
'Highland Lord' (d)	SDay
'Hint of Bluc' **new**	LSde
'Holiday Mood'	ELan ERou
'Hope Diamond'	CCol CRDP MCAu SDay
'Hornby Castle'	CBro LRHS NHol NVic WPer
'Hot Ticket'	SRos
'Houdini'	EChP EGle EGol WMnd WWye
'Humdinger'	SRos
'Hyperion'	CPrp CSev EBre ECGP ECha ECtt
	EGol EPfP GKir LAst LPVe MCAu
	MGrG MLan MNFA MRav NGdn
	NHol SApp SChu SHBN SPer SUsu
	WTMC WWye
'I Shine' **new**	LSde
'Ice Cap'	EBee LCaP SChu WFar WPnP
'Ice Carnival'	CBre CKel EBee EGle EPfP LPVc
	LRHS MAvo MBNS MBri MNFA
	NGdn SApp SVil
'Ice Cool'	SRos
'Icy Lemon'	SRos
'Ida Duke Miles'	SDay SRos

'Ida Munson' **new**	EGol
'Ida's Magic'	WAul
'Iditarod' **new**	LSde
'Imperator'	EPla LPBA NHol NPPs WViv
'In Depth' (d) **new**	EGle EPfP MBNS WCot
'Indian Giver' **new**	LSde
'Indian Paintbrush'	EBee EChP EGle EWoo GKir
	LHop MBri MCAu NBir SVil
'Inner View'	EChP ECtt LHop LPVe LPan
	MBNS NLar SApp STes WAul
	WMnd
'Inspired Word'	SRos
'Invictus'	SRos
'Irish Elf'	GBuc GMac SApp WTin
'Iron Gate Glacier'	MBNS
'Isle of Dreams' **new**	CAbx
'Jake Russell'	MNFA
'James Marsh'	CCol CPar EChP EGle EWes MBri
	MCAu MNrw NSti SRos SSpe
	WAul WHil WMnd WWye
'Janet Gordon' **new**	LSde
'Janice Brown'	CKel SApp SDay SRos
'Jan's Twister'	SApp
'Jason Salter' **new**	SDay WAul
'Jay Turman' **new**	LSde
'Jedi Dot Pierce'	SApp SRos
'Jedi Rose Frost' **new**	SApp
'Jenny Wren'	EMar EPPr GSki LRHS MBNS SSpe
	SUsu WAul
'Jo Jo'	MCAu WWin
'Joan Senior'	More than 30 suppliers
'Jock Randall'	MNFA SDay
'Jockey Club' (d) **new**	MBNS
'John Bierman'	SRos
'John Robert Biggs'	SApp
'Jovial'	SApp SDay
'Joylene Nichole'	SApp SRos
'Judah'	SDay SRos
'Justin June'	CCol
'Kabuki Ballet' **new**	LSde
'Kate Carpenter'	SRos
'Katie'	NHaw
'Katie Elizabeth Miller'	SRos
'Kecia'	MNFA
'Kelly's Girl'	SRos
'Kindly Light'	SRos
'King Haiglar'	CCol EGol SRos
'Kiss Me Tender' **new**	LSde
N 'Kwanso Flore Pleno'	see H. fulva 'Green Kwanso'
N 'Kwanso Flore	see H. fulva 'Kwanso Variegata'
Pleno Variegata'	
'La Peche'	SDay
'Lacy Marionette'	SApp
'Lady Fingers' **new**	CCol
'Lady Neva'	SApp SDay
'Ladykin'	SRos
'Lake Norman Spider' **new**	CAbx
'Lambada' **now**	LSde
'Lark Song'	EBre EGol EOrc WBcn WFar
'Lavender Bonanza'	WCFE
'Lavender Deal' **new**	EMar
'Lavender Illusion'	SApp
'Lavender Memories'	SApp
'Lavender Spider'	CAbx
'Lavender Tonic' **new**	SApp
'Leebea Orange Crush' **new**	LSde
'Lemon Bells' ♀ H4	EBee ECha EFou EGle EMFW
	EMar EPPr EPfP GSki MBNS
	MNFA MWgw NGdn SApp SChu
	SDay SMrm SRos
'Lemon Mint'	EGol MTed
'Lemon Starfish' **new**	SApp
'Lenox'	SApp SRos

'Leonard Bernstein' SApp
'Light the Way' ECha
'Lilac Wine' ECha
§ *lilioasphodelus* ♀ H4 More than 30 suppliers
'Lillian Frye' EGol
'Lilting Belle' **new** CCol
'Lilting Lady' SApp SDay
'Lilting Lavender' **new** SApp SDay
'Lime Frost' SRos
'Limoncello' SApp
'Linda' CMGP ERou EWll MLwd MRav
  NHol
* 'Liners Moon' EGol
'Little Audrey' EGle
'Little Bee' EFou MBNS
'Little Beige Magic' EGol
'Little Big Man' SDay
'Little Bugger' MBNS NGby NLar
'Little Bumble Bee' CFir COIW EGle EGol MBNS
  MCAu MNFA WPGP WTin
'Little Business' EFou MBNS SApp SDay
'Little Cadet' MNFA
'Little Cameo' EGol
'Little Carnation' SCro
'Little Carrot Top' **new** MCAu
'Little Cranberry Cove' EGol
'Little Dandy' EGol
'Little Deeke' MNFA SDay SRos
'Little Fantastic' EGol
'Little Fat Dazzler' SApp SDay
'Little Grapette' CHad CPlt CPrp EBee EGle EGol
  LBBr LRHS MBNS MCAu NLar
  NSti SApp SBod SCro SRos SVil
  WAul WBcn WHrl WTin
'Little Greenie' SDay
'Little Gypsy Vagabond' SDay SRos
'Little Heavenly Angel' SApp
'Little Lassie' MBNS
'Little Lavender Princess' EGol
'Little Maggie' MHar MSte SApp SDay
'Little Missy' EMar EMil MBNS
'Little Monica' SDay
'Little Print' **new** LSde
'Little Pumpkin Face' EGol
'Little Rainbow' EGol
'Little Red Hen' EMar LRHS MBNS MNFA NBro
  NGdn SDay
'Little Sweet Sue' MNFA
'Little Tawny' MCAu
'Little Toddler' SApp
'Little Violet Lace' GSki SDay
'Little Wart' EGol SDay
'Little Wine Cup' More than 30 suppliers
'Little Woman' SDay
'Little Zinger' SDay
'Littlest Angel' SDay
'Lochinvar' CAbx EBee ENot GBuc MRav SRos
'Longfield Purple EBee MBNS
  Edge' **new**
'Longfield's Beauty' EGle MBNS
'Longfield's Glory' CCol MBNS MLLN
'Longfield's Pride' **new** MBNS
longituba CPLG WCot
- B&SWJ 4576 WCru
'Love Glow' **new** CFir
'Luau Meow' **new** LSde
'Lullaby Baby' EGle EGol LPVe MBNS SApp SDay
  SRos STes
luna NOak
'Lupine' MTed
'Lusty Leland' CHea CPar EBee EGle EGol EMar
  MBNS SCro SRos
'Luxury Lace' More than 30 suppliers

'Lynn Hall' EGol WViv
'Mabel Fuller' MRav SCro
'Mad Max' CAbx
'Mae Graham' SApp
'Magic Carpet Ride' LSde
'Mahogany Magic' **new** LSde
'Mallard' EBre ECtt EFou EGol EHrv EMar
  EPla LLWP LRHS MBri MRav MTis
  NPPs SApp SRos WBcn WCot
  WCra WPer WTMC
'Manchurian Apricot' SRos
'Marble Faun' SRos
'Margaret Perry' CFee WAul
'Marion Vaughn' ♀ H4 CSev EBre ECot EFou EGle EGol
  EHrv ELan EMan EPfP EPla GMaP
  GSki LRHS MMil MNFA MWat
  NLon NPPs NSti SChu SDix SPer
  SSpi WCot
'Mariska' SApp SDay SRos
'Mark My Word' SApp
'Mary Todd' EGle EGol LPan MBNS MCAu
  MNFA NBlu SApp SCro
'Mary's Gold' SDay SRos
'Mata Hari' SDay
'Matt' SRos
'Mauna Loa' CCol EBee EFou MBNS MCAu
  SApp WAul WCot
'Mavoureen Nesmith' SCro
'May May' **new** SApp
'Meadow Mist' EBee EGle EGol
'Meadow Sprite' SApp SDay SRos
'Medieval Guild' SApp
'Melody Lane' EGol
'Meno' EGol
'Merlot Rouge' WAul
'Michele Coe' CM&M EBee EGol EHrv EMar
  LRHS MBNS MCAu MNFA MTed
  NGdn SChu SRos WElm WLRN
  WMoo
'Mico' **new** SApp
middendorffii CAvo EBee EMon EWTr GCal
  GMaP NFla NGdn NSti SDes WFar
  WPnP
- var. *esculenta* EMon
- 'Major' CFee
'Midnight Mantis' **new** SApp
'Midnight Raider' **new** LSde
'Mikado' EFou LRHS NBlu
'Milady Greensleeves' **new** CCol
'Millie Schlumpf' SApp SRos
'Mimosa Umbrella' **new** SApp
'Ming Porcelain' SApp SDay SRos
'Mini Pearl' CSpe EChP EGol EPfP GKir LRHS
  MBri SApp SChu SDay SRos SVil
  WPer WWye
'Mini Stella' CBro ECtt LPVe LRHS MBNS SMac
  WAul WBcn WFar WPnP
miniature hybrids SRms WPer
minor CBro EGol EMon GCal NGdn
  SRms
'Missenden' ♀ H4 MNrw NHaw
'Mission Moonlight' COtt EGol MCAu
'Missouri Beauty' CCol CPar EBee ERou LPVe LRHS
  MBNS NPri SDes WWeb
'Mokan Butterfly' **new** LSde
'Moment of Truth' MBNS
'Monica Marie' SRos
'Moon Witch' SRos
'Moonlight Mist' CCol SRos
'Moonlit Caress' EBee EWoo MBNS WAul
'Moonlit Crystal' CSpe
'Moonlit Masquerade' CPen EChP EGle EMar ENot LBuc
  MBNS MCCP MUlv WAul

'Mormon' **new**	CAbx
'Mormon Spider'	SApp
'Morning Dawn'	EFou EGle
'Morning Sun'	EMar MBNS WCot
'Morocco Red'	CBro CTri ELan GSki MMil NGdn
'Mountain Laurel'	LRHS MBri MNFA MRav SApp
	WFar
'Mrs B.F. Bonner'	WAul
'Mrs David Hall'	CMdw SCro
'Mrs Hugh Johnson'	CHad CMGP CPlt CSev ECGN
	ECot EHon MSte NHol SHBN
	WWpP
'Mrs Joan Cook'	EGle
'Mrs John J.Tigert'	ERou
'Mrs Lester'	SDay WCot
multiflora	EMon MNFA NHol WCot
'Munchkin	LSde
Moonbeam' **new**	
'My Darling	SDay
Clementine' **new**	
'My Melinda'	SDay
'Mynelle's Starfish' **new**	LSde SApp
'Mysterious Veil' **new**	EGol
'Nagasaki' (d) **new**	SDay
nana	EBee EPot
'Nanuq'	SDay SRos
'Naomi Ruth'	EGle EGol LAst MBNS MCAu
	SApp WTin
'Nashville'	CBro EBee EBre ELan ERou IBlr
	MMil
'Neal Berrey'	SRos
'Nefertiti'	CM&M EBee EChP LAst LHop
	SApp
'Netsuke'	SApp
'Neyron Rose' ♀ H4	CHea CMGP EGol EPfP EPla ERou
	GSki MBNS MCAu MNFA NGdn
	SChu SRos WMoo
'Night Beacon'	EBee ECtt EGol EMar EWes EWoo
	MBNS MBri MCAu NLar SApp
	SDay SDes SRos WHrl
'Night Raider'	SApp SDay SRos
'Nigrette'	LPBA MTed NHol
'Nile Cranc' **new**	MBNS SApp WAul WHil
'Nob Hill'	CMdw EGol EPla MNFA SRos
'North Star'	GCal MTed
'Norton Beauté'	WCot
'Norton Orange'	MNFA WFar
'Norwegian Woods' **new**	LSde
'Nova' ♀ H4	CPrp MNFA SApp
'Oachita Beauty' **new**	CAbx
'Ocean Rain'	SRos
x *ochroleuca*	SSpi
'Olive Bailey Langdon'	EGol SApp SDay SRos WCot
'Omomuki'	SApp SRos
'Oom-pa-pa'	ECha
'Open Hearth'	CAbx CCol SDay
'Optic Elegance'	SAsh
'Orange Dream' **new**	SDay
'Orange Velvet'	SRos
'Orange Vols' **new**	CAbx
'Orangeman' hort.	EPla GSki LRHS MBNS
'Orchid Beauty'	ECha
'Orchid Candy'	MBNS MBri NBir WHil
'Orchid Corsage'	SApp
'Orford'	WWin
'Oriental Ruby'	EGol MNFA
'Outrageous'	SApp
'Paige Parker'	EGol
'Painted Lady'	MNFA SDay
'Panchen Lama'	SApp
'Pandora's Box'	CSpe EBee EChP EFou EGle EGol
	ELan EMan EMar EPfP EWoo GKir
	IPot LPhx MBNS MBri MCAu

	MNrw NBir NGdn NPSI SApp
	SDay SRos STes WAul WHil WWpP
	WWye
'Paper Butterfly'	CKel SRos
'Paradise Pink'	NPri
'Paradise Prince'	EGol
'Pardon Me'	CM&M CMHG EGle EGol ELan
	LPVe LPio MBNS MCAu NGdn
	NHol SApp SRos WAul WBor
	WRus WWye
'Pastel Ballerina'	SRos
'Pastel Classic'	SRos
'Patchwork Puzzle'	SRos
'Paul Weber' **new**	SApp
'Peach Petticoats' **new**	SRos
'Peacock Maiden'	SDay
'Pear Ornament' **new**	SRos
'Penelope Vestey'	EBee EBla EGle EMar LRHS MBNS
	MNFA NGdn SPla SRos
'Penny's Worth'	EGol GKir LPVe WAul WCot
'Perfect Pleasure' **new**	LSde
'Permaquid Light'	CMHG
'Persian Princess'	WBcn
'Petite Ballerina'	LSde SDay
'Piccadilly Princess'	SRos
'Pink Attraction'	SApp
'Pink Ballerina'	EFou EGol
'Pink Charm'	CMGP COlW EBee EChP EMar
	ENot LPBA LRHS MCAu MNFA
	MWgw NGdn NHol NLon NOrc
	SChu SHBN SRos WCra WViv
'Pink Cotton Candy'	SRos
'Pink Damask' ♀ H4	More than 30 suppliers
'Pink Dream'	EBee EMar IPot LRHS MBNS
	MCAu MNFA NBir NHol
'Pink Glow'	CM&M
'Pink Grace'	CAbx
'Pink Heaven'	EGol
'Pink Lady'	ERou MBrN MNrw MRav NBur
	SHBN SRms
'Pink Lavender Appeal'	EGol
'Pink Peaches' **new**	LSde
'Pink Prelude'	EBee EChP EMar EWll LRHS
	MBNS MNFA SChu
'Pink Puff'	MBNS NBir NLar SDay
'Pink Salute'	SRos
'Pink Sundae'	ECha MTis
'Pink Super Spider'	SRos
'Pinocchio'	MBNS
'Piquante'	EBee
'Pirate's Patch'	SRos
'Pixie Pipestone'	CCol SApp
'Pompeian Purple'	EGol
'Poneytail Pink'	EGol
'Pony'	EGol SDay
'Pookie Bear'	SApp
'Prague Spring' **new**	CAbx SApp
'Prairie Bells'	CSWP EWTr MBNS MBro NCiC
	STes WBar WFar WHoo WLRN
	WWhi
'Prairie Blue Eyes'	CCol EBee EChP EGle EGol LRHS
	MBNS MCAu MNFA NPri SApp
	SCro SPlb WAul WBcn WCot
	WMnd WTMC
'Prairie Charmer'	EBee IPot
'Prairie Moonlight'	EBee SApp
'Prairie Queen'	IPot
'Prelude to Love' **new**	LSde
'Pretty Mist'	GKir MBri
'Pretty Peggy'	MNFA
'Prima Donna'	SCro
'Primrose Mascotte'	MTed NBir WWin
'Prince Redbird'	SDay

	'Princeton Grape'	SApp
	'Princeton Point Lace' **new**	SApp
	'Prize Picotee Elite'	SRos WTin
	'Protocol'	SDay
	'Proud Mary' **new**	LSde
§	'Puddin''	CM&M NHol SDay WAul
	'Pumpkin Kid'	SRos
	'Puppet Show'	SDay
	'Pure and Simple' **new**	LSde
	'Purple Pauper'	MCAu
	'Purple Rain'	EFou MBNS SApp
	'Purple Waters'	CCol EPfP EWll LPVe LRHS MBNS MWgw NPri WAul
	'Pursuit of Excellence'	ECtt SRos
	'Quannah' **new**	LSde
	'Queen Beatrice'	EBee
	'Queen of May'	WCot
	'Queen's Gift'	SApp
	'Quick Results'	SApp SRos
	'Quietness'	SRos
	'Radiant Ruffles' **new**	LSde
	'Raging Tiger' **new**	SDay
	'Rainbow Candy' **new**	MBNS
	'Raindrop'	EGol SSpe
	'Rajah'	EGra NBro
	'Rare Breed' **new**	LSde
	'Raspberry Candy'	EMar WAul WHrl
	'Raspberry Pixie'	EGol MTed SApp
	'Raspberry Wine'	SApp WBro
	'Red Precious' ♀ H4	EGol MNFA MNrw SAsh SRos
	'Red Ribbons'	CCol SDay
	'Red Rum'	EFou EWTr EWll MBNS MTis SDes SMrm WPnP WWhi
	'Red Suspenders' **new**	SApp
	'Red Twister'	CAbx
	'Red Volunteer' **new**	LSde SApp SRos
	'Renegade Lady' **new**	LSde
	'Rhine Maiden' **new**	LSde
	'Riptide'	SApp
	'Robin Coleman'	MNFA
	'Rocket City'	ELan
	'Rodeo Drive' **new**	LSde
	'Romantic Rose'	EMar MBNS
	'Romany'	LPBA
	'Root Beer'	MCAu WBcn WTin
	'Rose Emily'	SApp SDay SRos
	'Rose Festival'	MCAu
	'Rose Talisman' **new**	LSde
	'Rosella Sheridan'	SRos
	'Royal Braid' **new**	CPen EGle EPfP MBNS MCLN MNrw WAul WCot WHil
	'Royal Charm'	SRos
	'Royal Corduroy'	SRos
	'Royal Robe'	EBlw
	'Royal Saracen'	SDay
	'Royal Thornbird' **new**	LSde
	'Royalty'	NGdn WWpP
	'Ruby Spider' **new**	SDay
	'Rudolf Seyer'	MBNS
	'Ruffled Apricot'	CKel LPVe SDay SRos WElm WHoo
	'Russell Prichard'	ERou
	'Russian Rhapsody'	CKel
	'Rutilans'	CFee
	'Sabra Salina'	SDay SRos
	'Salieri' **new**	LSde
	'Salmon Sheen'	MNFA SDay
	'Sammy Russell'	More than 30 suppliers
	'Sandra Walker'	EGol
*	'Sassy Sally' **new**	LSde
	'Satin Clouds'	EGol
	'Satin Glass'	MNFA
	'Satin Glow'	ECha
	'Satin Silk'	EBre
	'Scarlet Flame'	ECha
*	'Scarlet Oak'	LRHS MBri MNFA
	'Scarlet Orbit'	SApp SDay SRos
	'Scarlet Tanager'	NCat
	'Scatterbrain'	CKel
	'Schoolgirl'	EBre
	'Scorpio' **new**	CCol
	'Scotland'	SApp
	'Searcy Marsh'	EGol
	'Sebastian'	SRos
	'Seminole Wind' **new**	LSde
	'Serena Madonna' **new**	CFir
	'Serena Sunburst'	SRos
	'Shaman'	SApp SRos
	'Sherry Lane Carr' **new**	LSde
	'Shooting Star'	SPla
	'Show Amber'	SRos
	'Showgirl'	GKir
	'Silken Fairy'	EGol SDay
	'Silken Touch' **new**	LSde
	'Siloam Angel Blush'	SDay
	'Siloam Baby Talk'	CM&M CRDP EChP EGle EGol LAst NBir SCro SRos WAul WHoo WPnP WTin
	'Siloam Bo Peep'	CRDP EGol MNFA WAul WTMC
	'Siloam Brian Henke'	SRos
	'Siloam Button Box'	EBee EChP EGol EMan EWoo WAul WHil
	'Siloam Byelo'	EGol SDay
	'Siloam Cinderella'	EGol SDay SRos
	'Siloam David Kirchhoff'	EBee MBNS MCAu SDay SRos
	'Siloam Doodlebug'	EGol SRos
	'Siloam Double Classic' (d)	EGol SRos
	'Siloam Dream Baby'	EPPr GBri MBNS
	'Siloam Edith Scholar'	EGol
	'Siloam Ethel Smith'	EGol SCro SDay SRos
	'Siloam Fairy Tale'	CRDP EChP EGol
	'Siloam Flower Girl'	SDay
	'Siloam French Doll'	CCol MBNS
	'Siloam Frosted Mint'	SApp
	'Siloam Gold Coin'	SDay
	'Siloam Grace Stamile'	SRos
	'Siloam Harold Flickinger' **new**	SRos
	'Siloam Jim Cooper' **new**	LSde
	'Siloam Joan Senior'	ECtt EGol MBNS SDay
	'Siloam John Yonski' **new**	SDay
	'Siloam June Bug'	EGle EGol ELan MCAu MNFA SApp
	'Siloam Justin Lee'	MBNS
	'Siloam Kewpie Doll'	EGol
	'Siloam Little Angel' **new**	EGol SApp
	'Siloam Little Girl'	EGol SDay SRos
	'Siloam Mama' **new**	SDay
	'Siloam Merle Kent'	SApp SRos
	'Siloam Mini Pearl'	EMan
	'Siloam New Toy' **new**	EGol
	'Siloam Nugget'	SApp
	'Siloam Orchid Jewel'	EGol SDay
	'Siloam Pee Wee'	EGol
	'Siloam Pink'	LAst
	'Siloam Pink Glow'	EGle EGol WAul
	'Siloam Pink Petite'	EGol
	'Siloam Plum Tree'	EGol SApp
	'Siloam Pocket Size'	EGol MSte SApp
	'Siloam Prissy'	EGol SApp
	'Siloam Purple Plum'	EGol
	'Siloam Red Ruby'	EGol
	'Siloam Red Toy'	EGol MNFA
	'Siloam Red Velvet'	EGol
	'Siloam Ribbon Candy'	EGol
	'Siloam Rose Dawn'	SApp SDay SRos
	'Siloam Rose Queen'	SDay

'Siloam Royal Prince' — CM&M EChP EGle EGol EMan EPfP NHol SApp SCro SDay
'Siloam Ruffled Infant' **new** — SDay
'Siloam Shocker' — EGol SApp
'Siloam Show Girl' — CCol EGle EGol GKir MBNS MBri SApp WAul
'Siloam Sugar Time' — EGol
'Siloam Tee Tiny' — EGle EGol
'Siloam Tinker Toy' — EGol
'Siloam Tiny Mite' — EGol SDay
'Siloam Toddler' — EGol
'Siloam Tom Thumb' — EGol EMar MBNS MBri
'Siloam Ury Winniford' — CBro CRDP EGol MBNS MCCP SDay SPer WAul WHoo WPnP
'Siloam Virginia Henson' — COtt EBee EGol MCAu MNFA SOkh SRos WRus
'Silver Ice' — SRos
'Silver Trumpet' — EGle EGol SCro
'Silver Veil' — SApp SDay WFar
'Sir Blackstem' — SApp
'Sir Modred' — CAbx
'Sirius' — NHol
'Sirocco' — EChP WTin
'Slender Lady' — SRos
'Smoky Mountain Autumn' — SApp SRos
'Snappy Rhythm' — MNFA
'Snowy Apparition' — EWTr EWll MBri MCLN MNFA MSte SMrm
'Snowy Eyes' — CHid EBee EGle EGol EMar GBuc GMac IPot MBNS NHol SApp WAul WWye
'So Excited' — LSde
'So Lovely' **new** — SApp
'Someone Special' — SRos
'Song of Singapore' **new** — LSde
'Song Sparrow' — GKir GMac IBal LRHS MBri WPer WWye
'South Seas' **new** — LSde
'Sovereign Queen' **new** — EGol
'Spacecoast Starburst' **new** — EBcc MBNS MCAu
'Spanish Glow' — SApp
'Spanish Sketch' **new** — LSde
'Spider Breeder' — CAbx
'Spiderman' — SRos
'Spindazzle' **new** — SApp
'Spinncret' — CAbx
'Spirit Weaver' **new** — LSde
'Spode' **new** — SDay
'Spring Willow Song' — SDay
'Stafford' — More than 30 suppliers
'Staghorn Sumach' — MBri
'Star of India' **new** — LSde
'Starling' — CFir CPar EBee EChP EGle EGol MCAu MSte WAul
'Stars and Stripes' — MNFA
'Stella de Oro' — More than 30 suppliers
'Stella Junior' — LBuc
'Stineette' — WCot
'Stoke Poges' ♀ H4 — CBro CSev EBee EChP EGle EMFW EMar EPfP EPla LAst LHop LRHS MBNS MCAu MMil MNFA SApp SChu SDay SPer SRos STes
'Stoplight' — CCol SApp
'Strawberry Candy' — CM&M EBee EChP EFou EMan EMar EPfP EWoo LAst LPan MBNS MBri NGdn SApp SOkh SRos SVil WAul WHoo
'Strawberry Fields Forever' **new** — MCLN
I 'Streaker' B. Brown (v) — SPar WCot
'Streaker' McKinney — MNFA
'Strutter's Ball' — CPar EChP EGle EMan EWoo IPot LHop MNFA NGdn SApp SDay

— SRos SVil WAul WCot WHoo WMnd
'Sugar Cookie' — CRDP SApp SDay SRos
'Summer Air' — LRHS MBri
'Summer Echoes' **new** — LSde
'Summer Interlude' — MCAu WMoo
'Summer Jubilee' — SDay
'Summer Wine' — More than 30 suppliers
* 'Summertime' — WBcn
'Sun Pixie' — SCro
'Sunday Gloves' — EGol
'Super Purple' — CKel
'Superlative' — SRos
'Suzie Wong' — MNFA SChu
'Svengali' **new** — SDay
'Sweet Obsession' **new** — LSde
'Sweet Pea' — EGol
'Taj Mahal' — SApp WFar
'Tang' — MBNS MNFA WHil
'Tasmania' — SPer
'Techny Peach Lace' — SRos
'Techny Spider' — SRos
'Tejas' — CElw EBee EMil MBNS
'Teller of Tales' **new** — LSde
'Tender Shepherd' — EGol MCAu
'Tetraploid Bubbles' — MBri
'Tetraploid Stella de Oro' — SDay
'Tetrina's Daughter' ♀ H4 — CMGP EPfP NHol SRos
'Texas Sunlight' — SDes WAul
'Thumbelina' — ECha MNFA
§ *thunbergii* — CAvo EBee ECha EMon MNFA MNrw SMac SSpi
'Time Lord' — SDay
'Timeless Fire' — SApp SRos
'Tinker Bell' — MSte SRos
'Tiny Talisman' **new** — SDay
'Tobacco Road' — SApp
'Todd Monroe' — LSde
'Tom Collins' — SRos
'Tom Wise' — SRos
'Tonia Gay' — CRDP SApp SRos
'Tootsie' — SDay
'Tootsie Rose' — SDay SRos
'Torpoint' — EMar LRHS MBNS MNFA
'Towhead' — EBee EGol ENot MRav MTed
'Toyland' — CCol CMGP CSev EBee EChP EGol EPPr GSki MBNS NBir NGdn NLon NPri SSpe SUsu WLRN WWeb
'Triple Threat' — SDay
'Tropical Toy' — SDay
'True Glory' — SApp
'Tuscawilla Bill Reed' **now** — LSde
'Tuscawilla Tigress' — EMar
'Twenty Third Psalm' — WTin
'Upper Class Peach' — SRos
'Uptown Girl' **new** — SRos
'Vanessa Arden' **new** — SApp
'Varsity' — EBrc EGol GMac MBri MCAu NBir SRos
'Veiled Beauty' — MCAu
'Velvet Rose' **new** — LSde
'Vera Biaglow' — SDay
'Vespers' — WCra WFar
vespertina — see *H. thunbergii*
'Victoria Aden' — CBro LBuc
'Vintage Bordeaux' — ELan
'Violet Hour' **new** — SDay
* 'Vohann' — CMdw
'Walking on Sunshine' — SRos
'Wally Nance' — SDay
'Water Witch' — EGol SApp
'Waxwing' — WPer
'Wayside Green Imp' — EBee EFou EGol SApp SCro

'Wayside Green Lamp'	EGle MNrw MSte
'Wedding Band' **new**	LSde
'Wee Chalice'	EGol
'Welchkins'	WAul
'Whichford' ♀ H4	CBro CHad EBre ECtt EGol ELan
	LAst LPhx LRHS MNFA NLon
	SChu SPer WWal WWin
'Whistling Swan'	SDes
'White Coral'	EMar LRHS
'White Dish'	EGol
'White Edged	EMar
Madonna' **new**	
'White Minx' **new**	LSde
'White Temptation'	CFir CM&M CSpe EBee EChP EGol
	EPfP EWoo MCAu NGdn SDay SRos
'Whooperie'	SRos
'Wide Eyed'	EPla
'Wild Mustang'	CCol MBNS
'Will Return' **new**	LSde
'Wind Frills'	SApp SDay
'Window Dressing'	EGol SApp
'Windsor Tan'	WCFE
'Wine Bubbles'	EGol SApp
'Wineberry Candy' **new**	CMGP EGle EPfP MCLN
'Wings of Song'	SApp
'Winnie the Pooh'	SDay
'Winsome Lady'	ECha WBro
'Winter Olympics'	SDay
'Wisest of Wizards' **new**	LSde
'Wishing Well'	SChu
* 'Witch Hazel'	COtt
'Witch Stitchery'	CAbx
'Witches Wink' **new**	LSde
'Women's Work'	SApp
'Wood Duck'	COtt EGle LBuc SApp
'Wren'	COtt
'Xia Xiang' **new**	SDay
'Yellow Explosion'	SApp
'Yellow Lollipop'	MNFA SApp SDay SRos
'Yellow Mantle'	MNFA
'Yellow Petticoats'	MTed
'Yellow Rain'	SAsh WCot
'Yesterday Memories'	SRos
'Zampa'	SDay
'Zara' CAbx SPer	

Hemiorchis (Zingiberaceae)
pantlingii	CKob EBot

Hemiphragma (Scrophulariaceae)
heterophyllum	EBee NLAp

Hepatica ✿ (Ranunculaceae)
acutiloba	CArn CBro CLAP EBee EPot GBuc
	GCrs GKir LAma LEur MAsh NBir
	NGar SIgm WCru WPnP
'Akane' **new**	LHop
americana	EBee EHrv GBuc GCrs MAsh NBir
	NLar WCru WPnP
angulosa	see *H. transsilvanica*
'Baien' **new**	LHop
'Hatsane' **new**	LHop
henryi	EBee LAma WCru
insularis	WCru
- B&SWJ 859	WCru
'Kasumino' **new**	WHil
maxima	EBee
- B&SWJ 4344	WCru
x *media*	WCom
- 'Ballardii'	GKir IBlr
- 'Harvington Beauty'	CLAP CWes GBuc IBlr MAsh NBir
	NGar
'Miyoshino' **new**	LHop

§ *nobilis* ♀ H4	More than 30 suppliers
- var. *asiatica*	MS&S
- blue	CRDP GBuc GDra LPio MAsh
	MS&S NGar NHar NSla SBla SRot
	WAbe WCru
- 'Cobalt'	WAbe
- dark blue	CLAP NGar
- double pink	see *H. nobilis* 'Rubra Plena'
- var. *japonica*	CArn CBro CRDP EBee GCrs
	LAma MAsh NBir NGar SBla SIgm
	SMrm WCru
- lilac	MTho SBla
- mottled leaf	EHrv LEur MTho
- 'Pearl Grey' **new**	NPar
- Picos strain	SBla
- pink	CLAP CRDP EHyt EPot ETow
	GCrs LEur MAsh MS&S NGar
	NWCA SBla SIng SRms SRot
* - var. *pyrenaica*	MAsh
* - - 'Apple Blossom' **new**	GCrs NBir
* - 'Pyrenean Marbles'	CLAP
- red	MAsh NGar WAbe
- 'Roger's Silver' **new**	NPar
- var. *rubra*	CLAP CRDP NMen NSla
§ - 'Rubra Plena' (d)	CRDP ECha EPot GCrs NGar
- violet	SBla
- white	CLAP CRDP EHyt GCrs LPio
	MAsh MS&S NGar NMen NSla
	SBla SIng SRot WCru WHil WIvy
'Noumurasaki' **new**	LHop WHil
'Oboroyo' **new**	LHop
'Oomurasaki' **new**	LHop
'Ryokka' **new**	LHop WHil
'Ryoustsu' **new**	LHop
'Saikaku' **new**	WHil
'Sakaya' **new**	LHop
'Sakuragari' **new**	LHop WHil
'Sayaka' **new**	WHil
'Sougetsu' **new**	LHop
'Tenjim Ume' **new**	LHop WHil
§ *transsilvanica* ♀ H4	CBro CLAP CRDP EBee ECha
	EHyt EPot GAbr GCrs GKir LAma
	LHop LRHS MAsh MS&S MWat
	NGar NHar NMen SBla SCro
	SMrm SPer WAul WCot WCru
* - *alba*	NGar
- 'Blue Jewel'	CFir CLAP EBee GCrs WPnP
- 'De Buis'	CFwr CLAP EBee EPot GCal GCrs
	GEdr LPio MDun NLar WPnP
- deep blue **new**	IBlr
- 'Eisvogel'	CBro EPot NGar NPar
- 'Elison Spence' (d)	IBlr NGar NPar SBla
- Jan/Feb flowering	NPar
- 'Lilacina'	ECha NGar NPar
- 'Loddon Blue'	IBlr NGar
- pink	EPot SBla
- 'Praecox'	NPar
triloba	see *H. nobilis*
'Wakana' **new**	LHop
yamatutai	LEur MAsh
aff. *yamatutai* **new**	EBee

x Heppimenes (Gesneriaceae)
I 'Purple Queen'	NMos

Heptacodium (Caprifoliaceae)
jasminoides	see *H. miconioides*
§ *miconioides*	CAbP CBot CFil CMCN CPMA
	CPle EBee ELan EOrc EPfP GEil
	GIBF GQui IArd ICrw IDee MBlu
	MCCP NBee SMac SMad SRkn
	WCot WCwm WMou WPGP WPnP
	WSHC

Heptapleurum see *Schefflera*

Heracleum (*Apiaceae*)
candicans	EBee EMan WCot
dulce <u>new</u>	EBee
lanatum 'Washington Limes' (v)	EBee EMan EPPr NCat WCot
lehmannianum	SDix WCot
mantegazzianum	CRow EPfP MFir SMad WFar
minimum 'Roseum'	WPat
moellendorfii <u>new</u>	EBee
sphondylium pink	CNat

Herbertia (*Iridaceae*)
§ **lahue**	CDes LRHS WCot
platensis <u>new</u>	CPLG
pulchella	CPLG

Hereroa (*Aizoaceae*)
odorata <u>new</u>	EShb

Hermannia (*Sterculiaceae*)
candicans	see *H. incana*
erodioides JCA 15523	CPBP
flammea	CPBP
§ **incana**	CHal MOak
* **stricta**	CPBP SIgm WAbe

Hermodactylus (*Iridaceae*)
§ **tuberosus**	CAvo CBos CBro CFwr CMea CTri EBee EBre ECGP ECha EMan EPar LAma LPhx LPio LRHS MNrw NRog STes WCot WHil

Herniaria (*Illecebraceae*)
glabra	EOHP GBar GPoy MSal SIde WHer WLHH WWye

Herpolirion (*Anthericaceae*)
novae-zealandiae	ECou

Hertia see *Othonna*

Hesperaloe (*Agavaceae*)
funifera	EOas
parviflora	CTrC EBee EMan EOas LPio SChu SIgm

Hesperantha (*Iridaceae*)
§ **baurii**	CLAP CLyd CNic CStu EBee EMan GBuc LBow NMen SSpi WAbe WCot
coccinea	see *Schizostylis coccinea*
cucullata <u>new</u>	EBee
* - 'Rubra'	NWCA
huttonii	EBee EMan GBuc GMac MFir MWrn NBir WCot
mossii	see *H. baurii*
petitiana	GCal
vaginata 'Stanfordiae'	LBow
woodii	CDes CFir

Hesperis (*Brassicaceae*)
dinarica	EBre
lutea	see *Sisymbrium luteum*
matronalis	More than 30 suppliers
§ - var. **albiflora**	CCge CPrp CSpe CTri EBee EFou ELau EMar EPfP ERou LHrt LRHS MBct MBow MWrn NDov NPri SPer SSvw WCot WFar WMnd WMoo WPer WWye
- - 'Alba Plena' (d)	CMea CRDP EBee ELan EMan EVFa GAbr LRHS MNrw NBir

	NPri SBla SIde SPoG WCot WFar WHHs
- double (d)	CHad GKir MBri SMrm
- 'Frogswell Doris' <u>new</u>	EOrc IFro
- 'Lilacina Flore Pleno' (d)	EMon GMac MBNS MCLN NDov NLar NPri SMrm
steveniana	ECoo SMrm

Hesperochiron (*Hydrophyllaceae*)
californicus	GDra

Heterocentron (*Melastomataceae*)
§ **elegans**	EMan

Heterolepis (*Asteraceae*)
aliena <u>new</u>	GFai

Heteromeles (*Rosaceae*)
arbutifolia	see *H. salicifolia*
salicifolia	CAgr

Heteromorpha (*Apiaceae*)
arborescens	CTrC SIgm SPlb

Heteropappus (*Asteraceae*)
altaicus	WPer

Heterotheca (*Asteraceae*)
mariana	see *Chrysopsis mariana*
pumila	ETow NWCA
§ **villosa**	CRDP EMan LBuc
- 'Golden Sunshine' <u>new</u>	EBee

Heuchera ✿ (*Saxifragaceae*)
abramsii	WLin
'Amber Waves'	CTal C3pt EBee EFou MBri NPri SAsh SHar SRot SUsu WWeb
§ **americana**	CHid CRDP EBee ECha EOrc GBar MHar NBir NSti WWeb
- Dale's strain	CBct ECGN ECha EMan GKir LRHS MGGn MNrw NCat NGdn NLar SPlb WGor WHrl WMnd WPnP WPrP WTMC
- 'Harry Hay'	LPhx MSte
- 'Ring of Fire'	CBcs CKno CLAP COtt EBee EBre EGle EHan EPfP GBri IArd LRHS MAvo MDun MSPs MSte NPPs NPri NSti SPar SPla WBea WCot WFar WPnP
'Amethyst Myst'	CFai COlW EBee EMan LRHS MMil SRot SUsu WFar
'Beauty Colour'	CFee EBee EBrc EDAr EFou EMan EPfP GKir IBal IHMH MAvo MBct MBri MRav MSPs NPPs SCoo WBea WCot WCra WFar
* 'Black Velvet'	EBee EFou
'Blackbird' ♀ H4	CFai EBee MBNS WMnd
'Blood Vein' <u>new</u>	EWll ITer
bracteata	CHid
Bressingham hybrids	EBre ENot GKir LAst LRHS MHdf NArg NBir NMir NOak SMac SPar SPer SRms WFar WMoo WPer
x **brizoides** <u>new</u>	IHMH
Cally hybrids <u>new</u>	GCal
'Can-can' ♀ H4	More than 30 suppliers
'Canyon Chimes'	COtt
'Canyon Delight'	WCot
'Canyon Duet'	COtt
'Canyon Pink'	NSti WCot
'Cappuccino'	CKno EBee EChP ECtt EMan MAvo MBNS NBro WCFE WWol WWpP
'Cascade Dawn'	CHid CMHG EBee EMan LHop LRHS MRav MSte NBir NHol

	NLar NPri SDes SMrm WAul WCot WFar WViv
'Champagne Bubbles'	SHar WCot
Charles Bloom = 'Chablo'	EBre
'Cherries Jubilee'	SHar WGor
'Chimes and Duet'	WWeb
'Chiqui'	SUsu
chlorantha	GBin GCal
'Chocolate Ruffles'PBR	More than 30 suppliers
'Chocolate Veil'	EBee SHar
'Color Dream' **new**	EBee
coral bells	see *H. sanguinea*
'Coral Bouquet'	SHar WCot
'Coral Cloud'	EBee MRav
'Crimson Curls'	EBee LRHS WWeb
'Crispy Curly'	COlW EMan EWll ITim MBNS MGGn MWrn WBVN
cylindrica	MBNS MRav MSte WPer
- var. *alpina*	NWCA
- 'Brownfinch' **new**	SMHy
- 'Chartreuse'	LPio
- 'Greenfinch'	CFee COlW EBre ECha ELan ENot EPfP ERou EWTr GCal GKir GTou LRHS MTis NBir NOrc SDes SHel SPar WBea WCot WPer
'Dainty Bells'	WCot
'Dennis Davidson'	see *H.* 'Huntsman'
'Dingle Mint Chocolate'	EVFa
'Ebony and Ivory'	EBee EChP EHrv EPPr LBuc NDov NSti SHar SRot SUsu WCot WWol
I 'Eco Magnififolia'	CLAP EBee
'Eden's Aurora'	EChP WMnd
'Eden's Joy'	EBee EChP EFou
'Eden's Mystery'	EBee ECtt EFou SHBN
'Eden's Shine'	EBee MOne
elegans	NMen
'Emperor's Cloak'	CBri CHar ECtt EMil ENot EWTr ITim LHrt MWrn NBur NDlv NLar NPro STes SWal WElm WMoo WSan
'Firebird'	NBir NVic
Firefly	see *H.* 'Leuchtkäfer'
'Fireworks' ♀ H4 **new**	GBin SHar WCot
'Florist's Choice'	SHar
glabra	EBee
glauca	see *H. americana*
'Green Ivory'	CHar CSam EBee EBre EMan EOrc LRHS MRav NGdn NSti
'Greenfinch'	EGle GKir MHer NHol SPer WElm WFar WGwG WMnd
grossulariifolia	EBee MBNS WPer
hallii	EBee ETow
'Helen Dillon' (v)	CHid CLAP EBla ECtt EGle EMan GBri LAst MCAu MGrG MLLN MRav NBir NPri SApp SDes SPar SPer SPla WCom WCot WFar WPnP WWpP
'Hercules'PBR	EBee EChP ECtt MAvo MBNS MBri
hispida	EMan MSte MWrn WPer
§ 'Huntsman'	EBee EChP ECha ELan EMan GBri GBuc MBNS MRav MWrn SAdn SMad WBcn WFar WMnd WRus
'Ibis'	EBee
'Jubilee'	EBee
'Lady in Red'	EBee EFou MBNS
'Lady Romney'	GCal
§ 'Leuchtkäfer'	CBcs CFee COlW EChP ECtt GBuc LAst LRHS MRav NHol NMir NOrc NPri SBla SDes SMac SPer SPlb SRms SWal SWat WFar WMnd WMoo WPer WPnP
'Magic Wand' ♀ H4	NGdn SHar
maxima	EMon
'Metallica' **new**	MWrn

micans	see *H. rubescens*
micrantha	EBee GCal MWgw MWrn SRms
- var. *diversifolia*	EBee EGle EPla LRHS MBri SPar
Bressingham Bronze = 'Absi'PBR	SPer SPla SVil WFar WWeb
N - - 'Palace Purple'	More than 30 suppliers
'Mini Mouse'	EBee GKir MBNS MBri SVil WWeb
'Mint Frost'PBR	CLAP CMGP CMHG COtt EFou EHan EMan EPPr GBin GBri GDaI LAst LHop LRHS MBri MCLN MLLN MRav MTis NHol NPSI NPri NPro SMad SPar WCot WFar WLin WOVN WWeb
'Monet'	see *H. sanguinea* 'Monet'
'Montrose Ruby' **new**	EBee
'Northern Fire'	CLAP CRez EBee
'Oakington Jewel'	CRez EBee EChP ELan EMan LRHS MOne SHBN
'Opal'	WCot
'Painted Lady'	GBuc LPio WCot
'Palace Passion'	WBrE
* 'Palace Purple Select' **new**	IBal
parishii NNS 93-384	NWCA
'Party Bells'	NGar
parvifolia var. *nivalis*	EBee
'Pearl Drops'	NCat
'Persian Carpet'	CHid EBee EBlw ECGN ECha EMan GKir LRHS MDun MLLN NBir NGdn NPri SPar SPer SSpi WBea WCom WCot WCra WFar WLin WRus WWeb
'Petite Marbled Burgundy'	CBos CMdw COtt CStr EBee EGle EVFa GBri IBal LAst LTwo MSte NDov NLar NPPs SUsu WBea WCot WFar WWhi
'Petite Pearl Fairy'	CHid CM&M COtt EBee EGle EMar EVFa GBin MBri MSte NGdn NLar NPro NSti SPla WCot WGor WLin WWeb WWhi
'Petite Pink Bouquet' **new**	EBee EChP GAbr IBal WCot
'Pewter Moon'	CBro EBee ELan EMil ENot EPfP GKir LPio LRHS MRav NBir SChu SDes SPar SPer WFar WMnd WPnP
'Pewter Veil'PBR	EBee EMan ENot EPfP EPyc EVFa SDes WEas WFar WPnP WWol
pilosissima	ECGN
§ 'Pluie de Feu'	CFir EBee EChP ECtt EMan EPfP EWsh GBri GCal MBNS MBri MRav WRHF WRus
'Plum Fairy' **new**	CM&M
'Plum Pudding'PBR	More than 30 suppliers
'Prince'	EBee MBNS
pringlei	see *H. rubescens*
* x *pruhonicana* Doctor Sitar's hybrids	COlW MWrn NCat SMac SRms
* 'Pruhoniciana'	EBee
pubescens	GBri
pulchella	CPBP CSam EBee MHer MWrn SMac SRms SUsu
- JCA 9508	NMen NWoo
'Purple Petticoats' ♀ H4	EFou SHar SRot
'Quilter's Joy' ♀ H4	EFou
'Rachel'	More than 30 suppliers
Rain of Fire	see *H.* 'Pluie de Feu'
'Raspberry Regal' ♀ H4	CMHG EBee ECtt EFou EGle EMan EVFa GAbr LAst MLLN MRav MSph NBir NDov NHol NPri NSti WAul WCom WCot
'Red Bird'	EBee
'Red Spangles'	EBee EBre EPfP LRHS MBNS NBir
'Regina' ♀ H4	CAbP EBee EFou GKir IBal MBNS MBri NBro WFar WWeb
richardsonii	GBin IIve MNrw

'Robert'	EBee LAst SChu
Rosemary Bloom = 'Heuros'PBR	EBre LRHS
§ *rubescens*	EDAr EHyt MTho NBro NMen SIng WPer WWin
rubra 'Redstart'	ECtt
'Ruby Veil'	EBee EBre EFou GKir SDes SMrm WGor
'Ruffles'	LRHS
'Sancyl'	SRms
§ *sanguinea*	CAgr CSBt EBee EDAr LRHS MHer MWgw NBir NBlu NFor SHel SPer WPer
– 'Alba' ♀ H4	EMon EVFa WBcn WMaN
– 'Geisha's Fan'	NBhm SHar
§ – 'Monet' (v)	EBee EMan ENot GKir MBNS WElm WWeb
– 'Sioux Falls'	EBee EChP LAst MWrn
§ – 'Snow Storm' (v)	EBee EBre ECtt ELan ENot EPfP EWes GKir MBar MHer MRav SPar SPer SPlb WAul WFar WMnd
– 'Splish Splash' (v)	EWsh
– 'Taff's Joy' (v)	CRow EMon EWes MNrw WCot
– 'Vivid Crimson' **new**	MWrn
– 'White Cloud' (v)	EBee LAst MWrn SRms
'Schneewittchen'	EBee EMan EPfP EWTr LRHS MRav WCot
'Scintillation' ♀ H4	EBee EBre ECtt LRHS NCat SRms
'Silver Indiana'PBR	EBee LBuc MBri SDes SMrm SPoG
'Silver Scrolls'	More than 30 suppliers
'Silver Shadows' **new**	SHar
'Silver Streak'	see x *Heucherella* 'Silver Streak'
'Smokey Rose'	EBee
'Snow Storm' (v)	see *H. sanguinea* 'Snow Storm'
'Stormy Seas'	More than 30 suppliers
'Strawberries and Cream' (v)	EBee NPPs
'Strawberry Candy' **new**	EBee
'Strawberry Swirl'	More than 30 suppliers
'Titania' **new**	EBee
'Van Gogh'	EBee EFou
'Veil of Passion'	SHar
'Velvet Cloak'	EHan
'Velvet Night'	EBee EFou EMan LBBr LBuc MAvo MBNS NBir SHar SVil WAul WFar
'Vesuvius'	SHar
villosa	ECGN ECha MRav
– 'Autumn Bride' **new**	MWrn
– 'Biddulph Brown'	WCot
– var. *macrorhiza* **new**	GCal
– 'Royal Red'	ECha GBuc GMac
'Wendy Hardy'	CLAP
'White Marble'	SHar
'Winter Red'	EBee EBre MCAu
'Yeti'	EBcc MBNS WPnP
'Zabelliana'	GBri GCal

x *Heucherella* (Saxifragaceae)

alba 'Bridget Bloom'	CElw CSam EChP ECha ELan GAbr GKir GMaP LGro LPVe MBro MCAu MRav NOrc NPri SDes SPar SPer SRms WFar WHoo WMnd WPnP WRus
§ – 'Rosalie'	CElw CFee CMHG CMea EBre ECha EMar EPri EWsh LPVe LRHS MBNS MBri MRav MSte MTis NBir NDov SPlb WFar WHoo WMnd WMoo WPnP WRus WWeb
'Burnished Bronze'	EBee EMan SHar SRot SUsu WAbe WFar WMoo
'Chocolate Lace' **new**	MBri SHar
'Cinnamon Bear'	SHar
'Dayglow Pink'	EBee SHar SRot WFar WGor WMoo

'Kimono' ♀ H4	EBee EMan MBri NGdn SHar SRot
'Ninja'	see *Tiarella* 'Ninja'
'Pearl Kohl' (v)	CCol
'Quicksilver'	CBcs CBct EBee ECGN EChP EMan EPPr GMaP LAst MBri MCAu MSte NCot NDov NGdn NPSI NSti SDes SMad SPer SSpi WAul WBea WCot WElm WFar WLin WMoo WPnP WWeb
§ 'Silver Streak'	CHid CMHG EBre EChP EFou EPPr GKir GMaP LHop MBri MGGn MSte NCot NSti NPri SDes SPar SPla SSpi WCot WMoo WWeb
tiarelloides ♀ H4	CSev EBee EMan EMil EPfP LRHS MWgw NCat NFor NLon NSti SDes SPer SVal WMnd WRus
'Viking Ship'	More than 30 suppliers

Hexastylis see *Asarum*

x *Hibanobambusa* (Poaceae)

I *tranquillans*	CDDB CMco EFul EPla LJus LPan MHdf MMoz SDry WJun
I – f. *kimmei*	EBee
I – 'Shiroshima' (v) ♀ H4	CAbb CDoC CFil CFwr EBee EBlw EPla ERod IFro LJus LPal MAvo MBrN MCCP MHdf MMoz MWhi MWht NMoo NVic SDry SPar WJun WNor WPGP

Hibbertia (Dilleniaceae)

aspera	CPLG CPle CRHN SBrw WBcn WFar
§ *cuneiformis*	CPle ERea WPat
pedunculata	ECou
procumbens	ESis ITim NLAp WAbe
§ *scandens* ♀ H1	CHEx CPlN CRHN ECou ELan ERca GQui LRHS SOWG WMul
stricta **new**	ECou
tetrandra	see *H. cuneiformis*
✴ *venustula* **new**	ECou
volubilis	see *H. scandens*

Hibiscus ✿ (Malvaceae)

cannabinus	SIde
coccineus	MSte SOWG SSpi
fallax	CHll
hamabo	CWSG SSta
huegelii	see *Alyogyne huegelii*
leopoldii	SPer SRms
manihot	see *Abelmoschus manihot*
militaris	EBee
✴ *moesiana*	MBri
moscheutos	CArn CFir MSte
– 'Galaxy' **new**	LPVe
mutabilis	SOWG
paramutabilis	SMad
rosa-sinensis	EBak LRHS MBri SOWG
– 'Casablanca'	MBri
– 'Cooperi' (v) ♀ H1	CHal SOWG
– 'El Capitolio'	SOWG
– 'Helene'	ELan
– 'Holiday'	MBri
– 'Kardinal'	MBri
– 'Koeniger'	MBri
– 'Thelma Bennell'	SOWG
– 'Tivoli'	MBri
sabdariffa	MSal
schizopetalus ♀ H1	SOWG
sinosyriacus	EPfP LRHS
– 'Lilac Queen'	LRHS WBcn
– 'Ruby Glow'	MGos WPGP
syriacus	WFar WNor
– 'Admiral Dewey' (d)	MGos SPla

- 'Aphrodite' — CPMA EBee ENot MRav
- 'Ardens' (d) — CEnd CWSG EBee EMui EPfP LRHS MGos SLim SPer
- Blue Bird — see *H. syriacus* 'Oiseau Bleu'
- 'Boule de Feu' (d) **new** — ELan
- 'Bredon Springs' ♀ H4 **new** — WBcn
- 'Coelestis' — EMil MGos SPer
- 'Comte d'Hainault' — EBee SLim
- 'Diana' — CDoC EBee EMil ENot EPfP LRHS MBNS MRav SLon WBcn WWeb
- 'Dorothy Crane' — CEnd EBee ENot LRHS MGos MRav MWeb WWes
- 'Duc de Brabant' (d) — CDoC CSBt EMil EMui LRHS SHBN SPer WBcn
- 'Elegantissimus' — see *H. syriacus* 'Lady Stanley'
- 'Hamabo' ♀ H4 — CSBt EBee EMil ENot EPfP LAst LPan LRHS MAsh MBri MGos MRav MWat NBlu NLar NPri SHBN SLim SPar SPer SPla SPlb WDin WFar WStl WWeb
- 'Helene' — CDoC EBee LRHS MBri MRav WBcn WWeb
- 'Jeanne d'Arc' (d) — SLon
§ - 'Lady Stanley' (d) — CSBt EBee LRHS SLim SPer
- Lavender Chiffon = 'Notwoodone'PBR — EBee ENot EPfP LRHS MGos MRav NPri SPer WWeb
- 'Lenny' ♀ H4 — EBee ENot MGos MRav WWeb
- 'Leopoldii' **new** — NBlu
- 'Marina' **new** — EMui
§ - 'Meehanii' (v) ♀ H4 — CEnd EBee ENot EPfP LRHS MAsh MBri MGos SCoo SLim SPer SPla SSta WBcn
§ - 'Oiseau Bleu' ♀ H4 — More than 30 suppliers
- Pink Giant = 'Flogi' — CBcs CDoC CMHG EBee EBre ELan EPfP LPan LRHS MBri MGos NBlu SLon SPer WDin
- 'Purpureus Plenus' (d) — SLim
- 'Purpureus Variegatus' (v) — CBot SLim
- 'Red Heart' ♀ H4 — CEnd CSBt ELan EPfP LAst LRHS MAsh MBNS MBri NBlu NLar NPri SPar SPer SPla SRms WDin WStl WWeb
- 'Rosalbane' — MBri
- 'Roseus Plenus' (d) — SLim WBcn WDin
- 'Russian Violet = 'Floru' — CEnd COtt EBee ELan EMil LRHS MBri MGos MRav
- 'Speciosus' — EMui ENot MRav SLon SPer
- 'Totus Albus' — CSBt EMil NBlu WSHC
- 'Variegatus' — see *H. syriacus* 'Purpureus Variegatus'
- White Chiffon = 'Notwoodtwo'PBR ♀ H4 — EBee ENot EPfP LRHS MGos MRav SPer WWeb
- 'William R. Smith' ♀ H4 — CWSG EBee ELan ENot LAst LPan LRHS MAsh MGos MRav SHBN SPer SRPI SSta WDin WWeb WWes
- 'Woodbridge' ♀ H4 — More than 30 suppliers
trionum — CPLG CSpe WBor WKif
- 'Sunny Day' — ELan

hickory, shagbark see *Carya ovata*

Hieracium (Asteraceae)

aurantiacum — see *Pilosella aurantiaca*
brunneocroceum — see *Pilosella aurantiaca* subsp. *carpathicola*
§ *glaucum* — WEas WWin
§ *lanatum* — CSpe EHol GBin NBir WEas WPer WRos WWin
maculatum — CRow ECoo EHoe EMar GGar GKir LRHS MFir MLwd MPEx MWod NBid NCat NPer NWCA WMoo WPer WRos

- 'Blue Leaf' — EMan
- 'Leopard' (v) — EFWa EMan SGar
pannosum MESE 409 — EBee
pilosella — see *Pilosella officinarum*
praecox — see *H. glaucum*
x *rubrum* — EBre
umbellatum — WOut
villosum — EBee EHoe EVFa LRHS MDun NBro NPri WHer WPer WRos WWin
waldsteinii — MBro NFor
welwitschii — see *H. lanatum*

Hierochloe (Poaceae)

occidental **new** — CBig
odorata — CBig CPen ELau EMan EMon EPPr GPoy Ilve LPVe MGol SRGP WPnP
redolens — GAbr GOrn

Himalayacalamus (Poaceae)

§ *asper* — CFil ERod WPGP
§ *falconeri* — CFil EBee EFul EPfP EPla MMoz SDix SDys WPGP
§ - 'Damarapa' — CFil EPla LJus MMoz SDes SDix WJun WPGP
§ *hookerianus* — CAbb CFil LJus WJun
porcatus **new** — CFil

Hippeastrum ✿ (Amaryllidaceae)

x *acramannii* — GCal
'Apple Blossom' — LAma NRog
'Beautiful Lady' — LAma
'Bestseller' ♀ H1 — LAma
bifidum — see *Rhodophiala bifida*
'Blossom Peacock' (d) **new** — ETub
'Byjou' — NRog
'Calimero' — ETub
'Christmas Gift' — ETub LRHS
'Dutch Belle' — LAma
elwesii — SBla
'Fairy Tale' — ETub
'Fantastica' — LAma
'Floris Hekker' — ETub
'Germa' — ETub
'Inca' — LAma
'Jewel' (d) — ETub LRHS
'Jungle Star' **new** — ETub
'Lemon Lime' — ETub LAma LRHS
'Lima' — LAma
'Ludwig's Goliath' — LAma
'Mary Lou' (d) — ETub LAma
'Oskar' — NRog
papilio ♀ H1 — LAma NRog
* - 'Butterfly' — ETub LRHS
'Papillon' — LAma
'Pasadena' — LRHS
'Philadelphia' (d) — ETub
'Picotee' — LAma LRHS
'United Nations' — LAma
'White Dazzler' — LAma
'Yellow Pioneer' — LAma

Hippocrepis (Papilionaceae)

§ *comosa* — CKin SSpi
§ *emerus* — CBcs CMHG CTrC CTri EBee ELan EPfP ERea GEil LAst LHop MMil STre WHCG WPat WSHC

Hippolytia (Asteraceae)

§ *herderi* — EBee EMan SMrm WCot

Hippophae (Elaeagnaceae)

rhamnoides ♀ H4 — More than 30 suppliers
- 'Askola' (f) — MGos

- 'Freisendorf Orange' (f) | MBlu
- 'Leikora' (f) | ELan ESim MBlu MGos SPer WMou WPat
- 'Pollmix' (m) | ELan ESim MBlu MGos SPer
salicifolia | CAgr CLnd WPGP

Hippuris (*Hippuridaceae*)
vulgaris | CBen CRDP EHon EMFW IHMH LMdh NPer WFar WMAq WWpP

Hirpicium (*Asteraceae*)
armerioides | NWCA

Histiopteris (*Dennstaedtiaceae*)
incisa | CFil

Hoheria ✿ (*Malvaceae*)
§ *angustifolia* | CFil CTrC ECou LAst WPGP
'Borde Hill' | EPfP SBrw SPer SSpi SSta WHCG
glabrata | CBcs CFil ECou EPfP GGar IMGH WPGP
- 'Silver Stars' | EPfP
'Glory of Amlwch' ♀ H3 | CFil CPMA CSam EPfP GCal LRHS SMad SSpi SSta WCru WPGP
'Hill House' **new** | CHll
§ *lyallii* ♀ H4 | CBcs CDoC CPLG CSam ECou ELan EPfP LAst NEgg NPSI SHBN SPer SSpi SSta WBod WDin
microphylla | see H. *angustifolia*
populnea | CBcs CBot CPle
- 'Alba Variegata' (v) | CTrC SMad
- 'Moonlight' **new** | NPSI
- 'Osbornei' | SBrw
- 'Sunshine' **new** | NPSI
sexstylosa | CAbb CBot CDoC CDul CFee CHEx CHid CMHG CTri Elan EPfP IKee IMGH ISea LAst MDun SBrw SLon SPer SSta WGer
- 'Pendula' | CBcs NPSI WDin
- 'Stardust' ♀ H4 | CAbP CDul CFil CMCN CPMA ELan EPfP LRHS MBri NLar NPal SBrw SKee SMad SMur SPer SPoG SReu SSpi WFar WPGP WSHC
* - 'Starshine' | ERea

Holboellia (*Lardizabalaceae*)
coriacea | CBcs CBot CHEx CPlN CRHN CRez CSam EBee EPfP LRHS MDun MGos SAPC SArc SBra SOWG SSta WCFE WCot WCru
fargesii DJHC 506 | WCru
latifolia | CHEx COtt CPlN CRHN CSBt CSam CTrG CTri EBce EPfP GCal LRHS MTPN SAPC SArc SBra SEND SLim SOWG SPar SPer WFar
- SF 95134 | ISea

Holcus (*Poaceae*)
lanatus | CKin
mollis 'Albovariegatus' (v) | More than 30 suppliers
- 'White Fog' (v) | CChe CPen EBee EHul MBlu MBri MGGn NHol SPar WFar WLeb

Holodiscus (*Rosaceae*)
discolor | CDul CFil CPle EBee ELan EPla EVFa EWes GKir LRHS MBlu MBri MBro NBlu NSti SBrw SDys SHBN SLon SMad SPer SPla SSpi SSta WDin WHCG WPat
- NJM 94044 | WPGP
- var. *ariifolius* | EPfP EWTr WPGP
- var. *discolor* | CBcs

Homalocladium (*Polygonaceae*)
§ *platycladum* | CHal LEdu SPar

Homeria (*Iridaceae*)
breyniana | see H. *collina*
- var. *aurantiaca* | see H. *flaccida*
§ *collina* | CPLG EMui
§ *flaccida* | LAma LBow NRog
ochroleuca | LAma LBow NRog

Homoglossum see *Gladiolus*

Homoranthus (*Myrtaceae*)
flavescens | SOWG

Honckenya (*Caryophyllaceae*)
peploides **new** | MLwd

Hordeum (*Poaceae*)
brachyantherum | CBig
chilense **new** | EBee EPPr
jubatum | More than 30 suppliers

Horkelia (*Rosaceae*)
fusca subsp. *capitata* | EBee

Horminum (*Lamiaceae*)
pyrenaicum | CElw CMHG CNic CPlt EBee ELan EMan GAbr GDra MAvo MBro MGrG NGar NMen SBla SRms WBca WCom WFar WMoo WPer WWin
- pale blue | MDKP MSte NLAp

horseradish see *Armoracia rusticana*

Hosta ✿ (*Hostaceae*)
AGSJ 302 | CDes
'Abba Dabba Do' (v) | CBdn EBee EGol EMic EPGN EVFa LRHS SApp
'Abby' | CBdn EGol EMic EPGN
'Abiqua Ariel' | CBdn EMic
'Abiqua Blue Crinkles' | CBdn NBir
'Abiqua Drinking Gourd' | CBdn EBee EFou EGol EMic EOrc EPGN GKir GSki IBal LRHS MHom NMyG
'Abiqua Ground Cover' **new** | EGol
'Abiqua Moonbeam' (v) | CBdn CRez CWin EBee EMic EPGN NMyG SApp
'Abiqua Recluse' | EGol LRHS
'Abiqua Trumpet' (*tokudama*) | CBdn EGol NMyG
'Abiqua Zodiac' | CBdn
aequinoctiiantha | EGol
albomarginata | see H. 'Paxton's Original'
§ *Albomarginata* | CBcs CBdn CHar EBee EGol EMic EPGN GKir MBar MNrw NBir NMyG SHBN SPar SPer
(*fortunei*) (v)
'Allan P. McConnell' (v) | CBdn EGol EMic EPGN NHar
'Alpine Aire' | EMic
'Alvatine Taylor' | CBdn EGol
'Amanuma' | EGol EMic MHom
'Amber Maiden' (v) | EGol
'Amber Tiara' **new** | EMic
'American Dream' (v) | EGol EMic EPGN IBal
'Amy Elizabeth' (v) | CBdn EGol EMic
'Angel Feathers' (v) **new** | EGol
'Annc' (v) | CBdn EGol
'Anne Arett' (v) | EPGN
'Antioch' (*fortunei*) (v) | CBdn EBee EGol EMic MIDC MRav MSte SApp WFar
'Aoki' (*fortunei*) | EMic EPGN NHol SDes

'Aphrodite'	CFir EBee EGol EMic EMon EPGN
(*plantaginea*) (d)	MBri MSte NLar WCot
'Apple Green'	EMic
'Aqua Velva'	EGol LRHS
'Archangel'	EGol
'Argentea Variegata'	see *H. undulata* var. *undulata*
(*undulata*)	
'Aristocrat' **new**	CBdn EGol EPGN WRus
'August Beauty'	CBdn EMic
'August Moon'	More than 30 suppliers
aureafolia	see *H.* 'Starker Yellow Leaf'
'Aureoalba' (*fortunei*)	see *H.* 'Spinners'
'Aureomaculata' (*fortunei*)	see *H. fortunei* var. *albopicta*
* 'Aurcomarginata' (v)	CPrp GAbr GKir LPVe WHoo
§ 'Aureomarginata'	CBdn CBos CBri CSBt EBre EGol
(*montana*) (v)	EHoe EMic EPGN GCal LSyl MBri
	NHol NLar NMyG NVic SApp
	SCro SPar SPla SSpi SUsu WRus
	WWeb WWol
§ 'Aureomarginata'	CBdn CBro EBre ECha EGol EMic
(*ventricosa*) (v) ♀ H4	EPGN EPfP IBal LRHS MBri NGdn
	NVic SApp SRms WRus WWye
'Aureostriata' (*tardiva*)	see *H.* 'Inaho'
'Aurora Borealis'	EGol EPGN
(*sieboldiana*) (v)	
'Austin Dickinson'	EGol EMic
'Azure Snow'	CBdn EGol LRHS WBcn
'Babbling Brook'	EGol
'Baby Bunting'	CBdn EGol EMic EPGN MBNS
	NMyG WRus
'Ballerina' **new**	EGol
'Banyai's Dancing Girl'	EGol EMic
'Barbara Ann' (v)	CBdn EPGN MBri
'Barbara White'	EGol
'Beauty Substance'	CBdn EGle EGol EMic EPGN NMyG
'Bees' Colossus'	CWin SApp
bella	see *H. fortunei* var. *obscura*
'Bennie McRae'	EGol
'Betcher's Blue'	EGol
'Betsy King'	EBee EGol EPGN MRav NHol NMyG
'Bette Davis Eyes'	EGol
'Betty'	EGol EPGN
'Big Boy' (*montana*)	EGol EPGN GKir
'Big Daddy'	More than 30 suppliers
(*sieboldiana* hybrid)	
'Big Mama'	EGol EPGN LRHS MBNS NLar
(*sieboldiana* hybrid)	
'Bigfoot' **new**	EGol
'Bill Brincka' (v)	EGol
'Birchwood Blue' **new**	EGol
'Birchwood Elegance'	CBdn
'Birchwood Parky's Gold'	CBdn CMHG EGol EMic EPGN
	EPfP EWTr EWes LPVe LRHS
	MBNS MIDC MTed NHar NHol
	NOak SApp SDes SHBN SIng
	SMrm SSpi WRus WWeb
'Birchwood Ruffled	EGol EMic
Queen'	
'Bitsy Gold'	EGol
'Bitsy Green'	EGol
'Black Beauty'	EGol EPGN
'Black Hills'	CBdn EGol EPGN LRHS
'Blave Venus' **new**	EGol
§ 'Blonde Elf'	EGol EMic EPGN NMyG SApp
'Blue Angel' misapplied	see *H. sieboldiana* var. *elegans*
'Blue Angel'	CBdn CRez EBee EGol EHan
(*sieboldiana*) ♀ H4	EHoe ELan EMic EOrc EPGN EPfP
	GBin GKir GMaP LAst LRHS MBro
	MWat NMyG NOrc SCro SHBN
	SMrm WMnd WRus WTMC WWye
'Blue Arrow'	CBdn EGol EPGN
'Blue Belle'	CBdn EGol EMic EPGN MBro
(Tardiana Group)	MSte NGdn WHoo WTin

'Blue Blazes'	LRHS
'Blue Blush'	CBdn EGol EPGN WTMC
(Tardiana Group)	
'Blue Boy'	CBdn EGol EMic EPGN EWes
	LCaP NHol
'Blue Cadet'	CBcs CBdn CFwr EBee EGol EMic
	GEdr GKir GSki LAst LPVe MBar
	MCAu MHFa NBee NBir NLar
	NOak SBod SPar WCra WFar
	WMnd WRus WStl WWeb WWpP
'Blue Cup'PBR	CBdn ENot EPGN MRav
(*sieboldiana*)	
'Blue Danube'	CBdn EGol EMic MHom
(Tardiana Group)	
'Blue Diamond'	CBdn CMHG CWin EGol EMic
(Tardiana Group)	EPGN SApp WFar
'Blue Dimples'	CBdn CWin EGol IPot LRHS
(Tardiana Group)	
'Blue Edger'	CBdn NBir
'Blue Heart' (*sieboldiana*)	ECha EMic LPio
'Blue Ice' (Tardiana Group)	CBdn EGol
'Blue Impressions' **new**	EMic
'Blue Jay'	CBdn EGol
'Blue Lady'	CBdn EMic
'Blue Mammoth'	CBdn EGol EMic EPGN LRHS
(*sieboldiana*)	
'Blue Moon'	CBdn EBre EFou EGol EOrc EPGN
(Tardiana Group)	EPfP ERos IPot LPhx MBNS NHol
	NMyG
'Blue Seer' (*sieboldiana*)	CBdn EGol
'Blue Shadows'	CBdn CWin EBee EPGN LRHS
(*tokudama*) (v)	NMyG SApp SHBN WRus
'Blue Skies'	CBdn EGol EPGN MHom SApp
(Tardiana Group)	
'Blue Umbrellas'	CBdn EBee EGol EHan ELan EMic
(*sieboldiana* hybrid)	EOrc EPGN EPfP GSki IPot LBuc
	LRHS MBri MIDC NGdn NHol
	NLar NMyG
'Blue Velvet'	CBdn
'Blue Vision'	EPGN LRHS
'Blue Wedgwood'	CBdn CBro CRow EGol ELan
(Tardiana Group)	EMic EOrc EPGN GKir IBal LAst
	MBri MIDC NHol NMyG SApp
	SChu SPar SPla WCFE WHil WRus
	WTMC WWpP
'Bold Edger' (v)	CBdn EGol EPGN
'Bold Ribbons' (v)	CBdn CWin EGol EMic WTin
'Bold Ruffles' (*sieboldiana*)	EGol LRHS
'Bonanza' (*fortunei*)	EMic
'Border Bandit' (v)	EGol
'Borsch 1'	CBdn
'Borwick Beauty'	CBdn EMic EPGN NGdn NMyG
(*sieboldiana*) (v)	
'Bountiful'	EGol EMic
'Bouquet'	EGol
'Bressingham Blue'	CBdn CPrp CWin EBre ECtt EGol
	ETub LPVe LRHS MCAu MRav
	NMyG SPar SPer WFar WMnd
	WTMC WWpP
'Brigadier' **new**	EGol
'Bright Glow'	EGol
(Tardiana Group)	
'Bright Lights'	CBdn CRez CWin EGol EMic
(*tokudama*) (v)	EPGN IBal LAst NMyG WTMC
'Brim Cup' (v)	CBdn CWin EBee EGol EMic
	EPGN GKir IBal MBNS MBri NBro
	NGdn SApp WRus
'Brooke'	EGol EMic EPGN
'Brother Ronald'	CBdn EGol EMic LRHS
(Tardiana Group)	
'Bruce's Blue'	EGol GSki
'Buckshaw Blue'	CBdn EFou EGol EPGN ETow
	NBir NGdn SSpi WBcn WTMC

'Butter Rim' (*sieboldii*) (v)   EGol
'Cadillac' **new**   CBdn
I   'Calypso'   EGol EPGN
'Camelot'   CBdn EGol LRHS NGdn
   (Tardiana Group)
'Canada Blue'   EFou WTMC
'Candy Hearts'   CBdn CMHG CSam EGle EGol
   EMic EPGN MHom
capitata B&SWJ 588   WCru
   - MSF 850   CFil WPGP
caput-avis   see *H. kikutii* var. *caput-avis*
'Carnival' (v)   CBdn EGol EPGN IBal WRus
'Carol' (*fortunei*) (v)   CBdn CLAP CWin EBee EGol EMic
   EWsh IBal LAst MSte NMyG WHal
'Carousel' (v)   EGol
'Carrie Ann'   see *H.* 'Carrie'
§   'Carrie' (*sieboldii*) (v)   EGol SApp
'Cascades' (v)   EGol
'Celebration' (v)   EGol ELan EMic EPGN LRHS
   MDKP WRus
'Challenger'   EMic
'Change of Tradition' (v)   CBdn EMic
'Chantilly Lace' (v)   CBdn EGol EMic EPGN IBal WTin
'Chartreuse Waves'   EGol
'Chartreuse Wiggles'   EPGN LRHS
   (*sieboldii*)
'Cheatin Heart'   EGol
'Chelsea Babe' (v)   EGol
'Chelsea Ore'   CHad
   (*plantaginea*) (v)
'Cherry Berry' (v)   CBdn CPen CRez CWin EBee
   EGol EMic EPGN MBNS MCLN
   MIDC NBro NGdn NHar NMyG
   SApp SVil WRus
'Cherub' (v)   EGol
'China' (*plantaginea*) **new**   EMic
'Chinese Sunrise'   CBdn EBee EChP EGol EMic EOrc
   (*cathayana*) (v)   EPGN IPot MBNS MHom NHol
   NMyG SCro WHil
'Chiquita'   EGol
§   'Chôkô Nishiki'   CBdn CFir EBee EGle EGol EMic
   (*montana*) (v)   EPGN IPot MIDC NABC NGdn
   NMyG SChu SPar
'Christmas Tree' (v)   CBdn CM&M CWin EBee EGle
   EGol EMic EPGN GBri IPot LRHS
   MIDC MNrw NGdn NMyG SApp
   SVil WHil WRus WTMC
'Citation' (v)   EGol LRHS
'City Lights'   EGol
'Clarence'   CBdn
clausa   WRus
   - var. *normalis*   CBdn EBee EBre EGol GCal GQui
   LRHS NBir NGdn NLar
'Collectors Choice'   EGol
'Color Glory'   CCol CWin EBee EChP EGle EGol
   (*sieboldiana*) (v)   EPGN GBin LAst NGdn NLar
   NMyG SApp WBcn WRus WTMC
'Colossal'   EGol EMic
'Columbus Circle' (v)   CBdn EGol
'Coquette' (v)   CBdn EGol EMic
'Cotillion' (v)   EGol
'County Park'   EGol
'Craig's Temptation'   CBdn
'Cream Cheese' (v)   EGol
'Cream Delight' (*undulata*)   see *H. undulata* var. *undulata*
'Cream Edge'   see *H.* 'Fisher Cream Edge'
'Crepe Suzette' (v)   CBdn EGol EPGN LRHS
'Crested Reef'   CBdn EGol EMic
'Crested Surf' (v)   EGol EMic
§   *crispula* (v) ♀ H4   CBdn CHad CRow EGol EHon
   EMic EPGN EPar GMac LGro
   MBar MHom NChi NLon SChu
   SHBN WWpP

'Crown Jewel' (v)   EPGN
'Crown Prince'   CBdn EGol EPGN
§   'Crowned Imperial'   CBdn EMic NHol
   (*fortunei*) (v)
'Crusader' (v)   CBdn EGol EMic EPGN LRHS
   NMyG WRus
'Cupid's Dart' (v)   EGol
'Curlew' (Tardiana Group)   CBdn EGol
'Dark Star' (v)   CBdn EGol EPGN SApp
'Dartmoor Forest'   CBdn
'Darwin's Standard'   CBdn
'Dawn'   CBdn EGol EPar
'Daybreak'   CBdn CWin EGol EMic EPGN
   LAst LRHS MBri NBro SApp SVil
   WHil WTMC WWye
'Days End' (v)   EGol
decorata   CBdn EGol EMic EMil MBar
'Delia'   EPGN
'Devon Blue'   CBdn EGol LCaP
   (Tardiana Group)
'Devon Desire' (*montana*)   CBdn
'Devon Discovery'   CBdn
'Devon Giant'   CBdn
'Devon Gold'   CBdn
'Devon Green'   CBdn CLAP EHan EPGN GBri IPot
   MIDC MLLN MSte NBro NGdn
   NMyG NPPs NPro SApp WAul
   WFar WRus
'Devon Hills'   CBdn
'Devon Mist'   CBdn LPVe
'Devon Tor'   CBdn EPGN
'Dew Drop' (v)   CBdn EGol EMic NMyG WWol
'Diamond Tiara' (v)   CBdn EGol EMic EPGN IBal LAst
   LRHS NMyG SChu
'Domaine de Courson'   CBdn GBin WFar
'Don Stevens' (v)   CBdn EGol
'Donahue Piecrust'   CBdn EGol
'Dorset Blue'   CBdn EGol EPGN GSki LRHS
   (Tardiana Group)
'Dorset Charm'   CBdn EGol
   (Tardiana Group)
'Dorset Flair'   EGol EMic
   (Tardiana Group)
'Doubloons'   EGol
'Drummer Boy'   CBdn EGol EMic MGan
'Duchess' (*nakaiana*) (v)   EGol
'DuPage Delight'   CBdn EGol EPGN
   (*sieboldiana*) (v)
'Dust Devil' (*fortunei*) (v)   EGol
'Edge of Night'   CBdn EGol
'El Capitan' (v)   CBdn EGol EMic EPGN LRHS
§   *elata*   EBee EGol EGra EMic
'Elatior' (*nigrescens*)   CBdn EMic
'Eldorado'   see *H.* 'Frances Williams'
'Electrum Stater' **new**   CBdn
'Elegans'   see *H. sieboldiana* var. *elegans*
'Elfin Power' (*sieboldii*) (v)   EGol
'Elisabeth'   CBdn EPGN LBuc NMyG
'Elizabeth Campbell'   CBdn CLAP EGol EMic EPGN
   (*fortunei*) (v)   MSte SApp SSpi
'Ellen'   EMic
'Ellerbroek' (*fortunei*) (v)   EGol EMic GSki
'Elsley Runner'   EGol
'Elvis Lives'   CBdn EGol IPot LAst LRHS NGdn
   NMyG NPPs
'Embroidery' **new**   MIDC
'Emerald Carpet'   EGol
'Emerald Necklace'   EGol
   (v) **new**
'Emerald Skies'   EGol
'Emerald Tiara' (v)   CBdn EGol EMic EPGN LRHS
   NMyG SApp SVil
'Emeralds and Rubies'   EGol

'Emily Dickinson' (v)	CBdn EGol IBal LRHS SApp
'Eric Smith'	CBdn EGol EMic EPGN LPhx
(Tardiana Group)	MHom SChu WFar
'Evelyn McCafferty'	EGol
(*tokudama* hybrid)	
'Evening Magic' (v)	EGol EPGN
'Everlasting Love' (v) **new**	EGol
'Excitation'	CBdn EGol LPio
'Fair Maiden' (v)	CBdn EGol EPGN
'Fall Bouquet'	EGol
(*longipes hypoglauca*)	
'Fall Emerald'	CBdn EMic
'Fan Dance' (v)	EGol
'Fantastic'	EGol LRHS
(*sieboldiana* hybrid)	
'Feather Boa'	EGol EPGN NHar
'Fenman's Fascination'	EMic
'Fire and Ice' (v)	CBdn CCol CHid CMGP CPen
	CWin EBee EGle EGol EMic
	ENot EPGN EPfP GBin GKir LAst
	MBNS MBri MCLN MHom MIDC
	NBro NGdn NMyG NSti SApp
	WAul WRus WTMC
§ 'Fisher Cream Edge'	CBdn
(*fortunei*)	
'Flame Stitch' (v) **new**	EGol
'Floradora'	CBdn EGol EMic EPGN IBal
'Flower Power'	CBdn EGol
fluctuans	GIBF
'Fond Hope' (*sieboldiana*)	CBdn
'Fool's Gold' (*fortunei*)	CBdn EMic LBuc
'Formal Attire'	CBdn EGol EMic LRHS
(*sieboldiana* hybrid) (v)	
'Forncett Frances' (v)	EGol
'Fortis'	see *H. undulata* var. *erromena*
fortunei	CBdn CHar CNic CRow EGol EMic
	IBal MIDC NHol SChu SPer
	WEas WFar WPnP WWal WWye
§ - var. *albopicta* ♀ H4	More than 30 suppliers
- - f. *aurea* ♀ H4	CBdn CBos CHad CMGP CMHG
	CRow EBee ECha EFou EGol
	EHoe ELan EPla GKir GMaP LRHS
	MBar NLar NMyG SChu SCro SPer
	SPla SRms WFar WRus
- - - dwarf	EMic
§ - var. *aureomarginata*	More than 30 suppliers
♀ H4	
- var. *gigantea*	see *H. montana*
§ - var. *hyacinthina* ♀ H4	CBdn EBee EGol EMic EOrc EPfP
	GCal LRHS MBar MRav NMyG
	NOrc SPar SSpi WFar WWeb WWin
- - variegated (v)	see *H.* 'Crowned Imperial'
§ - var. *obscura*	CBdn EBee ECho EGol EMic WLin
- var. *rugosa*	EMic
'Fountain'	NHol
'Fourth of July' **new**	EGol
'Fragrant Blue'	CBdn EGol EMic LBuc LRHS
	NMyG WRHF
'Fragrant Bouquet' (v)	CBdn CWin EFou EGol EMic
	EPGN IBal LRHS NGdn NHol NLar
	NMyG SApp SChu SVil WRus
'Fragrant Dream' **new**	CBdn
'Fragrant Gold'	EGol
'Francee' (*fortunei*)	More than 30 suppliers
(v) ♀ H4	
§ 'Frances Williams'	More than 30 suppliers
(*sieboldiana*) (v) ♀ H4	
'Frances Williams' seedlings	NSti
'Frances Williams	EGol EPfP MWat
Improved'	
(*sieboldiana*) (v)	
'Freising' (*fortunei*)	EBee
'Fresh' (v)	EGol EPGN

'Fried Bananas'	CBdn EGol EMic
'Fried Green Tomatoes'	CBdn EGol EMic EPGN LRHS NLar
'Fringe Benefit' (v)	CWin EBre EGol EMic EPGN GKir
'Frosted Jade' (v)	CBdn EGol EPGN LRHS NMyG
I 'Fulva' **new**	EGol
'Gaiety' (v)	EGol EPGN
'Gaijin' (d)	CBdn
'Gala' (v)	CBdn EPGN
'Gay Blade' (v)	EGol
'Gay Feather' **new**	NPro SPoG
'Gay Search' (v)	EPGN
'Geisha' (v)	CBdn EGol EPGN GBin IBal MBNS
	MCCP NMyG WBcn
'Gene's Joy'	EPGN
'Gigantea' (*sieboldiana*)	see *H. elata*
'Gilt Edge' (*sieboldiana*) (v)	EMic LCaP NMyG
'Ginko Craig' (v)	More than 30 suppliers
glauca	see *H. sieboldiana* var. *elegans*
* 'Glauca' (*fortunei*)	WLow
'Glockenspiel'	CBdn EGol
I 'Gloriosa' (*fortunei*) (v)	EGol EPGN
'Glory'	CBdn EGol
'Goddess of Athena' (v)	EGol
'Gold Drop' (*venusta*)	CBdn EBee ECho EGol EMic EOrc
	LPhx LRHS NHol
'Gold Edger'	More than 30 suppliers
§ 'Gold Haze' (*fortunei*)	CBdn EGol EMic EOrc EPGN NBir
	NHol NMyG
'Gold High Fat	EPGN
Cream' **new**	
'Gold Leaf' (*fortunei*)	EGol
'Gold Regal'	CBdn CWin EGol EMic EPGN LCaP
	MHom MSte NMyG SMrm WMnd
'Gold Rush' PBR **new**	CBdn EPGN
'Gold Splash'	MBro WHoo
'Gold Standard'	More than 30 suppliers
(*fortunei*) (v)	
'Goldbrook' (*fortunei*) (v)	EGol WBcn
'Goldbrook Genie'	EGol
'Goldbrook Girl'	EGol
'Goldbrook Glamour' (v)	EGol
'Goldbrook Glimmer'	EGol
(Tardiana Group) (v)	
'Goldbrook Gold'	EGol
'Goldbrook Grace'	EGol
'Goldbrook Gratis' (v)	EGol
'Goldbrook Grayling'	EGol
'Goldbrook Grebe'	EGol
'Golden Age'	see *H.* 'Gold Haze'
'Golden Anniversary'	CBdn EBee LRHS NHol WTMC
'Golden Ben' **new**	ITim
'Golden Bullion'	CBdn EGol EPGN GBri LRHS
(*tokudama*)	
'Golden Circles'	see *H.* 'Frances Williams'
'Golden Decade'	EGol
'Golden Fascination'	EGol
'Golden Guernsey' (v)	EMic
'Golden Isle'	EGol
'Golden Medallion'	CBdn CMHG EGol ELan EOrc
(*tokudama*)	GKir IBal LRHS MBNS MBri NGdn
	NHol NMyG WFar
'Golden Nakaiana'	see *H.* 'Birchwood Parky's Gold'
'Golden Oriole'	CBdn
'Golden Prayers'	EHan
'Golden Prayers'	CBdn EGle EGol ELan ENot EPGN
(*tokudama*)	ERos GSki LPhx LRHS MIDC MRav
	NBir NBro NGdn NHol NMyG
	NOrc SChu SPer SPla WRus
'Golden Scepter'	CBdn CMHG EChP EGol EMic
(*nakaiana*)	EPGN NHol WFar
'Golden Sculpture'	CBdn EGol LRHS
(*sieboldiana*)	
'Golden Spider'	EGol EMic

'Golden Sunburst'	CBdn EBee EGol ELan EMic EPGN
(*sieboldiana*)	GSki IBal NGdn NHol SMrm WFar
'Golden Tiara' (v) ♀ H4	More than 30 suppliers
'Goldpfeil'	EMic
'Goldsmith'	EGol SApp
'Good as Gold'	EMic EPGN
'Gosan' (*takahashii*)	EGol
gracillima	CRow EPGN EPar
'Granary Gold' (*fortunei*)	CBdn EGol EPGN LRHS NABC SChu
'Grand Master'	EGol EPGN IBal LCaP
'Grand Tiara' (v)	CBdn EGol EPGN SApp
'Gray Cole' (*sieboldiana*)	CBdn EGol EMic
'Great Expectations'	More than 30 suppliers
(*sieboldiana*) (v)	
'Green Acres' (*montana*)	EGle EPGN LPhx MSte SApp
	SChu WFar
'Green Angel'	EGol
'Green Eyes' (*sieboldii*) (v)	EGol
'Green Fountain' (*kikutii*)	CBdn EFou EGol EMic EPGN
	LRHS MSte
'Green Gold'	EMic
'Green Gold' (*fortunei*) (v)	CBdn
'Green Piecrust'	CBdn EGol EPGN LRHS
'Green Ripples'	CHid
'Green Sheen'	EGol EPGN
'Green Summer Fragrance'	CBdn
'Green Velveteen'	CBdn EGol
'Green with Envy' (v)	CBdn EGol
'Grey Piecrust'	EGol
'Ground Master' (v)	CBdn CMHG COIW COtt EBre
	ECha ECtt EGol FLan EOrc EPGN
	EPfP GMaP GSki LRHS MBri MRav
	NBro NHol NMyG NSti SDes SPar
	SPer SPla WAbe WFar WRus
'Ground Sulphur'	EGol EPGN
'Guacamole' (v)	CBdn EBee EGle EGol EMic EPGN
	IPot NLar NMyG SUsu SVil WTin
'Guardian Angel' **new**	EPGN WRus
'Gum Drop'	CBdn EMic EPGN
'Gun Metal Blue'	EGol
'Hadspen Blue'	More than 30 suppliers
(Tardiana Group)	
'Hadspen Hawk'	EGol LPhx NMyG SApp
(Tardiana Group)	
'Hadspen Heron'	CBdn EGol MAvo MHom SChu
(Tardiana Group)	
'Hadspen Rainbow'	CBdn IBal
'Hadspen Samphire'	EGol EMic EPGN LRHS NBir WRus
'Hadspen Seersucker'	CHad
'Hadspen White' (*fortunei*)	EGol EMic
'Haku-chu-han'	CBdn
(*sieboldii*) (v)	
'Hakujima' (*sieboldii*)	EGol LPhx
§ 'Halcyon'	More than 30 suppliers
(Tardiana Group) ♀ H4	
'Happiness'	CBdn CWin EGol EHoe EMic
(Tardiana Group)	EPGN MHom MRav NMyG
'Happy Hearts'	EGol EMic
'Harmony'	CBdn EGol EMic
(Tardiana Group)	
'Harvest Glow'	EGol
'Harvest Moon'	GKir
'Heart Ache'	EGol
'Heartleaf'	EMic
'Heart's Content' (v)	CBdn EGol
'Heartsong' (v)	EGol EPGN
'Helen Doriot'	EGol EMic
(*sieboldiana*)	
helonioides	see *H. rohdeifolia*
hort. f. ***albopicta***	
'Herifu' (v)	CBdn EGol
'Hilda Wassman' (v)	EGol
'Hirao Majesty'	CBdn EGol

'Hirao Splendor'	EGol
'Hirao Supreme'	CBdn EGol
'Hirao Tetra'	CBdn
'Holstein'	see *H.* 'Halcyon'
'Honey Moon'	CBdn EGol
§ 'Honeybells' ♀ H4	More than 30 suppliers
'Honeysong' (v)	CBdn EMic EPGN
'Hoosier Harmony' (v)	CBdn EGol EMic LRHS
'Hoosier Homecoming'	CBdn SApp
'Hope' (v)	EGol
§ 'Hyacintha Variegata'	CMHG GBri LPVe
(*fortunei*) (v)	
'Hydon Gleam'	EMic EPGN
'Hydon Sunset' (*nakaiana*)	CBdn CM&M CMHG EBre EGol
	EMic EOrc EPGN GKir LHyd MIDC
	NHol NMyG NOak NSti WMnd
hypoleuca	EGol
'Ice Cream' (*cathayana*) (v)	EGol
'Ilona' (v) **new**	EGol
§ 'Inaho'	CBdn EGol EPGN
'Inca Gold'	EGol
'Ingeborg' **new**	WTin
'Inniswood' (*montana*) (v)	CBdn CLAP CWin EBee EFou
	EGle EGol EPGN IBal IPot LRHS
	MBNS NGdn NMyG NSti SApp
	WMnd WPnP
'Invincible'	CBdn CLAP EFou EGle EGol EMic
	EPGN IBal LPhx LRHS MBNS
	MIDC NLar NMyG SApp SVil
	WRus WTin WWye
'Iona' (*fortunei*)	CBdn EBee EGol EMic EPGN SSpi
'Irische see'	EGol
(Tardiana Group)	
'Irish Breeze'	EPGN
'Iron Gate Delight' (v)	CBdn
'Iron Gate Glamour'	EGol EPGN WBen
'Iron Gate Special' (v)	EMic
'Iron Gate Supreme' (v)	EPGN
'Island Charm' (v)	CBdn EGol EMic IBal
'Iwa Soules'	EGol
'Jade Beauty'	CBdn
'Jade Cascade'	CBdn CLAP CMil EBee EFou EGol
	EMic LRHS MSte NBir NChi NHol
	NLar NMyG SApp SMrm WCot
	WLin WOVN
'Jade Scepter' (*nakaiana*)	EGol EMic
'Jadette' (v)	EGol EPGN NHar SChu
'Janet' (*fortunei*) (v)	CBdn CMil CWin EBee EGol EOrc
	GMaP LCaP LRHS NGdn NHol
	NMyG WBar
'Japan Girl'	see *H.* 'Mount Royal'
'Jimmy Crack Corn'	EGol
'Joker' (*fortunei*) (v)	CBdn EBee GKir
'Jolly Green Giant'	EMic
(*sieboldiana* hybrid)	
'Journeyman'	EBre EGol EMic
'Julia' (v)	EGol IBal
'Julie Morss'	CBdn CWin EBee EGol EMic
	EPGN MAvo WRus WWpP
'Jumbo' (*sieboldiana*)	EMic
'June' PBR (Tardiana	More than 30 suppliers
Group) (v)	
'Just So' (v)	CBdn EGol EMic EPGN LRHS
'Kabitan'	see *H. sieboldii* var. *sieboldii* f.
	kabitan
'Karin' **new**	CBdn
'Katherine Lewis'	CBdn
(Tardiana Group) (v)	
'Kelsey'	EGol EMic
'Kifukurin' (*kikutii*) (v)	CBdn
'Kifukurin Ko Mame'	CBdn
(*gracillima*) (v)	
I 'Kifukurin' (*pulchella*) (v)	CBdn EGol EMic

Name	Suppliers
'Kifukurin Ubatake' (*pulchella*)	CBdn EPGN
kikutii	EGol EMic EOrc WTin
§ - var. ***caput-avis***	EBre EGol EMic
- var. ***polyneuron***	CLAP EGol SApp
- var. ***tosana***	EGol
§ - var. ***yakusimensis***	CBdn CRDP EGol EMic ETow GDra SMad
'Kingfisher' **new**	EGol
§ 'Kirishima'	CBdn EPGN NHar
'Kiwi Cream Edge' (v)	EMic
kiyosumiensis	NHol
'Klopping Variegated' (*fortunei*) (v)	EGol
'Knave's Green'	EPGN
'Knockout' (v)	CBdn CWin EGol EPGN IBal MBNS MBri MNrw NBro NGdn NHar NLar NMyG WRus
'Koriyama' (*sieboldiana*) (v)	CBdn EBee EMic IBal
'Krossa Cream Edge' (*sieboldii*) (v)	EPGN
'Krossa Regal' ♀ H4	More than 30 suppliers
'Lacy Belle' (v)	CBdn CWin EGol EMic LRHS NBro NGdn WRus
'Lady Helen'	EMic
'Lady Isobel Barnett' (v)	CBdn EMic EPGN
***laevigata* new**	EGol
'Lakeside Black Satin'	CBdn EPGN
'Lakeside Cha Cha' (v) **new**	CBdn EGol EMic
'Lakeside Neat Petite'	EGol
'Lakeside Ninita' (v)	EGol EMic
'Lakeside Symphony' (v)	EGol EMic
§ ***lancifolia*** ♀ H4	CBdn CBro CMHG CRow EBre ECha EGol EHrv ELan EMic EPGN EPar GKir GMaP LGro LPVe MRav NGdn NHol NMyG NSti SApp SPer SRms SSpi WAul WGwG WPGP WWal
'Leather Sheen'	EGol EMic EPGN
'Lee Armiger' (*tokudama* hybrid)	EGol
'Lemon Delight'	CBdn CWin EGol EPGN SApp
'Lemon Lime'	CBdn EGol EMic IBal LRHS MHom MNrw NMyG NPro WIvy WPat WTin WWhi WWye
'Lemon Twist'	LRHS
'Leola Fraim' (v)	CBdn EGol EMic EPGN LRHS WBcn
'Leviathan'	EMic
* ***lilacina***	SCro WFar WMoo
'Lily Pad' **new**	EPGN
'Lime Piecrust' **new**	EGol
'Limey Lisa'	EMic
'Little Aurora' (*tokudama* hybrid)	EGol EMic EPGN
'Little Black Scape' **new**	EGol
'Little Blue' (*ventricosa*)	EGol
'Little Bo Beep' (v)	EGol
'Little Caesar' (v)	EGol
'Little Doll' (v)	EGol
'Little Razor'	EGol
'Little Sunspot' (v) **new**	EGol
'Little White Lines' (v)	CBdn EGol EPGN
'Little Wonder' (v)	CBdn EGol SChu
longipes	EGol LPhx
longissima	CMHG EGol SRPl WCru
'Louisa' (*sieboldii*) (v)	ECha EGol MSte
'Love Pat' (*tokudama*) ♀ H4	CBdn CCol CFir CWin EBee EGol EMic EPGN EPfP GAbr GBin GSki IBal LAst LBBr MCCP MIDC MRav NMyG SApp SDes SPla SVil
'Loyalist' **new**	CBdn
'Lucky Charm'	EMic
'Lucy Vitols' (v)	CBdn EGol EMic
'Lunar Eclipse' (v)	CWin EGol LPhx
'Lunar Orbit' (v)	CBdn
'Maekawa'	EGol
'Mama Mia' (v)	EGol EMic EPGN
'Maraschino Cherry'	EGol EMic
'Margin of Error' **new**	EPGN
N 'Marginata Alba' (*fortunei*) (v)	CBot CHad ECha GKir LPBA WWin
'Marilyn'	EGol EPGN LRHS
'Marquis' (*nakaiana* hybrid)	EGol
'Maruba Iwa' (*longipes* var. *latifolia*)	CBdn
'Maruba' (*longipes* var. *latifolia*)	EGol
'Mary Jo'	EMic
'Mary Marie Ann' (*fortunei*) (v)	CBdn EGol EPGN NMyG
§ 'Masquerade' (v)	CBdn EGol EMic EPGN NABC NHar WFar
'Mediovariegata' (*undulata*)	see *H. undulata* var. *undulata*
'Medusa' (v)	EGol
'Mentor Gold'	EGol
'Mesa Fringe' (*montana*)	CBdn
* 'Metallic Sheen'	CBdn LRHS
* 'Metallica'	CBdn
'Midas Touch' (*tokudama* hybrid)	CBdn EGol EOrc NHol NLar WRus
'Middle Ridge'	EBee NHol
§ 'Midwest Gold'	MHom SApp
'Midwest Magic' (v)	CBdn EGol EMic LRHS WBcn
'Mildred Seaver' (v)	CBdn CWin EGol EMic EPGN LRHS MBri MWat
'Millie's Memoirs' (v)	EGol
'Ming Jade' **new**	SApp
'Minnie Klopping'	EMic EPGN
§ ***minor***	CBdn CBro EBee EBre EGol EMic EPGN ERos EWTr GDra GEdr GGar GSki MTho NHol NMyG SSpi WFar
- from Korea **new**	EGol
- Goldbrook form	EGol
minor hort. f. ***alba***	see *H. sieboldii* var. *alba*
'Minor' (*ventricosa*)	see *H. minor*
'Minuteman' (*fortunei*) (v)	CBdn CBos CWin EBee EGle EPGN EPfP EVFa GBin IBal IPot LAst LPVe LRHS MBNS MIDC NGdn NMyG SApp WGor WTMC WTin WWol
'Moerheim' (*fortunei*) (v)	CBdn EGol EMic EPGN EPar GBin LRHS MBar MBri MIDC NHol SChu WHal WLin WTMC
N ***montana***	CBdn CHad ECha EGol EMic EPGN NHol
- B&SWJ 4796	WCru
- B&SWJ 5585	WCru
- 'Aureomarginata'	see *H.* 'Aureomarginata' (*montana*)
- f. ***macrophylla* new**	EGol
'Moon Glow' (v)	EGol EPGN
'Moon River' (v)	CBdn EGol EMic EPGN LRHS
'Moon Shadow' (v)	EGol
'Moon Waves' **new**	EGol
'Moonbeam'	CBdn WTMC
'Moonlight' (*fortunei*) (v)	CBdn EChP EGol EMic EPGN GMaP LRHS NABC NMyG SApp WBcn WRus
'Moonlight Sonata'	CBdn EGol
'Morning Light' **new**	CBdn CMGP EGol EPGN WRus
'Moscow Blue'	EGol LRHS

*	'Mount Hope' (v)	EGol
	'Mount Kirishima'	see H. 'Kirishima'
	(sieboldii)	
§	'Mount Royal' (sieboldii)	NHol
	'Mountain Snow'	CBdn CWin EBee EGol EMic
	(montana) (v)	EPGN LRHS SApp WTMC
	'Mountain Sunrise'	EGol
	(montana)	
	'Mr Big' **new**	WCot
	'Munchkin' (sieboldii)	CBdn
	'Myerscough Magic'	CBdn MSte NMyG
	'Naegato' **new**	SApp
	nakaiana	EBee EMic GCal NDlv
	'Nakaimo'	CBdn GBin NHol
	'Nameoki'	NHol SRPl
	'Nana' (ventricosa)	see H. minor
§	'Nancy Lindsay'	CBdn CTri EBee EGol EMic EPGN
	(fortunei) (v)	NGdn SApp SChu WTMC
	'Neat Splash' (v)	CBdn EChP NBir NHol
	'Neat Splash Rim' (v)	EPGN
	'New Wave'	EGol
	'New Zealand Nugget'	SApp
	'Nicola' (Tardiana Group)	EGol EMic EPGN MHom NMyG
		WRus
	'Night before	CBdn CFir COtt CWin EBee EGle
	Christmas' (v)	EGol EPGN GBin IBal IPot LAst
		MCLN MIDC MNrw NBro NGdn
		NHol SApp SHBN WRus WSan
		WTMC WWpP WWye
	nigrescens	CBdn CWin EBee EGol EPGN
		GCal MTed SApp
	'Nokogiryama'	EGol EMic
	'North Hills' (fortunei) (v)	CBdn EGol EMic LPio LRHS NBir
		NGdn SChu SMrm SPar
	'Northern Exposure'	CFir CWin EBee EGol EMic NGdn
	(sieboldiana) (v)	NMyG SApp
	'Northern Halo'	EChP EGol EMic
	(sieboldiana) (v)	
	'Northern Lights'	EGol
	(sieboldiana)	
	'Obscura Marginata'	see H. fortunei var.
	(fortunei)	aureomarginata
	'Obsession'	EGol
	'Okazuki Special'	CBdn EGol
	'Old Faithful'	EGol
	'Olga's Shiny Leaf'	EGol EMic
	'Olive Bailey Langdon'	CBdn
	(sieboldiana) (v)	
	'Olive Branch' (v)	EGol
	'Oriana' (fortunei)	EGol
	'Osprey' (Tardiana Group)	EGol LRHS
	'Oxheart'	EMic
	pachyscapa	EMic
	'Pacific Blue Edger'	CBdn CFir CM&M CWin EFou
		EGle EGol EMic EPGN LAst MBri
		WWye
	'Pandora's Box' (v)	CBdn EGol EMic IBal WCot
	'Paradigm' (v)	CBdn EGol EMic EPGN IBal
	'Paradise Joyce'	CBdn EBee EGol EMic EPGN
		MCLN MIDC WRus
	'Paradise Power'	CBdn EGol EMic
	'Paradise Puppet' (venusta)	CBdn EPGN
	'Paradise Red Delight'	CBdn
	(pycnophylla)	
	'Paradise Standard' (d)	CBdn
	'Pastures Green'	EGol
	'Pastures New'	EFou EGol EMic EPGN LPhx
		MHom NHol NMyG SApp
	'Patrician' (v)	EMic EPGN
	'Patriot' (v)	More than 30 suppliers
	'Paul's Glory' (v)	CBdn CWin EGle EGol EMic
		EPGN GBin IBal LAst LRHS MBri

		MCLN NGdn NMyG NPPs SApp
		SUsu SVil WRus WTMC WWye
§	'Paxton's Original'	CHar CMGP EGol EHrv EPGN
	(sieboldii) (v) ♀ H4	GKir MBar NLar SRms WBro WPer
	'Peace' (v)	CBdn EGol EMic EPGN
	'Pearl Lake'	CBdn EBee EGol EMic EPGN LPan
		LPhx LRHS MHom MWat NHol
		NMyG SApp SVil WTin
	'Peedee Gold Flash'	CBdn EPGN NHar
	'Pelham Blue Tump'	EGol EMic
	'Permanent Wave'	EGol
	'Perry's True Blue'	CBdn
	'Peter Pan'	CBdn EGol EMic
	'Phoenix'	EGol GBin SApp
	'Photo Finish' **new**	EGle EPGN
	'Phyllis Campbell'	see H. 'Sharmon'
	(fortunei)	
	'Picta' (fortunei)	see H. fortunei var. albopicta
	'Piecrust Power'	CBdn EGol
	'Piedmont Gold'	CBdn EGol EMic EOrc EPGN IBal
		LPhx MSte WTMC
	'Pilgrim' **new**	CBdn EGol EMic IBal
	'Pineapple Poll'	CBdn EMic EPGN MIDC NMyG
		WTin
	'Pineapple Upside	EPGN
	Down Cake' **new**	
	'Pizzazz' (v)	CBdn CWin EBee EGle EGol EMic
		EPGN IBal LAst MHom MIDC
		NGdn NHol NLar NMyG SApp
		WHil WTMC
	plantaginea	CBdn EGol EMic EOrc EPar LEdu
		LPhx MHom MIDC NMyG SSpi
		WCFE WCru
	- var. *grandiflora*	see H. plantaginea var. japonica
§	- var. *japonica* ♀ H4	CBos CBot CHad CLAP CStu ECha
		EHrv EMic EPGN EPar GBri
		MCAu SApp SChu SMHy
	'Platinum Tiara'	CBdn EMic EPGN IBal NBir
	(nakaiana) (v)	
	'Pooh Bear' (v)	CBdn EGol
	'Popo'	CBdn EGol
	'Potomac Pride'	CBdn EPGN LRHS
	'Pretty Flamingo' **new**	EMic
	'Puck'	EGol
	'Purple and Gold'	CBdn
	'Purple Dwarf'	CBdn EGol EMic GKir LRHS
		NGdn NHol NLar WCra
	'Purple Profusion'	EGol EMic
	pycnophylla	EGol SIgm
	'Queen Josephine' (v)	CBdn COtt CWin EBee EGol EMic
		EPGN EVFa IBal IPot LAst MBNS
		MBri MHom NGdn SApp WRus
		WTMC WWye
	'Queen of Islip'	CBdn
	(sieboldiana) (v)	
	'Quilting Bee'	EGol
	'Radiant Edger' (v)	CBdn CWin EBee EGol EMic
		EPGN LRHS NHol SApp
	'Raleigh Remembrance'	EGol
	'Rascal' (v)	CBdn EGol EMic LRHS
	'Raspberry Sorbet'	CBdn EGol EPGN LRHS
	rectifolia	NHol
	'Red Neck Heaven'	CBdn
	'Red October' **new**	CBdn
	'Regal Splendor' (v)	CBdn CWin EBee EGol EMic EPGN
		GSki LRHS MBri MHom NBro NDov
		NHol NMyG NPSI SDes SMrm SPla
		SVil WMnd WRus WWpP
	'Resonance' (v)	EPGN LRHS MBri NGdn WTMC
	'Reversed' (v)	CBdn CLAP CWin EBee EGol ELan
		EMic EPGN EPfP EWsh LRHS
		MDKP MIDC MSte NBro NDov
		NGdn NHol NMyG WRus WTMC

'Revolution' (v) **new**   CBdn CWin EBee EGle EGol IPot MBNS MBri MIDC WRus WWeb
'Rhapsody' (*fortunei*) (v)   EGol
'Richland Gold' (*fortunei*)   CBdn EBee EGol EMic EPGN LPhx
'Rippled Honey' **new**   EPGN IBal NMyG
'Rippling Waves'   EGol EMic
'Rising Sun'   EGol
'Robert Frost' (v)   CBdn EGol EMic
'Robusta' (*fortunei*)   see *H. sieboldiana* var. *elegans*
§ *rohdeifolia* (v)   CLAP EGol LBuc WHal
§ - f. *albopicta*   CBdn EGol ELan EPar NHol SChu
'Rosemoor'   CBdn EGol
'Rough Waters'   SApp
§ 'Royal Standard' ♀ H4   More than 30 suppliers
'Royalty'   EGol
rupifraga   EGol
§ 'Sagae' (v) ♀ H3-4   CBdn CHid CLAP CWin EBre EChP EGle EGol EMic EPGN EPfP EVFa IBal IPot LPan LRHS MBri MIDC MNrw MSte NGdn NMyG SApp SDes SMrm WFar WTMC
'Saint Elmo's Fire' (v)   CBdn EGol EMic IBal MCCP
§ 'Saishu Jima'   EPla NHol WCru
    (*sieboldii f. spathulata*)
'Salute'   CBdn EGol
'Samurai' (*sieboldiana*) (v)   CBdn CWin EBee EGol IBal IPot MRav NBro NGdn SApp
'Sarah Kennedy' (v)   EPGN
'Savannah'   EGol LRHS
'Sazanami' (*crispula*)   see *H. crispula*
'Scooter' (v)   CBdn EGol EMic EPGN NMyG
'Sea Bunny'   EGol
'Sea Dream' (v)   CBdn CWin EGol EMic EPGN WBcn
'Sea Drift'   EGol
'Sea Fire'   EGol LRHS
'Sea Gold Star'   CBdn EGol EPGN
'Sea Hero' **new**   EGol
'Sea Lotus Leaf'   CBdn EGol EMic EPGN NLar
'Sea Mist' (v)   CBdn
'Sea Monster'   EGol
'Sea Octopus'   EGol
'Sea Sapphire'   EGol LRHS
'Sea Sprite' (v)   EPGN LBuc LRHS
'Sea Thunder' (v)   CBdn EGol EMic EPGN
'Sea Yellow Sunrise'   CBdn EGol EMic IBal SApp
'Second Wind'   CBdn EMic EPGN LRHS NMyG
    (*fortunei*) (v)
'See Saw' (*undulata*)   EGol SApp WPnP
'Semperaurea'   GSki
    (*sieboldiana*)
'September Sun' (v)   CBdn EGol EPGN LRHS NMyG
'Serendipity'   CBdn EGol EMic EPGN MHom
'Shade Beauty' (v) **new**   EGol
'Shade Fanfare' (v) ♀ H4   CBdn EBre EGol ELan EMic ENot EOrc EPGN EPar EPfP GKir LRHS MBNS MBri MCAu MIDC MRav NBir NGdn NLar NMyG NSti SCro WFar WMnd
'Shade Master'   CBdn EBre EGol GKir LAst NHol SMer SVil
§ 'Sharmon' (*fortunei*) (v)   CBdn CWin EBee EGol EMic EPGN IPot LPVe MBNS NHol NMyG SApp SChu
'Sheila West'   CBdn
'Shelleys' (v)   EGol
'Sherborne Profusion'   CBdn EMic
    (Tardiana Group)
'Sherborne Swift'   CBdn EGol
    (Tardiana Group)
'Shining Tot'   CBdn EGol
'Shirley Vaughn' (v)   EGol

'Shogun' (v)   EGol
'Showboat' (v)   CBdn EGol EPGN
§ *sieboldiana*   CMHG CRow CSBt EBee EBot EFou EGol ELan EMic EPar EPfP LPVe MRav NChi NFor NHol SPer SPlb SRms WCru WFar WGwG WWpP
§ - var. *elegans* ♀ H4   More than 30 suppliers
§ *sieboldii* var. *alba*   CHad CMGP EGol SSpi
§ - var. *sieboldii*   CBdn CLAP EBre EGol EPGN
    f. *kabitan* (v)   MIDC NABC NHar SChu WGwG
- - f. *shiro-kabitan* (v)   EGol EMic EPGN
'Silver Bowl' **new**   EGol
'Silver Crown'   see *H.* 'Albomarginata'
'Silver Lance' (v)   CBdn EGol EMic EPGN
'Silvery Slugproof'   CBdn NMyG SApp
    (Tardiana Group)
'Sitting Pretty' (v)   EGol EPGN
'Slick Willie' **new**   EGol
'Slim Polly'   CBdn
'Snow Cap' (v)   CBdn CWin EGle EGol EMic EPGN IBal MIDC MUlv NABC NMyG SApp
'Snow Crust' (*elata*) (v)   CBdn EGol EMic LRHS
'Snow Flakes' (*sieboldii*)   CBdn CHEx EBee EGol EPGN EPfP GCal GKir LPio LRHS MBar MBri NBro NGdn NHol NMyG NPro SDes SPer WFar WGwG WTMC
'Snow White'   EGol
    (*undulata*) (v)
'Snowden'   CBdn CHad CMHG EBee EBre ECha EFou EGol EMic EOrc EPGN MBro NBir NGdn NHol NMyG NPar SCro SMrm SSpi WHoo WPnP WRus
'Snowstorm' (*sieboldii*)   CBdn NHol
'So Sweet'   CBdn CLAP CWin EBee EGol EHan EMic EMil EOrc EPGN GSki MBri MHom MIDC MSte NGdn NHol NMyG SApp SMrm WRus
'Solar Flare' **new**   EGol
'Something Blue'   CBdn
'Something Different'   EPGN
    (*fortunei*) (v)
'Sparkling Burgundy'   CBdn EGol
'Sparky' (v) **new**   EGol
'Special Gift'   CBdn EBee EGol EMic LBuc LRHS
'Spilt Milk' (*tokudama*) (v)   CBdn EGol EPGN
'Spinners'   EBre
§ 'Spinners' (*fortunei*) (v)   CBdn ECha EGol EMic SChu SSpi
'Spinning Wheel' (v) **new**   EGol
'Spritzer' (v)   CBdn EGol EMic EPGN WBcn
'Squash Casserole'   EGol
'Squash Edge'   EPGN
    (*sieboldiana*) (v)
'Squiggles' (v)   EGol
§ 'Starker Yellow Leaf'   EMic
'Stenantha' (*fortunei*)   EMic
'Stenantha Variegated'   NHol
    (*fortunei*) (v)
'Stetson' (v) **new**   EGol
'Stiletto' (v)   CBdn EBee EGol EMic EPGN IPot LAst MBNS MIDC NBro NGdn NHar NMyG NPro NSti
'Striptease' (*fortunei*) (v)   CBdn CWin EGol EMic EPGN GBin GKir LAst MBNS MCLN MIDC NGdn NHol NLar SApp SHBN SVil WRus WTMC
'Sugar and Cream' (v)   CM&M CRez CWin EBee EGol EMic EOrc EPGN GMac LAst LPio LRHS NGdn SApp SChu WTMC
'Sugar Plum Fairy'   EGol
    (*gracillima*)
'Sultana' (v)   EMic
'Sum and Substance' ♀ H4   More than 30 suppliers

'Summer Breeze' (v) **new**	EGol
'Summer Fragrance'	CBdn EGol EMic EPGN LRHS
'Summer Joy' (v)	CBdn
'Summer Music' (v)	CBdn CWin EBee EGle EGol EMic
	EPGN LAst MBri SApp WRus
'Summer Serenade' (v)	CBdn EGol EMic
'Summer Snow'	EPGN
(sieboldiana) (v)	
'Sun Glow'	EGol
'Sun Power'	CBdn CPen CWin EBee EBre EGol
	EMic EOrc EPGN EPar LRHS MCLN
	NBro NLar NMyG NSti WRus
'Sundance' (fortunei) (v)	EGol
* 'Sunflower'	NOak
'Super Bowl'	EGol
'Super Nova' (v)	CBdn EGol EMic EPGN IBal LRHS
'Sweet Bo Beep'	EGol
'Sweet Home	EGol
Chicago' (v) **new**	
'Sweet Marjorie'	EGol
'Sweet Susan'	EGol EMic EOrc LRHS MBNS
	SApp SPer WWpP
'Sweet Tater Pie'	CBdn EGol EPGN
'Sweetheart'	EMic
'Sweetie' (v)	CBdn EGol EMic IBal LRHS
'Swirling Hearts'	EGol LRHS
'Tall Boy'	CBdn CSev EBee ECha EGol EPla
	GCal MWgw NBir SSpi
'Tamborine' (v)	CBdn EGol EPGN LRHS SApp
Tardiana Group	CBdn CBro CMGP EGol ELan
	MCAu MHom NGdn NHol SPer
tardiflora	CBdn CBos CFil EGol ERos SApp
	WCot WPGP
tardiva	CBdn EBre LRHS
'Tattoo' **new**	CBdn EGol EHan EPGN
'Tea and Crumpets' (v)	CBdn EPGN
'Temple Bells'	EGol LRHS
'Tenryu'	EGol EPGN
'The Twister'	EGol EMic
'Thomas Hogg'	see H. undulata var. albomarginata
'Thumb Nail'	CBdn ECha EGol GSki
'Thunderbolt'	EPGN MBNS
(sieboldiana) **new**	
tibae	CBdn
'Tiny Tears' (venusta)	CBdn EGol LRHS
tokudama	EGol EPGN LRHS MHom NABC
	NBir NGdn NHol NSti SChu SDes
§ - f. *aureonebulosa*	CBdn CWin EGol EMic EPGN IPot
	LPhx LRHS MSte NGdn NMyG
	NSti WMnd
- f. *flavocircinalis* (v)	CBdn CWin EBee EBlw EGol EMic
	EPGN LRHS NBro SApp SSpe
	WFar WHoo WMnd WWye
'Torchlight' (v)	CBdn EGol EMic LRHS
'Tot Tot'	EGol
'Touchstone' (v)	CBdn MBri NMyG SApp
'Trail's End'	EMic
'True Blue'	CBdn CWin EBee EGol EMic LAst
	SApp
'Tutu'	EGol MIDC
'Twilight' (fortunei) (v)	CBdn CWin EBee EGol EMic
	EPGN EVFa MBNS MBri SApp
	SPar WRHF WRus WWol
'Twinkle Toes'	EGol
'Twist of Lime' (v)	CBdn EGol
'Ultraviolet Light'	EGol
undulata	CHar MIDC NLon WBrE WFar
	WWpP
§ - var. *albomarginata*	More than 30 suppliers
§ - var. *erromena* ♀ H4	CBdn CMGP EHon EMic EPfP IBal
	LPBA MBro MWgw NBid NFla
	NHol SPer WWpP
§ - var. *undulata* (v) ♀ H4	CBdn CBot CBro CRow EHoe

	EHon EHrv ELan ENot EPGN EPfP
	LAst LGro LPBA LPVe MRav MTis
	NBlu NMyG NVic SChu SPar SPer
	WEas WFar WKif WRus WWeb
	WWin WWpP
- var. *univittata* (v) ♀ H4	CBro CRow ECha EGol EPGN
	EPfP NBir NPro SDes SPla WFar
	WKif WMoo
'Urajiro Hachijo'	EGol
'Urajiro (hypoleuca)	EGol
'Valentine Lace'	CBdn EGol EMic LRHS
'Van Wade' (v)	CBdn EGol EPGN
'Vanilla Cream'	EGol EPGN LRHS
(cathayana)	
'Variegata' (gracillima)	see H. 'Vera Verde'
'Variegata' (tokudama)	see H. tokudama f.
	aureonebulosa
'Variegata' (undulata)	see H. undulata var. undulata
'Variegata' (ventricosa)	see H. 'Aureomarginata'
	(ventricosa)
'Variegated' (fluctuans)	see H. 'Sagae'
ventricosa ♀ H4	CBcs CBdn CBro CHid EBre EGol
	EGoo EMic EPfP GDra GMaP
	LPBA MHer MNrw MRav NHol
	WCFE WFar WWye
- var. *aureomaculata*	CBdn EBee EGol EPGN NBir NSti
- 'Aureomarginata'	see H. 'Aureomarginata'
	(ventricosa)
I 'Venucosa'	EGol EMic WFar
'Venus Star'	EPGN GSki
venusta ♀ H4	More than 30 suppliers
- B&SWJ 4389	WCru
- dwarf	CSWP LPhx
- *yakusimensis*	see H. kikutii var. yakusimensis
§ 'Vera Verde' (v)	CBdn EBee EPGN ERos GQui
	MHom NBir NMyG
'Verna Jean' (v)	CBdn EGol
'Veronica Lake' (v)	CBdn EGol EMic LRHS
'Vilmoriniana'	EGol EMic
'Viridis Marginata'	see H. sieboldii var. sieboldii f.
	kabitan
'Wagtail' (Tardiana Group)	CBdn EMic
'Wahoo' (tokudama) (v)	EGol
'Warwick Choice' (v)	CBdn
'Warwick Curtsey' (v)	EGol
'Warwick Delight' (v)	EGol
'Warwick Edge' (v)	CBdn EGol
'Warwick Essence'	EGol EMic
'Waving Winds' (v)	EGol
'Waving Wuffles'	EMic
'Wayside Blue'	EMic
'Wayside Perfection'	see H. 'Royal Standard'
'Weihenstephan'	EGol EMic
(sieboldii)	
'Weser' **new**	EGol
'Wheaton Blue'	CBdn EMic LRHS
'Whirlwind' (fortunei) (v)	CBdn CCol CRez CWin EBee
	EGol EOrc EPGN GBin IBal IPot
	MBri MCLN MIDC MNrw NBro
	NGdn NMyG SApp SVil WAul
	WMnd WRus WTMC WWye
'Whirlwind Tour' (v)	EGol
'White Christmas'	CBdn EBee
(fortunei) (v)	
'White Christmas'	EGle EGol EPGN LRHS WRus
(undulata) (v)	
'White Fairy'	CBdn EBee EPGN IBal NMyG
(plantaginea) (d)	
'White Feather' (undulata)	CBdn
'White Gold'	CBdn EGol EPGN
'White Tacchi'	EMon
'White Triumphator'	CBdn EGol MBri
(rectifolia)	

'Wide Brim' (v) ♀ H4 — More than 30 suppliers
'Wind River Gold' — EGol
'Windsor Gold' — see *H.* 'Nancy Lindsay'
'Winfield Blue' — EGol LRHS
'Winfield Gold' — CBdn EGol
'Wogon Giboshi' — see *H.* 'Wogon' (*sieboldii*)
§ 'Wogon' (*sieboldii*) — CBdn CM&M CRDP CRow EPGN GMaP MAvo NDlv NHar NHol NMen NSti
'Wogon's Boy' — CBdn EGol EPGN
'Wolverine' (v) — EGol WCot
'Wrinkles and Crinkles' — EGol EPGN
'Yakushima-mizu' (*gracillima*) — CBdn EGol
* **yakushimana** — GCrs NHar
'Yellow Boa' — EGol
'Yellow Edge' (*fortunei*) — see *H. fortunei* var. *aureomarginata*
'Yellow Edge' (*sieboldiana*) — see *H.* 'Frances Williams'
'Yellow River' (*montana*) (v) — CBdn EGol EMic EPGN LRHS MBri NGdn NMyG
'Yellow Splash' (v) — CBdn EBee ECha EPGN LRHS MBNS MHom NMyG SChu
'Yellow Splash Rim' (v) — EGol MBri WBcn
'Yellow Splashed Edged' (v) — EMic
'Yellow Waves' — CBdn
yingeri — EGol
– B&SWJ 546 — WCru
'Zager Blue' — EMic
'Zager Green' — EMic
'Zager White Edge' (*fortunei*) (v) — CLAP EGol EMic EPGN NMyG
'Zounds' — More than 30 suppliers

Hottonia (Primulaceae)
palustris — CBen ECoo EHon ELan EMFW LPBA MSta NVic SBHF SWat WWpP

Houstonia (Rubiaceae)
caerulea hort. — see *H. michauxii*
caerulea L. — ECho NLAp SIng WWin
– var. **alba** — IHMH WPer
michauxii 'Fred Mullard' — EWes

Houttuynia (Saururaceae)
cordata — CAgr EWTr GBar IBlr SWat WBrE WFar
§ – 'Boo-Boo' (v) — EChP EMan EPfP EPla LHop MCLN
§ – 'Chameleon' (v) — More than 30 suppliers
– 'Flame' (v) — LRHS
– 'Flore Pleno' (d) — CBen CRow EChP ECha EHon ELan EPfP EPla GBar LPBA MCCP MRav MSta MWgw NBir NBlu NBro NPer SGar SIde SLon SPer SRms SWat WFar WPnP WWin WWpP
– 'Joker's Gold' — EBee EMan EPPr EPfP EVFa LBuc MBNS NBro
* – 'Pied Piper' — CDoC ENot LRHS SAga
– 'Tequila Sunrise' — CHEx
– 'Terry Clarke' (v) — see *H. cordata* 'Boo-Boo'
– 'Tricolor' — see *H. cordata* 'Chameleon'
– Variegata Group (v) — EBla EPot GBar IBlr LPBA NBro SIng WWpP

Hovenia (Rhamnaceae)
acerba — CFil WPGP
dulcis — CAgr CBcs CMCN CPle EPfP IArd LEdu MBlu SDes
tomentella — CPLG

Howea (Arecaceae)
§ **belmoreana** ♀ H1 — LPal
forsteriana ♀ H1 — EPVP LPal LRHS MBri

Hoya (Asclepiadaceae)
§ **australis** — LRHS SOWG
bella — see *H. lanceolata* subsp. *bella*
carnosa ♀ H1 — CBcs CPIN CRHN EBak ELan EOHP ESlt GQui LRHS MGol SRms
– 'Compacta' — CHal
* – **compacta** 'Hindu Rope' — NPer
* – 'Krinkle' — NPer
– 'Red Princess' — MBri
– 'Rubra' — SYvo
– 'Tricolor' — NPer
– 'Variegata' (v) — MBri SMur
cinnamomifolia — SOWG
* **compacta** 'Tricolor' — NPer
darwinii hort. — see *H. australis*
lacunosa — LRHS
§ **lanceolata** subsp. **bella** ♀ H1 — CHal GQui SRms
linearis — SOWG
multiflora — SOWG

Humata (Davalliaceae)
pyxidata — see *Davallia solida* var. *pyxidata*
tyermannii — NMar

Humea (Asteraceae)
elegans — see *Calomeria amaranthoides*

Humulus (Cannabaceae)
japonicus — ECoo MSal
lupulus — CArn CBcs CPIN ECoo ELau EPfP GBar GPoy ILis MHer MSal SIde WDin WHer WSel WStl WWye
– 'Aureus' ♀ H4 — More than 30 suppliers
– 'Aureus' (f) ♀ H4 — CFwr CRHN GBar MAnH MCCP MPRe SMad SPla WCot
– 'Aureus' (m) ♀ H4 — MCCP
* – **compactus** — GPoy
– 'Fuggle' — CAgr GPoy SDea
– (Goldings Group) 'Cobbs' — SDea
– – 'Mathons' — CAgr SDea
– 'Hallertauer' — SDea
– 'Hip-hop' — EMon EWes
– 'Prima Donna' **new** — CBct CFwr GBin SPoG
– 'Taff's Variegated' (v) — EMon EVFa EWes WBcn WHil
– 'Wye Challenger' — CAgr GPoy
– 'Wye Northdown' — CAgr SDea

Hutchinsia see Pritzelago

Hyacinthella (Hyacinthaceae)
millingenii — EHyt

Hyacinthoides (Hyacinthaceae)
§ **hispanica** — CBro CHid CMea EPot ETub IBlr MBri NBir NCel WFar WWye
– 'Alba' — CMea EPot
– 'Excelsior' — LRHS
– 'La Grandesse' — CBro
– 'Rosabella' — CBro
– 'Rose' — CMea EPot NCat
– 'Rosea' — CPom
– white — ETub
§ **italica** — WShi
§ **non-scripta** — CArn CAvo CBro CKin EPar EPot ETub IBlr LAma LRHS MBow MHer NCel NMir NRog SHFr WHer WShi
– pink — WShi
§ **vicentina** — ERos

Hyacinthus ✿ (*Hyacinthaceae*)

amethystinus	see *Brimeura amethystina*
azureus	see *Muscari azureum*
comosus 'Plumosus'	see *Muscari comosum* 'Plumosum'
fastigiatus	see *Brimeura fastigiata*
multiflowered blue	ETub
multiflowered pink	ETub
multiflowered white	ETub
'Nereus' **new**	ETub
orientalis 'Amethyst'	LAma NRog
- 'Amsterdam'	LAma NRog
- 'Anna Liza'	NRog
- 'Anna Marie' ♀ H4	CAvo CBro ETub LAma MBri NRog
- 'Ben Nevis' (d)	LAma MBri NRog
- 'Bismarck'	LAma NRog
- 'Blue Giant'	LAma NRog
- 'Blue Jacket' ♀ H4	CBro ETub LAma NRog
- 'Blue Magic'	LAma NRog
- 'Blue Orchid' (d)	LAma
- 'Blue Star'	LAma
- 'Borah' ♀ H4	LAma NRog
- 'Carnegie'	CAvo CBro ETub LAma NRog
- 'City of Haarlem' ♀ H4	CBro ETub LAma NRog
- 'Colosseum'	LAma
- 'Delft Blue' ♀ H4	CAvo CBro ETub LAma MBri NRog
- 'Fondant'	LAma
- 'Gipsy Queen' ♀ H4	ETub LAma MBri NRog
- 'Hollyhock' (d)	LAma MBri NRog WHil
- 'Jan Bos'	ETub LAma NRog
- 'King Codro' (d)	LAma MBri NRog
- 'King of the Blues'	LAma NRog
- 'La Victoire'	LAma NRog
- 'Lady Derby'	CBro LAma
- 'L'Innocence' ♀ H4	CBro LAma NRog
- 'Lord Balfour'	LAma
- 'Marconi' (d)	LAma NRog
- 'Marie'	LAma NRog
- 'Mulberry Rose'	LAma NRog
- 'Myosotis'	LAma
§ - 'Oranje Boven'	LAma
- 'Ostara' ♀ H4	CBro LAma MBri NRog
- 'Peter Stuyvesant'	ETub LAma NRog
- 'Pink Pearl' ♀ H4	CBro LAma NRog
- 'Pink Royal' (d)	LAma NRog
- 'Princess Margaret'	LAma
- 'Queen of the Pinks'	LAma NRog
- 'Queen of the Violets'	NRog
- 'Rosette' (d)	LAma
- 'Salmonetta'	see *H. orientalis* 'Oranje Boven'
§ - 'Sneeuwwitje'	LAma NRog
- Snow White	see *H. orientalis* 'Sneeuwwitje'
- 'Violet Pearl'	CBro LAma NRog
- 'Vuurbaak'	LAma
- 'White Pearl'	CAvo LAma NRog
* 'Woodstock'	ETub LAma MBri

Hydrangea ✿ (*Hydrangeaceae*)

angustipetala	CFil CSam
- B&SWJ 3454	WCru
- B&SWJ 3814	WCru
- B&SWJ 6038 from Yakushima	WCru
* - f. **macrosepala** B&SWJ 3476	WCru
anomala	SSpi WBcn
subsp. **anomala**	
- - B&SWJ 2411	WCru
- subsp. **glabra** B&SWJ 3117 **new**	WCru
§ - subsp. **petiolaris** ♀ H4	More than 30 suppliers
- - B&SWJ 6337	WCru
- - from Yakushima B&SWJ 6081 **new**	WCru
§ - - var. **cordifolia**	CFil EPla MBNS
- - dwarf	see *H. anomala* subsp. *petiolaris* var. *cordifolia*
- - **tiliifolia**	EBee EPfP GCal SNut WFar WSHC
- - 'Yakushima'	CFil WCru WPGP
§ **arborescens**	CArn CFil MRav WFar WPGP
- 'Annabelle' ♀ H4	More than 30 suppliers
§ - subsp. **discolor**	WCru WPat
- - 'Sterilis'	CFil SSpi WCru WPGP
- 'Grandiflora' ♀ H4	CBcs CBot CFil EFpt EPfP EWTr MRav SPar SPer WBod WCru WDin WHCG WSHC WWin
- subsp. **radiata**	CAbP CFil CMil GEil GIBF LRHS MAsh NHlc SSpi WBcn WCru WFar WPGP
aspera	CFil GKir SLon SSpi SSta WCru WKif
- 'Anthony Bullivant'	SSpi
- Kawakamii Group	CFil CMil CSpe EPla NLar SSpi WCru WPGP
- - B&SWJ 1420	WCru
- - B&SWJ 3462	WCru
§ - 'Macrophylla' ♀ H3	CFil CMil EFpt EPfP LRHS MBri NBee NBlu NPal SPer SSpi WCru WGer WPGP
- 'Mauvette'	CBcs CFil CMil MBlu NPal SPer SSpi SSta WBcn WCru WGer WPGP
- 'Peter Chappell'	NLar SSpi
§ - subsp. **robusta**	CFil SNut WCru WPGP
- 'Rocklon'	CFil CMil NLar WCru WPGP
- 'Rosthornii'	see *H. aspera* subsp. *robusta*
- 'Sam MacDonald'	CFil CHad LRHS NLar SSpi WPGP
§ - subsp. **sargentiana** ♀ H3	More than 30 suppliers
- - large leaved	WGor WPGP
- 'Spinners'	SSpi
- subsp. **strigosa**	CFil CMil EPfP WCru WPGP
- 'Taiwan'	LRHS SSpi
- 'Taiwan Pink'	EPfP NLar
§ - Villosa Group ♀ H3	More than 30 suppliers
- 'Brilliant'	NHlc
cinerea	see *H. arborescens* subsp. *discolor*
glandulosa B&SWJ 4031 **new**	WCru
- 'Hallasan' (H) **new**	CBcs
§ **heteromalla**	CFai CFil CMHG CTrG EPfP SSpi WPGP
- DJHC 493	WCru
- HWJCM 180	WCru
- SF 338	ISea
- B&SWJ 2602 from Sikkim	WCru
- Bretschneideri Group	EPfP GQui MBlu NHlc WBod WCru WFar
- 'Morrey's Form'	WCru
- 'Snowcap'	GQui IArd WBcn WCru
- f. **xanthoneura**	CFil SSpi
- - 'Wilsonii'	WCru WKif WSHC
- 'Yalung Ridge'	NHlc WCru
* **heterophylla**	MGos
hirta	CFil
- B&SWJ 5000	WCru
'Hobergine'PBR **new**	CBcs
indochinensis B&SWJ 8307 **new**	WCru
integerrima	see *H. serratifolia*
integrifolia	CFil CPlN GGGa
- B&SWJ 022	WCru
involucrata	CFil CPLG EPfP GEil LRHS NHlc SBrw SSpi SSta WBcn WCru WDin
- dwarf	CFil GEil WCru
- 'Hortensis' (d) ♀ H3-4	CElw CFil CMil CPle EFpt EPfP MRav SBrw SPer SSpi SSta

		WAbe WBod WCru WKif WPGP WSHC
*	- 'Plena' (d)	WCot WCru
*	- 'Sterilis'	EPfP SSpi
	- 'Viridescens' **new**	SSpi
	'Korale Red'	WBcn
	lobbii B&SWJ 3214	WCru
	longipes	CFil CMil WCru WPGP
	'Love You Kiss' (L)	see *H. serrata* 'Kiyosumi'
	luteovenosa	CFil WCru
	- B&SWJ 5602	WCru
*	*macrocephala* **new**	SSpi
	macrophylla	LRHS
	- Alpen Glow	see *H. macrophylla* 'Alpenglühen'
§	- 'Alpenglühen' (H)	CBcs CFil CSBt ELan NHlc SHBN SRms WPGP
	- 'Altona' (H) ♀ H3-4	CBcs CFil CSBt CWSG EFpt IArd ISea LRHS MGos MRav NHlc NPri SBod SPer WLRN WPGP WStI
	- 'Amethyst' (H/d)	CFil WPGP
	- 'Ami Pasquier' (H) ♀ H3-4	CBcs CDoC CFil CMac EBee EFpt EPfP GKir LRHS MRav NHlc SCoo SGar SLim SPla SSpi WBcn WGer WPGP WWeb
*	- 'Aureomarginata' (v)	EPfP EVFa
	- 'Aureovariegata' (v)	CFil ELan LRHS SNut SPar WBcn WPGP
	- 'Ayesha' (H)	More than 30 suppliers
	- 'Ayesha Blue' (H)	ENot MAsh
	- 'Beauté Vendômoise' (L)	CFil CMil SSpi WPGP
	- 'Benelux' (H)	CBcs CWSG WGwG
*	- 'Bicolour'	MAsh
§	- 'Blauer Prinz' (H)	CFil CSBt LRHS SHBN WLRN
§	- 'Blauling' (L)	CDoC
§	- 'Blaumeise' (L)	CFil MAsh MRav NHlc SSpi WBod WGer WPGP
	- 'Blue Bonnet' (H)	CFil COtt CSBt EPfP IBal MAsh SPer WHen WLRN WPGP
	- Blue Butterfly	see *H. macrophylla* 'Blauling'
	- Blue Prince	see *H. macrophylla* 'Blauer Prinz'
	- Blue Sky	see *H. macrophylla* 'Blaumeise'
	- Blue Tit	see *H. macrophylla* 'Blaumeise'
	- 'Blue Wave'	see *H. macrophylla* 'Mariesii Perfecta'
	- 'Bluebird' misapplied	see *H. serrata* 'Bluebird'
	- 'Bodensee' (H)	CBcs ENot GKir LRHS SBod SPla WStI
	- 'Bouquet Rose' (H)	CWib ECtt MRav NBlu WBod
	- 'Bridal Bouquet' (H)	CDoC
	- 'Brunette' (H)	CFil CMil
	- 'Buchfink' (L)	CFil SSpi WPGP
	- 'Chaperon Rouge' **new**	EFpt
	- 'Cordata'	see *H. arborescens*
	- 'Deutschland' (H)	CTri
	- 'Domotoi' (H/d)	CFai CFil SNut
	- Dragonfly	see *H. macrophylla* 'Libelle'
*	- 'Dwaag Pink'	MRav
	- 'Eldorado' (H)	EHol
§	- 'Enziandom' (H)	CBcs CFil CSBt SSpi WPGP
	- 'Europa' (H) ♀ H3-4	CBcs CMac CTrw CWSG EFpt GKir LRHS MAsh MGos NPri SBod SEND WStI WWal
§	- 'Fasan' (L)	CFil NHlc WPGP
	- Firelight	see *H. macrophylla* 'Leuchtfeuer'
	- Fireworks	see *H. macrophylla* 'Hanabi'
	- 'Fireworks Blue' (L) **new**	CBcs
	- 'Fireworks Pink' (L)	CBcs
	- 'Fischers Silberblau' (H)	CFil
	- 'Forever Pink'	EBre WGer
§	- 'Frau Katsuko'	LRHS
	- 'Frillibet' (H)	CAbP CDoC CFil EPfP LRHS NHlc WPGP
	- 'Gartenbaudirektor Kuhnert' (H)	SMer
§	- 'Générale Vicomtesse de Vibraye' (H) ♀ H3-4	CBcs CDoC CEnd CFil CMHG CTri CWSG EBee EFpt EPfP GKir LRHS MBar MBri NHlc SHBN SLim SNut SPer SSpi WBVN WLRN WPGP WWin
	- Gentian Dome	see *H. macrophylla* 'Enziandom'
	- 'Geoffrey Chadbund'	see *H. macrophylla* 'Möwe'
	- 'Gerda Steiniger'	CBcs
	- 'Gertrud Glahn' (H)	CBcs
	- 'Glowing Embers'	CFil IArd MBri SEND WPGP
	- 'Gold Dust' (v)	CFil EPla WPGP
	- 'Goliath' (H)	CFil EPfP LRHS WPGP
	- 'Hamburg' (H)	CEnd CFil CTri CWSG EBee ECtt ENot EPfP LPVe LPan LRHS MGos MRav NBlu SDix WBrE WFar WStI WWeb
	- 'Hanabi' (L/d)	CBcs CFee CMil MBlu WBcn WWeb
	- 'Harlequin'	CFil CMil WPGP
	- 'Harry's Pink Topper' (H)	MAsh
	- 'Hatfield Rose' (H)	CBcs
	- 'Heinrich Seidel' (H)	CBcs CFil NHlc WBrE WPGP
	- 'Holstein' (H)	CFil MAsh WPGP
§	- 'Hörnli' (H)	CFil LPan WPGP
	- 'Intermezzo'	NHlc
	- 'Izu-no-hana' (L/d)	CBcs CFil CMil MBlu
	- 'Jogosaki' (L/d)	MBlu WPGP
§	- 'Joseph Banks' (H)	CBcs
	- 'Kardinal' (L)	CFil WPGP
	- 'King George' (H)	CBcs CDoC CFil CSBt CWSG EBee EBre GEil GKir LAst LRHS MBar MGos MRav MWat SLim SPer SRPl WFar WMoo WPGP WStI WWal
	- 'Kluis Superba' (H)	CBcs CFil CTri MRav NHlc WPGP
§	- 'Koningin Wilhelmina' (H)	CFil WBcn WPGP WTel
	- 'Kuro-hime' (L) **new**	CBcs
	- 'La France' (H)	CBcs COtt CTri CWSG LRHS MBar MRav SMer SRPl WFar
	- 'Lady Fujiyo' (H)	CPLG LRHS
	- Lady Katsuko (H)	see *H. macrophylla* 'Frau Katsuko'
	- 'Lady Mariko' (H)	LRHS SPer
	- 'Lady Nobuko' (H)	LRHS SPer
	- 'Lady Taiko Blue' (H)	LRHS SPer
	- 'Lady Taiko Pink' (H)	LRHS
	- 'Lanarth White' (L) ♀ H3-4	CBcs CDoC CFil CTbh CTri EBee EFpt EPfP MRav NHlc SHBN SLim SPer SReu SRms SSpi WBod WCru WPGP WPnP WWeb
	- lavender blue **new**	EFpt
	- 'Leuchtfeuer' (H)	ENot LRHS MBri WBcn WGer WWeb
	- 'Libelle' (L)	CBcs CDoC CFil EBee EFpt EPfP EVFa MAsh NHlc SLim SNut SPar SPer SPoG WKif WPGP WWeb
	- 'Lilacina'	see *H. macrophylla* 'Mariesii Lilacina'
§	- 'Maculata' (L)	CSBt EHol ELan GEil GQui SGar WGwG
	- 'Madame A. Riverain' (H)	CFil CPLG CWSG LRHS SBod WBcn WLRN
§	- 'Madame Emile Mouillère' (H) ♀ H3-4	More than 30 suppliers
	- 'Maréchal Foch' (H)	CFil CTri WPGP
	- 'Mariesii' (L)	CFil CMHG CSBt CTri CWib EBee ELan ENot EPla ISea LHop LRHS NBee NHlc SDix SPer WGwG WKif WLRN WPnP WStI
§	- 'Mariesii Grandiflora' (L) ♀ H3-4	CFil EBee ENot EPfP LRHS MBar NBlu NPri SBod SEND SHBN SNut

		SRms SSpi WBod WDin WFar WLRN WPGP WStI
§	- 'Mariesii Lilacina' (L) ♀ H3-4	CFil EPfP MWhi NHlc SPer SSpi WKif WPGP
§	- 'Mariesii Perfecta' (L) ♀ H3-4	More than 30 suppliers
	- 'Masja' (H)	CBcs COtt EGra IArd LRHS MGos NBee NBlu SHBN
	- 'Mathilda Gutges' (H)	CDoC CFil SSpi WPGP WStI
	- 'Merveille Sanguine' (H)	IArd WPGP
	- 'Messalinde' **new**	MBri
	- 'Mini Hörnli'	see H. macrophylla 'Hörnli'
	- 'Miss Belgium' (H)	CFil CTri NHlc
	- 'Miss Hepburn'	CSBt NHlc SPer
	- 'Mousmée'	CFil IArd
	- 'Mousseline' (H)	LPan
§	- 'Möwe' (L) ♀ H3-4	CBcs CDoC CEnd CFil CPLG EBee ECtt ENot LHop MBri NPri SChu SCoo SDix SGar SNut SPer SRms SSpi SSta WPGP WWeb
	- 'Nachtigall' (L) **new**	SNut SSpi
	- 'Niedersachsen' (H)	CDoC CFil MRav NHlc SMer WPGP
	- Nightingale	see H. macrophylla 'Nachtigall'
	- 'Nigra' (H) ♀ H3-4	CBcs CChe CFil CMil CPLG CWib EBee EFpt ELan EPfP EPla MGos SDix SHBN SNut SPer WCru WFar WGwG WPGP WStI WWal
	- 'Nikko Blue' (H)	CBcs CFil CWSG EBee EPfP MBar NBlu SEND WBod WPGP
§	- 'Nymphe' (H)	ENot LRHS
	- 'Oamacha'	NHlc
	- 'Otaksa' (H)	CFil NHlc
	- 'Parzifal' (H) ♀ H3-4	CBcs CFil CTrw EFpt EPfP NHlc WBod WLRN WPGP WWal
	- 'Pax'	see H. macrophylla 'Nymphe'
	- 'Pfau' (L) **new**	SSpi
	- Pheasant	see H. macrophylla 'Fasan'
	- 'Pia' (H)	CBcs CDoC CFil CPLG CPla EBee EHyt ELan GKir IArd MAsh MBNS MRav MTho NWCA SBod SLim SMad SPer SPla SPoG SRms WAbe WCru WFar WPGP WPat WPnP
	- Pigeon	see H. macrophylla 'Taube'
	- 'Prinses Beatrix'	CBcs CChe CFil WPGP
	- 'Quadricolor' (L/v)	CAbb CFil CMil CTbh EBee EHoe EPfP LRHS MBri MRav SDix SGar SHBN SLim SNut SPer SPla SPlb SRPl SRms WCot WCru WHCG WPGP WSHC WWeb
	- Queen Wilhelmina	see H. macrophylla 'Koningin Wilhelmina'
	- 'R.F. Felton'	CBcs
	- 'Ramis Pietis' (H) **new**	CBcs
	- 'Red Baron'	ENot MBri
	- Redbreast	see H. macrophylla 'Rotkehlchen'
	- 'Regula' (H)	CTrw
	- 'Renate Steiniger' (H)	CFai ENot MPWC WBcn WBod WGwG WWeb
	- 'Rosita' (H)	ENot LPan LRHS MAsh
§	- 'Rotkehlchen' (L)	CFai CFil WGer WPGP
	- 'Rotschwanz' (L)	CFil CMil NHlc SSpi
	- 'Saint Claire'	CBcs CPLG
	- 'Sanguinea' **new**	EFpt NPPs
	- 'Schwabenland'	NPri
	- 'Sea Foam' (L)	EBee NBlu WBan WCot
*	- 'Shower'	LRHS MBri
	- 'Shower Pink' **new**	EFpt
	- 'Sibylla' (H)	CBcs CFil NHlc WPGP
	- Sister Therese	see H. macrophylla 'Soeur Thérèse'
	- 'Snow' **new**	MBri
§	- 'Soeur Thérèse' (H)	CBcs CFil CSBt ENot LPan LRHS MAsh MBri MGos WGwG WPGP WStI
§	- 'Taube' (L)	CBcs CFil CPLG GQui NBlu
N	- Teller Blau (L)	CDoC COtt EBee ENot EPfP NHlc NSti SCoo SLim SPoG WDin WWeb
N	- Teller Rosa (L)	CDoC EBee ENot EPfP MAsh SCoo WWeb
N	- Teller Rot (L)	CDoC EBee ENot MAsh SCoo SPlb WDin WWeb
N	- Teller Variegated	see H. macrophylla 'Tricolor'
N	- Teller Weiss	see H. macrophylla 'Libelle'
	- 'Tokyo Delight' (L) ♀ H3-4	CBrd CChe CDoC CEnd CFil CPLG EBee SSpi WBcn WPGP
	- 'Tovelit'	IArd LRHS
	- 'Tricolor' (L/v)	CBcs CBot CDoC CFil LAst LRHS MAsh MGos MTis NBee SBod SLon SPer WFar WKif WMoo WPGP WPnP WWal
	- 'Val de Loire'	CWSG
	- 'Variegata'	see H. macrophylla 'Maculata'
	- 'Veitchii' (L) ♀ H3-4	CBcs CBot CFil CMHG CMil CPLG CSBt EFpt ENot EPfP MBri MRav SBod SDix SGar SPer SSpi WPGP
	- 'Vicomte de Vibraye'	see H. macrophylla 'Générale Vicomtesse de Vibraye'
	- 'Vulcain'	EVFa
	- 'Westfalen' (H) ♀ H3-4	IArd LRHS SDix SPla WLRN WWal
	- 'White Lace' (L)	ELan
	- 'White Wave'	see H. macrophylla 'Mariesii Grandiflora'
	'Midori' (H) **new**	CBcs
	paniculata	CFil CMCN CPne CTrw GIBF GKir LAst
	- B&SWJ 3556 from Taiwan	WCru
	- B&SWJ 5413 from Japan	WCru
	- 'Brussels Lace'	CABP CFil LRHS MAsh SNut SSpi
	- 'Burgundy Lace'	CBcs CMil MBlu
	- 'Everest'	CABP LRHS SNut
	- 'Floribunda'	CFil EPfP EWTr LRHS SPer SSpi WPGP
	- 'Grandiflora' ♀ H4	More than 30 suppliers
	- 'Greenspire'	CBcs LBuc LRHS MBlu WDcn
	- 'Kyushu' ♀ H4	More than 30 suppliers
	- 'Limelight'PBR **new**	CBcs
	- 'Phantom' **new**	WPat
	- Pink Diamond = 'Interhydia' ♀ H4	CABP CDoC CMCN CTbh CTri EBee EBre ENot LAst LRHS MAsh MBlu MBri NPri SLim SMad SSpi SSta WBod WCru
	- 'Pink Jewel' **new**	CWib
	- 'Praecox'	SLon SPer WCru WWin
	- 'Tardiva'	CBcs CBot CDoC LPan LRHS MGos MRav NHol SBrw SDix SPer SRms WBan WFar WHCG WPGP WPat WWeb
	- 'Unique' ♀ H4	CBcs CDoC CFil CHad CMil EBee EFpt ENot EPfP LRHS MAsh MBri NBee SNut SPer SPla SSpi WBan WBod WCru WDin WFar WPGP WPat
	- 'White Lace'	CBcs MBlu WWes
	- 'White Moth'	CBcs CFil SNut
	peruviana x **serratifolia**	SSpi
	petiolaris	see H. anomala subsp. petiolaris
	'Pink Showers'	NHlc
§	'Preziosa' ♀ H3-4	More than 30 suppliers
	quelpartensis	CBcs CPIN CRHN GQui SSpi
	quercifolia ♀ H3-4	More than 30 suppliers
	- 'Burgundy'	EPfP NLar
	- 'Flore Pleno'	see H. quercifolia 'Snow Flake'
	- 'Harmony'	CEnd CFil IArd SSta WHCG WPGP WPat
	- 'Pee Wee'	EPfP GEil LRHS MAsh SReu WBcn WPat

- 'Sike's Dwarf'	CEnd CFil GCal SSpi WPGP WPat
§ - 'Snow Flake' (d)	CAbP CBcs CDoC CDul CEnd CFil CMil CPle CSPN ELan EMil EPfP GKir LRHS MAsh SBrw SLon SMur SPer SPla SSpi SSta WHCG
- Snow Queen = 'Flemygea'	CBcs CDoC CKno CPMA CWSG EBee EPfP ISea MGos MRav MSte MWgw SDes SLim SPer SPla SRPl SSta WFar WHCG
- 'Tennessee Clone'	CFil WPGP
robusta	SLPl
sargentiana	see *H. aspera* subsp. *sargentiana*
scandens	CFil
- B&SWJ 5893	WCru
§ - subsp. *chinensis* B&SWJ 1488	WCru
- - B&SWJ 3420	WCru
- subsp. *liukiuensis*	WCru
- - B&SWJ 6022	WCru
seemannii	More than 30 suppliers
serrata	CTrw CWib NHlc WCru WDin
- B&SWJ 6241	WCru
- 'Acuminata'	see *H. serrata* 'Bluebird'
- 'Aigaku'	WPGP
- 'Amacha'	CFil CMil WPGP
- 'Amagyana'	CMil CPLG WPGP
- 'Belle Deckle'	see *H. serrata* 'Blue Deckle'
- 'Beni-gaku'	CBcs CFil CMil CPLG EBee NLar WLRN WPGP
- 'Beni-yama' **new**	CMil
- 'Blue Deckle' (L)	CFil CMHG MAsh MRav NHlc SNut SPla SSpi WBcn WPGP
§ - 'Bluebird' ♀ H3-4	More than 30 suppliers
* - *chinensis*	NHlc
- 'Diadem' ♀ H3-4	CFil CMil CPLG NHlc SDix WCru WLRN WPGP WSHC
- dwarf white **new**	WCru
- 'Fuji Snowstorm' **new**	CMil
- 'Golden Sunlight'PBR **new**	LRHS SLon SPoG
- 'Grayswood' ♀ H3-4	CBcs CEnd CFil CSBt CWSG EFpt GEil GKir GQui LRHS MRav SDix SGar SPer WKif WLRN WPGP
- 'Intermedia'	CFil WPGP
- 'Jogasaki'	CFil
§ - 'Kiyosumi'	CBcs CDoC CEnd CFil CMil SSpi WBcn WCru
- 'Koreana'	CMil
- 'Kurenai' (L) **new**	SSpi
- 'Maiko'	CBcs CMil
- 'Mikamba' **new**	EFpt
- 'Miranda' (L) ♀ H3-4	CBrd CFil CPLG CSam SSpi WFar WPGP
- 'Miyama-yae-murasaki' (d)	CFil CMil WPGP
- 'Preziosa'	see *H.* 'Preziosa'
- 'Red Brocade' **new**	WCot
- 'Rosalba' ♀ H3-4	CFil CPLG EFpt EPfP MRav SPer SPla WFar WPGP WSHC
- 'Shichidanka-nishiki' (d/v)	CBcs CFil WGer WPGP
- 'Shinonome' **new**	CMil
- 'Shirofugi'	CFil
- 'Shirotae' (d)	CBcs CFil
- 'Shishiva' **new**	EFpt
- var. *thunbergii*	CBcs CFil CMHG GQui WFar WPGP
* - - 'Plena' (d) **new**	WCru
- 'Tiara' ♀ H3-4	CFil CMil EBee SSpi WBcn WPGP WWes
- 'Uzu Azisai'	CFil WPGP
- subsp. *yezoensis*	CFil NHlc WPGP
'Wryneck' (H)	
§ *serratifolia*	CFil CHEx CPIN EPfP EPla MBlu SAPC SArc SBra SSpi SSta WCru WGer WPGP

sikokiana B&SWJ 5035	WCru
'Sunset' (H) **new**	CBcs
tiliifolia	see *H. anomala* subsp. *petiolaris*
villosa	see *H. aspera* Villosa Group
xanthoneura	see *H. heteromalla*
'Ya-no-amacha' **new**	CBcs
'Yola Blue'	WWeb

Hydrastis (*Ranunculaceae*)

canadensis	CArn EBee EOHP GBuc GPoy LEur WCru

Hydrocharis (*Hydrocharitaceae*)

morsus-ranae	CBen CRDP CRow EHon EMFW LMdh LPBA MSta NPer SWat

Hydrocotyle (*Apiaceae*)

asiatica	see *Centella asiatica*
moschata	WPer
ranunculoides	WWpP
* *sibthorpioides*	CBgR CDes CPLG EBee EMan
'Variegata' (v)	EMon GCal WCHb WCot WPer
vulgaris	CRDP EMFW MSta NPer WWeb

Hydrophyllum (*Hydrophyllaceae*)

canadense	EMar WCru
virginianum	CRDP MSal

Hylomecon (*Papaveraceae*)

erectum **new**	EBee
§ *japonica*	CRDP EChP EPar ERos ETow GCrs GEdr GKir MSte NBir NDov NGar NMGW NMen NRya SBla WAbe WCot WCru WFar WHil

Hylotelephium see *Sedum*

Hymenanthera see *Melicytus*

Hymenocallis (*Amaryllidaceae*)

'Advance'	LAma LRHS
§ *caroliniana*	LAma WCot
x *festalis* ♀ H1	ERea LAma LRHS MBri NRog SDeJ SYvo WCot
harrisiana	LRHS WCot
littoralis	NRog
§ *longipetala*	LRHS WCot
occidentalis	see *H. caroliniana*
'Sulphur Queen' ♀ H1	LRHS NRog SDeJ WCot

Hymenolepis (*Asteraceae*)

parviflora	see *Athanasia parviflora*

Hymenosporum (*Pittosporaceae*)

flavum	CPLG LRHS SOWG

Hymenoxys (*Asteraceae*)

brandegeei	see *Tetraneuris brandegeei*
§ *hoopesii* **new**	WLin
lapidicola	CGra

Hyophorbe (*Arecaceae*)

indica	CRoM
§ *lagenicaulis*	CRoM LPal
verschaffeltii	CRoM LPal

Hyoscyamus (*Solanaceae*)

albus	GBar MChe MGol MSal
niger	CArn EMFP GPoy MChe MGol MSal WWye

Hypericum ❀ (*Clusiaceae*)

ACE 2467	WOBN

acmosepalum CFil GEil GIBF WPGP
§ *addingtonii* EPla
aegypticum CLyd CPBP EDAr EHyt EMlt EPot
LBee LRHS MHer NLAp NMen
NWCA NWoo SBla SIgm SRot
WCom WLin WOld WPat WPer
– long-styled SIng
amblycalyx SIgm
androsaemum CAgr CArn ECha EGoo ELan ELau
ENot GKir ISea MHer MRav MSal
NPer NSco SHFr WDin WWpP
§ – 'Albury Purple' CBcs CBos CElw GBuc GEil GKir
MCCP MRav
– 'Autumn Blaze' MGos
§ – 'Dart's Golden Penny' SPer WBcn
– 'Excellent Flair' MGos NPro
– 'Orange Flair' EWTr WWpP
§ – f. *variegatum* 'Mrs CWib MWgw NBir NSti SBod SPer
Gladis Brabazon' (v) WBcn WCom WCot WHrl WWeb
WWpP
§ *annulatum* EMon
ascyron EBee GIBF IIve
athoum CLyd EHyt MBro NBir SScr WPat
atomarium EBee WPGP
attenuatum GIBF IIve
balearicum CFil CLyd EHrv IFro MTho SDry
SIgm WAbe WCom WPGP
barbatum NRya
– MESE 371 EBee
bellum CPle EPfP GCal
buckleyi WAbe WPat
calycinum CBcs CChe CSBt EBee ELan ENot
EPfP GKir IHMH IIve LBuc LGro
MAsh MBar MGos MRav MWat
NBlu NLon NWea SHBN SPer
WDin WGwG WMoo WTel WWpP
§ *cerastioides* CMea CWib EDAr ESis GKir LBee
LRIIS SIgm SIng SRms WAbe WPer
WWin
coris CLyd ECha EWes LRHS MBro
MTho MWat SRms
cuneatum see *H. pallens*
x *cyathiflorum* CDoC CMac
'Gold Cup'
x *dummeri* EBee EMil MBri NHol
'Peter Dummer'
'Eastleigh Gold' SLon
elatum see *H.* x *inodorum*
elodeoides MSta
elodes EMFW
empetrifolium CPle
– 'Prostatum' see *H. empetrifolium* subsp.
tortuosum
§ – subsp. *tortuosum* CLyd EWes
§ *forrestii* ♀ H4 CFil CPle EBee EPfP LRHS NWea
WFar WPGP
– Hird 54 WPGP
N *fragile* hort. see *H. olympicum* f. *minus*
frondosum 'Sunburst' EBee EPfP LRHS MGos MWgw WFar
N 'Gemo' MGos
'Gold Penny' see *H. androsaemum* 'Dart's
Golden Penny'
grandiflorum see *H. kouytchense*
henryi L 753 SRms
'Hidcote' ♀ H4 More than 30 suppliers
'Hidcote Silver Ghost' **new** WBcn
'Hidcote Variegated' (v) CWib EBee MCCP SLim SPer
SRms WBrE WFar WWeb
hircinum EOHP
– subsp. *cambessedesii* LRHS
– subsp. *majus* EMon
hirsutum CKin
humifusum EHyt IIve

§ x *inodorum* GGar NBir
– 'Albury Purple' see *H. androsaemum* 'Albury
Purple'
– 'Elstead' ECtt ELan EWTr GKir MBar MGos
MRav MWat NBid NBlu SHBN
SRms WBan WDin WHCG WWin
– 'Summergold' (v) CBos WBod
– 'Ysella' EHoe EWes MRav MTPN NSti
SDry SPer
japonicum EWes
kalmianum EWes
kelleri EHyt ETow ITim
§ *kiusianum* MBar MTho SIng
var. *yakusimense*
§ *kouytchense* ♀ H4 CBcs EMil EMon EPfP EWes GQui
LRHS MBri MRav SDry WBVN
WCFE WCwm WKif WPat
lancasteri EBee EPfP LRHS MAsh WBcn
leschenaultii hort. see *H. addingtonii, H.* 'Rowallane'
linarioides CLyd GTou
'Locke' LAst
maclarenii GCal
'Milkmaid' GEil
x *moserianum* ♀ H4 EBee EBre ENot EPfP MBar MRav
NPer SHBN SPer SRms WDin WStl
§ – 'Tricolor' (v) More than 30 suppliers
– 'Variegatum' see *H.* x *moserianum* 'Tricolor'
'Mrs Brabazon' see *H. androsaemum* f.
variegatum 'Mrs Gladis
Brabazon'
nummularium NBir
oblongifolium WLRN
– CC 1706 GGar
olympicum ♀ H4 CAgr CBrm CNic COIW ECha EFer
ELan EMlt EPfP EPot GDra GKir
LGro LRHS MBrN MFir MHdf MHer
MWat MWgw NFor NLon SBla SIng
SPer SRms WDin WHen
I – 'Calypso' MWgw
– 'Eden Star' NPro
– 'Grandiflorum' see *H. olympicum* f. *uniflorum*
§ – f. *minus* CNic ECtt EGoo EMNN GCal GDra
LRHS MOne MWhi NBlu SPlb
SRms WCom WPer WStl WWin
– – 'Sulphureum' CBot ESis EWes MLLN NBir SPer
SRms WCFE WSHC WWin
§ – – 'Variegatum' (v) EHyt EVFa EWes LBee NBir WPat
§ – f. *uniflorum* CM&M EDAr GDra GMaP IHMH
LIck MBar MBro NBro NPri NVic
SEND
– – 'Citrinum' ♀ H4 CLyd CMea ECha ECtt EDAr EHyt
EPot LBee LRHS MBro MWat
NBro NDlv NLon SBla SIgm SUsu
WAbe WCom WEas WHoo WKif
WPGP WPat
orientale EBee EWes NMen
§ *pallens* ECho NMen
patulum var. *forrestii* scc *H. forrestii*
– var. *henryi* see *H. pseudohenryi*
Rehder et hort.
perforatum CAgr CArn CKin EBee ELau EOHP
EPfP GBar GPoy MChe MGas MHer
MPEx NCWG NMir SIde WHer
WJek WMoo WSel WWye
– 'Crusader' (v) WHer
polyphyllum see *H. olympicum* f. *minus*
– 'Citrinum' see *H. olympicum* f. *minus*
'Sulphurcum'
– 'Grandiflorum' see *H. olympicum* f. *uniflorum*
prolificum CFai ECtt MMHG
§ *pseudohenryi* L 1029 GBuc
pseudopetiolatum GTou
– var. *yakusimense* see *H. kiusianum* var. *yakusimense*

pulchrum	IIve
quadrangulum L.	see *H. tetrapterum*
reptans hort.	see *H. olympicum* f. *minus*
reptans Dyer	CNic CPBP ECha ESis EWes
§ 'Rowallane' ♀ H3	CBot CTrw EPfP EPla IDac ISea
	SDix SHBN SMrm
stellatum	EMon WBcn WCFE
subsessile B&L 12486	EMon
'Sungold'	see *H. kouytchense*
tenuicaule KR 743	ISea
§ *tetrapterum*	CArn CKin MSal NSco
trichocaulon	CLyd EHol ELan EWes MBro WPat
	WWin
xylosteifolium	SLon
yakusimense	see *H. kiusianum* var.
	yakusimense
yezoense	WBrE

Hyphaene (*Arecaceae*)
petersiana	NBlo XBlo

Hypocalymma (*Myrtaceae*)
angustifolium	SOWG

Hypocalyptus (*Papilionaceae*)
sophoroides **new**	SPlb

Hypochaeris (*Asteraceae*)
maculata **new**	WHer
radicata	CKin IIve NMir

Hypocyrta see *Nematanthus*

Hypoestes (*Acanthaceae*)
aristata	ERea
§ *phyllostachya* (v) ♀ H1	MBri
- 'Bettina' (v)	MBri
- 'Carmina' (v)	MBri
- 'Purpuriana' (v)	MBri
- 'Wit' (v)	MBri
sanguinolenta misapplied	see *H. phyllostachya*

Hypolepis (*Dennstaedtiaceae*)
millefolium	EFer
punctata	EFer

Hypoxis (*Hypoxidaceae*)
hirsuta	EBee EWes
hygrometrica	CRDP ECou LTwo NMen WAbe
	WOBN
krebsii	LTwo
parvula	ITim NMen SBla
- var. *albiflora*	EPot
§ - - 'Hebron Farm Biscuit'	CBro EWes SAga SBla WAbe
- pink-flowered	EPot
- x *Rhodohypoxis*	see x *Rhodoxis hybrida*
baurii	
* *tasmanica* **new**	WCot

Hypsela (*Campanulaceae*)
RB 94066	MNrw
longiflora	see *H. reniformis*
§ *reniformis*	EDAr EMNN EMan EMlt GDea
	GKir LBee LRHS MOne MRav
	NHar NJOw NLAp NRya NWCA
	SIng WFar WWin
- 'Greencourt White'	GBuc GDra

Hyssopus (*Lamiaceae*)
officinalis	More than 30 suppliers
- f. *albus*	CBod CPrp CSev ECha EGoo
	ELau GPoy MChe MHer NBlu
	NGHP SIde SPlb WBry WCHb

	WCer WHHs WHer WJek WPer
	WSel WWye
§ - subsp. *aristatus*	CArn CBod CPrp EBee EBre EDAr
	ELau ESis GPoy LLWP MChe
	MHer NBlu NChi SIde SWal WCHb
	WEas WJek WSel WWin WWye
- - white **new**	WEas
- 'Roseus'	CBod CPrp CSev EBee ECha EGoo
	ELau GPoy LLWP MBNS MBow
	MChe MHer NBlu NChi NFor
	NGHP SIde WCHb WCer WHHs
	WHer WJek WKif WPer WWye
* *schugnanicus*	EBee LLWP MHar
* - *albus*	EBee
seravschanicus	EOHP IIve
tianschanicus	LLWP

Hystrix (*Poaceae*)
patula	More than 30 suppliers

Iberis (*Brassicaceae*)
amara	WBWf
aurosica 'Sweetheart'	CBrm EBee LPVe NMen
'Betty Swainson'	EBee GBri SMrm WCot
candolleana	see *I. pruitii* Candolleana Group
commutata	see *I. sempervirens*
'Correvoniana'	WEas
'Dick Self'	EBre LRHS
gibraltarica	EMan NFor NPri SRms WBVN
	WGor
'Golden Candy' **new**	ENot WWeb
jordanii	see *I. pruitii*
§ *pruitii* Candolleana Group	MWrn
saxatilis	EDAr GDra WPer
- *candolleana*	see *I. pruitii* Candolleana Group
semperflorens	WCFE WCom WCot
§ *sempervirens* ♀ H4	CBcs CTri ELan EMan EPfP LAst
	LGro LHrt MHer MWat NArg NBid
	NBro NFor NLon NOrc NVic
	SEND SPar SRms STre SWal WBrE
	WCFE WFar WPer WWal
- 'Compacta' **new**	MWrn SBod
- 'Little Gem'	see *I. sempervirens* 'Weisser
	Zwerg'
- 'Plena' (d)	WCom
- 'Pygmaea'	CNic ECtt MWat NHar NMen SBla
	WHil
§ - 'Schneeflocke' ♀ H4	COIW EMlt ENot GDra GKir LPVe
	LRHS LRav MBro NJOw SPar SPer
	WHoo
- Snowflake	see *I. sempervirens*
	'Schneeflocke'
- 'Variegata' (v)	WCom
§ - 'Weisser Zwerg'	CMea EBre ECha ECtt ELan
	EMNN GMaP LBee LRHS MBro
	MHer MRav NBlu NHar NMen
	SBla SRms WAbe WHoo WWin

Idesia (*Flacourtiaceae*)
polycarpa	CAgr CBcs CFil CMCN CTho EBee
	EPfP EWTr LHop SMad SSpi SSta
	WBVN WDin WFar WPGP WPat

Ilex ✿ (*Aquifoliaceae*)
N x *altaclerensis*	GKir SHHo STop
- 'Atkinsonii' (m)	SHHo
- 'Belgica' (f)	SHHo

§ - 'Belgica Aurea' (f/v) ♀ H4 — CBcs CDoC CSBt CTho EBee EPfP GKir LNet LPan MBar MBri MWat NBee NHol NWea SEND SHBN SHHo SKee WBcn WFar

- 'Camelliifolia' (f) ♀ H4 — CDul CMCN CSBt CTho CWib EBee EPfP GKir LPan MBlu MBri MRav MWat NWea SHHo SMad SPer STop WBcn WFar

- 'Golden King' (f/v) ♀ H4 — More than 30 suppliers

- 'Hendersonii' (f) — SHHo WBcn

- 'Hodginsii' (m) ♀ H4 — CMCN CWib ECot MBar MRav NWea SEND SHHo WFar

- 'Howick' (f/v) — SHHo WBcn

- 'James G. Esson' (f) — SBir SHHo

- 'Lady Valerie' (m) — IArd SHHo

- 'Lawsoniana' (f/v) ♀ H4 — More than 30 suppliers

- 'Maderensis' — NRib

- 'Maderensis Variegata' — see I. aquifolium 'Maderensis Variegata'

- 'Marnockii' (f) — SHHo WBcn

- 'Moorei' (m) — SHHo

- 'Mundyi' (m) — CWib SHHo

- 'Purple Shaft' (f) — GKir MAsh MRav SHHo

- 'Ripley Gold' (f/v) — EBee GKir LPan MAsh NHol SAga SCoo SHHo STop

- 'Silver Sentinel' — see I. x altaclerensis 'Belgica Aurea'

- 'W.J. Bean' (f) — SHHo

- 'Wilsonii' (f) — LPan MWat NWea SHHo

angustifolia — see I. cassine var. angustifolia

aquifolium ♀ H4 — More than 30 suppliers

- 'Alaska' (f) — CDoC CDul CMCN CTho EBee EBre EMil ENot GKir LBuc MAsh NSti SBir SHHo STop WFar WRHF

- 'Amber' (f) ♀ H4 — CTri MWat SBir SHHo WBcn WLRN

- 'Angustifolia' (f) — EPla WFar

- 'Angustifolia' (m or f) — EPfP MBar MWat NHol SHHo WBVN WBcn WFar

§ - 'Argentea Marginata' (f/v) ♀ H4 — More than 30 suppliers

§ - 'Argentea Marginata Pendula' (f/v) — CDoC CSBt CTri CWib ENot EPfP GKir LPan LRHS MAsh NHol NWea SHHo SLim SPer SRms WFar WPat

- 'Argentea Pendula' — see I. aquifolium 'Argenta Marginata Pendula'

- 'Argentea Variegata' — see I. aquifolium 'Argentea Marginata'

- 'Atlas' (m) — CBcs CDoC LBuc

- 'Aurea Marginata' (f/v) — CMHG CTho EBee EHoe GKir LPan MGos NBlu NHol NWea SBod SHBN SHHo SKee WCFE WDin WFar WPat WRHF

- 'Aurea Marginata Pendula' (f/v) — CDoC NHol SLim SPer WPat

- 'Aurea Ovata' — see I. aquifolium 'Ovata Aurea'

- 'Aurea Regina' — see I. aquifolium 'Golden Queen'

- 'Aureovariegata Pendula' — see I. aquifolium 'Weeping Golden Milkmaid'

- 'Aurifodina' (f) — GKir IMGH SHHo WBcn WLRN

§ - 'Bacciflava' (f) — More than 30 suppliers

- 'Bowland' (f/v) — NHol SHHo

- 'Cookii' (f) — SHHo

- 'Copper' — WBcn

- 'Crassifolia' (f) — CWib EPla SHHo SMad

- 'Crispa' (m) — CPle MBlu NHol SBir SHHo

- 'Crispa Aureomaculata' — see I. aquifolium 'Crispa Aureopicta'

§ - 'Crispa Aureopicta' (m/v) — NBlu SHHo WBcn WPat

- 'Elegantissima' (m/v) — SHHo

- 'Ferox' (m) — CDul ELan EPfP GKir LRHS SHHo STop WBcn WDin WGwG

- 'Ferox Argentea' (m/v) ♀ H4 — More than 30 suppliers

* - 'Ferox Argentea Picta' (m/v) — LRHS

- 'Ferox Aurea' (m/v) — CDoC CLnd CPle CSBt EBee ELan EPfP EPla GKir LAst MAsh NHol SHHo SPer

§ - 'Flavescens' (f) — CBot EBee EPfP EPla NDlv NHol SHHo WBcn WLRN

* - 'Forest Weeping' — LRHS

- 'Foxii' (m) — SHHo

- 'Fructo Aurantiaco' (f) — EBee

- 'Fructo Luteo' — see I. aquifolium 'Bacciflava'

- 'Gold Flash' (f/v) — EBee GKir LRHS MAsh MBri MGos NBee NBlu NHol SHHo SLim WBcn WDin

- 'Golden Hedgehog' — EPfP GKir

- 'Golden Milkboy' (m/v) — CWib EBee EMil EPfP GKir LNet MAsh MBlu MGos SHHo WCFE WDin WPat

- 'Golden Milkmaid' (f/v) — CWib EHol

§ - 'Golden Queen' (m/v) ♀ H4 — CDoC CWSG CWib EBee ENot GKir LHyr LNet LRHS MBri MGos NBir NHol NWea SHHo SPer SRPl SReu SRms WPat

- 'Golden Tears' — SHHo WBcn

- 'Golden van Tol' (f/v) — CBcs CDoC CSBt CTri EBee EBre ELan ENot EPfP GKir IMGH LAst LNet LPan LRHS MBar MBlu MBri MGos NBee NHol NSti SHBN SHHo SPer SRms WDin WStl WWal WWeb

- 'Green Pillar' (f) — CMCN EPfP LBuc SHHo

- 'Handsworth New Silver' (f/v) ♀ H4 — More than 30 suppliers

- 'Harpune' (f) — CPle SHHo

§ - 'Hascombensis' — EHol GDra LHop LPhx MBro MGos NHar NHol NMen WFar

- 'Hastata' (m) — CWib IArd

- 'Ingramii' (m/v) — SBir SHHo WBcn

- 'J.C. van Tol' (f) ♀ H4 — More than 30 suppliers

- 'Latispina' (f) — SHHo

- 'Laurifolia Aurea' (m/v) — SHHo WWal

- 'Lichtenthalii' (f) — IArd SHHo

- 'Madame Briot' (f/v) ♀ H4 — CDoC CMHG CSBt CTri CWib EBee ENot EPfP GKir IMGH LHyr LRHS MAsh MBar MBri NHol NWea SHHo SPer SPla SReu SRms WDin WFar WTel WWal

§ - 'Maderensis Variegata' (m/v) — SHHo

- 'Monstrosa' (m) — SHHo

- 'Moonlight holly' — see I. aquifolium 'Flavescens'

- 'Myrtifolia' (m) — CDoC ELan EPfP GKir MBar MBlu MGos MRav MTed NBlu SPar WFar

- 'Myrtifolia Aurea' (m/v) — SBir WBcn

§ - 'Myrtifolia Aurea Maculata' (m/v) ♀ H4 — CBrm CDoC CSam EBee EHoe ELan EPfP GKir IMGH LAst LNet LRHS MAsh MBri MRav NHol NSti NWea SHHo SLim SPer SRPl WFar WPat

- 'Myrtifolia Aureovariegata' — see I. aquifolium 'Myrtifolia Aurea Maculata'

§ - 'Ovata Aurea' (m/v) — SHHo

- 'Pendula' (f) — EPfP MWat SHHo

- 'Pendula Mediopicta' — see I. aquifolium 'Weeping Golden Milkmaid'

- 'Purple Lady' — WBcn

- 'Purple Lord' — WBcn

- 'Pyramidalis' (f) ♀ H4 — CDoC CEnd CSBt CTho CTri EBee ELan ENot GKir LHyr LRHS MAsh MBar MBri MGos MLan

	MRav NBee NBlu NHol NWea SHHo SPer SRms WDin
– 'Pyramidalis Aureomarginata' (f/v)	CDoC LRHS MGos MLan NBlu SHHo WBcn WWal
– 'Pyramidalis Fructu Luteo' (f) ♀ H4	GKir MBar NWea SHHo WBcn
– 'Rubricaulis Aurea' (f/v)	NHol SHHo STop WBcn
– 'Sharpy' (f)	SBir
– Siberia = 'Limsi'PBR (f)	EBee SHHo
– 'Silver King'	see *I. aquifolium* 'Silver Queen'
– 'Silver Lining' (f/v)	SHHo STop
– 'Silver Milkboy' (f/v)	CTho EHoe EMil LRHS MBlu MGos SBir WFar
– 'Silver Milkmaid' (f/v)	CDoC CSBt CWSG EBee EPfP GKir LAst LRHS MBar MRav NHol SHBN SHHo SLim SPar SPer SPla SSta WMoo WRHF WWal
§ – 'Silver Queen' (m/v) ♀ H4	More than 30 suppliers
– 'Silver Sentinel'	see *I.* x *altaclerensis* 'Belgica Aurea'
– 'Silver van Tol' (f/v)	CDoC EBee ELan ENot IMGH LAst LRHS MBri NHol NPer NWea SHHo SPer SPoG WBcn WLRN WStI WWeb
– 'Victoria' (m)	WBcn
§ – 'Watereriana' (m/v)	EHol LRHS MAsh SMur WBcn
– 'Waterer's Gold'	see *I. aquifolium* 'Watereriana'
§ – 'Weeping Golden Milkmaid' (f/v)	SHHo WPat
x *aquipernyi*	SHHo
– Dragon Lady = 'Meschick' (f)	COtt LPan SHHo
– 'San Jose' (f)	CMCN SHHo
x *attenuata*	WFar
– 'Sunny Foster' (f/v)	CDul CMCN ENot EPla MBlu MGos SHHo WBcn WFar
§ *bioritsensis*	CMCN CTri NWea SBir WBcn
buergeri	CMCN
cassine	CMCN
§ – var. *angustifolia* (f)	STop
chinensis misapplied	see *I. purpurea*
ciliospinosa	CMCN WPGP
colchica	CMCN SBir SHHo
corallina	CBcs CMCN
cornuta	ERom LPan SHHo WBcn WFar
* – 'Aurea'	SHHo
– 'Burfordii' (f)	SHHo
§ – 'Dazzler' (f)	LPan SHHo
– 'Fine Line' (f) **new**	SHHo
– 'Ira S. Nelson' (f/v)	SHHo
– 'O. Spring' (f/v)	CMHG EPla SHHo WBcn
– 'Rotunda' (f)	SHHo
I – 'Willowleaf' (f) **new**	SHHo
crenata	CMCN CTri ERom ESis GKir LPan MBar NWea SHHo SPar WDin WFar WHCr WNor
– 'Akagi'	WFar
– 'Aureovariegata'	see *I. crenata* 'Variegata'
– 'Braddock Heights' (f)	SHHo
– 'Cape Fear' (m)	SHHo
– 'Carolina Upright' (m)	SHHo
– 'Cole's Hardy' (f)	SHHo
– 'Convexa' (f) ♀ H4	CBcs EBee ENot EPfP GDra GKir IMGH LPan LRHS MBar MBri NHol NWea SHHo WFar WPat
– 'Convexed Gold'	MBri
– 'Fastigiata' (f)	CChe CDoC CEnd EBee EBre EPfP EPla GKir LAst LPan LRHS MAsh MBNS MBar MBri MGos NBlu SCoo SHHo SPar SPer WFar WWes
– 'Fructo Luteo'	see *I. crenata* f. *watanabeana*
– 'Fukarin'	see *I. crenata* 'Shiro-fukurin'
* – 'Glory Gem' (f)	CSBt SHHo
– 'Gold Tips' **new**	MGos
– 'Golden Gem' (f) ♀ H4	More than 30 suppliers
– 'Green Dragon' (m)	EPla WWes
– 'Green Hedge'	LBuc
– 'Green Island' (m)	SHHo
– 'Green Lustre' (f)	SHHo
– 'Helleri' (f)	CMCN EPla MBar MBro SBla SHHo WPat
– 'Hetzii' (f)	SHHo
– 'Ivory Hall' (f)	EPla SHHo
– 'Ivory Tower' (f)	SHHo
* – 'Kobold'	SHHo
– 'Korean Gem'	EPla SHHo
– var. *latifolia* (m)	SHHo
– 'Luteovariegata'	see *I. crenata* 'Variegata'
– 'Mariesii' (f)	IMGH MBlu MBro SBla SHHo SIng WPat
– 'Mount Halla' (f)	CMCN
– 'Nakada' (m)	SHHo
– var. *paludosa*	EBee WPGP
– 'Pride's Tiny'	SHHo
I – 'Pyramidalis' (f)	CMil NHar NHol NWea WPat
§ – 'Shiro-fukurin' (f/v)	CMCN CMHG EBee ELan EPfP GKir LAst LRHS NHar NHol SHHo
– 'Sky Pencil' (f)	CMCN
– 'Snowflake'	see *I. crenata* 'Shiro-fukurin'
– 'Stokes' (m)	LRHS SHHo
– upright	CMCN
§ – 'Variegata' (v)	CMCN EPla GKir LRHS MBar MBlu NHol SHHo
§ – f. *watanabeana* (f)	SHHo
'Dazzler'	see *I. cornuta* 'Dazzler'
decidua	CMCN CPle
dimorphophylla	CBcs CDoC CMCN SHHo SMad
– 'Somerset Pixie'	CWib SHHo
'Doctor Kassab' (f)	CMCN SHHo
'Drace' (f)	SHHo
'Elegance' (f)	WFar
fargesii	CPne CTho
ficoidea	CMCN
glabra	SHHo
'Good Taste' (f)	SHHo WFar
hascombensis	see *I. aquifolium* 'Hascombensis'
hookeri	SHHo
'Indian Chief' (f)	MBlu SMad WFar
insignis	see *I. kingiana*
'John T. Morris' (m)	SHHo
§ *kingiana*	CFil CPne EBee EPla WFar WPGP
x *koehneana*	CBot CDul CPne
– 'Chestnut Leaf' (f) ♀ H4	CDoC CMCN CMHG EWTr MBri MRav SHHo SMad WBcn WCru WFar WLeb WPGP WWeb
latifolia	CHEx CMCN SHHo
'Lydia Morris' (f)	CSam SHHo WFar
'Mary Nell' (f)	SBir SHHo
x *meserveae*	SHHo
– Blue Angel (f)	More than 30 suppliers
– Blue Maid = 'Mesid' (f)	EMil
– Blue Prince (m)	CBcs CBrm CDoC CDul COtt EBee EHoe EWTr GKir LBuc MBar MBlu NBlu NHol NWea SBir SHBN SHHo SLim SPer WDin WFar WStI WWeb
– Blue Princess (f)	CBcs CBrm COtt ENot EPfP EWTr GKir LAst LBuc LPan MBar MBlu MRav NHol NSti NWea SHBN SHHo SLim SPer WStI
– Golden Girl = 'Mesgolg' (f)	EMil
muchagara	CBcs CMCN

myrtifolia	CMCN ECot MLan MRav NEgg NHar NPri SPar WCFE WLRN
'Nellie R. Stevens' (f)	CDoC LPan NWea SBir WBcn
opaca	CMCN
pedunculosa	CMCN SHHo
perado latifolia	see *I. perado* subsp. *platyphylla*
§ – subsp. *platyphylla*	CBcs CHEx CMCN CSam EPla MBlu SAPC SArc SHHo WPGP
pernyi	CMCN CTrG GKir SHHo SLon SSta WBVN WBcn WFar WPic
– var. *veitchii*	see *I. bioritsensis*
§ *purpurea*	CMCN
'Pyramidalis'	see *I. aquifolium* 'Pyramidalis'
rugosa	CMCN
'September Gem' (f)	CMCN
serrata	CMCN
'Sparkleberry' (f)	LRHS
suaveolens	CMCN
verticillata	CDul CMCN CPne EPla GKir IMGH LPan NWea WDin WFar
– (f)	EPfP NWea WFar
– (m)	CDoC EPfP WLRN
– 'Afterglow' (f)	MBlu
– f. *aurantiaca* (f)	MBlu
– 'Christmas Cheer' (f)	WFar
– f. *chrysocarpa* (f)	CMCN
– 'Compacta'	see *I. verticillata* 'Nana'
– 'Jim Dandy' (m)	MBlu
§ – 'Nana' (f)	MBlu
– 'Red Sprite'	see *I. verticillata* 'Nana'
– 'Southern Gentleman' (m)	MBlu
– 'Stop Light' (f)	MBlu
– 'Sunset' (f)	MBlu
– 'Winter Red' (f)	CMCN GKir MBlu MMHG
vomitoria	CMCN
x *wandoensis*	CMCN SBir SHHo
'Washington' (f)	CPle SBir
yunnanensis	CMCN

Iliamna see *Sphaeralcea*

Illicium (Illiciaceae)

anisatum	CArn CBcs CFil CPle EPfP SRPl SSpi WFar WOTO WPGP WPat WSHC
floridanum	CBcs CFil EPfP NLar SBrw SSpl WPGP
– 'Halley's Comet'	SSpi
– variegated (v)	SSpi
henryi	CFil CMCN CMHG CPle SSpi WPGP WSHC
parviflorum **new**	SSpi
simonsii **new**	SSpi
'Woodland Ruby' **new**	SSpi

Impatiens ✿ (Balsaminaceae)

from China	CDes EBee EMan GCal WCot WPGP
apiculata	CPLG GCal
arguta **new**	GCal WCru
auricoma	CHal EBak SHFr
balfourii	EBee EHrv EMan EMon NBir WCot
'Cardinal Red'	CHal
congolensis	EPfP
cristata	CPLG
'Diamond Rose'	CHal
double-flowered (d)	EBak
falcifer CC 3208 **new**	WCot
(Fiesta Series) 'Burgundy Rose' [PBR] (d)	NPri WWol
– 'Appleblossom' **new**	NPri
– 'Blush' **new**	NPri
– Fiesta Coral Bells = 'Balfiecobl' (d)	NPri
– Fiesta Orange Spice = 'Balficorce' [PBR] (d) **new**	NPri
– Fiesta Purple Piñata = 'Balfipuna'	NPri
– 'Fiesta Salmon' [PBR]	see *I.* (Fiesta Series) 'Salmon Sunrise', 'Sparkler Salmon'
– Fiesta Stardust Lavender = 'Balfiesala' **new**	LIck
– 'Fiesta White' [PBR] (d)	NPri WWol
– 'Lavender Orchid' [PBR] (d)	NPri WWol
I – 'Ole Cherry' **new**	NPri
– 'Ole Frost' **new**	NPri
– 'Ole Stardust' **new**	NPri
– 'Pink Ruffle' [PBR] (d)	LIck NPri
§ – 'Salmon Sunrise' [PBR] (d)	NPri
– 'Salsa Red' [PBR] (d)	NPri
– 'Sparkler Red' [PBR] (d)	NPri WWol
– 'Sparkler Rose' [PBR] (d)	NPri
§ – 'Sparkler Salmon' [PBR] (d)	LIck WWol
glandulifera	MCCP MHer WHer WWpP
– 'Candida'	CBre EMon
– 'Sugar Loaf Peach'	WAlt
hawkeri	EBak
hians	SHFr
aff. *kerriae* B&SWJ 7219 **new**	WCru
kilimanjari x *pseudoviola* **new**	GCal
longiloba B&SWJ 6623	WCru
'Madame Pompadour'	CHal
New Guinea Group	CHal EBak MBri WLRN WWol
niamniamensis	EBak ERea SSte
– 'Congo Cockatoo'	CHal EOHP ESlt LIck SHFr SRms
– 'Golden Cockatoo' (v)	CHal EBak ESlt IFro MCCP WWol
omeiana	CDes CHEx CLAP CSpe EBee EMan EPPr GCal ITer MNrw SAga SSpi SSte WCot WCru WPGP
pseudoviola	SDix SHFr
'Raspberry Ripple'	CHal
'Salmon' [PBR]	see *I.* (Fiesta Series) 'Salmon Sunrise', 'Sparkler Salmon'
'Salmon Princess'	CHal
sodenii	SDys SHFr WPGP
sulcata	SHFr
sultani	see *I. walleriana*
tinctoria	CDoC CFil CFir CHEx CHll CPLG CPlt CPom EBee GCal MNrw SIgm SSpi SSte WCot WCru WPGP WPrP
– subsp. *elegantissima*	CFee
– subsp. *tinctoria*	IFro
ugandensis	CFil SSpi WPGP
violeta B&SWJ 6608 **new**	WCru
walkeri **new**	CFee
§ *walleriana*	EBak MBri
– (Summer Ice Series) 'Blackberry Ice' [PBR] (d/v)	CHal WWol
– – 'Cherry Ice' [PBR] (d/v)	CHal WWol
– – 'Dapper Dan' (d/v)	CHal
– – 'Orange Ice' [PBR] (d/v)	WWol
– – 'Peach Ice' (d/v)	CHal WWol
– – 'Pink Ice' [PBR] (d/v) **new**	WWol
– – 'Raspberry Ice' (d/v) **new**	WWol
✱ – 'Variegata' (v)	CHal
zombensis	EBee SHFr WCot

Imperata (Poaceae)

brevifolia	CBrm CFwr
cylindrica	EPar MSal
– 'Red Baron'	see *I. cylindrica* 'Rubra'
§ – 'Rubra'	More than 30 suppliers

Incarvillea (*Bignoniaceae*)

§ **arguta**	CBot CPLG EBee LPio SBla WAbe WCot WWin
brevipes	see *I. mairei*
compacta	MDKP NHar NSla
– ACE 1455	EBee
delavayi	More than 30 suppliers
– 'Alba'	see *I. delavayi* 'Snowtop'
– 'Bees' Pink'	EBee GBuc GCal
§ – 'Snowtop'	CBot COtt EBee EChP ELan ENot EPfP EPot ERou EWTr GBuc GCal LAst MCCP MDun MLLN MMil NLar SBla SPer SPla WBrE WCot WFar WPGP
diffusa	EHyt SBla
forrestii	LPio NSla
– KGB 43	EHyt
grandiflora	EBee ELan GCrs SBla
himalayensis	GBuc GDra NHar SIgm
'Frank Ludlow'	
– 'Nyoto Sama'	GBuc GDra
§ **mairei**	EBee EGoo EHyt EMan GCrs GDra GSki LHop LRHS MLLN NLar SIgm WPer WWin
– ACE 2420	EBee
– var. **mairei**	EPot GBuc
– – CLD 101	GCrs
– – f. **multifoliata**	see *I. zhongdianensis*
– pink	EHyt
§ **olgae**	CBri EBee EMan GSki LPVe MDKP NLar NWCA SSvw
przewalskii	WAbe
sinensis 'Alba'	WBro
younghusbandii	EBee
§ **zhongdianensis**	EBee EPot GBri GBuc GCrs GDra GEdr NSla SBla SMrm WPGP
– CLD 233	EHyt

Indigofera (*Papilionaceae*)

amblyantha ♀ H4	CBcs CFwr EBee EPfP GCal IDee MBlu NLar NLon SBrw SDry SSpi WDin WPat WSHC
articulata	CFil
australis	LRav SOWG
cytisoides new	GFai
decora f. **alba**	EPfP GEil IArd IDee
dielsiana	CBcs EPfP
'Dosua' new	NPSI
gerardiana	see *I. heterantha*
hebepetala	WCru WDin WSHC
§ **heterantha** ♀ H4	More than 30 suppliers
kirilowii	CFil EPfP IArd SOWG WSHC
pendula	EPfP WPGP
potaninii	CBcs SHBN WCru WHer
pseudotinctoria	CFil EBee EGFP EPfP LRav SRms WFar WPGP
tinctoria	CArn MSal WHHs

Indocalamus (*Poaceae*)

hamadae	EPla ERod SDry WJun
latifolius	EPPr EPla ERod LJus LPal MMoz MWht SDry WJun
– 'Hopei'	EPla
longiauritus	EPla SDry
solidus	CBig CDDB CHEx EPla ERod LJus LPal MHdf MMoz MWht NPal SDry WJun WMul
§ **tessellatus** ♀ H4	CAbb CDDB CDoC CFil CHEx CMCo CTrC EBee EFul EPfP EPla ERod IFro LJus MCCP MHdf MMoz MWht NGdn NMoo SMad WDyG WFar WJun WPGP WPnP

Inula (*Asteraceae*)

acaulis	MLLN WCot WWeb
barbata	EBre LHop MLLN
cappa	EBee
conyzae	MSal
crithmoides	WHer
dysenterica	see *Pulicaria dysenterica*
ensifolia	EPfP GKir LHrt MCAu MLLN MSte MTho NBro SAga SDes SMac SYvo WBea WFar WHoo WOld WPnP WWpP
– 'Compacta'	EFou
– 'Gold Star'	CMGP EBee EMan EPfP LPVe MHer MLLN NBid NBir NFor NLon NOak SBla WFar WHHs WLRN WMnd WPer
glandulosa	see *I. orientalis*
* **harassii**	CHll
helenium	CArn CSam CSev EFWa ELau GBar GPoy ILis LRHS MBow MCAu MChe MHer MLLN MSal NArg NBid NMir SDes SRms WCer WHHs WHbs WHer WMoo WPer WWye
– 'Goliath'	ELau MLLN
helianthus-aquatilis	MLLN
heterolepis	EBee
hirta	MLLN WPer
hookeri	More than 30 suppliers
macrocephala misapplied	see *I. royleana*
– Boiss.	EBee MLLN
magnifica	More than 30 suppliers
– 'Sonnenstrahl'	LPhx
oculus-christi	EBee EWes MLLN
* 'Oriental Star'	WHil
§ **orientalis**	COIW EBee EChP EFWa EPPr EPfP EWTr GIBF LRHS MAnH MBri MCAu NLon NMir SBri SDes SMac SPer WFar WLin WMnd WOld WPGP WPer WWeb
racemosa	EBee EMon EPla EWes GBin GCal IBlr MNrw MSte NBid NSti SRms WFar WWpP
– 'Sonnenspeer'	ECGN EMan NLar SMad WPer
rhizocephala	EHyt IFro MLLN WPer
royleana	GCal GMac MNrw MRav MSte
salicina new	EBee

Iochroma (*Solanaceae*)

§ **australe**	CBcs CHEx CKob CPle CSpe LHop MOak SBrw SGar SHFr SOWG SSte WCom WCot WEas
§ – 'Andean Snow'	CBot CPLG MOak
§ – 'Bill Evans'	CPLG EWll
cyaneum	CKob CPLG ERea SOWG SSte SYvo WMul
– purple	CHll
§ – 'Trebah'	CBcs ERea MOak SYvo
gesnerioides	WMul
'Coccineum'	
§ **grandiflorum**	CHEx CHll CSev SOWG SYvo WMul
violaceum hort.	see *I. cyaneum* 'Trebah'
warscewiczii	see *I. grandiflorum*

Ipheion (*Alliaceae*)

'Alberto Castillo'	CAvo CBro CLAP CMea CPlt EBee EGrW EHyt ELan EMan EPot ERos EWes LTwo MAsh MBro MNrw MTho SBla SIgm SIng WCom WCot WHoo WIvy WPGP
dialystemon	CMea SBla SOkd WAbe
'Rolf Fiedler' ♀ H2-3	CAvo CBro CMea CPom CStu

	ECho EGle EGrW EHyt ELan EPar
	EPfP EPot ESis ETub EWes LAma
	LHop MAsh MRav MTho NMen
	SIng WCom WFTG WFar WHil
sellowianum	WCot
uniflorum	CAvo CBri CBro CHal CTri EBee
	ECha ETub LAma MBri MBro
	MLwd MNrw MRav NMen NRog
	NWCA NWoo SAga SIng SRms
	WAbb WAul WBea WCot WFar
	WHoo WPer WPnP
- 'Album'	CBro CMea ECha EHyt ELan EPar
	EPot ERos EWes LPio LRHS MAsh
	MRav MTho NMGW SBla SIng
	WCot WPnP
- 'Charlotte Bishop'	CAvo CBro CDes CElw CMea CPlt
	ECha EGle EHyt EWes LTwo MAsh
	MBro MRav SBla SDys SIng SUsu
	WCom WCot WHoo WIvy WPGP
- 'Froyle Mill' ♀ H4	More than 30 suppliers
- 'Wisley Blue' ♀ H4	More than 30 suppliers

Iphigenia (Liliaceae)

indica new	EBee

Ipomoea (Convolvulaceae)

acuminata	see *I. indica*
alba	CPIN
* *andersonii*	CPIN
batatas 'Blackie'	CPIN WCot WFar WMul
carnea	LRHS SOWG
coccinea	CSpe
horsfalliae ♀ H1	CPIN
§ *indica* ♀ H1	CBcs CHEx CHal CHll CPIN CSpe
	FRea MPRe SOWG SYvo WMul
learii	see *I. indica*
§ *lobata*	CSpe LRHS SGar SHFr SUsu SYvo
purpurea 'Kniola's Purple-black'	CSpe
quamoclit	CPIN
tuberosa	see *Merremia tuberosa*
versicolor	see *I. lobata*

Ipomopsis (Polemoniaceae)

§ *aggregata*	EBee LTwo
multiflora new	EBee
rubra	EBee

Iresine (Amaranthaceae)

herbstii	CHal EBak ERea SMur
- 'Aureoreticulata'	CHal MOak
- 'Brilliantissima'	CHal MOak SMrm
lindenii ♀ H1	CHal MOak

Iris ✿ (Iridaceae)

AGSJ 431	EWoo
CLD 1399	NHol
'Abridged Version' (MTB)	NZep
'Acapulco Gold' (TB)	SCro
'Ace of Clubs' (SDB)	NZep
'Acoma' (TB) new	EWoo
'Action Front' (TB)	COtt EBee EChp EHrv ERou EWTr
	MWgw NGdn SCoo SLon WLRN
'Actress' (TB)	EFou
'Adobe Rose' (TB)	ESgI
'Afternoon Delight' (TB)	ESgI MCAu
'Agatha Dawson' (Reticulata/v) new	EMon
'Agnes James' (CH) ♀ H3	CBro
'Ahead of Times' (TB) new	EFam
'Ain't She Sweet' (IB)	SCro
'Albatross' (TB)	CKel SMrm
albicans ♀ H4	SCro WHal
§ *albomarginata*	WWst
'Alcazar' (TB)	EBee EPfP EWTr NMoo SDes
	SWat WEas WFar WMnd
'Alenette' (TB)	MCAu
'Alice Harding' (TB) new	ESgI
'Alien Mist' (TB)	LIri
'Alizes' (TB) ♀ H4	ESgI EWoo LIri
'All Right' (IB)	NZep SCro
'Allegiance' (TB)	WEas
'Alpine Lake' (MDB)	NZep WCot
'Alpine Twilight' (TB) new	EFam
'Alsterquelle' (SDB)	WTin
'Altruist' (TB)	MCAu SCro
'Amadora' (TB)	CKel
'Ambassadeur' (TB)	EBee ERou EWTr SDes
'Amber' (SDB)	WWeb
'Amber Blaze' (SDB)	NZep
'Amber Queen' (DB)	EBee ECtt ELan EMan ERos MSte
	NBir NCiC NMen SPer WLRN
	WWal
'Ambroisie' (TB) new	ESgI
'Amethyst Flame' (TB)	EBee EBre ENot ERou ESgI
	NMGW SRms
'Amigo' (TB)	ESgI SCro
'Amphora' (SDB)	CBro ERos GBuc
'Andalou' (TB)	ESgI
'Angelic Wings' (TB) new	EFam
'Angel's Tears'	see *I. histrioides* 'Angel's Eye'
anglica	see *I. latifolia*
'Anna Belle Babson' (TB)	ESgI SCro
'Anna Marie' (TB) new	EFam
'Annabel Jane' (TB)	CKel MCAu SCro SIri
'Anne Elizabeth' (SDB)	CBro ERos
'Annikins' (IB) ♀ H4	CKel
'Anniversary Celebration' (TB) new	CKel
'Antigone' new	ESgI
'Anvil of Darkness' (TB) new	LIri
aphylla	GIBF NOrc
'Apollo' (Dut) new	CTwr MSph
'Apollo's Touch' (IB)	NZep
* 'Apple Court'	SApp
N 'Apple Court White' (CH)	CBos
'Appledore' (SDB)	CBro ERos MBro
'Appointer'	CRow
'Apricorange' (TB) ♀ H4	CKel
'Apricot Frosty' (BB) new	LIri
'Apricot Skies' (BB)	NZep
'Arabi Pasha' (TB)	SCro WLRN
'Arctic Fancy' (IB) ♀ H4	CKel MMil
'Arctic Star' (TB)	CKel
'Arnold Sunrise' (CH) ♀ H3	GMac WWst
'Around Midnight' (TB)	SCro
'Art School Angel' (TB)	LIri
'Artistic Gold' (TB) new	EFam
'Artist's Whim' (TB) new	EFam
'Ask Alma' (IB)	CKel EFou ESgI NZep SCro
'Astrid Cayeux' (TB)	ESgI EWoo
* 'Atlantique' (TB)	CKel
'Attention Please' (TB)	CHar CKel
§ *attica*	CBro CPBP EHyt EPPr EPot ERos
	LBee LRHS LTwo SIng WHal WLin
- lemon	GCrs
§ *aucheri* ♀ H2	CBro EBee GKev LAma WWst
'Audacious' (BB)	NZep
'Aunt Martha' (BB)	MBri NMGW
'Aurean' (IB) new	CKel
'Austrian Sky' (SDB)	CDes CSam EBee EBre ENot MBro
	MMil WPGP
'Autumn Clouds' (TB) new	EFam
'Autumn Leaves' (TB)	MMil
'Autumn Mists' (TB) new	EFam

'Autumn Orangelite' (TB) **new** — EFam
'Avanelle' (IB) — EFou ERou
'Az Ap' (IB) — NZep SCro
'Azure Excho' (IB) — MMil
'Babbling Brook' (TB) **new** — MRav
'Baboon Bottom' (BB) — LIri
'Baby Bibs' (MTB) — NZep
'Baby Blessed' (SDB) — CBro EFam NZep
'Baby Face' (TB) — MMil
'Baby Prince' (SDB) **new** — EFam
'Back in Black' (TB) — CKel
'Back Street Affair' (TB) **new** — LIri
'Baked Alaska' (TB) — MMil
bakeriana — LAma
'Bal Masque' (TB) — ESgI
baldschuanica — WWst
'Ballerina' — NBir
'Ballerina Blue' (TB) — ERou
'Ballet Lesson' (SDB) ♀ H4 **new** — LIri
'Ballyhoo' (TB) — MCAu
'Banbury Beauty' (CH) ♀ H3 — CLAP CPlt
'Banbury Fair' (CH) — WWst
'Banbury Melody' (CH) — CFee GMac
'Banbury Ruffles' (SDB) — ESgI MMil NMGW NMen
'Banbury Welcome' (CH) — IBlr
'Bandera Waltz' (TB) **new** — MCAu
'Bang' (TB) — CKel
'Bar de Nuit' (TB) — ESgI
'Baria' (IB) — NFla
barnumae — EHyt EPot
'Baroque Prelude' (TB) — CKel MMil
'Basso' (IB) — SCro
'Batik' (BB) — LIri SCro WCot
'Batsford' (SDB) — CBro EHyt
'Battle Royal' (TB) — LIri
'Bayberry Candle' (TB) — LIri
'Be Dazzled' (SDB) — EFou
'Be Happy' (SDB) — NZep
'Beachgirl' (TB) **new** — LIri
'Beauty Mark' (SDB) — NZep
'Bedford Lilac' (SDB) ♀ H4 — LIri NZep
'Bee Wings' (MDB) — NZep WEas
'Before the Storm' (TB) — CKel ESgI LIri MCAu SCro
'Beguine' (TB) — ESgI
'Bel Azur' (IB) — SCro
'Bellboy' (MTB) — NZep
'Belvi Cloud' (TB) **new** — EFam
'Belvi Queen' (TB) — EFam MNrw
* 'Ben Hasel' — ECha
N 'Benton Arundel' (TB) — SCro
'Benton Dierdre' (TB) — SCro SRms
'Benton Evora' (TB) — ENot
N 'Benton Lorna' (TB) — SCro
'Benton Sheila' (TB) — SCro
'Berkeley Gold' (TB) — COtt CPrp EBee EBre ECtt EPfP
EWes GMac NGdn NMGW NOrc
NVic SCoo SDes SPer WLRN
'Berlin Tiger' ♀ H4 **new** — CRow SApp
'Best Bet' (TB) — EFam
'Best Man' (TB) **new** — EFam
'Bethany Claire' (TB) — ESgI
'Betty Chatten' (TB) — NMen WLRN
'Betty my Love' (Spuria) — LIri
'Betty Simon' (TB) — CKel ESgI EWoo
'Beverly Sills' (TB) — ESgI LIri MCAu SCro
'Bewilderbeast' (TB) — LIri
'Beyond' (TB) — SCro
'Bibury' (SDB) ♀ H4 — EGle MMil
N 'Big Day' (TB) — CKel

'Big Dipper' (TB) **new** — EWoo
'Big Money' (CH) ♀ H3 — GBuc WWst
'Big Wheel' (CH) — GMac
biglumis — see *I. lactea*
biliottii — CBro
'Bionic Comet' (AB) — SCro
'Black Dragon' (TB) — SCro WBrE
'Black Gamecock' (La) — SSpi WMAq
'Black Ink' (TB) — COlW
'Black Knight' (TB) — EBee MRav NGdn SDes SIri
'Black Swan' (TB) — CHad COtt EBee EBre EChP ECha
ECtt EMan MCLN MMil MSte
NGdn NLon SDes WCot WWal
'Black Taffeta' (TB) **new** — CKel
'Black Tie Affair' (TB) **new** — ESgI EWoo
'Black Watch' (IB) — CKel
'Blackbeard' (BB) ♀ H4 — CKel MCAu
'Blast' (IB) **new** — CKel
'Blazing Saddles' (TB) — NZep
'Blenheim Royal' (TB) — ESgI SCro
'Blessed Assurance' (IB) **new** — EFam
'Blitz' (SDB) — NZep
'Blood Covenant' (SDB) — NZep
'Blue Ballerina' (CH) ♀ H3 — GBuc
'Blue Crusader' (TB) **new** — LIri
'Blue Denim' (SDB) — CBro CM&M EBee ECtt EGle EHyt
ENot GMaP MBNS MLwd MRav
NBir NBro NCot SIri SMrm WHoo
WLin
'Blue Doll' (MDB) — NZep
'Blue Duchess' (TB) — CKel SMrm
'Blue Emperor' — SRPl
'Blue Eyed Blond' (IB) — SCro
'Blue Hendred' (SDB) — MCAu NBir
'Blue Horizon' (TB) — ERos NMen
'Blue Icing' (IB) — EFou
'Blue Line' (SDB) ♀ H4 — NZep
'Blue Luster' (TB) ♀ H4 — CHar CKel SCro
'Blue Magic' (Dut) — NRog
'Blue Moonlight' (TB) **new** — EFam
'Blue Petticoats' (TB) — ETub
'Blue Pigmy' (SDB) — EBee ERos NMen NSti SDes SIri
SPer SPet WLRN WWal
'Blue Pools' (SDB) — EFou EGle EHyt MBri NBir NZep
WTin
'Blue Reflection' (TB) — MMil
'Blue Rhythm' (TB) — CKel CM&M CSBt EBee EChP
EMan ERou EWTr GMaP GMac
MCAu MRav MSte MWgw NMoo
SChu SCoo SCro SDes SPer WLRN
WMnd
'Blue Sapphire' (TB) — CHad
'Blue Shimmer' (TB) — COtt EBee ECGN ELan EMan
ENot EPfP MEHN MRav NGdn
SCoo SCro SPer SWat WBVN
WElm WWal
'Blue Staccato' (TB) — CKel ESgI SCro SMrm
'Blue Velvet' (TB) — WMoo
'Blue Warlsind' **new** — GKev
'Bluebeard' (TB) — EHyt
'Blushes' (IB) — SCro
'Blushing Pink' (TB) — SCro
'Bodacious' (TB) — ESgI
'Bohemian' (TB) — ESgI
'Boisterous' (BB) **new** — LIri
'Bold Lassie' (SDB) — WHer
'Bold Look' (TB) **new** — LIri
'Bold Print' (IB) — MCAu SCro WWin
'Bonnie Davenport' (TB) **new** — LIri
'Bonny' (MDB) — CBro
'Boo' (SDB) — CKel MCAu NZep WDav WWin

'Bourne Graceful'	CBct EBee EPPr GCal SSpi WLRN WWal	
'Bouzy Bouzy' (TB)	ESgI	
bracteata	CFil NWoo WPGP WPer	
- JCA 13427	CLAP	
'Braithwaite' (TB)	CKel EBee EBre ELan ENot ERou MCAu MSte NGdn SCro SDes SRms SWat WElm WLRN	
'Brandy' (TB) **new**	LIri	
'Brannigan' (SDB)	CBro EHyt GKir MBri MMil NBir	
'Brasilia' (TB)	EBee NBir	
'Brass Tacks' (SDB)	NZep	
'Brassie' (SDB)	CBro CKel ERos MBNS NBro SMrm WHil	
'Bravita' (SDB) **new**	ESgI	
'Breakers' (TB) ♀ H4	CKel ESgI	
'Bridal Crown' (TB)	SCro	
§ 'Bride' (DB)	MBro WMnd	
'Bride's Halo' (TB)	EWoo SCro	
'Bright Button' (SDB)	CKel EWoo WDav	
'Bright Vision' (SDB)	ESgI NZep	
'Bright White' (MDB)	CBro CKel EHyt ERos MBNS MBri NMen WDav	
'Bright Yellow' (DB)	MRav	
'Brighteyes' (IB)	EBre ESis GKir MBro SCro SRms WPer	
'Brilliant Excuse' (TB)	NZep	
'Brindisi' (TB)	CKel ESgI MCAu SCro	
'Bristo Magic' (TB)	SCro	
'Bristol Gem' (TB)	SCro	
'Broadleigh Ann' (CH)	CBro WWst	
'Broadleigh Carolyn' (CH) ♀ H3	CBro	
'Broadleigh Charlotte'	CBro WWst	
'Broadleigh Clare' (CH)	CBro	
'Broadleigh Dorothy' (CH)	CBro GGar WWst	
'Broadleigh Elizabeth' (CH)	CBro	
N 'Broadleigh Emily' (CH)	CBro WWst	
N 'Broadleigh Florence' (CH)	CBro	
'Broadleigh Jean'	CBro WWst	
'Broadleigh Joan' (CH)	CBro	
'Broadleigh Joyce' (CH)	CBro WWst	
'Broadleigh Lavinia' (CH)	CBro MRav SApp WWst	
'Broadleigh Mitre' (CH)	CBro CPBP	
'Broadleigh Nancy' (CH)	CBro SApp	
'Broadleigh Peacock' (CH)	CBro CNic EBla IBal IBlr MMil MRav	
N 'Broadleigh Rose' (CH)	CBro CElw CHad CPlt EBla EHrv EPPr GBuc GKir IBlr MAvo MBrN MRav SAga SIri SMrm SWal WLin	
'Broadleigh Sybil' (CH)	CBro	
'Broadleigh Victoria' (CH)	CBro GBuc	
'Broadway' (TB)	EBee NZep SCro	
'Broadway Baby' (IB)	ESgI	
'Broadway Doll' (BB) **new**	EFam	
'Brom Bones' (SDB) **new**	EFam	
'Bromyard' (SDB) ♀ H4	CBro MMil	
'Bronzaire' (IB) ♀ H4	CKel MCAu	
'Bronze Beauty' Werckmeister 1992 (*boogiana* hybrid)	EPPr NBir	
'Bronze Cloud' (TB)	CKel	
'Bronze Perfection' (Dut)	WElm	
'Bronze Queen' (Dut)	LRHS WRHF	
'Brown Lasso' (BB) ♀ H4	EFou LIri MCAu SCro	
'Brown Trout' (TB)	NBir	
'Bubbling Over' (TB)	SCro	
bucharica Foster.	see *I. orchioides* Carriere	
bucharica ambig. **new**	WBor	
§ *bucharica* Foster ♀ H3-4	CBro EMar EPar EPot GIBF LAma NRog SUsu	
- 'Yellow Dushanbe'	EBee	
bulleyana	GCrs GIBF GKev NWoo SIgm SRms WAbe	

- ACE 1890	CStu	
- ACE 2296	EBee EHyt GBuc	
- black SDR 1792 **new**	GKev	
- - SDR 1793	GKev	
aff. *bulleyana* SDR 1986 **new**	GKev	
'Bumblebee Deelite' (MTB) ♀ H4	MCAu NZep WDav	
'Burgundy Brown' (TB)	NZep	
'Burgundy Bubbles' (TB)	LIri	
'Burnt Toffee' (TB)	ESgI	
'Butter Pecan' (IB)	SCro	
'Buttercup Bower' (TB)	MCAu NMGW	
'Buttercup Charm' (MDB)	NZep	
'Buttermere' (TB)	SRms	
'Butterpat' (IB)	ESgI NZep	
'Butterscotch Kiss' (TB)	EBee EBre EChP ELan EMan ERou MMil MRav MTis MWgw NBir SCoo SCro	
'Button Box' (SDB)	NZep	
'Cabaret Royale' (TB)	ESgI MCAu	
'Cable Car' (TB)	CKel	
'Caliente' (TB)	EBee EPfP MCAu MRav SDes	
'California Style' (IB)	NZep	
§ Californian hybrids	CElw CPBP EHyt EPot MRav NBir SIng SSpi WAbe WCFE WCot WWhi	
'Calypso Mood' (TB)	SCro	
'Cambridge Blue'	see *I.* 'Monspur Cambridge Blue'	
'Camelot Rose' (TB)	MCAu	
'Cameo Blush' (BB) **new**	EFam	
'Cameroun' (TB) **new**	ESgI	
'Campbellii'	see *I. lutescens* 'Campbellii'	
canadensis	see *I. hookeri*	
'Candyland' (BB) **new**	EFam	
'Candylane' (MTB) **new**	CKel	
'Cannington Ochre' (SDB)	CBro	
'Cannington Skies' (IB)	MMil	
'Cantab' (Reticulata)	CAvo CBro EBre EHyt EPar EPot ETub LAma NCel NRog WLin	
'Cantina' (TB) **new**	EFam	
capnoides	WWst	
'Capricious' (TB)	ESgI SCro	
'Caption' (TB)	ESgI	
'Caramba' (TB)	SCro	
'Cardew' (TB) ♀ H4	CKel	
'Carilla' (SDB)	ERos LPhx	
'Carnaby' (TB)	EFou ESgI MCAu	
'Carnival Time' (TB)	EFou	
'Carnton' (TB)	WEas	
'Carolina Gold' (TB)	SCro	
'Carolyn' (CH)	CFir	
'Carolyn Rose' (MTB) ♀ H4	NZep	
'Carved Pink' (TB)	SCro	
'Casbah' (TB)	SCro	
'Cascade Sprite' (SDB)	SRms	
'Cascadian Skies' (TB)	ERou	
'Catalyst' (TB)	SCro	
'Cayenne Capers' (TB)	MMil	
* 'Cedric Morris'	EWes	
'Cee Jay' (IB) ♀ H4 **new**	EWoo LIri	
'Celebration Song' (TB)	ESgI	
'Centre Court' (TB)	SCro	
'Certainly Certainly' (TB) **new**	EFam	
chamaeiris	see *I. lutescens*	
'Champagne Elegance' (TB)	ESgI MCAu MMil NBir	
'Champagne Waltz' (TB)	LIri	
'Change of Pace' (TB)	SCro	
'Chanted' (SDB)	ESgI	
'Chanteuse' (TB)	SCro	
'Chantilly' (TB)	CM&M COtt CSBt EBee EBre EChP ELan EMan EPfP MRav	

	MTis NBir NGdn NOrc SCro SPer WCra WFoF
'Chapeau' (TB)	MCAu
'Charger' (TB)	MMil
I 'Charming' (TB)	CKel
'Chartreuse Ruffles' (TB)	EWoo SCro
'Chasing Rainbows' (TB) **new**	LIri
'Chaste White' (TB) **new**	EFam
'Cheers' (IB)	NZep
'Cherokee Lace' (Spuria)	WTin
'Cherry Garden' (SDB)	CBro CFwr CKel EBee ECtt EGoo EHrv ELan EVFa EWes GKir IPot LPhx MBNS MBri MBro MMil MRav NBir NCot NSti NWCA SMrm WCot WEas WElm
'Cherry Glen' (TB) **new**	LIri
'Cherry Orchard' (TB)	NFor NLon
'Cherry Smoke' (TB)	SCro
'Cherub Tears' (SDB)	EHyt NZep
'Cherub's Smile' (TB)	ESgI SCro
'Chickee' (MTB) ♀	CKel NZep
'Chicken Little' (MDB)	CBro EBee NMoo
'Chief Quinaby' (TB)	SCro
'Chief Waukesha' (TB)	SCro
I 'Chieftain' (SDB)	MRav WWin
'China Dragon' (TB)	SCro
'Chivalry' (TB)	WTin
'Chocolate Vanilla' (TB)	LIri
'Chorus Girl' (TB)	CKel
'Christmas Angel' (TB)	EBre ERou
'Christmas Time' (TB)	NMGW
Chrysofor Group	WPGP
chrysographes ♀ H4	CHid CPrp EBre EChP GKir GMac IKee LPVe LRHS MCCP MRav MTho MWrn NSti SMac SRms SScr WAbe WAul WHil WPnP WRHF WWeb WWhi WWin
- *alba*	NBir
- black	More than 30 suppliers
I - 'Black Beauty'	CFir
I - 'Black Knight'	CBot CHid EPfP GBuc GCal MDun MHer MSte NBid NChi NFor NLar SWat WCom WViv WWin
- crimson	IBlr NWoo
N - 'Inshriach'	CFai EHyt GBuc GDra IBlr SPer WAbe
- 'Kew Black'	CDes NBir NChi WHer WHil
- 'Mandarin Purple'	EBee GBuc GCal GMac SWat WCot WMoo
- purple	MBro
§ - 'Rubella'	CPlt CRow GMac MMil MRav MSte WFar WPrP
* - var. *rubella* 'Wine'	CHad
- 'Rubra'	see *I. chrysographes* 'Rubella'
chrysographes x *forrestii*	GDra NBir WViv
chrysophylla	GBuc
- JCA 13233	CLAP
'Chubby Cheeks' (SDB)	CKel
'Chuck Waltermire' (TB) **new**	EFam
N 'Cider Haze' (TB)	CKel
'Cimarron Rose' (SDB)	ESgI NZep
'City of David' (TB)	SCro
'Clairette' (Reticulata)	CBro EPar LAma
'Clara Garland' (IB) ♀ H4	CKel
'Clarence' (TB)	ESgI LIri
clarkei	EPot GIBF WFar
- CC 3320	WCot
- CC 3408	WCot

'Classic Bordeaux' (TB) **new**	LIri
'Classic Look' (TB)	ESgI LIri
'Clay's Caper' (SDB)	EFou
'Clear Morning Sky' (TB) ♀ H4	LIri
N 'Cleo' (TB)	CKel ESgI NBir NSti
'Cliffs of Dover' (TB)	CKel SDes SIri SRms
'Cloudcap' (TB)	SRms
'Cloudless Sunrise' (TB)	ERou
'Coalignition' (TB)	LIri
'Cobalt Mesa' (Spuria) **new**	LIri
'Colette Thurillet' (TB) **new**	ESgI MCAu
collettii	EBee
'Color Brite' (BB)	SCro
'Color Splash' (TB)	SCro
'Columbia Blue' (TB)	SCro
'Combo' (SDB)	CKel
'Condottiere' (TB)	SCro
'Confetti' (TB)	LRHS
confusa ♀ H3	CHEx CKel CPla CSev EPla IFro SAPC SArc SChr SEND SSpi SSte WDyG WFar WMul WPic WWst
§ - 'Martyn Rix'	CBct CDes CHad CHid CLAP CPou CRez CSev CSpe EBee EMan GCal LPio MBct MHer SSpi WCot WDyG WFar WHrl WMnd WOld WPGP WPer
'Conjuration' (TB)	ESgI EWoo LIri MMil
'Conspiracy' (TB) **new**	LIri
'Constant Wattez' (IB)	CKel EBee ESgI EWTr LBuc WMnd
'Consummation' (MTB)	NZep
'Cool Treat' (BB) ♀ H4 **new**	LIri
'Copatonic' (TB) **new**	LIri
'Copper Classic' (TB)	ESgI NZep SCro SIri
'Cops' (SDB)	NZep
'Coquetterie' (TB)	ESgI
'Coral Chalice' (TB)	ERou
'Coral Strand' (TB)	MCAu
'Coral Wings' (SDB)	NZep
'Cordoba' (TB) **new**	LIri
'Corn Harvest' (TB)	EFam MMil NZep
'Corrida' (TB)	LBuc
'Côte d'Or' (TB)	SCro
'Cozy Calico' (TB)	ESgI SCro
'Cracklin Burgundy' (TB)	SCro
'Cranapple' (BB) ♀ H4	LIri
'Cranberry Ice' (TB)	EWoo SCro SIri
'Cream Beauty' (Dut) **new**	ETub
'Cream Cake' (SDB)	NZep
'Cream Soda' (TB) ♀ H4	CKel
'Creative Stitchery' (TB)	SCro
'Creme d'Or' (TB)	ESgI
cretensis	see *I. unguicularis* subsp. *cretensis*
'Cricket Lane' (SDB)	NZep
'Crimson Fire' (TB)	SCro
'Crimson Tiger' (TB)	EFam LIri
'Crispette' (TB)	MCAu
cristata ♀ H4	EBla EPot GBuc MDHE NPro SIng SRms WCru
- 'Alba'	EBee ERos LBee LRHS NHar NWCA
- x *lacustris*	EPot ETow NMen
crocea ♀ H4	EBee ETow GKev
'Croftway Lemon' (TB)	SCro
'Cross Stitch' (TB)	MMil NZep
'Crown Sterling' (TB)	SCro
'Crowned Heads' (TB) **new**	LIri
'Crystal Glitters' (TB)	ESgI
'Cum Laude' (IB)	SCro
cuniculiformis ACE 2224	GBuc
'Cupid's Cup' (SDB) **new**	ESgI

'Curtain Up' (TB) **new** — EFam
'Cutie' (IB) — ESgI NZep SDes
'Cyanea' (DB) — EFam SIng SIri SMrm
cycloglossa — CFwr EBee LRHS WWst
– HW&E 7727 — CLAP
'Dance Away' (TB) — ESgI
'Dancers Veil' (TB) — CHar CKel EBre ECtt EFou ERou GKir MRav NVic SCro SIri SMer
'Dancin'' (IB) — NZep
'Dancing Gold' (MTB) — NZep
danfordiae — CAvo CBcs CBro CPMA EBre EPar EPot ETub EWTr LAma LRHS MBNS NRog WCot WLin
'Dante' (TB) — CKel
'Dardanus' (Aril) — EPot
'Dark Blizzard' (IB) — NZep
'Dark Crystal' (SDB) **new** — ESgI
'Dark Spark' (SDB) — MCAu
'Dark Vader' (SDB) — ESgI
'Darkside' (TB) — SCro
'Dauntless' (TB) **new** — ESgI
'Dawn Candle' (Spuria) — SApp
'Dawn Glory' (TB) — SCro
'Dawning' (TB) — LIri
'Dazzling Gold' (TB) — ESgI SCro
§ *decora* — CBro EBee GIBF LEdu MNrw
– B&SWJ 2122 — WCru
'Deep Black' (TB) — COtt EBee EChP EMan EPfP MCAu MWgw NOrc SChu SCro SDes SHBN SPer SWat
'Deep Caress' (TB) — ESgI
'Deep Dark Secret' (TB) **new** — LIri
'Deep Fire' (TB) — SCro
'Deep Pacific' (TB) — LRHS MBri
'Deep Space' (TB) — MCAu
delavayi ♀ H4 — EBee GIBF GMaP IBlr LSyl MLLN WCot
– SDR 50 — GKev
'Delicate Lady' (IB) ♀ H4 **new** — CKel
'Delphi' (TB) — SCro
'Delta Butterfly' (La) — WMAq
'Demon' (SDB) — CKel CMil CPlt EFou EHyt LRHS WDav
'Denys Humphries' (TB) — CKel
'Deputé Nomblot' (TB) — ESgI
'Derwentwater' (TB) — MMil SRms
'Desert Dream' (AB) — GGar
'Desert Dream' (Sino-Sib) — GDra
'Desert Echo' (TB) — EFou
'Desert Song' (TB) — CKel
'Designer Gown' (TB) — ERou
'Devilry' (SDB) — EHyt
'Dew Point' (IB) — SCro
'Diabolique' (TB) — LIri
dichotoma **new** — EBee
'Die Braut' — see *I.* 'Bride'
'Dilly Green' (TB) **new** — LIri
'Discretion' (TB) — SCro
'Ditto' (MDB) — EFam
'Dixie Darling' (TB) **new** — ESgI
'Dixie Pixie' (SDB) — EGle ESis WTin
'Doll' (IB) **new** — EWoo
'Dolly Madison' (TB) **new** — ESgI
* 'Don Brownsay' — MMil
'Don't Be Cruel' (TB) **new** — LIri
'Dorcas Lives Again' (TB) **new** — EFam
'Dorothy Robbins' (CH) — WWst
'Double Lament' (SDB) — CBro ERos MMil WOut
'Double Time' (TB) **new** — EFam

douglasiana ♀ H4 — EChP EPar EPla GKev IBlr SMac SSpi WAbe WFar WOut
– 'Amiguita' — CFir WCom WWst
* – Bandon strain — SSpi
'Doxa' (IB) — SCro
'Draco' (TB) **new** — ESgI
'Dream Builder' (TB) — NMGW
'Dreamsicle' (TB) — SCro
'Dress Circle' (Spuria) — LIri
'Dualtone' (TB) — CKel
'Duke of Earl' (TB) **new** — EFam
'Dundee' (TB) — SCro
'Dunlin' (MDB) — CBro EHyt ERos NBir NMen
'Dusky Challenger' (TB) — ESgI EWoo LIri MCAu SCro
'Dutch Chocolate' (TB) — ESgI MMil SIri
'Dwight Enys' (TB) ♀ H4 — CKel
dykesii — CRow EBee
'Dynamite' (TB) — LIri
'Eagle's Flight' (TB) — NMGW
'Eardisland' (IB) ♀ H4 — MMil
'Earl' (TB) — MMil
'Earl of Essex' (TB) — EFam MCAu MMil SCro
'Early Edition' (IB) — EFou
'Early Frost' (IB) — CKel SCro
'Early Light' (TB) ♀ H4 — LIri
'Echo de France' (TB) — ESgI
'Ecstatic Echo' (TB) — ESgI
'Edith Wolford' (TB) — ESgI EWoo LIri MCAu SCro
'Ed's Blue' (DB) — ELan
'Edward' (Reticulata) — EPot LAma
'Edward of Windsor' (TB) — CHad CMil EBee ELan ERou NBir NOrc SCoo SDes WLRN WMnd
'Elainealope' (TB) — EFam LIri
'Eleanor's Pride' (TB) — CKel ESgI MMil
elegantissima — see *I. iberica* subsp. *elegantissima*
'Elizabeth Arden' (TB) — CKel
'Elizabeth of England' (TB) — EBee
'Elizabeth Poldark' (TB) — ESgI LIri
'Elvinhall' — CBro
'Ember Days' (TB) — MMil
'Empress of India' (TB) — EBee LBuc SDes
'Enchanted Gold' (SDB) — NZep
'Encircle' (CH) — GBuc WWst
'English Charm' (TB) **new** — EFam
'English Cottage' (TB) — EBee GCal MCAu MMil MWat SCro SDes WIvy
'English Knight' (TB) **new** — EFam
'Ennerdale' (TB) — SRms
§ *ensata* ♀ H4 — CBen CMHG COlW CPLG CSBt EBee ECGP ELan ENot EPfP GMac LPBA LRHS LSyl MNrw MSta NBro NGdn NLar SPlb SRms SWat WFar WHil WPer WWin WWpP
– 'Activity' — CLAP CRow NBro SMrm WFar WOBN
– 'Alba' — ECha
– 'Aldridge Prelude' **new** — WAul
– 'Apollo' — CBen CRow EWTr
– 'Artist' — NBro
– 'Barnhawk Sybil' — SSpi
– 'Barr Purple East' ♀ H4 — CRow
– 'Beni-tsubaki' — WOBN
I – 'Blue King' — CLAP NBro
I – 'Blue Peter' — CBen CRow
– 'Blush' — NBro
– 'Caprician Butterfly' ♀ H4 — EPfP WHil
– 'Carnival Prince' — CFir CLAP NBro SBod SMrm WFar WMoo WPnP
– 'Charm' — EBre
– 'Chitose-no-tomo' — CRow

'Feed Back' (TB) **new** — EFam
'Feminist' (TB) — SCro
fernaldii NNS 95-296 — NWCA
'Festive Skirt' (TB) — CKel
'Feu du Ciel' (TB) — ESgI LIri
'Fierce Fire' (IB) ♀ H4 — CKel
'Fiery Song' (TB) — CKel
filifolia — CBro
'Film Festival' (TB) — ESgI
N 'Fire and Flame' (TB) — NBir
'Fire Siren' (TB) — MMil
'Firecracker' (TB) — ERou MRav
'First Interstate' (TB) — ESgI LIri SCro
'First Step' (SDB) — NZep
'Five Star Admiral' (TB) — SCro
'Flaming Dragon' — CKel EBee SRPl
'Flapjack' (SDB) — NZep
'Flash' — NHol
'Flashing Beacon' (MTB) — NZep
'Flea Circus' (MDB) — NZep
'Flirty Mary' (SDB) — EGle
§ 'Florentina' (IB/TB) ♀ H4 — CArn CBro CKel ECha EFou EMFP
    ESgI EWoo GPoy IBlr ILis MCAu
    MChe MHer MRav NBid NBir
    SCro SIde WCot WPic WWye
'Flower Shower' (SDB) **new** — EFam
'Flumadiddle' (IB) — CBro
'Focal Point' — LBuc
'Focus' (TB) — SCro
§ *foetidissima* ♀ H4 — More than 30 suppliers
 - *aurea* — WCot
 - *chinensis* — see I. *foetidissima* var. *citrina*
§ - var. *citrina* — CFil CFir CRow EBee EGle EPPr
    EPla GAbr GCal GKir IBlr ITer
    LFlo MDcl MBri MRav SSpi STcs
    SUsu WAbe WCom WCot WEas
    WRus WWin WWye
 - 'Fructu Albo' — CNat EBee EChP MMHG SUsu
    WCot WRus
 - var. *lutescens* — CHid EMon EPPr IBlr MTed
 - 'Moonshy Seedling' — CSWP EGol
 - 'Variegata' (v) ♀ H4 — CBro CElw CFil CRow EBee ECtt
    EGle EHrv EOrc EPPr EPfP EPla
    GMaP MBri MCCP MLwd MRav
    NBir NLar NLon NMRc NPar NPer
    SSpi SUsu WPGP WRus WWhi
 - yellow seeded — EFou MTed WCot
'Foggy Dew' (TB) — GKir
'Folkwang' (TB) — EBee EWTr SDes
'Fondation Van Gogh' (TB) — ESgI LIri
'Forest Light' (SDB) — CBro EHyt ESgI MBro
'Forever Yours' (TB) **new** — EFam
'Forge Fire' (TB) — ESgI
'Forgotten Dreams' (CH) — WWst
formosana B&SWJ 3076 — WCru
forrestii ♀ H4 — More than 30 suppliers
 - hybrids — GDra IBlr
'Fort Apache' (TB) — ESgI EWoo SCro
fosteriana — WWst
'Foxy Lady' (TB) — ESgI
'Frank Elder' (Reticulata) — CAvo CBro EHyt EPot ERos GCrs
    LAma LPio LRHS MRav MTho
    NMen WCot WIvy
'Frans Hals' (Dut) — EWTr MNrw
'French Fashion' (TB) **new** — LIri
'Fresno Calypso' (TB) — ESgI MCAu
'Fresno Flash' (TB) — SCro
'Frimousee' (TB) **new** — ESgI
'Fringe of Gold' (TB) — EBee SCro
'Frison-roche' (TB) — ESgI
'Fritillary Flight' (IB) — CKel
    ♀ H4 **new**

'Frontier Marshall' (TB) — NMoo
'Frost and Flame' (TB) — CM&M EBee EBre EChP ECtt
    ELan ENot EPfP ERou EWll GKir
    MBri MCAu MRav NGdn NMoo
    NOrc SChu SCro SDes SPer SWat
'Frosted Angel' (SDB) — WDav
'Frosted Velvet' **new** — EFam
'Frosty Crown' (SDB) — CDes
'Full Tide' (TB) — SCro
fulva — CDes CRow EBee GCal IBlr NBir
    NBro NPPs NSti SIri SMrm SSpi
    WCot WEas WPGP
 - 'Marvell Gold' (La) — CDes CRow EBee
x *fulvala* ♀ H4 — CDes CMea CSam EBee EMon IBlr
    NBir NSti SCro WPGP
 - 'Violacea' — EBee
'Furnaceman' (SDB) — CBro EHyt ERos MBri MBro MMil
'Fuzzy' (MDB) — ERos
'Fuzzy Face' (SDB) — NZep
'Gala Gown' (TB) — MCAu
§ *galatica* — WWst
'Galleon Gold' (SDB) — NZep
§ 'Gelbe Mantel' (Sino-Sib) — CBgR CBot CHid CLAP CRez
    EBee EBla EChP LHop NBir NBro
    NGdn NHol NSti WCot WFar WHil
'Gentius' (TB) **new** — EBee WMnd
'George' (Reticulata) ♀ H4 — CAvo CBro EBre EPar EPot ERos
    ETub GCrs LRHS WCot WRHF
'Gerald Darby' — see I. x *robusta* 'Gerald Darby'
germanica ♀ H4 — EHol NFor
 - var. *florentina* — see I. 'Florentina'
* - 'Mel Jope' — NBir
 - 'Nepalensis' — EGoo
'Gibson Girl' (TB) — MMil
'Gigglepot' (SDB) — LPhx MMil
'Ginger Swirl' (TB) — SCro
'Gingerbread Man' (SDB) — CBro CHad CMca EFou EGle EHrv
    ERos ESgI LPhx LPio MBrN MBro
    MMil NMen SIri SMrm SWal
    WHoo WIvy WWin
'Glacier' (TB) — CKel
'Glacier King' (TB) **new** — EFam
'Glad Rags' (TB) — ESgI NZep
'Glenwillow' (MDB) — NZep
'Gnu' (TB) — LIri
'Gnus Flash' (TB) — LIri
'Godfrey Owen' (TB) — CKel MCAu
'Godsend' (TB) — LIri
'Going My Way' (TB) — ESgI EWoo LRHS MCAu SCro SIri
'Gold Burst' (TB) — SCro
'Gold Galore' (TB) — SCro
'Gold Mania' (Spuria) **new** — LIri
'Gold of Autumn' (TB) — CKel SMrm
'Golden Alps' (TB) — ENot
'Golden Child' (SDB) **new** — EFam
'Golden Encore' (TB) — CKel EFam MCAu MWat
'Golden Fair' (SDB) — NBir
'Golden Harvest' (Dut) — LRHS
'Golden Inmortal' (TB) **new** — EFam
'Golden Muffin' (IB) — NZep
'Golden Opportunity' (TB) **new** — LIri
'Golden Planet' (TB) — CKel
'Golden Ruby' (SDB) — ESis
'Golden Waves' (Cal-Sib) ♀ H3 — CBro
goniocarpa — EBee
 - var. *grossa* **new** — EBee
'Good and True' (IB) — SCro
'Good Looking' (TB) — LIri MCAu
'Good Show' (TB) — SCro
'Gordon' (Reticulata) — EPot LAma LRHS

'Goring Ace' (CH) ♀ H3   WWst
'Goring Steeple'   WWst
  (CH) ♀ H4 **new**
gormanii   see *I. tenax*
'Gosh' (SDB)   CKel
'Gossip' (DB)   CBro
gracilipes   GEdr
 - 'Alba'   GEdr SCnR
 - x *lacustris*   GEdr WAbe
graeberiana   EPot
 - white fall   LRHS WWst
 - yellow fall   LRHS WWst
graminea ♀ H4   More than 30 suppliers
 - 'Hort's Variety'   GCal
 - var. *pseudocyperus*   CRow NSti SDys
graminifolia   see *I. kerneriana*
'Granada Gold' (TB)   ENot SRms
'Grand Baroque' (TB)   EFam MMil
'Grand Waltz' (TB)   SCro
'Grandma's Hat' (SDB) **new**   EBee
'Grape Reprise' (TB) **new**   EFam
'Grapelet' (MDB)   ERos NZep
'Grapesicle' (SDB)   NZep
'Great Lakes' **new**   ESgI
'Grecian Goddess'   EFam
  (TB) **new**
'Grecian Skies' (TB)   SCro
'Green Halo' (DB)   EGle LPhx
'Green Ice' (TB)   CKel
'Green Prophecy' (TB)   LIri
'Green Spot' (SDB) ♀ H4   More than 30 suppliers
'Green Streak' (TB)   LIri
'Greenstuff' (SDB)   LPhx MMil
'Gypsy Beauty' (Dut) **new**   ETub
'Gypsy Boy' (SDB)   MMil NMGW NZep
'Gypsy Caravan' (TB)   SCro
'Gypsy Jewels' (TB)   CKel ESgI
'Gypsy Romance' (TB)   LIri
'H.C. van Vliet' (Dut)   NRog
* 'Haizon Bleu' **new**   EWoo
'Hallowed Thought' (TB)   MMil MWat
halophila   see *I. spuria* subsp. *halophila*
'Hand Painted' (TB) **new**   EFam
'Handshake' (TB)   LIri
'Happening' (SDB)   NZep
'Happy Birthday' (TB) **new**   ESgI
'Happy Mood' (IB) ♀ H4   EFou SIri
'Happy Pal' (TB) **new**   EFam
'Harbor Blue' (TB)   CKel EBee MWat SCro SDes
'Harlow Gold' (IB)   EFou ESgI NZep
'Harmony' (Reticulata)   CAvo CBro EBre EPot LAma LRHS
      MBri NCel NRog
'Harriette Halloway' (TB)   CPrp EBee SMrm
'Harvest King' (TB)   ESgI LIri
'Headlines' (TB)   CKel MCAu
'Heaven's Bounty' (BB) **new**   EFam
'Helen Boehm' (TB)   SCro
'Helen Proctor' (IB)   ESgI NZep SCro
'Helge' (IB)   COIW EBee EPfP SDes SWat
'Hellcat' (IB)   NZep
'Hello Darkness' (TB)   ESgI LIri
'Hell's Fire' (TB)   SCro
'Hercules' (Reticulata)   LAma
'Hers' (IB)   SCro
'High Command' (TB)   CKel SCro SMrm
'High Energy' (TB) **new**   EFam
'High Life' (TB)   SCro
'His' (IB)   SCro
histrio   LAma
 - subsp. *aintabensis*   EHyt EPot LAma
histrioides   GCrs WAbe WLin
§ - 'Angel's Eye'   CLAP ERos
 - 'Angel's Tears'   see *I. bistrioides* 'Angel's Eye'

 - 'Lady Beatrice Stanley'   CLAP EPot GCrs
N - 'Major'   CBro CLAP GCrs LAma
 - 'Reine Immaculée'   ERos
 - var. *sophenensis*   CLAP
'Hocus Pocus' (SDB)   EFou EHyt EPPr EWoo
'Holden Clough'   CBos CBot CHad CHar CKel
  (SpecHybrid) ♀ H4   CRow EBee EFou ELan EMFW
      EPPr EPfP EPla EPri GMaP LRHS
      MFir MMil MRav NBir NGdn NSti
      SSvw WAul WEas WFar WLin WPrP
      WSan WWin
'Holy Night' (TB)   CKel
'Honey Behold' (SDB)   CKel
'Honey Glazed' (IB)   ESgI NZep
'Honey Mocha' (TB)   SCro
'Honey Scoop' (TB) **new**   EFam
'Honington' (SDB)   MCAu MMil
'Honky Tonk Blues' (TB)   ESgI LIri
'Honorabile' (MTB)   MCAu SMrm
hoogiana ♀ H3   EBee GKev LRHS MBow
 - 'Alba'   WWst
 - 'Gypsy Beauty' **new**   EPPr
 - 'Purpurea'   LRHS
§ *hookeri*   CHad CSpe EDAr ELan GEdr GIBF
      NJOw NWoo SAga SOkd WAbe
hookeriana   WCot
'Hopscotch' (BB)   SCro
'Hot Chocolate' (TB)   LIri
'Hot Spice' (IB)   MCAu NZep
'Howard Weed' (TB)   SDes
'Hubbub' (IB)   SCro
'Hula Doll' (MDB)   EGle NMen
'Hula Honey' (TB) **new**   EFam
hyrcana   CBro EBee LAma LRHS
'I Bless' (IB) **new**   EFam
'I Do' (TB)   MMil NZep
§ *iberica*   CMea EHyt EPot
  subsp. *elegantissima*
 - subsp. *iberica*   EHyt EPot WWst
'Ice Dancer' (TB) ♀ H4   CKel
'Iced Tea' (TB)   LIri
'Iced Vanilla' (IB)   CKel
'Ida' (Reticulata)   EPot LAma
illyrica   see *I. pallida*
'Immortality' (TB)   MCAu SCro
'Imperator' (Dut)   MTis
'Imperator' (TB)   EBee EWTr SDes
'Imperial Bronze' (Spuria)   EFou NFor
'Impetuous' (BB) ♀ H4   EFou
'Imprimis' (TB) **new**   LIri
'In Depth' (Spuria) **new**   LIri
'In Town' (TB)   ESgI EWoo
inconspicua **new**   WWst
'Indian Chief' (TB)   CM&M EBee EMil LRHS MCAu
      WAul
'Indian Dancer' (BB) **new**   CKel
'Indian Jewel' (SDB)   EGle
'Indian Pow Wow' (SDB)   CRDP CSev
N 'Indian Sunset' (TB)   CKel
'Indigo Flight' (IB)   EFou
'Infernal Fire' (TB)   LIri
'Infinite Grace' (TB)   SCro
'Innocent Heart' (IB) ♀ H4   SCro
innominata   CFil CHad CWCL EBee ECha IBlr
      LBee LHop LRHS MLwd MNrw
      MTho NBir NBro NHar NMen SChr
      SRms SWal WEas WPGP WWal
 - JCA 13225   CLAP SSpi
 - JCA 13227   SSpi
 - apricot   IBlr NWoo
 - Ballyrogan hybrids   IBlr
 - copper   IBlr
 - rose   CNic ERos

N – 'Spinners'   SSpi
   – yellow   CAvo NRya
   'Inscription' (SDB)   EGle EHyt
   'Interpol' (TB)   ESgI
   'Invitation' (TB) **new**   ESgI
   'Irish Doll' (MDB)   EGle
   'Irish Temper' (SDB)   MMil
   'Irish Tune' (TB)   ESgI SCro
   'Ishmael' (SDB)   EGle
   'Istanbul' (TB) **new**   EFam
   'It's Magic' (TB)   LIri
   'J.S. Dijt' (Reticulata)   CAvo CBro EBre EPar EPot LAma
                                   LRHS MBow MBri NCel NRog
   'Jade Mist' (SDB)   EGle GKir LRHS
   'Jan Reagan' (SDB)   NZep
   'Jane Phillips' (TB) ♀ H4   CHad CKel CPrp EBre ECGN
                                   EChP ECha ECtt EGle ELan ENot
                                   EPfP ERou GKir LHop MCAu
                                   MCLN MEHN MMil MRav MSte
                                   NGdn NOrc SCro SDes SHBN
                                   SMrm SPer SWat WFar
   'Jane Taylor' (SDB)   CBro EGle
   'Janet Lane' (BB) **new**   CKel
   'Janice Chesnik' (Spuria)   LIri
   japonica ♀ H3   CHEx EHrv LPio NPer WFar
   – L 638   SCro
   – 'Aphrodite'   WPnP WTin
      Sprenger C.1907 (v)
N – 'Ledger's Variety'   CAvo CBro CHll CKel CPrp CSpe
                                   EBee ECha EHrv ELan EPar EPfP
                                   EPla EPri IGor MRav SChr SIri
                                   SMad WPGP
   japonica pallescens **new**   EBee
   – 'Variegata' (v) ♀ H3   CAvo CBot CHEx CHad CKel
                                   CSpe EBee ECha EHrv EPar GGar
                                   LRHS NBro NOre NPer EAga EArc
                                   SDes SMad SSpi WCFE WEas WFar
                                   WHer WHil WPic
   'Jasper Gem' (MDB)   EGle ERos GKir MMil NBir
   'Java Charm' (TB)   MMil
   'Jazz Festival' (TB) **new**   MCAu
   'Jazzamatazz' (SDB)   ESgI
   'Jazzebel' (TB)   SCro
   'Jean Cayeux' (TB) **new**   ESgI
   'Jean Guymer' (TB)   EFam MMil NBir
   'Jeanne Price' (TB)   MCAu
   'Jeannine' (Reticulata)   LAma
   'Jephthah's Daughter'   EFam
      (TB) **new**
   'Jeremy Brian' (SDB) ♀ H4   MMil
   'Jesse's Song' (TB)   ESgI MCAu NZep SCro
   'Jewel Baby' (SDB)   CBro NMGW NZep
   'Jewel Bright' (SDB)   EFou
   'Jeweler's Art' (SDB) **new**   EWoo
   'Jiansada' (SDB)   CBro
   'Jitterbug' (TB)   EHrv
   'Joanna' (TB)   EBee SDes
   'Joanna Taylor' (MDB)   EHyt ERos NMen NZep
N 'Joe Elliott' (CH)   EGle
   'John' (IB)   SCro
   'John Taylor' (SDB)   CKel
   'Joyce' (Reticulata)   CBro EPar EPot LAma LRHS MBri
                                   NCel NRog
   'Joyce Terry' (TB)   ESgI GKir LRHS MBri
   'Joyful' (SDB)   ESgI
   'Jubilee Gem' (TB)   CKel
   'July Sunshine' (TB) **new**   EFam
   'June Prom' (IB)   SCro
   'Jungle Shadows' (BB)   LPhx MRav NBir SIri SMrm
   'Jurassic Park' (TB)   LIri
   'Just Dance' (IB) **new**   ESgI
   'Just Jennifer' (BB)   MCAu
   kaempferi   see *I. ensata*

   'Kaibab Trail' (Spuria) **new** LIri
   'Kangchenjunga' (TB) **new**   ESgI
   'Karen Christine' (TB)   SCro
   kashmiriana   CBcs
   'Katharine Hodgkin'   CAvo CBro CLAP EBee EHyt EPot
      (Reticulata) ♀ H4   ERos GAbr GCrs ITim LAma LPhx
                                   LRHS MRav MTho NHar NMen
                                   NRog NSla SMrm WAbe WCot
                                   WIvy WLin
   'Katie-Koo' (IB) ♀ H4   CKel WDav
   'Katinka' (CH)   WWst
   'Katy Petts' (SDB)   EFou NZep
   'Kayleigh Jayne Louise'   CKel
      (TB)
   'Kayo' (SDB)   EFou EGle EHyt MMil NZep
   'Kelway Renaissance' (TB)   CKel
   kemaonensis   EBee NHar
   'Kent Pride' (TB)   CHad CMil EBee EBre EChP EFou
                                   EPPr EPfP ERou GKir MCAu MMil
                                   MRav MWat SChu SCro SWat
                                   WWin
   'Kentucky Bluegrass' (SDB)   EFou MMil WWin
   'Kentucky Derby' (TB)   SCro
   'Kermit' (IB)   SCro
§ *kerneriana* ♀ H4   CBro CPom EBee ERos ETow
                                   GBuc LRHS MLLN MNrw NBir
                                   SIgm SMHy SScr SUsu WOBN
                                   WPen
   'Kevin's Theme' (TB) **new**   LIri
   'Kilt Lilt' (TB)   SCro
   kirkwoodii   SBla
   'Kissing Circle' (TB)   ESgI EWoo
   'Kitt Peak' (Spuria) **new**   LIri
   'Kiwi Capers' (SDB)   NZep
   'Kiwi Slices' (SDB)   ESgI NMGW
   hlattii   see *I. spuria* subsp
                                   musulmanica
   'Knick Knack' (MDB)   CBro CDes EBee EHyt EMan ERos
                                   ESis GCrs LBee LPhx LPio LRHS
                                   MRav MTis NCiC NMGW NMen
                                   SIng SMrm WHil WOBN WWal
                                   WWin
   'Kochii' (IB)   GCal
   kolpakowskiana   WWst
   korolkowii   GIBF
   – 'Violacea'   EBee WWst
   kuschakewiczii   WWst
   'La Senda' (Spuria)   WCot
   'Lace Artistry' (TB)   SCro
   'Laced Cotton' (TB)   SCro
   'Laced Lemonade' (SDB)   EFou GKir LRHS MBri
§ *lactea* ♀ H4   SCro
   lacustris ♀ H4   CBro ERos GCrs NBro NHar
                                   NMen NWCA WAbe
   'Lady Emma' (MTB) **new**   EFam
   'Lady Essex' (TB) **new**   EFam
   'Lady Friend' (TB)   ERou ESgI SCro
   'Lady Ilse' (TB)   MCAu
   'Lady Madonna' (TB)   SCro
   'Lady Mohr' (AB)   CKel
   'Lady of Fatima' (TB)   ESgI
   'Lady R' (SDB)   EHyt
   'Lady Snowflake' (TB) **new**   ETub
   laeuinea   EBee
§ *laevigata* ♀ H4   CKel CRow CWat ECha EGle
                                   EGol EHon ELan EPfP LPBA MRav
                                   MSta NBlu NBro NGdn NPer SPer
                                   SWat WFar WMAq WShi WWpP
   – 'Alba'   CBen CRow ECha EGol EHon
                                   EPfP GDea LEdu LPBA SSpi SWat
                                   WAbe WFar WWpP
   – 'Albopurpurea'   CLAP EMFW SLon WTMC
   – 'Atropurpurea'   CRow EGol IBlr LPBA

	- 'Colchesterensis'	CBen CLAP CRow CWat EGol EMFW LPBA MSta NPer SLon SWat WCra WHrl WMAq WTMC
	- 'Dark Pettale'	CLAP
I	- 'Dorothy'	LPBA MSta NGdn
*	- 'Dorothy Robinson'	SWat
	- 'Elegant'	see I. laevigata 'Weymouth Elegant'
I	- 'Elegante'	SWat
	- 'Elgar'	WMAq
	- 'Liam Johns'	CRow
	- 'Midnight'	see I. laevigata 'Weymouth Midnight'
	- 'Mottled Beauty'	CRow MSta
	- 'Murasama'	CRow
N	- 'Plum Purple'	EGle
I	- 'Reveille'	EGle
	- 'Richard Greany'	CRow
	- 'Rose Queen'	see I. ensata 'Rose Queen'
	- 'Shirasagi'	CRow
I	- 'Snowdrift'	CBen CLAP CRow CWat EGol EHon EMFW EPla LPBA MSta NBir NGdn NPer SCro SLon SPer SWat WFar WMAq WTMC WWpP
	- 'Variegata' (v) ♀ H4	More than 30 suppliers
	- 'Violet Garth'	CRow
	- 'Weymouth'	see I. laevigata 'Weymouth Blue'
§	- 'Weymouth Blue'	CRow SAWi
§	- 'Weymouth Elegant'	CBen CRow
§	- 'Weymouth Midnight'	CBen CFir CRow ECGP EGol EHon SWat WOBN
	'Lake Placid' (TB)	SCro
	'Land o' Lakes' (TB)	SCro
N	'Langport Chapter' (IB)	CKel
N	'Langport Chief' (IB)	CKel
N	'Langport Claret' (IB)	CKel
N	'Langport Curlew' (IB)	CKel
N	'Langport Duchess' (IB)	CKel WDav
N	'Langport Fairy' (IB)	CKel
N	'Langport Finch' (IB)	NBir WIvy
N	'Langport Flame' (IB)	CKel MMil
N	'Langport Flush' (IB)	SCro
N	'Langport Haze' (IB)	CKel
N	'Langport Hope' (IB)	CKel
N	'Langport Jane' (IB)	CKel
N	'Langport Magic' (IB)	MMil
	'Langport Midnight'	SMrm
	'Langport Minstrel' (IB)	CKel
N	'Langport Pagan' (IB)	WTin
	'Langport Phoenix' (IB)	CKel
N	'Langport Pinnacle' (IB)	CKel
N	'Langport Pleasure' (IB)	CKel
N	'Langport Prince' (IB)	MMil
N	'Langport Robe' (IB)	CKel
N	'Langport Song' (IB)	CKel MMil
N	'Langport Star' (IB)	CKel
	'Langport Storm' (IB)	CHad CKel EBee EChP EFou EMil MMil NGdn SChu WDav WIvy
N	'Langport Sun' (IB)	CKel SMrm
N	'Langport Sunbeam' (IB)	CKel
N	'Langport Swift' (IB)	CKel
	'Langport Sylvia' (IB)	CKel
N	'Langport Violet' (IB)	CKel
	'Langport Vista' (IB)	CKel
N	'Langport Warrior' (IB)	CKel
	'Langport Wren' (IB) ♀ H4	CBro CKel CMil GKir LPhx MBri MMil NBir SMrm WEas
	'Lark Rise' (TB) ♀ H4	CKel
	'Lascivious Dreams' (TB) new	EFam
§	latifolia ♀ H4	GIBF
	- 'Duchess of York'	EPot
	- 'Isabella'	EPot

	- 'King of the Blues'	EPot MBow WAul WCot
	- 'Mansfield'	EPot
	- 'Mont Blanc' new	EBee
	- 'Montblanc'	EPot
	- 'Queen of the Blues'	EBee EPot
	'Latin Rock' (TB)	MCAu SCro
	latiphilum new	GIBF
§	lazica ♀ H4	CAbP CBro CMea EBee ECre EHyt EMan EPPr EPot EWsh GGar GMac IBlr ITer MAvo MBri MRav MSte NBir NSti SChu SCro SIng SMHy SSpi SUsu WCot WEas WPGP IBlr
	- deep blue	IBlr
	- 'Joy Bishop' new	WCot
	'Leah Traded' (BB) new	EFam
	'Leda's Lover' (TB)	ESgI SCro
	'Lemon Brocade' (TB)	ESgI EWoo GKir MBri MCAu
	'Lemon Dilemma' (Spuria) new	LIri
I	'Lemon Drop' (TB)	CKel
	'Lemon Flare' (SDB)	EBre ECtt MRav SRms
	'Lemon Glitter' (TB)	EFou
	'Lemon Ice' (TB)	MMil
	'Lemon Mist' (TB)	ESgI MMil
	'Lemon Puff' (MDB)	CBro MCAu
	'Lemon Reflection' (TB)	MMil
	'Lemon Whip' (IB) new	EWoo
	'Lemon Wine' (IB)	CKel
N	'Lena' (SDB)	CBro EBee
	'Lenna M' (SDB)	CKel
	'Lenora Pearl' (BB)	ESgI
	'Lent A. Williamson' (TB)	SCro
	'Lenten Prayer' (TB) new	LIri
	'Lenzschnee' (TB)	EBee
	'Let's Elope' (IB)	ESgI
	'Light Cavalry' (IB)	ESgI EWoo NZep
	'Light Laughter' (IB)	MCAu
	'Lighted Within' (TB)	SCro
	'Lighten Up' (SDB)	NZep
	'Lilac and Lavender' (SDB)	MMil NZep
	'Lilac Stitchery' (TB) new	EFam
	'Lilli-white' (SDB)	CKel EBee EBre EGle ELan ENot MCAu MMil MRav NSti SIri
	'Lima Colada' (SDB)	SMrm
	'Limelight' (TB)	SRms
	'Lincoln Imp' (CH) ♀ H3	WWst
	'Linesman' (SDB)	NZep
	linifolia	WWst
	'Lions Share' (TB)	LIri
	'Liquid Smoke' (TB)	MMil
	'Little Amigo' (SDB)	NZep
N	'Little Amoena'	ERos NMen
	'Little Annie' (SDB)	NMGW NZep
	'Little Bill' (SDB)	EFou EGle
	'Little Black Belt' (SDB)	EFou NZep SIri SMrm
	'Little Blackfoot' (SDB)	MMil WHoo WWin
	'Little Chestnut' (SDB)	WWin
	'Little Dandy' (SDB)	EGle WIvy
	'Little Dogie' (SDB)	EGle EHyt
	'Little Dream' (SDB)	EGle MCAu NZep
	'Little Episode' (SDB)	NZep
	'Little Pearl' (MDB)	NZep
	'Little Rosy Wings' (SDB)	CBro ERos LPhx MMil
	'Little Shadow' (IB)	ENot MRav SRms
	'Little Snow Lemon' (IB)	EFam NZep
	'Little Tilgates' (CH) ♀ H3	WCot WWst
	'Live Coals' (SDB) new	LIri
	'Live Jazz' (SDB)	MMil NZep
	loczyi	EBee
	'Lodore' (TB)	SRms
	'Lois Parrish' (TB) new	LIri
	'London Pride' (TB) new	MMil
	longipetala	GIBF NBir

'Lookin' Good' (IB)	NZep
'Loop the Loop' (TB)	CFwr EBee EBre EGle EPfP ETub
	EWoo SWat
'Lord Baltimore' (TB)	SCro
'Lord Warden' (TB)	EBee EFou
'Loreley' (TB)	ESgl
'Lorenzaccio de	ESgl
Medecis' (TB)	
'Lorilee' (TB)	ESgl SCro
'Los Angeles'	LRHS
'Lothario' (TB)	WFoF
'Loud Music' (TB)	MBri
'Louisiana Lace' (TB)	SCro
'Louvois' (TB)	ESgl SDes
'Love for Leila'	LIri
(Spuria) **new**	
'Love the Sun' (TB)	ESgl
'Lovely Again' (TB)	MCAu MWat
'Lovely Dawn' (TB) **new**	LIri
'Lovely Fran' (TB) **new**	EFam
'Lovely Kay' (TB)	SCro
'Lovely Light' (TB)	MBri
'Love's Tune' (IB)	SCro
'Loveshine' (SDB)	MMil MRav NZep
'Low Ho Silver' (IB) **new**	EFam
'Low Snow' (SDB)	NZep
'Lugano' (TB)	ESgl MMil
'Lumiere d'Automne' (TB)	ESgl
'Luminosity' (TB) **new**	EFam
§ *lutescens* ♀ H4	ERos GEdr GKev
§ - 'Campbellii'	CBro EHyt ERos LPhx MBro NMen
* - 'Goldcrest'	MBro
- subsp. *lutescens*	WLin
'Lyme Tyme' (TB)	LIri
'Ma Mie' (IB) **new**	ESgl
macrosiphon	GKev
'Madeira Belle' (TB)	MCAu
'Magharee' (TB)	ESgl
'Magic Bubbles' (IB)	LIri
♀ H4 **new**	
'Magic Flute' (MDB)	EGle
magnifica ♀ H3-4	CBro EBee EHyt GKev SBla
- 'Agalik'	CMea LRHS WLin WWst
- 'Alba'	EHyt LRHS
'Mahogany Snow' (SDB)	MMil NZep
'Making Eyes' (SDB) **new**	ESgl EWoo
I 'Mandarin' (TB)	ESgl GDra
'Mandarin Purple'	EBee GGar IBlr NGdn NHol
(Sino-Sib)	
mandshurica	GIBF
'Mango Entree' (TB) **new**	LIri
'Many Moons Tales'	EFam
(TB) **new**	
'Maple Treat' (TB) **new**	LIri
'Marcel Turbat' (TB)	ESgl
'Marche Turque' (TB) **new**	ESgl
'Margaret Inez' (TB) **new**	LIri
'Margot Holmes' (Cal-Sib)	EBee GCal GDra GGar IBlr SChu
'Marhaba' (MDB)	CBro ERos
'Maria Tormena' (TB)	SCro
'Marilyn Holloway' (Spuria)	ECha
'Mariposa Skies' (TB)	LIri
'Marmalade Skies' (BB)	NZep
'Marshlander' (TB)	EFou SCro
'Martyn Rix'	see *I. confusa* 'Martyn Rix'
'Mary Constance'	CKel LIri
(IB) ♀ H4	
'Mary Frances' (TB)	MCAu SCro
'Mary McIlroy' (SDB) ♀ H4	CBro CKel MMil WTin
'Master Touch' (TB)	SCro
'Matinata' (TB)	CKel EBre
'Maui Moonlight' (IB)	CKel EFou LIri MMil NZep
♀ H4	

'May Melody' (TB)	MBri
'Meadow Court' (SDB)	CBro CFwr CKel CM&M CRez
	EBee ERos MCAu NBro NZep
	WDav WWin
'Meg's Mantle' (TB) ♀ H4	CKel
'Melissa Sue' (TB)	SCro
mellita	see *I. suaveolens*
- var. *rubromarginata*	see *I. suaveolens*
'Melon Honey' (SDB)	CKel EGle EHyt MCAu MMil
	NZep WDav WHrl WWin
'Memphis Blues' (TB) **new**	EWoo
'Memphis Delight' (TB)	MCAu
'Mer Du Sud' (TB)	ESgl
'Merseyside' (SDB)	EGle
'Mesmerizer' (TB)	LIri
'Metaphor' (TB)	MCAu MMil
'Mezza Cartuccia' (IB) **new**	ESgl
'Michael Paul' (SDB) ♀ H4	ESgl
'Michele Taylor' (TB)	SCro
'Midday Blues' (IB)	NZep
'Midnight Caller' (TB) **new**	EFam
'Midnight Fire' (TB)	ERou
'Midnight Mango' (TB) **new**	CKel
'Midnight Oil' (TB)	LIri
'Midnight Pacific' (TB) **new**	EFam
'Mil Byers' (TB) **new**	EFam
milesii ♀ H4	CDes CPou EBee EMon GBuc
	GIBF IGor MSph NBir WPer WPic
'Mind Reader' (TB)	LIri
'Mini Agnes' (DB)	CBro
'Minnesota Glitters' (TB)	SCro
'Minnie Colquitt' (TB)	SCro
'Miss Carla' (IB)	CKel MMil SCro
'Miss Scarlett' (BB) **new**	EFam
'Mission Sunset' (TB)	EBre EHrv
'Missouri Lalieu'	LIri
(Spuria) **new**	
'Missouri Rivers'	LIri
(Spuria) **new**	
missouriensis ♀ H4	IBlr IGor SSpi
- var. *arizonica*	EBee
'Mister Roberts' (SDB)	ESgl NZep
'Mme Chereau' (TB) **new**	ESgl
'Mme Louis Aureau'	ESgl
(TB) **new**	
'Modern Classic' (TB)	EWoo
'Mogul' (TB) **new**	LIri
* 'Mohogang Mountain'	EFam
(TB) **new**	
'Monaco' (TB)	EFou
'Money' (TB)	SCro
monnieri	IBlr NLar SDix
Monspur Group	CDes EBee ECGP GCal SSpi WCot
	WPGP WPic
§ 'Monspur Cambridge	MCAu WPic
Blue' (Spuria)	
'Moon Pearl' (CH)	WWst
'Moon Sparkle' (IB)	CKel EBee SIri
'Moonbeam' (TB) **new**	CKel
'Moonlight' (TB)	NFor WCot
'Moonlight Waves'	see *I. ensata* 'Moonlight Waves'
'Moonstruck' (TB) **new**	EWoo
'Morning Hymn' (TB)	SCro
'Morning Show' (IB)	SCro
'Morning's Blush' (SDB)	LIri
♀ H4 **new**	
'Morocco' (TB)	SCro
'Morwenna' (TB) ♀ H4	CKel
* 'Mount Stewart Black'	GCal
'Mrs Horace Darwin' (TB)	CFir EBee SWat WMnd
'Mrs Nate Rudolph' (SDB)	CDes EBee EFou EGle ESis LPhx
	SMrm
'Mrs Tait' (Spuria)	GCal NChi

'Mulled Wine' (TB) **new**	ESgI
'Music Box' (SDB)	NZep
'My Friend Jonathan' (TB) **new**	EFam
'My Impulse' (Spuria) **new**	LIri
N 'My Seedling' (MDB)	CBro ERos NMen WIvy
'My Smoky' (TB)	CKel
'Mystique' (TB)	SCro
'Naivasha' (TB)	CKel
'Nancy Hardy' (MDB)	CBro ERos NMen
narbutii **new**	WWst
narcissiflora **new**	CFir EBee
narynensis **new**	WWst
'Natascha' (Reticulata)	CMea EHyt EPot LAma SWal WLin
'Natchez Trace' (TB)	ETub
'Navajo Blanket' (TB)	SCro
'Navajo Jewel' (TB)	ESgI
'Needlecraft' (TB)	MMil
'Needlepoint' (TB)	ESgI SCro
'Neon Pixie' (SDB)	NZep
nepalensis	see *I. decora*
nertschinskia	see *I. sanguinea*
'New Idea' (MTB)	ESgI
'New Snow' (TB)	CKel
'Nibelungen' (TB)	EBee EPfP MLwd WFar
'Nice 'n' Nifty' (IB)	NZep WTin
nicolai	WWst
'Nigerian Raspberry' (TB)	LIri
'Night Game' (TB)	LIri
'Night Owl' (TB)	CKel EBee MBct MMil SCro SDes
'Night Ruler' (TB)	ESgI
'Nightfall'	EBee WWeb
'Nights of Gladness' (TB)	ESgI
'Noces Blanches' (IB)	ESgI
'Noon Siesta' (TB)	ESgI
'Northern Flame' (TB) **new**	EFam
'Northwest Progress' (TB) **new**	LIri
'O Shenandoah' (TB) **new**	EFam
'Ochraurea' (Spuria)	GCal NGdn
ochroleuca	see *I. orientalis*
'October' (TB) **new**	EFam
'Oklahoma Crude' (TB)	LIri
'Oktoberfest' (TB)	ESgI
'Ola Kala' (TB)	CM&M CMGP EBee EBre ECle ERou ESgI EWTr MCAu MSte SCro SDes SPer WLRN
'Old Black Magic' (TB) **new**	LIri
'Old Flame' (TB)	NMGW
'Olympiad' (TB)	ESgI
'Olympic Challenger' (TB)	ESgI MCAu
'Olympic Torch' (TB)	MCAu
'One Desire' (TB)	NZep
'Open Sky' (SDB)	MMil NZep
'Orageux' (IB) **new**	ESgI
'Orange Blaze' (SDB)	CBro
'Orange Caper' (SDB)	EBee EBre EGoo ESgI MBri MRav NCiC NZep SIri SPet
'Orange Grove' (TB)	MBri
'Orange Harvest' (TB) **new**	EFam
'Orange Petals' (IB) **new**	LIri
N 'Orange Plaza'	NMen WIvy
'Orange Tiger' (SDB)	NZep
'Orchid Cloud' (TB) **new**	EFam
'Orchidarium' (TB)	CKel
orchioides hort.	see *I. bucharica* Foster
§ *orchioides* Carrière	CMea EBee EChP EHyt ELan ERos ETow MBow NWCA SBla WLin
'Oregold' (SDB)	NZep
'Oregon Skies' (TB) **new**	EWoo
'Oregon Skles' (TB)	SCro
'Oriental Baby' (IB)	CKel EWoo

'Oriental Glory' (TB)	MCAu
'Oriental Touch' (SpecHybrid)	CRow
§ *orientalis* Mill. ♀ H4	CBot CMil EBee EPPr GIBF IFro LPBA MCAu MNrw MSte MWgw SChu SSpi WPic WWin WWst
§ *orientalis* Thunb.	see *I. sanguinea*
- 'Alba'	see *I. sanguinea* 'Alba'
'Orinoco Flow' (BB) ♀ H4	CHar CKel LIri
'Oritam' (TB)	SCro
'Out Yonder' (TB)	MCAu
'Ovation' (TB)	ESgI SCro
'Overnight Sensation' (TB)	SCro
'O'What' (SDB) **new**	ESgI
'Owyhee Desert' (TB)	LIri
'Ozone Alert' (TB)	LIri
'Pacer' (IB)	NZep
Pacific Coast hybrids	see *I.* Californian hybrids
'Pacific Gambler' (TB)	EFou
'Pacific Mist' (TB)	SCro
'Pacific Panorama' (TB) **new**	ESgI
'Pageant' (TB) **new**	WTin
'Paint It Black' (TB)	EWoo
'Pale Primrose' (TB)	MCAu WBar WEas
'Pale Shades' (IB) ♀ H4	CBro CKel ERos
§ *pallida*	CHad CPrp EBot EFou GKir GMaP ITer MCAu MCCP MRav MSte WBrE WMnd
- 'Argentea Variegata' (v)	More than 30 suppliers
- 'Aurea'	see *I. pallida* 'Variegata'
- 'Aurea Variegata'	see *I. pallida* 'Variegata'
- var. *dalmatica*	see *I. pallida* subsp. *pallida*
§ - subsp. *pallida* ♀ H4	CBot CKel EBee EBre EChP ECha ELan MBri MWgw SCro SDes SDix SMrm SPer WCot WWal
N - 'Variegata' (v) ♀ H4	More than 30 suppliers
'Palomino' (TB)	MCAu
'Paltec'	CHad CPlt CPou EBee LPhx
'Pandora's Purple' (TB)	SCro
'Paradise' (TB)	EPfP SCro
paradoxa	WWst
- f. *choschab*	EHyt EPot SBla SOkd
'Paricutin' (SDB)	CBro EGle
'Paris Lights' (TB)	SCro
'Party Dress' (TB)	CM&M CMGP EBee ENot ERou EWTr LAst MRav NBir NGdn NOrc SDes SPer WBVN WWal
parvula	WWst
'Pastel Charm' (SDB)	CM&M CRez EBee NSti SIri WMnd
'Pastel Delight' (SDB)	NZep
'Patches' (TB) **new**	ESgI
'Path of Gold' (DB)	CBro
'Patina' (TB)	EWoo
'Patterdale' (TB)	NBir NMGW NVic
'Pauline' (Reticulata)	CBro EPot LAma LRHS NRog
'Peace and Harmony' (TB)	LIri
'Peach Band' (TB)	ERou
'Peach Eyes' (SDB)	CBro NZep
'Peach Float' (TB)	MCAu
'Peach Melba' (TB)	ESgI
'Peach Petals' (BB)	NZep
'Peach Picotee' (TB)	ESgI SCro
'Peach Spot' (TB)	MMil
'Peacock'	see *I. ensata* 'Peacock'
'Pearly Dawn' (TB)	CHad EBee EChP ECha MWat NGdn SChu SCoo SCro SPer WLRN
'Pegasus' (TB)	SCro
'Peggy Chambers' (IB) ♀ H4	EFou MMil SMrm
'Peking Summer' (TB)	SCro
'Pennies' (MDB)	NZep
'Pennyworth' (IB)	SCro

	'People Pleaser' (SDB)	NZep
	'Peppermint Twist' (SDB)	NZep
	'Perfume Counter' (TB) **new**	EFam
	'Persian Berry' (TB)	SCro
	'Persian Doll' (MDB)	NZep
	'Pet' (SDB)	NZep
	'Phaeton' (TB) **new**	LIri
	'Pheasant Feathers' (TB) **new**	LIri
	'Phil Keen' (TB) ♀ H4	CKel
	'Phillida' (CH)	WWst
	'Picacho Peak' (Spuria) **new**	LIri
	'Picadee' **new**	EPfP WElm
	'Piero Bargellini' (TB) **new**	LIri
	'Pigeon' (SDB)	NZep
	'Pigmy Gold' (IB)	ENot ERos
	'Pinewood Amethyst' (CH)	CPlt WWst
	'Pinewood Delight' (CH) **new**	CPlt
	'Pinewood Prelude' (CH)	WWst
	'Pinewood Sunshine' (CH)	CPlt
	'Pink Angel' (TB)	SCro
	'Pink Attraction' (TB)	EFam ESgI
	'Pink Bubbles' (BB)	EFou NZep
	'Pink Charming' (TB)	LIri
	'Pink Confetti' (TB)	ESgI SCro
	'Pink Divinity' (TB)	MMil
	'Pink Fawn' (SDB) **new**	LIri
	'Pink Horizon' (TB)	CSBt EBee EPfP SCro SGar
	'Pink Kitten' (IB)	MCAu NZep
N	'Pink Lavender' (TB)	SCro
	'Pink Light' **new**	EBee
	'Pink 'n' Mint' (TB)	SCro
	'Pink Pussycat'	MBri
N	'Pink Randall' (TB)	SCro
	'Pink Ruffles' (IB)	CHar
	'Pink Swan' (TB)	ESgI
	'Pink Taffeta' (TB)	ESgI MPWC SCro
	'Pinkness' (TB) **new**	EFam
	'Pinnacle' (TB)	CKel SWat
	'Piper's Tune' (IB)	SIri SMrm
	'Pipes of Pan' (TB)	MRav
	'Piquant Lass' (MTB)	NZep
	'Pirate's Patch' (SDB) **now**	ESgI
	'Piroska' (TB)	ESgI
	'Pixie' (Reticulata)	EPot
	'Pixie Flirt' (MDB)	ERos
	'Playgirl' (TB)	SCro
	'Pleased as Punch' (IB) **new**	EFam
	'Pledge Allegiance' (TB)	MCAu MMil SCro
	plicata	MCAu
	'Plickadee' (SDB)	CBro EPot
	'Pogo' (SDB)	EBee EChP ECtt EGle EHyt ENot EWoo GKir MMil MRav NBir NWCA SRms
	'Point Made' (TB)	LIri
	'Pond Lily' (TB) **new**	LIri
	'Post Time' (TB)	SCro
	'Power Surge' (TB)	LIri
	'Prancing Pony' (TB)	CKel SCro
	'Precious Heather' (TB) ♀ H4	CKel
	'Pretender' (TB)	LRHS MBri
	'Prettie Print' (TB)	SCro
	'Pretty Please' (TB) **new**	ESgI
	'Priceless Pearl' (TB)	SCro
	'Pride of Ireland' (TB)	SCro
	'Primrose Drift' (TB)	MCAu
	'Prince' (SDB)	EFou EGle ESis
	'Prince Indigo' (TB)	EBee ENot
	'Prince of Burgundy'	LIri

	(IB) ♀ H4 **new**	
	'Prince of Earl' (TB) **new**	EFam
	'Princess Beatrice'	see *I. pallida* subsp. *pallida*
	'Princess Pittypat' (TB) **new**	EFam
	'Princess Sabra' (TB) ♀ H4	CKel
	'Princesse Caroline de Monaco' (TB) **new**	LIri
	prismatica	CPLG EPla WTin
	'Professor Blaauw' (Dut)	CFwr ETub LRHS MSph WAul
	'Progressive Attitude' (TB)	LIri
	'Prophetic Message' (AB)	EFou
	'Prosper Laugier' (IB)	SCro
	'Proud Tradition' (TB)	SCro
	'Provencal' (TB)	CKel ESgI MCAu
	'Prudy' (BB) ♀ H4	CKel
	pseudacorus ♀ H4	More than 30 suppliers
	- 'Alba'	CRow SSpi WPnP
	- var. *bastardii*	CRDP CRow CWat ECGP ECha EGol EMFP EMFW LPBA NPer SLon WFar WWpP
	- 'Beuron'	CRow
	- cream	EGol MTed NBir WAul
N	- 'Ecru'	CRow
	- 'Esk'	GCal MTed
N	- 'Flore Pleno' (d)	CBot CRow EBee EMFW EPPr MInt NLar NPer WCot WFar WViv
	- 'Golden Daggers'	CRow
I	- 'Golden Fleece'	SPer
	- 'Golden Queen'	CRow MSta WWpP
	- 'Ilgengold'	CRow
N	- 'Ivory'	CRow
	- 'Lime Sorbet' (v)	WCot
*	- *nana*	CRow LPBA
	- 'Roy Davidson' ♀ H4	CBgR CKel CLAP CRow SLon
*	- 'Sulphur Queen'	WCot
	- 'Sun Cascade'	CRow
	- 'Tiggah'	CRow
	- 'Turnipseed'	CRow EBee WTin
	- 'Variegata' (v) ♀ H4	More than 30 suppliers
	pseudacorus x *versicolor*	SCro
	'Pulse Rate' (SDB)	CBro
	pumila	EPla EPot GKev LRHS MBro MHer NFor NMen NWCA SRPl WLin WRHF WWin
	- *atroviolacea*	CKel NFla SMrm WMnd
	- subsp. *attica*	see *I. attica*
	- 'Aurea'	WMnd
	- blue	SWal
*	- 'Gelber Mantel'	NBir
	- 'Jackanapes'	WEas
	- 'Lavendel Plicata'	EBee MOne NBro NSti
	- 'Lavender Glow'	LBuc
	- 'Purpurea'	EHyt
	- 'Violacea'	MBro SRms
	- yellow	NFla SWal
	'Pumpin' Iron' (SDB) **new**	ESgI WDav
	'Pumpkin Center' (SDB)	NZep
	'Puppet' (SDB)	EGle
	'Puppet Baby' (MDB)	NZep
	'Puppy Love' (MTB)	NZep
	'Pure Allure' (SDB)	NZep
	'Purple Duet' (TB) **new**	EFam
	'Purple Gem' (Reticulata)	CBro EPot LAma
	'Purple Sensation' (Dut)	MSph
	'Purple Streaker' (TB)	SCro
	purpurea	see *I. galatica*
	'Pussycat' (MDB)	GKir
	'Quaker Lady' (TB) **new**	ESgI
	'Quark' (SDB)	CBro CKel NZep
	'Quechee' (TB)	EBee EChP EMan EPfP ERou

	EWTr GMaP MRav MSte MWat
	NGdn SChu SCro SWat WLRN
'Queen in Calico' (TB)	ESgI MCAu SCro
'Queen of Hearts' (TB)	SCro
'Queen of May' (TB) **new**	ESgI
'Queen's Circle' (TB) **new**	LIri
'Queen's Pawn' (SDB)	NMGW NZep
'Quietly' (SDB) **new**	EFam
'Quintana' (CH)	WWst
'Radiant Apogee' (TB) **new**	ESgI
'Radiant Summer' (TB)	SCro
'Rain Dance' (SDB) ♀ H4	ESgI NMGW NZep
'Rajah' (TB)	CSBt EBee EChP EPfP ERou MRav
	NGdn NOrc SChu SCoo SDes
	SLon WMnd WWal
'Rameses' (TB) **new**	ESgI
'Rancho Rose' (TB)	SCro
'Rapture in Blue' (TB)	EWoo
'Rare Edition' (IB)	CKel EBre EFou EWoo GKir MBri
	NZep SCro WAul
'Rare Treat' (TB)	NZep
'Raspberry Acres' (IB)	LRHS MCAu
'Raspberry Blush'	CHad CKel EBee EChP EFou EPfP
(IB) ♀ H4	NZep SCro SWat WElm
'Raspberry Jam' (SDB)	EGle EHyt MMil NZep
'Raspberry Sundae' (BB)	NZep
'Rathe Primrose' (IB)	SCro
'Raven Hill' (TB)	MCAu
'Razoo' (SDB)	CKel
'Red Duet' (TB) **new**	EFam
I 'Red Flash' (TB)	CKel SMrm
'Red Hawk' (TB)	LIri MCAu
'Red Heart' (SDB)	ESgI GMaP LIri MRav WPer
'Red Lion' (TB)	EFou NZep
'Red Orchid' (IB)	EBee ELan EWTr WWeb
'Red Revival' (TB)	MCAu MWat SCro
N 'Red Rum' (TB)	CKel
'Red Tornado' (TB)	ESgI
'Red Zinger' (IB)	ESgI NZep SCro
'Redelta' (TB) **new**	EFam
'Redwing' (TB)	WPer
'Redwood Supreme'	SApp
(Spuria)	
'Regal Surprise'	CRow
(SpecHybrid)	
'Regards' (SDB)	CBro EGle
§ **reichenbachii**	ERos LBee LTwo
– NS 700	CPou
'Repartee' (TB)	ESgI EWoo SCro
§ **reticulata** ♀ H4	CBcs CBro CMea EPar EPot ETub
	LRHS MBNS NCel NRog SWal
* – 'Violet Queen'	EPot
'Returning Chameleon'	EFam
(TB) **new**	
'Returning Peace'	EFam
(TB) **new**	
'Riches' (SDB)	NZep
'Ride the Wind' (TB)	SCro
'Right Royal' (TB)	ENot
'Rime Frost' (TB)	MCAu MMil
'Rimfire' (TB) **new**	EBee
'Ringo' (TB)	CKel ESgI LIri MCAu NMGW SCro
'Ripple Chip' (SDB)	NZep WTin
'Rippling Waters' (TB)	ESgI
'Rising Moon' (TB)	SCro
'Rive Gauche' (TB) **new**	ESgI
'River Avon' (TB)	LIri
♀ H4 **new**	
'River Hawk' (TB)	SCro
'River Pearl' (TB) **new**	LIri
§ x **robusta** 'Dark Aura'	CRDP WCot
§ – 'Gerald Darby' ♀ H4	More than 30 suppliers
§ – 'Mountain Brook'	CRow

– 'Nutfield Blue'	NSti
§ 'Rocket' (TB)	CMGP EBee ECGN EChP GMaP IPot
	MRav NBir NGdn SCoo SCro WLRN
'Rogue' (TB)	LIri
'Romance' (TB)	ERou
'Romano' (Dut)	CFwr ETub MNrw MSph
'Ron' (TB)	EWoo SCro SIri
'Roney's Encore' (TB) **new**	EFam
'Rosalie Figge' (TB) **new**	EFam
'Rose Queen'	see I. ensata 'Rose Queen'
'Rose Violet' (TB)	NMGW
'Roselene' (TB)	NMGW
'Rosemary's Dream' (MTB)	CKel
rosenbachiana	WWst
'Roseplic' (TB)	ESgI MCAu
'Rosette Wine' (TB)	LIri MCAu
'Rosy Veil' (TB) **new**	ESgI
'Rosy Wings' (TB)	EHyt
'Roustabout' (SDB)	EGle
N 'Roy Elliott'	LHop MBro NHol NMen SIng WPer
'Royal Cadet' (Spuria) **new**	LIri
'Royal Contrast' (SDB)	MMil NZep
♀ H4	
'Royal Elegance' (TB) **new**	EWoo
'Royal Intrigue' (TB)	SCro
'Royal Magician' (SDB)	WHoo WTin
'Royal Regency' (TB)	SCro
'Royal Summer' (TB) **new**	EFam
'Royal Touch' (TB)	EFou
'Royal Yellow' (Dut)	NRog
'Ruban Bleu' (TB)	ESgI EWoo
'Rubistar' (TB) **new**	ESgI
'Ruby Chimes' (IB)	LPhx MCAu SCro
'Ruby Contrast' (TB)	CHad MCAu
rudskyi	see I. variegata
'Ruffled Ballet' (TB)	SCro
'Ruffled Copper	LIri
Sunset' (TB)	
'Ruffled Surprise' (TB)	SCro
'Ruffles and Lace' (TB)	SCro
'Rustic Cedar' (TB)	EPfP ESgI
'Rustic Royalty' (TB) **new**	LIri
'Rustler' (TB)	LIri SCro
'Rusty Dusty' (SDB)	NZep
ruthenica	ERos GIBF NMen WPer
– **leucantha** **new**	EBee
– var. **nana** SDR 428	GKev
– – SDR 914	GKev
'Sable' (TB)	CHad CPrp EBee EChP EMan ESgI
	MCAu MCLN MRav MWat MWgw
	NGdn NOrc SCoo SCro SPer WLRN
'Sable Night' (TB)	CHar CKel ERou
'Saffron Jewel' (AB)	WTin
'Sager Cedric' (TB)	MCAu
'Sahara Sands' (Spuria)	ECha
'Saharan Sun' (TB)	LIri
'Saint Crispin' (TB)	CM&M EBee ERou ESgI MRav
	MWat MWgw SChu SCro SPer
	WLRN WWal
'Salonique' (TB)	MCAu SDes WFar
* 'Saltbox' (SDB)	WIvy
'Saltwood' (SDB)	CBro ESgI
'San Francisco' (TB) **new**	ESgI
'Sand Princess' (MTB)	EFou SMrm
'Sandstone' (BB) **new**	LIri
'Sangreal' (IB)	LBuc
§ **sanguinea** ♀ H4	GIBF
§ – 'Alba'	IBlr
§ – 'Snow Queen'	More than 30 suppliers
– x **laevigata**	SCro
'Santana' (TB)	SCro
'Sapphire Beauty' (Dut)	NRog
'Sapphire Gem' (SDB)	CKel MCAu SMrm WDav

'Sapphire Hills' (TB)　MCAu SCro
'Sapphire Jewel' (SDB)　NZep
'Sarah Taylor' (SDB)　♀ H4　CBro EFou EHyt EWoo MCAu
'Sarajaavo' (AB) **new**　CKel
sari　EHyt EPot SBla
'Sass with Class' (SDB)　CKel WTin
'Satin Gown' (TB)　EPri GKir MBri MCAu
'Saturday Night Live'　LIri
　(TB) **new**
'Saturnalia' (TB)　SCro
'Saxon' (TB) **new**　EFam
'Scented Bubbles' (TB)　EFam
schachtii purple　SBla
'Schortman's Garnet　SCro
　Ruffles' (TB)
'Scintilla' (IB)　♀ H4　MMil SCro
'Scintillation' (TB)　SCro
'Scribe' (MDB)　CBro EBee EGle ESis GKir LRHS
　　MBri NBir
'Scrimmage' (SDB)　NZep
'Sea Double' (TB)　MMil
'Sea Fret' (SDB)　CBro
'Sea of Joy' (TB)　SCro
'Second Opinion' (MTB)　NZep
'Seneca Rebound'　EFam
　(SDB) **new**
'Senlac' (TB)　LBuc WBro WMnd
'September Frost'　EFam
　(TB) **new**
serbica　see *I. reichenbachii*
'Serengeti Spaghetti'　LIri
　(TB) **new**
'Serenity Prayer' (SDB)　MCAu
setosa ♀ H4　CBro CFwr EBee EGle EMNN
　　ERos GKev LRHS MFir MNrw
　　MOne MSta NDlv NGdn NLAp
　　SCro SWal
- *alba*　EBee MBro MSte NLar WLin
- var. *arctica*　CRDP CSWP EMon EPot MBro NHol
　　NMen NWCA SBla WHoo WPer
- subsp. *canadensis*　see *I. hookeri*
- dwarf　see *I. hookeri*
§ - 'Hondoensis'　EMon MSte
- 'Hookeri'　see *I. hookeri*
- 'Kasho En'　CHad
- 'Kirigamini'　see *I. setosa* 'Hondoensis'
- var. *nana*　see *I. hookeri*
- *tricuspis*　GEdr
* 'Sevenly Seven' (TB) **new**　EFam
'Severn Side' (TB)　♀ H4　CKel
'Shampoo' (IB)　EFou
'Sheer Ecstasy' (TB) **new**　LIri
'Sheila Ann Germaney'　EHyt EPot
　(Reticulata)
'Shelford Giant'　LIri NBir
　(Spuria)　♀ H4
'Shepherd's Delight' (TB)　GKir MBri
'Sherbet Lemon' (IB)　CKel MCAu
　♀ H4
'Short Distance' (IB)　EWoo
'Show Me Yellow' (SDB)　NZep
'Showcase' (TB)　NMGW
'Showman' (TB)　ERou
shrevei　see *I. virginica* var. *shrevei*
'Shurton Inn' (TB) **new**　CKel
'Shy Violet' (SDB)　NZep
'Si Senor' (TB)　EFou
sibirica ♀ H4　More than 30 suppliers
- 'Alba'　see *I.* 'Sibirica Alba'
- 'Ann Dasch'　EFou WLin
- 'Annemarie Troeger'　EFou SBla
　♀ H4
- 'Annick'　LPhx

- 'Anniversary'　CBos CDes CLAP EBee LRHS
　　MBNS SCro WPGP
- 'Baby Sister'　CMHG EBee EFou EGle GMac
　　LRHS MBri WAul WHil WRus
- 'Baxteri'　see *I.* 'Sibirica Baxteri'
- 'Berlin Bluebird'　LPhx
- 'Berlin Sky' **new**　CAbx
- 'Bickley Cape'　EBee
- 'Blue Brilliant'　WLin
- 'Blue Burgee'　SCro
* - 'Blue Emperor'　EBee WBrE
- 'Blue King'　CHid CKel COtt EBee EChP
　　EGle EPfP GMaP LPVe LRHS
　　MBNS MBro MRav MWrn NGdn
　　NMoo SMrm WLin WLow WMnd
　　WMoo
- 'Blue Meadow Fly'　CLAP EBee EGle
- 'Borbeleta'　LPhx
- 'Bracknell'　LPhx
- 'Brynmawr'　CAbx WLin
- 'Butter and Sugar'　♀ H4　More than 30 suppliers
- 'Caesar's Brother'　CHid CMGP CPrp EBee EChP
　　EGle EMil IBlr LPVe LRHS MCAu
　　MOne MSta SMer SPer SWal SWat
　　WPnP WWin
- 'Caezar'　CRow GKir NCat SDys SRms WLin
- 'Camberley'.　WLin
- 'Cambridge'　♀ H4　EBla MTed NHol SWat WFar
- 'Canonbury Belle'　WLin
- 'Castlegrace' **new**　WLin
- 'Chartreuse Bounty'　EBee EChP EGle ERou EWes
　　MBNS MLLN NLar
- 'Chilled Wine' **new**　GMac
- 'Circle Round'　LPhx
- 'Clee Hills'　CAbx WLin
- 'Clouded Moon'　see *I. sibirica* 'Forncett Moon'
- 'Connie A' **new**　WLin
- 'Cool Spring'　WLin
- 'Coquet Waters'　WLin
- cream　see *I. sibirica* 'Primrose Cream'
- 'Crème Chantilly'　♀ H4　SCro
- 'Dance Ballerina Dance'　CPen CRow EBee EChP EPPr
　　ERou GBri MHar SUsu SWat WAul
- 'Dancing Nanou'　SWat
- 'Dark Desire'　MRav SCro
- 'Dear Delight'　EBee EBrE
- 'Dear Dianne'　CKel EFou
- 'Dewful'　WLin
- 'Dragonfly'　GMac WWhi
- 'Dreaming Spires'　♀ H4　GBin GKir GMac WLin
- 'Dreaming Yellow'　♀ H4　CBre CFee EBee EBre ECha EFou
　　EGle EPfP EPri GMac MCAu
　　MCLN MNFA MRav NBro NChi
　　NGdn NLon SApp SBla SCro
　　SHBN SMrm SPer SSpe WMoo
- 'Ego'　CHid COtt CSam CSpe EBee ECha
　　GKir GMaP GMac LBBr LRHS
　　MCLN NGby NHol SWat WHil
　　WLin WPrP
- 'Ellesmere'　NGdn
- 'Emperor'　EBee ERou LPBA LPhx MSte
　　MWgw NBur NHol NSti SMrm
　　SWat WCra WLin
- 'Eric the Red'　IBlr NBur
- 'Ewen'　CBot CHid CLAP CPou CRow
　　CSam EBee EFou EGle EMan IBlr
　　MNrw MTed NGdn SCro SWat
　　WCot WFar
- 'Flight of Butterflies'　More than 30 suppliers
- 'Floating Island'　WLin
§ - 'Forncett Moon'　WLin
- 'Fourfold Lavender'　EBee
- 'Fourfold White'　EBee GMac LPhx LRHS

	– 'Gatineau'	CDes CLAP EBee GBuc GDra NCat NHol WLin
	– 'Gerbel Mantel' **new**	GBin
	– 'Glaslyn' ♀ H4	CAbx
	– 'Granaat' **new**	EBee
	– grey **new**	SApp
	– 'Harpswell Hallelujah'	SCro
	– 'Harpswell Happiness' ♀ H4	CLAP CPrp EBee EGle EPfP LPio MUlv SWat WAul WMoo
	– 'Harpswell Haze'	ECha WMoo
	– 'Heavenly Blue'	EHon LPBA MWat SSpe WWpP
	– 'Helen Astor'	CBos CDes CLAP CMea CRow CSam CTri EBee EGle LRHS MBNS MHar MRav MTed NHol SMrm SWat
	– 'Hoar Edge'	CAbx
	– 'Hubbard'	SCro
	– 'Illini Charm'	CHid EBee EChP EMan NBro SSpe WMoo
	– 'Jac-y-do'	WLin
	– 'Kemugami' **new**	EBee
	– 'Lady of Quality'	SCro
	– 'Lady Vanessa'	CPou EGle MRav SCro WLin
	– 'Langthorns Pink'	CRDP EGle ELan MRav WLin
	– 'Laurenbuhl'	CPLG SCro WLin
	– 'Lavender Bounty'	EBee EGle EMan MCAu SCro
	– 'Lavender Light'	WLin
	– 'Limeheart'	CPou CSev EGle ELan ERou WLin
N	– 'Limelight'	EGle LRHS
	– 'Little Blue'	LRHS SCro
	– 'Little Twinkle Star' **new**	CHid GBin NPro
	– 'Looks Mohrish'	SCro
	– 'Maranatha'	EFou SMrm
	– 'Marcus Perry'	CRow MSte
	– 'Marilyn Holmes'	EGle NFor WCot
	– 'Marlene Ahlburg'	WLin
§	– 'Melton Red Flare'	EHon ELan GMac SDys SOkh WCot WHer
	– 'Mountain Lake'	GBin SWat
	– 'Mrs Rowe'	CFee CPou CRow EBee EBlw EFou EGle EGra EPPr LLWP MCAu MNFA MRav MSte MWat SWat WLin WRus
	– 'Mrs Saunders'	CAbx SApp
	– 'My Love'	WLin
	– 'Navy Brass'	EGle GBuc
	– 'Nottingham Lace'	EGle GMac SWat WBcn WLin
	– 'Oban' ♀ H4	CAbx GMac WLin
	– 'Orville Fay'	EChP EFou EGle GMac SCro WCot
	– 'Ottawa'	CPou CRow EBee ELan ERou GMac LRHS MBNS SCro SPer SWat WFar
	– 'Outset'	SCro
	– 'Papillon'	CSam EBee ECGN EChP ECtt EGle ELan EMFW EPPr ERou GIBF GKir LRHS MCLN MWat NBir NBro NCat NGdn NLar NPri NSti SChu WFar WHil WLin WPer WPnP WWeb
N	– 'Pearl Queen'	MTPN WFar
	– 'Perry's Blue'	More than 30 suppliers
I	– 'Perry's Favourite'	CFee CRow
	– 'Perry's Pigmy'	GBuc WLin
	– 'Persimmon'	CFir CHid EBee ECtt EGle EMFW EMan ERou GKir LRHS MArl MWat NMoo SAga WMoo WPGP
*	– 'Phosphor Flame'	GBin WLin
	– 'Pink Haze'	CHar CPen CRow CSam EBee EGle MBri NSti SCro WHil WRus
	– 'Pirate Prince'	CAbx MBro NPer WHoo
	– 'Pirouette'	WLin
	– 'Placid Waters'	EGle SCro
	– 'Plant World hybrids' **new**	MDKP SWal
	– 'Polly Dodge'	GMac
	– 'Pounsley Purple'	CPou
§	– 'Primrose Cream'	CMea MTed WCot
	– 'Purple Cloak'	MSte WBcn
	– 'Purple Mere'	WLin
N	– 'Red Flag'	WLin
	– 'Reddy Maid'	SCro
	– 'Redflare'	see *I. sibirica* 'Melton Red Flare'
	– 'Rejoice Always'	GMac WTin
	– 'Rimouski'	WLin
N	– 'Roger Perry'	CFee
	– 'Rowden Aurelius'	CRow
I	– 'Royal Blue'	ECha GBuc WLin
	– 'Ruffled Velvet' ♀ H4	CHar CHea CHid CKel EBre EChP EFou EGle EPPr EPfP GKir IPot MBNS MCLN MRav MSte NBro SCro SDes SHBN SVil WAul WFar WHil WHoo WOBN WPGP WWeb
	– 'Sally Kerlin'	SCro
	– 'Savoir Faire'	CRDP ECha EGle
	– 'Sea Horse'	GBuc NCat WLin
	– 'Sea Shadows'	NBir SIri WLin
	– 'Shirley Pope' ♀ H4	CDes CMil EBee EBre EGle GKir GMac LPhx LRHS MBri MNFA NSti SDes SSpi WCot WMoo
	– 'Showdown'	EBee ECtt EGle LRHS SAga SCro WFar
	– 'Shrawley'	CAbx
	– 'Silver Edge' ♀ H4	More than 30 suppliers
	– 'Sky Wings'	CRow ECha EGle MArl
	– 'Snow Queen'	see *I. sanguinea* 'Snow Queen'
	– 'Snowcrest'	CBre WLin
	– 'Soft Blue' ♀ H4	CDes CMil EBee SCro WLin
N	– 'Southcombe White'	COlW CRow GBuc GCal LPio MHar NGdn SIri SMHy
	– 'Sparkling Rosé'	More than 30 suppliers
	– 'Splashdown' (Sino-Sib)	SWat
	– 'Steve'	EBee EBre EChP EPPr NBro SUsu SWat WAul WMoo
	– 'Steve Varner'	SCro
	– 'Summer Sky'	CAbx CBre EBla MCAu SApp SCro SSpi SWat WCot WLin WTin
	– 'Super Ego'	WTin
	– 'Superba'	WLin
	– 'Swank'	CAbx
	– 'Taldra' **new**	WLin
	– 'Tal-y-Bont' **new**	WLin
	– 'Teal Velvet'	EBee
	– 'Tealwood'	WLin
	– 'Temper Tantrum'	CKel
	– 'Thelma Perry'	WLin
	– 'Towanda Redflare'	EGle
	– 'Tropic Night'	More than 30 suppliers
	– 'Tycoon'	CHid CSBt EBee IBlr LRHS MNFA NCat NChi SPer WLRN WLin WPGP
	– 'Vee One' **new**	WLin
	– 'Velvet Night'	CAbx
	– 'Vi Luihn'	CBcs ECha EGle
	– 'Violetmere'	WLin
	– 'Weisse Etagen'	EBee
	– white	EGle
I	– 'White Swan'	LAst
	– 'White Swirl' ♀ H4	More than 30 suppliers
	– 'Winscombe'	CHid
	– 'Wisley White'	EGle GMac MWgw SRms WLin
	– 'Yellow Court'	CRow
§	– 'Sibirica Alba'	CRow ECha EHon EPfP GAbr GGar LLWP MHer NChi SRms SWat WFar WWpP WWye
§	– 'Sibirica Baxteri'	CFee
	– *sichuanensis*	EBee
	– *sieboldii*	see *I. sanguinea*
	– 'Sierra Blue' (TB) **new**	ESgI
	– 'Sierra Grande' (TB)	EWoo
	– 'Sierra Nevada' (Spuria)	EFou
	– 'Sign of Leo' (TB) **new**	EFam

'Sunshine Isle' (SDB)	MMil NZep	
'Superlation' (TB)	SCro	
'Superstition' (TB) ♀ H4	EFou ESgI GBin MCAu MMil SCro SIri SMrm WAul	
'Supreme Sultan' (TB)	ESgI EWoo LIri MCAu SCro	
'Surprise Orange' (MDB)	NZep	
'Susan Bliss' (TB)	CKel EBee ELan EPfP ESgI GMaP MBNS SIri SMrm	
susiana	LAma	
'Swaledale' (TB)	MCAu	
'Swazi Princess' (TB)	CKel ESgI MCAu SCro	
'Sweet Kate' (SDB) ♀ H4	MCAu	
'Sweet Musette' (TB)	MCAu SCro	
'Sweeter than Wine' (TB)	LIri MCAu SCro	
'Swingtown' (TB)	LIri	
'Sybil'	GBin GMaP	
'Sylvia Murray' (TB)	MCAu	
'Symphony' (Dut)	LRHS NBir	
tadshikorum	WWst	
'Tall Chief' (TB)	EBre SCro	
'Tan Tingo' (IB)	EFou	
'Tangerine Sky' (TB)	MCAu SCro	
'Tantara' (SDB)	WTin	
'Tanzanian Tangerine' (TB)	LIri	
'Tarheel Elf' (SDB)	WTin	
'Tarn Hows' (TB)	SIri SRms	
'Tea Leaves' (TB) **new**	EFam	
tectorum	CSWP ERos GIBF GSki ITer MNrw NMGW WHil	
- 'Alba'	CPou EPPr	
- 'Variegata' (v)	CHid CPrp EBee EPPr MCCP MRav NCot SPar SVil WWpP	
'Tell Fibs' (SDB)	CBro EGle	
'Temple Gold' (TB)	CKel	
'Temple Meads' (IB)	CKel	
'Templecloud' (IB) ♀ H4	CHar CKel	
'Temptone' (TB) **new**	LIri	
'Ten' (SDB)	NZep	
§ *tenax*	CLAP CNic CPBP ECho ETow GBuc GSki	
'Tender Years' (IB) **new**	WAul	
'Tennessee Vol' (TB)	LIri	
tenuifolia **new**	EBee	
tenuissima	GBuc SSpi	
'Terra Rosa' (TB) **new**	LIri	
'Thais' (TB) **new**	ESgI	
'The Bride'	see *I.* 'Bride'	
'The Citadel' (TB)	CKel SCro	
'The Rocket'	see *I.* 'Rocket'	
'Theatre' (TB)	MMil SCro	
'Theda Clark' (IB)	SCro	
'Theseus' (Aril)	EHyt	
'Third Charm' (SDB)	CBro EFam	
'Third World' (SDB)	CBro	
thompsonii	WTin	
'Thornbird' (TB) ♀ H4	ESgI LIri	
'Thousand Lakes' (SDB)	NZep	
'Three Cherries' (MDB)	CBro EGle	
'Thriller' (TB)	ESgI MCAu MMil	
'Throb' (TB)	LIri	
thunbergii	see *I. sanguinea*	
'Thunder Echo' (TB)	ESgI	
'Tide's In' (TB)	ERou EWoo SCro	
'Tiger Blues' (Spuria) **new**	LIri	
'Tiger Butter' (TB)	ESgI	
'Tiger Honey' (TB)	LIri	
tigridia	EBee	
'Timeless Moment' (TB)	SCro	
'Tinkerbell' (SDB)	CPBP CStu EBee EGle EMan ESis LPhx MSte NBir SChu SPet WLRN WWal WWin	
'Tintinara' (TB) ♀ H4	CKel	
'Tiny Freckles' (MDB)	NZep	
'Tiny Lou' (Spuria) **new**	LIri	
'Tirra Lirra' (SDB) ♀ H4	MMil	
'Titan's Glory' (TB) ♀ H4	CKel ESgI LIri MCAu MRav SCro WCot	
'To the Point' (TB) **new**	LIri	
'Tol-Long'	MSte	
'Tom Johnson' (TB) **new**	LIri	
'Tom Tit' (TB)	MCAu	
'Tomingo' (SDB)	MCAu	
'Tomorrow's Child' (TB)	ESgI SCro	
'Toni Lynn' (MDB)	EHyt	
'Toots' (SDB)	EGle EHyt WTin	
'Top Flight' (TB)	EBee EChP ELan ENot ERou LAst SCoo SPer SRms WLRN	
N 'Topolino' (TB)	CKel SIri SMrm	
'Total Eclipse'	SRms	
'Touch of Spring' (TB)	MMil	
'Toy Boat' (SDB)	NMGW	
'Tracy Tyrene' (TB)	ESgI	
transylvanica **new**	GIBF	
tridentata **new**	WOBN	
subsp. 'Trillion' (TB) **new**	LIri	
'Triple Whammy' (TB)	ESgI	
'Triplicate' (SDB)	LPhx MBri	
'Tu Tu Turquoise' (SDB)	NZep	
tuberosa	see *Hermodactylus tuberosus*	
'Tumbleweeds' (SDB)	NZep	
'Tumultueux' (TB)	ESgI	
N 'Tuscan' (TB)	CKel CMil	
'Tut's Gold' (TB)	ESgI MCAu SCro	
'Twist of Fate' (TB)	SCro	
'Two Rubies' (SDB)	NZep	
'Tyke' (MTB)	NZep	
§ *unguicularis* ♀ H4	More than 30 suppliers	
- 'Abington Purple'	CBro WCot	
- 'Alba'	CBro ECha WAbe WMnd	
N - 'Bob Thompson'	CAvo CBro SAga WCot	
- subsp. *carica* var. *angustifolia*	IBlr WCot	
§ - subsp. *cretensis*	EPot NMen WAbe	
- - MS 860	WCot	
- - white	SBla	
- var. *lazica*	see *I. lazica*	
- 'Marondera'	CAvo	
- 'Mary Barnard' ♀ H4	CAvo CBro CFee CHar CPou CSam CSpe ECGP ECha EHrv IBlr MAvo NBir NMen SBla SDes SIng WCot WGwG WMnd	
N - 'Oxford Dwarf'	CBro ECho	
- 'Palette'	ELan	
§ - 'Walter Butt'	CAvo ECGP ECha NBir SRot WFar WMnd	
uniflora var. *caricina*	MNrw	
uromovii	GBuc MArl WHoo	
'Vague a l'Ame' (TB)	ESgI	
'Vamp' (IB)	CKel SMrm	
'Vanity' (TB) ♀ H4	ESgI SCro	
'Vanity's Child' (TB)	ERou	
§ *variegata* ♀ H4	CPou CRDP EGoo EPar GCal MCAu SIng SUsu WCot WWst SCro	
- var. *pontica*	SCro	
'Vegas Showgirl' (SDB)	NZep	
'Velvet Caper' (SDB)	WTin	
'Velvet Robe' (TB)	EBee	
* *venaidae* **new**	WWst	
'Veneer' (TB) **new**	LIri	
'Verity Blamey' (TB) **new**	CKel	
verna	EBee EPot ERos NHol	
versicolor ♀ H4	CArn CBen CRow EGol EHon EMFW EPar GBin IBlr LPBA LRHS MNrw MSal MSta NGdn SPlb SRms SWat WAbe WFar WMAq WShi WWpP	

- 'Between the Lines'	CRow	
- 'China West Lake'	CRow	
- 'Dottie's Double'	CRow	
N - 'Goldbrook'	EGol	
- 'Kermesina'	CRDP CRow EBee ECha EGol EHon	
	ELan EMFW EPar GCal GGar GMac	
	IBlr MSta NBlu NPer NSti SLon	
	SRms SWat WEas WFar WMoo	
- 'Mysterious Monique'	CMdw CRDP CRow	
- 'Party Line'	CRow	
- var. *rosea*	CRow	
- 'Rowden Allegro'	CRow	
- 'Rowden Aria'	CRow	
- 'Rowden Cadenza' **new**	CRow	
- 'Rowden Concerto' **new**	CRow	
- 'Rowden Fugue' **new**	CRow	
- 'Rowden Lyric'	CRow	
- 'Rowden Mazurka'	CRow	
- 'Rowden Nocturne' **new**	CRow	
- 'Rowden Rondo'	CRow	
- 'Rowden Sonata'	CRow	
- 'Rowden Symphony'	CRow	
- 'Rowden Waltz' **new**	CRow	
⚹ - 'Signagoniga Ridska'	NCat	
- 'Silvington'	CRow	
- 'Whodunit'	CRow	
'Vert Gallant' (TB) **new**	ESgI	
vicaria	WWst	
'Victor Herbert' (TB)	SCro	
'Victoria Falls' (TB)	ESgI SCro	
'Vigilante' (TB)	LIri	
'Vinho Verde' (IB) ♀ H4	CKel	
violacea	see *I. spuria* subsp. *musulmanica*	
'Violet Beauty' (Reticulata)	EPot LAma LPhx LRHS MBow	
'Violet Classic' (TB)	EFou MCAu MMil	
'Violet Icing' (TB) ♀ H4	CKel EFou	
'Violet Lass' (SDB)	NZep	
'Violet Miracle' (TB)	MMil	
virginica 'De Luxe'	see *I.* x *robusta* 'Dark Aura'	
- 'Pond Crown Point' **new**	CRow	
- 'Pond Lilac Dream' **new**	CRow	
N - 'Purple Fan'	CRow	
§ - var. *shrevei*	CRow	
'Visual Arts' (TB)	SCro	
'Vitality' (IB)	SCro	
'Vive la France' (TB)	ESgI EWoo	
'Vivien' (TB)	SCro	
'Voila' (IB)	EFou NZep	
'Voltage' (TB)	LIri	
'Volute' (TB)	ESgI	
'Voyage' (SDB) **new**	Ewoo	
'W.R. Dykes' (TB)	WTin	
'Wabash' (TB)	EBre ERou ESgI MMil	
'Walter Butt'	see *I. unguicularis* 'Walter Butt'	
'War Chief' (TB)	ESgI	
'War Sails' (TB)	MCAu	
warleyensis	WWst	
'Warl-sind' (Juno)	EBee WWst	
'Warrior King' (TB)	MCAu	
'Waterboy' (SDB)	NZep	
'Watercolor' (SDB)	NZep	
wattii	EBee GCal	
'Webelos' (SDB)	EGle LPhx MBri	
'Wedding Candles' (TB)	SCro	
'Well Suited' (SDB)	EWoo	
'Westar' (SDB) ♀ H4	NZep	
'Westwell' (SDB)	MCAu WWin	
'What Again' (SDB)	SCro	
'Wheels' (SDB)	WTin	
'White Bridge' (Dut)	MSph NRog	
'White City' (TB)	CHad CMGP CPrp EBee ECGP	
	EMan EOrc EPfP MCAu MMil MRav	
	MWat NGdn NPer SChu SCoo SDes	

	SIri SPer SRms SWat WMnd	
'White Excelsior' (Dut)	LAma LRHS	
'White Gem' (SDB)	WWin	
'White Knight' (TB)	EBee ELan EPfP SCoo WMnd	
	WWeb	
'White Shimmer'	LIri	
(Spuria) **new**		
'White Superior' (Dut)	NBir	
'White van Vliet' (Dut)	NRog	
'Whoop 'em Up' (BB)	NZep	
'Why Not' (IB)	NMGW NZep	
'Widdershins' (TB) **new**	LIri	
'Widecombe Fair' (SDB)	WIvy WWin	
N 'Wild Echo' (TB)	CKel	
'Wild Jasmine' (TB) **new**	MCAu	
'Wild Thing' (TB)	SCro	
willmottiana	WWst	
- 'Alba'	EBee	
'Willow Ware' (IB)	SCro	
'Willowmist' (SDB)	NZep	
wilsonii ♀ H4	EBee GBuc GEdr GIBF MMil SSpi	
	WOBN	
- 'Gelbe Mantel'	see *I.* 'Gelbe Mantel'	
'Windsor Rose' (TB)	CHar SCro	
'Winged Melody' (TB)	MBri	
winogradowii ♀ H4	CBro EHyt EPot ERos GCrs LAma	
	MTho NHar SDix WAbe WLin	
'Winter Olympics' (TB)	EFou ESgI	
'Wise Gift' (Cal-Sib)	WWst	
♀ H4 **new**		
'Witch of Endor' (TB)	MMil	
'Wizard of Id' (SDB)	EGle NZep WTin	
'Wondrous' (TB)	ESgI	
'World News' (TB)	SCro	
'Wow' (SDB)	EGle EHyt	
'Wyoming Cowboys'	LIri	
(Spuria) **new**		
xiphioides	see *I. latifolia*	
xiphium	GIBF SSpi	
'Yaquina Blue' (TB) **new**	EWoo LIri	
'Yellow Girl' (SDB)	NMGW NZep	
'Yo-yo' (SDB)	NZep	
'Zantha' (TB)	MCAu	
'Zen'	EBre	
'Zinc Pink' (BB)	SCro	
'Zing Me' (TB)	CKel	
'Zowie' (SDB)	NZep	
'Zua' (IB)	LPhx SCro	

Isatis (Brassicaceae)

tinctoria	CArn CBri COld CPrp CSev EBee
	EOHP GPoy ILis LRHS MChe MHer
	MSal NVic SIde WBri WChb WHHs
	WHer WJck WPer WSel WWye

Ischyrolepis (Restionaceae)

ocreata	CTrC WNor
§ *subverticillata*	CCtw CHEx CTrC IArd

Ismene see *Hymenocallis*

Isolepis (Cyperaceae)

§ *cernua*	CHal EMFW EMan EPfP MAvo
	MBri WDyG WFar WHil WMAq
nodosa	LEdu

Isoloma see *Kohleria*

Isomeris see *Cleome*

Isoplexis (Scrophulariaceae)

canariensis	CAbb CBot CFil CRHN CSpe
	CTrC EBee EMan EWll SHFr WEas

* ***cernua* new**	SBHF
isabelliana	CFil EBee MGol SSte WCot WEas
sceptrum	CBcs CBot CFil CFir CHEx CPLG
	CSpe EMan GCal SAPC SArc SHFr
- pink	CSpe

Isopogon (Proteaceae)
anethifolius	SPlb

Isopyrum (Ranunculaceae)
biternatum	EBee GBuc LEur NLar
***nipponicum* new**	WCru
thalictroides	SIng
'Flore Pleno' **new**	

Isotoma (Campanulaceae)
§ ***axillaris***	CSpe EBre LIck LRHS MOak NPri
	SCoo SHFr SMrm SPet WWin
- 'Fairy Carpet'	EMan
'Blue Star'	WWeb
fluviatilis	ECou WCru ▼
- white	ECou

Itea (Escalloniaceae)
ilicifolia ♀ H3	More than 30 suppliers
japonica 'Beppu'	MGos SLPl
virginica	CAbP CBcs CMCN CMHG CPle
	ELan EPfP EWTr MBlu MGos MRav
	SLon SPer WBVN WFar WHCG
§ - 'Henry's Garnet'	CDoC CEnd CFai CMCN CPMA
	CWSG EBee EPfP LAst MBlu NLar
	NPSI NPri SBrw SLim SRPl SSpi
	WDin
- Little Henry = 'Sprich' **new**	SSpi
- 'Long Spire'	CPMA
- 'Merlot'	CPMA
- 'Sarah Eve'	CMCN
- Swarthmore form	see *I. virginica* 'Henry's Garnet'

Itoa (Flacourtiaceae)
orientalis SF 92300	ISea

Ixia (Iridaceae)
Bird of Paradise	see *I.* 'Paradijsvogel'
'Blue Bird'	LAma
dubia	EGrW WCot
flexuosa	LBow NRog WCot
'Hogarth'	LAma
hybrids	SDeJ
'Mabel'	NRog
maculata	LBow NRog SSpi WCot
'Marquette'	NRog
monadelpha	EGrW LBow WCot
paniculata	EGrW LBow NRog WCot
§ 'Paradijsvogel'	LAma
polystachya	LBow NRog
pumilio	EGrW WCot
rapunculoides	EGrW
'Rose Emperor'	LAma NRog
thomasiae	WCot
'Venus'	LAma
viridiflora	LBow WCot
'Yellow Emperor'	ETub WCot WFTG

Ixiolirion (Ixioliriaceae)
pallasii	see *I. tataricum*
§ ***tataricum***	CHar EBee EMan LAma MBow
	MBri
- Ledebourii Group	CAvo LAma

Ixora (Rubiaceae)
chinensis 'Apricot Queen'	SOWG

'Golden Ball'	SOWG
'Pink Malay'	SOWG

J

Jaborosa (Solanaceae)
integrifolia	CFir CPLG EBee ELan GCal ITer
	MNrw WAul WBor WCot WCru
	WDyG WPGP WPnP
***sativa* new**	IIve

Jacaranda (Bignoniaceae)
acutifolia hort.	see *J. mimosifolia*
acutifolia Kunth	MBri
§ ***mimosifolia***	CBcs ERea ESlt GQui LRHS MGol
	MPRe SMur SOWG SPlb

Jacobinia see *Justicia*

Jamesbrittenia (Scrophulariaceae)
§ ***jurassica***	EHyt
- H&B 19148	EHyt
'Pink Pearl' **new**	COtt WWeb
pristisepala 'Sani' **new**	SScr
Sumatra Indigo =	SMrm
'Yagemon'	

Jamesia (Hydrangeaceae)
americana	CPle WWin

x *Jancaemonda* (Gesneriaceae)
vandedemii	EHyt

Jasione (Campanulaceae)
§ ***heldreichii***	GAbr MWrn SBla SRms WElm WWin
jankae	see *J. heldreichii*
§ ***laevis***	ECot EHol IHMH LRHS MDKP
	SRms WGwG
§ - 'Blaulicht'	CCge CFis EBee ECha EDAr EMan
	EPfP GMaP LRHS MBNS MBri MLan
	MWgw MWrn NBlu NFla NLar
	NPPs SMrm SPet SPla SPlb SSvw
	WMoo WPer WRos WWal WWeb
- Blue Light	see *J. laevis* 'Blaulicht'
montana	EDAr GKir MBow MChe MDKP
	NLAp WHer
perennis	see *J. laevis*

Jasminum (Oleaceae)
angulare ♀ H1	CPIN EHol ERea LRHS SOWG
azoricum ♀ H1	CPIN CRHN ELan EPfP ERea EShb
	ESlt GQui LRHS NPal WMul
beesianum	More than 30 suppliers
bignoniaceum	CPIN WSHC
dispermum	CRHN
floridum	EBee EWes SLim
fruticans	CMac CPle EBee ELan EPla WBcn
	WCru
grandiflorum 'De Grasse' ♀ H1	CPIN EBee ERea LRHS SOWG
humile	CPLG CPle EBee EHol EVFa GSki
	IKee IMGH MHer MRav SHFr
	WBod WFar WKif
- f. ***farreri***	WCru
§ - 'Revolutum' ♀ H4	More than 30 suppliers
- f. ***wallichianum***	CPle
- - B&SWJ 2559	WCru
§ ***laurifolium*** f. ***nitidum***	CPIN ERea
leratii	CPIN

§ *mesnyi* ♀ H2-3 — CFRD CMac CRHN CSBt CTri CWib EBak EBee ELan EPfP ERea IGor NBea SBra SLim SOWG SPar SSte SYvo WCot WEas WSHC

multipartitum bushy — CSpe

nitidum — see *J. laurifolium* f. *nitidum*

nudiflorum ♀ H4 — More than 30 suppliers

- 'Argenteum' — see *J. nudiflorum* 'Mystique'
- 'Aureum' — CRow EBee ELan EPfP EPla GQui LRHS MAsh MBro MCCP MRav NSti SLim SPer SPla WCot WHCG WPat WTel WWeb

§ - 'Mystique' (v) — EBee ELan LRHS SLon SMur SPer SSta WCot WPat WWeb

- 'Nanum' — MBro

odoratissimum — ERea LRHS SOWG

officinale ♀ H4 — More than 30 suppliers
- CC 1709 — WCot WHCr

§ - f. *affine* — CBcs CRHN CSPN CSam CTri CWSG CWib EBee EBre ELan ENot EOrc EPfP EPla ERea MAsh MRav NHol SDix SLim SMad SPar SRms WCru WWeb

§ - 'Argenteovariegatum' (v) ♀ H4 — More than 30 suppliers

- 'Aureovariegatum' — see *J. officinale* 'Aureum'
- 'Aureum' (v) — More than 30 suppliers
- 'Crûg's Collection' B&SWJ 2987 — WCru
- 'Devon Cream' PBR — SPar
- Fiona Sunrise = 'Frojas' PBR — More than 30 suppliers
- 'Grandiflorum' — see *J. officinale* f. *affine*
- 'Inverleith' ♀ H4 — CDoC CWSG EBee ELan EPfP GCal IArd LAst LHop LRHS MAsh MBNS MBri MCCP MLan MRav SBra SCoo SLim SMad SPar SPer SVil WFar WGwG WPat WWal WWeb
- 'Variegatum' — see *J. officinale* 'Argenteovariegatum'

parkeri — CBcs CBot CFee CTri EBee EHyt EPfP EPla ESis GMaP IMGH ITim LHop MBNS MBro NRya NWCA SHGC SIgm SIng SPar SRot WAbe WCru WFar WPat

polyanthum ♀ H1-2 — CArn CBcs CPIN CRHN CSBt CTri CTrw EBak EBee EPfP ERea ERom EShb GQui LPan LRHS MBri NPal NRog SLim SOWG SPar SRms WCFE

primulinum — see *J. mesnyi*

reevesii hort. — see *J. humile* 'Revolutum'

sambac ♀ H1 — CHll CPIN CRHN EHol ELan EPfP ESlt LPan LRHS NPal SOWG SYvo WMul
- 'Grand Duke of Tuscany' (d) — ERea LRHS SOWG
- 'Maid of Orleans' (d) ♀ H1 — FRea LRHS SOWG

x *stephanense* — More than 30 suppliers

tortuosum — CPIN

Jatropha (Euphorbiaceae)

integerrima — ESlt LRHS SOWG
podagrica ♀ H1 — ESlt LRHS

Jeffersonia (Berberidaceae)

diphylla — CArn CBro CElw EBee EChP EHrv EPar GKir GSki IBlr LAma LEur LRHS MDun MSal MTho NBir NDov NGar NHar NRog SRot WAbe WCot WCru WFar WWye

dubia — CFir EBee EHyt EWes GCrs IBlr LEur LRHS NBir NGar NHar NMen NRog SBla SIgm SRot WAbe WCot WCru
- 'Alba' — LEur SBla WCru

jostaberry see *Ribes* x *culverwellii* Jostaberry

Jovellana (Scrophulariaceae)

procumbens — CPne
punctata — CDoC CPLG CPle CSpe EBee IBlr MBlu
repens — CFir EBee IBlr IDac WCot WCru
sinclairii — CHll CPLG ECou EHyt IBlr SSpi WCru
violacea ♀ H3 — More than 30 suppliers

Jovibarba ✿ (Crassulaceae)

§ *allionii* — CMea CTri CWil EHol EMlt EPot GAbr LBee LRHS MBro MHer NHol SBla SIng WAbe WCom WPer WWin
- 'Oki' — CWil MOne
- x *hirta* — CWil GAbr MBro MOne NHol NMen SDys SIng WLRN

§ *arenaria* — CWil EHol ESis GAbr MApt MBro MDHE NMen SIng
- from Murtal, Austria — MDHE
- from Passo Monte Crocecar Nico — CWil
'Emerald Spring' — CWil NMen

§ *heuffelii* — CWil LRHS MApt NHol NMen NPri WPer
- 'Aga' — NHol
- 'Aiolos' — NHol
- 'Alemene' — NHol
- 'Almkroon' — NHol
- 'Angel Wings' — CWil NHol NMen
- 'Aquarius' — CWil
- 'Artemis' — NHol
- 'Be Mine' — CWil
- 'Beacon Hill' — CWil MBro
- 'Belcore' — CWil
- 'Benjamin' — NHol
- 'Bermuda' — CWil
- 'Bermuda Sunset' — NHol
- 'Big Red' — NHol
- 'Brandaris' — NHol SDys
- 'Brocade' — NHol
- 'Bronze Ingot' — CWil
'Chocoleto' — WTin
- 'Cleopatra' — NHol
- 'Dunbar Red' — NHol
- 'Fandango' — CWil MHom
- 'Genio' — CWil NHol
- 'Geronimo' — NHol
- 'Giuseppi Spiny' — CWil NHol
- var. *glabra* — MBro WHoo
- - from Anabakanak — CWil MHom NHol WTin
- - from Anthoborio — CWil NMen WTin
- - from Backovo — NHol
- - from Galicica — NHol
- - from Haila, Montenegro/ Kosovo — CWil NHol NMen
- - from Jakupica, Macedonia — CWil
- - from Kapaenianum — WTin
- - from Koprovnik, Kosovo — CWil
- - from Ljuboten — CWil NHol NMen WTin
- - from Pasina Glava — CWil
- - from Rhodope — CWil MHom NHol
- - from Treska Gorge, Macedonia — CWil MBro NMen WTin
- - from Vitse, Greece — CWil
- 'Gold Rand' — NHol
- 'Green Land' — CWil
- 'Greenstone' — CWil MBro NHol NMen WTin

– 'Henry Correvon'	CWil
– 'Inferno'	CWil MHom NHol
– 'Inge'	CWil
– 'Ithaca'	NHol
– 'Iuno'	CWil
– 'Jade'	CWil NMen
– var. *kopaonikensis*	CWil NMen
– 'Mary Ann'	MHom
– 'Miller's Violet'	CWil WTin
– 'Minuta'	CWil NHol NMen WTin
– 'Mystique'	CWil MBro NMen
– 'Opele'	NHol
– 'Orion'	CWil NHol NMen
– 'Pink Skies'	MBro
– 'Prisma'	CWil WTin
– 'Purple Haze'	MBro
– 'Sungold'	NHol
– 'Suntan'	CWil NHol
– 'Sylvan Memory'	CWil
– 'Tan'	CWil MBro NHol
– 'Torrid Zone'	WTin
– 'Tuxedo'	CWil
– 'Violet'	CWil SDys
§ *hirta*	CHal CWil GAbr GCrs MDHE MOne NHol NMen SBla SIng STre WBVN WPer
– subsp. *borealis*	CWil EGln MBro MOne NDlv NHol
– from Wintergraben	SIng SPlb
– subsp. *glabrescens*	EPot ESis
– – from Belansky Tatra	CWil LBee MDHE MOne NDlv
– – from High Tatra	MDHE
– – from Smeryouka	CWil MBro SIng
– – var. *neilreichii*	LRHS
– 'Lowe's 66'	MOne
– var. *neilreichii*	MHom
– 'Preissiana'	CWil GEdr LBee MBro MOne NDlv NHol NMen SIng
§ *sobolifera*	CHEx CWil ELau ESis GEdr MBro MOne NHol NJOw NMen SIng SPlb WAbe WPer
– 'August Cream'	CWil LBee
– 'Green Globe'	CWil ELau MDHE SDys
– 'Miss Lorraine'	CWil

Juanulloa (Solanaceae)

aurantiaca	see *J. mexicana*
§ *mexicana*	EAmu ESlt SOWG

Jubaea (Arecaceae)

§ *chilensis*	CBrP CRoM EAmu LPJP LPal WMul
spectabilis	see *J. chilensis*

Juglans ✿ (Juglandaceae)

§ *ailanthifolia*	CMCN ESim WPGP
– var. *cordiformis*	CAgr CTho
cathayensis (F)	WGWT
– B&SWJ 6778	WCru
cinerea (F)	CDul CMCN EGFP
– 'Booth' seedlings (F) **new**	CAgr
– 'Craxezy' (F)	CAgr
§ *elaeopyren*	EGFP WGWT
hindsii **new**	CMCN EGFP
x *intermedia*	SKee WGWT
mandschurica	CMCN EGFP WGWT
microcarpa	WGWT
– subsp. *major*	see *J. elaeopyren*
nigra (F) ♀ H4	More than 30 suppliers
– 'Emma Kay' (F)	CAgr
– 'Laciniata'	CMCN CTho GKir MBlu WGWT
– 'Purpurea'	MBlu
– 'Thomas' (F)	ESim
– 'Weschke' (F)	CAgr

'Paradox' **new**	WGWT
'Red Danube' (F) **new**	WGWT
regia (F) ♀ H4	More than 30 suppliers
– 'Broadview' (F)	CDoC CDul CEnd CTho EMui ERea ESim GTwe LRHS MBlu MBri MCoo MGos SCoo SDea SKee WGWT
– 'Buccaneer' (F)	CDul CTho ERea ESim GTwe LRHS SDea SKee WGWT
– 'Cascade' (F)	ESim
– 'Coenen' (F)	WGWT
– 'Fernette'PBR **new**	SKee
– 'Fernor'PBR **new**	SKee
– 'Franquette' (F)	CTho ENot GTwe LRHS MCoo SKee WDin
– 'Hansen' (F)	WGWT
– 'Hartley' (F)	SKee
– 'Laciniata'	CMCN GKir WGWT
– 'Lara'	GTwe SKee
– 'Leopold' **new**	WGWT
– 'Mayette' (F)	SKee WDin
– 'Metcalfe' (F) **new**	WGWT
– 'Meylannaise' (F)	SKee
– number 139 (F)	ESim
– number 16 (F)	WGWT
– number 26 (F)	ESim
– 'Parisienne' (F)	SKee
– 'Pendula' **new**	WGWT
– 'Plovdivski' (F)	WGWT
– 'Proslavski' (F)	WGWT
– 'Purpurea'	CMCN WGWT
– 'Rita'	WGWT
– 'Ronde de Montignac' (F)	SKee
sieboldiana	see *J. ailanthifolia*

jujube see *Ziziphus jujuba*

Juncus (Juncaceae)

acutus	WRos WWye
articulatus	CKin
* *balticus* 'Spiralis'	ECho WBea WCot
bulbosus	CKin
compressus	CKin
conglomeratus	CKin EHoe
– 'Spiralis'	NGdn WCot
§ *decipiens* 'Curly-wurly'	More than 30 suppliers
– 'Spiralis'	see *J. decipiens* 'Curly-wurly'
effusus	CHEx CKin EMFW LPBA NBlu NPer NSti SRGP SWat WMAq WWpP
– 'Cuckoo' (v)	CNat
– 'Gold Strike' (v)	CRow CWCL EPPr EPla LIck MAvo WWpP
– f. *spiralis*	More than 30 suppliers
ensifolius	CRow CWat EBee EHoe EMFW EWes LIck MSta NPer SBHF SWal WFar WRos
filiformis 'Spiralis'	CBig CBrm GIBF LPVe MAvo MLwd NVic WCot WRus WWeb
inflexus	CKin EHon SWat WWpP
– 'Afro'	CBcs CBig CKno CMea EBee EMan EMon EPGN LRHS MAvo MBrN MCCP NBro SPlb SWal WCot
membranaceus HLMS 94.0541	NRya
pallidus	EBee EPPr GCal GGar LIck NBid
patens 'Carman's Gray'	CFee CFil CHar CKno EBee EMan EPPr EPla GCal LPan LRHS MAvo MCCP MMoz MTed NGdn NPSI NSti SApp WCot WHil WPGP WWpP
– 'Elk Blue' **new**	CKno
'Silver Spears'	EBee EMan EPPr LPhx MAvo SRGP WCot WWpP
squarrosus	CKin
xiphioides	EHoe EPla LRHS NOGN SWal

- JLS 86096LACA	EMon
- JLS 8609LACA	EPPr

Junellia (Verbenaceae)

odonnellii new	EBee
thymifolia F&W 9341 new	EBee
wilczekii	WFar
- F&W 7770	NWCA

Juniperus ✿ (*Cupressaceae*)

chinensis	CMac SEND
- 'Aurea' ♀ H4	CBcs CKen CMac EHul EOrn LCon LLin MAsh MBar MGos
§ - 'Blaauw' ♀ H4	CDoC CMac EHul ENot EOrn GKir LCon LLin MBar MGos SCoo SHBN SLim STre WStI
- 'Blue Alps'	CDoC CSBt CSli EBre EHul EOrn GKir IMGH LCon LPan MAsh MBar MBri MGos NBee SEND SLim WDin WFar WOrn
- 'Blue Point'	ENot MBar MGos
- 'Densa Spartan'	see *J. chinensis* 'Spartan'
- 'Echiniformis'	CKen CMac EOrn
- 'Expansa Aureospicata' (v)	CDoC CKen CMac EBre EHul EOrn EPfP LCon LLin MBar MGos SLim SRms
§ - 'Expansa Variegata' (v)	CDoC CMac CSBt CWib EBre EGra EHul EOrn EPfP GKir IMGH LCon LLin MAsh MBar MGos SLim SMer SRms WDin WFar WMoo WStI WTel
- 'Globosa Cinerea'	MBar
- 'Japonica'	EOrn MBar SMer
- 'Japonica Variegata' (v)	EBre SLim
- 'Kaizuka' ♀ H4	CDoC CMac EBre EHul EOrn GKir LBee LCon LRHS MAsh MBar SLim SMad SMer SPoG
- 'Kaizuka Variegata'	see *J. chinensis* 'Variegated Kaizuka'
- 'Keteleeri'	LCon MBar WCwm
- 'Kuriwao Gold'	see *J.* x *pfitzeriana* 'Kuriwao Gold'
- 'Obelisk' ♀ H4	EHul LCon LRHS MBar MGos SBod
- 'Oblonga'	EHul LLin MAsh MBar SMer STre WOrn
§ - 'Parsonsii'	CMac MBar SHBN STre WCFE
- 'Plumosa'	MBar
- 'Plumosa Albovariegata' (v)	EOrn MBar
- 'Plumosa Aurea' ♀ H4	EHul ENot EOrn LCon MBar SIng WDin WFar
- 'Plumosa Aureovariegata' (v)	CKen EOrn LCon MBar SLim
- 'Pyramidalis' ♀ H4	CBrm CDoC EBre EHul ENot EPfP GKir IMGH LCon LLin MAsh MGos NBlu SBod SRms WDin WFar WWeb
- 'Pyramidalis Variegata'	see *J. chinensis* 'Variegata'
- 'Robust Green'	EOrn GKir LCon MBar SLim
- 'San José'	CDoC EHul EOrn LCon LLin MAsh MBar SCoo SLim WDin WLRN
§ - var. **sargentii**	STre
- 'Shimpaku'	CKen EGra EOrn EPla LLin MBar NLar
§ - 'Spartan'	EHul
- 'Stricta'	CKen CSBt EHul ENot GKir LBee LRHS MAsh MBar MGos NBee NBlu SLim SPla WDin WStI
- 'Stricta Variegata'	see *J. chinensis* 'Variegata'
- 'Sulphur Spray'	see *J.* x *pfitzeriana* 'Sulphur Spray'
§ - 'Variegata' (v)	MBar

§ - 'Variegated Kaizuka' (v)	CBrm EHul EOrn EPla GKir LCon LLin MAsh MBar SPoG WEve
- 'Wilson's Weeping'	LLin WBcn
communis	CArn CKin CTrG EHul GPoy MHer MSal NCWG NWea SIde
- (f)	SIde
- 'Arnold'	LCon MBar MGos
- 'Arnold Sentinel'	CKen
- 'Atholl'	CKen
I - 'Aureopicta' (v)	MBar
- 'Barton'	LLin MBar NHol
- 'Berkshire'	CKen
- 'Brien'	CDoC CKen
- 'Brynhyfryd Gold'	CKen WBcn
§ - var. **communis**	ECho MBar NDlv
- 'Compressa' ♀ H4	More than 30 suppliers
§ - 'Constance Franklin' (v)	ECho EHul MBar WBcn
- 'Corielagan'	CKen CNic LCon MBar MGos
- 'Cracovia'	CKen EHul
- var. **depressa**	GPoy MBar
- 'Depressa Aurea'	CKen CMac CSBt CWib EHul ENot GKir LBee LCon LLin LPan LRHS MBar MGos NDlv SHBN SMer WTel
- 'Depressed Star'	EHul LCon MBar
- 'Derrynane'	EHul
- 'Effusa'	CKen
- 'Gelb'	see *J. communis* 'Schneverdingen Goldmachangel'
§ - 'Gold Cone'	CKen CSBt CSli EBre EHul ENot GKir LBee LCon LLin LRHS MAsh MBar MBri MGos NDlv SLim SMer WDin WWeb
- 'Golden Showers'	see *J. communis* 'Schneverdingen Goldmachangel'
- 'Green Carpet' ♀ H4	CAgr CDoC CKen CSBt EBre EHul EOrn EPla GKir IMGH LBee LBuc LCon LLin LRHS MAsh MBar MBri NHol SLim SMer WCFE WDin WEve WWeb
- 'Haverbeck'	CKen
- var. **hemispherica**	see *J. communis* var. *communis*
- 'Hibernica' ♀ H4	CDoC CKen CMac CSBt EHul ENot EOrn EPfP GBin GKir IMGH LBee LCon LRHS MBar MGos NWea SBod SHBN SLim SMer SPer SPla WBrE WCFE WDin WOrn WStI WTel
- 'Hibernica Variegata'	see *J. communis* 'Constance Franklin'
- 'Hornibrookii' ♀ H4	CMac EHul ENot EOrn LLin MBar MGos SBod SHBN SMer STre WDin WWin
I - 'Horstmann'	EPla MBar SLim
- 'Horstmann's Pendula'	CDoC LCon LLin WBcn
- 'Kenwith Castle'	CKen
§ - 'Minima'	SBod
- 'Oblonga Pendula'	LCon
- 'Prostrata'	ISea
- 'Pyramidalis'	WGor
- 'Repanda' ♀ H4	CBcs CBrm CDoC CMac CSBt CSli CWib EHul ENot EPfP GKir LCon LLin MAsh MBar MGos NBee NBlu NDlv NWea SLim SMer SPer SPla WCFE WDin WEve WFar
§ - 'Schneverdingen Goldmachangel'	EOrn GKir LLin MAsh SLim SMer SPoG WWeb
- 'Sentinel'	CSli EBre EHul EPfP LCon LRHS MBar MBri NBee NBlu SLim WCFE WDin WStI
- 'Sieben Steinhauser'	CKen
- 'Silver Mist'	CKen
- 'Spotty Spreader' (v)	GKir SCoo SLim
- Suecica Group	EHul ENot MBar NWea

– 'Suecica Aurea'	EHul EOrn
– 'Zeal'	CKen
conferta	see *J. rigida* subsp. *conferta*
– 'Blue Tosho'	SLim
– var. *maritima*	see *J. taxifolia*
– 'Silver Mist' **new**	CKen
davurica	EHul
– 'Expansa'	see *J. chinensis* 'Parsonsii'
– 'Expansa Albopicta'	see *J. chinensis* 'Expansa Variegata'
– 'Expansa Variegata'	see *J. chinensis* 'Expansa Variegata'
deppeana 'Silver Spire'	EGra MBar MGos
x *gracilis* 'Blaauw'	see *J. chinensis* 'Blaauw'
horizontalis	ENot NWea
– 'Alpina'	CKen
§ – 'Andorra Compact'	CKen MAsh MBar SCoo
– 'Bar Harbor'	CKen CMac EHul GKir MBar MGos NWea SBod WGor
§ – 'Blue Chip'	CKen CMac CWib EBre EHul ENot EOrn EPfP GKir LBee LLin LRHS MAsh MBar MGos NBlu SBod SLim SPer WDin
– 'Blue Moon'	see *J. horizontalis* 'Blue Chip'
– 'Blue Pygmy'	CKen
– 'Blue Rug'	see *J. horizontalis* 'Wiltonii'
– 'Douglasii'	CKen CMac EHol EHul MBar WGor
– 'Emerald Spreader'	CKen EHul ENot GKir MBar MGos SLim
– 'Glacier'	CKen WEve
– Glauca Group	CMac CSBt EHul ENot GKir LLin MBar MGos SMer SPer WDin
– 'Glomerata'	CKen MBar
– 'Golden Carpet'	CSBt EOrn GKir IMGH LBee MAsh MBri NHol NPro SCoo SLim SPer WEve
– 'Golden Spreader'	CDoC GKir WBcn
– 'Grey Pearl'	CKen CSli EBre EHul GKir SBod SLim
– 'Hughes'	CMac EBre EHul ENot GKir LBee LLin LRHS MAsh MBar MGos NDlv SBod SLim SPla
– 'Jade River'	CKen EHul GKir LRHS MGos SCoo SLim WLRN
– 'Limeglow'	CKen
– 'Mother Lode'	CKen
– 'Neumänn'	CKen
– 'Plumosa'	NDlv
– 'Plumosa Compacta'	see *J. horizontalis* 'Andorra Compact'
– 'Prince of Wales'	CKen CSli EBre EHul GKir LLin LRHS MAsh MGos SLim WLRN WWeb
– var. *saxatalis* E.Murray	see *J. communis* var. *communis*
– 'Turquoise Spreader'	CKen CSBt EHul GKir MBar SCoo WWeb
– 'Variegata' (v)	MBar
– 'Venusta'	see *J. virginiana* 'Venusta'
– 'Villa Marie'	CKen
– 'Webber'	MBar SLim
§ – 'Wiltonii' ♀ H4	CKen CSli EHul ENot EOrn MGos
– 'Winter Blue'	LBee LCon LRHS SLim
– 'Youngstown'	CMac CSWP EBre GKir LCon LLin MBar MGos SBod WGor
– 'Yukon Belle'	CKen
N x *media*	see *J.* x *pfitzeriana*
§ x *pfitzeriana*	CSBt
– 'Armstrongii'	EHul
– 'Blaauw'	see *J. chinensis* 'Blaauw'
– 'Blue and Gold' (v)	CKen EHul EOrn LLin MBar SHBN SLim SPer
– 'Blue Cloud'	see *J. virginiana* 'Blue Cloud'
§ – 'Carbery Gold'	CDoC CMac CSBt CSam CSli EHul

	EOrn GKir LBee LCon LLin LRHS MAsh MBar MBri MGos SLim SPoG
– 'Gold Coast'	CDoC CKen CMac CSBt EBre EHul ENot EPfP GKir LBee LCon LRHS MAsh MBar MBri MGos MWat SLim WDin
– Gold Sovereign = 'Blound' PBR	EBre EOrn GKir LBee MAsh MGos NHol SMer
– 'Gold Star'	EOrn WBcn
* – 'Golden Joy'	SLim
– 'Golden Saucer'	MAsh MBar MBri NBlu SCoo
– 'Goldkissen'	MBri
§ – 'Kuriwao Gold'	CMac EBre EHul ENot EPfP GKir LBee MBar MGos NHol SBod SLim SMer STre WFar WOrn WStI
– 'Milky Way' (v)	SLim
– 'Mint Julep'	CMac CSBt EBre EHul ENot GKir IMGH LBee LCon LLin LPan LRHS MAsh MBar MGos NBlu SLim SPer WBrE WDin WFar WMoo WOrn
– 'Mordigan Gold'	LPan
– 'Old Gold' ♀ H4	CBrm CKen CMac EHul ENot EOrn EPfP GKir IMGH LBee LCon LLin LRHS MAsh MBar MGos NBlu NDlv NHol NWea SBod SLim SMer SPer WDin WEve WFar WTel WWeb
– 'Old Gold Carbery'	see *J.* x *pfitzeriana* 'Carbery Gold'
– 'Pfitzeriana'	see *J.* x *pfitzeriana* 'Wilhelm Pfitzer'
– 'Pfitzeriana Aurea'	CBcs CDoC CDul CMac CSBt CWib EHul ENot EPfP GKir LCon LLin LRHS MBar MBri MGos MWat NBlu NWea SHBN WCFE WDin WFar WOrn
– 'Pfitzeriana Compacta' ♀ H4	CMac ECho EHul MBar SLim SPer
– 'Pfitzeriana Glauca'	EHul ENot IMGH LPan LRHS MBar SCoo SLim WGor
– 'Richeson'	MBar
– 'Saybrook Gold'	LPan
– 'Silver Cascade'	EHul
§ – 'Sulphur Spray' ♀ H4	CBrm CDoC CKen CMac CSBt CWib EBre EHul ENot EOrn EPla GKir LBee LCon LLin LRHS MAsh MBar MBri MGos NBlu NHol SLim SPer SPla WCFE WDin WFar WMoo WTel
§ – 'Wilhelm Pfitzer'	CMac EHul ENot EPfP MBar NWea WStI
– 'Winter Surprise' (v)	MGos
§ *pingii* 'Glassell'	CDoC ECho LLin MBar MGos
§ – 'Pygmaea'	EOrn ESis MBar
§ – var. *wilsonii*	CDoC CKen ECho EHul EOrn MBar
procumbens 'Bonin Isles'	LLin MGos SLim
– 'Nana' ♀ H4	CDoC CKen CMac CSBt EBre EHul ENot EOrn EPfP GKir IMGH LBee LCon LLin LRHS MAsh MBar MBri MGos MWat NHol SHBN SLim SPla WCFE WDin
	LCon
recurva	
– 'Castlewellan'	EOrn LCon MGos WCwm
– var. *coxii*	CDoC CMac EHul EOrn EPla GGGa GKir ISea LCon LLin MBar MBri MGos SLim SRms WCFE WCwm WEve WPic
§ – 'Densa'	CDoC CKen EHul EOrn MBar NHol SHBN
– 'Embley Park'	EHul MAsh MBar
– 'Nana'	see *J. recurva* 'Densa'
rigida	EHul LBee LLin MBar MWat
§ – subsp. *conferta*	LCon SLim SPer SPla STre WEve WStI
* – – 'Blue Ice'	CKen EOrn LLin

- - 'Blue Pacific'	CMac COtt EHul GKir MBar MBri SLim SPoG
- - 'Emerald Sea'	EHul
sabina	NWea
§ - 'Blaue Donau'	CSBt EHul MBar MGos SRms WEve
- Blue Danube	see *J. sabina* 'Blaue Donau'
- 'Broadmoor'	EHul
- 'Buffalo'	EHul
- Cupressifolia Group	MBar
- 'Hicksii'	CBcs CMac MBar NWea
- 'Knap Hill'	see *J.* x *pfitzeriana* 'Wilhelm Pfitzer'
- 'Mountaineer'	see *J. scopulorum* 'Mountaineer'
- 'Rockery Gem'	EHul EOrn MGos SLim SPla WGor
- 'Skandia'	CKen
- 'Tamariscifolia'	CBcs CDoC CMac CSBt CWib EBre EHul ENot GKir LBee LCon LLin LPan LRHS MAsh MBar MBri MGos NBlu NWea SBod SHBN SLim SMer SPer WCFE WDin WFar WTel
- 'Tripartita'	see *J. virginiana* 'Tripartita'
- 'Variegata' (v)	CMac EHul MAsh MBar NWea WBcn
sargentii	see *J. chinensis* var. *sargentii*
scopulorum	CKen MBar
§ - 'Banff'	CSBt
- 'Blue Arrow'	CDoC CKen COtt CSBt CWib ENot EOrn EPfP GKir IMGH LBee LCon LLin LPan LRHS MAsh MBar MBri MGos MWat NBee NBlu SCoo SLim SPar SPer SPla WDin WEve
- 'Blue Banff'	CKen
- 'Blue Heaven'	EHul LCon MAsh MBar
- 'Blue Pyramid'	EHul
- 'Boothman'	EHul
- 'Moonglow'	CSli EBre EHul MBar
§ - 'Mountaineer'	EHul
- 'Mrs Marriage'	CKen
- 'Repens'	MBar MGos
- 'Silver Star' (v)	EHul MBar MGos WEve
- 'Skyrocket'	More than 30 suppliers
- 'Springbank'	CMac EHul LBee LRHS MBar
- 'Tabletop'	MBar WBcn
- 'Tolleson's Blue Weeping'	LCon
- 'Wichita Blue'	EHul EPfP LCon LPan SEND WGor
squamata 'Blue Carpet' ♀ H4	More than 30 suppliers
- 'Blue Spider'	CKen LRHS MBar SCoo SLim WGor WLRN
- 'Blue Star' ♀ H4	More than 30 suppliers
'Blue Star Variegated'	see *J. squamata* 'Golden Flame'
- 'Blue Swede'	see *J. squamata* 'Hunnetorp'
- 'Chinese Silver'	EHul LCon MBar SLim WBcn WLRN
- 'Dream Joy'	CKen SLim
- var. *fargesii*	see *J. squamata*
- 'Filborna'	CKen LBee MBar MWat SLim SMer
- 'Glassell'	see *J. pingii* 'Glassell'
§ - 'Golden Flame' (v)	CKen
- 'Holger' ♀ H4	CBrm CDoC CKen CMac CSBt EBre EHul EOrn EPfP EPla GKir LBee LCon LLin LRHS MAsh MBar MBri MGos SBod SLim WCFE WStl WWeb
§ - 'Hunnetorp'	EOrn GKir MBar MBri MGos NBlu WEve WGor
- 'Loderi'	see *J. pingii* var. *wilsonii*
- 'Meyeri'	CTri EHul ENot EOrn GKir IMGH MBar MGos SBod SCoo SLim SMer STre WDin WFar WStl WTel WWin
- 'Pygmaea'	see *J. pingii* 'Pygmaea'
- 'Wilsonii'	see *J. pingii* var. *wilsonii*
- 'Yellow Tip'	WBcn
§ *taxifolia*	EOrn IMGH LBee
virginiana	CAgr CPne

§ - 'Blue Cloud'	EHul MBar SLim WEve WGor WLRN
- 'Burkii'	CDoC EHul LCon WGer
- 'Frosty Morn'	CKen ECho EHul MBar SCoo
- 'Glauca'	CSWP EHul NWea
- 'Golden Spring'	CKen
- 'Grey Owl' ♀ H4	CMac CSli CWib EHul ENot EPfP GKir LCon MBar MGos NWea SLim SLon SMer SRms STre WDin WFar WGor WTel
- 'Helle'	see *J. chinensis* 'Spartan'
- 'Hetzii'	CBcs CMac ECho EHul MBar NBlu NWea WDin WFar WLRN
- 'Hillii'	MBar
- 'Hillspire'	EHul
- 'Nana Compacta'	MBar
- 'Silver Spreader'	CKen CSBt EHul LCon MGos SCoo WBcn
- 'Staver'	EHul
- 'Sulphur Spray'	see *J.* x *pfitzeriana* 'Sulphur Spray'
§ - 'Tripartita'	MBar
§ - 'Venusta'	CKen

Jurinea (Asteraceae)

alata	EMan
cyanoides	EMan
dolomiaea CC 3719 **new**	ITim
mollis	GBuc

Jurinella see *Jurinea*

Jussiaea see *Ludwigia*

Justicia (Acanthaceae)

aurea	ERou
§ *brandegeeana* ♀ H1	CHal MBri SOWG
- 'Lutea'	see *J. brandegeeana* 'Yellow Queen'
§ - 'Yellow Queen'	CHal
§ *carnea*	CFwr CHEx CHal CSev EBak EHol ERea GCal LRHS MBri SLdr SMad SOWG WMul
guttata	see *J. brandegeeana*
'Nørgaard's Favourite'	MBri
ovata	SMad
pohliana	see *J. carnea*
rizzinii ♀ H1	CHal CHll CPle CSev ERea EShb SOWG
spicigera	ERea
suberecta	see *Dicliptera suberecta*

K

Kadsura (Schisandraceae)

japonica	CBcs CPIN EMil
- B&SWJ 1027	WCru
- 'Shiromi'	CPIN EMil EPfP SBra SBrw
- 'Variegata' (v)	EPfP SBra SBrw WSHC

Kaempferia (Zingiberaceae)

galanga	LEur
linearis	CKob LEur
rotunda	LAma LEur

kaffir plum see *Harpephyllum caffrum*

Kageneckia (Rosaceae)

oblonga	IFro

Kalanchoe (Crassulaceae)

beharensis ♀ H1	CHal EShb MBri
blossfeldiana	EOHP LRHS
- 'Variegata' (v)	CHal
daigremontiana	CHal EShb SRms
§ **delagoensis**	CHal EShb SMur STre
fedtschenkoi	CHal
manginii ♀ H1	CDoC EOHP
pumila ♀ H1	CHal EMan ERea EWoo SPet STre WEas
'Tessa' ♀ H1	MBri MLan SPet
tomentosa ♀ H1	CHal SMur SPet WEas
tubiflora	see K. delagoensis
'Wendy' ♀ H1	WGwG

Kalimeris (Asteraceae)

§ **incisa**	EWll GMac IHMH WCot WFar WMoo WTin
- 'Alba'	EBee EFou EMon NLar SHel SSvw WFar
- 'Blue Star'	EBee EFou LHop NLar WFar
* - 'Variegata' (v)	EBee
integrifolia	ECha GMac WTin
intricifolia new	EBee
§ **mongolica**	EBee ECha MAnH WFar WPGP WPer
§ **pinnatifida**	EBee EMan EPPr WCot
§ **yomena** 'Shogun' (v)	CRDP EBee ECha EFou EHoe ELan EMan EMar EMon EPPr GBri GBuc GEdr GKir MAvo MLLN MTis NBid NBir NPri NSti SAga SCro SDes SPer SPlb WCot WCra WFar WWeb
- 'Variegata'	see K. yomena 'Shogun'

Kalmia ✿ (Ericaceae)

angustifolia ♀ H4	GKev MBar NBlu NLAp SPar SRms WDin WFar
- var. **angustifolia** f. **candida**	WAbe
- var. **pumila**	SReu WAbe
- f. **rubra** ♀ H4	CBcs CDoC CMHG CPLG EBre ELan EPfP GKir ISea ITim LRHS MAsh MGos NDlv NHol SBrw SHBN SPer SReu SSta WFar WHar WPat
latifolia ♀ H4	CBcs CEnd CTrG ELan EMil EPfP GGGa LNet MBar MDun MGos MLan NBee NBlu NWea SBrw SPar SPer SReu SSpi SSta WAbe WBod WBrE WDin WFar WGer WNor WStI WWeb
- 'Alpine Pink'	CBrm NLar SBrw
- 'Bullseye'	CBcs GGGa SBrw
- 'Carousel'	CAbP EPfP GGGa GKir LRHS MGos
- 'Elf'	GEdr LRHS MGos MLea NLar WWeb
- 'Freckles' ♀ H4	CBcs ELan EPfP GEdr GGGa GKir ISea LRHS MAsh MDun MGos NDlv SBrw WGwG
- 'Fresca'	LRHS MDun MHFa
- 'Galaxy'	GGGa
- 'Heart of Fire'	CAbP GGGa GKir LRHS MAsh NDlv
- 'Keepsake' new	GGGa
- 'Little Linda' ♀ H4	GGGa GKir IMGH LRHS MAsh MBri NDlv SBrw
- 'Minuet'	CAbP CDoC CWSG EPfP GEdr GGGa GKir IMGH LRHS MAsh MDun MLan MLea MMHG NDlv SBrw SPoG SSpi WBrE WWeb
- f. **myrtifolia**	GEdr LPan MLea
- 'Olympic Fire' ♀ H4	CBrm CEnd ELan EPfP GGGa GKir LPan LRHS MAsh MGos NDlv NHol SBrw SSpi
- 'Ostbo Red'	CBcs CDoC EMil EPfP GEdr GGGa GKir IMGH ISea MBri MGos MLea

	NDlv NHol SBrw SHBN SPer SReu SSpi SSta WBod WGwG WLRN
- 'Peppermint'	GGGa
- 'Pink Charm' ♀ H4	CAbP ELan GGGa GKir GWCH LPan MAsh NDlv SBrw SMer SPer WBan WLRN
- 'Pink Frost'	CBcs GEdr GGGa NDlv NHol SBrw SPer
- 'Pristine'	GGGa SBrw
- 'Quinnipiac'	NHol
- 'Raspberry Glow'	GGGa
- 'Richard Jaynes'	GEdr LRHS SPer WBrE
- 'Sarah'	GGGa MBri NLar SSpi
- 'Silver Dollar'	GGGa NHol
- 'Snowdrift'	GGGa LRHS SPer
§ **microphylla**	GGGa WAbe
polifolia	CBcs CPLG MBar MBro NHol WPat
- var. **compacta**	WAbe WSHC
- 'Glauca'	see K. microphylla
- f. **leucantha**	GGGa SSta WAbe WPat
- 'Nana'	SSta

Kalmiopsis (Ericaceae)

leachiana ♀ H4	EPot GCrs NHar SOkd SSta WAbe
- 'Glendoick'	GGGa LTwo MBro MDun NHar WPat
- 'Hiawatha'	SReu
- 'Marcel le Piniec'	GGGa
* - 'Shooting Star'	LTwo WPat

x Kalmiothamnus (Ericaceae)

ornithomma 'Cosdon'	WAbe
- 'Haytor'	WAbe

Kalopanax (Araliaceae)

pictus	see K. septemlobus
§ **septemlobus**	CBcs CFil CHEx CLnd ELan EWTr GIBF NPal SDes WBVN WOTO
- var. **maximowiczii**	CDoC EPfP MBlu NBee SMad WCot

Keckiella (Scrophulariaceae)

§ **cordifolia**	EMan

Kelseya (Rosaceae)

uniflora	CGra WAbe

Kennedia (Papilionaceae)

beckxiana	LRHS SOWG
coccinea	CBcs CPIN GQui LRHS
macrophylla	CPIN CTrC
nigricans	CPIN ESlt SOWG
prostrata	SPlb
rubicunda	CHal CPIN CRHN CSpe

Kentia (Arecaceae)

belmoreana	see Howea belmoreana

Kentranthus see Centranthus

Kerria (Rosaceae)

japonica misapplied (single)	see K. japonica 'Simplex'
japonica (d)	see K. japonica 'Pleniflora'
- 'Albescens'	CBot CFai NPro WBcn WFar
- 'Golden Guinea' ♀ H4	CChe CPLG CPom CWSG EBee ECtt ELan EPfP GKir LRHS MAsh MGos MNrw NPro SCoo SPer SPoG SSte WDin WFar WWeb WWpP
§ - 'Picta' (v)	CBcs CDul CWib EBee EBre EHoe ENot EPfP LAst MBar MBri MGos MRav NBee SGar SLim SLon SPar SPer SRms WDin WFar WSHC WTel WWal WWeb WWpP

§ – 'Pleniflora' (d) ♀ H4 — More than 30 suppliers
§ – 'Simplex' — CBcs CSBt ENot GKir NWea SGar WDin WFar WOTO WTel
  – 'Variegata' — see *K. japonica* 'Picta'

Keteleeria (Pinaceae)
davidiana new — LCon

Khadia (Aizoaceae)
sp. — CTrC

Kickxia (Scrophulariaceae)
spuria — MSal

Kirengeshoma (Hydrangeaceae)
palmata ♀ H4 — More than 30 suppliers
  – dwarf — WCot
§ – Koreana Group — CHid CLAP CRDP EBee EChP ECha EGle EHrv ELan EMan EPar EPfP GKir IPot LAst LPhx MBri MRav NDov NEgg SCro SMad SPer WAbe WCot WFar WHil WOVN WTMC

Kitagawia (Apiaceae)
§ **litoralis** — EBee

Kitaibela (Malvaceae)
balansae new — EBee
vitifolia — CFee CPLG CSpe EBee ELan EMar EMon EWTr GCal IFro MNrw NBid SPlb WCer WCot WHer WPer WPic WRHF WRos WTMC WWin
  'Chalice' — CStr

Kitchingia see *Kalanchoe*

kiwi fruit see *Actinidia deliciosa*

Kleinia (Asteraceae)
articulata — see *Senecio articulatus*
grantii — ERea
repens — see *Senecio serpens*
senecioides — WEas

Knautia (Dipsacaceae)
§ **arvensis** — CArn CKin EC00 MBow MChe MGas MHer MLLN MWya NLan NMir NSco WFar WHer
  – 'Lawley's White' **new** — NPar
dipsacifolia — SHar
godetii new — EBee
* **jankiae** — WHer
§ **macedonica** — More than 30 suppliers
  – 'Crimson Cushion' **new** — NCot
  – 'Macedonia Lilac' — EBlw
  – 'Mars Midget' **new** — CFwr
  – Melton Pastels — CFwr EChP FMar ENot EPfP GKir IBal MWgw MWrn SCro SDes SRot SWal SWat WBar WFar
  – pink — CMil CSam
  – 'Red Dress' — EBee EMon
  – tall, pale — LPhx
sarajevensis — CMdw EBee
§ **tatarica** — EBee

Knightia (Proteaceae)
excelsa — CTrC

Kniphofia ❀ (Asphodelaceae)
'Ada' — ECGP ERou EWes MLLN MRav
'Alcazar' — More than 30 suppliers
'Amsterdam' — LBuc MWat
angustifolia new — WHil

'Apple Court' — NBir
'Apricot' — CMdw
'Apricot Sensation' — ECha
'Apricot Souffle' — EMan GBri MLLN WCot
'Atlanta' — CFil GCal IBlr LRHS SHel WCot
'Barton Fever' **new** — WCot
baurii — WCot
'Bees' Flame' — EBee
'Bees' Lemon' — CBcs CM&M CMdw CPen EBee EChP ECtt EGle EMan EMil GKir LAst LHop LPio MBri MCLN MDKP MLLN NGdn NLar NSti SAga WCot
'Bees' Sunset' ♀ H4 — CDes CFwr EBee EGle GBri MRav MWgw NBir SHBN SMHy SMrm SUsu WCot WLRN WPGP WPrP WTMC
* **bicolor** — EBee NSti WCot
'Border Ballet' — ECtt EMan ERou LRHS MFir MRav MWgw NBir NBro NLar NMir SDes SWat WFar
brachystachya — CPou EBee GCal SIgm SPlb WCot
  – 'Bressingham Court' **new** — CRez
'Bressingham Comet' — EBee EBre ECtt EMan EPfP GKir LRHS MBri MRav NBir SBla SDes SDys WCot WHil WRus
'Bressingham Gleam' — WCot
Bressingham hybrids — EBre LRHS NBir
Bressingham Sunbeam = 'Bresun' — CPen EBee WCot
'Brimstone' ♀ H4 — More than 30 suppliers
buchananii — EBee WCot
'Buttercup' ♀ H4 — CMHG CMdw SOkh
'C.M. Prichard' hort. — see *K. rooperi*
'C.M. Prichard' Prichard — WCot
'Candlelight' — CDes CFwr CPlt EBee EMan SChu SCro SDys SUsu WCot WPGP
* 'Candlemass' — LPio
caulescens ♀ H3-4 — More than 30 suppliers
  – 'Coral Breakers' **new** — WCot
  – short — SMrm
citrina — CBot CFir EBee FBlw EGGN EChP EMan EPfP LAst LRHS NLar WPer
'Cobra' — CDes CRDP CStr EBee LRHS SCro WCot WPGP
'Corallina' — EBee LCaP NHaw NPri WCot WFar WPnP WViv
'Dingaan' — CPrp EBee EChP EMan GBri GCal MNrw WCot WFar
'Doctor E.M. Mills' — CFwr CPrp CSam
'Dorset Sentry' — CHea CKno CMdw CSam EBee EChP EGle EMan EMar GBuc GCal GMac LAst MAnH MLLN MNrw MSte NLar NSti WCot WElm
'Dropmore Apricot' **new** — CM&M
'Drummore Apricot' — CAbb CFwr CKno CMHG CSam CTrC EBee EChP EGle EMan EWll LAst MCLN MSte NBir NDov NPPs NSti SMrm WCot WHrl WPGP WPrP WWhi
'E.C. Mills' **new** — WCot
'Earliest of All' — COtt EBee EBre EMan EWll GSki LCaP LRHS MBNS SPer
'Early Buttercup' — CFwr CPrp ECot EPfP GBri MRav NCat NHaw SApp SPar WCot WFar WViv
§ **ensifolia** — CPou NGdn SIgm WBcn
'Erecta' — WCot
'Ernest Mitchell' — EGle MRav SMrm WCot
Express hybrids — EBee NLar
'Fairyland' — EMan LPio MNrw WBro WCot WRHF WTin
* 'Fat Yellow' — MWgw
fibrosa — CFir WCot WHil

'Fiery Fred'	CMil EGle ELan EMan LRHS NHaw WCot WEas
'Flamenco' **new**	MPWC
fluviatilis **new**	EBee
foliosa	EBee EBre EMan LRHS SChr SMrm
'Forncett Harvest'	EFou
'Frances Victoria'	WCot
galpinii hort.	see *K. triangularis* subsp. *triangularis*
– Baker ♀ H4	CBot CMGP EBee EMar GBri SAga SPer SRms
'Gilt Bronze'	WCot
'Gladness'	MRav NBir NSti SChu WCot WPrP
'Goldelse'	EGle IBlr NBir SMad WViv
'Goldfinch'	CMdw EBee MRav SUsu
gracilis	SApp WCot
'Green and Cream'	MNrw
'Green Jade'	CDes CFir CMdw COtt CRow EBre ECha EPar EPfP GBri GKir LPhx MCLN MRav NBir NSti SChu SEND SGar SIgm SMrm WBro WPGP
'H.E. Beale'	GCal MRav NHaw SMrm WCot
hirsuta	EBee EBre ELan EMan EMar LPio MSte WCot
– JCA 3.461.900	WCot
– JCA 346 900	SSpi
'Hollard's Gold'	WCot
'Ice Queen'	CBri CFir CFwr CPar EBee ECGP EGle EOrc ERou EVFa GBri LPhx MMil MRav NChi SMad SMrm SPar WCot WTin
ichopensis	CFil EBee GBuc WCot
'Ingénue'	EMan LPio WCot
'Innocence'	SPar WCot
'Jenny Bloom'	More than 30 suppliers
'John Benary'	CFwr COtt CPou CPrp CSam EBee ECtt EGle EMan EMar GAbr GBin GCal GMaP GMac LHop LPio LRHS NDov NPSl NSti SMrm SPer SUsu WCFE WCot WHrl WKif WLin
'Johnathan'	MWat WCot
laxiflora	CFil CPou EBee SSpi
'Lemon Ice'	WCot
'Light of the World'	More than 30 suppliers
'Limelight'	EMar
linearifolia	CFil CPou CTrC EBee GGar MNrw SApp SPlb WCot
'Little Elf'	LPhx LPio MWat SBla SDys WSHC
'Little Maid'	More than 30 suppliers
'Lord Roberts'	CPen EBee EMan ENot SMad WCot
'Luna'	WCot
'Lye End'	EBee SMrm
macowanii	see *K. triangularis* subsp. *triangularis*
'Maid of Orleans'	CRow GBri GKir NHaw WCot
'Mellow Yellow'	IBlr
'Mermaiden'	CMHG CRow EBee EChP EMan LAst MNrw WCot
'Minister Verschuur'	CFwr EBee WFar WMnd WViv
'Modesta'	EBee EPla GBri SBla WPGP WSHC
'Mount Etna'	WCot
multiflora	SMrm
'Nancy's Red'	More than 30 suppliers
natalensis	EBee GBuc LPio WCot
nelsonii	see *K. triangularis* subsp. *triangularis*
'Nobilis'	see *K. uvaria* 'Nobilis'
northiae	CBot CFil CFir CHEx CPou EBee EMan GBin GCal LEdu SAPC SArc SIgm SPlb SSpi WAbe WCru WPGP
'Notung'	IBlr
I 'Old Court Seedling'	WCot
'Painted Lady'	CTri GCal MAnH MBct MBro MRav SMrm WHoo
parviflora	CPou
pauciflora	CBro EMan EMar LHop SDys SIgm WCot
'Percy's Pride'	More than 30 suppliers
'Perry's White'	WViv
'Pfitzeri'	SRms
porphyrantha	WCot
x *praecox*	CFil EBee WCFE WCot
'Primulina' hort.	CPou EBre EMan
'Prince Igor'	CFir ECha EMan NBir SChu SIgm SMad SPar
pumila	EBee MNrw
'Ranelagh Gardens'	SArc
ritualis	CFil EBee WCot
§ *rooperi*	CBot CFil CHEx CMdw CMil EBee EMan GBri GCal GGar IGor LPhx LPio MHer MLwd MMil MNrw NBir NRib SCro SMrm WCot WPGP WPic WViv
– 'Torchlight'	CFwr CPne CPrp WViv
'Ross Sunshine'	EOrc
'Rougham Beauty'	ERou
'Royal Caste'	EBee MMil MRav NBir NOrc NPri SDes WFar
'Royal Standard' ♀ H4	CBcs COtt EBee ELan EMan ENot EPfP ERou GBri GSki LRHS MNrw MRav SCro SDes SMad SPar SRms WCot WFar WWeb
rufa	CPou EBee WCot
aff. *rufa* **new**	SSpi
'Safranvogel'	IBlr SMrm SUsu WCot
'Samuel's Sensation' ♀ H4	EBee EChP EMan GBri LRHS MBri NSti SHBN WCot
sarmentosa	CDes CFil CPou EBee SIgm WCot WPGP
'September Sunshine'	MRav
'Shining Sceptre'	CFwr CSam EBee EBre ECha ECtt EFou ERou GSki LIck LPio LRHS MLLN MRav MWat SGar SIgm SMad SPar WCot WLRN
splendida	SMrm
'Springtime'	WCot
'Star of Baden-Baden'	ECGN NBir WCot WPGP
'Strawberries and Cream'	EBee EMan EPfP GSki LPhx LPio MSte SAga SUsu WWye
stricta	SIgm WCot
'Sunbeam'	NBir
'Sunningdale Yellow' ♀ H4	CDes CMdw COlW CPou EBee ECha EHry EMan ENot ERou EVFa GMaP MFir MWat SChu SMHy SPar SRms WCot WEas WPGP
'Tawny King'	More than 30 suppliers
'Tetbury Torch' PBR	LRHS WWeb
thodei	CPou
thomsonii	GCal
– orange	GCal
– var. *snowdenii* misapplied	see *K. thomsonii* var. *thomsonii*
– var. *snowdenii*	CHEx CPou EBee EVFa WCru WHrl WPGP WSHC
§ – var. *thomsonii*	CBot CDes CFir ECha EMan EMar EOrc ETow GBri IBlr MNrw SCro SMrm SPar WCot WFTG WHal WPrP
– – triploid variety	GSki
– yellow	GCal
'Timothy'	More than 30 suppliers
'Toffee Nosed' ♀ H4	CPar ECGP EFou EGle EMan EPfP ERou GBin GBri GCal LPio MMil MRav NBir SChu SMrm SPer SUsu WCot WPrP WSHC
'Torchbearer'	WCot WFar WTre

triangularis	CBot CHad CMHG EBee ECGN EPfP GCal GSki LRHS NPPs SAga SScr WFar
§ – subsp. *triangularis*	CBot CBri CBro CHad CKno COIW CPrp EChP EMar ENot EWsh GBuc IBlr LRHS MRav NBro NHaw NPri SCoo SDes SLon SMrm SPar SPla SRms SWat WBrE WViv
'Tubergeniana'	WCot
I 'Tuckii'	CStu EMan EWll MNrw
tuckii Baker	see *K. ensifolia*
typhoides	EBee SPlb SSpi WCot WHal
tysonii	SPlb
uvaria	CPou CTrC EBee GSki LPio LRHS MHer NBir NPri NVic SDes SPer SRms SSpi WCot WHoo WHrl WMnd
* – Fairyland hybrids	EWTr LIck
– 'Flamenco'	CFwr EWll LPVe NGdn SDes WHil
§ – 'Nobilis' ♀ H4	EBee EChP EMan ERou GBin GBri MLLN SAPC SArc SMHy SMad SPar SPoG WCot
'Vanilla'	CPen EBec EGle EMan LPio MRav SMrm WAul
'Wrexham Buttercup'	CDes CKno EBee EChP ECtt EMan GBri GCal MLLN MRav WCot WHal WTMC
'Yellow Cheer'	CPen LRHS
'Yellow Hammer'	CBot EBee ECha EVFa NCat SPar WFar
'Zululandiae'	EBee WCot

Kochia see *Bassia*

Koeleria (Poaceae)

cristata	see *K. macrantha*
glauca	More than 30 suppliers
§ *macrantha*	CBig CBrm EMan EPPr NHol NNor NOGN
vallesiana	EHoe EMon EPPr ESis LRHS MNrw WPrP

Koellikeria (Gesneriaceae)

'Red Satin'	NMos

Koelreuteria (Sapindaceae)

* *bipinnata* var. *integrifoliola*	CFil WPGP
paniculata ♀ H4	More than 30 suppliers
– var. *apiculata*	CMHG
– 'Fastigiata'	EBee EPfP MBlu NPal SKee
– 'Rosseels'	MBlu NPal

Kohleria (Gesneriaceae)

'Clytie'	MBri
'Dark Velvet'	CHal WDib
eriantha ♀ H1	CHal EShb MBri WDib
* x *hybrida*	NMos
'Jester' ♀ H1	CHal WDib
* 'Linda'	CHal
'Strawberry Fields' ♀ H1	MBri NMos
§ *warscewiczii* ♀ H1	CHal LRHS WDib

Kolkwitzia (Caprifoliaceae)

amabilis	CBcs CSBt CTrw EBee ELan EMil EPfP GIBF ISea LPan MGos NFor NWca SPar SPlb SRms WCFE WDin WGwG WHCG WHar WMoo WNor WStI WTel
– 'Maradco'	EBee EPfP LRHS MAsh NPro SPla WPat
– 'Pink Cloud' ♀ H4	More than 30 suppliers

Kosteletzkya (Malvaceae)

virginica	EMan SPlb

Kuhnia (Asteraceae)

eupatorioides new	EBee

Kunzea (Myrtaceae)

ambigua	CTrC ECou SBrw SOWG SPlb
baxteri	CTrC ECou SOWG
capitata	CTrC SOWG
ericifolia	SPlb
§ *ericoides*	CTrC ECou GGar SOWG
– 'Auckland'	ECou
– 'Bemm'	ECou
parvifolia	CTrC ECou SOWG
pomifera	ECou

L

Lablab (Caesalpiniaceae)

§ *purpureus*	SMur

+ *Laburnocytisus* (Papilionaceae)

'Adamii'	CDul CLnd COtt CPMA EBee EPfP GKir LBuc LPan MBlu MGos SHBN SMad SSpi

Laburnum ✿ (Papilionaceae)

alpinum	CNic EBee EPfP NWea SSpi WDin
– 'Pendulum'	CBcs CDoC CWSG EBre ELan EPfP GKir LNet LPan LRHS MHar MBri MGos MRav MWat NBee NEgg SHBN SKee SLim SPer WDin WOrn WStI
§ *anagyroides*	CWlb ECrN ISca NWea SEND SRms WDin
– 'Pendulum'	CLnd
vulgare	see *L. anagyroides*
x *watereri* 'Vossii' ♀ H4	More than 30 suppliers

Lachenalia (Hyacinthaceae)

§ *aloides*	EPot LBow MBri SRob
– var. *aurea* ♀ H1	LBow LRHS MSte
* – var. *bicolor*	WCot
– var. *luteola*	LBow
– 'Nelsonii'	LBow LRHS
– 'Pearsonii'	LRHS
– var. *quadricolor* ♀ H1	ETub LBow LRHS WCot
– var. *vanzyliae* ♀ H1	LBow
§ *bulbifera* ♀ H1	LBow MBri
– 'George' ♀ H1	LBow
contaminata ♀ H1	LBow LRHS WCot
mathewsii	LBow
mediana	LBow
mutabilis	LBow LRHS WCot
orchioides var. *glaucina*	WCot
pendula	see *L. bulbifera*
purpureocoerulea	WCot
pustulata ♀ H1	LBow LRHS WCot
reflexa	WCot
splendida new	WCot
tricolor	see *L. aloides*
unicolor new	WCot
violacea new	WCot
viridiflora ♀ H1 new	LRHS WCot

Lactuca (Asteraceae)

alpina	see *Cicerbita alpina*

perennis	EBee ECoo EVFa LHop MTho
	NMGW WCot WFTG WHer
virosa	CArn MSal

Lagarosiphon (Hydrocharitaceae)

§ *major*	CBen CRow EHon EMFW EPfP
	NBlu WFar WMAq

Lagarostrobos (Podocarpaceae)

§ *franklinii*	CBcs CDoC CTrG LCon LLin WPic

Lagerstroemia (Lythraceae)

indica ♀ H1	EShb LPan SEND SMur SPlb WCom
- 'Rosea'	CBcs LPan SEND
subcostata	CBcs

Lagunaria (Malvaceae)

patersonii	CFil CPLG WPGP
- 'Royal Purple'	EREa

Lagurus (Poaceae)

ovatus ♀ H3	LHrt SAdn SWal

Lamiastrum see *Lamium*

Lamium ✿ (Lamiaceae)

album	CKin GWCH
- 'Aureovariegatum'	see *L. album* 'Goldflake'
- 'Brightstone Gem' (v)	WCHb
- 'Friday' (v)	CBgR EHoe EMan EMar EMon
	EWTr MTho WCHb WHer
§ - 'Goldflake' (v)	WCHb
armenum	EHyt
barbatum new	EBee
§ *galeobdolon*	CArn CHEx CNat CTri CWib
	EWTr LGro MHar MHer MPWC
	MSal MWat NCot NSco SRms
	WBrE WWpP
- 'Hermann's Pride'	More than 30 suppliers
- 'Kirkcudbright Dwarf'	EBee EWes
- subsp. *montanum*	WCHb WWpP
'Canfold Wood'	
§ - - 'Florentinum'	CHal CRow CSBt EBee EChP
	ECha EHoe ELan EMan EPar EPfP
	GKir MRav NLon NVic SHel SIng
	WFar WPer WPnP
- 'Purple Heart'	EMon
§ - 'Silberteppich'	CRow ECha EFou ELan EMan
	EMar LRHS MRav MTho NFor
	WCot WPer
- 'Silver Angel'	EMan NSti
- Silver Carpet	see *L. galeobdolon* 'Silberteppich'
- 'Variegatum'	see *L. galeobdolon* subsp.
	montanum 'Florentinum'
garganicum new	WTMC
- subsp. *garganicum*	CDes CPom EWes GBri GEil
	MCAu SUsu WPer WWpP
- subsp. *pictum*	see *L. garganicum* subsp. *striatum*
- subsp. *reniforme*	see *L. garganicum* subsp. *striatum*
§ - subsp. *striatum*	SBla
- - DS&T 89011T	EPPr
luteum	see *L. galeobdolon*
maculatum	CArn EGoo EMon MBow NArg
	NCot SEND SHFr SRms WGwG
	WWye
- AL&JS 90226JU	EMon
- 'Album'	EBee ELan EMon EPfP LGro NLon
	SAga SPer SRms
- 'Anne Greenaway' (v)	GBri MCAu MGrG SChu SPet WBea
	WCHb WCot WEas WElm WMoo
- 'Annecy'	MInt
§ - 'Aureum'	CArn COIW EBre ECha EHoe
	ELan GGar GKir LGro MBro

	MTho NBlu SDes SPar SPer SPet
	SUsu WCHb WEas WFar WPer
- 'Beacon Silver'	More than 30 suppliers
- 'Beedham's White'	NBir NSti WCot
- 'Brightstone Pearl'	EGoo EPPr EWes WCer
- 'Cannon's Gold'	EBee ECha ECtt EHoe ELan ERou
	EWes GBuc NBlu NSti SDes
N - 'Chequers'	CDoC EBee LRHS SDes SPer SPla
	WCFE WPnP WWpP
- 'Dingle Candy'	CMdw EMon EVFa
- 'Elaine Franks'	CHid CSam NCat
- 'Elisabeth de Haas' (v)	CHal EWes SDes WCHb WCer
	WPer WWpP
- 'Forncett Lustre' new	EBee
- 'Gold Leaf'	see *L. maculatum* 'Aureum'
- Golden Anniversary =	EBee ERou GAbr LAst LRHS
'Dellam'PBR (v)	MBow MCCP NArg NBro NGdn
	SDes SPla WFar WPnP WWeb
- 'Golden Nuggets'	see *L. maculatum* 'Aureum'
- 'Golden Wedding'	COtt
- 'Hatfield'	EBee GAbr GBuc NCot
- 'Ickwell Beauty' (v)	EWes GBri WElm
- 'Immaculate'	EBee
- 'James Boyd Parselle'	EGle EGil MCAu MLLN SCro
	WCFE WCHb WCot WRHF
- 'Margery Fish'	SRms WEas
- 'Pink Nancy'	CBot EGoo GAbr GKir MTho
	MWrn WCer WFar
- 'Pink Pearls'	COIW CSBt EWTr LHrt LRHS
	NCiC NCot SDes SPet WMoo
- 'Pink Pewter'	EBre ECGP ECha ECtt EFou EPla
	EWTr GKir LGro LRHS NChi NCot
	NGdn NSti SCro SPer SPla SPlb
	SRPl SUsu WBrE WCHb WPer WRus
- 'Purple Winter'	LRHS
- 'Red Nancy'	EBee EMar EMon GCal NChi WCer
§ - 'Roseum'	CWib EBee EFer ELan EMar EPar
	EPfP EPla GKir LGro LHop MRav
	MWat MWgw NArg NFor NLon
	NSti SGar SPer WGwG WPer WWpP
- 'Shell Pink'	see *L. maculatum* 'Roseum'
- 'Silver Shield'	EWes
- 'Sterling Silver'	EBee NCot WPer
- 'White Nancy' ♀ H4	More than 30 suppliers
- 'Wootton Pink'	CBos GBuc GCal GMac LRHS MBri
	MHer NBir NChi NCot NLar SSvw
	WBro WCra WEas WElm WPer
microphyllum	CPBP EHyt
orvala	More than 30 suppliers
- 'Album'	CBos CBot CPle EBre EChP ELan
	EMon EOrc EPPr LRHS MFir MSte
	SGar SHar SIng SMrm SUsu WCot
	WHer
- 'Silva'	WCot
sandrasicum	CPBP EHyt NWCA SBla WPat
'Silberlicht'	CHEx

Lampranthus (Aizoaceae)

CDPR 3096 new	CFil
aberdeenensis	see *Delosperma aberdeenense*
aurantiacus	CBcs CHEx SPet
aureus	CTrC
'Bagdad'	CHEx
blandus	CBcs CHEx
§ *brownii*	CBcs CHal ECho ELan EMlt NBir
	SChr SEND SPet
coccineus	SPet
coralliflorus	CTrC
edulis	see *Carpobrotus edulis*
glaucus	SEND
haworthii	CHal
multiradiatus	CTrC SEND
roseus	EMlt SPet WEas

scaber	CTrC
spectabilis	CBcs CHal SAPC SArc SMur SPar SPet WBrE
- 'Tresco Apricot'	CBcs
- 'Tresco Brilliant'	CBcs CHEx SPet
- 'Tresco Fire'	CHal
- 'Tresco Peach'	CHEx CHal CStu EMlt
- 'Tresco Red'	CBcs
'Tresco Pearl'	CHEx

Lamprothyrsus (*Poaceae*)

CDPR 3096 **new**	WPGP

Lantana (*Verbenaceae*)

'Aloha' (v)	CHal SWal WWol
camara	ELan EPfP LRHS MBri MOak SRms SYvo
- 'Firebrand'	SYvo
- orange-flowered **new**	SWal
- pink-flowered **new**	NPri SWal
- 'Radiation' **new**	SGar
- red-flowered	SWal WWol
- 'Snow White'	MOak
- white-flowered **new**	SWal
- yellow-flowered **new**	NPri
§ *montevidensis*	CHal MOak SPet
- 'Boston Gold'	CHal MOak
- 'Whiteknights'	MOak
selloviana	see *L. montevidensis*
'Spreading Sunset'	SOWG

Lapageria (*Philesiaceae*)

rosea ♀ H3	CBcs CPlN CRHN EPfP EPla ERea GKir GQui IDee IMGH MDun MGol NRib NSla SAdn SHBN SSpi WNor
- var. *albiflora*	CPlN
'Flesh Pink'	CRHN
- 'Nash Court'	ECot EMil ERea

Lapeirousia (*Iridaceae*)

cruenta	see *Anomatheca laxa*
laxa	see *Anomatheca laxa*

Lapsana (*Asteraceae*)

communis 'Inky'	CNat WAlt

Lardizabala (*Lardizabalaceae*)

biternata	see *L. funaria*
funaria	CPLG CPlN CTrG

Larix (*Pinaceae*)

decidua ♀ H4	CBcs CCVT CDoC CDul CSBt ECrN ENot EWTr GKir LCon LPan MBar NWea SHBN SPar SPer WDin WEve WFar WHar WMou WStI
- 'Autumn Gold Weeping'	GKir
- 'Corley'	CKen LCon LLin MBlu
- 'Croxby Broom'	CKen
- 'Globus'	NHol SLim
- 'Horstmann Recurved'	SCoo SLim
- 'Little Bogle'	CKen MAsh NHol
- 'Oberförster Karsten'	CKen
- 'Pendula'	CBcs GKir
- 'Puli'	CEnd COtt GKir LLin MAsh MBlu SCoo SLim SPer SPoG
x *eurolepis*	see *L. x marschlinsii*
europaea Middend.	see *L. sibirica*
gmelinii	GIBF
- var. *olgensis*	NLar
- var. *principis-rupprechtii*	GIBF LCon
- 'Tharandt'	CKen
§ *kaempferi* ♀ H4	CDoC CDul CLnd CSBt CTri

	CWib ECrN EMil ENot GKir LBuc LCon LNet MBar MGos NWea SLim SPar SPer STre WDin WEve WFar WMou WNor WStI
- 'Bambino'	CKen
- 'Bingman'	CKen
- 'Blue Ball'	CKen LLin WEve
- 'Blue Dwarf'	CKen COtt GKir LCon LLin LNet MAsh MGos NBlu SLim WOrn
- 'Blue Haze'	CKen
- 'Blue Rabbit'	CKen CTho
- 'Blue Rabbit Weeping'	COtt GKir LCon LLin MGos NHol SCoo SLim WDin WEve WOrn
- 'Cruwys Morchard'	CKen
- 'Cupido'	LLin MAsh NHol
- 'Diane'	CEnd CKen GKir LCon LLin MAsh MBlu MBri MGos NHol SLim SPoG
- 'Elizabeth Rehder'	CKen
- 'Grant Haddow'	CKen
- 'Grey Green Dwarf'	MAsh NHol
- 'Grey Pearl'	CKen
- 'Hobbit'	CKen
- 'Jakobsen'	LCon
* - 'Jakobsen's Pyramid'	CEnd LLin NHol SCoo
- 'Nana'	CKen LLin MAsh NLar WWes
I - 'Nana Prostrata'	CKen
- 'Pendula'	CDul CEnd ECrN EPfP GKir LLin MBar MBlu MGos NHol SKee SPer
- 'Stiff Weeping'	GKir MAsh NLar SLim
- 'Swallow Falls'	CKen
- 'Varley'	CKen
- 'Wehlen'	CKen
- 'Wolterdingen'	CKen MBlu
- 'Yanus Olieslagers'	CKen
laricina	LCon SMad
- 'Arcthusa Bog'	CKen
- 'Bear Swamp'	CKen
- 'Bingman' **new**	CKen
- 'Hartwig Pine' **new**	CKen
- 'Newport Beauty'	CKen
leptolepis	see *L. kaempferi*
§ x *marschlinsii*	CSBt ECrN ENot GKir NWea WMou
- 'Domino'	CKen LLin NLar
- 'Gail'	CKen
- 'Julie'	CKen
* x *pendula* 'Pendulina'	ECrN
potaninii var. *himalaica* SF 95206	ISea
russica	see *L. sibirica*
§ *sibirica*	ISea MBar

Larrea (*Zygophyllaceae*)

tridentata	CArn

Laserpitium (*Apiaceae*)

siler	CArn NLar SIgm SMHy SPlb

Lasiagrostis see *Stipa*

Latania (*Arecaceae*)

loddigesii	LPal
verschaffeltii	LPal

Lathyrus ✿ (*Papilionaceae*)

albus	CEnd
amphicarpos	EBee
§ *articulatus*	ELan WCHb
aurantius	WLin
§ *aureus*	CBos CDes CHEx CHad EBee EMar EMon GBuc GCal LPhx

	MCAu MGrG MTho NBir NChi	– hybrids	LPhx
	SBla WCom WCru WEas WHal	– 'Tillyperone'	EMon WWpP
	WPGP WPat WSan WViv	§ **sativus**	CHad CHid CSpe ELan LCTD SSth
azureus hort.	see *L. sativus*		WCHb
chloranthus	EWll	– var. **azureus**	see *L. sativus*
cirrhosus	CDes EMon	– **caeruleus**	SAga
clymenum articulatus	see *L. articulatus*	**sphaericus**	WCHb
cyaneus hort.	see *L. vernus*	**sylvestris**	CAgr CKin CNat CPLG EBee
* – 'Alboroseus'	MTho SWat		EMon MHer MLLN MNrw MSte
davidii	EMon		SPet WPnP
fremontii hort.	see *L. laxiflorus*	– 'Wagneri'	EBee WCot
§ **gmelinii**	NLar WSan	**tingitanus**	CRHN LCTD WCHb
– 'Aureus'	see *L. aureus*	– 'Roseus'	CRHN
grandiflorus	CSev CStr EBee EChP ECha EMon	**tuberosus**	CAgr EBee EMon MNrw SSpi WCot
	LPhx NLar SMac SMrm SWat	'Tubro'	EMon
	WCom WCot	**undulatus**	SSpi
heterophyllus	EBee EMon EWsh MNrw	**venetus**	MNrw
inermis	see *L. laxiflorus*	§ **vernus** ♀ H4	More than 30 suppliers
japonicus	WHer	– 'Alboroseus' ♀ H4	More than 30 suppliers
– subsp. **maritimus**	EBee	– var. **albus**	CDes EWes LCTD
laevigatus	NLar	– **aurantiacus**	see *L. aureus*
latifolius ♀ H4	CAgr CArn CRHN EBee EBre	– 'Caeruleus'	CBos CDes CRDP EBee EMon
	ECGP EChP GBar GKir MFir		LHop LPhx SMrm WPGP
	MWgw NBlu NChi NPer SIng	* – 'Cyaneus'	SAga SOkh SWat WCot WRus
	SRms WEas WFar WHer WPer		WSan WWpP
	WStI WWin WWye	– 'Flaccidus'	EBee EChP EGle EMon WCom
§ – 'Albus' ♀ H4	CBot EBee ELan EMan GDra GKir		WCot WKif WTin
	LPhx MNrw SRms SSpi SUsu	* – 'Gracilis' **new**	WViv
	WBry WEas	– 'Indigo Eyes'	WCom
– 'Blushing Bride'	WCot	– 'Rainbow' **new**	WHil
– deep pink	NSti	– 'Rosenelfe'	CBot CDes EMan SOkh WHil
– pale pink	NSti		WPGP WSan WViv
– Pink Pearl	see *L. latifolius* 'Rosa Perle'	– f. **roseus**	ECGN ECha MRav NBir WCot
– 'Red Pearl'	CPlN ECtt EFou ELan ERou MBri	– 'Spring Beauty'	WViv
	MTis MWrn NPri SMrm SPer SPlb	– 'Spring Melody'	EBee LPio MRav SOkh WCot WPat
	SSvw WFar WPer WRus WViv WWeb	– 'Subtle Hints' **new**	EMon
§ – 'Rosa Perle' ♀ H4	CChe COlW CTri EBee ECtt EFou		
	EMan ERou GKir LHop MBri MSte	*Laurelia* (*Monimiaceae*)	
	NLar NPer NPri SBla SBra SMrm	**novae-zealandiae new**	CTrC
	SPer SSvw STes WRus WViv WWeb	§ **sempervirens**	CBcs CFil CTrw WPGP
I – 'Rubra'	EPfP	**serrata**	see *L. sempervirens*
– Weisse Perle	see *L. latifolius* 'White Pearl'		
– 'White Pearl' misapplied	see *L. latifolius* 'Albus'	*Laurentia* see *Isotoma*	
§ – 'White Pearl' ♀ H4	More than 30 suppliers		
§ **laxiflorus**	EBee EChP ECoo MCCP MHar	*Laurus* (*Lauraceae*)	
	MNrw MTho NChi NLar WCom	§ **azorica**	CBcs WFar
	WViv WWin	**canariensis**	see *L. azorica*
linifolius	EMon	**nobilis** ♀ H4	More than 30 suppliers
– var. **montanus**	CKin EBee WViv	– f. **angustifolia**	CMCN CSWP EBee EPla GQui
luteus (L.) Peterm.	see *L. gmelinii*		MBlu MRav SAPC SArc SDry
– 'Aureus'	see *L. aureus*		WCHb WPGP WSel
magellanicus	WCot	– 'Aurea' ♀ H4	CBcs CDul CFwr CMHG CSBt
F&W 9309 **new**			EBee ELau ELau EMil EPfP EPla
maritimus new	WFTG		ERea GQui LHop LNet LRHS
montanus	EBee		MBlu MBro MChe SBrw SLim
§ **nervosus**	CPlN CPou CSpe MTho SBla SRms		SLon SMad SPer WCHb WCot
neurolobus	CNic MOne		WDin WFar WPat WSel
niger	CPom EBee EMar EMon LHop	– 'Crispa'	MRav
	MLLN NLar SHFr SUsu WFar WHil	– 'Sunspot' (v) **new**	WCot
nissolia	ELan		
odoratus	CHar EWll	*Lavandula* ❀ (*Lamiaceae*)	
– 'Bicolor'	ELan	N 'Alba'	CArn CBcs CBot CSev CWib NYoL
– 'Cupani'	SUsu		SAdn SIde SPer SWat WEas WPer
– 'Matucana'	CSpe EBee	§ x **allardii**	CArn CPLG CPrp CSev EBee EMil
– 'Painted Lady'	SMrm WBry		EOHP GBar MChe MHer NHHG
palustris	NLar		WBad WJek WLav WOut WSel
polyphyllus	WCot	– 'African Pride'	GBar SDow
pratensis	CKin MGol	§ **angustifolia**	More than 30 suppliers
pubescens	CRHN GBuc WCot	– 'Alba'	CChe EBee EDAr EHoe ELau EPfP
roseus	EMon		GPoy LBuc MBNS MChe MHer
rotundifolius	CPlN EBee ECoo EMon GCal		MRav NLon NMen SLon SPar SPlb
	GDra LPhx MNrw MTho SUsu		WBry WDin WFar WHHs WSel
	WCom WCot WFar WHoo	– 'Alba Nana'	see *L. angustifolia* 'Nana Alba'

- 'Arctic Snow' **new**	CFai SPoG
- 'Arctic White' **new**	WLav
- 'Ashdown Forest'	CLvH CSev EBee ELau GBar MChe
	MHer NCot SAdn SDow SIde
	SMrm WBad WHHs WHoo WJek
	WLRN WLav
- 'Beechwood Blue' ♀ H4	NYoL SDow WBad WLav
- Blue Cushion =	EBre ENot GKir MBNS NPri SDow
'Lavandula Schola'PBR	
- 'Blue Mountain'	GBar SDow
- 'Blue Mountain	SDow
White' **new**	
§ - 'Bowles' Early'	CLvH CSam GBar MChe SAdn
	SDow WBad
- 'Bowles' Grey'	see *L. angustifolia* 'Bowles' Early'
- 'Bowles' Variety'	see *L. angustifolia* 'Bowles' Early'
- 'Cedar Blue'	CLvH CSev EGoo ELau GBar
	MHer NGHP NYoL SDow SHDw
	SIde SMrm SPla WBad WBar WFar
	WHHs WLav
- 'Compacta'	WBad
- 'Dwarf Blue'	CLvH CWSG EMil MHer MWhi
	WBad WFar
I - 'Eastgrove Nana'	WEas
- 'Folgate'	CArn CBcs CLvH CWCL ELau
	GBar MChe MHer NHHG NLon
	NYoL SDow SIde WBad WLav
	WMnd WSel WTel
- 'Fring Favourite'	SDow
- 'Heacham Blue'	SDow
§ - 'Hidcote' ♀ H4	More than 30 suppliers
- 'Hidcote Pink'	CArn CLvH CWib EDAr ESis GBar
	MHer MRav MWat NFor NMen
	NSti SDow SPer SRPl WBad WHHs
	WHen WHrl WKif WPer WSel
- 'Hidcote Superior' **new**	LPVe
- 'Imperial Gem' ♀ H4	CArn CLvH CSBt CSLe CWCL
	CWib EBee ELau ESis GBar LRHS
	MAsh MBri MChe MHer MLan
	MWat NHHG NPri SDow SIde
	SMur SPar SVil WBad WHoo WTel
	WWeb WWpP
§ - 'Jean Davis'	CLvH EBee GBar MAsh NHHG
	NPri SAdn SDow SIde WBad
	WHHs WLav WSel
- 'Lady'	CLvH MChe NOrc SEND SHDw
	WBad
- 'Lady Anne' **new**	WBad
N - 'Lavender Lady'	ELau EOHP NPer NYoL SAdn WPer
- 'Lavenite Petite' **new**	CFai LRHS
- Little Lady = 'Batlad'PBR	CWSG MAsh MBNS MHer SDow
	WBad WLav
- Little Lottie = 'Clarmo'	CWSG EBee ECGP EMil ENot
♀ H4	EPfP LRHS MAvo NCot SCoo
	SDow SLim SVil WBad WLav
- 'Loddon Blue' ♀ H4	CBcs ELau GBar NHHG NLon
	NYoL SAdn SDow SIde WBad WLav
§ - 'Loddon Pink' ♀ H4	CLvH CSLe EBee ENot EPfP ERea
	GBar GKir LRHS MAsh MChe
	MRav MTis NBid NPri NYoL SAdn
	SDow SPar SRPl WBad WEas WFar
	WHHs WHoo WPGP WWal
- 'Maillette'	SDow SIde WHHs WLav
- 'Middachten' **new**	CLvH
- 'Miss Donnington'	see *L. angustifolia* 'Bowles' Early'
- 'Miss Katherine'PBR ♀ H4	CFai CSBt CWSG ELan EPfP LRHS
	MAsh SDow SVil WBad WLav
- Miss Muffet = 'Scholmis'	EBee EMil MAsh SDow WBad
♀ H4	WLav
- 'Munstead'	More than 30 suppliers
§ - 'Nana Alba' ♀ H4	More than 30 suppliers
- 'Nana Atropurpurea'	SDow WBad WSel
- No.9	SDow

- 'Peter Pan'	CLvH MLan SDow WLav
- 'Princess Blue'	CLvH CWCL EBee ELan ELau
	ENot GBar LRHS MAsh MBNS
	NPri NYoL SAga SDow SIde SRPl
	WBad WLav WPer WWeb WWpP
§ - 'Rosea'	More than 30 suppliers
- 'Royal Purple'	CArn CLvH CSLe EBee ELau
	EWTr EWes GBar LRHS MAsh
	MBNS MHer NGHP NHHG NPri
	NYoL SAdn SDow SIde SMur
	WBad WLav WWpP
N - 'Twickel Purple'	CLvH CSBt CWSG EBee ENot
	EPfP GKir LHop LRHS MAvo
	MChe MHer MRav NHHG NPri
	NYoL SDix SDow SIde SPar SPer
	WBad WCom WHHs WLav WSel
	MHer WLav
aristibractea	NPro WLav
augustifolia	
'Lavenite Petite' **new**	CBcs GBar MHer SDow WLav
'Avonview'	CBcs GBar MHer SDow WLav
'Blue River'PBR **new**	CLvH
* 'Blue Star'	CLvH NBlu WHHs
'Bowers Beauty'	WBad WLav
buchii var. *buchii*	SDow
- var. *gracilis*	SDow
N 'Cambridge Lady'	WLav
canariensis	CSev EOHP ERea MHer NHHG
	SDow SHDw WBad WCHb WJek
	WLav
x *christiana*	CLvH CWCL EBee ELau GBar MHer
	SDow SHDw WBad WJek WLav
'Cornard Blue'	see *L.* 'Sawyers'
dentata	CArn CLvH CPrp CSev CTca CWCL
	EBee ELan ELau EOHP FPri ERea
	GBar MChe MHer MTis NHHG
	SAdn SDow SDry WBad WHHs
	WHer WPat WPic WWpP WWye
§ - var. *candicans*	CLvH CSev CTca EBee ELau
	EOHP GBar LHop MChe MHer
	NHHG SDow SMrm SPar WBad
	WCHb WLav WPer WWye
- 'Dusky Maiden' **new**	SDow WLav
- 'Linda Ligon' (v)	CFwr EBee EOHP GBar SDow
	WBad WLav
- 'Ploughman's Blue'	CWCL SDow WBad
'Royal Crown' ♀ H2-3	CLvH GBar MHer SDow WBad
	WFar
'Royal Standard'	SHBN
- silver	see *L. dentata* var. *candicans*
- 'Silver Queen'	WLav
- variegated **new**	CWib
'Devantville Cuche'	ELau NSti SDow WJek WLav
I 'Edelweiss'	CFwr EBee NGHP SVil WLav
'Fathead'	COtt CWCL EBee EPfP GAbr
	GBar LAst LRHS MAsh MHer
	MLan NGHP SAdn SDow SLim
	SMrm WBad WBrE WHHs WJek
'Fragrant Memories'	CLvH CSLe EBee ELau ERea GBar
	MAsh NPri SDow SIde WBad
	WLav
Goldburg = 'Burgoldeen'	CLvH CSBt EHan ELan ENot MAsh
	MBNS MBri MHer
(v)	NGHP NPri SCoo SDow SLim
	SPer WBad WHHs WLav WWeb
'Goodwin Creek Grey'	CLvH CWCL GBar MChe NBlu
	SDow WBad WLav WOut
'Helmsdale'PBR	More than 30 suppliers
heterophylla hort.	see *L.* x *allardii*
'Hidcote Blue'	see *L. angustifolia* 'Hidcote'
x *intermedia* 'Abrialii'	CLvH SDow WLav
- 'Alba' ♀ H4	CLvH CMea CPrp ECle GBar NChi
	NHHG SDow SGar WBad WLRN
N - 'Arabian Night' ♀ H4	CLvH COtt ELau MHer SDow

	SIde WBad WHHs WLav WPat WWeb
- 'Bogong'	CLvH
- 'Chaix' **new**	GBar
§ - Dutch Group	CArn CLvH CWCL CWSG EDAr ELan ENot EPfP EWTr GBar GKir MAsh MBar MBri MHer MRav NYoL SCoo SDow SLim SPar SPer SWat WBad WCom WHHs WHen WJek WPer WSel
§ - - Walberton's Silver Edge = 'Walvera' (v)	LRHS MAsh SCoo SDow SIde
- 'Grappenhall'	More than 30 suppliers
- 'Grey Hedge'	CLvH CSLe SDow WBad WHHs WLav
- 'Grosso'	CChe CFwr CLvH COkL COtt CSLe CSev EBee ECle ELau EPfP GBar MHer MRav NGHP NSti NYoL SAdn SDow SMrm SSvw WBad WDin WFar WJek WLRN WSel WWeb
- 'Hidcote Giant'	CLvH CSLe EBee ELan GBar LRHS MAsh NPer SDow WBad WKif WLav WRHF WSel
* - 'Hidcote White'	CLvH MHer WBad WLav
- 'Impress Purple'	GBar SDow WLav
- 'Lullingstone Castle'	CBod CLvH CPrp CSLe ELau GBar LHop NYoL SDow WBad WHHs WJek WLav
- 'Old English'	CSLe SDow
- Old English Group	CArn CBod CLvH ECGP ELau MBow NYoL SDow WBad WHoo WJek WLav WSel
- 'Seal'	CArn CLvH CPrp CSLe ECle ELau GBar MBow MChe MHer NGHP NHHG NYoL SDow SMrm WBad WHCG WHHs WMnd WPer WSel WWal
- 'Super'	SDow
- 'Sussex' **new**	SDow WLav
N - 'Twickel Purple'	CArn CMHG CSev CWib ECGP ELau ENot EWes NHHG SMrm SPar SWat WJek WMnd WPnn
'Jean Davis'	see L. angustifolia 'Jean Davis'
lanata ♀ H3	CArn CBot ECha GBar GPoy MBro MChe MHer MWat NHHG NLon NSti NWCA SDow SDry SHFr WBad WEas WWye
- x *angustifolia*	GBar NHHG WBad
§ *latifolia*	CArn LPVe SDow WBad
'Loddon Pink'	see L. angustifolia 'Loddon Pink'
mairei x *intermedia*	WBad
'Marshwood' PBR	CBri CSLe CTri CWSG EBee EBre ENot EPfP LBuc LRHS MHer MRav NYoL SCoo SDow SIde SLim SPar SPer SPla WBad
minutolii	MHer SDow WBad
multifida	CArn CSev EHol EOHP ERea MChe MHer SDow WBad WBry WCHb WHer WLav WWal
- 'Blue Wonder' **new**	CLvH WBad
officinalis	see L. angustifolia
§ *pinnata*	CArn CSev CWCL EBee EOHP GBar MAsh MChe MHer NHHG NPri SDow SDry SRob WBad WCHb WEas WHHs WHal
pterostoechas pinnata	see L. pinnata
pubescens	SDow
'Regal Splendour'	CWCL ELan EPfP MAsh MBri NPri SDow WWeb
'Richard Gray' ♀ H4	CCge CLvH CSLe EBee ECGP EMon GBar LRHS MAsh MHer SDow WAbe WBad WBcn WHen WLav WMnd
'Rosea'	see L. angustifolia 'Rosea'
rotundifolia	EBee MHer SDow
'Roxlea Park'	EBee SVil WLav
'Saint Brelade'	EBee EPfP GBar MAsh SDow WBad WLav
§ - 'Sawyers' ♀ H4	More than 30 suppliers
'Silver Edge'	see L. x *intermedia* (Dutch Group) Walberton's Silver Edge = 'Walvera'
N *spica* nom. rejic.	see L. angustifolia, L. latifolia, L. x intermedia
- 'Hidcote Purple'	see L. angustifolia 'Hidcote'
stoechas ♀ H3	More than 30 suppliers
- var. *albiflora*	see L. stoechas f. leucantha
- 'Aphrodite' **new**	LRHS
- subsp. *atlantica*	SDow WBad
- subsp. *cariensis*	SDow
- dark	WBad
- 'Devonshire' **new**	CLvH MHer WBad
- 'Evelyn Cadzow' **new**	WBry
- 'Kew Red'	CFai CMea CSBt EBee ELau ENot EPfP LRHS MBNS MHer MLan MWat NGHP SAga SDow SHDw SLim SMrm SPer WBad WBcn WBrE WHoo
§ - f. *leucantha*	CArn CBot CLvH CMHG CSBt CSev CTCP CWib ECha ELan ELau EPfP GBar LAst MAsh MBri MChe MHer NWoo SChu SDow SPer SPla WAbe WBad WCHb WPer
- 'Liberty' **new**	ENor SDow
- subsp. *luisieri*	GBar SDow WBri
- subsp. *lusitanica*	CLvH MHer SDow WBad WLav
- 'Papillon'	see L. stoechas subsp. pedunculata
§ - subsp. *pedunculata* ♀ H3	More than 30 suppliers
- - 'James Compton'	CLvH CWib EBee ECha LRHS MAsh SDow SLim WBad WLav WTel
- 'Pippa'	WBad
- 'Pukehou'	ENor EPfP LRHS MAsh SDow WBad WLav WPat
- 'Purple Ribbon' **new**	CLvH
- 'Rocky Red' **new**	CBcs
- 'Rocky Road' **new**	CFai WLav
- subsp. *sampaioana*	SDow WBad WLav
- 'Snowman'	CLvH CSBt EBee EPfP LAst LRHS MAsh MBNS MHer MSPs MTPN MWat NPri NYoL SAdn SDow SLim SPar SPer SRPl SVil WBad WFar WHHs WWal
- subsp. *stoechas*	CSLe
- 'Sugar Plum'	WBad WLav
- 'Summerset Mist'	CLvH WBad WLav
- 'Willow Vale' ♀ H4	CFai CMHG CMea COtt CSLe CWCL CWSG EBee EPfP GBar LPhx LRHS MAsh MBNS MHer MWat SAdn SAga SDow SMHy SPar WBad WCom WEas WHoo WJek WPGP WWeb
- 'Willowbridge Calico' **new**	NPro WLav
* - 'Wine Red'	CLvH MHer WBad WBcn WLav
subnuda	WBad
'Tickled Pink'	CWCL ELan MAsh MBri SDow WLav WWeb
vera hort.	see L. x *intermedia* Dutch Group
vera DC.	see L. angustifolia
viridis	More than 30 suppliers

Lavatera (Malvaceae)

acerifolia	WEas
arborea	SChr WHer
- 'Rosea'	see Lavatera x clementii 'Rosea'

- 'Variegata' (v)	ELan EMan NPer NSti SBod SDix SEND SMad WCHb WCot WEas WHer WHil WWal WWpP	
assurgentiflora	CPLG EPfP	
bicolor	see *L. maritima*	
cachemiriana	EBee ELan GBuc GCal MFir NBur NPer NSti	
x **clementii** 'Barnsley'	More than 30 suppliers	
- 'Blushing Bride'	CDoC EBre EPfP LRHS MLLN NPri SBod SDix SHBN SMrm SPer SPla WBcn WHar	
- 'Bredon Springs' ♀ H3-4	CDoC CWSG EBee EBre ECha ECtt EMil ENot EPfP GBri GKir LHop LRHS MAsh MBri MNrw MRav SBod SLim SMrm SPar SPer SPla SRPl WFar WStl WWal WWeb	
- 'Burgundy Wine' ♀ H3-4	More than 30 suppliers	
- 'Candy Floss' ♀ H3-4	EBee EPfP LRHS MBNS MBar MGos NPer SAdn SMrm SPar SPer WDin WStl WWal	
- 'Eye Catcher'	CFai GKir LRHS MBNS SPer	
- 'Kew Rose'	CDoC EBee EMil EPfP LRHS MAsh NPer SLim SPar SPla WGwG WWeb	
- 'Lavender Lady'	EBee ECtt GKir MGrG	
- 'Lilac Lady'	CElw CFai CFwr ECha ELan LRHS MAsh MBNS MCCP MCLN NLon SPer WWeb	
- 'Lisanne'	EBee EOrc LRHS MCCP MLLN MNrw NPri SMrm WFTG	
- 'Mary Hope'	CFai LRHS MAsh NPro	
Memories - 'Stelav'PBR	CFai CHid CWSG EBee ELan ENot EPfP EVFa LRHS MAsh MCCP MLan NBlu NPer NPri NPro SLim WRHF	
- 'Pavlova'	CDoC EBee EPfP LRHS MCCP SMrm	
- 'Poynton Lady'	EVFa MGos NEgg	
- 'Rosea' ♀ H3-4	CBcs CChe COlW CSBt CWSG EBee EBre ECtt ENot EPfP LRHS MAsh MBar MGos NBlu NFor NPri SAga SBod SHBN SLon SPar SPer WDin WTar WGwG WTel WWeb WWin	
- 'Shorty'	WFar	
- 'Wembdon Variegated' (v)	NPer	
'Linda'	WBcn	
§ **maritima** ♀ H2-3	CBot CDoC CMHG CRHN EBee ECtt ELan EPfP LHop LHrt NPri SDry SHBN SPar SPer SUsu WCFE WEas WFar WHCG WKif	
- **bicolor**	see *L. maritima*	
oblongifolia	CBot	
N **olbia**	CTrl GKir MHer MWat SPlb SRms	
- 'Pink Frills'	CBot EBee EBre LHop LRHS MBar MNrw MRav NPri SDry SHBN SMrm SPla WCot WStl	
'Peppermint Ice'	see *L. thuringiaca* 'Ice Cool'	
'Pink Frills'	see *L. olbia* 'Pink Frills'	
plebeia	EBee	
'Rosea'	see *Lavatera* x *clementii* 'Rosea'	
'Shadyvale Star'	MGrG NPro	
tauricensis	EMan NLar	
N **thuringiaca**	MWhi NPri WFar	
§ - 'Ice Cool'	CBot CElw ECha ECtt GCal LRHS MBar MGos NBee NPer SBla SHBN SMrm SPar SPer WFar	
'White Satin'PBR	CFai MBri	

Lawsonia (Lythraceae)

inermis	MSal

Ledebouria (Hyacinthaceae)

adlamii	see *L. cooperi*
§ **cooperi**	CDes CFwr CHal CRDP CStu EBla

	EHyt ELan EMan ERos ESis GCal ITim SDes SRot WPrP	
§ **socialis**	CHEx CHal CMdw CSWP CSev CSpe CStu EPem ERos EShb MBro NRog	
violacea	see *L. socialis*	

x *Ledodendron* (Ericaceae)

§ 'Arctic Tern' ♀ H4	CDoC CSBt GEdr GGGa GKev GKir LMil LRHS MAsh MBar MDun MGos MLea NHar NHol NWCA SLdr SPer SReu WBrE WPic

Ledum (Ericaceae)

§ x **columbianum**	GGGa
groenlandicum	GEil GGGa MBar MGos MLea WAbe WDin WGer WSHC
- 'Compactum'	MAsh NLar
macrophyllum	CFir
palustre	GGGa GPoy MGos WAbe
- subsp. **decumbens**	EPot GCrs GGGa IIve SOkd
§ - f. **dilatatum**	IIve

Leea (Leeaceae)

coccinea	see *L. guineensis*
§ **guineensis**	MBri

Leersia (Poaceae)

oryzoides <u>new</u>	EBee

Legousia (Campanulaceae)

'Devon Sky'	EMan

Leibnitzia (Asteraceae)

anandria	EBee NWCA
nepalensis	CPLG EBee
pusilla	EBee NWCA

Leiophyllum (Ericaceae)

buxifolium ♀ H4	EPfP EPot GCrs GKir ITim LRHS MBro NHol SBrw SSpi WPat
- var. **hugeri**	NHar

Lembotropis see *Cytisus*

lemon see *Citrus limon*

lemon balm see *Melissa officinalis*

lemon grass see *Cymbopogon citratus*

lemon verbena see *Aloysia triphylla*

Lemna (Lemnaceae)

gibba	CWat LPBA NPer
minor	CWat EHon EMFW LPBA MSta NPer SWat
polyrhiza	see *Spirodela polyrhiza*
trisulca	CWat EHon EMFW LPBA MSta NPer SWat

Leonotis (Lamiaceae)

leonitis	see *L. ocymifolia*
leonurus	CHEx CHll CTbh CTrC GGar MGol SMad
nepetifolia	EMan MGol WCot
§ **ocymifolia**	CFee CPLG NSti WHer WWye
- var. **ocymifolia**	EMan WCot
'Staircase'	NPPs WRos

Leontodon (Asteraceae)

autumnalis	CKin
crispus asper	EBee

MESE 307 **new**

hispidus	CKin MGas NMir
§ *rigens*	EMan GBri GBuc GKir ITer MWrn
	NBid NSti SBri SDix SGar SMad
	SMrm WCot WFar WMoo
– 'Girandole'	CMCo EBee LIck MNrw SUsu
	WPer WRos WWal

Leontopodium (*Asteraceae*)

alpinum	EBot EBre GAbr GKir GTou LRHS
	MHdf NBlu NFor NMen SIng SPlb
	SRms WLin WPer WWin
– 'Mignon'	CMea EMNN EWes GDra GTou
	NMen WAbe WHoo
– subsp. *nivale*	WPat
– *pirinicum*	WLin
coreanum **new**	GKev
§ *discolor*	WAbe
§ *ochroleucum*	MDKP WPer
var. *campestre*	
palibinianum	see *L. ochroleucum* var.
	campestre

Leonurus (*Lamiaceae*)

artemisia	EOHP MSal
cardiaca	CArn EBee EGoo EMan EMon
	GBar GPoy LHrt MChe MHer MSal
	NCWG SIde WBri WHbs WHer
	WMoo WSel WWye
– 'Crispus'	EMon
– subsp. *villosus*	EBee
macranthus	EFEx
– var. *alba*	EFEx
sibiricus	MGol MSal SDes WSan

Leopoldia (*Hyacinthaceae*)

comosa	see *Muscari comosum*
tenuiflora	see *Muscari tenuiflorum*

Lepechinia (*Lamiaceae*)

§ *chamaedryoides*	CHll CPLG CSpe
floribunda	CPle
hastata	CBrd
salviae **new**	EBee WCot

Lepidium (*Brassicaceae*)

campestre	CArn
nanum	EHyt WLin
ruderale	MSal
virginicum	MSal

Lepidothamnus (*Podocarpaceae*)

§ *laxifolius*	CMHG

Lepidozamia (*Zamiaceae*)

hopei	LPal NRog
peroffskyana	CBrP CRoM LPal NRog

Leptinella (*Asteraceae*)

§ *albida*	CStu GCrs LGro
§ *atrata*	IHMH
– subsp. *luteola*	GGar NWCA SChu SDys
§ *dendyi*	EWes GGar LBee MHer NLAp
	NMen WMAq
filicula	ECou
hispida	see *Cotula hispida*
§ *minor*	CFwr ECou MOne
pectinata var. *sericea*	see *L. albida*
– subsp. *villosa* CC 475	NWCA
§ *potentillina*	CTri EBee ECha EHoe ESis MBNS
	MWgw NJOw SChu SIng SRms
	WCru WPer WWin
§ *pusilla*	SDys

§ *pyrethrifolia*	EBee GKev NMen
– var. *linearifolia*	ELan
§ *rotundata*	ECou WPer
§ *serrulata*	MBar WCru WLRN
§ *squalida*	CNic ECha GGar IBlr MBar NRya
	NSti STre WPer
§ – 'Platt's Black'	EBee EDAr EMan EWes GCrs GEdr
	GGar LRHS NRya NSti SDys SIng
traillii **new**	GGar

Leptodactylon (*Polemoniaceae*)

§ *californicum*	CPBP
pungens NNS 98-347	NWCA

Leptospermum ✿ (*Myrtaceae*)

citratum	see *L. petersonii*
* *compactum*	CPLG
'Confetti' **new**	ECou
'County Park Blush'	ECou
cunninghamii	see *L. myrtifolium*
ericoides	see *Kunzea ericoides*
flavescens misapplied	see *L. glaucescens*
flavescens Sm.	see *L. polygalifolium*
§ *glaucescens*	CMHG ECou
§ *grandiflorum*	CFil CPLG CTrG ELan GGar ISea
	LRHS SBrw SOWG SSpi WSHC
grandifolium 'Silver Sheen'	see *Leptospermum* 'Silver Sheen'
'Green Eyes' (*minutifolium* x *scoparium*)	ECou
'Havering Hardy'	ECou
humifusum	see *L. rupestre*
juniperinum	SPlb
laevigatum 'Yarrum'	ECou
§ *lanigerum*	CMHG CMac CPLG CTrC CTri
	ECou SLim SOWG WAbe WWin
– 'Cunninghamii'	see *L. myrtifolium*
– 'Silver Sheen'	see *L.* 'Silver Sheen'
– 'Wellington'	ECou
liversidgei	CPLG
macrocarpum	SOWG
minutifolium	CPLG ECou
§ *myrtifolium*	CTri ECou EPla EWes GGar SDry
	SOWG SPer SSta WPat WPic
– 'Newnes Forest'	ECou
– 'Silver Sheen'	see *L.* 'Silver Sheen'
– x *scoparium*	ECou
nitidum	CTrC ECou EGFP SOWG SPlb
– 'Cradle'	ECou
obovatum	CMHG
§ *petersonii*	CArn ECou EOHP SOWG
phylicoides	see *Kunzea ericoides*
'Pink Surprise' (*minutifolium* x *scoparium*)	ECou SOWG
§ *polygalifolium*	CTrC GGar SPlb SRms
prostratum	see *L. rupestre*
pubescens	see *L. lanigerum*
'Red Cascade' **new**	MGos
rodwayanum	see *L. grandiflorum*
rotundifolium	CTrC ECou
§ *rupestre* ♀ H4	CDoC CPne CTri ECou EPot GDra
	GGar GTou MBar MGos NHar
	SDry SPlb SRms WFar WSHC
– x *scoparium*	ECou
scoparium	CArn CTrC ECou ELau ERom
	NBlu SPlb WDin
– 'Adrianne'	ELan MAsh
– 'Album'	CBrm
– 'Autumn Glory'	CWSG EBee EHoe SBrw SLim
– 'Avocet'	ECou
– 'Black Robin'	LRHS SOWG
– 'Blossom' (d)	CBcs ECou SOWG WGer

- 'Boscawenii' — SBrw SHGC
- 'Burgundy Queen' (d) — CBcs ECou
- 'Chapmanii' — CMHG CTrG EBee GGar
- 'Coral Candy' — CBcs SOWG
- 'County Park Pink' **new** — ECou
- 'County Park Red' **new** — ECou
- 'Elizabeth Jane' — GGar GQui
- 'Essex' — ECou
- 'Fred's Red' — EWes WPat
- 'Gaiety Girl' (d) — CBrm
- 'Grandiflorum' — WGer
- var. *incanum* 'Keatleyi' — ECou MGos SOWG
  ♀ H3
- - 'Wairere' — ECou
- 'Jubilee' (d) — CBcs ISea
- 'Kerry' — MAsh
- 'Leonard Wilson' (d) — CTri ECou EWes
- 'Lyndon' — ECou
- 'Martini' — CDoC CTrG LRHS MGos SOWG
  WCot WWeb
- 'McLean' — ECou
- (Nanum Group) 'Huia' — CBcs ENot WOBN
- - 'Kea' — ECou GQui MGos WGer
- - 'Kiwi' ♀ H3 — CBcs CBrm CDoC CTrC EBee
  ECou ELan ENot EPfP EPot EWes
  GQui ISea LRHS MAsh MDun
  MGos SBrw SLim SPla WFar WGer
  WPat WWeb
- - 'Kompakt' — EPot
- - 'Nanum' — ECou EPot NJOw NMen SBod
  SHRN SIng
- - 'Pipit' — EPot EWes ITim
- - 'Tui' — CTrC
- 'Nichollsii' ♀ H3 — CBcs CTrC CTri GQui SOWG
  WHar WSHC
- 'Nichollsii Nanum' — CDoC CMca EPot ITim NSla SBrw
  ♀ H2-3 — SIng SRms WAbe WEas WPat
- 'Pink Cascade' — CBcs CTri IMGH SBrw SLim SPer
- 'Pink Pearl' (d) — SAga
- 'Pink Splash' — ECou
- var. *prostratum* hort. — see *L. rupestre*
- 'Red Damask' (d) ♀ H3 — More than 30 suppliers
- 'Red Falls' — CDoC ECou SOWG
- 'Redpoll' — ECou
- 'Roseum' — MTPN WBrE
- 'Rosy Morn' — ISea
- 'Ruby Glow' (d) — LRHS
* - 'Ruby Wedding' — ELan LRHS SPla WWeb
- var. *scoparium* **new** — GGar
* - 'Silver Spirc' — SOWG
- 'Snow Flurry' — CBcs CTrC EBee ISea SLim SRPl
  SSte
- 'Sunraysia' — CTrw
- 'Winter Cheer' — CBcs
- 'Wiri Joan' (d) — MGos
- 'Zeehan' **new** — ECou
  sericeum **new** — SOWG
§ 'Silver Sheen' ♀ H3 — CEnd EBee ECou ELan LRHS SBrw
  SLon SPar WCot WGer WPGP

  spectabile **new** — SOWG
  squarrosum — CTrC
  'Wellington Dwarf' — ECou

Leschenaultia (Goodeniaceae)
  biloba — ECou
- 'Big Blue' — SOWG
* 'Eldorado' — SOWG
  formosa red — ECou
- 'Scarlett O'Hara' — SOWG
- yellow — ECou
  hirsuta **new** — SOWG
  pink — ECou

Lespedeza (Papilionaceae)
  bicolor — CBcs LAst MGol SEND SPar WDin
  WFar WHCG
  buergeri — CBcs SMur WSHC
  capitata **new** — EBee MSal
  thunbergii ♀ H4 — CBcs CDul EBee EChP ELan EMil
  EPfP EVFa EWTr IDee IMGH LRHS
  MAsh MBlu NBlu SHGC SLon
  SOWG SPar SPer SSpi SSta WAul
  WDin WFar WHCG WOTO WSHC
- 'Summer Beauty' — EPfP MGos
* - 'Variegata' (v) — LRHS
  tiliifolia — see *Desmodium elegans*
  virginica **new** — EBee WSHC

Lesquerella (Brassicaceae)
  arctica var. *purshii* — WPat
  hemiphysaria — WLin

Leucadendron (Proteaceae)
  argenteum — CHEx CTrC CTrF SIgm
  'Bell's Supreme' **new** — CTrC
  daphnoides **new** — SPlb
  discolor — CTrC
  eucalyptifolium — CTrC SPlb
  galpinii — CTrC
  laureolum — CTrC
  'Maui Sunset' — CTrC
  'Safari Sunset' — CTrC
  salicifolium — CTrC
  salignum — CTrC
- 'Early Yellow' — CTrC
- 'Fireglow' — CDoC CTrC
  strobilinum — CDoC CTrC
  uliginosum — CTrC

Leucanthemella (Asteraceae)
§ *serotina* ♀ H4 — More than 30 suppliers

Leucanthemopsis (Asteraceae)
§ *alpina* — GCrs LRHS
  hosmariensis — see *Rhodanthemum hosmariense*
§ *pectinata* — LBee
  radicans — see *L. pectinata*

Leucanthemum ✿ (Asteraceae)
  atlanticum — see *Rhodanthemum atlanticum*
  catananche — see *Rhodanthemum catananche*
  'Fringe Benefit' — EMon
  hosmariense — see *Rhodanthemum hosmariense*
  mawii — see *Rhodanthemum gayanum*
  maximum hort. — see *L.* x *superbum*
§ *maximum* (Ramond) DC. — NBro NLon NPer WBea WCer
- *uliginosum* — see *Leucanthemella serotina*
  nipponicum — see *Nipponanthemum nipponicum*
§ x *superbum* — EHol MBow MHer MNrw MWgw
  NBlu NSti NVic WFar
- 'Aglaia' (d) ♀ H4 — More than 30 suppliers
- 'Alaska' — EBee EFou EMan LAst LRHS
  NGdn NOak NPri SPer SWal WPer
  WWal WWpP
- 'Anita Allen' (d) — CElw CPou EBee MAvo WCot
  WFar WWpP
- 'Antwerp Star' — NCat WWpP
- 'Barbara Bush' (v/d) — CFai EBee EChP EGle EMan EVFa
  MSph MTis NBir SPla SPoG WCot
- 'Beauté Nivelloise' — EBee ECha EMan MAvo MCAu
  NDov SUsu WCot WFar WPer
  WRHF WRha

– 'Becky'	ECha
– 'Bishopstone'	CBos CMGP ELan EMan ERou NLon SChu SCou WEas
– 'Christine Hagemann'	CFwr EBee EFou LRHS MAvo MBri MRav SUsu WHoo WWpP
– 'Cobham Gold' (d)	CElw EBee ECha EMan EREa GBuc NFla NOrc SOkh SUsu WWpP
– 'Coconut Ice'	WPer
I – 'Crazy Daisy'	WRHF WWpP
– 'Droitwich Beauty'	EBee MAvo MBct MNrw WHoo
– 'Duchesse of Albercorne'	CStr
– 'Esther Read' (d)	CElw CFwr CHar CM&M CPrp EBee ECtt EGle EHol ELan EMan EREa ERou IKee LAst MFir NChi NDov NFla NPri SHel SRms STes SWat WCot WFar WViv WWol
– 'Everest'	EMan NOak SHar SRms
– 'Fiona Coghill' (d)	CElw CHea CMil CStr EBee ECGP EFou EGle GBri IBlr MAvo MFir MHer MLLN WCot WHoo WMaN
– 'H. Seibert'	CMil
– 'Highland White Dream'PBR	WFar WWeb
– 'Horace Read' (d)	CElw CHea CMdw CMea CMil CRDP EBee ELan EMan EREa MCAu MGas NBir SAga WEas WPer
– 'Jennifer Read'	EREa
– 'John Murray'	NBir WAbb
– 'Little Miss Muffet'	LRHS MBri
– 'Little Princess'	see L x superbum 'Silberprinzesschen'
– 'Manhattan'	CMdw EBee EBre EFou EWes GBuc LRHS MTed NCat
– 'Mayfield Giant'	ERou MWgw WPer
– 'Mount Everest'	SRms WCot
– 'Northern Lights'	MLwd SMac
– 'Phyllis Smith'	CFwr CHea COIW EBee ECha EFou EGle EMan LRHS MAvo MCLN MHer MTis MWrn NGdn NSti SAga SHel SMad SPer STes WAbb WBea WCot WFar WMoo WWpP
– 'Polaris'	CFwr LRHS NOak WMoo
– 'Rags and Tatters' new	MAvo
– 'Rheinblick'	WLRN
* – 'Schneehurken'	EBee LCTD MAvo SAsh
– 'Shaggy'	EChP GMaP MLLN NFla SWat
§ – 'Silberprinzesschen'	COIW EBee EChP EFou EPfP GKir LRHS NMir NOak NPri SPlb SRms WBea WFar WHen WMoo WPer WWpP
– 'Snow Lady'	CM&M EBee LRHS NMir NPer SPet SRms WFar WHen WWpP
– 'Snowcap'	EBee EBre ECha EGle EMan ENot LRHS MRav NGdn NLon SBla SLon SPer SPla SSpe WLRN WWpP
– 'Snowdrift' new	CFwr WHil
§ – 'Sonnenschein'	More than 30 suppliers
– 'Starburst' (d)	EMan LRHS SHel SRms WHen
– 'Summer Snowball' (d)	CElw EGle EMan EWes LRHS MAvo SHel SUsu WCot WFar WTel WWpP
– 'Sunny Side Up' new	EGle EWes
– 'Sunshine'	see L. x superbum 'Sonnenschein'
– 'T.E. Killin' (d) ♀ H4	CElw EBee ECha EGle EMan LRHS MCLN SApp WCot WFar
– 'White Iceberg' (d)	WPer
– 'White Knight'	LRHS
– 'Wirral Pride'	EBee NPri WWol
§ – 'Wirral Supreme' (d) ♀ H4	More than 30 suppliers
'Tizi-n-Test'	see Rhodanthemum catananche 'Tizi-n-Test'

§ vulgare	CArn CKin ECoo EFWa EPar GBar GWCH IHMH MBow MHer NLan NMir NSco SIde WHen WHer WJek WShi WWpP WWye
– 'Avondale' (v)	MCCP NGdn
– 'Filigran' new	WWeb
– 'Jenny Swales' new	WAlt
§ – 'Maikönigin'	EBee GCal IHMH NSti WHrl WRHF WWpP
– May Queen	see L. vulgare 'Maikönigin'
– 'Sunny'	CBre WAlt

Leucocoryne (Alliaceae)

ixioides	CPLG LBow
odorata	WCot
purpurea ♀ H1	LBow LRHS WCot

Leucogenes (Asteraceae)

acklandii	NHar
grandiceps	GCrs GTou NHar NSla
leontopodium	EPot GCrs GDra GEdr GGar GTou NHar NLAp NSla WAbe
tarahaoa	EPot WAbe

Leucojum ✿ (Amaryllidaceae)

aestivum	CBcs CFee EBee EChP EPfP GCrs LAma LRHS MAvo MBri MLwd MWgw NEgg NMGW NRog SPar SRms SYvo WAbe WBod WCot WCra WEas WFar WHil WShi WWpP WWye
– 'Gravetye Giant' ♀ H4	CAvo CBro CFwr CHad CPLG CPom EBee ECha EHrv ELan EMar EPar EPot ETub LAma LPhx LRHS MMil MNrw MRav NRog SBla WAbb WAul WCot WFTG WFar WPGP WPnP WShi
autumnale ♀ H4	More than 30 suppliers
– 'Cobb's Variety'	WCot
– var. oporanthum	EPot ERos NRog
– var. pulchellum	CBro EPot ERos
nicaeense ♀ H2-3	CGra CLyd CPBP CRDP CStu EBur EHyt EPot ERos MTho NGar NMen SSpi WCom WIvy
roseum	CLyd EBur EHyt EPot LAma NRya SIgm
tingitanum	CBro EHyt EPot WCot
trichophyllum	CBro ERos
– f. purpurascens	EPot
valentinum	CBro SCnR
vernum ♀ H4	CAvo CBro EHrv EMon EPar EPot ETub GCrs GDra LAma LPio LRHS MAvo MBri MNrw MRav NGar NMGW NMen SRms WAbe WBod WCot WFTG WFar WHer WHil WShi
– var. carpathicum	CLAP ECha EHrv GEdr LAma MRav NMen
– var. vagneri	CLAP ECha EHrv EMon GDra GEdr LHop WTin

Leucophyllum (Scrophulariaceae)

frutescens	SOWG

Leucophyta (Asteraceae)

§ brownii	ECou EMan MOak MRav SVen

Leucopogon (Epacridaceae)

ericoides	MBar WPat
§ fasciculatus	ECou
§ fraseri	ECou GCrs
parviflorus	see Cyathodes parviflora

x *Leucoraoulia* (Asteraceae)
§ hybrid (**Raoulia hectorii** x   EPot GTou NSla SIng WAbe
  Leucogenes grandiceps)
§ **loganii**   CPBP EPot GCrs ITim NWCA
                                 WAbe WLin

Leucosceptrum (Lamiaceae)
  canum   CPLG CTrG
  stellipilum formosanum   SSpi
  - - B&SWJ 1804   EBee WCru WCot

Leucospermum (Proteaceae)
  cordifolium   SOWG

Leucothoe (Ericaceae)
  axillaris Red Lips =   MGos
    'Lipsbolwi'PBR
  - 'Royal Red'   WLRN
  carinella   MBri MGos
  davisiae   SBrw SSta
§ **fontanesiana** ♀ H4   LRHS NBea SPer STre WBrE WStI
  - 'Lovita'   CEnd EBee GCal LRHS MBri MRav
                                 SCoo SSta WWeb
  - 'Nana'   LRHS MAsh
  - 'Rainbow' (v)   More than 30 suppliers
  - 'Rollissonii' ♀ H4   MBar MRav SRms WBod
  keiskei   EPfP LRHS MAsh
  - 'Royal Ruby'   CWSG EBee NHol WDin WWeb
  populifolia   see *Agarista populifolia*
  racemosa   NLar
  Scarletta = 'Zeblid'   More than 30 suppliers
  walteri   see *L. fontanesiana*

Leuzea (Asteraceae)
  carthamoides new   MSal
§ **centauroides**   EBee EBlw EBre ECGP ECha EGle
                                 EVFa GCal LPhx MAnH NBid SAga
                                 WCot WHoo
  conifera   EBee
§ **rhapontica**   EMan

Levisticum (Apiaceae)
  officinale   CAgr CArn CPrp CSev ELau GBar
                                 GMaP GPoy MBar MBow MChe
                                 MHer NBid NBlu SDix SIde SPlb
                                 SWat WBri WGwG WHHs WHbs
                                 WHer WPer WSel WWye

Lewisia ❀ (Portulacaceae)
  'Archangel'   NRya
  Ashwood Carousel hybrids   ENot GCrs MAsh MDHE
  'Ashwood Pearl'   MAsh
  'Ben Chace'   MAsh WAbe
  Birch strain   CBcs ECho ELan
  brachycalyx ♀ H2   EWes GMaP GTou ITim MAsh
                                 MTho NHar NWCA
  cantelovii   EPot MAsh
  columbiana   GTou ITim MAsh MDHE MWod
                                 NHar SIng WAbe
  - 'Alba'   MAsh WAbe
  - subsp. **columbiana**   CGra
  - 'Rosea'   GCrs MAsh NSla WAbe WGor
  - subsp. **rupicola**   EHyt LTwo MAsh MMHG NWCA
                                 WGor WOBN
  - subsp. **wallowensis**   EHyt MAsh MDHE NMen WGor
  congdonii   MAsh
  cotyledon ♀ H4   LRHS LTwo MAsh MNrw MOne
                                 NWCA SPet WBrE WFar WPat
  - J&JA 12959   NWCA
  - f. **alba**   EPot GDra GKev GTou LHop
                                 MAsh MBro
  - 'Ashwood Ruby'   MAsh

  - Ashwood strain   CWCL EBre ENot ESis EWes LBee
                                 LRHS MAsh MBri MOne NRya
                                 SRms WGor
  - 'Fransi'   ESis
  - var. **heckneri** ♀ H4   WGor
  - var. **howellii**   EHyt LTwo SRms WGor
  - hybrids   CBrm CNic EDAr EMNN EPot
                                 GDra GTou ITim LHop MBro
                                 NBlu NHar NMen SDes SIng
                                 WAbe WBod WGor WLin WWin
  - 'John's Special'   GCrs GDra
  - magenta   MAsh WGor
§ - 'Regenbogen' mixed   ESis LPVe WGor WPer
  - 'Rondo'   ESis
  - 'Rose Splendour'   ESis
  - Sunset Group ♀ H4   EMlt GAbr GDra GKir MBri MHer
                                 NHar NHol NJOw NLAp SRms WPer
  - 'White Splendour'   MAsh SIng WGor
  'George Henley'   EBre EPot ETow EWes MAsh
                                 NMen NRya SIng SRms WAbe
* 'Holly'   MDHE
  'Joyce Halley'   GCrs
  leeana   EHyt MAsh
  'Little Plum'   ESis GDra GEdr GMaP ITim LPVe
                                 MAsh NDlv NHar NHol NRya
                                 NSla SIng WGor
§ **longipetala**   GTou MAsh MOne NWCA
  - x **cotyledon**   GTou
§ **nevadensis**   ERos ESis GDra GEdr GTou ITim
                                 MAsh MBri MBro MNrw MTho
                                 NLAp NMen NRya NWCA SRms
                                 SRot WHoo WPer
  - **bernardina**   see *L. nevadensis*
  - 'Rosea'   CGra GCrs MAsh
  oppositifolia   GCrs MAsh
  - J&JA 13450   NWCA
  'Richeyi'   MAsh
  'Phyllellia'   MAsh
  'Pinkie'   CPBP EDAr GCrs IHMH LTwo
                                 MAsh MDHE NLAp NMen
  pygmaea   CGra EHyt ESis EWes GCrs GTou
                                 ITim LRHS MAsh MBri MDCh
                                 NBir NHar NHol NLAp NMen
                                 NWCA WPer
  - **alba**   ITim
  - subsp. **longipetala**   see *L. longipetala*
  Rainbow mixture   see *L. cotyledon* 'Regenbogen'
                                 mixed
  'Rawreth'   LTwo
  rediviva   CGra ETow EWes GCrs GTou
                                 ITim MAsh NHar NMen NSla
                                 NWCA SIgm WAbe WLin
  - M&PS 99/072   NMen
  Jolon strain   GKev WGor
  - subsp. **minor**   CGra
  - var. **rediviva**   EHyt
  - white   MAsh NMen NWCA
  serrata   MAsh
  sierrae   MAsh MBro NMen WPer
  'Stadbrook Victoria' new   EHyt
  'Trevosia'   EHyt EPot MAsh MDHE
  tweedyi ♀ H2   EBre EHyt ETow GCrs GDra GTou
                                 ITim LHop LRHS MAsh MOne
                                 NBir NHar NMen NWCA SIgm
                                 SIng WAbe WGor
  - 'Alba'   EHyt GCrs ITim LRHS MAsh
                                 NWCA WAbe
  - 'Elliott's Variety'   MAsh WGor
  - 'Rosea'   EHyt GDra LHop LRHS MAsh
                                 NMen SIng WGor

Leycesteria (Caprifoliaceae)
  crocothyrsos   CArn CBrm CCge CHar CPle

	CWib GDrg GEil GQui IFro MMil
	MWrn SLon SMad SWal WBod
	WFar WHrl WLRN WMoo WPic
	WWpP
formosa ♀ H4	More than 30 suppliers
- Golden Lanterns =	ENot NPri WWeb
'Notbruce' **new**	
- 'Golden Pheasant' (v)	CPMA MRav
- 'Purple Rain' **new**	NLar WBcn

Leymus (*Poaceae*)

from Falkland Islands	EPPr
§ *arenarius*	More than 30 suppliers
hispidus	see *Elymus hispidus*
'Niveus'	EHul
§ *racemosus*	LHrt MMHG

Lhotzkya see *Calytrix*

Liatris (*Asteraceae*)

aspera	EBee EMan SIgm WPer
cylindracea	EBee IIve
elegans	EShb
lancifolia **new**	EBee
ligulistylis	EBee EMan SIgm WMoo
punctata	EBee IIve
pycnostachya	EMan EMon MHar MLLN NLar
	SRms WMoo WPer
- 'Alexandra' **new**	EBee
scariosa **new**	EBee
- 'Gracious'	EWll
- 'Magnifica'	CBcs
§ *spicata*	More than 30 suppliers
- 'Alba'	CBri CHor CPrp CSBt EBee EBot
	ECha ECtt EFou ELan EMlt EPfP
	GKir LAma LAst LPio MNrw
	MWgw SDeJ SDes SPar SPer SPlb
	WBea WBrE WHoo WLow WPer
- 'Blue Bird'	WViv
- *callilepis*	see *L. spicata*
- 'Floristan Violett'	CBrm CFwr CHar EBee EChP
	EMar EPfP LAst LPVe LRHS MHer
	MTis NCot NLon NPri SCoo SDes
	SPlb WBar WFar WLRN WMnd
	WMoo WPer WWeb
- 'Floristan Weiss'	CArn CBrm CFwr CHar COlW
	EBre ECGN EChP ELau EPfP GBuc
	GMaP LAst LPVe LRHS MHer
	MRav MTis NCot NOak SPla WFar
	WHHs WLRN WMnd WMoo WPer
	WWeb WWin
- Goblin	see *L. spicata* 'Kobold'
§ - 'Kobold'	CBcs CHar COlW EBee ECGN
	EChP ECtt ENot EPfP GKir GMac
	LRHS MBow MBri MRav MWgw
	NGdn NLar SPar SPla SRms WFar
	WHoo WMnd WMoo WPer WWeb
squarrosa	EBee IIve

Libertia ✿ (*Iridaceae*)

HCM 98.089 **new**	EBee
from New Zealand	EPla
'Amazing Grace'	CDes CPne EBee EPPr IBlr SUsu
	WPGP
'Ballyrogan Blue'	IBlr
Ballyrogan hybrid	IBlr
* *breunioides*	CPLG IBlr
caerulescens	CFil CPLG EBee EChP EGoo EMan
	ERos EVFa GSki IBlr LHop LPio
	NBir NLar SDes WCot WFar WHer
	WPGP WPic WSan
chilensis	see *L. formosa*
elegans	CPLG GBuc IBlr

§ *formosa*	More than 30 suppliers
- brown-stemmed	IBlr
grandiflora ♀ H4	More than 30 suppliers
- Cally strain	GCal
ixioides	CBcs CElw ECha ECou EMan
	GMac GSki IBlr MFir NSti WLeb
	WLin WPic WRHF
- hybrids **new**	SDix
- 'Tricolor'	GGar IBlr
'Nelson Dwarf'	IBlr
paniculata	CPLG
peregrinans	CAbb CBri CFee CHEx EBre ECha
	EGle EGoo EHrv EMar EPla ESis
	GCal GGar GSki IBlr LHop LPio
	MFir MRav NWCA SDes SDix
	SUsu WAbe WHal WOld WPat
- East Cape form	IBlr
- 'Gold Leaf'	CBcs CElw CPrp EHrv EVFa IBlr
	LAst LPio SMad SOkh WCot WCru
	WPic WViv
* *procera*	CFil EBee IBlr WPGP
pulchella	EBre EMan IBlr
sessiliflora	CFee EBee IBlr NBir WPic
- RB 94073	EPPr MNrw SMad
Shackleton hybrid	IBlr
tricolor	EBee GBuc
* *umbellata*	IBlr

Libocedrus (*Cupressaceae*)

bidwillii	CDoC
chilensis	see *Austrocedrus chilensis*
decurrans 'Berruma	ENot
Gold' **new**	
decurrens	see *Calocedrus decurrens*
plumosa	CBcs CDoC

Libonia see *Justicia*

Licuala (*Arecaceae*)

grandis	MBri
ramsayi	CBrP
spinosa	LPal

Ligularia ✿ (*Asteraceae*)

B&SWJ 1158 from Korea	WCru
B&SWJ 2977	WCru
alatipes	GBin
altaica	EBee
amplexicaulis	EBee IBlr
calthifolia	CRow EBee
clivorum	see *L. dentata*
§ *dentata*	CPLG CRow EBee ECtt GIBF GKir
	NBro SRms SWat WFar WWeb
- 'Britt-Marie	WCot
Crawford' **new**	
- 'Dark Beauty'	EMan ERou GSki
- 'Desdemona' ♀ H4	More than 30 suppliers
- 'Megamona' **new**	EBee
- 'Orange Princess'	EBee NPer WPer
- 'Othello'	CHEx CRow EBlw EChP EGle
	EPfP GKir GSki IBlr LAst LRHS
	MBri MCAu NBlu NGdn NHol
	NLar NPri SCro SDes SPar SSpe
	SWat WAul WCot WCra WFar WHil
	WLin WPnP
- 'Ox-eye'	WGer
- 'Sommergold'	ECha GSki IBlr SPer WFar
fischeri	EBee GSki MLLN NFor WCot WPer
- B&SWJ 1158	WFar
- B&SWJ 2570	WCru
- B&SWJ 4478	WCru
- B&SWJ 5540	WCru
glabrescens	CRow

§ 'Gregynog Gold' ♀ H4 | CHad CRow EBee EBlw ECha EGle EMFW EMan EPfP ERou GKir GMaP GSki IBlr LRHS MBri NBro NGdn NOrc SChu SCro SPer WCru WElm WFar WHil
× **hessei** | EBee EBre GKir GMaP GSki NLar SWat WFar WPnP
hodgsonii | CRow EBre EMan GKir GSki IBlr LRHS MBri MNrw WFar WPer
intermedia | WFar
- B&SWJ 4383 | WCru
- B&SWJ 606a | WCru
japonica | CHar CRez CRow EBee ECha GSki NLar WCot WFar
- B&SWJ 2883 | WCru
aff. **kaialpina** | WCru
   B&SWJ 5806 **new**
- - B&SWJ 6185 | EBee
kanaitzensis | WCru
   ACE 1968 **new**
macrophylla | CRow MWhi WCot WFar
× **palmatiloba** | CFai CFir CHEx EBee EGle EMan EPar EPla ERou EWTr GCal GKir GSki IBlr LPhx MRav NHol NOak NSti SBla SCro SLon SWat WAul WCot WCra WFar WPnP
§ **przewalskii** ♀ H4 | More than 30 suppliers
- variegated (v) | EBlw
sachalinensis | EBee GBin GCal WCot
sibirica | EBee GSki MCAu NLar WCot WFar WLin WMoo WPer WPnP
- 'Hietala' | EBee
- var. **speciosa** | WCru
   B&SWJ 5841
smithii | see Senecio smithii
* **speciosa** | ECha GSki
stenocephala | EBee EMil GKir IBlr NBro SWat WCot WFar
- B&SWJ 283 | WCru
'Sungold' | WPnP
tangutica | see Sinacalia tangutica
'The Rocket' ♀ H4 | More than 30 suppliers
tussilaginea | see Farfugium japonicum
veitchiana | CHEx CRow EBee EMan EMar EPfP GCal GDra GKir IBlr MBri MCAu MSte NGdn NSti SWat WFar WTMC
vorobievii new | EBee GSki
'Weihenstephan' | GKir IBlr LRHS MBri
wilsoniana | CBct CHEx CRow EBee ECtt EMan MCAu MLLN MRav SDes SWat WFar
'Zepter' | EBee GBuc GCal LRHS MBri MTed NLar WCot

Ligusticum (Apiaceae)

jeholense | EBee
lucidum | CDul CMCN EHol EPfP IIve LPhx MSal SIgm WFar
porteri | MSal
scoticum | EOHP EWes GBar GPoy IIve ILis MSal
striatum B&SWJ 7259 | WCru

Ligustrum ✿ (Oleaceae)

chenaultii | see L. compactum
§ **compactum** | CLnd NLar
§ **delavayanum** | CBcs EMon ERom LHyr LPan LRHS MBar SAPC SArc WFar
ionandrum | see L. delavayanum
japonicum | ENot LPan SEND SMur SPer WDin WFar
- 'Coriaceum' | see L. japonicum 'Rotundifolium'
- 'Macrophyllum' | EPfP LRHS MAsh

§ - 'Rotundifolium' | CDoC CHEx CPLG CPle EBee EMil EPfP EPla LNet LRHS MAsh MRav SBod SLim SMad SPer WAbe WBcn WFar
§ - 'Texanum' | LPan LRHS NPSI
* - 'Texanum Argenteum' | LPan
lucidum ♀ H4 | CDoC CSBt CTho EBee ELan ENot EWTr LAst LPan MBar MGos MRav NLar NWea SAPC SArc SMad SPar SPer SRPl SSpi WBVN WDin WFar WGer
- 'Excelsum Superbum' (v) ♀ H4 | CABP CLnd CPMA CWib ELan ENot EPfP LAst LPan LRHS MAsh MBar MGos SBrw SPer SRPl SSpi WCot
- 'Golden Wax' | CABP CPMA EBee ENot LRHS MRav WBcn
- 'Tricolor' (v) | CPMA EBee ELan ENot EPfP LRHS SHBN SLim SPer SPla SSpi SSta WDin WFar
obtusifolium | SLPl
   'Darts Perfecta'
- var. **regelianum** | WFar
ovalifolium | CBcs CCVT CChe CDoC CLnd CSBt CTri EBre EPfP GKir LBuc LHyr LPan LRHS MBar MBri MGos NBee NWea SLim SPer WDin WGwG WMou WWal
§ - 'Argenteum' (v) | CBcs CDoC CDul CWib EBee EHoe GKir LBuc LRHS MBar MBri NBlu NHol SLim SPar SPer SPla WDin WFar WTel WWin
- 'Aureomarginatum' | see L. ovalifolium 'Aureum'
§ - 'Aureum' (v) ♀ H4 | More than 30 suppliers
* - 'Lemon and Lime' (v) | NLar
- 'Taff's Indecision' (v) | CPMA
- 'Variegatum' | see L. ovalifolium 'Argenteum'
quihoui ♀ H4 | ECre ELan EPfP SDix SMad SPer SSpi SSta WBcn WFar WHCG WPat
§ **sempervirens** | EPfP SMad SSta
sinense | CHEx CPLG EPfP MRav WFar WPGP
- 'Multiflorum' | WFar
- 'Pendulum' | CFil CLnd EPla WPGP
- 'Variegatum' (v) | CLnd CMHG CPMA EPfP EPla LAst LHop MRav SPer
- 'Wimbei' | EPla NPro SSpi WFar
strongylophyllum | WFar
texanum | see L. japonicum 'Texanum'
tschonoskii | SLPl
'Vicaryi' | CMHG CPMA EBee EBre ELan EPfP EPla IArd LRHS MAsh MBar MGos NPro SDix SPer SPla WFar
vulgare | CCVT CKin CTri EBre ENot EPfP GKir LBuc LHyr NBlu NWea SHFr WDin WHer WMou
- 'Lodense' | MBar SLPl

Lilium (Liliaceae)

F&W 7445 | CStu
'Acapulco' (VIId) | LAma MCLN NCel
African Queen Group (VIa) ♀ H4 | CHar EBre ECot ETub LAma MBNS NCel NRog SCoo SDeJ
albanicum | see L. pyrenaicum subsp. carniolicum var. albanicum
'Alliance' (VII) | NCel
amabile (IX) | CLAP LRHS WDav WWst
- 'Luteum' (IX) | CLAP LRHS WDav
'Amber Gold' (Ic) | CLAP
'America' **new** | NCel WDav
amoenum (IX) | EBee EPot LAma LEur
'Angela North' (Ic) | CLAP
'Apeldoorn' (Ic) | ECri LRHS NCel

'Aphrodite' (Ia/d)	NBir NCel
'Apollo' (Ia) ♀ H4	CBro EPot LAma LRHS MBNS
	MBri NCel NOak SDeJ
'Apricot Beauty' (Ib)	NCel
'Arena' (VIIb)	LRHS NCel SCoo
'Ariadne' (Ic)	CLAP
'Aristo'	see L. 'Orange Aristo'
'Ascari' (VIIb) **new**	NCel
* Asiatic hybrids (VI/VII)	LAma NCel NGdn SDeJ SGar
auratum (IX)	EBee EFEx LAma NCel
- 'Classic' (IX) **new**	CLAP
- 'Gold Band'	see L. auratum var. platyphyllum
- 'Golden Ray'	NCel
§ - var. **platyphyllum** (IX)	ECri WDav WWst
- Red Band Group (IX)	WFar
- var. **virginale** (IX)	LAma LRHS WDav
Aurelian hybrids (VI)	SMrm
'Avignon' (Ia)	ECri LAma LRHS NCel
Backhouse hybrids (II)	CLAP
bakerianum (IX)	LAma LEur
bakerianum aureum **new**	EBee
bakerianum var. **aureum new**	GKev
- var. **delavayi** (IX)	LAma
- var. **rubrum new**	EBee GKev LAma LEur WDav
- var. **yunnaense new**	GKev
'Barbara North' (Ic)	CLAP
'Barbaresco' (VII)	CSut SCoo
'Barcelona' (Ia)	MNrw NOak
'Batist' (Ia)	ECri LAma NCel
Bellingham Group (IV)	CLAP GBuc SSpi
'Bellona' (Ia)	NRog
'Bergamo' (VIId)	NCel SCoo
'Berlin' (VIId)	NCel
'Bestseller' (VIII) **new**	NCel
'Black Beauty' (VIId)	CLAP LAma LRHS NCel
'Black Dragon' (VIa)	CHar ECri LAma SGar
'Blazing Dwarf' (Ia)	MBri WWeb
'Blue Eyes' (Ia) **new**	NCel
bolanderi (IX)	EBee
'Bonfire' (VIIb)	SDeJ
'Bright Pixie' **new**	IBal
'Bright Star' (VIb)	EBre LAma SDeJ
'Brocade' (II)	CLAP
brownii (IX)	EBee LAma LEur
- var. **australe** (IX) B&SWJ 4082	WCru
'Buff Pixie'PBR (Ia)	LAma LPVe NCel WWeb
bulbiferum	CLAP ETub GBuc NCel
- var. **croceum** (IX)	GIBF
'Bums' (Ia/d)	EMon
'Butter Pixie'PBR (Ia)	LAma LPVe NCel WGor WGwG WHHs WWeb
callosum **new**	EBee
- var. **luteum new**	WWst
camtschatcense **new**	GIBF
§ *canadense* (IX)	EBee GBuc GCrs GGGa LAma LPio NRog SDeJ SSpi
- var. **coccineum** (IX)	WWst
- var. **editorum** (IX)	LAma
- var. **flavum**	see L. canadense
'Cancum'	ECri LRHS NCel
candidum (IX) ♀ H4	CArn CAvo CBcs CBro CHar CSWP CTri EBot EBre ECha EHrv ELan EPfP ETub GIBF IBal LAma LRHS MBri MHer MRav MWgw NCel NGHP NRog SDeJ SIgm WBrE WCot
- 'Plenum' (IX/d)	EMon
- var. **salonikae new**	GIBF
carniolicum	see L. pyrenaicum subsp. carniolicum
'Casa Blanca' (VIIb) ♀ H4	CBro EBre ECri IBal LAma MBNS MCLN MLLN NCel NRog SCoo SDeJ
§ 'Casa Rosa' (V)	CSWP NBir NCel SGar SWat
'Celene' **new**	NCel
cernuum (IX)	CLAP EBee ETub WCot
'Charisma' (Ia)	MBri
'Chianti' (Ia) **new**	NCel
'Chinook' (Ia)	NRog
'Chippendale' (Ic) **new**	CLAP
'Chris North' **new**	CLAP
'Cinnabar' **new**	ECri
Citronella Group (Ic)	CAvo ECri ETub LAma LRHS NCel NRog WFar
'Colibri' **new**	MBri
columbianum (IX)	GBuc GCrs NMen SSpi
- dwarf **new**	NMen
'Compass' (Ia)	NCel
'Con Amore' (VIIb)	LRHS NCel SCoo
concolor (IX)	EBee WWst
- var. **coridion new**	WWst
- var. **stictum new**	GIBF
'Connecticut King' (Ia)	ECri LAma NCel NRog SDeJ SVen
'Coral Butterflies' **new**	CLAP
cordatum **new**	CBri
'Corina' (Ia)	ECri MBNS MBri NOak SGar WGor
'Corsage' (Ib)	NCel NRog
'Côte d'Azur' (Ia)	CBro EBre EPot ETub LAma NCel SDeJ WGor
'Coulance' (VIId)	ETub
'Crimson Pixie' (Ia)	CBro LPVe NCel WWeb
x *dalhansonii* (IX)	CLAP WCot
§ - 'Marhan' (II)	CLAP
'Dame Blanche' (VII)	LAma
'Dante' (VIIIa/b) **new**	NCel
§ *dauricum* (IX)	EBee GCrs GEdr LEur
davidii (IX)	EBee GIBF LAma NCel WCru WDav WWst
- var. **unicolor**	EBee
§ - var. **willmottiae** (IX)	GIBF WViv
debile	GIBF
'Destiny' (Ia)	NRog
'Disco' (Ia)	MBri
distichum **new**	EBee GIBF
'Doeskin' (Ic) **new**	CLAP
'Dominique' (VII)	NRog
'Dreamland' (Ia)	ECri NCel
duchartrei (IX)	CLAP EBee GBuc GCrs GEdr GMaP LAma LEur NSla SMac SSpi WCru WDav
- white (IX)	WDav
§ 'Ed' (VII)	EPot LAma NCel
'Eileen North' (Ic) **new**	CLAP
'Electric' (Ia)	ECri LAma
'Elfin Sun'	LAma
'Ellen Willmott' (II)	CLAP
'Enchantment' (Ia)	ECri LAma MBNS MBri MCLN NRog SDeJ
'Eros'	CLAP
'Eurydike' (Ic) **new**	CLAP
'Evelina'	LRHS
'Everest' **new**	WDav
'Exception' (Ib/d)	LAma
'Expression' (VII) **new**	NCel
'Fairest' (Ib-c/d) **new**	CLAP
'Fangio' (VIIIa/b) **new**	NCel
fargesii (IX)	EBee LAma
'Fata Morgana' (Ia/d) ♀ H4	LRHS SCoo
'Festival' (Ia)	LAma
'Fire King' (Ib)	CBro CLAP ECGP ECri LAma NBir NRog SCoo SDeJ WDav
formosanum (IX)	EBee EBre EPPr EPyc GKir IBal LCTD MWrn NBro SEND STes WCot WViv

– B&SWJ 1589	WCru
– var. *pricei* (IX)	CSam EBee ELan EPfP EPot ESis
	GEdr LBee LEur LHop LRHS LSyl
	MBri MHer MNrw MTho NJOw
	NLAp NMen NWCA SBla SCoo
	SIng SRot WFar WHer WPer
– 'Snow Queen' (IX)	MDKP
'Full Speed' **new**	MBri
'Garden Party' (VII) ♀ H4	LPVe LRHS
'George Slate' (Ic/d) **new**	CLAP
'Golden Flair' **new**	WWeb
'Golden Melody' (Ia)	ECri
Golden Splendor Group	ECri ETub LAma MBNS NCel
(VIa) ♀ H4	NRog SCoo SWat
'Gran Cru' (Ia)	EBre NCel
'Gran Paradiso' (Ia)	ECri LAma
'Grand Cru' (Ia) ♀ H4	ECri LAma NOak SDeJ
grayi (IX)	GCrs NSla SSpi
'Green Magic' (VIa) **new**	CHid
hansonii (IX)	CLAP EBee ETub IBlr LAma NCel
	NRog WDav
henryi (IX) ♀ H4	CAvo CFwr CHar CLAP CSWP
	EBee EPot GIBF LAma LRHS
	MLLN NCel NRog SDeJ WCot
	WCru WDav
– 'Carlton Yerex' **new**	WWst
– var. *citrinum* **new**	WWst
– x Pink Perfection Group	CLAP
'Hit Parade' (VII)	LAma
humboldtii	SIgm
var. *humboldtii* **new**	
Imperial Silver	LAma
Group (VIIc)	
'Inzell' **new**	WDav
'Iona' (Ic)	CLAP
'Italia' (Ia) **new**	NCel
§ 'Jacques S. Dijt' (II)	CLAP
japonicum (IX)	EFEx WCru
'Jaqueline' **new**	ETub WDav
'Jetfire' (Ia)	EPot SDeJ
'Journey's End' (VIId)	CHar EBre LAma LRHS MBNS NRog
§ 'Joy' (VIIb) ♀ H4	CHar LAma LPVe NCel
'Karen North' (Ic)	CLAP
§ *kelleyanum* (IX)	CLAP GBuc GGGa
– NNS 98-373	WCot
'King Pete' (Ib) ♀ H4	NOak SDeJ
'Kiss Proof' (VIIb)	LRHS
'Kiwi Fanfare'	CBrm
'Kyoto' (VIId)	LAma
'Lady Alice' (VI)	CLAP
'Ladykiller' (Ia)	NRog
§ *lancifolium* (IX)	EMFP GIBF LAma SDeJ SSpi WFar
– B&SWJ 539	WCru
– var. *flaviflorum* (IX)	CLAP ECri GBuc
– 'Flore Pleno' (IX/d)	CBro CLAP CMil CSWP CSam
	EBot EBre EMFP EMon EPPr GBuc
	GCal GSki IBlr LRHS NBir NSti
	SMrm WCom WCot WCru WFar
– Forrest's form (IX)	CLAP GKir IBlr
§ – var. *splendens* (IX) ♀ H4	CBro EBee EBot LAma LRHS
	MLLN MWgw SDeJ WCot
langkongensis **new**	GIBF
lankongense (IX)	GEdr LAma WCot WDav WWst
'Last Dance' (Ic) **new**	CLAP
'Latvia' (Ia/b)	ETub NCel
'Le Rêve'	see *L.* 'Joy'
leichtlinii **new**	CLAP ECri WDav
– 'Iwashimiza' (IX)	WCot
– var. *maximowiczii* **new**	EBee WWst
'Lemon Pixie'PBR (Ia)	CSut GKir LAma LPVe NCel
leucanthum (IX)	EBee GIBF LAma LEur
– var. *centifolium* (IX)	WCru WWst
'Liberation' (I)	NBir NCel

'Little Girl' (VIIb)	WWeb
'Lollypop' (Ia)	EMar ETub LRHS MDKP MLLN
	MNrw NCel SCoo
longiflorum (IX) ♀ H2-3	EBee ECri LAma LRHS NRog
	SCoo WCot
– 'Casa Rosa'	see *L.* 'Casa Rosa'
– 'Gelria' (IX)	SDeJ
§ – 'White American' (IX)	CBro CSWP EMar ETub LRHS
	MBri MLLN NCel WWeb
lophophorum (IX)	EBee GIBF LAma WCru WDav
– ACE 1767	EPot
'Lovely Girl' (VIIb)	ECri ETub WDav
'Luxor' (Ib)	CSut ECri LRHS NBir
mackliniae (IX)	CLAP EChP EHyt GBuc GCal
	GCrs GEdr GGGa GTou IBlr ITim
	NHar SBla SIgm SSpi WAbe
x *maculatum*	see *L. dauricum*
var. *davuricum*	
– Japanese double (IX)	EMon
– *monticola* (IX)	EHyt
'Madras' (Ia) **new**	NCel
'Marco Polo' (Ia)	LAma NCel SCoo
'Marhan'	see *L.* x *dalhansonii* 'Marhan'
'Marie North' (Ic)	CLAP
'Marlène' (Ia) **new**	NCel
martagon (IX) ♀ H4	More than 30 suppliers
– var. *album* (IX) ♀ H4	More than 30 suppliers
– 'Inshriach' (IX)	GDra WCot
– 'Inshriach Ivory' **new**	GDra
– var. *pilosiusculum* (IX)	EBee
– 'Plenum' (IX/d)	EMon
'Medaillon' (Ia) ♀ H4	LAma NRog
medeoloides (IX)	EBee EFEx EHyt GBuc GCrs
	GGGa NMen SSpi
'Mediterrannee' (VIIb/d)	ETub
'Mero Star' (VII) **new**	NCel
michiguense (IX)	CSWP GCrs
'Milano' (Ia)	ECri
minima **new**	GIBF
'Miss America'	NCel
'Miss Burma' (VII)	LPVc NCel
'Miss Rio' (VII)	LRHS NCel SCoo
'Mona Lisa' (VIIb/d)	EPot ETub IBal LAma LAst LPVc
	LRHS MBri MLLN NCel WBVN
	WWeb
§ *monadelphum* (IX)	CBro CLAP EBee EHyt GBuc GCrs
	LAma NRog SIgm SSpi WDav
'Mont Blanc' (Ia)	LAma MLLN NBir NCel SDeJ
'Montana'	LRHS
'Monte Negro' (Ia)	CSut ECri ETub LPVe NCel WDav
'Montreux' (Ia)	LAma NCel
'Moulin Rouge' (Ib)	NRog
'Mr Ed'	see *L.* 'Ed'
'Mr Ruud'	see *L.* 'Ruud'
'Muscadet'PBR (VII)	CSut ETub LRHS NCel
'My Romance' (VIId)	MBri WWeb
§ *nanum* (IX)	EBee EHyt EPot GBuc GCrs GEdr
	GGGa GKev LAma LEur NMen
	NRog NSla WCru
– var. *flavidum* (IX)	EHyt EPot GCrs NMen WCru
– from Bhutan (IX)	EHyt GCrs GEdr WCru
– 'Len's Lilac' (IX)	WCru
– McBeath's form (IX)	WCru
'Navona' (Ia) **new**	CSut NCel
neilgherrense (IX)	CFil WPGP
nepalense (IX)	CBro CFwr CLAP CMil CSWP
	EBee EBla EPot GCrs GDrg GEdr
	GIBF GKir LAma LEur LRHS
	MDun SBla SDeJ WCot WCru
	WFar WPnP
– B&SWJ 2985	WCru
– CC 3669	WCot
'New Yellow'	MBri

	nobilissimum (IX)	EFEx
	'Noblesse' (VII)	LRHS
	'Olivia' (Ia)	ECri ETub LAma MLLN WDav
	Olympic Group (VIa)	LAma
	'Omega' (VII)	LAma NCel
§	'Orange Aristo' (Ia)	MBri
	'Orange Pixie' (Ia)	CSut EBre ECri EPfP GKir IBal LAma LPVe MBri NCel SCoo WGor WWeb
	'Orange Splendens' **new**	NCel
	'Orange Triumph' (Ia)	EPot LAma
	'Orchid Beauty' (Ia)	MBri NCel
	'Orestes' (Ib)	CLAP
*	Oriental Superb Group	NGdn
§	*oxypetalum* (IX)	GCrs GGGa
	- var. *insigne* (IX)	CLAP EHyt EPot ETow GCrs GDra GGGa GIBF LAma NHar NMen NSla SSpi WAbe WCru
	papilliferum	EBee LAma
	pardalinum (IX) ♀ H4	CAvo EBee IBlr LRHS NSla WCot WCru WWhi
	- var. *giganteum* (IX)	CBro CFwr CLAP ECri MNrw WDav
	- subsp. *shastense*	GCrs NMen SSpi
	parryi (IX)	GBuc SSpi
	- NNS 93-452	WCot
	- NNS 98-376	WCot
	'Partner' **new**	MBri
	'Peach Butterflies' (Ic/d)	CLAP
	'Peach Pixie' (Ia)	LAma LPVe MBri NBir NCel SCoo WWeb
	'Peggy North' (Ic)	CLAP
	'Perugia' (VIId)	LAma
	'Pesaro' (VIIb) **new**	NCel
	Petit Pink = 'Hobozi' (Ia)	LPVe
	philippinense (IX)	ETow SIgm
	- B&SWJ 4000	WCru
	Pink Perfection Group (VIa) ♀ H4	CAvo CBro EBre ECri LAma MBNS NRog SCoo SWat WFar
	'Pink Pixie'PBR (Ia)	ECri MAvo MBri NCel
	'Pink Tiger' (Ib)	CBro CLAP ECri LRHS NCel WFTG WGor
	pitkinense (IX)	EMon SOkd WWst
	'Pompei' (VIIb/d) **new**	NCel
§	*pumilum* (IX) ♀ H4	CAvo CBro CLAP EBee ECri EPot GBuc GCal GIBF LAma LRHS MLLN MTho NCel SDeJ WCot WCru WFTG WPrP WViv
	- 'Golden Gleam' (IX)	WWst
	pyrenaicum (IX)	CAvo CBrm CBro CLAP IBlr LPio WCot WDav WPGP WRha WShi WViv
§	- subsp. *carniolicum* (IX)	CBrm NMen NSla SSpi
§	- - var. *albanicum* (IX)	GCrs SSpi
	- subsp. *pyrenaicum* var. *rubrum* (IX)	CLAP WCot
	'Raspberry Butterflies' (Ic/d)	CLAP
	Red Carpet' (Ia)	ECri LRHS MAvo MBri NBir WGor
	'Red Dwarf' (Ia) **new**	CSut IBal
	'Red Flair' **new**	WWeb
	Red Jewels Group (Ic)	LAma
	'Red Night' (I)	EGoo LRHS NRog
	'Red Tiger' (Ib)	CLAP NCel
	'Red Velvet' (Ib) **new**	CLAP
	regale (IX) ♀ H4	CArn CAvo CBro CHEx CHar CSam CSut EBre EHrv EPfP ETub GIBF LAma LEdu LPVe LRHS MLLN MRav MWgw NCel NEgg NRog SDeJ SMac WBrE WCom WFar WViv
	- 'Album' (IX)	CAvo CBri CSWP EBee EBre ECri ETub LAma LRHS MCLN NCel NCot NRog SCoo SDeJ SGar WCot WFar
§	- 'Royal Gold' (IX)	MBNS MWgw SDeJ WDav
	'Reinesse' (Ia)	NCel WWeb

	'Roma' (Ia)	LAma LPio LRHS MBNS NBir
	'Rosefire' (Ia)	NOak
	'Rosemary North' (I)	CLAP
	Rosepoint Lace Group (Ic)	CLAP
	'Rosita' (Ia)	ECri MBri NRog
	rosthornii	WCot WCru
	'Rosy Wonder' (VIIa/c) **new**	NCel
	'Royal Dream' (VIII) **new**	NCel
	'Royal Fantasy' (VIII) **new**	NCel
	'Royal Gold'	see *L. regale* 'Royal Gold'
	'Royal Sunset' (VIII) **new**	NCel
	'Royal Trinity' (VIII) **new**	NCel
	rubellum (IX)	EFEx GBuc
§	'Ruud' (VII)	CBro EPot LAma LPVe LRHS MAvo NCel
	sachalinense **new**	WWst
	'Salmon Classic' (VIII) **new**	NCel
	'Sam' (VII) ♀ H4	EPot LAma LRHS NCel SCoo
	'Samur' (VIIIa/b) **new**	NCel
	'Sans Souci' (VIId)	MBri
	sargentiae (IX)	CLAP EBee GCrs GGGa NMen WCot WCru
	sempervivoideum (IX)	EBee EPot LAma LEur WDav
	shastense	see *L. kelleyanum*
	'Showbiz' (VIII)	LAma
	'Shuksan' (IV)	CLAP
	'Siberia'PBR **new**	NCel
	'Silly Girl' (Ia)	ECri
	'Sissi' (VII) **new**	NCel
	'Snow Flair' **new**	WWeb
	'Snow Princess'	LAma
	'Snow Trumpet' (V)	CSam
	'Sombrero' (VIIb)	MBri
	'Sorbonne' (VII) **new**	NCel
	speciosum	CBro EBee ECri EPot GBuc LAma
	var. *album* (IX)	LPio LRHS NBir SDeJ
	- 'Coral Queen' (IX)	CSut
	- var. *gloriosoides* (IX)	EBee EPot LAma
	- var. *roseum* (IX)	ECri GBuc
	- var. *rubrum* (IX)	CAvo CBro CHar CLAP ECri EPot ETub LAma LRHS MLLN NBir NCel NRog SDeJ
	- 'Twinkle' (IX)	ETub
§	- 'Uchida' (IX)	ECri SDeJ WDav
	'Sphinx' (Ia/d)	NCel
	'Spring Pink' (Ia)	SGar
	'Staccato' (Ia)	NCel
	'Star Gazer' (VIIc)	CBro EBre ECot IBal LAma LPVe LRHS MBNS NCel NRog SCoo SDeJ WGor WWeb
	'Starfighter' (VIId)	ETub LRHS NCel
*	'Sterling Silver'	LPVe NOak
	'Sterling Star' (Ia)	CLAP ECri LAma NRog
	stewartianum (IX)	LAma
	sulphureum	EBee LAma LEur
	'Sun Ray' (Ia)	CBro LRHS NCel NRog
	'Sunset' (Ia)	NCel
	superbum (IX)	CBro CLAP EBee LAma NRog WCru WDav WPrP
	'Sutton Court' (II)	CLAP IFro
	'Sweet Kiss' (Ia)	NCel
	'Sweet Surrender' (I)	CHar ECri LRHS
	szovitsianum	see *L. monadelphum*
	taliense (IX)	EBee GEdr GIBF LAma LEur WCru
	'Tamara' (Ib)	MBNS MBri NRog
	tenuifolium	see *L. pumilum*
	x *testaceum* (IX) ♀ H4	LAma NRog
	'Theseus' (Ic)	CLAP
	tianschanica **new**	EBee LEur
	'Tiger White' (Ic)	NCel
	tigrinum	see *L. lancifolium*
	'Time Out'PBR **new**	NCel
	'Tinkerbell' (Ic) **new**	CLAP

'Trance' (VIIb)	MBri
tsingtauense (IX)	GIBF WDav
'Uchida Kanoka'	see *L. speciosum* 'Uchida'
'Vanity Flair' **new**	WWeb
'Viva' (Ic)	CLAP
vollmeri (IX)	GCrs SSpi WAbe
wallichianum (IX)	EBee LAma NRog SDeJ
wardii (IX)	WWst
wenshanense **new**	EBee LEur
'White American'	see *L. longiflorum* 'White American'
'White Butterflies' (Ic/d) **new**	CLAP
'White Happiness' (Ia)	LAma
'White Henryi' (VId)	CLAP
'White Kiss' (Ia/d)	LAma LRHS
I 'White Lace' (Ic/d) **new**	CLAP
'White Lion' (VIIa/b) **new**	NCel
'White Paradise' (V)	SCoo
White Pixie = 'Snow Crystal' (I)	EPfP LPVe MBNS NCel
'White Tiger' (Ib)	CLAP
'Wiener Blut' (VIIIa/b) **new**	NCel
wigginsii (IX)	EHyt GCrs GGGa SSpi
willmottiae	see *L. davidii* var. *willmottiae*
Yellow Blaze Group (Ia)	LAma NRog
'Yellow Bunting' (I)	WWst
'Yellow Star' (Ib)	LRHS

lime see *Citrus aurantiifolia*

lime, Djeruk see *Citrus amblycarpa*

lime, Phillipine see x *Citrofortunella microcarpa*

Limnophila (Scrophulariaceae)
aromatica	MSal

Limonium (Plumbaginaceae)
bellidifolium	EBee ECha EDAr ESis ETow ITer SBla SIng WEas WHoo WPer
- 'Dazzling Blue' **new**	MWrn
binervosum	EBee
cosyrense	CMea MHer NMen SIng WPer WWin
dumosum	see *Goniolimon tataricum* var. *angustifolium*
globulariifolium	see *L. ramosissimum*
gmelinii	MLLN SPlb WPer
* - subsp. *hungaricum*	ECGN NLar
- 'Perestrojka'	EBee
gougetianum	ETow WPer
latifolium	see *L. platyphyllum*
minutum	CNic EBee
'Misty Blue' PBR **new**	EMui
'Misty Pink' **new**	EMui
'Misty White' **new**	EMui
paradoxum	MOne
perezii	CTrF EDAr WPer
§ *platyphyllum*	COIW CPrp EBee EPfP EPla LHop LRHS MCAu MHer MNrw MWat MWgw MWrn NMir SDes SGar SPer SPla SRms WBrE WCot WFar WGwG WHoo WMoo WPer WWal WWin
- 'Robert Butler'	EBee EMan GCal LBuc LRHS MRav
- 'Violetta'	CTri EBee EBlw EBre ECGP ECha ELan ERou GKir GMac LRHS MBri MCAu MMHG MRav NLar SPer SUsu WHoo
§ *ramosissimum*	EBee
sinense **new**	EShb
speciosum 'Blue Diamond'	see *Goniolimon incanum* 'Blue Diamond'
'Stardust' **new**	MPWC
tataricum	see *Goniolimon tataricum*
vulgare	WHer

Linanthastrum see *Linanthus*

Linanthus (Polemoniaceae)
nuttallii	CDes
- subsp. *floribundus*	CPBP

Linaria (Scrophulariaceae)
aeruginea	CSpe EMlt
aeruginosa subsp. *nevadensis* 'Gemstones'	LRHS
alpina	CMea CSpe ECtt EMlt GMaP GTou LPVe MPWC MTho SRms SScr WPer
'Anstey'	CElw
anticaria 'Antique Silver'	CFwr CHea CPou EBee ECha EMan GBuc LRHS MGGn MSte NLar SSvw WPGP WWeb
Blue Lace = 'Yalin'	EBee NPri SAsh
* 'Blue Pygmy'	SScr
capraria	CPBP WCot
cymbalaria	see *Cymbalaria muralis*
§ *dalmatica*	EBee EChP ECha ELan ERou LPhx MCAu MFir MHar MWhi NBid NBro NDov NPri SChu WCot WKif WMoo WPer
x *dominii* 'Carnforth'	CMdw CMea EBee MBrN NBro WBry WCot WWpP
- 'Yuppie Surprise'	CHid EBee EChP ECtt EMan EMon LPio NBir NDov NGdn SPer WCra WLRN WPGP
genistifolia	ECtt MDKP
- subsp. *dalmatica*	see *L. dalmatica*
'Globosa Alba'	see *Cymbalaria muralis* 'Globosa Alba'
hepaticifolia	see *Cymbalaria hepaticifolia*
* *lobata alba*	SPlb
'Natalie'	SBla
origanifolia	see *Chaenorhinum origanifolium*
pallida	see *Cymbalaria pallida*
§ *peloponnesiaca*	EBee
pilosa	see *Cymbalaria pilosa*
purpurea	CKin COIW EBee EFWa EHrv ELan EWTr MCAu MChe MFir MHer MWgw NBro NCat NLon NPPs NPer NPri SRms WHen WMoo WPer WWye
- 'Alba'	see *L. purpurea* 'Springside White'
- 'Canon Went'	More than 30 suppliers
- 'Chariton White' **new**	CNat
- pink	MBow
- 'Radcliffe Innocence'	see *L. purpurea* 'Springside White'
§ - 'Springside White'	CElw EBee ECha ECtt EMan ERou GBuc LPhx MAnH MCAu MGGn MSte NBid NBir NPri SBla SSvw SUsu WBea WCot WFTG WLRN WMoo WPer WRha
- 'Thurgarton Beauty'	MDKP WCot
- 'Vainglorious'	CNat
repens	CKin MNrw WCot WHbs WHer
sibthorpiana	see *L. peloponnesiaca*
'Sue'	EBee EMan
supina	WWpP
'Toni Aldiss'	CSpe EBee WFTG WKif
triornithophora	CBot CElw CFir CHar CSpe EBee ECha EMan EMar GBuc IGor MAnH MFir MWgw MWrn WBea WCot WMoo WPer WRha WWye

- purple	ELan STes WBea WMoo
vulgaris	CArn CKin ELau GWCH LDai
	MBow MChe MGas MHer NMir
	NSco WHer WJek WLHH WPer
- 'Peloria'	CNat EBee EMon WAlt
'Winifrid's Delight'	CHea EBee EMan EPfP LAst WLRN

Lindelofia (Boraginaceae)

anchusoides hort.	see *L. longiflora*
§ **anchusoides**	EPPr GBri NBid
(Lindl.) Lehm.	
§ **longiflora**	CFir CPlt ECGN EMan GBin GBuc
	GCal GDea LRHS MLLN NLar
	WBro WFTG WPGP WPer

Lindera (Lauraceae)

angustifolia	CFil
benzoin	CFil EPfP GIBF MSal WDin WPGP
erythrocarpa	CFil EPfP WPGP
- B&SWJ 6271	WCru
megaphylla	CBcs
obtusiloba ♥ H4	CAbP CFil EPfP IArd LRHS NLar
	SSpi WNor WPGP
praecox	CFil WPGP
praetermissa	CFil EPfP WPGP
reflexa <u>new</u>	EPfP
strychnifolia	EPfP
triloba	CFil WPGP
umbellata	WCru
var. **membranaceae**	
B&SWJ 6227 <u>new</u>	

Lindernia (Scrophulariaceae)

grandiflora blue	ECou SSpi
- pink	ECou

Linnaea (Caprifoliaceae)

borealis	GDra ILis MHar NSla
- subsp. **americana**	NHar NWCA

Linum ❀ (Linaceae)

africanum <u>new</u>	CDes
arboreum ♥ H4	EBee MBro SBla SIgm WAbe WKif
	WPat
- NS 529	NWCA
austriacum	EBee
campanulatum	SMac
capitatum	EBee WHoo
dolomiticum	WPat
flavum	CTri EPfP GDra GTou WHoo
- 'Compactum'	GAbr LHop MBro NPri SBla SMrm
	SRms WCot WHrl WWin
'Gemmell's Hybrid' ♥ H4	CLyd CMea EPot EWes LRHS
	MBro MDKP NBir NHar NMen
	NRya NWCA SBla SIng WAbe
	WLin WPat
kingii var. **sedoides**	LTwo WLin
leonii	EBee LRHS WCom WKif
monogynum	CDes EBee ECou WPGP
§ - var. **diffusum**	ECou
- dwarf	GTou
- 'Nelson'	see *L. monogynum* var. *diffusum*
narbonense	CSam CSpe EBee EMan LGro LPhx
	LRHS MBri MBro NOak SDes SIgm
	SMrm SRms WHoo WKif
- 'Heavenly Blue'	ERou SMac SUsu SVal WEas WHen
nervosum	WLin
§ **perenne**	More than 30 suppliers
- 'Album'	EBee ECha ELan EMan EOHP EPfP
	ERou SPer WBro WHen WPer
- subsp. **alpinum**	WPer
- - 'Alice Blue'	CPBP LBee NMen SBla WWin
- - var. **julicum** <u>new</u>	EBee

§ - 'Blau Saphir'	CBod CSam EBee LPVe LRHS
	MLLN MPWC NLar NOrc NPri
	SRms WBVN WHen WMoo
- Blue Sapphire	see *L. perenne* 'Blau Saphir'
- 'Diamant'	CBod EBee LPVe LRHS NCiC NPri
	WMoo
- subsp. **extra-axillare**	CLyd
- 'Himmelszelt'	NLar
- subsp. **lewisii**	EBee EHyt NBir SAga
- 'Nanum Diamond' <u>new</u>	NLar
- 'White Diamond'	NPri WHen WHer
rubrum	CSpe MChe
sibiricum	see *L. perenne*
suffruticosum	CPBP
- subsp. **salsoloides**	LTwo NWCA SBla WPat
'Nanum'	
- - 'Prostratum'	GBuc SIgm

Liparis (Orchidaceae)

coelogynoides	ECou
cordifolia	EFEx
fujisanensis	EFEx
krameri var. **krameri**	EFEx
kumokiri	EFEx
makinoana	EFEx
nigra	EFEx
sootenzanensis	EFEx

Lippia (Verbenaceae)

alba	MSal
canescens	see *Phyla nodiflora* var.
	canescens
chamaedrifolia	see *Verbena peruviana*
citriodora	see *Aloysia triphylla*
dulcis	CArn CFir EOHP MSal
graveolens	EOHP
nodiflora	see *Phyla nodiflora*
repens	see *Phyla nodiflora*
scaberrima	EOHP

Liquidambar ❀ (Hamamelidaceae)

acalycina	CPMA MGos SBir SSpi SSta WNor
	WPat
'Elstead Mill'	LPan
formosana	CDul CEnd CMCN CPle CTho EBee
	ECrN EPfP IMGH LPan MBlu MGos
	SBir SPar SPer SSta WNor WPGP
- B&SWJ 6855	WCru
- Monticola Group	CPMA EPfP SBir SSta
orientalis	CDul CLnd CMCN CPMA EPfP
	LPan SBir SSta
styraciflua	More than 30 suppliers
- 'Andrew Hewson'	CLnd CPMA LRHS MAsh SBir SSpi
	SSta
- 'Anja'	CPMA MBlu SBir SSta
- 'Anneke'	CLnd CPMA LRHS SBir SSta
* - 'Argentea'	CLnd
- 'Aurea'	see *L. styraciflua* 'Variegata'
- 'Aurea Variegata'	see *L. styraciflua* 'Variegata'
- 'Aurora' (v)	CPMA SBir SCoo SLim
- 'Burgundy'	CLnd CPMA CTho MAsh NHol
	SBir SSta WPat
- 'Fastigiata' <u>new</u>	MBlu
- 'Festeri'	CEnd SBir SSta WPat
- 'Festival'	CPMA SSta
- 'Globe'	CPMA
- 'Golden Treasure' (v)	CPMA LNet LRHS SMad SSpi WPat
- 'Gum Ball'	CLnd CMCN CPMA EBee EPfP
	EWes MGos NLar SMad SSta WPat
- 'Happidaze' <u>new</u>	WPat
- 'Jennifer Carol'	CPMA
- 'Kia'	CEnd CLnd CPMA WPat
- 'Kirsten'	CPMA SSta

- 'Lane Roberts' ♀ H4	CDoC CDul CLnd CMCN CTho EBee EPfP LPan LRHS MAsh MBlu MBri MGos NLar SBir SKee SLim SMad SReu SSta WDin WPGP WPat
- 'Manon' (v)	CDoC CEnd CPMA NBhm SLim
- 'Midwest Sunset' **new**	WPat
- 'Moonbeam' (v)	CEnd CPMA CTho MAsh NHol NLar SBir SCoo SLim SSta WPat
- 'Moraine'	CPMA
- 'Naree'	CPMA
- 'Oconee' **new**	WPat
- 'Palo Alto'	CPMA MAsh NHol SBir SSta WPat
- 'Parasol'	CEnd CPMA SBir SSta
- 'Pendula'	CLnd CPMA LNet SBir SSta WBod
- 'Penwood'	CPMA SSpi SSta
- 'Rotundiloba'	CLnd CPMA SSpi SSta
- 'Silver King' (v)	CDul CPMA EBee ECrN EHoe EPfP IMGH MGos SCoo SKee SLim SPer SPoG SSta
- 'Stared'	CLnd CPMA SBir WPat
- 'Stella'	CLnd
- 'Thea'	CLnd CPMA LNet LRHS MAsh SBir SSta
§ - 'Variegata' Overeynder (v)	CBcs CBot CDul CLnd COtt CPMA CTho ECrN ELan EPfP LNet LPan LRHS MAsh MGos NBee NHol NPal SHBN SKee SLim SPer SSpi SSta WDin WPat
- 'Worplesdon' ♀ H4	More than 30 suppliers

Liriodendron ✿ (*Magnoliaceae*)

chinense	CBcs CLnd CMCN CTho EPfP MBlu SSpi WPGP
'T. Jackson' **new**	NLar
tulipifera ♀ H4	More than 30 suppliers
- 'Ardis'	CMCN SSpi
- 'Arnold'	CMCN
- 'Aureomarginatum' (v) ♀ H4	LTwo NWCA SBla WPat
- 'Aureum'	CMCN
- 'Crispum'	CMCN
- 'Fastigiatum'	CBcs CDoC CDul CEnd CLnd CMCN COtt CTho EBee ECrN ELan ENot EPfP IMGH LPan LRHS MAsh MBlu MBri NPal NRog SKee SPer SSta WOrn
- 'Glen Gold'	CEnd CMCN MBlu MGos SMad
- 'Mediopictum' (v)	CBcs CMCN CTho LBuc LNet MBlu

Liriope ✿ (*Convallariaceae*)

'Big Blue'	see *L. muscari* 'Big Blue'
§ *exiliflora*	CEnd CLAP EBee EGle EMan EPar GCal LRHS NLar WAul WFar WRus
§ - 'Ariaka-janshige' (v)	CRDP EMan SPar SWat
§ *gigantea*	CLAP EMan SWat WWal
graminifolia hort.	see *L. muscari*
hyacinthifolia	see *Reineckea carnea*
kansuensis	ERos
koreana	GCal
'Majestic'	CBct EGle ENot ERou GSki MBri SDes WCot WFar
§ *muscari* ♀ H4	More than 30 suppliers
- B&SWJ 561	WCru
- 'Alba'	see *L. muscari* 'Monroe White'
- 'Aztec Gold'	WWal
§ - 'Big Blue'	CBct CKno CLAP CPrp EBee EMan EPfP EWll LBBr LHop LRHS MRav NArg NLar SDes WCFE WMoo
- 'Christmas Tree'	CPrp WWal
- 'Evergreen Giant'	see *L. gigantea*
- 'Gold-banded' (v)	CHea CPrp EBlw EGle EMan EPfP GCal LRHS NRib SDes SHBN SPer SWat WFar WGwG WRus WViv WWal
- 'Ingwersen'	CPrp EBee EDAr GBin
- 'John Burch' (v)	CFwr CLAP CPrp EBee EMan ENot GBin LHop MCCP SPar SUsu WPer
- 'Majestic' misapplied	see *L. exiliflora*
- 'Mini Mondo'	WGwG WWal
§ - 'Monroe White'	More than 30 suppliers
- 'Paul Aden'	CFil EPfP WPGP
- 'Royal Purple'	CBct CLAP CPrp EBee EMan ENot EPfP GSki NFla NGdn NLar NOrc NWCA SDes WCot WGwG WPer WWal
- 'Silver Ribbon'	CLAP CPrp EBee EMan EPfP MGrG ENgg NSti SPer WPGP WPrP
- 'Silvery Midget' (v)	CPrp SUsu WMoo WWal
- 'Superba'	WCot
§ - 'Variegata' (v)	More than 30 suppliers
* - 'Variegated Alba' (v)	CFir
- 'Webster Wideleaf'	WPer
platyphylla	see *L. muscari*
'Samantha'	CKno CPrp EBee ECha LRHS
§ *spicata*	CBro CHor EBee ERos LPio MBro NOrc SPar SSpi SWat WAul WHoo WWeb
- 'Alba'	CRow EBee GCal MRav MTed MTho WTin WWin
§ - 'Gin-ryu' (v)	CBct CCge CFir CKno CLAP CMdw CSpe EBee EPPr EVFa EWes GSki LEdu LPio MRav MStc SDes SUsu WCot WPGP WViv WWal
- 'Silver Dragon'	see *L. spicata* 'Gin-ryu'
- 'Small Green'	EBee MGGn

Lisianthius (*Gentianaceae*)

russelianus	see *Eustoma grandiflorum*

Listera (*Orchidaceae*)

ovata	WHer

Lithocarpus ✿ (*Fagaceae*)

densiflorus	WCot
var. *echinoides*	
NNS 00-504 **new**	
edulis	CHEx SArc
pachyphyllus	CBcs CHEx
* *pathisapsis* SF 96178 **new**	ISea

Lithodora (*Boraginaceae*)

§ *diffusa*	MAsh SGar
- 'Alba'	ECtt EMil EPfP GDra GKir LBee LRHS MBri MGos NLap SDes SGar SPer WFar WWeb
- 'Cambridge Blue'	LRHS SDes SLdr SPer
- 'Compacta'	CLyd EGle EWes GDra NWCA
- 'Grace Ward' ♀ H4	CWCL EWes GDra GKev MBro MGos MWya NHar NHol SBod WAbe WBod WPat
- 'Heavenly Blue' ♀ H4	More than 30 suppliers
- 'Inverleith'	EWes WFar
- 'Pete's Favourite'	WAbe
- 'Picos'	CMea EDAr EGle EHyt EPot GCrs GTou MBro NMen SIgm WAbe WPat
- 'Star' PBR	CBcs CLyd ECtt EPfP GKir LRHS MAsh SBod SCoo SIng SPer SPoG WBod WWol
graminifolia	see *Moltkia suffruticosa*
hispidula	SIgm WAbe
x *intermedia*	see *Moltkia* x *intermedia*
§ *oleifolia* ♀ H4	CLyd CMea MBro MWat NBir NMen NSla WLin WPat
rosmarinifolia	CSpe EHyt GKir LRHS

zahnii	CMHG EBee EPot SIgm WAbe WLin WPat

Lithophragma (Saxifragaceae)

parviflorum	CMea CPom EHyt GDra MNrw MSte MTho NBir NMen NRya NWCA SSpi WCru WFar

Lithospermum (Boraginaceae)

diffusum	see *Lithodora diffusa*
doerfleri	see *Moltkia doerfleri*
erythrorhizon	MSal WWye
incisum **new**	EBee
officinale	GBar GPoy IIve MGol MSal
oleifolium	see *Lithodora oleifolia*
purpureocaeruleum	see *Buglossoides purpurocaerulea*

Litsea (Lauraceae)

glauca	see *Neolitsea sericea*
japonica	CHEx

Littonia (Colchicaceae)

modesta	CHal CRHN

Livistona (Arecaceae)

australis	CBrP CRoM CTrC EAmu EPVP LPal
benthamii **new**	CRoM
chinensis ♀ H1	CAbb CBrP CRoM EAmu EPVP LPJP LPal MPRe WMul
decipiens	CBrP CRoM CTrC LPal MPRe
jenkinsiana	WMul
mariae	LPal

Lloydia (Liliaceae)

ixiolirioides **new**	EBee
oxycarpa **new**	EBee
serotina	EBee
tibetica **new**	EBee
yunnanensis **new**	EBee

Loasa (Loasaceae)

lateritia	see *Caiophora lateritia*
triphylla var. *volcanica*	EMan EWes GCal WCot WSHC

Lobelia (Campanulaceae)

'Alice'	WCot WFar WOut
anatina	CFai CFir LRHS WDyG
angulata	see *Pratia angulata*
'Bees' Flame'	CFir CLAP EBee EBlw EMan ERou ETub MAnH MLLN SChu SHel SUsu SVil SWat WLRN
Big Blue = 'Weslobigblue'PBR **new**	LAst
Blue Star = 'Wesstar'PBR	ECtt
bridgesii	CPLG CPne CSpe EFou EMan GCal GGar GMac IFro ITer LRav MWrn SSte WHil
'Brightness'	ELan
'Butterfly Blue'	CBcs EBee EBre EChP EGle GBuc LRHS MTis SPla
'Butterfly Rose'	EBre EGle GBuc SRot WCHb
cardinalis ♀ H3	More than 30 suppliers
- subsp. *graminea* var. *multiflora*	CFir
'Cherry Ripe'	CLAP CM&M ECoo ELan EMan EPfP LHop LRHS NHlc NHol SMrm WCHb WEas WLRN
'Cinnabar Deep Red'	see *L.* 'Fan Tiefrot'
'Cinnabar Rose'	see *L.* 'Fan Zinnoberrosa'
comosa **new**	SPlb
'Complexion'	LRHS
Compliment Blue	see *L.* 'Kompliment Blau'
Compliment Deep Red	see *L.* 'Kompliment Tiefrot'
Compliment Purple	see *L.* 'Kompliment Purpur'
Compliment Scarlet	see *L.* 'Kompliment Scharlach'
coronopifolia **new**	EShb
'Cotton Candy' **new**	EFou NSti
'Dark Crusader'	CPrp EBee EBlw ECtt EFou ELan EMan EMar LRHS MBri MCLN NGdn NPro SAga SChu SMrm SPla WCHb WCru WEas WMnd WRus WSan
dortmanna	EMFW
erecta **new**	MGol
erinus 'Kathleen Mallard' (d)	ECtt WBVN WFoF WWol
- 'Richardii'	see *L. richardsonii*
'Eulalia Berridge'	CLAP CSam EBee EChP EGle EMil GBuc LPhx MBri MMil SAga SMrm WCru WDyG WMoo
excelsa	CPle CTbh MGol SIgm WCot WFar WPic
Fan Deep Red	see *L.* 'Fan Tiefrot'
'Fan Deep Rose'	see *L.* 'Fan Orchidrosa'
§ 'Fan Orchidrosa' ♀ H3-4	CFwr EMan MPWC NGdn SRot WLRN WWeb
'Fan Scharlach' ♀ H3-4	IBal LPVe MWgw NLar SRot WWeb
§ 'Fan Tiefrot' ♀ H3-4	ERou GBuc LAst LPVe MPWC MWgw NGdn NLar SGar SHel SPar SRms SSpi SWat WCHb WHil WLRN WPer WWeb
§ 'Fan Zinnoberrosa' ♀ H3-4	CBcs CBrm CFir EMan ERou LAst LRHS MAnH MGol MPWC SRms SRot WCHb WPer WWin
'Flamingo'	see *L.* 'Pink Flamingo'
fulgens	EPfP IBlr NBlu NPer WEas WFar
§ - 'Elmfeuer'	EBee EMar ERou LPVe MAnH MAvo MTis NLar SMrm SPlb WFar WGor
- 'Illumination'	GBuc
- Saint Elmo's Fire	see *L. fulgens* 'Elmfeuer'
galpinii **new**	WCot
x *gerardii*	CBri CLAP CSam EWll SSte SWal WBor WHil WWpP
- 'Eastgrove Pink'	WEas
- 'Rosencavalier'	EBee EMar LRHS MBri MMil WFar WOut
§ - 'Vedrariensis'	More than 30 suppliers
gibberoa	CHEx
'Hadspen Blue' **new**	LBuc
'Hadspen Purple' **new**	CWes
'Hadspen Royal Purple'	MBri WWeb
imperialis **new**	WSan
inflata	CArn GPoy MSal WCHb WWye
'Jack McMaster'	SUsu
'Kimbridge Beet'	CMac
§ 'Kompliment Blau'	CFir CHor EMan ERou LRHS NArg SPar WPer
§ 'Kompliment Purpur'	ERou MNrw SPar
§ 'Kompliment Scharlach' ♀ H3-4	CBri CHor CSWP EBee EBre ECGN EPfP ERou LRHS MBNS MPWC NPer SPar SSpi WCHb WFar WMnd WPer WWpP
§ 'Kompliment Tiefrot'	CHor ERou MAnH MNrw MPWC NArg SPar WAul WPer
laxiflora	CBot EGra MTho SAga SIgm
- var. *angustifolia*	CHEx CPrp CSam CSpe CTbh CWCL EMan ERea GCal IBlr MOak MSte SHFr SMrm SRms SSte WPer WWye
'Lena'	SWat
lindblomii	CFee
linnaeoides	EMan SPlb WEas
longifolia from Chile	CFee
§ *lutea*	EBee LRHS LRav MOak

pedunculata	see *Pratia pedunculata*
perpusilla	see *Pratia perpusilla*
'Pink Elephant' ♀ H4	CHar CLAP CSWP EBee EPri
	GMac IKee MAnH MDKP SChu
	WFar WPGP WRha
§ 'Pink Flamingo'	EBee EBlw EBre EPar LRHS NLon
	SMrm SOkh SWat WCHb WFar
	WHoo WWye
polyphylla	MGol SIgm
'Pope's Velvet'	WHil
puberula	CFir
'Purple Towers'	GBuc
'Queen Victoria' ♀ H3	More than 30 suppliers
* *rediviva*	EBre
regalis	WCHb WHal
§ *richardsonii* ♀ H3	ECtt LIck WLRN
roughii	EMan NLAp
'Ruby Slippers'	CBcs CFai EBee NPro
N 'Russian Princess'	CPrp CRDP CSam EBee EBlw
	ECGN EChP ECtt EMan EMar
	LRHS MAnH MAvo MBri MMil
	MOak SChu SMad SPer SUsu
	WCHb WFar WLRN
seguinii var. *doniana*	CPLG
CC 3673 **new**	
sessilifolia	EBee EGle GBuc GCal WBVN
	WCot WLRN WPer WSan WWye
– B&L 12396	EMon
siphilitica	More than 30 suppliers
– 'Alba'	CSam EBee EBlw EPfP EPri LPVe
	LRHS MLLN MWrn SRms SWal
	WCHb WFar WHoo WHrl WMoo
	WPer WSan WWpP WWye
– Blue selection	LPVe NLar WSan
– 'Rosea'	MNrw
'Spark'	GBuc
'Sparkle DeVine'	EFou WCot WWpP
x *speciosa*	EFou MNrw
– dark	CMHG EGle SMrm
– deep pink **new**	LPVe
splcula	IIve
'Tania'	More than 30 suppliers
treadwellii	see *Pratia angulata* 'Treadwellii'
Tresahor Series **new**	CHEx
tupa	More than 30 suppliers
– JCA 12527	EBlw LAst MTPN WCot
– Archibald's form **new**	MCCP
– dark orange	SMrm
urens	CFil EBee SSpi WPGP
valida	EBee EMan GBuc GQui SPet
	WLRN WOut
– 'South Seas'	WBar
vedrariensis	see *L.* x *gerardii* 'Vedrariensis'
'Wildwood Splendour'	EFou
'Will Scarlet'	CLAP EBre
'Zinnoberrosa'	see *L.* 'Fan Zinnoberrosa'

Loeselia (Polemoniaceae)

mexicana	WCot

loganberry see *Rubus* x *loganobaccus*

Loiseleuria (Ericaceae)

procumbens from Japan	GCrs WAbe

Lomandra (Lomandraceae)

hystrix	WCot
longifolia	ECou GCal WCot

Lomaria see *Blechnum*

Lomatia (Proteaceae)

ferruginea	CAbb CBcs CDoC CFil CHEx

	CPne CTrG EPfP ICrw ISea
	SAPC SArc SBrw WCru WPGP
fraseri	SSpi
hirsuta	CFil
longifolia	see *L. myricoides*
§ *myricoides*	CAbb CDoC CFil CPLG CTrG
	CTrw EPfP LRHS SArc SLon SPer
	SSpi WPGP
polymorpha **new**	WPGP
silaifolia	CDoC EPfP
§ *tinctoria*	CDoC CTrC CTrw EPfP LRHS
	SArc SSpi

Lomatium (Apiaceae)

brandegeei	SIgm
columbianum	SIgm
dissectum	EBee
– var. *multifidum*	SIgm
grayi	SIgm
– NNS 00-522	EPPr
hallii NNS 00-526 **new**	SIgm
macrocarpum	SIgm
martindalei	EBee GCrs SIgm
nudicaule	SIgm
utriculatum	EBee MSal SIgm

Lonicera ✿ (Caprifoliaceae)

B&SWJ 2654 from Sikkim	WCru
KR 291	EPla
PC&H 17A	SBra
from China	WCru
§ *acuminata*	CPIN GIBF IArd LRHS SLim
	WGwG WSHC
– B&SWJ 3480	WCru
alberti	CFai MBNS MRav SLon SMac
	WGwG WHCG WSHC
albiflora	WSHC
– var. *albiflora*	SBra
alpigena	GIBF
alseuosmoides	CPIN CTrC GBin IArd SAga SBra
	SLon SMac WBcn WCru WSHC
	WWeb
N x *americana* hort.	see *L.* x *italica*
§ x *americana*	CHad CRHN EPfP LAst LHop
(Miller) K. Koch	LRHS MGos NBea NBlu NPer
	NWea SBra SLPI SLim SPla SReu
	SSta WBod WCru WWeb
x *brownii*	CMac SGar
§ – 'Dropmore Scarlet'	More than 30 suppliers
N – 'Fuchsioides'	EPfP MBro NBrk NSti WSHC
caerulea	MRav WHCG
– var. *edulis*	ESim LEdu
canadensis **new**	SBra
§ *caprifolium* ♀ H4	CDoC CRHN EBee ECtt ELan
	EOrc EPfP EPla LBuc LRHS MAsh
	MBar MBri NBea NMGW SBra
	SHBN SPer WCru
– 'Anna Fletcher'	CRHN CSPN EBee MBNS NHaw
	SBra SCoo SLim WCFE WCru WWeb
– 'Inga' **new**	SBra
– f. *pauciflora*	see *L.* x *italica*
chaetocarpa	CMHG CPle GEil WPat
chamissoi **new**	GIBF
§ *chrysantha*	GBin GEil GIBF NRya
ciliosa	CPIN NBea
'Clavey's Dwarf'	see *L.* x *xylosteoides* 'Clavey's Dwarf'
deflexicalyx	EPfP GIBF
demissa	GIBF
dioica	SBra
'Early Cream'	see *L. caprifolium*
edulis **new**	GIBF
etrusca	EPla GIBF MRav WCom WWeb

- 'Donald Waterer' ♀ H4	EBee LRHS MAsh SBra SCoo SPla WFar WGor	
- 'Michael Rosse'	EBee EBre ELan IArd LRHS MBNS MSte SBra SRms WRHF	
- 'Superba' ♀ H4	CPIN CRHN EBee ECtt EPfP LRHS MAsh MLLN NBrk SBra SEND SLim SPar SPer SPla WCru WPen WSHC	
ferdinandii	GIBF WWes	
flexuosa	see *L. japonica* var. *repens*	
fragrantissima	More than 30 suppliers	
gibbiflora Maxim.	see *L. chrysantha*	
gibbiflora Dippel	NRya	
giraldii hort.	see *L. acuminata*	
giraldii Rehder	CBot CFRD CPIN EBee EPfP LBuc MAsh NHol SBra SLim SPar WCot WCru	
glabrata	EBee GEil LBuc SBra SCoo SLPl SLim WCru	
- B&SWJ 2150	SBra WCru	
gracilipes **new**	GIBF	
gracilis	MBlu	
grata	see *L* x *americana* (Miller) K. Koch	
x *heckrottii*	CDoC CFRD CMac CRHN EBee ECtt LRHS MBar NBea NBee NSti WDin WLRN WStI WWeb	
N - 'Gold Flame'	More than 30 suppliers	
§ *henryi*	More than 30 suppliers	
- var. *subcoriacea*	see *L. henryi*	
hildebrandiana	CPIN ERea LRHS SBra SOWG SSpi WPGP	
'Hill House'	CHll	
hirsuta	NBea SBra	
'Honey Baby'PBR	MBlu MGos MRav NBlu NHol SPoG WPat WRHF	
implexa	CPIN EHol EPla EVFa GCal LPhx NPro SBra WCru WSHC	
infundibulum var. *rockii*	EPfP	
insularis	CMCN MBlu	
involucrata	CFee CMCN CMHG CPMA CPle CWib EPla LHop MBNS MBar MBlu MRav NChi NHol SPer WCFE WCom WDin WFar	
- var. *ledebourii*	CPle EBee ELan EPfP EPla GKir MTis NHol SDys WTel WWin	
§ x *italica* ♀ H4	CMac COIW CRHN CWSG EBee EBre ECtt ELan ENot LRHS MBri MRav MWgw NPer NSti SBra SDix SLim SMer SPar SPer SSpi WBod WCru WDin WFar WTel WWeb	
- Harlequin = 'Sherlite'PBR (v)	More than 30 suppliers	
§ *japonica* 'Aureoreticulata' (v)	More than 30 suppliers	
- 'Cream Cascade'	EBee LBuc MLLN	
- 'Dart's World'	CFRD EBee NHol SPla SVil WLRN WStI	
- 'Halliana' ♀ H4	More than 30 suppliers	
- 'Hall's Prolific'	More than 30 suppliers	
§ - 'Horwood Gem' (v)	EBee ECtt NHol NPro SBra SCoo WBcn WWeb	
- 'Mint Crisp' (v)	ELan EPfP LRHS MAsh MBri SMur WWeb	
- 'Peter Adams'	see *L. japonica* 'Horwood Gem'	
- 'Red World'	MTis NBrk	
§ - var. *repens* ♀ H4	More than 30 suppliers	
- 'Variegata'	see *L. japonica* 'Aureoreticulata'	
korolkowii	CBot CPMA EBee EPfP GEil LRHS MBNS MBri NBir SLon SUsu WCom WCot WHCG WLeb WSHC WWin	
- var. *zabelii* misapplied	see *L. tatarica* 'Zabelii'	
- var. *zabelii* Rehder	ELan	

lanceolata AC 3120	GGar	
maackii	CHll CMCN CPMA EPfP WHCG	
* *macgregorii*	CMCN	
'Mandarin'PBR	CDoC CWSG EBee ENot EPfP GKir LRHS MAsh MBNS MBri MRav SBra SCoo SPar	
maximowiczii **new**	GEil GIBF	
morrowii	GIBF	
x *muscaviensis*	GEil	
nervosa	GIBF	
nigra	EPla	
nitida	CBcs CCVT CChe CTri EBee ENot EPfP LHyr MRav NBlu NWea SHBN SPer SRPl STre WDin WFar WHar WHen WStI	
- 'Baggesen's Gold' ♀ H4	More than 30 suppliers	
- 'Cumbrian Calypso' **new**	NPro	
- 'Eden Spring'	NPro	
- 'Elegant'	LBuc	
- 'Ernest Wilson'	MBar	
- 'Fertilis'	ENot SPer	
- 'Hohenheimer Findling'	WDin	
- 'Lemon Beauty' (v)	CDoC EBee EHoe EPfP EPla EVFa GEil LAst LHop LRHS MBNS MBar MBri MGos MTis NBir NBlu NHol NRib SLPl SPar SPer WBcn WDin WEas WFar WLeb WMoo WWeb	
- 'Lemon Queen'	CWib ELan WLRN	
- 'Lemon Spreader' **new**	LBuc	
§ - 'Maigrün'	CBcs EBee EMil ENot LRHS MBri NPro SPer WDin WFar WGwG	
- Maygreen	see *L. nitida* 'Maigrün'	
- 'Red Tips'	EBee EHoe EPla EVFa GEil LRHS MBNS MBri MGos MLLN NHol WDin WFar WLRN WPnP WWeb	
- 'Silver Beauty' (v)	More than 30 suppliers	
* - 'Silver Cloud'	NHol	
- 'Silver Lining'	see *L. pileata* 'Silver Lining'	
- 'Silver Queen'	WEas	
- 'Twiggy' (v)	LBuc LHop LRHS MBri MGos NPro WLRN	
periclymenum	CArn CKin CTri ELau EPla GPoy MDun MHer NBea NFor NLon NSco NWea SHFr SPlb WDin WHCG WWye	
§ - 'Belgica'	More than 30 suppliers	
- 'Belgica' misapplied	see *L.* x *italica*	
* - 'Cream Cascade'	GKir	
- 'Cream Cloud' **new**	SBra	
- 'Florida'	see *L. periclymenum* 'Serotina'	
- 'Graham Thomas' ♀ H4	More than 30 suppliers	
- 'Heaven Scent'	EMil SBra	
- 'Honeybush'	CSPN EBee SCoo WBcn WWeb	
- 'La Gasnaérie'	EBee SBra SLim	
- 'Liden'	SBra	
- 'Llyn Brianne' **new**	WBcn	
- 'Munster'	CFRD EBee MBri NBrk SBra WBcn WSHC	
- 'Red Gables'	CFRD CSam EBee MBNS MBri MRav MSte NHol SBra SLim SPla SVil WCot WGor WPat	
N - 'Serotina' ♀ H4	More than 30 suppliers	
- - EM '85	ENot WCru	
- 'Serpentine'	EBee SBra	
* - *sulphurea*	EPla EWll NBlu WFar WWeb	
- 'Sweet Sue'	CRHN CSPN EBee ECtt ELan EPfP EVFa GCal LAst LRHS MAsh MBNS MLan MSte MTis NFor NSti SBra SCoo WBcn WFar WWeb	
- 'Winchester'	EBee LBuc WWeb	
pileata	More than 30 suppliers	
- 'Moss Green'	CDoC EBee MGos WHCG	
- 'Pilot'	SLPl	

§	- 'Silver Lining' (v)	EPla GBuc WCot
	- 'Stockholm'	SLPl
	pilosa Willd. CD&R 1216	SBra
	praeflorens	CPle
*	*pulsata* **new**	CTrC
	x *purpusii*	CDoC CPle CSBt CWSG CWib EBee ECle ENot EPfP EWTr MBNS MBar MGos MWat NBea SLim SPer SPla SRms WBod WCFE WEas WFar WHCG WHar WSHC WTel WWin
	- 'Spring Romance'	SLon
	- 'Winter Beauty' ♀ H4	More than 30 suppliers
	pyrenaica	CPle WPat
	quinquelocularis	GIBF MBlu
	f. *translucens*	
	rupicola	see *L. syringantha*
	var. *syringantha*	
	saccata	EPfP
	sempervirens ♀ H4	CBot CPlN CSBt EBee EPar EPfP MBNS MCCP MRav NBea SBra SPer WCru WFar WLRN WSHC
	- 'Dropmore Scarlet'	see *L.* x *brownii* 'Dropmore Scarlet'
	- 'Leo'	CSPN
N	- f. *sulphurea*	CPlN EBee EPfP LRHS NBea SBra SPer WSHC
	- - 'John Clayton' **new**	SBra
	serotina 'Honeybush'	CDoC CPle MAsh MBlu MTis NHol NPri SBra SLim
	setifera	CBot CPle
	- 'Daphnis'	EPfP
	similis var. *delavayi* ♀ H4	CBot CPlN CRHN CSPN CSam EBee EPfP EPla IArd LRHS MAsh MLan MRav NBea NSti SBra SDix SLPl SPla WCru WGwG WPGP WPen WSHC
	'Simonet'	SBra
	splendida	CBot SBra WSHC
	standishii	CBcs CSBt CTri EBee EHol MGos MRav SPer WDin WFar WHCG WRha WWin
	- 'Budapest'	MBlu MGos
	'Stone Green'	NPro SPla
§	*subequalis* **new**	CFil
§	*syringantha*	More than 30 suppliers
	'Grandiflora'	GQui
	tatarica	CFai CWib MRav MWhi SLon WFar WHCG WTel WWin
	- 'Alba'	CFai MTed
	- 'Arnold Red'	CBcs CBot EBee ELan EPfP EWTr MBlu MHer NBlu SGar WDin WTel
	- 'Hack's Red'	CBcs CWib EBee EPfP MRav SDes SPer WDin WFar WHCG WWeb
§	- 'Zabelii'	EBee EPfP MGos
	x *tellmanniana*	More than 30 suppliers
	- 'Joan Sayer'	EBre MBNS MBri MGos SBra SLim WBcn WCFE WCru WWeb
	thibetica	GIBF MBlu SPer WFar
	tragophylla ♀ H4	CBcs CDoC CPlN EBee ELan EPfP EPla GCal GIBF LHop LRHS MAsh MBNS MBlu MBri NSti SBra SLim SPer SSpi SSta WCru WDin WSHC WWeb
	- 'Maurice Foster'	EBee GCal SBra SMad
*	- 'Pharoah's Trumpet'	ERea LRHS MAsh WBcn
	trichosantha	GIBF
	var. *acutiuscula* **new**	
	vesicaria	CPle
	webbiana	ELan
	x *xylosteoides*	MRav WFar
	- 'Clavey's Dwarf'	CPLG MBlu MGos NBrk SLPl
	- 'Miniglobe'	ESis NPro
	xylosteum	EWTr

Lopezia (Onagraceae)

racemosa	CSpe SHFr

Lophomyrtus (Myrtaceae)

§	*bullata*	CAbP CHEx CTrC EBee ECou GQui IDee SPer WCHb
	- 'Matai Bay'	CBcs CTrC EBee
	'Gloriosa' (v)	CAbP CDoC CPle CTrC LAst MAsh SBrw WCHb WWeb
§	*obcordata*	SSpi
§	x *ralphii*	LAst WCHb WPic
§	- 'Kathryn'	CBcs CDoC CPLG CPle CTrC EBee WCHb WSHC
	- 'Little Star' (v)	CAbP CBcs LRHS MAsh WPat WWeb
I	- 'Multicolor' (v)	CTrC EBee
	- 'Pixie'	CAbP CDoC CTrC SBrw WPat
	- 'Red Dragon'	CTrC EBee WPat
	- 'Traversii' (v)	LRHS SMur WWeb
	- 'Variegata' (v)	EBre
	'Red Wing' **new**	WWeb
	'Tricolor' (v)	CPle

Lophospermum (Scrophulariaceae)

§	*erubescens* ♀ H2-3	CBot CBri CHEx CHal CRHN MSte MTis SMur SYvo
	- 'Bridal Bouquet' **new**	CPla
§	'Red Dragon'	CPla CSpe SGar SYvo
§	*scandens*	CBcs CRHN ELan SMur
§	- 'Pink Ice'	LRHS SOWG

loquat see *Eriobotrya japonica*

Loropetalum (Hamamelidaceae)

	chinense	CFil CMCN SSpi
	- 'Ming Dynasty'	SBrw
	- f. *rubrum*	CFil SLon WPGP
	- - 'Blush'	CFil WBcn WPGP
	- - 'Fire Dance'	CDoC CFai CPMA SBrw SSpi WCot
I	- - 'Zhuzhou Fuchsia'	CMCN

Lotononis (Papilionaceae)

pulchella	SPlb

Lotus (Papilionaceae)

	berthelotii	CFee CHEx CHal CSpe ECtt ELan ERca ESlt MOak NBlu SChu SPar SPet SPoG
	- deep red ♀ H1+3	LIck
	- x *maculatus* ♀ H113	CSpe WIvy
	corniculatus	CArn CKin GWCH MBow MCoo MHer NLap NLan NSco SIde WBri
	- 'Plenus' (d)	EPot MTho WAlt WPer
	creticus **new**	SHFr
§	*hirsutus* ♀ H3-4	More than 30 suppliers
	- 'Brimstone' (v)	ECtt EPPr LHop LRHS MCCP SBrw SPar SPer SPla SVil WBro WWeb
	- dwarf	LHop
	- 'Lois'	EBee
	maculatus	CSpe ESlt NPri SHFr SOWG SPet WIvy
	maritimus	CPLG EBee EWll LPhx MOne MWgw SHFr SRot WWin
	mascaensis hort.	see *L. sessilifolius*
	pedunculatus	see *L. uliginosus*
	pentaphyllus	GCal
	subsp. *herbaceus*	
§	- subsp. *pentaphyllus*	EChP
§	*sessilifolius*	ERea
	suffruticosus	see *L. pentaphyllus* subsp. *pentaphyllus*
	tetragonolobus	SRot WHer

§ *uliginosus*	MGas NMir NSco

lovage see *Levisticum officinale*

Luculia (Rubiaceae)

grandifolia	LRHS SOWG
gratissima 'Rosea'	LRHS

Ludwigia (Onagraceae)

grandiflora	WMAq WWpP
palustris	SBHF
uruguayensis	LPBA

Luetkea (Rosaceae)

pectinata	EBee GDra NRya WAbe

Luma (Myrtaceae)

§ *apiculata* ♀ H3	More than 30 suppliers
§ - 'Glanleam Gold' (v) ♀ H3	More than 30 suppliers
- 'Variegata' (v)	CMHG CTri ISea SAga SLim WCru WWye
§ *chequen*	CBcs CFee EBee GGar IDee MHer NCWG WCHb WCwm WJek

Lunaria (Brassicaceae)

§ *annua*	GWCH MBow MWgw SIde SWat WHer
- var. *albiflora* ♀ H4	MWgw NBir SIde SWat WCer WCot
I - - 'Alba Variegata' (v)	CCge CSpe EBla EMon MCAu MFir MGGn MHer WCot
- 'Munstead Purple'	EBla
* - 'Stella'	WHen
- 'Variegata' (v)	CHar EBla IBlr MCAu MCCP MTho NBid NBir SWat WCot WEas WHer WSan
- violet	NBir WFar
biennis	see *L. annua*
rediviva	CBos CFwr CSpe EBee EBre ECGP ECha EMon EPla GCal GGar GKir GLil IBlr LPhx LRHS MBct NBid NChi NPer NSti SSpi SUsu WCot WEas WFar WHen WHer WPGP

Lupinus ✿ (Papilionaceae)

'African Sunset'	CWCL
'Alan Titchmarsh'	MWoo
albifrons	EBee MWgw SIgm
'Amber Glow'	CWCL
'Anne Gregg'	MWoo
'Approaching Storm'	SMrm
'Apricot Spire'	CWCL
arboreus ♀ H4	More than 30 suppliers
- *albus*	CSpe WBry WCom
- 'Barton on Sea'	CFwr CNat MAnH MWrn NLar
- blue	CBri CBrm CHar CMea CWes CWib ECGP ERou MAnH MCCP MPRe MTis MWrn NLar SMac SPer SPlb WBry WFar WHer WMoo WWeb
- 'Blue Boy'	CFwr
- cream	ECGP NLon SMac
- 'Mauve Queen'	CBri CHEx MAvo SUsu
- mixed	SMac
- prostrate **new**	CFwr
- 'Snow Queen'	CBrm CTCP MCCP MWrn
- 'Sulphur Yellow'	CBri CHEx ERou WHil
- white	MAnH
arcticus	CDes EBee WPGP
'Aston Villa'	CWCL MWoo
'Baby Doll' **new**	CWCL
Band of Nobles Series ♀ H4	CBri ECtt SSth WFar
'Barnsdale'	MWoo
'Beryl, Viscountess Cowdray'	GBuc

'Bishop's Tipple'	CWCL EWes
'Blue Moon'	CWCL
'Blue Streak'	CWCL
'Blueberry Pie'	CWCL
'Cashmere Cream' **new**	CWCL
chamissonis	CAbb CFwr CPla CSpe CStr EBee EChP EHrv EMan EWes LHop LRHS MTho MTis MWrn SDry SGar SMrm SPer WCom WFTG WFar
'Chandelier'	CBri CHad CSBt CTri EBre ECtt ELan EPfP ERou EWTr GAbr GKir LRHS MBri MCAu MWgw NMir NPPs NVic SMer SPer SRPl WFar WHen WPer WRHF
'Chelsea Pensioner'	MWoo
'Cherry Belle' **new**	CWCL
'Copperlight'	CWCL
'Deborah Woodfield'	MWoo
'Desert Sun'	CWCL
'Dolly Mixture'	CWCL
'Dorset Cream'	MWoo
Dwarf Gallery hybrids	ENot GKir LIck
'Dwarf Lulu'	see *L.* 'Lulu'
'Esmerelder'	MWoo
Gallery Series	COIW CSBt EBre SCoo SPlb WFar WLRN
- 'Gallery Blue'	ECtt EPfP MWrn NLar NLon NNor NPri SCoo SPer WHil WWeb
- 'Gallery Pink'	EPfP LRHS MPWC NBlu NLar NPri SCoo SPer SPla WBry WHil
- 'Gallery Red'	ECtt EPfP LRHS MWrn NLar NPri SCoo SPer SPla WBry WHil WWeb
- 'Gallery Rose' **new**	NLon
- 'Gallery White'	EPfP LPVe LRHS MWrn NBlu NLar NPri SCoo SPer SPla WHil
- 'Gallery Yellow'	ECtt EPfP LRHS NLar NLon NPri SCoo SPer SPla WHil WWeb
'Garden Gnome'	WPer
'Helen Sharman'	MWoo
'Household Brigade'	MWoo
'Judith Chalmers'	MWoo
'Kayleigh Ann Savage'	MWoo
'Lady Penelope'	CWCL
lepidus	EMan
- var. *lobbii*	SIgm
- var. *sellulus*	SIgm
'Little Eugenie'	MWoo
littoralis	EMan GDra SIgm WPer
'Lollipop'	CWCL
longifolius	EBee
§ 'Lulu'	CBri COtt CSam EBre EChP ECtt ENot LRHS MRav NPPs SPer WFar WMoo
microcarpus	EBee
Minarette Group	ECtt LRHS MBri SPet SRms WFar WGor
'Misty'	MWoo
mutabilis	IIve
'My Castle'	CSBt CTri EBre ECtt ELan EPfP ERou EWTr GAbr GKir GLil LRHS MBow MBri MCAu MRav MWgw NBlu NMir NOak NVic SMer SPer WFar WHen WPer
'Nigel Colborn'	MWoo
'Noble Maiden' (Band of Nobles Series)	CSBt EBre ECtt ELan EPfP ERou EWTr GAbr GKir GLil LRHS MBow MBri MCAu MWgw NMir NOak NPPs NVic SMer SPer WFar WHen WPer WRHF
nootkatensis	EBee
'Olive Tolley'	MWoo
'Pagoda Prince'	CWCL
'Pam Ayres'	MWoo

'Party Dress'	MWoo
perennis	CAgr EBee ECGN
'Pink Cadillac' **new**	CWCL
'Plum Duff'	CWCL
'Plummy Blue' **new**	EMan
'Poached Salmon'	SMrm
'Polar Princess'	CWCL ERou EWes MGrG SWat
polyphyllus	EBee WOut
'Pope John Paul'	MWoo
'Queen of Hearts'	CWCL
'Red Arrow'	CWCL
x *regalis* 'Morello	WElm
Cherry' **new**	
'Rote Flamme'	EWes LPVe MPWC
'Royal Wedding'	MWoo
Russell hybrids	COlW CSBt CSam ELan ENot EPfP
	GKir LHop MHer SPet SPlb SRms
	WFar WMnd
'Sand Pink'	EWes
sericeus	EMan
'Sherbert Dip'	CWCL
'Silk Rain' **new**	CWCL
'Snowgoose'	CWCL
'Storm'	CWCL
'Stuart Ogg V.M.H.'	MWoo
'Sunset'	MWoo
'Terracotta' **new**	CWCL
'The Chatelaine'	CBri CHad CSBt EBre ECtt ELan
(Band of Nobles Series)	EPfP ERou GKir GLil LRHS MBow
	MBri MCAu MRav MWgw NLon
	NMir SMer SPer WFar WHen WHil
	WMoo WPer
'The Governor'	CBri CSBt CTri EBre ECtt ELan
(Band of Nobles Series)	EPfP ERou GAbr GKir GLil LPVe
	LRHS MBow MBri MCAu MRav
	MWgw NMir NVic SMer SPer SPla
	WFar WMoo WPer
'The Page'	CBri EBre ELan EMan EPfP ERou
(Band of Nobles Series)	LRHS MBri MRav MWgw NMir
	SMer SPer WFar WHil WMoo WPer
'Thundercloud'	CHad CPlt SMrm
'Troop the Colour'	MWoo
variicolor	CHid CSpe SIgm SSpi
versicolor	EBee EMan LDai LGro MCCP MEHN
	MHer MLLN MLwd SGar SMad
	WBVN WBea WBry WPGP WPrP
'Windermere'	MWoo

Luzula (*Juncaceae*)

from New Guinea	EBee EWes
alpinopilosa	CBig EPPr GBin
banksiana	CElw
var. *rhadina* **new**	
x *borreri* **new**	EPPr
- 'Botany Bay' (v)	ECtt EPPr EPla GBin
campestris	CKin
canariensis	CFwr WDyG WWye
forsteri	CBrm EPPr EVFa
lactea	EMon EPGN EPPr LRHS
luzuloides	CBig WPer
- 'Schneehäschen'	EBee EMan EMon EPPr GBin GCal
	MWgw WPrP WWpP
maxima	see *L. sylvatica*
multiflora	EBee
nivea	More than 30 suppliers
pilosa	EPla GCal IBlr
pumila	ESis
purpureosplendens	CElw
'Ruby Stiletto' **new**	MAvo
rufa	CTrC ECou
§ *sylvatica*	CKin CRow CSWP CTrC EFou
	EPPr EPfP EPla GDea GKir GOrn
	MBow MFir MHdf MLLN MMoz

	MRav NBro NOrc SDes SPar SPer
	WDin WFar WHer WPGP WShi
- 'A. Rutherford'	see *L. sylvatica* 'Taggart's Cream'
- 'Aurea'	More than 30 suppliers
- 'Aureomarginata'	see *L. sylvatica* 'Marginata'
I - 'Auslese'	CBig EBee EPPr GBin LRHS WMoo
- 'Bromel' **new**	CRez
- 'Hohe Tatra'	More than 30 suppliers
§ - 'Marginata' (v)	More than 30 suppliers
* - f. *nova*	EPPr
- 'Select'	CTrC
§ - 'Taggart's Cream' (v)	CElw CRez CRow EBee EHoe
	EMar EMon EPla EVFa LRHS NBid
	WBea WDyG WLeb WMoo WPGP
- 'Tauernpass'	CBgR CCol EBee EHoe EMon
	EPPr EPla GCal LRHS NBea NBid
	NHol WPrP
- 'Wäldler'	EHoe EPPr LRHS NHol
- 'Waulkmill Bay'	SLPl
ulophylla	CBig CBod CFir CTrC EBee ECou
	EGoo EMan EPPr ESis GBin GBuc
	GDra MDCh NWCA

Luzuriaga (*Philesiaceae*)

radicans	CFee EBee ERos IBlr WCot WCru
	WFar WSHC
- MK 92	SSpi

x Lycene (*Caryophyllaceae*)

§ *kubotae*	EBee

Lychnis (*Caryophyllaceae*)

alpina	CMHG EBee EMlt EPfP GDra
	GIBF GKir GTou NBln NLon NPri
	NVic SRPl WBea WPer WWal
- 'Alba'	GTou NBir
- compact	GTou
- dark-flowered **new**	GKev
- 'Rosea'	NBir
- 'Snow Flurry'	EMlt NLar
x *arkwrightii* 'Orange	LAst WWeb
Zwerg' **new**	
§ x *arkwrightii*	EBee EBre ECha ELan LBee NNor
	SRot WAbe WBea WFar
- 'Vesuvius'	CBcs ENot EPfP EPla GKir LAst
	LPVe LRHS MHer MNrw MRav
	MTis NBir NBlu SDes SGar SPer
	SRms STes SWal WPer
chalcedonica ♀ H4	More than 30 suppliers
- var. *albiflora*	CM&M EBee ECha IBlr LAst LRHS
	MBri MWgw NBid NBro NLon
	NOak NSti SPer WCer WFar
	WHen WMoo WPer
- - 'Snow White'	EWll
- apricot	MBro NBid WBry WHrl
- 'Carnea'	GCal LBuc LPVe LRHS MFir WBea
	WHil
- 'Dusky Salmon'	ITer MDKP MLwd WElm WWpP
- 'Flore Pleno' (d)	CMil EBee ECha ELan ERou GBuc
	GCal GKir IFro MCCP MLLN
	MOne NLar NPri NSti WCot WFar
- 'Morgenrot'	MCCP NLar WBea
- 'Pinkie'	EBee ELan SBod WFTG
- 'Rauhreif'	WBea
- 'Rosea'	CSam EBee EBre EMan EPfP GKir
	LIck LRHS NBir STes WCer WFar
	WHen WHrl WMoo WPer
* - 'Salmonea'	CM&M EBee GBri LAst LPio MBri
	MTis NBir SPer SRms
- salmon-pink	COlW WWhi
- 'Summer Sparkle'	SWal
cognata	CDes EBee
- B&SWJ 4234	WCru

§ ***coronaria*** ♀ H4 — More than 30 suppliers
  - MESE 356 — EBee
  - 'Abbotswood Rose' — see *L* x *walkeri* 'Abbotswood Rose'
  - 'Alba' ♀ H4 — CStr ECha EFou EHoe ELan EPfP ERou LHrt LPio LRHS MBNS MBow MBri MBro MCAu NBid NBir NOak NOrc SAga SGar SPar SPer SRms WFar WHer WPGP WPer WWin

I   - 'Alba Variegata' (v) — MCCP
  - 'Angel's Blush' — CBri EBee EMan LHop LRHS MRav NBir SMac SPer SRPl WFTG WPer WRHF WRha WRus WWal
  - Atrosanguinea Group — CBre EBee EFou EMan ERou IBlr LBBr LHop LPio LRHS MPWC MRav NCot NPri SPer WPer
  - 'Cerise' — MArl NBir WBry
  - 'Flottbek' — MOne NCat NLar
  - 'Hutchinson's Cream' (v) — EMan EMon MCAu NPro WCot
  - Oculata Group — CSpe EBee EGoo ERou GKir IBlr MFir MTho NOak NPPs NPri SPlb WCer WFar WHen WHer WPer

coronata new — SBla
§ - var. ***sieboldii*** — EBee WBar WSan
dioica — see *Silene dioica*
flos-cuculi — CArn CKin CNic CSam EBee EBre EHon EMFW GDra LPBA MBow MHer MSal MSta NLan NMir SGar WHen WHer WMAq WMoo WWpP
  - var. ***albiflora*** — CBre CSam ECoo EPar GDea MLLN NBro WCHb WHer
  - 'Nana' — CNic CSpe EDAr EMar EMlt GAbr MLwd NRya WBea WCot WPat WPer WWeb WWin
flos-jovis ♀ H4 — EBee EPfP EWTr IGor LPVe MFir MTis NOak SMer SRms WLRN WPer
  - 'Hort's Variety' — ERou GKir MRav NSti SBla SUsu WBea
  - 'Minor' — see *L.* *flos-jovis* 'Nana'
§ - 'Nana' — NBid NPro NWCA WCom
  - 'Peggy' — CM&M EBee ERou MCCP NLar
fulgens — EBee
x ***haageana*** — EBee LAst LRHS NWCA SAga SIng SRms
kubotae — see x *Lycene kubotae*
lagascae — see *Petrocoptis pyrenaica* subsp. *glaucifolia*
miqueliana — WMoo
  - 'Variegated Lacy Red' (v) — WCot
'Molten Lava' — CFir GMaP LPVe LRHS NArg NOrc NPro SDes WMoo WPer WWeb
nutans — MSal
preslii minor — EBee
sibirica new — EBee
* ***sikkimensis*** — EBee
'Terry's Pink' — EBee MLLN NLar WFar
§ ***viscaria*** — CArn CElw ECha GIBF IGor LDai MSal NCiC NFor SCro SGar WBea WHer WMoo
  - ***alba*** — EBee ECha GCal MCCP MLLN NBro WRha WWeb
  - ***alpina*** — see *L. viscaria*
  - subsp. ***atropurpurea*** — CBri EBee NLon WBea
  - 'Feuer' — NLar WLRN WMoo
  - 'Firebird' — EWes NBur WWpP
  - 'Plena' (d) — EChP MDun MInt NPSI SUsu WTin
  - 'Schnee' — EMar EWTr
  - 'Snowbird' — WWpP
  - 'Splendens' — EPfP
  - 'Splendens Plena' (d) ♀ H4 — EBee ECha GMac MArl MBri MWgw NBro NLon WBea WEas WFar
  - 'White Cloud' new — MSph
§ x ***walkeri*** 'Abbotswood Rose' ♀ H4 — GBuc

wilfordii — CFir EBee MLLN MTis SHar
§ ***yunnanensis*** — CSam EBee GBuc GKev MSte NBid NHol SIng WBea WMoo WPer
  - ***alba*** — see *L. yunnanensis*

Lycianthes (Solanaceae)
rantonnetii — see *Solanum rantonnetii*

Lycium (Solanaceae)
barbarum — IIve NBlu SMad
chinense — CArn

Lycopodium (Lycopodiaceae)
clavatum — GPoy

Lycopsis see *Anchusa*

Lycopus (Lamiaceae)
americanus — EBee GPoy MSal
europaeus — CArn ELau GBar GPoy MChe MHer MSal WBri WGwG WHer WJek WWye
lucidus new — MSal
virginicus — CFwr COld MSal SDys WWye

Lycoris (Amaryllidaceae)
albiflora — WCot
aurea — EBee EBot ETub LRHS
chinensis new — EBee
haywardii new — WCot
longituba — EBee
radiata — CStu EBee EBot LRHS
sanguinea new — EBee

Lygodium (Schizaeaceae)
japonicum — WRic
§ ***microphyllum*** — NMar
scandens — see *L. microphyllum*

Lygos (Papilionaceae)
monosperma new — SSpi
sphaerocarpa — see *Retama sphaerocarpa*

Lyonia (Ericaceae)
ligustrina — LRHS SMur

Lyonothamnus (Rosaceae)
floribundus — CAbb SAPC SArc SIgm SMad SSpi
  subsp. ***aspleniifolius*** — WCru WFar WPGP

Lysichiton (Araceae)
americanus ♀ H4 — More than 30 suppliers
camtschatcensis ♀ H4 — CBcs CBen CLAP CRow CWat EBee ECha EHon ELan EMFW EPar EPfP LPBA MDun MSta NOrc NPer SDes SMad SMrm SPer SSpi SWat WCot WFar WPnP
  - x ***americanus*** — SSpi

Lysimachia ✿ (Primulaceae)
§ ***atropurpurea*** — CArn CBri CHal CHar CSpe ECGN EChP EGle ELan EShb EWTr GIBF LHop LRHS MCCP MGrG MHer MNrw NPri SMad STes SUsu WCot WFar WMoo WPGP WPer WRos WSan
  - 'Beaujolais' — MSPs NPPs WSan WWeb WWpP
  - 'Geronimo' — CSpe
barystachys — CHea CRow EBee EBlw EBre EVFa GMac MAnH MRav SMac SMer WCot WFar
candida new — EBee
ciliata — CMHG CRow EBee ECha EFer

	EHoe ELan EMar EPPr EPar GMac
	MBri MCAu MFir MNrw NArg
	NGdn NSti SChu WBea WCot
	WEas WFar WMnd WPer WWin
§ - 'Firecracker' ♀ H4	More than 30 suppliers
- 'Purpurea'	see L. ciliata 'Firecracker'
clethroides ♀ H4	More than 30 suppliers
- 'Geisha' (v) new	WCot
- 'Lady Jane'	NBur SRms
§ *congestiflora*	LPVe MOak NPer SHFr SPet WLRN
- 'Outback Sunset' PBR (v)	ECtt LRHS MOak NPri WCot
	WGwG WLRN WWol
decurrens	EBee
- JCA 4.542.500	WCot
ephemerum	More than 30 suppliers
fortunei	EBee SHel SMac WCot
henryi	EWes GBuc MOak
hybrida new	EBee WCot
japonica	CRow CStu EBee GBuc MTho
var. *minutissima*	MWod SIng SRot WPer
lichiangensis	CFir CSam EBre EMFP EMan GKir
	GSki MLLN NArg NCot SHFr
	WMoo WPer WPnP
lyssii	see L. congestiflora
mauritiana	CSpe EBee EMan MWrn WWpP
melampyroides new	EBee
minoricensis	CArn CMGP EBee EEls EHrv ELan
	EMan EPri MAnH STes SWat WHer
	WLeb WPer WWin WWpP
nemorum	EFer WPer
- 'Little Sun'	WAlt
- 'Pale Star'	CBre WAlt
nummularia	CBen CHal COlW CSBt CTri CWat
	EBre ECtt EHon EPfP GPoy LPBA
	MBar MBow MBri MWgw NFor SHFr
	SWat WCot WGwG WWpP WWye
- 'Aurea' ♀ H4	More than 30 suppliers
paridiformis new	EBee
pseudohenryi	EBee
punctata misapplied	see L. verticillaris
punctata L.	More than 30 suppliers
§ - 'Alexander' (v)	More than 30 suppliers
- 'Gaulthier Brousse' new	WCot
- 'Golden Glory' (v)	WCot
- 'Ivy Maclean' (v)	EBee EMan WCot
- 'Senior'	EMil
‡ - 'Snow Lady'	WCot
- 'Sunspot'	EBee WCot
- 'Variegata'	see L. punctata 'Alexander'
- *verticillata*	see L. verticillaris
serpyllifolia	ECtt SHFr
thyrsiflora	EBee EHon EMFW MSta NPer SBHF
	SWat WCot WHer WMAq WWpP
§ *verticillaris*	WBea WCot
vulgaris	CArn EHon GDea LPBA MBow
	SIde WBWf WCot WFar WMoo
	WPer WWpP WWye
- subsp. *davurica*	WCot
yunnanensis new	CElw CHar EBee EChP EMan
	GIBF GMac MAnH MDKP MTis
	MWrn WCot WPrP WWpP

Lysionotus (Gesneriaceae)

pauciflorus	ETow GCrs
- B&SWJ 189	WCru
- B&SWJ 303	WCru
- B&SWJ 335	WCru

Lythrum (Lythraceae)

alatum	EBee WSan
anceps new	NLar
salicaria	More than 30 suppliers
- 'Blush' ♀ H4	More than 30 suppliers

- 'Brightness'	EBee NArg WHil
§ - 'Feuerkerze' ♀ H4	More than 30 suppliers
- Firecandle	see L. salicaria 'Feuerkerze'
- 'Florarose'	NCat
- 'Happy'	EBee SChu SMrm
- 'Lady Sackville'	CBos EBee GBuc GMaP LRHS MBNS
	NCat SSvw SUsu WTMC WTel
- 'Morden Pink'	CFwr EBee EGle LPhx LRHS MBri
	MSte WBry WFar
- 'Prichard's Variety' new	EBee
- 'Robert'	More than 30 suppliers
- 'Rose'	ELan MWgw NBir
- 'Rosencaule'	EBee NCat
- 'Stichflamme'	NCat
- 'Swirl' new	EFou
- 'The Beacon'	CMHG EBee EMan GCal SRms
- Ulverscroft form	MTed
- 'Zigeunerblut'	CMHG CPlt CRDP EBee EGle
	EMan LPhx MRav MSte SAga
	SMrm SWat WAul WRus
virgatum	CMHG LPhx NCat SMHy SMrm
	SOkh
- 'Dropmore Purple'	CRDP CSBt EBee EFou EPPr ERou
	LHop LPhx LRHS MBri MCAu
	MSte SOkh WFar WWpP
- 'Rose Queen'	CBos ECha EMan MRav WPer
- 'Rosy Gem'	CM&M EBee EBlw ECtt EPfP GKir
	GMac MBNS MFir MWat MWgw
	NBid NBlu NBro NOak SDes SMer
	SRms SWal WBea WFar WHil
	WHoo WPer WViv WWpP
- 'The Rocket'	CM&M CTri EBee EChP EGle
	EPfP ERou LAst LRHS NCat NSti
	SMer SPer WWin

Lytocaryum (Arecaceae)
§ *weddellianum* ♀ H1	LPal MBri

M

Maackia (Papilionaceae)
amurensis	CDes CMCN CPle EBee ELan EPfP
	SBrw WDVN WNor WSHC
- var. *buergeri*	CLnd GBin
chinensis	CMCN MBlu
fauriei	CPle

Macbridea (Lamiaceae)
caroliniana	CDes EBee

Macfadyena (Bignoniaceae)
uncata	SOWG
§ *unguis-cati*	CPlN CRHN CTCP

Machaeranthera (Asteraceae)
§ *bigelovii*	EBee EHyt
shastensis	EBee

Machaerina (Cyperaceae)
rubiginosa 'Variegata' (v)	CKno WCot

Machilus see Persea

Mackaya (Acanthaceae)
§ *bella* ♀ H1	CHll CSpe ERea EShb SOWG SYvo

Macleania (Ericaceae)
ericae new	WCot
insignis	CPlN

Macleaya (Papaveraceae)

cordata misapplied	see *Macleaya* x *kewensis*
§ **cordata** (Willd.) R. Br. ♀ H4	More than 30 suppliers
- 'Flamingo' ♀ H4	CPrp EBee ECha GCal SMrm SPar WWye
§ x **kewensis**	EBee MBro MTed WHoo WPGP
§ **microcarpa**	MAnH MGGn MGol NPSI SGar SWat WHer WSel
- 'Kelway's Coral Plume' ♀ H4	More than 30 suppliers
- 'Spetchley Ruby'	EMan LPhx NBir NDov WCot

Maclura (Moraceae)

pomifera	CBcs CFil CMCN CWib EGFP IDee SLon WDin WPGP
tricuspidata	CAgr EGFP

Macrodiervilla see *Weigela*

Macropiper (Piperaceae)

§ **excelsum**	CHEx ECou

Macrozamia (Zamiaceae)

communis	CBrP CRoM LPal WNor
diplomera	CBrP
dyeri	see *M. riedlei*
johnsonii	CBrP
lucida	CBrP
miquelii	CBrP LPal
moorei	CBrP CRoM CTrC LPal
mountperiensis	CBrP
§ **riedlei**	CBrP CRoM LPal
spiralis	CRoM

Madia (Asteraceae)

elegans	EMan NBur SWal

Magnolia ✿ (Magnoliaceae)

'Aashild Kalleberg' **new**	SSpi
acuminata	CBcs CMCN EPfP NBhm NPal
- 'Golden Glow'	CBcs CMHG
* - 'Kinju'	CEnd WPGP
- 'Koban Dori'	CBcs CFil CPMA CTho NPSI
§ - var. **subcordata**	LBuc WPGP
§ - - 'Miss Honeybee'	LRHS SSpi
'Advance' **new**	CPMA
'Albatross'	CBcs CDoC CEnd CTho SSpi
amoena	CBcs CTho WNor
- 'Multiogeca'	CBcs
'Ann' ♀ H4	CSdC CTrh SSpi
'Apollo'	CBcs CEnd CPMA NPSI SSpi
ashei	see *M. macrophylla* subsp. *ashei*
'Athene'	CBcs CMHG CPMA LRHS SSpi
'Atlas'	CBcs CEnd CMHG CPMA CTho EMil MGos SSpi WPGP
'Betty' ♀ H4	CBcs CDoC CLAP CSdC LNet LPan MGos SBrw SSta WDin WFar WLRN
'Big Dude'	CFil IArd SSpi WPGP
biondii	CBcs CFil NLar SSpi WNor WPGP
I 'Black Tulip' **new**	ENot LRHS MBri NPri
x **brooklynensis**	SSpi
'Daybreak'	
- 'Evamaria'	CTho
- 'Hattie Carthan'	WPGP
- 'Woodsman'	LBuc SBrw SSta
- 'Yellow Bird'	CEnd CMCN COtt CPMA CTho ENot EPfP LRHS MBlu MDun MGos MNes SLim SSpi SSta
'Butterflies'	CBcs CDoC CFai CFil CMHG CPMA CTho EPfP ISea LRHS MAsh

	MDun SSpi SSta WFar WPGP
'Caerhays Belle'	CBcs SSpi
'Caerhays Surprise'	CBcs CPMA
campbellii	CBcs CDul CFil CMCN CPMA CSam CTho ELan EPfP ISea LRHS MAsh MDun MNes SSpi WFar WPGP WPic
- Alba Group	CBcs CEnd CTho MGos SPer WFar WPGP
- - 'Strybing White'	CTho
- 'Betty Jessel'	CMHG CTho
- 'Darjeeling'	CBcs CTho EMil
- 'Lamellan Pink'	CTho
- 'Lamellan White'	CTho
- 'Landicla'	CTho
- subsp. **mollicomata**	CBcs CEnd CHEx CSam CTrw EPfP ISea WFar WHCr WPGP
- - 'Lanarth'	CBcs CEnd SSpi WBod
- - 'Maharanee' **new**	CBcs NPSI
- - 'Peter Borlase'	CDoC CTho
- (Raffillii Group) 'Charles Raffill'	CAbP CBcs CLnd ELan EMil EPfP MDun MGos MLan SHBN SKee SLim SPer SPoG SRPl WDin
- - 'Kew's Surprise'	CBcs CPMA
'Candy Cane'	SSpi
'Cecil Nice'	WPGP
'Charles Coates'	MDun
'Columbus'	CFil CPMA SSpi WPGP
'Coral Lake' **new**	MDun
cordata	see *M. acuminata* var. *subcordata*
- 'Miss Honeybee'	see *M. acuminata* var. *subcordata* 'Miss Honeybee'
cylindrica hort.	see *M.* 'Pegasus'
cylindrica Wilson	CMCN CPMA EPfP IArd LRHS SSpi
* 'Dan Quing'	LPan
'Dark Shadow'	WPGP
'David Clulow'	CBcs CPMA CTho SSpi
dawsoniana	CBcs CMCN
I - 'Chyverton Alba'	CTho
- 'Chyverton Red'	CTho SSpi
- 'Clarke'	CTho
delavayi	CBcs CBrP CFil CHEx CMCN EPfP GGGa LRHS SAPC SArc SSpi WPGP
§ **denudata** ♀ H3-4	CBcs CMCN CPMA CTho CTrw EMil EPfP IDee LPan LRHS MAsh NPSI SMur SPer SRPl SReu SSpi SSta WBod WDin WFar WNor
- 'Dubbel' **new**	CBcs
- 'Forrest's Pink'	CBcs
- 'Gere'	CBcs
- 'Yellow River'	LPan MDun NLar
'Elisa Odenwald'	CFil SSpi WPGP
'Elizabeth' ♀ H4	CDoC CEnd CFil CLAP CMCN CPMA CTho ELan EPfP GGGa ISea LAst LRHS MAsh MDun MGos MNes NHol SHBN SKee SPer SSpi SSta WPGP
'Fireglow'	CTho
'Frank Gladney'	CPMA CTho SSpi
'Frank's Masterpiece' **new**	MDun
fraseri AM	SSpi
'Full Eclipse'	CFil WPGP
'Galaxy' ♀ H4	CBcs CDoC CEnd CFil CLAP CSdC CTho EPfP IArd IMGH ISea LPan LRHS MBar MBri MGos MSte NBhm SKee SLdr SLim SSpi SSta WBod WBrE WDin WPGP
'George Henry Kern'	CBcs CDoC COtt EBee IArd ISea LRHS MAsh MBri MGos MSte NBlu SSpi SSta WBod WDin WFar WDin WPGP
globosa	CFil GGGa WFar WPGP
- from India	SSpi
'Gold Crown'	SSpi

'Gold Star'	CBcs CFil CPMA CTho EBee MBlu SSpi WBcn WPGP WWeb
'Golden Endeavour' **new**	MDun
'Golden Gift'	SSpi
grandiflora	CDul CHEx CMCN EBee EBre EPfP LAst LRHS MRav NBlu SAPC SArc SRPl WDin WFar WNor WOrn
- 'Edith Bogue'	CPMA ENot MRav WBVN
- 'Exmouth' ♀ H3-4	More than 30 suppliers
- 'Ferruginea'	CBcs EBee SLim SPar
- 'Galissonnière'	CBcs COtt EBee IMGH LPan LRHS MGos MRav NPSI SBrw SLim SPar SSpi WDin
I - 'Gallissonnière Nana'	LPan
- 'Goliath'	CBcs CDul CEnd CFil CHEx CSBt EBee ELan EPfP LNet SBrw SPar SPoG SSpi SSta WPGP
- 'Little Gem'	CDoC CPMA CPne EBee LRHS SSpi WBcn WGer WStI
- 'Nannetensis'	CPMA EBee SPoG
- 'Russet'	CPMA LNet
- 'Saint Mary'	CPMA
- 'Samuel Sommer'	CPMA SAPC SArc WGer WPGP
- 'Victoria' ♀ H3-4	CDoC CFil CPMA CTho EBee ELan EPfP ISea LHyd LRHS MAsh MBlu MBri SBrw SLim SPla SReu SSpi SSta WCwm WFar WPGP
'Hawk'	CFil WPGP
'Heaven Scent' ♀ H4	More than 30 suppliers
'Helen Fogg'	WPGP
heptapeta	see *M. denudata*
§ 'Hong Yur'	CEnd CPMA
'Hot Lips'	WPGP
hypoleuca	see *M. obovata* Thunb.
'Iolanthe'	CBcs CEnd CFil CMCN CMHG CPMA CSdC CTho ELan GKir LRHS MGos NBhm NHol SPer SSpi SSta WFar WPGP
'J.C.Williams' **new**	CDoC
'Jane' ♀ H4	CDoC COtt CSdC ELan EPfP LRHS MAsh MBri MGos NHol SBrw SLdr SPer SSta WGer
'Judy'	COtt
x *kewensis*	
'Wada's Memory' ♀ H4	CBcs CDoC CFil CLAP CMCN CMHG CPMA CTho ELan EPfP GKir LRHS MAsh MBri MSte SBrw SPer SSpi SSta WDin WFar
kobus	CBcs CDul CMCN CLnd CSBt CTho ENot EWTr IMGH LPan MDun NMoo SHBN SPer WBod WDin WFar WNor
- var. *borealis*	CPMA CTho
- 'Norman Gould'	see *M. stellata* 'Norman Gould'
'Lamellan Surprise'	CTho
'Leda'	SSpi
'Lilenny'	SSta
§ *liliiflora*	CTrw MBar
§ - 'Nigra' ♀ H4	CBcs CDoC CDul CWlb EBre ELan ENot EPfP EWTr LPan LRHS MGos MRav NBlu SBrw SHBN SLdr SLim SPer SPla SReu SSpi SSta WBod WDin WFar WOrn WStI
- 'Oldfield'	WPGP
* 'Limelight'	SSpi
x *loebneri*	CBcs LRHS WNor
- 'Ballerina'	CDoC COtt SBrw SSta
- 'Donna'	SSpi
- 'Leonard Messel' ♀ H4	More than 30 suppliers
- 'Merrill' ♀ H4	CBcs CFil CMCN CMHG CTho CTrh EBre ELan EPfP ISea LPan LRHS MAsh MBri MGos NHol SPer SReu SSpi SSta WBod WDin WPGP

- 'Snowdrift'	CMCN SSta
- 'Spring Snow'	CMCN
§ *lotungensis* **new**	SSpi
macrophylla	CBrP CFil CMCN EPfP IDee MBlu SAPC SArc SSpi WMul WNor WPGP
§ - subsp. *ashei*	SSpi WNor
'Manchu Fan'	CBcs CDoC CPMA CSdC EMil IArd SMur SSpi SSta
'Margaret Helen' **new**	CBcs CPMA
'Marj Gossler'	SSpi
'Marwood Spring'	CBcs CMHG CTho
'Maryland'	CFil CPMA SBrw SSpi SSta WPGP
'Milky Way' ♀ H4	CBcs CMHG CPMA CTho MGos NPSI SMur SSpi
'Nimbus'	CPMA SSpi
obovata Diels	see *M. officinalis*
§ *obovata* Thunb. ♀ H4	CFil CHEx CMCN CPMA CTho EPfP IDee IMGH MDun MLan NLar SHBN SPer SSpi SSta WDin WPGP
§ *officinalis*	CFil EPfP NLar WFar WPGP
- var. *biloba*	EPfP
§ 'Pegasus'	CEnd ISea SSpi
'Peppermint Stick'	CBcs CSdC MGos SKee SSta
'Peter Smithers'	CPMA CTho
'Phelan Bright'	CFil WPGP
'Phillip Tregunna'	CTho
'Pickard's Sundew'	see *M.* 'Sundew'
'Pink Goblet' **new**	MAsh
'Pinkie' ♀ H4	COtt LRHS MBri NLar SSpi SSta WGer
'Pirouette'	SSpi
'Princess Margaret'	CPMA SSpi
x *proctoriana*	CABP CDoC CFil EBee EPfP LRHS MAsh SPer WPGP
- 'Slavin's Snowy'	LRHS
quinquepeta	see *M. liliiflora*
'Randy'	COtt EPfP
'Raspberry Ice'	CDoC CEnd CLAP CMHG COtt CSdC CTho CTrw EPfP LRHS MAsh SSta WFar
'Ricki'	COtt CSdC EMil LBuc MBlu MBri MGos NBlu NLar SSta WFar
'Rouged Alabaster'	LRHS
'Royal Crown'	CDoC CSdC EMil NBhm SLim SSta
'Ruby'	CBcs CPMA MGos
salicifolia ♀ H3-4	CFil CMCN EPfP ISea LRHS MAsh SPer SSpi SSta
- 'Jermyns'	SSpi
sargentiana	CFil
- var. *robusta*	CBcs CBrd CEnd CLnd CMCN ELan EPfP IMGH ISea MDun MGos SPer SSpi SSta WDin WFar WPGP
- - 'Blood Moon'	SSpi
- - 'Multipetal'	CBrd
'Sayonara' ♀ H4	COtt CPMA EPfP SBrw SSpi WDin
'Schmetterling'	see *Magnolia* x *soulangeana* 'Pickard's Schmetterling'
'Serene'	CMHG CPMA SSpi SSta
'Shirazz' **new**	CPMA
sieboldii	CBcs CMCN CPMA ELan EMil EPfP GKir IMGH LPan MBar MBri MDun MGos MLan MWya NBlu SHBN SKee SLim SLon SPer SSpi SSta WBod WFar WNor WOrn
- B&SWJ 4127	WCru
- from Korea hardy selection	GGGa
- 'Colossus' **new**	SSpi
- 'Genesis' **new**	SSpi
- 'Michiko Renge' **new**	NLar
- subsp. *sinensis*	CBcs CDoC CMCN CPMA CSam CTho ELan EPfP GGGa GGar

IMGH MDun MWya SKee SPer SSpi
SSta WBod WCwm WDin WLRN
More than 30 suppliers

x *soulangeana*
§ - 'Alba' CBcs CDul CEnd CSBt ENot EPfP LPan LRHS MGos NBlu SBrw SLim SPer SSpi
- 'Alba Superba' see *M.* x *soulangeana* 'Alba'
- 'Alexandrina' CBcs EPfP LRHS MGos NLar
- 'Amabilis' COtt
- 'Brozzonii' ♀ H3-4 CDoC CMHG EPfP LRHS NLar SBrw SSpi
- 'Burgundy' Clarke CBcs CBot CDoC ISea LRHS SBrw SSta
- 'Darrell Dean' CTho WPGP
- 'Joe McDaniel' CDoC IArd SKee SSpi
- 'Lennei' ♀ H3-4 CBcs CDoC CEnd CMCN CMHG CSBt EPfP EWTr LPan LRHS MAsh MGos NHol NPri SBrw SHBN SLim SPer SRms SSta WFar WNor WOrn WPGP WStI
- 'Lennei Alba' ♀ H3-4 CDoC CMCN CSdC MMHG SLdr SSta WFar
- 'Nigra' see *M. liliiflora* 'Nigra'
- 'Pickard's Ruby' COtt IArd MDun
§ - 'Pickard's Schmetterling' CDoC CSdC SSta
- 'Pickard's Sundew' see *M.* 'Sundew'
- 'Picture' CDoC WDin
- Red Lucky see *M.* 'Hong Yur'
- 'Rubra' misapplied see *M.* x *soulangeana* 'Rustica Rubra'
§ - 'Rustica Rubra' ♀ H3-4 CBcs CDoC CMCN CPMA CSBt EBee EBre ELan EMui ENot EPfP IMGH LNet LPan LRHS MAsh MBri MDun SHBN SPer SReu SSpi SSta WDin WFar WPGP
- 'San José' CBcs LRHS MAsh MBri NLar SSpi SSta
- 'Sweet Sixteen' WPGP
- 'Verbanica' LRHS MAsh SSpi
- 'White Giant' SBrw WPGP
'Spectrum' CBcs CEnd CFil CPMA CSdC IArd MAsh MGos SSpi WPGP

sprengeri WNor WWes
- 'Copeland Court' CBcs CTho
- var. *diva* CBcs CEnd CFil SSpi WPGP
- - 'Burncoose' CBcs CDoC
- - 'Claret Cup' SSpi WBod WPGP
- - 'Lanhydrock' CFil CTho SSpi WPGP
- var. *elongata* COtt
- 'Eric Savill' CPMA CTho SSpi
'Star Wars' ♀ H4 CBcs CDoC CEnd CFil CPMA CSdC CTho EMil EPfP MAsh SBrw SMur SSpi SSta WPGP
'Stellar Acclaim' **new** MDun
§ *stellata* ♀ H4 More than 30 suppliers
- 'Centennial' CDoC MAsh MBri SSta
- 'Chrysanthemiflora' SSpi
- 'Jane Platt' MDun SSpi
- f. *keiskei* CEnd COtt CSdC
- 'King Rose' CBcs CDoC COtt CSdC EPfP LRHS MAsh MBri MSte SBrw SPer WBod
§ - 'Norman Gould' CDoC COtt EPfP MBri NLar SBrw SSta WDin
- 'Pink Perfection' **new** MDun
- 'Rosea' COtt ELan LRHS MDun MGos NLar SHBN WDin WWeb
I - 'Rosea Massey' **new** WFar
- 'Royal Star' CBcs CBrm CDoC CEnd CLAP CMCN CSam CTri CWSG ENot EPfP ISea LPan LRHS MAsh MBri MGos MRav NHol NPri SBrw SPer SSpi SSta WBrE WDin WHar WOrn WStI

- 'Waterlily' ♀ H4 CBcs CMCN ELan EMil EPfP GKir LAst LRHS MAsh SLim SPer SPla SSpi SSta WDin
'Summer Solstice' CPMA SSpi
'Sunburst' **new** MDun
'Sundance' CFil CPMA EMil MDun MGos NPSl WPGP
I 'Sundew' CBcs CDoC CMCN EBee EPfP IArd MGos SBrw SHBN SMrm WBVN WPGP
'Susan' ♀ H4 More than 30 suppliers
'Susanna van Veen' CBcs
x *thompsoniana* AM CMCN EPfP
- 'Olmenhof' SSpi
'Tiffany' WPGP
'Tina Durio' CDoC
'Todd Gresham' CPMA WPGP
'Tranquility' **new** MDun
'Treve Holman' CSdC
tripetala CBcs CHEx CLnd CMCN CPne EPfP IMGH LPan MBlu MLan NWea SHBN SMad SSpi SSta WCwm WDin WOrn WPGP
x *veitchii* CDoC CSBt EPfP SSpi SSta
- 'Isca' CTho
- 'Peter Veitch' CFil CTho SSta
virginiana CDul CMCN CPMA CPne CTho EBee EPfP SSpi WDin WPGP
- 'Havener' IArd IDee
- 'Henry Hicks' SSpi
'Vulcan' CBcs CEnd CMHG COtt CPMA CTho MDun
x *watsonii* see *Magnolia* x *wieseneri*
'White Chalice' **new** CPMA
§ x *wieseneri* CBcs CMCN CPMA ELan EPfP GKir ISea LRHS MAsh MBlu SPer SSpi SSta WFar
wilsonii ♀ H4 More than 30 suppliers
- 'Gwen Baker' CEnd
- 'Winelight' CFil
'Yellow Fever' CBcs CMHG CPMA CTho EMil ICrw MDun SMur SSta
'Yellow Lantern' CAbP CBcs CFil EPfP LRHS MAsh MBlu SSpi SSta WPGP WWeb

x *Mahoberberis* (Berberidaceae)

aquisargentii ENot EPfP GBin GEil GKir MRav NHol SHGC SLon WDin WFar WPat
'Dart's Treasure' EPla WFar
'Magic' MGos
miethkeana MBar SRms

Mahonia ✿ (Berberidaceae)

§ *aquifolium* CAgr CBcs CDul CSBt CTrG EBee ENot EWTr GKir LAst MBar MBri MGos MRav MWat NBlu NFor NWea SHBN SPer SPlb SReu WCFE WDin WFar WStI
- 'Apollo' ♀ H4 CMac EBee ELan EMil ENot EPfP GKir LRHS MAsh MBar MBri MGos MRav NBee NBlu NPri SCoo SHBN SMer SPer SReu SSta WDin WWeb
- 'Atropurpurea' CBcs ELan ENot EPfP EPla GKir LRHS MAsh NBee NLar SHBN SPer SPla WDin
* - 'Cosmo Crawl' MGos
- 'Fascicularis' see *M.* x *wagneri* 'Pinnacle'
- 'Green Ripple' EPfP MBri MGos NLar WBcn WFar
- 'Mirena' MGos
- 'Orange Flame' EPfP MBlu
- 'Smaragd' CBcs CDoC CMac EBee ELan

	ENot EPfP LRHS MBlu MGos MRav WHCG
- 'Versicolor'	MBlu
bealei	see *M. japonica* Bealei Group
confusa	CDoC CFil EPla NLar SSpi WBcn WCru WFar WPGP
eutriphylla	see *M. trifolia*
fortunei	EPla WBcn WSHC
fremontii	GCal SIgm
gracilipes	CFil MDun
haematocarpa	SIgm
japonica ♀ H4	More than 30 suppliers
§ - Bealei Group	CBcs CDul CSBt EBee EBre ELan EPfP EPla GKir LAst LRHS MAsh MBar MGos MRav NBlu NPer SLim SMer SPar SRPl WDin WFar WWeb
- 'Hiemalis'	see *M. japonica* 'Hivernant'
§ - 'Hivernant'	EPla MGos NBlu
x *lindsayae*	WPGP
lomariifolia ♀ H3	CBcs CBot CPLG ENot EPfP LRHS SAPC SArc SDry SPar SSpi WBor WSHC
x *media* 'Arthur Menzies'	EPla
- 'Buckland' ♀ H4	CAbP CBcs CDul CMac CSBt CSam CTrw CWSG EPfP ISea LAst LRHS MBri MDun NHol SPar SPer SRPl SRms WBod WPat WStI
- 'Charity'	More than 30 suppliers
- 'Charity's Sister'	EBee EPla MBri
- 'Faith'	EPla
- 'Lionel Fortescue' ♀ H4	CBcs CMac CSam CTrw CWSG EBee EBre ELan ENot EPfP EPla ISea LHop LRHS MAsh MBri MRav SLon SMad SPer SReu SSpi SSta WFar WHCG
- 'Underway' ♀ H4	CSam EBee EPfP EPla LRHS MAsh MBri SMur WWes
- 'Winter Sun' ♀ H4	More than 30 suppliers
nervosa	CBcs COtt CPLG EPfP EPla IDee MBlu NBee SBrw SPer WBcn WCru WPGP
pallida	CFil EBee EPla SIgm WPGP
N *pinnata*	EBee ENot EPfP EPla MBar
pumila	SSpi WCru
repens	EPla MWhi
- 'Rotundifolia'	EPla
russellii	CFil
x *savilliana*	CFil CWib EPla
§ *trifolia*	EPla
trifoliolata	EPfP
var. *glauca*	CEnd NLar
x *wagneri* 'Fireflame'	EPla
- 'Moseri'	EMil SSpi WPat
§ - 'Pinnacle' ♀ H4	ENot EPfP EPla EWTr LRHS MAsh MGos MLan NFor SBrw SMur SPer
- 'Sunset'	MBlu
- 'Undulata'	ENot EPfP MBlu SDix SPer SRms WHCG

Maianthemum (Convallariaceae)

bifolium	CAvo CDes CHid CPLG CRDP CRow EBee EMan EMon EPot GBuc LEur MDun MNrw MTho NBro NMen SRms WCru WPGP WPnP WTin WWye
- from Yakushima	EBee SOkd
§ - subsp. *kamtschaticum*	CAvo CCol CLAP CRDP CRow EPar GKir LBuc LEur LSyl SMac SUsu WCot WTin
- - B&SWJ 4360	WCru
* - - var. *minimum*	WCru
canadense	EBee GCal GKir NMen

dilatatum	see *M. bifolium* subsp. *kamtschaticum*

Maihuenia (Cactaceae)

poeppigii **new**	SPlb
- JCA 2.575.600	WCot

Maireana (Chenopodiaceae)

georgei **new**	SPlb

Malacothamnus (Malvaceae)

fremontii	EMan WLin
marrubioides **new**	EMan

Malephora (Aizoaceae)

crassa **new**	CTrC

Malpighia (Malpighiaceae)

coccigera	ESlt

Malus ✿ (Rosaceae)

§ 'Adirondack'	CDoC EPfP MAsh MBri MGos SKee
Admiration	see *Malus* 'Adirondack'
x *adstringens* 'Almey'	ECrN
- 'Hopa'	CLnd SCrf
- 'Simcoe'	CLnd MGos
'Aldenhamensis'	see *M.* x *purpurea* 'Aldenhamensis'
'Amberina' **new**	CLnd
* *arborescens*	CLnd CTho
x *atrosanguinea*	CLnd
§ - 'Gorgeous'	CCAT CDul CLnd COtt CWSG EBee ECrN GKir GTwe MAsh MBri MGos SCoo SCrf SKee SLim WDin WJas WOrn
baccata	CFil CLnd CMCN CTho GTwe NWea SEND WNor
- W 264	GIBF
- 'Dolgo'	CCAT CDoC CLnd COtt SKee
- 'Gracilis'	CWSG
- 'Lady Northcliffe'	CLnd SFam
- var. *mandshurica*	EPfP
- 'Street Parade'	MBri
aff *baccata*	NWea
- - MF 96058	SSpi
§ *bhutanica*	CMCN CTho EPfP GIBF SPer SRPl WHCr WNor
brevipes	CLnd CTho
'Butterball'	CLnd ECrN EPfP GKir LRHS MBlu SCoo SKee WDin WJas
* 'Cheal's Weeping'	ECrN LAst NBea
Coccinella =	WDin
'Courtarou'PBR **new**	
'Coralburst'	MBri
coronaria	
var. *dasycalyx*	CDoC CDul CLnd EBee ENot EPfP
'Charlottae' (d)	LRHS MAsh MBri MHFa SCrf SFam SPer
- 'Elk River'	MAsh SKee
- 'Nieuwlandiana'	GIBF
'Crimson Brilliant' **new**	CLnd
'Crittenden'	EBee ECrN ENot MRav
denticulata **new**	GIBF
* 'Directeur Moerlands'	CDoC EPfP GKir LRHS MBri MGos WDin WJas
domestica (F)	MGos
- 'Acme' (D)	SDea SKee
- 'Adams's Pearmain' (D)	CCAT CTho GKir GTwe LBuc LRHS SDea SFam SKee WJas
- 'Advance' (D)	SKee
- 'Akane' (D)	SDea

- 'Akerö' (D) **new** — SKee
§ - 'Alexander' (C) — SKee
- 'Alfriston' (C) — SKee
- 'Alkmene' (D) ♀ H4 — GTwe SDea SKee
- 'All Red Gravenstein' (D) — NRog
- 'Allen's Everlasting' (D) — GTwe SDea SKee
- 'Allington Pippin' (D) — CCVT CSBt CSam CTho CTri
  ECrN LRHS NRog SDea SKee WJas
- 'American Golden — CTho
  Russet' (D) **new**
- 'American Mother' — see *M. domestica* 'Mother'
- 'Anna Boelens' (D) — SDea
- 'Annie Elizabeth' (C) — CCAT CTho CWib ECrN GKir
  GTwe LRHS MBri SDea SFam
  SKee WJas
- 'Anniversary' (D) — SDea
- 'Api Rose' (D) — SKee WJas
- 'Ard Cairn Russet' (D) — GTwe SDea SKee
- 'Arkansas' (D) — SKee
- 'Aromatic Russet' (D) — SKee
- 'Arthur Turner' (C) ♀ H4 — CCVT CDoC EMui ENot GKir
  GTwe LBuc LRHS MGos MHFa
  NRog SCrf SDea SFam SKee WJas
- 'Ashmead's Kernel' — CCAT CSBt CTho CTri CWib EBre
  (D) ♀ H4 — ECrN EMui EPfP ERea GKir GTwe
  LBuc LRHS MRav MWat NRog NWea
  SCrf SDea SFam SKee WHar WJas
- 'Ashton Bitter' (Cider) — CCAT CCVT CTho GTwe SFam
- 'Ashton Brown — CCAT CTho
  Jersey' (Cider)
- 'Autumn Pearmain' (D) — CTho SDea WJas
- 'Backwell Red' (Cider) — CCAT
- 'Baker's Delicious' (D) — ECrN SDea SKee
- 'Ball's Bittersweet' — CCAT CTho
  (Cider)
- 'Ballyfatten' (C) **new** — CTho
- 'Balsam' — see *M. domestica* 'Green Balsam'
- 'Banns' (D) — SKee
- 'Barnack Beauty' (D) — CTho SKee
- 'Barnack Orange' (D) — SKee
- 'Barnhill Beauty' **new** — CTho
- 'Baron Wood' (C) **new** — SKee
- 'Baumann's Reinette' (D) — SKee
- 'Baxter's Pearmain' (C/D) — SKee
- 'Beauty of Bath' (D) — CCAT CCVT CDoC CTho CTri
  CWib ECrN GKir GTwe LBuc
  LRHS MHFa NRog SCrf SDea
  SFam SKee WJas
- 'Beauty of Bedford' (D) — SKee
- 'Beauty of Hants' (D) — ECrN SKee
- 'Beauty of Kent' (C) — SDea SKee
- 'Beauty of Moray' (C) — SKee
- 'Bedwyn Beauty' (C) — CTho
- 'Beeley Pippin' (D) — GTwe SDea SKee
- 'Belfleur Kitaika' (D) — SKee
- 'Bell Apple' (Cider/C) — CCAT CTho
- 'Belle de Boskoop' — CCAT CTho GTwe NRog SDea SKee
  (C/D) ♀ H4
- 'Belle Flavoise' — SKee
- 'Belvoir Seedling' — SKee
  (D/C) **new**
- 'Bembridge Beauty' (F) — SDea
- 'Ben's Red' (D) — CCAT CEnd CTho SKee
- 'Bess Pool' (D) — SDea SFam SKee WJas
- 'Bewley Down Pippin' — see *M. domestica* 'Crimson King'
- 'Bickington Grey' — CTho
  (Cider) **new**
- 'Billy Down Pippin' (F) — CTho
- 'Bismarck' (C) — CCAT CTho NRog SKee
- 'Black Dabinett' (Cider) — CCAT CTho
- 'Black Tom Putt' (C/D) — CTho
- 'Blackamore — CTho
  Red' (C) **new**

- 'Blenheim Orange' — CCAT CCVT CDoC CSBt CTho
  (C/D) ♀ H4 — CTri CWib ECrN EMui ENot GKir
  GTwe LBuc LRHS MBri MHFa
  MWat NRog SCrf SDea SFam SKee
  SPer WJas
- 'Blenheim Red' (C/D) — see *M. domestica* 'Red Blenheim'
- 'Bloody Butcher' — CTho
  (C) **new**
- 'Bloody Ploughman' (D) — GKir SKee
- 'Blue Pearmain' (D) — SDea SKee
- 'Blue Sweet' (Cider) — CTho
- Bolero = 'Tuscan'PBR — ENot LRHS MGos SDea
  (D/Ball)
- 'Bonum' (D/C) **new** — CTho
- 'Boston Russet' — see *M. domestica* 'Roxbury
  Russet'
- 'Bountiful' (C) — CCAT COtt CSBt CTri CWib ECrN
  EMui GKir GTwe LBuc LRHS MBri
  MGos MHFa SDea SKee WHar WStI
- 'Bow Hill Pippin' (D) — SKee
- 'Box Apple' (D) — SKee
- 'Braddick Nonpareil' (D) — SKee
- 'Braeburn' (D) — ECrN EMui SDea SKee
- 'Bramley's Seedling' — More than 30 suppliers
  (C) ♀ H4
- 'Bramley's Seedling' — SCoo SDea
  clone 20
- 'Bramshott Rectory' — SKee
  (D/C) **new**
- 'Bread Fruit' (C/D) — CEnd
- 'Breakwell's — CCAT CTho
  Seedling' (Cider)
- 'Breitling' (D) — SKee
- 'Bridgwater Pippin' (C) — CCAT CTho WJas
- 'Broad-eyed Pippin' (C) — SKee
- 'Brown Crofton' (D) — SKee
- 'Brown Snout' (Cider) — CCAT CTho
- 'Brown Thorn' (Cider) — CCAT
- 'Brownlees Russet' (D) — CTho EMui GTwe NRog NWea
  SDea SFam SKee
- 'Brown's Apple' (Cider) — CCAT GTwe
- 'Broxwood Foxwhelp' — CCAT CTho
  (Cider)
- 'Budimka' (D) **new** — SKee
- 'Bulmer's Norman' — CCAT
  (Cider)
- 'Burn's Seedling' (D) — CTho
- 'Burr Knot' (C) — SKee
- 'Burrowhill Early' — CTho
  (Cider)
- 'Bushey Grove' (C) — SDea SKee
- 'Buttery Do' **new** — CTho
- 'Caledon' **new** — CTho
- 'Calville Blanc d'Hiver' — SKee
  (D)
- 'Cambusnethan — SKee
  Pippin' (D)
- 'Camelot' (Cider/C) — CCAT CTho
- 'Cap of Liberty' (Cider) — CCAT
- 'Captain Broad' — CCAT CEnd CTho
  (D/Cider)
- 'Captain Kidd' (D) — SKee
- 'Captain Smith' (F) — CEnd
- 'Carlisle Codlin' (C) — GKir GTwe
- 'Catherine' (C) — SKee
- 'Catshead' (C) — CCAT CCVT GKir GQui SDea
  SKee WJas
- 'Cellini' (C/D) — SDea
- 'Charles Ross' (C/D) — CCAT CDoC CMac CSBt CSam
  ♀ H4 — CTho EBre ECrN EMui GBon GKir
  GTwe LBuc LRHS MBri MHFa
  MRav MWat NRog NWea SDea
  SFam SKee WHar WJas WOrn

- 'Charlotte'^{PBR} (C/Ball)   ENot LRHS MGos SDea
- 'Chaxhill Red' (Cider/D)   CCAT CTho
- 'Cheddar Cross' (D)   CTri SKee
- 'Chelmsford Wonder' (C)   SKee
- 'Chisel Jersey' (Cider)   CCAT CTri
- 'Chivers Delight' (D)   CCAT CSBt ECrN EMui GTwe
                             LRHS SCrf SDea SKee WJas
- 'Chorister Boy' (D)   CTho
- 'Christmas Pearmain' (D)   CTho GTwe SDea SFam SKee
- 'Cider Lady's Finger'   CCAT CTho
  (Cider)
- 'Cistecké' (D)   SKee
- 'Claygate Pearmain'   CCAT CTho GTwe SDea SFam
  (D) ♀ H4   SKee WJas
- 'Clopton Red' (D)   SKee
- 'Coat Jersey' (Cider)   CCAT
- 'Cockle Pippin' (D)   CTho GTwe SDea
- 'Coeur de Boeuf' (C/D)   SKee
- 'Coleman's Seedling'   CTho
  (Cider)
- 'Collogett Pippin'   CCAT CEnd CTho
  (C/Cider)
- 'Colonel Vaughan' (C/D)   CTho SKee
- 'Cooper's Seedling' (C)   SCrf
- 'Cornish Aromatic' (D)   CCAT CTho EMui GTwe SCrf
                             SDea SFam SKee WJas
- 'Cornish Crimson   GTwe
  Queen' (F)
- 'Cornish Gilliflower' (D)   CCAT ECrN SDea SFam SKee WJas
- 'Cornish Honeypin' (D)   CTho
- 'Cornish Longstem' (D)   CEnd CTho
- 'Cornish Mother' (D)   CEnd
- 'Cornish Pine' (D)   CEnd CTho SDea SKee
- 'Coronation' (D)   SDea SKee
- 'Costard' (C)   GTwe SKee
- 'Cottenham Seedling' (C)   SKee
- 'Coul Blush' (D)   SKee
- 'Court of Wick' (D)   CCAT CTho SKee
- 'Court Pendu Plat' (D)   CCAT CTho GKir LBuc MWat NRog
                             NWea SDea SFam SKee WJas WOrn
§ - 'Court Royal' (Cider)   CCAT CTho
§ - 'Cow Apple' (C) **new**   CTho
- 'Cox's Orange   CBcs CCAT CCVT CMac CSBt
  Pippin' (D)   CWib EBre ECrN ENot GTwe
                   LBuc LRHS MHFa MWat NPri
                   NRog NWea SCrf SDea SFam SKee
                   SPer WJas WOrn WWeb
- 'Cox's Pomona' (C/D)   CTho SDea SKee WJas
- 'Cox's Rouge de   SKee
  Flandres' (D)
- 'Cox's Selfing' (D)   CWSG CWib EMui EPfP ERea
                          GTwe LBuc MBri MGos SCrf SDea
                          SKee WHar WJas WWeb
- 'Crawley Beauty' (C)   CCAT GTwe SDea SFam SKee WJas
- 'Crimson Bramley' (C)   CCAT
- 'Crimson Cox' (D)   SDea
§ - 'Crimson King' (Cider/C)   CCAT CTho
- 'Crimson Peasgood' (C)   GKir
- 'Crimson Queening' (D)   SKee WJas
- 'Crimson Victoria'   CTho
  (Cider)
- Crispin   see *M. domestica* 'Mutsu'
§ - 'Crowngold'^{PBR} (D)   EMui GTwe
- 'Cummy Norman' (Cider)   CCAT
- 'Curl Tail' (D)   SKee
- 'Cutler Grieve' (D)   SDea
- 'Dabinett' (Cider)   CCAT CCVT CTho CTri EMui
                         GTwe LBuc SCrf SDea SKee WOrn
  'D'Arcy Spice' (D)   CCAT CLnd EPfP GKir SDea SFam
                         SKee
- 'Dawn' (D)   SKee
- 'De Boutteville' (Cider)   CTho
- 'Deacon's Blushing   SDea

  Beauty' (C/D)
- 'Deacon's Millennium'   SDea
- 'Decio' (D)   SKee
- 'Delkid' (F)   GTwe
- 'Devon Crimson   CTho
  Queen' (D)
- 'Devonshire   CEnd CTho
  Buckland' (C)
- 'Devonshire Crimson   SDea
  Queen' (D)
- 'Devonshire   CCAT CEnd CTho EMui SDea
  Quarrenden' (D)   SFam SKee WJas
- 'Devonshire Red' (D/C)   CTho
- 'Dewdney's Seedling' (C)   GTwe
- 'Diamond Jubilee' (D)   SKee
- 'Discovery' (D) ♀ H4   More than 30 suppliers
- 'Doctor Hare's' (C)   MCoo
- 'Doctor Harvey' (C)   ECrN SFam
- 'Doctor Kidd's   see *M. domestica* 'Kidd's Orange
  Orange Red'   Red'
- 'Dog's Snout' (C/D)   NRog
- 'Doll's Eye' **new**   CTho
- 'Domino' (C)   SKee
- 'Don's Delight' (C)   CTho
- 'Doux Normandie'   CCAT
  (Cider)
- 'Dove' (Cider)   CTho
- 'Downton Pippin' (D)   SKee WJas
- 'Dredge's Fame' (D)   CTho
- 'Duchess of Oldenburg'   SKee
  (C/D)
- 'Duchess's Favourite' (D)   SKee
- 'Dufflin' (Cider)   CCAT CTho
- 'Duke of Devonshire' (D)   CSam CTho SDea SFam SKee
                               WJas
- 'Duke of Gloucester' (C)   WJas
N - 'Dumeller's Seedling' (C)   see *M. domestica* 'Dummellor's
                                   Seedling'
§ - 'Dummellor's Seedling'   CCAT CTho SDea SKee
  (C) ♀ H4
- 'Dunkerton Late Sweet'   CCAT CTho
  (Cider)
- 'Dunn's Seedling' (D)   SDea
§ - 'Dutch Mignonne' (D)   SKee
- 'Dymock Red' (Cider)   CCAT
- 'Early Blenheim' (D/C)   CEnd CTho
- 'Early Bower' (D)   CEnd
- 'Early Julyan' (C)   SKee WJas
- 'Early Victoria'   see *M. domestica* 'Emneth Early'
- 'Early Worcester'   see *M. domestica* 'Tydeman's
                       Early Worcester'
- 'Easter Orange' (D)   GTwe SCrf SKee
- 'Ecklinville' (C)   SDea SKee WJas
- 'Edward VII' (C) ♀ H4   CDoC GTwe SCrf SDea SFam
                              SKee WJas
- 'Egremont Russet'   CCAT CCVT CDoC CSBt CTho
  (D) ♀ H4   CWSG CWib EBre EMui ENot
                 EPfP GBon GKir GTwe LBuc
                 LRHS MBri MGos MHFa MWat
                 NBee NRog NWea SCrf SDea
                 SFam SKee SPer WJas WOrn
- 'Ellis' Bitter' (Cider)   CCAT CTho GTwe
- 'Ellison's Orange' (D)   CCAT CSBt CTri CWib ECrN ENot
  ♀ H4   GBon GKir GTwe LBuc LRHS
            MHFa NRog NWea SDea SFam
            SKee WHar WJas WStI
- 'Elstar' (D) ♀ H4   ECrN EMui GTwe MRav SDea SKee
- 'Elton Beauty' (D)   SDea SKee
§ - 'Emneth Early' (C) ♀ H4   EMui GTwe MHFa NRog SDea
                                  SFam SKee WJas WOrn
- 'Emperor Alexander'   see *M. domestica* 'Alexander'
  (C/D)
- 'Empire' (D)   SKee

- 'Encore' (C) — SDea
- 'English Codling' (C) — CTho
- 'Epicure' (D) — see *M. domestica* 'Laxton's Epicure'
- 'Ernie's Russet' (D) — SDea
- 'Eros' (D) — SKee
- 'Essex Pippin' (D) — SKee
- 'Evening Gold' (C) — SDea
- 'Eve's Delight' (D) — SDea
- 'Excelsior' (C) — SKee
- 'Exeter Cross' (D) — CCAT SDea SFam
- 'Fair Maid of Devon' (Cider) — CCAT
- 'Fairfield' (D) — CTho
- 'Fall Russet' (D) — GTwe
- 'Falstaff' PBR (D) ♀ H4 — CCAT CDoC ECrN EMui EPfP GKir GTwe MGos SDea SKee WJas
- 'Fearn's Pippin' (D) — SKee
- 'Fiesta' PBR (D) ♀ H4 — CCAT CCVT CDoC CSBt CWSG CWib EBre ECrN EMui ENot EPfP GBon GTwe LBuc LRHS MBri MGos MHFa NBlu NPri NRog SDea SFam SKee WHar WJas WOrn
- 'Fillbarrel' (Cider) — CCAT CTho
- 'Firmgold' (D) — SDea
- 'Five Crowns' (D) — SKee
- 'Flamenco' (D) — ENot MGos SDea
§ - 'Flower of Kent' (C) — CCAT SCrf SDea SKee
- 'Flower of the Town' (D) — SKee
- 'Forfar' — see *M. domestica* 'Dutch Mignonne'
- 'Forge' (D) — SDea SKee
- 'Fortune' — see *M. domestica* 'Laxton's Fortune'
- 'Foster's Seedling' (D) — SKee
- 'Foulden Pearmain' (D) — SKee
- 'Francis' (D) — SKee
- 'Frederick' (Cider) — CCAT CTho
- 'French Crab' (C) — CTho SDea
- 'Freyberg' (D) — SKee
- 'Fuji' (D) — SDea SKee
- 'Gala' (D) — CSBt GBon GTwe MBri NBlu NPri SCrf SDea SFam SKee
§ - 'Gala Mondial' (D) — WJas
I - 'Gala Royal' — see *M. domestica* 'Royal Gala'
- 'Galloway Pippin' (C) — GKir GTwe SKee
- 'Garnet' (D) — SKee
- 'Gascoyne's Scarlet' (D) — CCAT NRog SDea SFam SKee
- 'Gavin' (D) — SDea SKee
- 'Genesis II' (D/C) — SDea
- 'Genet Moyle' (C/Cider) — CCAT CTho WJas
- 'George Carpenter' (D) — CTho SDea SKee
- 'George Cave' (D) — CTho ECrN GTwe NBee NRog SCrf SDea SFam SKee WJas
- 'George Neal' (C) ♀ H4 — CTho SDea SFam
- 'Gilliflower of Gloucester' (D) — CTho
- 'Ginny Lin' **new** — CTho
- 'Gladstone' (D) — CTho SKee WJas
- 'Glasbury' (C) — SKee
§ - 'Glass Apple' (C/D) — CEnd
- 'Gloria Mundi' (C) — SDea SKee
- 'Gloster '69' (D) — GTwe SDea SKee
- 'Gloucester Cross' (D) — SKee
- 'Gloucester Underleaf' — CTho
- 'Golden Ball' — CTho
- 'Golden Bittersweet' (D) — CCAT CTho
- 'Golden Delicious' (D) ♀ H4 — CSBt CWib EBre ECrN EMui ENot GBon MBri MHFa NBlu NRog NWea SCrf SDea SKee SPer WHar WOrn WStI WWeb
- 'Golden Glow' (C) — SDea
- 'Golden Harvey' (D) — CCAT CTho
- 'Golden Knob' (D) — CCAT CTho SKee

- 'Golden Noble' (C) ♀ H4 — CCAT CDoC CSam CTho ECrN EMui GKir GTwe SDea SFam SKee WOrn
- 'Golden Pippin' (C) — CTho SKee
- 'Golden Reinette' (D) — GTwe SKee
- 'Golden Russet' (D) — GTwe SDea SKee
- 'Golden Spire' (C) — CTho NRog SDea SKee
- 'Goldilocks' (D) — GTwe
- 'Gooseberry' (C) — SKee
- 'Goring' (Cider) — CCAT CTho
- 'Grand Sultan' (D) — CTho
- 'Grandpa Buxton' (C) — NRog
- 'Granny Smith' (D) — CLnd CWib ECrN GTwe NBlu NPri SCrf SDea SKee SPer
- 'Gravenstein' (D) — CCAT SDea SFam SKee
- 'Greasy Butcher' **new** — CTho
- 'Greasy Pippin' (D/C) **new** — CTho
§ - 'Green Balsam' (C) — CTri NRog
- 'Green Roland' — SKee
- 'Greensleeves' PBR (D) ♀ H4 — CCAT CDoC CSBt CWSG CWib EBre ECrN EMui GKir GTwe LRHS MBri MGos MHFa NBee NRog NWea SDea SKee WHar WJas WOrn
- 'Greenup's Pippin' (D) — SKee
- 'Grenadier' (C) ♀ H4 — CCAT CDoC CSBt CTri ECrN GKir GTwe LRHS MGos MHFa NBee NRog SCrf SDea SKee WBVN WJas WOrn WStI
- 'Grosse Saulette' (Cider) **new** — SKee
- 'Halstow Natural' (Cider) — CTho
- 'Hambledon Deux Ans' (C) — SDea SKee
- 'Hambling's Seedling' (C) — SKee
- 'Hangy Down' (Cider) — CCAT CTho
- 'Hanwell Souring' (C) **new** — SKee
§ - 'Harry Master's Jersey' (Cider) — CCAT CTho CTri SDea
- 'Harvester' (D) — CTho
- 'Harvey' (C) — SDea SKee
- 'Hawthornden' (C) — SKee
- 'Hereford Cross' (D) — SKee
- 'Herefordshire Beefing' (C) — SKee WJas WOrn
- 'Herefordshire Pippin' (D) — CTho
- 'Herring's Pippin' (D) — CTri GTwe SDea SKee
- 'Heusgen's Golden Reinette' (D) — CCAT SKee
- 'Hibb's Seedling' (C) **new** — SKee
- 'Hibernal' (C) **new** — SKee
- 'High View Pippin' (D) — SKee
- 'Histon Favourite' (D) — SKee
- 'Hoary Morning' (C) — CCAT CTho SDea SKee
- 'Hocking's Green' (C/D) — CCAT CEnd CTho
- 'Holland Pippin' (C) — SKee
- 'Hollow Core' (C) — CTho
- 'Holstein' (D) — COtt CSam CTho GTwe SDea SKee
- 'Honey Pippin' (D) — SKee
- 'Hormead Pearmain' (C) — SKee
- 'Horneburger Pfannkuchen' (C) — SKee
- 'Horsford Prolific' (D) — SKee
- 'Horsham Russet' (D) **new** — SKee
- 'Houblon' (D) — SKee
- 'Howgate Wonder' (C) — CCAT CDoC CSBt CWib ECrN EMui GBon GKir GTwe LBuc LRHS MBri MHFa NBee NPri NRog SCrf SDea SFam SKee WJas
- 'Hubbard's Pearmain' (D) — SKee

- 'Idared' (D) ♀ H4	ECrN GBon GKir MGos SDea SKee
- 'Improved Cockpit' (D)	NRog
- 'Improved Dove' (Cider)	CCAT
- 'Improved Keswick' (C/D)	CEnd
- 'Improved Lambrook Pippin' (Cider)	CCAT CTho
- 'Improved Redstreak' (Cider)	CTho
- 'Ingrid Marie' (D)	NRog SCrf SDea SKee WJas
- 'Irish Johnnies' **new**	CTho
- 'Irish Peach' (D)	CCAT ECrN GTwe LBuc LRHS NRog SDea SFam SKee WJas
- 'Isaac Newton's Tree'	see M. domestica 'Flower of Kent'
- 'Isle of Wight Pippin' (D)	SDea
- 'Isle of Wight Russet' (D)	SDea
- 'Jackson's' (Cider)	see M. domestica 'Crimson King'
- 'Jacques Lebel' (C)	SKee
- 'James Grieve' (D) ♀ H4	More than 30 suppliers
- 'Jefferies' **new**	SKee
- 'Jerseymac' (D)	SDea
- 'Jester' (D)	ECrN GTwe NRog SDea SKee
- 'John Apple' (C)	SKee
- 'John Standish' (D)	CCAT CTri GTwe NRog SCrf SDea
- 'John Toucher's'	see M. domestica 'Crimson King'
- 'Johnny Andrews' (Cider)	CCAT CTho
- 'Johnny Voun' (D)	CCAT CEnd CTho
- 'Jonagold' (D) ♀ H4	ECrN EWTr GTwe LBuc MBri MHFa NWea SCrf SDea SFam SKee SPer WJas
- 'Jonagold Crowngold'ᴾᴮᴿ	see M. domestica 'Crowngold'
§ - 'Jonagored'ᴾᴮᴿ (D)	NRog SDea SKee
§ - 'Jonared' (D)	GTwe
- 'Jonathan' (D)	SDea SKee
- 'Jordan's Weeping' (C)	GTwe SDea WJas
- 'Josephine' (D)	SDea
- 'Joybells' (D)	SKee
- 'Jubilee'	see M. domestica 'Royal Jubilee'
- 'Jupiter'ᴾᴮᴿ (D) ♀ H4	CCAT CDoC CSBt CTri CWib ECrN FWTr GBon GKir GTwe MGos MHFa NRog SDea SKee WJas WOrn
- 'Kapai Red Jonathan' (D)	SDea
- 'Karmijn de Sonnaville' (D)	SDea SKee
§ - 'Katja' (D)	CCAT CCVT CDoC CTri CWib ECrN EMui EPfP EWTr GBon GKir GTwe LBuc LRHS MBri NBee NBlu NRog SCrf SDea SKee SPer WHar WJas WOrn
- Katy	see M. domestica 'Katja'
- 'Keegan' **new**	CTho
- 'Kent' (D)	GTwe SCrf SDea SKee
- 'Kentish Fillbasket' (C)	SKee
- 'Kentish Pippin' (C/Cider/D)	SKee
- 'Kerry Pippin' (D)	SKee
- 'Keswick Codling' (C)	CTho ECrN GKir GTwe NRog NWea SDea SKee WJas
§ - 'Kidd's Orange Red' (D) ♀ H4	CCAT EBre EMui GTwe LBuc LRHS NRog SCrf SDea SFam SKee WJas
- 'Kilkenny Pippin' (F)	GTwe
- 'Kill Boy' **new**	CTho
- 'Killerton Sharp' (Cider)	CTho
- 'Killerton Sweet' (Cider)	CTho
- 'King Byerd' (C/D)	CEnd CTho
- 'King Charles' Pearmain' (D)	CTho SKee
- 'King George V' (D)	SKee
- 'King Luscious' (D)	SDea
§ - 'King of the Pippins' (D) ♀ H4	CCAT CTho CTri GTwe LBuc SCrf SDea SFam SKee WOrn
- 'King of Tompkins County' (D)	NRog
- 'King Russet' (D) ♀ H4	SDea
- 'King's Acre Bountiful' (C)	SKee WJas
- 'King's Acre Pippin' (D)	CCAT SDea SFam SKee WJas
- 'Kingston Bitter' (Cider)	CTho
- 'Kingston Black' (Cider/C)	CCAT CTho GTwe SDea SKee
- 'Kirton Fair' (D) **new**	CTho
- 'Knobby Russet' (D)	GTwe SKee
- 'Lady Henniker' (D)	CCAT CTho ECrN GTwe NRog SDea SKee WJas
- 'Lady of the Wemyss' (C)	SKee
- 'Lady Sudeley' (D)	CTho SDea SKee
- 'Lady's Finger' (C/D)	CEnd GKir
- 'Lady's Finger of Lancaster' (C/D)	NRog SKee
- 'Lady's Finger of Offaly' (D)	SDea
- 'Lakeland' (D) **new**	SKee
- 'Lamb Abbey Pearmain' (D)	SKee
- 'Landsberger Reinette' (D)	SKee
- 'Lane's Prince Albert' (C) ♀ H4	CCAT CSBt ECrN EMui ENot GBon GKir GTwe LRHS MGos MHFa MRav MWat NRog NWea SCrf SDea SFam SKee WJas WOrn
- 'Langley Pippin' (D)	SDea SKee
§ - 'Langworthy' (Cider)	CCAT CTho
§ - 'Lass o' Gowrie' (C)	SKee
§ - 'Laxton's Epicure' (D) ♀ H4	CDoC ECrN GBon GTwe NRog SCrf SDea SFam SKee WJas
- 'Laxton's Favourite' (D)	ECrN SKee
§ - 'Laxton's Fortune' (D) ♀ H4	CCAT CDoC CMac CSBt EMui GKir GTwe MGos NPri NRog NWea SCrf SDea SFam SKee WHar WJas
- 'Laxton's Rearguard' (D)	SKee WJas
- 'Laxton's Royalty' (D)	SDea SFam
§ - 'Laxton's Superb' (D)	CBcs CCAT CCVT CDoC CSBt CTri CWib ECrN EMui ENot GBon GKir GTwe LBuc LRHS MBri MHFa NBlu NPri NRog SCrf SDea SKee WHar WJas WOrn
- 'Leathercoat Russet' (D)	CTho SKee
- 'Lemon Pippin' (C)	CCAT CTho SDea SKee WJas
- 'Lewis's Incomparable' (C)	SKee
- 'Liberty' (D)	SDea
- 'Limberland' (C)	CTho
- 'Limelight' (D) **new**	SKee
- 'Linda' (D)	SKee
- 'Listener' (Cider/D)	CCAT CTho
- 'Lobo' (D)	SCrf
§ - 'Loddington' (C)	SKee
- 'Lodi' (C)	SDea
- 'London Pearmain' (D)	SKee
- 'London Pippin' (C)	CTho
- 'Longkeeper' (D)	CEnd CTho
- 'Longstem' (Cider)	CTho
- 'Lord Burghley' (D)	GTwe SDea SKee
- 'Lord Derby' (C)	CCAT CMac CTho CWib ECrN EMui GKir GTwe MBri MHFa MWat NRog SCrf SDea SFam SKee
- 'Lord Grosvenor' (C)	GTwe SKee
- 'Lord Hindlip' (D)	GTwe SDea SFam SKee WJas
- 'Lord Lambourne' (D) ♀ H4	CCAT CDoC CSBt CTri CWib EBre ECrN EMui GKir GTwe LRHS MHFa MWat NRog SCrf SDea SFam SKee SPer WHar WJas WOrn
- 'Lord Nelson' (C) **new**	SKee
- 'Lord of the Isles' (F)	CCAT
- 'Lord Rosebery' (D)	SKee

- 'Lord Stradbroke' (C) — SKee
- 'Lord Suffield' (C) — CTri
- 'Lucombe's Pine' (D) — CEnd CTho
- 'Lucombe's Seedling' (D) — CTho SKee
- 'Mabbott's Pearmain' (D) — SDea
- 'Madresfield Court' (D) — SDea SKee WJas
- 'Major' (Cider) — CCAT CTho
- 'Malling Kent' (D) — EMui SDea SFam
- 'Maltster' (D) — SKee WJas
- 'Manaccan Primrose' (C/D) — CEnd CLnd
- 'Manks Codlin' (C) — CTho
- 'Margil' (D) — CCAT GTwe SDea SFam SKee
- 'Mary Golds' **new** — CTho
- 'Maxton' (D) — SKee
- 'May Queen' (D) — SDea SFam SKee WJas
- 'Maypole'PBR (D/Ball) — LRHS MGos SDea WJas
- 'Maypole 2000' (C/Ball) **new** — ENot
- 'McIntosh' (D) — SKee
- 'Measday's Favourite' (C) **new** — SKee
- 'Médaille d'Or' (Cider) — CCAT
- 'Medina' (D) — GTwe
- 'Melba' (D) — SKee
- 'Melcombe Russet' (D) — CTho
- 'Melon' (D) — SDea
- 'Melrose' (D) — ECrN GTwe SKee
- 'Merchant Apple' (D) — CCAT
- 'Merchant Apple of Illminster' (D) — CCAT CTho
- 'Mère de Ménage' (C) — SFam
- 'Meridian' (D) — EMui SDea SKee
- 'Merton Knave' (D) — GTwe MGos SDea SFam
- 'Merton Russet' (D) — SDea
- 'Merton Worcester' (D) — ECrN SDea SKee
- 'Michaelmas Red' (D) — GTwe NRog SKee WJas
- 'Michelin' (Cider) — CCAT CCVT EMui GTwe SDea SKee WOrn
- 'Miller's Seedling' (D) — GTwe SKee WJas
- 'Millicent Barnes' (D) — SDea
- 'Mollie's Delicious' (D) — SKee
- 'Monarch' (C) — CCAT CTri ECrN GTwe NRog SDea SFam SKee WJas
I - 'Mondial Gala' — see *M. domestica* 'Gala Mondial'
- 'Monidel'PBR — SKee
- 'Morgan's Sweet' (C/Cider) — CCAT CTho CTri SDea SKee
- 'Moss's Seedling' (D) — SDea
§ - 'Mother' (D) ♀ H4 — CCAT CDoC CSBt CTri GTwe SCrf SDea SFam SKee WJas
- 'Munster Tulip' (D/C) **new** — CTho
- 'Muscadet de Dieppe' (Cider) — CCAT
§ - 'Mutsu' (D) — CCAT CTri ECrN GTwe MBri MHFa NRog SCrf SDea SKee
- 'Nemes Szercsika Alma' (C) **new** — SKee
- 'Nettlestone Pippin' (D) — SDea
- 'Newton Wonder' (D/C) ♀ H4 — CCAT CDoC CMac CSBt CTho CTri CWib ECrN GTwe LRHS MHFa NRog SCrf SDea SFam SKee WJas
- 'Newtown Pippin' (D) — SDea
- 'Nine Square' (D) — CTho
- 'Nittany Red' (D) — SDea
- 'No Pip' (C) — CTho
- 'Nolan Pippin' (D) **new** — SKee
- 'Nonpareil' (D) — SKee
- 'Norfolk Beauty' (C) — SKee
- 'Norfolk Beefing' (C) — SDea SFam SKee
- 'Norfolk Royal' (D) — CDoC ECrN GTwe SDea SKee

- 'Norfolk Summer Broadend' (C) — SKee
- 'Norfolk Winter Coleman' (C) — SKee
- 'Northcott Superb' (D) — CTho
- 'Northern Greening' (C) — GTwe SKee
§ - 'Northwood' (Cider) — CCAT CTho
- 'Nutmeg Pippin' (D) — ECrN SDea SKee
- 'Oaken Pin' (C) — CCAT CTho
- 'Old Pearmain' (D) — CTho SDea SKee
- 'Old Somerset Russet' (D) — CTho
- 'Opalescent' (D) — SKee
- 'Orange Goff' (D) — SKee
- 'Orkney Apple' (F) — SKee
- 'Orleans Reinette' (D) — CCAT CCVT CTho CWib ECrN EMui GTwe LRHS MWat NRog SCrf SDea SFam SKee WJas
- 'Osier' (Cider) — CCAT
- 'Oslin' (D) — SKee
- 'Owen Thomas' (D) — CTri SKee
- 'Oxford Conquest' (D) **new** — SKee
- 'Paignton Marigold' (Cider) — CTho
- 'Palmer's Rosey' (D) — SKee
- 'Pascoes Pippin' (D/C) **new** — CTho
- 'Payhembury' (C/Cider) — CTho
- 'Peacemaker' (D) — SKee
- 'Pear Apple' (D) — CEnd CTho
- 'Pearl' (D) — SDea
- 'Peasgood's Nonsuch' (C) ♀ H4 — CCAT ECrN GKir GTwe LRHS MBri NRog SCrf SDea SFam SKee WJas WOrn
- 'Peck's Pleasant' (D) — SKee
- 'Pendragon' (D) — CTho
- 'Penhallow Pippin' (D) — CTho)
- 'Pennard Bitter' (Cider) — CCAT
- 'Peter Lock' (C/D) — CCAT CEnd CTho
- 'Peter's Pippin' (D) — SDea
- 'Peter's Seedling' (D) — SDea
- 'Pickering's Seedling' (D) — SKee
- 'Pigeonette de Rouen' (D) — SKee
- 'Pig's Nose Pippin' (D) — CEnd SKee
- 'Pig's Nose Pippin' Type III (D) — CTho
- 'Pig's Snout' (Cider/C/D) — CCAT CEnd CTho
- 'Pine Golden Pippin' (D) — SKee
- 'Pitmaston Pine Apple' (D) — CCAT CTho ECrN LRHS MHFa NRog SCrf SDea SFam SKee WJas WOrn
- 'Pitmaston Russet Nonpareil' (D) — SKee
- 'Pixie' (D) ♀ H4 — CCAT CSam CWib GTwe SDea SFam SKee WJas
- 'Plum Vite' (D) — CTho CTri
- 'Plympton Pippin' (C) — CEnd CTho
- 'Polka' = 'Trajan'PBR (D/Ball) — ENot LRHS MGos SDea
- 'Polly' (C/D) — CEnd
- 'Polly Prosser' (D) — SKee
- 'Polly Whitehair' (C/D) — CTho SDea SKee
- 'Pomeroy of Somerset' (D) — CCAT CTho SKee
- 'Ponsford' (C) — CCAT CTho
- 'Pónyik Alma' (c) — SKee
- 'Port Wine' — see *M. domestica* 'Harry Master's Jersey'
- 'Porter's Perfection' (Cider) — CCAT CTho
- 'Pott's Seedling' (C) — SKee
- 'Princesse' — GKir SDea SKee

- 'Purpurroter Cousinot' (D)	SKee	
- 'Quarry Apple' **new**	CTho	
- 'Queen' (C)	CTho SKee	
- 'Queen Cox' (D)	EMui GBon MHFa MRav SDea SKee	
- 'Queen Cox' self-fertile	SDea	
- 'Queens' (D)	CTho	
- 'Quench' (D/C) **new**	CTho	
- 'Red Alkmene' (D)	MBri	
§ - 'Red Blenheim' (C/D)	SKee	
- 'Red Bramley' (C)	CWib	
- 'Red Charles Ross' (C/D)	SDea	
- 'Red Delicious' (D)	SCrf	
- 'Red Devil' (D)	COtt CWSG ECrN EMui EPfP GKir GTwe LRHS MBri NBee SCoo SDea SKee SPoG WJas	
- 'Red Ellison' (D)	CCAT CTho CTri GTwe NRog SCrf SDea	
- 'Red Elstar' (D)	SCrf	
- 'Red Falstaff' PBR (D)	GKir LBuc LRHS MBri MCoo SKee WBVN	
- 'Red Fuji' (D)	SDea	
- 'Red Gravenstein' (D)	NRog	
- 'Red James Grieve'	see *M. domestica* 'Redcoat Grieve'	
- 'Red Jersey' (Cider)	CCAT	
- 'Red Joaneting' (D)	SKee	
- 'Red Jonagold' PBR	see *M. domestica* 'Jonagored'	
- 'Red Jonathan' (D)	SDea	
- 'Red Miller's Seedling' (D)	SCrf SDea	
- 'Red Rattler' (D)	CTho	
- 'Red Robin' (F)	CEnd	
- 'Red Ruby' (F)	CTho	
- 'Red Victoria' (C)	GTwe SKee	
- 'Red Windsor'	EMui SKee	
§ - 'Redcoat Grieve' (D)	CDoC GKir SDea SKee	
- 'Redsleeves' (D)	GTwe SDea SKee	
- 'Redstrake' (Cider)	CCAT	
- 'Reine de Pommes' (Cider)	CCAT	
- 'Reine des Reinettes'	see *M. domestica* 'King of the Pippins'	
- 'Reinette d'Obry' (Cider)	CCAT	
- 'Reinette Dorée de Buediker' (D)	GTwe	
- 'Reinette du Canada' (D)	SKee	
- 'Reinette Rouge Etoilée' (D)	CCAT SDea	
- 'Reverend Greeves' (C)	SDea	
- 'Reverend W. Wilks' (C)	CCAT CCVT CDoC COtt CTri ECrN EMui GKir LBuc LRHS MBri MHFa MWat NRog SCrf SDea SFam SKee WJas	
- 'Ribston Pippin' (D) ♀ H4	CCAT CTho CWib ECrN EMui GTwe LBuc LRHS MWat NRog SCrf SDea SFam SKee WJas	
- 'Rival' (D)	SDea SKee WJas	
- 'Robert Blachford' (c)	SKee	
- 'Robin Pippin' (D)	GTwe	
- 'Rome Beauty' (D)	SDea	
- 'Rosemary Russet' (D) ♀ H4	CCAT CSam CTho GTwe MCoo NRog SCrf SDea SFam SKee	
- 'Rosmarina Bianca' (D/C)	SKee	
- 'Ross Nonpareil' (D)	GTwe SDea SKee	
- 'Roter Ananas' (D)	SKee	
- 'Roter Eiserapfel' (D)	SKee	
- 'Rough Pippin' (D)	CEnd CTho	
- 'Roundway Magnum Bonum' (D)	CCAT CTho SDea SFam SKee	
§ - 'Roxbury Russet' (D)	SKee	
§ - 'Royal Gala' (D) ♀ H4	ECrN EMui LRHS SDea SKee WWeb	
§ - 'Royal Jubilee' (C)	CCAT SKee	
§ - 'Royal Russet' (C)	SDea	

- 'Royal Snow' (D)	SKee	
- 'Royal Somerset' (C/Cider)	CCAT CTho	
- 'Rubens' (D)	SKee	
- 'Rubinette' (D)	CDoC COtt ECrN GTwe MBri MGos MHFa SDea SKee WJas	
- 'Sabaros' (C) **new**	SKee	
- 'Saint Albans Pippin' (D)	SKee	
- 'Saint Augustine's Orange' (D)	SKee	
- 'Saint Cecilia' (D)	SDea WJas	
§ - 'Saint Edmund's Pippin' (D) ♀ H4	CTho ECrN ERea GTwe LBuc SCrf SDea SFam SKee	
- 'Saint Edmund's Russet'	see *M. domestica* 'Saint Edmund's Pippin'	
- 'Saint Magdalen' (D)	SKee	
- 'Saltcote Pippin' (D)	SKee	
- 'Sam Young' (D)	SKee	
- 'Sandlands' (D)	SDea	
- 'Sandringham' (C)	ECrN SKee	
- 'Sanspareil' (D)	SKee	
- 'Saturn' PBR	CDoC EMui GTwe SDea SKee	
- 'Saw Pits' (F)	CEnd	
- 'Scarlet Nonpareil' (D)	SDea SKee	
- 'Scarlet Pimpernel' (D)	SCrf	
- 'Scilly Pearl' (C)	WJas	
- 'Scotch Bridget' (C)	GKir SKee WJas WOrn	
- 'Scotch Dumpling' (C)	GKir GTwe LRHS MCoo	
- 'Scrumptious' (D)	GKir LBuc MBri SCoo SKee SPer	
- 'Sercombe's Natural' (Cider)	CCAT CTho	
- 'Severn Bank' (C)	CCAT CTho	
- 'Shakespeare' (D)	WJas	
- 'Sharleston Pippin' (D) **new**	SKee	
- 'Sheep's Nose' (C)	CCAT SDea SKee	
- 'Shenandoah' (C)	SKee	
- 'Sidney Strake' (C)	CEnd	
- 'Sikulai Alma' (D) **new**	SKee	
- 'Sir Isaac Newton's	see *M. domestica* 'Flower of Kent'	
- 'Sir John Thornycroft' (D)	SDea	
- 'Sisson's Worksop Newtown' (D)	SKee	
- 'Slack Ma Girdle' (Cider)	CCAT CTho	
- 'Smart's Prince Arthur' (C)	SDea	
- 'Snell's Glass Apple'	see *M. domestica* 'Glass Apple'	
- 'Somerset Lasting' (C)	CTho	
- 'Somerset Redstreak' (Cider)	CCAT CTho GTwe	
- 'Sops in Wine' (C/Cider)	CCAT CTho SKee	
- 'Sour Bay' (Cider)	CTho	
- 'Sour Natural'	see *M. domestica* 'Langworthy'	
- 'Spartan' (D)	CCAT CDoC CSBt CWib EBre ECrN EMui ENot EPfP EWTr GBon GKir GTwe LBuc LRHS MGos MHFa NBlu NPri NRog SCrf SDea SFam SKee SPer WJas WOrn WStI	
- 'Spencer' (D)	CTri ECrN SKee	
- 'Spotted Dick' (Cider)	CTho	
- 'Stable Jersey' (Cider)	CCAT	
- 'Stamford Pippin' (D)	SDea SKee	
- 'Stanway Seedling' (C)	SKee	
- 'Star of Devon' (D)	CCAT SDea	
- 'Stark' (D)	SDea	
- 'Starking' (D)	ECrN	
- 'Starkrimson' (D)	SKee	
- 'Starkspur Golden Delicious' (D)	SKee	
- 'Stembridge Cluster' (Cider)	CCAT	
- 'Stembridge Jersey' (Cider)	CCAT	

- 'Steyne Seedling' (D)   SDea
- 'Stirling Castle' (C)   GKir GTwe SKee
- 'Stobo Castle' (C)   SKee
- 'Stockbearer' (C)   CTho
- 'Stoke Edith Pippin' (D)   SKee
- 'Stoke Red' (Cider)   CCAT CTho
- 'Stone's'   see *M. domestica* 'Loddington'
- 'Stoup Leadington' (C)   SKee
- 'Striped Beefing' (C)   SKee
- 'Strippy' **new**   CTho
- 'Stub Nose' (F)   SKee
- 'Sturmer Pippin' (D)   CSBt ECrN GTwe LRHS MWat
                                 NRog SCrf SDea SFam SKee WJas
* - 'Sugar Apple'   CTho
- 'Sugar Bush' (C/D)   CTho
- 'Summer Golden   SKee
  Pippin' (D)
- 'Summerred' (D)   ECrN
- 'Sunnydale' (D/C)   SDea
I - 'Sunrise' (D)   EMui LRHS SKee
- 'Sunset' (D) ♀ H4   CCAT CCVT CDoC CSBt CSam
                                 CTri CWib EMui EPfP EWTr GKir
                                 GTwe LBuc LRHS MBri MHFa
                                 NBee NPri NRog NWea SCrf SDea
                                 SFam SKee SPer WHar WJas WOrn
- 'Suntan' (D) ♀ H4   CCAT CWib ECrN GBon GTwe
                                 MHFa MWat NBee SDea SKee
- 'Superb'   see *M. domestica* 'Laxton's Superb'
- 'Surprise' (D)   GTwe
- 'Sweet Alford' (Cider)   CCAT CTho
- 'Sweet Bay' (Cider)   CTho
- 'Sweet Cleave' (Cider)   CCAT CTho
- 'Sweet Coppin' (Cider)   CTho
- 'Tale Sweet' (Cider)   CCAT CTho
- 'Tamar Beauty' (F)   CEnd
- 'Tan Harvey' (Cider)   CCAT CEnd CTho
- 'Taunton Cross' (D)   SKee
- 'Taunton Fair   CCAT CTho
  Maid' (Cider)
- 'Taylor's' (Cider)   CCAT SDea
- 'Ten Commandments'   CCAT SDea WJas
  (D/Cider)
- 'Téton de Demoiselle' (D)   SKee
- 'The Major'   CWib
- 'The Rattler' (F)   CEnd
- 'Thomas Rivers' (C)   SDea SKee
- 'Thorle Pippin' (D)   SKee
- 'Tidicombe Seedling' (D)   CTho
- 'Tom Putt' (C)   CCAT CCVT CTho CTri CWib
                                 ECrN GKir GTwe LBuc LRHS
                                 SDea SKee WJas WOrn
- 'Tommy Knight' (D)   CCAT CEnd CTho
- 'Tower of Glamis' (C)   GTwe SKee
- 'Town Farm Number 59   CTho
  (Cider)
- 'Transparente de   CTho
  Croncels' (C)
- 'Tregoana King' (C/D)   CEnd CTho
- 'Tremlett's Bitter' (Cider)   CCAT CTho SDea
- 'Trumpington' (D) **new**   CTho
- 'Twenty Ounce' (C)   CCAT GTwe MHFa SKee WJas
- 'Twinings Pippin' (D)   SKee
§ - 'Tydeman's Early   CLnd CWib ECrN GTwe LRHS
  Worcester' (D)   NBee NRog SDea SKee WJas
- 'Tydeman's Late   ECrN GTwe NRog SDea SFam
  Orange' (D)   SKee
- 'Tyler's Kernel' (C)   SKee
- 'Underleaf' (D)   CCAT
- 'Upton Pyne' (D)   CCAT CSam CTho SCrf SDea SKee
- 'Veitch's Perfection' (C/D)   CTho
- 'Venus Pippin' (D)   CEnd
- 'Vicar of Beighton' (D)   SKee
- 'Vickey's Delight' (D)   SDea

- 'Vileberie' (Cider)   CCAT
- 'Vista-bella' (D)   ECrN GTwe NBee SDea SKee
                                 WJas
- 'Vitgylling' (D/C)   SKee
- 'Wagener' (D)   NRog SDea SKee
- Waltz = 'Telamon'PBR   LRHS MGos SDea
  (D/Ball)
- 'Wanstall Pippin' (D)   SKee
- 'Warner's King' (C) ♀ H4   CTho CTri NRog SCrf SDea SKee
                                 WJas
- 'Warrior'   CTho
- 'Wealthy' (D)   SDea SKee
- 'Wellington' (C)   see *M. domestica* 'Dummellor's
                                 Seedling'
- 'Wellington' (Cider)   CTho
§ - 'Wellspur' (D)   GTwe
- 'Wellspur Red Delicious'   see *M. domestica* 'Wellspur'
- 'Welsh Russet' (Cider)   SDea
- 'White Alphington'   CTho
  (Cider)
- 'White Astrachan'   CTho
  (D) **new**
- 'White Close Pippin'   CTho
  (Cider)
- 'White Jersey' (Cider)   CCAT
- 'White Joaneting' (D)   GTwe SKee
- 'White Melrose' (C)   GTwe SDea SKee
- 'White Paradise' (C)   SKee
- 'White Quarrenden' (D)   SKee
- 'White Transparent' (C/D)   SDea SKee
- 'William Crump' (D)   CCAT CTho ECrN SDea SFam
                                 SKee WJas
- 'Winston' (D) ♀ H4   CCAT CCVT CDoC CSBt CTri
                                 ECrN GTwe NRog NWea SCrf
                                 SDea SFam SKee
- 'Winter Banana' (D)   ECrN NRog SDea SKee
- 'Winter Gem' (D)   COtt ECrN EMui GKir LBuc LRHS
                                 MBri MGos SDea SKee WBVN
                                 WWeb
- 'Winter Majetin' (C)   SKee
- 'Winter Peach' (D/C)   CEnd CTho
- 'Winter Pearmain' (D)   SKee
- 'Winter Quarrenden' (D)   SDea
- 'Winter Queening' (D/C)   CTho SDea
- 'Winter Stubbard' (C)   CTho
- 'Woodbine'   see *M. domestica* 'Northwood'
- 'Woolbrook Pippin' (D)   CCAT CTho
- 'Woolbrook Russet' (C)   CCAT CTho SKee
- 'Worcester Pearmain'   CBcs CCAT CCVT CSBt CTho
  (D) ♀ H4   CWib ECrN EMui ENot GBon
                                 GKir GTwe LBuc LRHS MBri
                                 MHFa MWat NPri NRog NWea
                                 SDea SFam SKee SPer WHar WJas
                                 WOrn WStI WWeb
- 'Wormsley Pippin' (D)   ECrN SKee
- 'Wyatt's Seedling'   see *M. domestica* 'Langworthy'
- 'Wyken Pippin' (D)   CCAT ECrN GTwe SDea SFam
                                 SKee WJas
- 'Yarlington Mill' (Cider)   CCAT CTho CTri SDea SKee
- 'Yellow Bellflower' (D/C)   SKee
- 'Yellow Ingestrie' (D)   SFam SKee WJas
- 'Young America' (D)   SKee
- 'Zabergäu Renette' (D)   SKee
'Echtermeyer'   see *M. x gloriosa* 'Oekonomierat
                                 Echtermeyer'
§ 'Evereste' ♀ H4   More than 30 suppliers
florentina   CTho EPfP GIBF MRav WMou
floribunda ♀ H4   More than 30 suppliers
'Gardener's Gold'   CEnd
§ x *gloriosa* 'Oekonomierat   CCAT EBee GKir GQui SCrf SDea
  Echtermeyer'   WDin WJas
'Golden Gem'   CRez EPfP GTwe MDun SCoo SKee
'Golden Hornet'   see *M. x zumi* 'Golden Hornet'

'Goldsworth Purple'	CTho
'Gorgeous'	see *M.*x *atrosanguinea* 'Gorgeous'
'Harry Baker' **new**	ERea
'Hillieri'	see *M.* x *schiedeckeri* 'Hillieri'
hupehensis ♀ H4	CCAT CEnd CLnd CMCN CSBt
	CTho CWib EBee ENot EPfP GKir
	GTwe LRHS MBlu MBri MHFa MRav
	SCrf SFam SHBN SLPl SPer WMou
'John Downie' (C) ♀ H4	More than 30 suppliers
'Kaido'	see *M.* x *micromalus*
kansuensis	CLnd EBee GIBF WCwm
'Laura'PBR	COtt EBee EMui ENot EPfP GKir
	LRHS MAsh MBlu MGos SCoo
	SKee SLim WGer
'Louisa'	MAsh
x *magdeburgensis*	CLnd CSBt MHFa NWea
§ x *micromalus*	CLnd
x *moerlandsii*	CLnd
- 'Liset'	CDul CEnd CLnd COtt CWib EBee
	ECrN ENot MAsh MHFa MRav
	SFam SKee SPer WFar WJas WStI
§ - 'Profusion'	CDul CLnd CSBt EBee EBre ECrN
	ELan ENot GKir LPan LRHS MAsh
	MBri MGos MHFa MRav NBee
	NWea SCrf SHBN SKee SPer SRPl
	SSta WDin WJas WStI
- 'Profusion Improved'	CCAT CEnd COtt CSBt CWSG
	GKir MWat SCoo SKee SLim WOrn
orthocarpa	CLnd
Perpetu	see *M.* 'Evereste'
'Pink Glow'	MAsh SCoo SLim SPoG
'Pink Perfection'	CDoC CEnd CLnd EBee ENot
	MAsh MBri MDun SHBN SKee
Pom'Zaï = 'Courtabri'	CDoC
'Prairie Fire' **new**	MBri SKee
prattii	CLnd CTho
'Profusion'	see *M.* x *moerlandsii* 'Profusion'
prunifolia 'Cheal's	NRog
Crimson'	
- 'Fastigiata'	GIBF
- *var. prunifolíus* **new**	GIBF
- var. *rinkii* **new**	GIBF
pumila 'Cowichan'	GKir LRHS MBri
- 'Dartmouth'	CCAT CDul CLnd CSBt CSam
	CTho CTri NRog SFam
- 'Montreal Beauty'	GKir LRHS MBri SKee WJas WOrn
- 'Niedzwetzkyana'	CLnd
§ x *purpurea*	CLnd CTho NRog SCrf SDea
'Aldenhamensis'	WDin WOrn
- 'Eleyi'	CDul CLnd EBee ENot MRav
	NWea SCrf WDin WStI
- 'Lemoinei'	CLnd ECrN EMui EWTr
- 'Neville Copeman'	CDoC CDul CLnd EBee ECrN
	EPfP LPan MGos WJas WOrn
- 'Pendula'	see *M.* x *gloriosa* 'Oekonomierat
	Echtermeyer'
'R.J. Fulcher'	CLnd CTho
'Ralph Shay' **new**	CLnd
'Red Ace'	CDul
'Red Barron' **new**	CLnd
'Red Glow'	CDoC CLnd COtt EBee ECrN GQui
	MHFa SCrf WJas WLRN WWeb
'Red Jade'	see *M.* x *schiedeckeri* 'Red Jade'
§ x *robusta*	CDoC CLnd CTri EBee GTwe
	LPan NWea SCrf SLon SRPl
- 'Red Sentinel' ♀ H4	More than 30 suppliers
- 'Red Siberian'	ECrN MHFa SDea SHBN SPer
- 'Yellow Siberian'	CLnd
rockii	GIBF
'Royal Beauty' ♀ H4	CLnd CWib EBee EBre ENot EPfP
	GKir GTwe LPan LRHS MAsh
	MBri MGos MRav SCoo SCrf SKee
	WDin WHar WOrn WWeb

'Royalty'	More than 30 suppliers
'Rudolph'	CCAT CCVT CDul CLnd EBee
	ENot LPan LRHS MAsh MHFa
	MRav SCoo SLim WJas
'Ruth Ann' **new**	CLnd
sargentii	see *M. toringo* subsp. *sargentii*
'Satin Cloud' **new**	CLnd
§ x *schiedeckeri* 'Hillieri'	CCAT CLnd ECrN SCrf SFam
§ - 'Red Jade'	CDul CLnd CSBt CWib EBee EBre
	ECrN ELan ENot EPfP GKir GTwe
	LPan LRHS MAsh MBar MBri MGos
	MHFa MRav MWat NBee NBlu
	NWea SHBN SPer WDin WJas WOrn
Siberian crab	see *M.* x *robusta*
sieboldii	see *M. toringo*
sikkimensis	GIBF WHCr
- B&SWJ 2431	WCru
'Silver Drift' **new**	CLnd
'Snowcloud'	CCAT CDul CEnd CLnd EBee
	ECrN ENot EPfP LRHS MBri SHBN
	SPer WOrn
spectabilis	CLnd
'Street Parade'	CLnd
'Sun Rival'	CCAT CDoC CDul CEnd COtt CSBt
	CWSG EBee EMui EPfP GTwe
	LRHS MAsh MBri MDun MGos
	SCoo SFam SKee SLim WHar WJas
sylvestris	CCVT CDul CKin CLnd CTri
	ECrN EPfP GKir LBuc MRav NBee
	NRog NWea WDin WLRN WOrn
§ *toringo*	CLnd GIBF SSpi
- var. *arborescens* **new**	GIBF
§ - subsp. *sargentii*	CDul CLnd CMCN EBee ECrN
	ENot GKir LRHS MBri MGos MRav
	NWea SFam SPer SPoG WNor
- - 'Tina'	CLnd
toringoides	see *M. bhutanica*
transitoria ♀ H4	CCAT CEnd CFil CLnd CTho EBee
	EPfP GIBF GKir LRHS MBlu MBri
	MRav NWea SCoo SPer SSpi
	WPGP
- 'Thornhayes Tansy'	CLnd CTho MBri
trilobata	CCAT CLnd CTho EPfP MBri
	MGos SCoo SKee WMou
- 'Guardsman'	MBri
tschonoskii ♀ H4	More than 30 suppliers
- 'White Star'	see *M.* 'White Star'
'Van Eseltine'	CCAT CDoC CDul CLnd CSBt
	CWSG CWib EBee EMui GKir
	GTwe LRHS MAsh MBri MHFa
	MWat SFam SKee SPer WJas
'Veitch's Scarlet'	CDul CLnd CSBt CTho GQui
	GTwe NRog SFam
§ 'White Star'	CBrm CCAT CDoC CDul CSBt
	CWSG ECrN LRHS SCoo SKee
	SLim WWeb
'Winter Gold'	CDoC CDul CLnd CSam LCaP
	SCrf WStI
'Wisley Crab'	CLnd EBee EMil GTwe SDea SFam
	SKee
yunnanensis var. *veitchii*	CTho GIBF
x *zumi* var. *calocarpa*	CLnd
§ - 'Golden Hornet' ♀ H4	More than 30 suppliers
- 'Professor Sprenger'	CLnd

Malva (Malvaceae)

alcea	CAgr EPfP
- var. *fastigiata*	EMan ERou LRHS MBow NBid
	NBro NBur NCat SAga SPer SRms
	WPer
bicolor	see *Lavatera maritima*
'Gibbortello'	CCge MCLN NBur
moschata	More than 30 suppliers

- f. *alba* ♀ H4 — More than 30 suppliers
- - 'Pirouette' — MGGn WHen
- 'Kirikee Sunrise' — IIve
- 'Pink Perfection' — EFWa MTis
- 'Romney Marsh' — see *Althaea officinalis* 'Romney Marsh'
- *rosea* — ECha EVFa GDra NCot NPer WPnP
'Park Allee' — EBee EChP EMan MCCP WHil WRus
sylvestris — CAgr CKin GWCH MBow MChe NBro NFla NPri NSco SMad SWat WHHs WHer WJek WMoo WPer WRos WWin WWye
- 'Brave Heart' — CM&M GBri NBur NCot NLar SRkn WGwG WHHs
- 'Highnam' — WAlt
- 'Knockout' **new** — EWes
I - 'Magic Hollyhock' (d) — SGar
- Marina = 'Dema' PBR — EBee ELan LRHS MBri
- subsp. *mauritanica* — CHea EBee EBlw ECoo EMar EPfP GBri NCot NFor NPer WMoo
- - 'Bibor Fehlo' — CSpe NBur NGdn
- 'Mystic Merlin' **new** — WGwG WHHs
- 'Perry's Blue' — NPer
- 'Primley Blue' — CBcs CBot CElw EBee EBlw EChP ECha ECtt ELan EMan EPfP GBri MRav MTho NCot NEgg NGdn NPer NPri NSti SMad SPer WFar WSan WWin
- 'Richard Perry' — NPer
- 'Zebrina' — CM&M EBee EMar EWTr GBri LDai MCLN NBur NGdn NJOw NPPs NPri WHil WMoo WRha
verticillata 'Crispa' — MChe

Malvastrum (Malvaceae)
x *hypomadarum* — see *Anisodontea* x *hypomadara* (Sprague) Bates
lateritium — More than 30 suppliers

Malvaviscus (Malvaceae)
arboreus — CHll CKob
- var. *mexicanus* — ERea SYvo
- pink — CKob

mandarin see *Citrus reticulata*

mandarin, Cleopatra see *Citrus reshni*

Mandevilla (Apocynaceae)
x *amabilis* 'Alice du Pont' ♀ H1 — CBcs CPIN CRHN ELan EMil EPfP ERea ESlt LRHS SMur SOWG WMul
x *amoena* — see *M.* x *amabilis*
boliviensis ♀ H1 — CPIN ELan ESlt LRHS SOWG
§ *laxa* ♀ H2 — CBot CHEx CHll CPIN CTrC CWib ELan ERea ESlt LRHS SHFr SOWG WCot WCru WSHC
sanderi — EPfP MBri
- 'Rosea' — ERea
splendens ♀ H1 — EBak LRHS SOWG
suaveolens — see *M. laxa*

Mandragora (Solanaceae)
autumnalis — EEls GCal MGol MSal WCot
caulescens **new** — EBee
§ *officinarum* — CBrd FEls GCal GPoy LEdu MGol MSal WCot WWye

Manettia (Rubiaceae)
inflata — see *M. luteorubra*
§ *luteorubra* — CPIN ELan EPfP

Manfreda see *Agave*

Manglietia (Magnoliaceae)
insignis — CFil CHEx SSpi

Manihot (Euphorbiaceae)
esculenta — CKob
- 'Variegata' **new** — CKob

Mansoa (Bignoniaceae)
hymenaea — CPIN

Maranta (Marantaceae)
leuconeura var. *kerchoveana* ♀ H1 — CHal LRHS MBri NBlo XBlo

Margyricarpus (Rosaceae)
§ *pinnatus* — CFee CPLG CPle ESis GEdr GEil GGar NWCA WCom WPer
setosus — see *M. pinnatus*

marjoram, sweet see *Origanum majorana*

marjoram, pot see *Origanum onites*

marjoram, wild or oregano see *Origanum vulgare*

Mariscus see *Cyperus*

Marrubium (Lamiaceae)
candidissimum — see *M. incanum*
catariifolium — MGGn
cylleneum — EBlw ECha MGGn WPer
* - 'Velvetissimum' — CPom SBla WCHb
'Gold Leaf' — ECha
§ *incanum* — EBee EMan IFro IIve MBri MGGn SMrm WEas
libanoticum — ECha MGGn MSte WPer
pestalloziae — EBee WCot
supinum — CArn NWoo
vulgare — CArn ELau GBar GPoy GWCH MChe MGGn MHer NOrc SIde WCHb WCer WHer WPer WSel WWye
- 'Green Pompon' — ELau IIve MCCP MGGn NLar

Marsdenia (Asclepiadaceae)
erecta — see *Cionura erecta*

Marshallia (Asteraceae)
grandiflora — EBee SIgm
trinerva — SCro WCot

Marsilea (Marsileaceae)
quadrifolia — WWpP

Mascagnia (Malpighiaceae)
macroptera — CPIN

Mascarena see *Hyophorbe*

Massonia (Hyacinthaceae)
echinata — CStu
pustulata — CPLG CStu

Mathiasella (Apiaceae)
from Mexico **new** — SIgm

Matricaria (Asteraceae)
chamomilla — see *M. recutita*
parthenium — see *Tanacetum parthenium*
§ *recutita* — GPoy MChe

Matteuccia (*Woodsiaceae*)

intermedia	see *Onoclea intermedia*
orientalis	CFil CPLG GCal LEur NHar NMar NOrc WFar WRic
pensylvanica	EBee EMon NHar SMrm
struthiopteris ♀ H4	More than 30 suppliers
- 'Bedraggled Feathers'	EMon

Matthiola (*Brassicaceae*)

* **arborescens alba**	LHrt WBVN
§ **fruticulosa**	EBee
- 'Alba'	CDes EBee WPGP
- subsp. **perennis**	EBee NWCA
incana	CBgR CWes MArl WCot WPer WRHF WRus
- **alba**	ELan GMaP NBir
thessala	see *M. fruticulosa*
white perennial	CArn CHad CMea CMil CSev CSpe ECGP ERou EVFa LPhx LRav MBct MWgw NPer SEND SSth WEas WHoo

Maurandella (*Scrophulariaceae*)

§ **antirrhiniflora**	LRHS

Maurandya (*Scrophulariaceae*)

§ **barclayana**	CBot CHll CPlN CRHN CSpe MBri SGar SYvo
- **alba**	CBot
erubescens	see *Lophospermum erubescens*
lophantha	see *Lophospermum scandens*
lophospermum	see *Lophospermum scandens*
'Pink Ice'	see *Lophospermum scandens* 'Pink Ice'
'Red Dragon'	see *Lophospermum* 'Red Dragon'
scandens	see *Lophospermum scandens*
§ 'Victoria Falls'	LRHS SOWG

Maytenus (*Celastraceae*)

boaria	CHEx CMCN CPle EPfP GEil LEdu SAPC SArc SLon WFar WPGP WPic
- 'Worplesdon Fastigiate'	CFil
magellanica	CFil WFar

Mazus (*Scrophulariaceae*)

miquelii	EBee
radicans	CStu WCru
reptans	CBrm CNic EBee EDAr EMan EMlt EPfP EWTr GEdr NFla NWCA WOut WPer
- 'Albus'	CNic EBee EDAr EMlt GMaP MDKP SPlb WCru WPer
surculosus	CPom

Meconopsis ❀ (*Papaveraceae*)

CC 3315	WRos
aculeata	EBee GGGa GTou
baileyi	see *M. betonicifolia*
Ballyrogan form	GEdr IBlr
x **beamishii**	GBuc NLon
§ **betonicifolia** ♀ H4	More than 30 suppliers
- var. **alba**	EBee EDAr EWTr GAbr GBuc GDra GGGa GGar GMaP GMac IMGH ITim LHop LSyl MBri MCAu MUlv NBlu NChi NHar NLar SLon SRms WCru
- 'Hensol Violet'	EBee EChP GBuc GCal GCrs GFlc GGGa ITim LHop NLar WViv
'Branklyn'	CDes CFil GAbr GBri IBlr WPGP
cambrica	CKin EBee EBre EHrv ELan EMar GGar GTou LHrt MBow NCat NCot NHol NPri SChu SIng SPer
	WAbe WBea WCru WFar WHen WHer WPer WWye
- 'Anne Greenaway'	ELan LHop SPer
- var. **aurantiaca new**	SWal WWeb
- **flore-pleno** (d)	CBos CHar EPar GBuc MTho NBid SChr
- - orange (d)	NBid NBir NMGW WCot WCru WHen
- - yellow (d)	WCot WCru
§ - 'Frances Perry'	ETow GBuc GCal IBlr WCru WFar WRos
- 'Muriel Brown' (d)	NCot WCru
- 'Rubra'	see *M. cambrica* 'Frances Perry'
chelidoniifolia	CFil GCal GKir IBlr SSpi WCru WFar
delavayi	GGGa
dhwojii	GBri GFle GGGa GKev LRHS MNes WPnP
(Fertile Blue Group) 'Blue Ice'	see *M.* (Fertile Blue Group) 'Lingholm'
N - 'Lingholm'	CLAP EBee GBuc GCal GCrs GDrg GEdr GFle GGar GTou ITim SSpi WBVN WLin
N George Sherriff Group	CLAP GBuc GCal GMac IBlr NBir GCrs
- 'Ascreavie' **new**	GCrs
- 'Huntfield' **new**	GCrs
- 'Jimmy Bayne'	GBuc GCrs GMaP
gracilipes	MNes
grandis misapplied	see *M.* George Sherriff Group
N **grandis** ambig.	CBrd CHar CPla CSam EBee EDAr EGle ENot GAbr GEdr GGGa GGar GIBF ITim LRHS MNes MNrw NChi NCot NHar NSla SBla SLon WAbe WHen WLin WPnP WViv
- Balruddry form	GGGa
- GS 600	see *M.* George Sherriff Group
henrici new	GGGa
horridula	EBee GFle GGGa GKev ITer LRHS MTho SMrm
- Rudis Group	EBee
N (Infertile Blue Group) 'Bobby Masterton'	GBuc
- 'Crewdson Hybrid'	CLAP GBuc GCrs GDra GMaP MNes
- 'Cruickshank' **new**	GCrs
- 'Dawyck'	GCrs
- 'Mrs Jebb'	GBuc GCrs GMac
- 'Slieve Donard' ♀ H4	CDes CFil CLAP EBee GBri GBuc GCrs GDra GGar GMaP ITim MNes NHar SBla WPGP
integrifolia	EBee GFle GGGa
ACE 1798	GTou
§ subsp. **integrifolia** 'Wolong'	GCrs
'James Cobb'	see *M. integrifolia* subsp. *integrifolia* 'Wolong'
Kingsbarns hybrids	GCrs GGGa
lancifolia	EBee GBuc
'Mrs McMurtrie'	IBlr
§ **napaulensis**	CFil CSam EBee EDAr ENot GCrs GDra GFle GGGa GGar GKir IBlr IMGH ITer ITim LHop LRHS MBri MNes MWod NChi NLar SLon WLin WRos WViv
- KEKE 103	MNes
- pink	EBee GDrg WViv
- red	EBee GBuc GDrg ITer ITim WCru ITim
§ - Wallich's form	ITim
- Wallich's Form, white-flowered **new**	GKev
nudicaulis	see *Papaver nudicaule*
'Ormswell'	GBuc IBlr
paniculata	EBee GFle GGGa IBlr ITim LRHS NBir WAbe WLin

– CC&McK 296	GTou
* – Ghunsa Group	CLAP EGle MNes
pseudointegrifolia	GGGa GKir
– SDR 1749	GKev
– SDR 1911	GKev
– SDR 1922	GKev
punicea	EGle GCrs GGGa GIBF GMac
quintuplinervia ♀ H4	CLAP CPBP GBri GCrs GDra GEdr
	GFle GGGa GGar GKev GTou IBlr
	MLLN NBid NBir NCot NGar
	NHar NMGW NRya NSla
* – 'Kaye's Compact'	GBuc IBlr
racemosa var. **racemosa**	GKev
– – SDR 1734	GKev
regia	CSam EBee EDAr GAbr GFle GIBF
	LHop LRHS NLar WBar WLin WViv
– x **grandis**	GBuc
robusta	EBee ITim
x **sarsonsii**	GFle
N x **sheldonii** ambig.	CBcs CBrd EBee EDAr ENot EPfP
	GBin GBuc GDra GGGa GKir
	GMaP ITer LAst LHop MBri MDun
	MFir NBir NBlu NHar NLon SLon
	SPer WCru WFar WPGP WPnP WViv
– fertile	see *Meconopsis* Fertile Blue Group
– sterile	see *Meconopsis* Infertile Blue Group
'Spring Hill'	GBuc IBlr
superba	GBuc GFle GGGa MNes
villosa	GBuc GCal GFle GGGa GKev
	GTou IBlr ITim WBVN WCru WLin
wallichii hort.	see *M. napaulensis* Wallich's form
wallichii ambig.	EBee GDrg ITim
'Willie Duncan'	GCrs

Medeola (Convallariaceae)
virginica	EBee LAma WCru

medlar see *Mespilus germanica*

Medicago (Papilionaceae)
arborea	IBlr
sativa	CKin IIve WHer WMoo
– subsp. **sativa**	IBlr

Medinilla (Melastomataceae)
magnifica ♀ H1	LRHS MBri SMur
myriantha 'Pink Pixie'	ESlt

Meehania (Lamiaceae)
cordata	CDes EBee NLar
urticifolia	CDes CPom EBee EMon EPPr
	MHar MSte WPGP WTMC
– B&SWJ 1210	WCru
– 'Wandering Minstrel' (v)	CDes EBee EMan EMon WPGP

Melaleuca (Myrtaceae)
acerosa	SOWG
acuminata	SPlb
alternifolia	CArn ECou ELau EOHP EShb
	GPoy MGol MHer MSal SOWG
	SSte WHer
armillaris	CDoC CTrC SGar SOWG SPlb
– pink	SOWG
bracteata	CTrC ECou
citrina	SOWG
coccinea	SOWG
cuticularis	SPlb
decora	SOWG
decussata	CTrC ECou SOWG SPlb SSte
§ **diosmatifolia**	CTCP
elliptica	SOWG SSte
ericifolia	CTri SOWG SPlb
erubescens	see *M. diosmatifolia*

filifolia	SOWG
fulgens	CTrC SOWG SPlb
– 'Apricot' **new**	SOWG
* – 'Hot Pink'	SOWG
– purple-flowered **new**	SOWG
gibbosa	CPLG EBee ECou IDee SBrw
	SOWG SSte WSHC
holosericea hort.	see *M. smartiorum*
huegelii	SOWG SSte
hypericifolia	CPLG CTrC ECou SOWG SPlb SSte
incana	CTrC SOWG SSte
lateritia	ECou SOWG SSte
leucadendra	MSal
linariifolia	CTrC ECou LRHS SPlb SSte
nesophila	CTrC ECou SOWG SPlb SSte
platycalyx	SOWG
pulchella	SOWG SSte
pungens	SPlb
pustulata	ECou SOWG SSte
radula	SOWG
* **rosmarinifolia**	SOWG
§ **smartiorum**	SOWG
spathulata	SOWG
squamea	CTrC EBee IDee IKee WPic
squarrosa	CPLG CTrC ECou GKir NNEX
	SOWG SPlb SSte
thymifolia	ECou MSal SOWG SPlb SSte
viridiflora	CPLG GQui
wilsonii	CTrC ECou SOWG

Melandrium (Caryophyllaceae)
rubrum	see *Silene dioica*

Melanoselinum (Apiaceae)
§ **decipiens**	CArn CHEx CTrF ITer LPhx SIgm

Melasphaerula (Iridaceae)
graminea	see *M. ramosa*
§ **ramosa**	CBre CPLG WCot

Melia (Meliaceae)
azadirachta	GPoy
§ **azedarach**	CArn CBcs CHEx ECre ELau LPan
	NPSI
– var. **japonica**	see *M. azedarach*

Melianthus (Melianthaceae)
comosus	CHEx CTrC EWes SPlb SSte
major ♀ H3	More than 30 suppliers
minor	CFir SIgm
villosus	CFir MAnH MCCP NLar SIgm SPlb

Melica (Poaceae)
altissima	LRHS
– 'Alba'	EHoe
– 'Atropurpurea'	More than 30 suppliers
ciliata	CBig CBrm COlW CSam EBee
	ECGN EHoe EPPr EPla EWsh GBin
	MHdf MMoz NHol NNor SRGP SWal
	WHil WPer WRos WWeb WWpP
– subsp. **taurica**	EPPr
macra	EBee EHoe EPPr WPGP
* – 'Purpurea' **new**	WPGP
nutans	CBig CBod CBrm CWCL EHoe
	EPPr EPla EWsh GBin GWCH
	NHol NPPs NWCA SYvo WHal
	WRos WWeb WWye
penicillaris	EBee EPPr WPer WWpP
persica **new**	EBee EPPr
torreyana **new**	EPPr
transsilvanica	ECGN MHdf NNor
– 'Atropurpurea'	EBee EChP EWll NHol SDes SMac
– 'Red Spire'	CBig IBal LRav MHdf MWhi WWpP

uniflora	CBrm CKin
- f. ***albida***	CFil EBee EHoe EMan EMon EVFa
	MBct SLPl SUsu WCot WRHF
- 'Variegata' (v)	CBre CFil EBee ECha EHoe EMan
	EMon EPPr EPla GCal MBrN MBri
	MMoz NGdn WCot WWye

Melicope (*Rutaceae*)

ternata	ECou

Melicytus (*Violaceae*)

alpinus	ECou
angustifolius	CPle ECou
crassifolius	CPle ECou EPla WHCG
obovatus	ECou EMan
ramiflorus	ECou

Melilotus (*Papilionaceae*)

officinalis	CArn CKin CWCL GPoy MChe
	MGol SIde WHer WSel WWye
- subsp. ***albus***	SIde WHer

Melinis (*Poaceae*)

nerviglumis	EBee EPPr
repens	EShb SYvo
roseus	EBee EHul MCCP

Melissa (*Lamiaceae*)

officinalis	CAgr CArn CChe CHal CPrp EDAr
	EFer ELau GPoy MBar MBow MBri
	MChe MHer NArg NBlu NPri SIde
	SPar SPlb SWal SYvo WBea WHHs
	WPer WWpP WWye
- 'All Gold'	CArn CBre CHal CMGP CPrp
	CSev ECha EHoe ELan ELau GBar
	MBow MBri MChe MHer NBid
	NVic SPer WMoo WWye
§ - 'Aurea' (v)	More than 30 suppliers
* - 'Compacta'	GPoy MHer
- 'Quedlinburger	CArn
Niederliegende'	
- 'Small-Ness'	MNes
N - 'Variegata' misapplied	see *M. officinalis* 'Aurea'

Melittis (*Lamiaceae*)

melissophyllum	CBrm CFir CPlt CRDP EBee EMan
	LPio MCAu MHar MTis NSti SIgm
	SIng SRms SSpi SSvw WAbb WCot
	WFTG WSan WWye
- subsp. ***albida***	EBee SSpi
- pink	EMon SOkh
- 'Royal Velvet	CPen MDri MLLN WHil
Distinction'PBR **new**	

Melliodendron (*Styracaceae*)

xylocarpum **new**	IArd

Menispermum (*Menispermaceae*)

canadense	CPlN GPoy MSal SHBN
davuricum	MSal

Menstruocalamus (*Poaceae*)

sichuanensis **new**	CFil

Mentha ❀ (*Lamiaceae*)

* ***angustifolia*** **new**	EOHP
aquatica	CAgr CArn CBen CKin CPrp
	CRow CWat ECoo EHon ELau EPfP
	GPoy IHMH LPBA MBow MChe
	MHer MSta NPer SLon SPlb SWat
	WFar WHHs WHer WMAq WWpP
§ - var. ***crispa***	IHMH IIve
- krause minze	see *M. aquatica* var. *crispa*

- 'Mandeliensis'	EOHP IHMH IIve
arvensis	CArn ELau EOHP GIBF IHMH IIve
	MHer MSal NSco WHer WJek
- 'Banana'	EOHP
- var. ***piperascens***	EOHP MSal SAga
§ - - 'Sayakaze'	ELau
asiatica	ELau EOHP IIve MHer SIde WHer
Bowles' mint	see *M. x villosa* var.
	alopecuroides Bowles' mint
* ***brevifolia***	EOHP IHMH WHer
§ ***cervina***	CBen CWat EMFW EOHP IHMH
	LPBA MSta SBHF SLon SWat WBar
- ***alba***	EOHP IHMH SLon WMAq WWpP
citrata	see *M. x piperita* f. *citrata*
'Clarissa's Millenium' **new**	EOHP
cordifolia	see *M. x villosa*
corsica	see *M. requienii*
crispa L. (1753)	see *M. spicata* var. *crispa*
- L. (1763)	see *M. aquatica* var. *crispa*
- x ***piperita***	EDAr GBar
'Dionysus'	EOHP IHMH IIve
x ***dumetorum*** **new**	IHMH
'Eau de Cologne'	see *M. x piperita* f. *citrata*
eucalyptus mint	ELau EOHP GBar MHer WBea
	WHHs WRha
gattefossei	CArn ELau
x ***gentilis***	see *M. x gracilis*
§ x ***gracilis***	CArn ELau EOHP GBar GWCH
	IHMH MBow MChe NPri SIde
	WBea WJek WRHF WWye
- 'Aurea'	see *M. x gracilis* 'Variegata'
§ - 'Variegata' (v)	CAgr CBrm CPrp CSev ECha
	EHoe ELau EMar GGar GPoy ILis
	MBar MHer MRav NArg NBlu
	NPri NVic SGar SPlb SWal WFar
	WHHs WHer WPer WSel
haplocalyx	ELau EOHP MSal
* 'Hillary's Sweet Lemon'	EBee ELau EOHP
I 'Julia's Sweet Citrus'	EOHP MHer
* ***lacerata***	IHMH SIde
lavender mint	CBod CPrp ELau EMan GBar
	GPoy IIve MHer MRav NGHP
	WBea WBry WJek WRha
§ ***longifolia***	CAgr CPrp CRDP ECoo ELau EMar
	GBar IIve MBow MRav NSti SPlb
	WEas WHer WJek WPer WSel WWye
- Buddleia Mint Group	CArn ELau EMan GAbr GGar GKir
	IHMH MHer MRav WBea WBry
	WHHs WRha WSel
- subsp. ***capensis***	GGar
- silver	CArn ELau GWCH MHer WBea
* - 'Variegata' (v)	CBod CPrp ELau NCat NSti WJek
Nile Valley mint	CArn CBod CPrp ELau EOHP
	NBlu SHDw SIde WCHb
x ***piperita***	CArn COkL CSev ECha EDAr EHoe
	ELau GBar GGar GPoy ILis MBow
	MBri MChe MHer NArg NBlu NFor
	NPri NVic SGar SPlb SWal WBea
	WHHs WHbs WPer WWyc
- 'After Eight'	IHMH IIve
* - alba	GBar MHer WHHs
- 'Black Mitcham'	EOHP GBar
- black peppermint	CAgr GWCH IHMH NHol WHHs
§ - f. ***citrata***	More than 30 suppliers
* - - 'Basil'	CBod CPrp ELau EOHP GBar
	IHMH IIve LHrt LLWP MHer
	MRav SHDw SIde WBea WBry
	WHHs WJek WRha
- - 'Bergamot'	EOHP IHMH IIve
- - 'Chocolate'	CAgr CArn CBod CPrp ELau EMan
	EOHP GBar GGar GKir IHMH ILis
	MHer NArg NBlu NGHP NPri SHDw
	SIde WBea WBry WHHs WJek WPer

– – 'Grapefruit'	EOHP GBar ILis WJek	
– – 'Lemon'	CPrp ELau EMan EOHP GAbr	
	GBar IHMH MBow MBri MHer	
	NGHP SHDw SIde WBea WCHb	
	WHHs WJek WPer WRha WSel	
– – 'Lime'	CPrp EMan EOHP GBar ILis LHrt	
	MHer MTed NGHP SHDw SIde	
	SPlb WBea WCHb WHHs WJek	
– – orange	EOHP GBar MHer	
– – 'Swiss Ricola'	EOHP MHer	
I – 'Extra Strong	IHMH	
Peppermint' **new**		
– 'Logee's' (v)	EBee EMan EOHP EWes GBar MHer	
	NGHP NPri WBea WBry WCHb	
	WCot WHHs WHer WJek WRha	
§ – 'Multimentha'	EOHP	
– f. **officinalis**	ELau IHMH SIde	
– 'Oma Streib'	EOHP IIve WAlt	
– var. **ouweneellii**	IHMH	
Belgian mint **new**		
– 'Reine Rouge'	EOHP IHMH IIve	
– 'Reverchonii'	IHMH IIve	
– Swiss mint	CPrp WHHs	
pulegium	CArn CPrp CSev EDAr ELau GBar	
	GPoy IHMH MChe MHer MPEx	
	NVic SIde SPlb SRms WCHb	
	WHHs WHbs WHer WJek WPer	
	WWpP WWye	
– 'Upright'	CArn CBod CPrp EOHP GBar	
	GPoy MHer NBlu SHDw SIde WBry	
	WCHb WHHs WJek WPer WSel	
§ **requienii**	More than 30 suppliers	
rotundifolia hort.	see M. suaveolens	
rotundifolia (L.) Hudson	see M. x villosa	
rubra var. **raripila**	see M. x smithiana	
'Sayakarze'	see M. arvensis var. piperascens	
	'Sayakaze'	
§ x **smithiana**	CAgr CArn CPrp ELau EOHP GAbr	
	GBar GPoy IHMH ILis MChe MHer	
	NBir NGHP NPri WBea WBry WHer	
	WPer WRha WWye	
– 'Capel Ulo' (v)	ELau EOHP WHer	
§ **spicata**	CArn CPrp CSev EDAr GBar GPoy	
	IHMH ILis LHrt MBar MBow MBri	
	MChe MHer NBlu NFor NHol	
	SPlb SRms SWal WBea WHHs	
	WHer WJek WPer WWpP WWye	
– Algerian fruity	EOHP IHMH IIve	
* – 'Brundall'	ELau EOHP ILis	
– 'Canaries'	EOHP IHMH IIve	
* – var. **crispa**	CArn CPrp ECha EDAr ELau	
	EOHP GAbr GBar GGar IHMH	
	LHop MHer NArg NBlu NHol NPri	
	SIde SPlb WCHb WCer WCot	
	WPer WRha WSel WWye	
– – large-leaved **new**	IHMH	
– – 'Moroccan'	More than 30 suppliers	
– – 'Persian'	IHMH IIve	
– 'Guernsey'	EOHP SHDw	
– 'Kerry'	IIve	
– 'Newbourne'	ELau	
– 'Rhodos'	IHMH IIve	
– 'Russian'	NHol	
– 'Small Dole' (v)	SHDw	
– 'Spanish Furry'	EOHP MHer	
– 'Spanish Pointed'	ELau EOHP	
– 'Tashkent'	CArn ELau EOHP GWCH MHer	
	MTed SHDw SIde WBea WBry	
	WCHb WHHs WJek WWpP	
– subsp. **tomentosa**	IHMH IIve	
– 'Ukraine'	IIve	
* – 'Variegata' (v)	SHDw WHer	
– 'Verte Blanche'	IHMH IIve	

– 'Westmeath'	IIve	
§ **suaveolens**	CAgr CArn ELau GBar GPoy	
	GWCH IHMH ILis MBow MBri	
	MHer NPri SIde SWal WBea WHHs	
	WHer WLHH WPer	
* – 'Grapefruit'	CPrp IHMH IIve NPri WHHs	
– 'Jokka'	IIve	
* – 'Mobillei'	EOHP WJek	
* – 'Pineapple'	COkL IIve WHHs	
– subsp. **timija**	ELau WJek	
§ – 'Variegata' (v)	More than 30 suppliers	
I 'Sweet Pear'	EOHP	
sylvestris L.	see M. longifolia	
Thüringer minze	see Mentha x piperita	
	'Multimentha'	
§ x **villosa**	CArn EOHP IHMH IIve	
§ – var. **alopecuroides**	CAgr CBre CPrp ELau EMan GBar	
Bowles' mint	GGar GPoy IHMH IIve ILis MChe	
	MHer NGHP NSti SGar SIde STre	
	SWat WHHs WHer WJek WWye	
viridis	see M. spicata	

Menyanthes (Menyanthaceae)

trifoliata	CBen CRow CWat ECoo EHon	
	ELau EMFW GBar GPoy LPBA	
	MCCP MSta NPer NVic SLon WFar	
	WMAq WShi WWpP WWye	

Menziesia (Ericaceae)

alba	see Daboecia cantabrica f. alba	
ciliicalyx	SSpi	
– dwarf	SReu SSta	
– **lasiophylla**	see M. ciliicalyx var. purpurea	
– var. **multiflora**	CPLG GGGa MDun SReu SSta	
§ – var. **purpurea**	CPLG GGGa	
ferruginea	SReu SSta	
polifolia	see Daboecia cantabrica	
'Spring Morning'	WAbe	

Mercurialis (Euphorbiaceae)

perennis	GPoy MGol NSco WHer WShi	
– 'Cae Rhos Lligwy'	WHer	

Merendera (Colchicaceae)

eichleri	see M. trigyna	
kurdica	LAma	
§ **montana**	ERos WIvy WOBN	
pyrenaica	see M. montana	
raddeana	see M. trigyna	
sobolifera	EHyt EPot WFar	
§ **trigyna**	LAma	

Merremia (Convolvulaceae)

pinnata new	MSal	
§ **tuberosa**	CPlN SOWG	

Mertensia (Boraginaceae)

ciliata	CMdw CPom EBre GDra GKir	
	LRHS MArl MBri MNrw SWat WRus	
echioides	ETow	
franciscana	EBee GCal WCru	
lanceolata	EBee	
var. **nivalis new**		
macdougalii new	EBee	
maritima	EWll GPoy MSal NGby WWin	
– subsp. **asiatica**	see M. simplicissima	
primuloides	CPlt GDra GEdr WAbe	
pterocarpa	see M. sibirica	
pulmonarioides	see M. virginica	
§ **sibirica**	CLAP CSpe EBee ETow LPhx	
	NChi NDlv NLAp NLar NPri	
	SMrm SPlb WBVN WPnP WWin	
§ **simplicissima**	CBot CFir ECho EHyt ELan EMan	

virginica ♀ H4
GKir LPhx MBro MNrw NBir
NWCA SBla SCro SPlb WCom
WCru WFar WHoo WPnP
CBos CBot CBro CElw CFwr
CLAP CRDP EBre ELan EPfP EPot
EWTr GGar GKir LAma MCAu
NLar SIng SMac SMrm SRms
WCru WFar WPnP

Merxmuellera see Rytidosperma

Meryta (Araliaceae)
sinclairii   CHEx

Mesembryanthemum (Aizoaceae)
'Basutoland'   see Delosperma nubigenum
brownii   see Lampranthus brownii

Mespilus (Rosaceae)
germanica (F)
CBcs CDul CLnd CTri ECrN ELan
LPan MWat SHBN WDin WFar
WMou WOrn
- 'Bredase Reus' (F)   SKee
- 'Dutch' (F)   SDea SFam SKee
- 'Large Russian' (F)   ERea ESim GTwe
- 'Macrocarpa'   SKee
- 'Monstrous' (F)   SDea
- 'Nottingham' (F)
CCVT CEnd CSam CTho CWib
EBee EMui ENot EPfP ERea ESul
GKir GTwe LBuc LPan LRHS MBlu
MLan NBee SCoo SDea SFam
SKee SPer WJas WMou
- 'Royal' (F)   ESim SKee
- 'Westerveld' (F)   SKee

Metapanax see Pseudopanax

Metasequoia (Cupressaceae)
glyptostroboides ♀ H4   More than 30 suppliers
- 'Gold Rush'
CDoC CEnd CTho CWSG EPfP
GKir LCon LLin LRHS MAsh
MBlu MBri MGos SCoo SKee
SLim
- 'Green Mantle'   EHul
- 'Sheridan Spire'   CEnd CTho LNet WPGP
- 'Spring Cream' new   SLim
- 'White Spot' (v) new   SLim SPoG

Metrosideros (Myrtaceae)
carmineus   CHEx CTrC
- 'Carousel' (v)   ERea
- 'Ferris Wheel'   ERea
diffusus   CPIN
§ excelsus   CHEx CTrC CTrG EBak ECou
- 'Aureus'   ECou
- 'Fire Mountain'   CTrC
- 'Parnell'   CBcs CTrC
- 'Scarlet Pimpernel'   ERea SOWG
- 'Spring Fire'   CBcs GQui
- 'Upper Hut' (v)   CTrC
- 'Vibrance'   CTrC
'Goldfinger' (v)   ERea
kermadecensis   ECou
- 'Radiant' (v)   CPLG
- 'Variegatus' (v)   CBcs CDoC CTrC ECou ERea GQui
lucidus   see M. umbellatus
'Mistral'   ECou
'Moon Maiden'   SOWG
'Pink Lady'   CTrC
robustus   CTrC GQui
'Thomasii'   ELan EPfP EShb ESlt LRHS SOWG
tomentosus   see M. excelsus
§ umbellatus   CHEx CPne CTrC ECou GGar SBrw

villosus   SOWG
- 'Tahiti'   CBcs GQui IDee

Meum (Apiaceae)
athamanticum
CBos CRDP CRez CSev CSpe
EBee EBre EFou EGle EHrv
EMan EMar GBri GCal GPoy
MAvo MRav MSal MTho NBid
NPPs NSti SBla SIgm WFar WPer
WPrP

Michauxia (Campanulaceae)
campanuloides   WLin WSan
tchihatchewii   CBot CSpe

Michelia (Magnoliaceae)
chapensis   WPGP
compressa   EPfP
doltsopa   CBcs CFil CHEx EMil GQui IDee
SSpi
- 'Silver Cloud'   CBcs
figo   CAbb CFil CPLG ERea GQui SBrw
SSpi WPGP
- var. crassipes   WPGP
martinii   SSpi
maudiae   CPLG SSpi WPGP
sinensis   see M. wilsonii
§ wilsonii   CFil
yunnanensis   CFil SSpi

Micranthus (Iridaceae)
plantagineus   LBow

Microbiota (Cupressaceae)
decussata ♀ H4
CBcs CDoC CKen CMac CSBt
EBre EHul EOrn EPla GKir LBee
LCon LLin LRHS MAsh MBar
MBri MGos MWat SLim WBod
WFar
- 'Jakobsen'   CKen
- 'Trompenburg'   CKen

Microcachrys (Podocarpaceae)
tetragona   CDoC ECho ECou EHul EOrn
IMGH LCon LLin MBri SCoo

Microcoelum see Lytocaryum

Microglossa (Asteraceae)
albescens   see Aster albescens

Microlaena see Ehrharta

Microlepia (Dennstaedtiaceae)
speluncae   MBri

Micromeria (Lamiaceae)
chamissonis   GPoy
corsica   see Acinos corsicus
croatica   CPBP EHyt ETow
rupestris   see M. thymifolia
§ thymifolia   EMan GPoy NMen SPlb

Microseris (Asteraceae)
ringens hort.   see Leontodon rigens

Microsorum (Polypodiaceae)
diversifolium   see Phymatosorus
diversifolius

Microstrobos (Podocarpaceae)
fitzgeraldii   CKen
niphophilus   ECou

Mikania (Asteraceae)

§ **dentata** — CPln MBri
ternata — see M. dentata

Milium (Poaceae)

effusum — CKin COld CTrC
- 'Aureum' ♀ H4 — More than 30 suppliers
- var. **esthonicum** — EBee EMon EPPr NHol WWpP
- 'Yaffle' (v) — CBgR CFir CFwr EBee EBlw EFou
EGle EMan EPPr GCal MAnH
MCCP SDes WCot WLeb

Millettia (Papilionaceae)

§ **japonica** — LNet
murasaki-natsu-fuji — see M. reticulata
§ **reticulata** — LNet

Milligania (Asteliaceae)

densiflora — IBlr

Mimosa (Mimosaceae)

pudica — LRHS MLan SMur

Mimulus (Scrophulariaceae)

'A.T. Johnson' — NVic
alatus — EBee
'Andean Nymph' — see M. naiandinus
aridus — EBee
§ **aurantiacus** ♀ H2-3 — CBot CElw CFee CHal CPle CSpe
EBak EBre EOrc EPot ERea LHop
MOak NBir NPer SAga SDry SGar
SHFr SIng SMrm SPlb SUsu SYvo
WAbe WCom WEas WPer
§ - var. **puniceus** — CBot CHal CSpe CTri EBee EDif
EMan LHop MHar MOak SAga
SDry SMrm SUsu WCom WEas
- 'Pure Gold' **new** — EDif
- 'Tangerine' **new** — EDif
'Aztec Trumpet' — EDAr
x **bartonianus** — see Mimulus x harrisonii
bifidus — CSpe EBee SIng
- subsp. **fasciculatus new** — EBee
- 'Tapestry' — CSpe
§ - 'Verity Buff' — CSpe EDif LIck MOak WEas
- Verity hybrids — ERea
§ - 'Verity Purple' — CSpe EDif LIck SAga SOWG
- 'Wine' — see M. bifidus 'Verity Purple'
x **burnetii** — EMan LPBA NPri SRms
cardinalis ♀ H3 — EBee EChP EHon ELan LPBA MFir
MNrw MTho NFor NMGW SBHF
SHFr SPer WBor WCom WCot
WFar WHal WMoo WPGP WPer
WWin WWpP
- NNS 95-344 — EMan
- NNS 95-345 — WCot
- 'Dark Throat' — SGar
cupreus 'Minor' — ECho SIng
- 'Whitecroft Scarlet' ♀ H4 — EDAr ELan EPfP GDra LPBA LRHS
MDKP MHer SRms WPer WWeb
WWin WWpP
DK hybrid — MDKP
'Eleanor' — SAga SMrm SUsu
glutinosus — see M. aurantiacus
- **atrosanguineus** — see M. aurantiacus var. puniceus
- **luteus** — see M. aurantiacus
§ **guttatus** — CBen CKin CRow GDea MGas
NPer SRms WMAq WMoo WPer
WWpP
- 'Richard Bish' (v) — CRDP CWat EBee EMan LHop
MCCP
x **harrisonii** — CDes EBee EMan EPfP EWes
GMac WDyG

'Highland Orange' — EDAr EMlt GKir MHer NBlu SPlb
WGor WPer
'Highland Pink' — EDAr EMan EPfP GKir NBlu NLon
SIng SPlb WCom WGor WPer
I 'Highland Pink Rose' — SWal
'Highland Red' ♀ H4 — ECtt EDAr EMFW EMar EMlt EPfP
GDra GKev GKir LPBA NArg NPri
SIng SPlb SRms WCom WHen
WPer WWeb WWin
'Highland Yellow' — ECtt EDAr EMlt GKir MHer NBlu
SPlb WHen WPer WWeb
hose-in-hose (d) — EBee EMFW NChi NPer
'Inca Sunset' — EDAr EWes
langsdorffii — see M. guttatus
lewisii ♀ H3 — CHll EBee GDra GGar GTou
MTho SLon SPer SRms WFTG
WPGP WPer WRha
- JCA 1.624.009 — CDes
- f. **albus** — SGar
longiflorus — CBot MOak
- 'Santa Barbara' — LIck MOak
'Lothian Fire' — WMAq WWpP
luteus — CBen CRow CWat EHon ENot
EPfP IKee LPBA MHer MSta NLon
NPer NSco SHFr SWal WFar
WMAq WWpP
* - 'Variegatus' (v) — CRow GDra NGdn NPer
* 'Major Bees' — EPfP
'Malibu Ivory' — MDKP
'Malibu Pink' — MDKP
'Malibu Red' — MDKP
'Mandarin' — EBre
minimus — EMlt
moschatus — CRow NCat WCru
naiandinus ♀ H3 — CM&M CPBP EBee GKir LRHS
SPlb WFar WLin
- C&W 5257 — CPlt EBre ELan NMGW SRot SWat
WRos
'Old Rose' — EBee
'Orange Glow' — EPfP WHal
orange hose-in-hose (d) — NBir
§ 'Orkney Gold' (d) — EBee WAlt
'Popacatapetl' — CHal CHll CSpe EBee EDif EMan
LHop LIck MHar MOak MSte SAga
SChu SMrm SOWG SUsu
primuloides — ELan EPot NMen NWCA SPlb
- var. **linearifolius new** — EBee
'Puck' — GKir GMac LRHS
'Purple Mazz' **new** — SAga
'Quetzalcoatl' — LIck MOak SAga SMrm
Red Emperor — see M. 'Roter Kaiser'
ringens — CBen CRow CWat EBee EHon
EMFW EPfP GBri GDea LPBA MSta
NBir NBlu NPer SPer SPlb SRms
WFar WHil WMAq WPer WWpP
§ 'Roter Kaiser' — LPVe WBar WWpP
'Royal Velvet' — SAga
'Tawny' **new** — CSpe
'Threave Variegated' (v) — EBee EMan GBuc GCal MBri
MDKP NBir SBHF WCom WFar
WWpP
'Tigrinus' — see M. 'Popacatapetl'
tilingii — CHal ECho GTou
'Trish' **new** — CSpe
'Western Hills' — MGrG MLLN
'Wine Red' — see M. bifidus 'Verity Purple'
'Wisley Red' — ECot ELan SIng SRms
yellow hose-in-hose (d) — see Mimulus 'Orkney Gold'

Mina see Ipomoea

mint, Bowles see Mentha X villosa var. alopecuroides

mint, curly see M. spicata var. crispa

mint, eau de cologne see *M.* x *piperita f. citrata*

mint, ginger see *M.* x *gracilis*

mint, horse/long-leaved see *M. longifolia*

mint, pennyroyal see *M. pulegium*

mint, peppermint see *M. piperita*

mint, round-leaved see *M. suaveolens*

mint, spearmint see *M. spicata*

Minuartia (Caryophyllaceae)

caucasica	see *M. circassica*
§ *circassica*	CLyd CStu ESis ETow NWCA WPer
juniperina	CBrm ESis
laricifolia	CLyd LRHS
parnassica	see *M. stellata*
§ *stellata*	EPot ETow NDlv NMen SIng
- NS 758	NWCA
§ *verna*	NMen
- subsp. *caespitosa* 'Aurea'	see *Sagina subulata* var. *glabrata* 'Aurea'

Mirabilis (Nyctaginaceae)

jalapa	CArn EBot ELan ETub LAma LHrt LRHS MBri MGol MSal SEND SHFr SRms SYvo
multiflora **new**	MGol

Miscanthus (Poaceae)

flavidus B&SWJ 3697	WCru
floridulus misapplied	see *Miscanthus* x *giganteus*
floridulus **new**	MBrN MSPs NOak WPrP
x *giganteus*	CFir CHEx CSev EBee EFou EHoe EWsh GCal LBBr LRHS MAvo MCCP MMoz MWgw NBea NPSI NVic SDes SDix SEND SMad SPlb WCot WFar
nepalensis	CKno CPLG EHoe EPPr EWes LEdu MAnH SMrm WCot
- CC 3619	EPPr
oligostachyus	CBig GCal NGdn
§ - 'Afrika'	CFwr LPhx
I - 'Nanus Variegatus' (v)	CBrm CKno CRow EBee EHoe EMan EMon FVFa EWes LRHS MMoz SApp WCot WPGP
- 'Purpurascens'	see *Miscanthus* 'Purpurascens'
§ 'Purpurascens'	CBrm CFwr CKno EBee EBlw ECGN ECha EGol EHoe EHul EMan EPPr EPla EWsh GSki LAst MBrN MMoz MWgw NGdn SApp SDes WBro WCot
sacchariflorus	More than 30 suppliers
sinensis	CAgr CBig CHEx EPfP GBin GKir LHrt MHdf MMoz MWgw MWrn NOak WDin WMoo WRos
- 'Adagio'	CFwr CKno EGle EMan EPPr LEdu LPhx NPPs SMHy WCot
- 'Afrika'	see *M. oligostachyus* 'Afrika'
- 'Arabesque'	EFou EGle EPPr IPot LPan MMoz SApp
- 'Augustfeder'	EBre EGle
- 'Autumn Light'	EPPr IPot
- 'Blütenwunder' **new**	SApp
- 'China'	CBig CBrm CDes CFir CFwr CHar CWCL EBee ECGN EHoe EMan

	EPGN EPPr EPla EWes EWsh GBin IPot LRHS MBri NDov NHol NOrc SAga SChu SDes SMad SWat WPGP
- var. *condensatus*	EPPr
- - 'Cabaret' (v)	CKno CSpe CWCL EBee EBlw EFou EHoe EMan EPPr GBin IPot LAst NCot NGdn SRos WCot WHal
- - 'Central Park'	see *M. sinensis* var. *condensatus* 'Cosmo Revert'
- - 'Cosmo Revert'	CKno EMil MMoz SApp
- - 'Cosmopolitan' (v)	More than 30 suppliers
- - 'Emerald Giant'	see *M. sinensis* var. *condensatus* 'Cosmo Revert'
- 'Dixieland' (v)	CBig EGle EHoe EPPr GBin IPot LEdu LPan MMoz
- dwarf form	SMad
- 'Federriese'	EBre
- 'Ferner Osten'	More than 30 suppliers
- 'Flamingo'	More than 30 suppliers
- 'Gearmella'	CBig EBcc EBre EGle EPPr GKir LEdu
- 'Gewitterwolke'	CFwr LPhx
- 'Ghana'	CFwr LHop LPhx
- 'Giraffe'	CDes CFwr GKir
- 'Goldfeder' (v)	CFwr EBee EPla WBcn
- 'Goliath'	CFwr EHoe EPPr IPot LPan
- 'Gracillimus'	More than 30 suppliers
- 'Graziella'	CEnd CHar CKno CWib EBre EGle EHoe EPGN EPPr EPla LPan LPhx LRHS MBri MMoz MSte NDov NGdn NHol NOrc NPPs SCro SDes SPer SUsn WLRN WPGP WPrP WTMC
- 'Grosse Fontäne'	CBrm CKno EBee ECha EGle EHoe EPGN EPPr EPla EWsh GKir LEdu LRHS NHol SDes SMad WAul WMoo
- 'Haiku'	CFwr LPhx
- 'Helga Reich' **new**	CBig
- 'Hercules'	MAvo MMoz SApp
- 'Hermann Müssel'	CFwr LPhx SApp
- 'Juli'	CKno IPot LPan
- 'Kaskade'	CBig CKno CWCL EBee EBre EGle EHoe EPGN EPPr EPla GKir LPhx MAvo MBri MMoz MSte NOGN SMrm WBcn WFar WMoo
- 'Kirk Alexander' (v) **new**	SApp
- 'Kleine Fontäne'	More than 30 suppliers
- 'Kleine Silberspinne'	More than 30 suppliers
- 'Krater'	LEdu MBrN SWat
§ - 'Little Kitten'	CDes CKno EBee EGle EPla EWsh LEdu MBar SMad WPGP
- Little Nicky = 'Hinjo' (v)	CDes SApp
- 'Malepartus'	More than 30 suppliers
- 'Morning Light' (v)	More than 30 suppliers
- new hybrids	CFwr CPen CTrC EChP EHul LRav
- 'Nippon'	More than 30 suppliers
- 'Nishidake' **new**	CFwr
- 'November Sunset'	EGle EPPr EWes IPot MMoz
- 'Poseidon'	EPPr SDys
- 'Positano'	CDes CKno EBee MMoz WPGP
- 'Professor Richard Hansen'	CFwr
- 'Pünktchen' (v)	CBrm CPen EBee ECha EFou EGle EPPr EPla LPan LPhx NPro SMHy SMad SMrm
- var. *purpurascens* hort.	see *Miscanthus* 'Purpurascens'
- 'Roland'	CFwr EBee GBin LBBr LPhx SAga
- 'Roterpfeil'	LPhx
- 'Rotfuchs'	GKir LPhx WFar

– 'Rotsilber'	CBig CBrm CFwr CKno CSpe CWCL CWib EBre ECha EFou EGle EHoe EPGN EPPr EPla EWsh GKir IArd LEdu LPan LRHS MWgw SHBN STes WFar WPnP WViv
– 'Samurai'	EBee MAvo
– 'Sarabande'	CBig CBrm CFwr CKno ECGN EFou EGle EHoe EHul EPPr EWsh GKir IPot LPan SApp SMHy WFar
§ – 'Silberfeder'	More than 30 suppliers
– 'Silberpfeil' (v)	MSte
– 'Silberspinne'	CBig CMdw EBee EFou EGle EPla GKir LEdu LPhx LRHS MCCP NGdn SAga SPlb WAul WDin
– 'Silberturm'	CFwr SVil
– Silver Feather	see M. sinensis 'Silberfeder'
– 'Sioux'	CBig CFwr EBee EGle EHoe EPPr EPla EWsh GKir LRHS MLwd MMoz SMHy WBcn
– 'Sirene'	CBig CFwr EBee EBre EGle EHoe EMan EPGN EPPr EPla GKir LPan LRHS MBNS MBlu MGrG NHol WFar WPrP
– 'Slavopour'	EPla
– 'Spätgrün'	EPla
– 'Strictus' (v)	More than 30 suppliers
– 'Tiger Cub' (v)	CBig CWCL
– 'Undine'	CFwr CKno CMea EBlw EBre ECha EGle EHoe EPGN EPPr EPla EWsh LEdu LPhx LRHS MCLN MMoz NHol SChu SDix SHFr SPla SRGP WLRN
– 'Variegatus' (v)	More than 30 suppliers
– 'Vorläufer'	CFwr EBee EBre EFou EHoe EPPr EPla EWsh GKir LPhx
– 'Wetterfahne'	CFwr EBre EGle
§ – 'Yaku-jima'	EBee ECha EGle EPPr
– 'Yakushima Dwarf'	More than 30 suppliers
– 'Zebrinus' (v)	More than 30 suppliers
– 'Zwergelefant'	CFwr MMoz SMHy
tinctorius 'Nanus Variegatus' misapplied	see M. oligostachyus 'Nanus Variegatus'
transmorrisonensis	CBig CBod CFwr CKno EHoe EMan EPPr EWsh GBin LEdu LHrt LPhx LRav MAnH MMoz NHol SApp SMad SWal WHil
yakushimensis	see M. sinensis 'Yaku-jima' , M. sinensis 'Little Kitten'

Mitchella (Rubiaceae)

repens	EBee WCru
undulata B&SWJ 4402	WCru

Mitella (Saxifragaceae)

breweri	CHal CNic CSam EBee ECha GBin GGar LSyl MRav MSte NHol NSti SHFr SHel SRms SSpi WBea WEas WFar WMoo WPer WPnP WWye
caulescens	ECha MRav NBro NHol WPer WPnP
diphylla	EBee
formosana B&SWJ 125	EBee NCat WCru
japonica B&SWJ 4971 **new**	WCru
kiusiana new	CLAP
makinoi new	CLAP
ovalis	EBee
pauciflora B&SWJ 6361 **new**	WCru
stauropetala	EBee NCat NWoo
yoshinagae	EBee
– B&SWJ 4893	WCru WPnP

Mitraria (Gesneriaceae)

coccinea	CAbb CBcs CMac CNic CPLG CPln CPle CTrG CTrw CWib ELan ERea EShb GEil GGGa IDee MBlu MDun SArc SLon SPer SSpi WBod WBor WCot WGwG WPat WSHC
– Clark's form	CSam GGar LAst
– from Lake Puyehue	CDoC CFee ERea GQui LRHS MAsh MGos SBra SBrw SSta WCru WCwm WFar WWal
– 'Lake Caburgua'	GCal GGar NSti WCot

Molinia (Poaceae)

altissima	see M. caerulea subsp. arundinacea
caerulea	CBig CFwr COtt EBee EHul EPPr LPhx MBlu MWod WWpP
§ – subsp. **arundinacea**	CBig CBrm CWCL EBre ECGN ECha EFou GBin GKir SLPl SPer SRGP WPer
– – 'Bergfreund'	EBee ECGN EHoe EMon EPPr EWsh GCal LPhx MAvo SCou SDys SHel SMad SUsu WDyG WMoo WWye
– – 'Cordoba' **new**	LPhx
– – 'Fontäne'	CPen CSam EBee EFou EHoe EPPr GBin LPan LPhx MSte
– – 'Karl Foerster'	More than 30 suppliers
– – 'Skyracer'	EBre EFou EGle EHoe EPPr GBri LBBr LIck LPan LPhx MMoz SApp SMHy SMad WCot WFar WMoo WWpP
– – 'Staefa'	EHoe
– – 'Transparent'	CHad CKno CWCL EBre ECha EFou EGle EHoe EPGN EPPr GBri GCal IGor LPan LPhx MBri MMoz MSte SDes SMad SMrm WCot WHal WPrP
– – 'Windsaule'	EBee LPhx
– – 'Windspiel'	CKno CRow CSam CWCL EBee ECGN ECha EFou EGle EHoe EMan EMil EMon EPPr EWsh GCal LEdu LPan LPhx MAnH MWgw NSti SApp SMrm SWal WBro WCot WMoo WPGP
– – 'Zuneigung'	EHoe EPPr LPan LPhx
– subsp. **caerulea new**	CMdw
– – 'Carmarthen' (v)	CElw CNat EBee EMon EPPr IPot MAvo SApp SUsu WPrP
– – 'Claerwen' (v)	EMan EPPr GBuc GCal
– – 'Dauerstrahl'	EPPr GBin MAvo NHol WLin WPrP
– – 'Edith Dudszus'	More than 30 suppliers
– – 'Heidebraut'	CBig CElw CFwr EBee ECGN ECGP ECha EGle EHoe EHul EMon EPPr GBin LPhx LRHS MAvo MBri NBro NDov SApp SVil WFar
– – 'Moorflamme'	CBig EPPr LPan LPhx
– – 'Moorhexe'	More than 30 suppliers
– – 'Strahlenquelle'	CElw CKno CSam EBee EGle ELan EMan EMon EPGN EPPr EPla GBin GCal LRHS MAvo MMoz NBro NOGN WPGP WPrP
– – 'Variegata' (v) ♀ H4	More than 30 suppliers
litoralis	see M. caerulea subsp. arundinacea

Molopospermum (Apiaceae)

peloponnesiacum	CFwr EBee EMan LEdu LPhx MLLN NChi NLar SIgm SMrm WCot WCru

Moltkia (Boraginaceae)

§ **doerfleri** CPle NChi
  graminifolia see *M. suffruticosa*
§ x **intermedia** ♀ H4 CMea CNic SOkd WWin
  petraea NWCA SIgm WPat
§ **suffruticosa** NBir

Momordica (Cucurbitaceae)

  balsamina CPlN MSal
  charantia MSal

Monadenium (Euphorbiaceae)

  lugardae MBri
  'Variegatum' (v) MBri

Monarda ❀ (Lamiaceae)

'Adam'	EBee GAbr GCal LRHS MAnH MLLN MSte WViv
'Amethyst'	EWes SOkh
'Aquarius'	CElw EBlw EChP EFou EGle EMon EPfP ERou GKir LRHS MBri MCAu MCLN MSte MWgw NPro NSti SChu SCro SDes SPla WAul WCHb WFar WHil WRus WViv WWeb
austromontana	CArn CFwr EBee ECoo EMan EVFa MDKP MWrn NBir SCro SDes SIde WCot WFar WPer
'Baby Spice'	EBee ENot LRHS
§ 'Balance'	EBee EBlw EChP EFou EGle EMan EPPr GCal LPhx LRHS MAnH MCAu NPPs NSti NVic SChu SCro SOkh SPla WCHb WFar WHoo WPGP WPnP WRus
'Beauty of Cobham' ♀ H4	EChu ELan EOrc EPfP ERou EWsh GAbr GKir GMaP LHop LPhx LRHS MAnH MBri MHer MSte NChi NDov NLar NSti SChu SDes SMad SPer WCIIb WHil WLin WSan WViv
'Blaukranz'	EFou SChu SMrm
§ 'Blaustrumpf'	CElw EBee GBri MHer MSte NCiC NLar NOrc SPer WFTG WRus
Blue Stocking	see *M.* 'Blaustrumpf'
Dowman	see *M.* 'Sagittarius'
bradburyana	EBee WCHb
'Cambridge Scarlet' ♀ H4	More than 30 suppliers
'Capricorn'	CStr EFou EGle EMan EMar ERou GBuc LRHS MSte NCat SChu SCro SOkh WCHb WRus WWal
'Cherokee'	GBar GBri LPhx MRav WCHb WFar
citriodora	CArn GPoy LRHS MChe MHer MSal SIde SPlb SRms SWat WHHs WJek WLHH WPer WSel
'Comanche'	CStr EBee EFou EHrv EPfP EWes LPhx MAnH SAga WCHb WFar WRus WViv
'Croftway Pink' ♀ H4	CBcs COlW CSBt CStr EBre ECha ECtt EFou ELan ELau EPfP ERou EWTr GBar GKir LRHS MCAu MGrG MHer NOrc NPPs NSti SPer SRms WCHb WFar WViv
didyma	CAgr CArn EDAr EPfP GKir LSyl MChe MFir MHdf MPWC MSal NArg NBlu NBro NLon SWal SWat WBrE WBri WHbs WJek
- 'Alba'	CBot MGol MHer WBea
- 'Duddiscombe'	CSam
- 'Goldmelise'	WBea
'Donnerwolke'	SChu
'Elsie's Lavender'	CStr EBee EFou EGle EMon GBri GBuc LPhx LRHS MAnH NBro WAul WCHb

§ 'Feuerschopf'	WOut
'Fireball' **new**	ERou GBin WHil
Firecrown	see *M.* 'Feuerschopf'
§ 'Fishes'	EBee EChP EFou EHrv ELan EMar EWes GBar GCal LPhx MAnH MCLN MMil MRav MSte NCat NLar NPPs NVic SAga SChu SPla WCHb WFar WHil WMnd WPnP WViv
fistulosa	CAgr CArn EBee EWTr GPoy MBow MChe MSal MWrn SIde WHHs WHer WJek WLHH WMoo WPer
fistulosa alba **new**	EBee
'Gardenview'	CMdw EWes GBar GCal MAnH NSti SMrm WRHF
'Gardenview Scarlet'	EBee EBre ECtt EFou EOrc GBri GKir LPhx LRHS MBri NCat NChi WCHb WPer WSan
Gemini	see *M.* 'Twins'
'Hartswood Wine'	SMad
'Jacob Cline'	EFou
'Kardinal'	EBee EFou
'Lambada'	LRHS MHdf NPPs WSan
Libra	see *M.* 'Balance'
'Loddon Crown'	CBos CHea EBee ECGP EFou EMar EMon LRHS MAnH MBri MWrn NChi WCHb WFar WMaN WRha WWeb WWpP
* 'Mahogany'	CElw CSam CStr EBre EChP EFou EGle EMar ERou EWTr GBri GKir GMaP LRHS MHer MRav MTis NChi NCiC NPPs NSti SPer WCHb WSan WViv
'Marshall's Delight'	CBos EBee EBre EChP GKir MCLN SMrm WGwG WHHs WHil WRus
* **media**	EBee
* **Melissa**	EBee EFou EGle WSan
menthifolia	CAgr CArn EWTr GCal LRHS MCCP SAga SMrm STes WHHs WHer
'Mohawk'	EBee EChP EFou EGle EHrv EMan EMon EPPr ERou LPhx LRHS MAnH MCLN NCat NChi NCiC NDov WCHb WLRN WViv
'Mrs Perry'	EFou EWes MHer
'Ou Charm'	CElw CFwr CSu EBre ECGP EChP EPPr ERou EWes GBri LRHS MCAu MCLN MLLN MMil MWrn NChi NCiC NDov NPPs SAga SMad STes WAul WCHb WCom WCot WFar WSan WViv
'Panorama'	ECtt MSal SPlb SWal WElm WMoo WPer
'Panorama Red Shades' (Panorama Series)	MWrn
'Pawnee'	SChu WCHb
'Petite Delight'	EBee EFou LHop LRHS NLar WAul WCot WFar
'Petite Pink Supreme' **new**	MBri WHil
'Pink Tourmaline'	EBee EChP ERou LPhx LRHS MCLN NGby SMad SMrm WCHb WFar WRus
Pisces	see *M.* 'Fishes'
'Poyntzfield Pink'	GPoy
Prairie Glow	see *M.* 'Prärieglut'
Prairie Night	see *M.* 'Prärienacht'
'Präriebrand'	MBri
§ 'Prärieglut'	MBri
§ 'Prärienacht'	More than 30 suppliers
punctata	CArn CBot EBee ELan EMan GCal LPhx LRHS MLLN MSal SMrm SWat WCHb WMoo
'Purple Ann'	CFwr LPhx NDov SAga SMrm

	'Raspberry Wine'	EFou GBri
	'Ruby Glow'	CHad EBee ECGN EChP EHrv
		EMan LPhx LRHS MArl MBri
		MCLN MTis NCat NChi NDov
		NPPs SChu SOkh WCHb WFar
		WLRN WRus
§	'Sagittarius'	EBee EBlw EChP EGle EMan
		EMon GBar GKir LRHS MAnH
		MCLN MMil MWgw NCat NGdn
		NSti SChu SPla WCHb WHil WLRN
		WPGP WWal WWeb
	'Sahin's Mildew-free'	WCHb
§	'Schneewittchen'	CFwr CStr EChP ECha ECtt EHrv
		ELan EMan ERou EWTr GKir
		LRHS MAnH MBri MLLN NBro
		NLar NOrc NSti SChu SDes SIde
		SPer WAul WHHs WMnd WSan
		WViv
§	'Scorpion'	More than 30 suppliers
	'Sioux'	EHrv EWes GBar GBuc GKir
		LRHS SMrm WCHb WFar WHil
		WRha
	'Snow Maiden'	see M. 'Schneewittchen'
	'Snow Queen'	EBee EBlw ECtt EFou EPfP GKir
		LRHS NPPs SPla WMnd WSan
	Snow White	see M. 'Schneewittchen'
	'Squaw'	More than 30 suppliers
	'Talud'	NCat
§	'Twins'	CBod CMil CPrp EBee EChP
		EFou EGle EMar ERou EWTr
		GAbr LRHS MBri MLLN NPri
		SDes SWat WCHb WHil WPnP
		WRus WSan
	'Velvet Queen'	SMrm
	'Vintage Wine'	ECtt EFou EGle ELan GBri NFla
		SMrm WCHb WCot WFar WHil
		WRus WWye
*	violacea	WCHb WWpP
	'Violet Queen'	EBee EBre EChP EMar EWes LRHS
		NPro

Monardella (Lamiaceae)

	macrantha	CPBP SBla
	nana subsp. arida	CPBP
	- subsp. tenuiflora	NWCA
	NNS 95-352	
	odoratissima	CArn ECoo EMan LRav MWrn
		WJek
	palmeri	NWCA
	villosa subsp. globosa	WCot
	NNS 95-355 new	
	- 'Russian River' new	CSpe

Monopsis (Campanulaceae)

	lutea	see Lobelia lutea
	Midnight = 'Yagemon'PBR	CSpe
	unidentata	EMan

Monstera (Araceae)

	deliciosa (F) ♀ H1	MBri NBlo SRms XBlo
	- 'Variegata' (v) ♀ H1	MBri SRms

Montbretia see Tritonia

	x crocosmiiflora	see Crocosmia x
		crocosmiiflora
	pottsii	see Crocosmia pottsii

Montia (Portulacaceae)

	australasica	see Neopaxia australasica
	californica	see Claytonia nevadensis
	parvifolia	see Naiocrene parvifolia
	perfoliata	see Claytonia perfoliata
	sibirica	see Claytonia sibirica

Moraea (Iridaceae)

	alpina	GCrs
§	aristata	LBow
§	bellendenii	LBow WCot
	bipartita new	WCot
*	drakensbergensis	CPBP
§	fugax	IBlr WCot
	gawleri	WCot
	glaucopsis	see M. aristata
	huttonii	CDes CFir EBee SBla WCru WSHC
	iridioides	see Dietes iridioides
	longifolia Sweet	see M. fugax
	lurida new	WCot
	natalensis	SBla
	papilionacea	EBee WCot
	pavonia var. lutea	see M. bellendenii
	polyanthos new	WCot
	polystachya	EBee LRHS
	ramosissima	LBow
	robusta	SIgm
	spathacea	see M. spathulata
§	spathulata	CBro CPLG CStu EBee EMan GCal
		GMac LPio MFir WCot WPGP WSHC
	thomsonii	LBow LPio
	vegeta	WCot
	villosa	LBow SIgm WCot

Moricandia (Brassicaceae)

	moricandioides	CSpe

Morina (Morinaceae)

	alba	EBee NChi
	longifolia	More than 30 suppliers
	nepalensis	SScr
	persica	EChP GBuc MBro SIgm WHoo
	polyphylla	GPoy

Morisia (Brassicaceae)

	hypogaea	see M. monanthos
§	monanthos	CPla GMaP IHMH MBar NLAp
		NWCA
	- 'Fred Hemingway'	EBre EHyt EPot GCrs ITim LRHS
		NHar NLAp NMen NSla SBla SIng
		WPat

Morus (Moraceae)

§	alba	CArn CBcs CDul CLnd CMCN
		CTho EBee ECrN ELan ERea
		EWTr GKir GTwe LBuc NPSI
		NWea SHBN SPar SPer WDin
	- 'Laciniata'	IDee
	- 'Macrophylla'	SMad
	- var. multicaulis	ERea
	- 'Pendula'	CBcs CDoC CEnd ELan EPfP ERea
		GTwe LHyr LNet LPan LRHS MBlu
		MBri MLan MWat NBee NPSI
		SHBN SPer WDin WOrn
	- 'Platanifolia'	LPan MBlu
	- var. tatarica	LEdu WOTO
	bombycis	LPan
	- 'Atomic Blast'	WBcn
	'Illinois Everbearing' (F)	ESim
	nigra (F) ♀ H4	More than 30 suppliers
§	- 'Chelsea' (F)	CEnd COtt CTho CTri CWSG
		EMui EPfP ERea GTwe MBri MGos
		MLan SKee SLim SPer SPoG
	- 'King James'	see M. nigra 'Chelsea'
	- 'Large Black' (F)	EMui
	- 'Wellington' (F)	CEnd

Mosla (Lamiaceae)

	dianthera new	GCal

Mucuna (*Papilionaceae*)
bennettii	CPlN
macrocarpa	CPlN
sempervirens	CPlN

Muehlenbeckia (*Polygonaceae*)
astonii	ECou
axillaris hort.	see *M. complexa*
§ – Walp.	CTri ECou GCal GGar MHdf NCat SDry
– 'Mount Cook' (f) **new**	ECou
– 'Ohau' (m) **new**	ECou
§ **complexa**	CBcs CDoC CHEx CHal CPLG CPlN CTrC CWib EBee ECou EPla ESlt GQui IBlr LRHS MCCP MHdf NSti SAPC SArc SBra SDry SLim SLon SMac SPar WCFE WSHC
– (f) **new**	ECou
– 'Nana'	see *M. axillaris* Walp.
– var. **trilobata**	CPlN EPla IBlr MHdf WCru
– 'Ward' (m) **new**	ECou
ephedroides	ECou
– 'Clarence Pass'	ECou
– var. **muricatula**	ECou
gunnii	CPlN ECou
platyclados	see *Homalocladium platycladum*

Muhlenbergia (*Poaceae*)
capillaris	CKno
dubia new	CBrm
emersleyi new	CBrm
japonica 'Cream Delight' (v)	EBee EHoe EMan EMon EPPr LRIIS MCCP WWpP
lindheimeri	WCot
mexicana	CBig EBee EPPr SRGP
rigens	CBig CBrm CKno

Mukdenia (*Saxifragaceae*)
acanthifolia	WCru
rossi variegated (v) **new**	EMon
§ **rossii**	CRDP EBee EMan EMon EPla GCal MTed NGar SHar SMac SMad SSpi WCot WCru WTMC
– dwarf **new**	GCal
– 'Ogon' **new**	WCru

mulberry see *Morus*

Murraya (*Rutaceae*)
* **elliptica**	SOWG
exotica	see *M. paniculata*
koenigii	EOHP GPoy
§ **paniculata**	CArn ERea SMur

Musa (*Musaceae*)
from Yunnan, China	CKob EAmu NBlo NPal WPGP XBlo
§ **acuminata**	MBri
– 'Double' (AAA+ Group) (F)	WMul
§ – 'Dwarf Cavendish' (AAA Group) (F) ♀ H1	CKob EAmu ELan EPfP ESlt MSPs NBlo WMul XBlo
– 'Dwarf Red' (AAA Group) (F)	NBlo XBlo
– 'Dwarf Red Jamaican' (AAA Group) (F)	CKob
– 'Grand Nain' (AAA Group) (F)	WMul
– 'Pisang Berlin' (AA Group) (F)	CKob
– 'Pisang Lidi' (AA Group) (F)	CKob
– 'Red Iholena' (AAA Group) (F)	NBlo WMul XBlo
* – 'Rose' (AA Group) (F)	CKob
– 'Tapo' (AA Group) (F)	CKob
– 'Williams' (AAA Group) (F)	EAmu WCot WMul
– 'Zebrina' ♀ H1+3	CKob EAmu NBlo WMul XBlo
– 'Zebrina' x **acuminata** 'Grand Nain'	EAmu WMul
balbisiana	CKob EAmu NBlo WCot XBlo
– 'Cardaba' (BBB Group) (F)	WMul
– 'Tani' (BB Group) (F)	CKob
basjoo	More than 30 suppliers
– 'Sakhalin'	CKob WMul
beccarii	CKob
'Brazilian'	see *Musa* x *paradisiaca* 'Pome'
'Burmese Blue' **new**	CKob
'Butuhan' (*balbisiana* x *textilis*)	CKob
cavendishii	see *M. acuminata* 'Dwarf Cavendish'
coccinea	see *M. uranoscopus*
'Ele-ele' (AAB Group) (F)	CKob
ensete	see *Ensete ventricosum*
(Fe'i Group) 'Utafun' (F)	CKob
hookeri	see *M. sikkimensis*
* 'Kru' (F)	NBlo WMul XBlo
§ **lasiocarpa**	CHEx CKob EAmu ESlt LRHS WMul WPGP
laterita	CKob
mannii	CKob
nana Lour.	see *M. acuminata*
– auct.	see *M. acuminata* 'Dwarf Cavendish'
ornata ♀ H1	LPal NBlo WMul XBlo
– 'African Red'	CKob
– 'Macro'	CKob
– 'Purple'	CKob
– 'Royal Red Salmon' **new**	EAmu
x **paradisiaca** AAB Group	NBlo XBlo
– 'Dwarf Orinoco' (ABB Group) (F)	CKob
– Goldfinger = 'FHIA-01' (AAAB Group) (F)	CKob
– 'Hajaré' (ABB Group) (F)	CKob
– 'Malbhog' (AAB Group) (F)	CKob
– 'Monthan' (ABB Group) (F)	CKob
– 'Mysore' (AAB Group) (F)	WMul
– 'Ney Poovan' (AB Group) (F)	CKob
– 'Orinoco' (ABB Group) (F)	EAmu WMul
– 'Pisang Awak' (AAB Group) (F)	CKob
§ – 'Pome' (AAB Group) (F)	WMul
– 'Rajapuri' (AAB Group)	EAmu WMul
– 'Safet Velchi' (AB Group) (F)	CKob
– 'Silk' (AAB Group) (F)	CKob
– 'Yawa Dwarf' (F)	CKob
'Royal Pink' (*ornata* hybrid)	CKob
'Royal Purple' (*ornata* hybrid)	CKob
'Royal Red' (*ornata* hybrid)	CKob
'Saba' ambig. (F)	CKob
§ **sikkimensis**	CHid CKob EAmu ELan ESlt EWes LPJP NBlo SChr WMul WPGP XBlo
textilis	CKob
§ **uranoscopus** ♀ H1	CKob EAmu NBlo WMul XBlo
velutina ♀ H1+3	CKob EAmu NBlo SSte WMul WPGP XBlo
* 'Violacea' (*ornata* hybrid)	LPal

Muscari ✿ (Hyacinthaceae)

ambrosiacum	see M. muscarimi
armeniacum ♀ H4	CBro EPar EPfP ETub IHMH LRHS MBri NCel NDov NMGW NRog SChr SRms WCot WPer WShi
- 'Argaei Album'	CMea EPot LAma NEgg
- 'Babies Breath'	see M. neglectum 'Baby's Breath'
- 'Blue Pearl'	LRHS NCel
- 'Blue Spike' (d)	CBro EPar EPfP LAma LRHS MBri NBir NBlu NCel NEgg NRog SChr WCot WPer
- 'Christmas Pearl'	WCot
- 'Early Giant'	LAma
- 'Fantasy Creation'	CFwr EChP EPot ETub LRHS MBNS NCel WAul WCot WFTG
- 'Heavenly Blue'	LAma
- 'Saffier'	LAma LRHS
- 'Valerie Finnis'	CAvo CBro CFwr EPot GCrs ITim LRHS MSte WAbe WCot WFTG
§ aucheri ♀ H4	CAvo EPar LAma NCel NRog NRya WHoo
- 'Tubergenianum' new	ETub
§ azureum ♀ H4	CAvo CBro CNic EPar EPfP ERos LAma LRHS NMen NRog WCot
- 'Album'	CBro EPar ERos ETub LAma LRHS MAvo NRog SChr WBry WCot
botryoides	LAma NCel NRog
- 'Album'	CAvo CBro EChP EPfP LAma LRHS MBNS MBri NCel NRog WFTG WShi
caucasicum	SChr
chalusicum	see M. pseudomuscari
§ comosum	CBro EPar LRHS WPer
- 'Monstrosum'	see M. comosum 'Plumosum'
§ - 'Plumosum'	CAvo CBro CRDP EBot EMan EMon EPar EPot LAma LRHS MAvo MBri NCel WCot
dionysicum	WCot
HOA 8965 new	
grandifolium	EHyt
- JCA 689.450	WCot
'Ken Aslett'	GCrs
latifolium	CAvo CBro CMea CStu EHyt EPar GGar LAma LRHS MAvo MBNS MLLN NCel NChi NRog WBry WCot WHil WHoo WPer
* - 'Blue Angels'	NBir
§ macrocarpum	CAvo CBro ECha LAma WAbe WCot
mirum	EHyt
moschatum	see M. muscarimi
§ muscarimi	CBro EPar LAma WCot
- var. flavum	see M. macrocarpum
§ neglectum	CMea CSWP LAma SEND WFTG WShi
§ - 'Baby's Breath'	CMil SCnR SMad SMrm WCot
pallens	NWCA
paradoxum	see Bellevalia paradoxa
§ pseudomuscari ♀ H4 BSBE 842	EHyt
racemosum	see M. neglectum
'Sky Blue'	EPot
'Superstar'	ETub
§ tenuiflorum	WCot
tubergenianum	see M. aucheri 'Tubergenianum'
'White Beauty'	EPot LRHS

Muscarimia (Hyacinthaceae)

ambrosiacum	see Muscari muscarimi
macrocarpum	see Muscari macrocarpum

Musella (Musaceae)

lasiocarpa	see Musa lasiocarpa

Musschia (Campanulaceae)

wollastonii	CHEx CPla CTrF EMan

Mutisia (Asteraceae)

clematis	CRHN
coccinea	CPIN
decurrens	CPIN
ilicifolia	CPIN EBee IBlr LRHS MTPN SIgm WSHC
microphylla	EBee WCot
oligodon	CPIN IBlr SGar
- F&W 9400	EBee
retusa	see M. spinosa var. pulchella
spinosa	EBee
§ - var. pulchella	SSpi
subulata f. rosea new	CFil

Myoporum (Myoporaceae)

acuminatum	see M. tenuifolium
debile	ECou
laetum	CDoC CHEx CPLG CTbh CTrC

Myosotidium (Boraginaceae)

§ hortensia	More than 30 suppliers
- white	CBos CPla EVFa NCot WNor
nobile	see M. hortensia

Myosotis (Boraginaceae)

alpestris 'Ruth Fischer'	NBir NMen
arvensis	GWCH
australis	EShb GCal MMHG MSPs
'Bill Baker'	CPLG EMon
colensoi	ECou EDAr MTho NMen NWCA
explanata	NMen WEas
palustris	see M. scorpioides
pulvinaris	CPBP
rakiura	EVFa GCrs GTou
rupicola	see M. alpestris
§ scorpioides	CBen CRow CWat EHon EMFW EPfP LPBA MBow MGrG MSta NCot NGdn SCoo SLon SPlb SRms SWat WEas WMAq WMoo WWpP
- Maytime = 'Blaqua' (v)	EMan EMon LPBA NBir NCot NGdn WWpP
- 'Mermaid'	CBen CRow CWat ECha EHon EPfP GMac LPBA LRHS MFir MSta NCat NDov SDix SWat WFar WPer WRus WWpP
- 'Pinkie'	CRDP CRow CWat EMFW GMac NGdn SWat WWpP
- 'Snowflakes'	CRow CWat WWpP
secunda	CKin
sylvatica alba	see M. sylvatica f. lactea
§ - f. lactea	CRow
- 'Snowdrift' (v)	CRDP

Myrceugenia (Myrtaceae)

ovata	CTrG
planipes	CTrG

Myrcia (Myrtaceae)

pennsylvanica new	GIBF
tomentosa new	GIBF

Myrica (Myricaceae)

californica	CFil CPle WPGP
cerifera	CAgr CArn CPle IIve LEdu
gale	GPoy MGos SWal SWat WDin WSel WWye
pensylvanica	CAgr IFro IMGH NBlu

Myriophyllum (Haloragaceae)

§ **aquaticum** — CRow CWat EHon ELan EMFW LPBA MSta SCoo SLon SWat WFar WMAq WWeb
brasiliense — see *M. aquaticum*
* **propium new** — EMFW
proserpinacoides — see *M. aquaticum*
* 'Red Stem' — LPBA WWpP
spicatum — EHon EMFW SBHF WWpP
verticillatum — EHon SCoo

Myrrhis (Apiaceae)

odorata — More than 30 suppliers
- 'Forncett Chevron' — EFou

Myrsine (Myrsinaceae)

africana — CPLG CPle
divaricata — CTrC

Myrteola (Myrtaceae)

§ **nummularia** — GDra ISea NMen WAbe

Myrtus (Myrtaceae)

apiculata — see *Luma apiculata*
bullata — see *Lophomyrtus bullata*
chequen — see *Luma chequen*
communis ♀ H3 — More than 30 suppliers
- 'Flore Pleno' (d) — GQui
- 'Jenny Reitenbach' — see *M. communis* subsp. *tarentina*
- 'Merion' new — WJek
- 'Microphylla' — see *M. communis* subsp. *tarentina*
- 'Nana' — see *M. communis* subsp. *tarentina*
§ - subsp. **tarentina** ♀ H3 — More than 30 suppliers
§ - - 'Microphylla Variegata' (v) — CPle SAga SPer STre WBrE WHHs WJek WSHC
- 'Tricolor' — see *M. communis* 'Variegata'
§ - 'Variegata' (v) — More than 30 suppliers
dulcis — see *Austromyrtus dulcis*
'Glanleam Gold' — see *Luma apiculata* 'Glanleam Gold'
lechleriana — see *Amomyrtus luma*
luma — see *Luma apiculata*
nummularia — see *Myrteola nummularia*
obcordata — see *Lophomyrtus obcordata*
* **paraquayensis new** — CTrC
x **ralphii** — see *Lophomyrtus* x *ralphii*
'Traversii' — see *Lophomyrtus* x *ralphii* 'Traversii'
ugni — see *Ugni molinae*
* **variegata** 'Penlee' (v) — CTrG

N

Nabalus (Asteraceae)

albus new — EBee
aspera new — EBee

Naiocrene (Portulacaceae)

§ **parvifolia** — CNic

Nandina (Berberidaceae)

domestica ♀ H3 — More than 30 suppliers
- B&SWJ 4923 — WCru
- 'Fire Power' ♀ H3 — More than 30 suppliers
- 'Harbor Dwarf' — LRHS WFar
- var. **leucocarpa** — EPla MBlu
- 'Little Princess' — EPla
- 'Nana' — see *N. domestica* 'Pygmaea'

- 'Nana Purpurea' — EPla
§ - 'Pygmaea' — WBod WDin
- 'Richmond' — CBcs ELan EPfP LRHS MAsh MGag MGos SBod SHBN SPar SPer SPla WBrE WFar

Nannorrhops (Arecaceae)

ritchieana — CBrP LPal

Napaea (Malvaceae)

dioica — EBee

Narcissus ✿ (Amaryllidaceae)

'Aberfoyle' (2) ♀ H4 **new** — GEve
'Accent' (2) ♀ H4 — CQua
'Achduart' (3) — CQua GEve
'Achentoul' (4) — CQua
'Achnasheen' (3) — CQua GEve
'Acropolis' (4) — CQua LAma LRHS
'Actaea' (9) ♀ H4 — ETub LRHS MBri NRog
'Admiration' (8) — CQua
'Advocat' (3) — CQua
'Aflame' (3) — LAma MBri
'Ahwahnee' (2) — IRhd
'Aintree' (3) — CQua
'Aircastle' (3) — CQua
I **albidus** subsp. **occidentalis** (13) — ERos
'Albus Plenus Odoratus' — see *N. poeticus* 'Plenus'
'Alston' (2) — IRhd
'Alto' (2) **new** — IRhd
'Altruist' (3) — CQua
'Altun Ha' (2) — CQua EHof IRhd
'Amazing Grace' — IRhd
'Amber Castle' (2) — CQua
'Ambergate' (2) — GEve LAma
'American Heritage' (1) — CQua IRhd
'American Shores' (1) — CQua IRhd
'Amstel' (4) — CQua
'Andalusia' (6) — ERos
'Angel Face' (3) — EHof IRhd
'Angel Wings' — see *N.* 'Celtic Wings'
'Angelito' (2) **new** — IRhd
Angel's Tears — see *N. triandrus* subsp. *triandrus* var. *triandrus*
'Angkor' (4) — CQua
'An-gof' (7) — CQua
'Annalong' (3) — IRhd
'Applins' (2) — IRhd
'Apricot' (1) — CBro
'April Love' (1) — CQua
'April Snow' (2) — CBro CQua
'April Tears' (5) ♀ H4 — NRog
'Aranjuez' (2) — CQua
'Arctic Gold' (1) ♀ H4 — CQua
'Ardglass' (3) — IRhd
'Ardress' (2) — CQua
'Ardview' (3) **new** — IRhd
'Areley Kings' (5) — CQua
'Arish Mell' (5) — CQua
'Arkle' (1) ♀ H4 — CQua GEve
'Arleston' (2) — IRhd
'Armidale' (3) **new** — IRhd
'Arndilly' (2) — CQua
'Arpege' (2) — CQua
'Arran Isle' (2) — IRhd
'Arthurian' (1) — IRhd
'Arwenack' (11a) — CQua
'Ashmore' (2) — CQua IRhd
'Ashton Wold' (2) — EHof
'Asila' (2) — IRhd
'Aspasia' (8) — CBro
'Assertion' (2) **new** — IRhd

§ *assoanus* (13) CBro CLAP EBre EPar EPot ERos GKir LAma

§ *asturiensis* (13) ♀ H3-4 CBro CSam EPar EPot IBlr MNrw
- x *cyclamineus* NGar
'Atholl Palace' (4) IRhd
atlanticus (13) CLAP
'Atricilla' IRhd
'Audubon' (2) CQua
'Aunt Betty' (1) IRhd
'Auntie Eileen' (2) CQua

§ *aureus* (13) CQua
'Auspicious' (2) IRhd
'Avalanche' (8) ♀ H3 CQua LRHS
'Avalon' (2) CQua
'Avril Amour' (1) **new** IRhd
'Azocor' (1) **new** IRhd
'Baby Moon' (7) CQua EPar EPot ETub LAma LRHS MBNS MBri NRog
'Baccarat' (11a) MBri
'Badanloch' (3) CQua
'Badbury Rings' (3) ♀ H4 CQua IRhd
'Balalaika' (2) CQua
'Baldock' (4) CQua
'Ballinamallard' (3) **new** IRhd
'Ballygarvey' (1) CQua
'Ballygowan' (3) IRhd
'Ballykinler' (3) IRhd
'Ballymorran' (1) IRhd
'Ballynahinch' (3) IRhd
'Ballynichol' (3) IRhd
'Ballyrobert' (1) CQua
'Baltic Shore' (3) IRhd
'Balvenie' (2) CQua
'Bambi' (1) CBro ERos NRog
'Banbridge' (1) IRhd
'Bandesara' (3) IRhd
'Bandit' (2) **new** CQua
'Banstead Village' (2) CQua
'Bantam' (2) ♀ H4 CBro CQua ERos
'Barleywine' (2) IRhd
'Barlow' (6) CQua
'Barnesgold' (1) IRhd
'Barnsdale Wood' (2) CQua
'Barnum' (1) ♀ H4 IRhd
'Barr Hall' (9) **new** IRhd
'Barrett Browning' (3) MBri NRog
'Bear Springs' (4) **new** IRhd
'Bebop' (7) CBro
'Bedruthan' (2) CQua
'Belbroughton' (2) CQua
'Belcanto' (11a) CQua
'Belisana' (2) LAma
'Bell Rock' (1) CQua
'Bell Song' (7) CBro CQua ERos LRHS
'Ben Aligin' (1) CQua
'Ben Armine' (2) GEve
'Ben Avon' (1) GEve
'Ben Hee' (2) ♀ H4 CQua
'Ben Loyal' (2) GEve
'Benbane Head' (9) **new** IRhd
'Berceuse' (2) IRhd
'Bere Ferrers' (4) CQua
'Bergerac' (11a) CQua
'Berlin' (2) ERos
'Beryl' (6) CBro CQua ERos LAma LRHS
'Best of Luck' (3) IRhd
'Betsy MacDonald' (6) CQua
'Biffo' (4) CQua
'Big John' (1) GEve
'Bilbo' (6) CQua
'Binkie' (2) CBro CQua LAma MBri
'Birdsong' (3) CQua
'Birkdale' (2) GEve

'Birma' (3) EFam LAma
'Birthday Girl' (2) IRhd
'Bishops Light' (2) CQua
'Blarney' (3) CQua
'Blisland' (9) CQua
'Blossom' (4) **new** CQua
'Blue Danube' (1) IRhd
'Blushing Maiden' (4) CQua
'Bob Minor' (1) CQua
'Bobbysoxer' (7) CBro CQua ERos LAma MTho
'Bobolink' (2) CQua
'Bodwannick' (2) CQua
'Bolton' (7) CBro
'Bosbigal' (11a) CQua
'Boscastle' (7) CQua
'Boslowick' (11a) CQua
'Bosmeor' (2) CQua
'Bossa Nova' (3) CQua
'Bossiney' (11a) CQua
'Bosvale' (11a) CQua
'Bouzouki' (2) IRhd
'Bowles' Early Sulphur' (1) CRow
'Boyne Bridge' (1) **new** IRhd
'Brandaris' (11a) CQua GEve
'Bravoure' (1) ♀ H4 CQua
'Brentswood' (8) CQua
'Bridal Crown' (4) EPfP ETub LAma LRHS
'Bright Flame' (2) CQua
'Brindle Pink' (2) IRhd
'Broadland' (2) CQua
'Broadway Star' (11b) ETub LAma LRHS
'Brodick' (3) GEve IRhd
'Broomhill' (2) ♀ H4 CQua
broussonetii (13) CFil
'Budock Bells' (5) CQua
'Bugle Major' (2) EHof
bulbocodium (13) ♀ H3-4 CBro CFil CMea CNic EHyt ETub LBee LPhx LRHS NGar NMGW NRya NWCA SRms WCom WPGP
§ - subsp. *bulbocodium* (13) CBro
§ - - var. *citrinus* (13) EHyt EPot SSpi
§ - - var. *conspicuus* (13) CArn CAvo CBro CNic CPMA CQua CSam EHyt EPar EPot ERos GCrs ITim LAma MBri MS&S NMen NRog NRya SChr
* - - *filifolius* (13) CBro SChr
- - var. *genuinus* CAvo
x *cantabricus*
subsp. *tananicus* (13)
- - - x 'Jessamy' EHyt
§ - - var. *graellsii* (13) NSla
- - var. *nivalis* (13) ERos
§ - - var. *tenuifolius* (13) CNic EHyt EPot MNrw
- - - x *triandrus* (13) EHyt NGar
§ - 'Golden Bells' (10) CBro CFwr EPot ETub GEdr LRHS MBri MWgw WWeb
- var. *mesatlanticus* see *N. romieuxii* subsp. *romieuxii* var. *mesatlanticus*
I - subsp. *viriditubus* (13) ERos
- subsp. *vulgaris* see *N. bulbocodium* subsp. *bulbocodium*
'Bunclody' (2) CQua
'Bunting' (7) ♀ H4 CQua
'Burning Bush' (3) IRhd
'Burntollet' (1) CQua
'Busselton' (3) **new** IRhd
'Buttercup' (7) CBro
'Butterscotch' (2) CQua
'Cabernet' (2) IRhd
'Cacatua' (11a) **new** IRhd
'Cadgwith' (2) CQua
'Caedmon' (9) CQua
'Cairntoul' (3) CQua

'Calamansack' (2)	CQua	
'California Rose' (4)	IRhd	
'Camellia' (4)	EFam	
'Cameo King' (2) **new**	CQua	
'Campernelli Plenus'	see *N.* x *odorus* 'Double Campernelle'	
'Campion' (9)	CQua IRhd	
'Canaliculatus' (8)	CBro CQua EHyt EPar ERos ETub LAma LRHS MBri NMen	
canaliculatus Gussone	see *N. tazetta* subsp. *lacticolor*	
'Canarybird' (8)	CBro	
'Canasta' (11a)	CQua	
'Canisp' (2)	CQua	
'Cantabile' (9) ♀ H4	CBro CQua IRhd	
cantabricus (13)	CFil SSpi WPGP	
- subsp. *cantabricus* (13)	CLAP EHyt ERos	
- - var. *foliosus* (13) ♀ H2	EPot SCnR	
- - var. *petunioides* (13)	LAma	
I - subsp. *monophyllus* var. *laciniatus* (13)	EHyt	
- x *romieuxii* (13)	NHar	
'Canticle' (9)	IRhd	
'Capax Plenus'	see *N.* 'Eystettensis'	
'Cape Cornwall' (2)	CQua	
'Cape Helles' (3) **new**	IRhd	
'Cape Point' (2)	IRhd	
'Capisco' (3)	CQua IRhd	
'Caramba' (2)	CQua	
'Carbineer' (2)	EFam LAma	
'Carclew' (6)	CQua	
'Cardinham' (3)	CQua	
'Cargreen' (9)	CQua	
'Cariad' (5)	CQua	
'Carib Gipsy' (2) ♀ H4	CQua EHof IRhd	
'Caribbean Snow' (2)	EHof	
'Carlton' (2) ♀ H4	EFam ETub LAma MBri NRog	
'Carnearny' (3)	CQua GEve	
'Carnkief' (2)	CQua	
'Carnyorth' (11a)	CQua	
'Carole Lombard' (3) **new**	IRhd	
'Carrickbeg' (1)	CQua	
'Cassata' (11)	CQua EFam ETub LAma LRHS NBir NRog	
'Castanets' (8)	IRhd	
'Casterbridge' (2)	CQua IRhd	
'Castlehill' (3)	IRhd	
'Catalyst' (2) **new**	IRhd	
'Catistock' (2)	CQua	
'Cauldron' (2)	CQua	
'Cavalryman' (3)	IRhd	
'Cavendish' (4)	IRhd	
'Caye Chapel' (3)	EHof	
'Cazique' (6)	CQua	
'Ceasefire' (2)	IRhd	
'Cedric Morris' (1)	CBro CDes CElw CLAP ECha EHyt NDov SMrm SSpi WCot	
'Celestial Fire' (2)	EHof	
'Celtic Gold' (2)	CQua	
'Centannées' (11b)	ETub	
'Centrefold' (3) **new**	CQua	
'Cha-cha' (6)	CBro CQua	
'Chanson' (1) **new**	IRhd	
'Chanterelle' (11a)	LAma NRog	
'Chapman's Peak' (2)	IRhd	
'Charity May' (6) ♀ H4	CBro CQua IRhd LAma MBri NRog	
'Charleston' (2)	CQua	
'Chaste' (1)	IRhd	
'Chat' (7)	CQua	
'Cheer Leader' (3)	CQua GEve	
'Cheerfulness' (4) ♀ H4	CAvo CQua ETub ITim LAma LRHS MBNS MBri NRog	
'Cheetah' (1)	IRhd	
'Chelsea Girl' (2)	GEve	
'Cheltenham' (2) **new**	CQua	
'Chérie' (7)	CBro CQua	
'Cherrygardens' (2)	CQua IRhd	
'Chesapeake Bay' (1) **new**	EHof	
'Chesterton' (9) ♀ H4	CQua	
'Chickadee' (6)	CBro CQua	
'Chickerell' (3)	CQua	
'Chief Inspector' (1)	CQua IRhd	
'Chilmark' (3)	IRhd	
'Chiloquin' (1)	CQua	
'Chinchilla' (2)	CQua IRhd	
'Chinita' (8)	CBro CQua	
'Chit Chat' (7) ♀ H4	CBro	
'Chobe River' (1)	IRhd	
'Chorus Line' (8) **new**	IRhd	
'Chukar' (4) **new**	IRhd	
'Churchman' (2)	IRhd	
'Churston Ferrers' (4)	CQua	
'Cisticola' (3)	IRhd	
citrinus	see *N. bulbocodium* subsp. *bulbocodium* var. *citrinus*	
'Citronita' (3)	CQua	
'Clare' (7)	CBro CQua	
'Clashmore' (2)	GEve	
'Clearbrook' (2) **new**	CQua	
'Close Harmony' (4)	IRhd	
'Cloud Nine' (2)	CBro	
'Clouded Yellow' (2)	EHof IRhd	
'Clouds Rest' (2)	IRhd	
'Codlins and Cream'	see *N.* 'Sulphur Phoenix'	
'Colley Gate' (3)	CQua	
'Colorama' (11a)	CQua	
'Colour Sergeant' (2)	IRhd	
'Colourful' (2)	IRhd	
'Columbus' (2)	CQua	
'Colville' (9)	CQua	
'Comal' (1)	CQua	
'Compressus'	see *N.* x *intermedius* 'Compressus'	
'Compton Court' (3) **new**	CQua	
concolor (Haworth) Link	see *N. triandrus* subsp. *triandrus* var. *concolor*	
'Conestoga' (2)	IRhd	
'Confuoco' (2)	EFam	
'Congress' (11a)	CQua	
* 'Connie Number 1'	EHyt	
* 'Connie Number 2'	EHyt	
'Cool Crystal' (3)	CQua IRhd	
'Cool Evening' (11a)	IRhd	
'Cool Pink' (2) **new**	CQua	
'Cool Shades' (2)	EHof	
'Coombe Creek' (6)	CQua	
'Copper Nob' (2)	IRhd	
'Cora Ann' (7)	CBro	
'Corbiere' (1)	CQua IRhd	
cordubensis (13)	EHyt EPot SSpi	
'Cornet' (6)	CQua	
'Cornish Chuckles' (12)	CQua	
'Corofin' (3)	CQua	
'Coromandel' (2)	IRhd	
'Corozal' (3)	EHof	
'Cosmic Dance' (3)	IRhd	
'Cotinga' (6)	CQua	
'Crackington' (4) ♀ H4	CQua IRhd	
'Cragford' (8)	LAma	
'Craig Stiel' (2)	CQua	
'Craigarusky' (2)	IRhd	
'Creag Dubh' (2)	CQua GEve	
'Crevenagh' (2) **new**	IRhd	
'Crimson Chalice' (3)	IRhd	
'Cristobal' (1)	CQua	
'Crock of Gold' (1)	CQua	
'Crofty' (6) **new**	CQua	
'Croila' (2)	CQua	

'Crown Royalist' (2)	IRhd
'Crowndale' (4) **new**	IRhd
'Cryptic' (1)	IRhd
'Cuan Gold' (4)	IRhd
cuatrecasasii (13)	EPot ERos
'Cul Beag' (3)	CQua
'Culmination' (2) **new**	CQua
'Cupid's Eye' (3)	IRhd
'Curlew' (7) **new**	CQua
cyclamineus (13) ♀ H4	CBro CFil CRDP CWoo EPar GCrs
	LAma LCTD MS&S NRog SBla SCnR
	Slgm SRms SSpi WAbe WCru WPGP
'Cyclataz' (8)	CQua
'Cyclops' (3) **new**	CQua
cypri (8)	CBro CQua
'Cyros' (1)	CQua
'Dailmanach' (2)	CQua IRhd
'Dailmystic' (2) **new**	IRhd
'Dainty Miss' (7)	CQua
'Dallas' (3)	CQua
'Dan du Plessis' (8) **new**	CQua
'Dancing Queen' (2) **new**	IRhd
'Dardanelles' (2) **new**	IRhd
'Dateline' (3)	CQua IRhd
'David Alexander' (1)	CQua
'Dawn' (5)	CBro
'Dawn Run' (2)	IRhd
'Dawn Sky' (2)	EHof
'Daydream' (2) ♀ H3	CQua LAma
'Debutante' (2)	CQua
'Decoy' (2)	IRhd
'Delia' (6)	IRhd
'Delibes' (2)	LAma
'Delnashaugh' (4)	CQua
'Delos' (3)	CQua
'Delphin Hill' (4)	IRhd
'Delta Flight' (6)	IRhd
'Demand' (2)	CQua
'Denali' (1)	IRhd
'Derryboy' (3)	IRhd
'Descant' (1) **new**	IRhd
'Desdemona' (2) ♀ H4	NRog
'Desert Bells' (7)	CQua
'Desert Orchid' (2)	CQua
'Diatone' (4)	GEve
'Dick Wilden' (4)	LAma
'Dickcissel' (7)	CBro CQua ERos
'Dimity' (3)	CQua
'Dinkie' (3)	CBro
'Diversity' (11a) **new**	IRhd
'Doctor Hugh' (3) ♀ H4	CQua GEve IRhd
'Doctor Jazz' (2)	EHof
'Doombar' (1) **new**	CQua
'Dorchester' (4)	IRhd
'Double Campernelle'	see *N.* x *odorus* 'Double Campernelle'
double pheasant eye	see *N. poeticus* 'Plenus'
double Roman	see *N.* 'Romanus'
'Doubleday' (4)	IRhd
'Doublet' (4) **new**	CQua
'Doubtful' (3)	CQua
'Dove Wings' (6) ♀ H4	CBro CQua IRhd LAma
'Dover Cliffs' (2)	CQua
'Downpatrick' (1)	CQua
'Dragon Run' (2)	CQua
'Drama Queen' (11a) **new**	IRhd
'Drumbeg' (2)	IRhd
'Drumlin' (1)	IRhd
dubius (13)	CBro
'Duiker' (6) **new**	IRhd
'Duke of Windsor' (2)	EFam
'Dulcimer' (9)	CQua
'Dunadry Inn' (4)	IRhd

'Dunkerry' (4) **new**	CQua
'Dunkery' (4)	IRhd
'Dunley Hall' (3)	IRhd
'Dunskey' (3)	CQua
'Dusky Lad' (2) **new**	IRhd
'Dusky Maiden' (2) **new**	IRhd
'Dutch Delight' (2)	IRhd
'Dutch Master' (1) ♀ H4	CQua ETub LAma MBri NRog
'Early Splendour' (8)	CQua LAma
'Easter Bonnet' (2)	LAma
'Eastern Dawn' (2)	ETub
'Eaton Song' (12) ♀ H4	CBro CQua
'Eddy Canzony' (2)	CQua
'Edenderry' (1) **new**	IRhd
'Edgbaston' (2)	CQua EHof
'Edward Buxton' (3)	LAma MBri
'Egard' (11a)	CQua
'Eland' (7)	CQua
'Electrus' (11a) **new**	IRhd
'Elf' (2)	CBro CQua
'Elfin Gold' (6)	CQua IRhd
'Elizabeth Ann' (6)	CQua
'Elka' (1)	CQua IRhd
'Elphin' (4)	CQua GEve
'Elrond' (2)	CQua
'Elven Lady' (2)	IRhd
'Elvira' (8)	CBro CQua
'Embo' (2)	GEve
'Emily' (2)	CQua
'Emperor's Waltz' (6)	CQua IRhd
'Empress of Ireland' (1) ♀ H4	CQua IRhd
'Englander' (6)	EPot
'English Caye' (1)	EHof
'Ensemble' (4)	CQua
'Eribol' (2)	GEve
'Eriskay' (4)	GEve
'Erlicheer' (4)	CQua
'Escapee' (3) **new**	IRhd
'Estrella' (3)	CQua
'Ethereal Beauty' (2)	IRhd
'Ethos' (1)	IRhd
'Euphonic Grace' (2) **new**	IRhd
'Euryalus' (1)	CQua
'Evelix' (2)	GEve
'Evening' (2) **new**	CQua
'Evesham' (3)	IRhd
'Eye Level' (9)	IRhd
'Eyeglass' (3) **new**	IRhd
'Eyelet' (3)	IRhd
'Eype' (4) **new**	IRhd
'Eyrie' (3) **new**	IRhd
§ 'Eystettensis' (4)	CBro CRDP ECha ERos IBlr
'Fair Head' (9)	CQua
'Fair Prospect' (2)	CQua
'Fairgreen' (3)	CQua
'Fairlawns' (3)	CQua
'Fairsel' (3)	IRhd
'Fairy Chimes' (5)	CBro CQua
'Fairy Footsteps' (3)	IRhd
'Fairy Gold' (6)	CAvo
'Fairy Island' (3)	CQua
'Fairy Magic' (2) **new**	IRhd
'Fairy Spell' (3)	IRhd
'Falconet' (8) ♀ H4	CBro CQua ERos
'Falmouth Bay' (3) **new**	CQua
'Falstaff' (2)	CQua
'Famecheck Giant' **new**	EFam
'Famecheck Luck' (2) **new**	EFam
'Famecheck Silver' (11b) **new**	EFam
'Fanad Head' (9)	IRhd
'Far Country' (2)	GEve

Name	Nurseries
'Faro' (1)	IRhd
'Farranfad' (2)	IRhd
'Fastidious' (2)	CQua
'Favor Royal' (3)	IRhd
'February Gold' (6) ♀ H4	CAvo CBro EPar EPot ERos ETub IRhd LAma LRHS MBri MWgw NBir NMGW NRog SRms WShi
'February Silver' (6)	CBro EPar ETub LAma LRHS NRog
'Felindre' (9)	CQua IRhd
'Feock' (3)	CQua
fernandesii (13)	CBro SCnR
'Ferndown' (3)	CQua IRhd
'Ffitch's Ffolly' (2)	CQua
'Fiji' (4)	CQua
'Filoli' (1)	IRhd
'Fine Gold' (1)	CQua
'Fine Romance' (2)	CQua EHof
'Fiona MacKillop' (2)	IRhd
'Fionn' (2)	GEve
'Firebrand' (2)	CQua
'Firestorm' (2)	IRhd
'First Formal' (3) **new**	CQua
'Flirt' (6)	CQua
'Flomay' (7)	CBro
'Florida Manor' (3)	IRhd
'Flower Carpet' (1)	LAma
'Flower Drift' (4)	LAma
'Flower Record' (2)	LAma
'Fly Half' (2)	CQua
'Flycatcher' (7)	CQua IRhd
'Flying Colours' (4) **new**	IRhd
'Foresight' (1)	EFam
'Forge Mill' (2)	CQua
'Fortissimo' (2)	ETub
'Fortune' (2)	CQua EFam LAma NRog
'Foundling' (6) ♀ H4	CBro CQua GEve IRhd
'Fragrant Breeze' (2)	ETub
'Fragrant Rose' (2)	CQua IRhd
'Francolin' (1)	IRhd
'Frank's Fancy' (9)	IRhd
'Freedom Rings' (2)	CQua
'Fresco' (11a) **new**	IRhd
'Fresh Lime' (1)	EHof
'Fresno' (3)	IRhd
'Frogmore' (6) **new**	CQua
'Front Royal' (2)	CQua
'Frostbite' (4)	CQua
'Frosted Pink' (2) **new**	IRhd
'Frostkist' (6)	CBro CQua
'Frou-frou' (4)	CQua
'Fruit Cup' (7)	CQua
'Furnace Creek' (2)	IRhd
'Fynbos' (3)	IRhd
gaditanus (13)	CBro ERos
'Garden News' (3)	IRhd
'Garden Princess' (6)	CBro
'Gay Cavalier' (4)	CQua
'Gay Kybo' (4) ♀ H4	CQua
'Gay Song' (4)	CQua
§ *gayi* (13)	CBro CQua
'Geevor' (4)	CQua
'Gemini Girl' (2) **new**	CQua
'George Leak' (2)	CQua
'Georgie Girl' (6)	CQua
'Geranium' (8) ♀ H4	CBro CQua LAma LRHS MBri NRog
'Gettysburg' (2)	CQua
'Gigantic Star' (2)	LAma MBri
'Gilda' (2)	IRhd
'Gillan' (11a)	CQua
'Gin and Lime' (1) ♀ H4	CQua
'Gipsy Moon' (2) **new**	EHof
'Gipsy Queen' (1)	CQua EHyt
'Gironde' (11)	CQua
'Glen Cassley' (3)	CQua GEve
'Glen Clova' (2)	CQua
'Glen Lorne' (2)	GEve
'Glencalvie' (2) **new**	GEve
'Glenfarclas' (1) ♀ H4	GEve
'Glenmorangie' (2)	GEve
'Glenside' (2)	CQua
'Glissando' (2)	CQua IRhd
'Gloriosus' (8)	CQua
'Glowing Red' (4)	CQua
'Goff's Caye' (2)	EHof IRhd
'Gold Bond' (2)	IRhd
'Gold Charm' (2) **new**	CQua
'Gold Convention' (2) ♀ H4	CQua IRhd
'Gold Ingot' (2)	IRhd
'Gold Medal' (1)	LAma
'Gold Mine' (2)	IRhd
'Golden Amber' (2)	CQua IRhd
'Golden Aura' (2) ♀ H4	CQua
'Golden Bells'	see *N. bulbocodium* 'Golden Bells'
'Golden Cheer' (2)	CQua
'Golden Cycle' (6)	CQua
'Golden Dawn' (8) ♀ H3	CQua ETub
'Golden Ducat' (4)	CQua LAma MBri NBir NRog
'Golden Halo' (2)	IRhd
'Golden Harvest' (1)	LAma LRHS MBri NRog
'Golden Incense' (7) **new**	CQua
'Golden Jewel' (2) ♀ H4	CQua GEve
'Golden Joy' (2)	CQua
'Golden Orbit' (4) **new**	CQua
'Golden Quince'PBR (12)	CBro CQua
'Golden Radiance' (1)	IRhd
'Golden Rapture' (1) ♀ H4	CQua
'Golden Sceptre' (7)	CBro
'Golden Sovereign' (1)	IRhd
'Golden Strand' (2)	IRhd
'Golden Topaz' (2)	IRhd
'Golden Vale' (1) ♀ H4	CQua
'Golden Wings' (6)	IRhd
'Goldfinger' (1) ♀ H4	CQua
'Goldhanger' (2)	EHof
'Goldsithney' (2)	CBro
'Golitha Falls' (2)	CQua
'Good Measure' (2)	CQua
'Goose Green' (3)	IRhd
'Gorran' (3)	CQua
'Grace Note' (3)	CQua
graellsii	see *N. bulbocodium* subsp. *bulbocodium* var. *graellsii*
'Grand Monarque'	see *N. tazetta* subsp. *lacticolor* 'Grand Monarque'
'Grand Opening' (4)	IRhd
'Grand Primo Citronière' (8)	CQua
'Grand Prospect' (2)	CQua
'Grand Soleil d'Or' (8)	CQua EPfP LAma NRog
'Gransha' (3)	IRhd
'Grapillon' (11a)	GEve
'Grasmere' (1) ♀ H4	GEve
'Greatwood' (1)	CQua
'Green Chartreuse' (2)	EHof
'Green Lodge' (9)	IRhd
'Greenlet' (6)	CBro CQua LRHS
'Greenodd' (3)	CQua
'Greenpark' (9)	IRhd
'Gresham' (4)	CQua IRhd
'Gribben Head' (4)	CQua
'Grullemans Senior' (2)	EFam
'Gulliver' (3)	CQua
'Gunwalloe' (11a) **new**	CQua
'Guy Wilson' (2) **new**	EHof
'Gwennap' (1)	CQua
'Gwinear' (2)	CQua

'Halley's Comet' (3)	CQua IRhd
'Halvose' (8)	CBro
'Hambledon' (2) ♀ H4	CQua
'Happy Fellow' (2)	EHof
'Harbour View' (2) **new**	IRhd
'Harmony Bells' (5)	CQua
'Harpers Ferry' (1) **new**	CQua
'Hartlebury' (3)	CQua
* 'Hat' (10)	EHyt
'Hawangi' (3)	IRhd
'Hawera' (5) ♀ H4	CAvo CBri CBro CQua EPar EPfP EPot ETub LAma LRHS MBri MWgw NMGW NRog
'Hazel Rutherford' (2)	GEve
'Heamoor' (4)	CQua
hedraeanthus (13) SG 13	WCot
'Helen's Tower' (2)	IRhd
'Helford Dawn' (2)	CQua
hellenicus	see *N. poeticus* var. *hellenicus*
henriquesii	see *N. jonquilla* var. *henriquesii*
'Hero' (1)	CQua
'Hesla' (7)	CBro
'Hexameter' (9)	CQua
'High Society' (2) ♀ H4	CQua IRhd
'Highfield Beauty' (8) ♀ H4	CQua
'Highgrove' (1) **new**	EHof
'Highlite' (2)	CQua
'Hilford' (2)	IRhd
'Hill Head' (9)	IRhd
'Hillstar' (7)	CQua IRhd
'Hilltown' (2)	IRhd
'Holland Sensation' (1)	LAma
'Holly Berry' (2)	CQua
'Hollypark' (3)	IRhd
'Holme Fen' (2)	EHof
'Honey Guide' (5)	CQua
'Honeybird' (1)	CQua
'Honeyorange' (2)	IRhd
'Honolulu' (4)	CQua ETub
'Hoopoe' (8)	CBro CQua
'Horace' (9)	CQua
'Horn of Plenty' (5)	CBro CQua
'Hornpipe' (1) **new**	IRhd
'Hors d'Oeuvre' (8)	CBro
'Hot Gossip' (2)	CQua EHof
'Hotspur' (2)	CQua
'Hugh Town' (8)	CQua
'Hunting Caye' (2)	EHof
'Huntley Down' (1)	CQua
'Ice Diamond' (4) **new**	CQua IRhd
'Ice Follies' (2) ♀ H4	CQua EFam ETub LAma MBri NBir NRog
'Ice King' (4)	NBir
'Ice Wings' (5) ♀ H4	CAvo CBro CQua EPot ERos LRHS WShi
'Idless' (1)	WQua
'Immaculate' (2)	CQua
'Impresario' (2)	IRhd
'Inara' (4)	CQua
'Inca' (6)	CQua
x *incomparabilis* **new**	GIBF
'Indian Chief' (4)	EFam
'Indian Maid' (7)	CQua
'Indora' (4)	CQua
'Inglescombe' (4)	LAma
'Inner Glow' (2) **new**	IRhd
'Innovator' (4)	IRhd
'Inny River' (1)	IRhd
'Interim' (2)	CQua
§ x *intermedius* (13)	CBro ERos
§ - 'Compressus' (8)	CQua

'Interval' (2)	IRhd
'Intrigue' (7) ♀ H4	CQua IRhd
'Inverpolly' (2)	GEve
'Ipi Tombi' (2)	ERos
'Ireland's Eye' (9)	IRhd
'Irish Light' (2)	CQua
'Irish Linen' (3)	CQua
'Isambard' (4)	CQua
'Islander' (4)	CQua
'Islandhill' (3)	IRhd
'Ita' (2)	IRhd
'Itzim' (6) ♀ H4	CBro CQua ERos ETub
'Ivory Gull' (5)	CQua
'Jack Snipe' (6) ♀ H4	CAvo CBro CNic CQua EPfP EPot ERos LAma LRHS MBNS MBri NRog WShi
'Jack Wood' (11a)	CQua
'Jackadee' (2)	IRhd
'Jacobin' (1)	IRhd
'Jake' (3)	IRhd
'Jamage' (8)	CQua
'Jamaica Inn' (4)	CQua
'Jambo' (2)	IRhd
'Jamboree' (2)	CQua
'Jamestown' (3)	IRhd
'Jana' (4)	CQua
'Jane Frances' (1)	GEve
'Jane MacLennan' (4)	GEve
'Jantje' (11a)	CQua
jeanmonodii (13) JCA 701.870	WCot
'Jenny' (6) ♀ H4	CAvo CBro CQua EPar EPot ERos ETub IRhd LAma LRHS MWgw NBir NRog WShi
'Jessamy' (10)	EHyt
'Jetage' (6)	CBro
'Jetfire' (6) ♀ H4	CBro CQua EPot ERos ETub GEve GKir LAma LRHS MLLN
'Jezebel' (3)	CBro
'Johanna' (5)	CBro
'John Ballance' (1)	IRhd
'John Daniel' (4)	CQua
'John's Delight' (3)	CQua
jonquilla (13) ♀ H4	CAvo CBro CQua EPar EPot ERos LAma LPhx LRHS NGar NRog WPGP WShi
§ - var. *henriquesii* (13)	CBro CFil SCnR WPGP
'Joppa' (7)	CQua
'Joy Bishop'	see *N. romieuxii* 'Joy Bishop'
'Joybell' (6)	CQua
'Jules Verne' (2)	CQua
'Julia Jane'	see *N. romieuxii* 'Julia Jane'
'Jumblie' (12) ♀ H4	CBro CQua EPot ERos ITim LAma LRHS MBri NRog WShi
juncifolius	see *N. assoanus*
'June Lake' (2)	IRhd
'Kabani' (9)	CQua
'Kamau' (9)	IRhd
'Kathleen Munro' (2)	GEve
'Kathy's Clown' (6)	CQua
'Kaydee' (6) ♀ H4	CQua IRhd
'Kea' (6)	CQua
'Keats' (4)	CBro CQua
'Kehelland' (4)	CBro
'Kenbane Head' (9)	IRhd
'Kenellis' (10)	CBro CQua
'Kernow' (2)	CQua
'Kidling' (7)	CQua
'Killara' (8)	CQua
'Killearnan' (9)	CQua
'Killeen' (2)	IRhd
'Killyleagh' (3)	IRhd
'Kilmood' (2)	IRhd

'Kiltarn' (2) **new** — IRhd
'Kiltonga' (2) — IRhd
'Kilworth' (2) — CQua EFam LAma
'Kimmeridge' (3) — CQua
'King Size' (11a) — GEve
'Kinglet' (7) — CQua
'King's Grove' (1) ♀ H4 — CQua IRhd
'Kings Pipe' (2) — CQua
'Kingscourt' (1) ♀ H4 — CQua
'Kirkcubbin' (3) — IRhd
'Kit Hill' (7) — CQua
'Kitty' (6) — CBro ERos
'Kiwi Magic' (4) **new** — CQua IRhd
'Kiwi Sunset' (4) — CQua
'Kokopelli' (7) **new** — CBro
'Korora Bay' (1) **new** — IRhd
'Kuantan' (3) **new** — EHof
'La Argentina' (2) — EFam
'Ladies' Choice' (7) — IRhd
'Lady Ann' (2) — IRhd
'Lady Be Good' (2) — EHof
'Lady Emily' (2) — IRhd
'Lady Eve' (11a) **new** — IRhd
'Lady Serena' (9) — CQua
'Lagan Valley' (1) **new** — IRhd
'Lake Tahoe' (2) — IRhd
'Lalique' (3) — CQua
'Lamanva' (2) — CQua
'Lanarth' (7) — CBro
'Lancaster' (3) — IRhd
'Lapwing' (5) — CBro ERos IRhd
'Larkelly' (6) — CBro ERos
'Larkhill' (2) — CQua
'Larkwhistle' (6) ♀ H4 — CBro ERos
'Late Call' (3) — IRhd
'Lauren' (3) **new** — IRhd
'Lavender Lass' (6) — CQua
'Lee Moor' (1) — CQua
'Lemon Beauty' (11b) — CQua LRHS
'Lemon Drops' (5) — CBro ERos MSte
'Lemon Grey' (3) — IRhd
'Lemon Heart' (5) — CBro
'Lemon Silk' (6) — CQua
'Lemon Snow' (2) — IRhd
'Lemonade' (3) — CQua
'Lennymore' (2) — CQua IRhd
'Lewannick' (2) — CQua
'Lewis George' (1) **new** — CQua
'Libby' (2) — IRhd
'Liberty Bells' (5) — CBro CQua EPot LAma LRHS MBri NRog
'Life' (7) — CQua
'Lighthouse' (3) — GEve
'Lighthouse Reef' (1) — EHof IRhd
'Lilac Charm' (6) — CQua IRhd
'Lilac Hue' (6) — CBro
'Lilac Mist' (2) **new** — EHof
'Limbo' (2) — CQua IRhd
'Limehurst' (2) — CQua
'Limpopo' (3) — IRhd
'Lindsay Joy' (2) **new** — CQua
'Lingerie' (4) ♀ H4 — NZep
'Lintie' (7) — CBro CMea CQua ERos LAma LRHS MBri NRog
'Lisbarnett' (3) — IRhd
'Lisnamulligan' (3) — IRhd
'Lisnaruddy' (3) **new** — IRhd
'Little Beauty' (1) ♀ H4 — CAvo CBro CMea CQua EPot ERos LAma
'Little Dancer' (1) — CBro
'Little Gem' (1) ♀ H4 — CAvo CBro CQua EPot LAma NRog
'Little Karoo' (3) **new** — IRhd

'Little Sentry' (7) — CBro CQua
'Little Soldier' (10) — CQua
'Little Spell' (1) — CBro
'Little Witch' (6) — CAvo CBro CQua EPot ERos ITim LAma LRHS MBri NRog
'Liverpool Festival' (2) — CQua
lobularis — see *N. pseudonarcissus* 'Lobularis'
'Loch Alsh' (3) — IRhd
'Loch Assynt' (3) — CQua
'Loch Brora' (2) — CQua GEve
'Loch Fada' (2) — CQua
'Loch Hope' (2) — CQua GEve
'Loch Leven' (2) — GEve
'Loch Lundie' (2) — CQua
'Loch Maberry' (2) — CQua
'Loch Naver' (2) — CQua GEve
'Loch Stac' (2) — CQua
'Logan Rock' (7) — CQua
longispathus — SSpi
    (13) MS 546
'Lorikeet' (1) — CQua NZep
'Lothario' (2) — LAma NRog
'Lough Bawn' (2) — GEve
'Lough Cuan' (1) — IRhd
'Lough Gowna' (1) — IRhd
'Lough Ryan' (1) — IRhd
'Loughanisland' (1) — IRhd
'Loveny' (2) — CQua
'Lubaantun' (1) **new** — EHof
'Lucky Chance' (11a) **new** — IRhd
'Lundy Light' (2) — CQua
'Lyrebird' (3) — CQua
'Lyric' (9) — CQua
'Lysander' (2) — CQua
macleayi **new** — CQua
'Madam Speaker' (4) — CQua
'Magician' (2) — IRhd NZcp
'Magnet' (1) — LAma MBri
'Magnificence' (1) — LAma
'Majarde' (2) — EFam
'Majestic Star' (1) — CQua
'Makasa Sun' (2) — IRhd
'Malin Head' (5) — IRhd
'Mallee' (11a) **new** — IRhd
'Manaccan' (1) **new** — CQua
'Manly' (4) — CQua
'Mantle' (2) — CQua
'March Sunshine' (6) — CBro LAma
'Marjorie Treveal' (4) — CQua
'Marlborough' (2) — CQua
'Martha Washington' (8) — CBro CQua
'Martinette' (8) — CQua LRHS
marvieri — see *N. rupicola* subsp. *marvieri*
'Mary Copland' (4) — LAma
'Mary Kate' (6) — CQua IRhd
'Mary Lou' (6) — IRhd
'Mary Schouten' (2) — GEve
'Marzo' (7) — IRhd
'Matador' (8) — CQua IRhd
'Max' (11a) — CQua
'Maya Dynasty' (2) — CQua
'Mayan Gold' (1) — IRhd
'Mazzard' (4) **new** — CQua
'Media Girl' (2) — IRhd
x *medioluteus* (13) — CBro
'Medusa' (8) — CBro
'Melancholy' (1) — IRhd
'Melbury' (2) — CQua
'Menabilly' (4) — CQua
'Men-an-Tol' (2) — CQua
'Menehay' (11a) ♀ H4 — CQua IRhd
'Mentor' (2) — GEve
'Mercato' (2) — LAma

'Merida' (2)	IRhd
'Merlin' (3) ♀ H4	CQua GEve
'Merry Bells' (5)	CQua
'Merrymeet' (4)	CQua
'Mexico City' (2)	IRhd
'Michaels Gold' (2)	EHof
'Midas Touch' (1)	CQua
'Midget'	CAvo CBro CMea CQua EPot ERos ETub
'Milan' (9)	CQua
'Millennium' (1)	CBro
'Millennium Sunrise' (2)	CQua
'Millennium Sunset' (2)	CQua
'Minicycla' (6)	CAvo CBro
minimus hort.	see *N. asturiensis*
'Minnow' (8) ♀ H3	CAvo CBro CQua EPot ERos ETub LAma LRHS MBri NRog WShi
§ *minor* (13) ♀ H4	CBro CQua ECha LAma WShi
- 'Douglasbank' (1)	GCrs
- var. *pumilus* 'Plenus'	see *N.* 'Rip van Winkle'
- Ulster form	IBlr
'Minute Waltz' (6) **new**	CQua
'Mission Bells' (5) ♀ H4	CQua IRhd
'Misty Dawn' (3)	IRhd
'Misty Glen' (2) ♀ H4	CQua
'Mite' (6) ♀ H4	CAvo CBro CMea ERos
'Mitylene' (2)	CQua
'Mockingbird' (7)	IRhd
'Mondragon' (11a)	CQua EFam
'Mongleath' (2)	CQua
'Monks Wood' (1)	EHof
'Monksilver' (3)	CQua
'Montclair' (2)	CQua
'Montego' (3)	CQua
'Monza' (4)	IRhd
'Moon Ranger' (3)	IRhd
'Moon Rhythm' (4)	IRhd
'Moon Shadow' (3) **new**	IRhd
'Moon Tide' (3)	IRhd
'Moon Valley' (2)	GEve IRhd
'Moonshine' (5)	CBro
'Moonspell' (2)	IRhd
'Moralee' (4)	IRhd
§ *moschatus* (13) ♀ H4	CBro EPot
'Mother Catherine Grullemans' (2)	EFam
'Mount Fuji' (2)	CQua
'Mount Hood' (1) ♀ H4	ETub LAma MBri NBir
'Mount Oriel' (2)	IRhd
'Mount Royal' (2) **new**	IRhd
'Mourneview' (1)	IRhd
'Movie Star' (2)	IRhd
'Mowser' (7)	CQua
'Moyle' (9)	IRhd
'Mrs Langtry' (3)	CQua WShi
'Mrs R.O. Backhouse' (2)	LAma MBri WShi
'Muirfield' (1)	GEve
'Mullion' (3)	CQua
'Mulroy Bay' (1)	IRhd
'Murlough' (9)	CQua IRhd
'Muscadet' (2)	CQua
'My Sunshine' (2) **new**	EHof
'Naivasha' (2)	IRhd
'Namraj' (2)	CQua
'Nancegollan' (7)	CBro CQua
'Nangiles' (4)	CQua
'Nanpee' (7) **new**	CQua
'Nansidwell' (2)	CQua
'Nanstallon' (1)	CQua
'Nederburg' (1) **new**	IRhd
'Nether Barr' (2)	IRhd
§ *nevadensis* (13)	SSpi
'New Hope' (3) **new**	CQua
'New-baby' (7)	CQua
'Newcastle' (1)	CQua
'Night Music' (4)	CQua
'Nightcap' (1)	CQua
'Nirvana' (7)	CBro
'Niveth' (5)	CAvo CQua
nobilis var. *nobilis* (13)	EPot
'Nonchalant' (3)	IRhd
'Norma Jean' (2) **new**	CQua
'Nor-nor' (2)	CBro ERos
'Northern Sceptre' (2)	IRhd
'Noss Mayo' (6)	CBro CQua
'Notre Dame' (2) ♀ H4	IRhd
'Nouvelle' (3)	IRhd
'Numen Rose' (2)	IRhd
Nylon Group (10)	CBro CLAP CNic EHyt EPot SSpi
Nylon Group yellow (10)	EPot
'Obelisk' (11a)	CQua
obesus (13)	CLAP EHyt EPot ERos
obvallaris (13) ♀ H4	CAvo CBro EPar EPot ERos GBin MWgw NRog WBWf WHer WPnP WShi
'Ocarino' (4)	CQua
'Ocean Blue' (2)	IRhd
x *odorus* (13)	WShi
§ - 'Double Campernelle' (4)	CQua EPar ETub LAma WCot WShi
- 'Rugulosus'	see *N.* 'Rugulosus'
'Odyssey' (4)	IRhd
'Oecumene' (11a)	CQua
old pheasant's eye	see *N. poeticus* var. *recurvus*
'Omaha' (2)	IRhd
'Orange Monarch' (2)	EFam
'Orange Walk' (3)	EHof IRhd
'Orangery' (11a)	EFam LAma LRHS MBri NRog
'Oregon Pioneer' (2)	IRhd
'Ormeau' (2) ♀ H4	CQua
'Oryx' (7) ♀ H4	CQua IRhd
'Osmington' (2)	CQua
'Ottoman Gold' (2)	IRhd
'Ouma' (1)	CQua
'Outline' (2) **new**	IRhd
'Ouzel' (6)	CQua
'Oykel' (3)	CQua GEve
'Oz' (12)	CBro CQua
'Pacific Rim' (2) **new**	IRhd
'Painted Desert' (3)	CQua
'Pale Sunlight' (2)	CQua
§ *pallidiflorus* (13)	ECha
'Palmares' (11a)	CQua
'Panache' (1)	CQua
'Paper White'	see *N. papyraceus*
'Papillon Blanc' (11b)	LAma
'Papua' (4) ♀ H4	CQua
§ *papyraceus* (13)	CQua EPfP LAma MBri NRog
'Paradigm' (4)	IRhd
'Parcpat' (7)	CBro
'Parisienne' (11a)	LAma NRog
'Park Springs' (3)	CQua
'Party Time' (2)	IRhd
'Passionale' (2) ♀ H4	CQua IRhd LAma NBir
'Pastiche' (2)	CQua
'Patabundy' (2)	CQua
'Patois' (9)	IRhd
'Paula Cottell' (3)	CBro
'Pay Day' (1)	CQua
'Peach Prince' (4)	CQua
'Pearlshell' (11a)	CQua GEve
'Peeping Tom' (6) ♀ H4	CBro EPar ERos LAma MBri NRog SRms
'Peggy's Gift' (3) **new**	IRhd
'Pencrebar' (4)	CAvo CBro CQua EPot ERos LAma LRHS MBri WShi
'Pengarth' (2)	CQua

'Penjerrick' (9) **new**	CQua
'Penkivel' (2)	CQua
'Pennance Mill' (2)	CQua
'Pennine Way' (1)	CQua
'Pennyghael' (2)	GEve
'Penpol' (7)	CBro CQua
'Penril' (6)	CQua ERos
'Pentille' (1)	CQua
'Pepper' (2)	CBro
'Pequenita' (7)	CBro
'Percuil' (6)	CQua
'Perdredda' (3) **new**	CQua
'Perimeter' (3)	CQua IRhd
'Peripheral Pink' (2)	CQua
'Permissive' (2) **new**	IRhd
'Perseus' (1)	GEve
'Petit Four' (4)	LAma NRog
'Petrel' (5)	CBro CQua EPot ETub LRHS
'Phalarope' (6)	CQua
'Phantom' (11a)	CQua
'Phinda' (2)	IRhd
'Picoblanco' (2)	CBro CQua
'Pink Angel' (7)	CQua
'Pink Champagne' (4)	CQua
'Pink Flush' (2) **new**	IRhd
'Pink Holly' (11a) **new**	CQua
'Pink Pageant' (4)	CQua IRhd
'Pink Paradise' (4)	CQua IRhd
'Pink Perry' (2) **new**	IRhd
'Pink Silk' (1)	CQua IRhd NZep
'Pink Tango' (11a)	CQua
'Pipe Major' (2)	CQua
'Pipers Barn' (2)	CBro CQua
'Piper's Gold' (1)	IRhd
'Pipit' (7) ♀ H4	CAvo CBro CMea CQua EPot ERos LAma LRHS MNrw NBir WShi
'Piraeus' (4)	IRhd
'Pismo Beach' (2)	CQua
'Pitchroy' (2)	CQua
poeticus (13)	CAvo LAma LRHS WHer
§ - var. *hellenicus* (13)	CBro CQua
- old pheasant's eye	see *N. poeticus* var. *recurvus*
- var. *physaloides* (13)	CQua
N - 'Plenus' (4)	CBro CQua EPot ETub GQui WCot WShi
- 'Praecox' (9)	CBro CQua
§ - var. *recurvus* (13) ♀ H4	CBro CQua EPar EPot ETub LAma NBir WShi
'Poet's Way' (9)	CQua
'Pol Crocan' (2) **new**	CQua IRhd
'Pol Dornie' (2)	CQua
'Pol Voulin' (2)	IRhd
'Polglase' (8)	CBro
'Polly's Pearl' (8)	CQua
'Polnesk' (7)	CBro
'Polwheveral' (2) **new**	CQua
'Pooka' (3)	IRhd
'Pops Legacy' (1)	CQua IRhd
'Port Logan' (3) **new**	IRhd
'Port Patrick' (3)	IRhd
'Port Salon' (3) **new**	IRhd
'Port William' (3)	IRhd
'Portfolio' (1)	IRhd
'Porthchapel' (7)	CQua
'Portrush' (3)	CQua
'Portstewart' (3)	IRhd
'Powerstock' (2)	IRhd
'Prairie Fire' (3)	CQua IRhd
'Prcamblc' (1)	CQua IRhd
I 'Precocious' G.E. Mitsch (2) ♀ H4	CQua
'Premiere' (2)	CQua
'Pretty Baby' (3)	EHof

'Pride of Cornwall' (8)	CBro
'Primrose Beauty' (4)	CQua
'Prince of Brunswick' (2)	IRhd
'Princeps' (1)	CQua WShi
'Princess Alexandra' (6)	CQua
'Princess Zaide' (3)	CQua
'Prism' (2) **new**	CQua
'Probus' (1)	CQua
'Professor Einstein' (2)	LAma NRog
'Prototype' (6)	IRhd
pseudonarcissus (13) ♀ H4	CBro CQua CRow ETub LAma MBow SSpi WBWf WHer WShi
- subsp. *eugeniae* **new**	EPot
- subsp. *gayi*	see *N. gayi*
§ - 'Lobularis'	CAvo CBro CQua EPar EPot ERos LRHS NRog
- subsp. *moschatus*	see *N. moschatus*
- subsp. *nevadensis*	see *N. nevadensis*
- subsp. *pallidiflorus*	see *N. pallidiflorus*
'Ptolemy' (1)	LRHS
'Pueblo' (7)	CAvo ERos ETub LRHS WShi
pulchellus	see *N. triandrus* subsp. *triandrus* var. *pulchellus*
'Pulsar' (2) **new**	IRhd
pumilus (13)	EPot ERos LRHS
'Puppet' (5)	CQua
'Purbeck' (3) ♀ H4	CQua IRhd
'Quail' (7) ♀ H4	CBro CQua EPot ERos ETub LAma LRHS NRog
'Quasar' (2)	CQua GEve NZep
Queen Anne's double daffodil	see *N.* 'Eystettensis'
'Queen's Guard' (1) **new**	IRhd
'Quetzal' (9)	CQua
'Quick Step' (7)	CQua IRhd
'Quiet Hero' (3) **new**	IRhd
'Quiet Waters' (1)	EHof
'Quince' (12)	CBro CMea CQua CSam EPot ETub
'Quirinus' (2)	LAma
radiiflorus var. *poetarum* (13) **new**	CBro
'Radjel' (4)	CQua
'Rainbow' (2) ♀ H4	CQua
'Rame Head' (1)	CQua
'Rameses' (2)	CQua
'Ramore Head' (9) **new**	IRhd
'Rapture' (6) ♀ H4	CQua IRhd
'Raspberry Ring' (2)	CQua
'Ravenhill' (3)	CQua
'Red Ember' (3)	IRhd
'Red Goblet' (2)	LAma
'Red Hugh' (9)	IRhd
'Redman' (2)	IRhd
'Refrain' (2)	CQua
'Regal Bliss' (2)	CQua
'Reggae' (6) ♀ H4	CBro CQua IRhd
'Rembrandt' (1)	LAma MBri
'Rendezvous Caye' (2)	EHof
'Replete' (4)	CQua
requienii	see *N. assoanus*
'Ridgecrest' (3)	IRhd
'Rijnveld's Early Sensation' (1) ♀ H4	CAvo CBro CQua ERos MBri
'Rikki' (7)	CBro CQua ERos
'Rima' (1)	CQua
'Rimmon' (3)	CQua
'Ring Fence' (3)	IRhd
'Ringhaddy' (3)	IRhd
'Ringing Bells' (5)	CQua
'Ringleader' (2)	IRhd
'Ringmaster' (2)	CQua
'Rio Bravo' (2)	IRhd
'Rio Gusto' (2)	IRhd
'Rio Lobo' (2)	IRhd

'Skywalker' (2) **new**	IRhd	
'Sligachan' (1)	GEve	
'Slim Whitman' (2)	ETub	
'Slipstream' (6) **new**	IRhd	
'Small Talk' (1)	CQua	
'Smokey Bear' (4)	CQua	
'Snoopie' (6)	CQua	
'Snow Bunting' (7)	CBro	
'Snowcrest' (3)	CQua	
'Snowshill' (2)	CQua	
'Soft Focus' (2) **new**	IRhd	
'Solar System' (3)	IRhd	
'Solar Tan' (3)	CQua IRhd	
'Soleil d'Or' (8)	MBri	
'Solveig's Song'	EHyt EPot	
'Sonata' (9)	CQua	
'Soprano' (2)	IRhd	
'Sorcerer' (3)	CQua	
'South Street' (2)	CQua	
'Sovereign' (11a)	ETub IRhd	
'Spaniards Inn' (4)	CQua	
'Sparkling Eye' (8)	IRhd	
'Sparnon' (11a)	CQua	
'Special Envoy' (2) ♀ H4	CQua IRhd	
'Speenogue' (1) **new**	IRhd	
'Spellbinder' (1) ♀ H4	EFam LAma MBri	
'Sperrin Gold' (1)	IRhd	
'Spirit of Rame' (3)	CQua	
'Split Image' (2)	IRhd	
'Sportsman' (2)	CQua	
* 'Spring Joy'	ERos	
'Spring Morn' (2)	CQua IRhd	
'Stainless' (2)	ETub	
'Standard Value' (1)	LAma	
'Stann Creek' (1) **new**	EHof	
'Stanway' (3)	CQua IRhd	
'Starfire' (7)	CQua	
'State Express' (2)	CQua	
'Steenbok' (3)	IRhd	
'Step Forward' (7)	ERos	
'Stilton' (9)	CQua	
'Stinger' (2) **new**	CQua	
'Stint' (5)	CBro CQua	
'Stocken' (7)	CBro	
'Stoke Charity' (2)	FHof	
'Stoke Doyle' (2)	EHof	
'Stormy Weather' (1)	CQua IRhd	
'Strathkanaird' (1)	GEve	
'Stratosphere' (7)	CQua	
'Strines' (2)	CQua	
'Suave' (3)	CQua	
'Sugar and Spice' (3)	EHof	
'Sugar Bird' (2)	IRhd	
'Sugar Loaf' (4)	CQua	
'Sugarbush' (7)	CBro MBri NRog	
'Suilven' (3)	GEve	
'Suisgill' (4)	CQua	
'Sulphur Phoenix' (4)	CQua	
'Summer Solstice' (3) **new**	IRhd	
'Sumo Jewel' (6)	CQua	
'Sun Disc' (7) ♀ H4	CBro CQua EPot ERos ETub LAma LRHS MBri	
'Sun 'n' Snow' (1) **new**	GEve	
'Sunday Chimes' (5) **new**	CQua	
'Sundial' (7)	CAvo CBro CQua EPot ERos LAma LRHS	
'Suntory' (3)	CQua	
'Suntrap' (2)	IRhd	
'Surfside' (6) ♀ H4	CBro CQua ERos LRHS	
'Surrey' (2)	CQua	
'Suzie Dee' (6)	IRhd	
'Suzie's Sister' (6)	IRhd	
'Suzy' (7) ♀ H4	CBro LAma MBri NRog	

'Swaledale' (2)	CQua	
'Swallow Wing' (6)	IRhd	
'Sweet Blanche' (7)	CQua	
'Sweet Lorraine' (2) **new**	EHof	
'Sweet Pepper' (7)	CBro GEve	
'Sweet Sue' (3)	EHof	
'Sweetness' (7) ♀ H4	CAvo CBro CMea CQua IRhd LAma NRog WShi	
'Swift Arrow' (6) ♀ H4	CQua	
'Swing Wing' (6)	CQua	
'Sydling' (5)	CQua	
I 'Sylph' G.E. Mitsch (1)	CQua	
'Sylvan Hill' (1)	IRhd	
'Taffeta' (10)	CBro EHyt	
'Tahiti' (4) ♀ H4	CQua ETub LAma LRHS MBri NRog	
'Tain' (1)	GEve	
'Tamar Fire' (4) ♀ H4	CQua	
'Tamar Lad' (2)	CQua	
'Tamar Lass' (3) **new**	CQua	
'Tamar Snow' (2)	CQua	
'Tamara' (2)	CQua	
'Tangent' (2)	CQua	
'Tarlatan' (10)	CBro ERos	
'Taslass' (4)	CQua	
'Tater-Du' (5)	CQua	
tazetta subsp. *aureus*	see *N. aureus*	
§ – subsp. *lacticolor* (13)	CQua WPGP	
§ – – 'Grand Monarque' (8)	CQua	
– subsp. *papyraceus*	see *N. papyraceus*	
'Tehidy' (3)	CQua	
§ 'Telamonius Plenus' (4)	CBro IGor LAma WShi	
'Temple Cloud' (4)	IRhd	
tenuifolius	see *N. bulbocodium* subsp. *bulbocodium* var. *tenuifolius*	
'Terracotta' (2)	IRhd	
'Terrapin' (3)	IRhd	
'Tête-à-tête' (12) ♀ H4	CAvo CBro CMea CQua EPar EPfP EPot ERos ETub GKir LAma LRHS MBNS MBri MWgw	
'Texas' (4)	LAma MBri	
'Thalia' (5)	CAvo CBro CMea ERos ETub ITim LAma LRHS MBri MWgw NBir NRog WShi	
'The Alliance' (6)	CQua	
'The Grange' (1)	CQua	
'The Knave' (6)	CQua	
'The Little Gentleman' (6)	CBro	
'Thistin' (1) **new**	IRhd	
'Thoughtful' (5)	CBro CQua	
'Tibet' (2)	LRHS	
'Tiercel' (1)	CQua	
'Tiffany Jade' (3)	CQua	
'Timolin' (3)	CQua	
'Tinderbox' (2) **new**	IRhd	
'Tiritomba' (11a)	CQua	
'Titania' (6)	CQua	
'Tittle-tattle' (7)	CBro CQua IRhd	
'Toby' (2)	CBro ERos	
'Toby the First' (6)	CQua	
'Top Hit' (11a)	CQua	
'Top of the Hill' (3)	IRhd	
'Topkapi' (2)	IRhd	
'Topolino' (1) ♀ H4	CAvo CBro CQua EPot LAma NRog	
'Torianne' (2)	CQua	
'Torr Head' (9)	IRhd	
'Torridon' (2)	CQua GEve	
'Toscanini' (2)	EFam	
'Toto' (12) ♀ H4 **new**	CBro	
'Tracey' (6) ♀ H4	CBro CQua	
'Trebah' (2)	CQua	
'Treble Two' (7)	CQua	
'Trecara' (3) **new**	CQua	
'Trefusis' (1)	CQua	

'Trehane' (6)	CQua	
'Trena' (6) ♀ H4	CBro CQua	
'Tresamble' (5)	CBro CQua LAma	
'Treverva' (6)	CQua	
'Treviddo' (2)	CQua	
'Trevithian' (7) ♀ H4	CBro CQua IRhd LAma LRHS NRog	
'Trewarvas' (2)	CQua	
'Trewirgie' (6)	CBro CQua	
triandrus (13) ♀ H3	NSla WPGP	
- var. *albus*	see *N. triandrus* subsp. *triandrus* var. *triandrus*	
§ - subsp. *triandrus* var. *concolor* (13)	CBro MS&S	
§ - - var. *pulchellus* (13)	LAma	
§ - - var. *triandrus* (13)	EPot	
'Trident' (3)	CQua	
'Trigonometry' (11a)	IRhd	
'Tripartite' (11a) ♀ H4	CQua GEve NZep	
'Triple Crown' (3) ♀ H4	CQua IRhd	
'Tropic Isle' (4)	CQua	
'Tropical Heat' (2)	IRhd	
'Trousseau' (1)	CQua	
'Troutbeck' (3)	CQua	
'Trueblood' (3) **new**	IRhd	
'Trumpet Warrior' (1)	IRhd	
'Tudor Minstrel' (2)	CQua	
'Tuesday's Child' (5) ♀ H4	CQua ERos MBNS	
'Tullynagee' (3) **new**	IRhd	
'Tullyroyal' (2)	IRhd	
'Turncoat' (6)	CQua	
'Tutankhamun' (2)	CQua	
'Twink' (4) **new**	CQua	
'Tyee' (2)	CQua	
'Tyrian Rose' (2)	IRhd	
'Tyrone Gold' (1) ♀ H4	IRhd	
'Tywara' (1)	EHof	
'Ulster Bride' (4)	CQua	
'Ulster Bullion' (2)	IRhd	
'Una Bremner' (2)	GEve	
'Uncle Duncan' (1)	CQua EHof IRhd	
'Unique' (4)	CQua LAma	
'Unsurpassable' (1)	LAma	
'Urchin' (2)	IRhd	
'Utiku' (6)	CQua	
'Val d'Incles' (3)	IRhd	
'Valdrome' (11a)	CQua MBri	
'Valinor' (2)	CQua	
'Value' (2)	IRhd	
'Van Sion'	see *N.* 'Telamonius Plenus'	
'Vandyke' (2)	IRhd	
'Vanellus' (11a) **new**	IRhd	
'Veneration' (1) **new**	CQua	
'Verdin' (7)	CQua	
'Verger' (3)	LAma MBri	
'Vernal Prince' (3) ♀ H4	CQua GEve	
'Verona' (3) ♀ H4	CQua	
'Verran Rose' (2) **new**	IRhd	
'Vers Libre' (9)	CQua	
'Vickie Linn' (6) **new**	IRhd	
'Victorious' (2)	CQua	
'Vigil' (1) ♀ H4	CQua	
'Viking' (1) ♀ H4	CQua GEve	
'Violetta' (2)	CQua	
viridiflorus (13)	SSpi	
- MS 500	SSpi	
'Vulcan' (2) ♀ H4	CQua	
'W.P. Milner' (1)	CAvo CBro CMea EPot LAma LRHS MBri NRog WShi	
'Wadavers' (2)	CQua	
'Waif' (6)	CQua	
'Waldorf Astoria' (4)	CQua IRhd	
'War Dance' (3)	IRhd	

'Warbler' (6)	CQua	
'Watamu' (3) **new**	IRhd	
'Waterperry' (7)	CBro LAma NRog	
watieri	see *N. rupicola* subsp. *watieri*	
'Wavelength' (3)	IRhd	
'Waxwing' (5)	CQua	
'Wee Bee' (1)	CQua	
'Welcome' (2) **new**	CQua	
'Westward' (4)	CQua	
'Whang-hi' (6)	CQua ERos	
'Wheal Coates' (7) ♀ H4	CQua	
'Wheal Honey' (1)	CQua	
'Wheal Jane' (2)	CQua	
'Wheal Kitty' (7)	CQua ERos	
'Wheatear' (6) **new**	IRhd	
'Whetstone' (1)	CQua	
'Whipcord' (7)	IRhd	
'Whisky Galore' (2) **new**	EHof	
'Whisky Mac' (2)	EHof	
'White Hill' (3)	IRhd	
'White Lady' (3)	CAvo CQua WShi	
'White Lion' (4) ♀ H4	CQua EFam LAma NRog	
'White Marvel' (4)	CQua LAma LRHS NRog	
'White Nile' (2) **new**	CQua	
'White Star' (1)	CQua IRhd	
'Whiteabbey' (2)	IRhd	
'Wicklow Hills' (3)	CQua	
willkommii (13)	CBro	
'Winholm Jenni' (3)	CQua	
'Witch Doctor' (3)	IRhd	
'Witch Hunt' (4)	IRhd	
'Wodan' (2)	EFam	
'Woodcock' (6)	CBro CQua	
'Woodland Prince' (3)	CQua	
'Woodland Star' (3)	CQua	
'Woodley Vale' (2)	CQua	
'Woolsthorpe' (2)	CQua	
'Xit' (3)	CAvo CBro CQua EHyt GCrs SCnR	
'Xunantunich' (2)	EHof IRhd	
'Yellow Cheerfulness' (4) ♀ H4	LAma LRHS MBri NRog	
'Yellow Sun' (3)	LAma	
'Yellow Xit' (3)	CQua	
'York Minster' (3)	CQua IRhd	
'Young American' (1)	CQua	
'Young Blood' (2)	IRhd	
'Your Grace' (2)	EHof	
'Yum-Yum' (3)	IRhd	
zaianicus	see *N. romieuxii* subsp. *albidus* var. *zaianicus*	
- *lutescens*	see *N. romieuxii* subsp. *albidus* var. *zaianicus* f. *lutescens*	
'Zekiah' (1) **new**	CQua	

Nardophyllum (Asteraceae)
bryoides	GTou

Nardostachys (Valerianaceae)
grandiflora	GPoy

Narthecium (Melanthiaceae)
ossifragum	WShi

Nassella (Poaceae)
cernua	CBig CBrm EBee EPPr EWsh WRos
lepida	CBig CBrm
pulchra	CBig
trichotoma	CBrm CFwr EBee EHoe EMan EMon EPPr EPla EWsh LJus LRHS MAvo MBNS MCCP MMoz SApp SAsh SLim SMrm SPla WCot WDyG WPGP WRos

Nasturtium (Brassicaceae)
officinale	CPrp EMFW SWat WHer

Natal plum see *Carissa macrocarpa*

Nautilocalyx (Gesneriaceae)
pemphidius	WDib

nectarine see *Prunus persica* var. *nectarina*

Nectaroscordum (Alliaceae)
bivalve	ERos
§ *siculum*	CArn CAvo CBre CBro CMea CMil EBre EChP ELan EOrc EPar GMaP LLWP LPhx MBro MCLN NBir NCel NChi NEgg SSvw SUsu SYvo WFar WHil WHoo WLin WRHF
§ - subsp. *bulgaricum*	More than 30 suppliers
tripedale	CLAP CMea

Neillia (Rosaceae)
affinis	ENot MTis NBid NLar NPro WBVN WDin WHCG
longiracemosa	see *N. thibetica*
sinensis	CMCN CPle MRav
§ *thibetica*	More than 30 suppliers

Nematanthus (Gesneriaceae)
'Apres'	WDib
'Black Magic'	CHal WDib
'Christmas Holly'	WDib
'Freckles'	WDib
§ *gregarius* ♀ H1	CHal EBak WDib
§ - 'Golden West' (v)	CHal WDib
- 'Variegatus'	see *N. gregarius* 'Golden West'
radicans	see *N. gregarius*
'Tropicana' ♀ H1	CHal WDib

Nemesia (Scrophulariaceae)
Blue Cloud = 'Penblu' ♀ H3	SAga
Blue Lagoon = 'Pengoon' (Maritana Series)	LIck SCoo WWeb
Bluebird = 'Hubbird' PBR	CHll SGar
Blushing Bride = 'Yablush'	WGor WWeb
§ *caerulea*	ECtt MTho WPer
- 'Joan Wilder' (clonal)	ECtt EMan WEas
N - 'Joan Wilder' (seed raised)	see *N. caerulea* lilac/blue
§ - lilac/blue	WPer
- 'Woodcote'	CFox
Candy Girl = 'Pencand' (Maritana Series) **new**	SCoo WWeb
'Delphi'	EOrc
§ *denticulata* ♀ H3-4	More than 30 suppliers
- 'Confetti'	see *N. denticulata*
foetens	see *N. caerulea*
'Fragrant Cloud' PBR	CChe CHea EBee EOrc EPfP LRHS MAsh MCCP MNrw SPla WWeb
fruticans misapplied	see *N. caerulea*
fruticans Benth.	NBlu
'Georgina'	MOak
Honey Girl = 'Penhon' (Maritana Series) **new**	LIck SCoo WWeb
'Innocence' ♀ H3	CFox CHal COIW CSpe EBee EMan EOrc LHop LIck MArl MOak WGwG
'Karoo Blue' **new**	NPri SCoo
'Karoo Pink' **new**	NPri
Melanie = 'Fleuron' PBR ♀ H3	EPfP LRHS WWeb
'Morning Haze' **new**	WWeb
Mystic Blue = 'Penmys' **new**	WWeb

'Orchard Blue' | EBee EOrc EPfP
'Rose Wings' | EPfP
Sugar Girl = 'Pensug' (Maritana Series) **new** | NPri WWeb
sylvatica **new** | CSpe
'Tufty' | WCot
umbonata hort. | see *N. caerulea* lilac/blue
'Vanilla Mist' **new** | EPfP
'White Wings' PBR | CHar EPfP

Nemopanthus (Aquifoliaceae)
mucronatus	CPle

Neodypsis (Arecaceae)
decaryi	see *Dypsis decaryi*

Neolitsea (Lauraceae)
glauca	see *N. sericea*
§ *sericea*	CBcs CHEx SSpi

Neomarica (Iridaceae)
gracilis	WCot

Neopanax see *Pseudopanax*

Neopaxia (Portulacaceae)
§ *australasica*	ECou GDra
- blue-leaved	see *N. australasica* 'Kosciusko'
- bronze-leaved	see *N. australasica* 'Ohau'
- grey	see *N. australasica* 'Kosciusko'
§ - 'Kosciusko'	GDra GGar
- 'Lyndon'	ECou
§ - 'Ohau'	ECou

Neoregelia (Bromeliaceae)
carolinae	MBri
- (Meyendorffii Group) 'Flandria' (v)	MBri
- - 'Meyendorffii'	MBri
- f. *tricolor* (v) ♀ H1	CHal MBri
§ Claret Group	MBri
marmorata ♀ H1	ESlt

Neottianthe (Orchidaceae)
cucullata	EFEx

Nepenthes (Nepenthaceae)
alata	CSWC
- x *ventricosa*	SHmp
x *coccinea*	MBri
fusca x *maxima* **new**	SHmp
gracilis	CSWC
khasiana	SHmp
maxima x *mixta*	SHmp
rafflesiana	CSWC
sanguinea	SHmp
spectabilis	SHmp
stenophylla	SHmp

Nepeta (Lamiaceae)
DS&T 89048T	CStr
§ *argolica*	EBee MSte WPer
'Bide-a-Wee Variegated' (v)	NBid
'Blue Beauty'	see *N. sibirica* 'Souvenir d'André Chaudron'
bucharica	GBuc WOut
* *buddlejifolium*	NLar
camphorata	GBar GTou MLLN MNrw MSte SAga SBla SCro SGar SIde WOut
cataria	CArn CPrp CSam CSev EBee ELau GBar GPoy MBow MChe MHer

	MSal MWrn NBlu NBro SCro SIde WHer WMoo WPer WSel WWye
§ - 'Citriodora'	CArn CBot CHar CPrp EBee ELau EWTr GBar GPoy Ilve MHer MSal MWrn NVic SChu SIde SSpe WBar WBea WCHb WHHs WHer WHil WSel
citriodora Dum.	see *N. cataria* 'Citriodora'
clarkei	CBri CHar CStr EBee EFou EMan LPhx MDKP MMHG MNrw MSte MWrn NCat SAga SBla SBod SCro SWat WCom WPer
curviflora	Ilve
* *darcyi* **new**	EBee
'Dropmore' **new**	EBee
§ x *faassenii* ♀ H4	More than 30 suppliers
- 'Alba'	COlW CStr EBee ECtt EPfP MGGn NLar WBea WHil
glechoma 'Variegata'	see *Glechoma hederacea* 'Variegata'
'Gottfried Kühn'	GBar
govaniana	More than 30 suppliers
grandiflora	EFou EWsh MGrG MRav SBri SIde WFar WHer WOut WWhi
- 'Bramdean'	CMea CPrp CRDP CSam CStr EBee EMan LPhx MBri NCat NDov SAga SUsu WKif WOut
- 'Dawn to Dusk'	More than 30 suppliers
- 'Pool Bank'	CRDP CStr EBee EGoo EMan NCat SChu SCro SGar SUsu WViv
hederacea 'Variegata'	see *Glechoma hederacea* 'Variegata'
italica	MAnH SBla SHar
* *kubabiana*	EBee
kubanica	EMan LPhx
laevigata	EBee
lanceolata	see *N. nepetella*
latifolia	EBee LPhx MLLN
'Lilac Cloud' **new**	NBir
longibracteata **new**	EBee
* *longipes* hort.	More than 30 suppliers
macrantha	see *N. sibirica*
melissifolia	EBee MHer WCHb WOut WPer WWye
mussinii hort.	see *N. x faassenii*
mussinii Spreng.	see *N. racemosa*
§ *nepetella*	EBee GBri NBir NChi WFar WOut WPer WPrP
nervosa	More than 30 suppliers
- 'Blue Carpet'	GCal WOut
- 'Forncett Select'	CSam EBee EFou EMan NDov NGar SDys SMrm
§ *nuda*	CSam EBee EChP ECha EMan LDai MCAu MLLN SPoG WFar WPer
- subsp. *albiflora*	CStr ECha NCat SBla
* - 'Anne's Choice'	EBee MSte SWat
* - 'Grandiflora'	WMoo WPic
- 'Isis' **new**	EFou
- subsp. *nuda*	CBre CStr
parnassica	CBri CMea CSam CStr EBee EChP ECoo EMan EWTr GBar ITim LRHS MAnH MBct MWrn NLar SAga SCro SMad WBri WCot WHer WMoo WPic WWhi
phyllochlamys	CBot CPBP
'Porzellan'	CPrp CStr EBee ECGP EChP EFou EMan EVFa MMil MSte SAga SMrm SVil
§ *prattii*	CBri CHar COlW CRDP EBee ECoo ERou SBod SMrm SPoG STes WElm
§ *racemosa* ♀ H4	CArn CBot CFwr COlW CSBt CSev EBee EBre ECGN ELau EPfP GBar GKir LRHS MChe MRav NBlu SIde WMoo WWin WWye
- *alba*	WFar
- 'Blue Ice'	CStr GBuc WHoo
- 'Grog'	CStr EBee EFou MLLN WCot
- 'Karen's Blue'	EFou
- 'Little Titch'	CStr EBee EFou EMan EVFa GCal LAst LRHS MSte SAga SChu SMrm SPla SSpe SWat WFar WOut
- 'Snowflake'	CBot CMea EFou ELan EMil EPfP GCal GKir LPio LRHS MAnH MHer MSte NBir NCat NPri SChu SPar SPer SPla SRPl SSpe STes WFar WGwG WHHs WHil WSel
§ - 'Superba'	EFou ELan EMon GBuc MBro WHoo
- 'Walker's Low'	More than 30 suppliers
reichenbachiana	see *N. racemosa*
§ *sibirica*	CBri EBlw ECGN ECha EFou ELau EPfP EWTr GKir LRHS MAnH MHer MNrw MRav MWrn NBid NBro NDov NPri SChu SCro SIgm WCot WFar WHal WPer
§ - 'Souvenir d'André Chaudron'	More than 30 suppliers
sibthorpii	see *N. argolica*
sintenisii	CSWP CStr IFro
'Six Hills Giant'	More than 30 suppliers
stewartiana	CBri CStr EPPr GBuc LDai MBro MCAu MLLN MWrn NLar STes WElm WHoo WOut WSan
- ACE 1611	EBee GBuc SMrm
- CLD 551	EMan
subsessilis	More than 30 suppliers
- AGSJ 251	MNes
- pink	CSam CStr ECha EGle EPPr EVFa GBuc GEil MAnH SAga WMaN WViv
* - *sensibilis*	SWat
- 'Sweet Dreams'	EBee GBri SHar SSvw
- var. *yesoensis*	CPlt CStr
tenuifolia	EBee MSal
transcaucasica	CArn CStr EBee LPio WOut
- 'Blue Infinity'	EWTr NArg NPPs SMac
troodii	CBri EMan
tuberosa	CBri CSpe CStr EBee EChP ECha ECoo EMan GBri MAnH MAvo MRav MWrn SChu STes WCot WPic WWhi WWye
'Veluws Blauwtje' **new**	EBee
yunnanensis **new**	EMan MAnH

Nephrolepis (Oleandraceae)

cordifolia	GQui MBri NMar
exaltata ♀ H2	ERea LRHS
- 'Bostoniensis'	MBri
- 'Smithii'	MBri
- 'Smithii Linda'	MBri
- 'Teddy Junior'	MBri
- 'Todeoides'	NMar
- 'Whitmanii Improved'	NMar

Nephrophyllidium (Menyanthaceae)

crista-galli	IBlr

Nerine ✿ (Amaryllidaceae)

from Lime Close	LPhx
'Administrator' **new**	SSpr
'Afterglow'	LAma MBNS SSpr
'Airies'	SSpr
'Alexandra' **new**	SSpr
'Amalfi'	SSpr
'Angelico'	SSpr
angulata **new**	EBee
'Atlanta'	SSpr
'Audrey' **new**	WCot
'Baghdad'	SSpr

'Belladonna'	SSpr	'Kasmir'	SSpr
'Berlioz'	SSpr	'Kilwa'	SSpr
'Blanchefleur'	SSpr	'King Leopold'	SSpr
* 'Borde Hill White'	SSpr	'King of the Belgians'	LAma SSpr
bowdenii ♀ H3-4	More than 30 suppliers	'Kingship'	SSpr
- 'Alba'	CBro ELan LRHS SCoo	'Kola'	SSpr
- 'Manina'	SSpr WCot	'Konak'	SSpr
- 'Mark Fenwick'	CBcs CBro EBee GCal WCot WOld	'Koriba'	SSpr
- 'Marnie Rogerson'	CBro WCot	**krigei**	EBee
§ - 'Mollie Cowie' (v)	EBee EMon EVFa IBlr MTed WCot	'Kymina'	SSpr
	WCru	'Kyoto'	SSpr
- pale pink striped	CDes	'Kyrie'	SSpr
darker **new**		'Lady Cynthia Colville'	SSpr
- 'Pink Triumph'	CAbP CBcs CFwr CLyd EBee EBla	'Lady Eleanor Keane'	SSpr
	EMan EPyc GBuc IBlr LAma LRHS	'Lambourne'	SSpr
	NRog SDeJ SPer WDav	**laticoma**	EBee WCot
- 'Quinton Wells'	LPhx	'Latu'	SSpr
- 'Variegata'	see *N. bowdenii* 'Mollie Cowie'	'Lawlord'	SSpr
- 'Wellsii'	CMil CRDP EBee WCot	'Leila Hughes'	SSpr
'Brahms'	SSpr	'Locharber'	SSpr
'Branstone' **new**	SSpr	'Lord Grenfell'	IBlr
'Canasta'	SSpr	'Lottery'	SSpr
'Cardinal'	SSpr	'Lucinda'	SSpr
'Carisbrooke' **new**	SSpr	'Lyndhurst Salmon'	SSpr
'Carnival'	SSpr	'Mandarin'	SSpr
'Caroline'	SSpr	'Mansellii'	SSpr
'Catherine'	SSpr	'Maria'	SSpr WCot
'Clarabel'	SSpr	**masoniorum**	CBro CStu EBee EHyt ERos LPhx
'Clarissa'	SSpr		MTho NMen SChr WCot
'Clent Charm'	SSpr	'Meadowbankii'	SSpr
corusca 'Major'	see *N. sarniensis* var. *corusca*	'Miss Edith Godman'	SSpr
crispa	see *N. undulata*	'Monet'	SSpr
'Curiosity'	SSpr	'Mrs Goldsmith'	SSpr
'Cynthia Chance'	SSpr	'Natasha'	SSpr
'Dame Alice Godman'	SSpr	'Noreen'	SSpr
'Darius'	SSpr	'Oberon'	EEpr
'Dorellia'	SSpr	'Orange Queen'	SSpr
'Drucilla'	SSpr	'Osborne' **new**	SSpr
'Dunkirk'	SSpr	**peersii**	WCot
'Elspeth'	SSpr	'Penelope'	SSpr
'Eve'	SSpr	'Pink Galore'	SSpr
'Evening'	SSpr	'Plain Jane'	SSpr
'Ffiske'	SSpr	'Plymouth'	SSpr
filamentosa	CBro	**pudica**	WCot
filifolia	CRDP EBee EHyt EPot ERos GCal	'Quarr' **new**	SSpr
	ITim MNrw WCot	'Red Pimpernel'	GAbr LAma MBNS
flexuosa	MRav SSpr WViv	'Rembrandt'	SSpr
- 'Alba'	CAvo CBro CPne EBee ECha EPot	'Rose Godman' **new**	SSpr
	ETub LAma LPhx LRHS MRav	'Rushmere Star'	SSpr
	SDeJ SSpr WCot WViv	'Salmonia'	SSpr
'Fortune'	SSpr	**sarniensis** ♀ H2-3	CBro CFwr ECha LRHS NRog
'Fucine' **new**	CDes		SYvo WDav
'Gaby Deslys'	SSpr	* - 'Alba'	WCot
'Glensavage Gem'	SSpr	§ - var. **corusca**	CAvo LAma
'Glensavage Spider'	SSpr	- - 'Major'	LBow SSpr
'Gloaming'	SSpr	- var. **curvifolia**	SSpr WCot
'Goya'	SSpr	f. **fothergillii**	
'Hamlet'	SSpr	- 'Mottistone' **new**	SSpr
'Harlequin'	SSpr	'Smokey Special'	SSpr
'Harry Dalton'	SSpr	'Snowflake'	SSpr
'Hawaii'	SSpr	'Solent Swan'	SSpr
'Helen Smith'	SSpr	'Springbank Alice' **new**	SSpr
'Helena'	SSpr	'Springbank Matthew' **new**	SSpr
'Hera'	EMon LPhx	'Stephanie'	LAma LRHS SSpr WDav
humilis	WCot	'Stephanie' x 'Moscow'	SSpr
'Inchmery Kate'	SSpr	§ **undulata**	CBgR CBro CFwr EBee ECha EPot
innominata	SSpr		ERos LAma LBow LPhx LRHS
'Janet'	SSpr		MBri WCot WViv
'Jenny Wren'	SSpr	'Vestal'	SSpr
'Jill'	SSpr	'Virgo'	GAbr
'Joan'	SSpr	'White Swan'	LAma MBNS SSpr
'Judith'	SSpr	'Wolsey'	SSpr
'Juliet Berkeley'	SSpr	'Yaverland' **new**	SSpr

'Zeal Giant' ♀ H3-4   CBro CFir LPhx

Nerium ❀ (Apocynaceae)

oleander	CAbb CHEx CMdw CTri EBak EEls LPan LRHS MTis SArc SPar SRms
– 'Album'	EEls
– 'Album Plenum' (d)	EEls
– 'Alsace'	EEls ERea
– 'Altini'	EEls
– 'Angiolo Pucci'	EEls
– 'Bousquet d'Orb'	EEls
§ – 'Carneum Plenum' (d)	EEls
– 'Cavalaire' (d)	EEls
* – 'Clare'	ERea SOWG
– 'Cornouailles'	EEls
– 'Docteur Golfin'	EEls
– 'Emile Sahut'	EEls
– 'Emilie'	EEls ERea
– 'Flavescens Plenum' (d)	CFee EEls
– 'Géant des Batailles' (d)	EEls SOWG
– 'Hardy Red'	EEls
– 'Hawaii'	EEls
* – 'Isabelle'	EEls
– 'Isle of Capri'	EEls SOWG
– 'J.R.'	EEls
– 'Jannoch'	EEls
– 'Louis Pouget' (d)	EEls
– 'Madame Allen' (d)	EEls
– 'Maresciallo Graziani'	EEls
– 'Margaritha'	EEls
– 'Marie Gambetta'	EEls
– 'Mont Blanc'	EEls
– 'Mrs Roeding'	see N. oleander 'Carneum Plenum'
– 'Nana Rosso'	EEls
– 'Oasis'	EEls
– subsp. oleander	EEls
– 'Papa Gambetta'	EEls
– 'Petite Pink'	EEls
– 'Petite Red'	EEls
– 'Petite Salmon'	EEls
– 'Professeur Granel' (d)	EEls
– 'Provence' (d)	EEls SOWG
– 'Rose des Borrels'	EEls
– 'Rosée du Ventoux' (d)	EEls SOWG
– 'Roseum Plenum' (d)	CRHN EEls
– 'Rosita'	EEls
– 'Sealy Pink'	EEls
* – 'Snowflake'	SOWG
– 'Soeur Agnès' (d)	EEls
– 'Soleil Levant'	EEls
– 'Souvenir d'Emma Schneider'	EEls
– 'Souvenir des Iles Canaries'	EEls
– 'Splendens' (d)	SOWG
– 'Splendens Giganteum' (d)	EEls
– 'Splendens Giganteum Variegatum' (d/v)	EEls
– 'Tito Poggi'	EEls SHFr
– 'Variegatum' (v) ♀ H1+3	CBot
– 'Variegatum Plenum' (d/v)	WCot
– 'Villa Romaine'	EEls
– 'Ville de Carpentras' (d)	EEls

Nertera (Rubiaceae)

balfouriana	ECou
granadensis	MBri

Neviusia (Rosaceae)

alabamensis	WWes

Nicandra (Solanaceae)

physalodes	CArn EMan EWll MGol MSal NCWG SWal SYvo WRos
– alba	SWal
* – 'Blacky'	SMrm
– 'Splash of Cream' (v)	EMan EWll SWal WWpP
– 'Violacea'	CSpe GGar SRms

Nicotiana (Solanaceae)

glauca	CFwr CPLG EBee EMan MGol MOak MSte SSte WHer
knightiana	CSpe WEas
langsdorffii ♀ H3	CBcs CBri CFox CHad EBee EBla EMan EMon GBri LHrt LPio MGol SMrm SPet SUsu WEas WMaN WPer WRus
– 'Cream Splash' (v)	CPla EBee EChP EMon WBar WHer
– 'Lime Green' ♀ H3 new	CSpe
longiflora new	CStr
* mutabilis	CHll CSpe EBee
quadrivalvis	MGol
var. bigelovii new	
rustica	IIve MGol
suaveolens	WRus
sylvestris ♀ H3	CBri CFox CHad COIW CSpe CStr EBee EChP EMan EPfP EWTr LPVe MGol MOak SEND SMrm SPar WEas WHer WRus WWye
tabacum	CArn MGol WWye
– Hungarian	IIve

Nidorella (Asteraceae)

auriculata new	CTrC

Nidularium (Bromeliaceae)

flandria	see Neoregelia carolinae (Meyendorffii Group) 'Flandria'

Nierembergia (Solanaceae)

§ caerulea ♀ H1	CAbP EBee ECha EHrv EMan EWTr MLLN
frutescens	see N. scoparia
hippomanica	see N. caerulea
§ repens	CFee ECGP EDAr EMlt EPot GKir LRHS NLAp WWin
rivularis	see N. repens
§ scoparia	NFla SScr
– 'Mont Blanc'	LRHS
– 'Purple Robe'	LRHS

Nigella (Ranunculaceae)

sativa new	WJek

Niphaea (Gesneriaceae)

oblonga	NMos

x Niphimenes (Gesneriaceae)

'Lemonade'	NMos

Nipponanthemum (Asteraceae)

§ nipponicum	CDes CFwr CNic CSam EBee GCal GMac LAst LPio MNrw NSti SMrm SRms WCot
– roseum	CSam

Noccaea see Thlaspi

Nolina (Dracaenaceae)

beldingii	SIgm
brevifolia	SIgm
greenii	SIgm
longifolia	EOas

palmeri	SIgm
§ *recurvata* ♀ H1	CTrC EOas LPal MBri
texana	CTrC NWCA SIgm

Nomocharis (*Liliaceae*)

aperta	EBee EHyt EPot GBuc GCrs GDra GEdr GKev GKir ITim LAma SSpi WCru
- CLD 229	GBuc GKir
basilissa	EBee
farreri	EBee EPot GCrs GEdr GKir WCru
x *finlayorum*	GCrs
mairei	see *N. pardanthina*
meleagrina	EBee EPot GBuc LAma
nana	see *Lilium nanum*
oxypetala	see *Lilium oxypetalum*
§ *pardanthina*	EMan GBuc GMac LAma NHar WAbe WCru
- f. *punctulata*	GBuc GGGa GKir WCru
saluenensis	EBee GTou ITim WAbe WCru

Nonea (*Boraginaceae*)

lutea	CBri EChP MFir MLLN NOrc NSti WAhh WCHb WHal WRos WWye

Nothochelone see *Penstemon*

Nothofagus ✿ (*Fagaceae*)

§ x *alpina*	CLnd CMCN NWea SPer WMou WNor
antarctica	CBen CCVT CLnd CMCN CMHG CTho ELan EPfP EWTr ISea LPan MBar MBlu MBri MGos NBee NPal NWea SPer STre WDin WFar WNor WSHC
cunninghamii	GGGa ISea STre WNor
dombeyi	CBcs CDoC CDul CLnd CTho ISea LHyd SAPC SArc SBir SSpi WBod WNor
fusca	CBcs CDoC CTrC
menziesii	CBcs CDul
§ *nervosa*	CDul LPan WDin
obliqua	CBcs CDoC CDul CLnd CMCN CSam NWea WDin WMou WNor
procera misapplied	see *N.* x *alpina*
procera Oerst.	see *N. nervosa*
solanderi	CMHG
- var. *cliffortioides*	CBcs WCwm

Notholaena see *Cheilanthes*

Notholirion (*Liliaceae*)

bulbuliferum	EBee GDra GKir WCot
campanulatum	EBee
macrophyllum	EBee EPot GBuc GDra GEdr NLar WCru
thomsonianum	GCrs

Nothopanax see *Polyscias*

Nothoscordum (*Alliaceae*)

gracile	EBee
inodorum	GBuc
neriniflorum	see *Caloscordum neriniflorum*

Notobuxus (*Buxaceae*)

natalensis	SLan

Notospartium (*Papilionaceae*)

carmichaeliae	ECou
- 'Hodder'	ECou
- 'Seymour'	ECou
glabrescens	ECou

- 'Ben More'	ECou
- 'Woodside'	ECou
'Joy' ECou	
torulosum	ECou
- 'Blue Butterfly'	ECou
- 'Malvern Hills'	Ecou
- x *glabrescens*	ECou

Nuphar (*Nymphaeaceae*)

japonica	CRow
var. *variegata* (v)	
lutea	CBen CRow EHon EMFW LPBA MSta SCoo SLon SWat WFar
pumila	MSta
* - *variegata* (v)	MSta

Nylandtia (*Polygalaceae*)

spinosa new	SPlb

Nymphaea ✿ (*Nymphaeaceae*)

alba (H)	CBen CRow CWat EHon EMFW EPfP LPBA MSta NBlu SCoo SWat WFar WMAq WStI WWeb
§ - subsp. *occidentalis* (H)	MSta
'Alba Plenissima' (H)	MSta
alba var. *rubra* (H)	MSta
'Albatros' Latour-Marliac (H)	EHon LMdh LPBA MSta SBHF SWat WBcn
'Albatros' misapplied	see *N.* 'Hermine'
'Amabilis' (H)	CBen CRow EMFW LPBA MSta SWat WBcn WMAq
'American Star' (H)	CWat EMFW MSta SBHF SWat WMAq
'Andreana' (H)	CWat LPBA MSta SWat
'Arc-en-ciel' (H)	MSta SWat WMAq
'Arethusa' (H)	MSta
'Atropurpurea' (H)	CBen EMFW LPBA MSta SWat WMAq
'Attraction' (H)	CBen CRow EHon EMFW LPBA MSta NBlu NPer SWat WMAq
'Aurora' (H)	EMFW LMdh LPBA MSta SBHF SWat WMAq
'Barbara Davies' (H)	MSta
'Barbara Dobbins' (H)	MSta
'Baroness Orczy' (H)	MSta
'Bateau' (H)	MSta
'Berit Strawn' (H)	EMFW
'Berthold' (H)	CBen MSta
'Blue Beauty' (T/D)	CBen
'Bory de Saint-Vincent' (H)	MSta
'Brakeleyi Rosea' (H)	LPBA MSta
'Burgundy Princess' (H)	EMFW LMdh
candida (H)	CBen EHon EMFW LPBA MSta WMAq
- var. *rubra* (H)	MSta
'Candidissima' (H)	MSta
'Candidissima Rosea' (H)	MSta
§ *capensis* (T/D)	MSta
'Caroliniana' (H)	CWat MSta
'Caroliniana Nivea' (H)	CBen EMFW MSta
'Caroliniana Perfecta' (H)	CBen LPBA MSta SWat
'Caroliniana Rosea' (H)	MSta
'Celebration' (H)	MSta SBHF
§ 'Charlene Strawn' (H)	EMFW MSta SWat WBcn WMAq
'Charles de Meurville' (H)	CBen CRow EMFW LMdh LPBA MSta NPer WMAq
'Château le Rouge' (H)	MSta
'Chrysantha' (H)	MSta
'Chubby' (H)	EMFW MSta
'Colonel A.J. Welch' (H)	CBen CRow EHon EMFW LMdh LPBA MSta NPer SCoo SWat WFar WMAq
colorata	see *N. capensis*

	'Colossea' (H)	CBen CWat EHon EMFW LPBA MSta NBlu
	'Comanche' (H)	CBen EMFW MSta NPer SWat WMAq
	'Comte de Bouchaud' (H)	MSta
	'Conqueror' (H)	EMFW IArd LPBA MSta SWat WFar WWeb
	'Dallas' (H)	SBHF
	'Danieda'	SWat
§	'Darwin' (H)	CBen CWat MSta SWat WMAq
	'David' (H)	CWat MSta
	'Deva' (H)	MSta
	'Ellisiana' (H)	CBen EMFW LPBA MSta SLon SWat
	'Elysée' (H)	MSta
	'Escarboucle' (H) ♀ H4	CBen CRow CWat EHon EMFW LMdh LPBA MSta NPer SBHF SWat WBcn WMAq
	'Esmeralda' (H)	MSta SWat
	'Eucharis' (H)	MSta
	'Eugénia de Land' (H)	MSta
	'Evelyn Randig' (T/D)	MSta
	'Exquisita'	see N. 'Odorata Exquisita'
§	'Fabiola' (H)	CBen CRow EHon EMFW EPfP LMdh LPBA MSta SCoo SWat WBcn WFar WMAq
	'Fire Crest' (H)	CBen EHon EMFW LMdh LPBA MSta NBlu SCoo SLon SWat WBcn WFar WMAq
	'Formosa' (H)	MSta
	'France' (H)	MSta
	'Fritz Junge' (H)	MSta
	'Froebelii' (H)	CBen CRow CWat EHon EMFW LMdh LPBA MSta SWat WBcn WMAq
	'Fulva' (H)	MSta
	'Galatée' (H)	MSta
	gigantea (T/D)	MSta
	'Gladstoneana' (H) ♀ H4	CBen CRow CWat EHon EMFW LMdh LPBA MSta NPer SBHF SWat WMAq
	'Gloire du Temple-sur-Lot' (H)	CBen EMFW MSta SWat WMAq
	'Gloriosa' (H)	CBen LPBA MSta SWat WFar WWeb
	'Gold Medal' (H)	CBen
	'Goliath' (H)	MSta
	'Gonnère' (H) ♀ H4	CBen CRow CWat EHon EMFW LMdh LPBA MSta SWat WBcn WMAq
	'Graziella' (H)	LPBA MSta SWat WBcn WMAq
	'Grésilias' (H)	MSta
	'Hal Miller' (H)	MSta
	'Helen Fowler' (H)	EMFW MSta SBHF SLon SWat WMAq
	x *helvola*	see N. 'Pygmaea Helvola'
§	'Hermine' (H)	CBen EMFW MSta SWat WMAq
	'Hever White' (H)	MSta
	'Hollandia' misapplied	see N. 'Darwin'
	'Indiana' (H)	CBen EMFW LPBA MSta SWat WMAq
	'Irene Heritage' (H)	CBen
	'James Brydon' (H) ♀ H4	CBen CRow CWat EHon EMFW EPfP LMdh LPBA MSta NPer SCoo SWat WBcn WFar WMAq
	'James Hudson' (H)	MSta
	'Jean de Lamarsalle' (H)	MSta
	'Jean Laydeker' (H)	MSta
§	'Joanne Pring' (H)	MSta SWat
	'Joey Tomocik' (H)	CWat LMdh SBHF SCoo SLon WMAq
	'Lactea' (H)	MSta
	'Laydekeri Fulgens' (H)	CBen EMFW LPBA MSta SWat WMAq
	'Laydekeri Liliacea' (H)	CBen CRow EMFW LMdh LPBA MSta SWat WMAq

	'Laydekeri Purpurata' (H)	LPBA MSta SWat WBcn WMAq
	'Laydekeri Rosea' misapplied'	see N. 'Laydekeri Rosea Prolifera
§	'Laydekeri Rosea Prolifera' (H)	CBen EMFW LPBA MSta
	'Lemon Chiffon' (H)	EMFW
	'Leviathan' (H)	MSta
	'Limelight'	SWat
	'Little Sue' (H)	EMFW
	'Livingstone' (H)	CWat MSta
	'Luciana'	see N. 'Odorata Luciana'
	'Lucida' (H)	CBen CWat EMFW LPBA MSta SWat WMAq
	'Lusitania' (H)	MSta
	'Madame Bory Latour-Marliac' (H)	MSta
	'Madame de Bonseigneur' (H)	MSta
	'Madame Julien Chifflot' (H)	MSta
	'Madame Maurice Laydeker' (H)	MSta
	'Madame Wilfon Gonnère' (H)	CBen CWat EHon EMFW LMdh LPBA MSta SWat WBcn WMAq WWeb
	'Marliacea Albida' (H)	CBen CWat EHon LPBA MSta SWat WFar WMAq
	'Marliacea Carnea' (H)	CBen CRow EHon EMFW EPfP LMdh LPBA MSta NBlu NPer SCoo SWat WBcn WFar WMAq
§	'Marliacea Chromatella' (H) ♀ H4	CBen CRow CWat EHon EMFW EPfP LMdh LPBA MSta SBHF SCoo SLon SWat WBcn WFar WMAq
	'Marliacea Flammea' (H)	MSta
	'Marliacea Ignea' (H)	MSta
	'Marliacea Rosea' (H)	EMFW MSta WMAq
	'Marliacea Rubra Punctata' (H)	MSta
	'Mary Exquisita' (H)	MSta
	'Mary Patricia' (H)	MSta
	'Masaniello' (H)	CBen CRow EHon EMFW LPBA MSta SWat WBcn WMAq
	'Maurice Laydeker' (H)	MSta
	'Maxima'	see Nymphaea 'Odorata Maxima'
	'Mayla'	SBHF
§	'Météor' (H)	CBen CWat EMFW MSta WBcn WMAq
	mexicana	MSta
	'Moorei' (H)	CBen EHon EMFW LPBA MSta SLon SWat WMAq
	'Mrs C.W.Thomas' (H)	MSta
	'Mrs Richmond' Latour-Marliac (H) **new**	SBHF
	'Mrs Richmond' misapplied	see N. 'Fabiola'
	'Murillo' (H)	MSta
	'Neptune' (H)	MSta
	'Newchapel Beauty'	WMAq
	'Newton' (H)	EMFW MSta SWat WMAq
	'Nigel' (H)	MSta SWat
	'Nobilissima' (H)	MSta
	'Norma Gedye' (H)	CBen MSta SWat WMAq
	'Occidentalis'	see N. alba subsp. *occidentalis*
	'Odalisque' (H)	CWat EMFW MSta
§	*odorata* (H)	CBen CRow EHon LPBA MSta SBHF SCoo WBcn WMAq
	'Odorata Alba'	see N. odorata
§	'Odorata Exquisita' (H)	MSta
	odorata var. *gigantea* (H)	MSta
	'Odorata Juliana' (H)	EMFW MSta
§	'Odorata Luciana' (H)	EMFW MSta
§	'Odorata Maxima' (H)	WMAq

§ *odorata* var. *minor* (H)   CBen CRow EMFW LPBA MSta SWat WFar WMAq
- 'Pumila'   see *N. odorata* var. *minor*
- var. *rosea* (H)   MSta
- f. *rubra* (H)   MSta
'Odorata Sulphurea' (H)   MSta NBlu SBHF SLon SWat WBcn WFar
§ 'Odorata Sulphurea Grandiflora' (H)   CBen CRow CWat EMFW LPBA MSta SCoo SLon SWat
odorata subsp. *tuberosa* (H)   CBen LPBA MSta WMAq
- subsp. *tuberosa* 'Maxima' (H)   MSta
§ 'Odorata Turicensis' (H)   LPBA MSta
'Odorata William B. Shaw' (H)   see *N.* 'W.B. Shaw'
'Pam Bennett' (H)   CBen MSta
'Pamela' (T/D)   CBen
'Paul Hariot' (H)   CWat EHon EMFW LPBA MSta SWat WBcn WMAq
Pearl of the Pool (H)   MSta SWat
'Perry's Baby Red' (H)   CBen LMdh SBHF WMAq
'Perry's Double White' (H)   CBen
'Perry's Pink' (H)   MSta SWat WMAq
'Perry's Viviparous Pink' (H)   CBen
'Perry's Yellow Sensation'   see *Nymphaea* 'Yellow Sensation'
'Peter Slocum' (H)   EMFW MSta SWat
'Philippe Laydeker' (H)   MSta
'Phoebus' (H)   MSta SWat WBcn
'Phoenix' (H)   MSta
'Picciola' (H)   MSta
'Pink Opal' (H)   CBen CWat EMFW LPBA MSta SLon
'Pink Peony' (H)   EMFW
'Pink Platter' (T/D)   CBen
'Pink Sensation' (H)   CBen EMFW MSta SWat WMAq
'Pink Sunrise' (H)   EMFW MSta
'Pöstlingberg' (H)   MSta
'Président Viger' (H)   MSta
'Princess Elizabeth' (H)   EHon LPBA MSta SBHF
'Pygmaea Alba'   see *N. tetragona*
§ 'Pygmaea Helvola' (H) ♀ H4   CBen CRow CWat EHon EMFW LMdh LPBA MSta NPer SAWi SBHF SCoo SLon SWat WMAq WWeb
'Pygmaea Rubis' (H)   CRow EHon LPBA MSta SWat WMAq
'Pygmaea Rubra' (H)   CBen CWat EMFW LMdh MSta NBlu NPer SCoo WMAq
'Ray Davies' (H)   EMFW MSta SBHF
'Red Spider' (H)   EMFW
'Rembrandt' misapplied   see *N.* 'Météor'
'René Gérard' (H)   CBen CWat EHon EMFW LPBA MSta SWat WBcn WFar WMAq
'Robinsonii' (H)   MSta
'Rosanna Supreme' (H)   MSta SWat
'Rose Arey' (H)   CBen CRow CWat EHon EMFW LMdh LPBA MSta SCoo SWat WBcn WMAq
'Rose Magnolia' (H)   MSta SLon SWat
§ 'Rosea' (H)   CBen LPBA MSta WMAq
'Rosennymphe' (H)   CBen LPBA MSta SWat WFar WMAq
'Rosita' (H)   MSta
'Rosy Morn' (H)   MSta
'Sanguinea' (H)   MSta
'Seignouretti' (H)   EMFW MSta WBcn WMAq
'Senegal' (H)   MSta
'Sioux' (H)   CBen EHon EMFW LMdh LPBA MSta NBlu NPer SBHF SLon SWat WMAq
'Sirius' (H)   CBen EMFW MSta SWat
'Solfatare' (H)   MSta
'Somptuosa' (H)   MSta WMAq
'Souvenir de Jules Jacquier' (H)   MSta

'Speciosa' (H)   MSta
'Spectabilis' (H)   MSta
'Splendida' (H)   MSta WMAq
'Suavissima' (H)   MSta
'Sultan' (H)   MSta
'Sunrise' (H)   see *N.* 'Odorata Sulphurea Grandiflora'
'Superba' (H)   MSta
'Sylphida' (H)   MSta
'Temple Fire' (H)   MSta
§ *tetragona* (H)   CBen CRow CWat EHon EMFW LMdh LPBA MSta SLon WFar WMAq
- 'Alba'   see *N. tetragona*
- 'Johann Pring'   see *Nymphaea* 'Joanne Pring'
§ - var. *rubra* (H)   MSta
'Texas Dawn' (H)   MSta SAWi SLon WMAq
'Tuberosa Flavescens'   see *N.* 'Marliacea Chromatella'
'Tuberosa Richardsonii' (H)   EHon EMFW MSta WFar WWeb
tuberosa 'Rosea'   see *N.* 'Rosea'
'Tulipiformis' (H)   MSta
'Turicensis'   see *Nymphaea* 'Odorata Turicensis'
'Venusta' (H)   MSta
'Vera Louise' (H)   MSta
'Vésuve' (H)   EMFW MSta SLon SWat
'Virginalis' (H)   MSta SWat
'Virginia' (H)   MSta
§ 'W.B. Shaw' (H)   CBen EHon EMFW LPBA MSta SWat WMAq
'Walter Pagels' (H)   MSta SLon WMAq
'Weymouth Red' (H)   CBen
'William Doogue' (H)   MSta WBcn
'William Falconer' (H)   CBen CWat EMFW LPBA MSta SLon SWat
'Wow' (H)   SLon
§ 'Yellow Sensation' (H)   CBen
'Yul Ling'   SWat

Nymphoides (Menyanthaceae)

peltata   CRDP CWat EMFW EPfP LMdh NPer SBHF SCoo SLon SWat WFar WMAq WWpP
§ - 'Bennettii'   CBen EHon LPBA MSta

Nyssa (Cornaceae)

aquatica   CLnd CTho EPfP SSpi SSta
sinensis ♀ H4   CAbP CBcs CDoC CDul CEnd CLnd CMCN CPMA CTho ELan EPfP GKir LPan MBlu MBri NHol SBrw SPer SRPl SRcu SSpi SSta WBod WCwm WNor WPGP
- Nymans form **new**   EPfP
sylvatica ♀ H4   More than 30 suppliers
- 'Autumn Cascades'   EPfP IArd MBlu
- var. *biflora*   CMCN
- 'Jermyns Flame'   EPfP MAsh SSpi
- 'Red Red Wine'   EPfP
- 'Sheffield Park'   CAbP EPfP LRIIS SSpi
- 'Windsor'   EPfP LRHS SSpi
- 'Wisley Bonfire'   EPfP LRHS MAsh SSpi

O

Oakesiella see *Uvularia*

Ochagavia (Bromeliaceae)

carnea   CPne
rosea   CHEx CPne

Ocimum (Lamiaceae)

'African Blue'	CArn ELau EMan EOHP GPoy MHer
§ *americanum*	WHer WPer
- 'Meng Luk'	see *O. americanum*
- 'Spice'	see *Ocimum* 'Spice'
basilicum	CArn CSev EEls GPoy LRHS MBow MBri MChe NPri SIde SWat WHer WPer WSel WWye
- 'Anise'	see *O. basilicum* 'Horapha'
- 'Ararat' **new**	WHHs
* - 'Cinnamon'	EMan LRHS MBow MChe MHer MSal NPri SHDw WHHs WHer WJek WPer WSel
- 'Fine Verde' **new**	WHHs
- 'Genovese'	ELau MHer NVic WHHs
- 'Glycyrrhiza'	see *O. basilicum* 'Horapha'
- 'Green Globe'	MChe
- 'Green Ruffles'	LRHS MChe SWat WJek WSel
- 'Holy'	see *O. tenuiflorum*
§ - 'Horapha'	CArn CSev EOHP MBow MChe MHer MSal NGHP SIde WJek WPer
* - 'Horapha Nanum'	NGHP WJek
- 'Napolitano'	CBod MChe MHer SIde SWat WJek WPer
- var. *purpurascens*	CArn CSev MBri MChe SIde WHer WPer
- - 'Dark Opal'	CBod SHDw WJek WSel
- - 'Purple Ruffles'	EOHP MBow MChe SIde SWat WHHs WJek WPer WSel
- - 'Red Rubin'	EOHP MChe MHer WJek
- 'Thai'	see *O. basilicum* 'Horapha'
canum	see *O. americanum*
x *citriodorum*	CArn LRHS MBow MChe MHer MSal NGHP SHDw SIde SWat WHHs WJek WPer WSel
- 'Lime'	MHer WJek
- 'Siam Queen'	LRHS MHer WJek
gratissimum	ELau MHer WHHs
kilimandscharicum	GPoy
x *basilicum* var. *purpurascens*	
minimum	CArn CBod CSev ELau GPoy LRHS MBri MChe MHer NPri SIde WHHs WHer WJek WPer WSel WWye
sanctum	see *O. tenuiflorum*
'Spice'	MChe WPer
'Spicy Globe'	WHHs WJek
§ *tenuiflorum*	CArn CSev GPoy LRHS MChe MSal NGHP SHDw SIde SWat WHHs WHer WJek WPer

Odontonema (Acanthaceae)

strictum	WMul

Oemleria (Rosaceae)

§ *cerasiformis*	CBcs CFwr CPLG CPle EPfP EPla MWat SSpi WCot WEas WHCG WPGP WSHC WWin

Oenanthe (Apiaceae)

aquatica **new**	IHMH
- 'Variegata' (v)	EMFW
* *javanica* 'Atropurpurea'	EHoe
- 'Flamingo' (v)	CBen CPLG CRow EChP ELan EMan EMar EMon EPfP EPri EWsh GGar LRHS MAvo MBNS NBlu NBro SGar SLon SPar WCom WCru WFar WHer WMAq WPer WWpP

Oenothera ✿ (Onagraceae)

from South America	MTho

§ *acaulis*	CBot CSpe EBee GCal MNrw MWgw SBri SGar WRos
- 'Aurea'	NEgg SRot WPer
- 'Lutea'	see *O. acaulis* 'Aurea'
affinis	IDac
'Apricot Delight'	CBri ECoo EFWa EMan LRHS MCCP MWgw NBur NEgg NPPs WMoo
argillicola	WPer
berlandieri	see *Calylophus berlandieri*
§ *biennis*	CArn CKin CPrp CRow CSev EBre EHoe GPoy MBow MChe MHer MRav NBro NGHP SGar SIde WFar WHer WJek WPer
bistorta	see *Camissonia bistorta*
brachycarpa	EBee
caespitosa	EMan MTho NRib
- subsp. *caespitosa* NNS 93-505	NWCA
* *campylocalyx*	EBee LDai NBur
cheiranthifolia	see *Camissonia cheiranthifolia*
cinaeus	see *O. fruticosa* subsp. *glauca*
'Colin Porter'	CCge EBee EBur EDAr MNrw NEgg NGHP NWCA SGar
coryi	EBee
'Crown Imperial'	EBee EVFa GKir LBuc SLon SPer SSpi SVil
deltoides var. *howellii*	SMrm
§ *elata* subsp. *hookeri*	EBee EMan WPer
erythrosepala	see *O. glazioviana*
flava	EBee EFWa
fremontii	SIng
§ *fruticosa*	CSam EBre SPlb WWpP
- 'African Sun'[PBR]	EBee EFWa EMan EWes SBod SRot
- 'Camel' (v)	CBct CPlt EBee EFWa EGle EMan EPPr LDai LHop MAvo MHar SAga SUsu WCot WHrl
- Fireworks	see *O. fruticosa* 'Fyrverkeri'
- subsp. *fruticosa*	EBee
§ - 'Fyrverkeri' ♀ H4	EBre ECtt EFou ELan ENot EPla GKir LHop LRHS MCAu MRav NArg NGar NGdn NHol NVic SBla SBod SDes SPar SPer SPla WAul WEas WHil WHoo WRos WWal WWin
§ - subsp. *glauca* ♀ H4	CElw COlW EBre EFWa EPfP ERou LPVe MAnH MBct MDKP MNrw MTho MWgw MWhi NBlu NEgg NGar NPro SPet SRms SWal SYvo WEas WHil WPer
- - 'Erica Robin' (v)	More than 30 suppliers
- - 'Frühlingsgold' (v)	CBct EBee SUsu
- - narrow grey-leaved	SUsu
- - Solstice	see *O. fruticosa* subsp. *glauca* 'Sonnenwende'
§ - - 'Sonnenwende'	CBre CElw EBee EBre EMon LPVe LRHS MAvo MLLN NPro SGar WMoo WTel
- - 'Sunspot' (v)	GBuc SScr
- Highlight	see *O. fruticosa* 'Hoheslicht'
§ - 'Hoheslicht'	EBee
- 'Lady Brookeborough'	MRav NGar
- 'Longest Day' **new**	IHMH
- 'Michelle Ploeger'	EBee EBre EGle EMan
- var. *riparia*	SOkh WRus
- 'Silberblatt'	EBee EPPr MGrG
- 'W. Cuthbertson'	EBee
- 'Yellow River'	EBee LRHS MHar WWeb
- 'Youngii'	EBee EPfP ERou LIck MCCP MLLN NBlu SDes WPer
glabra hort.	ECha NSti SIgm SIng SUsu WCom
- Miller	see *O. biennis*
glazioviana	CMil CSam EBee ECoo IBlr NBir SIde WFar WHrl WPer WWpP WWye
hookeri	see *O. elata* subsp. *hookeri*

howardii	WLin
kunthiana	CBri CStr EBee EDAr EFWa EGoo
	EMan ERou GCal IFro MDKP NWCA
	SBri SCro WCot WMoo WPer
lamarckiana	see *O. glazioviana*
'Lemon Sunset'	ECoo LHop MCCP NBur SWal
	SWat WFTG WMoo
linearis	see *O. fruticosa*
'Longest Day'	EChP EFou EPfP LRHS MArl MBrN
	SAsh
§ *macrocarpa* ♀ H4	More than 30 suppliers
- 'Greencourt Lemon'	LPhx WHrl
- subsp. *incana*	EMan LPVe SMad
macrosceles	EBee
* *minima*	EBee MDKP
missouriensis	see *O. macrocarpa*
* *mollis*	EBee
muricata	EBee
neomexicana	GCal
oakesiana	EBee
odorata hort.	see *O. stricta*
odorata Hook. & Arn.	see *O. biennis*
odorata Jacquin	CArn GCal IBlr NOrc
- 'Sulphurea'	see *O. stricta* 'Sulphurea'
organensis	CDes EBee EFWa MLLN
pallida	IBlr MAnH SWat
- 'Innocence'	CBot ECtt LRHS MBNS MCCP
	MGol SPar SRot WPer
- 'Wedding Bells'	EFWa NPer
'Penelope Hobhouse'	CBct EBee GBuc SAga SUsu SWat
§ *perennis*	CNic EBee EBrc EMIT GKir MTho
	SRms SWat WEas WPer
pumila	see *O. perennis*
rosea	CMea CSam
speciosa	CMHG CSev EBee EMon LPVe
	MBow MRav SAga SEND SPer STes
	SWat WCot WElm WPer WSan
- 'Ballerina'	EMan LHop WCFE
- var. *childsii*	see *O. speciosa*
- 'Pink Petticoats'	ECha ECoo ECtt EFWa EMlt LAst
	MArl MCCP MWgw NPer SIde
	SWat WBea WElm WSan
§ - 'Rosea'	CBot CFir CNic CPrp CRDP EBee
	ECoo LAst LIck LRHS MCCP
	MNrw SGar SPlb SWat WPGP
	WPer WWin
- 'Siskiyou'	More than 30 suppliers
- 'Woodside White'	SMrm
- yellow-leaved	EBee
§ *stricta*	CKin CMea EBee ECGP EWTr LItrt
	MBri SCro SIng WBry WPer WWye
* - 'Moonlight'	SGar
§ - 'Sulphurea'	CHad CMIIG CMil EBee ECoo
	EGoo ELan EMan GCal IFro IFro
	MWgw NPer SChu SCro SMrm
	SUsu WAbb WBea WCot WPer
'Summer Sun'	EBee LBuc LRHS MCLN SPoG SSpe
'Sunburst' (v)	EMan
taraxacifolia	see *O. acaulis*
tetragona	see *O. fruticosa* subsp. *glauca*
- var. *fraseri*	see *O. fruticosa* subsp. *glauca*
- 'Sonnenwende'	see *O. fruticosa* subsp. *glauca*
	'Sonnenwende'
tetraptera	NWCA
texensis	SWat
- 'Early Rise'	EMan LHop
versicolor	MCAu NPPs
- 'Sunset Boulevard'	More than 30 suppliers

Olea (Oleaceae)

africana **new**	CTrC
europaea (F)	More than 30 suppliers
- 'Aglandau' (F)	ERea

- 'Amygdalolia' (F)	ERea
* - 'Aragones' **new**	CGOG
- 'Arbequina' (F)	CGOG
- 'Bouteillan' (F)	ERea
- 'Cailletier' (F)	ERea
- 'Chelsea Physic Garden'	WPGP
§ - 'Cipressino' (F)	ERea LPan SPar
- 'El Greco' (F)	CBcs ERea
- 'Gordal Sevillana' **new**	CGOG
- 'Manzanillo' (F)	ERea
- 'Picholine' (F)	ERea
- 'Picual' (F)	CGOG
- 'Pyramidalis'	see *O. europaea* 'Cipressino'
* - 'Sativa' (F)	EMui
- 'Serrana del Espadán' **new**	CGOG
- 'Villalonga' **new**	CGOG

Olearia ✿ (Asteraceae)

albida Hook. f.	CBcs
algida	ECou
arborescens	GEil GGar GSki
* - 'Variegata' (v)	NPro
argophylla	ECou GGar
avicenniifolia	CBcs CHEx ECou GGar WGer
	WLRN WSHC
capillaris	CDoC CPle CPne ECou GGar
	NLon SDry SIgm WCwm
chathamica	CPLG GGar
§ *cheesemanii*	CDoC CMHG CPLG CPle EBee
	GGar IDee SPer WGer WSHC
coriacea	ECou GGar
'County Park'	ECou
erubescens	CDoC CPle
floribunda	CPle GGar
forsteri from Tresco	CDoC
frostii	WKif
furfuracea	CDoC CPle
glandulosa	ECou GGar
gunniana	see *O. phlogopappa*
x *haastii*	More than 30 suppliers
- 'McKenzie'	ECou
hectorii	ECou
§ 'Henry Travers'	CDoC CPLG CPle CTrC EBee
	EPfP GGar GQui IBlr MDun NLar
	WGer
hookeri	GGar
§ *ilicifolia*	CDoC CFil CPle GGar GSki LRHS
	MDun SDry SPer SSpi
§ - x *moschata*	GGar IDee LRHS
insignis	CTrC GGar
- var. *minor*	WCru
lacunosa	MDun
lepidophylla	CPle ECou
- silver	ECou
lirata	CPle ECou GGar
macrodonta ♀ H3	More than 30 suppliers
- 'Intermedia'	GGar
- 'Major'	GGar SHBN
- 'Minor'	CBcs CDoC CTrC ELan EPfP GEil
	GGar GQui SPlb WFar WPat WStI
x *mollis* hort.	see *O. ilicifolia* x *O. moschata*
x *mollis* (Kirk) Cockayne	CPle GQui SPer SSpi WSHC
- 'Zennorensis' ♀ H3	CBcs CDoC CPLG CPle GGar ISea
	MDun SDry SOWG WCru WDin
	WEas WGer
moschata	CPle GGar
myrsinoides	CFai CPle IDee
§ *nummulariifolia*	CDoC CPle CPne CTrC CTri ECou
	EPfP EPla GGar NLon SDry SEND
	SPar SPer STre WBod WDin WFar
	WKif WSHC WTel WWal
- var. *cymbifolia*	CNic ECou
- hybrids	ECou

- 'Little Lou' | ECou
odorata | CPLG CPle ECou GGar NLar WBod WFar WHCG
oleifolia | see *O.* 'Waikariensis'
paniculata | CMHG CPle CTrC CTri EPfP GGar GSki IDee ISea SDry WGer WPic
§ *phlogopappa* | CSBt CTri EBee ECou GGar SVen WBrE WPic
- 'Comber's Blue' | CBcs EBee EPfP GGar IBlr LRHS NPer SPer SSta
§ - 'Comber's Pink' | CBcs CDoC CPLG EBee EPfP GGar IBlr LRHS MPRe NPer SBrw SPer WBod WEas WKif
- pink | CTrG
- 'Rosea' | see *O. phlogopappa* 'Comber's Pink'
- Splendens Group | CAbb WFar
- var. *subrepanda* | CPle CTrC GGar LEdu SEND WAbe WBod
§ *ramulosa* | CDoC CPLG CPle WKif WSHC WWal
- 'Blue Stars' | ECou GGar LRHS
- var. *ramulosa* | ECou
- 'White Stars' | ECou
rani hort. | see *O. cheesemanii*
rani Druce | ISea
x *scilloniensis* hort. | see *O. stellulata* DC.
x *scilloniensis* Dorrien-Smith ♀ H3 | GGar NBlu
- 'Master Michael' | CBot CDoC EBee MPRe SBrw SOWG SPer WBea WSHC WWeb
semidentata misapplied | see *O.* 'Henry Travers'
solandri | CDoC CFwr CHEx CPle CSam CTrC EBee ECou GGar SDix SDry SHFr SPar SPer STre
- 'Aurea' | CBcs GQui
stellulata hort. | see *O. phlogopappa*
§ *stellulata* DC. | More than 30 suppliers
- 'Michael's Pride' | CPLG
§ - 'Talbot de Malahide' | EHol GGar
traversii | CAbb CBcs CDoC CFai CHEx CMHG CSBt CTrC EBee GGar SEND SPar SVen WGer WLRN
§ - 'Tweedledum' (v) | CDoC CWib ECou EHoe GGar MOak
virgata | CPle ECou GGar GSki WCot
- var. *laxiflora* | CTrC
- var. *lineata* | CPLG CPle ECou GGar NLar SEND WCru WDin WPic WSHC
- - 'Dartonii' | CBcs CTrC EBee ECou EHol GGar MBlu SLPl WGer WSHC
viscosa | CPle GGar
§ 'Waikariensis' | CBot CMHG CPLG CPle CSam CTrC ECou GGar IDee LRHS SChu SEND WBod WCFE WDin WGer WPat

Oligostachyum (Poaceae)
lubricum | see *Semiarundinaria lubrica*

olive see *Olea europaea*

Olsynium (Iridaceae)
§ *biflorum* | LTwo
§ *douglasii* ♀ H4 | CBro EDAr EHyt ELan EPar EPot ETow GAbr GCrs GDra GEdr GMaP LTwo NGar NHar NMen NRya SIng WAbe WCot WLin
- 'Album' | EHyt EPar EPot GAbr GCrs GDra GEdr NHar NRya NSla
- var. *inflatum* | EWes
§ *filifolium* | MNrw NMen
§ *junceum* | CBri CFil SBla WCot

- JCA 12289 | MTho
- JCA 14211 | CFir
lyckolmii **new** | WCot

Omphalodes (Boraginaceae)
cappadocica ♀ H4 | CBos CElw CRow EBre ECGN ECha EOrc EPar EPot GKir LLWP LPio LRHS MBro NBro NCot NFor NLon NPer SDix SGar SIng SPer SRms SSpi SWat WHoo WPat
- 'Alba' | GKir LLWP SRms
- 'Anthea Bloom' | GBuc IBlr
- 'Blue Rug' **new** | IHMH
- 'Cherry Ingram' ♀ H4 | More than 30 suppliers
- 'Lilac Mist' | CElw EBee EMan ENot LLWP LPio MAvo MLwd MRav SRms SSvw SWat WPnP
- 'Parisian Skies' **new** | CLAP
- 'Starry Eyes' | More than 30 suppliers
§ *linifolia* ♀ H4 | CMea CRDP CSpe ECoo NMen WEas WWeb
- *alba* | see *O. linifolia*
luciliae | WHoo
nitida | EMon GGar NRya SSpi WCot
verna | More than 30 suppliers
- 'Alba' | CBot CBre CDes CPLG EBee EChP ECha EGle ELan EMon GAbr LAst LHop MHar MTho NChi NCot NHol NLar SAga SDes SPer SRPl SRms SSvw SWat WBea WEas WFar WWpP
- 'Elfenauge' | CElw CMil EBee EGle EMon EPPr NCot NDov SMrm SUsu
- *grandiflora* | WCot

Oncostema see *Scilla*

onion see *Allium cepa*

Onixotis (Colchicaceae)
triquetra | WCot

Onobrychis (Papilionaceae)
cornuta **new** | EBee
gracilis | CPom
tournefortii **new** | EBee
viciifolia | EBee EMan EPyc MSal SHar WBWf WWye

Onoclea (Woodsiaceae)
§ *intermedia* **new** | EMon
sensibilis ♀ H4 | More than 30 suppliers
- copper | CFil CRow WPGP

Ononis (Papilionaceae)
repens | CArn CKin MSal NMir
rotundifolia | CWCL MSal
spinosa | CKin CPom EBee EVFa EWll MHer MSal WFar WPer

Onopordum (Asteraceae)
acanthium | CArn CHEx EBlw EChP ECha ECoo ELan EPfP GAbr GBar GKir GMac LHrt LPhx MCAu MHer MWat MWgw NBid NVic SGar SIde SPar WCHb WCot WHer WHil WWpP WWye
acaule | EBee
arabicum | see *O. nervosum*
bracteatum | WPer
§ *nervosum* ♀ H4 | CArn CSpe EBee NBro SMad SRms WFar

Onosma (*Boraginaceae*)

alborosea	CMdw CSev EBee ECha EGoo EOrc EVFa GBri GCal GEdr NMRc SAga SChu WEas WKif WPGP WPat
arenaria	EGoo
bourgaei **new**	EBee
graeca MESE 50 **new**	EBee
helvetica	MBro WPat
nana	CStu
sericea	EBee
stellulata	CLyd EGoo SSpi
taurica ♀ H4	EBee ETow MOne NBir SGar WWin
visianii **new**	EBee

Onosmodium (*Boraginaceae*)

molle subsp. occidentale **new**	
	EBee

Onychium (*Adiantaceae*)

contiguum	EFer
japonicum	CFil CRDP EFer GQui SBla SChu WAbe WCot WHer
- 'Dali' L 1649	SBla

Ophiopogon ✿ (*Convallariaceae*)

'Black Dragon'	see *O. planiscapus* 'Nigrescens'
bodinieri	CBct ERos EWes LEur SApp SMac WRHF
- B&L 12505	CLAP EBee EPPr EPla MTed
chingii	GCal LEdu
formosanus B&SWJ 3659	EBee WCru
'Gin-ryu'	see *Liriope spicata* 'Gin-ryu'
graminifolius	see *Liriope muscari*
intermedius	CBct EPla ERos ESis LEur MSte WCot WPGP
§ - 'Argenteomarginatus'	ERos EWes WPGP
- *parviflorus*	NSti
'Variegatus'	see *O. intermedius* 'Argenteomarginatus'
§ *jaburan*	CHid CMGP EBee EShb LAma LEdu MHdf MSte NHol WPnP
- 'Variegatus'	see *O. jaburan* 'Vittatus'
§ - 'Vittatus' (v)	CFwr CMHG EBee EHoe EMan EPfP EWes ITer LEur LRHS MCCP NEgg SAga SDes SPer SYvo WCot WFar WRus
japonicus	CBro CRow EPPr EPfP EPla NSti SSte
- B&SWJ 1842	WCru
- 'Albus'	CLAP NHol
- 'Compactus'	CFil CStu EBee LRHS SMac SPla SSpi WPGP WWye
- 'Kigimafukiduma'	CBrm CFwr GBin MRav SDes WGwG
- 'Minor'	CBct EPfP EPla NLar WPGP
- 'Nanus Variegatus' (v)	CDes EBee EVFa
- 'Nippon'	CM&M EBee LAst LBuc LPio LRHS
- 'Tama-ryu'	EHyt
* - 'Tama-ryu Number Two'	ECho ESis NHar
- 'Torafu' (v) **new**	EPPr
* - 'Variegatus' (v)	EPla SIng SLPl
malcolmsonii B&SWJ 5264	WCru
planiscapus	CFee CKno CMHG CSWP CSev EBee EPar EPla GCal GOrn MSte MTho MWod NBro NHar NLon SAga SPla STre WPrP WWal
* - 'Albovariegatus' **new**	SPoG
- *leucanthus*	EPPr WCot
- 'Little Tabby' (v)	CDes CLAP CSpe EBee ESis MMoz MWrn NPro SAga SPar SRGP WCot WDyG WPGP
* - *minimus*	ERos

Ophrys (*Orchidaceae*)

- 'Nigrescens' ♀ H4	More than 30 suppliers
- 'Silver Ribbon'	SWat
scaber B&SWJ 1871 **new**	WCru
'Spring Gold'	EMon
wallichianus	EPla EVFa GGar GIBF LEur MHdf NLar SSpi WCom WCot WPGP

Ophiorrhiza (*Rubiaceae*)

intermedius **new**	EBee
japonicus	EBee
mairei **new**	EBee

Ophrys (*Orchidaceae*)

apifera	CHdy WHer
bombyliflora	SBla

Oplismenus (*Poaceae*)

§ *africanus* 'Variegatus' (v) ♀ H1	CHal
undulatifolius	EBee NBro

Opopanax (*Apiaceae*)

chironium	IIve

Opuntia ✿ (*Cactaceae*)

cantabrigiensis	EOas SChr
compressa	CTrC CTrF SChr
engelmannii	SChr
erinacea var. *utahensis*	WCot
x *polycantha*	
NN8 99 263 **new**	
ficus-indica	SAPC
grahamii	SChr
grandiflora	see *O. macrorhiza*
humifusa	ELau EOas SMad
§ *lindheimeri*	CHEx CTrC CTrF EOas SAPC SArc SChr
linguiformis	see *O. lindheimeri*
§ *macrorhiza*	SChr
paraguayensis	EOas
phaeacantha	CHEx CTrF EOas SAPC SArc SClu
- var. *major*	WCot
NNS 95-285 **new**	
polyacantha	SChr SPlb
rhodantha	EOas SClir
robusta	CTrC CTrF EOas SChr
santa-rita	EOas
scheeri	CTrF
stenopetala **new**	CAbb
tardospina	see *O. lindheimeri*

orange, sour or Seville see *Citrus aurantium*

orange, sweet see *Citrus sinensis*

Orbea (*Asclepiadaceae*)

variegata (v) ♀ H1 **new**	CHEx

Orchis (*Orchidaceae*)

elata	see *Dactylorhiza elata*
foliosa	see *Dactylorhiza foliosa*
fuchsii	see *Dactylorhiza fuchsii*
maculata	see *Dactylorhiza maculata*
maderensis	see *Dactylorhiza foliosa*
majalis	see *Dactylorhiza majalis*
§ *mascula*	CHdy GPoy WHer
morio	CHdy

Oreopanax (*Araliaceae*)

dactylifolius **new**	LEdu

Oreopteris (*Thelypteridaceae*)

§ *limbosperma*	EMon SRms

Oreoxis (Apiaceae)

alpina **new**	EBee

Oresitrophe (Saxifragaceae)

rupifraga	EBee WCru

Origanum ✿ (Lamiaceae)

from Santa Cruz	CArn
from Yunnan, China	NWoo
acutidens	EHyt NWCA WCHb
amanum ♀ H2-3	CPBP CRDP EGle EHyt ELan ETow EWes LRHS MBro NBir NMen SBla SChu SIgm SIng WAbe WCom WHoo WPat WWye
- var. *album*	CPBP CRDP ECho EGle SBla WAbe WPat
x *applii*	EDAr ELau
'Barbara Tingey'	CRDP CSpe EBee ECou EGle EHyt ELan EPot EWes LBee LRHS MBro MHer MNrw MSte MTho NWCA SAga SBla SChu SIng SUsu WAbe WCFE WCru WHoo WPat
I 'Bristol Cross'	CNic CStr ECha GBar NCWG WPat
'Buckland'	CHea CPlt CRDP EHyt EPot ESis LPhx LRHS MSte NWCA SBla SIng WCom WPat
caespitosum	see *O. vulgare* 'Nanum'
§ *calcaratum*	CMea EMan ETow LRHS MTho SBla SMrm WAbe WCru WPat
creticum	see *O. vulgare* subsp. *hirtum*
dictamnus	CArn EEls EHyt GPoy LRHS LTwo SBla SHDw WAbe WJek WRus
'Dingle Fairy'	CM&M EBee EGoo EMan EMar EWes GBar MHer MLLN MMHG MNrw NBir NCWG SIde SIng WBry WMoo WWye
'Erntedank'	EBee
'Frank Tingey'	CPBP ECho EHyt ELan SUsu WAbe
'Gold Splash'	EDAr GBar SIde
'Goudgeel'	CStr
heracleoticum L.	see *O. vulgare* subsp. *hirtum*
§ x *hybridinum*	SAga SBla WLin WPat WWin
'Ingolstadt'	EBee LPhx SAga SCro WWye
'Kent Beauty'	More than 30 suppliers
'Kent Beauty Variegated' (v)	ELan
laevigatum ♀ H3	CArn CLyd CMHG CStr ELan EPfP EPot MBro MHar MHer NBro NMir NPer NWCA SAga SBla SGar SMer WCom WMoo WPer WWin WWye
- 'Herrenhausen' ♀ H4	More than 30 suppliers
- 'Hopleys'	More than 30 suppliers
- 'Purple Charm'	EBee ELau WCot
- 'Springwood'	WCot WWye
'Lynda Windsor' **new**	CRDP
majorana	CArn CSev ELan ELau GWCH MBow MChe MHer MSal NCWG SIde SWal SWat WHHs WJek WPer WSel WWye
microphyllum	CArn CBot CFee CMHG EDAr EGle EHyt ESis GBar LPhx LRHS MTho NMen SBla SChu SIng WAbe WCru WPat WWye
minutiflorum	ECho EMan LTwo
'Norton Gold'	CBre CElw EBee EBre ECha EPot GBar GBuc LRHS NCWG NPer
'Nymphenburg'	CFee EBee EMan MSte SAga SChu SDys SMrm SUsu WCru WHer WWhi
onites	CArn ELau GBar GPoy ILis MChe MHer MSal MWat NBlu SIde SPlb WHHs WHer WJek WPer WSel WWpP WWye

'Pilgrim'	EBre
'Pink Cloud'	EDAr
* *prismaticum*	GBar
pulchellum	see *O.* x *hybridinum*
'Purple Cloud'	EDAr NBir
'Rosenkuppel' zur Linden	More than 30 suppliers
'Rotkugel'	CPrp EBee EGle EMan LPhx MSte NCat WCot WCru
rotundifolium ♀ H4	CArn CRDP CSev CStr CStu ELan ESis LEdu MDKP MHer NBir SBla SChu WAbe WRus WSan
- hybrid	MDKP
- 'Pagoda Bells'	EBee SIng
scabrum	CArn NCWG WWye
- subsp. *pulchrum*	CStu
- - 'Newleaze'	LHop
sipyleum	EBee EHyt NWCA SBla WAbe
'Thundercloud' **new**	WWeb
tournefortii	see *O. calcaratum*
virens	CArn GBar ILis MCCP
vulgare	CAgr CArn CKin CSev ECoo EDAr GBar GKir GPoy LHrt MBar MBow MChe MHer NBlu NBro NCWG NLan NMir NPri SGar SIde SPlb SWal WHHs WHer WPer WWpP WWye
- 'Acorn Bank'	CArn CBod CPrp EBee ELau EWes MHer SAga SIde WBry WCHb WHHs WHer WJek
- var. *album*	CElw LPhx WHer WJek
- - 'Aureum Album'	MCLN WHer WWhi
- 'Aureum' ♀ H4	More than 30 suppliers
- 'Aureum Crispum'	CPrp ECha EDAr EGoo ELau ESis GAbr GBar GPoy ILis NBid NBlu NCWG SIde SWat WCer WHHs WJek WRha WSel WWpP WWye
- 'Compactum'	More than 30 suppliers
- 'Corinne Tremaine' (v)	NBir SAga WHer
- 'Country Cream' (v)	More than 30 suppliers
- 'Curly Gold'	CPrp
- *formosanum*	WCru
B&SWJ 3180	
- from Israel	ELau
§ - 'Gold Tip' (v)	CMea CPrp CSev CStr EDAr EHoe ELau GBar ILis MHer NArg NCWG NGHP NHol NPri SDes SIde SPlb SWat WCHb WHer WWpP WWye
- 'Golden Shine'	CM&M EBee EWes MWat NGHP WRHF WRha
§ - subsp. *hirtum*	CArn GPoy LEdu MSal NWoo SPlb WBri WJek WPer WWpP
- - 'Greek'	CBod CPrp ELau GWCH IIve MBow MHer NBlu NGHP NPri WHHs
§ - 'Nanum'	ESis GBar LRHS NCat WJek
- 'Pink Mist' **new**	WWeb
- 'Polyphant' (v)	CHar CMHG CSev EBee EChP EDAr EGle EMan EOHP ESis GBar LHop LPio MLLN NBir NCWG NWoo WBea WBrE WCHb WCot WHHs WHer WJek WMoo WSel WWye
- 'Thumble's Variety'	CBod CElw CPrp EBre ECGP ECha ECoo EGle EGoo EHoe GBar GKir LHop LPhx LRHS MBri MHer MRav MUlv NCWG NHol SIde SLon SSvw SWat WMnd WMoo WPer
- 'Variegatum'	see *O. vulgare* 'Gold Tip'
- 'Webb's White'	GBar
- yellow long-leaved **new**	ECha
'White Cloud'	EDAr
'Z'Attar'	MHer

Orites (Proteaceae)
myrtoidea new CFil

Orixa (Rutaceae)
japonica CBot EPfP SSpi WFar WPGP
- 'Variegata' (v) EPfP LRHS MAsh

Orlaya (Apiaceae)
grandiflora CRDP WCot WFar

Ornithogalum (Hyacinthaceae)
arabicum CBro EBot EChP LAma LRHS
　　MAvo MBri MLLN WCot WDav
arcuatum WCot
balansae see *O. oligophyllum*
caudatum see *O. longibracteatum*
chionophilum CFwr
ciliiferum new EBee
dubium ♀ H1 CSut ETub LPio LRHS MMHG
　　NWCA WCot WHil
fimbriatum EBee EPot WCot
lanceolatum CAvo EHyt WCot
§ **longibracteatum** CHEx CPLG CStu EBee EPem
　　SChr SYvo WHer
magnum CAvo CFwr CMea EBee ETub
- 'Saguramo' **new** WCot
'Mount Everest' **new** CSut
nanum see *O. sigmoideum*
narbonense CFwr CHar EBee GBuc LRHS
　　WCot WDav
nutans ♀ H4 CAvo CBro CFwr CMea CRDP EChP
　　EMan EMon EPar EPfP EPot ETub
　　LAma LPhx MAvo MEHN MLLN
　　MMil MNrw NMen NRog SYvo
　　WAul WBea WBro WCot WHil WPer
§ **oligophyllum** CBro CStu EBee EPot MNrw WDav
orthophyllum CStu WCot
platyphyllum new EBee
polyphyllum WCot
ponticum EROS
pyramidale CDes CFwr CSpe EBee EBot EPot
　　MNrw WCot
pyrenaicum CAvo CMea CPLG CStu EBee
　　ECha ERos WCot WShi
reverchonii CDes CMea EBee WCot
saundersiae EBee LRow
sibthorpii see *O. sigmoideum*
§ **sigmoideum** WAbe
sintenisii new WWst
tenuifolium see *O. orthophyllum*
thyrsoides ♀ H1 LAma LRHS MBri WBea
umbellatum CBro CNic CPLG ELan EMon EPar
　　GPoy LAma LRHS MBri MNrw
　　NBlu NMen NRog SRms SYvo
　　WBea WCot WFar WHil WPer
　　WShi WViv WWye

Orontium (Araceae)
aquaticum CBen CWat EHon EMFW LMdh
　　LPBA MSta SAWi SWat WMAq
　　WWeb

Orostachys (Crassulaceae)
§ **aggregata** SChr
furusei CBgR EBee EMan LHop NSti
　　WCot WFTG WFar WWhi
iwarenge CStu
malacophylla see *O. aggregata*
§ **spinosa** EMan ETow NMen WCot WFar

Orphium (Gentianaceae)
frutescens CPLG WCot

Orthrosanthus (Iridaceae)
chimboracensis CDes CFir EMan WCot WFar WPer
　　WPic
- JCA 13743 CPou
laxus CPBP CPle EBee ERos GBuc SMad
　　WFTG WWin
multiflorus CDes EBee ETow WPGP
polystachyus CMdw CPle CRez CSpe EChP
　　EMan ERos MAvo MLwd WElm
　　WFTG WSHC

Oryzopsis (Poaceae)
lessoniana see *Stipa arundinacea*
miliacea CBig EBee ECha EHoe EMan EPPr
　　LHrt SRGP WCot WDyG WPGP WPrP
paradoxa EBee EPPr

Oscularia (Aizoaceae)
§ **deltoides** ♀ H1-2 CHEx MRav SPet WCot WEas

Osmanthus (Oleaceae)
americanus WBcn
armatus CFil CTri EBee EPfP LPan WFar
§ x **burkwoodii** ♀ H4 More than 30 suppliers
§ **decorus** CBcs CDul CPLG CSBt CTri ELan
　　EPfP EWTr GKir MGos MRav NWea
　　SPer SSta WBcn WBod WDin WFar
- 'Angustifolius' MGos WBcn
delavayi ♀ H4 More than 30 suppliers
- 'Latifolius' GKir LRHS WBcn WFar
forrestii see *O. yunnanensis*
x **fortunei** CPle EBee EPfP LPan LRHS SLPl
　　WFar WPGP
fragrans LPan SAPC SArc
- f. *thunbergii* SSpi
§ **heterophyllus** CBcs CDul EMil ENot EPfP LPan
　　MBar NFor SDes SPer SRPl SReu
　　SRms SSpi SSta WDin WFar
　　WGwG WStI
§ - all gold CAbP CDoC EGra LAst MBlu SPer
　　SPla WSHC
- 'Argenteomarginatus' see *O. heterophyllus* 'Variegatus'
§ - 'Aureomarginatus' (v) CBcs CBrm CDoC CFil CHar
　　CMHG CSBt EBee EHoe EMil EPfP
　　LRHS SHBN SLon SPer
- 'Aureus' misapplied see *O. heterophyllus* all gold
- 'Aureus' Rehder see *O. heterophyllus*
　　'Aureomarginatus'
§ - 'Goshiki' (v) More than 30 suppliers
N - 'Gulftide' ♀ H4 CDoC EBee EMil EPfP LRHS MGos
　　MWht SDes SPar WFar WRHF WStI
- 'Purple Shaft' CAbP ELan EPfP LRHS MAsh
- 'Purpureus' CAbP CBcs CBot CDoC CMHG
　　CWib EHoe EPfP LRHS MBri MDun
　　MGos MRav MSph NDlv SDry SLim
　　SLon SSpi WDin WRHF WStI
- 'Rotundifolius' CFil
- Tricolor see *O. heterophyllus* 'Goshiki'
§ - 'Variegatus' (v) ♀ H4 CBcs CBot CSBt CTrC CWib EBee
　　EBre ELan EMil ENot EPfP LAst
　　LRHS MAsh MBar MRav MWat
　　NBlu SDes SLim SPar SPer SPla
　　SReu SSta WDin WFar WHar WPat
　　WWeb
ilicifolius see *O. heterophyllus*
serrulatus CBot CFil WPGP
suavis CFil EPfP GKir LRHS SSpi
§ **yunnanensis** CMHG EPfP LRHS MBlu SAPC
　　SArc SSpi WFar WPGP

x *Osmarea* (Oleaceae)
burkwoodii see *Osmanthus* x *burkwoodii*

Osmaronia see *Oemleria*

Osmorhiza (Apiaceae)

aristata B&SWJ 1607	WCru

Osmunda ✿ (Osmundaceae)

cinnamomea ♀ H4	CFil CLAP CPLG EBee GBin LEur
	NHar NMar SSpi WPGP WRic
claytoniana ♀ H4	CFil CLAP CPLG EBee EPfP GCal
	LEur NHol NMar NOGN SCou
	WCru WMoo WRic
japonica	EBee
regalis ♀ H4	More than 30 suppliers
§ - 'Cristata' ♀ H4	CFil CFwr CLAP CPLG CRDP
	ELan GBin GCal LPBA MBri NHol
	SLon WFib WPGP WRic
- 'Purpurascens'	More than 30 suppliers
- var. **spectabilis**	WRic
§ - 'Undulata'	ELan GBin NHol NMar WFib WRic

Osteomeles (Rosaceae)

schweriniae	WCot
- B&L 12360	CPle SAga

Osteospermum ✿ (Asteraceae)

'African Queen'	see *O.* 'Nairobi Purple'
'Antaris'	COIW LHop
'Arctur'PBR	CBcs
'Bamba'PBR	LIck
barberae hort.	see *O. jucundum*
'Blackthorn Seedling'	see *O. jucundum* 'Blackthorn Seedling'
'Blue Streak'	LPio NBur SMrm
'Brickell's Hybrid'	see *O.* 'Chris Brickell'
'Brightside'PBR	WWol
(Side Series) **new**	
'Buttermilk' ♀ H1+3	CHal CSpe CTbh ELan GGar LAst
	LHop LRHS MBri MOak SMrm
	SRms SWgG WWeb
'Cannington Katrina'	MOak SRms
'Cannington Roy'	CMHG CSam CTbh ECtt EPfP LPio
	MBri NBur NLon SIng SRms WAbe
caulescens hort.	see *O.* 'White Pim'
§ 'Chris Brickell'	CHal GCal MOak MSte NBur
	WHen
'Countryside'	WWol
(Side Series) **new**	
'Cream Symphony'	CBcs CTbh SMrm
'Darkside' (Side Series) **new**	WWol
ecklonis	CHea CHll CTbh EChP GGar IBlr
	ISea MCLN MHer NBro NFla
	NGdn SMrm WBar WFar WGwG
	WMoo WPer WWin
- var. **prostratum**	see *O.* 'White Pim'
'Edna Bond'	MCLN WEas
'Gemma'PBR **new**	WGor
'Giles Gilbey' (v)	CHEx CHal CTbh MBNS MOak
	NBur NCiC SVen
'Gold Sparkler' (v)	LRHS SMrm
'Gweek Variegated' (v)	MOak
'Helen Dimond' **new**	COtt WWeb
'Hopleys' ♀ H3-4	LHop MBNS MHer MWrn SEND
'Irish'	EPot NLAp
'James Elliman'	MOak SRms
'Jewel' (v)	COtt
§ **jucundum** ♀ H3-4	More than 30 suppliers
§ - 'Blackthorn Seedling' ♀ H3-4	CPlt ECha MBri MSph NFla NGdn NLon SAga SBla
- var. **compactum**	CHEx CLyd CMea CPBP MBro MHar NPer WAbe WCom WHen WHoo
- 'Elliott's Form'	MBri
- 'Jackarandum'	MDKP

§ - 'Killerton Pink'	CMHG WPer
§ - 'Langtrees' ♀ H3-4	ECtt EOrc LHop SMrm
'Kalanga' **new**	LIck
'Killerton Pink'	see *O. jucundum* 'Killerton Pink'
§ 'Lady Leitrim' ♀ H3-4	CBri CHEx EBlw ECha EOrc GBri
	GDea GGar IBlr LHop LHrt LPio
	MArl MBNS MBow MCLN MOak
	MWrn NPer SAga SChu SSvw
	WAbe WCom WFTG WRus WWeb
	WWpP
'Langtrees'	see *O. jucundum* 'Langtrees'
'Lemon Symphony'PBR	CBcs LAst LIck SMrm
'Lubango'PBR	CBcs
§ 'Nairobi Purple'	CFee CHEx CHal ELan GBuc
	GGar MOak NBur SAga SVen
Nasinga Series	CBcs CElw
'Orange Symphony'	CTbh LAst LIck SMrm
Orania Peach = 'Akope'PBR **new**	LIck
'Pale Face'	see *O.* 'Lady Leitrim'
'Peggyi'	see *O.* 'Nairobi Purple'
'Penny Pink'	ECtt LPio
'Pink Whirls' ♀ H1+3	CBot CHal CWCL LRHS MBri
	MOak NBur SRms
'Pollux'PBR	MBNS
'Port Wine'	see *O.* 'Nairobi Purple'
'Seaside'PBR	WWol
(Side Series) **new**	
'Seaspray'	COtt
'Silver Sparkler' (v) ♀ H1+3	CSLe CSpe EBre ELan EShb LRHS MBNS MHer MOak NBur SChu SRms SVen WBrE
'Sirius'PBR	SMrm
'Snow White'	CHal
'Sparkler'	CHEx EBre MSte
'Stardust'PBR	COtt LRHS MAsh NPer SCoo WWeb
'Stringston Gemma'	CHal
'Sunny Alex'PBR	LRHS
'Sunny Martha'PBR	LRHS
* 'Superbum'	CHEx
'Svelte'	MSte
'Tauranga'	see *O.* 'Whirlygig'
'Tresco Peggy'	see *O.* 'Nairobi Purple'
'Tresco Pink'	IBlr
'Tresco Purple'	see *O.* 'Nairobi Purple'
'Vega'	COIW CTbh LHop WGor
'Weetwood' ♀ H3-4	CMHG EBlw ECtt EPot LHop MBNS MBri MHar MHer MSte SAga SBla SMrm WAbe WCot WEas WWeb
'Westside' (Side Series) **new**	WWol
§ 'Whirlygig' ♀ H1+3	CHal EBre GGar MBri MHer MOak SRms
§ 'White Pim' ♀ H3-4	CHll CMHG ELan LPhx LRHS NPer SChu SDix SPer SUsu
'Wildside'PBR	WWol
(Side Series) **new**	
'Wine Purple'	see *O.* 'Nairobi Purple'
Wisley hybrids	GGar WEas
'Wisley Pink'	EPyc WFTG
'Zambesi'	LRHS
'Zimbar'	ELan LRHS
'Zulu'PBR	LRHS MHer

Ostrowskia (Campanulaceae)

magnifica	MTho

Ostrya (Corylaceae)

carpinifolia	CBcs CDul CLnd CMCN CTho
	IMGH LRHS MBar MBlu WDin
	WNor WOrn
japonica	CFil CMCN
virginiana	CFil CMCN EPfP IMGH WNor

Otatea (Poaceae)
aztecorum new   CFil

Othonna (Asteraceae)
capensis   CHal
§ *cheirifolia*   CBot CNic CSam CSev EBee EBlw ECha EGoo ELan EMan EVFa NBir NFor NLon SDry SIgm SMac SPer SRms WCom WCot WEas WPer

Othonnopsis see *Othonna*

Ourisia (Scrophulariaceae)
caespitosa   EPot GCrs IBlr NGar NMen NRya
- var. *gracilis*   GEdr GGar GTou IBlr NMen
§ *coccinea*   EBee EMan GAbr GBuc GEdr GGar GKev IBlr LRHS NBir NGar NGby SSpi WAbe
crosbyi   GGar IBlr
- x *macrocarpa*   IBlr
elegans   scc *O. coccinea*
lactea   IBlr
'Loch Ewe'   CPLG CPla GAbr GBuc GDra GEdr GGar IBlr MDun NGar NHar NLAp WCru WPGP
macrocarpa   IBlr
macrophylla   EBee GAbr GBuc GDra GGar IBlr IGor NHar SPoG WAbe
- x *modesta*   IBlr
microphylla   FHyt NWCA WAbe
* - f. *alba*   EHyt WAbe
modesta   IBlr
polyantha   EHyt
- F&W 8487   FHyt WAbe
'Snowflake' ♀ H4   EBee EMan EPot GAbr GCrs GDra GEdr GKev IBlr MDun MOne NBir NGar NHar NMen WAbe WWin

Oxalis ✿ (Oxalidaceae)
F&W 8673   CPBP
acetosella   CKin CNat ERos IIve MBow MHer NMir NSco WHer WShi
- var. *subpurpurascens*   WCot
adenophylla ♀ H4   More than 30 suppliers
- dark   GDra MTho
anomala   EBee EMan WCot
arborescens   CHEx
§ *articulata*   EMan LGro MTho NPer SEND WCot WWin
- 'Alba'   ETow LRHS
- 'Aureoreticulata'   MTho
- 'Festival'   CFwr
'Beatrice Anderson'   FHyt GCrs MBro MTho NHar NHol NMen SBla WAbe
bowiei   CRDP EPot
- 'Amarantha' new   EBee
'Bowles' White'   MTho
brasiliensis   CNic CStu EMlt EPot MTho NMen WOBN
brick orange   WCot
chrysantha   EMlt IHMH SIng
compacta F&W 8011   CPBP
compressa double   CSpe
 (d) new
corniculata   MTho
 var. *atropurpurea*
debilis 'Aureoreticulata'   WCot
deppei   see *O. tetraphylla*
§ *depressa*   CStu CTri EBee EPot EWes GEdr LTwo MTho NBir NHol NMen NRya NSla SIng SRms WBea WBrE WCot WFar

enneaphylla ♀ H4   EMan EPot GCrs GGar LRHS MTho NHol NMen NRya
- 'Alba'   EHyt EPot ERos ETow GBuc ITim MBro NHol NMen NSla WAbe WCom WIvy
I - 'Hythe Seedling'   EHyt
- 'Lady Elizabeth'   SBla
- 'Minutifolia'   EPot ERos GCrs LRHS LTwo MBro MTho NHol NMen NRya WAbe WCom WIvy
* - 'Minutifolia Rosea'   CGra
- 'Rosea'   CBro EPot ERos GDra MTho NHar NHol NMGW NRya NSla SBla SIng
- 'Rubra'   GDra NHar
- 'Ruth Tweedie'   ETow NSla
- 'Sheffield Swan'   EHyt EPot NMen SBla SOkd WAbe
europaea new   GWCH
falcatula new   WCot
flava   LAma LBow
floribunda hort.   see *O. articulata*
geminata   NBir
'Gwen McBride'   GCrs
'Hemswell Knight'   ETow NHar NMen
hirta   CBro CSpe LBow MTho NJOw
- 'Gothenburg'   CPBP EMan ERos LBow MTho NMen
imbricata   LBow
inops   see *O. depressa*
'Ione Hecker' ♀ H4   CBro CGra CLyd EHyt EPot ERos GCrs GEdr GGar GMaP GTou ITim LBee MTho NHar NHol NMen NRya NSla NWoo SBla SIgm WAbe WCom WIvy WLin
§ *laciniata*   EHyt ERos GCrs MTho NHar NHol NMen NSla SBla
- dark   EHyt
- hybrid seedlings   NHar
- 'Seven Bells' new   SBla
lactea double   see *O. magellanica* 'Nelson'
lasiandra   CFwr EPot ERos
lobata   CBro CNic CPBP CStu EBee EHyt EMan EPot ERos ETow EWes LBow LHop LRHS MTho WAbe WCom
magellanica   CFee CHal CMHG CSpe CTri EBla EMlt ESis GDra GGar GMaP LBee MTho NHol SIng SPlb WBea WHrl WPer
- 'Flore Pleno'   see *O. magellanica* 'Nelson'
§ - 'Nelson' (d)   CElw CHal CRDP CRow CSpe EBee EMlt EPot EWes GCal GDra GGar GMac LBee LRHS MTho NBir NBro NHar NPer NWoo WCru WPer WPnP
massoniana new   SIng
melanosticta   LBow
nahuelhuapiensis   CPBP
 F&W 8469
namaquana new   WCot
obtusa   CLyd CSpe CStu EMan EPot ETow MTho NWCA SCnR WCot
- apricot   SOkh WCot
oregana   CDes CNic CRDP CRow EBee GBuc GGar NChi WCru WPGP
- f. *smalliana*   EBee EWes WCru WHal
palmifrons   CPBP CStu LTwo MTho
patagonica   EPot ERos GCrs NHar NMen
pes-caprae   CPLG
* *pulchra*   CSpe
§ *purpurea*   CSpe WAbe
- 'Ken Aslet'   CBro CFee CLyd CNic CStu EHyt EMan EPot GCrs LTwo NJOw WAbe WLin WOBN

regnellii   see *O. triangularis* subsp.
                                papilionacea
rosea hort.   see *O. rubra*
§ **rubra**   EBee
  semiloba   EBee EMan GCal WCot
  speciosa   see *O. purpurea*
  squamata   WPat
  squamosoradicosa   see *O. laciniata*
  stipularis   CNic
  succulenta   CFwr CSpe
  'Sunny' **new**   CFwr
  'Superstar'   WAbe
§ **tetraphylla**   CM&M EBee EPot LAma LRHS
                                MBri MTho NCat NOrc NPer
                                NRog SWal WRha
  – *alba*   EBee
  – 'Iron Cross'   CHEx EBee EMan LAma MMHG
                                NBir SWal WBVN WBea WBrE
                                WBro WHal
  triangularis   CHEx EOHP LAma NBir NPer
                                SPar WBrE WFar
  – 'Birgit' **new**   CFwr
  – 'Cupido'   CRDP WPer WWin
§ – subsp. *papilionacea*   EBee LAma LRHS MMHG NRog
    ♀ H1   WWin
  – – 'Atropurpurea'   CPLG EBee WBVN
  – subsp. *triangularis*   EBee EPyc
  tuberosa   GPoy ILis LEdu WHer
  – blush   IIve
  – 'Bolivian Giant' **new**   IIve
  – 'Fat Red' **new**   EOHP
  – 'Fat White'   EOHP IIve
  – golden red node   IIve
  – orange   IIve
  – pink   IIve
  – red   IIve
  – yellow   IIve
  'Ute'   CGra
  valdiviensis   EMan MDKP NBur WSan
  versicolor ♀ H1   CPBP CSpe CStu EHyt EMan EPot
                                ERos ITim MTho NMen SBla SCnR
                                SOkd SUsu WAbe WCot

         Torr. & A. Gray
  vesperilionis Zucc.   see *O. latifolia*
  vulcanicola   NPri SDix SMrm WLRN
  zeekoevleyensis   WCot

Oxera (Verbenaceae)
  pulchella   CPlN

Oxycoccus see *Vaccinium*

Oxydendrum (Ericaceae)
  arboreum   CAbP CBcs CDoC CEnd CMCN
                                EPfP GKir IDee IMGH LEdu LPan
                                MBri MGos NLar SBrw SRPl SSpi
                                SSta WCru WDin WFar WNor
                                WPGP
  – 'Chameleon'   EPfP LRHS SPer SSpi SSta

Oxylobium (Papilionaceae)
  ellipticum   ECou

Oxypetalum (Asclepiadaceae)
  caeruleum   see *Tweedia caerulea*

Oxyria (Polygonaceae)
  digyna   CAgr EMan GGar NBro NLar
                                WHer

Oxytropis (Papilionaceae)
  hailarensis   CPBP
     var. *chankaensis*

lambertii   LTwo
– var. *bigelovii* **new**   CPBP
megalantha **new**   EMan
purpurea **new**   EMan LTwo MAvo
shokanbetsuensis   LTwo SOkd
uralensis   LTwo

Ozothamnus (Asteraceae)
  antennaria   WSHC
§ **coralloides** ♀ H2-3   EPot GCrs GGar ITim NJOw
                                NLAp NRya NWCA SIng
§ 'County Park Silver'   EPot EWes GEdr ITim NDlv NHar
                                NWCA SBla WCom WPat
§ **hookeri**   CAbb CDoC ECou GGar NWCA
                                SBrw SChu SPer WPat
§ **ledifolius** ♀ H4   CBcs CDoC CMHG CPle CSam
                                ELan EPfP GGar GTou IKee LRHS
                                MBri NBir NLon SBrw SChu SLon
                                SPar SPer SSpi WDin WHCG WHar
                                WPat WSHC
§ **microphyllus**   ITim
§ **rosmarinifolius**   CBcs CDoC CMHG CPLG CTrG
                                EBee ELan EPfP ERea GGar LRHS
                                MNrw NLon SBrw SChu SPar SPer
                                WBod WBrE WDin WEas WFar
                                WHCG WPic
  – 'Kiandra'   ECou
  – 'Silver Jubilee' ♀ H3   CBcs CDoC CEnd CHEx CPLG
                                CSBt CSam CTrC CTrG EBee ELan
                                EPfP LRHS MAsh SBrw SHBN
                                SLon SPar SPer SRPl SRkn SSpi
                                WDin WFar WHCG
  scutellifolius   ECou
§ **selago**   ECou ITim NRya WCot
  – var. *intermedium* **new** GGar
  – 'Minor'   NWCA
§ – var. *tumidus*   SIng
  'Sussex Silver'   NBlu SBrw
  'Threave Seedling'   CDoC CSam LRHS SBrw
§ **thyrsoideus**   CBcs CPLG WFar

P

Pachyphragma (Brassicaceae)
§ **macrophyllum**   CDes CSev ECha EGle EHrv ELan
                                EMon EPPr IBlr LRHS MRav MTed
                                NCiC NLar NSti SSpi WCot WCru
                                WEas WPGP WWin

Pachypodium (Apocynaceae)
  bispinosum   CRoM
  geayi ♀ H1   CRoM
  horombense **new**   CRoM
  lamerei ♀ H1   CRoM EAmu MBri SMur
  lealii subsp. *saundersii* CRoM
  rosulatum var. *gracilius* CRoM
  succulentum   CRoM

Pachysandra (Buxaceae)
  axillaris **new**   GCal
  procumbens   EBee EPla NLar WCot WCru
  stylosa   CBct CDoC EPla MRav SMad
  terminalis   More than 30 suppliers
  – 'Green Carpet' ♀ H4   CBcs CDoC CElw EBee EBre
                                ECot EGol EPfP GKir LRHS MAsh
                                MBar MBri MGos NBlu NHol
                                NPro SCoo SPer SPla WRus
                                WWeb
  – 'Variegata' (v) ♀ H4   More than 30 suppliers

Pachystachys (Acanthaceae)
lutea ♀ H1   CHal ERea LRHS MBri

Pachystegia see *Olearia*

Pachystima see *Paxistima*

Packera (Asteraceae)
§   *aurea*   ECha EMan MSal WHil
   cymbalaria **new**   EBee

Paederia (Rubiaceae)
   scandens   CPLG CPln WCru WSHC
   - var. *mairei*   WCru
      B&SWJ 989 **new**

Paederota (Scrophulariaceae)
§   *bonarota*   CLyd NWCA
   lutea   CDes NWCA

Paeonia ❀ (Paeoniaceae)
albiflora	see *P. lactiflora*
'America'	MBri MCAu
'Angel Cobb Freeborn'	MCAu
anomala	CFil CFir MPhe SSpi
- subsp. *veitchii*	see *P. veitchii*
arietina	see *P. mascula* subsp. *arietina*
'Auten's Red'	MCAu
'Avant Garde'	MBri WKif
bakeri	MBri
banatica	see *P. officinalis* subsp. *banatica*
beresovskii	CFil MPhe
'Black Pirate'	CKel
Blue and Purple Giant	see *P. suffruticosa* 'Zi Lan Kui'
broteroi	CLAP ETow SCou SSpi
'Buckeye Belle'	CKel EBee EFou GKir MBri MPhe SHar
cambessedesii ♀ H2-3	CBrd CBro CFil CKel CLAP EGle EHyt EPot ETow LRHS MFir MTho NBir NMen SAga SDla SIgm SRot SSpi WAbe WCot WPGP
'Carol'	MCAu
caucasica	see *P. mascula* subsp. *mascula*
'China Pink' **new**	MBri
'Chinese Dragon'	CKel
'Claire de Lune'	MCAu MPhe NEgg WCot
'Claudia'	MCAu
clusii	MPhe
'Coral Charm'	WCot
'Coral Fay'	MSte
corallina	see *P. mascula* subsp. *mascula*
coriacea var. *atlantica*	CBro
Crimson Red	see *P. suffruticosa* 'Hu Hong'
'Cytherea'	MCAu
'Dancing Butterflies'	EBee ENot MCAu
daurica	see *P. mascula* subsp. *triternata*
decomposita	EBee MPhe
decora	see *P. peregrina*
'Defender'	MCAu
delavayi ♀ H4	CBcs CHad CKel CSam EBre EChP EOrc EPfP EPla GAbr GCal GKir IBlr LHop LRHS MAsh MDun NBir NEgg NSti SLPl SMad SPar SPer SRms SSpi STes WBod WBrE WTin
- from China	MPhe
- hybrid	ENot
§ - var. *ludlowii* (S) ♀ H4	CBcs CKel CSam EBee EChP ELan EOrc EPfP EWTr GGGa GKir ISea LRHS MDun MPhe NBir NPer SBrw SLPl SMad SPer SPlb SRPl SSpi WDin WEas WFar
§ - var. *lutea* (S)	CHad ENot EPfP LRHS MBro MLan SAga SHBN SLon SPar SRms STre WAul WBrE WHar WHil WHoo WTin SLPl SWat
§ - Potaninii Group (S)	SSpi
- x *delavayi* var. *lutea*	GKir
Drizzling Rain Cloud	see *P. suffruticosa* 'Shiguregumo'
'Early Bird'	GKir
'Early Scout' **new**	EBee
'Eastgrove Ruby Lace'	WEas
'Ellen Cowley'	MCAu
emodi	CLAP LPio WCot
'Fairy Princess' **new**	MBri
'Flame'	EBee MBri MCAu MNrw NLar
Fragrance and Beauty	see *P. suffruticosa* 'Lan Tian Yu'
Gansu Mudan Group	CKel MPhe
'Golden Bowl'	CKel
Great Violet	see *P. suffruticosa* 'Da Zong Zi'
Green Dragon Lying on a Chinese Inkstone	see *P. suffruticosa* 'Qing Long Wo Mo Chi'
'Hei Hua Kui'	see *P. suffruticosa* 'Hei Hua Kui'
'High Noon'	CKel ENot MCAu MPhe NBlu
'Honor'	MCAu
§ 'Huang Hua Kui' (S)	MPhe
humilis	see *P. officinalis* subsp. *microcarpa*
'Illini Warrior'	MCAu
'Isani Gidui'	see *P. lactiflora* 'Isami-jishi'
japonica hort	see *P. lactiflora*
jishanensis **new**	MPhe
'Joseph Rock'	see *P. rockii*
'Joyce Ellen' **new**	MCAu
kavachensis	GIBF
kevachensis	see *P. mascula* subsp. *mascula*
'Kinkaku'	see *P.* x *lemoinei* 'Souvenir de Maxime Cornu'
'Kinko'	see *P.* x *lemoinei* 'Alice Harding'
'Kinshi'	see *P.* x *lemoinei* 'Chromatella'
'Kintei'	see *P.* x *lemoinei* 'L'Espérance'
Kohlein's hybrid	CLAP
'Kokkou-Tsukasa'	CKel
'Kun Shan Ye Guang'	CKel
§ *lactiflora*	EHrv MPhe SSpi
- 'A.F.W. Hayward'	CKel
- 'Adolphe Rousseau'	CBcs EBee MCAu NBlu
* - 'Afterglow'	CKel
- 'Agida'	EBee
- 'Albert Crousse'	CBcs CKel GKir MCAu NBir NBlu
- 'Alexander Fleming'	CKel EBee EChP ECot GKir MCAu NBir
- 'Algae Adamson'	CKel
- 'Alice Balfour' **new**	CKel
- 'Amabilis' **new**	MCAu
- 'Angel Cheeks'	MCAu
- 'Anna Pavlova'	CKel
- 'Antwerpen'	ERou
- 'Arabian Prince'	CKel
- 'Argentine'	NBlu
- 'Artist'	CKel
- 'Asa Gray'	CKel
- 'Auguste Dessert'	CKel EBee MCAu MPhe
§ - 'Augustin d'Hour'	EBee ERou
- 'Aureole'	CKel
- 'Ballerina'	CKel
- 'Barbara'	CKel
- 'Baroness Schröder'	EBee ELan MCAu
- 'Barrington Belle'	EBee EMan GKir LRHS MBri MSte
- 'Barrymore'	CKel
- 'Beatrice Kelway'	CKel
- 'Belle Center'	MCAu
- 'Bethcar'	CKel
- 'Better Times'	MCAu
- 'Big Ben' **new**	SVil
- 'Blaze of Beauty'	CKel

- 'Blenheim'	CKel
- 'Bloodshot'	CKel
- 'Blush Queen'	EBee ELan LBuc MCAu SMrm
- 'Border Gem'	GKir
- 'Bouchela'	EBee
- 'Boulanger'	EBee
- 'Bower of Roses'	CKel
- 'Bowl of Beauty' ♀ H4	More than 30 suppliers
- 'Bowl of Cream'	EBee EMan LAst MBri MCAu
- 'Boy Kelway'	CKel
- 'Bracken'	CKel
- 'Break o' Day'	MCAu
- 'Bridal Veil'	CKel
- 'Bridesmaid'	CKel
- 'British Beauty'	CKel
- 'British Empire'	CKel NPar
- 'Bunker Hill'	CKel EBee GKir MCAu SLdr SMur SVil
- 'Butter Bowl'	MBri MCAu
- 'Calypso'	CKel
- 'Canarie'	CKel MBri
- 'Candeur'	CKel EBee
- 'Cang Long'	CKel
- 'Captivation'	CKel
- 'Carnival'	CKel EBee
- 'Caroline Allain' new	CKel
- 'Casablanca' new	WCGr
- 'Catherine Fontijn'	CKel EBee LBuc
- 'Challenger' new	CKel
- 'Charlemagne' new	CKel
- 'Charles' White'	EBee EGle LPVe MCAu
- 'Charm'	CKel MCAu
- 'Cheddar Charm'	GKir
- 'Cheddar Cheese'	GKir MBri
- 'Cheddar Gold' ♀ H4	GKir MBri
- 'Chestine Gowdy'	CKel
- 'Christine Kelway'	CKel
- 'Chun Xiao'	CKel
- 'Claire Dubois'	CKel ERou GKir MCAu WCGr
- 'Colonel Heneage'	CKel
- 'Cornelia Shaylor'	MCAu
- 'Coronation'	CKel
- 'Country Girl'	CKel
- 'Couronne d'Or'	MCAu
- 'Crimson Glory'	CKel MPhe
- 'Crimson Velvet'	CKel
- 'Cringley White'	SBod
- 'Da Fu Gui'	CKel
- 'Dark Lantern'	CKel
- 'Dark Vintage'	CKel
- 'Dawn Crest'	CKel
- 'Dayspring'	CKel
- 'Delachei' new	CKel
- 'Desire'	CKel
- Diana Drinkwater	CKel
- 'Dinner Plate'	LRHS MBri MCAu WCot
- 'Display'	CKel
- 'Do Tell'	EBee SVil
- 'Docteur H. Barnsby'	CKel
- 'Doctor Alexander Fleming' new	CKel WCGr
- 'Dominion'	CKel
- 'Doreen'	EBee EChP MCAu
- 'Doris Cooper'	MCAu
- 'Dorothy Welsh'	CKel
- 'Dresden'	CKel
- 'Duchess of Bedford'	CKel
- 'Duchess of Somerset'	CKel
- 'Duchesse de Nemours' ♀ H4	CKel COtt EBee EBre EChP EFou ENot EPfP GKir GMaP LHop LPVe MBri MBro MCAu MSte NBir NLar SDes SMrm SPer SRms WAul WCot WHoo WLow WViv
- 'Duchesse de Orleans' new	MCAu
- 'Duke of Devonshire'	CKel
- 'Eden's Temptation' new	SVil
- 'Edmund Spencer'	CKel
- 'Edulis Superba'	CKel EBee EBre EChP EGle ELan ENot GKir LEdu LPVe LRHS MCAu SMrm SPer SRPl
- 'Elizabeth Stone' new	CKel
- 'Ella Christine Kelway'	CKel
- 'Elma' new	CKel
- 'Elsa Sass'	MCAu WCGr
- 'Elwood Pleas' new	CKel
- 'Emma Klehm'	EBee
- 'Emperor of India'	CKel
- 'Enchantment'	CKel
- 'English Princess'	CKel
- 'Ethelreda'	CKel
- 'Ethereal' new	CKel
- 'Eugénie Verdier'	MTed
- 'Evening Glow'	CKel
- 'Evening World'	CKel MRav
- 'Faire Rosamond'	CKel
- 'Felicity' new	CKel
- 'Félix Crousse' ♀ H4	CKel CTri EBee ELan EMil ENot EPfP ERou GKir GMaP LAst LPVe MBri MCAu NBir SPer SRms SWat
- 'Fen Chi Jin Yu'	CKel
- 'Fen Mian Tao Hua'	CKel
- 'Festiva Maxima' ♀ H4	CKel CSBt CTri EBee EBre EChP ECot ELan EPfP ERou GKir LPVe LRHS MBri MBro MCAu MSte NLar SDes SPer SPla SRms WAul WHoo WViv
- 'Florence Ellis' new	MCAu
- 'Flower of Chivalry' new	CKel
- 'France'	CKel
- 'Gainsborough'	CKel
- 'Gardenia' new	WCGr
- 'Gay Paree'	EBee MBri MCAu
- 'Gay Sister'	CKel
- 'Gayborder June'	CKel EBee MBri MCAu
- 'Général MacMahon'	see P. lactiflora 'Augustin d'Hour'
- 'General Wolfe'	CKel
- 'Georgiana Shaylor' new	WCGr
- 'Germaine Bigot'	CKel MCAu
- 'Gilbert Barthelot'	MCAu
- 'Gleam of Light'	CKel
- 'Gloriana'	MCAu
- 'Glory Hallelujah'	MCAu
- 'Gold Mine'	CKel
- 'Golden Fleece' new	MCAu
- 'Goodform' new	CKel
- 'Great Sport'	CKel
- 'Grover Cleveland'	CKel
- 'Guidon' new	MCAu
- 'Gypsy Girl'	CKel
- 'Hakodate' new	CKel
- 'Heartbeat'	CKel
- 'Hei Hai Bo Tao'	CKel
- 'Helen Hayes'	MCAu
- 'Henri Potin'	CKel EBee
- 'Her Grace'	CKel
- 'Her Majesty'	NBir
- 'Herbert Oliver'	CKel
- 'Hiawatha'	MCAu
- 'Hit Parade'	MCAu
- 'Honey Gold'	EBee EChP EMan MCAu SVil
- 'Huang Jin Lun'	CKel
- 'Hyperion'	CKel
- 'Immaculée'	EBee ENot NLar SDes
- 'Ingenieur Doriat'	CKel
- 'Inspecteur Lavergne'	CKel CM&M EBee EFou LRHS MBri MCAu WAul WCot WSan

- 'Instituteur Doriat'	CKel EBee MPhe
§ - 'Isami-jishi'	MBri
- 'Israel' **new**	CKel
- 'Jacques Doriat'	CKel
- 'James Kelway'	CKel
- 'James Pillow'	MCAu
- 'James William Kelway' **new**	CKel
- 'Jan van Leeuwen'	CPen EBee EPfP ERou GKir MCAu
- 'Jappensha-Ikhu'	MBri
- 'Jeanne d'Arc'	CKel
- 'Jewel' **new**	CKel
- 'Jin Chi Yu' **new**	CKel
- 'Jin Dai Wei' **new**	CKel
- 'Joan Kelway'	CKel
- 'John Howard Wigell'	MCAu
- 'Joseph Plagne'	CKel
- 'Joy of Life'	CKel
- 'June Morning'	CKel
- 'June Rose'	MCAu
- 'Kansas'	CKel EBee ELan ERou MCAu MPhe WCGr WFar
- 'Karen Gray'	MBri MCAu
- 'Karl Rosenfield'	CKel CSBt EBee EBre EChP ECot EGle ENot EPfP GKir LRHS MAvo MBri MBro MSte NBee SDes SPla SRms WFar WHil WHoo WLow WViv
- 'Kathleen Mavoureen'	CKel EBee
- 'Kelway's Betty' **new**	CKel
- 'Kelway's Brilliant'	CKel
- 'Kelway's Circe' **new**	CKel
- 'Kelway's Daystar' **new**	CKel
- 'Kelway's Exquisite'	CKel
- 'Kelway's Fairy Queen'	CKel
- 'Kelway's Glorious'	CKel EBee ERou GKir LPVe MBri MTed SMrm
- 'Kelway's Gorgeous'	CKel EBee
- 'Kelway's Lovely'	CKel
- 'Kelway's Lovely Lady'	CKel
- 'Kelway's Majestic'	CKel
- 'Kelway's Queen'	CKel
- 'Kelway's Scented Rose'	CKel
- 'Kelway's Supreme'	CKel SWat
- 'King of England'	CKel
- 'Knighthood'	CKel
- 'Konigin Wilhelmina' **new**	EBee
- 'Krinkled White'	EBee GDin LPio LRHS MBri MCAu MPhe NLar WAul
- 'La Belle Hélène' **new**	CKel
- 'La Lorraine'	CKel
- 'La Perle' **new**	CKel
- 'Lady Alexandra Duff' ♀ H4	CKel COtt EBee EChP EPfP GKir LPVe MBri MCAu MRav MTis NFla SCoo SRms
- 'Lady Ley'	CKel
- 'Lady Mayoress'	CKel
- 'Lady Orchid'	MCAu
I - 'Langport Cross' **new**	CKel
- 'Langport Triumph'	CKel
- 'Laura Dessert' ♀ H4	CKel EBee ELan ERou EWll GKir MBri MCAu SPer
- 'Le Cygne'	SLdr
- 'Le Jour'	MBri
- 'Leading Lady' **new**	CKel
- 'L'Eclatante'	CKel EBee WViv
- 'Legion of Honor'	CKel
- 'Lemon Ice'	CKel
- 'Lemon Queen' **new**	CKel
- 'Letitia'	CKel
- 'Lillian Wild'	MCAu
- 'Longfellow' **new**	CKel
- 'Lord Calvin' **new**	MCAu

- 'Lord Cavan'	MCAu
- 'Lord Derby' **new**	CKel
- 'Lord Kitchener'	CKel MBri MPhe
- 'Lorna Doone'	CKel
- 'Lotus Queen'	MCAu
- 'Louis Barthelot'	CKel MCAu
- 'Louis Joliet'	EBee EChP MSte
- 'Louis van Houtte'	CKel EBee
- 'Louise Lossing' **new**	WCGr
- 'Lowell Thomas'	MCAu
- 'Lyric'	CKel
- 'Madame Calot'	EBee MCAu MSph SRms
- 'Madame Claude Tain'	NBlu WCot
- 'Madame de Verneville' **new**	CKel
- 'Madame Ducel'	CKel MCAu
- 'Madame Edouard Doriat' **new**	CKel
- 'Madame Emile Debatène'	CKel EBee MCAu
- 'Madame Geissler' **new**	WCGr
- 'Madame Jules Dessert'	MCAu
- 'Madelon'	CKel
- 'Magic Melody'	CKel
- 'Magic Orb'	CKel
- 'Maman Millet' **new**	CKel
- 'Margaret Truman'	CKel EBee MCAu NLar
- 'Marie Clutton' **new**	CKel
- 'Marie Crousse'	MCAu
- 'Marie Lemoine'	CKel EBee MCAu SMur
- 'Marquisite'	CKel
- 'Mary Brand'	MCAu
- 'Masterpiece' **new**	CKel
- 'Meteor Flag' **new**	CKel
- 'Mikado'	GKir
- 'Mischief'	CKel MCAu
- 'Miss America'	MCAu
- 'Miss Eckhart'	CKel EBee ERou MCAu
- 'Monsieur Jules Elie' ♀ H4	CBot CKel CM&M EBee EBre EChP EFou EMan EPfP ERou GKir LPVe LRHS MBri MCAu MPhe SPer SPla SVil WCGr WViv
- 'Monsieur Martin Cahuzac'	EBee EMan
- 'Moon of Nippon' **new**	MPhe
- 'Moon River'	EBee EMan SVil
- 'Mother's Choice'	EBee MCAu
- 'Mr G.F. Hemerik'	CKel EBee GKir LRHS MBri MCAu MPhe
- 'Mrs Edward Harding'	MCAu
- 'Mrs F.J. Hemerik'	MCAu
- 'Mrs J.V. Edlund'	MCAu
- 'Mrs Livingston Farrand' **new**	MCAu
- 'My Pal Rudy'	MCAu
- 'Myrtle Gentry'	WCGr
- 'Nancy Nora'	EBee SVil
I - 'Nellie' **new**	CKel
- 'Neon' **new**	WCGr
- 'Newfoundland'	CKel
- 'Nick Shaylor'	GKir MCAu
- 'Nippon Beauty' **new**	CPen EGle MBri
- 'Nobility'	CKel
- 'Noemie Demay' **new**	WCGr
- 'Ornament'	CKel
- 'Orpen'	CKel
- 'Othello'	CKel
- 'Paola' **new**	CKel
- 'Paul M. Wild'	EBee MCAu
- 'Pauline Maunder'	CKel
- 'Peche'	CPen EBee LPVe MCAu
- 'Peregrine'	CKel
- 'Persier'	EBee

– 'Peter Brand'	EBee LBuc
– 'Philippe Rivoire'	WCGr
– 'Philomèle'	MCAu
– 'Pillow Talk'	EBee MCAu
– 'Pink Cameo' **new**	MCAu WCot
– 'Pink Giant'	LRHS
– 'Pink Jazz' **new**	EBee
– 'Pink Parfait'	CKel MCAu
– 'Pink Princess'	LRHS MBri MCAu
– 'Polar King' **new**	MCAu
– 'President Franklin D. Roosevelt'	EBre GKir SWat
– 'Président Poincaré'	CKel EBre GKir SMur SWat
– 'President Taft'	see *P. lactiflora* 'Reine Hortense'
– 'Pride of Somerset'	CKel
– 'Primevere'	EBee EPfP EWll LBuc LRHS
– 'Princess Beatrice'	CKel
– 'Princess Margaret' **new**	WCGr
– 'Qi Hua Lu Shuang'	CKel
– 'Qing Wen'	CKel
– 'Queen of Sheba'	MCAu
– 'Raoul Dessert'	MCAu
– 'Raspberry Sundae'	EBee ERou MCAu NLar WCot
– 'Red Champion'	MBri
– 'Red Charm' **new**	MPhe
– 'Red Dwarf'	CKel
– 'Red King'	CKel
– 'Red Revival' **new**	CKel
§ – 'Reine Hortense'	CKel EBee MCAu
– 'Renato'	EBee EFou SVil
– 'Rose of Delight'	CKel
– 'Ruth Cobb'	MCAu
– 'Sante Fe'	MCAu
– 'Santorb' **new**	CKel
– 'Sarah Bernhardt' ♀ H4	More than 30 suppliers
– 'Shen Tao Hua'	CKel
– 'Shimmering Velvet'	CKel
– 'Shirley Temple'	CKel CMGP EBee ELan GKir LPVe MAvo MBri MBro MCAu MRav MSte SHar SMrm WCot WHil WHoo WViv
– 'Silver Flare'	CKel
– 'Sir Edward Elgar'	CKel
– 'Snow Swan' **new**	CKel
– 'Solange'	CKel EBee EChP LPVe MCAu
– 'Sorbet'	COtt CPen EBee EMan EPfP LRHS MPhe WHil
– 'Spearmint'	CKel
– 'Strephon'	CKel
– 'Surugu'	SLdr
– 'Sword Dance'	EBee EGle GBin MPhe
– 'Tamate-boko'	MBri MCAu
– 'The Nymph'	CPen
– 'Thérèse'	MCAu
– 'Top Brass'	CBot EBee MCAu MPhe MRav
– 'Toro-no-maki'	MCAu
– 'Translucient'	CKel
– 'Van Dyck' **new**	CKel
– 'Victoire de la Marne'	EBee SMur
– 'Vogue'	CKel EBee MBri MCAu SMur
– 'Westerner'	MCAu
– 'White Wings'	CBcs CKel COtt CPen EBee EGle ELan EPfP GKir MBri MCAu MSte NBee WCot
– 'Whitleyi Major' ♀ H4	GKir
– 'Wiesbaden'	MCAu
– 'Wladyslawa'	EBee NLar
– 'Xuan Li Duo Cai'	CKel
– 'Xue Feng'	CKel
– 'Yan Fei Chu Yu'	CKel
– 'Yan Zi Dian Yu'	CKel
– 'Zhu Sha Dian Yu'	CKel
– 'Zus Braun'	EBee
'Late Windflower'	ECha

§ x *lemoinei* 'Alice Harding' (S)	CKel ENot MCAu SPer
§ – 'Chromatella' (S)	CKel ENot LAma
§ – 'L'Espérance' (S)	LAma MGos
§ – 'Souvenir de Maxime Cornu' (S)	CKel ENot LAma LRHS MBri MCAu MGos MPhe SPer
lithophila	see *P. tenuifolia* subsp. *lithophila*
lobata 'Fire King'	see *P. peregrina*
ludlowii	see *P. delavayi* var. *ludlowii*
lutea	see *P. delavayi* var. *lutea*
– var. *ludlowii*	see *P. delavayi* var. *ludlowii*
macrophylla	MPhe
'Mai Fleuri'	GKir
mairei	MPhe
§ *mascula*	CAvo CBro EPfP GIBF LRHS NBir SCou
– from Sicily	MPhe
§ – subsp. *arietina*	ECha ETow SCou SIgm WEas WKif
– – 'Northern Glory'	GKir
– subsp. *bodurii* **new**	MPhe
– subsp. *hellenica* **new**	MPhe
– – from Sicily **new**	MPhe
– subsp. *icarica* **new**	MPhe
§ – subsp. *mascula*	CBro EBee EGle EPot GIBF WCot
– – DC 151	MDCh
– – from Georgia	MPhe
– – from SE Georgia	WPGP
§ – subsp. *russoi*	GIBF SIgm SSpi
§ – subsp. *triternata*	CLAP MPhe SSpi
– – from Crimea	WPGP
mlokosewitschii ♀ H4	CAvo CBro CFil CKel CLAP EBre ECha EOrc EPot ETow GEdr GKir LHop LRHS MBro MNrw MPhe NBir SBla SChu SMad SUsu WCom WCot WEas WHoo WPGP
mollis	see *P. officinalis* subsp. *villosa*
'Montezuma'	MBri
'Nymphe'	CMGP EBee EChP LRHS MBNS MBri MCAu MRav SCou WAul WHoo
obovata ♀ H4	CFir CLAP GIBF GKir MPhe MSal SSpi WCot
– var. *alba* ♀ H4	NWoo WAbe WEas
– 'Grandiflora'	GKir
– var. *willmottiae* **new**	MPhe
officinalis	CFil GPoy SBla SCou
– 'Alba Plena'	CKel CPou EBee GKir GMaP MBri MRav SMrm
– 'Anemoniflora Rosea' ♀ H4	EBee EGle EPfP GKir LRHS MBri MCAu MHom
§ – subsp. *banatica*	MCAu MHom MPhe SSpi
– 'China Rose'	GKir
– from Slovenia WM 9821	MPhe
– subsp. *humilis*	see *P. officinalis* subsp. *microcarpa*
– 'James Crawford Weguelin'	WCot
– 'Lize van Veen'	GKir MCAu
§ – subsp. *microcarpa*	SSpi
– 'Mutabilis Plena'	EBee IBlr MCAu
– 'Rosea Plena' ♀ H4	CKel EBee ECtt EPfP GAbr GBin GKir LAst LHop LPVe MBri MCAu MRav NMGW SMrm SWat WLRN
– 'Rosea Superba Plena'	EBee EFou MCAu SLdr
– 'Rubra Plena' ♀ H4	CKel CPou EBee ECtt EFou EMil EPfP GBin GKir LAst LHop LPVe MBri MCAu MHom NGdn SMrm SPer SRms SWat WCot WFar
§ – subsp. *villosa*	EBee ELan GAbr MBri MCAu SCou
'Oriental Gold'	CKel
ostii (S)	CKel MPhe
– dark-flowered (S)	CKel
papaveracea	see *P. suffruticosa*
paradoxa	see *P. officinalis* subsp. *microcarpa*
parnassica **new**	MPhe

'Paula Fay'	MBri MCAu MPhe MRav
Peony with the Purple Roots'	see *P. suffruticosa* 'Shou An Hong
§ *peregrina*	CFil CLAP ECho GCal MCAu MHom MPhe NSla NWoo SBla SIgm SSpi
– from Macedonia	WPGP
§ – 'Otto Froebel' ♀ H4	EBre GKir LRHS MBri MCAu WCot
– 'Sunshine'	see *P. peregrina* 'Otto Froebel'
'Phoenix White' (S) **new**	MBlu
'Postilion'	MBri
potaninii	see *P. delavayi* Potaninii Group
Purple Shawl	see *P. suffruticosa* 'Ge Jin Zi'
'Red Charm'	MBri MCAu
'Red Magic'	CMGP NLar
'Requiem'	MCAu
rhodia	MPhe
§ *rockii* (S)	EPfP MPhe SSpi WViv
– 'Bing Shan Xue Lian' (S)	MPhe
– 'Fen He' (S)	MPhe
– (Gansu Mudan Group) 'Bai Bi Fen Xia' **new**	MPhe
– – 'Bai Bi Lan Xia' **new**	MPhe
– – 'Lan He' **new**	MPhe
– – 'Li Xiang' **new**	MPhe
– 'He Ping Lian' (S)	MPhe
– 'Hong Lian' (S)	MPhe
– 'Hui He' (S)	MPhe
– 'Shu Sheng Peng Mo' (S)	MPhe
– 'Zi Die Ying Feng' (S)	MPhe
romanica	see *P. peregrina*
'Rose Garland'	MCAu
Rouge Red	see *P. suffruticosa* 'Zhi Hong'
russoi	see *P. mascula* subsp. *russoi*
'Scarlett O'Hara'	MBri MCAu
Shandong Red Lotus	see *P. suffruticosa* 'Lu He Hong'
'Shi-pen-kue' **new**	MBri
sinensis	see *P. lactiflora*
'Smouthii'	GKir
'Soshi' **new**	MBri
steveniana	CLAP MPhe
§ *suffruticosa* (S)	CWlb EBee ELan LPan MGos MPhe NBlu SPar SRPl SSpi WStI
– 'Akashigata' (S)	CKel
– 'Alice Palmer' (S)	CKel
– 'Bai Yu' (S)	CBcs
– 'Bai Yuan Hong Xia' **new**	MCAu
– 'Bang Ning Zi' (S)	MPhe
– Bird of Rimpo	see *P. suffruticosa* 'Rimpo'
– Black Dragon Brocade	see *P. suffruticosa* 'Kokuryû-nishiki'
– Black Flower Chief	see *P. suffruticosa* 'Hei Hua Kui'
– 'Cai Die' (S)	MPhe
* – 'Cai Jing Qui' (S)	MPhe
– 'Cang Zhi Hong' (S)	MPhe WViv
– 'Cardinal Vaughan' (S)	CKel
– 'Chen Hong' (S)	MPhe
– 'Chojuraku' **new**	MPhe
– 'Da Hong Ye' **new**	MPhe
– 'Da Hu Hong' **new**	MPhe
§ – 'Da Zong Zi' (S)	MCAu MPhe
– 'Dou Lu' (S)	CBcs CKel MPhe
– Double Cherry	see *P. suffruticosa* 'Yae-zakura'
– 'Duchess of Kent' (S)	CKel
– 'Duchess of Marlborough' (S)	CKel
– 'Er Qiao' (S)	CBcs CKel MPhe
– Eternal Camellias	see *P. suffruticosa* 'Yachiyo-tsubaki'
§ – 'Fei Yan Hong Zhuang' (S)	MCAu
– 'Fen Lan Zhu' (S)	MPhe
– 'Fen Qiao' (S)	CBcs
§ – 'Feng Dan Bai' (S)	CKel MCAu MPhe WViv
– 'Feng Zhong Guan' (S)	CKel
– Flight of Cranes	see *P. suffruticosa* 'Renkaku'
– Floral Rivalry	see *P. suffruticosa* 'Hana-kisoi'

– Flying Swallow Lady in Red	see *P. suffruticosa* 'Fei Yan Hong Zhuang'
– 'Fuji Zome Goromo' **new**	CKel
§ – 'Ge Jin Zi' (S)	MPhe
* – 'Glory of Huish' (S)	CKel
– 'Godaishu' (S)	LAma LRHS MBri MPhe SPer
– 'Guan Shi Mo Yu' (S)	CKel MPhe
§ – 'Hakuojisi' (S)	EBee ENot MCAu
– 'Hana-daijin' (S)	LAma LRHS MBri MCAu NBlu SPer
§ – 'Hana-kisoi' (S)	LAma MBri MCAu MPhe NBlu SPer
– 'Haru-no-akebono' (S)	CKel
§ – 'Hei Hua Kui' (S)	CKel MCAu
§ – 'Higurashi' (S)	EBee ENot
– 'Hong Cai Qiu' (S)	MPhe
– 'Hu Die Qun Wu' (S)	MPhe
§ – 'Hu Hong' (S)	MPhe WBrE
– Jewel in the Lotus	see *P. suffruticosa* 'Tama-fuyo'
– Jewelled Screen	see *P. suffruticosa* 'Tama-sudare'
– 'Jia Ge Jin Zi' (S)	CKel WViv
– 'Jiao Rong San Bian' (S)	MPhe
– 'Jin Pao Hong' (S)	MPhe
– 'Jitsugetsu-nishiki' (S)	CKel
– Joseph Rock	see *P. rockii*
§ – 'Kamada-fuji' (S)	CKel LAma MCAu
§ – 'Kaow' (S)	MCAu
– King of Flowers	see *P. suffruticosa* 'Kaow'
– King of White Lions	see *P. suffruticosa* 'Hakuojisi'
* – 'Kingdom of the Moon' (s)	LRHS
– 'Kinkaku'	see *P.* x *lemoinei* 'Souvenir de Maxime Cornu'
– 'Kinshi'	see *P.* x *lemoinei* 'Alice Harding'
§ – 'Kokuryû-nishiki' (S)	CKel LAma SPoG
– 'Koshi-no-yuki' (S)	CKel
– 'Lan Fu Rong' **new**	CBcs
§ – 'Lan Tian Yu' (S)	CKel MPhe
– 'Li Hua Xue' (S)	MPhe
– 'Ling Hua Zhan' (S)	MPhe
– 'Liu Li Guan Zhu' (S)	MPhe
§ – 'Lu He Hong' (S)	MCAu
– 'Luo Han Hong' (S)	MPhe WViv
– 'Luo Yang Hong' (S)	MPhe
– Magnificent Flower	see *P. suffruticosa* 'Hana-daijin'
– 'Masudore' **new**	NBlu
– 'Mikasayama' **new**	MPhe
– 'Montrose' (S)	CKel
* – 'Mrs Shirley Fry' (S)	CKel
– 'Mrs William Kelway' (S)	CKel
– 'Nigata Akashigata' (S)	CKel
– Pride of Taisho	see *P. suffruticosa* 'Taisho-no-hokori'
§ – 'Qing Long Wo Mo Chi' (S)	CKel MCAu
– 'Qing Shan Guan Xue' (S)	WViv
– 'Raphael' (S)	CKel
– 'Reine Elisabeth' (S)	CKel
§ – 'Renkaku' (S)	CKel LRHS MBri MPhe
§ – 'Rimpo' (S)	CKel EBee ENot LAma MPhe SPer
– subsp. *rockii* (S)	see *P. rockii*
– 'Rou Fu Rong' (S)	MCAu MPhe
– 'Ruan Zhi Lan' (S)	MPhe WViv
– 'Sai Xue Ta' **new**	MPhe
§ – 'San Bian Sai Yu' (S)	MPhe WViv
– Seven Gods of Fortune	see *P. suffruticosa* 'Sitifukujin'
– 'Sheng Hei Zi'	CBcs
§ – 'Shiguregumo' (S)	CKel
– 'Shimadaijin' **new**	MPhe
– 'Shimane-chojuraku' (S)	CKel
– 'Shimane-hakugan' (S)	CKel
– 'Shimane-seidai' (S)	CKel
– 'Shin Shima Kagayaki' **new**	CKel
– 'Shintoyen' (S)	CKel
– 'Shirotae' (S)	CKel

§ – 'Shou An Hong' (S)   MPhe
   – 'Si He Lian' (S)   MPhe
§ – 'Sitifukujin' (S)   MBri
   – 'Sumi-no-ichi' (S)   CKel
   – 'Superb' (S)   CKel
§ – 'Taisho-no-hokori' (S)   LRHS MCAu
§ – 'Taiyo' (S)   ENot LAma LRHS MBri MPhe SPer
§ – 'Tama-fuyo' (S)   LAma
§ – 'Tama-sudare' (S)   CKel
   – The Sun   see *P. suffruticosa* 'Taiyo'
   – 'Tian Xiang' **new**   MPhe
   – Top Table Red   see *P. suffruticosa* 'Sho An Hong'
   – Twilight   see *P. suffruticosa* 'Higurashi'
   – 'Wen Gong Hong' (S)   MPhe
   – Wisteria at Kamada   see *P. suffruticosa* 'Kamada-fuji'
   – 'Wu Jin Yao Hui' (S)   CBcs
   – 'Wu Long Peng Sheng'   CKel MPhe
   – 'Xiao Tao Hong' **new**   CBcs
   – 'Xue Gui' (S)   MPhe
   – 'Xue Ta' (S)   CKel
§ – 'Yachiyo-tsubaki' (S)   CKel ENot LAma
§ – 'Yae-zakura' (S)   LAma MCAu
   – 'Yan Long Zi Zhu Pan' (S)   CKel
   – 'Yin Hong Qiao Dui' (S)   CKel CMGP MPhe
§ – 'Ying Luo Bao Zhu' (S)   WViv
   – 'Yomo-zakura' (S)   LRHS
   – 'Yoshinogawa' (S)   EBee ENot LRHS MBri
   – 'Yu Lu Dian Cui' (S)   WViv
   – 'Yu Pan Zheng Yan' (S)   MPhe
   – 'Yu Xi Ying Xue' (S)   CKel MPhe
   – 'Zhao Fen' (S)   MPhe
§ – 'Zhi Hong' (S)   CKel
   – 'Zhong Sheng Hong' (S)   MPhe
   – 'Zhu Sha Lei' (S)   CKel MPhe
   – 'Zi Ban Bai' (S)   CKel
   – 'Zi Er Qiao' (S)   CKel MPhe
   – 'Zi Jin Pan' (S)   WViv
§ – 'Zi Lan Kui' (S)   CKel MPhe
   'Sunshine'   see *P. peregrina* 'Otto Froebel'
   tenuifolia   CBot CLAP GCal GIBF LPio MDun
     NSla SIgm SIng SMad SSpi WCot
   – subsp. *biebersteiniana*   MPhe
   – subsp. *carthalinica*   MPhe
§ – subsp. *lithophila*   GKir MPhe
   – 'Plena'   GKir LPio LRHS MBri MPhe
   – 'Rosea'   WCot
   Three-Sided Jade   see *P. suffruticosa* 'San Bian Sai Yu'
   tomentosa **new**   MPhe WWst
   turcica   MPhe
   veitchii   CKel CLAP EBee GIBF GMaP
     MHom MTho MWgw NBid NDlv
     SCou SDys SIgm SSpi WAbe
   – dwarf   MPhe
   – from China   MPhe
   – var. *leiocarpa*   EBee
   – var. *woodwardii*   CLyd CPne ERos GDra MTho NGar
     NSla NWCA SIgm SSpi WCot WHoo
   White Phoenix   see *P. suffruticosa* 'Feng Dan Bai'
   wittmanniana   CBot CLAP GKir
§ 'Yao Huang' (S)   CBcs CKel MCAu MPhe
   Yao's Yellow   see *P.* 'Yao Huang'
   'Yellow Dream'   WCot
   'Yellow Emperor'   WCot
   Yellow Flower of Summer   see *P.* 'Huang Hua Kui'

Paesia (Dennstaedtiaceae)
   scaberula   CFil GCal NBir SSpi WAbe

Paliurus (Rhamnaceae)
   spina-christi   CArn CLnd CPle EBee SLon SMad

Pallenis (Asteraceae)
   maritima   CStu LLck SPet WWol

   – 'Golden Dollar'   NPri

Panax (Araliaceae)
   ginseng   GCal GPoy
   japonicus   GPoy WCru
   quinquefolius   GPoy MSal

Pancratium (Amaryllidaceae)
   maritimum   EBee EBot LRHS WCot

Pandanus (Pandanaceae)
   utilis   EAmu LPal

Pandorea (Bignoniaceae)
   jasminoides   CHal CPIN CRHN CSpe EBak
     ECot LRHS MRav SOWG
§ – 'Charisma' (v)   CBcs CPIN CTrC EHol EMil EPfP
     EShb SOWG WCot
§ – 'Lady Di'   CPIN ERea LRHS SOWG SYvo WCot
   – 'Rosea'   MCCP
   – 'Rosea Superba' ♀ H1   CBcs CHEx CRHN EBee EHol
     EMil ERea LRHS
   – 'Variegata'   see *P. jasminoides* 'Charisma'
   lindleyana   see *Clytostoma calystegioides*
   pandorana   CPIN CRHN CTrC ERea SLim
     SYvo WCot
   – 'Golden Rain'   CBcs CMdw CPIN CRHN EBee
     ERea SLim SOWG
   – 'Ruby Heart'   CPIN
   – 'Snowbells'   CPIN

Panicum (Poaceae)
   bulbosum   EHoe EPPr EPla SMHy
   clandestinum   EHoe EPPr EPla EWes LEdu MAvo
     MCCP NPro WHil
   miliaceum   EGle MSal
   – 'Violaceum'   CSpe EMan SWal
   virgatum   CBig CTri EBlw LRav SDes SRGP
     WPer
   – 'Blue Tower'   LPhx MAnH SApp
   – 'Cloud Nine'   CKno EFou EPPr LHop LPhx
     MAnH SApp
   – 'Dallas Blues'   EFou EPPr
   – 'Hänse Herms'   CBrm CMil EGle EHoe EPPr IPot
     LPhx SCou SMad SPla WFar WWpP
   – 'Heavy Metal'   More than 30 suppliers
   – 'Northwind'   EFou EPPr SApp SMHy
   – 'Prairie Sky'   CKno EPPr LPhx MAnH SApp WCot
   – 'Red Cloud' **new**   SApp
   – 'Rehbraun'   CBrm CFwr CSBt CSpe EBee EBre
     ECGN EGle EHoe EPPr EPfP EWTr
     IArd IPot LEdu LPan LPhx MCAu
     MWgw NGdn NOak NPPs SApp
     SMad WRus
   – 'Rotstrahlbusch'   CSpe EBee EBre ECGN EFou EGle
     EHoe EMan EPPr IArd MAnH
     MAvo MSte MWgw MWhi NBea
     STes SWal WCot WHil WPGP
   – 'Rubrum'   CBos CKno CSBt EBlw EBre EChP
     ECha ECot EHoe ELan ENot EPPr
     EPfP EWsh LRHS MRav NDov
     NSti SApp SChu SDix SHBN SPar
     SPer SPla WMoo
   – 'Shenandoah'   CAbb CKno EBee IPot MBri WCot
   – 'Squaw'   CHar CKno CWCL EBee EBlw
     EBre EFou EGle EHoe EPGN EPPr
     EWsh GKir IPot MAnH MCAu
     MSte NPPs NPro SApp SHBN
     SMad WBro WCot WDyG WFar
     WLin WPnP WPrP WWye
   – 'Strictum'   EBee EHoe EHul EMan EMil EPPr
     EWes LPhx SApp SHel
   – 'Warrior'   More than 30 suppliers

'Wood's Variegated' (v)	EPPr LEdu

Papaver ✿ *(Papaveraceae)*

alboroseum	CSam EDAr EHyt GTou WPat
'Alpha Centauri'	SWat
(Super Poppy Series)	
§ *alpinum* L.	CSpe EDAr EMNN EMlt GDra
	GKir GTou ITim LRHS MMHG
	NBlu SIng SRms WFar WWin
- 'Flore Pleno' (d)	NBir
amurense	EBee GCal
anomalum album	CBri CSpe EBee EMon MWgw NArg
apokrinomenon	EBee ELan MWrn
§ *atlanticum*	EBee ECoo EMar GBuc LDai MLan
	NBro SBri SIng SPlb
- 'Flore Pleno' (d)	CM&M CSpe EBee MCCP MLwd
	NBro WFar WOld
'Aurora'	SWat
(Super Poppy Series)	
bracteatum	see *P. orientale* var. *bracteatum*
burseri	SRot
'Cathay'	
(Super Poppy Series)	SWat
'Celebration'	SWat
(Super Poppy Series)	
commutatum ♀ H4	ELan WBry WEas
'Eccentric Silk' **new**	SWat
* *ecoanense* **new**	EBee
fauriei	EBee
§ 'Fireball'	CMHG CPlt CRow EHcP ECha EGle
	ETow GCal IGor LHop MLLN MTis
	MWat WBry WCot WRHF WViv
'Harlequin'	SWat
(Super Poppy Series)	
heldreichii	see *P. spicatum*
X *hybridum* 'Flore	EBee EMon SWat WWal
Pleno' (d)	
involucratum **new**	EHyt
'Jacinth'	SWat
(Super Poppy Series)	
lateritium	CPou CSpe MDow MLLN SRms
	WPGP WWpP
- 'Flore Pleno' (d)	EBee EGle
'Medallion'	SWat
(Super Poppy Series)	
§ *miyabeanum*	CSpe EDAr ELan EWTr GAbr
	GDra GKir GTou LRHS MPWC
	NWCA WFar WPer WTMC WWin
- *album*	ECho
- 'Pacino'	CWes EDAr EMil EMlt ESis EWll
	GBuc IHMH LRHS NDlu WWcb
- *tatewakii*	see *P. miyabeanum*
'Mulberry Moods'	SWat
(Super Poppy Series)	
nanum 'Flore Pleno'	see *P.* 'Fireball'
§ *nudicaule*	ELan NBlu WPer
- Champagne Bubbles	EBre GWCH LRHS WFar WLRN
Group	WWeb
- Constance Finnis Group	EMon GBuc LRHS
- var. *croceum* 'Flamenco'	ERou LRHS
- Garden Gnome Group	see *P. nudicaule* Gartenzwerg Series
§ - Gartenzwerg Series	COlW CSpe EMil GAbr MBri NBlu
	NPri SDes SPlb WGor WWeb
- 'Pacino'	SGar SRms WFar WLRN
- 'San Remo'	WWeb
- 'Solar Fire Orange'	EWll WWeb
- 'Summer Breeze Orange'	NPri WWeb
- 'Summer Breeze Yellow'	NPri WWeb
- Wonderland Series	EHrv LPVe SDes
- - 'Wonderland Gold'	WWeb
- - 'Wonderland Orange'	NPri WWeb
- - 'Wonderland Pink	NPri
Shades'	

- - 'Wonderland Pink'	WWeb
- - 'Wonderland	WWeb
Rose' **new**	
- - 'Wonderland White'	NPri WWeb
- - 'Wonderland Yellow'	NPri
orientale	CBcs EPfP MBow MBro NBlu SRms
	SWat WBrE WCFE WFar WPer
- 'Abu Hassan'	SWat
- 'Aglaja' ♀ H4	CFai CMil EBee EMan EMil EVFa
	GBin LPhx MSph MSte NCot
	NDov NGdn NHaw NSti SPoG
	SUsu SWat WCot WHoo WWhi
- 'Aladin'	SWat
- 'Ali Baba'	SWat WWeb
- 'Allegro'	CPrp CSBt CSam EBlw EBre ECtt
	EFou EGle GAbr GKir LASt LRHS
	MBNS MBri MCAu MHer MRav
	NVic SDes SPer SPlb SSvw SWat
	WViv WWal WWeb
- 'Arwide'	CMil SWat
- 'Aslahan'	ECha SWat WBro
- 'Atrosanguineum'	SWat
- 'Avebury Crimson'	LPhx MBct MWat SWat WMaN
- 'Ballkleid'	ECha SWat WBro
- 'Beauty of Livermere'	see *P. orientale* (Goliath Group)
	'Beauty of Livermere'
- 'Beauty Queen'	EBee EBre ECha ECot EGle EMan
	GKir GMac LRHS MAvo MBri
	MRav MWgw NGdn SDix SRPl
	SWat WLRN
- 'Bergermeister Rot'	SWat
- 'Big Jim'	EBee SWat
- 'Black and White' ♀ H4	CElw CHad CPrp CRDP CSpe EBee
	EChP ECha EGle EHrv ELan EPfP
	ERou GKir LRHS MAnH MBow
	MCAu MRav MSph ECru EPer SPlb
	SWat WCot WPGP WSan WWin
- 'Blackberry Queen'	EBee EMan LPio MBow NCot
	SWat WCot
- 'Blickfang'	SWat
'Bloomsbury' **new**	EChP
- 'Blue Moon'	SApp WHal WLRN
- 'Bonfire'	CSam EHrv SOkh
- 'Bonfire Red'	CStr EBee ELan LRHS SWat
§ - var. *bracteatum* ♀ H4	CRDP CSam EChP ECha EWll
	GDra MLwd NBir SMHy SWat SYvo
- 'Brilliant'	EBee LRHS NLar WFar WMoo
	WRHF
* - 'Carneum'	EBee EChP LRHS WHil
- 'Carnival'	CMil EBee EFou SWat
- 'Catherina'	EBee SWat
'Cedar Hill'	EBee EWes LRHS MMil SMrm SWat
- 'Cedric Morris' ♀ H4	CHad CMil CSpe EBlw EChP
	ECha EFou EGle ELan EPri ERou
	GCal GMac MAnH MRav MSte
	MWat MWgw NSti SChu SMrm
	SWat WCot WEas WLRN WMaN
	WMnd WPGP WWin
- 'Charming'	CHad CMil CPar EBee EChP EGle
	EMan LPhx LRHS MBri MMil
	NDov SAga SWat WElm
- 'China Boy'	CMil EBee SWat WWeb
- 'Choir Boy'	CM&M CRDP EBee ECtt EGle
	MBct NCot SGar STes WBry WHrl
	WRHF
- 'Coral Reef'	EBee EWll MHer SAga SWat WBry
	WCra WElm WHrl WPen WRHF
- 'Corrina'	EBee SWat
- 'Curlilocks'	CFwr CMGP CPar EBre EChP ECtt
	ELan EPfP ERou LASt LRHS MBow
	MCLN MRav NPSI SAga SRms
	SWat WMnd WSan WWin
- 'Derwisch'	SWat

*	– 'Diana'	SMrm SWat
	– double orange (d) **new**	IBal
	– 'Double Pleasure' (d) **new**	MCLN
	– double red shades (d)	EBlw
	– 'Doubloon'	EBee EBre ERou GKir NGdn NHaw SWat WFar
	– 'Dwarf Allegro'	GBuc MFir NFor NLon NOak WMnd
	– 'Effendi' ♀ H4	CMil EFou IPot LPhx MBct SBla SDys SMHy SUsu SWat WBro
	– 'Elam Pink'	CMil EBee EGle LPhx MAvo MBri MLLN MSph MTis SWat WCot
	– 'Erste Zuneigung'	CBos EBee EGle LPhx WBro
	– 'Eskimo Pie'	SWat
	– 'Fatima'	CHad CMil EBee EFou SMrm SWat WWeb
	– 'Feuerriese'	SWat
	– 'Feuerzwerg'	SWat
	– 'Fiesta'	CMil SWat
	– 'Flamenco'	ECtt SWat
	– 'Forncett Summer'	EBee EChP EFou EMan EMar LPio MAvo MCAu NGdn SChu SWat WCot WMaN WPGP
	– 'Garden Glory'	CPar CPlt CRDP EBee EChP ECtt EFou EMan LAst LRHS MCAu NBro NCat SMrm SRPl SWat WLRN WTMC
	– 'Garden Gnome'	ENot GKir SPet
	– 'Glowing Embers'	EBre ERou GKir LRHS SMrm SWat
	– 'Glowing Rose'	SWat
*	– 'Goldie'	ELan
	– Goliath Group	CElw CMil EBee ECha EMan GKir LHop LRHS MAvo MCLN MTis NBro NOak NPri NVic SDix SPer SRPl SRms SWat WEas WFar WMnd WPen
	– – 'Beauty of Livermere'	More than 30 suppliers
	– 'Graue Witwe'	CMil EBee EFou EGle GBuc MBow MBri NCot SWat WCot WMaN WPGP
	– 'Halima'	ECha SWat
	– 'Harvest Moon'	CMHG EBee EBre EChP EHol ERou EWTr GKir LPio LRHS MBow MBri NHaw NPri SWat WHil
	– 'Helen Elisabeth'	CMHG COlW CSpe EBre EChP ECtt EFou EGle EMar ERou GCal GKir LAst LPio MBow MCLN MLLN MSte NGdn NPri SApp SWat WCom WFar WTMC
	– 'Hewitt's Old Rose'	WCot
	– 'Hula Hula'	ECha SWat
	– 'Indian Chief'	CM&M CMHG COlW CPrp CRDP EBee EBlw EChP EGle ERou GBin GMac LPio LRHS MSte MTis NBro NGdn NPer NPri SDes STes WBar WMnd
	– 'Joanne'	NLar
	– 'John III' ♀ H4	EBee EFou LPhx MSph SMHy SWat
	– 'John Metcalf'	CMil CRDP EBee EFou EGle LPio LRHS MAvo MCAu MLLN NSti SChu SMrm SWat WCot
	– 'Juliane'	CPlt EBee ECha EGle EPri LHop LPhx MBct MSte MWgw NDov NSti SAga SWat WBro WCot WWhi
	– 'Karine' ♀ H4	More than 30 suppliers
	– 'Khedive' ♀ H4	SWat
	– 'King George'	GBuc SWat
	– 'Kleine Tänzerin'	CMil CPou EBee EChP EFou EGle LPhx LRHS MAvo MCAu MCLN MLLN MWgw NDov NGdn NSti SAga SBla SUsu SWat WCot WLRN WWeb
	– 'Kollebloem'	SWat
	– 'Lady Frederick Moore'	EBee LPio MBow MLLN SWat WCra

	– 'Lady Roscoe'	SWat
	– 'Ladybird'	EBee ELan ENot ERou GKir LRHS MSte SCro
	– 'Lambada'	SWat
I	– 'Lauren's Lilac'	CMil LPhx SWat
	– 'Lavender Girl'	CFir
	– 'Leuchtfeuer' ♀ H4	EBee LPhx MSph SWat
	– 'Lighthouse' ♀ H4	SWat
	– 'Lilac Girl'	CElw CMil CPlt CSpe EBee EChP ECha EGle EMan EWll LHop LPhx LPio MAvo MBow MCLN MSph MSte NLar NSti SWat WCot WCra WHoo WMaN WWhi
	– 'Little Dancer' **new**	GMac
	– 'Little Dancing Girl'	EBee GBin GBri NCot NPri WHil
	– 'Maiden's Blush'	CMil EBee NSti SWat
	– 'Marcus Perry'	CStr EBee ENot EPfP ERou EWes GMaP LRHS MCAu MRav NPri SDes SWat WFar
	– 'Mary Finnan'	EBee EGle LPio SWat
	– 'Master Richard'	SWat
	– 'May Queen' (d)	CM&M CPou EBee EChP EWes IBlr LRHS MRav NBro NSti SLon SMrm WCot WElm WPen
	– 'May Sadler'	COlW EBee EBlw ENot SWat
	– 'Midnight'	EBee ERou SCro
	– 'Mrs H.G. Stobart'	CRDP MBow SWat
	– 'Mrs Marrow's Plum'	see *P. orientale* 'Patty's Plum'
	– 'Mrs Perry'	CM&M CSBt CSam CSpe EBlw EBre ELan EPfP ERou GKir LRHS MCAu MCLN MFir MRav MWat NGdn NPPs NPer NSti SCro SPer SPla SRms SWat WFar WHoo WTMC WTel
	– 'Nanum Flore Pleno'	see *P.* 'Fireball'
	– 'Noema'	SWat
	– 'Orange Glow'	EBee EWTr NCot NPri
	– 'Orangeade Maison'	CPou CStr EBee LPio SWat WBro
	– 'Oriana'	EBee EHol LRHS MMil SWat WLRN
	– 'Oriental'	SWat
	– 'Pale Face'	ERou SWat
§	– 'Patty's Plum'	More than 30 suppliers
	– 'Perry's White'	More than 30 suppliers
	– 'Peter Pan'	EBee MLLN SWat
	– 'Petticoat'	EBee EChP EFou ELan EMan IPot LAst SWat
	– 'Picotée'	More than 30 suppliers
	– 'Pink Lassie'	SWat
	– 'Pink Panda'	SWat
	– 'Pink Ruffles' PBR **new**	EBee EMan MBri MCLN
	– 'Pinnacle'	CMil CSWP EBee ERou GLil LRHS NGdn NHaw NPri SDes SMrm SWat WFar WPGP WSan
	– 'Pizzicato'	CHor CM&M CPar CWib EChP EHrv ERou EShb EWTr ITer LHop LPhx LRHS MBri NArg NChi NPer SGar SPet SSvw STes SWal SWat WFar WGwG WLRN WMoo WViv WWeb
	– 'Polka'	IPot SWat
	– 'Prince of Orange'	EBee SWat WHil
	– Princess Victoria Louise	see *P. orientale* 'Prinzessin Victoria Louise'
	– 'Prinz Eugen'	CMil CRDP EFou MAnH SWat
§	– 'Prinzessin Victoria Louise'	CFwr CSWP EBee EChP EMan GKir GMaP LPVe LRHS MLLN MMil NBro SApp SSvw SWat WCer WFar WPer
	– 'Prospero'	EBee
	– 'Queen Alexandra'	EBee EHrv NChi NLar
	– 'Raspberry Queen'	More than 30 suppliers
	– 'Raspberry Ruffles'	CMil LPhx SWat
	– 'Rembrandt'	EBee ECot EHrv ERou LRHS MMil

	NMoo NPri SWat WBar WPer WRus WViv
- 'Rosenpokal'	CM&M CMil EBee EChP LRHS NGdn SWat WBro
- 'Roter Zwerg'	ECha
- 'Royal Chocolate Distinction'	SWat
- 'Royal Wedding'	EChP EGle ERou EWTr GKir ITim LAst LPVe LPio LRHS MHer MMil MRav NGdn NLar NPri SChu SMrm SPer SPla SSvw SWat WCot WLRN WMoo WViv WWeb
* - 'Saffron'	CHad CMil EVFa SAga SWat
- 'Salmon Glow'	CBcs EBee EChP EWTr GKir GLil LAst MHer SDes SWat WFar WPer
- 'Salome'	SWat
- scarlet	MWgw NCot
- 'Scarlet King'	EBee EMan EWll LRHS MMil SWat WLRN
- 'Shirley Temple' **new**	SDes
- 'Showgirl'	CRDP CSam EBee MBow MLLN MSPs SOkh SWat
- 'Silberosa'	ECha
- 'Sindbad'	EBee EFou GMac LPhx LRHS NLar SWat
- 'Snow Goose'	CMil LPhx MAnH SWat
- 'Spätzünder'	SWat
- 'Springtime'	CSpe EBee EChP EFou EGle EMan EWes LRHS MCAu SWat WHoo W3an WTMC WTin
- 'Stokesby Belle'	MWgw
- Stormtorch	see *P. orientale* 'Sturmfackel'
§ - 'Sturmfackel'	EBee EGle ERou SWat
'Suleika'	SWat
- 'Sultana'	EBee EBlw ECha EGle ERou GMac LPhx MAnH MWat SWat WBro
- 'The Promise'	SWat
- 'Türkenlouis'	CFwr CHar CMHG COlW CSBt EBre ECtt EFou EGle ENot EPfP ERou GKir GLil GMaP GMac LAst LCaP LRHS MCAu SCro SMrm STes SWat WElm WFar WHoo
- 'Turkish Delight'	EBee ELan EPfP ERou GKir GMaP GMac LRHS MBow MMil MRav MTis NBid NBir NBro NCat NPri SMer SWat WFar
- 'Tutu'	SWat
- 'Victoria Dreyfuss'	SWat
- 'Viola'	SWat
- 'Water Babies'	SWat
- 'Watermelon'	CMil COtt CRDP EBre EChP ECtt EFou ERou GKir LAst LCaP LRHS MAnH MAvo MBri MCAu MCLN MLLN NCot NPri NSti SApp SCro SWat WElm WFar WHoo WTMC
- 'Wild Salmon'	SPar STes WRHF
- 'Wisley Beacon'	SWat
- 'Wunderkind'	CM&M EBee EChP EGle EMan LAst MCAu SWat
'Party Fun' **new**	WWeb
pilosum	EMan GBuc GDea LHrt NCat SRms SSvw SWat WCot
'Pink Lightning' (Super Poppy Series)	SWat
pseudocanescens **new**	EBee
rhaeticum	EHyt
rhoeas	CArn GPoy MBow WJek
- Angels' Choir (d)	ERou SWat
- 'Mother of Pearl'	SWat
- Shirley	MBow
rupifragum	CBri CFir CHar CMco CPLG CTCP EBee EChP ECha ECtt GAbr

	LPio MFir MLLN NPPs SGar SWal WCot WEas WFar WHrl WPer WRha WTMC
- 'Double Tangerine Gem' (d) **new**	CPen
- 'Flore Pleno' (d)	CSWP CSam CSpe EBee EMan LPio LRHS MLwd NChi SScr STes WCru WHen WHer WMoo WWhi
- 'Orange Bubbles' **new**	EWsh
- 'Tangerine Dream'	MCCP
sendtneri	MHer
'Serena' (Super Poppy Series)	SWat
'Shasta' (Super Poppy Series)	SWat
somniferum	CArn GPoy MSal SWat
- 'Black Beauty'	CSpe SWat WEas
- 'Chedglow Variegated' (v)	CPla EMan
- 'Flemish Antique' **new**	WHer
- 'Pink Chiffon'	SWat WEas
§ *spicatum*	CSpe EBee ECGP ECha EGle EGoo EMan GCal MFir MSte MWgw NBir NPPs SIgm SMrm SUsu WCot WMoo WWeb
'Tequila Sunrise' (Super Poppy Series)	SWat
'The Cardinal' **new**	WRHF
triniifolium	EMan SIgm
'Viva' (Super Poppy Series)	SWat
* 'Witchery'	NCot WWeb

papaya (paw paw) see *Carica papaya*

Parabenzoin see *Lindera*

Parachampionella see *Strobilanthes*

Paradisea (Asphodelaceae)

liliastrum ♀ H4	CHid CMdw EBee EMan EPPr ERos GIBF LPio NCat NChi NWoo WBVN WCFE WCot
lustianica	CAvo CDes CHid CMHG CPom CRDP EBee EChP ERos LPio MWrn NEgg SOkh SSpi WCot WLin WMoo WPGP WWeb

Parahebe ✿ (Scrophulariaceae)

'Arabella'	LRHS
'Betty'	GGar
x *bidwillii*	ECou EMNN MIlcr NDlv NWCA SRms SRot
- 'Kea'	CFee ECou ECtt EMNN ESis MDKP NHar SBla SHel SRot WPer
- 'Rosea'	WCom
canescens	ECou
§ *catarractae*	CHar CMHG CPLG EBee ECou EMNN EMlt GGar GKir MFir MNrw MWat NBee NBro NLAp SAga SPar SUsu WBrE WCom WCru WFar WHen WPer WWhi
- 'Baby Blue'	CAbP EPfP MAsh SReu SSta
- blue	EPfP GKir NBee SPer SPla
- 'County Park' **new**	ECou
- 'Cuckoo' **new**	ECou
§ - 'Delight' ♀ H3	ECou ESis EWes GGar LPVe LRHS MHer NLAp NPer SDix SHFr SIgm SMrm SRot STre WEas WFar WHen
- subsp. *diffusa*	ECou EMNN LRHS MHer MMil NHar NPer NVic WCom
- - 'Annie'	ECou NJOw
- - 'Pinkie'	ECou
- from Chatham Island	EWes
- garden form	ECha LLWP NLAp SBla
- subsp. *martinii*	ECou

- 'Miss Willmott'	NLAp NPri NVic SPer SPlb SVen WBVN WBea WCom WPer
- 'Porlock Purple'	see *P. cataractae* 'Delight'
- 'Rosea'	COkL ESis WBrE
- 'Tinycat'	ITim
- white	CBot ECha EMNN ESis IBlr LHop MFir NCat SHel SPar SPla WEas WPer WWhi
decora	ECou
densifolia	see *Chionohebe densifolia*
derwentiana	ECou
§ *formosa*	CPle ECou WHCG
- erect	ECou GGar
- white	ECou
'Gillian'	ECou ECtt WPer
'Greencourt'	see *P. cataractae* 'Delight'
§ *hookeriana*	GGar SAga
'Joy'	ECou EWes
'Julia'	GGar
'June'	GGar
'Lesley'	GGar
linifolia	CTri EMNN
- 'Blue Skies'	ECou EDAr
§ *lyallii*	CBot COkL ECou EDAr EMlt ESis LAst MBar MHer MWat NChi NDlv NHol NWCA SBla SPlb SRms WCom WWin
- 'Baby Pink'	EPfP MAsh
- 'Clarence'	CLyd ECou EHol
- 'Glacier'	ECou
- 'Julie-Anne' ♀ H3	CAbP COkL ECou EPfP ESis GCal LRHS MAsh
- 'Rosea'	CTri GGar WPer
- 'Summer Snow' **new**	ECou
'Mervyn'	CLyd CTri ECou ECtt EDAr NDlv NLAp NLon WHen WPer
olsenii	ECou GGar
§ *perfoliata* ♀ H3-4	More than 30 suppliers
- dark blue	GBuc GCal MBro SMad SMrm
- 'Pringle'	CAbP EPfP LRHS MAsh SMrm
'Snowcap'	CDoC EPfP LRHS MAsh SPlb

Parajubaea (Arecaceae)

cocoides	LPJP LPal

Parakmeria (Magnoliaceae)

lotungensis	see *Magnolia lotungensis*

Paraquilegia (Ranunculaceae)

adoxoides	see *Semiaquilegia adoxoides*
§ *anemonoides*	GCrs GGGa GTou NHar SBla WAbe WLin
- SDR 1555	GKev
- SDR 1768	GKev
grandiflora	see *P. anemonoides*

Paraserianthes (Mimosaceae)

distachya	see *P. lophantha*
§ *lophantha* ♀ H1	CHEx CRHN CTCP CTrC EBak ERea IDee SAPC SArc SOWG SPar WMul

Parasyringa see *Ligustrum*

x *Pardancanda* (Iridaceae)

norrisii	CFir EBee EMan EWes GSki LIck LRHS MGrG WAul WFoF

Pardanthopsis (Iridaceae)

dichotoma	EBee

Parietaria (Urticaceae)

§ *judaica*	GEil GPoy MSal WHer

Paris ✿ (Trilliaceae)

axialis var. *rubra* **new**	LEur
bashanensis	EBee LEur SSpi WCru
chinensis	EBee LEur WCru
cronquistii **new**	EBee
- var. *cronquistii* **new**	LEur
delavayi **new**	EBee LEur WCru
- var. *petiolata* **new**	EBee
fargesii	EBee LAma LEur WCru
- var. *petiolata*	EBee SSpi WCru
forrestii	WCru
incompleta	CAvo GCrs LEur SSpi
japonica	SOkd WCru
lanceifolia B&SWJ 3044 from Taiwan **new**	WCru
luquanensis	LEur
mairei	EBee LAma LEur WCru
marmorata **new**	EBee WCru
§ *polyphylla*	CBro CFir EBee EMar LAma LEur MPhe WCot WCru WPnP
- F 5947	ITim
- HWJCM 475	WCru
- var. *stenophylla*	EBee LAma WCru
- var. *yunnanensis*	CFir EBee
* - - *alba*	EBee LEur
quadrifolia	CFil CFir CLAP EBee GPoy LPhx MDun SSpi WCot WCru WHer WPnP WShi
tetraphylla	WCru
thibetica	EBee LEur WCru
- var. *apetala*	LEur
- var. *thibetica*	SSpi
verticillata	EBee LAma LEur WCru

Parnassia (Parnassiaceae)

nubicola	NHar
palustris	WHer

Parochetus (Papilionaceae)

africanus ♀ H2	CHid EWes GBuc
communis	CBcs CFee CNic CPLG GDra GKev IFro MRav NPer WBea WBor WPnP WRha WWhi
- B&SWJ 7215 from Golden Triangle **new**	WCru
- from Himalaya	IBlr
- - HWJCM 526	EBee WCru
* - 'Blue Gem'	IHMH
- dark	GCal

Paronychia (Illecebraceae)

argentea	CLyd NLAp WPat WPer
§ *capitata*	CHal CLyd CTri IFro SRms WHoo WPat WPer WWin
§ *kapela*	EMan ETow SPlb WPer
- 'Binsted Gold' (v)	EMan GEdr LRHS MBro
- subsp. *serpyllifolia*	NRya
nivea	see *P. capitata*
serpyllifolia	see *P. kapela* subsp. *serpyllifolia*

Parrotia (Hamamelidaceae)

persica ♀ H4	More than 30 suppliers
- 'Burgundy'	CPMA
§ - 'Lamplighter' (v)	CPMA
- 'Pendula'	CPMA EPfP
- 'Vanessa'	CEnd CMCN CPMA EWes GKir IArd LPan MBlu MBri NLar SBrw SKee WOrn
- 'Variegata'	see *P. persica* 'Lamplighter'

Parrotiopsis (Hamamelidaceae)

jacquemontiana	CBcs LBuc NLar NPal

Parrya (Brassicaceae)

albida new	EBee
menziesii	see *Phoenicaulis cheiranthoides*

parsley see *Petroselinum crispum*

Parsonsia (Apocynaceae)

capsularis	CPLG CPIN ECou
heterophylla	CPIN ECou

Parthenium (Asteraceae)

integrifolium	CArn GPoy IIve MSal

Parthenocissus (Vitaceae)

§ **henryana** ♀ H4	More than 30 suppliers
heptaphylla new	WWes
himalayana 'Purpurea'	see *P. himalayana* var. *rubrifolia*
§ - var. **rubrifolia**	EBee EPfP LRHS MAsh MRav SLim SLon SPoG WCru WFar
§ **quinquefolia** ♀ H4	More than 30 suppliers
- var. **engelmannii**	EBee LBuc MGos WCFE
semicordata B&SWJ 6551	WCru
striata	see *Cissus striata*
§ **tricuspidata** ♀ H4	CAgr CHEx CWib EBee ECtt EHoe EPfP GKir MGos NFor NLon SMer SPar SPer SReu WDin WFar
- 'Beverley Brook'	CMac EBee LBuc MBri SBra SPla SRms
- 'Crûg Compact' B&SWJ 1162	WCru
- 'Green Spring'	EBee IArd MBri MGos
- 'Lowii'	CMac EBee ECot EPfP EPla LBuc LRIIS MBlu MGos MRav SLon SPer
- 'Purpurea' **new**	MBlu
- 'Robusta'	CSam EBee LPan MBNS
§ - 'Veitchii'	More than 30 suppliers

Pasithea (Anthericaceae)

caerulea	EBee EMan WCot
- F&W 8766	EBee

Paspalum (Poaceae)

glaucifolium	LBBr LEdu WDyG
quadrifarium	EPPr

Passiflora ✿ (Passifloraceae)

actinia	CPas CPIN CRHN CSPN EBee SLim SSte
adenopoda	CPas
'Adularia'	CPas CWSG SSte
alata (F) ♀ H1	CAbb CPas CPIN CSPN EBak ELan ERea LRIIS SSte
- 'Shannon' (F)	CPas SSte
x **alatocaerulea**	see *P.* x *belotii*
allantophylla	CPas
'Allardii'	CPas
amalocarpa	CPas SSte
ambigua	CPas
§ 'Amethyst' ♀ H1	CChe CPas CRHN CSPN ELan EMil LHop LRHS SBra SPar SPet WFar WPGP WPat WWeb
amethystina misapplied	see *Passiflora* 'Amethyst'
§ **amethystina** Mikan	CBcs CDoC CPas CPIN ECre EHol ERea LRHS SSte
amoena (F)	CPas
ampullacea (F)	CPas
'Andy'	CPas
'Anemona' **new**	SSte
anfracta	CPas
'Anna'	CSPN
'Anna Christine' **new**	CSPN
N **antioquiensis** Karst ♀ H2	CBcs CHEx CPIN CTbh EBee EHol

	ERea GQui ISea LRHS MTis SAga SMur SOWG SVen WMul WOld
apetala	CPas
x **atropurpurea**	SSte
§ **aurantia**	CPas WCot
auriculata	CPas
banksii	see *P. aurantia*
§ x **belotii**	CPas EBee EHol ELan LRHS SSte
- 'Impératrice Eugénie'	see *P.* x *belotii*
biflora Lamarck	CPas
'Blue Carnival'	CSPN
'Blue Moon'	CPas CSPN
boenderi	CPas
'Byron Beauty'	CPas CSPN
§ **caerulea** ♀ H3	More than 30 suppliers
- 'Constance Elliot'	CBcs CBot CDoC CMac CPas CPIN CRHN CSBt CSPN CWSG EBee ELan EMil ENot EOrc EPfP LRHS MAsh MRav SBra SLim SOWG SPar SPer SPla SSta SSte WFar WGwG WWeb
- **rubra**	LRHS NHaw WFar
x **caponii**	ERea
capsularis	CHll CPas SSte
cerasina	CPas
chinensis	see *P. caerulea*
cincinnata	CPas
cinnabarina	CPas
cirrhiflora	CPas
citrina	CPas CPIN CWSG ELan ERea ESlt LRHS SOWG SSte
coccinea (F)	CPas CPIN LRHS
colinvauxii	CPas
x **colvillii**	CHll CPas CPIN
conzattiana	CPas
§ **coriacea**	CPas CPIN CSPN LRHS SSte
costaricensis	CPas
crenata	CPas
cuneata	CPas
§ - 'Miguel Molinari'	CPas
cuprea	CPas SSte
I 'Curiosa'	CPas ELan
cuspidifolia	CPas
§ **cyanea**	CPas
'Debby'	CPas CSPN
x **decaisneana** (F)	CPas CPIN
discophora	CPas
'Eclipse'	CSPN
edulis (F)	CAgr CPas CPIN CSPN CTCP LRHS SSte
- 'Crackerjack' (F)	ERea
- f. **flavicarpa** (F)	CPas ELan ESlt SSte
* - 'Golden Nuggett' (F)	CPas
elegans	CPas
'Elizabeth' (F)	CPas
'Empress Eugenie'	see *P.* x *belotii*
* 'Evatoria'	CSPN
x **exoniensis** ♀ H1	CBot CHll CPas CPIN CRHN ECre
exura	CPas
filipes	CPas
'Fledermouse'	CPas CSPN
foetida	CPas LRHS SOWG SSte
- var. **galapagensis**	CPas
- var. **hirsuta** (F)	CPas
- var. **hirsutissima**	CPas
- var. **orinocensis**	CPas
garckei	CPas
gibertii	CPas
gilbertiana	CPas WFar
glandulosa	CPas
gracilis	CPas
gracillima	CPas
gritensis	CPas SSte

guatemalensis	CPas
hahnii	CPas
helleri	CPas CPlN
herbertiana (F)	CPas CPlN SSte SVen
hirtiflora	CPas
holosericea	CPas
incana	see *P. seemannii*
incarnata (F)	CAgr CArn CPas EBot ITer MSal SPlb SSte
– 'Roseville'	SSte
'Incense' (F) ♀ H1	CPas CPlN EBak ELan LRHS SLim SPlb
indecora	CPas
jatunsachensis	CPas
'Jeanette'	CPas
'Jelly Joker'	CPas CSPN
jorullensis	CPas
juliana	CPas
kalbreyeri	CPas
karwinskii	CPas
x *kewensis*	CPas SSte
lancearia	CPas
lancetellesis	CPas
laurifolia (F)	CPas SLim
§ *ligularis* (F)	CPas LRHS SSte
'Lilac Lady'	see *P.* x *violacea* 'Tresederi'
lindeniana	CPas
lobata	CPas
lourdesae	see *P. cuneata* 'Miguel Molinari'
lowei	see *P. ligularis*
lutea	CPas
macrophylla	CPas
maliformis (F)	CPas CPlN
manicata (F)	CPas CPlN
matthewsii	CPas SSte
'Mavis Mastics'	see *P.* x *violacea* 'Tresederi'
mayana	see *P. caerulea*
mayarum	CPas
membranacea (F)	CPas SSte
microstipula	CPas
'Miranda' **new**	CSPN
misera	CPas
mixta (F)	CPlN CSPN ERea SBra
* – var. *pinanga*	CPas
– x *antioquiensis*	CDoC CTrC
mollissima (F) ♀ H1	CBcs CPas CPlN CRHN CTCP CTrC EBak EBee EPfP ERea EShb LRHS SMrm SOWG SPlb SSte WMul
mooreana	CPas
morifolia	CPas CPlN SSte WMul
mucronata	CPas
multiflora	CPas
murucuja	CPas SSte
naviculata	CPas
nephrodes	CPas
nitida (F)	CPas
oblongata	CPas
obtusifolia	see *P. coriacea*
oerstedii	CPas
– var. *choconhiana*	CPas
onychina	see *P. amethystina*
organensis	CPas
palmeri	CPas
penduliflora	CPas
perfoliata	CPas SSte
* 'Perfume'	CPas
pergrandis	CPas
phoenicea	CPas SSte
pilosicorona	CPas
'Pink Jewel'	CPas
pinnatistipula (F)	CPas
x *piresiae*	CPas
pittieri	CPas
platyloba	CPas CPlN
punctata	CPas
'Pura Vida'	CPas SSte
'Purple Haze'	CPas CRHN SBra WWeb
'Purple Rain'	CSPN
quadrangularis	CBcs CHll CPas CPlN CTbh
L. (F) ♀ H1	CWSG EBak ERea LPan LRHS SMur WMul
quadrifaria	CPas
quinquangularis	CPas SSte
racemosa ♀ H2	CPas CPlN CWSG EBee ELan ERea IBlr LAst LRHS SOWG
'Red Inca'	CPas
reflexiflora	CPas
resticulata	CPas
retipetala	see *P. cyanea*
rovirosae	CPas LRHS SSte
rubra	CPas SLim WBod WStI
* *rufa*	CPas
'Saint Rule'	CPas
sanguinolenta	CPas LRHS SSte
'Sapphire'	CPas
'Sarah Aimee'	CPas
§ *seemannii*	CPas
serrata	see *P. serratodigitata*
serratifolia	CPas
§ *serratodigitata*	CPas
serrulata	CPas
sexflora	CPas LRHS
'Simply Red'	CPas
'Smythiana'	CPas
sprucei	CPas
standleyi	CPas
'Star of Bristol' ♀ H2	CHEx CPas EBee SBra SLim
'Star of Clevedon'	CPas
'Star of Kingston'	CPas
stipulata	CPas
suberosa	CPas SSte
subpeltata	CPas SSte
subpurpurea	CPas
'Sunburst'	CHEx CPas CPlN LRHS SOWG SSte
'Susan Brigham' **new**	SSte
talamancensis	CPas
tenuifila	CPas
§ *tetrandra*	CPas ECou
x *tresederi*	see *P.* x *violacea* 'Tresederi'
trialata	CPas
tricuspis	CPas
tridactylites	CPas SSte
trifasciata	CPas CPlN CSPN SSte
tripartita	CPas
trisecta	CPas
tryphostemmatoides	CPas
tuberosa	CPas
tulae	CPas SSte
umbilicata	CPas CPlN WCru
urbaniana	CPas
vespertilio	CPas
§ x *violacea* ♀ H1	CPas CPlN CRHN ERea ESlt MBri
– 'Eynsford Gem'	CPas NHaw
– 'Lilac Lady'	see *P.* x *violacea* 'Tresederi'
§ – 'Tresederi'	CPas EBee MAsh SAga WFar
– 'Victoria'	CPas SLim WOld
viridescens	CPas
viridiflora	CPas
vitifolia (F)	CPas CPlN ELan ERea ESlt LRHS SMur SOWG
– 'Scarlet Flame' (F)	CPas
wurdackii	CPas
xiikzodz	CPas
yucatanensis	CPas

zamorana	CPas

passion fruit see *Passiflora*

passion fruit, banana see *Passiflora mollissima*

Pastinaca (Apiaceae)

sativa	CKin

Patrinia (Valerianaceae)

from Russia	SMrm
gibbosa	CLyd CRDP EBee EMan EOrc IFro MWrn SWal WCru WFar WPat WPnP WRus
rupestris	EBee IIve
saniculifolia	WCot WCru
scabiosifolia	More than 30 suppliers
– 'Nagoya'	MNrw
triloba	CLyd CPla CRDP EBre EDAr GBuc GCrs GKir LRHS MRav MWrn NWoo SMac SSpi SUsu
* – 'Minor'	ECho
– var. *palmata*	EBee WFar WMoo
– var. *triloba*	ETow GCal GDea WWin
villosa	EBee IIve

Paulownia (Scrophulariaceae)

catalpifolia **new**	CFil WPGP
fargesii Osborn	see *P. tomentosa* 'Lilacina'
– Franch.	SMad
fortunei	MBlu NPal WBVN WNor
kawakamii	CFil WPGP
– B&SWJ 6784	WCru
tomentosa ♀ H3	More than 30 suppliers
– 'Coreana'	CHll
§ – 'Lilacina'	CFil

Pavonia (Malvaceae)

missionum **new**	FShb
multiflora Jussieu ♀ H1	ERea
praemorsa	CBot EBee

paw paw (false banana) see *Asimina triloba*

Paxistima (Celastraceae)

canbyi	EHyt NLar NPro WPat WWes
myrsinites	see *P. myrtifolia*
§ *myrtifolia*	EPla ESis

peach see *Prunus persica*

pear see *Pyrus communis*

pear, Asian see *Pyrus pyrifolia*

pecan see *Carya illinoinensis*

Pecteilis (Orchidaceae)

* *dentata*	EFEx
§ *radiata*	EFEx
* – 'Albomarginata' (v)	EFEx
– 'Aureomarginata' (v)	EFEx

Pedicularis (Scrophulariaceae)

longiflora var. *tubiformis* **new**	GKev
rhinanthoides subsp. *tibetica* **new**	GKev

Peganum (Zygophyllaceae)

harmala	CArn CPLG MGol MSal WWye

Pelargonium ✿ (Geraniaceae)

B&SWJ 6497 from Thailand **new**	WCru
'A Happy Thought'	see *P.* 'Happy Thought'
'A.M. Mayne' (Z/d)	CWDa SPet
'Abba' (Z/d)	CWDa
'Abel Carrière' (I/d)	SKen SPet WFib
abrotanifolium (Sc)	CSev EWoo MHer SSea WFib
'Abundance' (Sc)	LDea
'Acapulco' (I)	NPri
acerifolium hort.	see *P. vitifolium*
acetosum	CSpe GCal MSte SHFr SMrm
* – 'Variegatum' (v)	MSte
acraeum	WFib
'Acushla by Brian' (Sc)	MWhe
'Ada Green' (R) **new**	LDea
'Ada Sutterby' (Dw/d)	SKen WFib
'Adagio' (Dw)	ESul
'Adam's Quilt' (Z/C)	SKen WEas
'Adele' (Min/d)	ESul WFib
'Ade's Elf' (Z/St)	NFir SSea
'Aerosol' (Min)	ESul WFib
'African Belle' (R)	SAga
'Afterglow' (Z)	WFib
'Ailsa' (Min/d)	ESul SKen
'Ainsdale Angel' (A)	LDea
'Ainsdale Eyeful' (Z)	LVER
'Akela' (Min)	ESul
Alba = 'Fisalb'PBR (Z/d)	WWol
'Alberta' (Z)	SKen WFib
'Albert's Choice' (R)	WFib
album	CWDa
alchemilloides	CRHN NClC WFib
'Alcyone' (Dw/d)	ESul SKen WTib
'Alde' (Min)	ESul MWhe NFir SKen WEas
'Aldenham' (Z)	WFib
'Aldham' (Min)	ESul WFib
'Aldwyck' (R)	ESul LDea WFib
'Alex' (Z)	CWDa SKen
'Alex Mary' (R)	SSea WFib
'Algenon' (Min/d)	ESul WFib
'Alice Crousse' (I/d) ♀ H1+3	WFib
'Alice Greenfield' (Z)	NFir
'Alison' (Dw)	ESul
'Alison Jill' (Z/d)	CWDa
'Alison Wheeler' (Min/d)	MWhc
'All My Love' (R)	LDea WFib
'Allicia' (R)	ESul
'Allure' (R) **new**	SKen
'Alma' (Min/C)	ESul
'Almost Heaven' (Dw/Z/v)	MWhe
'Alpine Glow' (Z/d)	MWhe
'Alpine Orange' (Z/d)	CWDa
'Alta Bell' (R)	WFib
'Altair' (Min/d)	ESul WFib
alternans	CSev
'Always' (Z/d)	WFib
'Alys Collins' (Z/d)	WFib
'Amari' (R)	LDea
'Ambrose' (Min/d)	ESul WFib
'Amethyst' (R)	ESul LDea SCoo SKen SPet WFib
§ Amethyst = 'Fisdel'PBR (I/d) ♀ H1+3	ECtt LDea LVER MWhe NPri WFib
'Ami' (R)	WFib
'Anabell Stephenson' (Dw/d)	WFib
'Andersonii' (Sc)	MHer MOak WFib
'Andrew Salvidge' (R)	LDea WFib
'Androcles' (A)	NFir
I 'Andromeda' (Min)	WFib
'Ange Davey' (Z/d)	WFib
'Angela' (R)	LDea

'Angela Brook'	CWDa
'Angela Read' (Dw)	ESul
'Angela Tandy' **new**	NFir
'Angela Woodberry' (I/d)	CWDa
'Angelique' (Dw/d)	ESul LVER NFir WFib
'Anglia' (Dw)	ESul
'Ann Field' (Dw/d) **new**	ESul
'Ann Hoystead' (R) ♀ H1+3	ESul WFib
'Ann Redington' (R)	LDea WFib
'Ann Sothern' (Z)	WFib
'Anna' (Min)	ESul WFib
'Anna Scheen' (Min)	ESul
'Annsbrook Aquarius' (St)	ESul NFir
'Annsbrook Beauty' (A/C)	ESul LDea LVER NFir
'Annsbrook Capricorn' (St/d)	ESul
'Annsbrook Jupiter' (Z/St)	ESul NFir
'Annsbrook Mars' (St)	ESul
'Annsbrook Pluto' (Z/St)	ESul NFir
'Annsbrook Squirrel' (Min) **new**	ESul
'Annsbrook Venus' (Z/St)	ESul
'Antigua' (R)	LDea WFib
'Antoine Crozy' (ZxI/d)	WFib
'Antoinette' (Min)	ESul
'Apache' (Z/d) ♀ H1+3	CHal CWDa WFib
'Aphrodite' (Z)	CWDa ECtt WFib
'Apollo' (R)	CWDa
'Apple Betty' (Sc)	EWoo LDea MHer WFib
'Apple Blossom Rosebud' (Z/d) ♀ H1+3	ECtt ESul LAst LRHS LVER MBri MWhe SKen SMrm SPet SSea SUsu WFib WGwG WWol
'Appledram' (R)	ESul LDea WFib
'Apri Parmer' (Min)	ESul
'Apricot' (Z/St)	ESul LAst SAga SKen
'Apricot Queen' (I/d)	LDea
'Apricot Star'	CSpe MSte MWhe
'April Hamilton' (I)	LDea WFib
'April Showers' (A) **new**	LDea
§ 'Arctic Star' (Z/St)	CSpe ESul LRHS NFir SAga SKen SSea WEas
'Arcturus' (Min)	WFib
'Ardens'	CSpe EBee EWoo LPio NFir SAga SMrm SOkh SSea SUsu WCot WEas
'Ardwick Cinnamon'	ESul EWoo LDea LVER NFir
'Aries' (Min)	ESul MWhe
'Arizona' (Min/d)	ESul SKen WFib
'Arnside Fringed Aztec' (R)	LDea
'Aroma' (Sc)	EWoo LIck WFib
'Arron Dixon' (A)	NFir
'Arthington Slam' (R)	LDea
'Arthur Biggin' (Z)	MWhe SKen
'Ashby' (U/Sc)	LVER
'Ashfield Blaze' (Z/d)	LVER WFib
'Ashfield Jubilee' (Z/C)	NFir SKen
'Ashfield Monarch' (Z/d) ♀ H1+3	LVER MWhe NFir WFib
'Ashfield Serenade' (Z) ♀ H1+3	SKen WFib
'Ashley Stephenson' (R)	WFib
'Askham Fringed Aztec' (R) ♀ H1+3	ESul LDea LVER
'Askham Slam' (R)	LDea
asperum Ehr. ex Willd.	see *P.* 'Graveolens'
'Athabasca' (Min)	ESul
§ 'Atomic Snowflake' (Sc/v)	CArn CHal ESul GBar LDea LVER MHer MSte MWhe SKen SPet SSea WFib WJek
'Attar of Roses' (Sc) ♀ H1+3	CArn CBrm CHal CRHN EOHP ESul GBar LDea LRHS LVER MHer MSte MWhe NFir NHHG SIde SKen SSea WFib WGwG WWye

'Attraction' (Z/Ca/d)	SSea WFib
'Aubusson' (R)	WFib
'Audrey' (Z/d)	WFib
'Audrey Baghurst' (I)	CWDa
'Audrey Clifton' (I/d)	SKen WFib
'Augusta'	SAga SMrm
'Aurora' (Z/d)	MWhe SKen
'Aurore' (U)	see *P.* 'Unique Aurore'
australe	CFir CRHN EWoo LPio SSpi WFib
'Australian Bute' (R) **new**	LVER
'Australian Mystery' (R/Dec)	CSpe ESul MSte NFir
'Autumn' (Z/d)	MWhe WFib
'Autumn Colours' (Min)	ESul
'Autumn Festival' (R)	WFib
'Autumn Haze' (R)	WFib
'Autumn Mist' (R)	WFib
'Avril'	ESul
'Aztec' (R) ♀ H1+3	ESul LDea LVER MSte NFir WFib
'Baby Bird's Egg' (Min)	ESul NFir WFib
'Baby Brocade' (Min/d)	ESul WFib
'Baby Face' (Dw)	EWoo
'Baby Helen' (Min)	ESul
'Baby James' (Min)	ESul
'Baby Snooks' (A)	ESul LDea MWhe
'Babylon' (R)	EWoo NFir WFib
'Badley' (Dw)	ESul
Balcon Imperial	see *P.* 'Roi des Balcons Impérial'
'Balcon Lilas'	see *P.* 'Roi des Balcons Lilas'
'Balcon Rose'	see *P.* 'Hederinum'
'Balcon Rouge'	see *P.* 'Roi des Balcons Impérial'
'Balcon Royale'	see *P.* 'Roi des Balcons Impérial'
'Ballerina' (Z/d)	MWhe
'Ballerina' (R)	see *P.* 'Carisbrooke'
'Bandit' (Min)	ESul
'Banstead Village' (Z) **new**	LVER
'Bantam' (Min/d)	ESul WFib
§ 'Barbe Bleu' (I/d)	ECtt EWoo LDea LVER MWhe NFir SKen SSea WFib
'Barham' (Min/d)	ESul
'Barking' (Min)	ESul NFir
'Barnston Dale' (Dw/d)	ESul NFir
'Barock '96'	NPri
'Baron de Layres' (Z/d)	WFib
'Baronne A. de Rothschild' (Z/d)	WFib
'Bath Beauty' (Dw)	SKen WEas
'Baylham' (Min)	ESul
Beach = 'Fisbea' (I/d)	NPri
'Beacon Hill' (Min)	ESul
'Beatrice Cottington' (I/d)	SKen WFib
'Beatrix' (Z/d)	LVER SKen WFib
'Beau Geste' (R)	ESul
'Beauty' (Z)	WFib
'Beauty of Calderdale' (Z/C)	WFib
'Beauty of Diane' (I/d)	LDea
N 'Beauty of Eastbourne'	see *P.* 'Lachskönigin'
'Beauty of El Segundo' (Z/d)	SKen WFib
'Beckwith's Pink' (Z)	EWoo SKen
'Belinda Adams' (Min/d) ♀ H1+3	MWhe NFir WFib
§ Belladonna = 'Fisopa' (I/d)	ECtt NPri SCoo
'Belvedere' (R)	ESul
'Bembridge'	SSea
'Ben Franklin' (Z/d/v) ♀ H1+3	ESul LVER MWhe NFir SPet WFib
'Ben Matt' (R)	LDea WFib
'Ben Nevis' (Dw/d)	ESul LVER
'Bentley' (Dw)	ESul
'Berliner Balkon' (I)	SKen
Bernardo = 'Guiber'PBR (I/d)	LAst

'Beromünster' (Dec)	CSpe ESul EWoo LDea MSte NFir WEas WFib
'Bert Pearce' (R)	EWoo LDea WFib
'Beryl Gibbons' (Z/d)	LVER MWhe
'Beryl Read' (Dw)	ERea ESul
'Beryl Reid' (R)	ESul LDea WFib
'Berylette' (Min/d)	ESul SKen WFib
'Bess' (Z/d)	ESul LVER SKen
'Bette Shellard' (Z/d/v)	LVER MWhe NFir
'Betty' (Z/d)	LVER
'Betty Hulsman' (A)	ESul LDea NFir
'Betty Read' (Dw)	ESul
betulinum	EWoo SSea WFib
'Betwixt' (Z/v)	SKen SSea WFib
'Bewerley Park' (Z/C/d)	WFib
'Bianca' (Min/d)	
'Bi-coloured Startel' (Z/St/d)	MWhe
'Bildeston' (Dw/C)	ESul NFir
'Bill Holdaway' (Z) **new**	LVER
'Billie Read' (Dw/d)	ERea ESul
'Bingo' (Min)	ESul
'Bird Dancer' (Dw/St) ♀ H1+3	CPlt CSpe ESul LVER MSte MWhe NFir SAga SHFr SKen SSea WEas WFib
'Birthday Girl' (R)	WFib
'Bitter Lemon' (Sc)	ESul
'Black Butterfly'	see P. 'Brown's Butterfly'
'Black Country Bugle' (Z/d)	CWDa
'Black Knight' (R)	CElw CMdw CSpe ESul EWoo LDea LVER MSte SAga WFib
'Black Knight' Tea (Dw/d/c)	MSte NFir
'Black Magic' (R)	WFib
'Black Night' (A)	ESul
'Black Pearl' (Z/d)	LVER WFib
'Black Prince' (R)	CElw ESul NFir
'Black Velvet' (R)	LDea
'Black Vesuvius'	see P. 'Red Black Vesuvius'
'Blakesdorf' (Dw)	ESul MWhe
Blanca = 'Penwei'PBR (Z/d)	LAst LVER
Blanche Roche = 'Guitoblanc' (I/d)	EWoo LAst SCoo
§ 'Blandfordianum' (Sc)	EWoo LDea MHer MSte
'Blandfordianum Roseum' (Sc) **new**	LDea
§ 'Blauer Frühling' (I x Z/d)	LVER
'Blaze Away'	SSea
'Blazonry' (Z/v)	MWhe SKen SSea WFib
'Blendworth' (R)	LDea
'Blooming Gem' (Min/I/d)	LDea
'Blue Beard'	see P. 'Barbe Bleu'
'Blue Fox' (Z)	CWDa
'Blue Orchid' (R)	WFib
'Blue Peter' (I/d)	SKen
Blue Spring	see P. 'Blauer Frühling'
'Bluebeard'	see *Pelargonium* 'Barbe Bleu'
Blue-Blizzard = 'Fisrain'PBR (I)	NPri SCoo WWol
§ Blues = 'Fisblu'PBR (Z/d)	CWDa WWol
'Blush Kleine Liebling' (Min)	WFib
'Blush Mariquita' (R)	WFib
'Blush Petit Pierre' (Min)	ESul
'Blushing Bride' (I/d)	LDea SKen
'Blushing Emma' (Dw/d)	ESul WFib
'Bob Legge' (Z/d)	WFib
'Bode's Trina' (I)	CWDa
'Bodey's Picotee' (R) ♀ H1+3	WFib
'Bold Candy' (R)	LDea
'Bold Carmine' (Z/d)	NFir
'Bold Dawn' (Z)	NFir
'Bold Flame' (Z/d)	WFib
'Bold Gypsy' (R)	LDea
'Bold Sunrise' (Z/d)	LVER NFir
'Bold Sunset' (Z/d)	LVER NFir WFib
'Bold White' (Z)	NFir
'Bolero' (U) ♀ H1+3	EWoo LVER MSte NFir NPri SSea WFib
'Bonito' (I/d)	LVER
'Bosham' (R)	ESul LDea WFib
'Both's Snowflake' (Sc/v)	EWoo
'Botley Beauty' (R)	ESul LDea WFib
'Brackenwood' (Dw/d) ♀ H1+3	ESul LVER NFir WFib
'Bramford' (Dw)	ESul
'Braque' (R)	LDea WFib
Bravo = 'Fisbravo'PBR (Z/d)	MWhe WFib
'Break o' Day' (R)	LDea WEas
'Bredon' (R) ♀ H1+3	ESul WFib
'Brenda' (Min/d)	ESul
'Brenda Hyatt' (Dw/d)	ESul WFib
'Brenda Kitson' (Z/d)	LVER MWhe
'Briarlyn Beauty' (A)	LDea MWhe NFir
'Briarlyn Moonglow' (A)	ESul LDea LVER SKen SSea
'Bridesmaid' (Dw/d)	ESul NFir SKen WFib
'Brightwell' (Min/d)	ESul WFib
'Brilliant' (Dec)	MHer WFib
'Brilliantine' (Sc)	EWoo MHer
'Bristol' (Z/v)	SKen SMrm SSea WFib
'Britannia' (R)	LDea
'Brixworth Boquet' (Min/C/d)	MWhe
'Brixworth Charmer' (Z/v)	MWhe
'Brixworth Melody' (Z/v)	MWhe
'Brixworth Pearl' (Z)	MWhe
'Brixworth Rhapsody' (Z/v)	MWhe
'Brixworth Starlight' (I/v)	MWhe
'Broadway' (Min)	WFib
'Brocade' (Z/d)	WFib
'Brockbury Scarlet' (Ca)	WFib
'Bronze Corinne' (Z/C/d)	SKen SPet
'Bronze Nuhulumby' (R)	ESul
'Bronze Queen' (Z/C)	MWhe
'Bronze Velvet' (R)	LDea WFib
'Brook's Purple'	see P. 'Royal Purple'
'Brookside Betty' (Dw/C/d)	ESul
'Brookside Bolero' (Z)	ESul
'Brookside Candy' (Dw/d)	ESul WFib
'Brookside Champagne' (Min/d)	ESul
'Brookside Flamenco' (Min/d)	ESul MWhe WFib
'Brookside Primrose' (Min/C/d)	ESul MWhe NFir WFib
'Brookside Rosita' (Min)	ESul
'Brookside Serenade' (Dw)	ESul WFib
'Brookside Spitfire' (Dw/d)	ESul
§ 'Brown's Butterfly' (R)	LDea NFir SMrm WFib
§ 'Bruni' (Z/d)	CHal MWhe
'Brunswick' (Sc)	ESul EWoo LDea LVER MHer MSte SSea WFib
'Brutus' (Z)	CWDa
'Bucklesham' (Dw)	ESul
'Burgenlandmädel' (Z/d)	LVER SKen WFib
'Burgundy' (R)	LVER WFib
'Burnaby' (R)	WFib
'Bushfire' (R) ♀ H1+3	ESul LDea WFib
'Bute' (Dec) **new**	ESul
'Butley' (Min)	ESul
'Butterfly' (Min/v)	ECtt NPri
§ Butterfly = 'Fisam'PBR (I)	NFir SCoo WFib

'Cal'	see *P.* 'Salmon Irene'
'Caledonia' (Z)	SKen
'Caledonian Maiden' (Z)	WFib
'California Brilliant' (U)	EWoo NFir
'Caligula' (Min/d)	WFib
Calypso = 'Fislypso'^{PBR} (Z)	WFib
'Cameo' (Dw/d)	MWhe WFib
'Camisole' (Dw/d) **new**	LVER
'Camphor Rose' (Sc)	ESul MHer MOak NFir SSea
'Can-can' (I/d)	WFib
candicans	LPio WFib
'Candy' (Min/d)	ESul
'Candy Kisses' (D)	ESul
canescens	see *P.* 'Blandfordianum'
'Capel' (Dw/d)	ESul
'Capella' (Min)	WFib
capitatum	EWoo MHer MOak WFib
'Capri' (Sc)	WFib
'Caprice' (R)	EWoo WFib
'Capricorn' (Min/d)	ESul
'Captain Starlight' (A)	ESul EWoo LDea LVER MHer NFir SKen SSea WEas WFib
'Caravan' (A)	LDea
'Cardinal Pink' (Z/d)	CWDa
'Carefree' (U)	EWoo MSte NFir WFib
'Cariboo Gold' (Min/C) ♀ H1+3	ESul
§ 'Carisbrooke' (R) ♀ H1+3	LDea SKen SSea WEas WFib
'Carmel' (Z)	EWoo WFib
'Carnival' (R)	see *P.* 'Marie Vogel'
'Carnival' (Z)	WFib
'Carol Gibbons' (Z/d)	LVER MWhe NFir
'Carole' (R)	ESul
'Carole Munroe' (Z/d)	LVER
'Caroline Plumridge' (Dw)	ESul
'Caroline Schmidt' (Z/d/v)	CHal ESul LAst LRHS LVER MSte MWhe NFir NWoo SKen SPet SSea SYvo WFib WLow
'Carolyn' (Min)	ESul
'Carousel' (Z/d)	CWDa
Cascade Lilac	see *Pelargonium* 'Roi des Balcons Lilas'
Cascade Pink	see *Pelargonium* 'Hederinum'
Cascade Red	see *Pelargonium* 'Red Cascade'
'Cassata' (R)	WFib
'Catford Belle' (A) ♀ H1+3	CSpe ESul LDea MWhe SKen SSea WFib
'Cathay' (Z/St)	ESul MWhe NFir SSea
'Cathy' (R)	NFir
caucalifolium subsp. *convolvulifolium*	WFib
'Celebration' (Z/d)	ESul
'Celia' (Min)	WFib
'Cézanne' (R)	LDea LVER WFib
§ Champagne (Z)	CWDa
'Chantilly Claret' (R)	LDea
'Chantilly Lace' (R)	ESul LDea
'Charity' (Sc) ♀ H1+3	CBrm ESul EWoo LDea LIck LVER MHer MSte MWhe NFir SSea WFib
'Charlie Boy' (R)	LDea WFib
'Charlotte Amy' (R) **new**	LDea
'Charlotte Bidwell' (Min)	ESul
'Charlotte Read' (Dw)	ERea
'Charm' (Min)	ESul
'Charmant'	CWDa
'Charmay Alf' (A) **new**	LDea
'Charmay Snowflake' (Sc/v)	WFib WHer
'Charmer' (R)	LDea
'Chattisham' (Dw/C)	NFir
'Chelmondiston' (Min/d)	ESul MWhe

§ 'Chelsea Gem' (Z/d/v) ♀ H1+3	LRHS LVER NFir SKen SSea WFib
'Chelsea Morning' (Z/d)	WFib
'Chelsworth' (Min/d)	ESul WFib
'Chelvey' (R)	LDea WFib
'Cherie' (Min)	WFib
'Cherie' (R)	ESul LDea WFib
'Cherie Bidwell' (Dw/d/v)	ESul
'Cherie Maid' (Z/v)	SSea WFib
'Cherry' (Min)	LVER WFib
'Cherry Baby' (Dec)	NFir
'Cherry Cocktail' (Z/d/v)	MWhe NFir
'Cherry Hazel Ruffled' (R)	LDea
'Cherry Orchard' (R)	LDea LVER SKen SSea WFib
'Cherry Sundae' (Z/d/v)	ESul WFib
'Cheryldene' (R)	LDea
'Chew Magna' (R)	WFib
'Chi-Chi' (Min)	ESul
'Chieko' (Min/d)	ESul MWhe WFib
'Chime' (Min/d)	ESul
'China Doll' (Dw/d)	WFib
'Chinz' (R)	CSpe NFir
'Chiquita' (R)	WFib
'Chirocco'	NPri
'Chocolate Drops' (Z) **new**	LVER
§ 'Chocolate Peppermint' (Sc)	CHal CSev ESul GBar LDea LHrt LRHS MHer MWhe NBur NFir NHHG SKen SSea SYvo WEas WFib WHer WJek
'Chocolate Tomentosum'	see *P.* 'Chocolate Peppermint'
'Chrissie' (R)	ESul
'Christina Beere' (R)	LDea
'Christopher Ley' (Z)	LVER SKen
'Cindy' (Dw/d)	ESul
'Circus Day' (R)	LDea WFib
'Citriodorum' (Sc) ♀ H1+3	CArn EOHP LDea LRHS MHer NHHG WFib WPer
'Citronella' (Sc)	CRHN LDea LRHS MHer MSte WFib
citronellum (Sc)	WFib WPer
'Clara Read' (Dw)	ESul
'Claret Cruz' (I)	CWDa
'Claret Rock Unique' (U)	EWoo LDea MHer MSte SKen WFib
'Clarissa' (Min)	ESul
'Clatterbridge' (Dw/d)	ESul LVER NFir WFib
'Claude Read' (Dw)	ERea ESul
'Claudette' (Min)	ESul
'Claudius' (Min)	ESul
'Claydon' (Dw/d)	ESul NFir
'Claydon Firebird' (R)	ESul
'Cleopatra' (Z)	WFib
'Clorinda' (U/Sc)	CHal CRHN ERea ESul EWoo GBar LVER MHer MOak MSte NBur SKen SSea WFib WHer WJek
'Clorinda Variegated'	see *P.* 'Variegated Clorinda'
'Clown' (R)	WFib
'Coconut Ice' (Dw)	ESul
§ Coco-Rico (I)	SKen
'Coddenham' (Dw/d)	WFib
'Colette' (Min)	WFib
§ 'Colonel Baden-Powell' (I/d)	LDea
Comedy = 'Fiscomedy'^{PBR} (I)	NPri WGwG
'Conspicuous' (R)	EWoo WFib
'Constance Spry' (Z) **new**	WEas
'Contrast' (Z/d/C/v)	LRHS MBri MWhe SCoo SKen SPoG SSea WEas WFib
'Cook's Golden Bird's Egg'	EWoo
'Cook's Red Spider' (Ca)	WFib
'Copdock' (Min/d)	ESul
'Copthorne' (U/Sc) ♀ H1+3	CMdw ESul LDea LVER MHer MSte SKen SSea WFib
'Coral Frills' (Min/d)	ESul

'Coral Sunset' (d) — CWDa
cordifolium — EWoo WFib
'Coriand' (Z/d) — WFib
'Cornell' (I/d) — ECtt WFib
'Coronia' (Z/Ca) — CWDa
'Corsair' (Z/d) ♀ H1+3 — MWhe WFib
'Cotta Lilac Queen' (I/d) — LVER
'Cottenham Beauty' (A) — EWoo LDea NFir
'Cottenham Charm' (A) — ESul
'Cottenham Delight' (A) — ESul LDea NFir
'Cottenham Gem' (A) — ESul
'Cottenham Harmony' (A) **new** — ESul
'Cottenham Surprise' (A) — ESul LDea MSte MWhe NFir
'Cottenham Treasure' (A) **new** — ESul
'Cotton Candy' (Dw/d) — ESul
'Cottontail' (Min/d) — ESul LVER
cotyledonis — WFib
'Countess Mariza' — see *P.* 'Gräfin Mariza'
'Countess of Scarborough' — see *P.* 'Lady Scarborough'
'Country Girl' (R) — SPet WFib
'Cover Girl' (Z/d) — WFib
'Cramdon Red' (Dw) — SKen WFib
'Crampel's Master' (Z) — LVER SKen
'Cranbrook Black' — EWoo
'Cranbrooks Unique' — EWoo
'Cransley Blends' (R) — ESul LDea WFib
'Cransley Star' (A) — LDea MWhe WFib
'Cream 'n' Green' (R/v) — NFir
'Creamery' (d) — WFib
§ 'Creamy Nutmeg' (Sc/v) — CArn CHal EOHP ESul GBar LDea LHrt LRHS LVER MHer MWhe NBur NFir SRob SSea
'Creeting St Mary' (Min) — ESul
'Creeting St Peter' (Min) — ESul
'Crescendo' (I/d) — ECtt
'Crimson Crampel' (Z) — CWDa
'Crimson Fire' (Z/d) — MBri MWhe SKen
'Crimson Unique' (U) ♀ H1+3 — CRHN CSpe EWoo MHer SAga SKen SSea WFib
§ *crispum* (Sc) — GBar GPoy LDea LHrt LPhx MOak NHHG WFib WJek WRha
 - 'Golden Well Sweep' (Sc/v) — NFir WFib
 - 'Major' (Sc) — ESul LRHS SKen WFib
 - 'Minor' (Sc) — MHer
 - 'Peach Cream' (Sc/v) — CHal ESul LRHS MWhe WFib WJek
 - 'Variegatum' (Sc/v) ♀ H1+3 — CHal CRHN CSev GBar GPoy LDea LRHS LVER MHer MOak MWhe NFir SPet SRob SSea WEas WFib
crithmifolium — MHer
'Crock O Day' (I/d) — LVER
'Crocketta' (I/d/v) — LVER NFir SSea
'Crocodile' (I/C/d) — ECtt EShb LDea LVER MWhe NFir SKen SSea SYvo WEas WFib
'Crowfield' (Min/d) — ESul LVER
'Crown Jewels' (R) — LDea
'Crystal Palace Gem' (Z/v) — LAst LRHS LVER MWhe SKen SMrm SSea WFib
cucullatum — ESul EWoo MHer SSea SVen WFib
'Culpho' (Min/C/d) — ESul
'Cupid' (Min/Dw/d) — ESul WFib
'Cyril Read' (Dw) — ERea ESul
§ 'Czar' (Z/C) — WFib
'Dainty Lassie' (Dw/v) — ESul
'Dainty Maid' (Sc) — ESul EWoo LVER NFir SSea SYvo
'Dale Queen' (Z) — WFib
'Dame Anna Neagle' (Dw/d) ♀ H1+3 — WFib

'Dancer' (Dw) — ESul
'Danielle Marie' (A) — LDea
'Dark Ascot' (Dec) **new** — ESul
'Dark Island' (Z) **new** — LVER
'Dark Lady' (Sc) — WFib
'Dark Red Blizzard' (I) **new** — NPri WWol
'Dark Red Irene' (Z/d) — LVER MWhe SKen WFib
'Dark Secret' (R) — CSpe ESul EWoo LDea MSte SKen WFib
'Dark Venus' (R) — LDea WFib
'Darmsden' (A) ♀ H1+3 — ESul LDea NFir
'David John' (Dw/d) — ESul
'Davina' (Min/d) — ESul MWhe WFib
'Dawn Star' (Z/St) — ESul NFir WFib
'Deacon Arlon' (Dw/d) — ESul LVER MWhe SKen
'Deacon Avalon' (Dw/d) — WFib
'Deacon Barbecue' (Z/d) — ESul MWhe SKen
'Deacon Birthday' (Z/d) — ESul LVER MWhe WFib
'Deacon Bonanza' (Z/d) — ESul MWhe SKen WFib
'Deacon Clarion' (Z/d) — ESul SKen
'Deacon Constancy' (Z/d) — ESul LVER MWhe
'Deacon Coral Reef' (Z/d) — ESul MWhe SKen WFib
'Deacon Delight' — EWoo
'Deacon Finale' (Z/d) — ESul LVER
'Deacon Finito' — see *P.* 'Finito'
'Deacon Fireball' (Z/d) — ESul LVER MWhe SKen WFib
'Deacon Flamingo' (Z/d) — ESul MWhe
'Deacon Gala' (Z/d) — ESul MWhe
'Deacon Golden Bonanza' (Z/C/d) — ESul WFib
'Deacon Golden Gala' (Z/C/d) — ESul SKen
'Deacon Golden Lilac Mist' (Z/d) — ESul SKen WFib
'Deacon Golden Mist' — see *P.* 'Golden Mist'
'Deacon Jubilant' (Z/d) — ESul MWhe SKen
'Deacon Lilac Mist' (Z/d) — ESul LVER MWhe SKen WFib
'Deacon Mandarin' (Z/d) — ESul MWhe SKen
'Deacon Minuet' (Z/d) — ESul LVER MWhe NFir SKen
'Deacon Moonlight' (Z/d) — ESul LVER MWhe
'Deacon Peacock' (Z/C/d) — ESul MWhe SKen
'Deacon Picotee' (Z/d) — ESul MWhe SKen
'Deacon Regalia' (Z/d) — ESul MWhe SKen WFib
'Deacon Romance' (Z/d) — ESul LVER MWhe SKen WFib
§ 'Deacon Summertime' (Z/d) — ESul LVER MWhe
'Deacon Sunburst' (Z/d) — ESul LVER MWhe SKen
'Deacon Suntan' (Z/d) — ESul LVER MWhe SKen WFib
'Deacon Trousseau' (Z/d) — ESul MWhe WFib
'Dean's Delight' (Sc) — LDea MOak
'Debbie Parmer' (Dw/d) — ESul
'Debbie Thrower' (Dw) — ESul
'Decora Impérial' (I) — LAst LVER
'Decora Lavender' — see *Pelargonium* 'Decora Lilas'
§ 'Decora Lilas' (I) — ECtt LAst LVER SPet
'Decora Mauve' — see *P.* 'Decora Lilas'
§ 'Decora Rose' (I) — CWDa ECtt LAst SPet
'Decora Rouge' (I) — ECtt SPet
'Deerwood Don Quixote' (A) — MWhe
'Deerwood Lavender Lad' (Sc) — ESul EWoo LDea MHer WFib
'Deerwood Lavender Lass' — LDea
'Degas' (R) — WFib
'Delhi' (R) — NPer WFib
'Delightful' (R) — WFib
'Delilah' (R) — LDea
'Delta' (Min/d) — ESul
'Denebola' (Min/d) — ESul LVER WFib
denticulatum — EWoo GBar MHer NHHG SKen SSea WFib WJek
§ - 'Filicifolium' (Sc) — CHal EWoo MHer NHHG SSea WFib WJek
'Destiny' (R) — WFib

'Diadem' (R) WFib
'Diana Palmer' (Z/d) SKen WFib
'Diane' (Min/d) ESul WFib
'Dibbinsdale' (Z) ESul NFir
dichondrifolium (Sc) EWoo LVER MHer NCiC NFir WFib
- x *reniforme* (Sc) NFir
'Diddi-Di' (Min/d) ESul
'Didi' (Min) ESul SKen WFib
'Dinky' (Min/d) ESul
§ Disco = 'Fisdis' (Z/d) CWDa
'Distinction' (Z) CSpe ESul MOak MWhe NFir
SAga SKen SSea WFib
'Doctor A. Chipault' (I/d) LDea WFib
'Doctor A. Vialettes' (Z/d) CWDa
'Doctor Margaret Sturgis' WFib
(Z/d)
'Dodd's Super Double' CHal SMrm
(Z/d)
'Dolce Vita' WWol
'Dollar Bute' (R) ESul LDea NFir
'Dollar Princess' (Z/C) SKen
'Dolly Read' (Dw) ERea ESul WFib
'Dolly Varden' (Z/v) ESul LDea LVER MWhe NFir SKen
♀ H1+3 SPet SSea WFib
dolomiticum WFib
'Dolphin' (Min) WFib
'Don Quixote' (A) EWoo LDea
'Don's Barbra Leonard' NFir
(Dw/B)
'Don's Helen Bainbridge' NFir
(Z/C)
'Don's Jubilee' (Dw/C) NFir
'Don's Mona Noble' NFir SKen
(Z/C/v)
'Don's Richard A. Costain' NFir
(Z/C)
'Don's Seagold' NFir
'Don's Shiela Jane' NFir
(Z/C/d) **new**
'Don's Silva Perle' (Dw/v) SKen
'Don's Southport' (Z/v) NFir
'Don's Stokesley NFir
Gem' (Z/C)
'Don's Swanland ESul
Girl' (Min)
'Don's Whirlygig' (Z/C) NFir
'Dorcas Brigham Lime' (Sc) EWoo
'Doreen' (Z/d) LVER
'Doreen Featherby' (R) WFib
'Doris Brook' (Z/d) WFib
'Doris Frith' (R) LDea WFib
'Doris Hancock' (R) WFib
'Doris Shaw' (R) WFib
'Dorothy May' (A) LDea
'Double Bird's Egg' (Z/d) CWDa SKen
'Double Grace Wells' ESul
(Min/d)
'Double Lilac White' (I/d) SKen
'Double New Life' (Z/d) CHal CWDa
'Double Orange' (Z/d) SKen
'Dove' (Z) WFib
'Dovedale' (Dw/C) ESul NFir
'Dragon's Breath' LVER
(Z/St) **new**
'Dream' (Z) CWDa WFib
'Dresden China' (R) EWoo LDea
'Dresden Pippa Rosa' (Z) SKen
Dresdner Coralit = LVER
'Coralit'PBR (I/d)
Dresdner Purpalit (I) LVER
Dresdner Rosalit = LVER
'Rosalit'PBR (I/d)
'Drummer Boy' (Z) CWDa SKen

'Dryden' (Z) SKen WFib
'Dubonnet' (R) LDea SYvo WFib
'Duke of Buckingham' LVER
(Z/d)
'Duke of Devonshire' (Z/d) LVER
'Duke of Edinburgh' see *P.* 'Hederinum Variegatum'
'Dulcie' (Min) ESul
'Dunkery Beacon' (R) WFib
'Dusty Rose' (Min) ESul WFib
§ 'Dwarf Miriam Baisey' LVER WFib
(Min)
'Dwarf Miriam Read' see *P.* 'Dwarf Miriam Baisey'
'E. Dabner' (Z/d) CWDa SKen WFib
'Earl of Chester' (Min/d) WFib
♀ H1+3
'Earliana' (Dec) ESul LDea SKen
'Earlsfour' (R) LDea MSte
'Eastbourne Beauty' (I/d) WFib
'Easter Morn' (Z/St) SSea WFib
echinatum EWoo MHer SAga
- 'Miss Stapleton' see *P.* 'Miss Stapleton'
'Eclipse' (I/d) MWhe SKen WFib
'Eden Gem' (Min/d) WFib
'Edith Steane' (Dw/d) ESul LVER
'Edmond Lachenal' (Z/d) WFib
'Edna' (Z/d) WFib
'Edward Hockey' (Z) WFib
'Edward Humphris' (Z) EWoo SKen
'Eileen' (I/d) LVER WFib
'Eileen' (Min/d) ESul NFir
'Eileen Postle' (R) ♀ H1+3 WFib
'Eileen Stanley' (R) LDea
'Elaine' (R) LDea
Elbe Silver = 'Pensil'PBR (I) NFir SCoo
'Electra' (Z/d) CWDa LVER SKen WFib
'Elfin Rapture' (R) WFib
'Elgar' (R) WFib
'Elizabeth Angus' (Z) SKen WFib
'Elizabeth Cartwright' (Z) WFib
'Elizabeth Read' (Dw) ERea ESul WFib
'Elmsett' (Dw/C/d) ESul LVER NFir
'Elna' (Min) ESul
'Els' (Min/St) ESul LVER SKen
'Elsi' (I x Z/d/v) LVER WFib
'Elsie Hickman' (R) LDea WFib
'Elsie Portas' (Z/C/d) ESul SKen
'Embassy' (Min) ESul WFib
'Emerald' (I) SKen
'Emilia Joy' (A) MHer
'Emma Bannister' (R) ESul
'Emma Hössle' see *P.* 'Frau Emma Hössle'
'Emma Jane Read' (Dw/d) ERea ESul MWhe NFir WFib
'Emma Louise' (Z) SKen
'Emmy Sensation' (R) LDea
'Emperor Nicholas' (Z/d) MWhe SKen
'Empress' (Z) SKen
'Ena' (Min) ESul
'Enchantress' (I) SKen
'Encore' (Z/d/v) LRHS LVER MWhe NFir
endlicherianum EPot NBhm NWCA SIgm WCot
'Endsleigh' (Sc) MHer
'Enid Blackaby' (R) WFib
'Enid Read' (Dw) ERea WFib
'Eric Ellis' (Z/d) WFib
'Eric Hoskins' (Z/d) WFib
* 'Eric Lee' CWDa
'Erwarton' (Min/d) ESul LVER NFir
'Escapade' (Min/d) ESul WFib
'Esteem' (Z/d) WFib
'Etna' (Min) WFib
'Evelyn' ESul
'Evesham Wonder' (Z/d) WFib
'Evka'PBR (I/v) LAst LVER NFir SCoo SSea

'Explosive' (I) — NPri

exstipulatum — EWoo WEas WFib

'Fair Dinkum' (Z/v) — ESul MWhe NFir

§ 'Fair Ellen' (Sc) — EWoo LDea MHer SKen WFib WPer

'Fairy Lights' (Dw/St) — ESul NFir

'Fairy Orchid' (A) — ESul LDea LVER SSea

'Fairy Princess' (R) — LDea

'Fairy Queen' — LDea MHer

'Fairy Tales' (Min) — WFib

'Falkland Brother' (Z/C/v) — WFib

'Falkland Hero' (Z/v) — LVER NFir WFib

'Fandango' (Z/St) — ESul MWhe NFir WFib

* 'Fanfare' — CWDa

'Fanny Eden' (R) — WFib

'Fantasia' white (Dw/d) — ESul MWhe WFib
  ♀ H1+3

'Fareham' (R) ♀ H1+3 — LDea MSte WFib

'Fascination' (Z/Ca) — WFib

'Feneela' (Dw/d) — ESul

'Fenton Farm' (Dw/C) — ESul NFir

'Festal' (Min/d) — ESul

'Feuerriese' (Z) — LVER SKen

'Fiat' (Z/d) — CWDa SKen

'Fiat Queen' (Z/d) — SKen WFib

'Fiat Supreme' (Z/d) — SKen WFib

'Fiery Sunrise' (R) — ESul EWoo LDea

'Fiesta' (R) — WFib

'Fiesta' (I/d) — LDea

'Fifth Avenue' (R) — CSpe EWoo MSte WFib

'Filename' (Min) **new** — ESul

'Filicifolium' — see *P. denticulatum* 'Filicifolium'

§ 'Finito' (Dw/d) — ERea

'Fir Trees Audrey B' — NFir
  (St) **new**

'Fir Trees Echoes of — EWoo NFir
  Pink' (A)

'Fir Trees Eileen' (St) **new** — NFir

'Fir Trees Flamingo' — NFir
  (Dw) **new**

'Fir Trees Jack' — NFir
  (Z/Dw) **new**

'Fir Trees Roseberry — NFir
  Topping' (Dw)

'Fir Trees Ruby — NFir
  Wedding' **new**

'Fir Trees Silver Wedding' — NFir
  (Z/C/d) **new**

'Fir Trees Sparkler' **new** — NFir

'Fire Dragon' (Z/St/d) — SKen SSea

'Fire Light' (Min/d) — WFib

'Firebrand' (Z/d) — LVER

'Firefly' (Min/d) — ESul WFib

'Firestone' (Dw) — ESul

'First Blush' (R) — WFib

'First Love' (Z) — LVER NFir

'Flair' (R) — WFib

'Flakey' (I/d/v) ♀ H1+3 — CSpe ESul LDea NFir SKen WFib

'Flame' (Z) — WFib

'Flarepath' (Z/C/v) — NFir

'Flesh Pink' (Z/d) — CWDa

'Fleur d'Amour' (R) — WFib

'Fleurette' (Min/d) — CHal ESul MWhe SKen SPet WFib

§ Flirt (Min) — ESul WFib

'Floral Cascade' (Fr/d) — WFib

'Florence Storey' (Z/C/d) — WFib

'Floria Moore' (Dec) — ESul EWoo NFir

'Flower Basket' (R/d) — LDea NFir

'Flower of Spring' (Z/v) — CHal LVER MWhe SKen SPet SSea
  ♀ H1+3 — SYvo WFib

'Flowerfield' (Z) — WFib

'Flowton' (Dw/d) — ESul

* 'Forever' (d) — CWDa

'Fox' (Z/d) — CHal

'Foxhall' (Dw) — ESul

Fragrans Group (Sc) — CHal CRHN CSev ESul EWoo GBar
  GPoy LRHS MHer MWhe NHHG
  SKen SPet WFib WHer WPer WWye

 – 'Creamy Nutmeg' — see *P.* 'Creamy Nutmeg'

§ – 'Fragrans Variegatum' — CSev ESul LIck MWhe NFir SKen
  (Sc/v) — WEas WFib WJek

 – 'Snowy Nutmeg' — see *P.* (Fragrans Group) 'Fragrans
  Variegatum'

'Fraiche Beauté' (Z/d) — CWDa WFib

'Francis James' (Z) — EWoo WFib

'Francis Parmenter' — SSea
  (MinI/v)

'Francis Parrett' (Min/d) — ESul LVER MWhe SKen WFib
  ♀ H1+3

'Francis Read' (Dw/d) — ERea ESul SPet

'Frank Headley' (Z/v) — CHal CSpe ESul LRHS LVER MSte
  ♀ H1+3 — MWhe NPer NVic SCoo SKen
  SMrm SPet SSea WEas WFib

'Frank Parrett' (Min/d) — ESul

§ 'Frau Emma Hössle' — ESul MWhe WFib
  (Dw/d)

'Frau Käthe Neubronner' — CWDa
  (Z/d)

'Freak of Nature' (Z/v) — ESul MWhe NFir SKen SSea WFib

'Freckles' (Z/d) — WFib

'Frensham' (Sc) — ESul EWoo MHer SSea WFib

'Freshfields Suki' (Dw) **new** — NFir

'Freshwater' (St/C) — ESul MWhe

'Freston' (Dw) — ESul

'Friary Wood' (Z/C/d) — ESul NFir WFib

'Friesdorf' (Dw/Fr) — ESul LVER MHer MWhe NFir
  SKen WEas WFib

'Frills' (Min/d) — ESul MWhe NFir WFib

'Fringed Angel' (A) — CFee LDea

'Fringed Apple' (Sc) — LDea NBur

§ 'Fringed Aztec' (R) ♀ H1+3 — ESul LDea LVER NFir SPet WFib

'Fringed Jer'Ray' (A) **new** — LDea

'Fringed Rouletta' (I) — LDea

'Frosty' misapplied — see *P.* 'Variegated Kleine Liebling'

'Frosty Petit Pierre' — see *P.* 'Variegated Kleine Liebling'

'Frühlingszauber Lila' (R) — ESul

frutetorum — MHer

fruticosum — EWoo LPio WFib

'Fuji' (R) — NFir

fulgidum — EWoo MHer WFib

'Funny Girl' (R) — WFib

'Fynn' (Dw) — ESul

'Gabriel' (A) — ESul EWoo LDea LVER

'Galilee' (I/d) ♀ H1+3 — LDea LVER SKen WFib

'Galway Star' (Sc/v) — MHer SKen WFib
  ♀ H1+3

'Garibaldi' (Z/d) — CWDa WFib

'Garland' (R) — ESul

'Garland' (Dw/d) — LVER

'Garnet' (Min) — NFir

'Garnet' (Z/d) — ESul LVER WFib

'Garnet Rosebud' (Min/d) — ESul LVER

'Garnet Wings' (R) — WFib

'Gartendirektor Herman' — EWoo NFir WFib
  (Dec)

'Gary Salvidge' (R) — LDea

'Gay Baby' (DwI) — ESul LDea MWhe

'Gay Baby Supreme' (DwI) — ESul

§ 'Gemini' (Z/St/d) — ESul MWhe NFir SSea WFib

'Gemma' (R) — NFir SAga

'Gemma' (Min/C) — WFib

'Gemma Finito' (R) — LDea

'Gemma Jewel' (R) ♀ H1+3 — ESul

'Gemma Rose' (R) — LDea

'Gemma Sweetheart' (R) — LDea

'Gemstone' (Sc) ♀ H1+3 — CBrm EWoo LDea MHer NFir WFib

'Genetrix' (Z/d) — WFib

'Genie' (Z/d) — LVER MWhe SKen WFib
'Gentle Georgia' (R) — WFib
'Geoff May' (Min) — ESul WFib
'Geoffrey Harvey' (Z/d) — WFib
'Geoffrey Horsman' (R) — WFib
'Georgia' (R) — WFib
'Georgia Peach' (R) — ESul WFib
'Georgie' (R) — LDea
'Georgina Blythe' (R) — WFib
   ♀ H1+3
'Geo's Pink' (Z/v) — MWhe
'Gerald Portas' (Dw/C) — ESul
'Gerald Wells' (Min) — ESul
'Geraldine' (Min) — ESul LVER
'Geronimo' (R) — WFib
'Gess Portas' (Z/v) — ESul
'Ghost Storey' (Z/C) — NFir
'Giant Butterfly' (R) — LDea
'Giant Oak' (Sc) — MHer MSte WFib
gibbosum — EWoo MHer WFib
'Gilbert West' (Z) — SKen
'Gilda' (R/v) — LDea NFir
'Gill' (Min/Ca) — ESul
'Ginger Rogers' (Z) — NFir
'Glacier Crimson' (Z) — SKen
'Gladys Evelyn' (Z/d) — WFib
'Gladys Stevens' (Min/d) — ESul
'Gleam' (Z/d) — LVER
'Glenn Barker' (Z/d) — WFib
'Glenshree' (R) — WFib
'Gloria Pearce' (R) — LDea WFib
'Glory' (Z/d) — WFib
'Glowing Embers' (R) — LDea LVER WFib
§ *glutinosum* — MHer
'Goblin' (Min/d) — ESul SKen WFib
'Godshill' (R) — LDea
'Gold Star' (Z/St/C) — ESul
'Golden Baby' (Dwl/C) — LDea MWhe NFir
'Golden Brilliantissium' — ESul LRHS LVER MWhe SKen SSea
   (Z/v) — WFib
'Golden Butterfly' (Z/C) — ESul
'Golden Chalice' (Min/v) — ESul LVER MWhe NFir
'Golden Clorinda' (U/Sc/C) — CRHN EWoo LDea MHer NFir WEas
'Golden Crest' (Z/C) — SKen SMrm
'Golden Ears' (Dw/St/C) — ESul MWhe NFir NPer WFib
'Golden Everaarts' (Dw/C) — ESul
'Golden Fleece' (Min/C/d) — ESul
'Golden Gates' (Z/C) — ESul SKen
'Golden Harry Hieover' — ESul MBri MHer
   (Z/C) ♀ H1+3
'Golden Little Darling' — LVER
   (Min/v) **new**
'Golden Mirage' (Z/v) — WFib
§ 'Golden Mist' (Dw/C/d) — LVER
'Golden Petit Pierre' — ESul
   (Min/C)
'Golden Princess' (Min/C) — WFib
'Golden Princess' (R) — LVER
'Golden Roc' (Min/C) — ESul
'Golden Ruth' (Z) — WFib
'Golden Staphs' (Z/St/C) — ESul LVER NFir SSea WFib
'Golden Starburst' — ESul
   (Dw/St/C) **new**
'Golden Stardust' (Z/St) — LVER
'Golden Wedding' (Z/d/v) — LRHS LVER MWhe NFir
'Golden Well Sweep' — see *P. crispum* 'Golden Well Sweep'
'Goldie' (R) — WFib
'Goldilocks' (A) — ESul LDea WFib
'Gooseberry Leaf' — see *P. grossularioides*
'Gordano Midnight' (R) — EWoo LDea WFib
'Gosbeck' (A) — LDea SSea
'Gossamer Carnival' — NFir
   (Z/d) **new**

'Gothenburg' — ESul
'Grace' (A) — LDea
'Grace Thomas' (Sc) — EWoo LDea MHer WFib
   ♀ H1+3
'Grace Wells' (Min) — ESul WFib
'Gracious Lady' (Z/d) — WFib
§ 'Gräfin Mariza' (Z/d) — SKen WFib
'Grand Duchess' (R) — LDea
'Grand Slam' (R) — ESul LDea LVER NFir WFib
'Grandad Mac' (Dw/St) — ESul NFir
grandiflorum — WFib
'Grandma Fischer' — see *P.* 'Grossmutter Fischer'
'Grandma Ross' (R) — ESul LDea
'Granny Hewitt' (Min/d) — ESul
graveolens — EWoo
§ 'Graveolens' (Sc) — CHal ESul GBar GPoy LRHS LVER
    — MHer MWhe SSea WFib WGwG WJek
'Great Blakenham' (Min) — ESul
'Great Bricett' (Min/d) — ESul LVER
'Green Ears' (Z/St) — ESul WFib
'Green Eyes' (I/d) — SKen
'Green Goddess' (I/d) — LDea SKen
'Green Gold Petit Pierre' — ESul
   (Min)
'Green Lady' (Sc) — WFib
'Green Woodpecker' (R) — LDea LVER SSea
§ 'Greengold Kleine — ESul SKen
   Liebling' (Min/C/v)
'Greengold Petit Pierre' — see *P.* 'Greengold Kleine Liebling'
'Greetings' (Min/v) — ESul LVER MBri WFib
§ 'Grenadier' (Z) — CWDa
'Grey Lady Plymouth' — ESul EWoo LDea MHer NFir WFib
   (Sc/v)
'Grey Sprite' (Min/v) — ESul WFib
griseum — WFib
* 'Groombridge Success' (d) — CWDa
§ 'Grossmutter Fischer' (R) — LDea WFib
§ *grossularioides* — EOHP ESul IFro MHer
'Grozser Garten' (Dw) — ESul
'Grozser Garten Weiss' (Dw) — ESul
'Guardsman' (Dw) — ESul
Guido = 'Kleugudo' (Z/d) — LAst LRHS
'Gustav Emich' (Z/d) — SKen WFib
'Gwen' (Min/v) — MWhe NFir
'H. Rigler' (Z) — SKen
'Hadleigh' (Dw) — ESul
'Hamble Lass' (R) — LDea
'Hänchen Anders' (Z/d) — WFib
§ 'Hannaford Star' (Z/St) — ESul NFir WFib
'Hannah' (A) — ESul
'Hans Rigler' (Z/d) — WFib
'Hansen's Pinkie' (R) — LDea
'Happy Appleblossom' — LVER NFir SKen
   (Z/v/d)
'Happy Birthday' (Z/T) **new** LVER
§ 'Happy Thought' (Z/v) — CHal ESul LAst LVER MBri MOak
   ♀ H1+3 — MWhe NFir NVic SCoo SKen SSea
'Happy Valley' (R) — ESul LVER WFib
'Harbour Lights' (R) — LDea WFib
'Harewood Slam' (R) — ESul EWoo LDea MSte WFib
'Harkstead' (Min) — ESul
'Harlequin' (Dw) — ESul
'Harlequin Alpine Glow' — LVER MWhe WFib
   (I/d)
'Harlequin Candy Floss' — CWDa
   (I/d)
'Harlequin Liverbird' (I) — WFib
'Harlequin Mahogany' (I/d) — LDea LVER MWhe SKen WFib
§ 'Harlequin Miss Liver — SKen
   Bird' (I)
'Harlequin Picotee' (I/d) — LDea LVER SKen
'Harlequin Pretty Girl' — LVER MWhe WFib
   (I x Z/d)

'Harlequin Rosie O'Day' (I)   LDea MWhe SKen WFib
'Harlequin Ted Day' (I/d)   LDea LVER
'Harmony' (R)   LVER
'Harold Bowie' (Z/d)   WFib
'Harriet Le Hair' (Z)   SKen
'Harvard' (I/d)   LVER WFib
'Harvey' (Z)   MWhe
'Hayley Charlotte' (Z/v)   MWhe
'Hay's Radiant' (Z/d)   WFib
'Hazel' (R)   LVER WFib
'Hazel Anson' (R)   LDea
'Hazel Barolo' (R)   LDea
'Hazel Birkby' (R)   ESul LDea WFib
'Hazel Blake' (R)   WFib
'Hazel Burtoff' (R)   ESul LDea WFib
'Hazel Carey' (R)   LDea
'Hazel Cerise' (R)   LDea
'Hazel Cherry' (R)   LDea MSte WFib
'Hazel Choice' (R)   ESul LDea NFir WFib
'Hazel Dean' (R)   NFir
'Hazel Glory' (R)   LDea WFib
'Hazel Gowland' (R)   LDea
'Hazel Gypsy' (R)   ESul LDea WFib
'Hazel Harmony' (R)   LDea
'Hazel Henderson' (R)   LDea
'Hazel Herald' (R)   ESul LDea
'Hazel Perfection' (R)   LDea NFir
'Hazel Rose' (R)   LDea
'Hazel Saga' (R)   ESul WFib
'Hazel Satin' (R)   LDea
'Hazel Shiraz' (R)   LDea
'Hazel Star' (R)   ESul
'Hazel Stardust' (R)   NFir
'Hazel Wright' (R)   LDea
§ 'Hederinum' (I)   SKen WFib
§ 'Hederinum Variegatum'   CHal SPet WFib
   (I/v)
'Heidi' (Min/d)   ESul
* 'Helen Bowie'   CWDa
'Helen Christine' (Z/St)   ESul MWhe NFir WFib
'Helena' (I/d)   LDea MWhe SKen WFib
'Hemingstone' (A)   LDea
'Hemley' (Sc)   LDea
'Henhurst Gleam' (Dw/d)   ESul WFib
'Henry Weller' (A) **new**   ESul NFir
'Hermione' (Z/d)   CHal MWhe WFib
'High Tor' (Dw/C/d)   SKen WFib
'Highfields Appleblossom'   LVER NFir SKen
   (Z)
'Highfields Attracta' (Z/d)   LVER SKen
'Highfields Ballerina' (Z/d)   LVER WFib
'Highfields Candy Floss'   LVER NFir
   (Z/d)
'Highfields Charisma' (Z/d)   LVER
'Highfields Choice' (Z)   LVER SKen
'Highfields Comet' (Z)   SKen
'Highfields Contessa' (Z/d)   LVER SKen WFib
'Highfields Dazzler' (Z)   LVER
'Highfields Delight' (Z)   LVER
'Highfields Fancy' (Z/d)   LVER NFir SKen
'Highfields Festival' (Z/d)   LVER MWhe NFir SKen
'Highfields Flair' (Z/d)   LVER
'Highfields Orange' (Z)   LVER MWhe
'Highfields Paramount' (Z)   SKen
'Highfields Perfecta' (Z)   CWDa
'Highfields Pride' (Z)   LVER SKen
'Highfields Prima Donna'   LVER MWhe SKen WFib
   (Z/d)
'Highfields Promise' (Z)   SKen
'Highfields Serenade' (Z)   LVER
'Highfields Snowdrift' (Z)   LVER SKen
'Highfields Sugar Candy'   SKen WFib
   (Z/d)

'Highfields Supreme' (Z)   LVER
'Highfields Symphony' (Z)   LVER WFib
'Highfields Vogue' (Z)   LVER
'Hilbre Island' (Z/C/d) **new**   NFir
'Hildegard' (Z/d)   CHal SKen WFib
'Hills of Snow' (Z/v)   CHal LVER MBri MHer SKen SSea
   WFib
'Hillscheider Amethyst'   see *P.* Amethyst = 'Fisdel'
'Hindoo' (RxU)   EWoo LVER NFir SSea WFib
'Hintlesham' (Min)   ESul
hispidum   MHer
'Hitcham' (Min/d)   ESul WFib
'Holbrook' (Dw/C/d)   ESul NFir
'Holmes C. Miller' (Z/d)   ESul
'Honeywood Hannah' (R)   WFib
'Honeywood Jonathan' (R)   WFib
'Honeywood Lindy' (R)   ESul
'Honeywood Margaret' (R)   ESul
'Honeywood Matthew'   ESul
   (Dw)
'Honeywood Suzanne'   ESul LVER NFir SKen WFib
   (Min/Fr)
'Honne Frühling' (Z)   SKen WFib
'Honneas' (Min)   ESul
'Honnestolz' (Min)   ESul SKen
'Hope Valley' (Dw/C/d)   ESul LVER MWhe NFir SKen
   ♀ H1+3
'Horace Parsons' (R)   WFib
'Horace Read' (Dw)   ERea ESul
'Horning Ferry' (Dw)   ESul
'House and Garden' (R)   NFir WFib
'Howard Stanton' (R)   WFib
'Howard's Orange' (R)   LDea
'Hugo de Vries' (Dw/d)   CWDa WFib
'Hula' (U x R)   EWoo MHer WFib
'Hulda Conn' (Z/Ca/d)   WFib
'Hunter's Moon' (Z/C)   ESul NFir
'Hurdy-gurdy' (Z/d/v)   ESul MWhe WFib
'Ian Read' (Min/d)   ERea ESul SPet WFib
'Icecrystal'PBR (Z/d)   CWDa
'Icing Sugar' (I/d)   ESul LDea SSea WFib
* 'Ilse Fisher'   CWDa
immaculatum (Z)   WFib
'Imperial Butterfly' (A/Sc)   ESul LDea LVER MSte MWhe NFir
   SKen WFib
'Improved Petit Pierre'   ESul
   (Min)
'Improved Ricard' (Z/d)   WFib
'Inca' (R)   WFib
incrassatum   NBur
inquinans   WFib
ionidiflorum   CSpe EShb EWoo MHer SAga
'Ipswich Town' (Dw/d)   ESul
'Irene' (Z/d) ♀ H1+3   SKen WFib
'Irene Cal' (Z/d) ♀ H1+3   SKen
'Irene Collet' (R)   LDea
* 'Iris Monroe'   CWDa
§ 'Isabell' (Z/d)   LAst WFib
'Isidel' (I/d) ♀ H1+3   SKen WFib
I 'Islington Peppermint' (Sc)   EWoo LVER SSea
'Italian Gem' (I)   SKen
'Ivalo' (Z/d)   MWhe SKen WFib
'Ivory Snow' (Z/d/v)   ESul EWoo LVER MWhe NFir
'Jacey' (Z/d)   LVER SKen
'Jack Read' (Dw)   ERea
'Jack Wood' (Z/d)   NFir
§ 'Jackie' (I/d)   EWoo LVER MBri SKen WFib
'Jackie Davies' (R)   LDea
'Jackie Gall'   see *P.* 'Jackie'
'Jackie's Gem' (I/d)   MWhe
'Jacko' (I/d)   EWoo
'Jacqueline' (Z/d)   SKen
'Jane Biggin' (Dw/C/d)   ESul MWhe SKen SPet

'Janet Dean' (R) — LDea
'Janet Hofman' (Z/d) — WFib
'Janet Kerrigan' (Min/d) — ESul MWhe WEas WFib
'Janet Scott' (Z) — CWDa
'Jasmin' (R) — ESul LDea SKen
'Jaunty' (Min/d) — ESul WFib
'Jayne' (Min/d) — ESul
'Jayne Eyre' (Min/d) — CHal ESul MWhe NFir SKen WFib
§ 'Jazz' — CWDa
'Jean Bart' (I) — CWDa LVER
'Jean Beatty' (Dw/d) — LVER
'Jean Oberle' (Z/d) — SKen WFib
'Jeanetta' (R) — LDea
§ 'Jeanne d'Arc' (I/d) — SKen WFib
'Jenifer Read' (Dw) — ERea ESul
'Jennifer' (Min) — ESul
'Jer'Ray' (A) — ESul LDea MHer
'Jessel's Unique' (U) — LDea LRHS MHer MSte SPet SSea
'Jetfire' (d) — CWDa
'Jewel' (R) — ESul
'Jeweltone' (Z/d) — WFib
'Jim Field' (R) — WFib
'Jimmy Read' (Min) — ERea
'Jinny Reeves' (R) — ESul LDea WFib
'Joan Cashmore' (Z/d) — ESul WFib
'Joan Fairman' (R) — WFib
'Joan Fontaine' (Z) — WFib
'Joan Hayward' (Min) — ESul
'Joan Morf' (R) — ESul EWoo LDea LVER NFir SKen SSea WFib
'Joan of Arc' — see P. 'Jeanne d'Arc'
'Joan Sharman' (Min) — ESul
'Joanna Pearce' (R) — ESul LDea SKen
'John Thorp' (R) — LDea
'John's Angela' — LVER
'John's Pride' — MBri NFir
'Joseph Haydn' (R) — ESul
'Joseph Haydon' (R) — LDea MSte
'Joseph Wheeler' (A) — ESul LDea MWhe
'Joy' (R) ♀ H1+3 — ESul LDea LRHS LVER NFir WFib
'Joy' (I) — SPet
Joy = 'Fiseye'PBR (Z/d) — CSpe SKen
'Joy Lucille' (Sc) — CSev ESul EWoo LDea MHer WFib
'Joyce Delamere' (Z/C/d) — WFib
'Joyden' — CWDa
'Joyful' (Min) — ESul
'Jubel Parr' (Z/d) — CWDa
'Judy Read' (Dw) — ESul
'Julia' (R) ♀ H1+3 — ESul LDea
'Juliana' (R) — LDea
'Julie' (A) — ESul
'Julie Bannister' (R) — ESul
'Julie Smith' (R) — LDea WFib
'Jungle Night' (R) — ESul WFib
'Juniper' (Sc) — MHer WFib
'Jupiter' (Min/d) — SKen WFib
'Jupiter' (R) — ESul NFir
'Just Rita' (A) — SSea
'Just William' (Min/C/d) — ESul
'Kamahl' (R) — WFib
'Karl Hagele' (Z/d) — LVER SKen SYvo WFib
'Karmin Ball' — CWDa WFib
karrooense Knuth — MHer
'Kath Peat' (Z/d) — WFib
'Kathryn' (Min) — ESul
'Kathryn Portas' (Z/v) — ESul SKen
'Katie' (R) — EWoo
'Kayleigh West' (Min) — ESul
'Keepsake' (Dw/d) — ESul LVER WFib
'Keith Vernon' (Z) — NFir
'Kelvedon Beauty' (Min) — WEas
'Ken Salmon' (Dw/d) — ESul
'Kennard Castle' (Z) — CWDa

'Kenny's Double' (Z/d) — WFib
'Kensington' (A) — LDea
'Kerensa' (Min/d) — ESul SKen
'Kesgrave' (Min/d) — ESul LVER
'Kettle Baston' (A) ♀ H1+3 — ESul LDea WFib
'Kimono' (R) — ESul EWoo LDea NFir
'Kinder Gaisha' (R) — NFir
'King Edmund' (R) — LDea WFib
'King of Balcon' — see P. 'Hederinum'
'King of Denmark' (Z/d) — LVER SKen WFib
'King Solomon' (R) new — LDea
'King's Ransom' (R) — LDea
'Kirton' (Min/d) — ESul
§ 'Kleine Liebling' (Min) — ESul MWhe WFib
'Kosset' (Min/d) — LVER
'Krista' (Min/d) — ESul WFib
'Kyoto' (R) — NFir
'Kyra' (Min/d) — ESul WFib
'L.E. Wharton' (Z) — SKen
'La France' (I/d) ♀ H1+3 — LDea LVER MWhe SKen WFib
'La Paloma' (R) — WFib
'Laced Mini Rose Cascade' (I) — NFir
Laced Red Mini Cascade = 'Achspen' (I) — NFir
Lachsball (Z/d) — SKen
§ 'Lachskönigin' (I/d) — LVER SKen SPet WFib
'Lady Alice of Valencia' — see P. 'Grenadier' (Z)
'Lady Cullum' (Z/C/v) — MWhe
'Lady Ilchester' (Z/d) — SKen WFib
'Lady Love Song' (R) — ESul LVER NFir
'Lady Mary' (Sc) — ESul EWoo LVER MHer WFib
'Lady Plymouth' (Sc/v) ♀ H1+3 — CHal CRHN CSpe ESul GBar LDea LHrt LRHS LVER MHFa MHer MOak MSte MWhe NFir NHHG SKen SMrm SPet SSea SYvo WEas WFib WHer WWye
§ 'Lady Scarborough' (Sc) — EWoo LDea MHer WFib
'Lady Woods' (Z) new — SSea
'Lakeland' (I) — ESul
'Lakis' (R) — LDea
Lambada = 'Fiofetti' (I/d) — NPri
'Lamorna' (R) — LDea SKen WFib
'Lancastrian' (Z/d) — WFib
'Land of Song' (A) new — NFir
'Langley' (R) — LDea
'Lanham Lane' (I) — LDea MWhe
'Lanham Royal' (Dw/d) — ESul
'Lara Aladin' (A) — LDea WFib
'Lara Candy Dancer' (Sc) ♀ H1+3 — CRHN EOHP ESul LDea MHer MOak WFib
'Lara Jester' (Sc) — EWoo MHer WFib
'Lara Maid' (A) ♀ H1+3 — MWhe WEas WFib
'Lara Nomad' (Sc) — EWoo LDea
'Lara Starshine' (Sc) ♀ H1+3 — ESul EWoo MHer NFir SSea WFib
'Lara Susan' new — EWoo NFir
'Lark' (Min/d) — ESul
'Larkfield' (Z/v) — SSea
N 'Lass o' Gowrie' (Z/v) — ESul LRHS LVER MSte MWhe NFir SKen WFib
'Lass o' Gowrie' (American) (Z/v) — SMrm WFib
'Laura Parmer' (Dw/St) — ESul
'Laura Wheeler' (A) — ESul LDea MWhe
'Laurel Hayward' (R) — WFib
'Lavender Grand Slam' (R) ♀ H1+3 — ESul LDea LVER NFir WFib
'Lavender Harewood Slam' (R) — ESul LDea
'Lavender Mini Cascade'PBR — see P. Lilac Mini Cascade = 'Lilamica'

'Lavender Sensation' (R)	WFib	
'Lavender Wings' (I)	LDea	
'Layham' (Dw/d)	ESul	
'Layton's White' (Z/d)	CWDa	
'Le Lutin' (Z/d)	CWDa WFib	
'L'Elégante' (I/v) ♀ H1+3	CHal EWoo LAst LDea LVER	
	MWhe NFir SKen SSea WEas WFib	
	WGwG WLRN	
'Lemon Air' (Sc)	ESul	
'Lemon Crisp'	see *P. crispum*	
'Lemon Fancy' (Sc)	EWoo LDea LVER MHer MWhe	
	NFir WFib WJek	
'Len Chandler' (Min)	ESul	
'Lenore' (Min/d)	ESul	
'Leo' (Min)	ESul	
'Leonie Holbrow' (Min)	ESul	
'Leopard' (I/d)	CWDa	
'Leslie Judd' (R)	WFib	
'Leslie Salmon' (Min/C)	ESul MWhe	
§ 'Leucht-Cascade'	WFib	
'Levington' (Min/d)	WFib	
Lila Compakt-Cascade	see *P.* 'Decora Lilas'	
Lilac Cascade	see *P.* 'Roi des Balcons Lilas'	
'Lilac Domino'	see *P.* 'Telston's Prima'	
'Lilac Elaine' (R)	LDea	
'Lilac Gem' (Min/I/d)	LDea LVER MWhe NFir WFib	
'Lilac Jewel' (R)	ESul	
§ Lilac Mini Cascade =	ESul LDea LVER NFir	
'Lilamica'PBR (I)		
'Lili Marlene' (I)	LVER SPet	
'Lilian' (Dw)	ESul	
'Lilian Pottinger' (Sc)	CArn CHal CRHN ESul GBar LDea	
	MHer MWhe NFir SKen SSea	
	WEas WFib	
'Lilo Cascade'	MOak	
'Limelight' (Z/v)	SSea	
'Limoncum' (Sc)	CScv LDca LRHS MIIcr NBur	
	SKen WFib	
'Linda' (R)	ESul LDea WFib	
'Linda' (Z/d)	WFib	
'Lindscy' (Min)	ESul	
'Lindy Portas' (I/d)	SKen	
'Lisa' (Min/C)	ESul WFib	
'Little Alice' (Dw/d)	ESul MWhe NFir WFib	
♀ H1+3		
'Little Blakenham' (A)	ESul LDea	
'Little Fi-fine' (Dw/C)	ESul NFir WFib	
'Little Gem' (Sc)	EWoo LDea LVER MHer SSea	
	WFib	
'Little Jip' (Z/d/v)	LVER NFir	
'Little John' (Min/d)	WFib	
'Little Margaret' (Min/v)	ESul	
'Little Perky' (MinI)	ESul	
'Little Primular' (Min)	ESul	
'Lively Lady' (Dw/C)	ESul	
'Liverbird'	see *P.* 'Harlequin Miss Liver Bird'	
'Lolette' (Min)	ESul	
'Lollipop' (Z/d)	WFib	
'Longshot' (R)	WFib	
'Lord Baden-Powell'	see *P.* 'Colonel Baden-Powell'	
'Lord Bute' (R) ♀ H1+3	CElw CSpe ESul EWoo LDea LIck	
	LRHS LVER MHer MSte NCiC NFir	
	NPer SKen SMer SMrm SPet SUsu	
	WEas WFib	
'Lord Constantine' (R)	LDea	
'Lord de Ramsey'	see *P.* 'Tip Top Duet'	
'Lord Roberts' (Z)	WFib	
'Lorelei' (Z/d)	CWDa WFib	
'Loretta' (Dw)	ESul	
'Lorna' (Dw/d)	ESul	
'Lotusland' (Dw/St/C) **new**	LVER NFir	
'Louise' (Min)	ESul	
'Love Song' (R/v)	ESul LDea LVER NFir SSea	

'Love Story' (Z/v)	ESul	
* 'Loverly' (Min/d)	ESul	
'Lowood' (R)	WFib	
'Lucilla' (Min)	ESul	
'Lucinda' (Min)	ESul	
'Lucy' (Min)	ESul	
'Lucy Gunnett' (Z/d/v)	ESul MWhe NFir WFib	
'Lucy Jane' (R)	LDea	
'Lulu' (I/d)	NPri	
Luna = 'Fisuna' (I/d)	NPri	
'Lustre' (R)	ESul WFib	
'Luz del Dio' (R)	WFib	
'Lyewood Bonanza' (R)	ESul LDea LVER	
'Lynne Valerie' (A)	LDea	
'Lyric' (Min/d)	ESul LVER WFib	
'Mabel Grey' (Sc) ♀ H1+3	CHal CRHN CSev CSpe ESul	
	EWoo LIck LRHS LVER MHer	
	MSte MWhe NBur NFir NHHG	
	SKen WEas WFib WGwG WJek	
§ 'Madame Auguste	CHal ESul EWoo LVER MHer	
	NFir	
Nonin' (U/Sc)	NWoo SKen WFib	
'Madame Butterfly' (Z/d/v)	ESul MWhe NFir SKen	
'Madame Crousse' (I/d)	WFib	
♀ H1+3		
'Madame Dubarry' (Z)	WFib	
'Madame Fournier' (Min/C)	ESul	
'Madame Hibbault' (Z)	SKen	
'Madame Layal' (A)	ESul EWoo LDea LIck MSte NFir	
	SAga SKen WFib	
'Madame Margot'	see *P.* 'Hederinum Variegatum'	
'Madame Recamier' (Z/d)	WFib	
'Madame Salleron'	LDea LRHS LVER MHer MSte	
(Min/v) ♀ H1+3	SKen SPet	
'Madame Thibaut' (R)	LDea MSte WFib	
'Madge Taylor' (R)	NFir	
'Magaluf' (I/C/d)	SSea WFib	
'Magda' (Z/d)	ESul LVER WFib	
'Magic Lantern' (Z/C)	NFir	
'Magic Moments' (R)	WFib	
'Magnum' (R)	WFib	
'Maid of Honour' (Min)	ESul	
'Maiden Sunrise' **new**	WGor	
'Mairi' (A)	LDea WFib	
'Maja' (R)	WFib	
'Maloya' (Z)	SKen WFib	
'Mamie' (Z/d)	SKen	
'Mandarin' (Z)	ESul	
'Mangles' Variegated' (Z/v)	SPet SSea	
'Mantilla' (Min)	ESul SKen	
'Manx Maid' (A)	ESul LDea NFir SKen WFib	
'Maple Leaf' (Sc)	EWoo	
'Marble Sunset'	see *P.* 'Wood's Surprise'	
'Marchioness of Bute' (R)	CSpe EMan ESul LDea MSte NFir	
	NPer WFib	
'Maréchal MacMahon' (Z/C)	SKen SPet WFib	
'Margaret Parmenter' (I/C)	ESul	
'Margaret Pearce' (R)	LDea	
'Margaret Salvidge' (R)	LDea WFib	
'Margaret Soley' (R) ♀ H1+3	EWoo LDea	
'Margaret Stimpson' (R)	LDca	
'Margaret Thorp'	LVER	
'Margaret Waite' (R)	WFib	
'Margery Stimpson' (Min/d)	ESul LVER WFib	
'Maria Wilkes' (Z/d)	WFib	
'Marie Rober' (R)	SKen WFib	
'Marie Thomas' (Sc)	LDea MHer SSea	
§ 'Maric Vogel' (R)	MSte WFib	
'Marilyn' (Dw/d)	ESul	
Marimba = 'Fisrimba'PBR	NPri SCoo	
'Marion' (Min)	ESul	
'Marion Bannister' (R)	ESul WFib	
'Mariquita' (R)	WFib	

'Marja' (R)   LDea
'Marktbeherrscher' (Z/d)   WFib
'Marmalade' (Min/d)   ESul MWhe WFib
'Marquis of Bute' (R/v) **new**   LVER
'Martha Parmer' (Min)   ESul
'Martin Parrett' (Min/d)   WFib
'Martin's Splendour' (Min)   ESul
'Martlesham'   ESul
'Mary Read' (Min)   ERea ESul
'Mary Rose' (R)   LDea
'Mary Spink' (Z/C/d)   LVER
'Mary Webster' (Min)   ESul
'Masquerade' (R)   ESul SPet
'Master Paul' (Z/v)   ESul
'Masterpiece' (Z/C/d)   ESul SKen
'Matthew Salvidge' (R)   ESul WFib
'Maureen' (Min)   NFir
'Mauve Beauty' (I/d)   SKen WFib
'Maxime Kovalevski' (Z)   WFib
'Maxine' (Z/C)   NFir
'Maxine Colley' (Z/d/v)   LVER
'May Day' (R)   LDea
'May Magic' (R)   NFir WFib
'May Rushbrook' (Z)   NFir
'Mayor of Seville' (Z/d)   WFib
'Maytime' (Z/d)   WFib
I   'Meadowside Dark and   NFir
        Dainty' (St)
'Meadowside Fancy'   LVER
        (Z/d/C)
'Meadowside Harvest'   ESul NFir
        (Z/St/C)
'Meadowside Julie   NFir
        Colley' (Dw) **new**
I   'Meadowside Mahogany'   LVER
        (Z/C)
'Meadowside Mardi Gras'   NFir
        (Dw/d) **new**
'Meadowside Midnight'   MHer MWhe SHFr
        (St/C)
'Meadowside Orange' (Z/d)   LVER
'Medallion' (Z/C)   MHer SSea WFib
'Meditation' (Dw)   ESul
'Medley' (Min/d)   LVER MWhe WFib
'Melanie' (R)   ESul LDea WFib
*   'Melissa' (Min)   ESul
'Melva Bird' (Z/d)   WFib
'Memento' (Min/d)   ESul SKen WFib
'Memories' (Z/d)   WFib
'Mendip' (R)   WFib
'Meon Maid' (R)   ESul LDea WFib
'Mere Caribbean' (R)   NFir
'Mere Casino' (Z)   LVER
'Mere Cocktail' (R)   WFib
'Mere Flamenco' (R)   WFib
'Mere Greeting' (Z/d)   MWhe
'Mere Iced Cocktail' (R)   WFib
'Mere Meteor' (R)   WFib
'Mere Sunglow' (R)   LDea WFib
'Merle Seville' (Z/d)   SKen
'Merry-go-round' (Z/C/v)   LVER MWhe WFib
'Mexica Tom' **new**   LAst WGor
'Mexically Rose' (R)   WFib
'Mexican Beauty' (I)   CHal MWhe WFib
'Mexicanerin'   see *P.* 'Rouletta'
'Michael' (A)   LDea
'Michelle' (Min/C)   LDea WFib
'Michelle West' (Min)   ESul
'Midas Touch' (Dw/C/d)   ESul
'Milden' (Z/C)   ESul NFir
'Milkmaid' (Min)   WFib
'Millbern Choice' (Z)   MWhe
'Millbern Clover' (Min/d)   ESul MWhe

'Millbern Engagement'   MWhe
        (Min/d)
'Millbern Peach' (Z)   MWhe
'Millbern Serenade'   MWhe
'Millbern Sharna' (Min/d)   ESul MWhe
'Millbern Skye' (A) **new**   MWhe
Millennium Dawn (Dw)   LVER
'Miller's Valentine' (Z/v)   ESul LVER WFib
'Millfield Gem' (I/d)   LVER SKen WFib
'Millfield Rival' (Z)   WFib
'Millfield Rose' (I/d)   LVER MWhe
'Millie' (Z/d)   CWDa WFib
'Mimi' (Min/C/d)   ESul SSea
'Minah's Cascade'   LVER
        (Z/d) **new**
'Mini-Czech' (Min/St)   ESul
'Minnie' (Z/d/St)   LVER
'Minstrel Boy' (R)   ESul LDea NFir WFib
'Minuet' (Z/d)   WFib
'Minx' (Min/d)   WFib
*   'Mirage'   CWDa
'Miranda' (Dw)   ESul
'Miriam Basey'   see *P.* 'Dwarf Miriam Baisey'
'Miss Australia' (R/v)   LDea WFib
'Miss Burdett Coutts' (Z/v)   ESul LVER MWhe SKen SPet SSea
        WFib
'Miss Flora' (I)   CWDa MWhe
'Miss Liverbird' (I/d)   ECtt
'Miss McKinsey' (Z/St/d)   NFir
§   'Miss Stapleton'   MHer
'Miss Wackles' (Min/d)   ESul WFib
'Mistress' (Z/C)   NFir
'Misty' (Z)   ESul
'Modesty' (Z/d)   SKen WFib
'Mohawk' (R)   ESul EWoo NFir WFib
Molina = 'Fismoli'[PBR] (I/d)   NPri
'Mollie' (R)   CSpe WFib
'Molly' (A)   NFir
'Mona Lisa'[PBR]   ESul
'Monarch' (Dw/v)   ESul
'Monica Bennett' (Dw)   ESul SKen WEas
'Monks Eleigh'   ESul
'Monkwood Charm' (R)   LDea
'Monkwood Rose' (A)   LDea NFir
'Monkwood Sprite' (R)   LDea
'Monsal Dale' (Dw/C/d)   ESul SKen
'Monsieur Ninon' hort.   see *P.* 'Madame Auguste Nonin'
§   'Monsieur Ninon' (U)   CRHN EWoo MSte WFib
'Mont Blanc' (Z/v)   ESul LVER MWhe SKen WFib
'Moon Maiden' (A)   ESul WFib
'Moonflight' (R)   WFib
'Moor' (Min/d)   ESul
'Moppet' (Min/d)   ESul
'Morello'[PBR] (R)   WFib
'More's Victory' (U/Sc)   SSea
'Morf's Red' (R)   WFib
'Morning Cloud' (Min/d)   ESul
'Morning Star' (Z/St)   WFib
'Morse' (Z) **new**   SKen
'Morval' (Dw/C/d) ♀[H1+3]   ESul LVER MWhe SKen WFib
'Morwenna' (R)   CMdw ESul EWoo LDea LVER
        MSte NFir SKen WFib
'Mosaic Silky' (Z/C/d/v)   LVER
'Mountie' (Dw)   ESul
'Mr Everaarts' (Dw/d)   ESul MWhe WFib
'Mr Henry Apps' (Dw/C/d)   MWhe
'Mr Henry Cox' (Z/v)   ESul LVER MHer MWhe NFir
        ♀[H1+3]   SKen WFib
'Mr Wren' (Z)   CHal LVER MWhe SKen SPet WFib
'Mrs A.M. Mayne' (Z)   SKen
'Mrs Cannell' (Z)   SKen
'Mrs Dumbrill' (A)   ESul LDea LIck SKen
'Mrs E. G. Hill' (Z)   CWDa

'Mrs Farren' (Z/v) — MWhe SKen SSea WFib
'Mrs G.H. Smith' (A) — ESul EWoo LDea MSte MWhe NFir WFib
'Mrs G. Morf' (R) — SSea WFib
'Mrs J.C. Mappin' (Z/v) ♀ H1+3 — EWoo SAga SKen SSea
'Mrs Kingsbury' (U) — EWoo WEas WFib
'Mrs Langtry' (R) — LDea
'Mrs Lawrence' (Z/d) — SKen WFib
'Mrs Margaret Thorp' (R) — WFib
'Mrs Martin' (I/d) — WFib
'Mrs Mary Bard' (R) — WFib
'Mrs McKenzie' (Z/St) — WFib
'Mrs Morf' (R) — LDea NFir
'Mrs Parker' (Z/d/v) — ESul LRHS LVER MWhe NFir SKen SPet WFib
'Mrs Pat' (Min/St/C) — ESul MWhe NFir
'Mrs Pollock' (Z/v) — LAst LRHS LVER MWhe NVic SCoo SKen SPet SSea WFib
'Mrs Quilter' (Z/C) ♀ H1+3 — MBri MHer MWhe NVic SAga SKen SMrm SSea WFib
'Mrs Salter Bevis' (Z/Ca/d) — ESul LVER WFib
'Mrs Strang' (Z/d/v) — MWhe SKen SSea
'Mrs Tarrant' (Z/d) — CHal WFib
'Mrs W.A.R. Clifton' (I/d) — LDea SKen WFib
'Music Man' (R) — WFib
'Müttertag' (R) — ESul LDea MSte
§ 'Mutzel' (I/v) — LVER NFir
'My Chance' **new** — NFir
'My Choice' (R) — LDea
'Mystery' (U) ♀ H1+3 — EWoo LVER NFir SAga SSea WFib
'Nacton' (Min) — ESul MHer
'Nadine' (Dw/d) — ESul
'Nancy Grey' (Min) — ESul NFir
'Nancy Hiden' (R) — WFib
'Naomi' (R) — LDea
'Narina' (I) — NPri SCoo
'Natalie' (Dw) — ESul
'Naughton' (Min) — ESul
'Navajo' (R) — WFib
'Needham Market' (A) — ESul LDea MSte
'Neene' (Dw) — ESul
'Neil Clemenson' (Sc) — EWoo WFib
'Neil Jameson' (Z/v) — LVER SKen
'Nell Smith' (Z/d) — WFib
'Nellie' (R) — LDea
'Nellie Nuttall' (Z) — WFib
'Nels Pierson' (I) — WFib
'Neon Fiat' (Z/d) — WFib
'Nervosum' (Sc) — ESul MOak
'Nervous Mabel' (Sc) ♀ H1+3 — ESul EWoo LDea MHer NFir WFib
'Nettlecombe' (Min/St) — ESul
'Nettlestead' (I) — ESul
'Nettlestead' (Dw/d) — LVER WFib
'Neville West' (Z) — SSea
'New Day' (A) **new** — LDea
'New Life' (Z) — ESul MWhe NFir
'New Phlox' (Z) — WFib
'Nicola Buck' (R) — LDea
'Nicor Star' (Min) — ESul WFib
'Nikki' (A) — LDea
'Nimrod' (R) — LDea
'Noblesse' **new** — WWol
'Noche' (R) — LDea SKen SMrm WFib
'Noel' (Z/Ca/d) — LVER WFib
'Noele Gordon' (Z/d) — LVER WFib
'Nomad' (R) — NFir
'Nomad's Sweetheart' (A) **new** — LVER
'Nono' (I) — WFib
* 'Norvic' (d) — CWDa
'Notting Hill Beauty' (Z) — SKen

'Obergärtner Held' (Z/d) — WFib
'Occold Embers' (Dw/C/d) — ESul NFir WFib
'Occold Lagoon' (Dw/d) — ESul
'Occold Orange Tip' (Min/d) — ESul
'Occold Profusion' (Dw/d) — ESul NFir
'Occold Ruby' (Dw/C) — CWDa
'Occold Shield' (Dw/C/d) — LAst LRHS NFir WFib WLow
'Occold Surprise' (Min/d) — ESul
'Occold Tangerine' (Dw) — ESul
* 'Odessy' (Min) — WFib
odoratissimum (Sc) — CHal ESul GBar GPoy LDea LRHS LVER MHer NFir NHHG SKen WFib WJek
'Offton' (Dw) — ESul
'Old Orchard' (A) — LDea SSea
'Old Rose' (Z/d) — WFib
'Old Spice' (Sc/v) — ESul GBar MHer NFir WFib
'Oldbury Cascade' (I/v) — EWoo
'Oldbury Duet' (A/v) **new** — LDea NFir
'Olga Shipstone' (Sc) — EWoo
'Olivia' (R) — ESul
'Olympia' (Z/d) — CWDa WFib
'Onnalee' (Dw) — ESul
'Opera House' (R) — WFib
'Orange Fizz' (Sc) **new** — ESul
'Orange Fizz' (Z/d) — LDea
'Orange Imp' (Dw/d) — ESul
'Orange Parfait' (R) — WFib
'Orange Puff' (Min) — WFib
'Orange Ricard' (Z/d) — MWhe SKen WFib
'Orange River' (Min/d) — ESul SKen WFib
'Orange Ruffy' (Min) — ESul
'Orange Splash' (Z) — LVER SKen
'Orangeade' (Dw/d) — ESul LVER SKen WFib
'Orangesonne' (Z/d) — LVER WFib
'Orchid Paloma' (Dw/d) — ESul SKen
'Oregon Hostess' (Dw) — ESul
'Orion' (Min/d) — ESul MWhe SKen WFib
'Orsett' (Sc) ♀ H1+3 — EWoo LDea LVER
'Oscar' (Z/d) — CWDa
'Osna' (Z) — LAst SKen
'Otto's Red' (R) — NFir
'Our Gynette' (R) **new** — NFir
ovale subsp. *ovale* — WFib
'Oyster' (Dw) — ESul
PAC cultivars — see under cultivar name
'Paddie' (Min) — ESul
'Pagoda' (Z/St/d) — CSpe ESul LVER MSte MWhe SKen WFib
'Paisley Red' (Z/d) — NFir WFib
'Palais' (Z/d) — LRHS SKen
'Pam Craigie' (R) — LDea
'Pamela Underwood' (R) — WFib
'Pampered Lady' (A) — LDea
panduriforme — EWoo MHer WFib
papilionaceum — CHEx CRHN CTbh EWoo MHer MOak WEas
'Parasol' (R) — WFib
'Parisienne' (R) — ESul LDea
'Parmenter Pink' (Min) — ESul
'Party Dress' (Z/d) — MWhe SKen WFib
'Pascal' (Z) — SKen
'Pat Thorpe' (R) — WFib
'Patience' (Z/d) — WFib
'Paton's Unique' (U/Sc) ♀ H1+3 — CHal CRHN CTbh EWoo LIck LVER MHer MSte NFir SSea WEas WFib WOld
* 'Patricia' (I) — CWDa
'Patricia Andrea' (T) — LVER NFir NPer
'Patricia Read' (Min) — ERea ESul
'Patsy 'Q'' (Z/C) — SKen
'Paul Crampel' (Z) — CHal LVER MHer WFib
'Paul Gotz' (Z) — SKen

'Paul Gunnett' (Min) — MWhe
'Paul Humphries' (Z/d) — WFib
'Paul Sloan' (Z) — WFib
'Paul West' (Min/d) — ESul
'Paula Scott' (R) — EWoo LDea
'Pauline' (Min/d) — ESul MWhe WFib
'Pax' (R) — LDea WFib
'Peace' (Min/C) — ESul WFib
'Peace Palace' (Dw) — ESul
'Peach Princess' (R) — ESul LVER NFir
'Pearl Brocade' (R) — WFib
'Pearly Queen' (Min/d) — ESul
'Peggy Sue' (R) — ESul LDea LVER
PELFI cultivars — see under cultivar name
peltatum — WFib
 - 'Lateripes' — SKen
'Penny' (Z/d) — MWhe SKen WFib
'Penny Dixon' **new** — NFir
'Penny Serenade' (Dw/C) — ESul SKen
'Pensby' (Dw) — ESul NFir
'Peppermint Lace' (Sc) — EWoo LDea
'Peppermint Star' (Z/St) — ESul
'Perchance' (R) — SSea
'Perfect' (Z) — SKen
* 'Perle Blanche' (I) — CWDa
§ Perlenkette Orange = — LAst
   'Orangepen'PBR (Z/d)
'Perlenkette Sabine' — LAst
   (Z/d) **new**
'Persian King' (R) — LDea
'Persimmon' (Z/St) — WFib
'Petals' (Z/v) — MSte SKen
'Peter Godwin' (R) — ESul LDea WFib
'Peter Grieve' (Z/v) — SSea WFib
'Peter Read' (Dw/d) — ERea ESul
'Peter's Choice' (R) — ESul LDea
'Peter's Luck' (Sc) ♀ H1+3 — ESul
'Petit Pierre' — see P. 'Kleine Liebling'
'Petite Blanche' (Dw/d) — WFib
'Petronella' (Z/d) — ESul
'Phil Rose' (I) — CWDa MWhe
'Philomel' (I/d) — SPet
'Phlox New Life' (Z) — ESul
'Phyllis' (Z) **new** — LDea
'Phyllis' (U/v) — ESul EWoo LVER MHer NFir SSea
'Phyllis Mary' (R) — WFib
'Phyllis Read' (Min) — ERea ESul WFib
'Phyllis Richardson' (R/d) — LDea LVER WFib
'Phyllis Variegated' (v) — LHop
'Picardy' (Z/d) — SKen
'Picotee Kleiner Leibling' — LVER
   (Min) **new**
'Pin Mill' (Min/d) — ESul
'Pink Aura' — ESul
'Pink Aurore' (U) — MHer MSte
'Pink Black Vesuvius' — WFib
   (Min/C)
'Pink Boar' — EWoo
'Pink Bonanza' (R) — ESul LDea WFib
'Pink Bouquet' (R) — ESul WFib
'Pink Capitatum' — see P. 'Pink Capricorn'
§ 'Pink Capricorn' (Sc) — CRHN EWoo MHer WFib
'Pink Carnation' (I/d) — LDea
'Pink Cascade' — see P. 'Hederinum'
'Pink Champagne' (Sc) — CRHN ESul MHer WFib
'Pink Cloud' (Z/d) — WFib
'Pink Countess Mariza' (Z) — SKen
'Pink Crampel' (Z) — CWDa
'Pink Dolly Varden' (Z/v) — SSea
'Pink Flamingo' (R) — LDea
'Pink Fondant' (Min/d) — ESul
'Pink Gay Baby' — see P. 'Sugar Baby'
'Pink Golden Ears' — ESul

(Dw/St/C)
'Pink Golden Harry — ESul
   Hieover' (Z/C)
'Pink Happy Thought' — LRHS LVER SPet SSea WFib
   (Z/v)
'Pink Ice' (Min/d) — ESul LVER NFir
'Pink Margaret Pearce' (R) — WFib
'Pink Mini Cascade' — see P. 'Rosa Mini-cascade'
'Pink Needles' — ESul
   (Min/St) **new**
'Pink Paradox' **new** — MOak
'Pink Pearl' (Z/d) — WFib
'Pink Rambler' (Z/d) — MWhe SKen WFib
'Pink Raspail' (Z/d) — WFib
'Pink Rosebud' (Z/d) — SKen WFib
'Pink Snow' (Min/d) — ESul
'Pink Splash' (Min/d) — ESul
'Pink Star' (Z/St) — WFib
'Pink Tiny Tim' (Min) — ESul WFib
Pink-Blizzard = — NPri WWol
   'Fispink'PBR (I)
'Pinocchio' (R) — WFib
'Pixie' (Min) — ESul
'Pixie Rose' (Z/St/d) — WFib
'Playmate' (Min/St) — ESul SKen WFib
'Plenty' (Z/d) — CWDa WFib
'Plum Rambler' (Z/d) — SKen WFib
'Poetesse' (A) — LDea MWhe
'Polka' (U) — ESul EWoo LVER MHer NFir SAga
   SSea WFib
'Pom Pom' (Z/d) — WFib
'Pompeii' (R) — ESul EWoo LDea NFir WFib
'Porchfield' (Min/St) — ESul
'Potpourri' (Min) — SKen
'Potter Heigham' (Dw) — ESul
'Powder Puff' (Dw/d) — ESul
'Prairie Dawn' (Z/d) — WFib
'Presto' (Min) — ESul MWhe
'Preston Park' (Z/C) — SKen SPet WFib
'Pretty Girl' (I) — LDea
'Pretty Polly' (Sc) — LDea MHer WFib
'Pride of Exmouth' — CStu
'Prim' (Min/St/d) — ESul
'Primavera' (R) — LDea
'Prince' (R) **new** — SKen
'Prince Consort' (R) — LDea LVER
'Prince of Orange' (Sc) — CArn CRHN CSev EOHP ESul
   EWoo GBar GPoy LDea LIck LRHS
   LVER MHer MOak MSte MWhe
   NFir NHHG WFib
'Prince of Wales' (Z) — WFib
'Princeanum' (Sc) ♀ H1+3 — EWoo MHer WFib
'Princess Alexandra' (R) — LVER SSea
'Princess Alexandra' — MWhe NFir WFib
   (Z/d/v)
'Princess Anne' (Z) — MSte
'Princess Josephine' (R) — LDea WFib
'Princess of Balcon' — see P. 'Roi des Balcons Lilas'
'Princess of Wales' (R) — ESul WFib
'Princess Virginia' (R/v) — LDea LIck WFib
'Professor Eckman' (R) — WFib
'Promenade' (Z/d) — WFib
'Prospect' (Z/d) — MWhe
pseudoglutinosum — EWoo WFib
'Purple Ball' — see P. Purpurball
'Purple Emperor' (R) — ESul LDea WFib
'Purple Heart' (Dw/St/C) — ESul NFir SSea
'Purple Muttertag' (R) — ESul
'Purple Orchard' (R) — LDea
'Purple Pride' (I/d) — CWDa
'Purple Rambler' (Z/d) — MWhe
'Purple Unique' (U/Sc) — EWoo LDea MHer MOak MSte
   NFir SKen WFib

§	'Purpurball' (Z/d)	LAst SKen
	'Pygmalion' (Z/d/v)	SSea WFib
	'Quakeress' (R)	WFib
	'Quantock' (R)	WFib
	'Quantock Beauty' (A)	LDea MWhe NFir
	'Quantock Blonde' (A) **new**	LDea
	'Quantock Kirsty' (A)	LDea
	'Quantock Marjorie' (A)	NFir
	'Quantock Matty' (A)	ESul EWoo LDea MWhe NFir
	'Quantock May' (A)	LDea NFir
	'Quantock Medoc' (A) **new**	LDea
	'Quantock Millennium' (A)	LDea NFir
	'Quantock Philip' (A) **new**	NFir
	'Quantock Plume' (A) **new**	NFir
	'Quantock Rory' (A)	LDea
	'Quantock Rose' (A)	EWoo LDea NFir
	'Quantock Sapphire' (A)	LDea
	'Quantock Sarah' (A) **new**	NFir
	'Quantock Shirley' (A) **new**	NFir
	'Quantock Star' (A)	LDea NFir
	'Quantock Ultimate' (A) **new**	NFir
	'Queen of Denmark' (Z/d)	LVER SKen WFib
	'Queen of Hearts' (I x Z/d)	LVER WFib
I	'Queen of the Lemons'	EWoo
N	*quercifolium* (Sc)	CHal CRHN CSev EWoo GPoy MHer NFir NHHG SKen SSea SYvo WFib WGwG WJek WWye
	- 'Fair Ellen'	see *P.* 'Fair Ellen'
	- variegated (v)	MHer
	quinquelobatum	CSpe
	'R.A.Turner' (Z/d)	WFib
	'Rachel' (Min)	ESul
	'Rachel Fisher' (Z)	WFib
	radens (Sc)	EPfP WFib
	'Radiance' (Z/d)	WFib
	'Radiant' (Z/d)	WFib
	'Radio' (Z/d)	WFib
	'Radior' (Min)	WFib
	'Rads Star' (Z/St)	ESul NFir SSea WFib
	'Radula' (Sc) ♀ H1+3	CSev ESul GBar LDea LIck MHer MOak MWhe SKen WFib
	'Radula Roseum' (Sc)	SSca
	'Ragamuffin' (Dw/d)	ESul MWhe WFib
	'Rager's Pink' (Dw/d)	ESul
	'Rager's Star' (Min)	ESul
	'Rager's Veri-Star' (Min/C)	ESul
	'Ragtime' (St)	NPri SCoo
	'Rakastani' (Z)	SKen
	'Rapture' (R)	WFib
	'Raspberry Parfait' (R)	LDea
	'Raspberry Ripple' (A)	ESul LDea MWhe NFir SAga
	'Raspberry Surprise' (R) **new**	LVER
	'Raspberry Sweet' (Z/St/d)	WFib
	'Raviro' (I/d)	WFib
	'Ray Bidwell' (Min)	ESul MWhe NFir
	'Ray Coughlin' (Z/C/d)	WFib
	'Raydon' (Min/St)	ESul
	'Rebecca' (Min/d)	ESul WFib
	'Red Admiral' (Min/d/v)	ESul SKen
§	'Red Black Vesuvius' (Min/C)	CHal ESul LVER MWhe SKen WEas WFib
	'Red Cactus' (St)	NFir
§	'Red Cascade' (I) ♀ H1+3	MWhe WFib
	'Red Gables'	CSpe
	'Red Galilee' (I/d)	MWhe
	'Red Glow' (Min)	ESul
	'Red Ice' (Min/d)	ESul LVER MWhe NFir
*	'Red Irene' (Z/d)	CWDa
	'Red Light' (Z/d)	WFib
	'Red Magic Lantern' (Z/C)	SKen
	'Red Pandora' (T)	LVER
	'Red Rambler' (Z/d)	CHal LVER MWhe SKen WFib
	'Red Silver Cascade'	see *P.* 'Mutzel'
	'Red Spangles' (R)	WFib
	'Red Spider' (Min/Ca)	ESul WFib
	'Red Startel' (Z/St/d)	MWhe SKen WFib
	'Red Susan Pearce' (R)	ESul LDea
	'Red Sybil Holmes' (I)	LVER
	'Red Tiny Tim' (Min)	WFib
	'Red Velvet' (R)	WFib
	'Red Witch' (Dw/St/d)	ESul LVER WFib
	Red-Blizzard = 'Fizzard' PBR (I)	NPri SCoo WWol
§	Red-Mini-Cascade = 'Rotemica' (I)	LDea LVER MWhe SKen WFib
	'Redondo' (Min/d)	ESul LVER MWhe SPet WEas WFib
	'Reflections' (Z/d)	WFib
	'Reg "Q"' (Z/C)	NFir
	'Regina' (Z/d)	LVER NFir SKen SPet WFib
	'Reifi Vanderlea'	EWoo
	'Rembrandt' (R)	LDea LVER SKen SSea SYvo WFib
	'Renate Parsley'	NFir WFib
	'Rene Roué' (Dw/d/v)	ESul NFir
	'Renee Ross' (I/d) ♀ H1+3	CWDa WFib
	reniforme	GBar MHer SAga SUsu WEas WFib
	'Retah's Crystal' (Z/v)	ESul LRHS LVER MWhe NFir
	'Rhodamant' (I/d)	WFib
	'Rhodo' (R)	WFib
	'Richard Gibbs'	EWoo MHer
	'Richard Key' (Z/d/C)	WFib
	'Richard West' (I/d)	CWDa
	'Ricky Promise' (A)	LDea
	'Rietje van der Lee' (A)	ESul WFib
	'Rigel' (Min/d)	ESul MWhe NFir SKen WFib
	'Rigi' (I/d)	MBri SKen WFib
	'Rigoletto' (I)	EWoo LDea NFir
	'Rimey' (St)	NFir
	'Rimfire' (R)	ESul LDea LVER NFir WFib
	Rio = 'Fisrix' PBR (Z)	WWol
	'Rio Grande' (I/d)	LDea LVER MWhe NFir NWoo SKen SPet WFib
	'Rising Sun'	NFir
	'Rita Brook' (Z/d)	WFib
	'Rita Coughlin' (R)	WFib
	'Rita Scheen' (A/v)	ESul EWoo LDea MWhe SSea WFib
	'Rita Thomas' (Z)	WFib
	'Ritchie' (R)	ESul
	'Robbie Hare' (R)	WFib
	'Robe' PBR (Z/d)	LAst LRHS LVER
	'Rober's Lavender' (Dw)	ESul
	'Rober's Lemon Rose' (Sc)	CRHN ESul EWoo GBar LDea MHer SKen SSea WEas WFib WHer WJek WWye
	'Rober's Salmon Coral' (Dw/d)	ESul
	'Robert Fish' (Z/C)	ESul LRHS SPet
	'Robert McElwain'	WFib
	'Robin' (Sc)	LDea LVER
	'Robin' (R)	LDea
	'Robin's Unique' (U)	EWoo NFir
	'Roger's Delight' (R/Sc)	EWoo LDea
	'Rogue' (R)	ESul EWoo LDea MSte WFib
	'Roi des Balcons'	see *P.* 'Hederinum'
§	'Roi des Balcons Impérial' (I) ♀ H1+3	MWhe
§	'Roi des Balcons Lilas' (I) ♀ H1+3	MWhe SKen WFib
	'Roi des Balcons Rose'	see *P.* 'Hederinum'
§	Rokoko = 'Fisfid' PBR (Z)	CWDa
	'Roller's David' (I/d)	CWDa
	'Roller's Echo' (A)	ESul LDea LIck MWhe
	'Roller's Gabriella' (A)	LDea
	'Roller's Pathfinder' (I/d/v)	LDea LVER
	'Roller's Pioneer' (I/v)	EWoo LDea LVER SAga SKen

'Roller's Satinique' (U) ♀ H1+3   EWoo LIck MHer SSea WFib

'Rollisson's Unique' (U)   MHer MSte NBur WFib

'Romeo' (R)   LVER

§ Romy (I)   LDea

§ 'Rosa Mini-cascade' (I)   ESul LVER MWhe NFir

'Rosaleen' (Min)   ESul

'Rosalie' (Min)   ESul

'Rosamunda' (Z/d)   WFib

'Rose Bengal' (A)   CRHN ESul LDea MWhe WFib

Rose Evka = 'Penevro'PBR (Dw/I/v)   NFir

'Rose Irene' (Z/d)   MWhe WFib

'Rose Jewel' (R)   ESul

'Rose of Amsterdam' (Min/d)   ESul

'Rose Silver Cascade' (I)   LDea LVER

'Rose Slam' (R)   WFib

'Rosecrystal'PBR (Z/d)   LVER

'Rosee Normande' (Z/d)   WFib

* 'Roselo'   CWDa

'Rosemarie' (Z/d)   MWhe

'Rosemine' (Z/d)   WFib

'Rosette' (Dw/d)   WFib

'Rosina Read' (Dw/d)   ERea ESul LVER WFib

'Rosmaroy' (R)   ESul LDea LVER NFir

§ 'Rospen' (Z/d)   SKen SYvo WFib

'Rosy Dawn' (Min/d)   WFib

'Rosy Morn' (R)   NFir

'Rote Mini-cascade'   see P. Red-Mini-Cascade = 'Rotemica'

'Rotlieb' (Z/d)   WFib

§ 'Rouletta' (I/d)   ECtt LDea LVER MWhe NPri SKen WFib

'Rousillon' (R)   LDea WFib

'Rousseau' (Min/C)   ESul WFib

'Royal Ascot' (R)   CHal CSpe ESul EWoo LDea MSte NFir SMrm SPet

'Royal Carpet' (Min/d)   ESul

'Royal Court' (R) new   LDea

'Royal Decree' (R)   LDea

'Royal Norfolk' (Min/d)   ESul LVER MWhe NFir SKen

'Royal Oak' (Sc) ♀ H1+3   CBrm CElw CSev EWoo GBar LDea MHer MWhe NBur SPet SSea WEas WFib WPer WRha

§ 'Royal Purple' (Z/d)   CHal WFib

* 'Royal Salmon'   CWDa

'Royal Sovereign' (Z/C/d)   LDea

'Royal Star' (R)   LDea

'Royal Surprise' (R)   LDea NFir

'Royal Wedding' (R)   LDea

'Rubella' (Z/d)   WFib

'Rubi Lee' (A)   MWhe

* 'Rubican'   CWDa

'Rubin Improved' (Z/d)   SKen WFib

'Ruby' (Min/d)   ESul WFib

'Ruby Orchid' (A)   LDea NFir

'Ruffled Velvet' (R)   EWoo SSea

'Rumba' new   WWol

'Rushmere' (Dw/d)   ESul WFib

'Russet Wings' (R)   WFib

'Rustler' (Min/d)   WFib

'Rusty' (Dw/C/d)   ESul SPet

'Ryecroft Pride' (Z/d)   WFib

'Ryecroft White' (Z/d)   WFib

'Sabine'PBR (Z/d)   LVER

'Sally Munro' (R)   LDea

'Sally Read' (Dw/d)   ERea ESul

'Salmon Beauty' (Min/d)   WFib

'Salmon Black Vesuvius' (Min/C)   ESul SPet

§ 'Salmon Irene' (Z/d)   WFib

'Salmon Queen'   see P. 'Lachskönigin'

'Salmon Slam' (R)   WFib

'Salmon Startel' (Z/St/d)   ESul MWhe

'Saltford' (R)   WFib

'Samantha' (R)   ESul WFib

'Samantha Stamp' (Dw/d/C)   SAga WFib

Samba = 'Fissamba'PBR (R)   WFib

'Sancho Panza' (Dec) ♀ H1+3   CSpe ESul EWoo LDea LVER MHer MSte SKen SSea WFib

'Sanguineum'   CSpe SAga

'Santa Maria' (Z/d)   LVER SKen WFib

'Santa Marie' (R)   LDea

'Santa Paula' (I/d)   ECtt LDea MWhe SKen

'Sasha' (Min)   WFib

'Sassa'PBR (Z/d)   CWDa LAst

§ Satellite (Z/St)   WFib

'Satsuki' (R)   ESul LDea NFir

'Saturn' (Z)   NFir

§ scabrum   WFib

'Scarlet Nosegay'   CHal

'Scarlet Pet' (U)   CFee CRHN ESul MHer NFir

'Scarlet Pimpernel' (Z/C/d)   ESul WFib

'Scarlet Rambler' (Z/d)   EWoo LVER SKen WEas WFib

'Scarlet Unique' (U)   EWoo LDea MHer MSte NFir SKen SSea WFib WOld

'Scatterbrain' (Z)   CWDa

§ 'Schneekönigin' (I/d)   ECtt LDea LVER MSte SKen

§ 'Schöne Helena'PBR (Z/d)   CWDa

'Secret Love' (Sc)   LDea WFib

'Seeley's Pansy' (A)   CSpe EWoo LDea MHer WFib

'Sefton' (R) ♀ H1+3   ESul LDea WFib

'Selby' (Z/C/d)   WFib

'Selina'   ESul

'Semer' (Min)   ESul SKen

* 'Serre de la Madone' (Sc)   WEas

'Shalimar' (St)   CSpe MSte NFir SAga WFib

'Shanklin' (Dw/St)   ESul

'Shanks' (Z)   NFir

'Sharon' (Min/d)   ESul WFib

'Sheila' (Dw)   ESul

'Shelley' (Dw)   ESul SKen

'Shenandoah' (Min)   WFib

'Sheraton' (Min/d)   MWhe

'Shimmer' (Z/d)   LVER MWhe WFib

'Shirley Ash' (A)   LDea WFib

'Shirley Maureen' (R)   LDea WFib

'Shocking Pink' (Z/d) new   LAst

'Shogan' (R)   NFir

'Shotley' (Min)   ESul

'Shottesham Pet' (Sc)   ESul EWoo MHer

'Show Off' (Z) new   LVER

'Shrubland Pet' (U/Sc)   EWoo MHer SKen

'Shrubland Rose' (Sc)   WFib

'Sid' (R) new   LDea

sidoides   CSpe CTrC EPyc IFro LPio MHer NFir SAga SMrm SSea WCom WCot WEas WGwG

– black   CSpe SUsu

– raspberry   CSpe SAga

'Sienna' (R)   LDea NFir

'Silberlachs' (Z/d)   WFib

'Silpen' (Z/d)   WFib

* 'Sils'   CWDa

'Silver Anne' (R/v)   ESul EWoo NFir WFib

'Silver Cascade Pink' (I) new   NPri

'Silver Kewense' (Dw/v)   ESul SKen WFib

* 'Silver Lights'   CWDa

'Silver Monarch'   ESul

'Silver Wings' (Z/v)   ESul EWoo LRHS MWhe NFir SSea WFib

'Silvia' (R)   ESul

'Simon Portas' (I/d)   SKen

'Simon Read' (Dw)	ERea ESul
'Simplicity' (Z)	LVER
'Single New Life' (Z)	LVER
'Sir Arthur Hort' (I)	WFib
'Sir Colin' (Z) **new**	SSea
'Sister Henry' (Z/d)	WFib
'Skelly's Pride' (Z)	LVER SKen WEas
'Skies of Italy' (Z/C/d)	CHal MBri MHer SKen SSea WFib
'Sleuring's Robin' (Min/d)	WFib
'Small Fortune' (Dw/d)	ESul SKen
'Smuggler' (R)	LDea
'Snape'	ESul
'Sneezy' (Min)	NFir
'Snow Cap' (MinI) **new**	NFir
Snow Queen	see P. 'Schneekönigin'
'Snow White' (Min)	ESul
'Snowbaby' (Min/d)	ESul
'Snowberry' (R)	ESul
'Snowdon' (Min)	WFib
'Snowdrift' (I/d)	LVER WFib
'Snowflake' (Min)	see P. 'Atomic Snowflake' (Sc/v)
'Snowmass' (Z/d)	CHal MWhe
'Snowstorm' (Z)	WFib
'Snowy Baby' (Min/d)	WFib
'Sofie'	see P. 'Decora Rose'
'Solent Waves' (R)	ESul LDea WFib
'Solferino' (A)	ESul EWoo LDea SKen
§ Solidor (I/d) ♀ H1+3	LDea NFir WFib
Solo = 'Guillio' (Z/I)	EWoo LVER
'Sombrero' (R)	WFib
'Somersham' (Min)	ESul
'Something Special' (Z/d)	LVER MWhe NFir WFib
'Sonata' (Dw/d)	ESul
'Sonnesport' (Z)	WFib
Sophie Casade	see Pelargonium 'Decora Rose'
'Sophie Dumaresque' (Z/v)	LVER MBri MWhe NFir SKen SSea WFib
'Sophie Koniger' (Z/d)	WFib
'Sorcery' (Dw/C)	ESul MWhe SKen
'Sound Appeal' (A)	ESul LDea
'South American Bronze' (R) ♀ H1+3	LDea SKen SMrm WFib
'South American Delight' (R)	LVER
'South Walsham Broad' (Dw)	ESul
'Southern Belle' (A)	LDea
'Southern Belle' (Z/d)	WFib
'Southern Charm' (Z/v)	NFir
'Southern Cherub' (A)	LDea
'Southern Gem' (Min/d)	ESul
'Southern Peach' (d)	ESul
'Souvenir' (R)	CHal LDea SSea
'Spanish Angel' (A) ♀ H1+3	ESul LDea NFir SSea
'Sparkler' (Z)	LVER
'Special Moment' (R)	WFib
'Spellbound' (R)	WFib
'Spital Dam' (Dw/d)	ESul NFir
'Spitfire' (Z/Ca/d/v)	ESul LVER SSea WFib
'Spithead Cherry' (R)	LDea WFib
§ 'Splendide'	CMdw CRDP CSpe MHer NFir SAga SSea WCot WEas
'Spotlite Hotline' (I)	LDea
'Spotlite Winner' (I)	LDea
'Spot-on-bonanza' (R)	ESul EWoo LDea NFir WFib
'Spring Bride' (R)	LDea
'Spring Park' (A)	ESul LVER MHer WFib
'Springfield Ann' (R)	ESul
'Springfield Black' (R)	ESul LDea LVER SSea
'Springfield Charm' (R)	ESul
'Springfield Mary Parfitt' (R)	ESul
'Springfield Moonbeam' (R)	ESul
'Springfield Pearl' (R)	LDea

'Springfield Purple' (R)	ESul
'Springfield Unique' (R)	LDea
'Springtime' (Z/d)	MWhe SKen WFib
'Sprite' (Min/v)	MWhe
'Sproughton' (Dw)	ESul
'St Helen's Favourite' (Min)	ESul
'Stacey' (R)	LDea
'Stadt Bern' (Z/C)	LRHS LVER MBri MSte MWhe NFir SKen WEas WFib
'Stanton Drew' (Z/d)	WFib
x stapletoniae	see P. 'Miss Stapleton'
'Star Flecks'	NFir
'Star of Persia' (Z/Ca/d)	WFib
'Starburst' (Z)	NFir
'Starflecks' (St)	LVER
'Starlet' (Ca)	WFib
'Starlight' (R)	WFib
'Starlight Magic' (A) ♀ H1+3	ESul LDea
'Starry Eyed' (Dw)	ESul
'Startel Salmon' (Z/St)	WFib
'Stella Read' (Dw/d)	ERea ESul WFib
'Stellar Arctic Star'	see P. 'Arctic Star'
'Stellar Cathay' (Z/St/d)	LRHS WFib
'Stellar Dawn Star' (Z/St)	WFib
'Stellar Grenadier'	see P. 'Grenadier'
'Stellar Hannaford Star'	see P. 'Hannaford Star'
* 'Stellar Orange Pixie' (St/d)	CWDa
'Stephen Read' (Min)	ERea ESul
'Stewart Meehan' (R) **new**	LDea
'Stewart Read' (Dw)	ERea
'Stirling Stent' (Z)	CWDa
'Strawberries and Cream' (Z/St)	NFir
'Strawberry Fayre' (Dw/St)	LVER
'Strawberry Sundae' (R)	ESul LDea LVER MSte NFir WFib
'Stringer's Delight'	ESul
'Stringer's Souvenir' (Dw/d/v)	ESul LVER
'Stuart Mark' (R)	LDea
'Stutton' (Min)	ESul
suburbanum **new**	EShb
'Suffolk Agate' (R)	ESul
'Suffolk Amethyst' (A)	ESul
'Suffolk Coral' (R)	ESul
'Suffolk Emerald' (A) **new**	ESul
'Suffolk Garnet' (A) **new**	ESul
§ 'Sugar Baby' (DwI)	ECtt ESul LDea MBri SKen WFib
'Summer Cloud' (Z/d)	SKen WFib
'Summer Rose Lilac' (I) **new**	NPri
'Summertime' (Z/d)	see P. 'Deacon Summertime'
'Sun Rocket' (Dw/d)	MWhe WFib
'Sundridge Moonlight' (Z/C)	WFib
'Sunraysia' (Z/St)	WFib
'Sunridge Moonlight' (Dw)	NFir
'Sunrise' (R)	ESul LDea LVER SKen WEas WFib
'Sunset' (Z)	WFib
'Sunset Snow' (R)	LVER NFir WFib
'Sunspot' (Min/C)	NFir
'Sunstar' (Min/d)	ESul WFib
'Super Rose' (I)	MWhe SKen SPet
'Super Spot-on-bonanza' (R)	LVER
'Supernova' (Z/St/d)	CWDa ESul MWhe SKen WFib
'Surcouf' (I)	WFib
'Susan Hillier' (R)	LDea
'Susan Payne' (Dw/d)	ESul MHer
'Susan Pearce' (R)	LDea LVER SKen WFib
'Susan Read' (Dw)	ERea ESul
* 'Susan Screen'	CWDa
'Susie 'Q' (Z/C)	LVER MWhe SKen SPet SSea

'Sussex Beauty' (Dw/d/v)	CWDa	
'Sussex Delight' (Min)	CWDa SKen SPet	
'Sussex Gem' (Min/d)	SKen	
'Sussex Lace'	see *P.* 'White Mesh'	
'Swanland Lace' (I/d/v)	WFib	
'Swedish Angel' (A)	ESul EWoo LDea LVER MWhe NFir SSea	
'Sweet Lady Mary' (Sc)	LDea WFib	
'Sweet Mimosa' (Sc) ♀ H1+3	CBrm CHal CRHN EWoo LIck LVER MHer MSte NFir SKen SSea WEas WFib	
'Sweet Miriam' (Sc)	LDea	
'Sweet Sue' (Min)	ESul WFib	
I 'Sweet William' (St)	LVER	
'Swilland' (A)	ESul LDea MWhe	
'Sybil Bradshaw' (R)	LDea WFib	
'Sybil Holmes' (I/d)	ECtt LVER MBri MWhe SKen SPet WFib	
'Sylvia Gale' (R)	WFib	
'Sylvia Marie' (Dw/d)	MWhe NFir SKen	
'Taffety' (Min)	ESul	
* 'Tamara'	CWDa	
'Tamie' (Dw/d)	ESul MWhe NFir	
'Tammy' (Dw/d)	ESul MWhe WFib	
'Tangerine' (Min/Ca/d)	ESul LVER SSea WFib	
'Tanzy' (Min)	ESul	
'Tapestry' (R)	WEas	
'Tattingstone' (Min)	ESul	
'Tavira' (I/d)	LVER SPet WFib	
'Tazi' (Dw) **new**	ESul	
'Ted Brooke' (Z/d)	WFib	
'Ted Dutton' (R)	WFib	
'Teddy Roosevelt' (Z/d)	WFib	
'Telstar' (Min/d)	ESul SKen WFib	
§ 'Telston's Prima' (R)	LDea	
'Tenderly' (Dw/d)	ESul	
'Tenerife Magic' (MinI/d)	ESul	
tenuicaule	WFib	
'Terence Read' (Min)	ERea	
tetragonum	MHer SSea SVen WFib	
'The Axe' (A)	ESul MWhe	
'The Barle' (A) ♀ H1+3	LDea	
'The Boar' (Fr) ♀ H1+3	CSpe EWoo LDea LVER MSte SRms WPer	
'The Bray' (A)	CSpe LDea	
'The Creedy' (A)	LDea	
'The Culm' (A)	ESul EWoo LDea MSte	
'The Czar'	see *P.* 'Czar'	
'The Dart' (A)	LDea	
'The Duchess' (I/d)	WFib	
'The Heddon' (A)	LDea	
'The Joker' (I/d)	WFib	
'The Kenn-Lad' (A)	LDea NFir	
'The Lowman' (A)	LDea	
'The Lyn' (A)	ESul LDea	
'The Mole' (A)	LDea LVER MHer MSte	
'The Okement' (A)	EWoo LDea MSte	
'The Otter' (A)	ESul LDea MWhe	
'The Speaker' (Z/d)	SKen WFib	
'The Tamar' (A)	CFee LDea	
'The Tone' (A) ♀ H1+3	ESul LDea MWhe	
'Thomas Earle' (Z)	WFib	
'Thomas Gerald' (Min/C)	ESul SKen	
'Tilly' (Min)	CHal NFir SAga	
'Tim' (Min)	ESul	
'Timothy Clifford' (Min/d)	ESul MWhe WFib	
'Tinkerbell' (A)	LDea	
§ 'Tip Top Duet' (A) ♀ H1+3	ESul EWoo LDea LIck LRHS LVER MHer MWhe NFir NWoo SMrm SSea WFib	
'Tom Portas' (Dw/d)	ESul	
'Tom Tit' (Z)	SPet	
'Tomcat'PBR (Z/d)	LAst LVER SSea WGor WGwG	

tomentosum (Sc) ♀ H1+3	CArn CHal CRHN CSev CSpe CTbh EWoo GBar GPoy IFro LDea MHer MOak MWhe NFir NHHG SKen SSea SVen WEas WFib WGwG WWye	
– 'Chocolate'	see *P.* 'Chocolate Peppermint'	
'Tommay's Delight' (R)	LDea WFib	
tongaense	WFib	
'Tony' (Min)	ESul	
'Topan' (R)	ESul	
'Topscore' (Z/d)	SKen WFib	
'Toreador' (Z/d)	WFib	
'Tornado' (R)	ESul NFir WFib	
'Torrento' (Sc)	ESul EWoo LDea MHer SKen WFib	
'Tortoiseshell' (R)	WFib	
'Toyon' (Z/d)	SKen WFib	
'Tracy' (Min/d)	ESul NFir	
transvaalense	WFib	
'Traute Hausler' (A)	LDea	
'Trautlieb' (Z/d)	CWDa WFib	
'Treasure Chest' (Z)	SKen	
'Trésor' (Z/d)	CWDa	
tricolor hort.	see *P.* 'Splendide'	
– Curt.	CPla	
trifidum	SSea WFib	
'Trimley' (Dw/d)	ESul	
'Trinket' (Min/d)	SKen	
'Triomphe de Nancy' (Z/d)	WFib	
triste	WFib	
'Trixie' (R)	LDea	
'Trudie' (Dw/Fr)	ESul LVER MHer SKen WFib	
'Trulls Hatch' (Z/d)	MWhe SKen	
'Tu Tone' (Dw/d)	ESul	
'Tuddenham' (Min/d)	WFib	
'Tuesday's Child' (Dw/C)	SKen	
'Tunias Perfecta' (R)	WFib	
'Turkish Coffee' (R)	ESul LVER NFir WFib	
'Turkish Delight' (Dw/C)	ESul MWhe NFir WFib	
'Turtle's Surprise' (Z/d/v)	SKen	
'Turtle's White' (R)	LDea	
'Tuyo' (R)	WFib	
'Tweedle-Dum' (Dw)	CSpe MWhe	
'Twinkle' (Min/d)	ESul WFib	
'Tyabb Princess' (R)	LDea WFib	
'Ullswater' (Dw/C)	ESul	
§ 'Unique Aurore' (U)	EWoo LVER MHer MSte NFir SKen WFib	
'Unique Mons Ninon'	see *Pelargonium* 'Monsieur Ninon'	
'Unity' (Dw)	LVER	
'Urchin' (Min)	ESul MWhe NFir SHFr WFib	
'Ursula Key' (Z/c)	SKen WFib	
'Valanza' (A)	ESul	
'Valenciana' (R)	WFib	
'Valentina' (Min/d)	ESul WFib	
'Valentine' (R)	ESul	
'Vancouver Centennial' (Dw/St/C) ♀ H1+3	CSpe ESul LRHS LVER MBri MHer MOak MWhe NFir SCoo SKen SMrm SPet SPoG SSea WFib	
'Vandersea'	EWoo	
§ 'Variegated Clorinda' (Sc/v)	EWoo WFib	
§ 'Variegated Fragrans'	see *P.* (Fragrans Group) 'Fragrans Variegatum'	
§ 'Variegated Kleine Liebling' (Min/v)	ESul LVER SSea WFib	
'Variegated La France' (I/v)	WFib	
'Variegated Madame Layal' (A/v) ♀ H1+3	EWoo WFib	
'Vasco da Gama' (Dw/d)	ESul WFib	
'Vectis Blaze' (I)	EWoo	
'Vectis Glitter' (Z/St)	CSpe LVER MWhe NFir	
'Velvet' (Z)	CWDa LVER	
'Velvet Duet' (A) ♀ H1+3	CHal EWoo LDea LIck LRHS LVER MWhe NFir SKen SSea	

'Venus' (Min/d)	ESul LRHS
'Vera Dillon' (Z)	SKen
'Verdale' (A)	LDea WFib
'Verity Palace' (R)	EWoo LDea WFib
'Verona' (Z/C)	CHal MBri SKen
'Verona Contreras' (A)	ESul LDea MWhe NFir WFib
I 'Veronica' (Z/d)	MWhe SKen
'Vicki Town' (R)	WFib
'Vicky Claire' (R)	ESul LDea NFir SKen SMrm WFib
'Victoria' (Z/d)	SKen
'Victoria Regina' (R)	LDea WFib
'Viking' (Min/d)	SKen
'Viking Red' (Z)	MWhe
'Village Hill Oak' (Sc)	ESul LDea LVER MHer
'Ville de Paris'	see P. 'Hederinum'
'Vina' (Dw/C/d)	ESul LVER MWhe SKen WFib
'Vincent Gerris' (A)	ESul LDea MWhe
Vinco = 'Guivin'[PBR] (I/d)	CWDa
violareum hort.	see P. 'Splendide'
'Violet Lambton' (Z/v)	WFib
'Violet Unique' (U) **new**	MHer
'Violetta' (R)	LDea WFib
'Virginia' (R)	LDea SPet WFib
'Viscossisimum' (Sc)	MHer SKen
viscosum	see P. glutinosum
§ *vitifolium*	MHer
'Viva' (R) **new**	ESul
'Vivat Regina' (Z/d)	WFib
'Voo Doo' (Dec)	ESul
'Voodoo' (U) ♀ H1+3	CBrm CSpe EWoo MHer MSte NCiC NFir SAga SSea SUsu WFib
'W.H. Heytman' (R)	WFib
'Wallace Fairman' (R)	LDea
'Wallis Friesdorf' (Dw/C/d)	ESul MWhe
'Wantirna' (Z/v)	ECtt EWoo LLck LVER MHer NFir
'Warrenorth Coral' (Z/C/d) **new**	LVER
'Warrion' (Z/d)	LVER WFib
'Washbrook' (Min/d)	ESul NFir
'Watersmeet' (R)	LDea
'Wattisham' (Dcc)	LDea
'Waveney' (Min)	ESul
'Wayward Angel' (A) ♀ H1+3	ESul LDea LVER SKen WFib
'Wedding Royale' (Dw/d)	ESul LVER
'Welcome' (Z/d)	WFib
'Welling' (Sc)	ESul GBar LDea LVER MHer NFir
'Wellington' (R)	LDea WFib
'Wendy Anne'	SKen
'Wendy Read' (Dw/d)	ERea ESul LVER MWhe SPet WFib
'Wensum' (Min/d)	ESul WFib
'Westdalc Appleblossom' (Z/d/C)	ESul LVER
* 'Westdale Beauty' (d)	CWDa
'Western Zoyland' (R)	WFib
'Whisper' (R)	WFib
'White Bird's Egg' (Z)	WFib
'White Boar' (Fr)	EWoo MSte
'White Bonanza' (R)	ESul WFib
'White Butterfly' (Z/C)	LVER
'White Charm' (R)	ESul LDea
'White Chiffon' (R)	CSpe LVER
'White Duet' (A)	LDea MWhe
'White Eggshell' (Min)	ESul LVER
'White Feather' (Z/St)	MHer WFib
'White Frills' (Z/d)	WFib
'White Glory' (R) ♀ H1+3	ESul LDea NFir WFib
'White Lively Lady' (Dw/C)	ESul
§ 'White Mesh' (I/v)	ECtt MBri MWhe SKen WFib
White Pearl Necklace	see P. Perlenkette Weiss = 'Perlpenei'
'White Queen' (Z/d)	CWDa

'White Roc' (Min/d)	ESul
'White Unique' (U)	CHal EWoo LDea MHer MSte NBur SPet SSea WFib
'White Velvet Duet' (A)	ESul
White-Blizzard = 'Fisbliz'[PBR]	NPri SCoo WWol
'Wickham Lad' (R)	LDea
'Wild Spice' (Sc)	LDea LVER
'Wilf Vernon' (Min/d)	ESul
'Wilhelm Kolle' (Z)	WFib
'Wilhelm Langath' **new**	SCoo
'William Sutton' (R)	WFib
'Winford Festival'	LVER
'Winnie Read' (Dw/d)	ERea ESul
'Winston Churchill' (R)	LDea
'Wirral Target' (Z/d/v)	ESul MWhe
'Wishing Star'	ESul
'Wispy' (Dw/St/C)	ESul
'Witnesham' (Min/d)	ESul
§ 'Wood's Surprise'	ESul LDea MWhe NFir SKen SWal
(MinI/d/v)	WFib
'Wookey' (R)	WFib
'Wrington' (R)	WFib
'Wroxham' (Dw)	ESul
'Wychwood' (A/Sc)	EWoo LDea
'Wyck Beacon' (I/d)	SKen
'Wycombe Maid' (Min/d)	WFib
'Yale' (I/d) ♀ H1+3	CHal LDea LVER MBri MSte MWhe SKen WFib
'Yarrabee Jane' (R)	WFib
'Yhu' (R)	ESul LDea NFir WFib
'Yolanda' (Min/C)	ESul
'York Florist' (Z/d/v)	LVER
'York Minster' (Dw/v)	SKen
'Yvonne' (Z)	WFib
'Zama' (R)	ESul NFir
'Zemmies' (MinI)	ESul
'Zena' (Dw)	ESul
'Zinc' (Z/d)	WFib
'Zoe' (A)	LDea
zonale	EWoo WFib
'Zulu King' (R)	WFib
'Zulu Warrior' (R)	WFib

Peliosanthes (Convallariaceae)

monticola B&SWJ 5183	WCru

Pellaea (Adiantaceae)

atropurpurea	EFer
cordifolia	WRic
falcata	MBri
rotundifolia ♀ H2	CHal MBri NMar SMur
sagittata	NMar

Pellionia see Elatostema

Peltandra (Araceae)

undulata	see P. virginica
virginica	CRow EMFW LPBA MSta NPer SLon SWat

Peltaria (Brassicaceae)

alliacea	EPPr LEdu
turkmena **new**	EMan

Peltiphyllum see Darmera

Peltoboykinia (Saxifragaceae)

§ *tellimoides*	CCol CLAP EBee GCal NHol SMac WFar WMoo
watanabei	EBee GIBF GTou SMac WCru WFar WMoo WPGP

Pennantia (Icacinaceae)

corymbosa	ECou
- 'Akoroa'	ECou
- 'Woodside'	ECou

Pennellianthus see *Penstemon*

Pennisetum (Poaceae)

B&SWJ 3854	WCru
§ **alopecuroides**	More than 30 suppliers
- Autumn Wizard	see *P. alopecuroides* 'Herbstzauber'
- 'Bruno Ears'	EHoe
- 'Cassian's Choice'	CBrm CKno EFou EHoe SMrm SUsu
- 'Caudatum' **new**	CKno CRez SApp
- 'Hameln'	More than 30 suppliers
§ - 'Herbstzauber'	CFwr CPen EBee EFou EGle EHoe EPfP GCal LHop LPan SApp SMrm
- 'Little Bunny'	CBrm CKno CPen CWes EBee EBlw EChP EHoe EMan ENot EPPr EPla GCal GKir LAst LPan LRHS NGdn NPro WCot WDin WPGP
- 'Little Honey' (v)	CKno EBee EMan EPPr LPan SMer SPla WCot
- 'Moudry'	CBrm CKno EFou EHoe EPPr SMrm
- 'National Arboretum'	EHoe LPan
- var. **purpurascens**	CBig CWCL
- - B&SWJ 5822	WCru
- f. **viridescens**	CBri CKno CStr EBee ECha EFou EGle EHoe ELan EMan EPfP EWsh LPan LRHS MLLN MMoz NSti WBea
- 'Weserbergland'	CFir CKno EBee EHoe EPPr LPan SApp
- 'Woodside'	CKno CMea CWCL CWes EBee EHoe EMan EPPr LBBr MBNS SApp SHel SPla
compressum	see *P. alopecuroides*
flaccidum	CBod EBee EHul EMan EMon EPPr LRHS MAvo SRGP WWpP
incomptum	CSam EBre EHoe GKir LRHS SMrm
- purple	CKno EBee MMoz SRGP
longistylum hort.	see *P. villosum*
macrourum	CBrm CFil CFwr CHea CKno CRDP EBee EGle EHoe EPGN EPPr EPla EWsh LHop LHrt MAnH SMad SMrm SUsu SWal SYvo WPGP
massaicum 'Red Buttons' **new**	CKno
orientale ♀ H3	More than 30 suppliers
I - 'Robusta'	SApp
* - 'Shogun' **new**	WCot
- 'Tall Tails'	CKno EPPr WCot
'Reine Saat'	CStr
rueppellii	see *P. setaceum*
§ **setaceum** ♀ H3	CBig CBrm CKno CPen CWCL EMan EPPr LHrt MAnH MGol MNrw MPWC MWat NPPs SWal WLRN WWpP
- 'Burgundy Blaze'	LPan
- 'Eaton Canyon' **new**	CKno
- 'Rubrum'	CBig CKno SApp
§ **villosum** ♀ H3	More than 30 suppliers

Penstemon ✿ (Scrophulariaceae)

P&C 150	CFee
West Col. USA	NLAp
'Abberley'	WPer
'Abbotsmerry'	CKno EBee LPhx MWrn SAga SDys SGar SKCG WEll WPPR
'Agnes Laing'	CWCL LPen LRHS MBNS SGar SPlb
alamosensis **new**	NLAp
albertinus	see *P. humilis*

albidus	NLAp WLin
§ 'Alice Hindley' ♀ H3	More than 30 suppliers
alpinus	CLyd EWes GAbr GTou MHar NLAp NOak SYvo WEll
ambiguus	EBee
'Amy Gray' **new**	SKCG
§ 'Andenken an Friedrich Hahn' ♀ H4	More than 30 suppliers
§ **angustifolius**	MNrw SCro SRms WPer
'Apple Blossom' ♀ H3-4	More than 30 suppliers
'Apple Blossom' misapplied	see *P.* 'Thorn'
arenicola **new**	NLAp
aridus	NSla
arizonicus	see *P. whippleanus*
arkansanus	MNrw NLAp
'Ashton'	EBee LPen
attenuatus	WPer
- NNS 96-176	WCot
'Audrey Cooper' **new**	EBee WPPR
auriberbis	EBee
azureus	CLyd WPer
'Barbara Barker'	see *P.* 'Beech Park'
§ **barbatus**	CBot CFee EBlw EBre ECha EHrv ELan ERou LPhx MLan MRav MWat NLAp SChu SMad SMrm SPer SRms WHCG WWin
§ - 'Blue Spring'	ECtt
- 'Cambridge Mixed'	ERou EWll LRHS LRav
- subsp. **coccineus**	CWCL EBee EWTr LPen LPhx LRHS MBNS MCCP MHer NDlv NLar WLin
- 'Jingle Bells'	CWCL EBee GKir LPen STes
- orange-flowered	SAga SMrm
- var. **praecox**	MBNS NJOw NLAp WPer
- - f. **nanus**	CBot EMan LRHS MSte SRms
- - - 'Rondo'	NLAp NLar WWeb
barrettiae	NLAp WLin
'Beckford'	EBee MWrn WEll
§ 'Beech Park' ♀ H3	CPrp EBee ECtt ELan ERou EWes LAst LPen LRHS MBNS MHdf MPWC NBir NHaw SAga SKCG SPar WCot WEll WHCG WRus
§ **berryi**	EBee EPot GKev LBee SMrm
'Bisham Seedling'	see *P.* 'White Bedder'
'Blackbird'	More than 30 suppliers
'Blue Spring' misapplied	see *P. heterophyllus* 'Blue Springs'
'Bodnant'	EBee MHar SKCG WBan WEll WPer
bradburii	see *P. grandiflorus*
'Bredon'	EBee WEll
breviculus	LTwo NLAp WLin
bridgesii	see *P. rostriflorus*
buckleyi **new**	NLAp
'Burford Purple'	see *P.* 'Burgundy'
'Burford Seedling'	see *P.* 'Burgundy'
'Burford White'	see *P.* 'White Bedder'
§ 'Burgundy'	More than 30 suppliers
caeruleus	see *P. angustifolius*
caespitosus	EBre NWCA
- subsp. **suffruticosus**	see *P. tusharensis*
§ **californicus**	WLin
calycosus	EBee
§ **campanulatus**	CMHG EBee ECtt EPfP EPot EWTr EWes GEdr LPen MAsh MLLN MWrn NHol NMen SRms WBea WEll WGwG WHCG WPer WWal
- PC&H 148	CHar EMan MSPs NOak SHFr STes WPPR
- **pulchellus**	see *P. campanulatus*
- **roseus** misapplied	see *P. kunthii*
'Candy Pink'	see *P.* 'Old Candy Pink'
cardinalis	WHil
cardwellii	CMea EPot EWes GTou SRms

- x *davidsonii* — WAbe
'Carolyn Orr' (v) — EBee EMan MHar WCot
'Castle Forbes' — GMac LAst LPen MBNS MHar MLLN NBur SKCG WBan WEas WHCG WPer
'Catherine de la Mare' — see *P. heterophyllus* 'Catherine de la Mare'
* 'Centra' — EBee LPen MLLN MWgw WEll WPPR
centranthifolius — SIgm
  JJA 13106
'Charles Rudd' — CBod CKno EBee ERou GEil GMac LPen LRHS MBNS MCLN MLLN SAga SBai SChu SGar SUsu SWal WEll WHCG WPPR
§ 'Cherry' ♥ H3 — EBee EOrc GMac LPen MBNS MGrG MHer MLLN NBur SAga SCro SGar SKCG SMrm SPla SPlb WHCG WPPR WPer
'Cherry Ripe' misapplied — see *P.* 'Cherry'
§ 'Chester Scarlet' ♥ H3 — CBri CMCo CPrp CWCL EBlw ENot GBri GMac LPen MNrw MOak MRav MSte SDix SGar SLon SMrm WCFE WEll WHCG WPPR WPer WWye
clutei — EBee EWTr WFTG WOut
cobaea — EBee GKev
'Comberton' — CHea EBee MAnH SAga WEll
confertus — CMHG CNic CTri EBee EHyt EMNN EPot LPen LPio MBNS MHer NChi NLAp NMen NWCA SRms WHCG WPPR WRHF
'Connie's Pink' ♥ H3 — EBee ENot LPen MBNS MLLN MSte NBur SKCG WEll WHCG WPPR
* 'Coral Pink' — CStr
cordifolius — see *Keckiella cordifolia*
'Cottage Garden Red' — see *P.* 'Windsor Red'
§ 'Countess of Dalkeith' — More than 30 suppliers
crandallii — CPBP
- subsp. *glabrescens* — WHCG WLin
§ - subsp. *taosensis* — NWCA SMrm
cristatus — see *P. eriantherus*
'Dad's Pink' **new** — SKCG
davidsonii — EWes NLAp SRms WAbe WPat
- var. *davidsonii* — CGra CPBP
§ - var. *menziesii* ♥ H4 — EBee GTou MDun NHar NWCA SRms
- - 'Broken Top Mountain' — CLyd
- - 'Microphyllus' — EPot LTwo NHar NMen NSla WAbe WLin
- var. *praeteritus* — EHyt EPot MDKP NHar
'Dazzler' — CBod CM&M CPrp CWCL EBee ERou LPen NChi WPPR WPer
deustus — SRms
'Devonshire Cream' — CElw CStr CWCL LPen LRHS MBNS SAga WHCG
diffusus — see *P. serrulatus*
digitalis — CBri CNic EBre ECha EMan EWTr LPen LPhx MBNS NChi NLAp WFar WHCG WPer
§ - 'Husker Red' — More than 30 suppliers
- 'Purpureus' — see *P. digitalis* 'Husker Red'
- 'Ruby Tuesday' **new** — CDes
- white-flowered — LPhx SWal WElm
discolor pale — NBir WFar
lavender-flowered
dissectus — NLAp
'Dorothy Wilson' — MLLN
§ 'Drinkstone' — EGoo EHol ERou EWTr LPen LRHS MWrn NChi SAga SDix SGar WHCG WPPR WPer
'Drinkwater Red' — see *P.* 'Drinkstone'
eatonii — EBee SRms
- subsp. *undosus* — NWCA
- - NNS 95-381 — WCot

'Edithae' — LPen NLon SChu SRms WEas WHCG WIvy WKif WLin
'Elmley' — EBee MLLN SAga SKCG WEll
§ *eriantherus* — CGra WHCG WLin
'Etna' — EBee ECtt GKir LRHS MBri MMil SPar SWal WEll
euglaucus — EBee LTwo SAga SGar
§ 'Evelyn' ♥ H4 — More than 30 suppliers
'Firebird' — see *P.* 'Schoenholzeri'
'Flame' — CBri EMan LHop LPen LRHS MWrn NBur WHCG WPPR WPer
'Flamingo' — CBri CWCL EBee ECtt EPfP ERou EWes LAst LPen LRHS MAsh MBNS MBro MSte SAga SBai SGar SWal WCFE WFar WHoo WLRN WPPR GTou
frutescens — GTou
fruticosus — MNrw NWCA SRms WAbe
§ - var. *scouleri* ♥ H4 — MAsh MOne NLAp SRms WPPR
- - f. *albus* ♥ H4 — LPen NWCA SChu WAbe WIvy WKif
- - 'Amethyst' — NLAp WAbe WLin
- var. *serratus* — LPen NLAp
- - 'Holly' — NMen SBla
Fujiyama = 'Yayama'PBR — ECtt LRHS MBow MBri NGdn WEll WFar
'Gaff's Pink' — SChu
'Gaiety' — CM&M
gairdneri — NLAp
'Garden Red' — see *P.* 'Windsor Red'
'Garnet' — see *P.* 'Andenken an Friedrich Hahn'
gentianoides — MNrw NBro NLAp
'Geoff Hamilton' — LHop LPen MBNS SAga SPar
'George Elrick' — LPen MBNS
§ 'George Home' ♥ H3 — CBri CWCL EBee ECGP ECtt EWes LPen LRHS MBNS MLLN MNrw MSte MWrn NDun NHaw SAga SChu SMrm SPar SSvw WBVN WHCG WRus
'Ghent Purple' **new** — CFee
glaber — CBri CMHG GMac LHop LLWP LPen LRHS MBNS MBri MBro MLLN MRav NBro NGdn NLAp SBai SHfr SMrm SPer WEas WEll WHCG WHoo WKif WPPR WPer WRus
- 'Roundway Snowflake' **new** — COt
'Gloire de Quatre Rue' — LPen
gracilis — EBee GCal WPer
§ *grandiflorus* — CBri EBee NLAp SMrm WLin
hallii — EBee EPot EWes GTou LRHS WLin WPPR
hartwegii ♥ H3-4 — GMac LHop LPen SChu WAbe WBan WHCG WPPR WPer WRus
- 'Albus' — EBee EVFa GEil LHop LPen LRHS MSte NFor SAga SGar WCom WEll WHCG WPPR WWeb
heterodoxus — EBee SGar
§ *heterophyllus* — CHea CWCL EBee EBre LGro LPen MNrw NBir SAga SChu SHfr SMer SRms STes WAbe WCFE WEas WHCG WPPR WPer
- 'Blue Fountain' — CHar LPen WPPR
- 'Blue Gem' — CBod CElw CTri EBre EOrc LRHS NChi SGar SIng SPla WHoo WPGP
§ - 'Blue Springs' — CBot EBee LPen LRHS MAnH MSte NBir NGdn NLAp SAga SBla WAbe
§ - 'Catherine de la Mare' ♥ H4 — CHad CStr EBre ELan GKir LHop CHad CStr EBre ELan GKir LHop LPen LRHS MBow MHer MMil MWat NBir NBro NLAp SAga SChu SMrm SPar WFar WKif WPPR WPer

- 'Heavenly Blue' — More than 30 suppliers
- 'Hergest Croft' — CElw SChu WPPR
- subsp. *purdyi* — WHCG
- 'Roehrsier' **new** — LPen
- 'True Blue' — see *P. heterophyllus*
- white-flowered **new** — EBee
- 'Züriblau' — CFai EBee LPen MSPs

'Hewell Pink Bedder' ♀ H3 — More than 30 suppliers

'Hewitt's Pink' — SAga

§ 'Hidcote Pink' ♀ H3-4 — More than 30 suppliers

'Hidcote Purple' — CElw CM&M NGdn SAga SChu

* 'Hidcote White' — CM&M CWCL EOrc MHer SKCG WAbe

'Hillview Pink' — WHil

'Hillview Red' — SAga WHil

§ *hirsutus* — CNic EBee LPen MNrw NLAp WPer WSan

- f. *albiflorus* — EBee LPen NLAp WAbe
- var. *minimus* — NLAp
- var. *pygmaeus* — CLyd CMea CNic CRDP EBee EDAr EPot EWTr GTou LBee LPen MBro MHer NHar NMen SBla SGar SPlb SRms SRot SWal WAbe WHoo WLin WPer WWin
- - f. *albus* — WPer
- - 'Purpureus' — WAbe
'Hopleys Variegated' (v) — EBee EMan MHar MHer MNrw NBir SAga SBai SGar WCot WPPR WWeb

§ *humilis* — EBee MLLN NLAp SRms WBar WLin

- 'Pulchellus' — NLAp NWCA

immanifestus — WLin

isophyllus ♀ H3-4 — CPrp CSam CStr CWCL EChP EGra EPfP ERou GEil LPen LRHS MAsh MMil SChu SWal WCom WEll WFar WHCG WPPR WPer

jamesii — CBrm EBee EChP WHrl

janishiae — CGra NWCA

'Jean Grace' — CHar EBre GKir LRHS SIng

'Jill Lucas' — SCro

'John Booth' — MSte WEas

'John Nash' — COlW EVFa MHer MTPN SAga SChu SHFr SIgm

'John Nash' misapplied — see *P.* 'Alice Hindley'

'John Spedan Lewis' **new** — SLon

'Joy' — EBee LPen MBro MLLN MSte SKCG WCFE WHoo WPPR WPer

'June' — see *P.* 'Pennington Gem'

'King George V' — More than 30 suppliers

'Knight's Purple' — CElw LPen MHar WEll WHCG

'Knightwick' — CElw EVFa LPen SAga WPPR WPer

§ *kunthii* — CBri CNic CPBP CWCL EBee LPen NLAp SAga WAbe WHrl WPPR

- upright — SGar

§ *laetus* subsp. *roezlii* — CMea EPot GCrs GDra GEdr LRHS MBar MLan MTis NHar NLAp NLon NSla NWCA SRms WAbe WWin

laricifolius — NWCA

§ 'Le Phare' — CBod EBee LPen LRHS MBNS MHar MHdf SKCG WEll WHCG WPPR WPer

'Lilac and Burgundy' — CHea CKno CMea CPlt CPrp EBee ERou LPen LRHS MBNS MBri MHar SAga SKCG WEll WPPR

linarioides — CPBP CStr LPen MBro NHol WPat

'Little Witley' — LPen SAga WEll WHCG WPer

* 'Logan Pink' — CStr

'Lord Home' — see *P.* 'George Home'

lyallii — CHar EBee EHrv ELan EMan LPen MCCP MLLN MNrw MWrn NLAp NLon NMRc SRms SSte WPPR WSan

'Lynette' — LPen LRHS MBNS SAga SPlb WEll WHCG WHil WPPR WPer

'Macpenny's Pink' — EBee LPen SChu

§ 'Madame Golding' — EBee GMac LPen LRHS MBNS MNrw SGar SKCG SPlb WHCG WPPR WPer

'Margery Fish' ♀ H3 — CElw ERou ESis EWes LPen LRHS MMil MNrw MSte NPPs SBai WEll WPPR WPer

'Maurice Gibbs' ♀ H3 — CBcs CBri CHar CM&M CMea COlW EBee EChP ECtt ERou EWes LPen LRHS MBNS MCLN MLLN NGdn SAga SBai SGar SIgm SPar SWal WEll WFoF WHCG WMnd WPPR WWeb WWol

mensarum — EBee

menziesii — see *P. davidsonii* var. *menziesii*

Mexicali hybrids — EBee LPen MLLN NLAp WPPR

mexicanus — WLin

'Midnight' — CBcs CHar CPrp CSam EChP EPfP GBri LLWP LPen MAnH MOak MRav MSte SBai SGar SIgm SMac WCFE WCom WHCG WPPR WPer WRus WWeb WWin

'Mint Pink' — SGar SScr WPPR

'Modesty' — EBee LPen LRHS MBNS NBur WEll WHCG WPPR

montanus — EBee NLAp SAga

- var. *montanus* — CGra

'Mother of Pearl' — More than 30 suppliers

'Mrs Miller' — LPen MBNS NBur

'Mrs Morse' — see *P.* 'Chester Scarlet'

multiflorus — EBee LPen

§ 'Myddelton Gem' — CHar LPen LRHS MBNS MNrw SKCG WEll WFoF WHCG WPPR

'Myddelton Red' — see *P.* 'Myddelton Gem'

neomexicanus — EBee

neotericus — NWCA SIgm

newberryi ♀ H4 — CMea EPot GKev GKir SRot WCom WKif WPat WWin

- subsp. *berryi* — see *P. berryi*
- f. *humilior* — EPot GEil

§ - subsp. *sonomensis* — EPot NHar NWCA WAbe

'Newbury Gem' — MBNS NBur SBai WPPR

§ *nitidus* — MNrw

'Oaklea Red' — ECtt EPyc ERou LPen LRHS MBri SWat

§ 'Old Candy Pink' — CFee EBee LLWP LPen MSte MWrn SBai WEll WPPR WPer

'Osprey' ♀ H3 — More than 30 suppliers

ovatus — CBrm EBee LPen LPhx LPio MAnH MLLN NDlv NLAp SBla SIgm SMrm SRms WCot WHCG WKif WSan WWeb

'Overbury' — EBee LPen

pachyphyllus — WLin

palmeri — CBri ECtt MSPs SAga WFTG

'Papal Purple' — CBri CMHG CWCL ERou EWTr LLWP LPen LRHS MBNS MSte MWrn NBir NChi SAga SBai SChu SMrm SRms WCom WElm WFar WHCG WHoo WPPR WRus WWhi

'Papal Purple' x 'Evelyn' — CBri CMHG LPen SAga SCro SGar

'Patio Pink' — ERou LPen LRHS MBri MLLN SWal WEll

'Patio Red' — CWCL

'Patio Shell' — GKir LRHS MBri

'Patio Wine' — GKir LRHS MBri

payettensis **new** — LTwo

'Peace' — EBlw LPen LRHS MBNS SKCG WHCG WPPR WRus

'Pearl' — EBlw

§ 'Pennington Gem' ♀ H3 — COlW EBre ECtt GBri GKir GMac LLWP LPen LRHS MHer MLLN MNrw MSte MWgw MWrn NGdn

	Name	Suppliers
		SBai SGar SIng SPer SSte WEas WHCG WPPR WPer
	'Pensham Arctic Sunset' new	SAga WPPR
	'Pensham Avonbelle' new	WEll WPPR
	'Pensham Barbara Dixon' new	WPPR
	'Pensham Bow Bells' new	SAga WPPR
	'Pensham Capricorn Moon'	SAga WEll WPPR
	'Pensham Cardinal' new	WPPR
	'Pensham Celebration' new	WPPR
	'Pensham Charles Romer' new	WPPR
	'Pensham Claret' new	WPPR
	'Pensham Daybreak' new	WEll WPPR
	'Pensham Dorothy Wilson' new	WPPR
	'Pensham Edith Biggs' new	WPPR
	'Pensham Fields' new	WPPR
	'Pensham Freshwater Pearl' new	CStr SAga WPPR
	'Pensham Great Expectations' new	SAga WPPR
	'Pensham Just Jayne'	WPPR
	'Pensham Marjorie Lewis' new	WEll WPPR
	'Pensham Mischief' new	WPPR
	'Pensham Miss Wilson' new	CStr WEll WPPR
	'Pensham Petticoat' new	WPPR
	'Pensham Plum Dandy' new	CStr WPPR
	'Pensham Plum Jerkum'	WPPR
	'Pensham Prolific' new	WPPR
	'Pensham Son of Raven' new	WPPR
I	'Pensham St. James's' new	WPPR
I	'Pensham The Dean's Damson' new	WPPR
	'Pensham Tiger Belle Coral' now	WPPR
I	'Pensham Tiger Belle Rose' new	SAga WPPR
	'Pensham Twilight'	CStr WPPR
I	'Pensham Victoria Plum' now	CStr WEll WPPR
	'Pershore Carnival'	NPro
	'Pershore Fanfare'	LPen WHrl
	'Pershore Pink Necklace'	LPen MLLN MWrn SAga SBai SKCG WBan WCot WEas WEll WHCG WPPR WSan
	'Phare'	see P. 'Le Phare'
	'Phyllis'	see P. 'Evelyn'
	pinifolius ♀ H4	More than 30 suppliers
	- 'Mersea Yellow'	More than 30 suppliers
	- 'Wisley Flame' ♀ H4	EPfP ESis GEdr SIgm SPar
	'Pink Bedder'	see P. 'Hewell Pink Bedder', 'Sutton's Pink Bedder'
	'Pink Dragon'	CLyd GDra WHCG
	'Pink Endurance'	CBri CMea CStr EBee EBre ELan ERou LPen MBro MCLN MSte SGar SWal WEas WEll WHCG WHal WHoo WPPR WPer
	'Pink Ice'	WHil
	'Pink Profusion'	MRav SIgm SUsu
	'Port Wine' ♀ H3	CHar CRDP CSam EBee LPen LRHS MBow MHar MLLN MWrn NBir NPPs SAga SBai SPer WCot WHCG WPPR WPer
	potosinus new	EWes
	'Powis Castle'	EBee EWes MHar WBan WPPR WPer WWye
	'Prairie Dusk'	LPen
	'Prairie Fire'	EBee ERou LPen SAga WPPR
*	'Prairie Pride'	LPen
	'Priory Purple'	WEll WHCG WPer
	procerus	CPom EBee EChP GBri LPen MDHE MLLN SRms WPer
	- var. brachyanthus	EBee SGar
§	- var. formosus	EPot WAbe
§	- 'Roy Davidson' ♀ H4	CMea CPBP LBee LRHS NHol NLAp SBla SOkd WAbe WFar WLin WPPR
	- var. tolmiei	EBee EPot GCal GEdr LBee LPen NChi NHol NSla NWCA WLin
	pruinosus	EBee EPot
	pubescens	see P. hirsutus
	pulchellus Greene	see P. procerus var. formosus
	- Lindl.	see P. campanulatus
*	pulcherrimus	NBro
	pumilus	SRms
	'Purple and White'	see P. 'Countess of Dalkeith'
	'Purple Bedder'	CBri CElw CHea COlW EBee EPfP ERou GAbr LAst LHrt LPen LRHS MAsh MCLN MLLN MNrw MWat NBir NGdn SAga SBai SWat WCFE WEll WFar WGor WHCG WPPR WWal WWeb
	'Purple Gem'	GDra
	'Purple Passion'	EBee EBre EChP EHrv EPfP EWcs LPen LRHS SCro SKCG WLRN
	'Purpureus Albus'	see P. 'Countess of Dalkeith'
	purpusii	SIgm
§	putus	WLin
	'Rajah'	EBee LPen
	'Raven' ♀ H3	More than 30 suppliers
	'Razzle Dazzle'	CWCL LPen LRHS MBNS SPlb WEll WPPR WPer
	'Red Ace'	MNrw
	'Red Emperor'	CStr ECtt LPen MBNS MHar NHaw SPlb WEas WEll WHCG WPer
	'Red Knight'	CWCL LPen LRHS MBNS
	'Rich Purple'	LLWP LRHS MBNS SPlb
	'Rich Ruby'	More than 30 suppliers
	richardsonii	MDKP MNrw SGar SIgm SRms WEll WGWG
	'Ridgeway Red'	EBee WPPR
	roezlii Regel	see P. laetus subsp. roezlii
§	rostriflorus NNS 95-407	WCot
	'Rosy Blush'	CBri EBee LPen LRHS MBNS MWgw SMrm SPlb WHCG
	'Roundhay'	CFee
	'Roy Davidson'	see P. procerus 'Roy Davidson'
	'Royal White'	see P. 'White Bedder'
	'Rubicundus' ♀ H3	EBee ECtt EGra EHrv ELan EPfP ERou LHop LPen LRHS MAsh MBNS SAga SBai SCro SMrm SPla WAbc WCot WCra WFar WHCG WMnd WPPR WRus WWal WWeb WWol
	'Ruby'	see P. 'Schoenholzeri'
	'Ruby Field'	EBee EOrc MWgw WHCG WPPR
	'Ruby Gem'	LPen LRHS MBNS MPWC
	rupicola ♀ H4	GCrs GDra GKev GTou LHop LRHS NSla NWCA SIgm WAbe WLin WWin
	- 'Albus'	NSla WAbe
	- 'Conwy Lilac'	WAbe
	- 'Conwy Rose'	WAbe
	- 'Diamond Lake'	CMea MBro NHar WPat
	- mauve hybrid	GDra
	'Russian River'	EBee EWes LAst LHrt LLWP LPen LRHS MCLN NBur NHaw SGar SMrm SOkh SPlb SWal WHCG WPPR WPer
	rydbergii	EPot NLAp
*	Saskatoon hybrids	EBee
§	'Schoenholzeri' ♀ H4	More than 30 suppliers
	scouleri	see P. fruticosus var. scouleri

	secundiflorus	EBee
§	*serrulatus*	CNic EBee EPot EWes GDea GTou LPen MSte MWgw NLAp SBri SGar SHFr SMad SRms WHrl
	– 'Albus'	EBee LPen MSte SIgm WPPR WWin
	'Shell Pink'	LPen SKCG WPPR WPer
*	'Sherbourne Blue'	GBuc WEll WPer
*	'Shrawley'	WPer
	'Sissinghurst Pink'	see *P.* 'Evelyn'
	'Six Hills'	NLAp SDys SRms WAbe WHCG WLin WPat
	'Skyline'	EPfP WWeb
	smallii	EBee EMan EWes LPVe LPen LPhx MHar NLAp SCro SGar SIgm WHoo
	'Snow Storm'	see *P.* 'White Bedder'
	'Snowflake'	see *P.* 'White Bedder'
	'Son of Raven' **new**	CStr
	sonomensis	see *P. newberryi* subsp. *sonomensis*
§	'Sour Grapes' M. Fish ♀ H3-4	More than 30 suppliers
	'Sour Grapes' hort.	see *P.* 'Stapleford Gem'
	'Southcombe Pink'	CWCL LPen MLLN MWrn SBai SKCG WEll WHCG WPPR
	'Southgate Gem'	GDea GKir LPen LRHS MNrw MWat SCro WHCG WPPR
	'Souvenir d'Adrian Regnier'	CBri LPen
	'Souvenir d'André Torres'	LLWP LPen WEll WPPR
	'Souvenir d'André Torres' misapplied	see *P.* 'Chester Scarlet'
	speciosus	EPot
§	'Stapleford Gem' ♀ H3	More than 30 suppliers
	'Strawberry Fizz' **new**	CWCL LPen MBNS
	strictus	EBee EMan EWTr LPVe LPen LPio MBNS MHar MLLN NLAp SCro SGar SIgm SRms WPer WWeb
	Stromboli = 'Yaboli'	MBri MMil
	subglaber	EBee
	'Sutton's Pink Bedder'	CWCL EBee LRHS MBNS SPlb
	'Sylvia Buss'	LPen
	tall pink	see *P.* 'Welsh Dawn'
N	'Taoensis'	EWes SGar SUsu
	taosensis	see *P. crandallii* subsp. *taosensis*
	teucrioides	EPot NLAp NWCA WLin
	– JCA 1717050	CPBP
	'The Juggler'PBR	EPfP LPen LRHS MBNS MWrn WWol
§	'Thorn'	More than 30 suppliers
I	'Thorn Cross'	NEgg
	'Threave Pink'	CWCL ERou LLWP SBai SMrm SPoG SWal WCom WPPR
*	'Threave White'	WPen
	'Torquay Gem'	CWCL GBuc LPen SDys SKCG WHCG WPer
	'True Sour Grapes'	see *P.* 'Sour Grapes'
I	'Tubular Rose' **new**	CWCL
§	*tusharensis*	CPBP SBla
	utahensis	CBot CMHG EBee EBre EVFa GBri SAga WPer
	venustus	CFir EBee GBuc GKev MHar MNrw SGar SRms SRot WHCG WRos WWye
	Vesuvius = 'Yasius'	CStr EBee GKir LPen MBri SPar WFar
	virens	MHer NLAp WLin WPat WPer
*	– *albus*	MDKP WWin
	virgatus subsp. *putus*	see *P. putus*
	– subsp. *virgatus*	NLAp
	washingtonensis	CGra WLin
	watsonii	EBee EMan MLLN SRms WHCG WPer
	'Wedding Bells' **new**	CStr

§	'Welsh Dawn'	LPen WEll WPPR
§	*whippleanus*	CBri CRDP EBee EWTr LPen MSte MWrn SAga WAbb WBea WPer
	– 'Chocolate Drop' **new**	WRHF
§	'White Bedder' ♀ H3	More than 30 suppliers
	whitedii **new**	CGra
	'Whitethroat'	LPen LRHS MBNS SOkh WCot WEll WHCG WPPR WPer WWin
	wilcoxii	EBee
	'Willy's Purple'	LPen WPPR
§	'Windsor Red'	CBod CPrp EBee ECtt EPfP ERou LPen LRHS MAsh MBNS MSte SBai SGar SUsu SWal WGor WHCG WPPR
§	*wislizeni*	EBee EPfP MLan MNrw MOne NOak SRms WWal

Pentaglottis (Boraginaceae)

§	*sempervirens*	CArn CKin EPfP MHer MSal WHen WWye

Pentapterygium see *Agapetes*

Pentas (Rubiaceae)

	lanceolata	CHal LRHS MBri

Peperomia (Piperaceae)

§	*argyreia* ♀ H1	MBri
	arifolia	CHal
	caperata	LRHS MBri
	– 'Little Fantasy' ♀ H1	CHal
	clusiifolia	CHal
	– 'Variegata' (v)	CHal
	glabella	CHal
	– 'Variegata' (v)	CHal
	griseoargentea ♀ H1	CHal
	magnoliifolia	see *P. obtusifolia* Magnoliifolia Group
	obtusifolia 'Jamaica'	MBri
	– (Magnoliifolia Group) 'Golden Gate' (v)	MBri
	– – 'Greengold'	CHal MBri
	– – 'USA' ♀ H1	MBri
	– 'Tricolor' (v)	MBri
	orba 'Pixie'	MBri
I	– 'Pixie Variegata' (v)	MBri
	pulchella	see *P. verticillata*
	sandersii	see *P. argyreia*
	scandens ♀ H1	MBri
	– 'Variegata' (v)	CHal MBri
§	*verticillata*	CHal

pepino see *Solanum muricatum*

Pereskia (Cactaceae)

	aculeata **new**	EShb

Perezia (Asteraceae)

	linearis	GBuc
	recurvata	GCrs GTou

Pericallis (Asteraceae)

§	*lanata* (L'Hér.) B. Nord.	CHll ELan MBlu SAga WDyG
	– Kew form	CRHN CSpe SAga SMrm
	multiflora	LHop SAga

Perilla (Lamiaceae)

§	*frutescens* var. *crispa* ♀ H2	CArn MChe WJek
	– green-leaved	EOHP
	– var. *nankinensis*	see *P. frutescens* var. *crispa*
	– var. *purpurascens*	CArn EOHP MChe WJek

Periploca (Asclepiadaceae)
  graeca CArn CBcs CMac CPlN CRHN
    CWib GQui SLon SYvo WSHC
  purpurea WCru
    B&SWJ 7235 **new**
  sepium CPLG CPlN

Peristrophe (Acanthaceae)
  speciosa ECre ERea

Pernettya see *Gaultheria*

Perovskia (Lamiaceae)
  atriplicifolia CArn CBot CDul CMea GPoy
    MHer WHCG
  - 'Little Spire'PBR ENot MBri NPro WWeb
  'Blue Haze' GCal
  'Blue Spire' ♀ H4 More than 30 suppliers
  'Filigran' ECGP EFou LRHS NSti SChu
  scrophulariifolia WCom

Persea (Lauraceae)
  americana 'Hass' (F) CGOG
  ichangensis CPLG
  indica CPLG
  lingue LEdu
  thunbergii CHEx

Persicaria (Polygonaceae)
§ **affinis** CBcs CHar CSBt EBlw GAbr GKir
    MBar MTho MWhi NBro NVic SGar
    SMer SWat WBrE WCFE WFar WMoo
  - 'Darjeeling Red' ♀ H4 CBcs CRow EBlw EChP ELan
    EMFW ENot EPfP GCal GKir LGro
    LRHS MBri MRav MWgw NBid
    NBir NBlu NChi NGdn SDes SPla
    WBea WFar WHen WHcr WPnP
    WViv WWpP
  - 'Dimity' see *P. affinis* 'Superba'
  - 'Donald Lowndes' ♀ H4 More than 30 suppliers
  - 'Kabouter' LBuc
  - 'Ron McBeath' CRow
§ - 'Superba' ♀ H4 More than 30 suppliers
  alata see *P. nepalensis*
  alpina CRow
  amphibia CRow
§ **amplexicaulis** CBre CFwr COld CPrp CRow
    ELan EMar GMaP LGro MBro
    MHer MWat MWgw NChi NFor
    NLon NOrc SChu SEND WFar
    WHoo WMoo WRHF WTel WWpP
  - 'Alba' CElw CHar CRow EBee ECGN
    ECha EFou EMan EPla ERou GMaP
    LHop LPhx LRHS MBri MCAu
    MLLN SHar SMrm SWat WAul
    WBea WCot WFar WMoo WPnP
  - 'Atrosanguinea' CNic CRow CTri EBee ECha EGra
    EMan EPla ERou GGar LPhx LRHS
    MFir MRav MWgw NBir NVic SPer
    SRms WFar WOld WWin WWpP
  - 'Cottesbrooke Gold' CRow WCot
  - 'Firedance' LPhx NCat SMrm SWat WCot
  - 'Firetail' ♀ H4 More than 30 suppliers
  - 'Inverleith' CBre CDes CKno CRow EBee
    EBre ECha ECtt EPla NCat SDes
    WMoo WOld WPGP
* - var. **pendula** CRow EBee ECha EMan NBir
    WBea WCot WFar WMoo
  - 'Rosea' CBos CRow EBee ECha ELan
    EMan EPla LPhx LRHS MBri
    MCAu MRav NBro NSti SDys SWat
    WBea WFar WMoo WPGP

  - 'Rowden Gem' CRow EPla
  - 'Rowden Jewel' CRow EPla
  - 'Rowden Rose Quartz' CRow
  - 'Summer Dance' EBee EFou
  - Taurus = 'Blotau' CElw CRow EBee EGle EPla ERou
    MLLN WFar
§ **bistorta** CAgr CArn CHar CKin CRow
    ELau GBar GPoy MChe MHer
    MSal MWhi NBir NGHP NSco
    SWat WCra WHHs WSel WWye
  - subsp. **carnea** CRow EBee ECha ELan EMan
    NBir WFar WMoo
  - 'Hohe Tatra' CRow EMan GKir LPhx MTed
    WFar WTMC
  - 'Superba' ♀ H4 More than 30 suppliers
  bistortoides MSal
* - 'Blush Clent' WTin
  campanulata CElw CRow EChP ECha EMar EWTr
    GAbr GBuc GCal GGar MHar MWat
    MWgw NBid NBro NFor NGdn
    NLon SPer WBcn WBea WCom
    WFar WMoo WOld WWin WWye
  - Alba Group CRow EWTr GCal GGar GKir
    MWgw NBro NGdn NSti SBri
    WHer WMoo WWye
  - 'Madame Figard' CRow
  - 'Rosenrot' CBre CKno CRow EMan EPPr
    GBuc GCal NBir NGdn NHol
    NLar SSpi SWat WBea WCot WFar
  - 'Southcombe White' CRow EPPr EPla GBri WBea
  capitata CHal CPLG CRow EMan SHFr SIng
    SRms WBea WCom WEas WMoo
  - CC 3693 WCot
  - from Afghanistan WBea
  - 'Pink Bubbles' ECtt SPet
  conspicua EBee
  coriacea CRow
  elata CHor CRez EMan EMar EMon
    GBuc GGar
  emodi CRow EBee
§ **longiseta** MSal
§ **macrophylla** CRow LDai MTed SMad WFar
  microcephala CRow EWes SAga SMac
  - 'Red Dragon' More than 30 suppliers
  - var. **wallichii** CRow
  milletii CRDP CRow EBee EBre ECha EPla
    EWes GBuc GKir LRHS MBri MCAu
    MTho NOak WCot WCru WMoo
§ **mollis** CRow EBee
* - var. **frondosa** CDcs EBee
  nakaii new EBee
  neofiliformis new EBee
§ **nepalensis** CRow EPPr SMad
§ **odorata** CArn EBlw ELau EOHP GPoy Ilve
    MHer MSal NGHP SHDw SIde WJek
  orientalis MSal SMrm
  polymorpha CBct CDes CFwr CKno CRow
    EBee EBre ECGN ECha EFou EGle
    EHrv EMan EMon LHop LPhx
    MTed NDov SDes SMad SMrm
    SSpe WCot WFar WMoo
  polystachya see *P. wallichii*
* **regeliana** EBee LRHS
§ **runcinata** CPLG CRow EBee EMar GGar
    NBid NBir NLar WBar WFar WHer
    WMoo WPer
  - Needham's form CDcs CRow
  scoparia see *Polygonum scoparium*
  sphaerostachya Meisn. see *P. macrophylla*
  tenuicaulis CLyd CRow EBee EMon EPPr EPar
    EPla GGar MFir NGar SBla WCot
    WCru WFar WMoo
§ **tinctoria** EBee EOHP

vacciniifolia ♀ H4	More than 30 suppliers
– 'Ron McBeath'	CRow
§ *virginiana*	CMHG CRow ECtt EMan MSal NLar SMad WMoo WTMC
– Compton's form	CBct CRow EBee EMan EPPr EVFa LDai MAvo NCat WCot WMoo WTMC
– 'Filiformis' **new**	WCot
– 'Lance Corporal'	CRow EBee EFou SMrm WMnd WMoo
– Variegata Group	CBot CM&M CRez CRow EBee EChP ECha EMan ERou GCal MBNS NLar SDes WAul WCot WMoo WOld WPnP
§ – – 'Painter's Palette' (v)	More than 30 suppliers
– white-flowered**new**	GCal
vivipara	CRow
§ *wallichii*	CRow EBee ECha GBri NLar NSti SBri SDix WBor WMoo WOld
§ *weyrichii*	EMan GCal MTed NBir NBro NLar SMrm WBea WCot WMoo

persimmon see *Diospyros virginiana*

persimmon, Japanese see *Diospyros kaki*

Persoonia (Proteaceae)

pinifolia **new**	ECou

Petalostemon see *Dalea*

Petamenes see *Gladiolus*

Petasites (Asteraceae)

albus	EBee EMon GGar GPoy
formosanus	LEdu
– B&SWJ 3025	WCru
fragrans	CNat EGra ELan EMon EPar MGas MHer MSta NLar SWat WFar WHer
§ *frigidus* var. *palmatus*	CRow EBee EPla LEdu MTed MWgw NLar NSti WCru
– – JLS 86317CLOR	SMad WCot
– var. *palmatus* 'Golden Palms'	EFou NSti SSpi
hybridus	CKin EMFW LEdu WHer
japonicus	EBee
– var. *giganteus*	CArn CHEx CRow EBot ECha EGol ELan EMon EPar EPfP LEdu NVic SDes WCra WCru WMoo WTMC
§ – – 'Nishiki-buki' (v)	CHEx CMCo CRow EBee EBot ECoo EEls EMon EPla IBlr ITer NSti SMad WCHb WCot WCru WFar WHil WPGP WTMC
– – 'Variegatus'	see *P. japonicus* var. *giganteus* 'Nishiki-buki'
– f. *purpureus*	EBee EPPr WCot WCru WPnP
palmatus	see *P. frigidus* var. *palmatus*
paradoxus	CDes EBee EMon LEdu MRav NLar SMad WCot WPGP

Petrea (Verbenaceae)

volubilis	CPlN LRHS SOWG WMul

Petrocallis (Brassicaceae)

lagascae	see *P. pyrenaica*
§ *pyrenaica*	WPer

Petrocoptis (Caryophyllaceae)

pseudoviscosa	EHyt WAbe
pyrenaica	CBrm EBur SBla SRms WPat
§ – subsp. *glaucifolia*	CNic EDAr EMan GTou MNrw NBir WPat WPer

Petrocosmea (Gesneriaceae)

kerrii	ETow
– B&SWJ 6634	WCru

Petromarula (Campanulaceae)

pinnata	EBee

Petrophytum (Rosaceae)

caespitosum	CGra GTou NHar NSla NWCA
cinerascens	NWCA SIng
§ *hendersonii*	GDra GGar NHol NWCA WAbe

Petrorhagia (Caryophyllaceae)

§ *saxifraga* ♀ H4	CBrm CNic EBur GDea MBow MNrw NJOw NPri SAga SRms WBea WGwG WMoo WPer WWhi
§ – 'Rosette'	MTho WWin

Petroselinum (Apiaceae)

§ *crispum*	CArn CSev EDAr GPoy GWCH ILis LRHS MBar MChe MDun NBlu SIde SWal WLHH WPer WSel WWye
– 'Bravour' ♀ H4	CPrp ELau MBow MHer
– 'Darki'	CSev NPri
– French	CArn CBod CPrp EDAr ELau IIve MBow MHer NBlu NPri NVic WJek WLHH WWye
– 'Greek'	ELau
– 'Green River'	EOHP
– 'Italian'	see *P. crispum* var. *neapolitanum*
– 'Italian Giant' **new**	WLHH
§ – var. *neapolitanum*	CBod CPrp ELau GWCH IIve MHer
– 'Super Moss Curled'	NVic
§ – var. *tuberosum*	CBod CPrp MHer SIde WHer
hortense	see *P. crispum*
tuberosum	see *P. crispum* var. *tuberosum*

Petteria (Papilionaceae)

ramentacea	CBcs CFil EGFP EPfP NLar SLPl

Petunia (Solanaceae)

(Conchita Series) 'Doble Dark Blue' **new**	LAst WWol
– 'Doble Lavender' **new**	LAst WWol
– 'Doble Pink' **new**	LAst
– 'Doble White' **new**	LAst WWol
Million Bells Cherry = 'Sunbelchipi'^{PBR}	NPri
Million Bells Lemon = 'Sunbelkic'^{PBR}	NPri WWol
Million Bells Terracotta = 'Sunbelkist' **new**	NPri
Million Bells Trailing Blue = 'Sunbelkubu'^{PBR}	NPri
Million Bells White **new**	NPri
(Petitunia Series)	WWol
Petitunia Bright Dream = 'Danpetbright'^{PBR} **new**	
– 'Petitunia Happy Dream' **new**	WWol
– Petitunia Violet Dream = 'Danpetviolet'^{PBR} **new**	WWol
Surfinia Blue = 'Sunblue'	CFox LAst NPri
Surfinia Blue Vein = 'Sunsolos'^{PBR}	CFox NPri
Surfinia Double Purple = 'Keidopuel' (d)	WWol
Surfinia Hot Pink = 'Marrose'^{PBR}	CFox NPri
Surfinia Lime = 'Keiyeul'	LAst NPri WWol
Surfinia Pastel 2000 = 'Sunpapi'	NPri

Surfinia Pink Ice = 'Hakice'^{PBR}	LAst NPri
Surfinia Pink Vein = 'Suntosol'^{PBR}	CFox GKir NPri WWol
Surfinia Purple = 'Shihi Brilliant'	NPri
Surfinia Purple Vein = 'Sunpurve'^{PBR}	WWol
Surfinia Sky Blue = 'Keilarbu'	NPri
Surfinia White = 'Kesupite' (Tumbelina Series) Priscilla = 'Kerpril'^{PBR}	CFox GKir NPri WWol LAst NPri
- Rosella = 'Kerros'^{PBR} **new**	LAst
- Tumbelina Candyfloss **new**	LAst NPri
- Tumbelina Julia = 'Kerjul'^{PBR}	LAst NPri
- Tumbelina Margarita **new**	LAst NPri
- Tumbelina Rosella Improved **new**	NPri

Peucedanum (Apiaceae)

aegopoides	EGle
decursivum **new**	EBee
formosanum B&SWJ 3647	WCru
friesiorum from Mt. Kilimanjaro **new**	SSpi
japonicum **new**	EBee
litorale	see *Kitagawia litoralis*
ostruthium	GPoy
- 'Daphnis' (v)	CDes CSpe EBee EGle EMan EMon EPPr EVFa LEdu MTed NChi NGby NProWComWCot WHil WHrl WPGP
siamicum B&SWJ 264 **new**	WCru
verticillare	CRDP EBee EMan LPhx MDun NBid NChi NDov NLar SDix SIgm SMad SSpi WCot

Phacelia (Hydrophyllaceae)

sericea subsp. *sericea*	GKev

Phacocapnos see *Cysticapnos*

Phaedranassa (Amaryllidaceae)

carmiolii **new**	WCot
dubia	WCot
* *montana*	LRHS
tunguraguae	WCot
viridiflora	WCot

Phaedranthus see *Distictis*

Phaenocoma (Asteraceae)

prolifera	SPlb

Phaenosperma (Poaceae)

globosa	CHar CKno EBee EGle EHoe EPPr EPla EWes EWsh LEdu LRHS NHol SMac WBor WDyG

Phaiophleps (Iridaceae)

nigricans	see *Sisyrinchium striatum*

Phaius (Orchidaceae)

minor	EFEx

Phalaris (Poaceae)

§ *aquatica*	MGol
arundinacea	CKin CWCL EPla EWTr LPVe MBNS MLan SPlb SWat WBan

- 'Elegantissima'	see *P. arundinacea* var. *picta* 'Picta'
- var. *picta*	CBri CHEx CWib GKir LHrt LRHS LSyl NBid NBur NPer SBri SHel SLon SYvo WDin WFar
- - 'Aureovariegata' (v)	CBcs CSWP MRav NGdn NPer SBHF SIng SWat WMoo
- - 'Feesey' (v)	More than 30 suppliers
- - 'Luteopicta' (v)	EBee EHoe EPPr EPfP EPla MMoz SPar WLeb WTin WWpP
- - 'Luteovariegata' (v)	EMon NGdn
§ - - 'Picta' (v) ♀ H4	COIW CRow EHoe EHon ELan ENot EPfP EPla GWCH LEdu LGro LPBA LRHS MBar MWgw MWod NFor NHol NLon NOak NSti SDes SIng SPer SWat WEas WMoo WWin WWpP WWye
- - 'Streamlined' (v)	EBee EMon EPla EWsh LRHS SLPl WFar WLeb
- - 'Tricolor' (v)	CPen EBee EHoe EMon EPla MBar WBea
canariensis	LIck SWal
tuberosa stenoptera	see *P. aquatica*

Phanerophlebia (Dryopteridaceae)

caryotidea	see *Cyrtomium caryotideum*
falcata	see *Cyrtomium falcatum*
fortunei	see *Cyrtomium fortunei*

Pharbitis see *Ipomoea*

Phaseolus (Papilionaceae)

caracalla	see *Vigna caracalla*

Phegopteris (Thelypteridaceae)

§ *connectilis*	EFer EMon LSyl NMar NVic SRms
decursive-pinnata	CLAP EMon GBri LEur NHol NMar WRic
hexagonoptera	LEur

Phellodendron (Rutaceae)

amurense	CBcs CFil CMCN EPfP GIBF LEdu LPan NLar SSpi WDin WNor WPic
- var. *sachalinense*	CBcs GIBF WPGP
lavalleei	EPfP WPGP

Phenakospermum (Strelitziaceae)

guianense	NBlo XBlo

Philadelphus ✿ (Hydrangeaceae)

ACE 1907	EPot
'Albâtre' (d)	LRHS
'Atlas' (v)	WCom
'Avalanche'	CMHG EBee EBre GKir LRHS NPro SPer SRms WDin WFar WHCG
'Beauclerk' ♀ H4	CDoC CDul CMHG CSBt CTri EBee EBre ENot EPfP EWTr GKir LRHS MAsh MBri MGos MRav NBee NHol NWea SLim SPer SReu SRms SSpi WHCG WWin
'Belle Etoile' ♀ H4	More than 30 suppliers
'Bicolore' **new**	MWya
'Boule d'Argent' (d)	CMHG
'Bouquet Blanc'	GKir GQui MRav SPer SRms WKif
brachybotrys	CFil ECre EPfP MRav NHol WHCG WPGP
'Buckley's Quill' (d)	MRav MWya WBcn
'Burfordensis'	EPfP SPer WCom
'Burkwoodii'	LRHS SMer
caucasicus	GEil
coronarius	CTri ENot LBuc LRHS MWat MWhi NFor NLon SGar SHBN SMer SPer SRPl WDin
- 'Aureus' ♀ H4	More than 30 suppliers

- 'Bowles' Variety'	see *P. coronarius* 'Variegatus'
- 'Gold Mound'	MGos MRav
§ - 'Variegatus' (v) ♀ H4	More than 30 suppliers
'Coupe d'Argent'	CPLG MRav
'Dame Blanche' (d)	EWTr LRHS MAsh MRav NPro
'Deberoux' (v)	EVFa
delavayi	CFil CPle EBee EPfP NWea SGar
	WCru WHCG WPGP
- AC 1648	GGar
- EDHCH 97170	EPPr
- var. *calvescens*	see *P. purpurascens*
'Enchantement' (d)	MRav SDix WLRN
§ 'Erectus'	CSBt CWib EBee EHol ENot EPfP
	ISea MRav SPer SPla WCom WDin
	WHCG WPat WTel
fragrans	CFil WPGP
'Frosty Morn' (d)	CBcs LBuc LRHS MBri MGos
	SMac SPer SPla WCom WGwG
henryi **new**	WPGP
incanus	CPLG
§ 'Innocence' (v)	CBot CEnd CHar CPLG CPle
	CWSG EHoe ELan EPfP EVFa GKir
	LAst LRHS MBNS MBri MGos
	MRav NBlu NPri NPro SAga SHBN
	SPar SPer SPla SReu SSta WFar
	WHCG WWeb
'Innocence Variegatus'	see *P.* 'Innocence'
§ *insignis*	MRav WBod
keteleeri	GEil
x *lemoinei*	CTri EBee EVFa EWTr GEil GKir
	MGos NFor SHBN SMer SRPl
	WDin WFar WGwG WStI WWal
- 'Erectus'	see *P.* 'Erectus'
- 'Lemoinei'	NWea
'Lemon Hill'	WBcn
lewisii	CFil GKir LPhx
- L 1896	WPGP
- 'Waterton'	LBuc
madrensis	CFil LHop WPGP
- CD&R 1226	WPGP
'Manteau d'Hermine'	More than 30 suppliers
(d) ♀ H4	
'Marjorie'	CHar
mexicanus	CFil EBee MWya WPGP
- 'Rose Syringa'	CFil WPGP
microphyllus	CBot CDul CFil CMHG EBee ELan
	EPfP ESis GKir LAst LPhx LRHS
	MAsh MBro MRav MWhi NHol
	SLon SPer SReu SSpi WHCG WPat
	WSHC
- var. *occidentalis*	CFil EPot
'Minnesota Snowflake' (d)	CBcs EBee ECtt EWes LBuc LRHS
	MRav NPro WFar WRHF
'Mont Blanc'	CBcs WFar
'Mrs E.L. Robinson' (d)	EBee ECtt LAst LRHS
'Natchez' (d)	ECtt GKir MBNS SVil WBcn WTel
'Norma'	WBcn
'Oeil de Pourpre'	EBee MRav
palmeri	CFil WPGP
pekinensis **new**	CPLG
'Perryhill'	SPer
§ *purpurascens*	CFil EWes GIBF GKir MRav SSpi
	WBcn WPat
'Russalka' **new**	MWya
schrenkii	CFil WPGP
§ 'Silberregen'	CDoC CFwr EBee ECtt EPfP EWTr
	LAst LRHS MAsh MBar MGos
	MRav NPro SHBN SPoG SRms
	WBod WFar WPat
Silver Showers	see *P.* 'Silberregen'
'Snow Velvet'	LRHS
'Snowflake'	CWSG EMil LAst NMoo WLRN
'Souvenir de Billiard'	see *P. insignis*

subcanus	CPLG MRav
'Sybille' ♀ H4	CMHG ENot EPfP GKir LRHS
	MBri MRav SPer SRms SSpi WBcn
	WHCG WKif WSHC
tenuifolius	CMCN GIBF
tomentosus	CFil CPLG WHCG WPGP
- B&SWJ 2707	WCru
'Velléda'	CFil
'Virginal' (d)	More than 30 suppliers
'Voie Lactée'	CFil GEil MRav
White Rock = 'Pekphil'	CDoC COtt CWSG EBee LAst
	LRHS MAsh NMoo SPer WLRN

Philesia (Philesiaceae)

buxifolia	see *P. magellanica*
§ *magellanica*	EMil GGGa GSki SOkd SSpi WBod
	WCru WSHC
- 'Rosea' **new**	CPLG

Phillyrea (Oleaceae)

angustifolia	CDul CFil CMCN CPle CTri EBee
	EPfP ERom MGos NPSI SEND SLPl
	SPar SPer SSpi WBVN WBcn WDin
	WPGP WSHC
- f. *rosmarinifolia*	CFil LAst WPGP
decora	see *Osmanthus decorus*
§ *latifolia*	CFil CHEx CPLG EBee EPfP LRHS
	SAPC SArc SLPl SSpi WBcn WDin
	WGer WPGP
media	see *P. latifolia*
I - 'Rodrigueziensis' **new**	WCFE

Philodendron (Araceae)

epipremnum	see *Epipremnum pinnatum*
erubescens	LRHS
'Burgundy' ♀ H1	
- 'Red Emerald'	CHal
scandens ♀ H1	CHal NBlo XBlo
selloum	EAmu WMul

Phlebodium see *Polypodium*

Phleum (Poaceae)

pratense	CBig EFWa EHoe SRGP
- subsp. *bertolonii*	CKin

Phlomis ✿ (Lamiaceae)

alpina	EBee
* *anatolica* 'Lloyd's Variety'	CAbP CSam EBee ELan GCal LAst
	LRHS MAsh MBri MSte SPer SSvw
	WCom WPen
anisodonta white-flowered	WPhl
aff. *anisodonta*	WPhl
armeniaca	WPhl
atropurpurea	GBin WPhl
betonicoides	EMon EPPr WPhl
bourgaei 'Whirling	WPhl
Dervish' JMT 271	
bovei subsp. *maroccana*	CBot EBee GCal IFro LPio WPhl
breviflora	WPhl
cashmeriana	CBot CPle ECha NLar WCFE WPhl
chrysophylla ♀ H3	CAbP CBot CPle CSam CStr EBee
	ECha ELan EMan EPfP LAst LRHS
	SDix SDry SIgm SPer WCFE
	WCom WCot WPhl
cretica	WPhl
* *cristata* **new**	CCge
cypria var. *occidentalis*	WPhl
§ 'Edward Bowles'	SDry SIgm SLPl SLon WCom
	WCot WPhl
* 'Elliot's Variety'	CPLG
fruticosa ♀ H4	More than 30 suppliers
grandiflora	CBot EBee SEND

- JMT 256	WPhl
italica	More than 30 suppliers
- 'Pink Glory'	WPhl
jeholensis **new**	EBee
lanata ♀ H3-4	CAbP CCge CStr EBee ELan EMan
	EPfP LRHS MSte NPro SBla SBrw
	SDry SPer WEas WGer WPhl WWye
- 'Pygmy'	SLon WPhl
leucophracta	EBee
- 'Golden Janissary'	EBee
longifolia	CBot CHad EBee EPfP LHop LRHS
	SIgm SPer
- var. *bailanica*	CPle LRHS SMac WFar WSHC
- var. *longifolia*	WPhl
lunariifolia JMT 258	WPhl
lychnitis	MWrn WPhl
lycia	LRHS SIgm WPhl
megalantha **new**	EBee
milingensis **new**	EBee
monocephala	WPhl
platystegia	WPhl
purpurea	CAbP CPle CSam ELan EPfP LRHS
	MAsh NBir SBrw SPar WCot WPhl
	WSHC
- *alba*	CBot EPfP LHop WSHC
- subsp. *almeriensis*	CStr WPhl
- 'Compact'	WPhl
rigida	EBee WCru
rotata **new**	EBee
§ *russeliana* ♀ H4	More than 30 suppliers
samia Boiss	see *P. russeliana*
samia L.	EBee EBlw EMar NChi NGdn
	SDes WFar
- JMT 285	LRHS WPhl
'Sunningdale Gold'	WPhl
tatsienensis	EBee
var. *tatsienensis* **new**	
tuberosa	CBot CFir CPou EBee EMan EMar
	ERou EWTr LAst LLWP MCAu NLar
	SIgm SMrm SSvw WCru WPGP WPhl
- 'Amazone'	CFir EBee EBlw EChP ECha EFou
	EHrv EMan EPfP LAst LPhx MBri
	MCLN NCot NSti SMad SMrm
	SUsu WCot WFar WTMC
viscosa misapplied	see *P. russeliana*
viscosa Poiret	WPhl

Phlox ✿ (Polemoniaceae)

adsurgens ♀ H4	EDAr ITim WAbe
- 'Alba'	SBla WAbe
- 'Red Buttes'	CLyd EPot LPio SBla
'Wagon Wheel'	CLyd CWCL EBre ECtt EDAr EHyt
	EPot EWes GEdr ITim LRHS NHar
	NSla SIng SMrm SPlb SRms WAbe
	WCFE WCom WFar WLin WRus
	WWin
x *arendsii* 'Anja'	EBee WCot
- 'Early Star'	CFwr EBee
- 'Hilda'	CStr EBee
- 'Lilac Star' **new**	CFir LAst WHil
§ - 'Luc's Lilac'	CPrp EBee EMar LPhx NBro
	NDov STes SVil
- 'Ping Pong'	CFwr EBee STes WHil
- 'Rosa Star' **new**	CFir LAst
- 'Sabine' **new**	CFir EBee
§ - (Spring Pearl Series)	CCol CHea CM&M EBee EChP
'Miss Jill'	EFou EGle GMaP NHol WCot
§ - - 'Miss Jo-Ellen'	EFou EGle GBri NPSI
§ - - 'Miss Karen'	CCol EChP EGle ERou NBro
§ - - 'Miss Margie'	EBee EChP EFou EGle ERou GBri
	GMaP LAst NBir NPSI WHil
§ - - 'Miss Mary'	CCol CM&M EBee EChP EFou
	EGle GBri NHol STes WHoo

§ - - 'Miss Wilma'	CCol GMaP NPSI WBar
- 'Suzanne'	EBee
austromontana	EPot GDra NWCA
bifida	ITim
- 'Alba'	LTwo WAbe
- blue	LRHS SBla SUsu
- 'Colvin's White'	CLyd CPlt EDAr SAga SBla
- 'Minima Colvin'	ECtt EPot
- 'Petticoat' zur Linden	CLyd CMea CPBP EPot GEdr
	LRHS SBla SUsu WLin
- 'Ralph Haywood'	CLyd GBuc ITim WAbe WOBN
- 'Starbrite'	CLyd LRHS SHar WFar
- 'Thefi'	EWes LTwo
'Black Buttes'	CLyd EPot
borealis	see *P. sibirica* subsp. *borealis*
* - *arctica*	EPot
bryoides	see *P. hoodii* subsp. *muscoides*
caespitosa	CMea EWes NDlv NMen SOkd
- subsp. *condensata*	see *P. condensata*
- subsp. *pulvinata*	see *P. pulvinata*
canadensis	see *P. divaricata*
carolina 'Bill Baker' ♀ H4	More than 30 suppliers
- 'Magnificence'	CM&M CPrp EChP EGle EWes GBuc
	GMac LAst MSte SOkh SSvw WCot
- 'Miss Lingard' ♀ H4	CHea CPrp CSam EChP EFou EGle
	EPfP GBuc GCal GMaP GMac LAst
	LRHS MMil MRav MSte NBir NChi
	NGdn NSti SAga SBla SChu SCro
	SPla WCot WHil WMaN WWin
* 'Chanel'	MLan
'Charles Ricardo'	CElw EBee EGle ETow EWes
	GBuc MBro MCLN SAga SBri
	SMrm SUsu SVil WHoo WRus
'Chattahoochee'	see *P. divaricata* subsp. *laphamii*
	'Chattahoochee'
§ *condensata*	NWCA WAbe WLin WPat
covillei	see *P. condensata*
'Daniel's Cushion'	see *P. subulata* 'McDaniel's
	Cushion'
diffusa	NMen
§ *divaricata* ♀ H4	EHol EWTr GKir MRav MSte SBod
	SHBN SPlb WPer WWin
- f. *albiflora*	ELan
- 'Blue Dreams'	CElw CFir CHea EBre EChP ECha
	EHrv GBuc GKir LRHS MNrw
	MSte MTis NDov NGdn NPPs
	SChu SCro SMrm SPla SUsu WFar
	WHal WPGP WRus WSan WWeb
- 'Blue Perfume'	CM&M CPen EChP EFou LPVe
	NBro NGdn NSti WWeb
- 'Charles' **new**	NHar
- 'Clouds of Perfume'	CHea CM&M EBee EChP EMan
	GBri GEdr GMaP LAst LPVe LRHS
	MWgw NCat NPPs NSti SBla SDod
	SHBN SMer SMrm SOkh SWat
	WAul WFar WRus WSan WWeb
- 'Dirigo Ice'	CLyd CPlt EBee EGle EHrv EMan
	LHop NLar SAga SBla WFar WIvy
- 'Eco Texas Purple'	CLAP CPlt CRez EBee EChP ECtt
	EMan GMac MHar NDov NHar
	SAga SIgm SMrm SUsu WPGP
	WRus WWeb
- 'Fuller's White'	CLyd SHBN
§ - subsp. *laphamii*	CLyd EGle EWes MCAu NSti SOkh
	SUsu WCru WFar WFoF
§ - - 'Chattahoochee' ♀ H4	CBot CPBP CSpe CWCL EChP
	ECtt EDAr EHyt ELan EMNN EPot
	EWes GBuc LHop LRHS MBro
	NLAp NPPs SBla SDes SIng SMrm
	WBro WCFE WCom WHil WLin
	WSHC WWin
- - 'Chattahoochee	EDAr LRHS
Variegated' (v)	

§	– 'Louisiana Purple'	EBee EGle NHar SVil	
	– 'May Breeze'	CLyd EBre EGle EHrv GKir GMaP	
		GMac LAst LHop LRHS MNrw	
		MSte NDov NGdn NHar SHBN	
		SMrm SPla WCom WFar WIvy	
		WPGP WRus	
	– 'Plum Perfect'	MSph NLar SHar	
*	– 'White Perfume'	CM&M CPen EChP EMil EWes	
		LPVe MBrN NBro NLar NSti SChu	
		SMrm WWeb	
	douglasii	NWCA SRms	
	– 'Apollo'	CLyd CTri EDAr EPot GDra LRHS	
		NHol NMen SBla WWin	
	– 'Blue Mist'	GDra	
	– 'Boothman's Variety'	CLyd ECha EDAr ELan EPar EPfP	
	♀ H4	EPot GKir LRHS MWat NMen	
		SRms WCom WEas WWin	
	– 'Concorde'	GDra	
	– 'Crackerjack' ♀ H4	CLyd COIW ECtt EDAr ELan	
		EMNN EMlt EPfP EPot GAbr GDra	
		GEdr GKev GKir GMaP LRHS	
		MHer NHar NLAp NLon NMen	
		NPro SBod SIng WAbe WFar WLin	
	– 'Eva'	CLyd CM&M COIW EBre EDAr	
		ELan EMNN EPot GKir GTou	
		LRHS NBir NHar NLAp NMen	
		NWCA SMrm WLin WPer WWin	
	– 'Galaxy'	CLyd EWes GDra NHar	
	– 'Ice Mountain'	ECho EDAr ELan EMlt NMen NPri	
		NWCA SRot WLin WRHF	
	– 'Iceberg' ♀ H4	CLyd EPot GDra GKev GMaP ITim	
		NHar NLAp NMen WRHF WWin	
	– 'J.A. Hibberson'	EPot	
	– Lilac Queen	see *P. douglasii* 'Lilakönigin'	
§	– 'Lilakönigin'	EDAr	
	– 'Napoleon'	CPBP NMen	
	– 'Ochsenblut'	MDHE MHer	
	– 'Red Admiral' ♀ H4	CNic EBre EMNN EPot ESis EWes	
		GDra GKir LRHS NHar NHol NLon	
		NMen SBod SMrm WCFE WFar	
	– 'Rose Cushion'	EDAr EWes GDra LRHS MDHE	
		MHer NMen	
	– 'Rose Queen'	CLyd GDra	
	– 'Rosea'	EBre EDAr ELan EMNN EPar ESis	
		GMaP LRHS NLAp NMen SBod	
		SMer WFar	
	– 'Silver Rose'	GTou NLAp NWCA	
	– 'Sprite'	SRms	
	– 'Tycoon'	see *P. subulata* 'Tamaongalei'	
	– 'Violet Queen'	EWes GDra NHar WFar WPat	
	– 'Waterloo'	CLyd EPot GDra LRHS NHar	
		NMen SChu	
I	– 'White Admiral'	SIng	
	'Geddington Cross'	MWgw	
	glaberrima 'Morris	CDes	
	Berd' **new**		
	hendersonii	CGra	
	hoodii	CLyd ECho	
§	– subsp. *muscoides*	EWes WLin	
	'Kelly's Eye' ♀ H4	CLyd CM&M CPBP CSam ECha	
		EDAr ELan EMNN EPot LRHS NLAp	
		NMen WFar WLin WPer WRHF	
	kelseyi	EHyt NWCA WAbe	
	– 'Lemhi Purple'	CGra CPBP SOkd	
	– 'Rosette'	CLyd EPot LRHS MDKP NMen WPer	
§	*latifolia*	EChP EMan MNrw SAga WRus	
	longifolia	SOkd	
	subsp. *brevifolia*		
	'Louisiana'	see *P. divaricata* 'Louisiana Purple'	
	maculata	NOrc WPer	
	– 'Alpha' ♀ H4	More than 30 suppliers	
	– Avalanche	see *P. maculata* 'Schneelawine'	
	– 'Delta'	CHea EBee EChP EMan EVFa	

		MCAu NHol NLon NSti SPer STes	
		WFar WHil WMaN WPnP	
	– 'Natascha'	More than 30 suppliers	
	– 'Omega' ♀ H4	CBri CHea CMHG EFou EPfP	
		EVFa GBuc GKir GMaP LRHS	
		MCAu MCLN MRav NBid NGdn	
		NHol NLar NSti SChu SMrm SPer	
		SPla SSpi WFar WMaN WPnP	
		WRus WSHC WWin WWye	
	– 'Princess Sturdza'	CBos SDix	
	– 'Reine du Jour'	CPlt EBee EFou LPhx NDov SAga	
		SDys SMrm SOkh SUsu	
	– 'Rosalinde'	EBee EMan EVFa MCAu MRav	
		MSte MWgw NHol SBla SChu SVil	
§	– 'Schneelawine'	EFou SChu	
	'Matineus'	LPhx	
	'Millstream'	see *P. x procumbens* 'Millstream'	
	missoulensis	SIng	
	muscoides	see *P. hoodii* subsp. *muscoides*	
	nivalis	NMen	
	– 'Camlaensis'	CLyd	
	– 'Jill Alexander'	CMea	
	– 'Nivea'	EPot LRHS WLRN	
	ovata misapplied	see *P. latifolia*	
	paniculata	CBos CHad EBee EChP LPhx	
		NBid NFor SDix WCot WOld	
		ERou	
	– 'A.E. Amos'	CBcs EBee MWat	
	– 'Aida' Pfitzer	CBcs EBee MWat	
	– var. *alba*	EBee GCal SDix WCot	
	– 'Alba Grandiflora' ♀ H4	EHrv SBla WEas	
	– 'Amethyst' Foerster	CFir CSam CWCL CWib EBee	
		EGle EHrv EPfP ERou GKir MCAu	
		MCLN NBir NBlu SBod SMer WFar	
		WHrl WWye	
	– 'Amethyst' misapplied	see *P. paniculata* 'Lilac Time'	
	– 'Anthony Six'	EBee	
	– 'Antoinette Six' **new**	CFwr	
	– 'Balmoral'	EBee ECtt GKir LLWP LRHS MLLN	
		MRav MSte NPri NSti SMer SWat	
	– 'Barnwell'	ELan GMac	
	– 'Becky Towe' (v)	COtt EBee EGle LRHS WWeb	
	– 'Betty Symons-Jeune'	CFwr	
	– 'Bill Green'	LRHS	
	– 'Blue Boy'	CBri CElw CFwr EBee EGle ENot	
		ERou LRHS NBir NBro NPSI WFar	
		WLow WMoo WViv	
	– 'Blue Evening'	LPhx SMrm	
	– 'Blue Ice' ♀ H4	CPen EBee EFou EMar LPhx LRHS	
		MRav MWat SChu SLon SMrm SPla	
	– 'Blue Mist'	EFou	
	– 'Blue Paradise'	CDes CElw CFwr CHar CMGP	
		CRDP EBre EChP EFou EGle LPVe	
		LPhx LRHS MAnH NGdn NPSI	
		NSti SAga SBla SMrm SVil SWat	
		WFar WHil WPGP WWeb WWye	
	– 'Blushing Bride'	SRms	
	– 'Border Gem'	CBcs CFwr CPen EBee EBre ECtt	
		EFou ENot ERou GKir MSte NChi	
		SMer SWat WCot WViv	
	– 'Branklyn'	EBee EBre GKir GMac LPhx LRHS	
		SMer WFar	
	– 'Brigadier' ♀ H4	CBla CFwr CSam EBee EBre ECtt	
		ELan ENot GBin GKir GMaP LRHS	
		MCAu MDKP MFir MWat NVic	
		SPer SPla SRms	
	– 'Bright Eyes' ♀ H4	CBla CBri COtt CRDP CSBt EBee	
		EBre ECtt ENot ERou GKir LRHS	
		MArl MCAu MDKP NPri SBod	
		SMer STes WTel	
	– 'Burgi'	CBos SDix	
	– 'Caroline van den Berg'	GKir SMer SRms WCot	
	– 'Cecil Hanbury'	EBee ERou SRms	
	– 'Chintz'	EFou MRav SRms	

	- 'Cinderella'	CFwr EBee EFou ERou MCLN NCat
	- 'Cool of the Evening'	CBos LPhx
	- Count Zeppelin	see *P. paniculata* 'Graf Zeppelin'
	- 'Crème de Menthe' **new**	CFwr
	- 'Danielle' **new**	CFwr
	- 'Darwin's Choice'	see *P. paniculata* 'Norah Leigh'
	- 'David'	CPen EBee EBre EChP EGle ERou
		IPot LPVe NChi NGby WAul WBor
		WCot WHil
	- 'Discovery'	EBee ECGP EMar EWes LBuc STes
		SWat
	- 'Dodo Hanbury-Forbes'	EHol
	♀ H4	
	- 'Doghouse Pink' **new**	CBos
	- 'Dresden China'	EBee SWat
	- 'Duchess of York'	CBos
§	- 'Duesterlohe'	CElw CPen CSam EFou EGle ERou
		GBuc GMac IPot LCaP MCLN
		NBir NCat NLar NSti SMrm SPer
		SSpe WAul WFar WHil
	- 'Eclaireur' Lemoine	EBee SWat
	- 'Eclaireur' misapplied	see *P. paniculata* 'Duesterlohe'
	- 'Eden's Crush'	CM&M EBee EChP EFou NVic WHil
	- 'Eden's Flash'	EFou EGle ERou WHil
	- 'Eden's Glory'	EChP EFou EGle
	- 'Eden's Glow'	CFwr EChP EFou WHil
	- 'Eden's Smile'	CFwr EBee EChP EFou ERou SHar
		WHil
	- 'Elizabeth Arden'	EBee EFou ERou MSte NCat SWat
		WMaN
	- 'Empty Feelings' **new**	CPen EBee EChP EGle IPot NSti
	- 'Étoile de Paris'	see *P. paniculata* 'Toits de Paris'
	- 'Europa'	CBcs COIW EBee ELan EPfP ERou
		LRHS MBri MCAu MFir MTis MWat
		NBir SBod SChu SPer SPla WFar
	'Eva Cullum'	CBos EBee EBre ECtt EFou EGle
		GKir LRHS MArl MLLN MRav
		NPPs SMer SPer SPet SWat WCot
		WHil WMoo
	- 'Eventide' ♀ H4	EBee EBre ECtt EFou ENot EPfP GKir
		LRHS MArl MCLN NLar NPri SChu
		SMer SPer SPet SWat WCot WViv
	- 'Excelsior'	MRav
	- 'Fairy's Petticoat'	MWat NCat
	- 'Flamingo'	EBee EBre ERou LRHS MAvo NLar
	- 'Franz Schubert'	CRez EBee EBre ECGP EFou EGle
		GKir GMac LRHS MAnH MRav
		NBir NChi NLar NSti SChu SMer
		STes SWat WCot WMaN WTel
§	- 'Frau Alfred von	COIW LBuc MBri SMrm
	Mauthner'	
	- 'Frosted Elegance' (v)	CPen EBee EChP EPPr
	- 'Fujiyama'	see *P. paniculata* 'Mount Fuji'
	- 'Glamis'	MWat
	- 'Goldmine' PBR **new**	CFai MLLN
§	- 'Graf Zeppelin'	CBla ELan EWll LRHS MWat SRms
	- 'Harlequin' (v)	CBos CElw CMGP CMil EBee EBre
		ECha EHoe ERou GBuc GKir MCAu
		MCCP NBid NLar NSti SPer SPla
		STes SUsu WCom WCot WFar WTel
I	- 'Hesperis'	LPhx MAnH SMHy SMrm SUsu
	- 'Iceberg'	MFir
	- 'Iris'	CDes EGle GBuc LPhx LPio SRms
	- 'Jubilee' **new**	CFwr
	- 'Judy'	LBuc MHdf NBro
	- 'Jules Sandeau'	EBee EBre MBri SDes SMrm
§	- 'Juliglut'	CFwr EChP ERou MWat SWat WCot
	- July Glow	see *P. paniculata* 'Juliglut'
	- 'Katarina'	CFwr EBee EChP ECtt EPfP
	- 'Kirchenfuerst'	CFwr CHar EBee EFou MBri NBir
		SMrm
	- 'Kirmeslaendler'	CBcs EBee ERou LRHS MLLN
		NDov SRPl SVil

	- 'Lady Clare'	SRms
	- 'Latest Red'	see *P. paniculata* 'Spätrot'
*	- 'Laura'	CM&M COtt EBee EGle ERou IPot
		NBro NVic SDes STes WFar WHil
		WHoo WLow
§	- 'Lavendelwolke'	CFwr EBee LPhx NBir SKCG
		SWat
	- Lavender Cloud	see *P. paniculata* 'Lavendelwolke'
	- 'Le Mahdi' ♀ H4	EBre ELan GBin MAvo MRav
		MWat SRms WCot
	- 'Lichtspel'	EFou LPhx
§	- 'Lilac Time'	CBla EBee EHrv EWll MCLN
		MDKP MSte MTis NCat
	- 'Little Boy'	CElw EBee EChP EFou EGle ERou
		LRHS NLar SDes STes WFar WWeb
	- 'Little Laura'	EFou MCLN NLar
	- 'Little Princess'	CFwr EGle NLar SDes
	- 'Lizzy' PBR	ERou MBri
	- 'Manoir d'Hézèques' **new**	WCot
	- 'Mary Christine'	EBee
	- 'Mary Fox'	CSam NDov
	- 'Mia Ruys'	CBos EFou ERou GMac MArl MBri
		MLLN SMrm
	- 'Mies Copijn'	EBee GMaP WFar
	- 'Milly van Hoboken'	CBos SCro
	- 'Miranda'	CStr
	- 'Miss Elie'	CHea CPen EBee EFou EGle ERou
		MCLN SSpe WFar WHil WHoo
	- 'Miss Holland'	CHea EGle LCaP WHoo WSan
	- 'Miss Jessica' **new**	ERou LAst
	- 'Miss Jill'	see *Phlox* x *arendsii* 'Miss Jill'
	- 'Miss Jo-Ellen'	see *Phlox* x *arendsii* 'Miss Jo-Ellen'
	- 'Miss Karen'	see *Phlox* x *arendsii* (Spring Pearl
		Series) 'Miss Karen'
	- 'Miss Kelly'	CFwr CM&M COtt CWib EBee
		EFou SSpe WHoo
	- 'Miss Margie'	see *Phlox* x *arendsii* (Spring Pearl
		Series) 'Miss Margie'
	- 'Miss Mary'	see *Phlox* x *arendsii* (Spring Pearl
		Series) 'Miss Mary'
	- 'Miss Pepper'	CMGP EBee EBre EMil ERou EWll
		IPot MCLN NLar SMrm WFar WHil
		WLow
	- 'Miss Universe'	CFwr CPen CRez EBee EGle LCaP
		MCCP WHil WHoo WSan
	- 'Miss Wilma'	see *Phlox* x *arendsii* 'Miss Wilma'
	- 'Monica Lynden-Bell'	CBos CDes CFai CM&M CSam
		EBee EChP EVFa GBri LAst MCLN
		NCat NLar SPla STes WCot WFar
		WLin
	- 'Mother of Pearl' ♀ H4	CHad EBee EBre ELan EMar LRHS
		MWat NVic SBla SPer SPet SVil
§	- 'Mount Fuji' ♀ H4	More than 30 suppliers
	- 'Mount Fujiyama'	see *P. paniculata* 'Mount Fuji'
	- 'Mrs A.E. Jeans'	SRms
	- 'Newbird'	SRms
	- 'Nicky'	see *P. paniculata* 'Duesterlohe'
§	- 'Norah Leigh' (v)	More than 30 suppliers
	- 'Orange Perfection'	see *P. paniculata* 'Prince of Orange'
	- 'Otley Choice'	EBee GMac LAst LRHS MRav MSte
		MWat NLar NSti SChu SCoo SVil
	- 'P.D. Williams'	WCot
	- 'Pastorale'	MWat NCat WCot WTel
	- 'Pat Coleman'	EFou
	- 'Pax'	EBee EMon ERou LPhx
	- 'Pike'	WCot
	- 'Pink Posie' PBR (v)	MAsh MBri SPer WCot WFar WWeb
	- 'Popeye'	CFwr EBee ECtt MBri NLar
§	- 'Prince of Orange' ♀ H4	More than 30 suppliers
	- 'Prospero' ♀ H4	CHar CSam EBee EHrv EOrc
		MCAu NBid NDov SChu SMer
		SUsu SVil WTel WViv
	- 'Rainbow'	CFwr EGle LPVe

	– 'Rapture'	MWat
	– 'Red Indian'	MWat SMer
	– 'Red Riding Hood' **new**	EBee LAst WHil
	– 'Rembrandt'	EBee EBre ERou GBri SBla WCot
	– 'Rijnstroom'	CBcs EBee EBre ECot ERou GMac LRHS MBow WFar WTel WViv
	– 'Rosa Pastell'	CFwr EBee EGle EHrv EMon LPhx SAga SKCG
§	– 'Rubymine' **new**	CFai ERou
	– 'Russian Violet'	MWat
	– 'San Antonio'	EBre WFar
	– 'Sandringham'	CFwr EBee EBre EHrv EPfP GKir LRHS MArl MNrw MRav MSte NBir NPri SMer SPer SRPl
§	– 'Schneerausch'	GKir LPhx WCot
	– 'Septemberglut'	EBee
	– 'Silvermine' (v) **new**	EBee
	– 'Skylight'	MWat NVic SPer WLin
	– 'Snow White'	NVic
	– Snowdrift	see *P. paniculata* 'Schneerausch'
§	– 'Spätrot'	NCat
	– 'Spitfire'	see *P. paniculata* 'Frau Alfred von Mauthner'
	– 'Starburst'	CRez EBee
	– 'Starfire'	More than 30 suppliers
	– 'Steeple Bumpstead'	EGle WCot
	– 'Sternhimmel'	CGra LPhx
	– 'Tenor'	CFir CFwr EBee EChP EFou ERou GKir LBBr LRHS MCAu MDKP MSte NGdn NPri SAga SChu SPet SPla SUsu WFar WHrl WLow WMoo WViv
	– 'The King'	EBee EChP EGle EWll LRHS NBro STes SUsu SWat WHil WTel
§	– 'Toits de Paris'	CBos EGle LPhx MWat NCat SUsu
	– 'Uspekh'	CFwr EBee EFou EWes MCLN MSte MTis NDov SChu SPer SVil WFar
	– 'Utopia'	LPhx
	– 'Van Gogh'	CFwr EHrv
	– 'Vintage Wine'	ENot GBin MSte
	– 'Violetta Gloriosa'	CBos LPhx
	– 'Visions'	EBee WHil
	– 'White Admiral' ♀ H4	More than 30 suppliers
	– 'Wilhelm Kesselring' **new**	CFai GBin
	– 'Windsor' ♀ H4	CBla CBri CFwr EBee EFou EPfP ERou GBri GKir LBBr LRHS MCAu MLLN MTis NDov NPri SCoo SRms
	pilosa	EBre ECha EMan GMac NPro WFar
	– subsp. *ozarkana*	SSpi
§	x *procumbens* 'Millstream' ♀ H4	EBee EDAr SAga SBla SHar
	– 'Variegata' (v)	EBee ECha EDAr EMNN EMlt EPot LRHS MDKP NHol NWCA SBla SPlb WCom WFar WLin WPat WWin
§	*pulvinata* **new**	CPBP
	'Scented Pillow'	LRHS
§	*sibirica* subsp. *borealis*	EDAr EWes ITim
	'Sileniflora'	CGra
	speciosa subsp. *woodhousei* **new**	SScr
	stolonifera	EPar GKir MNrw
	– 'Ariane'	EBee ECha EDAr EPar GEdr MNrw NHar SBla SMrm WAbe WFar WViv WWin
I	– 'Atropurpurea' **new**	MSph
	– 'Blue Ridge' ♀ H4	CBro CFir EBee ECha EDAr EGle EMan EPar EPfP EVFa GBuc GKir GMaP IMGH LAst MRav NHar SMer SMrm SRms WFar WSan WWin
	– 'Bob's Motley' (v)	EMan WCot
	– compact	EPot
	– 'Compact Pink'	WFar
	– 'Fran's Purple'	CLAP CLyd EBee EMan GMac NBro NHar SCro WCFE WFar WViv

	– 'Home Fires'	EBee EDAr MDKP MFir MNrw NBro NHar NLar SAga SBla SCro SMrm SPlb
	– 'Mary Belle Frey'	EBre EMan GKir MSte WFar WWin
	– 'Pink Ridge'	CLAP EWll GBuc MNrw NBir NHar
	– 'Purpurea'	EBee EVFa NHar
	– 'Sherwood Purple'	IFro
	– variegated (v)	MNrw WCot
	– 'Violet Vere'	CLAP CLyd CStr EDAr EGle GBuc MNrw NHar SMrm WCom WFar
	subulata	EPar GKir WBrE
	– 'Alexander's Surprise'	CMHG CMea ECtt EDAr EPfP EPot LBee LRHS MDKP NBir NFla SChu SPlb
	– 'Amazing Grace'	CWCL EDAr ELan ESis EWes GKir LBee LHop LRHS MHer NHol NWCA SChu SIng WPat WPer WRHF WWin
	– 'Apple Blossom'	EDAr GDra NPri NPro WAbe WLRN
	– 'Atropurpurea'	EBre LRHS NFor NJOw NLon WWin
	– 'Beauty of Ronsdorf'	see *P. subulata* 'Ronsdorfer Schöne'
	– 'Betty'	ECtt EMNN MBNS MDHE WPer
	– 'Blue Eyes'	see *P. subulata* 'Oakington Blue Eyes'
	– 'Blue Saucer'	MDHE
	– 'Bonita'	CPBP EMNN GKir LBee LRHS SMer WWin
	– 'Bressingham Blue Eyes'	see *P. subulata* 'Oakington Blue Eyes'
	– 'Brightness'	CNic GKir GTou LRHS
	– subsp. *brittonii* 'Rosea'	EPot WPer
	– 'Candy Stripe'	see *P. subulata* 'Tamaongalei'
	– 'Cavaldes White'	MDKP
	– 'Christine Bishop'	LRHS
	– 'Coral Eye'	EPfP
	– 'Drumm'	see *P. subulata* 'Tamaongalei'
	– 'Emerald Cushion'	CSam ECtt EDAr EMan EWTr MDKP MHer NFor NLAp NLon SDes WCFE WRHF
	– 'Emerald Cushion Blue'	CLyd CNic EBre EMlt EPfP GKir GTou NMen NPri NPro SBla SMrm SPlb WPer WWol
	– 'Fairy'	WPer
	– 'G.F. Wilson'	see *P. subulata* 'Lilacina'
	– 'Greencourt Purple'	EDAr NBur
*	– 'Holly'	EPot ITim MDHE NMen
	– 'Jupiter'	SChu
	– 'Kimono'	see *P. subulata* 'Tamaongalei'
§	– 'Lilacina'	CLyd CMea EDAr ELan GMaP GTou LGro LRHS MWat NFor SBla SChu WPer WWin
§	– 'Maischnee'	CLyd COIW ECtt EDAr EMNN EPfP EPot GKir LGro LRHS MHer MWat NFor NHol SIng SPlb WEas WWin
	– 'Marjorie'	CLyd CMHG ECtt EMNN LBee MHer NPri SMer WLRN
	– May Snow	see *P. subulata* 'Maischnee'
§	– 'McDaniel's Cushion' ♀ H4	CLyd CNic EBre ECha EDAr ELan EMNN EMlt EPfP EPot GKir GTou ITim LBee LRHS NFor NHol NLAp NLon NMen NWCA SPlb WFar WPer WTel WWin
	– 'Mikado'	see *P. subulata* 'Tamaongalei'
	– 'Model'	LGro
	– 'Moonlight'	CElw CLyd ECtt WPer
	– 'Nettleton Variation' (v)	EDAr EPot EWes GKir GMaP LBee LHop LRHS MBro MHer NFla NLAp SAga SIng SPlb SWal WAbe WCom WPat
§	– 'Oakington Blue Eyes'	CNic EBre EPar GDra GKir LRHS MLwd SMrm SRms WPer
	– 'Pink Pearl'	EWes

- 'Red Wings' ♀ H4	EBre ECtt EPfP GKir LRHS MHdf NMen SRms WFar
§ - 'Ronsdorfer Schöne'	EPot LBee LRHS
- 'Rose Mabel'	EDAr
- 'Samson'	GTou LRHS SMer WPer WWin
- 'Scarlet Flame'	CMea CSam EBre ECha ECtt EDAr ELan EMNN EPfP LGro MHer MWat NHol NPri SAga WPer WWin
- 'Schneewittchen'	CLyd
- 'Sensation'	GTou SBla SRms
- 'Snow Queen'	see P. subulata 'Maischnee'
- 'Starglow'	GTou WPer
§ - 'Tamaongalei'	CLyd CMea CPBP CWCL EDAr EHyt EPfP EPot EWes GDra GKir IMGH LRHS MHer NBlu NHar SBla SChu SCoo SIng SRms SWal WCFE WFar WWeb WWin
- 'Temiskaming'	ECha EDAr ELan EMNN ENot EWes GDra LBee LGro LRHS NMen SBla SChu SRms WCom WRHF
- violet seedling	CLyd
- 'White Delight'	CLyd EBre ECtt ELan EMNN GTou LBee NMen WPer
- 'Woodside'	CNic
'Tiny Bugles'	CGra
'Vivid'	EDAr MDHE SIgm

Phoenicaulis (Brassicaceae)

§ cheiranthoides	LTwo NWCA

Phoenix (Arecaceae)

canariensis ♀ H1+3	More than 30 suppliers
dactylifera (F)	CRoM EAmu LPal MPRe
reclinata	CRoM EPVP LPIP NPal WMul
roebelenii ♀ H1+3	CBrP CRoM EGln EPVP EPfP LPal MBri NPal WMul
rupicola	CRoM LPal
sylvestris	LPal
theophrasti	CFil EAmu LEdu LPJP LPal WMul

Phormium ✿ (Phormiaceae)

'Amazing Red'	CWil IBlr
'Apricot Queen' (v)	CAbb CBcs CDoC CMHG CSBt CTrC CWil EBee EPfP EPyc GQui IBal IBlr LRHS MAsh MDun MPRe NMoo NPal NPri SLim SPer WBcn WBod
Ballyrogan variegated (v)	IBlr
* 'Black Edge'	CWil IBlr MRav NPri
'Bronze Baby'	More than 30 suppliers
colensoi	see P. cookianum
§ coohianum	CHEx CTrC CWil EBee ECre EMil IBal IBlr MGos SAPC SArc SEND WFar WHil WMul
- 'Alpinum Purpureum'	see P. tenax 'Nanum Purpureum'
- dwarf	IBlr
- 'Flamingo'	CSpe CWil EBee ECre EPfP MBri SLim
- 'Golden Wonder'	IBlr
- subsp. hookeri 'Cream Delight' (v) ♀ H3-4	CAbb CDoC CElw CEnd CKno CSBt CTrC EBee EHoe ENot EPfP EPyc LRHS MBlu MDun MGos MPRe MRav SAga SHBN SPar SPer SRPl WCFE WCot WLRN WLeb WWeb
- - 'Tricolor' ♀ H3-4	CDoC CElw CFil CHEx CSBt CTrC CWil EBee EBlw ENot EPfP EPla IBal IBlr LRHS MAsh MRav SArc SHBN SHFr SLim SPar SPer SRms SSpi WCot WDin WLeb WPGP
* 'Copper Beauty'	COtt CTrC CWil EGln NMoo SPar WDyG WLRN
'Dark Delight'	IBlr
'Dazzler' (v)	IBlr MGos MRav WCot
'Duet' (v) ♀ H3	CBcs CDoC COtt CSBt CWil EHoe EPfP IBal IBlr LRHS MAsh SPla WBcn WFar
'Dusky Chief'	CSBt CWil LRHS WLeb WPat
'Emerald Isle' new	CWil
* 'Emerald Pink'	COtt CTrC CWil MPRe
'Evening Glow'	CSpe CTrC CWil EBee EPfP IBal IBlr LRHS MAsh MDun MPRe MRav SPla WCot WPat WWeb
'Firebird'	IBlr
'Flamingo'	CMHG CSBt CWil EBlw LRHS MDun SLim NFor WPat WWeb
'Gold Sword' (v)	COtt CTrC EBee ENot IBlr LRHS MAsh
'Guardsman' (v)	CHEx IBlr
'Jack Spratt' (v)	CBcs CBrm COtt CWil EBee ECou EHoe IBlr LRHS MAsh MBrN WLeb WPrP
'Jester'	More than 30 suppliers
'Limelight'	CWil
§ 'Maori Chief' (v)	CFil CSBt EPfP EWTr GQui IBal IBlr LRHS NFor NMoo SHBN SPar WAul WCot WLRN WPGP WPat
'Maori Eclipse'	CSBt CWil
'Maori Elegance' new	CWil
§ 'Maori Maiden' (v)	CBcs CDoC CMHG CSBt CTrC EBee ECre EHoe ENot GKir GQui IBal LRHS MAsh MGos MPRe MRav SMad WCot WFar WLeb WWeb
§ 'Maori Queen' (v)	CBcs CDoC CSBt CTrC EBee ENot EPfP GQui IBal IBlr LRHS MAsh MGos MPRe MRav NBlu NMoo WCot WFar WLRN WPat WWeb
§ 'Maori Sunrise' (v)	CBcs CDoC CKno CSam CTrC CWil EBee ENot EPfP IArd IBlr LPVe LRHS MBrN MCCP MGos MPRe MRav NPri SAga SLim SPar SPer WCot WFar WHil WLRN WLeb WWeb
'Pink Panther' (v)	CAbb CBcs CDoC CTrC CWil EBee ECtt ELan ENot EPfP EWil GKir GQui IBlr LRHS MAsh MDun MGos MPRe MRav NPri SLim WBod WDin WDyG WFar WLeb WPat WWeb
* 'Pink Stripe'	CSBt CSpe CWil EBee ENot IBlr LRHS MAsh MRav NBlu NPal WCot WPat
'Platt's Black'	CBcs CMHG CTrC CWil EPfP EWes GGar GKir LHop LJus LRHS SMad WLeb WPat WWeb
'Rainbow Chief'	see P. 'Maori Chief'
Rainbow hybrids	CSpe EBlw
'Rainbow Maiden'	see P. 'Maori Maiden'
'Rainbow Queen'	see P. 'Maori Queen'
'Rainbow Sunrise'	see P. 'Maori Sunrise'
I 'Rubrum' new	CWil
'Sea Jade'	IBlr
'Stormy Dawn'	WCot
'Sundowner' (v) ♀ H3	More than 30 suppliers
'Sunset' (v)	CSBt IBlr WCot
'Surfer' (v)	COtt CWil EHoe IBlr LPan MCCP SMad SPar WBcn WLeb WPat WWhi
'Surfer Boy' new	CWil
'Surfer Bronze' new	CWil EAmu NPal
'Surfer Green' new	NPal
tenax ♀ H4	More than 30 suppliers
- 'Bronze' new	CWil
- 'Co-ordination'	CTrC CWil EBee EPfP IBlr LRHS SPar WBcn
* - dwarf	IBlr
* - lineatum	NBlu SEND
§ - 'Nanum Purpureum'	CRDP IBlr MSte SEND
- 'Platinum'	IBlr

- Purpureum Group ♀ H3-4	More than 30 suppliers
- 'Radiance' (v)	IBlr
- 'Rainbow Queen'	see *P.* 'Maori Queen'
- 'Rainbow Sunrise'	see *P.* 'Maori Sunrise'
- 'Variegatum' (v) ♀ H3-4	CFil CHEx CSBt ENot EPfP IBlr LJus LPal LPan LRHS NBlu NMoo SAPC SArc SEND SPar SPlb SRms WBrE WFar WMul WPGP WPat
- 'Veitchianum' (v)	CHEx IBlr LRHS SPer WPGP
- 'Yellow Queen'	MRav
'Thumbelina'	CSBt CTrC CTri CWil EBee EHoe IBal LRHS MAsh MDKP MSte WPat
'Tom Thumb'	CBrm CWil GGar LPan SPar WDin WDyG WPrP
'Yellow Wave' (v) ♀ H3	More than 30 suppliers

Photinia ✿ (Rosaceae)

arbutifolia	see *Heteromeles salicifolia*
beauverdiana	CSam CTho SRms WFar
- var. **notabilis**	EPfP
§ **davidiana**	CDul CSam EBee ELan EPfP GIBF ISea MBar MRav SPer SRPl SRms WDin WFar WNor
- 'Palette' (v)	More than 30 suppliers
- var. **undulata**	CMHG LRHS WBcn
- - 'Fructu Luteo'	CMHG CSam CTrG EBee EPfP EPla LRHS MBri MRav SPer WFar
- - 'Prostrata'	ELan EPfP MBar MRav NLar SPer WDin WFar
x **fraseri**	CMCN
- 'Birmingham'	EBee EHoe GKir LPVe LPan LRHS MAsh SDes SLim SPar SRms WDin WLRN WSHC WWeb
- 'Purple Peter'	LRHS SKee SLim
- 'Red Robin' ♀ H4	More than 30 suppliers
- 'Robusta'	EBee EPfP LRHS SLim
glabra	SArc
§ - 'Parfait' (v)	CAbP ELan LRHS MAsh MRav SDry SHBN SPer SPla SPoG WAbe WFar
- 'Pink Lady'	see *P. glabra* 'Parfait'
- 'Rubens'	ELan EPfP LRHS MAsh MBri NHol SDry SPer SPla SSta WPat
- 'Variegata'	see *P. glabra* 'Parfait'
glomerata misapplied	see *P. prionophylla*
lasiogyna	CMCN WWes
niitakayamensis	GIBF
nussia	CDoC
'Paradise Super Hedge' **new**	WWeb
parvifolia	EPfP
prionophylla	CHEx
§ 'Redstart'	CEnd EBee EPfP LRHS MGos SLon SPer SSta WMoo WRHF
§ **serratifolia**	CBot CHEx CMHG CPLG EBee EPfP LRHS SAPC SArc SDry SPer SSta WBod WFar WPGP WSHC
serrulata	see *P. serratifolia*
villosa ♀ H4	CAbP CDul CTho GIBF MBar NPal SSpi
- var. **laevis**	EPfP EWTr LBuc LPan
- f. **maximowicziana**	EPfP GIBF

Phragmites (Poaceae)

from Sichuan, China	EPPr
§ **australis**	CTrC EMFW MGol SWat WFar WMAq
- subsp. **australis** var. **striatopictus**	EMon EPPr MTed
- - 'Variegatus' (v)	CFwr CNat CRDP CWCL CWat EBee ECGP EHoe EMFW EMan EMon EPPr EPar EPla EWsh IBlr LRHS MBri MMil MMoz MRav MTed NSti SHBN SLPI SMad SMer WFar WMoo WRus

---

- subsp. **pseudodonax**	EMon EPPr
communis	see *P. australis*
karka new	EPPr
- 'Variegatus' (v)	LRav

Phrynium (Marantaceae)

pubinerve	CKob

Phuopsis (Rubiaceae)

§ **stylosa**	More than 30 suppliers
- 'Purpurea'	CElw CPLG CWCL EBee ELan MNrw MRav NCat NChi SChu SDes WCom WHal

Phygelius ✿ (Scrophulariaceae)

aequalis	CBot CFee CHEx CSev MNrw MWgw SChu SDix SHom SMac SPla WMoo WPer WSHC WSan
- **albus**	see *P. aequalis* 'Yellow Trumpet'
- 'Aureus'	see *P. aequalis* 'Yellow Trumpet'
- Cedric Morris form	SHom
- 'Cream Trumpet'	see *P. aequalis* 'Yellow Trumpet'
- 'Indian Chief'	see *P.* x *rectus* 'African Queen'
* - 'Pink Trumpet'	CDoC CFwr GCal LRHS NFor NLon SCoo SMac SMrm SOkh SPer WRha
- Sensation = 'Sani Pass' PBR	CFwr CSpe EBee EBlw EChP ECtt EPfP GBri LRHS MAsh MCCP MOak SBla SCoo SMac SPer SWal
- 'Trewidden Pink' ♀ H4	More than 30 suppliers
§ - 'Yellow Trumpet' ♀ H3-4	More than 30 suppliers
'Bridgetown Beauty'	GCal
§ **capensis** ♀ H3-4	CBot CChe CWib EBlw EChP EFpt ELan ENot EOrc EPfP MBNS MHer MWgw NFor NLar SHom SMac SPer SPet SRms WBod WFar WMoo WPer WWpP WWye
- CD&R	EWes
- S&SH 50	SMac
- 'Caborn Flame' (v)	EBee
- **coccineus**	see *P. capensis*
- 'Janet's Jewel' (v)	SHom
- orange-flowered	LHop MOak SHom
- x **aequalis**	see *P.* x *rectus*
'Golden Gate'	see *P. aequalis* 'Yellow Trumpet'
'Hillview Green Trumpet' **new**	WHil
Logan form	EBee EBlw MCCP
'New Sensation' **new**	COtt
§ x **rectus**	SMac SYvo
§ - 'African Queen' ♀ H3-4	More than 30 suppliers
- 'Aylesham's Pride'	SHom
- 'Bridgetown Beauty'	SHom
- 'Devil's Tears' ♀ H4	More than 30 suppliers
- Logan form	EBlw SHom
* - 'Logan's Pink'	NGdn
- 'Moonraker'	More than 30 suppliers
- 'Pink Elf'	ELan ESis SHom SLon SMac
- 'Raspberry Swirl' **new**	SHom
- 'Salmon Leap' ♀ H4	More than 30 suppliers
- 'Sunshine'	CFwr COtt EBee EFpt EHoe EMan EWes LHop LRHS MAsh MLwd SPoG SSte SWal WCom WGwG WWpP
§ - 'Winchester Fanfare'	More than 30 suppliers
- 'Winton Fanfare'	see *P.* x *rectus* 'Winchester Fanfare'

Phyla (Verbenaceae)

§ **nodiflora**	CNic ECha EEls GKir NFla NWCA SEND SIng WPer
- 'Alba'	CNic
- var. **canescens**	WCru

Phylica (*Rhamnaceae*)

arborea 'Superba'	CBcs CPLG
ericoides	CPLG
plumosa	CPLG

x *Phylliopsis* (*Ericaceae*)

'Coppelia' ♀ H4	EPot GCrs GDra GGGa ITim LTwo NHar SReu SSta WAbe WPat
hillieri 'Askival'	GCrs GGGa WAbe
- 'Pinocchio'	CMHG EPot GCrs GGGa GTou ITim LRHS MDun NHar NLAp WAbe WPat
'Hobgoblin'	EPot SReu WAbe WPat
'Mermaid'	GGGa ITim SReu SSta WAbe
'Puck'	WAbe
'Sprite'	GCrs SReu SSta WAbe WPat
'Sugar Plum'	CWSG ITim MDun SBrw SSta WAbe
'Swanhilde' **new**	SSta

Phyllitis see *Asplenium*

Phyllocladus (*Phyllocladaceae*)

trichomanoides	CDoC CTrC LCon NLar
var. *alpinus*	

Phyllodoce (*Ericaceae*)

aleutica	EPot GCrs GGGa GKir MBar NDlv NHar NLAp NMen SRms WAbe
§ - subsp. *glanduliflora*	GDra
- x *caerulea*	GCrs GKir
§ - - 'Flora Slack'	CMHG GGGa
- - white-flowered	see *P. aleutica* subsp. *glanduliflora* 'Flora Slack'
x *alpina*	GDra
breweri	GDra GGGa GKir
caerulea ♀ H4	GDra GEdr GGGa GKir NDlv NHar NLAp WAbe
- *japonica*	see *P. nipponica*
- 'Viking'	GCrs
empetriformis	GDra GGGa MBar NHar SRms WAbe
glanduliflora	see *P. aleutica* subsp. *glanduliflora*
x *intermedia*	GDra
- 'Drummondii'	CMHG GKir
- 'Fred Stoker'	CMHG
§ *nipponica* ♀ H4	GCrs WAbe
- var. *oblongo-ovata*	GCrs GKir
tsugifolia	GCrs WAbe

Phyllostachys ✿ (*Poaceae*)

angusta	CFil EPla SDry WJun
arcana	CEbD EPla GKir SDry WJun
- 'Luteosulcata'	CBcs CDDB CFil EPla GKir LPal MHdf MMoz MWht NPal SDry WJun WNor
§ *atrovaginata*	EPla ERod SDry WJun
aurea ♀ H4	More than 30 suppliers
- 'Albovariegata' (v)	EFul SDry
- 'Flavescens Inversa'	CDDB EPla ERod SDry WJun
- 'Holochrysa'	CBrP CDDB EFul EPla ERod SDry WJun
- 'Koi'	CFil EFul EPla ERod LPal MMoz NMoo SDry
aureocaulis	see *P. vivax* 'Aureocaulis', *P. aureosulcata* 'Aureocaulis'
aureosulcata	EBee EFul EPfP EPla ERod GKir LRHS MMoz NMoo SDry WJun WMoo
- f. *alata*	CFil EPVP EPla SDry
- 'Argus'	EPla
§ - 'Aureocaulis' ♀ H4	More than 30 suppliers
- 'Harbin'	EPla ERod SDry
- 'Harbin Inversa'	EPla ERod
- 'Lama Temple'	CFil EPla

- 'Spectabilis' ♀ H4	More than 30 suppliers
bambusoides	CBcs CDDB EPla GKir SDix SDry WJun
§ - 'Allgold'	CFil EPla ERod GKir LJus NMoo NPal SDry WJun
- 'Castillonis'	CAbb CBcs CDDB CFil EBee EFul EPla ERod EWes GKir LEdu LJus LNet LPal MHdf MMoz MWht NBea NMoo NPal SDix SDry WJun WPGP
- 'Castillonis Inversa'	CFil EPla ERod LPal MMoz SDry WJun WPGP
- Holochrysa	see *P. bambusoides* 'Allgold'
- 'Katashibo'	EPla
- 'Kawadana'	EPla ERod SDry
- f. *lacrima-deae*	CFil
- 'Marliacea'	EPla ERod WJun
- f. *subvariegata*	CFil EPla SDry WPGP
- 'Sulphurea'	see *P. bambusoides* 'Allgold'
- 'Tanakae'	CDDB MMoz NMoo SDry
- 'Violascens'	NMoo
bissetii	CAbb CBcs CBig CDDB CDoC CFil CHEx CMCo EBee EFul EPfP EPla ERod GKir LJus LPal LPan MAvo MBrN MCCP MHdf MMoz MWgw MWht NMoo NOrc SDry WJun WNor WPGP
circumpilis	EPla
congesta hort.	see *P. atrovaginata*
decora	CAbb CDDB EBee EPla ERod LJus MHdf MMoz MWht NMoo NPal SDry WJun WPGP
dulcis	CDDB EPfP EPla ERod LEdu LJus LPJP WJun
§ *edulis*	CTrC EFul EHoe ERod IFro MMoz SDry WJun
- 'Bicolor'	SDry
§ - var. *heterocycla*	SDry
- f. *pubescens*	see *P. edulis*
- *subconvexa*	see *P. viridiglaucescens*
flexuosa	CFil EFul EPfP EPla IMGII LNet SDes SDry WJun WPGP
glauca	CAbb CEbD EBee EPla ERod MMoz MWht NMoo NPal
- 'Yunzhu'	EPla ERod LJus SDry WJun
§ *heteroclada*	NMoo SDry WJun
- 'Solid Stem' misapplied	see *P. heteroclada* 'Straight Stem'
§ - 'Straight Stem'	EPla MWht SDry
heterocycla	see *P. edulis* var. *heterocycla*
f. *pubescens*	see *P. edulis*
humilis	CDDB CDul EDcc EPla ERod LAst LPan MCCP MGos MMoz MWgw MWht NMoo NPal SDry WJun
iridescens	EPla SDry WJun
lofushanensis	CFil EPla WPGP
makinoi	ERod WJun
mannii	EPla SDry WJun
meyeri	EPla SDry WJun
nidularia	EPla ERod LJus MMoz SDry WJun
- f. *farcta* **new**	EPla
- smooth sheath	EPla
nigella	EPla
nigra ♀ H4	More than 30 suppliers
- 'Boryana'	CAbb CBig CDDB CDoC CFil EAmu EBee EFul EPfP EPla GKir LJus MGos MHdf MMoz MWht NMoo SArc SDix SDry SPar WFar WJun WMoo WPGP
- 'Fulva'	EPla
- 'Hale'	EPla
- var. *henonis* ♀ H4	CAbb CFil EAmu EBee EFul EMil EPla ERod LPal MHdf MMoz MWht NBea NMoo SDry WJun WPGP

- 'Megurochiku'	EPla ERod SDry WJun
- f. *nigra*	EPla SPer
- f. *punctata*	CDoC CFil EBee EPfP EPla ERod LJus MAvo MWht NGdn SDry SEND WJun WPGP
- 'Tosaensis'	EPla
- 'Wisley'	EPla
nuda	CDDB CEbD EAmu EBee EPla ERod GKir MGos MHdf MMoz MWht NPal SDry WJun
- f. *localis*	MWht SDry
parvifolia	EPla ERod WJun
platyglossa	CFil EPla ERod WPGP
praecox	EPla NMoo WJun
propinqua	CBig CDDB CDoC CDul EPla ERod LJus MCCP MHdf MMoz MWht SAPC SArc WJun WMul
- 'Bicolor'	EPla WJun
- 'Li Yu Gai'	CFil EPla WPGP
pubescens 'Mazel'	CDDB NMoo
purpurata	see *P. heteroclada*
rubicunda	CFil EPla WJun
rubromarginata	CDDB CFil EPla ERod SDry WJun
stimulosa	CDDB EPla ERod WJun
§ *sulphurea*	NMoo
- 'Houzeau'	EPla ERod SDry
- 'Robert Young'	EPla SDry
- 'Sulphurea'	see *P. sulphurea*
- var. *viridis*	CDDB EPla ERod GKir LPal LPan NMoo SDry
- - 'Mitis'	see *P. sulphurea* var. *viridis*
violascens	CDDB CFil EFul EPla ERod LJus LPal MMoz SDry WJun WPGP
virella	CFil EPla WPGP
§ *viridiglaucescens*	CAbb CBcs CDDB CEbD CFil CHEx EBee EFul EGln ELan EPfP EPla GKir LJus LPan MBrN MFir MHdf MMoz MWht SArc SDes SDry SEND SPla WJun
viridis	see *P. sulphurea* var. *viridis*
vivax	CDDB ECbD EFul EPfP EPla ERod LJus MMoz MPRe MWht SDry WJun WMul WNor
§ - 'Aureocaulis' ♀ H4	CAbb CDDB CDoC CFil CHEx CTrC EBee EFul EPfP EPla ERod GKir LJus LPJP LPal LRHS MHdf MMoz MPRe MWht NGdn NPal SAPC SDry SPar SPla WJun WMul WNor WPGP
- f. *huanvenzhu*	CFil EFul EPla ERod NMoo WJun

x *Phyllothamnus* (Ericaceae)

erectus	GCrs GGGa NHar SReu WAbe WPat

Phymatosorus (Polypodiaceae)

§ *diversifolius*	CFil

Phymosia (Malvaceae)

§ *umbellata*	CBot CRHN ERea LRHS SOWG

Phyodina see *Callisia*

Physalis (Solanaceae)

alkekengi ♀ H4	CAgr EBee EPfP EWTr GKir MLan NBir
- var. *franchetii*	More than 30 suppliers
- - dwarf	LPVe NLar WHil
- - 'Gigantea'	ECGP GBuc NFor NLar
- - 'Variegata' (v)	CRDP EBee ECha ECtt EMan EPla EWes IBlr MAvo NPro WOld WCru
angulata B&SWJ 7016	WCru

Physaria (Brassicaceae)

alpestris	WLin
didymocarpa	MDCh MWod

Physocarpus (Rosaceae)

opulifolius	GIBF IFro MSal
- 'Dart's Gold' ♀ H4	More than 30 suppliers
- 'Diabolo' PBR ♀ H4	More than 30 suppliers
§ - 'Luteus'	CBot CDoC CMHG CSam CWib EBee EPfP ESis GEil GKir IMGH ISea MBar MDun MRav MWhi NLon SPar SPer SRms WBod WDin WFar WMoo
ribesifolius 'Aureus'	see *P. opulifolius* 'Luteus'

Physochlaina (Solanaceae)

orientalis	CPLG CRDP EMan MGrG MSal WAul

Physoplexis (Campanulaceae)

§ *comosa* ♀ H2-3	ETow EWes LRHS NMen SBla WHoo

Physostegia (Lamiaceae)

angustifolia	CSam EBee
§ *virginiana*	CKno CPom CSBt EBee EWTr GBar GKir GMaP LAst MBNS NBlu NGar SGar SWat WFar WRHF
- 'Alba'	CBot CSBt EBee ECGN EChP EPfP EShb GBar GBri GKir GMaP LRHS MSte MTis NLar NOrc SBri SPet SPlb WEas WHrl WRHF WRha
§ - 'Crown of Snow'	CBri CFir CM&M EBee ECtt ERou EWTr GKir LPVe MBNS MBow MHer MRav MWrn NArg NLon NMir STes SWal WHil WMoo WPer WViv
- 'Grandiflora'	CFir WLRN
- 'Grandiflora Rose'	NArg NPri SWal
- 'Miss Manners'	WCot
- 'Olympic Gold' (v)	EMan ENot
- pale pink-flowered	EFou SWat
- 'Red Beauty'	CFir EBee ERou LRHS MDKP SPla WWin
- 'Rose Queen'	LPVe
- 'Rosea'	CBcs CBot CHar EBee EChP ERou GKir IGor MBow SRPl STes WFar WHrl WPer
- Schneekrone	see *P. virginiana* 'Crown of Snow'
- 'Snow Queen'	see *P. virginiana* 'Summer Snow'
- var. *speciosa*	EMon WFar
§ - - 'Bouquet Rose'	CElw EBee ECha EMan EMar EPfP LRHS MBri MCAu MFir MHer MRav MSte MWrn NBir NCat NGar NHol NMir SChu SMac SPer WAul WElm WFar WMoo WRos WRus WWeb
- - Rose Bouquet	see *P. virginiana* subsp. *speciosa* 'Bouquet Rose'
§ - - 'Variegata' (v)	More than 30 suppliers
§ - 'Summer Snow' ♀ H4	CBcs CElw EBee ECha EFou ELan ENot EPfP IBal LAst LHop LRHS MBri MCAu MFir MWat NHol SChu SPer SPla SRms WBea WCot WFar WHoo WMnd WRus WWin
- 'Summer Spire'	EBee ECha EHrv ELan EMan MSte NHol SPer WBea WFar
- 'Vivid' ♀ H4	More than 30 suppliers
- 'Wassenhove'	EBee EMon

Phyteuma (Campanulaceae)

comosum	see *Physoplexis comosa*
hemisphaericum	WPat
humile	EDAr
nigrum	CDes GCal ITer LBee LRHS MNrw NBid

orbiculare	ECGN
scheuchzeri	CNic CRDP EBee EMan EPfP GDra
	GEdr GTou MBro MHer MTis
	NChi NPri NWCA SBla SMad SPet
	SRms SRot WCom WRHF WWin
sieberi	CPBP GDra NBir
spicatum	CRDP GDra NBro

Phytolacca (Phytolaccaceae)

acinosa	GPoy MGol MSal NLar SWat WCot
	WHer
§ *americana*	More than 30 suppliers
- 'Silberstein' (v) **new**	WCot
- 'Variegata' **new**	ITer
clavigera	see *P. polyandra*
decandra	see *P. americana*
dioica	CHEx
esculenta	CHid EBee LHop
japonica B&SWJ 4897 **new**	WCru
octandra	CPLG ITer
§ *polyandra*	EBee ECha GBuc NBid NBro NCWG
	NChi SGar SRms WBan WWye
tibetica	MSal

Picea ✿ (Pinaceae)

from Japan	WHCr
§ *abies*	CCVT CDul CLnd CSBt CTri CWib
	EHul ENot EPfP GKir LBuc LCon
	LRHS MBar MBri MGos NBlu
	NWea WDin WEve WMou
'Acrocona'	CDoC ECho EHul EOrn GKir
	LCon LLin LRHS MAsh MBar MBlu
	MBri MGos SCoo
- 'Archer'	CKen
'Argenteospica' (v)	LCon MAsh NHol WEve
- 'Aurea'	ECho EOrn IMGH LLin
- 'Capitata'	CKen MBar NLar
- 'Clanbrassiliana'	CDoC CKen IMGH LCon MAsh
	MBar WEve
- Compacta Group	LBee LRHS
I - 'Congesta'	CKen
- 'Crippsii'	CKen
I - 'Cruenta'	CKen
- 'Cupressina'	CKen
- 'Diffusa'	CKen LCon MBar
- 'Dumpy' **new**	LCon
- 'Elegans'	MBar
- 'Ellwangeriana'	LCon NLar
- 'Excelsa'	see *P. abies*
- 'Fahndrich'	CKen
- 'Finedonensis'	LCon NLar
- 'Formanek'	CDoC CKen LCon LLin NLar
- 'Four Winds'	CAbP CKen
'Frohburg'	CDoC COtt GKir LRHS MBar MBri
	MGos SCoo
- 'Globosa'	MBar
- 'Globosa Nana'	MGos
- 'Gregoryana'	CKen CMac GKir IMGH LCon
	MBar NDlv NHol
- 'Humilis'	LCon
- 'Hystrix'	LCon NLar
- 'Inversa'	EHul EOrn LCon LLin LPan MBar
	MGos SCoo
- 'J.W. Daisy's White'	see *P. glauca* 'J.W. Daisy's White'
- 'Jana' **new**	CKen
- 'Kral' **new**	CKen
- 'Little Gem' ♥ H4	CDoC CKen CMac EBre EHul
	ENot EOrn GBin GKir IMGH LBee
	LCon LLin LRHS MAsh MBar MBri
	MGos NBee SLim SPer
- 'Mariae Orffii' **new**	LCon
- 'Maxwellii'	EHul GKir MBar MGos
- 'Nana'	MBar

- 'Nana Compacta'	CKen EHul IMGH LBee MAsh
	MBar MOne
- 'Nidiformis' ♥ H4	CDoC CKen CMac CSBt CTri EBre
	EHul ENot EOrn GBin GKir LCon
	LLin LPan LRHS MAsh MBar MBri
	MGos NBlu NWea SLim SRms
	WDin WStI
- 'Norrkoping'	CKen
- 'Ohlendorffii'	CKen EHul LCon LPan MAsh
	MBar NLar SCoo WStI
- 'Pachyphylla'	CKen
- 'Pendula Major'	SHBN
- 'Procumbens'	MBar
- 'Pumila'	EOrn
- 'Pumila Nigra'	CMac EHul LCon LLin MBar
	MGos NHar SCoo SLim
- 'Pusch'	CKen
- 'Pygmaea'	CKen MBar MGos
- 'Reflexa'	CDoC EHul GBin IMGH LCon
	MAsh
- 'Repens'	LRHS MBar MGos NBee
- 'Rydal'	LCon MAsh
- 'Saint James'	CKen
- 'Tabuliformis'	MBar
- 'Tufty'	EOrn
- 'Vermont Gold' **new**	CKen
- 'Waldbrunn' **new**	MAsh
- 'Walter Bron'	CKen
- 'Waugh'	MBar
- Will's Dwarf	see *P. abies* 'Wills Zwerg'
§ - 'Wills Zwerg'	LPan LRHS MAsh
ajanensis **new**	GIBF
alcoquiana	CDoC GKir LCon
- var. *alcoquiana* **new**	MAsh
I - 'Prostrata'	CDoC LCon MBar
breweriana ♥ H4	More than 30 suppliers
engelmannii	GKir LRav MBar
- subsp. *engelmannii*	LCon MBar
glauca	CAgr CTri WEve
- 'Alberta Blue'	CDoC CKen CSBt EOrn GKir
	LCon LLin LPan LRHS MAsh SCoo
	SLim WEve
- var. *albertiana* 'Alberta	CDoC CSBt EBre EHul EOrn GKir
Globe'	IMGH LBee LCon LLin MAsh
	MBar MBri MGos NBee NDlv
	SAga SLim SPoG WEve WFar
- - 'Conica'	More than 30 suppliers
- - 'Gnome'	CKen
- - 'Laurin'	CDoC CKen EBre EOrn GKir
	LBee LCon LRHS MAsh MBar
	MBri SCoo
- - 'Tiny'	CDoC CKen ENot EOrn LCon
	LLin MBar
- 'Arneson's Blue	CKen MAsh MBri SLim
Variegated' (v)	
- 'Blue Planet'	CKen
- 'Coerulea'	LCon MBar
I - 'Coerulea Nana'	NLar
- 'Cy's Wonder'	CKen
- 'Echiniformis' ♥ H4	CKen GKir LBee LCon LRHS
	MBar MBri NBlu
- var. *glauca* **new**	GIBF
- 'Goldilocks'	CKen
§ - 'J.W. Daisy's White'	CDoC CKen EOrn GKir LCon
	LLin LRHS MAsh MGos NPro
	SCoo SLim SMur SPer WEve
	WGor
- 'Lilliput'	EHul EOrn LCon MBar MGos WEve
- 'Nana'	CKen
- 'Piccolo'	CKen GKir LRHS MAsh MBri
	SLim
- 'Pixie' **new**	CKen
- 'Rainbow's End' (v)	CKen SLim

- 'Sander's Blue'	CKen EOrn LBee MBri SCoo SLim SPoG WEve
- 'Zucherhut'	LRHS MAsh MBar MBri
glehnii	LCon
- 'Sasanosei'	CKen
- 'Shimezusei'	CKen
jezoensis	LCon MGos
- subsp. *hondoensis*	WNor
- 'Yatsabusa' **new**	CKen
koraiensis **new**	GIBF GKir
kosteri 'Glauca'	see *P. pungens* 'Koster'
likiangensis	CMCN ISea LCon
- var. *balfouriana*	see *P. likiangensis* var. *rubescens*
- var. *purpurea*	see *P. purpurea*
§ - var. *rubescens*	CDoC GKir IDee NHol WWes
mariana	NWea
- 'Aureovariegata' (v)	LCon
- 'Doumetii'	EOrn LCon
- 'Fastigiata'	CKen EOrn
- 'Nana' ♀ H4	CDoC CKen CMac EBre EHul ELan ENot EPfP ESis GKir IMGH LCon LLin LRHS MAsh MBar MBri MGos MNrw MWat NBee NBlu NDlv NWea SLim SSta WBrE WDin
I - 'Pygmaea' **new**	CKen
x *mariorika*	MBar
obovata **new**	LCon
- var. *coerulea*	GIBF NLar
omorika ♀ H4	CBcs CDul CMCN ENot GKir LBuc LCon MBar MGos NBlu NWea SPer WBrE WCFE WDin WMou WPGP
I - 'Aurea'	LCon
- 'Frohnleiten'	CKen
- 'Karel'	CKen
- 'Nana' ♀ H4	CMac EHul LBee LCon LPan MAsh MBar SCoo SLim WEve
- 'Pendula' ♀ H4	CDoC GKir LCon LPan LRHS MBar MBlu NLar SHBN SSta
- 'Pimoko'	CKen GKir LCon LRHS MAsh
- 'Schneverdingen'	CKen
- 'Tijn' **new**	CKen
- 'Treblitsch'	CDoC CKen
orientalis ♀ H4	CDul CLnd LCon LPan LRav NWea
§ - 'Aurea' (v) ♀ H4	CMac EBre EHul ELan ENot GKir LCon LLin LPan MBar MBri NHol SHBN SLim WDin
- 'Aureospicata'	CDoC CTho ECho MAsh MBlu WEve
- 'Bergman's Gem'	CKen
- 'Early Gold' (v)	LPan MAsh
- 'Gowdy'	MBar NLar
- 'Kenwith'	CKen
- Pendula Group	MGos
- 'Professor Langner'	CKen
- 'Skylands'	CDoC CKen LCon LLin MAsh MGos SCoo SLim
* - 'Wittbold Compact'	LBee SCoo
pungens	MBar NWea WDin WNor
- 'Blaukissen'	CKen
- 'Erich Frahm'	CDoC EBre GKir LCon LPan LRHS MAsh MBar MBri MGos NBee NBlu SCoo SLim WOrn
- 'Fat Albert'	CWib EBre GKir LBee LNet LPan MBri SCoo
- Glauca Group	CLnd EWTr GKir GWCH LBee MBar NBee NWea WBVN WDin WMou WOrn WStI
N - 'Glauca Pendula'	GKir
- 'Glauca Procumbens'	LNet
§ - 'Glauca Prostrata'	EHul GKir MBar SLim
- 'Globe'	CKen LCon
I - 'Globosa' ♀ H4	CBcs CDoC CKen EBre EHul ELan EOrn GKir LBee LCon LLin LPan

	MAsh MBar MBri MGos MWat NBee NBlu NHol SHBN SLim SRms WEve
- 'Gloria'	CKen
- 'Hoopsii' ♀ H4	CBcs CDoC CMac CSBt EBre EHul ENot EOrn EPfP GKir IMGH LCon LNet LPan LRHS MAsh MBar MGos MWat NBee NPSI SHBN SKee SLim SPer WDin WEve
- 'Hoto'	EHul EOrn MBar SCoo
- 'Hunnewelliana'	EOrn
- 'Iseli Fastigiate'	CDoC COtt EBre GKir LCon LLin LNet MAsh WEve
§ - 'Koster' ♀ H4	CDoC CMac CSBt EHul EOrn GKir LCon LLin LNet LPan MAsh MBar MGos NWea SLim SPer SPoG SRms WDin WEve WFar
- 'Lucky Strike'	CDoC CKen LCon LLin MGos NLar
- 'Maigold' (v)	CKen LCon
- 'Moerheimii'	EHul EOrn LCon LNet MBar MGos NLar
- 'Montgomery'	CKen LCon LLin MBar NHol NLar
- 'Mrs Cesarini'	CKen
- 'Nimety' **new**	CKen
- 'Oldenburg'	ENot
- 'Omega'	GKir
- 'Procumbens'	CKen
- 'Prostrata'	see *P. pungens* 'Glauca Prostrata'
- 'Prostrate Blue Mist'	WEve
- 'Rovelli's Monument'	NLar
- 'Saint Mary's Broom'	CKen
- 'Schovenhorst'	EHul EOrn LPan
- 'Thomsen'	CKen EHul EOrn LCon MAsh
- 'Thuem'	EHul EOrn LCon LLin MGos NDlv NLar WEve
- 'Wendy'	CKen
§ *purpurea* **new**	GKir LCon
rubens	LCon
schrenkiana	LCon
sitchensis	CDul GKir LBuc LCon NWea WMou
- 'Nana'	CDoC NHol
- 'Papoose'	see *P. sitchensis* 'Tenas'
- 'Silberzwerg'	CKen
- 'Strypemonde'	CKen
§ - 'Tenas'	CDoC CKen LCon MAsh NHol NLar
smithiana	CDoC CMCN GKir LCon NLar SBir SLim
wilsonii	LCon

Picrasma (Simaroubaceae)

ailanthoides	see *P. quassioides*
§ *quassioides*	CFil CMCN EPfP WPGP

Picris (Asteraceae)

echioides	WHer

Picrorhiza (Scrophulariaceae)

kurrooa	GPoy

Pieris ✿ (Ericaceae)

'Bert Chandler'	CHig CSBt GKir LRHS SPer SSpi SLim
'Brouwer's Beauty'	SLim
'Firecrest' ♀ H4	CBcs CDoC CHig CMHG CTrG CTrh ENot SBrw SSpi WBod
'Flaming Silver' (v) ♀ H4	More than 30 suppliers
floribunda	MBar SPer
- 'Browers Beauty' **new**	MGos
'Forest Flame' ♀ H4	More than 30 suppliers
formosa	CHig
- B&SWJ 2257	WCru
- var. *forrestii*	CDoC CTrw CWib ISea NWea SBrw
- - 'Fota Pink'	WHar
- - 'Jermyns'	CHig SHBN
- - 'Wakehurst' ♀ H3	CAbP CBcs CHig CTrG CWSG EPfP

	LHyd LRHS MRav NHol NWea SBrw SRPl SReu SSta WBod WFar WWal
Havila = 'Mouwsvila' (v)	CDoC MAsh MBri MGos NHol SBrw SPar WFar
japonica	CBcs CTrw GIBF MBar MGos NWea SArc SReu WDin
– 'Bisbee Dwarf'	ITim MBar NHol
– 'Blush' ♀ H4	GKir LRHS MAsh MBri NHol SBod SHBN
– 'Bonfire'	CEnd MGos
– 'Brookside Miniature'	NHol
– 'Buchanan's Dwarf'	SReu SSta
– 'Carnaval' (v)	CEnd CWib EBee ENot MGos NPri
– 'Cavatine' ♀ H4	CMHG LRHS SBod
§ – 'Christmas Cheer'	MAsh MGos NHol SBrw WLRN WMoo
– 'Compacta'	NHol WAbe
– 'Crispa'	CHig
– 'Cupido'	CDoC EMil LRHS MAsh MBar MBri MGos NHol SPar WLRN
– 'Daisen'	CHig CTrw
§ – 'Debutante' ♀ H4	CDoC CHig CWSG CWib ENot EPfP GKir LRHS MAsh MBri MDun MOne NHol SBrw SPar SRPl SSpi WFar WGwG WLRN WStI
– 'Don'	see *P. japonica* 'Pygmaea'
– 'Dorothy Wyckoff'	CBcs CMHG CPLG CSBt CTrG CWSG GKir LRHS MAsh MBri MDun NDlv NHol SBrw SHBN SPer SSta WCwm
– 'Flaming Star'	ECot WBrE
– 'Flamingo'	CHig CTrw ENot LRHS MAsh MBar MGos NDlv NHol WBod WPat
– 'Geisha'	NHol WPat
– 'Grayswood' ♀ H4	CMHG EPfP LRHS MBri NHol
– 'Little Heath' (v) ♀ H4	More than 30 suppliers
– 'Little Heath Green' ♀ H4	CChe CDoC CHig CMHG CSBt CTrG GKir LHyd LRHS MAsh MBar MGos MHFa NDlv SBrw SPar SPer SSta WBrE WFar WOTO WPic WWeb
– 'Minor'	ITim MBar NHol
– 'Mountain Fire' ♀ H4	More than 30 suppliers
– 'Pink Delight' ♀ H4	CAbP CBcs CDoC CHig GKir LRHS MAsh MBar MGos MRav NHol SBrw SHBN SPar SPer SRms WBod WPat
– 'Prelude' ♀ H4	CChe CTrG CWSG GKir LRHS MAsh MBri MRav NHol WBod WPat
– 'Purity' ♀ H4	CBcs CDoC CHig CMHG CWSG EPfP LRHS MAsh MBar MGos MLan NHol SBrw SMer SRPl SReu SSta WBod WDin WFar WLRN WStI WWeb
§ – 'Pygmaea'	CMHG GDra NHol WAbe
– 'Red Mill'	CAbP CEnd CHig CWSG ENot EPfP GKir LRHS MAsh NBee NHol SPer SSpi WBod WFar WLRN
– 'Robinswood'	WBcn
– 'Rokujo's Dwarf'	SReu SSta
– 'Rosalinda'	MAsh WFar
– 'Rosea'	LHyd
– 'Sarabande' ♀ H4	CHig COtt LRHS MAsh MBar MBri MGos MOne NHol SBrw SSta WGwG WPat
– 'Scarlett O'Hara'	CSBt MGos
– 'Select'	MGos
– 'Silver Mills' **new**	MGos
– 'Snowdrift'	LRHS
– 'Spring Candy'	MGos
– 'Spring Snow'	LRHS
– Taiwanensis Group	CHig CMHG CWSG EPfP GGar LRHS MBar MRav NWea SRPl SRms SSta WFar WPat
– 'Temple Bells'	CHig CPLG CSBt ENot SMer SPar
– 'Tickled Pink'	CSBt NHol
– 'Valley Fire'	CTrh
– 'Valley Rose'	COtt CSBt CSam CTrh ENot EPfP GKir MGos NBee SPer SSpi WGwG WStI
– 'Valley Valentine' ♀ H4	CDoC COtt CSBt CTrh CWSG CWib ENot EPfP GKir LRHS MAsh MBri MGos NDlv SBrw SLim SPar SPer SReu SSta WBod WCwm WFar WPat WStI WWeb
– 'Variegata' hort.	see *P. japonica* 'White Rim'
§ – 'Variegata' (Carrière) Bean (v)	CMHG EPfP EPot GKir LHyd MAsh MBar MGos NBee NDlv NHol SHBN SLdr SPer SReu SSta WBod WDin WHar WPat WSHC
– 'Wada's Pink'	see *P. japonica* 'Christmas Cheer'
– 'White Cascade'	CHig SBrw
– 'White Pearl'	CAbP MAsh MGos NBee SBrw SPer
§ – 'White Rim' (v) ♀ H4	CBcs CWSG ENot EPfP GKir MAsh MGos SBrw SLim SLon SPlb WFar
– 'William Buchanan'	GCrs MBar NHol NLAp
– var. *yakushimensis*	WBod WSHC
koidzumiana	SSta
nana	MBar NHar
– 'Redshank'	SOkd
– 'Tilford'	LRHS MBri NHol SSta

Pilea (Urticaceae)

* 'Anette'	MBri
cadierei ♀ H1	CHal MBri
depressa	CHal
involucrata 'Norfolk' ♀ H1	CHal
§ *microphylla*	CHal EBak
muscosa	see *P. microphylla*
nummariifolia	CHal
peperomioides ♀ H1	CHal CSev EPem
repens	MBri

Pileostegia (Hydrangeaceae)

viburnoides ♀ H4	More than 30 suppliers
– B&SWJ 3565	WCru

Pilosella (Asteraceae)

§ *aurantiaca*	CMCo CNic EBee Elan MBow MCAu MFir MHer MWgw NArg NBid NBlu NOrc NPri NSti SIde SMad SPet WCer WHer WMoo WWye
§ – subsp. *carpathicola*	GGar
§ *officinarum*	CKin MGas NRya

Pilularia (Marsileaceae)

globulifera	CNat EFer

Pimelea (Thymelaeaceae)

coarctata	see *P. prostrata*
drupacea	ECou
ferruginea 'Magenta Mist'	SOWG
filiformis	ECou
ligustrina	GGar
§ *prostrata*	CLyd ECou EPot GCrs IKee MBar NHol NJOw SRot WPat WPer
– f. *parvifolia*	ECou
– Tennyson's form	SBla
tomentosa	ECou

Pimenta (Myrtaceae)

dioica	NBlo XBlo

Pimpinella (Apiaceae)

anisum	CArn MSal SIde WHHs WHer WSel
bicknellii	CDes EBee EPPr SIgm WPGP

flahaultii	CElw EBee NCat
major 'Rosea'	CBos CDes CHad CRDP CSpe
	EBee EMon LHop LPhx MBct SBla
	SMrm WEas WFar WHal WPGP
niitakayamensis	WCru
B&SWJ 6942 **new**	
saxifraga	EBee

pineapple guava see *Acca sellowiana*

Pinellia ✿ (*Araceae*)

cordata	CPom CRDP EBee EMan EPot
	LEdu SOkd WAbe WCot WCru
- variegated **new**	EBee
pedatisecta	CDes CRDP CRow EBee EMan
	ERos ITer LEur WCot WCru
pinnatisecta	see *P. tripartita*
ternata	CRDP CRow CStu EBee EPar EPot
	ERos LEur MSal NMen WCot
	WCru WWye
- B&SWJ 3532	LEur WCru
§ *tripartita*	CStu EBee ITer WAbe WCot WCru
	WPnP
- B&SWJ 1102	WCru
- 'Purple Face' B&SWJ 4850	WCru

Pinguicula ✿ (*Lentibulariaceae*)

acuminata	SHmp
crassifolia	SHmp
x *emarginata*	
cyclosecta	LHew SHmp
ehlersiae	EFEx
esseriana	EFEx
gigantea	SHmp
gracilis	LHew
grandiflora	CRDP CSWC EFEx GCrs GEdr
	IFro LRHS NHar NMen NRya
	WAbe WHer WPGP
- subsp. *coenocant-*	NWCA
abrica NS 307	
heterophylla	SHmp
jaumavensis	LHew
lauana	LHew
longifolia	EFEx WPGP
subsp. *longifolia*	
macrophylla	SHmp
moctezumae	SHmp
moranensis var. *caudata*	EFEx
- *moreana*	EFEx
- *superba*	EFEx
* *pilosa*	SHmp
rotundiflora	LHew SHmp
vallisneriifolia small	LHew
vulgaris	EFEx
zecheri x *macrophylla*	SHmp

pinkcurrant see *Ribes rubrum* (P)

Pinus ✿ (*Pinaceae*)

albicaulis	WNor
- 'Flinck'	CKen
- 'Nana'	see *P. albicaulis* 'Noble's Dwarf'
§ - 'Noble's Dwarf'	CKen
aristata	CAbP CDul CFil CLnd CMCN
	EBre EHul EOrn GKir LCon LLin
	MAsh MBar MGos NBee SIng
	SReu SSta STre WDin WEve
- 'Cecilia'	CKen
- 'Sherwood Compact'	CKen
armandii	CBcs CDul CMCN CSWP GKir
	LCon WEve
- 'Gold Tip' **new**	CKen
attenuata	LCon

austriaca	see *P. nigra* subsp. *nigra*
N *ayacahuite*	LCon
banksiana	CDul CLnd GKir IDee LCon
- 'Chippewa'	CKen
I - 'Compacta'	CKen
- 'H.J. Welch'	CKen
- 'Manomet'	CKen
- 'Neponset'	CKen LCon
- 'Uncle Fogy'	WEve
- 'Wisconsin'	CKen
brutia	LCon
bungeana	CAbb CDoC CLnd CMCN CTho
	EPfP GKir IDee LCon LLin MBlu
	SLPl SMad WEve WNor
- 'Diamant'	CKen
canariensis	EHul IDee ISea LCon
cembra	CAgr CDul CLnd EHul GIBF GKir
	LCon LPan MBar NLar NWea STre
	WEve
- 'Aurea'	see *P. cembra* 'Aureovariegata'
§ - 'Aureovariegata' (v)	CKen GKir LLin NDlv WEve
- 'Barnhourie'	CKen
- 'Blue Mound'	CKen
- 'Chalet'	CKen
- 'Compacta Glauca'	CDoC LCon MBri
* - 'Griffithii'	WDin
- 'Inverleith'	CKen
- 'Jermyns'	CKen
- 'King's Dwarf'	CKen
- 'Roughills'	CKen
- 'Stricta'	CKen
- witches' broom	CKen
contorta	CBcs CDoC CDul CTrC GKir IIve
	LCon MBar MGos NWea WDin
	WMou
- 'Asher'	CKen
- 'Frisian Gold'	CKen
- var. *latifolia*	CLnd LCon LRav WDin
- 'Spaan's Dwarf'	CDoC CKen GKir LCon LLin
	MAsh MBar MBri MGos NLar
	SCoo SLim
coulteri ♀ H4	CMCN EGra GKir LCon LLin
	SMad WNor WPGP
densiflora	CDul CMCN LCon LEdu WNor
- SF 99088	ISea
- 'Alice Verkade'	CDoC EHul GKir LBee LCon LLin
	LNet LRHS MAsh MBri NDlv SCoo
	SLim
- 'Aurea'	LCon MBar MGos SLim
- 'Jane Kluis'	CDoC CKen COtt EHul GKir LBee
	LCon LLin LNet LRHS MAsh MBri
	NDlv NLar SCoo SLim WEve
I - 'Jim Cross' **new**	CKen
- 'Low Glow'	CKen
- 'Oculus-draconis' (v)	GKir LLin MBar MBri MGos SCoo
	SLim
- 'Pendula'	CDoC CKen GKir LLin MBri SLim
- 'Pygmy'	CDoC
* - 'Pyramidalis'	ECho
- 'Umbraculifera'	CDoC GKir IMGH LCon LLin
	LPan MAsh MBar MBri MGos
	MOne NLar SCoo SSta WEve
I - 'Umbraculifera Nana'	LLin
§ *devoniana*	NNEX
edulis	LCon
- 'Juno'	CKen
flexilis	LCon
- 'Firmament'	CDoC LLin MAsh SLim
- 'Glenmore Dwarf'	CKen
- 'Nana'	CKen
- 'Pendula'	LLin
I - 'Pygmaea' **new**	NLar
- 'Vanderwolf's Pyramid'	EPfP GKir MAsh

- - 'Bright Eyes' — CKen ECho EOrn GKir IMGH LBee LCon LLin LRHS MAsh NLar SCoo SPoG
- - 'Helga' — CKen
- - 'Schovenhorst' — CKen
- - 'Strypemonde' — CKen
- - 'Yaffle Hill' — CKen
- - 'Obelisk' — CKen
- subsp. *pallasiana* — LCon NLar WPGP
- 'Pierrick Bregeon'PBR **new** — LLin
- 'Uelzen' — CKen

palustris — LCon LLin

parviflora — CTri LCon LPan STre WDin WNor
- 'Adcock's Dwarf' ♀ H4 — CDoC CKen GKir LCon LLin MBar MGos NLar SLim
- Aizu-goyo Group — LLin
- 'Al Fordham' — CKen
- 'Aoi' — CKen
- 'Ara-kawa' — CKen
- Azuma-goyo Group — CKen
I - 'Baasch's Form' — CKen
- 'Bergman' — LCon MAsh MBar NLar
- 'Blue Giant' — ECho MAsh NLar
- 'Bonnie Bergman' — CKen LLin
- 'Brevifolia' — LPan
- 'Dai-ho' — CKen
- 'Daisetsusan' — CKen
- 'Doctor Landis Gold' — CKen
- 'Fukai' (v) — CKen NLar
- 'Fukiju' — CKen
- Fukushima-goyo Group — CKen
- 'Fuku-zu-mi' — LLin
- 'Fu-shiro' — CKen
- Glauca Group — CDoC CMac EHul LCon LLin LPan MBar MBri MGos NBlu
I - 'Glauca Nana' — CKen
I - 'Goldilocks' — CKen
- 'Gyok-ke-sen' — CKen
- 'Gyo-ko-haku' — CKen
- 'Gyokuei' — CKen
- 'Gyokusen Sämling' — CKen NLar
- 'Gyo-ku-sui' — CKen LLin
- 'Hagaromo Seedling' — CKen LLin MAsh NLar
- 'Hakko' — CKen
- 'Hatchichi' — CKen
- 'Ibo-can' — CKen
- 'Ichi-no-se' — CKen
- 'Iri-fune' — CKen
- Ishizuchi-goyo Group — CKen
- 'Ka-ho' — CKen LLin
- 'Kanzan' — CKen
- 'Kiyomatsu' — CKen
- 'Kobe' — CKen LLin
- 'Kokonoe' — CKen LCon LLin
- 'Kokuho' — CKen
- 'Koraku' — CKen
- 'Kusu-dama' — CKen
- 'Meiko' — CKen
- 'Michinoku' — CKen
- 'Myo-jo' — CKen
- Nasu-goyo Group — CKen
- 'Negishi' — CDoC CKen LCon LLin LPan LRHS MAsh MBri NLar
- 'Ogon-janome' — CKen
- 'Ossorio Dwarf' — CKen
- 'Richard Lee' — CKen
- 'Ryo-ku-ho' — CKen
- 'Ryu-ju' — CKen
- 'San-bo' — CDoC CKen MBar
§ - 'Saphir' — CKen ECho
- 'Setsugekka' — CKen
- 'Shika-shima' — CKen
- Shiobara-goyo Group — CKen

- 'Shizukagoten' — CKen
- 'Shu-re' — CKen
- 'Sieryoden' — CKen
- 'Tani-mano-uki' — CKen
- 'Tempelhof' — COtt CTho GKir LNet LPan MBar SLim
- 'Templeflora' **new** — LCon
- 'Tenysu-kazu' — CKen
I - 'Torulosa' **new** — LLin
- 'Venus' — NDlv
I - 'Zelkova' — LLin
I - 'Zui-sho' — CKen

patula ♀ H2-3 — CAbb CBcs CDoC CDul CLnd CTrC ECre GKir LCon MBlu SAPC SArc SBir SCoo SLim SPar WEve

peuce — CDoC EHoe GKir LCon LRav MBar NWea STre
- 'Arnold Dwarf' — CKen
- 'Cesarini' — CKen

pinaster ♀ H4 — CAgr CDoC CDul CLnd EHul GKir LCon SEND WBVN

pinea ♀ H4 — CAgr CDoC CFil CKen CLnd CMac CTho EPfP GKir LCon LEdu LLin LPan MGos NPSI SAPC SArc SEND SPar WEve WNor
- 'Queensway' — CKen

ponderosa ♀ H4 — CAgr CLnd LCon LRav WPGP
- var. *scopulorum* — LCon

pumila 'Buchanan' — CKen
- 'Draijer's Dwarf' — CDoC EOrn GKir LLin MBri SCoo SLim
- 'Dwarf Blue' — MAsh NDlv
§ - 'Glauca' ♀ H4 — CKen LCon LLin LNet LRHS MAsh MBar MBri
- 'Globe' — GKir LBee LCon LLin LNet MAsh MBri
- 'Jeddeloh' — CKen
- 'Knightshayes' — CKen
- 'Säntis' — CKen
- 'Saphir' — see *P. parviflora* 'Saphir'

radiata ♀ H3-4 — CAgr CBcs CDoC CDul CSBt CTrC CTrw ECrN ENot EWTr GBin GKir LCon LRHS NWea SAPC SArc SHBN SKee SPar STre WDin WEve
- Aurea Group — CDoC CDul CKen GKir LBee LCon LLin LPan LRHS MAsh MBri SBir SCoo SLim SMur
- 'Bodnant' — CKen
- 'Isca' — CKen
- 'Marshwood' (v) — CKen LCon SCoo SLim
- var. *radiata* — NPal

resinosa — GIBF
- 'Don Smith' — CKen
- 'Joel's Broom' — CKen
- 'Quinobequin' — CKen

rigida — LCon

roxburghii — LCon

sabineana — LCon

x *schwerinii* — CDoC GKir LRHS
- 'Wiethorst' — CKen

sibirica — GIBF LCon

strobiformis — ISea LCon

strobus — CBcs CDul CTho EMil GKir ISea LCon LPan MBar NWea SEND SLim SPar STre WDin WEve WNor
§ - 'Alba' — LCon MGos
- 'Amelia's Dwarf' — CKen
- 'Anna Fiele' — CKen
- 'Aurea' — LCon
- 'Bergman's Mini' — CKen NLar
- 'Bergman's Pendula Broom' — CKen
I - 'Bergman's Sport of Prostrata' — CKen

- 'Bloomer's Dark Globe'   CKen
- 'Blue Shag'   CKen COtt EMil GKir LBee LLin
     MBri MGos NLar SCoo SLim SPoG
     WEve
- 'Cesarini'   CKen
- 'Densa'   CKen LCon MAsh
- 'Dove's Dwarf'   CKen
- 'Ed's Broom'   CKen
- 'Elkins Dwarf'   CKen
- 'Fastigiata'   CKen GBin GKir IMGH LLin LPan
- 'Greg'   CKen
- 'Hillside Gem'   CKen
- 'Horsford'   CKen LLin
- 'Jericho'   CKen NDlv
- 'Krügers Lilliput'   LCon LLin LRHS MBri NLar SCoo SLim
- 'Macopin'   LLin MGos NLar
- 'Mary Butler'   CKen
- 'Merrimack'   CKen
- 'Minima'   CKen LBee LCon LLin LRHS MBar
     MBlu MBri SCoo SLim
- 'Minuta'   CKen
- 'Nana'   see *P. strobus* Nana Group
- Nana Group   LLin
- 'Nivea'   see *P. strobus* 'Alba'
- 'Northway Broom'   CKen LCon LLin SLim
- 'Ontario' **new**   MBlu
- 'Pendula'   CKen GKir LCon SMad
§ - 'Radiata'   EHul EPla GKir LCon LNet MBar
     NBee NLar SLim
- 'Reinshaus'   CKen LLin
- 'Sayville'   CKen
- 'Sea Urchin'   CKen
- 'Uncatena'   CKen
- 'Verkade's Broom'   CKen
sylvestris ♀ H4   More than 30 suppliers
- 'Abergeldie'   CKen
- 'Alderly Edge' **new**   WEve
- 'Andorra'   CKen
§ - 'Argentea'   LNet
§ - Aurea Group ♀ H4   CKen CMac EBre EHul EPfP GBin
     GKir IMGH LBee LCon LLin LNet
     LRHS MAsh MBar SHBN SLim
     SPer SSta WLRN
- 'Aurea'   see *P. sylvestris* Aurea Group
- 'Avondene'   CKen
- 'Bergfield' **new**   NLar
- 'Beuvronensis' ♀ H4   CDoC CDul CKen CLnd CMac
     EOrn GKir IMGH LBee LCon LLin
     LNet LRHS MAsh MGos NHol
     SCoo SLim SSta WEve
- 'Blue Sky' **new**   MAsh
- 'Bonna'   GKir LCon SCoo
- 'Brevifolia'   MBar
- 'Buchanan's Gold'   CKen
- 'Burghfield'   CKen LLin WEve
- 'Chantry Blue'   CDoC EHul EOrn GKir IMGH
     LBee LCon LLin LRHS MAsh MBar
     MGos NLar SCoo SLim
- 'Clumber Blue'   CKen
- 'Compressa'   LLin
- 'Corley'   GKir LLin
- 'Dereham'   CKen LLin
- 'Doone Valley'   CKen GKir LLin WEve
- 'Edwin Hillier'   see *P. sylvestris* 'Argentea'
- Fastigiata Group   CDoC CEnd CKen EOrn GKir
     IMGH LBee LCon LLin LPan LRHS
     MAsh MBar MGos NDlv SCoo SLim
- 'Frensham'   CDoC CKen EOrn IMGH LBee
     LCon LLin MAsh MGos MOne WEve
- 'Globosa'   LRHS MBri
- 'Gold Coin'   CDoC CKen EOrn GKir LBee
     LCon LLin MAsh MBri MGos NDlv
     NLar SCoo SLim SPoG

- 'Gold Medal'   CKen GKir LCon LLin
- 'Grand Rapids'   CKen
- 'Hillside Creeper'   CKen GKir LCon LLin SLim
- 'Inverleith' (v)   EHul GKir LBuc LCon LLin MBar
     MGos NHol SCoo SLim SPoG
- 'Jeremy'   CKen LCon LLin SCoo SLim WEve
- 'John Boy'   LLin
- 'Kelpie'   LLin
- 'Kenwith'   CKen
- 'Lakeside Dwarf'   LLin
- 'Lodge Hill'   CDoC CKen EBre EOrn GKir
     IMGH LBee LCon LLin LRHS
     MAsh MOne SCoo SLim
- 'Longmoor'   CKen NLar
- 'Martham'   CKen LLin
- var. **mongolica**   GIBF
- 'Moseri'   CDoC ECho GKir LBee LRHS
     MAsh MBri WEve
- 'Nana Compacta'   GKir LLin
- 'Nana' misapplied   see *P. sylvestris* 'Watereri'
§ - 'Nisbet's Gem'   CKen LLin NLar
- 'Padworth'   CKen
- 'Pixie'   CKen LCon LLin NLar
I - 'Prostrata'   GKir SCoo
- 'Pulham'   LLin
- 'Pygmaea'   GKir SCoo SLim
- 'Reedham'   LLin
- 'Repens'   CKen
- 'Saint George'   CKen
- 'Sandringham'   LCon LLin
- 'Saxatilis'   CKen EOrn GKir LBee LCon LLin
     MAsh
- subsp. **scotica**   GIBF GTre
- 'Scott's Dwarf'   see *P. sylvestris* 'Nisbet's Gem'
- 'Scrubby'   LLin NLar
- 'Sentinel'   CKen
- 'Skjak I'   CKen
- 'Skjak II'   CKen
- 'Spaan's Slow Column'   CKen
- 'Tabuliformis'   LLin
- 'Tage'   CKen LLin
- 'Tanya'   CKen
- 'Tilhead'   CKen
- 'Treasure'   CKen LLin
§ - 'Watereri'   CDoC CMac EHul ENot GKir
     IMGH LBee LCon LLin LNet LPan
     LRHS MAsh MBar MBri MGos
     NHol SCoo SLim SPer WDin
     WEve
- 'Westonbirt'   CKen EHul LLin WEve
- 'Wishmoor'   LLin
- 'Wolf Gold'   CKen
* - 'Yaff Hill'   LLin
tabuliformis   CMCN GIBF LCon MBlu
- SF 96040   ISea
thunbergii   CDul CLnd EHul LCon LLin MGos
     STre WNor
- 'Akame'   CKen
- 'Aocha-matsu' (v)   CKen
- 'Arakawa-sho'   CKen
- 'Banshosho'   CKen NLar
- 'Beni-kujaku'   CKen
- 'Compacta'   CKen
- 'Dainagon'   CKen
- 'Kotobuki'   CKen NLar
- 'Koyosho'   GKir
- 'Kujaku'   CKen
- 'Kyushu'   CKen
- 'Miyajuna'   CKen NLar
- 'Nishiki-ne'   CKen
- 'Oculus-draconis' (v)   GKir LBuc LLin
- 'Ogon'   CKen
- 'Porky'   CKen

§ - 'Sayonara' CDoC CKen LCon LLin MAsh NHol NLar
- 'Senryu' CKen
- 'Shinsho' **new** CKen
- 'Shio-guro' CKen
- 'Suchiro Yatabusa' CKen
- 'Sunsho' CKen
- 'Taihei' CKen
I - 'Thunderhead' CKen
- 'Yatsubusa' see *P. thunbergii* 'Sayonara'
- 'Yumaki' CKen
uncinata see *P. mugo* subsp. *uncinata*
virginiana 'Wate's Golden' CKen
§ **wallichiana** ♀ H4 CDoC CDul CKen CMCN CTho EHul ENot EPfP GKir LCon LLin LPan MBar MGos NBee NPSI NWea SBir SLim SPar STre WDin WEve WFar WGer WNor WOrn
- CC 2045 WHCr
- 'Densa' MBri
- 'Nana' CKen EHul LCon LLin MBar SLim WEve
- 'Umbraculifera' LRHS MBri
- 'Zebrina' (v) CDoC GKir LBee LCon MAsh MBar MGos SMad WEve
yunnanensis CMCN GKir LCon WEve WNor

Piper (Piperaceae)
betle MSal
excelsum see *Macropiper excelsum*
nigrum MSal

Piptanthus (Papilionaceae)
forrestii see *P. nepalensis*
laburnifolius see *P. nepalensis*
§ **nepalensis** More than 30 suppliers
- B&SWJ 2241 WCru
aff. **nepalensis new** GIBF
tomentosus CFil SDry WPGP

Pistacia (Anacardiaceae)
atlantica EGFP
chinensis CBcs CBrd CMCN CPMA EPfP EWes SSpi WPic
lentiscus CBcs
terebinthus CFil

Pistia (Araceae)
stratiotes LMdh MSta NPer SCoo

Pittosporum ✿ (Pittosporaceae)
anomalum ECou SDry
- (f) ECou
- (m) ECou
- 'Falcon' ECou
- 'Raven' (f) ECou
- 'Starling' (m) ECou
'Arundel Green' CDoC CWSG EBee EPfP LRHS MTed SDry SLim SPar WWeb
bicolor CFil CPle ECou GQui SAPC SArc WBor WPGP
buchananii SGar SVen
colensoi ECou
- 'Cobb' (f) ECou
- 'Wanaka' (m) ECou
crassifolium CBcs CFil CPle CTrC ECou ERea WPGP
- 'Havering Dwarf' (f) ECou
- 'Napier' (f) ECou
- 'Variegatum' (v) CPne WBcn WPat
- x **tenuifolium** CWib ECou
'Craxten' (f) CPne ECou

'Crinkles' (f) ECou
cuneatum LHop SAga
daphniphylloides WPGP
  ETE 275
- var. **adaphniphylloides** CFil
'Dark Delight' (m) ECou
divaricatum ECou
'Essex' (f/v) ECou
eugenioides CBcs CHEx CMHG CTrC CTrG GGar SLon WLRN
- 'Platinum' (v) CBcs MGos
- 'Variegatum' (v) ♀ H3 CAbb CBcs CDoC EBee EMil EPfP GGar GQui LRHS NPSI NPal SAga SLim SPar WGer WPGP WWeb
'Garnettii' (v) ♀ H3 More than 30 suppliers
heterophyllum ECou IArd
- variegated (v) ECou SLim SSpi
'Humpty Dumpty' **new** ECou
illicioides var. **illicioides** WCru
  B&SWJ 6712
'Limelight' (v) CBcs CSBt CSPN CTrC EBee EMil ENot LRHS WWes
lineare ECou
§ 'Margaret Turnbull' (v) CBcs CMHG CTrC ECou EMil EWes LRHS MGos WBcn
michiei ECou
- (f) ECou
- (m) ECou
- 'Jack' (m) ECou
- 'Jill' (f) ECou
'Nanum Variegatum' see *P. tobira* 'Variegatum'
obcordatum ECou
- var. **kaitaiaense** ECou
omeiense CFil WPGP
phillyreoides CFil
pimeleoides ECou
  var. **reflexum** (m)
'Purple Princess' **new** ECou
ralphii EBee ECou
- 'Green Globe' ECou
- 'Variegatum' (v) SSpi
'Saundersii' (v) ENot
tenuifolium ♀ H3 More than 30 suppliers
- 'Abbotsbury Gold' (f/v) CAbb CChe CDoC CSam CTri CWSG EBee ECou ELan EMil EWes GBri LRHS NBlu SAga SDry SEND SHBN SLim SPar SPer SRPI WSHC
- 'Atropurpureum' CBcs SPar WBcn
- 'County Park Dwarf' ECou WCru
- 'Deborah' (v) CBcs ECou EHol LRHS WBcn
- 'Dixie' ECou
§ - 'Eila Keightley' (v) CMHG CSBt SAga
- 'Elizabeth' (m/v) CDoC CTrC EBee ECou LRHS NPSI WBcn WGer
* - 'French Lace' ECou WFar
- 'Gold Star' CBcs CDoC ECou EMil LRHS NPal SLim
- 'Golden King' CDoC CMHG CSBt EBee LRHS MRav SLim SRPI SRms WWeb
- 'Golden Princess' (f) ECou
- 'Green Elf' CTrC ECou
- 'Green Thumb' CWSG LRHS
- 'Irene Paterson' (m/v) ♀ H3 More than 30 suppliers
- 'James Stirling' EBee ECou EPfP LRHS
- 'John Flanagan' see *P.* 'Margaret Turnbull'
- 'Loxhill Gold' EBee LRHS SPar
- 'Marjory Channon' (v) CBcs LRHS NPer SRPI SSpi
- 'Mellow Yellow' CAbP LRHS WBcn
- 'Moonlight' (v) CTrC EBee NPSI
- 'Purpureum' (m) CBrm CPle CSBt CSam CTri CTrw ECou EPfP LAst LRHS SAga SDry SHBN SPer SPla SRms WGer WSHC

- 'Silver Magic' (v)	CBcs EMil MGos
- 'Silver 'n' Gold'	EBee LRHS
- 'Silver Princess' (f)	ECou
- 'Silver Queen' (f/v) ♀ H3	More than 30 suppliers
- 'Silver Sheen'	CBcs ECou LRHS
- 'Stirling Gold' (f/v)	ECou EPfP EWes EWll
- 'Sunburst'	see *P. tenuifolium* 'Eila Keightley'
- 'Tandara Gold' (v)	CAbb CTrC EBee ECou EMil ENot
	LPVe SLim SPla WFar
- 'Tiki'	CBcs CTrC ECou
- 'Tom Thumb' ♀ H3	More than 30 suppliers
- 'Tresederi' (f/m)	CTrw ECou LRHS
- 'Variegatum' (m/v)	CBcs CDoC ECou EMil GBri LRHS
- 'Victoria' (v)	CDoC CTrC EMil
- 'Warnham Gold' (m) ♀ H3	CBrm COtt CSBt CTrw CWSG
	CWib EBee ECou ELan EPfP GBri
	LAst LRHS MCCP MPRe SDry
	SLim SPar SSpi WAbe WDin
- 'Wendle Channon' (m/v)	CMHG CSam EBee ECot ECou
	EPfP LRHS NBlu SLim SRPl
- 'Winter Sunshine'	LRHS SSta
tobira ♀ H3	More than 30 suppliers
- B&SWJ 4362	WCru
* - *cuneatum*	SPer
* - 'Nanum'	CBcs CDoC EBee ECou ERea LPan
	MPRe SAPC SArc SLim WBcn
	WDin WGer
§ - 'Variegatum' (v) ♀ H2-3	CBcs CBot CPle CSam ECou EPfP
	GQui LHop LRHS NPal SAga SLon
	SPar SPer SSta WBcn WCru WDin
	WGer WPGP WWeb
truncatum **new**	EWes
undulatum	CHEx ECou
viridiflorum	ECou

Pityrogramma (Adiantaceae)

triangularis	CFil

Plagianthus (Malvaceae)

betulinus	see *P. regius*
divaricatus	CFil ECou GEil WPGP
lyallii	see *Hoheria lyallii*
§ *regius*	CTrC ECou GGar GQui LRHS

Plagiorhegma see *Jeffersonia*

Plantago (Plantaginaceae)

asiatica	IIve MSal
- 'Ki Fu' (v)	ITer WAlt
- 'Variegata' (v)	CRow EBee EMan GBuc MBNS
	NBro NEgg NLar WHer WMoo
	WRos WWye
coronopus	CKin IIve
cynops	MTho
lanceolata	IIve
- 'Ballydowling	CNat EBee EChP
Variegated' (v)	
- 'Blond Bomi-noka' **new**	CNat
- 'Bomi-noka' **new**	CNat
- 'Bottlebrush'	WAlt
- 'Burren Rose'	CNat CRow
- 'Golden Spears'	CBre CPla EBee EChP
- 'Keer's Pride' (v) **new**	WCot
- 'Martin's Freaky'	WAlt
- 'Pink Bomi-noka' **new**	CNat
- 'Sam'	WAlt
- 'Streaker' (v)	CRow MTed WCot WHal WHil
major	WHbs
- 'Atropurpurea'	see *P. major* 'Rubrifolia'
- 'Bowles' Variety'	see *P. major* 'Rosularis'
- 'Frills'	CBre CNat CRow EBee WHer
	WRHF
* - 'Karmozijn'	EMan

§ - 'Rosularis'	CArn CFwr CNat CRow CSpe
	EBee EChP ILis ITer MFir MHar
	MHer MTho MWgw NBid NBro
	NChi NEgg NSti SUsu WBea WHer
	WPer WWye
§ - 'Rubrifolia'	CArn CFwr CHid CRow CSpe
	EBee EChP ECoo ITer LDai MCAu
	MFir MHar MHer MWgw NBid
	NBro NChi NEgg NSti SGar WBar
	WBea WCer WHer WMoo WPer
	WRos WWye
- 'Subtle Streak' (v)	WAlt
- 'Tony Lewis'	CNat WAlt
maritima	CKin WHer
media	CBgR CKin MHer
nivalis	EBee ETow GEdr MBro SMad
	WWin
psyllium L.	CArn MSal
raoulii	WCot
rosea	see *P. major* 'Rosularis'
uniflora	WCot

Platanthera (Orchidaceae)

hologlottis	EFEx
metabifolia	EFEx

Platanus ❀ (Platanaceae)

x *acerifolia*	see *P.* x *hispanica*
§ x *hispanica* ♀ H4	CAgr CBcs CCVT CDul CLnd
	CMCN CTho EBee ECrN EMil
	ENot EPfP EWTr LBuc LHyr LPan
	MGos NWea SEND SHBN SKee
	SPer WDin WFar WMou
- 'Pyramidalis'	CTho WOrn
- 'Suttneri' (v)	CEnd CLnd CTho LNet SMad
	WBcn WMou
- 'Tremonia'	LRHS
orientalis ♀ H4	CDul CLnd CMCN EPfP LEdu
	LPan NWea SLPl SMad WDin
	WMou WPGP
- 'Cuncata'	CDoC GKir LRHS MBri
§ - f. *digitata* ♀ H4	CDoC CDul CLnd CTho EPfP
	ERod SLPl SMad WMou
- var. *insularis*	CEnd WPGP
- 'Laciniata'	see *P. orientalis* f. *digitata*
- 'Minaret' **new**	WMou
- 'Mirkovec'	CDoC LRHS MBri SMad SPer WMou

Platycarya (Juglandaceae)

strobilacea	EPfP IArd IDee

Platycerium (Polypodiaceae)

alcicorne hort.	see *P. bifurcatum*
§ *bifurcatum* ♀ H1	LRHS MBri

Platycladus (Cupressaceae)

orientalis 'Aurea	More than 30 suppliers
Nana' ♀ H4	
- 'Autumn Glow'	CKen LBee LRHS SCoo SLim WGor
- 'Beverleyensis'	LLin NLar
- 'Blue Cone'	MBar
- 'Caribbean Holiday'	MAsh
- 'Collen's Gold'	CTri EHul EOrn MAsh MBar SLim
	WBcn
- 'Conspicua'	CKen EHul LBee LRHS MBar
- 'Elegantissima' ♀ H4	CMac EHul EOrn LBee LRHS
	MAsh MBar SCoo
- 'Golden Minaret'	WBcn
- 'Golden Pillar'	EOrn
- 'Golden Pygmy'	CKen EOrn MAsh WBcn
- 'Juniperoides'	EHul LCon MBar WLRN
- 'Kenwith'	CKen
- 'Madurodam'	LLin MBar

– 'Magnifica'	EHul WCwm
– 'Meldensis'	CDoC CTri EBre EHul MBar WTel
– 'Minima'	EHul WGor
– 'Minima Glauca'	CKen MBar SRms
– 'Mint Chocolate'	LLin
– 'Purple King'	CSli LRHS SCoo SLim
I – 'Pyramidalis Aurea'	LBee LCon LPan LRHS
– 'Rosedalis'	CKen CMac CSBt CWib EBre EHul EOrn EPfP LBee LCon LLin LRHS MAsh MBar MBri MWat SLim SMer SPla SRms WEve WTel
– 'Sanderi'	MBar WCFE
– 'Semperaurea'	CMac IMGH
– 'Shirley Chilcott'	MAsh
– 'Sieboldii'	EHul
– 'Southport'	LBee LCon LLin LRHS
– 'Summer Cream'	CKen EHul MBar
– 'Westmont' (v)	CDoC CKen CSBt EOrn WBcn

Platycodon ✿ (Campanulaceae)

grandiflorus ♀ H4	CArn COlW EBee EBre ECha ELau EPot LHop MBro MHer MNrw MPEx MSal SGar SRms SWal WBrE WCom WHoo WMoo WWye
– albus	CBro CRDP EBee EChP EPfP LAst LHop MBri NOak SPer SPla WCom WHoo WPer
– 'Apoyama' ♀ H4	CLyd EBee ESis LBee LRHS WCot WHoo WPer WWin
– apoyama albus	WCFE WEas WHoo
– – 'Fairy Snow'	EMar WHil WHoo WSel
– 'Astra Blue' (Astra Series)	WHil WWeb
– 'Astra Double Blue' (Astra Series) new	WHil
– 'Baby Blue'	SRms
– 'Blue Haze'	EBee NCat WElm WLRN
– 'Blue Pearl'	WHoo
– 'Blue Pygmy'	SMac
– 'Florist Blue'	CMdw WMoo
– 'Florist Rose'	NOak WMoo WWye
– 'Florist Snow'	CMdw NOak WMoo WWye
– 'Fuji Blue'	ERou EWll LAst LIck NBro NLar WGwG WHHs WMnd WSel
– 'Fuji Pink'	CBro CRDP EBee EMar EPfP ERou ESis LAst LHop MRav MTis NBro NLar SMrm SPer SPoG WMnd WSel
– 'Fuji Red' new	LAst
– 'Fuji White'	ERou LAst NBro NLar SMrm WMnd WSel
– 'Hakone'	CRDP EMan LHop MBro MRav NCat SMrm WHoo WWal
– 'Hakone Blue'	CPen ERou ITim NLar
* – 'Hakone Double Blue' (d)	CBro EBee ECGP EMar LRHS MTis SRms WLRN
– 'Hakone White'	CBrm EBee ECGP ERou ITim MBro NChi NGby NLar SChu SPoG WElm WHoo WLin
– 'Lynda Windsor' new	CRDP
– 'Mariesii' ♀ H4	CBro CNic CSBt EBre EChP ECtt ENot EPfP ERou GKir GMaP LPVe LRHS MRav NBir NMen SMrm SPer SPet SPla SRms WEas WHoo WMnd WMoo WPer WWin
– mariesii albus	EBee ESis MBro WHoo
– 'Misato Purple'	EBee WCom WSel
– Mother of Pearl	see P. grandiflorus 'Perlmutterschale'
– 'Park's Double Blue' (d)	NOak WHoo WMoo
§ – 'Perlmutterschale'	CBrm EBee EChP EMar EPfP GMac MBri MCAu SPet WHoo
– pumilus	EBee MBro NChi NWCA WHoo
– roseus	CNic MNrw WHoo

– 'Sentimental Blue'	EBee LPVe NLar SMrm WHil WLRN
– 'Shell Pink'	see P. grandiflorus 'Perlmutterschale'
– 'Zwerg'	EBee

Platycrater (Hydrangeaceae)

arguta	WCru
– B&SWJ 6266	WCru

Plecostachys (Asteraceae)

§ serpyllifolia	CHal MOak SPet

Plectranthus (Lamiaceae)

from Puerto Rico	CArn
ambiguus new	EOHP
– 'Umigoye' new	EOHP
amboinicus	CHal EOHP EShb MOak NHor
* – 'Variegatus' (v)	EOHP
argentatus ♀ H2	CAbb CDoC CFwr CHad CMdw CSev CSpe EBee EBlw EMan EShb LHrt MOak MSte SAga SDix SGar SHFr SMrm SUsu WCom WDyG WKif
– 'Hill House' (v)	CHll EMan EOHP EShb LDai MOak
australis misapplied	see P. verticillatus
behrii	see P. fruticosus
ciliatus	EOHP MOak WEas
– 'Sasha' new	WWol
coleoides 'Marginatus'	see P. forsteri 'Marginatus'
– 'Variegatus'	see P. madagascariensis 'Variegated Mintleaf'
crassus	EOHP
Cuban oregano new	EOHP
dolichopodus new	EOHP
ecklonii new	EOHP
ernstii	EOHP MOak
excisus	CFwr EMon EOHP
§ forsteri 'Marginatus'	CHal EOHP ERea MOak
* fredericii new	NHor
§ fruticosus	CHal EOHP GBri MOak
– 'James'	EOHP
hadiensis var. tomentosus new	EOHP MOak
hirtellus gold	MOak
– variegated (v)	MOak
madagascariensis	EOHP
§ – 'Variegated Mintleaf' (v)	CHal EOHP MRav SHFr SPet SRms SVen
menthol-scented large-leaved	EOHP
menthol-scented small-leaved	EOHP
'Nostalgia' new	CSpe
§ oertendahlii ♀ H1	CHal EBak EOHP MOak SMur
– silver-leaved new	EOHP
ornatus	EOHP MOak
parviflorus new	SMur
rehmannii new	EOHP
saccatus	EOHP
spicatus new	EOHP
– 'Nelspruit' new	EOHP
Swedish ivy	see P. verticillatus, P. oertendahlii
§ thyrsoideus	CHal EOHP SVen
§ verticillatus	CHal EOHP
Vick's plant new	EOHP
zatarhendii	EMan EOHP
zuluensis	CFee CFwr CHal EOHP MOak
– dark-leaved new	EOHP
– light-leaved new	EOHP

Pleioblastus ✿ (Poaceae)

akebono	SDry
§ auricomus (v) ♀ H4	More than 30 suppliers

§ - 'Bracken Hill' SDry
- f. *chrysophyllus* EPla MMoz SDry SMad WJun
- 'Vagans' EBee
- *variegatus* (v) SAga WMoo
§ *chino* CHEx EPla SDry
§ - f. *angustifolius* SDry
- var. *argenteostriatus* EBee EPla WViv
(v)
- f. *aureostriatus* (v) EPla LJus MMoz SDry WCru
- f. *elegantissimus* CDoC CEnd CFir COtt EBee EGln
EPla ERod LAst LJus MGos MHdf
MMoz MWgw MWhi NMoo SDry
WJun WMoo WPGP
- 'Kimmei' SDry
- 'Murakamianus' SDry
fortunei see *P. variegatus*
'Gauntlettii' see *P. humilis* var. *pumilus*
glaber 'Albostriatus' see *Sasaella masamuneana* f.
albostriata
gramineus EPla SDry WJun
§ *hindsii* hort. EPla ERod LPan MMoz NMoo
SArc SDry
§ *humilis* ELan
§ - var. *pumilus* CDDB CDoC CRow CSam CTrC
EBee EHoe ENot EPar EPfP GKir
LAst LJus LRHS MBlu MBri MMoz
MWgw NHol SDry SPla SPlb WFar
WJun WNor WPat WPer WViv
kongosanensis EPla SDry
'Aureostriatus' (v)
linearis CAbb EAmu EBee EFul EPVP EPla
ERod LAst LPal MMoz NMoo SDry
WJun
longifimbriatus EPla WJun
oleosus EPla SDry WJun
§ *pygmaeus* More than 30 suppliers
§ - var. *distichus* CDDB EBee EBlw EFul EHul EPPr
EPla LAst LJus LRHS MGos MHdf
MMoz MWgw MWht NDlv NGdn
NMoo SDry SPar WJun WWin
✦ - - 'Mini' WCot WWpP
§ - 'Mirrezuzume' CPLG WFar
§ *simonii* CAgr CBcs EAmu EBee EBlw EBre
EFul ENot EPla GBin GCal LAst
LJus LPan LRHS MBNS MMoz
MWhi MWod SArc SDry
- var. *heterophyllus* see *P. simonii* f. *variegatus*
§ - f. *variegatus* (v) CFil EPla MBar MBlu NGdn SDry
SPer WJun WPGP
§ *variegatus* (v) ♀ H4 More than 30 suppliers
- 'Tsuboii' (v) CAbb CBig CBrm CDoC CEnd
CFwr COtt EBee EPPr EPla ERod
IFro LAst LJus LPJP LPal LRHS
MBNS MBrN MHdf MMoz MWhi
MWht NMoo SDry WCru WFar
WJun WPGP WPnP
- var. *viridis* (v) SDry
viridistriatus see *P. auricomus*

Pleione ✿ (Orchidaceae)

§ *albiflora* 'Pinchbeck EPot GCrs
Diamond'
Alishan g. CNic EPot GCrs LBut
- 'Merlin' NSpr
- 'Mount Fuji' LBut
- 'Soldier Blue' LBut
Asama g. 'Red Grouse' LBut
Bandai-san g. LBut
Barcena g. LBut
Berapi g. EPot LBut
Brigadoon g. GCrs LBut NSpr
- 'Stonechat' LBut
Britannia g. LBut

- 'Doreen' LBut NSpr
§ *bulbocodioides* EPot ERos LBut MBro NSpr WOBN
- Limprichtii Group see *P. limprichtii*
- Pricei Group see *P. formosana* Pricei Group
§ - 'Yunnan' EPot LBut NSpr
Burnsall g. NSpr
Captain Hook g. LBut NSpr
Chinese Dragon g. NSpr
§ *chunii* EFEx GCrs LAma NSpr
x *confusa* EFEx LBut
Danan g. LBut
Deriba g. LBut
Eiger g. EPot ERos LBut NSpr
- cream ERos LBut
El Pico g. GCrs
- 'Kestrel' LBut
- 'Pheasant' EPot LBut NSpr
- 'Starling' LBut
Erebus g. 'Quail' LBut
Erh Hai g. NSpr
Etna g. EPot GCrs LBut
formosana ♀ H2 CKob EFEx EPot ETow GCrs LAma
SAga SDeJ SIng WFar
- 'Achievement' LBut
I - 'Alba' GCrs SIng
- 'Arline' EPot
- 'Avalanche' LBut
- 'Blush of Dawn' CHdy GCrs LBut NSpr
- 'C.P. Diamond' EPot
- 'Cairngorm' NSpr
- 'Chen' CHdy EPot
- 'Christine Anne' NSpr
- 'Clare' EPot ERos GCrs LBut NSpr
- Eugene g. EPot
- 'Greenhill' LBut
I - 'Iris' EPot LBut
- Kate g. EPot
- 'Little Winnie' EPot
- 'Lucy Diamond' EPot LBut
- 'Lulu' EPot
- 'Pitlochry' LBut
- 'Polar Sun' CHdy EPot GCrs
§ - Pricci Group EPot ERos ETow
- - 'Oriental Grace' LBut MFir
- - 'Oriental Splendour' CHdy EPot LBut
- 'Red Spot' EPot
- 'Roydon' EPot
- 'Snow Bunting' LBut
- 'Snow White' GCrs LBut
- 'Snowy Owl' LBut
forrestii EFEx LAma
Foxhill g. NSpr
Fu Manchu g. NSpr
Fuego g. LBut NSpr
- 'Wren' LBut
Fujiyama g. LBut
Gerry Mundey g. LBut NSpr
Giacomo Leopardi g. NSpr
§ *grandiflora* NSpr
Heathfield g. NSpr
Hekla g. EPot ERos GCrs NSpr
- 'Partridge' LBut
Helgafell g. LBut
hookeriana GCrs
humilis NSpr
Irazu g. GCrs LBut NSpr
- 'Irazu Violet' GCrs
Jorullo g. LBut NSpr
- 'Long-tailed Tit' LBut
Katla g. LBut
Katmai g. LBut
Kilauea g. EPot LBut
- 'Curlew' LBut

Kituro g. LBut
Kohala g. **new** LBut
§ *limprichtii* ♀ H2 EFEx EPot ETow LBut WPnP
– pink GCrs
maculata EFEx
Marco Polo g. LBut NSpr
Matupi g. LBut NSpr
Mayon g. LBut
Mazama g. LBut
Myojin g. LBut
Novarupta g. LBut
Orinoco g. LBut
– 'Gemini' LBut
Orizaba g. LBut
Paricutin g. LBut
Pavlof g. LBut
pinkepankii see *P. grandiflora*
Piton g. EPot LAma LBut
pleionoides GCrs LBut
pogonioides hort. see *P. pleionoides*
pogonioides (Rolfe) Rolfe see *P. bulbocodioides*
Rainier g. LBut
Rakata g. LBut
– 'Blackbird' LBut
– 'Redwing' **new** LBut
– 'Shot Silk' LBut NSpr
– 'Skylark' LBut
San Pedro g. LBut
San Salvador g. LBut
Santorini g. LBut
scopulorum EFEx
Shantung g. CHdy EPot GCrs ITim LAma LBut
 NSpr
– 'Candy Floss' NSpr
– 'Ducat' EPot GCrs LAma LBut NSpr
– 'Gerry Mundey' LBut
– 'Golden Jubilee' NSpr
– 'Golden Plover' LBut
– 'Gwen' EPot
– 'Miki' NSpr
– 'Muriel Harberd' ♀ H2 CRDP NSpr
– 'R6.7' NSpr
– 'Ridgeway' EPot GCrs LBut NSpr
Sorea g. LBut
Soufrière g. LBut NSpr
speciosa Ames & Schltr. see *P. pleionoides*
Stromboli g. EPot GCrs NSpr
– 'Fireball' EPot GCrs LBut NSpr
– 'Robin' LBut
Surtsey g. LBut
– 'Stephanie Rose' NSpr
x *taliensis* LBut
Tarawera g. LBut
Tolima g. CNic EPot LBut
Tongariro g. CHdy EPot ERos GCrs LBut NSpr
– 'Jackdaw' LBut
Versailles g. EFEx EPot ERos LBut
– 'Bucklebury' ♀ H2 CNic EPot GCrs LBut NSpr
– 'Heron' LBut
– 'Muriel Turner' EPot NSpr
Vesuvius g. EPot LBut
– 'Aphrodite' EPot
– 'Grey Wagtail' **new** LBut
– 'Leopard' LBut NSpr
* – 'Phoenix' EPot LBut NSpr
– 'Tawny Owl' LBut
Volcanello g. GCrs LBut NSpr
– 'Honey Buzzard' **new** LBut
– 'Song Thrush' LBut
Wunzen g. LBut
yunnanensis hort. see *P. bulbocodioides* 'Yunnan'
– (Rolfe) Rolfe CHdy LAma LBut
Zeus Weinstein g. EPot LBut NSpr

– 'Desert Sands' LBut

Pleomele see *Dracaena*

Pleurospermum (Apiaceae)
brunonis EBee
calcareum WCru
 B&SWJ 8008 **new**

plum see *Prunus domestica*

Plumbago (Plumbaginaceae)
§ *auriculata* ♀ H1-2 CBcs CDoC CEnd CHEx CPIN
 CRHN CTri CWSG EBak EBee
 ELan EPfP ERea EShb LRHS MBri
 MLan MOak MRav MTis NEgg
 NPal NRog SIde SOWG SPar SPer
 SRms SYvo WBod
– var. *alba* ♀ H1-2 CBcs CBot CHEx CHal CRHN
 CSev CSpe EBak EBee ELan EMil
 EPfP ERea LRHS MLan MOak
 SEND SOWG SPar SPer SYvo
* – *aurea* LIck
– 'Crystal Waters' ELan
– dark blue-flowered CSpe SPar
capensis see *P. auriculata*
– 'Escapade' **new** EShb
§ *indica* ♀ H1 CHal LRHS SOWG
– *rosea* see *P. indica*
larpentiae see *Ceratostigma*
 plumbaginoides

Plumeria (Apocynaceae)
rubra ♀ H1 ESlt LRHS SOWG
– f. *acutifolia* LRHS MGol SOWG

Pneumatopteris see *Cyclosorus*

Poa (Poaceae)
alpina CBig NGdn NJOw
– *nodosa* CBig NFor SWal
bulbosa SWal
chaixii CBig CBod EHoe EMan EMon
 EPPr GKir LRHS NHol NNor SDes
 SLPl SWal WFoF WPrP WWpG
cita CTrC EPPr LEdu
colensoi CBod CCtw EHoe EMan EPPr
 MAvo NFor SPar WPnP
x *jemtlandica* EHoe EVFa NHol
labillardierei CBrm CKno CMea CSam CWCL
 ECGP ECha EGle EHoe EMan
 EPPr EVFa GGar GKir MAvo NBid
 SUsu WDyG WMoo WPrP

Podalyria (Papilionaceae)
calyptrata SPlb
canescens SPlb

Podocarpus (Podocarpaceae)
acutifolius CBcs CDoC ECou EPla GEil GGar
 LCon MBar STre
– (f) ECou
– (m) ECou
andinus see *Prumnopitys andina*
'Autumn Shades' (m) ECou
'Blaze' (f) ECou EPla LBuc LCon LLin MBrN
 SCoo SIng SLim
chilinus see *P. salignus*
'Chocolate Box' (f) ECou
'County Park Fire' PBR (f) CDoC CKen CWSG ECou EOrn
 EPfP EPla EVFa LCon LLin MGos
 NPal SCoo SLim WGor
cunninghamii CBcs CTrC ECou WCwm

- 'Kiwi' (f)	ECou
- 'Roro' (m)	ECou
- x *nivalis* (f)	ECou
dacrydioides	see *Dacrycarpus dacrydioides*
elongatus	CTrC
'Flame'	CDoC EPla
henkelii	CHEx CTrC WMul
latifolius	ECou
lawrencei	ECho EHul
- (f)	ECou MBar
- 'Alpine Lass' (f)	ECou
- 'Blue Gem' (f)	CDoC ECou EOrn EPla IArd LCon LLin MAsh MBar MBri MGos MOne NDlv NHol SCoo SLim SPoG WBcn WLRN
- 'Kiandra'	ECou
- 'Red Tip'	CDoC MAsh SCoo SLim
macrophyllus	CDoC CHEx EOrn LPan NLar SAPC SArc SMad WFar
- (m)	ECou
- 'Aureus'	CBcs
'Maori Prince' (m)	EPla
nivalis	CBcs CMac CPLG CTrC EBre ECou EOrn EPla GGar LLin MBar SRms
- 'Arthur' (m)	ECou
- 'Bronze'	EPla
- 'Clarence' (m)	ECou LLin
- 'Green Queen' (f)	ECou
- 'Jack's Pass' (m)	ECou
- 'Kaweka' (m)	ECou SIng
- 'Kilworth Cream' (v)	CBcs CDoC EPla LBuc LCon LLin MGos SCoo
- 'Little Lady' (f)	ECou SIng
- 'Livingstone' (f)	ECou SIng
- 'Lodestone' (m)	ECou
- 'Moffatt' (f)	ECou LLin SIng
- 'Otari' (m)	ECou LLin
- 'Park Cover'	ECou SIng
- 'Princess' (f)	ECou MBrN
- 'Ruapehu' (m)	ECou EPla SIng
* 'Redtip'	LBuc SLim
'Rough Creek'	LLin
§ *salignus* ♀ H3	CBcs CDoC CHEx EPla IDee ISea SAPC SArc WFar WSHC
- (f) ♀ H3	ECou
- (m) ♀ H3	ECou
spicatus	see *Prumnopitys taxifolia*
'Spring Sunshine' (f)	ECou EPla LLin NLar SIng
totara	CBcs CHEx CTrC ECou GGar LEdu STre WFar WPic
- 'Albany Gold'	CTrC IArd
- 'Aureus'	CBcs CDoC ECou EPla LCon LLin MBar SHBN WBcn WEve WLRN
- 'Pendulus'	CDoC ECou
'Young Rusty' (f)	CDoC ECou EPla LCon SIng

Podophyllum (Berberidaceae)

delavayi	LEur WCru
difforme	EBee LEur WCru
emodi	see *P. hexandrum*
- var. *chinense*	see *P. hexandrum* 'Chinense'
§ *hexandrum*	More than 30 suppliers
- 'Chinense'	CBro CRow EBee EMan GBuc GEdr IBlr LEur SMad WCru WPnP
- 'Majus'	EBee WCot WHal
peltatum	CArn CBct CBro CRow EBee EBla ECGN GPoy IBlr LAma LPhx MSal NHar NSti SSpi WCru WFar WPGP WPnP WViv
pleianthum	EBee LEur MMil WCru

- short	WCru
veitchii **new**	EBee
versipelle	EBee LEur SSpi WCru

Podranea (Bignoniaceae)

brycei	CPIN
§ *ricasoliana*	CPIN CRHN ERea SOWG WMul

Pogonatherum (Poaceae)

§ *paniceum*	LRHS MBri
saccharoideum	see *P. paniceum*

Pogonia (Orchidaceae)

ophioglossoides	CHdy SSpi

Pogostemon (Lamiaceae)

from An Veleniki Herb Farm, Pennsylvania	CArn
§ *cablin*	GPoy MGol MSal NBlo XBlo
heyneanus	MSal
patchouly	see *P. cablin*

Polemonium (Polemoniaceae)

acutiflorum	see *P. caeruleum* subsp. *villosum*
acutifolium	see *P. caeruleum* subsp
var. *nipponicum*.	*nipponicum*
ambervicsii	see *P. pauciflorum* subsp. *hinckleyi*
'Apricot Beauty'	see *P. carneum* 'Apricot Delight'
N *archibaldiae* ♀ H4	EBee MBro NBir SRms WCot
§ *boreale*	EBre EMan GCal GDra GEdr GKir IGor MBow MNrw MOne NArg SBla WFar WMoo
* - *album*	WBrE
- 'Heavenly Habit'	EBee LPVe NPro WWeb
§ *brandegeei*	NArg NBro SAga STes WBVN WPer
- subsp. *mellitum*	see *P. brandegeei*
'Bressingham Purple' **new**	EBre
caeruleum misapplied, Himalayan	see *P. cashmerianum*
§ *caeruleum*	More than 30 suppliers
- subsp. *amygdalinum*	see *P. occidentale*
- 'Bambino Blue'	EBee IBal LRHS WPer WWeb
- 'Blue Bell'	ELau
- Brise d'Anjou = 'Blanjou'[PBR] (v)	CCge CHid CM&M COtt EBee EBre EChP EMan ENot EOrc EPfP EWes GKir LAst LRHS MCLN MRav MSte NBir NPri NSti SAga SCoo SPer SPla WCot WLin WRus WSan WWeb
- subsp. *caeruleum* f. *album*	More than 30 suppliers
I - f. *dissectum*	NPol
- 'Everton White' **new**	MWrn
- 'Golden Showers' (v)	CCge CStr NPro
- var. *grandiflorum*	see *P. caeruleum* subsp. *himalayanum*
§ - subsp. *himalayanum*	EBee EPPr NChi WPer
* - - 'Album'	IIve
- 'Humile'	see *P.* 'Northern Lights'
- 'Idylle'	EMan GMac MAnH
- 'Iverna Jewel'	IIve
- 'Larch Cottage' (v)	NLar
- 'Newark Park'	EPPr
§ - subsp. *nipponicum*	EBee GBin WPer
- 'Snow and Sapphires' **new**	MBri
§ - subsp. *villosum*	CStr EBee IIve
carneum	ECha EGle EMan EOrc GKir LAst MCAu MCCP MNrw MTho NCot

	NHar NPPs NPol SPer SSpi STes WAul WBea WFar WMoo WPer WSan WWin
§ - 'Apricot Delight'	More than 30 suppliers
§ *cashmerianum*	EBee ECGN EPPr GBuc LPVe LRHS MBro MHar NBur NOak SPer WFar WHen WHil WHoo WSan
'Churchills'	CLAP EBee NCot WPGP WPrP
§ 'Dawn Flight'	WFar
delicatum	see *P. pulcherrimum* subsp. *delicatum*
'Eastbury Purple'	CElw CStr MAnH
elegans	NPol
'Elworthy Amethyst'	CElw EBee MAvo NCot WPGP
eximium	NPol WSan
flavum	see *P. foliosissimum* var. *flavum*
foliosissimum hort.	see *P. archibaldiae*
foliosissimum A. Gray	IGor MNrw WHoo WPer
- var. *albiflorum*	see *P. foliosissimum* var. *alpinum*
§ - var. *alpinum*	EBee MWrn NBir
- 'Cottage Cream'	CStr MAvo NCot NPol
§ - var. *flavum*	NCot NPol
- var. *foliosissimum*	EWes NPol
- - NNS 99-422	EPPr
'Glebe Cottage Lilac'	CCge CElw CHar CMil CStr EBee LPio MAvo NBir NCot WPGP
'Hannah Billcliffe'	CLAP MAnH MAvo NCot
§ 'Hopleys'	CLAP CStr EChP EMan GBar GBri GCal IFro NCot NGdn WFar
x *jacobaea*	CDes EBee EPPr NCot WCot
'Katie Daley'	see *P.* 'Hopleys'
kiushianum	EBee NCot
'Lace Towers'	NSti SHar
§ 'Lambrook Mauve' ♀ H4	More than 30 suppliers
mellitum	see *P. brandegeei* subsp. *mellitum*
'North Tyne'	NChi
§ 'Northern Lights'	CBos CDes CStr EBee ECGP EGle ELan EMan EMon EPPr EWes GBri GMac MAvo MBri MMil MNrw NCot NHar NPol NSti SAga SMrm STes WFar WMoo
'Norwell Mauve'	MNrw
§ *occidentale*	EBee
'Pam' (v) **new**	WWeb
pauciflorum	More than 30 suppliers
§ - subsp. *hinckleyi*	NCot NGar NPol SGar
- subsp. *pauciflorum*	LRHS SGar SMac WSan
- silver-leaved	see *P. pauciflorum* subsp. *pauciflorum*
- 'Sulphur Trumpets' **new**	WGwG WHHs
- subsp. *typicum*	see *P. pauciflorum* subsp. *pauciflorum*
§ 'Pink Beauty'	CBre CMGP EBee EFou ELan EPfP LRHS NCot NPol SUsu WCer
'Pink Pearl'	NCot
pulchellum Salisb.	see *P. reptans*
pulchellum Turcz.	see *P. caeruleum*
pulcherrimum hort.	see *P. boreale*
- 'Tricolor'	see *P. boreale*
pulcherrimum Hook.	EBee GAbr GTou NBro WHen WPer WWye
§ - subsp. *delicatum*	MTho NPol
- subsp. *pulcherrimum*	EHyt LTwo NPol
§ *reptans*	CAgr CArn CHea ECoo GBar GBri GPoy MHer MSal NBro SIng WFar WPer WWye
- 'Album'	see *P. reptans* 'Virginia White'
- 'Blue Pearl'	CElw CMea COlW EBee EMan EPar EPfP LRHS MLLN MNrw NBro NHol NLon SMrm SPer SPla SUsu SWal WFar WHen WHil WSan

- 'Dawn Flight'	see *P.* 'Dawn Flight'
- 'Firmament'	CDes EMon
- 'Lambrook Manor'	see *P.* 'Lambrook Mauve'
- 'Pink Beauty'	see *P.* 'Pink Beauty'
- 'Pink Dawn'	EChP EMil MCAu MLLN MUlv NCot NGdn
* - 'Sky Blue'	NBro
§ - 'Virginia White'	CBcs CBre CDes CElw CMea CStr EBee LRHS NChi NGar NPol SUsu WFar
- 'White Pearl'	COlW IGor WBVN
richardsonii hort.	see *P.* 'Northern Lights'
richardsonii Graham	see *P. boreale*
'Sapphire'	CStr ELan EMan EMon MBrN
scopulinum	see *P. pulcherrimum* subsp. *delicatum*
I 'Sonia's Bluebell'	CDes CElw CLAP CMil CStr EBee EPPr EVFa EWes LPhx MAvo MDKP MNrw MSte NCot SUsu WMaN WPGP WPrP
'Theddingworth'	WBar WFar
vanbruntiae **new**	EBee
viscosum	EPot GBuc MBrN SGar SYvo WHen
yezoense	CBre CStr GBri MNrw NCot NPol WFar WWhi
- *hidakanum*	CStr EBee NCot
- 'Purple Rain'	CHar CStr EBee EHrv EMan EPfP EWes GBuc MBct MCCP MLLN MNrw MTis NLon SPer WFar WRha WRus

Polianthes (Agavaceae)

nelsonii	CFir
tuberosa ♀ H1-2	CBcs CSpe LRHS NRog
- 'The Pearl' (d)	LAma

Poliomintha (Lamiaceae)

bustamanta	EBee ELan LPhx NBir SAga

Poliothyrsis (Flacourtiaceae)

sinensis ♀ H4	CABp CFil CPne CTho EPfP GIBF LAst MBri WBor WWes

Pollia (Commelinaceae)

japonica	EBee EMan IFro MAvo
minor B&SWJ 6843 **new**	WCru

Polygala (Polygalaceae)

alpicola	SOkd
amoenissima **new**	SOkd
calcarea	CLyd MBro NHar WAbe WPat
- Bulley's form	EPot LBee LRHS
- 'Lillet' ♀ H4	CLyd CPBP EHyt EPot GDra LHop LRHS LTwo MBro NHar NMen SBla SScr SSte WAbe WFar WPat WWin
chamaebuxus ♀ H4	CBcs GCrs GDra GEdr GKev MLLN NHar NLAp SRms WBVN WTin WWin
- *alba*	EHyt LBee LRHS WAbe
§ - var. *grandiflora* ♀ H4	CBcs EPot GDra GGar GKir LBee LHop MAsh MBar MBro MDun MGos NHar NLAp NMen NWCA SBla SChu SIng WAbe WBVN WBod WFar WPat WSHC WWin
- 'Kamniski'	CMHG EPot
- 'Loibl'	EPot SBla
- 'Purpurea'	see *P. chamaebuxus* var. *grandiflora*
- 'Rhodoptera'	see *P. chamaebuxus* var. *grandiflora*

§ x ***dalmaisiana*** ♀ H1 — CAbb CHEx CHll CRHN CSpe EBee ERea GQui LHop SBla SBrw SMur WAbe WBor WCFE

'Dolomite' — NHar

myrtifolia — CPLG CTrC LRHS SHFr SIgm SMrm SPlb WOBN WWye

- 'Grandiflora' — see *P.* x *dalmaisiana*

***pauciflora* new** — SOkd

'Rosengarten' — SBla

vayredae — GEdr

virgata — EPfP ERea EShb ESlt LRHS SSte

Polygonatum (Convallariaceae)

acuminatifolium — EBee LEur

altelobatum B&SWJ 286 — WCru

§ ***biflorum*** — CArn CBro CHid CPou EBee EBla EBre EGle EGol ELan EOrc EPot ERou GKir GSki IBlr LEur MSal NCat NLar SHar SMad SPar SSpi WAul WCot WCru WFar WPnP WViv

- dwarf — EPPr EPla IBlr LEur WCot
- polyploid — LEur

canaliculatum — see *P. biflorum*

cathcartii — EBee

cirrhifolium — CDes CLAP CPom EBee EBla ELan LEur NCat NPar WCot WCru WPGP

commutatum — see *P. biflorum*

cryptanthum — WCru

curvistylum — CAvo CBct CLAP CStu EBee EBla ECha EGle IBlr LEur LPhx MHtf NLar NRya WCru WFTG WFar WViv

cyrtonema hort. — see *Disporopsis pernyi*

cyrtonema Hua — EBee LEur

- B&SWJ 271 — WCru

falcatum hort. — see *P. humile*

§ ***falcatum*** A. Gray — CLyd EBee EGle EPla GGar IBlr LEur NOak SIng WHer WWin

- B&SWJ 1077 — WCru
- 'Variegatum' — see *P. odoratum* var. *pluriflorum* 'Variegatum'

'Falcon' — see *P. humile*

***filipes* new** — EBee WCru

***fuscum* new** — LEur WCru

geminiflorum — EBee IBlr SOkd WFar

- McB 2448 — GEdr

giganteum — see *P. biflorum*

glaberrimum — WCot

'Golden Gift' — CRDP

§ ***graminifolium*** — CBct CLAP CMGP CPBP EBee EPot ERos LEur MSte SCnR WCot WCru

- GW 803 — LEur WPnP

§ ***hirtum*** — CBct CHid CLAP CPom EMon EPla EPot IBlr LEur WCru WFar

- BM 7012 — EBee LEur

hookeri — More than 30 suppliers

- McB 1413 — GEdr

§ ***humile*** — CBct CFwr CLAP CRDP EBee EBla EHrv EHyt ELan EMan EPla ERos GBri GCal IBlr NHar NMen SBla SDes SMac SSpi SUsu WAbe WAul WCot WCru WFar WPnP WRus

§ x ***hybridum*** ♀ H4 — More than 30 suppliers

- 'Betberg' — CBct CRow EBee ECha LEur NBir WCot
- 'Flore Pleno' (d) — WHer
- 'Nanum' — CHid CNic LEur

§ - 'Striatum' (v) — More than 30 suppliers

- 'Variegatum' — see *P.* x *hybridum* 'Striatum'
- 'Wakehurst' **new** — EBla

inflatum — EBee LEur WCru

- B&SWJ 922 — WCru

involucratum — EBee LEur WCru

japonicum — see *P. odoratum*

kingianum — EBee LEur

- yellow-flowered B&SWJ 6562 — WCru

'Langthorns Variegated' (v) — ELan LEur

lasianthum — WCru

latifolium — see *P. hirtum*

maximowiczii — GCal GSki

multiflorum hort. — see *P.* x *hybridum*

multiflorum L. — CRow EBee EBot ECha EFou EPla EWTr EWsh GAbr GKir LRHS NVic SAga SPlb SRms SUsu SWal

- ***giganteum*** hort. — see *P. biflorum*

nodosum — EBee LEur WCru

obtusifolium — EBee

§ ***odoratum*** ♀ H4 — CAvo CBro CRow CSWP EBee ELau EPar EPfP EPla EPot GEdr GIBF IBlr LEur MSal NBid NLar NRya SAga SDes SMac SSpi WCot WCru

§ - dwarf — IBlr

- 'Flore Pleno' (d) ♀ H4 — CAvo CDes CLAP CMGP CRow EBee EHrv IBlr LEur SBla SCnR WHoo WPnP
- 'Grace Barker' — see *P.* x *hybridum* 'Striatum'
- var. ***pluriflorum*** — GBuc IBlr SSpi

§ - - 'Variegatum' (v) — More than 30 suppliers

- 'Red Stem' **new** — WCru
- 'Silver Wings' (v) — CLAP ERou LEur NBir NLar

officinale — see *P. odoratum*

oppositifolium — LEur WFar

- B&SWJ 2537 — EBee WCru

§ ***orientale*** — CHid CLAP IBlr

pluriflorum — see *P. graminifolium*

polyanthemum — see *P. orientale*

prattii — EBee LEur MPhe

pubescens — EBee WCru

pumilum — see *P. odoratum* dwarf

punctatum — LEdu LEur WFar

- B&SWJ 2395 — CBct WCru

racemosum — SIng SMac

roseum — EBee WHer

sewerzowii — EBee EPla

sibiricum — CAvo EBee GEdr IBlr WCru

- DJHC 600 — CDes

stenophyllum — CAvo LEur

stewartianum — CLAP EPar IBlr LEur

verticillatum — CAvo CBos CBro CHid CLyd CRow EBee EBre ECha EPla EPot GKir IBlr LEur MTho SMad WCot WCru WFar

- CC 1324 — CPLG

'Himalayan Giant' — CHid EBee LEur

* - ***rubrum*** — CArn CBct CRez CRow EGle EHrv EPPr EPar IBlr LEur LPhx MSte MTho NGby WCot WPrP

- 'Serbian Dwarf' — CHid EBee LEur

aff. ***verticillatum*** — LEur SDes

zanlanscianense — EBee LEur WCru

Polygonum ❀ (Polygonaceae)

affine — see *Persicaria affinis*

amplexicaule — see *Persicaria amplexicaulis*

aubertii — see *Fallopia baldschuanica*

aviculare — CArn

baldschuanicum — see *Fallopia baldschuanica*

bistorta — see *Persicaria bistorta*

compactum — see *Fallopia japonica* var. compacta

cuspidatum — see *Fallopia japonica*

equisetiforme hort. — see *P. scoparium*

filiforme	see *Persicaria virginiana*
longisetum	see *Persicaria longiseta*
molle	see *Persicaria mollis*
multiflorum	see *Fallopia multiflora*
odoratum	see *Persicaria odorata*
polystachyum	see *Persicaria wallichii*
reynoutria	see *Fallopia japonica*
runciforme	see *Persicaria runcinata*
§ *scoparium*	CBrm CRow EMan EPPr EPla GEil MFir SDry SDys SIng SMad WCot WTin
tinctorium	see *Persicaria tinctoria*
weyrichii	see *Persicaria weyrichii*

Polylepis (*Rosaceae*)

australis	LEdu SMad WCot

Polymnia (*Asteraceae*)

sonchifolia	IIve LEdu
- 'Munchy White' **new**	IIve
- 'Purple Gourmet' **new**	IIve
uvedalia	see *Smallanthus uvedalius*

Polypodium ✿ (*Polypodiaceae*)

australe	see *P. cambricum*
§ *cambricum*	EFer NHar NMar WCot WRic
§ - 'Barrowii'	NMar WRic
- 'Cambricum' ♀ H4	WRic WWye
- 'Cristatum'	WRic
- (Cristatum Group) 'Grandiceps Forster'	WRic
- - 'Grandiceps Fox' ♀ H4	WRic
- 'Oakleyae'	SMHy WPGP
- 'Omnilacerum Oxford'	CLAP WRic
- 'Prestonii'	WRic
- Pulcherrimum Group	CBgR EGol NHar WAbe
- 'Pulcherrimum Addison'	WAbe
- Pulcherrimum Group bifid	WRic
- 'Richard Keyse'	CDes WRic
- Semilacerum Group	NMar WRic
- - 'Carew Lane'	WRic
- - 'Falcatum O'Kelly'	WAbe WRic
- - 'Jubilee'	NMar
- - 'Robustum'	NMar WRic
- 'Whilharris' ♀ H4	CLAP WPGP WRic
x *coughlinii* 'Bifidograndiceps'	WRic
glycyrrhiza	LEur WRic
- Grandiceps Group	WRic
- 'Longicaudatum' ♀ H4	EBee EMon NMar WCot WFib WRic WWye
- 'Malahatense'	NMar
- 'Malahatense' (sterile)	WAbe WRic
interjectum	CLAP EBee EFer NMar NOrc NVic SPar WFib WRic
- 'Acutum'	NMar
- 'Bifidograndiceps'	SIng WPGP WRic
- 'Cornubiense' ♀ H4	CFil CLAP CRDP EFer EMon GCal NBir NBro NHar NHol NMar NVic SSpi WAbe WPGP WRic
- 'Ramosum Hillman'	WRic
x *mantoniae*	LEur
scouleri	NBro
vulgare	More than 30 suppliers
- 'Bifidomultifidum'	CBgR CLAP EBee EMon GBin MCCP NHar NHol NMar SIng SMac SPla WCot WFib
- 'Cornubiense Grandiceps'	SRms WFib WRic
* - 'Cornubiense Multifidum'	EBee NHar WCot
- Ramosum Group	NMar
- 'Trichomanoides Backhouse'	WAbe

Polypompholyx see *Utricularia*

Polyscias (*Araliaceae*)

'Elegans'	MBri
fruticosa	MBri
scutellaria 'Pennockii' (v)	MBri

Polystichum ✿ (*Dryopteridaceae*)

acrostichoides	CLAP CMHG CMil CPrp EBee GCal GQui LEur NHar SNut SSpi WRic
aculeatum ♀ H4	CFwr CLAP EBre ECha EFer EFou EHon ELan EMon ENot EPfP GKir GMaP GQui LEur MBri MWgw NBid NHar NHol NMar NOak NOrc SMer SPar SRms WCot WCru WFib WRic
I - Densum Group **new**	EFer
- Grandiceps Group	EFer NMar
andersonii	CLAP NHol
braunii	CBcs CMHG CPrp EBee EBre EGol GBin LEur LPVe MLan MMoz NOGN WPnP
caryotideum	see *Cyrtomium caryotideum*
deltodon **new**	EBee LEur
falcatum	see *Cyrtomium falcatum*
fortunei	see *Cyrtomium fortunei*
imbricans	CLAP NHar SArc
lonchitis	NWoo
luctuosum **new**	WRic
makinoi	CLAP NHol WFib WRic
munitum ♀ H4	More than 30 suppliers
- 'Incisum'	GCal
ovatopaleaceum **new**	WRic
polyblepharum ♀ H4	More than 30 suppliers
proliferum	GCal WRic
* - *plumosum*	CFwr NOak
retrorsopaleaceum	LEur NMar WRic
rigens	CElw CFwr CLAP EBee GCal NDlv NHol NMar NOGN SNut SPar SRms WCru WFib
§ *setiferum* ♀ H4	More than 30 suppliers
§ - Acutilobum Group	CBcs CFil CLAP CMHG CRDP EBee ECha ENot EPot NCat NHar NHol SDix SMad SPar SSpi STes WPGP WPnP
- Congestum Group	CRDP GBin MBri MMoz NHar NHol NMar SChu SPer SRms WFib WRic
- 'Congestum'	CFwr CPrp EBee ENot EPfP EPot GCal LRHS MDun NBir NBlu NSti SMer SMrm SNut SPla WGor
- 'Congestum Cristatum'	EFer
§ - 'Cristatogracile'	NHar NMar
- 'Cristatopinnulum'	CFil NHar NMar WPGP
- Cristatum Group	SRms
- Divisilobum Group	More than 30 suppliers
- - 'Dahlem'	CDoC CFwr CLAP CPen CTrC ECha EFer ELan EMon GKir LPVe MDun MMoz MSte SMac SMer SNut SPer WAbe WPnP WRic
- - 'Herrenhausen'	CFwr EBee EBlw EBre ECha EFer ELan EPfP GKir LRHS MAvo MBri MCCP MDun MWgw NMar NOGN NOrc NSti SApp SPer WAbe WFar WPnP WRic
- 'Divisilobum Densum' ♀ H4	CLAP ENot EPfP NMar NOrc SIng SMad SNut SSpi WCot
- 'Divisilobum Iveryanum' ♀ H4	GBin NHol SRms
- 'Divisilobum Laxum'	EPar SChu

- 'Grandiceps'	CLAP ELan
- 'Hamlet' **new**	GBin
- 'Helena' **new**	GBin
- 'Hirondelle'	SRms
- Lineare Group	CFil NHol WFib
- Multilobum Group	WRic
- Percristatum Group	see *P. setiferum* 'Cristatogracile'
- Perserratum Group	NMar
- 'Plumo-Densum'	see *P. setiferum* 'Plumosomultilobum'
- 'Plumosodensum'	see *P. setiferum* 'Plumosomultilobum'
- Plumosodivisilobum Group	CMil CRow ECha EGol NBid NHar SPla WAbe WCru WFib
§ - 'Plumosomultilobum'	CFwr CPrp EBee EFer ENot EPfP GBin LAst LRHS MCLN MWgw NSti SMer SMrm SNut SPar SPer SPla SRms WAbe WCot WMoo WPnP WRic
- Plumosum Group	CLAP CSam CSpe EBlw LEur NOrc SArc SBla SChu WFib WStI
- Plumosum Group dwarf	CBos
- Proliferum Group	see *P. setiferum* Acutilobum Group
* - 'Proliferum Wollaston'	CFwr ENot NRib SNut WWeb
- 'Pulcherrimum Bevis' ♀ H4	CLAP SHFr WFib WPGP
- 'Ray Smith' **new**	GBin
- Revolvens Group	EFer
- Rotundatum Group	CRDP NMar
- 'Wakeleyanum'	SRms
N - 'Wollaston'	CLAP GBin WAbe
tagawanum	WRic
triangulum	NMar
tripterum new	WRic
tsussimense ♀ H4	CBos CDoC CFwr CLAP CPrp CRDP EBee GKir GQui LEur MAvo MBri MSte NBir NBlu NHol NMar SNut SPer SPlb SRms SRot WFib WRic
vestitum	CTrC
xiphophyllum	WRic

Polyxena (Hyacinthaceae)

corymbosa	CStu LBow
§ **ensifolia**	ERos LBow
odorata	CLyd CStu WCot
pygmaea	see *P. ensifolia*

Pomaderris (Rhamnaceae)

apetala	CPLG
elliptica	CPLG ECou

pomegranate see *Punica granatum*

Poncirus (Rutaceae)

§ **trifoliata**	CAgr CArn CBcs CDoC CFil EBee ELan ENot EPfP ERea IDee LAst LRHS MBlu MRav NWea SAPC SArc SKee SLon SMad WDin WFar WPGP WPat WSHC WTel

Pontederia (Pontederiaceae)

cordata ♀ H4	CBen CHEx CRow CWat ECha EHon EMFW ENot EPfP LMdh LPBA MCCP MSta NPer SCoo SLon SPlb SWat WFar WMAq WWpP
- **alba**	CRow EMFW EPfP LMdh SAWi SLon WDyG WMAq
§ - var. **lancifolia**	CRow ECha EMFW LMdh MSta NPer SWat WDyG WWpP
- 'Pink Pons'	CRow
dilatata	EMFW SLon
lanceolata	see *P. cordata* var. *lancifolia*

Populus ✿ (Salicaceae)

x **acuminata**	WMou
alba	CCVT CDoC CDul CKin CLnd CSBt CTri EBee ECrN ENot GKir LBuc MBar NBee NWea SHBN SPer WDin WMou WOrn WStI
- 'Bolleana'	see *P. alba* f. *pyramidalis*
- 'Nivea'	EWTr
§ - f. **pyramidalis**	CBcs NBee SRms WMou
§ - 'Raket'	CLnd CTho ECrN ELan ENot MGos NWea SPer
- 'Richardii'	CDul CLnd CTho ECtt LPan MBar SPar SPer SRPl WCot WFar WMou
- Rocket	see *P. alba* 'Raket'
- x **grandidentata**	WMou
§ 'Balsam Spire' (f) ♀ H4	CDoC CDul CTho EBee ENot GKir LBuc NWea WDin WMou
§ **balsamifera**	CCVT CDoC CTho CTri EBee GKir MGos NWea SHBN SPer SRms WCot WDin WFar WHer
x **berolinensis**	CDoC
x **canadensis new**	CKin
- 'Aurea' ♀ H4	CDoC CDul CLnd CTho CWib EBee EMil ENot LPan MDun MRav SKee SPer WDin WGer WMou
- 'Aurea' x **jackii** 'Aurora'	MRav WDin
- 'Eugenei' (m)	CTho
- 'Robusta' (m)	CDoC CDul CLnd CTri EBee EMil ENot LBuc NWea WDin WMou
- 'Serotina' (m)	CDoC ECrN WDin WMou
x **candicans** misapplied	see *P.* x *jackii*
x **canescens**	CDoC GKir MBri WDin WMou
- 'De Moffart' (m)	ENot
- 'Tower'	WMou
x **generosa** 'Beaupré'	CTho GKir LBuc WDin WMou
§ x **jackii** (f)	WDin
- 'Aurora' (f/v)	CBcs CDul CLnd CSBt CTrw EBee ELan ENot EWTr GKir LBuc LRHS MBar MBri MGos MRav MWat NBee NBlu NWea SHBN SPar SPer SRms WDin WFar WHar WJas
lasiocarpa ♀ H4	CDoC CFil CLnd CMCN CTho EBee EPfP MBlu MRav SLPl SMad WMou WPGP
§ - var. **tibetica**	WMou
maximowiczii	WMou
nigra	CDul NWea SPer WDin
- (f)	ECrN SLPl
- (m)	SLPl
- subsp. **betulifolia**	CCVT CDul CKin CLnd CTho EBee ENot LBuc MGos NWea WDin WMou WOrn
- - (f)	WMou
- - (m)	WMou
N - 'Italica' (m) ♀ H4	CCVT CDoC CDul CLnd CSBt CTho CTri CWib EBee ECrN ELan ENot GKir LBuc LRHS MBri MGos NBee NWea SHBN SPer SRms WDin WOrn
- 'Italica Aurea'	see *P. nigra* 'Lombardy Gold'
§ - 'Lombardy Gold' (m)	CEnd CTho CWib MBlu SPer SRPl WMou
- 'Pyramidalis'	see *P. nigra* 'Italica'
simonii 'Fastigiata'	WMou
- 'Obtusata'	WMou
szechuanica	WMou
- var. **tibetica**	CFil WPGP
tacamahaca	see *P. balsamifera*
'Tacatricho 32'	see *P.* 'Balsam Spire'
tomentosa	WMou

tremula ♀ H4   CCVT CDoC CDul CKin CLnd CSBt CTho CWib EBee ECrN ELan ENot GKir GTre LBuc LHyr LRHS NBee NWea SHBN SKee SPer WDin WMoo WMou WOrn

§   - 'Erecta'   CDul CEnd CLnd CTho EBee LPan LRHS MBlu MBri SMad SPoG WFar WMou

- 'Fastigiata'   see *P. tremula* 'Erecta'
- 'Pendula' (m)   CEnd CLnd CTho ECrN SRPl WCFE WDin WGer WMou

trichocarpa   CDul CTho SPer
- 'Columbia River'   GKir
- 'Fritzi Pauley' (f)   CDul CTho WMou
violascens   see *P. lasiocarpa* var. *tibetica*
wilsonii   WMou
yunnanensis   CFil CLnd CMHG WMou WPGP

Porophyllum (Asteraceae)
ruderale   MSal

Portulaca (Portulacaceae)
grandiflora   MBri
oleracea   CArn MChe MHer SIde WHer WJek WLHH WWol
- var. *aurea*   MChe MHer WJek WLHH

Potamogeton (Potamogetonaceae)
crispus   EHon EMFW SBHF WMAq
pectinatus   EHon

Potentilla ✿ (Rosaceae)
alba   CPLG CSev EBee ECha EFou ELan EMar GBuc LGro MTho MWgw NChi NFla SCro SPer SUsu WAul WCot WPer
alchemilloides   MNrw SMer WPer
alpicola   WPer
ambigua   see *P. cuneata*
andicola   EBee
anserina   CArn CKin GBar MGas MHer WHbs WHer
- 'Golden Treasure' (v)   EBee EVFa ITer MLLN WCot WHer
- 'Shine'   EMan WAlt WCot
anserinoides   EBee EGoo EMan GCal WCot WMoo WPer
arbuscula hort.   see *P. fruticosa* 'Elizabeth'
'Arc-en-ciel'   CHid EBee EChP EMan IKee LAst MBri MCAu SBri SHar SUsu WHil
argentea   CSWP CSev LIck LPVe MBNS MPWC MWgw NNor SBri SPlb SSte WBea WFar WPat WPer
arguta   EBee
argyrophylla   see *P. atrosanguinea* var. *argyrophylla*
*   - *insignis rubra*   LPVe NChi
atrosanguinea   More than 30 suppliers
- CC 1384   CPou
§   - var. *argyrophylla*   EChP ECha ELan GCal GTou MRav MWat MWgw NBir NBro NChi NCot NMir NOak SCro SGar SRms SWal WBea WFar WMoo WPer WWhi WWin
- - SS&W 7768   GDra MSte NMGW
- - ex CC 2991   MDCh
- var. *leucochroa*   see *P. atrosanguinea* var. *argyrophylla*
aucheriana new   EHyt
aurea   EBee ECtt EDAr EMNN EPfP MBri MTho NArg NBlu NMen NMir NOrc NWCA SHFr SRms WPat

- 'Aurantiaca'   EDAr EWes SRot
§   - subsp. *chrysocraspeda*   GCrs NMen STre
§   - 'Goldklumpen' Foerster   ECtt MRav NPro SCro
- 'Plena' (d)   GDra GTou MBro SRot
'Blazeaway'   EBee EChP EMan EVFa LRHS MBri NBur NCat NGdn NHol SLon WFar WLRN
*   **bulleyana**   WWeb
burmiensis new   EBee
calabra   CMea ECha EDAr EMan SMer WHer WWin
§   **cinerea**   CTri LBee NHar SBla
collina   CNic EBee
§   'Craigieburn Cochineal'   EChP
§   **crantzii**   CBrm CMea EBee GCrs GTou MBar MSte SIng SRms
- 'Nana'   see *P. crantzii* 'Pygmaea'
§   - 'Pygmaea'   CNic ECtt EPfP MOne NBir NMen WBea
§   **cuneata** ♀ H4   CLyd EDAr ESis GDra GTou MTho NHar NLAp NRya NWCA SIng WOut WPer WWin
'Custard and Cream' new   EChP
delavayi   EBre GIBF MNrw
detommasii   MHar WPer
dickinsii   ETow SOkd
'Emilie'   CMea EBee EChP EFou EGle GCal LAco LPVe MBNS MBri NLar NSti SUsu WCra WFar WHil
§   **erecta**   CArn CKin EGle EOHP GBar GPoy GWCH MChe MHer MSal WBri WHbs WWye
eriocarpa   CLyd ECtt EHol EMNN EMlt GDra GEdr IMGH MWat NHar NMen SBri WAbe
- CC 2633   MDCh
'Etna'   CElw CKno CStr EBee EChP ECtt ELan EVFa GCal GKir GMac GTou MNrw MWrn NBir NCat NCot NFor NMRc NPPs SAga WBea WBro WCom WCru WHen WMoo WPGP WPer WWhi
'Everest'   see *P. fruticosa* 'Mount Everest'
'Fireflame'   EBee ECha NLar SBri
fissa   CTCP EBee MNrw MSte NBir WBar
'Flambeau'   CHad EBee EChP EMan MRav NDov NGdn NLar NPPs SLon
'Flamenco'   CBrm CSam CTri EBee EChP ECtt EFou ELan EMil ERou GKir IKee MArl MBri MNrw MRav NBir NFor SAga SUsu WAbb WFar WPGP
fragariiformis   see *P. megalantha*
fruticosa   LBuc NMen NWea
- 'Abbotswood' ♀ H4   More than 30 suppliers
- 'Abbotswood Silver' (v)   CLyd EBee ECtt LAst MBNS NLon SLim WFar WMoo WWal
- 'Annette'   LRHS MAsh MBri NPro WBod WWeb
- 'Apple Blossom' new   CWib
- var. *arbuscula* hort.   see *P. fruticosa* 'Elizabeth'
- 'Argentea Nana'   see *P. fruticosa* 'Beesii'
- 'Beanii'   SPer WWeb
§   - 'Beesii'   EBee EHyt ELan EPfP GKir LRHS MAsh MBNS MBar SIgm SPer SPla WHCG WLRN WSHC WTel WWeb WWin
- 'Bewerley Surprise'   EHol NBir NPro WHCG WWeb
- 'Cascade'   WBcn
- 'Charlotte' new   WBcn
*   - 'Chelsea Star' ♀ H4   WWeb
- 'Chilo' (v)   MGos WBcn

- 'Clotted Cream'	MBar
- var. *dahurica*	
'Farrer's White'	WFar
- - 'Hersii'	see *P. fruticosa* 'Snowflake'
- - 'Rhodocalyx'	CPle WFar
- 'Dart's Cream'	LRHS MBri
- 'Dart's Golddigger'	CTri EBee ECtt ENot WWeb
§ - 'Dart's Nugget'	WWeb
- 'Daydawn'	More than 30 suppliers
§ - 'Elizabeth'	More than 30 suppliers
- 'Farreri'	see *P. fruticosa* 'Gold Drop'
- 'Floppy Disc'	CWib EPfP LRHS MGos NHol NWoo SHBN SPer SPla SSta
- 'Frances, Lady Daresbury'	GKir WWeb
- 'Funny Face'	MBri
- 'Glenroy Pinkie'	CSam EBee EPfP LRHS MTis NPro SLon WWeb
§ - 'Gold Drop'	MHFa NFor WHCG WTel
- 'Golden Dwarf'	LRHS MGos
- 'Golden Spreader'	EBre GKir NPro
- 'Goldfinger'	CChe CDoC CSBt EBee ELan ENot EPfP GKir LHop LRHS MBri MGos MRav MWat SLim SMer SPer SPlb SRPl WDin WHar WStI WTel WWeb
- Goldkugel	see *P. fruticosa* 'Gold Drop'
- 'Goldstar'	EBee EBre ENot GKir IArd LRHS MBNS MBri MHFa WFar WHCG
- 'Goldteppich'	LBuc MBar SHBN
- 'Goscote'	MGos
- 'Grace Darling'	CAbP EPfP EWes GDra GGar NBir NEgg NHol WBod WGor WGwG WHCG WWeb
- 'Groneland' ♀ H4 **new**	WWeb
- 'Hachmann's Gigant'	EMil
- 'Haytor's Orange' **new**	CWib
- 'Honey'	LHop WHCG WWeb
- 'Hopleys Orange' ♀ H4	CChe EPfP EWes GKir LHop LRHS MAsh MBri MWat WBod WFar WGor WHCG WWeb WWin
- 'Hunter's Moon'	WWeb
- 'Hurstbourne'	NPro
- 'Jackman's Variety' ♀ H4	CSam CWib ECtt ENot SPer SRms WStI WWeb
- 'Jolina' **new**	WWeb
- 'Katherine Dykes'	CChe CDoC CSBt CWib EBee ENot EPfP GDra GKir LRHS MAsh MBar MDun MRav NWea SLim SLon SPer SRPl SRms WBod WDin WFar WGwG WHar WMoo WStI WTel WWeb
* - 'King Cup' ♀ H4	WWeb
- 'Kingdon Ward' **new**	WWeb
'Klondike'	CBcs CSBt EMil EPfP GKir NFor NWea
§ - 'Knap Hill'	EBee ENot GDra GEil MRav NFor WWeb
- 'Knap Hill Buttercup'	see *P. fruticosa* 'Knap Hill'
- 'Kobold'	GEil MBar
* - 'Lemon and Lime'	MBlu NBir NPro WWeb
- 'Limelight' ♀ H4	CSBt EBee ELan EPla GKir LRHS MAsh MBri MRav MWgw SPla SPoG SSta WBcn WFar WHCG WWeb
- 'Longacre Variety'	CTri ENot GDra GKir MBar NWea WBod WFar WTel WWeb
- Lovely Pink = 'Pink Beauty'PBR ♀ H4	CDoC COtt CSBt EBee ENot LRHS MBNS MRav NPri SCoo SPer WWeb
§ - 'Maanelys'	CSBt CTrw ECtt MWat NWea SPer SRms WDin WHCG WMoo
§ - 'Manchu'	CDoC CSBt CTri ENot GDra MBar MRav MWat NFor NPro SChu SHBN SPer SRms WCFE WHCG WTel WWin
- Marian Red Robin = 'Marrob'PBR ♀ H4	CDoC CSBt CWib EBee EBre ELan ENot EPfP GKir LAst LRHS MAsh MBri MRav MTis MWat NWea SCoo SLim SPer WDin WStI WWeb
- 'Medicine Wheel Mountain' ♀ H4	EBee ELan EWes LRHS MAsh MBri MRav NPro SLim SPer WHCG WWeb
- Moonlight	see *P. fruticosa* 'Maanelys'
§ - 'Mount Everest'	EHol MBar NHol NWea SLon SRms WWeb
- 'Nana Argentea'	see *P. fruticosa* 'Beesii'
- 'New Dawn'	CDoC EWTr GKir LRHS MAsh MBNS MBri SPer WBcn WFar
- 'Nugget'	see *P. fruticosa* 'Dart's Nugget'
- 'Orange Star'	CWib NHol WHCG WWeb
- 'Orangeade'	LRHS MAsh SMur SReu SSta WWeb
- 'Peaches and Cream'	WEas WHCG
* - 'Peachy Proud'	NPro
- 'Pink Glow'	GDra
- 'Pink Pearl'	EBre GKir WBcn WMoo WWin
- 'Pink Queen'	EMil MBri
- 'Pretty Polly'	CBrm CChe CSBt CWSG EBee ENot EPfP GKir LAst LRHS MAsh MBar MBri MGos SHBN SPer SPla SSta WBod WDin WFar WGwG WHCG WHar WMoo WStI WWal WWeb
- 'Primrose Beauty' ♀ H4	CDoC EBee ELan ENot EPfP EWTr GDra GKir LAst LRHS MBar MGos MRav MWgw NBlu NFor NJOw NLon SLim SMer SPlb WDin WFar WGwG WHar WMoo WStI WWeb
- Princess = 'Blink'PBR	CSBt CTri CWSG EBee EBre ELan ENot EWTr GKir LRHS MBNS MBar MRav NBlu SLim SPer SReu SRms WDin WFar WHar WStI WWeb
- 'Prostrate Copper'	NJOw
- var. *pumila*	MBro WPat
- 'Red Ace'	CDoC CSBt CWSG EBee EBre ECtt ELan ENot EPfP GKir LHop LRHS MBar MBri MDun MGos NBee NBir NWea SLim SPer SPla SRms WDin WFar WHCG WHar WMoo WWal WWeb
- var. *rigida* **new**	CPLG WBcn
- 'Royal Flush'	MBar MBri WStI
- 'Silver Schilling'	NPro
- 'Snowbird'	EBee EBre EPfP LRHS MBNS MBri MGos NPro SLim WFar WWeb
§ - 'Snowflake'	CBcs WLRN WMoo
- 'Sommerflor' ♀ H4	EBee ENot MRav
- 'Sophie's Blush'	CChe LAst MRav NHol NWea WDin WHCG WSHC WWeb
- 'Sunset'	More than 30 suppliers
- 'Tangerine'	More than 30 suppliers
- 'Tilford Cream'	CDoC CSBt EBee EBre ELan ENot EPfP GDra LAst LRHS MBar MBri MRav MWgw NBir NBlu NHol SHBN SPer SReu SRms WCFE WDin WFar WHCG WStI WWeb
- 'Tom Conway'	WHCG WWeb
- 'Tropicana' **new**	WBcn
§ - var. *veitchii*	CSBt SHBN SPer WStI
- 'Vilmoriniana'	CBot CHar CTri ELan EPfP EVFa LRHS MAsh MRav NFor NLon SIgm SLon SMac SPer SSpi WAbe WCFE WGwG WHCG WSHC WTel WWeb
- 'Wessex Silver'	WHCG
- 'Whirligig'	WHCG
- 'White Rain'	GDra GKir NFor NLon WWeb
- 'Wickwar Beauty' **new**	CWib

- 'Wickwar Trailer' — CLyd ESis WHoo
- 'William Purdom' — WHCG
- 'Yellow Bird' ♀ H4 — LRHS MGos
- 'Yellow Carpet' — WHCG
- 'Yellow Giant' — WWeb

gelida new — EHyt

'Gibson's Scarlet' ♀ H4 — More than 30 suppliers

glandulosa — EBee MNrw

'Gloire de Nancy' — CLAP CSpe EBee EBre ELan ERou GCal LHop LRHS MRav NBir WCot WPGP

'Gold Clogs' — see *P. aurea* 'Goldklumpen'

'Gold Sovereign' **new** — ENot LBuc

gracilis — CBrm CTCP EBee

- var. **glabrata** — EBee EPPr
- subsp. **nuttallii** — see *P. gracilis* var. *glabrata*

'Harlow Cream' — NBid

'Helen Jane' — EBee EBre EWTr GBuc GDra GKir LPio LRHS MBri MHer NBir NGdn NLar NPro STes WBea WCot WFar WPer

'Herzblut' — EBee EPfP GBuc MNrw NLar

x **hopwoodiana** — More than 30 suppliers

* x **hybrida** 'Jean Jabber' — EBee EWll GBuc GMac MRav NBur

hyparctica — MDKP

- **nana** — CLyd GCrs LBee LRHS MBro NHol WPat

'Jack Elliot' **new** — WWeb

§ **lineata** ex CC 2735 — MDCh

* **lutea** — EPPr

'Mandshurica' — see *P. fruticosa* 'Manchu'

§ **megalantha** ♀ H4 — More than 30 suppliers

- 'Gold Sovereign' **new** — NPro

'Melton' — EBee ECoo LAst MNrw NBir NChi NOak WHen

* 'Melton Fire' — ECtt GKir MWrn NArg NBir NBur NCot NJOw NPPs SBri SGar SMac SUsu SWal WBea WCot WElm WMoo

'Monarch's Velvet' — see *P. thurberi* 'Monarch's Velvet'

'Monsieur Rouillard' — CSam CTCP EBee EBre EMan EVFa GKir MHer MNrw MRav MWat NChi NDov NFor NPPs SUsu SWal WCot WCra WElm WHoo WLin WSan WWhi

'Mont d'Or' — LRHS MBri MRav

montana — NHol WHer WPer

nepalensis — EBee ECha EDAr GKir IMGH LAst LLWP MFir NBro NChi NFor NPro NSti SBri SGar SHFr SHel

- CC 2678 — MWod
- 'Master Floris' — SAga WFar WHer

§ - 'Miss Willmott' ♀ H4 — More than 30 suppliers

- 'Ron McBeath' — CBri CHea CPlt EChP ECtt EFou EMan EMar GBin LPVe MBNS MBro MCAu NSti SIng SMad WBro WHoo

- 'Roxana' — EBee ECGP ELan ERou GBuc GKir LAst LPVe MBNS MDKP MRav NBro NPPs WAbb WBea WFar WMoo WPer WRos

- 'Shogran' — EBee EChP EMlt ESis NGby WBea

§ **neumanniana** — EMlt NBir NPri WFar

- 'Goldrausch' — ECha MRav

§ - 'Nana' — EMNN EPot LBee LRHS MBro MHer MWat NHar NLAp NMen SIng SPlb SRms WEas WWin

- white-flowered **new** — SBri

nevadensis — CLyd CTri ECho GEdr SRms WPer

nitida — GEdr NHar NMen SRms WAbe WLin

- 'Alannah' — EHyt
- 'Alba' — EPot
- 'Lissadell' — CPBP

- 'Rubra' — CMea CNic EDAr GCrs GEdr GMaP GTou IMGH MBro MHer MWat NBir NHol NMGW NWCA SAga SBla SRms WAbe WPat

nivea — GTou SRot

'Nunk' — CStu LRHS MBar MWgw WWeb

* 'Olympic Mountains' — WPer

ovina — WPer

palustris — EBee LMdh MSta NLar WBea

pedata — LLWP

'Pink Orleans' **new** — WWeb

recta — CBrm CStr ELau EMan ERou GTou NPri WRos

- 'Alba' — EGoo GMaP LPVe MFir MWrn NBur WFTG WPer WWhi WWpP
- 'Citrina' — see *P. recta* var. *sulphurea*
- 'Macrantha' — see *P. recta* 'Warrenii'

§ - var. **sulphurea** — CHad CMil CSam EBee EChP EGoo EWTr GCal GMac IGor LPhx MFir MNrw MTis NBir NCat NPPs SAga SIng SUsu WBea WCom WCra WFar WHal WHer WHoo WMoo WPer

§ - 'Warrenii' — More than 30 suppliers

reptans — CKin

- 'Pleniflora' (d) — MInt WAlt
- 'Roxanne' (d) **new** — MHer

rupestris — CHea CM&M EBee EChP ECha EMan EPPr LAst MCAu MCLN MFir MLLN MNrw NChi NDlv NSti SBri SGar WBea WFar WHal WPer WWin

salesoviana — WLin

speciosa — EHyt EMan EWes MDKP WMoo

sterilis — CHid IHMH

'Sungold' — ECho ESis WHCG

tabernaemontani — see *P. neumanniana*

ternata — see *P. aurea* subsp. *chrysocraspeda*

thurberi — CHid EBee EGle EMan EPPr GCal LPhx LPio MNrw MRav NLar WMoo WWeb

§ - 'Monarch's Velvet' — More than 30 suppliers

- 'White Queen' — see *P.* 'White Queen'

tommasiniana — see *P. cinerea*

x **tonguei** ♀ H4 — More than 30 suppliers

tormentilla — see *P. erecta*

tridentata — see *Sibbaldiopsis tridentata*

verna — see *P. neumanniana*

- 'Pygmaea' — see *P. neumanniana* 'Nana'

'Versicolor Plena' (d) — CMea

villosa — see *P. crantzii*

'Volcan' — CBos CKno CMea CMil CPlt EBee EWes GCal LPhx MBNS MBri NChi WAbb WCra WFar WPGP

§ 'White Queen' — CWes EBee EWTr EWll GKir LAco LRHS MNrw MWrn NBur NPri SRot SWal

'William Rollison' ♀ H4 — More than 30 suppliers

willmottiae — see *P. nepalensis* 'Miss Willmott'

'Yellow Queen' — CBcs CHad CTri EMil ENot EPfP ERou MNrw MRav NHol SCro SPer SWat WFar

Poterium see *Sanguisorba*

sanguisorba — see *Sanguisorba minor*

Pratia (*Campanulaceae*)

§ **angulata** — EWll GGar NHar

- 'Jack's Pass' — NHar
- 'Messenger' — ECou
- 'Tim Rees' — IHMH

§	– 'Treadwellii'	ECha EDAr EMan GMac LBee LRHS MBNS NFla SPlb WHal WHen
	– 'Woodside'	ECou
	– x *pedunculata*	GGar
	'Celestial Spice'	ECou
	macrodon	WCru
§	*pedunculata*	More than 30 suppliers
	– 'County Park'	CMea CSpe CWCL ECha ECou EDAr ELan EMlt EPot ESis GGar IHMH MBar MBro NHar NMen NHar SAga SBla SIng SPlb SRms WFar WHal WHoo WPat WPer WWin
	– 'Kiandra'	ECou
	– 'Tom Stone'	EPot MBNS NHar
	– 'White Stars' **new**	LCTD
§	*perpusilla*	ECou
	– 'Fragrant Carpet'	ECou
	– 'Summer Meadows'	ECou WPer

Preslia see *Mentha*

Primula ✿ (*Primulaceae*)

	Lismore 79-26	EHyt
	(9) CC 3843 **new**	ITer
	acaulis	see *P. vulgaris*
	'Adrian Jones' (2)	EHyt ITim NHol WAbe
	'Aire Mist' (*allionii* hybrid) (2)	CGra GKev GNor ITim MFie NHar NHol NLAp NRya WAbe WLin
	'Alan Robb' (dPrim)(30)	MBri NHol SPer SUsu WFar WHil
	'Alexina' (*allionii* hybrid) (2)	EHyt ITim MFie NHar NHol
	algida (11)	ECho GFle NWCA
§	*allionii* (2) ♀ H2	EHyt EMNN GTou ITim MFie NHar NHol NWCA WAbe WCom
	– Hartside 383/3	NHol
	– KRW 420-67	EHyt
	– KRW 461/71	EHyt
	– KRW 509-76	EHyt
	– Lismore 81/19/3	MFie
	– 'Agnes' (2)	EHyt ITim
	– 'Aire Waves'	see *Primula* x *loiseleurii* 'Aire Waves'
	– var. *alba* (2)	EHyt EMNN NHar
	– 'Allen Queen' (2)	NHar
	'Anna Griffith' (2)	EHyt EPot GCrs ITim LRHS MFie NHol NRya NWCA WAbe WHil
	– 'Anne' (2)	EHyt GCrs ITim
	– 'Aphrodite' (2) **new**	NHar
§	– 'Apple Blossom' (2)	CGra GAbr ITim MDHE
	– 'Archer' (2)	EMNN ITim NHol
	– 'Ares' (2) **new**	NHar
	– 'Aries Violet' (2) **new**	NHar
	– x *auricula* 'Blairside Yellow' (2)	GNor ITim
	– x – 'Old Red Dusty Miller' hort. (2)	MFie NHar NHol
	– 'Austen' (2)	ITim NHol
	– 'Avalanche' (2)	ITim NHar NHol WAbe
	– 'Bill Martin' (2)	EPot ITim NLAp
	– 'Brilliant' (2)	WAbe
	– Burnley form (2)	NHol
	– 'Chivalry' (2) **new**	CGra
	– 'Clarence Elliott'	see *P.* 'Clarence Elliott' (2)
	– 'Claude Flight' (2)	EHyt ITim
	– 'Confection' (2)	EHyt
	– 'Crowsley Variety' (2)	CNic LRHS NHol NMen NWCA SBla WAbe WHil
	– 'Crusader' (2)	EHyt ITim
	– 'Crystal' (2)	EHyt ITim
	– 'Duncan' (2) **new**	CNic EHyt ITim
*	– 'E.G. Watson' (2)	EHyt
§	– 'Edinburgh' (2)	CNic EHyt EMNN EPot GKir ITim MFie NHol WAbe

	– 'Edrom' (2)	ITim NHol
	– 'Elizabeth Baker' (2)	EMNN GNor ITim MFie WAbe
	– 'Elizabeth Burrow' (2)	EHyt
	– 'Elizabeth Earle' (2)	EHyt EPot ITim NHol NLAp WAbe
	– 'Elliott's Large'	see *P. allionii* 'Edinburgh'
	– 'Elliott's Variety'	see *P. allionii* 'Edinburgh'
	– 'Fanfare' (2)	CGra EHyt ITim LRHS NHol WGwG
	– 'Flute' (2)	EHyt
	– 'Frank Barker' (2)	EPot NHol
	– GFS 1984 (2)	CGra
§	– 'Gilderdale Glow' (2)	CGra GKev MFie NHar
	– 'Giuseppi's Form'	see *P. allionii* 'Mrs Dyas'
	– 'Grandiflora' (2)	ITim
	– 'Hemswell Blush'	see *P.* 'Hemswell Blush'
	– 'Hemswell Ember'	see *P.* 'Hemswell Ember'
	– x *hirsuta* (2)	ITim MFie
	– 'Hocker Edge' (2)	ITim NHol
	– 'Horwood' (2)	EHyt WAbe
	– 'Huntsman' (2)	MFie
	– Ingwersen's form (2)	GTou NHol
	– 'Jenny' (2) JCA 4161/22	CGra EHyt EPot
	– K R W	see *P. allionii* 'Ken's Seedling'
§	– 'Kath Dryden' (2)	CNic EHyt
§	– 'Ken's Seedling' (2)	EPot NHol NLAp
	– 'Linda' (2) **new**	NHar
	– x 'Lismore Treasure' (2)	CGra CPBP NWCA
	– 'Lo 2' (2) **new**	NHar
	– 'Louise' (2)	EHyt
	– 'Malcolm' (2) **new**	EHyt
	– 'Margaret Earle' (2)	ITim NHol WAbe
	– 'Marion' (2)	EMNN EPot GNor ITim NHol
	– 'Marjorie Wooster' (2)	EHyt ITim NWCA WAbe
	– 'Martin' (2)	ITim NHol
	– 'Mary Anne'	GCrs
	– 'Mary Berry' (2)	EHyt EMNN ITim MFie WAbe
	– 'Maurice Dryden' (2)	EHyt
§	– 'Mrs Dyas' (2)	EHyt EMNN ITim NHar NHol WAbe
	– 'Neptunes Wave' (2) **new**	NHar
	– 'New Dawn' (2)	EHyt
	– pale (2)	WLin
	– 'Pale Venus' (2) **new**	NHar
I	– 'Paula' (2)	EHyt
	– 'Peace' (2) KRW 147-47 **new**	EHyt
	– x *pedemontana*	see *P.* x *sendtneri*
	– 'Peggy Wilson' (2)	EPot EWes NHol
	– 'Pennine Pink' (2)	EPot ITim NHol
	– 'Perkie' (2)	EHyt ITim
	– 'Picton's Variety' (2)	ITim NDlv NHol
	– 'Pink Aire'	see *P.* 'Pink Aire'
	– 'Pinkie' (2)	WLin
	– 'Posidon' (2) **new**	NHar
	– 'Praecox' (2)	ITim MFie NHol NSla
	– x *pubescens* 'Harlow Car' (2)	CLyd GMac ITim NHar
	– 'Raymond Wooster' (2)	EHyt ITim LRHS NHol
	– 'Robert' (2)	EHyt
	– 'Robin' (2) **new**	EHyt
	– 'Roger Bevan' (2)	EHyt
I	– 'Roy' (2)	EHyt
	– 'Scimitar' (2)	EHyt EMNN ITim NHol
	– 'Serendipity' (2)	EHyt
	– x 'Snow Ruffles' (2)	ITim
	– 'Snowflake' (2)	CGra CPBP EHyt EMNN EPot ITim LRHS NHar NWCA WAbe
	– 'Stanton House' (2)	NDlv NHol
	– 'Starburst' (2) **new**	NHar
	– 'Stephen' (2)	EHyt EMNN ITim
	– 'Superba'	EHyt
	– 'Tranquillity' (2)	EHyt ITim MFie NHar NHol
§	– 'Travellers' (2) JCA 4161/21	EHyt EPot

- 'Viscountess Byng' (2)	EMNN ITim
- x 'White Linda Pope' (2)	ITim MFie NHol WLin
- 'William Earle' (2)	EHyt EMNN EPot ITim LRHS
	MFie NDlv NHar NHol NWCA
	WAbe
- x *rubra* (2)	ITim NHol
alpicola (26)	CFee CRow CSWP EBre EPfP
	GCrs GDra GEdr GFle GGar GIBF
	GKir LPBA LRHS MFie NBid NBro
	NDlv SPer WAbe WLin WRus
- var. *alba* (26)	CPla CRow CSWP EBre GBuc
	GEdr GGar LSyl MBow MNrw
	SLon SPer SWat
§ - var. *alpicola* (26)	CSWP EBee GBuc GEdr GFle LSyl
	MNrw WAbe
- var. *luna*	see *P. alpicola* var. *alpicola*
- var. *violacea* (26)	CPla CRow CSWP GDra GGar
	LRHS LSyl MBow MBri MFie
	MNrw NHar SLon SPer SWat
	WAbe WLin WWhi
'Altaica'	see *P. elatior* subsp. *meyeri*
altaica grandiflora	see *P. elatior* subsp. *meyeri*
amoena	see *P. elatior* subsp. *meyeri*
angustifolia (20)	GFle
anisodora	see *P. wilsonii* var. *anisodora*
'April Rose' (dPrim)(30)	CMea ENot MRav NBid
x *arctotis*	see *P. x pubescens*
atrodentata (9)	GCrs WAbe
aurantiaca (4)	CFir CPla GBar GCrs GEdr GFle
	MSta SRms
aureata (21)	GCrs GGGa ITim WAbe
- subsp. *fimbriata* (21)	GCrs ITim
auricula ambig. (2)	NBlu
§ *auricula* L. (2) ♀ H4	EDAr ELan GCrs GKir GNor GTou
	LRHS MFie MHer NBro NSla SIng
	SPer SPet SPlb SWal WAbe WCom
	WMAq
- var. *albocincta* (2)	NWCA
- subsp. *auricula* (2)	GTou
- subsp. *balbisii*	see *P. auricula* subsp. *ciliata*
auricula hort A74 (A)	WBrE
- 'Abundance' (A)	MAln
- 'Achates' (A) **new**	MAln
- 'Admiral' (A)	MAln MCre
- 'Adrian' (A)	GAbr ITim MCre MFie NBro SPop
	WHil WLin
- 'Adrienne Ruan' (A) **new**	MAln
- 'Aga Khan' (A)	MAln
- 'Agamemnon' (A)	MAln MCre
- 'Alamo' (A)	MAln MCre SPop
- 'Alan Ravenscroft' (A)	MAln MFie
- 'Alansford' (A) **new**	MAln
- 'Albert Bailey' (S/d)	MAln MCre
- 'Alexandra Georgina' (A)	MAln
- 'Alf' (A) **new**	MAln
- 'Alfred Niblett' (S)	EMNN WLin
- 'Alice Haysom' (S)	CNic ELan MCre MFie SPop WHil
	WLin
- 'Alicia' (A)	ECGP SPop
- 'Alison Jane' (A)	CLyd MCre MFie NOak SUsu
- 'Allansford'	EMNN
- 'Allensford' (A)	MCre
- 'Almondbury' (S)	GNor
- alpine mixed (A)	CNic MBow SRms
- 'Amber Light' (S) **new**	MAln
- 'Amicable' (A)	MAln MCre SPop WHil
- 'Ancient Order' (A) **new**	MAln
- 'Andrea Julie' (A)	EMNN ITim MAln MCre MFie
	MOne NRya SPop WLin
- 'Andrew Hunter' (A)	MAln SPop
- 'Andy Cole' (A) **new**	MAln
- 'Angelo' (A) **new**	MAln
- 'Angie' (d) **new**	MAln

- 'Ann Taylor' (A)	MAln MCre
- 'Anne Hyatt' (d) **new**	MAln
- 'Anne Swithinbank' (d)	MAln
- 'Antoc' (S)	EMNN MFie
- 'Anwar Sadat' (A)	EMNN GAbr MAln MCre MFie
- 'Applecross' (A)	EMNN ITim MCre MFie NHar
	WHil WLin
- 'April Moon' (S) **new**	MAln
- 'April Tiger' (S) **new**	MAln
- 'Arabian Night' (A) **new**	MAln
- 'Arapaho' (A) **new**	MAln
- 'Arctic Fox'	MAln
- 'Argus' (A)	CLyd LAco MCre MFie NBir NHar
	SPop SUsu WHil WLin
- 'Aromanches' (A) **new**	MAln
- 'Arthur Delbridge' (A)	MCre MFie
- 'Arundel Star'	NLAp
- 'Arundell' (S/St)	EMNN GAbr ITim MCre NHar
	SPop WHil WLin
- 'Ashcliffe Gem' (A)	MAln
- 'Astolat' (S)	EMNN ITim MCre MFie NLAp
	NOak NRya SPop SUsu WLin
- 'Athene' (S) **new**	MAln
- 'Aurora' (A)	MFie
- 'Austin' (A)	MAln
- 'Avril Hunter' (A)	MCre MFie SPop WLin
- 'Bacchus' (A)	MCre MFie
- 'Balbithan' (B)	GAbr
- 'Ballet' (S)	MFie
- 'Barbara Mason'	MAln
- 'Barbarella' (A)	EMNN MAln MCre MFie SPop
	WLin
- Barnhaven doubles (d)	CSWP GAbr WLin
- 'Basuto' (A)	EMNN MCre MFie SPop
- 'Beatrice' (A)	CLyd EMNN GAbr GNor ITim
	LAco MAln MCre MFie SPop
	WLin
- 'Beauty of Bath' (S)	MAln
- 'Beckminster' (A)	MAln
- 'Bedford Lad' (A)	MAln MCre
- 'Beechen Green' (S)	EMNN GAbr ITim MAln SPop
- 'Belle Zana' (S)	MAln
- 'Bellezana'	MFie
- 'Ben Lawers' (S)	WLin
- 'Ben Wyves' (S)	MCre
- 'Bendigo' (S)	MAln
- 'Bewitched' (A) **new**	MAln
- 'Bilbao' (A) **new**	MAln
- 'Bilbo Baggins' (A) **new**	MAln
- 'Bilton' (S)	CLyd NLAp
- 'Black Ice' (S)	MAln
- 'Black Jack'	COtt WWeb
- 'Black Knight' (d)	MAln
- 'Blackfield' (S)	MFie
- 'Blackhill' (S)	EMNN
- 'Blackpool Rock' (St)	MAln
- 'Blairside Yellow' (B)	EWes NHar NSla
- 'Blakeney' (d)	MAln NLAp
- 'Blossom' (A)	EMNN ITim MFie WLin
- 'Blue Bonnet' (d) **new**	MAln
- 'Blue Bonnet' (A/d)	GAbr GNor MAln MCre NLAp SPop
- 'Blue Chips' (S) **new**	MAln
- 'Blue Cliffs' (S) **new**	MAln
- 'Blue Denim' (S) **new**	MAln
- 'Blue Frills' **new**	MAln
- 'Blue Jean' (S)	EMNN ITim MFie NLAp SPop
- 'Blue Mist' (B)	GNor
- 'Blue Moon' (S)	MAln
- 'Blue Nile' (S)	EMNN MFie SPop
- 'Blue Steel' (S)	ITim MAln
- 'Blue Velvet' (B)	EMNN GKev GNor MFie NBro
	SPop WLin
- 'Blue Wave' (d)	WLin

- 'Bob Dingley' (A)　MCre
- 'Bob Lancashire' (S)　EMNN GNor ITim MCre MFie NHar SPop SUsu WHil WLin
- 'Bold Tartan' (St) **new**　MAln
- 'Bolero' (A)　MAln SPop
- 'Bollin Tiger' (St)　MAln
- 'Bonanza' (S) **new**　MAln
- 'Bookham Firefly' (A)　EMNN GNor ITim MBro MCre MFie NHar SPop WHil WLin
- 'Boromir' (A) **new**　MAln
- 'Boy Blue' (S)　MAln
- 'Bradford City' (A)　MAln
- 'Brasso'　MAln
- 'Brazil' (S)　EMNN GAbr GNor LRHS MCre MFie NLAp NOak SPop WHil WLin
- 'Brazos River' (A) **new**　MAln
- 'Brenda's Choice' (A)　MCre MFie
- 'Bright Eyes' (A)　MCre MFie
- 'Broad Gold' (A)　MAln MCre
- 'Broadwell Gold' (B)　CLyd GAbr WLin
- 'Brompton' (S) **new**　MAln
- 'Brookfield' (S)　EMNN GNor ITim MCre MFie SPop WLin
- 'Broughton' (S)　MFie WLin
- 'Brown Ben' **new**　MFie
- 'Brown Bess' (A)　GNor ITim MCre MFie MOne NHar SPop WLin
- 'Brownie' (B)　NBir
- 'Bubbles' (A) **new**　MAln
- 'Buccaneer'　MAln
- 'Bucks Green' (S)　SPop
- 'Bunty' (A)　MFie
- 'Butterwick' (A)　ECGP GAbr GMaP LRHS MBNS MCre MFie NHar SPop WLin
- 'C.F. Hill' (A)　EMNN MAln
- 'C.G. Haysom' (S)　EMNN GAbr LAco MCre MFie NHar SPop WLin
- 'C.W. Needham' (A)　EMNN ITim MCre MFie WLin

I
- 'Calypso' (A)　MAln MCre
* - 'Cambodunum'(A)　MAln MCre MFie SPop
- 'Camelot' (d)　CLyd ELan EMNN GCrs ITim MCre MFie MOne NBro NChi NHar NPri SPop SUsu WFar
- 'Cameo' (A)　MAln MCre
- 'Camilla' (A)　MAln

I
- 'Candida' (d)　MAln MCre SPop
- 'Caramel' (A)　MAln
- 'Carioca' (A) **new**　MAln
- 'Carole' (A)　MFie WLin
- 'Cartouche' (A) **new**　MAln
- 'Catherine' (d)　ITim MCre
- 'Catherine Redding' (d) **new**　MAln
- 'Chaffinch' (S)　GNor ITim
- 'Chamois' (B)　GAbr
- 'Channel' (S) **new**　MAln
- 'Chantilly Cream' (d)　MAln MCre WLin
- 'Charles Bronson' (d) **new**　MAln
- 'Charles Rennie' (B) **new**　MAln
- 'Charlie's Aunt' (A) **new**　MAln
- 'Checkmate' **new**　MAln
- 'Chelsea Bridge' (A)　EMNN ITim MCre MFie
- 'Cherry' (S)　EMNN ITim
- 'Cherry Picker' (A)　MCre
- 'Cheyenne' (S)　EMNN GAbr ITim MCre MFie WLin
- 'Chiffon' (S) **new**　MAln
- 'Chirichua' (S)　MAln
- 'Chloris' (S)　MAln NBir
- 'Chocolate Soldier' (A)　MAln
- 'Chorister' (S)　CLyd ECGP ELan EMNN GAbr GNor ITim MCre MFie MOne NBir

NOak NPri SUsu WHil WLRN WLin
- 'Cicero' (A)　MAln

§ - subsp. *ciliata* (2)　GFle
I - 'Cinnamon' (d)　MAln MCre SPop WHil WLin
- 'Ciribiribin' (A) **new**　MAln
- 'Clare' (S)　ITim MAln MCre NRya
- 'Clatter-Ha' (d)　GCrs
- 'Claudia Taylor'　NHar WLin
- 'Clouded Yellow' (S) **new**　MAln
- 'Clunie' (S)　GNor ITim MCre
- 'Clunie II' (S)　GCrs NLAp WLin
- 'Cobden Meadows' (A) **new**　MAln
- 'Coffee' (S)　MCre MFie SUsu
- 'Colbury' (S)　MCre MFie NHar SPop WLin
- 'Colonel Champney' (S)　GNor ITim MFie SPop SUsu WLin
- 'Confederate' (S)　MAln
- 'Connaught Court' (A)　MAln SPop
- 'Conservative' (S)　GAbr MFie SUsu
- 'Consett' (S)　EMNN ITim MFie WHil
- 'Coppi' (A) **new**　MAln
- 'Coral' (S)　MFie
- 'Coral Sea' (S) **new**　MAln
- 'Cornmeal' (S)　MFie
- 'Corntime' (S) **new**　MAln
- 'Corrie Files' (d)　MAln
- 'Cortina' (S)　ECGP EMNN GNor ITim LAco MCre MOne NHar NOak NRya SPop SUsu WCot WHil WLin
- 'County Park Red' (B)　ECou
- 'Craig Vaughan' (A)　MCre MFie WLin
- 'Cranbourne' (A)　MAln MCre
- 'Crecy' (A)　MAln
▪ 'Crimple' (S)　MAln
- 'Crimson Glow' (d) **new**　MAln
- 'Cuckoo Fair'　SPop
- 'Cuckoo Fare' (S) **new**　MAln
- 'Cuddles' (A) **new**　MAln
- 'Daftie Green' (S)　EMNN GAbr ITim
- 'Dakota' (S)　EMNN
- 'Dales Red' (B)　MAln
- 'Dan Tiger' (St) **new**　MAln
- 'Daniel' (A) **new**　MAln
- 'Daphnia' (S)　MAln
- 'Dark Eyes' (d) **new**　MAln
- 'Dark Lady' (A) **new**　MAln
- 'Delilah' (d)　GAbr GNor MCre MFie WLin
- 'Denise' (S) **new**　MAln
- 'Denna Snuffer' (d)　EMNN GAbr GNor ITim MAln
- 'Devon Cream' (d)　GNor ITim MCre MFie WFar
- 'Diamond' (d) **new**　MAln
- 'Diane' (A)　EMNN MFie
- 'Digit' (d) **new**　MAln
- 'Digsby' (d)　MAln
- 'Dilemma' (A) **new**　MAln
* - 'Dill' (A) **new**　MAln
- 'Dilly Dilly' (A) **new**　MAln
- 'Divint Dunch' (A)　MAln MCre SPop
- 'Doctor Duthie' (S)　MAln
- 'Doctor Lennon's White' (B)　MFie SPop
- 'Dolly Viney' (d) **new**　MAln
- 'Donhead' (A)　MCre MFie
- 'Donna Clancy' (S)　MFie
- 'Doreen Stevens' (A) **new**　MAln
- 'Doris Jean' (A)　MFie
- 'Dorothy' (S)　MAln
- 'Doublet' (d)　CLyd EMNN GAbr GNor ITim MCre MFie NLAp NOak NRya SPop WHil WLin
- 'Doublure' (d)　GAbr GNor MAln MCre

- 'Douglas Bader' (A)   MCre
- 'Douglas Black' (S)   NLAp SPop
- 'Douglas Blue' (S)   MAln
- 'Douglas Gold'   WLin
- 'Douglas Green' (S)   MFie SPop
- 'Douglas Red' (A)   NHar WLin
- 'Douglas White' (S)   EMNN MFie
- 'Dovedale' (S)   MAln
- 'Dowager' (A)   MCre MFie
- 'Doyen' (d) **new**   MAln
- 'Drax' (A) **new**   MAln
- 'Dubarrie' (A) **new**   MAln
- 'Duchess of Malfi'   SPop
  (S) **new**
- 'Duchess of York' (2)   CLAP GBuc WBro
* - 'Dusky'   WLin
- 'Dusky Maiden' (A)   EMNN GNor MCre MFie SPop
    WHil WLin
- 'Dusty Miller' (B)   EBre MRav NBid NBir
- 'Eastern Promise' (A) **new**   MAln SPop
- 'Ed Spivey' (A)   MCre
- 'Eddy Gordon' (A)   MAln
- 'Eden Carmine' (B)   MFie
- 'Eden David' (B)   MFie
- 'Eden Peach' (B)   MFie
- 'Eden Picotee' (B)   MAln MFie
- 'Edith Allen' (A)   MAln MCre
- 'Elizabeth Ann' (A)   EMNN MCre
- 'Ellen Thompson' (A)   MCre MFie WLin
- 'Elsie' (A)   EMNN GNor MCre
- 'Elsie May' (A)   EMNN GNor MCre MFie SPop
    WLin
- 'Elsinore' (S)   MCre
- 'Embley' (S)   CLyd GNor NLAp
- 'Emery Down' (S)   ITim NLAp
- 'Emma Louise' **new**   MFie
- 'Emmett Smith' (A) **new**   MAln
- 'Enigma' (S) **new**   MAln
- 'Envy' (S)   MAln
I - 'Erica' (A)   EMNN MCre MFie NHar SUsu
    WHil WLin
- 'Erjon' (S)   MAln
- 'Error' (S)   MAln
- 'Ethel'   WHil
- 'Ettrick' (S)   MAln
- 'Eventide' (S)   SPop
- 'Everest Blue' (S)   SPop SUsu
- 'Excalibur' (d) **new**   MAln
- (Exhibition Series)   MFie
  'Exhibition Blau' (B)
- - 'Exhibition Gelb' (B)   MFie
- - 'Exhibition Rot' (B)   MFie
- 'Eye Opener' (A) **new**   MAln
- 'Eyeopener' (A)   MCre SPop
- 'Fairy' (A)   MAln
- 'Falaraki' (A) **new**   MAln
- 'Falstaff' (d) **new**   MAln
- 'Fanciful' (S)   CLyd MAln MFie WLin
- 'Fandancer' (A)   MAln
- 'Fanfare' (S)   MAln
- 'Fanny Meerbeck' (S)   EMNN GNor ITim MFie NOak
    SPop SUsu WLin
- 'Faro' (S)   MAln
- 'Favorite'   EMNN
- 'Favourite' (S)   MCre MFie SPop WHil
- 'Fen Tiger' (St) **new**   MAln
- 'Fennay' (S) **new**   MAln
- 'Figaro' (S)   MAln
- 'Finavon'   GCrs
- 'Finchfield' (A)   EMNN MCre MFie SUsu
- 'Firecracker' **new**   MAln
- 'Firenze' (A)   SPop
- 'Firsby' **new**   MAln

- 'Fishtoft' (d) **new**   MAln
- 'Flame' (A)   ITim MAln
- 'Fleminghouse' (S)   GNor
- 'Florence Brown' (S) **new**   ITim
- 'Forest Pines' (S) **new**   MAln
- 'Fradley' (A)   MAln
- 'Frank Bailey' (d)   MAln
- 'Frank Crosland' (A)   MFie
- 'Frank Faulkner' (A)   MAln
- 'Frank Jenning' (A) **new**   MAln
- 'Fred Booley' (d) **new**   SPop
- 'Fred Livesley' (A) **new**   MAln
- 'Fresco' (A)   MAln
- 'Friskney' (d) **new**   MAln
- 'Frittenden Yellow' (B)   WLin
- 'Fuller's Red' (S)   CLyd MFie
- 'Gaia' (d)   MAln
- 'Galen' (A)   MCre MFie WLin
- 'Ganymede' **new**   MAln
- 'Gary Pallister' (A) **new**   MAln
- 'Gavin Ward' (S) **new**   MAln
- 'Gay Crusader' (A)   EMNN GNor ITim MCre MFie
- 'Gazza' (A) **new**   MAln
- 'Gee Cross' (A)   EMNN MCre MFie
§ - 'Geldersome Green' (S)   EMNN GNor MCre MFie SPop
    WLin
- 'Generosity' (A)   MAln MCre SPop
- 'Geordie' (A) **new**   MAln
- 'George Harrison' (B)   GAbr
- 'George Jennings'   MAln
  (A) **new**
- 'George Stephens'   MAln
  (A) **new**
- 'Geronimo' (S)   EMNN GNor MFie SPop
- 'Girl Guide' (S) **new**   MAln
- 'Gizabroon' (S)   CLyd EMNN MCre MFie WLin
- 'Gleam' (S)   EMNN GCrs GNor LTwo MFie
    NLAp SPop WHil WLin
- 'Gleneagles' (S)   MAln MCre SPop
- 'Glenelg' (S)   GAbr MCre MFie SPop WCot
    WLin
- 'Gold Seam' (A) **new**   MAln
- 'Golden Boy' (A)   MAln
- 'Golden Chartreuse' (d)   GAbr MCre
- 'Golden Eagle' (A)   MAln
- 'Golden Eye' (S) **new**   MAln
- 'Golden Fleece' (S)   GNor
- 'Golden Girl' (A) **new**   MAln
- 'Golden Glory' (A) **new**   MAln
- 'Golden Hind' (d)   NHar SPop WLin
- 'Golden Splendour' (d)   MCre MFie SPop WLin
- 'Golden Wedding' (A)   MAln SPop
- 'Goldthorn' (A)   MCre
- 'Goldwin' (A)   MAln MCre
- 'Gollum' (A) **new**   MAln
- 'Good Report' (A)   SPop
- 'Gordon Douglas' (A)   MCre MFie SUsu
- 'Grabley' (S) **new**   MAln
- 'Green Finger' (S)   SPop
- 'Green Frill'   ITim
- 'Green Isle' (S)   EMNN GAbr MCre MFie NBir
    SPop WLin
- 'Green Jacket' (S)   GNor MCre
- 'Green Meadows' (S) **new**   MAln
- 'Green Mouse' (S)   MFie
- 'Green Parrot' (S)   CLyd EMNN ITim MCre WLin
- 'Green Shank' (S)   GNor MFie NHar SPop WHil
    WLin
- 'Greenfinger' (S)   MAln
- 'Greenheart' (S)   EMNN GNor ITim
- 'Greenpeace' (S)   CStu LRHS NHar WHil
- 'Greensleeves' (S)   GNor
- 'Greenways' (S) **new**   MAln

– 'Greta' (S)	ELan EMNN GNor MCre NHar NLAp NOak SPop WHil WLin
– 'Gretna Green' (S)	MFie
– 'Grey Dawn' (S) **new**	MAln
– 'Grey Edge'	ITim SUsu
– 'Grey Friar' (S)	MAln
– 'Grey Lady' (S)	MAln
– 'Grey Lag' (S)	EMNN GNor MFie
– 'Grey Monarch' (S)	GNor ITim MCre MFie WLin
– 'Grey Owl' (S) **new**	MAln
– 'Grey Shrike' (S)	MAln
– 'Grizedale' (S)	MAln
– 'Guildersome Green'	see *P. auricula* 'Geldersome Green'
– 'Guinea' (S)	EMNN GAbr ITim MCre MFie SPop WLin
– 'Gwen' (A)	MAln MCre
– 'Gwen Baker' (d)	MAln
– 'Gwen Gaulthiers' (S) **new**	MAln
– 'Gwenda' (A) **new**	MAln
– 'Gypsy Rose Lee' (A) **new**	MAln
– 'Habanera' (A)	SPop
– 'Haffner' (S)	MAln
– 'Hallmark' (A) **new**	MAln
– 'Hardley' (S)	MAln
– 'Harmony' (B)	MFie NBro
– 'Harry Hotspur' (A)	SPop
– 'Harry "O"' (S)	MCre SPop
– 'Haughmond' (A)	EMNN MCre
– 'Hawkwood' (S)	EMNN GNor ITim MCre NHar SPop SUsu WHil
– 'Hawkwood Fancy' (S)	MFie WLin
* – 'Hazel' (A)	MCre MFie
– 'Headdress' (S)	GAbr MCre MFie SPop
– 'Heady' (A)	SPop
– 'Heart of Gold' (A) **new**	MAln
– 'Hebers'	MAln
– 'Helen Ruane' (d) **new**	MAln
– 'Helena' (S)	EMNN GNor ITim MCre MFie NOak
– 'Helena Dean' (d) **new**	MAln
– 'Heliocentre' (A) **new**	MAln
– 'Hetty Woolf' (S)	EMNN GNor MCre
– 'Hillhouse' (A)	MCre
– 'Hinton Admiral' (S)	MAln WLin
– 'Hinton Fields' (S)	ECGP GNor MCre MFie SMrm SPop WHil WLin
– 'Hogton Gem' (d)	MAln
– 'Holyrood' (S)	GAbr MAln MFie
– 'Honey' (d) **new**	MAln
– 'Honeymoon' (S) **new**	MAln
– 'Hopleys Coffee' (d)	GNor MAln
– 'Howard Telford' (A)	MCre
– 'Hurstwood Midnight'	MFie
* – 'Hyacinth' (S)	LRHS NWCA
– 'Iago' (S)	MAln
– 'Ian Greville' (A) **new**	MAln
– 'Ibis' (S)	MAln MCre MFie
– 'Ice Maiden'	MAln SPop
– 'Idmiston' (S)	MCre SPop WLin
– 'Immaculate' (A)	MAln SPop
– 'Impassioned' (A)	MAln MFie SPop
– 'Impeccable' (A)	MAln
– 'Imperturbable' (A) **new**	MAln
– 'Indian Love Call' (A)	MAln MCre SPop WHil
– 'Isabel' (S) **new**	MAln
– 'Jack Dean' (A)	MAln MCre MFie SPop WHil
– 'James Arnot' (S)	GNor MFie NHar NOak NRya
– 'Jane' (S) **new**	MAln
– 'Jane Myers' (d)	MAln MFie
– 'Janie Hill' (A)	MAln MCre MFie
– 'Jeannie Telford' (A)	MCre MFie SPop

– 'Jenny' (A)	EMNN ITim LHop MBNS MCre MFie SPop WHil
– 'Jersey Bounce' (A) **new**	MAln
– 'Jesmond' (S)	MAln
– 'Jessica' (S) **new**	MAln
– 'Jessie' (d)	MAln
– 'Joan Elliott' (A)	CLyd GAbr
– 'Joanne' (A)	MCre
– 'Joe Perks' (A)	MAln MFie NRya
– 'Joe Perry' (A)	MCre
– 'Joel' (S)	MAln MFie SPop WLin
– 'Johann Bach' (B)	MFie
– 'John Gledhill' (A)	MCre
– 'John Stewart' (A)	EMNN MCre MFie
– 'John Wayne' (A)	MCre MFie
– 'Jonathon' (A) **new**	MAln
– 'Joy' (A)	CLyd EMNN GNor ITim LTwo MCre MFie SPop WHil
– 'Joyce' (A)	GAbr MCre MFie NBir SPop WLin
– 'Julia' (S)	MAln
– 'July Sky' (A)	MCre
– 'June' (A) **new**	MAln
– 'Jungfrau' (d)	MAln
– 'Jupiter' (S)	MAln MCre
– 'Jura' (A) **new**	MAln
– 'Karen Cordrey' (S)	GNor NHar SPop WLin
– 'Karen McDonald' (A) **new**	SPop
– 'Kath Dryden'	see *P. allionii* 'Kath Dryden'
– 'Kelso' (A)	MFie
– 'Ken Chilton' (A)	MAln
– 'Kercup' (A)	MFie
– 'Kevin Keegan' (A)	MCre
– 'Key West' (A) **new**	MAln
– 'Khachaturian' (A)	MAln
– 'Kim' (A)	EMNN MCre MFie WLin
– 'Kingcup' (A)	MCre MFie SPop
– 'Kingfisher' (A) **new**	SPop
– 'Kintail' (A)	MCre
– 'Kirklands' (d)	MFie SPop
– 'Klondyke' (A) **new**	MAln
– 'Königin der Nacht' (St)	MAln
– 'Kustard' (d) **new**	MAln
– 'Lady Daresbury' (A)	EMNN MCre MFie NRya SPop
– 'Lady Diana' (S)	MAln
– 'Lady Joyful' (S)	MCre
– 'Lady of the Vale' (A) **new**	MAln
– 'Lady Penelope' (S) **new**	MAln
– 'Lady Zoë' (S)	MFie SPop
– 'Lamplugh'	WHil
– 'Lancelot' (d) **new**	MAln
– 'Landy' (A)	GCrs MAln MCre MFie SPop
– 'Langley Park' (A)	MAln MCre MFie SPop
– 'Lara' (A)	MAln
– 'Laredo' (A) **new**	MAln
– 'Larry' (A)	MAln MCre SPop
– 'Lavenham' (S) **new**	MAln
– 'Laverock' (S)	MCre NBir NBro
– 'Laverock Fancy' (S)	EMNN GNor ITim MFie SUsu WLin
– 'Leather Jacket'	GAbr
– 'Lechistan' (S)	EMNN ITim MCre MFie NHar SPop WHil WLin
– 'Lee' (A)	MAln MCre
– 'Lee Clark' (A)	ITim MAln MCre
– 'Lee Paul' (A)	EMNN GNor ITim MCre MFie NRya SPop WHil WLin
– 'Lee Sharpe' (A)	MAln MCre
– 'Lemon Drop' (S)	MCre NBro
– 'Lemon Sherbet' (B)	MFie
– 'Lepton Jubilee' (S) **new**	MAln
– 'Letty' (S) **new**	MAln
– 'Leverton' (d) **new**	MAln

- 'Lewis Telford' (A)   MAln
- 'Lich' (S)   EMNN
- 'Lichfield' (A/d)   MAln MCre
- 'Light Hearted'   MFie
- 'Lila' (A) **new**   MAln
- 'Lilac Domino' (S)   MCre MFie NRya SPop WHil
                               WLin
- 'Lilac Domino' (A) **new**   ITim MAln SPop
- 'Lillian Hill' (A)   MAln
- 'Lima' (d) **new**   MAln
- 'Limelight' (A)   MAln SPop
- 'Limelight' (S) **new**   MAln
- 'Lindley' (S)   EMNN NHar
- 'Ling' (A)   EMNN MCre MFie SPop
- 'Lisa' (A)   CLyd ITim MCre MFie NHar SPop
                               WLin
- 'Lisa Clara' (S)   EMNN GNor ITim WLin
- 'Lisa's Smile' (S)   MFie NLAp WHil
- 'Little Rosetta' (d)   MAln
- 'Lord Saye and Sele' (St)   GAbr GNor ITim MCre MFie
                               NLAp SPop WHil WLin
- 'Louisa' (d)   MFie
- 'Louisa Woolhead' (d)   SPop
- 'Lovebird' (S)   EMNN GNor MCre MFie NHar
                               SPop SUsu
- 'Ludlow' (S)   MAln
- 'Lune Tiger' (St) **new**   MAln
- 'Lupy Minstrel' (S) **new** MAln
- 'Lynn' (A) **new**   MAln
- 'Madame Gina' (S)   MAln MFie
- 'Maggie' (S)   EMNN GNor ITim
- 'Magnolia' (B)   MFie
- 'Maid Marion' (d)   MCre
- 'Maizie' (S) **new**   MAln
- 'Mandarin' (A)   MAln MCre MFie SPop
- 'Mansell's Green' (S)   MAln MFie WHil
- 'Margaret Faulkner' (A)   EMNN GNor ITim MCre MFie
                               NRya WLin
- 'Margaret Irene' (A) **new** MAln SPop
- 'Margaret Martin' (S)   MAln
- 'Margot Fonteyn' (A)   MAln SPop
- 'Marie Crousse' (d)   CPBP GAbr GMaP MFie WLin
- 'Marigold' (d)   CLyd WFar
- 'Marion Howard   MAln MCre MFie
   Spring' (A)
- 'Marion Tiger' (St) **new** MAln
- 'Mark' (A)   EMNN ITim MCre MFie NBro
                               SPop WLin
- 'Marmion' (S)   MAln NLAp SPop WHil
- 'Martha Livesley' (A) **new** MAln
- 'Martin Luther King' (S)   MFie
- 'Mary' (d)   GNor MCre
- 'Mary Taylor' (S)   MAln
- 'Mary Zach' (S)   ITim MAln WHil
- 'Matthew Yates' (d)   CHad CStu ITim LHop MCre MFie
                               MOne NChi NPri SPop SUsu
                               WCot WHil WLin WRha
- 'Maureen Millward' (A)   EMNN MAln MCre MFie SPop
- 'May' (A)   MAln MCre
- 'Mazetta Stripe' (S/St)   ITim MAln SPop WLin
- 'McWatt's Blue' (B)   GAbr IGor WLin
- 'Meadowlark' (A)   MAln MCre
- 'Mease Tiger' (St) **new**   MAln
- 'Megan' (d) **new**   MAln
- 'Mehta' (A) **new**   MAln
- 'Mellifluous'   MAln MCre
- 'Mere Green' (S) **new**   MAln
- 'Merlin' (A)   NHar WLin
- 'Merlin' (S) **new**   MAln
- 'Merlin Stripe' (St)   MCre SPop
- 'Mermaid' (d)   GNor MCre
- 'Merridale' (A)   EMNN MCre MFie
- 'Mersey Tiger' (S)   GAbr

- 'Mesquite' (A) **new**   MAln
- 'Mexicano' (A) **new**   MAln
- 'Michael' (S)   MAln
- 'Michael Watham' (S) **new** MAln
- 'Mick' (A)   MAln
- 'Midnight' (S)   CLyd EMNN NHar
- 'Midnight' (A) **new**   ITim MAln
- 'Mikado' (S)   MCre MFie SPop
- 'Milkmaid' (A)   MAln
- 'Millicent' (A)   MAln MFie
- 'Mink' (A)   MFie WHil
- 'Minley' (S)   EMNN GCrs GNor ITim MCre
                               MFie NBir NBro NHar SPop WLin
- 'Minsmere' (S)   MAln
- 'Mirabella Bay' (A)   MAln
- 'Mirandinha' (A)   MAln MCre
- 'Miriam' (A)   MAln
- 'Miss Newman' (A)   MAln
- 'Mohawk' (S)   MCre
- 'Mojave' (S)   EMNN GNor ITim MCre MFie
                               NHar NLAp NRya SPop WHil
                               WLin
- 'Mollie Langford' (A)   MCre SPop
- 'Molly Langford' (A) **new** MAln
- 'Monet' (S) **new**   MAln
- 'Moneymoon' (S)   MFie
- 'Monica' (A)   MFie
- 'Monk' (S)   MCre MFie WHil
- 'Monk's Eleigh' (A) **new** MAln
- 'Moonglow' (S)   EMNN MFie
- 'Moonlight' (S)   GAbr MAln
- 'Moonrise' (S)   EMNN MFie
- 'Moonriver' (A)   MAln MCre SPop
- 'Moonshadow' (d) **new**   MAln
- 'Moonstone' (d)   MFie
- 'Moselle' (S)   MAln
- 'Mr 'A'' (S)   CLyd GCrs WLin
- 'Mrs A. Bolton' (A)   MCre
- 'Mrs L. Hearn' (A)   EMNN GNor ITim MCre MFie
                               SPop
- 'Mrs R. Bolton' (A)   WRha
- 'Murray Lanes' (A) **new**   MAln
- 'My Fair Lady' (A) **new**   MAln
- 'Myrtle Park' (A) **new**   MAln
- 'Nandy' (S) **new**   MAln
- 'Nankenan' (S)   MFie
- 'Nantenan' (S)   MAln
- 'Neat and Tidy' (S)   EMNN LRHS MCre MFie NHar
                               NOak NRya SPop WHil WLin
- 'Nefertiti' (A)   MAln SPop
- 'Nessundorma' (A) **new**   MAln
- 'Neville Telford' (S)   EMNN GNor ITim MCre MFie WLin
- 'Nickity' (A)   GAbr MAln MCre MFie SPop WLin
- 'Nicola Jane' (A) **new**   MAln
- 'Nigel' (d)   GAbr ITim MAln NLAp WLin
- 'Night and Day' (S)   EMNN MFie NLAp
- 'Nightwink' (S) **new**   MAln
- 'Nina' (A) **new**   MAln
- 'Nita' (d)   MAln
- 'Nocturne' (S)   EMNN GNor MCre MFie NBro
                               NLAp SPop WLin
- 'Noelle' (S) **new**   ITim
- 'Nonchalance' (A)   MCre MFie
- 'Norma' (A)   MFie WLin
- 'Notability' (A)   MAln
- 'Nureyev' (A)   MAln MCre
- 'Old England' (S)   MFie SPop
- 'Old Gold' (S)   GAbr SUsu WLin
- 'Old Irish Blue' (B)   CLyd IGor MCre MFie WLin
- 'Old Irish Scented' (B)   GAbr IGor NBro WLin
- 'Old Red Dusty Miller' (B)   ECha LTwo MFie NBir NJOw SIng
- 'Old Red Elvet' (S)   GNor MAln
- 'Old Smokey' (A)   MAln MCre SPop

- 'Old Suffolk Bronze' (B)   GAbr MFie
- 'Old Wine' (A)   CLyd MFie
- 'Old Yellow Dusty   CLyd EMNN EWes GAbr MFie
  Miller' (B)   MSte NBro NHol SIng WLin
      WWin
- 'Olton' (A)   MCre MFie
- 'Opus One' (A)   MAln
- 'Orb' (S)   CLyd EMNN MCre MFie SPop WLin
- 'Ordvic' (S)   MAln WLin
- 'Orlando' (S) **new**   MAln
- 'Osbourne Green' (B)   GAbr GNor IGor MFie NHar
      NLAp SPop SUsu WHil WLin
- 'Overdale' (A)   MAln MCre
- 'Paddlin Madeleine'   MAln
  (A) **new**
- 'Pagoda Belle' (A)   MAln
- 'Paleface' (A)   MAln MCre WHil
- 'Pam Tiger' (St) **new**   MAln
- 'Papageno' (St) **new**   MAln
- 'Paradise Yellow' (B)   EMNN MFie SPop
- 'Paragon' (A)   MAln MCre
- 'Paris' (S)   MAln
- 'Party Time' (S)   MAln
- 'Pastiche' (A)   MCre MFie
- 'Pat' (S)   EMNN MFie SPop
- 'Pat Mooney' (d) **new**   MAln
- 'Patience' (S)   SPop WHil
- 'Patricia Barras' (S)   MAln
- 'Pauline' (A)   MFie
- 'Pauline Taylor' (d) **new**   MAln
- 'Pear Drops' **new**   GAbr
- 'Pegasus' **new**   MAln
- 'Peggy' (A)   WHil
- 'Peggy's Lad' (A) **new**   MAln
- 'Pequod' (A) **new**   MAln
- 'Peruvian' (S) **new**   MAln
- 'Peter Beardsley' (A)   MAln
- 'Peter Hall' (d) **new**   MAln
- 'Phantom' **new**   MAln
- 'Pharaoh' (A)   MAln MFie SPop
- 'Phyllis Douglas' (A)   EMNN ITim MCre MFie SPop
- 'Pierot' (A)   MCre MFie SPop
- 'Piers Telford'   MCre MFie SPop
- 'Pink Fondant' (d) **new**   MAln
- 'Pink Lady' (A)   MFie NBro
I - 'Pink Lilac'   GNor
- 'Pinkie' (A)   MAln
- 'Pinstripe'   WHil
- 'Pioneer Stripe' (S)   NJOw WHil
- 'Pippin' (A)   MCre MFie NBro SPop WLin
- 'Pixie' (A)   MAln MCre
- 'Playboy' (A) **new**   MAln
- 'Plush Royal' (S)   MAln MFie
- 'Polestar' (S)   MAln MCre SPop WLin
- 'Pop's Blue' (S/d)   MAln SPop
- 'Portree' (S)   EMNN GAbr
- 'Pot o' Gold' (S)   GNor ITim MCre MFie NHar
      NLAp NOak SPop WHil
- 'Prague' (S)   GAbr GNor MCre MFie NBir NRya
      SPop SUsu
- 'Pretender' (A)   MAln SPop
- 'Prima' **new**   MAln
- 'Prince Bishop' (S) **new**   MAln
- 'Prince Charming' (S)   ITim MFie SPop SUsu WLin
- 'Prince Igor' (A) **new**   MAln
- 'Prince John' (A)   ITim MCre MFie NBro SPop WHil
      WLin
- 'Prince Regent' (B)   NBro
- 'Prometheus' (d) **new**   MAln
- 'Purple Glow' (d) **new**   MAln WLin
- 'Purple Sage' (S)   EMNN GNor NHar
- 'Purple Velvet' (S)   SPop
- 'Quality Chase' (A)   MAln MCre

- 'Quatro' (d)   MAln
- 'Queen Alexander'   GAbr
- 'Queen Bee' (S)   GAbr GNor ITim
- 'Queen of Sheba' (S)   MAln
- 'Queen's Bower' (S)   EMNN
- 'Quintessence' (A)   MAln MCre
- 'Rabley Heath' (A)   CLyd EMNN MCre MFie SPop
      WLin
- 'Rachel' (A) **new**   MAln
- 'Radiant' (A)   MFie
- 'Rajah' (S)   ELan GNor ITim MFie NHar NRya
      SPop WHil WLin
- 'Raleigh Stripe' (S) **new**   MAln SPop
- 'Ralenzano' (A) **new**   MAln
- 'Rameses' (A)   MAln MCre
- 'Red Admiral' **new**   MAln
- 'Red Beret' (S)   MFie
- 'Red Denna' (d) **new**   MAln
- 'Red Embers' (S) **new**   MAln
- 'Red Gauntlet' (S)   CMGP CStu EMNN ITim MFie
      MRav MSte NHar SPop WCot
      WHil WLin
- 'Red Mark' (A)   MCre MFie
- 'Red Rum' (S)   GAbr MFie
- 'Redcar' (A)   MAln MCre
- 'Redstart' (S)   MCre WHil
- 'Regency' (A) **new**   MAln
- 'Remus' (S)   ELan GAbr ITim LTwo MCre MFie
      NHar SPop SUsu WHil WLin
- 'Renata' (S)   MFie
- 'Rene' (A)   EMNN GAbr MAln MCre
- 'Reverie' (d) **new**   MAln
- 'Riatty' (d)   GAbr MAln MFie
- 'Richard Shaw' (A)   MFie NHar WHil WLin
- 'Ring of Bells' (S) **new**   MAln
- 'Robert Lee' (A) **new**   MAln
- 'Roberto' (S)   MAln
- 'Robin Hood' (A)   MAln
- 'Rock Sand' (S)   EMNN GNor MAln MFie NHar
      NLAp
- 'Rodeo' (A)   MCre MFie WPat
- 'Rolts' (S)   CLyd ELan EMNN GAbr GNor
      ITim MFie NBir NBro NHar NHol
      NLAp NOak SPop WHil
- 'Ronald Ward' (B) **new**   MAln
- 'Rondy' (S)   MAln
- 'Ronnie Johnson' **new**   MAln
- 'Ronny Simpson'   MCre
- 'Rosalie Edwards' (S)   EMNN ITim MFie
- 'Rose Conjou' (d) **new**   GAbr MAln
- 'Rose Kaye' (A)   GNor MAln MCre SPop
- 'Rosebud' (S)   GAbr GNor
- 'Rosemary' (S)   EMNN MCre MFie SUsu WHil
- 'Rothesay Robin' (A) **new**   MAln
- 'Rowena' (A)   CLyd ECGP EMNN MCre MFie
      NBro NHar SPop WLin
- 'Roxborough' (A) **new**   MAln
- 'Roxburgh' (A)   EMNN MCre MFie SPop
- 'Roy Keane' (A)   CStu MAln
- 'Royal Purple' (S)   NBir
- 'Royal Velvet' (S)   GAbr
- 'Ruby Hyde' (B)   GAbr
- 'Rusty Dusty'   IGor
- 'Rycroft' (A) **new**   MAln
- 'Saginaw' (A) **new**   MAln
- 'Sailor Boy' (S)   MFie
- 'Saint Boswells' (S)   GNor MCre MFie
- 'Saint Elmo' (A)   MFie
- 'Saint Gerrans' White' (B)   MFie
- 'Salad' (S)   MFie
- 'Sale Green' (S)   MFie
- 'Sally' (A)   MAln MCre
- 'Sam Gamgee' (A) **new**   MAln

– 'Sam Hunter' (A)	MAln SPop	
– 'San Antonio' (A) **new**	MAln	
– 'Sandhills' (A)	MAln MCre	
– 'Sandmartin' (S)	MFie	
– 'Sandra' (A)	ELan EMNN GAbr MCre MFie	
	SPop WHil WLin	
– 'Sandra's Lass' (A) **new**	MAln	
– 'Sandwood Bay' (A)	CLyd EMNN GAbr GNor LRHS	
	MCre MFie NBro NHar SPop WHil	
– 'Sarah Humphries'	MAln	
(d) **new**		
– 'Sarah Lodge' (d)	EMNN GAbr ITim MFie WLin	
– 'Sarah Woodhead' (D)	MAln	
– 'Satchmo' (S)	EMNN	
– 'Scipio' (S)	MAln	
– 'Scorcher' (S) **new**	MAln	
– 'Sea Mist' (d) **new**	MAln	
– 'Serenity' (S)	EMNN GNor MCre MFie	
– 'Shako' (A)	MAln	
– 'Shalford' (d)	MFie SPop WLin	
– 'Sharman's Cross' (S)	MAln	
– 'Sharon Louise' (S)	MCre	
– 'Sheila' (S)	ITim MAln MCre MFie NHar SPop	
	WHil WLin	
– 'Sherbet Lemon' (S) **new**	MAln	
– 'Shere' (S)	EMNN MCre MFie NLAp SPop	
	WLin	
– 'Shergold' (A)	MCre MFie	
– 'Sherwood' (S)	EMNN ITim MCre MFie NHar	
	SPop WLin	
– 'Shirley' (S) **new**	MAln	
– 'Shotley' (A)	EMNN MCre	
– 'Showman' (S) **new**	MAln	
– 'Sibsey' (d)	MAln SPop	
– 'Sidney' (A) **new**	MAln	
– 'Silmaril' **new**	MAln	
– 'Silverway' (S)	MCre NABC WLin	
– 'Sir John' (A) **new**	MAln	
– 'Sir John Hall'	MAln	
– 'Sir Robert' (d) **new**	MAln	
– 'Sirbol' (A)	MAln MCre MFie	
– 'Sirius' (A)	CLyd GAbr GNor ITim LRHS	
	MCre MFie MOne NHar SPop	
	WHil WLin	
– 'Sister Josephine' (d) **new**	MAln	
– 'Skipper' (d)	SPop	
– 'Skylark' (A)	MAln MCre	
– 'Skyliner' (A)	MAln	
– 'Slioch' (S)	EMNN GAbr GNor ITim MFie	
	NLAp SPop WLin	
– 'Slip Anchor' (A) **new**	MAln	
– 'Snooty Fox' (A)	EMNN MFie WHil WLin	
– 'Snooty Fox II' (A)	MCre SPop	
– 'Snowy Owl' (S)	GNor MCre MFie SPop	
– 'Somersby' (d) **new**	MAln WLin	
– 'Soncy Face' (A)	MAln	
– 'Song of India' (A) **new**	MAln	
– 'Sonny Boy' (A)	MAln	
– 'Sonya' (A)	ITim WLin	
– 'South Barrow' (d)	EMNN GAbr ITim MCre SPop SUsu	
– 'Sparky' (A) **new**	MAln	
– 'Spring Meadows' (S)	ECGP GAbr MCre MFie MOne	
	NChi NPri SPop SUsu WHil	
– 'Springtime' (A)	MAln SPop	
– 'Standish' (d)	GAbr	
– 'Stant's Blue' (S)	EMNN GNor ITim MCre MFie	
	NBro SPop	
– 'Star Wars' (S)	ITim MAln MFie SPop	
– 'Starburst' (S) **new**	MAln	
– 'Starry' (S)	NHar SPop WLin	
– 'Stella' (S)	MFie	
– 'Stella Coop' (d)	MAln	
– 'Stetson' (A) **new**	MAln	

– 'Stoke Poges' (A)	MAln	
– 'Stonnal' (A)	MCre MFie NHar SPop	
– 'Stormin Norman'	MAln	
(A) **new**		
– 'Stripey' (d)	MAln	
– 'Stuart West' (A)	MAln MCre	
– 'Stubb's Tartan' (S)	NHar	
– 'Subliminal' (A)	MAln MCre	
– 'Sue' (A)	MCre MFie	
– 'Sugar Plum Fairy' (S)	GAbr	
– 'Summer Sky' (A)	MCre	
– 'Summer Wine' (A) **new**	MAln	
– 'Sumo' (S)	MAln MCre SPop WLin	
I – 'Sunflower' (S)	GAbr MCre MFie NHar NLAp	
	SPop WLin	
– 'Sunsal' (S)	MFie	
– 'Sunstar' (S)	EMNN MFie	
– 'Super Para' (S)	EMNN GNor MCre MFie SPop	
	WLin	
– 'Superb' (A) **new**	MAln	
– 'Susan' (A)	ITim MCre MFie	
– 'Susannah' (d)	GAbr LRHS MFie MOne NChi	
	NHol NPri SPop WLRN WLin	
* – 'Sweet Chestnut' (S)	MAln WLin	
– 'Sweet Georgia Brown'	MAln	
(A) **new**		
– 'Sweet Pastures' (S)	EMNN GNor ITim MFie NHol	
	SPop	
– 'Swift' (S)	MFie	
– 'Sword' (d)	GAbr GNor MAln MCre MFie	
	MOne SPop WHil	
– 'Symphony' (A)	MFie SUsu WHil	
– 'Taffeta' (S) **new**	MAln	
– 'Tall Purple Dusty	SPop	
Miller' (B)		
– 'Tally-ho' (A)	MAln	
– 'Tamino' (S)	MAln	
– 'Tarantella' (A)	EMNN GAbr GNor MCre MFie WLin	
– 'Tawny Owl' (B)	NBro	
– 'Tay Tiger' (St) **new**	SPop	
– 'Ted Gibbs' (A)	MAln MCre MFie	
– 'Ted Roberts' (A)	EMNN MCre MFie NHar SPop	
	SUsu WLin	
– 'Teem' (S)	EMNN GNor MCre MFie NRya	
	SPop WLin	
– 'Temeraire' (A) **new**	MAln	
– 'Tenby Grey' (S)	MFie WLin	
– 'Tender Trap' (A) **new**	MAln	
– 'Terpo' (A) **new**	MAln	
– 'Tess' (A)	MAln	
– 'The Baron' (S)	GNor ITim MCre MFie MOne	
	NHar SPop	
– 'The Bishop' (S)	MFie	
– 'The Bride' (S)	EMNN	
– 'The Cardinal' (d)	SUsu	
– 'The Czar' (A)	MCre	
– 'The Egyptian' (A) **new**	MAln WHil	
– 'The Raven' (S)	EMNN MFie NLAp SPop	
– 'The Sneep' (A)	MAln MCre SPop WHil	
– 'The Snods' (S)	EMNN GNor MFie	
– 'Thebes' (A)	MAln	
– 'Thetis' (A)	MCre MFie SPop WLin	
– 'Thirlmere' (d)	MAln	
– 'Three Way Stripe' (St)	MCre	
– 'Thutmoses' (A)	MAln	
– 'Tiger Tim' **new**	MAln	
– 'Tinker' (S) **new**	MAln	
– 'Tinkerbell' (S)	MCre MFie WHil WLin	
– 'Toffee Crisp' (A) **new**	MAln	
* – 'Tomato'	WLin	
– 'Tomboy' (S)	MFie SPop	
– 'Toolyn' (S) **new**	MAln	
– 'Top Affair' (d) **new**	MAln	

- 'Tosca' (S)	EMNN GCrs GNor ITim MCre NRya SPop WHil WLin
- 'Trish'	GAbr
- 'Trouble' (d)	EMNN GAbr LHop LPio LRHS MBNS MCre MFie MOne NChi NHar SMrm SPop
- 'Troy Aykman' (A) **new**	MAln
- 'Trudy' (S)	EMNN GAbr GNor ITim MCre MFie MOne SPop
- 'True Briton' (S)	MCre MFie SPop
- 'Trumpet Blue' (S)	MAln MFie
- 'Tumbledown' (A)	MFie
- 'Tummel'	MAln SPop
- 'Twiggy' (S) **new**	MAln
- 'Tye Lea' (S)	MAln MCre
- 'Typhoon' (A)	MCre MFie SPop WHil
- 'Uncle Arthur' (A) **new**	MAln
- 'Unforgetable' (A)	MAln MCre
- 'Upton Belle' (S)	MAln
- 'Valerie' (A)	ITim MCre SPop
- 'Valerie Clare'	MAln
- 'Vee Too' (A)	MCre MFie SPop
- 'Vega' (A) **new**	MAln
- 'Velvet Moon' (A)	MAln
- 'Venetian' (A)	MAln MFie
- 'Venus' (A) **new**	MAln
- 'Vera Eden'	MFie
- 'Vera Hill' (A) **new**	MAln
- 'Verdi' (A)	EMNN ITim MCre
- 'Victoria' (S)	MAln
- 'Victoria de Wemyss' (A)	MCre MFie WHil
- 'Virginia Belle' (St) **new**	MAln
- 'Vivian' (S) **new**	MAln
- 'Vulcan' (A)	MFie NBro SPop
- 'Waincliffe Red' (S)	MFie
- 'Walhampton' (S)	FMNN
- 'Walter Lomas' (S) **new**	MAln
- 'Walton' (A)	MCre MFie
- 'Walton Heath' (d)	EMNN MCre MFie SPop WLin
- 'Waltz Time' (A)	MAln
- 'Watchett' (S) **new**	MAln
- 'Waterfall' (A) **new**	MAln
- 'Wayward' (S) **new**	MAln
- 'Wedding Day' (S)	MAln MFie
- 'Wentworth' (A)	MAln
- 'Whistle Jacket' (S) **new**	MAln
- 'White Ensign' (S)	EMNN GAbr GNor ITim MCre MFie NOak SPop WLin
- 'White Water' (A)	MAln SPop
- 'White Wings' (S)	EMNN GNor MCre MFie SPop WLin
- 'Whitecap' (S) **new**	MAln
- 'Whoopee' (A) **new**	MAln
- 'Wichita Falls' (S) **new**	MAln
- 'Wide Awake' (A)	MCre MFie
- 'Wilf Booth' (A)	MAln SPop
- 'Wincha' (S)	MFie SPop
- 'Windways Mystery' (B)	MFie
- 'Windways Pisces' (d) **new**	MAln
- 'Winifrid' (A)	CLyd EMNN GAbr GNor ITim LRHS MCre MFie NHar SPop WHil
- 'Winlation' (A) **new**	MAln
- 'Winnifred' (B) **new**	SPop
- 'Woodmill' (A)	MAln
- 'Wookey Hole' (A) **new**	MAln
- 'Wor Jackie' (S)	EMNN
- 'Wycliffe Midnight'	GAbr GNor
- 'Y.I. Hinney' (A)	EMNN MCre MFie
- 'Yellow Hammer' (S)	MAln
- 'Yellow Isle' (S) **new**	MAln
- 'Yelverton' (S)	MAln MFie
- 'Yitzhak Rabin' (A) **new**	MAln

- 'Yorkshire Grey' (S)	MFie NBro
- 'Zambia' (d)	CLyd GAbr MFie SPop SUsu WHil WLin
- 'Zircon' (S) **new**	MAln
- 'Zodiac' (S) **new**	MAln
- 'Zoe' (A) **new**	MAln
- 'Zoe Ann' (S)	MAln
I - 'Zona' (A)	MAln
auriculata (11)	ITim SBla
'Barbara Midwinter' (6x30)	CMea NDov NGar WAbe
Barnhaven Blues Group (Prim)(30) ♀ H4	CSWP GAbr
Barnhaven doubles (dPoly)(30)	CSWP
Barnhaven Gold-laced Group	see *P.* Gold-laced Group Barnhaven
Barnhaven hybrids	NCot WHrl
Barnhaven Traditional Group	CSWP MAvo
'Beamish Foam' (Poly)(30)	NDov
'Beatrice Wooster' (2)	CLyd CNic GAbr ITim LRHS MFie NDlv NHar NHol NLAp WAbe
'Bee' x 'Jo-Jo' **new**	GCrs
'Beeches' Pink'	GAbr
beesiana (4)	More than 30 suppliers
bella SDR 1653 **new**	GKev
- SDR 1758	GKev
'Bellamy's Pride'	CLyd WAbe
bellidifolia (17)	CPla GEdr
beluensis	see *P.* x *pubescens* 'Freedom'
Bergfrühling Julianas Group (Prim)(30)	MFie
§ x **berninae** 'Windrush' (2)	CLyd NHar WAbe
'Bewerley White'	see *P.* x *pubescens* 'Bewerley White'
bhutanica	see *P. whitei* 'Sherriff's Variety'
x **biflora** (2)	WAbe
'Big Red Giant' (dPrim)(30)	GAbr MBNS MDKP MOne NHar WHil
bileckii	see *P.* x *forsteri* 'Bileckii'
'Blue Riband' (Prim)(30)	CBgR EDAr ENot EPfP MRav WAbe WFar
'Blue Sapphire' (dPrim)(30)	CElw CMil EPfP EPot GAbr LRHS MBNS MFie MOne MWrn NChi SIng SPcr WHil WWol
Blue Striped Victorians Group (Poly)(30)	GAbr
'Blutenkissen' (Prim)(30)	GAbr
'Bon Accord Cerise' (dPoly)(30)	GAbr
'Bon Accord Purple' (dPoly)(30)	WFar WRus
'Bonfire' (4)	GDra
boothii alba (21)	CBos GCrs GGGa LTwo
- subsp. **autumnalis** (21)	GCrs GGGa WAbe
- subsp. **repens** (21)	MNrw
'Boothman's Ruby'	see *P.* x *pubescens* 'Boothman's Variety'
boveana (12)	MFie
§ **bracteosa** (21)	GCrs ITim NHar
Bressingham (4)	WFar
brevicula x **chionantha** subsp. **sinopurpurea** SDR 1794 **new**	GKev
brigantia **new**	GIBF
'Broadwell Pink' (2)	EHyt ITim
'Broadwell Ruby' (2)	WAbe WLin
'Bronwyn' (Prim)(30)	NBir
'Broxbourne'	CLyd ITim NHar NLAp
x **bulleesiana** (4)	CM&M EBee EChP IBal MTis NBro NLAp NLar SMrm SRms STes SWat WFar WHil WMoo WPer WViv

- Moerheim hybrids (4)　WFar
bulleyana (4)　♀ H4　More than 30 suppliers
- ACE 2484　WAbe
burmanica (4)　CPla GBuc GEdr GFle GGar GIBF
　　　MSta NHar SLon SRms WFar
'Butter's Bronze' (Prim)　WOut
　new
'Butterscotch' (Prim)(30)　CSWP
'Caerulea Plena'　GCal
　(dPrim)(30)
calderiana (21)　GDra GFle NHar
candelabra hybrids (4)　CBro CHar COlW EMNN GGar
　　　ITim NBir NPPs SWal WRos
Candy Pinks Group　CSWP GAbr
　(Prim)(30)
capitata (5)　CM&M CPla CSWP CSpe EBee
　　　EDAr GDra GFle GTou IFro ITim
　　　MBri MFie NHar NLAp NPPs
　　　WAbe WBea WCom WFar WGwG
　　　WMoo WPer
- subsp. *mooreana* (5)　CFir EChP EWTr GFle ITim LPBA
　　　NDlv SPlb
- subsp. *sphaerocephala*　GKev
　(5) SDR 1681
'Captain Blood'　CBos EPfP MFie MWrn NLar NSti
　(dPrim)(30)　SIng SUsu WFar WRha
'Carmen' (Prim)(30)　CLyd ITim
Carnation Victorians　MFie
　Group (Poly)(30)
carniolica (2)　GFle
Casquet mixture (Prim)(30)　CSWP
cernua (17)　GDra GFle ITim MFie NHar
'Charlen' (dPrim)(30)　NHar
Chartreuse Group　CSWP GAbr MFie WRha
　(Poly)(30)
'Cherry' (Prim)(30)　GAbr
'Chevithorne Pink'　NPar
　(Poly)(30)
§　*chionantha* (18)　♀ H4　EBee EDAr GCrs GDra GFle GGar
　　　GKir GMaP GTou ITim LRHS MBri
　　　MCAu MFie MNrw NBir NChi
　　　NFor NHar SPer WAbe WFar
　　　WGwG WViv
- SDR 1658　GKev
- subsp. *brevicaula*　GKev
　SDR 1576
- SDR 1750　GKev
§　- subsp. *melanops* (18)　EBee GFle GIBF LRHS NHar
§　- subsp. *sinopurpurea*　EBee GDra GFle GGar GIBF GTou
　(18)　SPer WAbe WCom WFar WPer
- - SDR 1757　GKev
chungensis (4)　EDAr GEdr GFle GGar GIBF GKir
　　　GTou MBri MLLN MLwd NDlv
　　　NHar SRms SUsu WAbe WMoo
§　- x *pulverulenta* (4)　EBee EBre GBuc GEdr MFie NHol
　　　NLar SMrm WAbe WFar WHil
x *chunglenta*　see *P.chungensis* x *pulverulenta* (4)
§　'Clarence Elliott' (2)　CGra CLyd CStu EHyt GCrs ITim
　　　NHar WAbe WCom WLin
clarkei (11)　CLyd GEdr GFle GTou NWCA
clusiana (2)　EBee GDra ITim
- 'Murray-Lyon' (2)　GCrs
cockburniana (4) ♀ H4　CRow GDra GEdr GFle GGar
　　　GIBF GTou MBri MFie NHar
　　　NWCA SRms WAbe WFar WLin
- L 913　MNes
- SDR 1967　GKev
- yellow-flowered **new**　GKev
concholoba (17)　CPla GFle GKev GTou ITim MFie
　　　NHar NLAp WAbe
'Corporal Baxter'　ENot EPfP EPot MBNS MBri
　(dPrim)(30)　MNrw MOne NChi WHil WRha
　　　WWol

cortusoides (7)　CPla EWTr GFle MNrw SRms
Cowichan (Poly)(30)　GAbr
Cowichan Amethyst　CSWP GAbr
　Group (Poly)(30)
Cowichan Blue Group　CSWP GAbr
　(Poly)(30)
Cowichan Garnet Group　CSWP EWoo GAbr GBuc MFie
　(Poly)(30)
Cowichan Red Group　WFar
　(Poly)(30)
Cowichan Venetian Group　CSWP GAbr
　(Poly)(30)
Cowichan Yellow Group　GAbr
　(Poly)(30)
'Craddock White'　CBos CVer
　(Prim) (30)
'Craven Gem' (Poly)(30)　GBuc MFie
Crescendo Series (Poly)(30)　GAbr
'Crimson Velvet' (2)　EMNN GAbr GNor ITim NHol WLin
crispa　see *P. glomerata*
*　*cuneata*　GTou
cuneifolia (8)　GFle GNor
- subsp. *heterodonta* (8)　GFle
daonensis (2)　GFle
darialica (11)　CNic ELan
'Dark Rosaleen' (Poly)　CVer
'David Green' (Prim)(30)　SIng
'David Valentine' (30)　GAbr
'Dawn Ansell' (dPrim)(30)　CElw CRow CSpe EPfP EPot EPri
　　　GAbr LRHS MBNS MBri MCLN
　　　MFie MOne MWrn NBir NEgg
　　　NHar SBla SIng SPer SSte SUsu
　　　WCot WHer WHil
Daybreak Group (Poly)(30)　CSWP MFie
deflexa (17)　GFle LRHS
denticulata (9) ♀ H4　More than 30 suppliers
- var. *alba* (9)　CTri EBre ECha EMNN EPfP EWTr
　　　GAbr GGar GKir GTou LRHS MBri
　　　MFie MWgw NBid NCot NHar
　　　NHol NLAp NOrc SDes SMer SPer
　　　WHen WMoo WPer WViv WWeb
　　　WWpP
- blue (9)　GKir NLar WLin
- 'Bressingham Beauty' (9)　EBre
- var. *cachemiriana*　EPfP NFla
　hort. (9)
- 'Glenroy Crimson' (9)　CLAP CRDP EBee SRms WCom
- 'Karryann' (9/v)　WCot
- lilac (9)　EHon GKir GTou MFie NCot
　　　NLAp NPri WViv WWeb
- purple (9)　GKir IBlr WMoo
- red (9)　EMNN EPar GGar GKir MWgw
　　　NCot NLAp NOrc WMoo
- 'Robinson's Red' (9)　EPot GBuc
- 'Ronsdorf' (9)　LRHS
- rose (9)　NHar
- 'Rubin'　EBee EHon EPfP GAbr GTou MBrN
　　　MBri MCLN MFie NBro NOak
　　　SRms WHen WHil WPer WWeb
- 'Rubinball' (9)　EBre EPfP GCrs GKir NHol WCot
- 'Snowball' (9)　MCLN NOak WHen
x *deschmannii*　see *P. x vochinensis*
'Desert Sunset' (Poly)(30)　CSWP MFie
deuteronana (21)　GCrs
'Devon Cream' (Prim)(30)　GBuc ITim WFar
'Dianne'　see *P. x forsteri* 'Dianne'
'Dorothy' (Poly)(30)　MRav NDov
'Double Lilac'　see *P. vulgaris* 'Lilacina Plena'
'Duckyls Red' (Prim)(30)　GBuc NChi
'Dusky Lady'　WBar WFar
'Easter Bonnet' (dPrim)(30)　CMil EPot LRHS MOne SPer WHil
edgeworthii　see *P. nana*
elatior (30) ♀ H4　More than 30 suppliers

– hose-in-hose (30)(d)	NBid
– hybrids (30)	SIng
– subsp. *intricata* (30)	NRya
– subsp. *leucophylla* (30)	EBee ECho
§ – subsp. *meyeri* (30)	GFle GNor NSla NWCA WAbe WLin
– subsp. *pallasii* (30)	GCrs GEdr
'Elizabeth Killelay' (dPoly)(30)	CBgR CBos CElw CMil EChP ELan LHop MAvo MSph NChi NCot NGdn NSti SUsu WCom WCot
'Ellen Page' (2)	MFie
ellisiae (21)	GFle SOkd
§ *erythra* (26)	ITim
'Ethel Barker' (2)	CGra GAbr ITim LRHS NDlv NHar NHol WAbe
'Eugénie' (dPrim)(30)	CHid CSpe ECle GAbr MBNS MFie MOne MWrn NHar NHol SIng WHil WLRN
'Fairy Rose' KRW 180/48 (2)	ITim WAbe
farinosa (11)	CLyd EBee GFle MBri MFie NHar NMen NRya WAbe WPer
fasciculata (11)	EHyt GEdr NLAp NSla SBla WHHs
– CLD 345	NHar WAbe
– SDR 1945	GKev
– ex CLD 345	GFle
'Fife Yellow' (dPoly)(30)	GBuc
'Fire Dance' (Poly)(30)	MFie
firmipes (26)	EBee GIBF
§ *flaccida* (28)	GDra GFle GGGa NHar WAbe
Flamingo Group (Poly)(30)	CSWP MFie
§ x *floerkeana* (2)	GCrs
– f. *biflora* 'Alba' (2)	SBla
florida (29)	GDra
– SDR 1855	GKev
florindae (26) ♀ H4	More than 30 suppliers
– bronze (26)	MFie NBir
I – 'Butterscotch' (26)	ITim WHrl
– hybrids (26)	EChP EHrv GAbr GDra GEdr GGar ITim MFie WHil
– orange (26)	CSam GMac IBlr LSyl MNrw NChi WCru WFar WWpP
– 'Ray's Ruby' (26)	CHar GBuc GMac MCLN MNrw NBir WElm WFTG WHrl WWhi WWpP
– red (26)	EBee GCal GGar ITim MFie MSta NBid NLar NPPs WCom WFar
– terracotta (26)	CSWP
Footlight Parade Group (Prim)(30)	CSWP
forrestii (3)	GGGa MFie NHar NLAp WAbe
– ACE 2474	GFle
– ACE 2480	EPot
– ACE 94-1875	IDac
– SDR 1533	GKev
§ x *forsteri* (2)	EMNN GFle MFie WAbe
§ – 'Bileckii' (2)	CStu EPar GCrs GFle ITim LRHS NBir NHar NLAp NWCA SRms WAbe WOBN
§ – 'Dianne' (2)	EHyt GAbr GBuc ITim NBro NHar WAbe WGwG
– 'Dianne' hybrids (2)	MFie
'Freckles' (dPrim)(30)	ECle MBNS MDun MOne NCot NHar NHol SPer WHil WLRN
'Freedom'	see *P.* x *pubescens* 'Freedom'
'Fritz Kummert' (2)	EHyt
frondosa (11) ♀ H4	CLyd EBee EHyt GFle GIBF LRHS MBri MBro MDKP MFie NHar NMen NWCA SHel WAbe WHoo WWeb
Fuchsia Victorians Group (Poly)(30)	MFie
'Garnet' (*allionii* hybrid) (2)	MFie
'Garryard Guinevere'	see *P.* 'Guinevere'

'Garryarde Crimson' **new**	WCot
gaubana (12)	MFie
gemmifera (11)	GFle GGGa
– var. *zambalensis* (11)	GFle WAbe
– – SDR 1611	GKev
– – SDR 1716	GKev
§ 'Gigha' (Prim)(30)	CSWP CSpe NGar
glabra **new**	WAbe
glaucescens (2)	CGra CLyd CNic GFle MFie WLin
§ *glomerata* (5)	GBuc GDra GFle GGGa
– CC 3321	WRos
'Glowing Embers' (4)	CSpe LRHS MFie NBir
glutinosa All.	see *P. allionii*
Gold-laced Group (Poly)(30)	CBre CElw CM&M CPla CRDP CSWP EBee EChP EWoo GAbr ITer MBri MCLN MHer MWod NBid NRya NWCA SPer SPet SUsu WFar WHer WHil
§ Gold-laced Group Barnhaven (Poly)(30)	CLAP GAbr ITer LPio MFie NBir NDov WViv
Gold-laced Group Beeches strain (Poly)(30)	SSth
'Gordon'	NGar
gracilipes (21)	GFle GGGa GGar ITim NHar NWCA SRms WAbe
– L&S 1166	WAbe
– early-flowering(21)	NHar WAbe
– late-flowering (21)	NHar
– 'Major'	see *P. bracteosa*
– 'Minor'	see *P. petiolaris*
Grand Canyon Group (Poly)(30)	MFie
grandis **new**	GFle
	GGGa
griffithii (21)	GFle
'Groeneken's Glorie' (Prim)(30)	EWTr GAbr GEdr LRHS MBri MRav NBir NBro SHar SPer WFar WViv
§ 'Guinevere' (Poly)(30) ♀ H4	More than 30 suppliers
'Hall Barn Blue'	GAbr
§ *halleri* (11)	EBee GFle GTou MFie NDlv NHar NMen NWCA WAbe
– 'Longiflora'	see *P. halleri*
Harbinger Group (Prim)(30)	CSWP GAbr LLWP
Harbour Lights mixture (Poly)(30)	CSWP MFie
Harlow Carr hybrids (4)	CSWP MLLN NDlv NGar WEas
Harvest Yellows Group (Poly)(30)	MFie
'Helge' (Prim)(30)	GAbr
'Helmswell Abbey' **new**	GKev
helodoxa	see *P. prolifera*
§ 'Hemswell Blush' (2)	GNor ITim NHol WLin
§ 'Hemswell Ember' (2)	CNic EMNN GCrs MFie NDlv NHar NLAp NRya
heucherifolia (7)	CPla GFle WBVN
hidakana (24)	SOkd
'High Point' (2) **new**	CGra
hirsuta (2)	CNic EHyt GCrs GEdr GFle GIBF GTou ITim MFie
– var. *exscapa* (2)	GFle
– 'Lismore Snow' (2)	ITim NHar
hose-in-hose (Poly)(30)(d)	CSWP ITer MHer MNrw
§ 'Hyacinthia' (2)	CLyd EMNN GIBF ITim MFie
hyacinthina	see *P. bellidifolia* subsp. *hyacinthina*
ianthina	see *P. prolifera*
iljinskyi **new**	NWCA
Indian Reds Group (Poly)(30)	CSWP MFie
'Ingram's Blue' (Poly)(30)	LRHS WPen
Inshriach hybrids (4)	CMHG CSWP EBre GDra MBri MFie NLar SPer WFar WWal

integrifolia (2)		GCrs GEdr GFle WAbe
§	'Inverewe' (4) ♀ H4	GAbr GBin GCal GKev NBir
	involucrata (11)	see *P. munroi*
	ioessa (26)	CBrm EWes GGGa ITer MBri WAbe
	'Iris Mainwaring' (Prim)(30)	GAbr GEdr MDHE MFie NHol
	irregularis (21)	GCrs GGGa
	issiori **new**	GIBF
	Jack in the Green Group (Poly)(30)	CMGP CSWP GAbr ITer MNrw MRav MWgw NCot WBVN WFar WHer WRha
	Jackanapes Group (Poly)(30)	EChP
	'Jackie Richards' (2)	WLin
	jaffreyana (11)	NGar WAbe
	japonica (4)	CMHG CRow CSam ECha GFle GGar GIBF GKir GLil GTou ITim LPBA LRHS MFir NBid NBro NChi NFor NHar NHol NLon SWat WAbe WCra WCru WFar WMoo WPer
	- 'Alba' (4)	EBee EHrv EWTr MCAu NHol NPri WAbe WFar WHil
	- 'Apple Blossom' (4)	GKev LHop SDes WFTG
*	- 'Carminea' (4)	EWTr NBro NHol WFar WHil WRHF
	- 'Fuji' (4)	CSWP GMac MBri MSta NBro
	- 'Fuji' hybrids (4)	NLar
	- hybrids (4)	SAWi
	- 'Miller's Crimson' (4) ♀ H4	More than 30 suppliers
	- 'Oriental Sunrise' (4)	CMil CSWP
	- 'Postford White' (4) ♀ H4	More than 30 suppliers
	- red (4)	WAbe
	- 'Valley Red' (4)	GBuc GFle GGar GMac ITim LHop
	jesoana (7)	GFle LTwo
	- B&SWJ 618	WCru
	'Joan Hughes' (*allionii* hybrid) (2)	CLyd ITim NHar NWCA SBla WAbe WLin
	'Joanna'	ECou EHyt
	'Johanna' (11)	GAbr GBuc GEdr GFle LSyl NGar NHar NPro NWCA WAbe
	'John Fielding' (6x30)	GEdr WCot
	'Jo-Jo' (2)	CLyd WAbe
	juliae (30)	CPla CRDP EHyt GFle GIBF LLWP LRHS SPlb WAbe WCom WCot WEas WHil
I	- 'Millicent' (3O) **new**	WCot
	'Kate Haywood'	CLyd WLin
	'Ken Dearman' (dPrim)(30)	CMea CSpe ENot EPfP EPot MBNS MFie MOne MRav MWrn NBid NBir NCot NEgg NHol NPPs SIng SPer WFar WHil WWol
	kewensis (12) ♀ H2	EShb GGar GKev MFie NWCA WAbe
	'Kinlough Beauty' (Poly)(30)	EBre EPar GAbr GEdr LRHS NRya NSti NWCA WEas
	'Kirk Ings' (2)	NGar
§	*kisoana* (7)	CPla EHyt GFle MTho WCru
	- var. *alba* (7)	CLAP CPla GGGa MTho
	- var. *shikokiana*	see *P. kisoana* (7)
	'Lady Greer' (Poly)(30) ♀ H4	CSam ECGN EDAr ELan GAbr GBuc GMaP LLWP MFie MRav NBir NChi NDov NHar NLap NRya NSti NWCA SIng SMac SUsu WCom WFTG WViv
	'Lambrook Lilac' (Poly)(30)	CElw
§	*latifolia* (2)	GFle GIBF WLRN
	- cream (2)	NLAp
	- x *pedemontana* (2)	GFle
§	*laurentiana* (11)	EBee GFle NWCA WAbe
	'Lea Gardens' (*allionii* hybrid) (2)	ITim MFie NHol
	'Lee Myers' (*allionii* hybrid) (2)	GNor ITim MFie NDlv NHar

	'Lilac Domino' (2)	NGar
	'Lilac Fairy'	ITim NGar NHar
	'Lilian Harvey' (dPrim)(30)	CElw EPfP LRHS MFie MOne MRav MWrn NBir NHol SIng WHil
	Limelight Group (Poly)(30)	MFie
	'Lindum Moonlight'	EHyt
	Lingholm hybrids (4)	NCat
	'Lingwood Beauty' (Prim)(30)	GAbr NHar
	'Linnet' (21)	ITim
	'Lismore' (2)	WLin
	'Lismore Pink' (2) **new**	GAbr
	'Lismore Yellow' (2)	EPot GKev GTou NHar NLAp WAbe
	Lissadel hybrids (4)	GFle GMac
*	'Little Poppet'	GAbr
	littoniana	see *P. vialii*
§	x *loiseleurii* (2)	EBre
§	- 'Aire Waves' (2)	EHyt GNor ITim NLAp
	longiflora	see *P. halleri*
	luteola (11)	GFle GGar LTwo MNrw NHol NPri SWal WFar
	macrophylla (18)	GFle GTou WAbe
	magellanica (11)	CGra GFle WAbe
	- subsp. *magellanica* J&JA 2.749.900 **new**	NWCA
	malacoides (3)	MBri
	mandarin red (4)	CSWP
	marginata (4) ♀ H4	EBre EMNN EPot GAbr GCrs GDra GFle LHop LRHS MBro NDlv NHar NHol NLAp SIng WAbe WFar
	- 'Adrian Evans' (2)	EHyt ITim
	- *alba* (2)	LRHS MBro NBro NDlv NGar NHar NHol SIng
	- 'Barbara Clough' (2)	CLyd ITim MFie NGar NLAp NSla SBla
	- 'Beamish' (2) ♀ H4	CLyd EPot NBro NGar NRya WCom
	- Beatrice Lascaris' (2)	EPot GCrs ITim MFie MOne NHar NHol SIng WAbe
	- 'Beverley Reid' (2)	ITim NHar
	- 'Boothman's Variety' (2)	ITim NGar NLAp
	- 'Caerulea' (2)	CLyd EPot ITim LBee MOne WAbe
	- 'Clear's Variety' (2)	CStu EMNN ITim NHar
	- 'Correvon's Variety' (2)	CLyd NGar
	- cut-leaved (2)	ITim NHol
	- dark (2)	NGar
	- 'Doctor Jenkins' (2)	ITim NHar NHol
	- 'Drake's Form' (2)	ITim NHol NLAp SOkd
	- dwarf (2)	LRHS MFie
	- 'Earl L. Bolton'	see *P. marginata* 'El Bolton'
	- 'El Bolton' (2)	NGar NHol WAbe
	- 'Elizabeth Fry' (2)	CLyd MBro NGar
	- 'F.W. Millard' (2)	NHar
	- from the Dolomites (2)	NHol NLAp
	- 'Gold Plate' (2)	NGar
	- 'Grandiflora' (2)	MBro NHar NHol SIng
	- 'Highland Twilight' (2)	CNic CPBP ITim NSla
	- 'Holden Clough' (2)	WCom
	- 'Holden Variety' (2)	EMNN ITim MBro NDlv NHar NHol NLAp SIng WAbe
	- 'Hyacinthia'	see *P.* 'Hyacinthia'
	- 'Ivy Agee' (2)	CLyd EPot ITim
	- 'Janet' (2)	CLyd EMNN NLAp WCom
	- 'Jenkins Variety' (2)	CLyd EPot
	- 'Kesselring's Variety' (2)	CLyd CM&M CMea CStu EHyt ELan EPot GNor ITim MBro MOne NDlv NHar NJOw NLAp SIng WAbe WWin
	- 'Laciniata'	ITim NGar SBla WCom
	- lilac-flowered	MFie NHar
	- 'Linda Pope' (2) ♀ H4	CLyd EHyt EMNN EPot ITim NBir NHar NHol NSla SUsu WAbe

	– maritime form (2)	NJOw
	– 'Millard's Variety' (2)	CLyd ITim
	– 'Miss Savory' (2)	EHyt
	– 'Mrs Carter Walmsley' (2)	NGar
	– 'Nancy Lucy' (2)	WAbe
	– 'Napoleon' (2)	ITim NGar NHar NHol
	– 'Oxember' **new**	NGar
I	– 'Peter's Variety' **new**	NGar
	– 'Prichard's Variety' (2) ♀ H4	CLyd ELan EMNN EMlt EPot ITim LBee MBro MFie NDlv NGar NHar NJOw NLAp NRya NWCA SIng WAbe WEas WFar
	– 'Rheniana'	see *Primula* 'Rheniana'
	– 'Rosea' (2)	NHol SIng
	– 'Sheila Denby' (2)	EMNN ITim NGar
	– 'Shipton' (2)	NGar
	– 'The President' (2)	EHyt ITim
	– violet-flowered (2)	EMNN NHar
	– 'Waithman's Variety' (2)	GCrs GTou ITim NLAp
	– wild-collected	ITim MFie
	'Maria Talbot' (*allionii* hybrid) (2)	EHyt NJOw
	'Marianne Davey' (dPrim)(30)	EPri MRav NBir NMGW
	'Marie Crousse' (dPrim)(30)	CBgR ENot LRHS MBNS MFie MOne MWgw MWrn NCot NHar NHol SIng WHil WRha
	Marine Blues Group (Poly)(30)	CSWP MFie
	'Mars' (*allionii* hybrid) (2)	GNor ITim NDlv NHar NHol
	'Marven' (2)	CLyd CStu NGar NHol
	'Mary Anne'	GAbr
	'Mauve Mist' (2)	NGar
	Mauve Victorians Group (Poly)(30)	CSWP MFie
	'McWatt's Claret' (Poly)(30)	GAbr LLWP NPar
	'McWatt's Cream' (Poly)(30)	CSWP EDAr GEdr GFle GGar LHop NBro NChi NHol NMen WCom
	melanops	see *P. chionantha* subsp. *melanops*
	x *meridiana* (2)	CStu EBre MFie NHar WLin
§	– 'Miniera' (2)	CLyd ITim WLin
	'Mexico'	MFie
	Midnight Group	CSWP GEdr MFie
	'Miniera'	see *P.* x *meridiana* 'Miniera'
	minima (2)	CLyd GFle GTou MFie NBro NHar NSla WAbe
	– var. *alba* (2)	GCrs GFle GGGa MFie
	x *hirsuta* (2)	see *P.* x *forsteri*
	x *wulfeniana* (2)	see *P.* x *vochinensis*
	'Miss Indigo' (dPrim)(30)	ENot EPfP GAbr LRHS MBNS MBri MCAu MCLN MFie MOne MRav MWrn NHar NHol SIng SPer WEas WGwG WHil WLin WViv
	mistassinica var. *macropoda*	see *P. laurentiana*
	miyabeana (4)	GFle
	– B&SWJ 3407	WCru
	modesta alba (11)	GFle WPat
	– var. *faurieae* (11)	MFie NWCA
	– var. *matsumurae* (11)	GFle
	mollis (7)	GEdr GIBF
	'Mother's Day' **new**	CElw
	moupinensis (21)	GGGa GKir WAbe
	– C&H 7038	GFle GGGa
*	'Mrs Eagland'	GAbr
	'Mrs Frank Neave' (Prim) **new**	GEdr
	'Mrs McGillivray' (Prim)(30)	GAbr
§	*munroi* (11)	GFle NBro NHar NWCA SIng SWat WAbe WLin

	– white-flowered (11) CC 1422	EHyt
§	– subsp. *yargongensis* (11)	CLyd EBee GAbr GCrs GFle GGar GTou LRHS MBri MFie NBro NHar SWat WAbe WFar
	muscarioides (17)	GFle GTou ITim MFie NHar WAbe
	Muted Victorians Group (Poly)(30)	CSWP MFie
§	*nana* (21)	GFle GKev ITim WAbe
	– 'Alba' (21) **new**	GCrs
	'Netta Dennis'	GCrs ITim
	New Pinks Group (Poly)(30)	CSWP MFie
	'Nightingale'	ITim WAbe
	nivalis Pallas	see *P. chionantha*
	nutans Delavay ex Franch.	see *P. flaccida*
	obconica (19)	LRHS MBri MFie WGwG
	'Old Port' (Poly)(30)	CElw CVer GEdr LLWP NHol NLAp WPat
	Old Rose Victorians Group (Poly)(30)	CSWP MFie
	'Olive Wyatt' (dPrim)(30)	EPri NBir
	'Oriental Sunrise' (4)	CSWP GAbr MBri MFie
	Osiered Amber Group (Prim)(30)	CSWP GAbr
	'Our Pat' (dPoly)(30)	GAbr ITim WPnP WRus
*	'Page' EHyt	
	Pagoda hybrids (4)	MBri
	palinuri (2)	GIBF WCom
	palmata (7)	GCrs GFle GGGa NHar WAbe
	'Paris '90' (Poly)(30)	CSWP GAbr MFie
	parryi (20)	CGra GCrs GFle GIBF MLLN NHar NWCA WFar
	'Pat Cottle' (d) (Poly) (30)	CBos CVer
	'Patrick' **new**	NCat
	pedemontana (2)	CGra GAbr NHol
	– 'Alba' (2)	EHyt
	'Perle von Bottrop' (Prim)(30)	GAbr
	'Peter Klein' (11)	CElw CNic CStu GBuc GEdr GFle LTwo NHar NLAp WAbe WTin
	petiolaris misapplied	see *P.* 'Redpoll'
§	*petiolaris* (21)	EHyt EPar GCrs GFle GGGa GNor ITim MDun NHar NWCA WAbe
	– Sherriff's form	see *P.* 'Redpoll'
§	'Pink Aire' (2)	EHyt ITim MFie NGar
	'Pink Fairy'	EHyt ITim
	'Pink Ice' (*allionii* hybrid) (2)	CGra CLyd CPBP ITim MFie NHol NRya
	planifolia (17)	GGGa
	poissonii (4)	CMHG CPla GCrs GFle GGar GIBF LPBA MFie NGby WAbe
	– ACE 1946	NWCA
	– CLD 193	LSyl
	polyanthus (30)	WFar
	polyneura (7)	CPla ECha EDAr GEdr GFle GGar GIBF GNor MFie MNes MNrw NBid NVic SRms WHil WLin
	– SDR 1732	GKev
	'Port Wine' (30)	GAbr
	praenitens	see *P. sinensis*
	prenantha (4)	GGGa ITim WAbe
	'Prince Silverwings' (dPoly)(30)	CVer WEas
§	*prolifera* (4) ♀ H4	CMHG CTrw EBee ECha EHon GCrs GEdr GFle GGar GIBF GMac ISea LPBA LSyl MFir MLLN MNrw MRav SIng SLon SPer SRms SSpi SWat WAbe WFar WPer
§	x *pubescens* (2) ♀ H4	EMan GAbr MBro NLAp WLRN WPer

- 'Alba' (2)   NHar WAbe
- 'Alison Gibbs' (2)   MOne
- 'Apple Blossom' (2)   CLyd EMNN ITim MFie SIng
- 'Balfouriana' (2)   CNic NHol
§ - 'Bewerley White' (2)   EBee EDAr ITim MBro MOne
                                                NDlv NHol WHoo WLin WWin
- 'Blue Wave' (2)   MFie
§ - 'Boothman's Variety' (2)   CLyd CStu EMNN ITim LRHS
                                                MBro MFie MSte NDlv NHar
                                                NHol NLAp SIng WCom WFar
                                                WWin
- 'Carmen'   see *P.* x *pubescens* 'Boothman's
                                                Variety'
- 'Chamois' (2)   MFie
- 'Christine' (2)   CLyd CMea EMNN MBro MFie
                                                NBir NDlv NHar NHol
- 'Cream Viscosa' (2)   EMNN ITim MFie NDlv NHol
                                                NMGW WCom
- 'Deep Mrs Wilson' (2)   SUsu
- 'Ellen Page'   see *Primula* 'Ellen Page'
- 'Faldonside' (2)   CLyd CNic EMNN MBro NDlv NHol
                                                NLAp NMGW WCom WHoo WWin
§ - 'Freedom' (2)   CLyd CStu EMNN GTou ITim LRHS
                                                MFie NBir NDlv NHar NHol NLAp
                                                SIng SRms WCom WEas WWin
- 'George Harrison' (2)   MFie
- 'Harlow Car' (2)   CLyd EMNN GMac ITim MFie
                                                NDlv NHar WFar
- 'Henry Hall' (2)   CLyd CStu EWes
- 'Herbert Beresford' (2)   EHyt GCrs
- 'Joan Danger' (2)   CLyd CStu ITim MFie NHol
- 'Joan Gibbs' (2)   CLyd ITim MFie MOne NHar NLAp
- 'Kath Dryden' (2)   MFie
- 'Lilac Fairy' (2)   ITim NDlv
- 'Mrs J.H.Wilson' (2)   CLyd EHyt ITim LRHS MFie NDlv
                                                NHol WLRN WPat
- 'Pat Barwick' (2)   CNic CStu EHyt EMNN GCrs ITim
                                                MFie NDlv NHol
- 'Peggy' (2) **new**   MFie
- 'Peggy Fell' (2)   GCrs MDHE
- 'Rufus' (2)   CLyd CNic GCrs ITim NHol NLAp
                                                WTin
- 'Sid Skelton' (2)   EMNN
- 'Snowcap'   GCrs
- 'Sonya' (2)   ITim
- 'The General' (2)   CLyd EHyt ITim MOne SPop WLin
                                                WWin
- 'Victoria' (2)   EMNN
§ - 'Wedgwood' (2)   EMNN GNor
- x 'White Linda Pope' (2)   ITim
- 'Winifred' (2)   NHol
pulchella (11)   WAbe
pulchra (21)   GCrs GEdr GKir
pulverulenta (4) ♀ H4   More than 30 suppliers
- 'Bartley'   SAWi
- Bartley hybrids (4) ♀ H4   CBot EBee GBuc GGar GMac
                                                NCat SMur
- 'Bartley Pink' (4)   CPla CPlt GBuc LSyl WEas
'Quaker's Bonnet'   see *P.vulgaris* 'Lilacina Plena'
'Rachel Kinnen' (2)   EHyt ITim MFie
'Ramona' (Poly)(30)   MFie
'Ravenglass Vermilion'   see *P.* 'Inverewe'
'Red Sunset' (4)   GDra
'Red Velvet' (dPrim)(30)   CMil ECGP MOne NPPs WHil
§ 'Redpoll' (21)   EHyt EPar GCrs NHar WAbe
reidii (28)   GFle MBri
- var. *williamsii* (28)   GDra GFle GGGa GNor GTou
                                                MBri NHar WLin
- - *alba* (28)   GDra GFle MBri
reptans (16)   GCrs
reticulata **new**   GFle
'Reverie' (Poly)(30)   CSWP MFie
'Rheniana' (2)   ITim NGar SIng

'Rose O'Day' (dPrim)(30)   MNrw MOne NBir NHol WHil
rosea (11) ♀ H4   CBot CPla CRow EBee EDAr EPar
                                                EPfP GEdr GFle GGGa GGar GKir
                                                GTou MFie MWgw NBid NBir
                                                NHar NLAp NSti NVic SIng SSpi
                                                SWal WFar
- 'Delight'   see *P. rosea* 'Micia Visser-de Geer'
- 'Gigas' (11)   EBre GAbr IBal MSta NHol WHil
- 'Grandiflora' (11)   EHon ELan EMNN EPar EWTr
                                                GBar GCrs GFle GKev LPBA LSyl
                                                MBri MRav NDlv NMen NWCA
                                                SRms WFar WPer WWpP
§ - 'Micia Visser-de Geer' (11)   LRHS
'Rowallane Rose' (4)   CBro GBuc MTed
'Roy Cope' (dPrim)(30)   MFie MWrn NBid NBir SIng WBor
                                                WFar
'Roydon Ruby'   WCot WViv
rubra   see *P.erythra*
rusbyi (20)   GFle GIBF
Rustic Reds Group   CSWP MFie
  (Poly)(30)
'Sapphire'   EHyt
saxatilis (7)   GCrs MFie
scandinavica (11)   GIBF MFie
x *scapeosa* (21)   GFle GGGa NHar
scapigera (21)   GGGa
§ - 'Schneekissen' (Prim)(30)   CBre CHid CMea GAbr ITim MBri
                                                MCLN MHer NBir NBro NChi
                                                NPro SBla WRus WViv
'Schneekissen Improved'   EBre
  (Prim)(30)
scotica (11)   GCrs GDra GFle GIBF GTou MFie
                                                NLAp WAbe
secundiflora (26)   CPla EBee ELan GAbr GCrs GDra
                                                GEdr GFle GGGa GGar GKir
                                                GTou LRHS LSyl MBro MNrw
                                                MTis NChi NWoo SPer SPlb SRms
                                                WAbe WBrE WFar WHoo
- SDR 1575   GKev
- SDR 1896   GKev
§ x *sendtneri* (2)   MFie
septemloba (7)   GFle WAbe
x *serrata*   see *P.* x *vochinensis*
serratifolia (4)   GGGa GGar
'Shizuko Hara'   EHyt
sibthorpii   see *P.vulgaris* subsp. *sibthorpii*
sieboldii (7) ♀ H4   CRow EHyt EMNN EPar GFle
                                                MBri MNrw NHar NMen NRya
                                                NWCA SMac SRms SSpi SUsu
                                                WAbe WCra WFar WLin
- *alba* (7)   CLAP GMac NBro NDov NMen
                                                SRot WCru WFar
- blue-flowered (7)   NMen
- 'Carefree' (7)   LTwo NBro NMen WOBN
- 'Dancing Ladies' (7)   CMil CSWP MFie NBro
- 'Galaxy' (7)   NBro
- 'Geisha Girl' (7)   CFir CLAP MRav WAbe WFTG
                                                WFar
- 'Lilac Sunbonnet' (7)   ENot EPfP LRHS LTwo NHol
- 'Manakoora' (7)   CSWP MFie NBro
- 'Mikado' (7)   CFir MFie MRav
- 'Pago-Pago' (7)   CLAP MFie NBro NHol
- 'Seraphim' (7)   GMac
- 'Snowflake' (7)   NGar NSla SBla WAbe
- 'Tah-ni' (7)   GAbr NBro
- 'Winter Dreams' (7)   CLAP CSWP MFie NBid NBro
§ *sikkimensis* (26) ♀ H4   CBot CRow EBee EBre EMNN
                                                GCrs GEdr GFle GGGa GGar GKir
                                                ITim LPBA LSyl MBri MBro MNrw
                                                MSta NHar WAbe WHil WRos
                                                WViv
- ACE 1422   GBuc WCru
- ACE 2234   GKev

- CC 3409	WRos
- CC&McK 1022	GTou
- crimson and gold (26)	MBro
- var. *hopeana* (26)	GCrs GFle
- var. *pudibunda* (26)	GEdr WAbe
- 'Tilman Number 2' (26)	GAbr GDra SPer
aff. *sikkimensis* (26)	ITim
- - ACE 2176	GBuc
Silver-laced Group (Poly)(30)	EPar
- 'Silver Lining' (Poly)(30)	LRHS
'Silverwells' (4)	GEdr
§ *sinensis* (27)	MBri
* *sino-ornata* **new**	NCat
sinopurpurea	see *P. chionantha* subsp. *sinopurpurea*
'Sir Bedivere' (Prim)(30)	CVer GAbr GBuc NGar
smithiana	see *P. prolifera*
'Snow Carpet'	see *P.* 'Schneekissen'
'Snow Cushion'	see *P.* 'Schneekissen'
'Snow White' (Poly)(30)	MRav
Snowcushion	see *P.* 'Schneekissen'
'Snowruffles'	ITim
sonchifolia (21)	CFir GGGa ITim MDun
- from Tibet (21)	MDun
sorachiana	see *P. yuparensis*
spectabilis (2)	EHyt GFle NHar
specuicola (11)	GIBF
Spice Shades Group (Poly)(30)	CSWP GAbr MFie WCot
x *steinii*	see *P.* x *forsteri*
'Stradbrook Dainty' (2)	EHyt ITim MFie NHol
'Stradbrook Dream' (2)	CNic EHyt EPot ITim MFie NHol
'Stradbrook Gem' (2)	ITim WAbe WLin
'Stradbrook Lilac Lustre' (2)	CGra MFie
'Stradbrook Lucy' (2)	EHyt ITim NHol WAbe
'Stradbrook Mauve Magic' (2)	MFie
stricta (11)	GFle WAbe
Striped Victorians Group (Poly)(30)	CSWP MFie NCot NDov
'Sue Jervis' (dPrim)(30)	GAbr MCAu NBir NHar NLar NSti SBla WBar WGwG WHal WRha
suffrutescens (8)	NSla WAbe
'Sunrise' (2)	ITim
'Sunshine Susie' (dPrim)(30)	ENot EPfP EPri GAbr LRHS MBNS MBri MCAu MCLN MFic MOnc MRav MWrn NHol SIng SUsu WCot WHil WLRN WWol
takedana (24)	GCrs GFle GGGa
tanneri subsp. *tsariensis* var. *alba* (21)	GGGa
'Tantallon' (21)	EPot GCrs GGGa GGar ITim NHar
§ Tartan Reds Group (Prim)(30)	CSWP
'Tawny Port' (Poly)(30)	CMea GAbr NBro SRms
tibetica (11)	GFle GGGa
'Tie Dye' (Prim)(30)	WCot
'Tinney's Moonlight'	EHyt
'Tipperary Purple' (Prim)(30)	GAbr GEdr WGwG WPnP
'Tomato Red' (Prim)(30)	WCot
'Tony'	NHar WAbe WLin
tosaensis var. *brachycarpa* (24)	GFle
'Tournaig Pink' (4)	GGar
'Val Horncastle' (dPrim)(30)	LRHS MBNS MDKP MFie MNrw MOne MWgw MWrn NBid NHar NLar SIng SPer WHil
Valentine Victorians Group (Poly)(30)	MFie
veris (30) ♀ H4	More than 30 suppliers
- hybrids (30)	WLin WWal

- 'Katy McSparron' (30/d)	CBgR MTed NCot WCot
- red-flowered(30)	CM&M GFle NBid
- 'Sunset Shades' (30)	NLar WBea
vernalis	see *P. vulgaris*
verticillata (12)	MFie
§ *vialii* (17) ♀ H4	More than 30 suppliers
Victorian shades (Poly)(30)	NPPs
§ *villosa* (2)	GCrs GFle GTou
- var. *cottica*	see *P. villosa*
Violet Victorians Group (Poly)(30)	CSWP MFie
viscosa All.	see *P. latifolia*
§ x *vochinensis* (2)	CFee CLyd CStu ITim LBee NHar SUsu
§ *vulgaris* (Prim)(30) ♀ H4	More than 30 suppliers
- *alba* (30)	CRow NSla WAbe WLin
- 'Alba Plena' (Prim)(30)	CHad CRow CSWP CVer GAbr GBuc GGar IBlr IGor NChi WRus
- 'Alex Brenton' (d) **new**	LHop
- green-flowered	see *P. vulgaris* 'Viridis'
§ - 'Lilacina Plena' (dPrim)(30)	CBot ECGP ENot EPfP GAbr IBlr ITim MBNS MCAu MNrw MRav NChi NCot NHol SPer WCom WGwG WHil WLin WViv
- 'Lutea' (Prim)(30)	CHar
§ - subsp. *sibthorpii* (Prim)(30) ♀ H4	CMHG CSam ENot GAbr GTou ITim LLWP LRHS MBro MHer MRav MWgw NBro NChi NPPs NWCA SBla SRms WAbe WCom WEas WHil WOut
- - HH&K 337	GFle
§ - 'Viridis' (Prim)(30)	CRow CVer IBlr NPar
waltonii (26)	CPla EBcc GCrs GEdr GFle GMac MNrw NChi
- hybrids (26)	GGar
'Wanda' (Prim)(30) ♀ H4	CBcs CRow CTri ELan GAbr LLWP LRHS NBid NSti NVic SBla SIng SMer SPer SRms WCFE WCom WEas WFar
Wanda Group (Prim)(30)	CNic NGar
'Wanda Hose-in-hose' (Prim)(30)(d)	GAbr MMHG NBir NChi NGar WCot WHer WHil
'Wanda Jack in the Green' (Prim)(30)	CRow MLLN WFar
Wanda Group pale mauve (30)	WGwG
wardii	see *P. munroi*
warshenewskiana (11)	CNic EHyt GAbr GEdr MDKP NHol NLAp NRya SIng WPat
watsonii (17)	GGGa GTou NHar NLAp SWat WAbe
'Wedgwood'	see *P.* x *pubescens* 'Wedgwood'
'Wharfedale Bluebell' (2)	CLyd NABC NBir NHar WGwG
'Wharfedale Buttercup' (2)	NABC NHar
'Wharfedale Butterfly' (2)	EHyt ITim NABC NHar NHol
'Wharfedale Crusader' (2)	ITim NHol
'Wharfedale Gem' (*allionii* hybrid) (2)	GNor ITim MFie NABC NGar NHar NHol NLAp NRya WAbe
'Wharfedale Ling' (*allionii* hybrid) (2)	CGra CPBP CStu EHyt EPot MFie NHar NHol NLAp NRya WAbe
'Wharfedale Superb' (*allionii* hybrid) (2)	ITim MFie NHar NHol NLAp
'Wharfedale Village' (2)	CLyd ITim NABC NHar NHol WGwG
'White Linda Pope' (2)	CLyd NGar NHar
'White Linda Pope' seedlings (2)	SIng
'White Wanda' (Prim)(30)	CRow GAbr
'White Waves' (*allionii* hybrid) (2) **new**	ITim
whitei (21)	GCrs MDun

§ - 'Sherriff's Variety' (21) GCrs IBlr
'Whitewaves' ITim
wigramiana (28) WAbe
'William Genders' GAbr
(Poly)(30)
wilsonii (4) CHid CPla GBuc GFle GMac
MNes MNrw MOne NDlv SWat
WAbe WBVN WHer WHoo
§ - var. *anisodora* (4) CNic CPla EBee GCrs GFle MFie
- - × *prolifera* **new** GKev
'Windrush' see *P.* × *berniniae* 'Windrush'
'Windward Blue' SBla
'Winter White' see *P.* 'Gigha'
'Wisley Crimson' see *P.* 'Wisley Red'
§ 'Wisley Red' (Prim)(30) CElw CVer
'Woodland Blue' NWoo
wulfeniana (2) CGra GFle MFie WAbe
xanthobasis (18) GIBF
yargongensis see *P. munroi* subsp.
yargongensis
§ *yuparensis* (11) EBee GFle IDac NMen WAbe

Prinsepia (Rosaceae)

sinensis CBcs CFee CMCN CPLG CPle
ESim GBin GEil MBlu WBVN
WBcn WPic WSHC
uniflora CBcs
utilis CTrG

Pritzelago (Brassicaceae)
alpina CNic NWCA

Proboscidea (Pedaliaceae)
louisianica EFEx
parviflora EFEx

Prostanthera (Lamiaceae)
aspalathoides EBee ECou EWes LPhx SOWG WCot
'Badja Peak' WAbe
baxteri ECou
chlorantha SOWG
cuneata ♀ H4 More than 30 suppliers
- 'Alpine Gold' CMHG CWSG EBee WFar
§ *incisa* CPLG CTbh CTrC CTrw SHDw
WLeb
- 'Rosea' WSHC
lasianthos CBcs CDoC CHll CSev ECou EWes
LPhx LRHS SAga SBrw SHDw
SOWG
- var. *subcoriacea* CPLG CRHN
'Mauve Mantle' **new** SOWG
melissifolia ESlt LRHS SBrw SPar WSel
- var. *parvifolia* CTrw EBee GGar WAbe WSHC
nivea ECou LPhx
ovalifolia ♀ H2 ECou NPPs SPar
'Poorinda Ballerina' CDoC CFwr CPLG CSev CWSG
EBee ECou EMan EOrc ESlt GKir
LHop LRHS MDun MGos SMur
SOWG SPer WFar WGwG WLeb
rotundifolia ♀ H2 CAbb CBcs CBrm CFwr CHEx
CPle CSBt CSev CTrG CTri CWSG
EBee EOHP EREa MWgw NGHP
SBrw SEND SOWG SPar SPer WLeb
- 'Chelsea Girl' see *P. rotundifolia* 'Rosea'
§ - 'Rosea' ♀ H2 CSBt CTrC CTrG EBee ECou
EOHP EREa GGar LHop MLan
SLon
* *scheelii* **new** SOWG
scutellarioides ECou
'Lavender Lady' **new**
sieberi see *P. incisa*
walteri CDoC ECou

Protea ✿ (Proteaceae)
aurea CHEx
compacta CHEx CTrF
coronata SPlb
cynaroides CBcs CCtw CHEx CTrC CTrF
SOWG SPlb
dracomontana **new** SPlb
eximia CTrC
grandiceps CTrC SPlb
lacticolor SPlb
laurifolia CTrC
obtusifolia **new** SPlb
'Pink Ice' **new** CTrC
repens CTrC
simplex CFil
speciosa CTrF
subvestita CTrC SIgm
susannae SPlb

Prumnopitys (Podocarpaceae)
§ *andina* WFar
elegans see *P. andina*
§ *taxifolia* ECou

Prunella (Lamiaceae)
§ *grandiflora* CArn EBee ECha EFer GBar GKir
MWat NLon SMac SPet SWat
WBrE WCHb WFar WMoo WPGP
WWye
- 'Alba' CElw CSBt EBee ECha EPfP EPyc
GKir GMaP LPio MRav MWgw
NBid NGdn NLar NOrc SPer
WCHb WMnd WWpP
- 'Blue Loveliness' EMan GAbr GTou SPla WCHb
WCom
- 'Carminea' EBee MNrw SPer
- light blue-flowered**new** NLar
- 'Little Red Riding Hood' see *P. grandiflora* 'Rotkäppchen'
- 'Loveliness' ♀ H4 CDoC EBee EBre ECha ECtt EPar
EWTr GKir MRav MWgw NBro
NGdn NSti NVic SApp SCro SPer
SPla SPlb WFar WMnd WWin
- 'Pagoda' LAst LIck NBlu NLar NOak SDes
SMac SWal WCHb WElm WMoo
- 'Pink Loveliness' CMCo CSBt EBre ENot EPar GTou
LRHS MWgw NArg SRms WCHb
WCom WFar WWin
- *rosea* CSBt EBee EPfP MWat WOut
§ - 'Rotkäppchen' ECtt MNrw WMoo
- 'Rubra' NLar WPer
- 'White Loveliness' EBee EBre EPar LRHS WCom WFar
WPer WRHF WRus WWin WWye
hyssopifolia EBee
incisa see *P. vulgaris*
* 'Inshriach Ruby' NBir WCHb
laciniata CMCo WCHb
§ *vulgaris* CAgr CArn CKin GAbr GBar GPoy
MBow MChe MGol MHer MSal
NLan NMir NSco NSti WCHb
WHbs WHer WWye
- 'Gleam' (v) EVFa WAlt WHrl
- 'Inner Glow' (v) WAlt
- var. *leucantha* GBar WAlt WHer
- 'Marbled White' (v) WAlt
- var. *rubrifolia* WRha
- 'Ruth Wainwright' (v) WCHb
- 'Voile' WAlt
× *webbiana* see *P. grandiflora*

Prunus ✿ (Rosaceae)
'Accolade' ♀ H4 More than 30 suppliers
§ 'Amanogawa' ♀ H4 More than 30 suppliers

	x *amygdalopersica*	ESim
	'Ingrid' (F)	
	- 'Pollardii'	CLnd EBee ENot MAsh WJas
	- 'Spring Glow'	CDoC CDul LRHS MBri WJas
	amygdalus	see *P. dulcis*
	'Aratama'	MBri
	armeniaca 'Alfred' (F)	CTho EMui ERea GTwe MBri SDea SKee SPer
	- 'Blenheim' (F)	ERea
	- 'Bredase' (F)	SDea
	- 'Early Moorpark' (F)	EPfP ERea GBon GTwe LRHS SDea SFam WWeb
	- 'Farmingdale' (F)	ERea SDea
	- 'Garden Aprigold' **new**	EMui ENot
	- 'Goldcot' (F)	ERea SDea
	- 'Golden Glow' (F)	GTwe LRHS MCoo
	- 'Hemskirke' (F)	ERea SKee
	- 'Hongaarse' (F)	SDea
	- 'Moniqui' (F)	CGOG
	- 'Moorpark' (F) ♀H3	CEnd CSBt CTri CWib EMui ENot ERea GKir GTwe LBuc MGos NRog SDea SKee SPer WStI
	- 'New Large Early' (F)	ERea GTwe SDea SEND SKee SPoG WBVN
	- 'Tross Orange' (F)	SDea
	'Asano'	see *P.* 'Geraldinae'
	avium ♀H4	More than 30 suppliers
	- 'Amber Heart' (F)	SKee
	- 'Bigarreau Gaucher' (F)	SKee
§	- 'Bigarreau Napoléon' (F)	GTwe MGos SFam SKee
	- 'Birchenhayes'	see *P. avium* 'Early Birchenhayes'
	- 'Black Eagle' (F)	CTho
	- 'Black Tartarian' (F)	SKee
	- 'Bottlers'	see *P. avium* 'Preserving'
	- 'Bradbourne Black' (F)	SKee
	- 'Bullion' (F)	CEnd CTho
	- 'Burcombe' (F)	CEnd CTho
	- Celeste =	COtt EMui GTwe LRHS SDea
	'Sumpaca'PBR (D)	SKee
	- 'Cherokee'	see *P. avium* 'Lapins'
	- 'Circassian' (F)	SKee
	- 'Colney' (F)	GTwe SFam SKee WJas
	- 'Dun' (F)	CTho
§	- 'Early Birchenhayes' (F)	CEnd CTho
	- 'Early Rivers' (F)	CSBt CWib ENot GTwe LRHS SDea SKee
	- 'Elton Heart' (F)	CTho
	- 'Fice' (F)	CEnd CTho
	- 'Florence' (F)	SKee
	- 'Governor Wood' (F)	CWib GTwe SKee
	- 'Grandiflora'	see *P. avium* 'Plena'
	- 'Greenstem Black' (F)	CTho
	- 'Hannaford' (D/C) **new**	CTho
	- 'Hertford' (F)	SFam
	- 'Inga' (F)	SFam SKee
	- 'Kentish Red' (F)	CTho
§	- 'Lapins' (F)	EMui GTwe LRHS SDea SFam SKee WHar WJas
	- 'May Duke'	see *P. x gondouinii* 'May Duke'
	- 'Merchant' (F) ♀H4	GTwe SKee
	- 'Merpet' (F)	GTwe
	- 'Merton Crane' (F)	SKee
	- 'Merton Favourite' (F)	SKee
	- 'Merton Glory' (F)	CSBt EMui ENot GTwe MGos SFam SKee
	- 'Merton Late' (F)	SKee
	- 'Merton Reward'	see *P. x gondouinii* 'Merton Reward'
	- 'Nabella' (F)	WJas
	- 'Napoléon'	see *P. avium* 'Bigarreau Napoléon'
	- 'Newstar' (F)	EMui
	- 'Noir de Guben' (F)	GTwe SKee
	- 'Noir de Meched' (D)	SKee
	- 'Nutberry Black' (F)	SKee
	- 'Old Black Heart' (F)	SKee
§	- 'Plena' (d) ♀H4	CBcs CCVT CDul CLnd CSBt CSam CTho CWSG EBee ECrN ELan ENot EPfP GKir LBuc LHyr LPan LRHS MGos MRav NWea SFam SKee SPer WDin WFar WHar WJas WOrn
§	- 'Preserving' (F)	CTho
	- 'Ronald's Heart' (F)	SKee
	- 'Roundel Heart' (F)	SKee
	- 'Sasha' (F)	GTwe
	- 'Small Black' (F)	CTho
	- 'Starkrimson' (F)	GTwe
	- 'Stella' (F) ♀H4	CEnd CMac CSam CWSG CWib EMui EPfP ERea EWTr GBon GKir GTwe LBuc LRHS MBri MGos MRav NBee NRog SDea SFam SKee SPer WHar WJas WOrn WStI WWeb
	- 'Stella Compact' (F)	COtt CWib ENot MBri SDea SKee WHar
	- 'Summer Sun' (D)	EMui GTwe MCoo SCoo SDea SKee
	- 'Summit' (F)	SKee
	- 'Sunburst' (F)	CCVT CEnd CTri EMui GTwe LBuc LRHS MBri SCoo SCrf SDea SFam SKee WBVN WJas WOrn WWeb
	- 'Sylvia' (F) **new**	SKee
	- 'Turkish Black' (F)	SKee
	- 'Upright' (F)	CTho
	- 'Van' (F)	ENot GTwe SKee
	- 'Vega' (F)	EMui GTwe SFam WJas
	- 'Waterloo' (F)	CTho SKee
	- 'White Heart' (F)	CTho CWib SKee
*	'Beni-no-dora'	SMur
*	'Beni-yutaka'	CEnd LBuc LRHS MBri SKee SLim
	'Blaze'	see *P. cerasifera* 'Nigra'
	x *blireana* ♀H4	CDoC CDul CEnd CSBt CTri EBec ENot EPfP LPan LRHS MAsh MBar MBri MRav MWat SCoo SKee SPer WHar
	'Blushing Bride'	see *P.* 'Shôgetsu'
	cerasifera	CAgr CTri ECrN GKir GTre LBuc NWea SKee WDin WMou
	- 'Cherry Plum' (F)	EMui SKee
	- 'Crimson Dwarf'	LPan
	- 'Hessei' (v)	CEnd EBee LRHS MAsh MBri MDun MGos MRav SLim
§	- Myrobalan Group (F)	CKin MRav SDea SKee
§	- 'Nigra' ♀H4	More than 30 suppliers
§	- 'Pendula'	CTho ECrN
§	- 'Pissardii'	CWib EBre ECrN GKir LPan MAsh MBar MRav NBea NFor NWea SFam SLim WFar WJas
*	- 'Princess'	CEnd CWSG EBee EMui SKee SLim
	- 'Rosea'	LRHS MBri
	- 'Spring Glow'	CEnd EBee EPfP LRHS SKee WOrn WWeb
	cerasus 'Montmorency' (F)	SKee
	- 'Morello' (C) ♀H4	CCVT CMac CSBt CTho CWSG CWib EBee EBre EMui ENot EPfP GBon GKir GTwe LBuc LRHS MBri MGos NBee NRog SDea SFam SKee SPer WJas WOrn WWeb
	- 'Nabella' (F)	SKee
	- 'Rhexii' (d)	CDul MAsh MGos SPer
	- 'Wye Morello' (F)	SKee
	'Cheal's Weeping'	see *P.* 'Kiku-shidare-zakura'
§	'Chôshû-hizakura'	GKir LNet MBri SPer
§	x *cistena* ♀H4	CBcs CSBt CWSG EBee EBre ELan ENot EPfP IKee LRHS MBri MDun MGos NBee NBlu SHBN SLim SPer SPla WDin WWeb

- 'Crimson Dwarf' see *P.* x *cistena*
'Collingwood Ingram' GKir LRHS MBri SKee
conradinae see *P. hirtipes*
davidiana CTho SPlb
domestica 'Allgroves ERea
Superb' (D)
- 'Angelina Burdett' (D) ERea GTwe NRog SDea SKee
- 'Anna Späth' (C/D) SKee
- 'Ariel' (C/D) SDea SKee
- 'Autumn Compote' (C) SKee
- 'Avalon'PBR (D) CCVT ECrN EMui GTwe SDea
SKee
- 'Belgian Purple' (C) SKee
- 'Belle de Louvain' (C) CTho ERea GTwe NRog SDea SKee
- 'Birchenhayes' (F) CEnd
- 'Black Diamond' see *P. salicina* 'Black Diamond'
- 'Blue Tit' (C/D) ♀ H4 CTho EMui ERea GTwe SDea SKee
- 'Bonne de Bry' (D) SKee
§ - 'Bountiful' (C) ERea
- 'Brandy Gage' (C/D) SKee
- 'Bryanston Gage' (D) CTho SKee
- 'Burbank's Giant' see *P. domestica* 'Giant Prune'
- 'Burcombe' CEnd
- 'Bush' (C) SKee
- 'Cambridge Gage' CDoC CTho CTri CWib EBre
(D) ♀ H4 EMui ERea GBon GKir GTwe
LRHS MBri MGos MWat NRog
SCrf SDea SFam SKee SPer WJas
WOrn WStl WWeb
- 'Chrislin' (F) CTho
- 'Coe's Golden Drop' (D) CTho EMui ERea GKir GTwe LRHS
MGos MRav SCoo SDea SFam SKee
- 'Count Althann's Gage' (D) ERea GTwe NRog SDea SFam SKee
- 'Cox's Emperor' (C) SKee
- 'Crimson Drop' (D) ERea SKee
- 'Cropper' see *P. domestica* 'Laxton's Cropper'
- 'Curlew' (C) SDea
- 'Czar' (C) ♀ H4 CDoC CSBt CTri EBre ECrN EMui
EPfP GKir GTwe LBuc LRHS
MGos NPri NRog NWea SDea
SFam SKee WOrn
- 'Delicious' see *P. domestica* 'Laxton's Delicious'
- 'Denniston's Superb' see *P. domestica* 'Imperial Gage'
- 'Diamond' (C) SKee
- 'Dittisham Black' (C) CTho
- 'Dittisham Ploughman' (C) CTho SKee
- 'Dunster Plum' (C) CTho CTri CWSG CWib
- 'Early Laxton' (C/D) ♀ H4 ERea GTwe SDea SFam SKee
- 'Early Prolific' see *P. domestica* 'Rivers's Early
Prolific'
- 'Early Rivers' see *P. domestica* 'Rivers's Early
Prolific'
- 'Early Transparent Gage' CSBt CTho CTri EMui ERea GTwe
(C/D) LBuc MCoo SDea SFam SKee
- 'Early Victoria' (C/D) SDea
- 'Edwards' (C/D) ♀ H4 CWib GTwe NRog SDea SFam
SKee
- 'Excalibur'PBR (D) GTwe SDea
§ - German Prune Group (C) SKee
§ - 'Giant Prune' (C) CWib ECrN GTwe NRog SDea SKee
I - 'Godshill Big Sloe' (F) SDea
- 'Godshill Blue' (C) SDea
- 'Godshill Minigage' (F) SDea
- 'Golden Transparent' (D) CTho ERea GTwe NRog SFam SKee
- 'Goldfinch' (D) GTwe NRog SKee
- 'Green Gage Group' see *P. domestica* Reine-Claude
Group
- - 'Old Green Gage' see *P. domestica* (Reine-Claude
Group) 'Reine-Claude Vraie'
- 'Grey Plum' (F) CTho
- 'Grove's Late Victoria' SKee
(C/D)
- 'Guthrie's Late Green' (D) SKee

- 'Herman' (C/D) GTwe LRHS MBri SDea SKee
- 'Heron' (F) GTwe SKee
- 'Impérial Epineuse' (D) SKee
§ - 'Imperial Gage' CSBt CTho CWib EMui ERea
(C/D) ♀ H4 GTwe SDea SFam SKee WBVN
WOrn
- 'Jan James' (F) CEnd
- 'Jefferson' (D) ♀ H4 EMui ERea GTwe NRog SDea
SFam SKee
* - 'Jubilaeum' (D) EMui GTwe SKee
- 'Kea' (C) CTho SKee
- 'Kirke's' (D) CTho ERea GTwe SDea SFam
SKee
- 'Landkey Yellow' (F) CTho
- 'Late Muscatelle' (D) ERea SKee
- 'Laxton's Bountiful' see *P. domestica* 'Bountiful'
§ - 'Laxton's Cropper' (C) CTri GTwe NRog SKee
§ - 'Laxton's Delicious' (D) GTwe SKee
- 'Laxton's Delight' GTwe
(D) ♀ H4
- 'Laxton's Gage' (D) SDea SKee
- 'Manaccan' (C) CTho
- 'Marjorie's Seedling' CDoC CSBt CTho CWib EBre
(C) ♀ H4 ECrN EMui ERea EWTr GBon
GTwe LBuc LRHS MGos MWat
NPri SCrf SDea SEND SFam SKee
WJas WOrn WWeb
- 'McLaughlin' (D) SKee
- 'Merton Gem' (C/D) GTwe SFam SKee
- 'Monarch' (C) GTwe SKee
- 'Ontario' (C/D) GTwe SKee
- 'Opal' (D) ♀ H4 CDoC CWSG ECrN EMui EPfP
ERea GTwe LBuc MBri MGos
MLan MWat NWea SDea SEND
SFam SKee WOrn WWeb
- 'Orleans' (C) SKee
- 'Oullins Gage' (C/D) ♀ H4 CDoC CSBt CWib ECrN EMui
ENot EPfP ERea GBon GKir GTwe
LBuc MBri MRav NRog SDea SFam
SKee SPer WJas WOrn WWeb
- 'Pershore' (C) ♀ H4 CTho CWib ERea GTwe NRog
SDea SFam SKee WOrn WStl
- 'Pond's Seedling' (C) CSBt SDea SKee
- 'President' (C/D) GTwe LPan SDea SKee
- 'Prince Englebert' (C) SKee
- 'Priory Plum' (D) SDea
- 'Purple Pershore' (C) CTri CWib ECrN ERea GTwe
NRog SDea SFam SKee
- 'Quetsche d'Alsace' see *P. domestica* German Prune
Group
- 'Reeves' (C) ♀ H4 GTwe SFam SKee
- 'Reine-Claude Dorée' see *P. domestica* Reine-Claude
Group
§ - Reine-Claude EMui GTwe NRog SDea SFam
Group (C/D) SKee SPer
- - 'Reine-Claude de CTho CTri ERea GTwe NRog
Bavais' (D) SDea SFam SKee
§ - - 'Reine-Claude Vraie' CSBt CWib EPfP ERea LBuc SKee
(C/D) WJas WOrn
§ - - 'Willingham Gage' (C/D) ERea GTwe LRHS MLan
- 'Reine-Claude Violette' (D) CTho ERea SKee
§ - 'Rivers's Early Prolific' (C) CSBt CTho ECrN ENot EPfP ERea
GTwe MCoo NRog NWea SCoo
SDea SKee
- 'Royale de Vilvoorde' (D) ERea SKee
- 'Sanctus Hubertus' CTri GTwe LCaP SDea SKee
(D) ♀ H4
- 'Severn Cross' (D) GTwe SKee
- 'Stanley' (C/D) LPan
- 'Stella' CCVT LPan
- 'Stint' (C/D) SKee
- 'Swan' (C) ECrN GTwe
- 'Transparent Gage' (D) ERea

	- 'Upright' (F)	CEnd
	- 'Utility' (D)	SKee
	- 'Valor' (C/D) ♀ H4	MCoo SKee
	- 'Victoria' (C/D) ♀ H4	More than 30 suppliers
*	- 'Violetta' (C/D)	EMui ERea GTwe SKee
	- 'Warwickshire Drooper' (C)	CTho CWib ERea GBon GTwe SDea SFam SKee
	- 'Washington' (D)	CTho ERea SDea SKee
	- 'White Magnum Bonum' (C)	CTho SDea
	- 'Willingham'	see *P. domestica* (Reine-Claude Group) 'Willingham Gage'
	- 'Wyedale' (C)	GTwe
§	*dulcis*	CDul CLnd CTri CWib ECrN EMui EWTr LPan MAsh MWat NBea NWea SCrf SDea SFam SKee SRPl WDin WOrn
	- 'Balatoni' (F)	LRHS MBri
*	- 'Macrocarpa' (F)	ESim
*	- 'Phoebe' (F)	ESim
	- 'Roseoplena'	CTri MBri
	- 'Titan' (F)	ESim
	Easter Bonnet = 'Comet'PBR	LRHS
	Fragrant Cloud = 'Shizuka'	CEnd CWSG EPfP GKir LRHS MAsh MBri SCoo SKee SLim SPer WBVN
§	x *fruticans* **new**	GIBF
	fruticosa 'Globosa'	CWSG LPan LRHS WGer
	'Fugenzô'	CSBt
	'Fuki'	MBri
§	'Geraldinae'	GKir LRHS MBri
	glandulosa 'Alba Plena' (d)	CEnd CPle CSBt CSam ECrN GEil LRHS MDun MGos MWat NBea SHBN SPer SPla SPlb SRms WAul WCFE WDin WMoo WSHC
	- 'Rosea Plena'	see *P. glandulosa* 'Sinensis'
§	- 'Sinensis' (d)	CEnd CPLG CPle CSBt ESis LRHS MGos MRav SHBN SPer SPla SRPl SRms WDin WSHC
§	x *gondouinii* 'May Duke' (F)	CTho SKee
§	- 'Merton Reward' (F)	SKee
	'Gyoikô'	CEnd CTho
	'Hally Jolivette'	CEnd COtt CPle ELan GKir LRHS MAsh MBri SKee WBcn WDin
	'Hanagasa'	MBri
	'Hana-kagoto'	MBri
	'Hillieri'	ECrN MBar MGos
	'Hillieri Spire'	see *P.* 'Spire'
	'Hilling's Weeping'	EBee GKir LRHS MBri
§	*hirtipes*	CTho SFam
	'Hisakura'	see *P.* 'Chôshû hizakura'
	Hollywood	see *P.* 'Trailblazer'
	'Ichiyo' (d) ♀ H4	MBri SCoo SKee
	incisa	CTri NBea SPer SSpi
	- 'Beniomi'	MRav
	- 'February Pink'	CAbP CPMA LRHS MBri MRav NPro WDin
	- 'Fujima'	EBee SMur
	- 'Kojo-nô-mai'	More than 30 suppliers
	- 'Mikinori'	CBcs MBri MGos
	- 'Oshidori'	LRHS MBri MGos MRav SCoo SKee SLim WFar
*	- 'Otome'	MBri WFar
	- 'Paean' **new**	NLar
	- 'Pendula'	GKir LRHS MBri SKee
	- 'Praecox' ♀ H4	CTho EPfP LRHS MBri SKee
	- 'The Bride'	CEnd GKir MAsh MBri SKee
§	- f. *yamadae*	CBcs CEnd EBee LBuc LRHS NLar SCoo SLim
§	*insititia* (F)	CAgr
	- 'Blue Violet Damson' (F)	SKee
§	- 'Bradley's King	CWib GTwe SKee

	Damson' (C)	
	- bullace (C)	SDea
	- 'Dittisham Damson' (C)	CTho
	- 'Farleigh Damson' (C) ♀ H4	CWib ERea GTwe LBuc SDea SFam SKee WJas
	- 'Godshill Damson' (C)	SDea
	- 'Golden Bullace'	see *P. insititia* 'White Bullace'
	- 'King of Damsons'	see *P. insititia* 'Bradley's King Damson'
	- 'Langley Bullace' (C)	CTho EMui ERea GTwe SKee
	- 'Merryweather Damson' (C)	CCAT CCVT CDoC CMac CSBt CTho CWib EBre EMui ENot ERea GBon GKir GTwe LBuc MBri NBee NBlu NRog SDea SFam SKee SPer WHar WJas WOrn WStI WWeb
	- 'Mirabelle de Nancy' (C)	CTho GTwe SDea SFam SKee
	- 'Mirabelle de Nancy (Red)' (C)	SDea
§	- 'Prune Damson' (C) ♀ H4	CDoC CTho CTri CWSG EMui ENot EPfP ERea GBon GTwe LBuc MBri MGos NRog SDea SFam SKee WHar WJas WOrn
	- 'Shepherd's Bullace' (C)	CTho ERea SKee
	- 'Shropshire Damson'	see *P. insititia* 'Prune Damson'
	- 'Small Bullace' (C)	SKee
§	- 'White Bullace' (C)	ERea SKee
§	- 'Yellow Apricot' (C)	ERea SKee
§	*jamasakura*	CTho
	japonica **new**	GIBF
	'Jô-nioi'	CEnd CLnd CTho
§	'Kanzan' ♀ H4	More than 30 suppliers
§	'Kiku-shidare-zakura' ♀ H4	More than 30 suppliers
	Korean hill cherry	see *P. verecunda*
	kurilensis	see *P. nipponica* var. *kurilensis*
	'Kursar' ♀ H4	CDul CLnd CTho CTri EBee EMui EPfP GKir LNet LRHS MBri NRog NWea SCoo SFam SKee SLim WOrn
	laurocerasus ♀ H4	CBcs CCVT CChc CDul CKin CWSG EBee ELan EPfP GKir GTre LHyr LNet LPan MRav MWat NBea NFor NWea SEND SPar SPer SRPl SReu WFar WMou WStI WWeb
I	- 'Albomaculata'	WBcn
	- 'Angustifolia' **new**	WDin
	- 'Aureovariegata'	see *P. laurocerasus* 'Taff's Golden Gleam'
	- 'Camelliifolia'	CTri EPla MBlu WBcn WCFE WDin WHCG WPGP
N	- 'Castlewellan' (v)	CBot CDoC CDul CPLG CTrw CWib EBee EPfP EPla ISea LAst MBar MGos NBea SDix SEND SPer SSta WDin WFar WGwG WHar WLeb WMoo
	- 'Caucasica'	MGos
	- 'Cherry Brandy'	EBee EGra ENot MRav SPer WBcn WCot WDin WLRN WStI
	- Etna = 'Anbri'PBR	EBee ENot EPfP LRHS MGos MRav NPri
	- 'Golden Splash'	WBcn
	- 'Green Marble' (v)	CTri EBee SPar WSHC
	- 'Herbergii'	WWeb
§	- 'Latifolia'	CHEx EPla GKir SAPC SArc SLPl SMad
§	- Low 'n' Green = 'Interlo'	EBee ENot MRav
	- 'Magnoliifolia'	see *P. laurocerasus* 'Latifolia'
	- 'Mano'	EMil MGos NBlu
	- 'Marbled White'	see *P. laurocerasus* 'Castlewellan'
	- 'Miky'	IArd
	- 'Milky'	WBcn
	- 'Mischeana'	MBri SLPl

– 'Mount Vernon'	EBee MBar MBri MGos MHFa WBcn WDin	
– 'Otinii'	CHEx	
– 'Otto Luyken' ♀ H4	More than 30 suppliers	
– Renault Ace = 'Renlau'PBR	EBee ENot MRav	
– 'Reynvaanii'	LRHS MBri WBcn	
– 'Rotundifolia'	CDoC CSBt CTri CWib EBee EMil ENot GKir LBuc LPan LRHS MBNS MBar MBri MGos NBea NBee NBlu NWea SLim SRms STop WDin WHar WTel	
– 'Schipkaensis'	NFor SPer	
§ – 'Taff's Golden Gleam' (v)	WBcn WCot	
– 'Van Nes'	EBee EMil WDin	
N – 'Variegata' (v)	CWib EPla MBNS MGos SRms	
– 'Zabeliana'	CDoC CDul CSBt EBee ENot EPfP GKir IBal MBar MGos NWea SHBN SPer SRms WDin WFar WTel WWin	
litigiosa	SKee	
* *longipedunculata*	LRHS MBri	
lusitanica ♀ H4	More than 30 suppliers	
– subsp. *azorica*	EPla MRav WFar WPGP	
– 'Myrtifolia'	EBee EPfP EPla GKir LAst LRHS MBri MLLN MRav WCFE WDin WGer	
– 'Variegata' (v)	More than 30 suppliers	
maackii	CTho EPfP GIBF MDun NBea SEND SSpi WDin	
– 'Amber Beauty'	CDoC CDul CEnd EPfP LRHS MRav NBee WDin	
mahaleb	CAgr CTho	
mandshurica	GIBF	
'Matsumae-beni-murasaki'	MBri	
'Matsumae-beni-tamanishiki'	MBri	
'Matsumae-hana-gasa'	MBri	
'Matsumae-hana-guruma'	MBri	
'Matsumae-usugasanesomei'	MBri	
'Matsumae-wakamushiyazakura'	MBri	
maximowiczii new	GIBF	
'Mount Fuji'	see *P.* 'Shirotae'	
mume	WDin WNor WOTO	
– 'Alboplena'	CChe	
§ – 'Beni-chidori'	CBcs CWib ECrN EPfP LBuc LRHS MBlu MBri MGos NBea SLim SPoG SSpi SSta WJas WPGP	
– 'Beni-shidori'	see *P. mume* 'Beni-chidori'	
* – 'Ken Kyo'	LRHS	
* – 'Kyo Koh'	LRHS	
§ – 'Omoi-no-mama' (d)	CEnd LRHS MBri MMHG	
– 'Omoi-no-wac'	see *P. mume* 'Omoi-no-mama'	
– 'Pendula'	LRHS	
– 'Yae-kankobane' (d)	LRHS	
myrobalana	see *P. cerasifera* Myrobalan Group	
§ *nipponica* var. *kurilensis*	CBcs MAsh	
– var. *kurilensis* 'Brilliant'	EBee GKir LPan MBri MGos WWeb	
– – 'Ruby'	CDul CEnd GKir LRHS MBri MGos NBee NBlu NEgg SMur	
– – 'Spring Joy'	LRHS MBri	
'Okame' ♀ H4	CLnd CSam CTho EBee EBre ENot EPfP GKir LRHS MAsh MBri MGos MRav NBlu NWea SCoo SKee SLim SPer SRPl WFar WOrn	
'Okumiyako' misapplied	see *Prunus* 'Shôgetsu' AGM	
padus	CCVT CDul CKin CLnd CSBt CTri ECrN GIBF GKir GTre LBuc LHyr LNet MDun MGos NBea NBee NWea SSpi WDin WMou WOrn	
– 'Albertii'	CTho LPan WJas	
– 'Colorata' ♀ H4	CDoC CDul CEnd CMHG CSam CTho ECrN ELan LBuc LNet LPan	
	MDun MGos NBee SHBN SPer SSpi WDin WJas	
– 'Dropmore'	EBee	
– 'Grandiflora'	see *P. padus* 'Watereri'	
– 'Plena' (d)	CTho	
– 'Purple Queen'	CEnd CTho EBee ECrN ENot WStI	
§ – 'Watereri' ♀ H4	CBcs CCVT CDoC CDul CLnd CTho CWib EBee ECrN ELan ENot EPfP LPan MGos NWea SCoo SHBN SKee SPer SRPl WDin WJas WOrn	
'Pandora' ♀ H4	CBcs CLnd EBee ECrN ENot EPfP GKir LHyr LPan LRHS MAsh MBri MDun MRav MWat NBea NBee NWea SCrf SEND SHBN SKee SPer SRPl WFar WOrn	
§ *pendula* 'Pendula Rosea' ♀ H4	CDoC CDul CEnd CSBt CWib ENot EPfP LPan LRHS MAsh MBri SPer WFar WJas WOrn	
§ – 'Pendula Rubra' ♀ H4	CDoC CEnd CLnd COtt CSBt CWib EBee ENot EPfP LNet LRHS MBri MGos SCoo SFam SHBN SLim SPer WWeb	
§ – 'Stellata'	LRHS MBri SPer	
* *persica* 'A. de Calande' new	CGOG	
– 'Amsden June' (F)	ERea GTwe SDea SFam SKee	
– 'Bellegarde' (F)	ERea GTwe SDea SFam SKee	
– 'Bonanza' (F)	EMil EMui ERea	
– 'Doctor Hogg' (F)	SDea	
– 'Duke of York' (F) ♀ H3	CTri ERea GTwe LRHS SDea SFam SKee WOrn WWeb	
– 'Dymond' (F)	ERea	
– 'Flat China' (F)	ERea	
– 'Foliis Rubris' (F)	CDul WPGP	
– 'Francis' (F)	SKee	
– 'Garden Anny' (F)	EMil ERea LRHS	
– 'Garden Lady' (F)	EMui ERea GTwe SKee	
– 'Hale's Early' (F)	ENot ERea GTwe SEND SFam SKee SPer	
– 'Hylands' (F)	SDea	
– 'Melred' (F)	MGos	
– 'Merrill O'Henry'	see *P. persica* 'O'Henry'	
– 'Natalia' (F)	SDea	
– var. *nectarina* 'Armking' new	CGOG	
– – 'Crimson Gold' (F)	SDea	
– – 'Early Gem' (F)	ERea SDea	
– – 'Early Rivers' (F) ♀ H3	CMac EMui ERea GTwe NRog SDea SFam	
– – 'Elruge' (F)	ERea GTwe SDea SEND SFam	
– – 'Fantasia' (F)	CGOG ERea SDea	
– – 'Fire Gold' (F)	SDea	
– – 'Garden Beauty' (F/d)	EMui ENot	
– – 'Humboldt' (F)	ERea GTwe SDea SKee	
– – 'John Rivers' (F)	ERea GTwe SDea SFam	
– – 'Lord Napier' (F) ♀ H3	CDoC CSBt CWSG CWib EMui ERea GKir LBuc LRHS MGos SDea SEND SFam SKee SPer SPoG WBVN WStI WWeb	
– – 'Nectared' (F)	CWib GTwe LCaP	
– – 'Nectarella' (F)	EMui ERea GTwe LRHS	
– – 'Pineapple' (F)	CTri ERea GTwe LRHS SDea SFam SKee	
– – 'Ruby Gold' (F)	SDea	
– – 'Terrace Ruby' (F)	ENot	
§ – 'O'Henry' (F)	CGOG	
– 'Peregrine' (F) ♀ H3	CMac CSBt CTri CWSG CWib EMui ENot EPfP ERea GBon GKir GTwe LBuc LRHS MBri MGos NRog SDea SFam SKee SPer WJas WOrn WStI	
– 'Purpurea'	EMui	
– 'Red Haven' (F)	GTwe SDea SKee	

- 'Reliance' (F)	SDea
- 'Robin Redbreast' (F)	SDea
- 'Rochester' (F) ♀ H3	CWSG EMui ENot ERea GBon GKir GTwe LRHS MBri SDea SFam SKee SPer WStI
- 'Royal George' (F)	GTwe NRog SFam
- 'Sagami-shidare'	LRHS MBri
- 'Saturne' (F)	EMui LRHS SKee
- 'Springtime' (F)	ERea SDea
- 'Terrace Amber'	EMui ENot
- 'Terrace Garnet'	ENot
- 'Weeping Flame' (F)	LRHS
- 'White Cascade'	LRHS MBri
'Pink Perfection' ♀ H4	CBcs CDoC CDul CLnd CSBt CWSG CWib EBee EBre ECrN ENot LHyr LPan LRHS MBri NBee SFam SHBN SKee SPer SRPl SSta WDin WFar WJas WOrn
'Pink Shell' ♀ H4	CLnd CTho EBee EPfP LRHS MBri NRog SFam SKee WOrn WStI
pissardii	see *P. cerasifera* 'Pissardii'
'Pissardii Nigra'	see *P. cerasifera* 'Nigra'
prostrata	WPat
* - 'Anita Kistler'	ECho
* - var. *discolor*	WNor
pumila var. *depressa*	MBar MBlu MRav NLar NPro
'Royal Burgundy'	CEnd CWSG EBee EMil GKir LRHS MAsh MBri MDun MGos MWat SCoo SKee SLim SPer WGer WOrn WWeb
rufa	CPMA CTho MDun SCoo SSpi
sachalinensis new	GIBF
salicina new	GIBF
§ - 'Black Diamond' (F)	SDea
- 'Methley' (D)	ESim
- 'Satsuma' (F)	ERea
- 'Shiro' (D)	ESim
sargentii ♀ H4	More than 30 suppliers
- 'Charles Sargent'	MBri
- 'Columnaris'	GKir LRHS MBri
- 'Rancho'	CLnd CMCN EBee ENot SLPl WOrn
x *schmittii*	CLnd EBee ECrN ENot MAsh SKee SPer WJas
'Sekiyama'	see *P.* 'Kanzan'
serotina	CDul
§ *serrula* ♀ H4	More than 30 suppliers
- Branklyn form	GKir MBri
- Dorothy Clive form	GKir MDun
- var. *tibetica*	see *P. serrula*
- x *serrulata*	CBcs CTho
serrulata	ENot
- 'Erecta'	see *P.* 'Amanogawa'
- 'Grandiflora'	see *P.* 'Ukon'
- 'Longipes'	see *Prunus* 'Shôgetsu' AGM
- 'Miyako' misapplied	see *Prunus* 'Shôgetsu' AGM
N - var. *pubescens*	see *P. verecunda*
- 'Rosea'	see *P.* 'Kiku-shidare-zakura'
- var. *spontanea*	see *P. jamasakura*
'Shidare-zakura'	see *P.* 'Kiku-shidare-zakura'
'Shimizu-zakura'	see *Prunus* 'Shôgetsu' AGM
'Shirofugen' ♀ H4	CBcs CDoC CDul CLnd CMCN CSBt CTho CWib EBee ECrN EMil ENot EPfP GKir LBuc LPan LRHS MAsh MBri MRav MWat NBee SCrf SFam SKee SPer WDin WJas WOrn
§ 'Shirotae' ♀ H4	More than 30 suppliers
§ 'Shôgetsu' ♀ H4	CBcs CDul CEnd CLnd CSBt CTho EBee ECrN ElaN EPfP GKir LPan LRHS MBri SFam SHBN SKee SLim SPer WDin WWeb
'Shosar'	CEnd CLnd CWib GKir LRHS MAsh MBri SKee SPer
'Snow Goose'	CDoC EBee GKir LRHS MBri
'Snow Showers'	CEnd CWSG EMui MAsh MDun NWea SKee WGer
spinosa	CCVT CDoC CDul CKin CTri ECrN ENot EPfP GTre LBuc LHyr LRHS MBar MBlu MBri NBee NWea SPer WDin WFar WHer WMou WNor
- 'Plena' (d)	CEnd CTho MBlu
- 'Purpurea'	MBlu WBcn WDin WHCG WMou WPat
§ 'Spire' ♀ H4	CDoC CDul CLnd CMCN CSBt CTho CWib EBee ECrN ENot EPfP GKir LBuc LHyr LPan LRHS MGos MRav NBlu NWea SKee SPer WDin WFar WJas WOrn WNor
x *subhirtella*	More than 30 suppliers
- 'Autumnalis' ♀ H4	More than 30 suppliers
- 'Autumnalis Rosea' ♀ H4	More than 30 suppliers
§ - 'Dahlem'	LRHS
- 'Fukubana'	CLnd CTho EBee GKir LPan LRHS MAsh MBri SCoo
- 'Pendula' hort.	see *P. pendula* 'Pendula Rosea'
- 'Pendula Rubra'	see *P. pendula* 'Pendula Rubra'
- 'Plena'	see *P.* x *subhirtella* 'Dahlem'
N - 'Rosea'	CLnd GKir MRav
- 'Stellata'	see *P. pendula* 'Stellata'
'Sunset Boulevard'	GKir LRHS MBri
'Taihaku' ♀ H4	More than 30 suppliers
'Taki-nioi'	ECrN NWea
'Taoyame'	CLnd LRHS MBri
tenella	CBcs CDul ElaN WCot WHCG
- 'Fire Hill'	CPMA CSBt ElaN EPfP GKir LNet LRHS MBar MGos SHBN SKee SPer SRPl SSpi WCot WDin WJas WOrn WPat
tibetica	see *P. serrula*
tomentosa	CRez ECrN
§ 'Trailblazer' (C/D)	CEnd CLnd CSBt CTho CWib LPan MGos NWea SKee WStI
triloba	CBcs CSBt CTri CWib ECrN EMil GIBF LBuc LPan LRHS NBee NWea SHBN SKee WDin
- 'Multiplex' (d)	EBre ENot LRHS MGos MRav NPri SPer SRms WJas
- Rosemund = 'Korros'	LRHS MBri MGos
§ 'Ukon' ♀ H4	CBcs CDoC CDul CLnd CMCN CTho CTri EBee ENot EPfP EWTr GKir LBuc LNet LRHS MBar MBri MGos MRav NBee NWea SFam SKee SPer SRPl WDin WFar WOrn WStI
'Umineko'	CDoC CLnd CWib EBee ECrN ENot GKir MGos SPer WDin WMoo
§ *verecunda*	CDoC CLnd NWea WJas
- 'Autumn Glory'	CTho NBea
virginiana 'Schubert'	CDoC CLnd CTho EBee ENot LPan WJas WOrn
yamadae	see *P. incisa* f. *yamadae*
§ x *yedoensis* ♀ H4	CLnd CMCN CSBt CSam CTho CTri EBee ECrN ENot EPfP NWea SFam SKee SLim SPer SRPl WDin WJas WOrn
- 'Ivensii'	CBcs CDoC CDul CSBt GKir LRHS MAsh MDun MGos NBee NRog SCoo SFam SHBN SKee SPer WDin WStI
- 'Pendula'	see *P.* x *yedoensis* 'Shidare-yoshino'
- 'Perpendens'	see *P.* x *yedoensis* 'Shidare-yoshino'
§ - 'Shidare-yoshino'	CEnd CLnd CTho EBee ECrN EPfP GKir LNet LRHS MBar MBri MGos MRav MWat NBee NWea SKee SLim SPer WOrn WWeb

- 'Tsubame' — LRHS
'Yoshino' — see *P.* x *yedoensis*
'Yoshino Pendula' — see *P.* x *yedoensis* 'Shidare-yoshino'

Pseuderanthemum (*Acanthaceae*)
seticalyx — ESlt

Pseudocydonia (*Rosaceae*)
§ sinensis — CAgr CBcs ECre LNet

Pseudofumaria see *Corydalis*

Pseudolarix (*Pinaceae*)
§ amabilis ♀ H4 — CDoC CEnd CFil CMCN CTho EHul EPfP GBin LCon LNet MBar MBlu MBri NBlu SCoo SLim SMad SPar SPoG STre WNor
kaempferi — see *P. amabilis*

Pseudomuscari see *Muscari*

Pseudopanax ✿ (*Araliaceae*)
(Adiantifolius Group) 'Adiantifolius' — CHEx CTrC GQui SMad
- 'Cyril Watson' ♀ H1 — CHEx
arboreus — CAbb CBcs CDoC CHEx CTrC LEdu
chathamicus — CDoC CHEx SAPC SArc
crassifolius — CAbb CBcs CBot CBrP EAmu SAPC SArc SMad SVen
- var. *trifoliolatus* new — CHEx
davidii — SLon
discolor — ECou
ferox — CAbb CBcs CBrP CHEx CTrC IDee ITer LEdu SAPC SArc SMad SSpi
laetus — CAbb CHEx CTrC ECou SAPC SArc
lessonii — CBcs CHEx ECou
- 'Gold Splash' (v) ♀ H1 — CBcs CHEx SEND
- hybrids — CHEx
'Linearifolius' — CHEx CTrC
'Purpureus' ♀ H1 — CHEx CTrC
'Sabre' — CHEx CTrC SMad
'Trident' — CDoC CHEx CTrC LEdu

Pseudophegopteris (*Thelypteridaceae*)
levingei — EFer EMon

Pseudophoenix (*Arecaceae*)
* nativo — MBri

Pseudosasa (*Poaceae*)
amabilis hort. — see *Arundinaria gigantea*
§ amabilis (McClure) Keng f. — LPal SDry WFar
§ japonica ♀ H4 — More than 30 suppliers
§ - 'Akebonosuji' (v) — CDDB EFul EPla LJus MHdf MMoz NMoo SDry WJun WNor
- 'Tsutsumiana' — CDoC CHEx EBee EPla ERod LJus MMoz MWht NBlu NMoo SDry WJun
- 'Variegata' — see *P. japonica* 'Akebonosuji'
owatarii — SDry
pleioblastoides — EPla SDry
usawai — EPla WJun
viridula — NMoo

Pseudotsuga (*Pinaceae*)
§ menziesii ♀ H4 — CBcs CDoC CDul CLnd ECrN EPfP GKir LBuc LCon LLin LRHS MBar MBlu NWea WDin WMou
- 'Bhiela Lhota' — CKen
- 'Blue Wonder' — CKen
- 'Densa' — CKen
- 'Fastigiata' — CKen LCon

- 'Fletcheri' — CKen LCon MBar SCoo SLim
- var. *glauca* — CTho LCon MBar
- 'Glauca Pendula' — LCon MBar MBlu MGos SMad
I - 'Gotelli's Pendula' — CKen
- 'Graceful Grace' — CKen
- 'Julie' — CKen
- 'Knaphill' new — NLar
- 'Little Jamie' — CKen MBar
- 'Little Jon' — SCoo SLim
- 'Lohbrunner' — CKen
- 'McKenzie' — CKen
- 'Nana' — CKen
- 'Stairii' — CKen
- 'Tempelhof Compact' — SLim
taxifolia — see *P. menziesii*

Pseudowintera (*Winteraceae*)
§ colorata — CBcs CDoC CPLG CPla CTrw CWib GCal GGar GKir IDee ISea MDun NRib SLon WBod WCru WFar WFoF WPat WPic
- 'Mount Congreve' — LRHS SSpi WGer

Psidium (*Myrtaceae*)
cattleyanum — see *P. littorale* var. *longipes*
friedrichsthalianum (F) — NBlo XBlo
guajava (F) — NBlo XBlo
littorale (F) — ERea
§ - var. *longipes* (F) — NBlo XBlo

Psilotum (*Psilotaceae*)
nudum — ECou

Psoralea (*Papilionaceae*)
bituminosa — WSHC
- HH&K 174 — CStr
glandulosa — CFil ECre WPGP WSHC
oligophylla new — SPlb
pinnata — CHEx CPLG CTrC CTrG IFro SSte

Psychotria (*Rubiaceae*)
capensis — EShb
carthagenensis new — MGol
viridis — MGol

Ptelea (*Rutaceae*)
trifoliata — CAgr CBcs CFil CLnd CMCN CTho CWib EBee EPfP EWTr GIBF MAsh MBlu SPer SRms SSpi WDin WFar WHCG WNor WOrn
- 'Aurea' ♀ H4 — CAbP CBcs CBot CDul CEnd CLnd CPMA CPle CTho EBee ELan ENot EPfP GBin GKir LRHS MBlu MBri MBro MGos SHBN SMur SPer SSpi SSta WDin WHCG WPGP WPat

Pteracanthus see *Strobilanthes*

Pteridophyllum (*Papaveraceae*)
racemosum — EFEx GCrs WCru

Pteris (*Pteridaceae*)
argyraea ♀ H1+3 — MBri NMar
cretica ♀ H1+3 — CHEx MBri SAPC SArc
- var. *albolineata* ♀ H1 — GQui MBri SRms
- 'Childsii' — NMar
- 'Cristata' — MBri
- 'Gautheri' — MBri
- 'Parkeri' — MBri NMar
- 'Rivertoniana' — MBri
- 'Rowei' — MBri
- 'Wimsettii' — MBri
ensiformis — MBri NMar

*	- 'Arguta'	MBri
	- 'Victoriae'	MBri
	gallinopes	WAbe
	longifolia	NMar
	tremula	GQui MBri NMar SRms
	umbrosa	MBri WRic
	vittata	SRms
	wallichiana	CHEx

Pterocarya (*Juglandaceae*)

	fraxinifolia ♀ H4	CAgr CBcs CDoC CDul CLnd CMCN CTrG EBee ECrN ENot EPfP EWTr MBlu NBee WDin WPGP
	x *rehderiana*	CTho MBlu WMou
	stenoptera	CBcs CFil CLnd CMCN CTho SLPl WPGP
	- 'Fern Leaf'	SMad WMou WPGP

Pteroceltis (*Ulmaceae*)

	tatarinowii	CMCN WHCr

Pterocephalus (*Dipsacaceae*)

	depressus	WPat
	parnassi	see *P. perennis*
§	*perennis*	EDAr ESis LBee LRHS MHer NBir NHar NMen NWCA SBla SMer SRms WAbe WEas WHoo WWin
	- subsp. *perennis*	WHrl
	pinardii	NWCA

Pterostylis (*Orchidaceae*)

	acuminata ingens	EPot
	coccinea	SSpi
	curta	CStu LEur SCnR WIvy
	truncata	SSpi

Pterostyrax (*Styracaceae*)

	corymbosa	CMCN CPMA MBlu SSpi WFar
	hispida ♀ H4	CBcs CFil CHEx CLnd CMCN CPMA CPne CSam CWib EPfP EPla GKir LAst MBlu MRav NLar SSpi WDVN WBod WDin WFar WOTO WPGP
	psilophylla	CMCN

Ptilostemon (*Asteraceae*)

	afer	EHrv EMan MAnH MLwd MWgw NChi WCot
§	*diacantha*	NLar WHil

Ptilotrichum see *Alyssum*

Ptilotus (*Amaranthaceae*)

	aervoides **new**	SPlb

Ptychosperma (*Arecaceae*)

	sanderianum **new**	CRoM

Pueraria (*Papilionaceae*)

	montana var. *lobata*	CAgr CArn CPlN MSal

Pulicaria (*Asteraceae*)

§	*dysenterica*	CArn CKin IHMH MChe MHer MSal NMir SIde WBri WCHb WJek WLHH WWye

Pulmonaria ❀ (*Boraginaceae*)

	WM 9206	SBla
	'Abbey Dore Pink'	EBee WAbb
	affinis	CElw CLAP EMon LRHS
	angustifolia ♀ H4	CSam EBee EPfP EWTr EWsh GDra GKev GKir LRHS MBro MSal NOrc SChu SMer SRms WEas WFar WWin

	- subsp. *azurea*	More than 30 suppliers
	- 'Blaues Meer'	CBct CFir CSam EBee EGle EPfP GBuc GKir LPio MBNS MNFA SBod WCru
	- 'Munstead Blue'	CElw CHea CLAP COlW EBee ECha EFou EGle EHrv ENot EPar IBlr LPio MRav MTho MWgw NHol NLon NRya NSti SRms WCru WRus
	- 'Rubra'	see *P. rubra*
	'Apple Frost'	EBee ECtt NBhm NSti WCra
	'Barfield Regalia'	CLAP CMHG EBee EMon IGor MAvo MBct MBro NCat NChi NSti SDys WCer
	'Benediction'	CBct CDes EBee LPhx NSti SAga
	'Berries and Cream'	NSti
§	'Beth's Blue'	ECha EMon LRHS MBri MGrG WCru
	'Beth's Pink'	CBct ECha GAbr WCru WFar WWpP
	'Blauer Hügel'	CElw EMon GKir NSti
§	'Blauhimmel'	CLAP EGle EMon LRHS MBro WCru
	'Blue Buttons'	CFir CHea EBee EPla GBin NSti SVil
	'Blue Crown'	CBct CDes CElw CLAP CSev EBee EHrv EMon EWes LRHS MAvo MBri NDov SAga SChu SSpe WEas WHal
	'Blue Ensign'	More than 30 suppliers
	'Blue Haze' **new**	EBee
	'Blue Moon'	see *P. officinalis* 'Blue Mist'
	'Blue Pearl'	EMon NHaw NSti
	'Blueberry Muffin'	CSpe
	'British Sterling'	CLAP EBee
	Cally hybrid	CBct CLAP EBee EMon GCal NSti
	'Cedric Morris'	CElw NSti
	'Chintz'	CLAP CSam EBee GBuc MAvo MMil NSti SVil WCru WHal
	'Clacton Red'	EMon NCat NSti WCru
	'Coral Springs'	EBee EBre GKir MAvo MBri NSti
	'Corsage'	EBee ECtt
	'Cotton Cool'	CBel CDes CElw CFil CKno EBee ECtt EMan EMon MAvo MCAu NSti SSpi WCot WCru WMoo WPGP
	'Crawshay Chance'	CBct WCru
	'Dark Vader'	NSti
	'De Vroomen's Pride' (v)	CBct CHld CLAP CSam EBee EChP EGle EMan EMar ITer LAst MOne MSte NSti SApp WMnd WPnP
	'Diana Clare'	More than 30 suppliers
	'Duke's Silver'	CLAP
	'Elworthy Rubies'	CElw MAvo
	'Emerald Isles'	NSti
	'Esther'	NSti
	'Excalibur'	CElw CHid CLAP EBee EBre EMan ENot GBin GBuc GKir ITer LAst MBct MBri MMil NSti WCot
	'Fiona'	CBct MCAu NHaw
	'Glacier'	CDes CElw CStr ECGP EMon EOrc EWTr LPio LRHS MArl MMil MSte NCat NChi NCot NSti SAga SDes SVil WCer WCot WCru WHal WWhi
	'Golden Haze' (v)	NSti
	'Hazel Kaye's Red'	CBel CElw LPio NSti
	'High Contrast' **new**	NSti
	'Highdown'	see *P.* 'Lewis Palmer'
	'Joan's Red'	CElw WBro WCot WTin
§	'Lewis Palmer' ♀ H4	More than 30 suppliers
	'Lime Close'	LPhx SAga
	'Little Blue' **new**	NSti
	'Little Star'	CBct CDes EBee EGoo EMon GBuc MTcd NDov NSti SChu SUsu WCru
	longifolia	CArn CBot CBro CFee CHar ECGN ECha ECoo ELan EPfP EPla EWTr GAbr GCal LLWP LRHS MSal

	NBir NOrc NSti SChu SDes SPar
	SPer SPet WCru WFar WRus WSel
§ – 'Ankum'	More than 30 suppliers
– 'Ballyrogan Blue'	IBlr
– 'Bertram Anderson'	CDes CLAP COlW EBre EChP
	ECtt EGle GGar GKir GMaP LAst
	LRHS MBri MCAu MLLN NBir
	NOrc NVic SBla SIng WCot WCra
	WCru WMnd WPnP
– subsp. *cevennensis*	CDes EBee EBre EChP EMan ENot
	EPfP GKir LAst MBri MCAu NSti
	SHar SSpe SSpi
– 'Coen Jansen'	see *P. longifolia* 'Ankum'
– 'Coral Spring'	EMan MBNS MCAu
– 'Dordogne'	CBct CLAP EBee EBre EFou EGle
	EMan GBuc GKir LRHS MAvo
	MCAu MGrG MRav NBir NOrc
	SBla WCru WHil WViv
– wild-collected	WCot
'Lovell Blue'	CElw NCot WRus
'Majesté'	More than 30 suppliers
§ 'Margery Fish' ♀ H4	More than 30 suppliers
'Mary Mottram'	CElw CLAP EBee EChP ECtt EFou
	EMan GMac LAst MBri MLLN
	MNFA NBir NHol NPPs NSti SAga
	SBla SMrm SSpe WCer WCot WCru
	WHal WMaN WMnd WMoo WWhi
'Mawson's Blue'	CLAP CMea EBee EBre ECha
	EMon GKir LPio LRHS MBri MRav
	MWat NBir NChi NSti WCru WEas
	WMaN WMoo WRHF WWye
'May Bouquet'	NSti
'Melancholia' new	IBlr
'Merlin'	CLAP EBee EMon LRHS NSti SSpi
'Middleton Red'	CElw
§ 'Milchstrasse'	CLAP NSti
Milky Way	see *P.* 'Milchstrasse'
mollis	CBot CLAP CSWP EBee EGoo EMon
	EOrc GCal IBlr LRHS MBri NCat
	NSti NWoo SMrm SSpi WCot WCru
– WM 9206	SBla
– 'Royal Blue'	EBee MRav
– 'Samobor'	CBct CLAP SDes WCot
'Monksilver'	CBel EMon NSti
'Moonstone'	CElw CLAP LAst LPhx LPio WRus
'Mournful Purple'	CBct CElw CLAP ECoo EGle EHrv
	SWat WCru
'Mrs Kittle'	CBct CElw CM&M EBee EChP
	EMan EWTr GBri MBro MCLN
	MGrG MNFA MRav NBir NSti
	SApp SBri SDys SSpi WCru WFar
	WHal WLin WMnd WRus
'Netta Statham'	ECha MGrG
'Northern Lights' new	SHar
'Nürnberg'	CElw EMon LRHS MAvo MBro
	NHaw WCru WHal
obscura	LRHS
officinalis	CAgr CArn CBro CHar EBlw EHon
	EMon EOrc EPar GBar GPoy ITer
	LLWP LRHS MChe MHer NChi
	NVic SIde WCru WFar WHal
	WHbs WWpP WWye
– 'Alba'	EBee ELan NLon WCru
§ – 'Blue Mist'	CDes CElw CLAP ECha EGle ELan
	EMon EOrc GBri GBuc GMac
	MBct MBro NBir NCot NPar NSti
	SMrm SSpi WAbb WBro WCot
	WCru WHal WHoo WMnd WMoo
	WRus WTin
– 'Bowles' Blue'	see *P. officinalis* 'Blue Mist'
– Cambridge Blue Group	EBee EBlw ECGN EChP EFou
	EMon LAst LRHS MRav NBir NLar
	NPPs NSti WCru WEas WHal

– 'Marjorie Lawley'	NPar
– 'Plas Merdyn'	IBlr
– *rubra*	see *P. rubra*
– 'Stillingfleet Gran'	EBee LPio NSti
– 'White Wings'	CElw CHea CLAP EBre EPla EPri
	GKir LPio LRHS MBNS MBro
	MCLN NDov NPri NSti SDes WEas
	WFar WMaN WMoo
'Oliver Wyatt's White'	CBct CDes EBee EMon WPGP
Opal = 'Ocupol'PBR	More than 30 suppliers
'Patrick Bates'	WCru
'Paul Aden'	CLAP
'Pewter'	LPio
'Pink Haze' new	EBee
'Polar Splash'	CBct EBee NSti SRot WFar
'Purple Haze'	NSti SHar
'Raspberry Ice'	NSti
'Raspberry Splash'	EMan NSti SHar SRot
* 'Rowlatt Choules'	SSpi
'Roy Davidson'	More than 30 suppliers
§ *rubra* ♀ H4	CElw COlW CSWP CStr EBlw
	ECha ELan EMar EOrc EWTr GKir
	IBlr LLWP MCAu MFir NBid NOrc
	NSti SChu SIng SRms WFar
– var. *alba*	see *P. rubra* var. *albocorollata*
§ – var. *albocorollata*	CBel CBre CElw CMHG EBee
	ECha ECtt EGle EHrv EMar
	EMon GAbr GKir LRHS MBro
	MCLN MFir MSte NCot NSti WCru
	WFar
– 'Ann'	CBct CBel CDes CElw CLAP EBee
	EChP EMon IBlr LPio LRHS MBNS
	MBct MBro MTed NSti SVil WCru
	WFar
* – *argentea*	SDes
– 'Barfield Pink'	CBro CElw EBee EChP ECtt EGle
	ELan EMar EMon GBar GCal GKir
	LAst LRHS MBro NBir NLar SChu
	SDes WCer WCru WHal WPnP
– 'Barfield Ruby'	CLAP EMon GBuc LRHS
– 'Bowles' Red'	CBel CBot EBee EBlw EBre ECtt
	EHrv ENot GKir LRHS MRav
	MWgw NBir NGdn SCro SDes
	SPer WFar WHal WMnd
– 'David Ward' (v)	More than 30 suppliers
– 'Prestbury Pink'	LRHS
– 'Rachel Vernie' (v) new	WCot
– 'Redstart'	More than 30 suppliers
– 'Warburg's Red'	CElw EMon
§ *saccharata*	EBee EBlw ECha EHrv ELan EWTr
	LGro MBro MCAu MFir NCot
	SChu SIng SPet SRms WCru WWin
– 'Alba'	CBro CElw ECha GBuc NOak SRms
– Argentea Group ♀ H4	CBro CSev EBee EBlw ECha ECoo
	EFou ELan EMar EOrc EPfP EWTr
	GMaP LAst LRHS MRav MTho
	NBro NGdn NLon SBla SPer SSpi
	WCot WSan
– 'Blauhimmel'	see *P.* 'Blauhimmel'
– 'Brentor'	CDes CElw EBee WWpP
– 'Diana Chappell'	NCat
– 'Dora Bielefeld'	More than 30 suppliers
– 'Frühlingshimmel'	CBct CBel CBro CDes CElw EBee
	ECha EFou EGle GKir LPhx LPio
	MAvo MRav SChu SMrm WFar
	WHal WLin WPrP WRus
– 'Glebe Cottage Blue'	CElw ECGP LPio NSti WWpP
– 'Jill Richardson'	ELan EVFa
– 'Lady Lou's Pink'	WCru
– 'Leopard'	CBos CDes CElw CLAP CMea
	CSam EBre EChP ECtt GBuc GKir
	GMaP GMac LAst LRHS MBro
	NBir NSti SApp SBla SDes SMrm

	SUsu WCot WCru WHoo WMnd WRus WWol
- 'Mrs Moon'	EBee ECtt ENot EPfP EWTr GKir GMaP LRHS MBNS MHer MWgw NBlu NOrc NPri SChu SDes SPer WCru WHen WMnd WPnP WWal
- 'Old Rectory Silver'	CLAP MWrn NBir
- 'Picta'	see *P. saccharata*
- 'Pink Dawn'	CMHG EBee EMan LRHS MBri WCru WMnd
- 'Reginald Kaye'	CElw ECha EMFP EWes MBro NDov SHBN
- 'Silverado'	CHid EBee IPot NLar NOrc NSti
- 'South Hayes'	CLAP
- 'White Barn'	see *Pulmonaria* 'Beth's Blue'
'Saint Ann's'	CBct CElw EMon LRHS MAvo NSti
'Silver Maid'	WCot
'Silver Mist'	MAvo
'Silver Sabre' **new**	IBlr
'Silver Shimmers' **new**	MBri SHar
'Silver Streamers'	NSti
'Silver Surprise'	WCot
'Sissinghurst White' ♀ H4	More than 30 suppliers
'Skylight'	CElw
'Smoky Blue'	CHid CLAP EBee ECtt EMan EMon ENot EPfP ITim LRHS MBro MHer MRav MWgw NCot NSti SDes SMer SWat WFar WHal WMnd WMoo
'Somibor'	SDes
'Spilled Milk'	CBct EBee EChP EMan MBri NLar NSti SDes
'Tim's Silver'	CBct ECha NPar WBcn
'Trevi Brooch' **new**	EBee
'Trevi Fountain'	EMan NSti SHar SRot
'Ultramarine'	EBee EMon
vallarsae	LAst
- 'Margery Fish'	see *P.* 'Margery Fish'
'Vera May'	MAvo SApp
'Victorian Brooch'	CBct CLAP EBee LRHS NSti SRot WFar
'Weetwood Blue'	CElw CLAP EBee EPfP EPla MSte
'Wendy Perry'	CBct CElw CLAP SHar
'Wisley White'	CBri CElw

Pulsatilla (Ranunculaceae)

alba	CBro NSla WCra
albana	CBro EBee EHyt GCrs LHop LRHS SBla
* - subsp. *alpina* **new**	GKev
- 'Lutea'	GKev
- white-flowered	SOkd
alpina	CBot EChP SRms
§ subsp. *apiifolia* ♀ H4	EHyt ELan GDra GKev GTou ITim NHar WCom WCot WPat
- subsp. *sulphurea*	see *P. alpina* subsp. *apiifolia*
ambigua	EBee SIgm
campanella	WAbc
- JJH 196	EBee
caucasica	CBro LRHS
cernua	CBri CBro EBee EBre GBuc LHop LRHS SIgm WAbe
chinensis	EBee
dahurica	EBee
x *gayeri*	EBee NBir
georgica	EBee SIgm WAbe WLin
halleri ♀ H4	EBee EBre EMan GAbr GKev GKir NSla SIgm
- subsp. *slavica* ♀ H4	CBro CLyd GCrs GEdr LRHS NSla NWCA WCom WWin
- subsp. *taurica*	GEdr MSte
koreana	CBro
lutea	see *P. alpina* subsp. *apiifolia*

millefolium **new**	EBee
montana	GBuc GCrs SIgm SPlb WLin
multifida	GIBF IIve
occidentalis	EBee EPot
§ *patens*	EBee
- var. *multifida*	GBuc
- - NNS 96221	IDac SIgm
pratensis	GPoy GTou IIve SRms
- subsp. *nigricans*	CBro LHop LRHS
rubra	CHar EBee GKir
turczaninovii	EBee SIgm
§ *vernalis* ♀ H2	GBuc GCrs GDra GEdr GTou NHar NSla SBla WAbe WLin
§ *vulgaris* ♀ H4	More than 30 suppliers
- 'Alba' ♀ H4	More than 30 suppliers
- 'Barton's Pink'	CBro EBee EHyt EWes EWll GKir LHop LRHS SBla SIng
- 'Blaue Glocke' **new**	SCro WHil
- Czech fringed hybrids	CNic ITim
- 'Eva Constance'	CBro CRDP EBre EHyt GKir LHop LRHS NBir SIng WAbe
- 'Flore Pleno' (d)	CLyd CNic EHyt
- 'Gotlandica'	CLyd SIgm
- subsp. *grandis* 'Budapest Seedling'	GCrs
- - 'Papageno'	CBot CFwr CSpe EBee EChP EDAr EMan EMar LHop LRHS NLar SAga SIgm SMrm SUsu WHil WLin
- Heiler hybrids	ECGP EMan EMar
- 'Miss Beveridge'	NOak
- pale pink-flowered	GKir
- Red Clock	see *P. vulgaris* 'Röde Klokke'
§ - 'Röde Klokke'	CBrm EBee ENot EWTr IBal LRHS MBro MCLN SCro WHil WSel
- *rosea*	SDes
- Rote Glocke	see *P. vulgaris* 'Röde Klokke'
- var. *rubra*	More than 30 suppliers
- violet blue-flowered	ITim SDes
§ - 'Weisse Schwan'	CFwr GAbr MHer NMen
- White Swan	see *P. vulgaris* 'Weisse Schwan'

pummelo see *Citrus maxima*

Punica (Lythraceae)

granatum	ERea EKom ESlt LPan LRHS MPRe SLim SOWG STre
- 'Fina Tendral'	ERea
- var. *nana* ♀ H3	CArn CHal CPle EPfP ERea ESlt LPan LRHS MPRe SBrw SLon SMrm SRms WPat
- 'Nana Racemosa' **new**	CBcs
- f. *plena* (d)	CBcs MRav WCFE
- - 'Rubrum Flore Pleno' (d) ♀ H3	LPan
* - 'Striata'	SOWG

Puschkinia (Hyacinthaceae)

scilloides	LRHS
§ - var. *libanotica*	CBro EPar EPot ETub LAma LRHS NRog WPer WShi
- - 'Alba'	EPar EPot LAma LRHS NRog

Putoria (Rubiaceae)

calabrica	CLyd NWCA

Puya (Bromeliaceae)

RCB WQ-0-1	WCot
alpestris	CBrP CHEx CTbh CTrC EOas IArd SAPC SChr SSpi
berteroana	CTrC
chilensis	CAbb CBcs CBrd CCtw CDoC CHEx CMdw CPne CStu CTbh

	CTrC EBee EOas IArd SAPC SArc SChr SPar SPlb
coerulea	CFir GBin SIgm SPlb
- F&W 8411	WLRN
- var. *violacea* F&W 7911	WLRN
ferruginea **new**	CHEx
gilmartiniae	CTrC EOas IArd
laxa	SChr
mirabilis	CHEx CKob CTrC EOas WCot

Pycnanthemum (*Lamiaceae*)

californicum	EBee
pilosum	CArn CHal CSev EBee ELau EMan GPoy MHer MSal NLar NPri SIde WBri WGwG WHHs WHer WPer WPic WWye
tenuifolium	CPLG EBee EMan NLar
virginianum	EBee IIve

Pycnostachys (*Lamiaceae*)

reticulata **new**	EShb

Pygmaea see *Chionohebe*

Pyracantha ✿ (*Rosaceae*)

Alexander Pendula = 'Renolex'	EHol MRav SRms WFar WHar
angustifolia	WCFE
- DWD 67	WCot
§ *atalantioides*	CMac SPlb WCFE
§ - 'Aurea'	WWin
'Brilliant'	EPfP
'Buttercup'	EPla WBcn
§ *coccinea* 'Lalandei'	CSBt NFor SMer SPer WGwG
- 'Red Column'	CChe CMac CWib EBee ECtt ELan EPfP GKir LAst LBuc LHop LRHS MBNS MBar MGos MRav MWat NBee NWea SCoo WBod WDin WGwG WHar WWeb
- 'Red Cushion'	CWSG EBee ENot LRHS MGos MRav SRms
crenulata	WCFE
Dart's Red = 'Interrada'	CSBt EBee LRHS MRav WBod
gibbsii	see *P.* *atalantioides*
- 'Flava'	see *P.* *atalantioides* 'Aurea'
'Gold Rush'	EBee MBri
'Golden Charmer' ♀ H4	CWSG EBee EBre ECtt ENot EPfP GKir LRHS MGos MRav NBlu NLon NWea SHBN SPer SRms WBod WDin WFar WGwG WHar
'Golden Dome'	LRHS
'Golden Glow'	LRHS
'Golden Sun'	see *P.* 'Soleil d'Or'
'Harlequin' (v)	ECtt EHol NPro SHBN SReu WCot WMoo
'Knap Hill Lemon'	CChe EBee MBlu
'Mohave'	CChe CMac CWib EBee EBre ELan GKir LRHS MBar MGos MWat NDlv NWea SHBN SPer SReu SRms WDin WGwG WStI
'Mohave Silver' (v)	CWSG EBee EGra LAst LRHS MBNS MGos MWat WBod
'Molten Lava'	MBri
'Monrovia'	see *P.* *coccinea* 'Lalandei'
'Mozart'	WWeb
'Navaho'	EBee EPfP MAsh WBcn WBrE
'Orange Charmer'	CBcs CChe CSBt CTri CWSG CWib EBee ELan ENot EPfP GKir MAsh MGos MRav MWat NBee NBlu NWea SHBN SMer SPer SPlb WFar WStI WTel WWeb
'Orange Glow' ♀ H4	More than 30 suppliers
'Orangeade' **new**	MBri
* 'Red Pillar'	GKir SRPl
'Renault d'Or'	SLPl
rogersiana ♀ H4	EBee ENot EPfP GKir MRav WTel
- 'Flava' ♀ H4	CSBt CTri EBee EHol ENot EPfP MAsh MBar MRav MWhi NLon NWea SMer SPoG SRPl WBVN WGwG WTel
'Rosedale'	MBri
Saphyr Jaune = 'Cadaune' PBR	CDoC CEnd CSBt CWSG EBee ENot EPfP GKir MAsh MBNS MGos MRav SMer SPoG WLRN WRHF WStI
Saphyr Orange = 'Cadange' PBR ♀ H4	CDoC CEnd COtt CSBt CWSG EBee EMil ENot EPfP EPla GKir LRHS MAsh MBri MGos MRav NBlu NPri SPer WLRN WRHF WStI WWeb
Saphyr Rouge = 'Cadrou' PBR ♀ H4	CDoC CEnd COtt CSBt CWSG EBee ENot EPfP GKir LRHS MBri MGos MRav SPer WLRN WRHF WWeb
'Shawnee'	CMac CSBt CWib EBee ECot EPfP MAsh MRav MWat NDlv WWeb
§ 'Soleil d'Or'	CMac CSBt CSam CWib EBee EBre ECtt ELan ENot EPfP GKir LBuc LRHS MAsh MBar MRav NFor NLon SLPl SLon SPer SReu WBod WDin WFar WGwG WHar WStI WTel WWeb
'Sparkler' (v)	CDoC CMac EHoe LAst LRHS MAsh MGos SPar SPer WFar WHar
'Teton' ♀ H4	CMac CWSG CWib EBee ELan ENot EPfP EPla ESis GKir LAst LHop LRHS MAsh MBar MBri MRav NBlu NDlv SRms WDin WFar WLRN WStI WWeb
'Watereri'	SLPl SPer WTel
'Yellow Sun'	see *P.* 'Soleil d'Or'

Pyrenaria (*Theaceae*)

spectabilis	see *Tutcheria spectabilis*

Pyrethropsis see *Rhodanthemum*

Pyrethrum see *Tanacetum*

Pyrola (*Ericaceae*)

decorata **new**	EBee
rotundifolia	SSpi WHer

Pyrostegia (*Bignoniaceae*)

venusta	CPIN ESlt LRHS SOWG WMul

Pyrrhopappus (*Asteraceae*)

carolinianus **new**	SSpi

Pyrrocoma (*Asteraceae*)

clementis	EBee
§ *lanceolata*	EBee

Pyrrosia (*Polypodiaceae*)

* *heterophylla*	NMar
lingua 'Variegata' (v)	EMon

Pyrus ✿ (*Rosaceae*)

amygdaliformis	CTho
- var. *cuneifolia*	CLnd CTho
betulifolia	CMCN WJas
calleryana 'Bradford'	CLnd
- 'Chanticleer' ♀ H4	CBcs CCVT CDoC CDul CEnd CLnd CTho EBee ECrN ENot EPfP

	EWTr GKir IArd LHyr LPan LRHS MAsh MBlu MGos MRav NWea SHBN SKee SLim SPer SSta WDin WJas WOrn
x *canescens*	CTho
communis (F)	CCVT CKin CTri GIBF LBuc NRog SKee SPer STre WMou
- 'Abbé Fétel' (D)	SKee
- 'Autumn Bergamot' (D)	CTho
- 'Barnet' (Perry)	CTho
- 'Baronne de Mello' (D)	CTho SFam SKee
- 'Beech Hill' (F)	CDul CLnd CTho EBee ECrN EMil ENot EPfP
- 'Belle Guérandaise' (D)	SKee
- 'Belle Julie' (D)	SKee
- 'Bergamotte Esperen' (D)	SKee
- 'Beth' (D) ♀ H4	CDoC CSBt CWib ECrN EMui EPfP GBon GTwe LBuc LRHS MBri MGos NBee NRog SDea SFam SKee SPer WHar
- 'Beurré Alexandre Lucas' (D)	SKee
- 'Beurré Bedford' (D)	SKee
- 'Beurré Bosc' (D)	SKee
- 'Beurré Clairgeau' (C/D)	SKee
- 'Beurré d'Amanlis' (D)	SKee
- 'Beurré d'Avalon' (D)	CTho
- 'Beurré de Beugny' (D)	SKee
- 'Beurré Dumont' (D)	SFam
- 'Beurré Hardy' (D) ♀ H4	CCAT CDoC CSBt CTho CWib ECrN EMui ENot ERea EWTr GKir GTwe LRHS MBri MRav MWat NRog SDea SFam SKee WOrn
- 'Beurré Mortillet' (D)	SKee
- 'Beurré Six' (D)	SKee
- 'Beurré Superfin' (D)	GTwe SFam SKee
- 'Bianchettone' (D)	SKee
- 'Bishop's Thumb' (D)	SDea
- 'Black Worcester' (C)	GTwe SDea SFam SKee WJas
- 'Blakeney Red' (Perry)	CTho SDea
- 'Blickling' (D)	SKee
- 'Brandy' (Perry)	CTho SDea SKee
- 'Bristol Cross' (D)	GTwe SKee
§ - 'Butirra Precoce Morettini' (D)	SDea
- 'Catillac' (C) ♀ H4	CTho GTwe NRog SFam SKee
- 'Chalk'	see *P. communis* 'Crawford'
- 'Chaumontel' (D)	SKee
- 'Clapp's Favourite' (D)	CTho ECrN GTwe SKee
- 'Colmar d'Eté' (D)	CTho
- 'Comte de Lamy' (D)	SKee
- 'Concorde'PBR (D) ♀ H4	CCVT CDoC CSBt CSam CTho CWib ECrN EMui ENot EPfP ERea EWTr GTwe LBuc LRHS MBri MGos MLan NBee NPri NRog NWea SDea SFam SKee WHar WJas WOrn WWeb
- 'Conference' (D) ♀ H4	More than 30 suppliers
- 'Crassane'	CTho
§ - 'Crawford' (D)	SKee
- 'Cromwell' (D)	ESim
- 'Deacon's Pear' (D)	SDea
- 'Devoe' (D)	SDea
- 'Docteur Jules Guyot' (D)	SDea SKee
- 'Double de Guerre' (C/D)	SKee
- 'Doyenné Blanc' (F)	SKee
- 'Doyenné Boussoch' (D)	SKee
- 'Doyenné d'Eté' (D)	ERea SFam SKee
- 'Doyenné du Comice' (D) ♀ H4	CCVT CDoC CMac CSBt CTho CWSG CWib EBre ECrN EMui ENot EPfP ERea GBon LBuc LRHS MBri MRav MWat NRog NWea

	SDea SFam SKee SPer WHar WJas WOrn WWeb
- 'Duchesse d'Angoulême' (D)	SKee
- 'Durondeau' (D)	CTho GTwe NRog SDea SFam SKee
- 'Emile d'Heyst' (D)	CTho GTwe
- 'Fertility' (D)	SKee
- 'Fertility Improved'	see *P. communis* 'Improved Fertility'
- 'Fondante d'Automne' (D)	CTho SKee
- 'Forelle' (D)	ERea SKee
- 'Gin' (Perry)	CTho
- 'Glou Morceau' (D)	CTho ECrN EMui GTwe LRHS MWat NRog SDea SFam SKee
- 'Glow Red Williams' (D)	SFam
- 'Gorham' (D)	CTho ECrN GTwe MCoo SFam SKee
- 'Gratiole de Jersey' (D)	CTho
- 'Green Horse' (Perry)	CTho
- 'Green Pear of Yair' (D)	SKee
- 'Hacon's Imcomparable' (D)	SKee
- 'Harrow Delight' (D)	SDea
- 'Harvest Queen' (D/C)	SDea
- 'Hessle' (D)	GTwe NRog SDea SFam SKee
- 'Highland' (D)	SKee
§ - 'Improved Fertility' (D)	CDoC GBon GTwe SDea SKee
- 'Jack Green'	CTho
- 'Jargonelle' (D)	CTho GTwe NRog SDea SFam SKee
- 'Joséphine de Malines' (D) ♀ H4	CTho GTwe LRHS SDea SFam SKee
- 'Laxton's Foremost' (D)	SKee
- 'Laxton's Satisfaction' (D)	SFam
- 'Louise Bonne of Jersey' (D)	CDoC CTho CTri ECrN EMui GTwe LRHS MBri MGos NRog SDea SFam SKee
- 'Marguérite Marillat' (D)	SDea
- 'Max Red Bartlett'	MCoo
- 'Merton Pride' (D)	CTho ECrN GTwe MWat SDea SFam SKee
- 'Merton Star' (D)	SKee
- 'Monarch' (D)	CLnd
- 'Moonglow' (D/C)	MCoo SDea SKee
- 'Morettini'	see *P. communis* 'Butirra Precoce Morettini'
- 'Nouveau Poiteau' (C/D)	CTho ECrN GTwe LRHS SKee
- 'Olivier de Serres' (D)	SFam SKee
- 'Onward' (D) ♀ H4	CLnd CTri CWib ECrN EMui GTwe MGos NRog NWea SDea SFam SKee WHar
§ - 'Packham's Triumph' (D)	CDoC CWib ECrN GTwe NRog SDea SKee
- 'Passe Colmar' (D)	CTho
- 'Passe Crassane' (D)	SKee
- 'Pear Apple' (D)	SDea
- 'Pitmaston Duchess' (C/D) ♀ H4	GTwe SDea SKee
- 'Red Comice' (D/C)	GTwe SKee
- 'Red Sensation Bartlett' (D/C)	EMui GTwe
- 'Robin' (C/D)	ERea SDea SKee
- 'Roosevelt' (D)	SKee
- 'Santa Claus' (D)	SDea SFam SKee
- 'Seckel' (D)	SFam SKee
- 'Soleil d'Automne' (F)	SKee
- 'Swan's Egg' (D)	CTho
- 'Terrace Pearl' new	EMui ENot WWeb
- 'Thompson's' (D)	GTwe SFam
- 'Thorn' (Perry)	CTho
- 'Triomphe de Vienne' (D)	SFam
- 'Triumph'	see *P. communis* 'Packham's Triumph'
- 'Uvedale's St Germain' (C)	CTho SKee

- 'Vicar of Winkfield' (C/D)   GTwe SDea SKee
- 'Williams' Bon Chrétien'   CCVT CMac CSBt CTho CWSG
   (D/C) ♀ H4   CWib EBre ECrN EMui ENot ERea
   GBon GKir LBuc LRHS MBri
   MGos MWat NRog SDea SFam
   SKee SPer WHar WJas WOrn WStI
   WWeb
- 'Williams Red' (D/C)   GTwe SKee
- 'Winnal's Longdon'   CTho
   (Perry)
- 'Winter Nelis' (D)   CTho CTri CWib ECrN GTwe
   SDea SFam SKee
cordata   CDul CTho SKee
cossonii   CTho
elaeagnifolia   CTho CWSG
- var. **kotschyana**   CEnd CLnd GIBF GKir LRHS
   MAsh MRav SLim WOrn
- 'Silver Sails' **new**   MBlu SCoo
korshinskyi new   GIBF
nivalis   CLnd CTho EBee ENot EPfP GIBF
   SHBN SLPI SPer
pyrifolia '20th Century'   see *P. pyrifolia* 'Nijisseiki'
- 'Chojuro' (F)   ERea ESim
- 'Hosui' (F)   LBuc
- 'Kumoi' (F)   SDea
* - 'Nashi Kumoi'   LPan
§ - 'Nijisseiki' (F)   ERea ESim
- 'Shinseiki' (F)   EMui ERea ESim LRHS SDea SKee
   SLim
- 'Shinsui' (F)   SDea SKee
salicifolia 'Pendula' ♀ H4   More than 30 suppliers
ussuriensis   GIBF

Q

Qiongzhuea see *Chimonobambusa*

Quercus ✿ (Fagaceae)

§ **acuta**   CBcs CHEx MBlu
acutifolia   CMCN
§ **acutissima**   CLnd CMCN EPfP SBir WDin
   WNor
aegilops   see *Q. ithaburensis* subsp.
   macrolepis
affinis   CMCN
agrifolia   CDul CMCN SBir
alba   CMCN NWea WDin
- f. **elongata**   EPfP LRHS
aliena   CMCN SBir
- var. **acutiserrata**   CMCN
alnifolia   CDul
arkansana   CMCN SBir
austrina   CMCN
x **beadlei**   see *Q.* x *saulii*
bicolor   CMCN SBir WDin WNor
borealis   see *Q. rubra*
breweri   see *Q. garryana* var. *breweri*
buckleyii new   SBir
x **bushii**   CMCN EPfP MBlu
x **byarsii new**   SBir
canariensis ♀ H4   CLnd CMCN CTho CTrG EPfP
   IArd IDee LRHS
castaneifolia   CLnd CMCN EPfP LPan WDin
- 'Green Spire' ♀ H4   CDoC CDul CMCN EPfP GKir
   IArd LRHS MBlu MBri SMad SPer
cerris   CBcs CDoC CDul CKin CLnd
   CMCN EBee ECrN EMil ENot EPfP
   GKir LPan LRHS MGos MLan NWea
   SBir SEND SPer SSta WDin WMou

§ - 'Argenteovariegata' (v)   CDul CEnd CLnd CMCN CRez
   CTho EBee EPfP GKir LRHS MBlu
   MBri SBir SKee SMad SPoG
* - 'Marmorata'   EPfP SBir
- 'Variegata'   see *Q. cerris* 'Argenteovariegata'
- 'Wodan'   CMCN EPfP GKir LRHS MBlu
chapmanii   CMCN
chrysolepis   CBcs CMCN
coccifera   CDul CFil CMCN IDee SSpi WDin
   WPGP WWes
- subsp. **calliprinos**   CMCN
coccinea   CBcs CDul CLnd CMCN CWSG
   ECrN EPfP GIBF GKir LRHS NBea
   NWea SBir SPer SSta STre WDin
   WNor WOrn
- 'Splendens' ♀ H4   CDoC CDul CEnd CMCN COtt
   CTho EBee ELan EPfP EWTr GKir
   LPan LRHS MBlu MBri SBir SHBN
   SMad SPer WDin
dentata   CMCN EPfP LRHS SBir WDin
- 'Carl Ferris Miller'   CMCN EPfP IArd LRHS MBlu SBir
   SMad
- 'Pinnatifida'   CMCN EPfP IArd LRHS MBlu
   SMad
- 'Sir Harold Hillier'   EPfP
- subsp. **yunnanensis new**   CMCN
douglasii   CLnd CMCN
dumosa   CMCN WNor
durata   CMCN
ellipsoidalis   CDul CMCN GKir LRHS SBir
   WNor
- 'Hemelrijk'   CDoC EPfP GKir LRHS MBlu
emoryi new   SBir
engelmannii   CMCN
fabrei   SBir
faginea   CLnd CMCN
falcata   CDul CLnd CMCN EPfP
- var. **pagodifolia**   see *Q. pagoda*
x **fernaldii**   CMCN
frainetto   CDoC CDul CLnd CMCN CTho
   EBee ECrN ENot EPfP EWTr GKir
   ISea LPan MBri SEND SPer WDin
   WMou WNor
- 'Hungarian Crown' ♀ H4   CMCN LRHS SMad
- 'Trump'   MBlu
fruticosa   see *Q. lusitanica* Lamarck
* **fungeana**   CLnd
gambelii   CMCN
garryana   CMCN SBir
§ - var. **breweri**   SBir
- var. **fruticosa**   see *Q. garryana* var. *breweri*
georgiana   CMCN SBir
glandulifera   see *Q. serrata*
§ **glauca**   CFai CMCN EPfP SAPC SArc SBir
   WNor
gravesii new   SBir
grisea new   SBir
x **hastingsii**   CMCN EPfP
hemisphaerica   CMCN EPfP SBir
x **heterophylla**   CMCN SBir
x **hickelii**   CMCN
- 'Gieszelhorst'   MBlu
hinckleyi   WDin
§ x **hispanica**   CLnd WPic
- 'Ambrozyana'   CMCN EPfP LRHS SBir SMad
   WDin
- 'Diversifolia'   CMCN EPfP MBlu
- 'Fulhamensis'   CMCN SEND
§ - 'Lucombeana' ♀ H4   CBcs CDul CMCN CSBt CTho
   EPfP IArd MBlu SBir SPer
§ - 'Pseudoturneri'   CBcs EPfP LPan MBlu
- 'Suberosa'   CTho
- 'Wageningen'   CMCN EPfP IArd SBir

ilex ♀ H4	More than 30 suppliers
ilicifolia	CDul CMCN LRHS SBir WNor
imbricaria	CDul CLnd CMCN LRHS MBlu
	SBir WDin
§ *incana* Bartram	CMCN
– Roxb.	see *Q. leucotrichophora*
infectoria	CDul
ithaburensis	CMCN EPfP
§ – subsp. *macrolepis*	CMCN GKir LEdu SBir
kelloggii	CMCN LRHS
x *kewensis*	CMCN
laevigata	see *Q. acuta*
laevis	CMCN EPfP SBir
§ *laurifolia*	CDul CMCN MBlu SBir
laurina	CMCN
§ *leucotrichophora*	CMCN
liaotungensis	see *Q. wutaishanica*
x *libanerris*	IArd SBir
– 'Rotterdam'	CMCN
libani	CDul CMCN EPfP WDin
lobata	CAgr CMCN LEdu
x *lucombeana*	see *Q.* x *hispanica*
– 'William Lucombe'	see *Q.* x *hispanica* 'Lucombeana'
x *ludoviciana*	CMCN EPfP SBir
§ *lusitanica* Lamarck	CMCN
lyrata	CMCN
'Macon'	LRHS
macranthera	CLnd CMCN EPfP GKir
macrocarpa	CLnd CMCN EPfP LRHS SBir
	WDin WNor
– x *turbinella*	CMCN
macrolepis	see *Q. ithaburensis* subsp.
	macrolepis
margarettiae new	SBir
marilandica	CDul CEnd CMCN EPfP IArd
	LRHS SBir
mexicana	CMCN SBir
michauxii	CMCN
mongolica subsp.	CMCN
crispula var.	
grosseserrata	
§ *montana*	CMCN
muehlenbergii	CDul CMCN EPfP MBlu NWea SBir
myrsinifolia	see *Q. glauca*
myrtifolia new	CMCN EPfP
nigra	CMCN CMHG SBir WNor
nuttallii	see *Q. texana*
obtusa	see *Q. laurifolia*
oglethorpensis new	SBir
§ *pagoda*	CMCN MBlu SBir
palustris ♀ H4	CDoC CDul CLnd CMCN CTho
	ECrN EPfP EWTr GKir LPan LRHS
	MAsh MBlu MBri NWea SBir SKee
	SMad SPer WDin WNor WOrn
* – 'Compacta'	EPfP
– 'Green Dwarf'	CMCN
– 'Pendula'	CEnd CMCN WPGP
* – 'Swamp Pygmy'	CMCN MBlu
§ x *pauciloba* new	SBir
pedunculata	see *Q. robur*
pedunculiflora	see *Q. robur* subsp. *pedunculiflora*
§ *petraea* ♀ H4	CDoC CDul CKin CLnd CSBt
	ECrN EPfP GKir IMGH LBuc MBlu
	NBee NWea SPer WDin WMou
§ – 'Insecata'	CDoC CEnd CMCN LRHS WPGP
§ – 'Laciniata'	see *Q. petraea* 'Insecata'
– 'Mespilifolia'	CTho
§ – 'Purpurea'	CLnd CMCN GKir LRHS MBlu
– 'Rubicunda'	see *Q. petraea* 'Purpurea'
– 'Westcolumn' new	IArd
§ *phellos*	CDul CLnd CMCN CTho EBee
	ECrN EPfP LRHS MBlu SLPl SLdr
	WDin WNor

phillyreoides	CBcs CDul CLnd CMCN EPfP SBir
	SLPl WDin WNor
polymorpha new	CMCN
'Pondaim'	CMCN LRHS SBir
pontica	CMCN EPfP LRHS MBlu NWea
prinoides	CMCN
prinus Engelm.	see *Q. montana*
* *prinus* L.	CMCN SBir
pubescens	CDul CFil CMCN GKir SBir
pumila Michx.	see *Q. montana*
pumila Walt.	see *Q. phellos*
pyrenaica	CLnd CMCN CTho IArd
– 'Pendula'	CMCN WDin
rhysophylla	EPfP MBlu SBir
§ *robur* ♀ H4	More than 30 suppliers
– 'Argenteomarginata' (v)	CDul CMCN MBlu SMad SSta
– 'Atropurpurea'	WDin
* – 'Compacta'	MBlu
– 'Concordia'	CBcs CDoC CEnd CFil CLnd
	CMCN COtt EBee EPfP GKir
	LRHS MBlu SMad WDin
– 'Contorta'	CMCN LRHS
– 'Cristata'	CDul CMCN MBlu
– 'Cucullata'	CMCN
* – *dissecta*	CMCN
– 'Facrist'	CDul CEnd
– f. *fastigiata*	CDoC CDul CLnd CTho EBee
	ECrN ENot EPfP GKir LBuc LHyr
	LPan LRHS MBar MGos NBee
	NWea SCoo SKee SLPl SPer WDin
	WOrn
– 'Fastigiata Koster' ♀ H4	CDoC CDul CMCN COtt EPfP
	GKir LPan NBee SSta
– 'Fennesseyi'	CMCN LRHS
– 'Filicifolia'	see *Q.* x *rosacea* 'Filicifolia'
– 'Filicifolia' misapplied	see *Q. robur* 'Pectinata'
– 'Fürst Schwarzenburg' (v)	CMCN MBlu
– 'Hentzei'	CMCN
– 'Hungaria'	LRHS
– 'Irtha'	EPfP
– 'Kosteri Fastigiata' new	MBlu
§ – 'Pectinata'	CTho MBlu WDin
§ – subsp. *pedunculiflora*	CLnd CMCN
– 'Pendula'	CDul CEnd CMCN CTho MBlu
– 'Purpurascens'	CEnd CMCN GKir MBlu
– 'Raba'	CMCN
§ – 'Salfast'	MBlu
– 'Salicifolia Fastigiata'	see *Q. robur* 'Salfast'
– 'Strypemonde'	CMCN
– f. *variegata* (v)	LRHS
– x *turbinella*	CMCN
§ x *rosacea* 'Filicifolia'	CEnd CLnd NDca WMou WWes
§ *rubra* ♀ H4	More than 30 suppliers
– 'Aurea'	CDul CEnd CFil CMCN CTho
	EPfP GKir LRHS MAsh MBlu SMad
	SSpi WPGP
– 'Boltes Gold' new	MBlu
– 'Magic Fire'	MBlu SMad
* – 'Sunshine'	CMCN LRHS MBlu SMad
rugosa	CMCN SBir
x *runcinata* new	SBir
sadleriana	CMCN
sartorii	SBir
§ x *saulii*	CMCN SBir
x *schochiana*	CMCN EPfP
schottkyana	CMCN SBir
x *schuettei*	SBir
§ *serrata*	CDoC CMCN SBir
sessiliflora	see *Q. petraea*
shumardii	CMCN EPfP LRHS SBir WDin WNor
stellata	CMCN SBir
suber	CAgr CBcs CDoC CDul CFil CLnd
	CMCN CTho ECrN EPfP IArd

	IDee ISea LRHS SAPC SArc SEND SPar SSpi WDin WPGP
- 'Cambridge'	EPfP
§ *texana*	CMCN EPfP SBir
trojana	CMCN
turbinella	CMCN
x *turneri*	CDoC CDul CLnd CMCN CTho WDin WMou
- 'Pseudoturneri'	see *Q.* x *hispanica* 'Pseudoturneri'
undulata Torr.	see *Q.* x *pauciloba*
vacciniifolia	CMCN
variabilis	CMCN EPfP NWea SBir
velutina	CLnd CMCN CTho EPfP LRHS SBir
- 'Albertsii'	MBlu
- 'Rubrifolia'	CMCN EPfP
'Vilmoriana' **new**	CMCN MBlu
virginiana	CMCN
'Warburgii'	CMCN EPfP
x *warei* **new**	SBir
wislizeni	CBcs CMCN SBir
§ *wutaishanica*	CMCN SBir

Quillaja (Rosaceae)

saponaria	CPle CTrG

quince see *Cydonia*

Quisqualis (Combretaceae)

indica	SOWG

R

Racosperma see *Acacia*

Ramonda (Gesneriaceae)

§ *myconi* ♀ H4	CLAP CPBP EHyt ITim LTwo NHar NMen NSla NWCA NWoo SBla SIgm SIng SRms WTel
- var. *alba*	MTho
- 'Jim's Shadow' **new**	WAbe
- 'Rosea'	CLAP SBla
nathaliae ♀ H4	CLAP CPBP NGar NHar NWCA SIgm
- 'Alba'	CLAP SBla SOkd
pyrenaica	see *R. myconi*
serbica	ETow SBla SIgm

Ranunculus ✿ (Ranunculaceae)

abnormis	ETow GCrs NRya SCnR SIng
aconitifolius	CMea EBee EChP ECha EMFP EPar NLar NSti SMrm WCot WMnd
- 'Flore Pleno' (d) ♀ H4	CBos CDes CHad CHea CRow EBre EPar EPfP EPri EWoo EVFa GAbr GBuc GKir GMaP GMac IBlr LPhx MBri MCLN NBir NPar SVal WAul WFar WHer WHil WMnd WMoo WPnP
acris	NBir NLan NPer
* - *citrinus*	CBgR CElw CMdw EChP ECoo ECtt EGle EPar EPri EWoo MHar MSte NRya SMrm WAlt WPrP WRha
- 'Cricket' (v)	WAlt
- 'Farrer's Yellow'	CRow LHop
- 'Flore Pleno' (d) ♀ H4	More than 30 suppliers
- 'Hedgehog'	CDes EPPr EVFa NDov
- 'Stevenii'	CFee CRow EPPr IGor SDix
- 'Sulphureus'	CBre CElw ECha NCat NMRc NSti WEas WFar WHal

alpestris	NMen NRya
- x *bilobus*	NMen
amplexicaulis	ERos GCrs GDra GMaP GTou MRav NHar NMen NSla SBla WAbe WCot
aquatilis	EHon EMFW LMdh SWat
x *arendsii* 'Moonlight'	CElw SCnR
asiaticus	EPot
- var. *albus*	SBla
- var. *flavus*	SBla
- var. *sanguineus*	EHyt SBla
- Tecolote hybrids	LAma
baurii	SSpi
bulbosus	CKin NSco
§ - 'F.M. Burton'	CBos CRDP EBee ECtt EGle EHrv ETow GCal MAvo NDov NRya NSti SCro WAlt WCot WHal WMoo WTMC WWin
- *farreri*	see *R. bulbosus* 'F.M. Burton'
- 'Speciosus Plenus'	see *R. constantinopolitanus* 'Plenus'
calandrinioides ♀ H2-3	CAvo EWes NBir SBla SIng SVal WAbe WCom WCot
- SF 137	WCot
chinensis **new**	EBee
§ *constantinopolitanus* 'Plenus' (d)	CElw CRDP CRow EBee ECha GCal GKir GMac MBri MBro MInt MLLN MRav NBid NBro NRya WCot WEas WFar WMoo
cortusifolius	CDes CFir CMHG EBee EMan EPPr MTed SHar WCot WCru
crenatus	CLyd EBee EHyt GEdr GTou LEur NHar NMen NRya SBla SOkd WHal
extorris 'Flore Pleno'	EMon
ficaria	CArn CKin CNat CRow ELau GBar MBow MChe MGas MHer MSal NSco NVic WFar WHbs WHer WShi WWye
- 'Aglow in the Dark'	CNat EBee
- var. *albus*	CElw CRow EMon ERos LRHS NRya SIng
- anemone-centred	see *R. ficaria* 'Collarette'
- 'Art Nouveau' **new**	CNat
- 'Ashen Primrose'	CRow EBee
§ - var. *aurantiacus*	CMea CNic CRow EBee ECha EMon EPar ERos GDra LEur LPhx LRHS MBro MRav NGar NJOw NRya SIng SRms WAbe WCom WFar
- 'Bantam Egg'	CRow
- 'Binsted Woods' **new**	SCro
- 'Blackadder'	CRow
- 'Bowles' Double'	see *R. ficaria* 'Double Bronze', 'Picton's Double'
- 'Brambling'	CBos CBre CHea CLAP CRow EBee EMon LEur LRHS MRav NGar NRya SIgm SSvw WCom WCot
- 'Brazen Child'	CRow EBee
- 'Brazen Daughter'	CRow
- 'Brazen Hussy'	More than 30 suppliers
- 'Bregover White'	CRow EBee LEur
- 'Broadleas Black' **new**	CNat
- 'Budgerigar'	CRow
- subsp. *bulbilifer* 'Chedglow'	CRow LEur
- 'Bunch' (d)	CRow
- 'Camouflage' (v) **new**	CNat
- 'Cartwheel' (d)	CRow
- 'Champernowne Giant'	CRow
- 'Chocolate Cream'	CRow
§ - subsp. *chrysocephalus*	CRow ECha EMon NGar NRya SIng SSvw WCot WFar WHer

- 'Clouded Yellow' (v) — CRow
- 'Coffee Cream' — CRow EBee LEur
- 'Coker Cream' — CRow
§ - 'Collarette' (d) — CRDP CRow CStu EBee EHyt EMon EPar EPot ERos GBar GBuc GGar LEur LPhx LRHS MAvo MRav MTho NBir NGar NMGW NMen NRya SBla SIng SMac WAbe WCom WFar
- 'Coppernob' — CBre CElw CHid CRDP CRow ECGP ECha GAbr LEur LPio NGar WCot WFar WPnP WWpP
- 'Corinne Tremaine' — WHer
- 'Coy Hussy' (v) — CNat LEur
- 'Crawshay Cream' — CElw CRow LPhx
- 'Cupreus' — see *R. ficaria* var. *aurantiacus*
- 'Custard Tart' — NGar
- 'Damerham' (d) — CRow EMon LRHS NGar
- 'Dappled Grey' **new** — WAlt
- 'Deborah Jope' — CRow
- 'Diane Rowe' — EMon
- 'Dimpsey' — CRow
§ - 'Double Bronze' (d) — CPLG CRow CStu EBee ECGP EMon EPar ERos LEur LRHS MDKP MTho NBir NGar NRya SIng WCot WWeb
- double cream (d) — see *R. ficaria* 'Double Mud'
- double green eye (d) — CRow
§ - 'Double Mud' (d) — CHid CLAP CRow CStu ECGP EMon ERos GAbr GBuc LEur LPhx LRHS MBro MTho NRya NWoo SBla SIng WCom WCot WFar WHal
- double yellow (d) — see *R. ficaria flore-pleno*
- 'Dusky Maiden' — CRow EMon LEur LRHS NGar WFar
- 'F A Bowles' — see *R. ficaria* 'Collarette'
- 'Elan' — CDes CRow
- subsp. *ficariiformis* — EMon NGar
§ - *flore-pleno* (d) — CFee CHid CRow CStu EBee ECha Elan EMar EMon EPPr EPar ERos GAbr GDra GGar LEur LRHS NRya NSti SIng SRms WAbe WCot WFar WWin
- 'Fried Egg' — CRow
- 'Green Mantle' — NGar
- 'Green Petal' — CElw CRow CStu EBee EMon EPar LEur LPhx MRav MTho NBir NJOw NRya SIng SSvw WHal WHer
- 'Greencourt Gold' (d) — CRow
- 'Holly' — see *R. ficaria* 'Holly Green'
- 'Holly Bronze' — CRow
§ - 'Holly Green' — CRow
- 'Hoskin's Miniature' — CRow
- 'Hoskin's Variegated' (v) — CRow
- 'Hyde Hall' — EMon LEur LRHS NGar WCot WFar
- 'Inky' — CNat LEur
- 'Jake Perry' — CBos
- 'Jane's Dress' — CHid CNat CRow LEur
- 'Ken Aslet Double' (d) — CDes CRow EMon LEur LRHS WHal
- 'Lambrook Black' — WHer
- 'Laysh On' (d) — CRow
- 'Leo' — EMon
- 'Limelight' — CRow
- 'Little Southey' — CRow EBee
- subsp. *major* — see *R. ficaria* subsp. *chrysocephalus*
- 'Martin Gibbs' — CNat
- 'Mimsey' (d) — CRow
- 'Mobled Jade' — CHid CNat CRow EBee LEur
- 'Newton Abbot' — CBre CRow
I - 'Nigrifolia' — NGar
- 'Oakenden Cream' — CRow
- 'Old Master' — MAvo NGar WCot
- 'Orange Sorbet' — CRow EMon LEur NGar

- 'Palest Cream' — CSam
§ - 'Picton's Double' (d) — CRow CStu EBee ECGP EHyt GBar MTho NGar NRya WAbe
- 'Primrose' — CRow EMon GGar LRHS MRav MTho NCat NRya WCot
- 'Primrose Elf' — CRow
- 'Quantock Brown' **new** — CBgR
- 'Quillet' (d) — CRow EMon
- 'Ragamuffin' (d) — CDes CRow EMon
- 'Randall's White' — CRDP CRow CSWP CStu EBee ECha LEur LPhx LSyl MRav MTho SIgm WCom WCot WElm WFar WWpP
- 'Rowden Magna' — CRow
- 'Salad Bowl' (d) — CRow
- 'Salmon's White' — CBre CFee CRow EBee ELan EMar EPPr EPar EPot LEur LPhx MRav NBir NRya SIng SSvw WAbe WFar WHal WHer WHrl
- 'Samidor' — CRow
- 'Sheldon' — CRow
- 'Sheldon Night' — CNat
- 'Sheldon Silver' — CFox CNat CRow LEur
- 'Silver Collar' **new** — EMon
- single cream — EMon NGar
- 'South Downs' — CNat
- 'Suffusion' — CNat CRow
- 'Sutherland's Double' (d) — CRow
- 'Sweet Chocolate' — CRow
- 'Torquay Elf' — CRow
- 'Tortoiseshell' — CElw CHid CRow EBee LEur MAvo MRav NGar WCom WFar
- 'Trenwheal' (d) — CRow
- 'Undercurrent' (v) — WAlt
- 'Winkworth' — EMon LEur
- 'Wisley White' — NGd
- 'Yaffle' — CBre CRow EBee EChP EMon LRHS MRav NGar WCot

flammula — CBen CKin CRow EHon EMFW LMdh LPBA MSta SWat WWpP
- subsp. *minimus* — CRow
gouanii — ETow NRya
gramineus ♀ H4 — CRDP CSam EBre EHyt EPot ERos GBuc GCrs GMaP LBee LPhx LRHS MBro MNrw MRav MTho MWat NMen NRya SIgm SIng SMad SRms SUsu WCom WCot WFar WHil WLin WPer SBla WFar
- 'Pardal' — MGrG
'Granhy Cream' — MGrG
illyricus — ECha NRya SRot WCru WHal
insignis — CBos CRDP
lanuginosus — EPPr EVFa MAvo
lappaceus — WPat
lapponicus — GIBF
lingua — CFir CKin COld ECoo EMFW LMdh MCCP SLon SPlb
- 'Grandiflorus' — CBen CRow EHon LPBA MSta NPer NRya SWat WHal WMAq WWpP WWye
lyallii — CPla GDra GGar ITim LEur SBla WAbe WSan
macauleyi — GCrs
macrophyllus — WCru
millefoliatus — CDes EBee EHyt ERos ETow GBuc MTho NGar NMen NRya WCot
montanus double (d) — EBee SBla
- 'Molten Gold' ♀ H4 — ECtt GCrs MRav MTho NBro NRya SBla SRot
parnassiifolius — CPBP ETow GTou NHar NMen SBla
platanifolius — LPhx MTed

pyrenaeus	NMen
repens	CKin
– 'Boraston O.S.' (v)	WCHb
– 'Broken Egg' (v) **new**	WAlt
* – 'Buttered Popcorn'	CRow EBee EPPr
– 'Cat's Eyes' (v)	CNat EMan WAlt
– 'Creeping Beauty'	WAlt
– 'Dinah Myte' (v)	WAlt
– 'Gathering Gloom' (v)	WAlt
– 'Gloria Spale'	CBre EMon WAlt
– 'In Vein' (v)	WAlt
– 'Joe's Golden'	EHoe NSti WAlt WCer
– 'Justin Time' (v)	WAlt
– 'Little Creep'	WAlt
– var. *pleniflorus* (d)	CBre CPLG CRow EChP ECha GGar GKir NSti WAlt WEas WFar
– semi-double (d)	WAlt
– 'Snowdrift' (v)	WAlt
– 'Time Bomb' (v) **new**	WAlt
– 'Timothy Clark' (d)	EMon MInt WAlt WHil
rupestris	see *R. spicatus*
sceleratus	WHer
serbicus	EBee EPPr GCal
sieboldii **new**	EBee
speciosus 'Flore Pleno'	see *R. constantinopolitanus* 'Plenus'
§ *spicatus*	CRDP
xinningensis **new**	EBee

Ranzania (Berberidaceae)
japonica	WCru

Raoulia (Asteraceae)
australis hort.	see *R. hookeri*
australis Hook.	CLyd EDAr EMNN EPot GGar ITim MBar MHer MWat NBro NFla NRya NWCA WHoo
– 'Calf'	ITim
§ – Lutescens Group	ECha EPot ITim WLin
grandiflora	SOkd WAbe
haastii	CLyd ECou WBrE
§ *hookeri*	CLyd ECha ECou EDAr EPot GEdr GKir ITim MLan NWCA SIng SPlb SRms WAbe WBrE WCom WFar WPat
– var. *laxa*	EWes
x *loganii*	see x *Leucoraoulia loganii*
lutescens	see *R. australis* Lutescens Group
monroi	ITim
* *nova*	ITim
petriensis	GCrs
x *petrimia*	CGra EHyt ITim WAbe
'Margaret Pringle'	
subsericea	CLyd ECou EWes GCrs NMen WBrE
tenuicaulis	ECha ECou GAbr SPlb

Raoulia x *Leucogenes* see x *Leucoraoulia*

raspberry see *Rubus idaeus*

Ratibida (Asteraceae)
columnifera	EBee EMan LRHS MGol WMoo
– f. *pulcherrima*	EGoo MBNS MCAu
– red	LRav
pinnata	CFwr EBee EBre LRHS MCAu SCro
tagetes **new**	EBee

Rauvolfia (Apocynaceae)
serpentina	MGol

Ravenala (Strelitziaceae)
madagascariensis	CRoM EAmu LPal NBlo WMul XBlo

Ravenea (Arecaceae)
rivularis	CRoM EAmu LPal

Rechsteineria see *Sinningia*

redcurrant see *Ribes rubrum* (R)

Regelia (Myrtaceae)
velutina	SOWG

Rehderodendron (Styracaceae)
macrocarpum	CBcs

Rehmannia (Scrophulariaceae)
angulata hort.	see *R. elata*
§ *elata* ♀ H2	CBct CBot CBri CSev CSpe EBee EBlw ELan EMan LAst LHop LPio LRHS MCLN MHer MPEx SAga SGar SMrm SRPl WCru WFar WMoo WPer WWin WWye
glutinosa ♀ H3	WWye
'White Dragon' **new**	CSpe

Reichardia (Asteraceae)
picroides	CAgr

Reineckea (Convallariaceae)
§ *carnea*	CDes CFee CHid CStu EBee EChP ECha ELan EMar EOrc EPar EPla ERos EWTr GCal GEdr LEur LRHS MFir MRav NSti SCro SDys SHel SPlb WCru WGwG WPGP WPer WWal
– 'Alba' **new**	SSpi
– 'Variegata' (v)	EMan MAvo WCot WCru WHil

Reinwardtia (Linaceae)
elata	SMrm
§ *indica*	LRHS
trigyna	see *R. indica*

Remusatia (Araceae)
vivipara **new**	EBee EBot

Reseda (Resedaceae)
alba	MHer
lutea	CKin MSal SIde
luteola	GBar GPoy MChe MGol MHer MSal NSco WBri WCHb WHer WWye

Restio (Restionaceae)
bifarius	CTrC
pachystachyus	IArd
quadratus	WNor
subverticillatus	see *Ischyrolepis subverticillata*
tetraphyllus	CFir CKno CTrC WCot

Retama (Papilionaceae)
§ *monosperma*	EShb ESlt
§ *sphaerocarpa*	SSpi

Reynoutria see *Fallopia*

Rhagodia (Chenopodiaceae)
triandra	ECou

Rhamnus (Rhamnaceae)
alaternus var. angustifolia	CFil WFar WHCr WPGP
§ – 'Argenteovariegata' (v) ♀ H4	More than 30 suppliers

- 'Variegata'	see *R. alaternus*
	'Argenteovariegata'
cathartica	CCVT CKin CLnd CTri ECrN GIBF
	LBuc MPEx NWea WDin WMou
	WTel
dahurica	GIBF IIve
frangula	CArn CCVT CKin CLnd CSam
	ECrN ENot LBuc MBlu NWea STre
	WDin WFar WMou
- 'Aspleniifolia'	CFai EBee ENot EPfP LBuc MBlu
	MBri MRav NLar SMur WBcn
	WDin WFar WPat
- 'Columnaris'	EMil SLPl
purshiana **new**	MSal

Rhaphiolepis (Rosaceae)

B&SWJ 4901 **new**	WPGP
x *delacourii*	CMHG CWSG CWib EBee EPfP
	GQui LAst LRHS SBrw SMur
	WBcn WBod WHCG WLRN
- 'Coates' Crimson'	CDoC EMil EPfP GQui IArd LHop
	SBra SBrw SHBN SLon SOWG
	WDin WSHC
- 'Enchantress'	CMHG SMur
- 'Spring Song'	SLon
indica	ERom
- Springtime = 'Monme'	SPer WDin
umbellata ♀ H2-3	CBot CHEx CSam CTri CWib
	EBee EPfP GQui LAst LHop LRHS
	MRav SBra SBrw SEND SLon
	SOWG WFar WHCG WPic
	WSHC
- f. *ovata*	CRez
- - B&SWJ 4706	WCru

Rhaphithamnus (Verbenaceae)

cyanocarpus	see *R. spinosus*
spinosus	CPle ERea WBod

Rhapidophyllum (Arecaceae)

hystrix	CBrP CRoM LPal NPal WCot

Rhapis (Arecaceae)

§ *excelsa* ♀ H1	CBrP CRoM EAmu EPVP LPal
	NPal WMul
multifida	LPal

Rhazya (Apocynaceae)

orientalis	see *Amsonia orientalis*

Rhektophyllum see *Cercestis*

Rheum ✿ (Polygonaceae)

§ 'Ace of Hearts'	More than 30 suppliers
'Ace of Spades'	see *R.* 'Ace of Hearts'
acuminatum	CRow EBee GBin WViv
alexandrae	CAgr CFir GCal GKir IBlr MTed
- SDR 1830	GKev
altaicum	IIve
'Andrew's Red'	GTwe
§ *australe*	CArn CRow EBee GCal LRHS
	MBro MLLN NBro NLar SDes
	WCot WFar WHoo
N x *cultorum*	see *R.* x *hybridum*
delavayi	EBee
- SDR 1668	GKev
emodi	see *R. australe*
forrestii	CAgr
x *hybridum*	CAgr
- 'Appleton's Forcing'	GTwe
- 'Baker's All Season'	GTwe
- 'Canada Red'	GTwe
- 'Cawood Delight'	GTwe MAsh SEND

- 'Champagne'	GTwe
- 'Daw's Champion'	GTwe
- 'Early Champagne'	GTwe
- 'Early Cherry'	GTwe
- 'Fenton's Special'	GTwe
- 'German Wine'	GTwe
- 'Goliath'	GTwe
- 'Grandad's Favorite'	EBre
- 'Greengage'	GTwe
- 'Hammond's Early'	GTwe SEND
- 'Harbinger'	GTwe
- 'Hawke's Champagne'	GTwe
- 'Holsteiner Blut'	CBct WCot
- 'Mac Red'	GTwe
- 'Prince Albert'	GTwe
- 'Red Prolific'	GTwe
- 'Reed's Early Superb'	GTwe
- 'Saint Kevin'	IIve
- 'Stein's Champagne'	GTwe
- 'Stockbridge Arrow'	CSut GTwe NGHP
- 'Stockbridge Bingo'	GTwe
- 'Stockbridge Emerald'	GTwe
- 'Stockbridge Guardsman'	GTwe
* - 'Strawberry'	EMui GTwe
- 'Sutton's Cherry Red'	GTwe
- 'The Sutton'	GTwe LBuc
- 'Timperley Early'	CDoC CMac CSam CTri EMui
	ENot EPfP GTwe LBuc LRHS
	MAsh NBlu NGHP SCoo SDea
	SPer WWeb
- 'Tingley Cherry'	GTwe
- 'Valentine'	GTwe
- 'Victoria'	GKir GTwe LRHS MHer NGHP WTel
- 'Zwolle Seedling'	GTwe
kialense	EBee EGle GCal NBid NMRc NSti
officinale	CHEx EPla GCal GKir LRHS MBri
	SWat
palmatum	CArn CBcs CHEx COIW EBee
	EBlw ECha ELan EMFW ENot
	EPfP EWTr GIBF GKir LPBA LRHS
	MRav MSal NGdn SPer SSpi SWat
	WCot WFar WMul WStI WViv
	WWeb
- 'Atropurpureum'	see *R. palmatum* 'Atrosanguineum'
§ - 'Atrosanguineum' ♀ H4	CBct CBot CRow EBre EChP
	ECha ELan EPar EPla GBuc GKir
	LRHS MBri MRav MWgw NBid
	NBro NFor NLon SDes SWat
	WCom WCru WWin
- 'Bowles' Crimson'	CHad GKir LRHS MBri SAga
- 'Da Huang'	IIve
'Hadspen Crimson'	CHad NPSI WCot
- 'Red Herald'	CBct LRHS MBri SBla SDes WCot
- *rubrum*	COtt EBre GKir LRHS MCCP NBir
	WFar WHil
- 'Saville'	CBct GKir LRHS MBri MLLN MRav
- var. *tanguticum*	More than 30 suppliers
I - - 'Rosa Auslese'	LPhx SDes WHil WViv
rhabarbarum	CRow
rhaponticum	CAgr EBee NLar WViv
ribes **new**	WCot
tataricum	EBee LEdu

Rhinanthus (Scrophulariaceae)

minor	NSco

Rhodanthe (Asteraceae)

§ *anthemoides*	ECou IDac
- 'Paper Cascade' PBR	GTwe LRHS

Rhodanthemum (Asteraceae)

from High Atlas, Morocco	SIng
'African Eyes' **new**	EBee SUsu

§ *atlanticum* — ECho EWes SScr
§ *catananche* — CPBP ECho EPot ETow EWes NWCA
- 'Tizi-n-Test' — LBee LRHS SBla
- 'Tizi-n-Tichka' — CPBP ETow EWes LBee LRHS NBir SBla SIng
§ *gayanum* — EBee EWes LRHS SAga SCro WCot WHen
- 'Flamingo' — see *R. gayanum*
§ *hosmariense* ♀ H4 — CMHG EBee ECha EDAr ELan EPot LHop LRHS MTis SAga SBla SCoo SCro SIng SPer SRms WAbe WCom WEas WHil

Rhodiola (*Crassulaceae*)

bupleuroides CLD 1196 — EMon
coccinea **new** — GCal
crassipes — see *R. wallichiana*
§ *fastigiata* — EMon GCal NMen
§ *heterodonta* — ECha EGle ELan EMon LPio MRav NPPs WCot
§ *integrifolia* NNS 99-456 — NWCA
§ *ishidae* — CTri
§ *kirilovii* — EMon GBin GKir GTou WCot
- var. *rubra* — EBre WFar
linearifolia **new** — EMon GCal
pachyclados — More than 30 suppliers
§ *primuloides* — NMen
rhodantha NNS 99-454 — NWCA
§ *rosea* — EBre ECha EHoe ELan EMan EPfP EPla GCal MFir MHer NBid NBir NFor NGdn NPPs NSti SCro SPar SPer SRms STre WAbb WEas WFar WWhi
semenovii — MHar NLar
§ *trollii* — CNic GCrs
§ *wallichiana* — GCrs NBid WCot

Rhodochiton (*Scrophulariaceae*)

§ *atrosanguineus* ♀ H1-2 — CArn CBcs CEnd CFox CPLG CPIN CRHN CSpe ELan EPfP ERea GGar LRHS MAsh MNes NPPs SGar SHFr SOWG SPar
volubilis — see *R. atrosanguineus*

Rhodocoma (*Restionaceae*)

arida — CTrC IArd
capensis — CAbb CFir CTrC IArd ITer
fruticosa — CTrC
gigantea — CAbb CCtw CFir CTrC ITer WNor

Rhododendron ✿ (*Ericaceae*)

'A.J. Ivens' — see *R.* 'Arthur J. Ivens'
'Abegail' — MGos NMun SLdr
'Abendrot' — MBri
aberconwayi — CWri LMil NMun SLdr SReu
- 'His Lordship' — GGGa LHyd
- pink — NMun
'Accomplishment' — CWri
acrophilum (V) — GGGa
  Argent 2768
'Actress' — NMun
'Ada Bruniere' (K) **new** — CSdC
'Addy Wery' (EA) ♀ H3-4 — CDoC ENot LKna MBar MGos MHdf NMun SCam SLdr SPoG SReu WBod WStI
adenogynum — GGGa LMil NMun SLdr
- CLD 795 — LMil
- Cox 6502 — GGGa
§ - Adenophorum Group — EMui
- - F 20444 — SLdr
- - R 11471 — NMun

- - 'Kirsty' — NMun
- white — NMun
adenophorum — see *R. adenogynum* Adenophorum Group
adenopodum — GGGa NMun SLdr SReu
adenosum — NHol NMun
- R 18228 — GGGa
- Kuluense Group — NMun
'Admiral Piet Hein' — SReu
'Adonis' (EA/d) — CMac LMil MBar SCam SLdr
'Adriaan Koster' (M) — SLdr
adroserum — see *R. lukiangense*
'Advance' (O) — LRHS NMun SLdr
aeruginosum — see *R. campanulatum* subsp. *aeruginosum*
aganniphum — GGGa LMil NMun
- CN&W 1174 — LMil
- EGM 284 — LMil
- pink, KR 3528 from Pe, Doshang La — LMil
- var. *aganniphum* F 16472 — NMun
§ - - Doshongense Group — GGGa NMun
- - - C&V 9541 — GGGa
- - - KW 5863 — NMun
- - Glaucopeplum Group — GGGa
- - Schizopeplum Group — GGGa
- var. *flavorufum* — GGGa NMun
- - Cox 5070 — GGGa
- - EGM 160 — LMil
- - 'Rusty' — NMun
agapetum — see *R. kyawii* Agapetum Group
x *agastum* — NMun SLdr
- PW 98 — LMil
'Ahren's Favourite' — MAsh SBrw
'Aida' (R/d) — CSBt SReu
'Aksel Olsen' — CTri ECho GKir MBar MDun NHol
'Aladdin' (EA) — CDoC ECho SLdr WFar WGwG
Aladdin Group — CWri SBrw SReu
'Aladdin' (*auriculatum* hybrid) — GGGa
Albatross Group — LKna LMil SBrw SLdr SReu SSta
'Albatross Townhill Pink' — LMil
'Albert Schweitzer' ♀ H4 — CWri EMil GGGa LMil MBar MDun NBlu SBrw SReu WWeb
albiflorum (A) — GGGa SReu
albrechtii (A) — GGGa LHyd LMil SReu SSpi WBod
- Whitney form (A) — LMil
'Alena' — GGGa
'Alexander' (EA) ♀ H4 — CDoC GQui LMil MAsh MBri MGos SHBN SReu
'Alfred' — LRHS NBlu
'Alice' (EA) — LHyd LKna
'Alice' (hybrid) ♀ H4 — CSBt LHyd LKna LMil NMun SBrw SLdr SReu
'Alice de Stuers' (M) — SLdr
Alison Johnstone Group — CBcs GGGa MBri MDun MLea NMun SLdr SReu WPic
'Aloha' — MBar NBlu NDlv SHBN SReu
Alpine Gem Group — GQui NHol
'Alpine Glow' — NMun
alutaceum — NMun
- var. *alutaceum* — GGGa
§ - - Globigerum Group — LMil
- - - R 11100 — GGGa NMun
§ - var. *iodes* — GGGa LMil NMun SLdr
§ - var. *russotinctum* — GGGa MDun
- - R 158 — SLdr
§ - - Triplonaevium Group — GGGa USDAPI 59442/R10923
amagianum (A) — LMil
Amaura Group — WBod

	ambiguum	LMil SLdr SReu WBod
	- KR 185 select*	GGGa
	- 'Jane Banks'	LMil
	'Ambrosia' (EA)	CSBt
	'America'	CBcs MBar MGos SBrw WFar
	amesiae	GGGa NMun
§	'Amethystinum' (EA)	LKna
	'Amity'	CDoC CWri ECho MAsh MLea SLdr
§	'Amoenum' (EA/d)	CDoC CMac CTrG CTrw LHyd LKna LRHS MBar MGos NBlu NMun SCam SLdr SPer SPoG WAbe WBod WFar WPic
	'Amoenum Coccineum' (EA/d)	SCam SReu WPat
	Amor Group	LHyd
	'Anah Kruschke'	MAsh SLdr
	'Analin'	see *R.* 'Anuschka'
	'Anchorite' (EA)	GQui LMil SLdr
	'Andre'	NMun SReu
*	'Andrea'	NMun
	'Angelo' **new**	LHyd
	Angelo Group	LHyd LMil SBrw SLdr SReu
	'Ann Callingham' (K)	CSdC
	'Ann Lindsay'	SBrw SReu
	'Anna Baldsiefen'	CSam ENot GLbr LMil MBri MOne NHol SBrw SReu SSta
	'Anna H. Hall'	MAsh SLdr
	'Anna Rose Whitney'	CBcs GGGa GKir LHyd LKna LMil LPan LRHS MAsh MBar MBri MDun MGos MLea NMun NPrl SBrw SHBN SLdr SPer SReu SSta WBVN WBod
	'Annabella' (K) ♀ H4	CSdC MAsh MBri SLdr SReu
	annae	GGGa LMil NMun SLdr
§	- Hardingii Group	NMun
	aff. *annae* C&H 7185	LMil
	'Anne Frank' (EA)	COtt MGos SReu WBod
	'Anne George'	LHyd
	'Anne Teese'	LMil SLdr
	'Annegret Hansmann'	GGGa
	'Anneke' (A)	MBar MDun SLdr SReu SSta WBod
	'Anny' (EA)	LKna SLdr
	anthopogon	GCrs LMil
	- 'Betty Graham'	GGGa LMil
	- from Marpha Meadow, Nepal	WAbe
§	- subsp. *hypenanthum*	LMil MDun
	- - 'Annapurna'	GGGa NHol WAbe
§	*anthosphaerum*	GGGa NMun SLdr SReu
	- KW 5684	NMun
	- Gymnogynum Group	NMun
§	- Heptamerum Group	NMun
§	'Antilope' (Vs)	CWri LMil SPer SReu SSta
	'Antje'	MAsh
	'Antonio'	LMil
	'Antoon van Welie'	SBrw
§	'Anuschka'	GKir LRHS SBrw
§	*anwheiense*	CWri LHyd LMil NMun SReu
	aperantum	GGGa
	- F 27022	GGGa
	- JN 498	GGGa
	'Aphrodite' (EA)	GQui
	apodectum	see *R. dichroanthum* subsp. *apodectum*
	'Apotheose' (EA)	NBlu
	'Apotrophia'	SLdr
	'Apple Blossom' (M)	NBlu SLdr
	'Apple Blossom'	CMac CTrh SBrw SReu
N	'Appleblossom'	see *R.* 'Ho-o'
	'Apricot Fantasy'	LMil
	'Apricot Surprise'	GKir LRHS

	'Apricot Top Garden'	SLdr
	'April Dawn'	GGGa
	'April Gem'	MBri
§	'April Glow'	LHyd
	'April Mist' **new**	MAsh
	'April Rose'	MBri
	'April Showers' (A)	ENot LMil
	'April White'	MBri
I	'Arabella'	MAsh
	'Arabesk' (EA)	SLdr WWeb
	araiophyllum	GGGa
	- KR 4029	LMil
§	*arborescens* (A)	GGGa LKna LMil NMun SLdr SReu
	- pink (A)	LMil
	arboreum	CHEx GGGa ISea LMil MDun NMun SReu
	- B&SWJ 2244	WCru
	- C&S 1651	NMun
	- C&S 1695	NMun
	- subsp. *arboreum* KR 966	NMun
	- 'Blood Red'	NMun SLdr
	- subsp. *cinnamomeum*	GGGa LMil NMun SLdr SReu
	- - var. *album*	SLdr SReu
	- - var. *cinnamomeum* Campbelliae Group	NMun SLdr
	- - var. *roseum*	CWri GGGa NMun
	- - - BB 151*	NMun
*	- - - *crispum*	NMun
	- - - 'Tony Schilling'	LHyd LMil NMun SLdr
§	- subsp. *delavayi*	GGGa ISea NMun SLdr
	- - C&H 7178	GGGa
	- - C&S 1515	NMun
	- - CN&W 994	LMil
	- - EGM 360	LMil
	- - KW 21796	NMun
	- 'Heligan'	CWri SReu
	- mid-pink	SLdr
§	- subsp. *nilagiricum*	GGGa SLdr
	- var. *roseum*	SLdr
§	- subsp. *zeylanicum*	NMun SLdr
	- - 'Rubaiyat'	NMun
	x *arbutifolium*	see *R.* Arbutifolium Group
	'Arcadia' (EA)	LKna
	'Arctic Fox' (EA)	GGGa
	'Arctic Regent' (K)	CSdC GQui
	'Arctic Tern'	see x *Ledodendron* 'Arctic Tern'
§	*argipeplum*	CWri GGGa LMil NMun SLdr
	'Argosy' ♀ H4	LMil NMun SBrw SLdr SReu
	argyrophyllum	CWri NMun SLdr
	- subsp. *argyrophyllum* W/A 1210	SLdr
§	- subsp. *hypoglaucum*	NMun
	- - 'Heane Wood'	GGGa
	- subsp. *nankingense*	GGGa LMil NMun
	- - 'Chinese Silver' ♀ H4	LHyd LMil LRHS MDun NMun SReu
§	*arizelum*	GGGa LMil LRHS MDun NMun SLdr
	- R 25	GGGa
	- SF 96228	ISea
	- subsp. *arizelum* Rubicosum Group	LMil LRHS MDun NMun
	'Armantine'	LKna
	armitii (V) Woods 2518	LKna
	'Arneson Gem' (M)	CDoC CSam GGGa LMil SLdr WWeb
	'Arneson Ruby' (K)	CDoC
	'Arpege' (Vs)	LMil MHFa MLea SReu
	'Arthur Bedford'	CSBt LHyd LKna LMil SBrw SReu
§	'Arthur J. Ivens'	SLdr
	'Arthur Osborn'	GGGa SLdr
	'Arthur Stevens'	SLdr
	'Arthur Warren'	LKna SBrw

'Arthur's Choice' (V) **new** SFai
'Asa-gasumi' (EA) LHyd SCam SLdr
'Ascot Brilliant' SBrw
asterochnoum LMil
– C&H 7051 GGGa
– EGM 314 LMil
Asteroid Group SLdr
'Astrid' ENot LMil NBlu
atlanticum (A) GGGa LMil NMun SSpi
– 'Seaboard' (A) LMil SLdr SPer
'Audrey Wynniatt' (EA) MAsh
Augfast Group CTrw ISea SLdr WBod
'August Lamken' MAsh MBri
augustinii CHig CSBt CTrG CTrw CWri
GGGa ISea LHyd LMil LRHS MLea
NMun SLdr SSpi SSta WAbe
WBod
– subsp. *augustinii* GGGa
C&H 7048
§ – subsp. *chasmanthum* GGGa LMil SLdr
– – C&Cu 9407 white GGGa
§ – Electra Group GGGa LHyd LMil MDun NMun SLdr
– Exbury best form LMil SReu
§ – subsp. *hardyi* GGGa SLdr
– pale lilac SLdr
§ – subsp. *rubrum* GGGa
– – 'Papillon' NMun
* – 'Trewithen' LMil
I – 'Werrington' SReu
§ *aureum* GGGa GPoy LMil NMun SLdr
auriculatum CWri GGGa LMil LRHS MDun
NMun SLdr SReu SSpi SSta
– PW 50 GGGa
– Reuthe's form SReu
auritum GGGa NMun SLdr WPic
'Aurora' (K) NMun SLdr
§ *austrinum* (A) LMil
– yellow (A) LMil
'Autumn Gold' LMil SBrw SLdr
'Avalanche' ♀ H4 LMil SReu
'Award' LMil
'Ayah' SBrw SReu
'Aya-kammuri' (EA) LHyd SLdr
Azamia Group LHyd
Azor Group CHig LHyd NMun SBrw SReu
'Azorazie' NMun
Azrie Group **new** SLdr
§ 'Azuma-kagami' (EA) CDoC LHyd LKna LMil WBod
'Azurika' NHol
'Azurro' GGGa MAsh WGer WWeb
'Azurwolke' LMil
'B. de Bruin' SBrw
'Babuschka' GGGa
'Baby Scarlet' SSta
'Baden-Baden' CDoC EBee GCrs GEdr LHyd
LKna MAsh MBar MDun MGos
NHol NMun NWea SBod SHBN
SLdr SSta WBrE WFar WWeb
'Bagshot Ruby' ENot LKna NBlu NWea
baileyi GGGa NMun SLdr WAbe
– LS&H 17359 NMun
bainbridgeanum USDAPI NMun
59184/R11190
balangense EN 3530 GGGa
balfourianum GGGa LMil NMun
– AC 1575 from Xian Rindong LMil
– SSNY 224 GGGa
– var. *aganniphoides* NMun
'Ballerina' (K) SReu
'Balsaminiflorum' see *R. indicum* 'Balsaminiflorum'
'Baltic Amber' (A) **new** GGGa
'Balzac' (K) LHyd MGos MLea SBrw SLdr
'Bambi' NMun SBrw SLdr SReu

'Bambino' LNet
'Bandoola' SReu
'Barbara Coates' (EA) SLdr
'Barbara Reuthe' SBrw SReu
barbatum GGGa LHyd LMil MDun NMun
SLdr SReu
– BL&M 325 NMun
'Barbecue' (K) LMil
'Barclayi Helen Fox' NMun SLdr
'Barclayi Robert Fox' NMun SLdr
'Bariton' **new** LMil
'Barmstedt' CWri
'Barnaby Sunset' GGGa GKir LMil LRHS MAsh NHol
'Barry Rodgers' GGGa
'Bashful' ♀ H4 CSBt EMui EPfP GKir LHyd LRHS
MGos NMun NPri SLdr SReu
§ *basilicum* GGGa IDee LMil LRHS NMun SLdr
– AC 3009 WCwm
– AC 616 NMun
– SF 381 ISea
x *bathyphyllum* NMun
– Cox 6542 GGGa
bauhiniiflorum see *R. triflorum* var. *bauhiniiflorum*
beanianum GGGa LMil NMun SLdr
– KW 6805 NMun
– compact see *R. piercei*
'Beatrice Keir' LMil NMun SLdr SReu
'Beattie' (EA) SLdr
Beau Brummel Group LMil
'Beaulieu Manor' GQui
'Beauty of Littleworth' LHyd LKna NMun SLdr SPer
SReu
beesianum GGGa LMil NMun SLdr
– CN&W 1316 ISea
– F 10195 NMun
– F 16375 SLdr
– SSNY 250 GGGa
– SSNY 303 GGGa
– red bud SLdr
'Beethoven' (EA) ♀ H3-4 CTrG LHyd NMun SCam SLdr
SReu WGor WPic
'Belkanto' ENot LMil
'Belle Heller' MBri SBrw SLdr
Bellerophon Group NMun
'Ben Morrison' (EA) SReu
'Bengal' GKir MAsh MBar MDun NHol
SReu WAbe
'Bengal Beauty' (EA) GQui SLdr
'Bengal Fire' (EA) CMac
'Beni-giri' (EA) CMac
'Bergie Larson' CDoC LMil MAsh MDun MLea SLdr
bergii see *R. augustinii* subsp. *rubrum*
'Berg's Yellow' CWri MAsh MDun MLea
'Bernard Shaw' SReu
'Bernstein' EMil NBlu WFar
'Berryrose' (K) ♀ H4 CBcs CWri ENot EPfP GKir LHyd
LKna LMil MBar MGos NBlu NMun
SBrw SLdr SPer SReu WBod WLRN
Berryrose Group MDun
'Bert's Own' CBcs SLdr
§ 'Beryl Taylor' GGGa NMun
'Betty' (EA) CTrG LHyd SLdr WBod
'Betty Anne Voss' (EA) CDoC GKir LHyd LMil LRHS NPri
SCam SCoo SLdr SReu WGwG
'Betty Wormald' CDoC CHig CSBt CWri GKir LKna
LMil MBri MGos MHFa MLea
NMun SBrw SHBN SLdr SReu SSta
bhutanense LMil
– AC 119 NMun
– AC 124 NMun
– CH&M GGGa
'Big Punkin' LMil
'Billy Budd' LHyd

'Birthday Girl'	COtt LMil MLea
'Birthday Greeting'	NMun
'Biscuit Box'	NMun
Biskra Group	GGGa NMun
'Blaauw's Pink' (EA) ♀ H3-4	CDoC CMac CTrh ENot GKir
	GQui LHyd LMil LRHS
	MAsh MBar MBri MGos NMun
	SBrw SCam SLdr SPer SPlb SReu
	SRms WBod WFar
'Black Hawk' (EA)	CBcs CTrG
'Black Knight' (A)	SLdr
'Black Magic'	CWri LMil MAsh
'Black Satin'	LMil
'Black Sport'	MLea
'Blatgold'	GGGa
Blaue Donau	see R. 'Blue Danube'
'Blazecheck'	LRHS MGos SCoo
'Blewbury' ♀ H4	CDoC LHyd LMil LRHS MDun
	NMun SLdr SReu SSta
'Blue Beard'	SLdr
'Blue Bell'	LKna SBrw
'Blue Boy'	LMil
'Blue Chip'	LHyd NMun SLdr
§ 'Blue Danube' (EA) ♀ H3-4	CDoC CMac CSBt CTrG CTrh CTri
	ENot GKir LHyd LKna LMil LRHS
	MAsh MBar MBri MDun MHFa
	NMun NPri SBod SCam SLdr SPer
	SReu SSta WBod WFar WSti
	WWeb
Blue Diamond Group	CBcs CBrm CChe CMHG CTrh
	ENot EPfP LKna LRHS MAsh MBar
	MDun MGos NHol NMun NWea
	SBrw SHBN SLdr SReu SRms
	WBod WPic
'Blue Diamond'	CSBt MLea WWeb
'Blue Gown'	LKna
'Bluc Monday'	SLdr WBod
'Blue Moon'	MBar
'Blue Mountain'	GDra NWea
'Blue Peter' ♀ H4	CDoC CSBt CWri EMil ENot EPfP
	GGGa LHyd LKna LMil MAsh
	MBar MBri MGos NBlu NMun
	SBrw SHBN SLdr SReu SSta
'Blue Pool'	LMil MBar WBod
Blue Ribbon Group	CMHG CTrw ISea
'Blue Silver'	GGGa LMil MAsh
'Blue Star'	GKir LHyd LRHS MAsh MBri
	MDun MLea NMen SReu WWeb
'Blue Steel'	see R. fastigiatum 'Blue Steel'
Blue Tit Group	CBcs CSBt CSam CTrG GDra GKir
	LHyd LKna LRHS NMun SBrw
	NMun SBrw SHBN SLdr SReu SSta
	STre WBod WWeb
Bluebird Group	CSBt ECho ENot LKna MBar
	MDun MGos NBlu NDlv NWCA
	SLdr SRms WBod
Bluestone Group	WBod
'Bluette'	ISca MDun MLca NDlv
'Blurettia'	CWri LMil NBlu
'Bobbie'	SReu
'Bob's Blue'	MDun
'Boddaertianum'	LHyd SReu
bodinieri USDAPI 59585/	NMun
R11281	
'Bodnant Yellow'	CSam
'Bold Janus' (V) **new**	SFai
'Bonfire'	SReu
'Bo-peep'	LHyd LRHS SReu
Bo-peep Group	CBcs CHig CSam LMil NMun SLdr
'Boskoop Ostara'	LMil
'Bountiful' (EA)	LMil
'Bouquet de Flore'	CDoC CSdC LMil MBar MBri SLdr
(G) ♀ H4	SPer SReu WGer

Bow Bells Group	CSam EBre ISea LHyd LKna LMil
	MAsh MBar MBri MDun MGos
	MLea SHBN
'Bow Bells' ♀ H4	GKir LRHS NBlu NMun NPri SLdr
	WFar WWeb
'Bow Street'	LHyd
brachyanthum	GGGa NMun
- subsp. *hypolepidotum*	GGGa LMil NMun
- - KW 7038	NMun
brachycarpum	GGGa NMun SLdr
- subsp. *brachycarpum*	SReu
Tigerstedtii Group	
§ - subsp. *fauriei*	NMun
- pink	NMun
- 'Roseum Dwarf'	GGGa NMun
brachysiphon	see R. *maddenii* subsp. *maddenii*
'Brazier' (EA)	CTrh LHyd LRHS NMun SCam SLdr
'Brazil' (K)	CSBt LKna SBrw SReu
'Bremen'	LMil SLdr
'Breslau' (EA)	SBrw
'Brets Own'	NMun
Bric-a-brac Group	CBcs CTrw NMun SLdr
'Bric-à-brac'	LHyd
'Bride's Bouquet' (EA/d)	SReu
'Bridesmaid' (O)	ENot EPfP SLdr
'Brigadoon'	LMil MAsh
'Bright Forecast' (K)	CWri SLdr WGor
'Brigitte'	CDoC CWri GGGa LMil LRHS
	MAsh SLdr
'Brilliant' (EA)	MGos WBod
'Brilliant' (hybrid)	MGos NHol
'Brilliant Crimson' (EA)	SLdr
'Britannia'	CSBt CSam CWri EPfP GKir ISea
	LHyd LKna LNet MAsh MBar MBri
	MGos NMun NWea SBrw SHBN
	SLdr SPer SReu SSta WFar
'Britannia' X	SLdr
griersonianum	
'Brocade'	CSam LHyd LKna LMil MBri
	MDun NMun SLdr
'Bronze Fire' (A)	SReu
'Broughtonii'	CWri NMun SLdr
'Brown Eyes'	CWri MDun MLea
'Bruce Brechtbill' ♀ H4	CDoC CHig CWri GGGa GKir
	LMil LRHS MAsh MDun NBlu
	NHol SBrw SLdr SReu SSta
'Bruns Gloria'	LMil
'Buccaneer' (EA)	SLdr
'Bud Flanagan'	LMil NMun SBrw
'Buketta'	GGGa MDun
bullatum	see R. *edgeworthii*
bulu C&V 9503	GGGa
'Bungo-nishiki' (EA/d)	CMac
bureavii ♀ H4	CAbP GGGa LHyd LMil MDun
	NMun SLdr SReu SSta WAbe
- C&H 7158	GGGa
- F 15609	NMun
- R 25439	NMun
SEH 211	LMil
- SF 517	ISea
- 'Ardrishaig'	GGGa
* - *cruentum*	LMil
I - 'Lem's Variety'	WAbe
- x Elizabeth Group	SReu
bureavioides	MDun NMun SReu
- Cox 5076	GGGa
'Burletta'	GGGa
burmanicum	GGGa LMil MDun NMun SLdr
	WBod
'Butter Yellow'	ECho MBri
'Buttercup' (K)	MBar
'Butterfly'	LKna MDun NMun SBrw SLdr
'Buttermilk' (V) **new**	ISea

'Buttermint'	MAsh MBri MDun MLea NBlu NMun SHBN SLdr SReu WBVN WGwG WWeb
'Buttons and Bows' (K)	GGGa LMil MAsh
'Buzzard' (K)	CSdC LKna LMil
'C.I.S.'	NMun
'Caerhays Lavender'	CBcs
caesium	GGGa
calendulaceum (A)	LHyd LMil SReu
- red (A)	LMil
- yellow	LMil
Calfort Group	NMun SLdr
'Calico' (K)	CSdC
caliginis (V)	GGGa
callimorphum	GGGa LMil NMun
- var. *myiagrum* F 21821a	NMun SLdr
- - KW 6962	NMun
calophytum ♥ H4	CBcs CHEx CWri GGGa LHyd LMil LRHS NMun WGer
- EGM 343	LMil
- Knott 151	NMun
- var. *openshawianum* C&H 7055	GGGa
- - EGM 318	LMil
- × *praevernum*	WCwm
calostrotum	CWri WAbe
- SF 357	ISea
- 'Gigha' ♥ H4	CDoC GGGa GKir LMil LRHS LTwo MBri MHFa MOne NHar SLdr WGwG
§ - subsp. *keleticum* ♥ H4	CTrG GDra GEdr LHyd MBar MGos NHol SBrw WGer WWeb
- - F 19915	NHol
- - F 21756	NMun
- - R 58	LMil
§ - - Radicans Group	GCrs GEdr LHyd LMil MBar MBri MBro MDun MLea NHol WAbe WPat
- - USDAPI 59182/R11188	MLea
- Radicans Group mound form	NHol
- subsp. *riparium*	LMil
- - SF 95089	ISea
- - Calciphilum Group	GGGa
§ - - Nitens Group	CDoC GGGa LMil MAsh NDlv NMen WAbe
§ - - Rock's form R 178	GGGa NHol
caloxanthum	see *R. campylocarpum* subsp. *caloxanthum*
'Calsap'	GGGa
Calstocker Group	LMil
calvescens var. *duseimatum*	NMun
camelliiflorum	GGGa MDun
'Cameronian' (Ad)	LKna
campanulatum	COtt LHyd LKna MDun NMun SLdr SReu WAbe
- HWJCM 195	WCru
- SS&W 9107	SLdr
- TSS 11	NMun
§ - subsp. *aeruginosum*	GGGa LMil NLar NMun SLdr SReu
- - Airth 10	GGGa
- *album*	NMun SLdr
- subsp. *campanulatum* BL&M 283	NMun
- - 'Roland Cooper'	NMun SLdr
- 'Knap Hill'	LHyd NMun SLdr SReu
- 'Waxen Bell'	LHyd NMun
§ 'Campfire' (EA)	SLdr
Campirr Group	LHyd
campylocarpum	GGGa LHyd LMil MDun NMun SLdr SReu
- LS&H 16495*	NMun

§ - subsp. *caloxanthum*	GGGa MDun NMun
- - KR 3516 from Pe, Doshang La	LMil
- - Telopeum Group	NMun
- - - KW 5718B	NMun
- subsp. *campylocarpum* TSS 12	NMun
- - Elatum Group	NMun
- East Nepal	NMun
campylogynum ♥ H4	GCrs MGos MLea NMen SSpi
- Cox 6051	GGGa
- Cox 6096	GGGa
- SF 95181	ISea
- 'Album'	see *R.* 'Leucanthum'
- 'Beryl Taylor'	see *R.* 'Beryl Taylor'
I - 'Bramble'	MDun
- Castle Hill form	LMil SReu
- Charopoeum Group	GCrs GGGa LMil MBar MDun MGos NHar NHol NLAp WAbe
- - 'Patricia'	ECho GBin MDun WAbe
- claret	ECho GGGa MDun WAbe
§ - Cremastum Group	CTrG GGGa LHyd NHol NMun WAbe
- - 'Bodnant Red'	GGGa LHyd MDun NMun WBod
- var. *leucanthum*	see *R.* 'Leucanthum'
- Myrtilloides Group	CBcs CDoC CTrw GGGa GQui LHyd LMil LRHS MDun NMen NMun SLdr SReu WAbe
- - Farrer 1046	GGGa
- pink	MBar WAbe
- plum	WAbe
- salmon pink	ECho EPot GEdr MDun NHar
camtschaticum	GGGa WAbe
- var. *albiflorum*	GGGa NMen
- from Hokkaido, Japan	GCrs NMen
- from Rishiri	GCrs
- red	GGGa
canadense (A)	GGGa NHol SLdr SReu
- f. *albiflorum* (A)	GGGa LMil
- dark-flowered (A)	LMil
- 'Deer Lake' (A)	SReu
'Canary'	LKna SLdr SReu
§ × *candelabrum*	NMun
canescens (A)	LMil
'Cannon's Double' (K/d) ♥ H4	CWri GGGa LMil MAsh MBri MGos MLea SLdr WWeb
'Cannon's Purple' **new**	GLbr
'Canzonetta' (EA) ♥ H4	GGGa LMil MGos SLdr
'Capistrano'	GGGa
capitatum	GGGa
'Caprice' (EA)	SReu
'Captain Jack'	GGGa SLdr
'Caractacus'	EMil MBar SBrw WFar
'Carat'	SLdr SReu
'Cardinal' **new**	SLdr
cardiobasis	see *R. orbiculare* subsp. *cardiobasis*
Carita Group	LKna SBrw SReu
'Carita Golden Dream'	LKna LMil NMun
'Carita Inchmery'	LHyd LKna NMun SBrw SLdr
'Carmen'	CSam GDra GGGa GKir ISea LHyd LKna LMil LRHS MAsh MBar MBri MDun MLea NHar NHol NLAp NMen NMun NWea SBrw SHBN SLdr SReu SRms WBod WWeb
carneum	GGGa
'Caroline Allbrook' ♥ H4	CDoC CSam CWri EMui GGGa GLbr ISea LHyd LMil MAsh MBri MDun MGos MHFa MLea NDlv NHol NMun SBrw SLdr SReu
'Caroline de Zoete'	LHyd
carolinianum	see *R. minus* var. *minus* Carolinum Group

'Cary Ann'	CBcs CSam CWri GKir ISea LRHS MLea NMun SLdr SReu WFar	
'Cassley' (Vs)	LMil SLdr	
'Castle of Mey'	SLdr	
catacosmum	GGGa	
§ 'Catalode'	SBrw	
catawbiense	CHig GGGa LHyd NMun SLdr	
'Catawbiense Album'	CWri GKir LRHS MAsh NWea WFar	
'Catawbiense Boursault'	CWri MAsh	
'Catawbiense Grandiflorum'	GKir LRHS MAsh SBrw WFar	
'Catherine Hopwood'	NMun SLdr	
caucasicum	NMun	
- ex AC&H	NMun	
§ - 'Cunningham's Sulphur'	MDun	
'Caucasicum Pictum'	GGGa LHyd LMil MBar MBri SBrw SLdr	
'Cayenne' (EA)	SLdr	
'Cecile' (K) ♀ H4	CBcs CSBt CWri GKir GLbr LHyd LKna LMil MBar MBri MDun MGos MHFa MLea NMun SLdr SPer SReu	
'Celestial' (EA)	CMac	
I 'Celtic Cross'	CBcs	
'Centennial'	see *R.* 'Washington State Centennial'	
cephalanthum	GGGa LMil	
- subsp. *cephalanthum* SBEC 0751	GGGa WAbe	
- - Crebreflorum Group	GGGa LMil LRHS WAbe	
- - Nmaiense Group C&V 9513	GGGa	
- subsp. *platyphyllum*	GGGa LMil	
- - CN&W 835	LMil	
cerasinum	GGGa ISea LMil NMun SLdr	
- C&V 9504	GGGa	
- KR 3460	LMil	
- KR 3490 from Pr, Doshang La	LMil	
- KW 11011	NMun	
- SF 95067	ISea	
- 'Cherry Brandy'	LHyd NMun	
- 'Coals of Fire'	NMun	
- deep pink-flowered	NMun	
'Cetewayo' ♀ H4	SBrw SReu	
chaetomallum	see *R. haematodes* subsp. *chaetomallum*	
'Chaffinch' (K)	LKna	
chamaethomsonii	GGGa LMil NHar NMun	
- CCH&H 8195	GGGa	
- SF 95084	ISea	
- var. *chamaethauma* KR 3506 from Pr, Doshang La	LMil	
- - KW 5847	LMil	
- var. *chamaethomsonii* F 21723	NMun	
chameunum	see *R. saluenense* subsp. *chameunum*	
§ 'Champagne' ♀ H3-4	CSBt GKir LHyd LKna LMil LRHS MAsh MGos MLea NMun SBrw SLdr SPer SReu	
championiae	GGGa	
'Chanel' (Vs)	SLdr SReu SSta	
'Chanticleer' (EA)	CTrh SCam SLdr SReu	
chapaense	see *R. maddenii* subsp. *crassum*	
'Chapeau'	LMil	
charitopes	GGGa LMil NMun SLdr	
- subsp. *charitopes* F 25570	SReu	
§ - subsp. *tsangpoense*	GGGa GQui LMil NHol	
- - C&V 9575*	GGGa	
'Charles Bagley'	SBrw	
* 'Charles Puddle'	WBod	

'Charlotte de Rothschild' (hybrid)	LMil NMun SLdr	
Charmaine Group	GGGa NHol WBod	
'Charme La'	GGGa	
'Charming Valentino' (V)	SFai	
chasmanthum	see *R. augustinii* subsp. *chasmanthum*	
'Cheer'	COtt CWri LMil LPan MAsh MBar MBri NBlu SBrw SLdr WFar WGor WWeb	
'Cheerful Giant' (K)	CDoC GKir LMil LRHS MGos	
'Chelsea Reach' (K/d)	CSdC LKna	
'Chelsea Seventy'	COtt ENot GKir LRHS MAsh NMun SLdr SReu	
'Chenille' (K/d)	LKna	
'Cherokee'	SCam SLdr	
'Cherries and Cream'	LMil	
'Chetco' (K)	CDoC LMil MBri	
'Chevalier Félix de Sauvage' ♀ H4	EMil LMil MGos NMun SBrw SReu	
'Cheyenne'	SLdr	
'Chicago' (M)	LKna	
'Chiffchaff'	LHyd NMen	
'Chikor'	CSBt CTrG GGGa GKir LKna MAsh MBar MBri MDun MGos NHar NHol NLAp NMun SLdr SReu SRms WBod WFar	
China Group	LKna SBrw SReu	
'China A'	LKna SBrw SLdr	
'Chinchilla' (EA)	GQui WGor	
'Chink'	CBcs ENot MAsh MBar MDun NMun SLdr WBod	
'Chintz'	WBod	
'Chionoides'	CHig GGGa LKna NBlu SLdr	
'Chipmunk' (EA/d)	LMil LRHS	
'Chippewa' (EA)	GGGa GKir LMil LRHS	
'Chocolate Ice' (K/d)	LKna SLdr	
'Chopin' (EA)	WBod	
'Choremia' ♀ H3	LMil NMun SReu WBod	
'Chorister' (K)	LKna	
christi (V)	GGGa	
'Christina' (EA/d)	CMac SLdr SReu WBod WGor	
'Christmas Cheer' (EA/d)	see *R.* 'Ima-shojo'	
'Christmas Cheer' (hybrid)	CBcs CHig CMac CWri GGGa ISea LHyd LKna LMil MAsh MGos MLea NMun SBrw SHBN SLdr SPer SReu WPic WWeb	
§ 'Christopher Wren' (K)	SLdr	
chrysanthum	see *R. aureum*	
chryseum	see *R. rupicola* var. *chryseum*	
chrysodoron	GGGa LMil NMun	
'Chrysomanicum'	NMun	
ciliatum	CBcs GGGa LHyd LMil NMun WAbe	
- 'Multiflorum'	see *R.* 'Multiflorum'	
ciliicalyx SF 535	ISea	
- subsp. *lyi*	see *R. lyi*	
Cilpinense Group	CBcs CHig ENot GKir LKna LMil LRHS MAsh MBar MDun NMun SBrw SLdr WBod WFar	
'Cilpinense' ♀ H3-4	CSBt CSam EBee EMil EPfP GGGa LHyd LRHS MHdf NPri SPoG SReu WBrE	
cinnabarinum	LMil MDun NMun SLdr	
- B&SWJ 2633	WCru	
- 'Caerhays Lawrence'	NMun SLdr	
- subsp. *cinnabarinum*	MDun SLdr	
- - BL&M 234	LMil	
- - ex LS&M 21283	LMil	
- - 'Aestivale'	LMil	
- - Blandfordiiflorum Group	GGGa NMun SLdr	

§ - - 'Conroy' GGGa LMil LRHS MDun MLea SReu
- - Ghunsa, Nepal MDun
- - 'Nepal' LHyd
- - Roylei Group GGGa LMil MDun MLea NMun SLdr SReu WBod
- - - 'Vin Rosé' LMil MDun
§ - subsp. *tamaense* GGGa NMun
- - KW 21003 NMun
- - KW 21021 GGGa NMun
§ - subsp. *xanthocodon* LMil MDun MLea NMun SLdr SReu
- - KW 8239 NMun
§ - - Concatenans Group CBcs CSam CWri GGGa MDun MLea NMun SLdr
- - - C&V 9523 GGGa
- - - KW 5874 LHyd LMil
- - - LS&T 6560 NMun
- - - 'Amber' LMil MDun MLea
- - - 'Copper' **new** SLdr
- - - 'Daffodilly' LHyd
- - Purpurellum Group GGGa MDun NMun SLdr
Cinnkeys Group GGGa LMil MDun
Cinzan Group LMil SReu
citriniflorum NMun
- CCH&H 8177 GGGa
- R 108 GGGa LMil
- var. *citriniflorum* LMil
- var. *horaeum* NMun
- - F 21850* GGGa
- - F 25901 NMun
'Claydian Variegated' (v) GGGa
clementinae GGGa MDun NMun SLdr SReu
- F 25705 LMil NMun
- JN 352 GGGa
- JN 722 GGGa
- JN 723 GGGa
- JN 729 GGGa
- x *pronum* GGGa
'Cliff Garland' GQui LMil
Clio Group NMun
'Coccineum Speciosum' CSBt CSdC GGGa LHyd LMil
(G) ♀ H4 MBar SReu SSta
'Cockade' (EA) LKna
'Cockatoo' (K) LKna
§ *coelicum* F 25625 GGGa
- KW 21075 NMun
- KW 21077 NMun
coeloneuron CBcs GGGa LMil MDun
- EGM 334 LMil
'Colin Kenrick' (K/d) LKna
collettianum H&W 8975 NMun
'Colonel Coen' CWri GGGa GLbr LRHS MAsh MGos MLea SHBN SLdr WGer WWeb
Colonel Rogers Group LHyd NMun SLdr SReu
x *columbianum* see *Ledum* x *columbianum*
'Colyer' (EA) SLdr
Comely Group LHyd NMun SLdr
- 'Golden Orfe' SLdr
complexum F 15392 GGGa
'Comte de Gomer' (hybrid) CBcs
concatenans see *R. cinnabarinum* subsp. *xanthocodon* Concatenans Group
concinnum CTrw CWri LHyd MDun MLea NMun SLdr
- Pseudoyanthinum Group GGGa GQui MDun NMun
'Concorde' NBlu
'Conroy' see *R. cinnabarinum* subsp. *cinnabarinum* 'Conroy'
'Consolini's Windmill' LMil
'Constable' LHyd NMun SLdr
'Constant Nymph' LKna
'Contina' GGGa
Conyan Group LHyd

cookeanum see *R. sikangense* var. *cookeanum* Cookeanum Group
'Coral Flare' (V) SFai
'Coral Mist' GGGa LMil
'Coral Reef' NMun SLdr SReu
'Coral Sea' (EA) SReu
'Cordial Orange' (V) SFai
coriaceum GGGa LMil LRHS NMun WCwm
- Cox 6531 GGGa
- R 120 NMun
'Corneille' (G/d) ♀ H4 LKna LMil SLdr SPer SReu
'Cornish Cracker' NMun SLdr
Cornish Cross Group LHyd NMun SLdr SReu
Cornish Early Red Group see *R.* Smithii Group
'Cornish Red' see *R.* Smithii Group
Cornubia Group NMun SLdr
'Corona' LKna
'Coronation Day' SLdr SReu
'Coronation Lady' (K) ENot LKna
'Corringe' (K) LMil
'Corry Koster' LKna SBrw
coryanum GGGa NMun
- KR 5775 LMil
- 'Chelsea Chimes' SLdr
- - ex KW 6311 GGGa LMil
'Cosmopolitan' CWri GGGa LMil LPan MBar MGos NBlu SBrw SLdr WFar
'Costa del Sol' NMun
'Cotton Candy' LMil NMun
'Countess of Athlone' LKna SBrw
'Countess of Derby' SBrw SReu
'Countess of Haddington' CBcs CWri LMil MDun NMun
♀ H2 SLdr
'Countess of Stair' WPic
'County of York' see *R.* 'Catalode'
cowanianum GGGa
Cowslip Group CSam CTri CWri GKir LHyd LKna LMil LRHS MAsh MBar MDun MGos MLea NMun SHBN SLdr SPoG SReu
coxianum C&H 475B GGGa
'Cranberry Swirl' LMil
'Cranbourne' SBrw SReu
'Crane' ♀ H4 GGGa GKir GQui LMil LRHS WAbe
crassum see *R. maddenii* subsp. *crassum*
'Cream Crest' GQui MDun SHBN WAbe
'Cream Glory' LHyd SReu
'Cream Supreme' (V) **new** SFai
'Creamy Chiffon' CDoC CWri GGGa MAsh MDun MGos MLea SBrw SLdr
§ 'Creeping Jenny' CBcs GGGa LHyd MBar MDun MLea NHol SLdr
cremastum see *R. campylogynum* Cremastum Group
§ 'Crest' ♀ H3-4 CSam CWri GGGa LHyd LKna LMil MAsh MDun MGos MLea SBrw SHBN SLdr SPoG SReu WBod
'Crete' COtt LMil SReu
'Crimson Pippin' GGGa LMil
crinigerum GGGa LMil MDun NMun SLdr
- JN 756 GGGa
- var. *crinigerum* NMun
KW 7123
- - KW 8164 NMun
- - R 100 NMun
- - R 38 NMun
- var. *euadenium* NMun
'Crinoline' (K) LRHS SBrw SLdr SReu
'Crinoline' (EA) SCam
'Croceum Tricolor' (G) CSdC
Crossbill Group CBcs SLdr WPic
* *crossium* SReu
'Crosswater Belle' **new** LMil

'Crosswater Red' (K)	LMil	
cruttwellii (V)	GGGa	
cubittii	see *R. veitchianum* Cubittii Group	
cucullatum	see *R. roxieanum* var. *cucullatum*	
§ **cumberlandense** (A)	GGGa LMil LRHS	
- 'Camp's Red' (A)	LMil	
- 'Sunlight' (A)	LMil LRHS	
cuneatum	GGGa NMun	
- F 27119*	NMun	
- R 11392	NMun	
§ - Ravum Group	WPic	
'Cunningham's Blush'	GGGa LRHS MAsh SHBN	
'Cunningham's Sulphur'	see *R. caucasicum* 'Cunningham's Sulphur'	
'Cunningham's White'	CBcs CSam CWri EPfP GGGa GKir LKna LRHS MAsh MBar MBri MDun MGos NBlu NMun NPri NWea SBrw SLdr SPer SReu WFar WStI WWeb	
'Cupcake'	see *R.* 'Delp's Cupcake'	
'Cupreum Ardens'	CSdC	
'Curlew' ♀ H4	CDoC CSBt EBre EPot GEdr GGGa GKir GLbr LMil LRHS MAsh MBar MBri MDun MGos MLea NHar NHol NLAp NMen NMun SHBN SLdr SReu WAbe WBod WOrn	
cyanocarpum	GGGa LMil NMun	
- AC 676	NMun	
- Bu 294	GGGa	
'Cynthia' ♀ H4	CSBt CWri ENot EPfP GGGa GLbr LHyd LKna LMil MAsh MBar MBri MGos MHFa MLea NMun NWea SBrw SHBN SLdr SReu SSta WFar	
'Dairymaid'	LHyd LKna NMun SBrw SReu	
dalhousieae	GGGa SLdr	
§ - var. **rhabdotum**	GGGa ISea SLdr	
Damaris Group	NMun SLdr	
'Damaris Logan'	see *R.* 'Logan Damaris'	
Damozel Group	WStI	
'Damozel' **new**	SLdr	
'Dandy' (hybrid)	LKna	
'Daphne Jewiss'	SReu	
'Dartmoor Blush'	SReu	
'Dartmoor Pixie'	SReu	
* 'Dartmoor Rose'	SReu	
dasycladum	see *R. selense* subsp. *dasycladum*	
dasypetalum	ECho GKev MBar MBri MDun MLea	
dauricum	SLdr WBod	
- 'Album'	see *R. dauricum* 'Hokkaido'	
- 'Arctic Pearl'	GGGa SLdr	
- dwarf	LHyd	
§ - 'Hokkaido'	LHyd	
- - x **leucaspis**	GGGa	
- 'Midwinter' ♀ H4	GGGa LHyd LMil SLdr	
* 'Dauricum Splendens' **new**	MAsh	
'David' ♀ H4	LHyd LKna NMun SBrw SLdr SReu	
davidsonianum ♀ H3-4	CTrw GGGa LHyd LMil NMun SLdr WBod	
- EGM 351	LMil	
- Bodnant form	LMil	
- 'Caerhays Blotched' **new**	SLdr	
- 'Caerhays Pink'	GGGa	
- 'Ruth Lyons'	LMil SLdr	
'Daviesii' (G) ♀ H4	CBcs CDoC CSdC CTri CWri ENot GGGa GKir LHyd LKna LMil MAsh MBri MDun MLea NBlu SLdr SPer SReu SSpi WBrE	
'Dawn's Delight'	NMun	
* 'Day Dawn'	SReu	
'Day Dream'	SReu	
Day Dream Group	LKna	
'Daybreak' (K)	GQui	

N 'Daybreak' (EA/d)	see *R.* 'Kirin'	
'Dayspring' (EA)	ENot	
'Dear Grandad' (EA)	CTri LMil LRHS NPri	
N 'Debutante'	EPfP	
x **decipiens**	SLdr	
decorum ♀ H4	CBrm COtt CWri GGGa LHyd LMil LRHS MDun NMun SLdr SReu	
- AC 757	NMun	
- Bu 286	NHol	
- C&H 7023	GGGa	
- Farrer 979	NMun	
- SF 252	ISea	
- 'Cox's Uranium Green'	SReu	
- subsp. **decorum**		
SBEC 1060	NMun	
- - SBEC 181	NMun	
§ - subsp. **diaprepes**	LMil NMun	
- - 'Gargantua'	NMun SReu	
- pink-flowered	SLdr	
degronianum	GGGa NMun SReu	
§ - subsp. **degronianum**	LMil NMun	
- - 'Gerald Loder'	GGGa LHyd	
§ - subsp. **heptamerum**	GGGa MDun NMun	
- - Doleshy 531	SLdr	
- - angel form	SLdr	
- - 'Ho Emma'	LMil	
- 'Rae's Delight'	LMil	
dekatanum	GGGa	
deleiense	see *R. tephropeplum*	
'Delicatissimum' (O)	CWri GGGa GQui MHdf MLea NLar SLdr WBVN WGwG	
'Delp's Cupcake'	GGGa	
dendricola	SLdr	
- KW 20981	GGGa	
dendrocharis	GGGa	
- CC&H 4012	GGGa	
- Cox 5016	GGGa NHol WAbe	
- 'Glendoick Gem'	GGGa	
- 'Glendoick Jewel'	GGGa	
* 'Denny's Rose' (A)	SReu	
'Denny's Scarlet'	SReu	
'Denny's White'	SReu	
denudatum C&H 70102	GGGa	
- C&H 7118	GGGa	
- EGM 294	LMil	
- SEH 334	LMil	
'Desert Orchid'	LHyd	
'Desert Pink' (K)	LKna	
desquamatum	see *R. rubiginosum* Desquamatum Group	
x **detonsum**	LMil NMun SLdr	
- F13784	SLdr	
'Devisiperbile' (EA)	SLdr	
'Devonshire Cream'	MAsh SLdr	
'Dexter's Spice'	LMil	
'Diabolo' (K)	LKna	
'Diadem' (V)	SBrw	
Diamant Group (EA)	GGGa	
- lilac (EA)	GGGa LMil MBri MLea	
- pink (EA)	ECho GGGa MDun MGos MLea SReu WAbe	
§ - purple (EA)	ECho MDun MGos MLea NBlu	
§ - red (EA)	MDun MLea WAbe	
- rosy red (EA)	ECho GGGa MBri WGor	
- white (EA)	ECho LRHS MDun MLea NBlu SLdr WAbe	
'Diamant Purpur'	see *R.* Diamant Group purple	
'Diamant Rot'	see *R.* Diamant Group red	
'Diana Pearson'	LHyd NMun	
'Diana van Herzeele'	SBrw	
'Diane'	LKna NMun SBrw SLdr	
diaprepes	see *R. decorum* subsp. *diaprepes*	

dichroanthum	GGGa LHyd LMil MDun NMun SLdr SReu
- CCH&H 8198	GGGa
§ - subsp. ***apodectum***	GGGa LMil NMun
- subsp. ***dichroanthum***	LMil
- - F 6781	NMun
- - SBEC 545	GGGa
§ - subsp. ***scyphocalyx***	GGGa NMun SLdr
- - F 24546	GGGa
- - F 27115	GGGa
- - F 27137	NMun
- - Farrer 1024	GGGa
dictyotum	see *R. traillianum* var. *dictyotum*
'Dido'	LHyd
didymum	see *R. sanguineum* subsp. *didymum*
'Dietrich'	SBrw SReu
dignabile C&V 9569	GGGa
dilatatum	LMil
dimitrum	MDun
'Diny Dee'	MGos
'Diorama' (Vs)	SLdr SReu SSta
'Diphole Pink'	SBrw
diphrocalyx	NMun
§ 'Directeur Moerlands' (M)	SLdr
'Direktor E. Hjelm'	SBrw
discolor	see *R. fortunei* subsp. *discolor*
'Doc'	EBee EMui ENot EPfP GKir LHyd LMil LRHS MBar MGos NDlv NMun SBrw SLdr SReu WFar WStI
'Doctor Arnold W. Endtz'	NMun SBrw
'Doctor Ernst Schäle'	GGGa
'Doctor H.C. Dresselhuys'	MBar SBrw SHBN
'Doctor Herman Sleumer' (V)	GGGa
'Doctor M. Oosthoek' (M) ♀ H4	SReu
'Doctor Stocker'	NMun
'Doctor Tjebbes'	ISea SBrw
'Doctor V.H. Rutgers'	MBar SBrw WFar
'Don Quixote' (K) **new**	CSdC
'Donald Waterer'	SBrw
'Doncaster'	ENot GKir LKna MBar MGos NMun NWea SBrw SHBN SLdr WFar
'Dopey' ♀ H4	CDoC CSBt CWri EMui ENot EPfP GGGa GKir LHyd LMil LRHS MAsh MBar MBri MGos MLea NBlu NDlv NHol NMun SBrw SHBN SLdr SReu WWeb
'Dora Amateis' ♀ H4	CBcs COtt GGGa GKir ISea LHyd LMil LRHS MAsh MBar MBri MGos NHol NMun NPri SBrw SLdr SPer SReu WBod WGwG WPic WWeb
Dormouse Group	CDoC GGGa LMil MHFa SBrw SLdr WBVN WWeb
'Dorothea'	SLdr
'Dorothy Corston' (K)	LKna
'Dorothy Hayden' (EA)	SLdr
'Dörte Reich' **new**	GGGa
doshongense	see *R. aganniphum* var. *aganniphum* Doshongense Group
'Double Beauty' (EA/d)	LKna SReu SSta
'Double Damask' (K/d) ♀ H4	LHyd LKna SBrw SLdr SReu
'Double Date' (d)	CDoC SLdr
'Doubloons'	NMun SLdr
'Douglas McEwan'	MDun SLdr
'Dracula' (K) **new**	GGGa
Dragonfly Group	SBrw SReu
- x ***serotinum***	SLdr
'Drake's Mountain'	ECho MBar MBri MDun

'Dreamland' ♀ H4	COtt CSBt CWri EBee ENot LHyd LMil MAsh MGos MLea SBrw SLdr SPoG SReu WFar WWeb
'Dresden Doll' (V)	SFai
'Driven Snow' (EA)	ENot SLdr
drumonium	see *R. telmateium*
'Drury Lane' (K)	GQui LMil LRHS
dryophyllum hort.	see *R. phaeochrysum* var. *levistratum*
'Duchess of Portland'	SReu
'Duchess of Rothesay'	NMun
'Duchess of Teck'	SReu
'Dusky Dawn'	NMun SLdr
'Dusky Orange'	SReu
'Dusty Miller'	CAbP CDoC COtt CSBt EBee GKir ISea LHyd LRHS MBar MGos NBlu NDlv SHBN SLdr
'Earl of Athlone'	LHyd SBrw SReu
'Earl of Donoughmore'	LHyd LKna SBrw SReu SSta
'Early Beni' (EA)	LHyd
Early Brilliant Group	LKna
'Ebony Pearl'	CBcs CWri GGGa MAsh MGos MLea SLdr
eclecteum	LMil MDun NMun SLdr
- Cox 6054	GGGa
- 'Rowallane Yellow'	NMun
'Eddy' (EA)	LKna NMun
§ ***edgeworthii*** ♀ H2-3	CWri GGGa ISea LMil NMun WAbe WBod
- AC 666	NMun
- x ***leucaspis***	CBcs
- x ***moupinense***	GGGa
'Edith Bosley'	GGGa
'Edith Mackworth Praed'	SReu
'Edna Bee' (EA)	GQui LMil SLdr
'Edward Dunn'	SBrw
'Effner' **new**	LMil
'Egret' ♀ H4	EPot GGGa GKir MAsh MBar MBri MDun MGos MLea NHar NHol SLdr WAbe WGer
'Ehrengold'	LMil
'Eider'	GGGa ISea MAsh NMun SLdr SReu WFar
'Eileen'	LMil SReu
'Eisprinzessin' (EA)	GGGa
'El Alamein'	SBrw
'El Camino'	COtt CWri MBri MLea NMun SHBN SLdr
'El Greco'	NMun SLdr
Eldorado Group	GQui
'Eleanor' (EA)	WBod
'Eleanor Habgood'	SLdr
Electra Group	see *R. augustinii* Electra Group
elegantulum	GGGa LHyd LMil MDun NMun SLdr
'Elfin Gold'	SReu
'Elisabeth Hobbie' ♀ H4	GDra GGGa LKna LMil MBar MDun MGos MHdf SLdr WWeb
Elizabeth Group	CBcs CDoC CTrh CTrw CWri GDra GGGa GLbr IMGH LHyd LKna LMil LRHS MAsh MBar MGos NHol NMun NWea SBrw SHBN SLdr SPer SReu WBod WFar
N 'Elizabeth' (EA)	CSBt CSam ENot EPfP GKir MGos NWCA WBod
'Elizabeth de Rothschild'	LMil MDun NMun SLdr
'Elizabeth Jenny'	see *R.* 'Creeping Jenny'
'Elizabeth Lockhart'	CWri GEdr GGGa GKir GQui MAsh MBar MDun MGos MLea WBod
'Elizabeth of Glamis'	GGGa

'Elizabeth Red Foliage' GGGa GKir LMil LRHS MAsh MDun NHol SPer
elliottii GGGa NMun SLdr SReu
- KW 7725 NMun
Elsae Group NMun SLdr SReu
'Else Frye' NMun
'Elsie Lee' (EA/d) ♀ H3-4 CDoC CTrh GGGa LMil MAsh SBrw SLdr SReu SSta
'Elsie Pratt' (A) MBar SReu SSta
'Elsie Straver' MAsh NHol SBrw SHBN SLdr SReu
'Elsie Watson' GGGa LMil
'Elspeth' LHyd LKna
'Emanuela' LMil
§ 'Emasculum' COtt LKna SReu
'Ember Glow' NMun
Emerald Isle Group SReu
'Empire Day' LKna SLdr
'Enborne' LHyd NMun
'Endsleigh Pink' WBod
'English Roseum' NBlu SLdr
'Erato' ENot GGGa LMil
eriogynum see *R. facetum*
eritimum see *R. anthospbaerum*
'Ernest Inman' LHyd NMun SLdr
erosum GGGa NMun SLdr
erubescens see *R. oreodoxa* var. *fargesii*
 Erubescens Group
§ x *erythrocalyx* NMun
 Panteumorphum Group
N 'Esmeralda' CMac CTrG
Ethel Group SLdr WBod
'Etna' (EA) SCam SLdr
'Etoile de Sleidinge' SBrw
'Etta Burrows' CWri GGGa MDun
'Euan Cox' GGGa NHar NHol NMen
euchaites see *R. neritflorum* subsp. *neriiflorum* Euchaites Group
euchroum NMun
eudoxum GGGa NMun
- KW 5879* NMun
- var *eudoxum* R 6c NMun
'Eunice Updike' (EA) LHyd
'Europa' SReu
eurysiphon NMun
- KW 21557* NMun
- Arduaine form GGGa
'Eva Goude' (K) LKna
'Evelyn Hyde' (EA) SLdr
'Evening Fragrance' (A) SReu
'Evensong' (EA) LKna
'Everbloom' (EA) NMun SLdr
'Everest' (FA) ENot LHyd MAsh SLdr WBod
'Everestianum' GGGa LKna MBar SBrw
exasperatum NMun
- KW 8250 GGGa
'Exbury Albatross' LKna
'Exbury Calstocker' LMil
'Exbury Fabia' SReu
'Exbury May Day' SReu
'Exbury Naomi' LHyd LKna LMil NMun SBrw SLdr
'Exbury White' (K) EPfP GQui
'Excalibur' GGGa
excellens LMil
- AC 146 GGGa
- SF 92074 ISea
- SF 92079 ISea
- SF 92303 ISea
eximium see *R. falconeri* subsp. *eximium*
'Exquisitum' (O) ♀ H4 CDoC CWri EPfP GGGa LMil MAsh MBri MLea NLar SLdr SSpi
exquisitum see *R. oreotrephes* Exquisitum Group

§ *faberi* GGGa LMil NMun SLdr
- subsp. *prattii* see *R. prattii*
'Fabia' ♀ H3 GGGa LHyd LMil SReu
Fabia Group LKna MDun NMun SBrw SLdr
'Fabia' x *bureavii* SLdr
§ 'Fabia Tangerine' COtt LHyd MLea SReu WBod
'Fabia Waterer' LMil
§ *facetum* GGGa LMil MDun NMun
- AC 3049 LMil
- Farrer 1022 NMun
- SF 612 ISea
'Faggetter's Favourite' LKna LMil MDun NMun SBrw SLdr SReu SSta
 ♀ H4
Fairy Light Group CSam LMil MAsh MBri SLdr
'Falcon' see *R.* (Hawk Group) 'Hawk Falcon'
falconeri ♀ H3-4 CHEx COtt GGGa ISea LHyd LMil LRHS MDun NMun SLdr SPer SReu WGer
- B&SWJ 2437 WCru
§ - subsp. *eximium* CDoC GGGa LMil MDun SLdr
'Fanal' (K) SLdr
'Fanny' see *R.* 'Pucella'
'Fantastica' ♀ H4 CDoC CWri GGGa LHyd LMil LRHS MAsh MBri MDun SReu WWeb
fargesii see *R. oreodoxa* var. *fargesii*
'Fashion' CTrG
fastigiatum GCrs GDra LMil MAsh MBar MBri NLAp NMun SLdr
- C&H 7159 GGGa
- SBEC 804/4869 GGGa MDun NHol
- SF 518 ISea
§ - 'Blue Steel' ♀ H4 CBcs CDoC COtt CWri GGGa GKir GLbr IMGH LMil LRHS MAsh MBri MBro MDun MGos NHar NHol NMun SPlb SReu WAbe WPat SReu
§ - 'Harry White' SReu
'Fastuosum Flore CSBt CWri GBin GGGa GKir ISea
 Pleno' (d) ♀ H4 LHyd LKna LMil MAsh MBar MBri MGos MLea NMun NWea SBrw SLdr SPoG SReu SSta WFar
§ *faucium* GGGa NMun
- C&V 9508 GGGa
 KR 3465 from Pe, LMil
 Doshang La
- KR 5024 GGGa
- KW 6401 NMun
aff. *faucium* KW 5732 NMun
fauriei see *R. brachycarpum* subsp. *fauriei*
'Favorite' (EA) CMac CTrw LHyd LKna LRHS MBri NMun SCam SLdr
'Fedora' (EA) CBcs LHyd LKna SLdr
'Fernanda Sarmento' (A) SReu
ferrugineum GGGa LHyd LKna LMil MBar MGos NMun SLdr SRcu WAbe WBod
- Ascreavie form NHol
* - *compactum* ECho
- Glenarn form NHol
* - 'Hill of Tarvit' NHol
- 'Plenum' (d) MDun
'Festive' LHyd
'Feuerwerk' (K) SLdr
fictolacteum see *R. rex* subsp. *fictolacteum*
Fine Feathers Group WBod
Fire Bird Group LHyd SLdr
'Fire Rim' GGGa
'Fireball' (K) ♀ H4 CBcs CDoC CTri CWri GGGa GLbr LHyd LMil LRHS MAsh MBri MHdf MLea NBlu SBrw SPer WOrn
'Fireball' (hybrid) GKir LRHS SLdr WLRN WWal
Firedrake Group SReu
'Firefly' (K) ENot EPfP

'Firefly' (EA)	see *R.* 'Hexe'
'Fireglow'	CSdC SLdr WFar WWeb
'First Light' (V)	SFai
'Flamenco Dancer' (V)	SFai
'Flaming Bronze'	SReu
'Flaming June' (K)	LKna
§ *flammeum* (A)	LMil
'Flanagan's Daughter'	LMil LRHS MAsh
I Flava Group	see *R.* Volker Group
flavidum	GGGa SLdr WAbe WBod
– Cox 6143	GGGa
– 'Album'	LMil LRHS
§ 'Flavour'	LKna
fletcherianum	NMun WAbe
– R 22302	NMun
– 'Yellow Bunting'	GGGa
fleuryi KR 3286	GGGa
§ *flinckii*	GGGa LMil LRHS MDun NMun
– CH&M 3080	GGGa
floccigerum	GGGa LMil NMun SLdr
– AC 1898 from Da Po Shan	LMil
– bicolored	NMun
'Flora Lockblott' **new**	SLdr
'Floradora' (M)	SReu
'Floriade'	LKna SBrw
floribundum	LMil LRHS NMun SLdr
– EGM 294	LMil
– 'Swinhoe'	SLdr
'Florida' (EA/d) ♀ H3-4	CMac LKna LMil MAsh SBrw SReu
	SSta WBod WFar
'Flower Arranger' (EA)	LMil NPri
formosanum	GGGa
formosum	CBcs GGGa GQui NMun
§ – var. *formosum*	GGGa LMil SLdr WAbe
Iteaphyllum Group	
– – 'Khasia' C&H 320	GGGa
– var. *inaequale* C&H 301	GGGa
forrestii	GGGa NMun
– subsp. *forrestii*	NMun
LS&T 5582	
– – Repens Group	GGGa LMil NMun SLdr
– – – 'Seinghku'	GGGa
– Tumescens Group	GGGa NHol NMun SLdr
– – C&V 9517	GGGa
Fortorb Group	NMun
Fortune Group	NMun SLdr
fortunei	CBcs CWri GGGa ISea LHyd LKna
	LMil MDun NMun SLdr SReu
§ – subsp. *discolor* ♀ H4	GGGa LMil NMun SLdr WGer
– – PW 34	GGGa
– – 'Hilliers Best'	SLdr
§ – – Houlstonii Group	LMil NMun
– – – 'John R. Elcock'	LMil
– – x 'Lodauric Iceberg'	SLdr
– 'Foxy'	NMun SLdr
– 'Lu-Shan'	MDun
– 'Mrs Butler'	see *R. fortunei* 'Sir Charles Butler'
§ – 'Sir Charles Butler'	LMil LRHS
'Fox Hunter'	LKna SLdr
fragariiflorum C&V 9519	GGGa
– LS&E 15828	GGGa
'Fragrantissimum' ♀ H2-3	CAbb CBcs CDoC CTrG CTrw
	CWri GGGa GGar ISea LHyd LMil
	MDun MRav NMun WAbe
'Francesca' **new**	GGGa
Francis Hanger	NMun SLdr SReu
(Reuthe's) Group	
'Frank Baum'	NMun SBrw SReu
'Frank Galsworthy' ♀ H4	LKna LMil SBrw SReu
'Frans van der Bom' (M)	LMil SLdr
'Fraseri' (M)	GGGa
'Fred Nutbeam' (EA)	LMil MGos

'Fred Peste'	CDoC LMil MDun MGos MLea
	SReu WBVN
'Fred Wynniatt'	CWri LHyd LMil NMun SLdr
	SReu
'Fred Wynniatt Stanway'	see *R.* 'Stanway'
'Frere Organ' (G) **new**	SLdr
'Freya' (R/d)	LMil SLdr
'Fridoline' (EA)	GGGa
'Frilled Petticoats'	NMun SLdr SReu
'Frilly Lemon' (K/d)	CDoC LMil NLar SLdr
'Frome' (K)	LKna
'Frosted Orange' (EA)	LMil MAsh SLdr
'Frosthexe'	GGGa WAbe
§ 'Frühlingstraum'	LHyd
'Fuko-hiko' (EA)	NMun
'Fulbrook'	NMun
fulgens	GGGa LHyd LMil MDun NMun SReu
fulvum ♀ H4	CDoC GGGa LHyd LMil LRHS
	MDun NMun SLdr SReu SSta
– AC 3083	LMil
– subsp. *fulvoides*	NMun SLdr
– – Cox 6026	GGGa
– – Cox 6532	GGGa
– – R 143	NMun
– – R 180	NMun
'Fumiko' (EA)	SLdr
'Furnivall's Daughter' ♀ H4	CSBt CWri ENot EPfP GGGa LHyd
	LKna LMil LRHS MBar MBri MGos
	MHFa NBlu NMun SBrw SLdr
	SReu SSta WFar
'Fusilier'	SLdr SReu
'Gabriele' (EA)	GQui SSpi
'Gabrielle Hill' (EA)	CDoC COtt LMil SLdr
'Gaiety' (EA)	LMil SBrw SReu
'Galactic'	NMun SLdr
galactinum	LMil NMun SLdr
– EN 3537	GGGa
– W/A 4254	NMun
'Galathea' (EA)	CDoC
'Gandy Dancer'	CWri MAsh MDun SLdr WBVN
'Garden State Glow' (EA/d)	SLdr SReu
'Gartendirektor Glocker'	CWri GGGa LMil MDun MLea
	MOne SLdr SSta WBVN WWeb
'Gartendirektor	CWri GGGa LMil MBri MDun
Rieger' ♀ H4	NHol SBrw SReu
'Gauche' (A)	GQui SLdr
'Gaugin'	GQui
Gaul Group	SLdr
'Geisha' (EA)	MBar
'Geisha Lilac' (EA)	COtt ECho GKir LMil LRHS MBar
	MBri MLea WLRN
§ 'Geisha Orange' (EA) ♀ H4	COtt CTrh GGGa GKir LMil LRHS
	MBar MBri MDun MGos MLea
	MOne NDlv NPri SLdr WLRN WWeb
'Geisha Purple' (EA)	COtt LMil MAsh MBar MDun
	MLea NBlu WFar WWeb
'Geisha Red' (EA)	COtt EPfP LMil MBar MBri MLea
	WAbe WFar WWeb
'Gekkeikan' (EA)	CBcs
'Gena Mae' (A/d)	GGGa LMil SLdr
'General Eisenhower'	CSBt SBrw SReu
'General Eric Harrison'	LHyd NMun SLdr
'General Practitioner'	ENot NMun SLdr
'General Sir John du Cane'	NMun
'General Wavell' (EA)	CMac LKna SLdr
'Gene's Favourite'	SReu
genestierianum	GGGa
CC&H 8080	
'Genghis Khan'	NMun
'Geoffroy Millais'	LMil
'Georg Arends' (EA)	NPri
'Georg Arends'	SLdr
'George Haslam' **new**	SLdr

'George Hyde' (EA)	LMil NPri
'George Reynolds' (K)	GKir MHFa
'George's Delight'	CSBt CWri GGGa MLea SLdr
'Georgette'	LHyd NMun SLdr
§ x *geraldii*	SLdr
'Germania'	LMil MAsh MBar WWeb
Gertrud Schäle Group	CTri MAsh MBar MDun NHol
	SReu WWeb
'Getsutoku' (EA)	SReu
'Gibraltar' (K) ♥ H4	CBcs CDoC CWri EBre ENot EPfP
	GGGa GKir LKna LMil LRHS MBar
	MBri MGos MLea NPri SBrw SLdr
	SPer SReu SSta WBod WWal
giganteum	see *R. protistum* var. *giganteum*
'Gilbert Mullier'	MBri NBlu
'Ginger' (K)	CDoC EPfP LMil LRHS NMun
	SLdr
'Ginny Gee' ♥ H4	More than 30 suppliers
§ 'Girard's Hot Shot' (EA)	CTrh ECho GGGa GQui SBrw
	SLdr SReu
'Girard's Hot Shot' variegated (EA/v)	GGGa
'Glacier' (EA)	MGos SLdr
'Glamora' (EA)	SLdr
glanduliferum	LRHS
- C&H 7131	GGGa
- EGM 347	LMil
- PW 044 from Miao Miao Shan	LMil
glaucophyllum	GGGa LHyd LMil MDun NMun
	SLdr WAbe
- var. *album*	GGGa
- Borde Hill form	LMil
§ - subsp. *tubiforme*	NMun
Glendoick Butterscotch **new**	GGGa
'Glendoick Crimson' (EA)	GGGa
'Glendoick Dream' (EA)	GGGa
Glendoick Ermine (EA) **new**	GGGa
'Glendoick Garnet' (EA)	GGGa
Glendoick Glacier **new**	GGGa
'Glendoick Gold'	GGGa
'Glendoick Ruby'	GGGa
Glendoick Velvet **new**	GGGa
'Glenroy Carpet'	SReu
'Glen's Orange'	CWri
'Gletschernacht'	CWri LMil
glischroides	GGGa
glischrum	GGGa NMun SReu
- C&Cu 9316	GGGa
- subsp. *glischroides*	LMil NMun
- subsp. *glischrum*	GGGa LMil
§ - subsp. *rude*	GGGa LMil NMun
- - C&V 9524	GGGa
globigerum	see *R. alutaceum* var. *alutaceum* Globigerum Group
'Glockenspiel' (K/d)	LKna SLdr
'Gloria'	see *Rhododendron* 'Bruns Gloria'
'Gloria Mundi' (G)	SReu
'Glory of Leonardslee'	SLdr
'Glory of Littleworth' (Ad)	LMil
'Glory of Penjerrick'	NMun SLdr
'Glowing Embers' (K)	CDoC CWri GKir LMil LRHS
	MAsh MBri MDun MHdf MLea
	SBrw SLdr SPer SReu WFar
Goblin Group	SLdr
'Gog' (K)	LHyd LKna WLRN
'Gold Crest' (K)	LKna
'Gold Dust' (K)	SBrw SLdr
'Gold Finger' **new**	MDun
'Gold Mohur'	SBrw SLdr SReu
'Goldball'	see *R.* 'Christopher Wren'

'Goldbukett'	GGGa LHyd MGos SBrw
'Golden Bee'	GGGa NHol
'Golden Belle'	LMil
'Golden Bouquet'	LRHS
'Golden Charm' (V) **new**	SFai
'Golden Clipper' **new**	LHyd
'Golden Coach'	COtt CWri MDun MGos MLea NMun
'Golden Eagle' (K)	CDoC COtt GKir LMil MDun MGos SCoo SLdr WOrn
'Golden Eye' (K)	LKna SLdr
'Golden Flare' (K)	CBcs CDoC LHyd MAsh MHdf NBlu SLdr SReu WBrE
'Golden Fleece'	LKna SReu
'Golden Gate'	CDoC LMil MDun NMun SLdr WGor WGwG WWeb
'Golden Horn' (K)	GQui SLdr WGor
Golden Horn Group	NMun SLdr
Golden Horn Persimmon	see *R.* 'Persimmon'
'Golden Lights' (A)	CDoC CWri GKir LMil LRHS MAsh MBri MDun NPri
'Golden Oriole'	LKna SReu
Golden Oriole Group	CBcs NHol NMun
§ - 'Talavera'	CBcs
'Golden Princess'	COtt LMil MDun NHol
'Golden Ruby'	MAsh
'Golden Splendour'	LMil
'Golden Sunset' (K)	COtt CSdC GLbr LMil MBar MDun MGos MLea SBrw SLdr
'Golden Torch' ♥ H4	CAbP CBcs CMHG COtt CSBt CWri EBee ENot EPfP GGGa GKir LHyd LMil LNet LRHS MAsh MBri MDun MGos MLea NBlu NDlv NMun SHBN SLdr SReu SSta WOrn WWeb
'Golden Wedding'	CBcs CSBt CWri LHyd LMil MAsh MDun MGos MHFa MLea SLdr WBVN
'Golden Wit'	ECho MDun SBrw SLdr
'Goldfinch' (K)	LKna
'Goldflamme' **new**	SLdr
'Goldflimmer' (v)	EBee EMil ENot GGGa GKir LRHS MAsh MGos NBlu NPri SBrw SLdr SPer SReu WFar WWeb
'Goldfort'	LKna SBrw SReu
'Goldika'	LMil
'Goldkrone' ♥ H4	CDoC CWri ENot GGGa ISea LHyd LMil MAsh MBri MDun MGos MLea NMun SBrw SLdr SReu WBVN WOrn
Goldschatz = 'Goldprinz'	GGGa
'Goldstrike'	SLdr
'Goldsworth Crimson'	LHyd SBrw
'Goldsworth Orange'	CSBt GGGa LHyd LKna MGos NMun SBrw SLdr SPer SReu
'Goldsworth Pink'	LKna SBrw SReu
'Goldsworth Yellow'	CSBt CSam LKna MGos SLdr SReu
'Golfer'	GGGa LMil
'Gomer Waterer' ♥ H4	CDoC CHig CSBt CSam CWri EPfP GGGa GKir GLbr LHyd LKna LMil MBar MBri MDun MGos MHFa MLea NBlu NMun NWea SBrw SLdr SPer SReu SSta WFar WOrn
'Good News'	SLdr
'Gorbella'	WWeb
'Gordon Jones'	GGGa
'Govenianum' (Ad)	LKna SLdr
'Grace Seabrook'	CDoC COtt CSam CTri CWri GGGa GKir GLbr LHyd LMil LRHS MAsh MDun MGos SLdr SReu
'Graciosum' (O)	LKna SReu
'Graf Lennart'	LMil
'Graham Thomas'	LMil SReu

'Grand Slam'	MDun SLdr
grande	GGGa NMun SLdr
– TSS 37	NMun
– pink	NMun
aff. *grande* KR 13649	NMun
'Grandeur Triomphante' (G)	CSdC SReu
gratum	see *R. basilicum*
'Graziella'	GGGa
'Greensleeves'	LKna LMil
'Greenway' (EA)	CBcs SLdr
Grenadier Group	SBrw
'Gretzel'	NMun SReu
griersonianum	CBcs GGGa LHyd MDun NMun
	SLdr
– F 24116	NMun
griffithianum	GGGa LMil NMun SLdr WPic
'Gristede' ♥ H4	CDoC COtt GGGa LMil MAsh
	MDun NHol SReu WWeb
groenlandicum	see *Ledum groenlandicum*
'Grosclaude'	NMun SLdr
'Grouse'	NHar
– x *keiskei* var. *ozawae*	ECho
'Yaku Fairy'	
'Grumpy'	CDoC CSBt CWri EMui ENot
	GGGa GKir LHyd LMil LNet LRHS
	MAsh MBar MBri MGos NBlu
	NDlv NMun SBrw SHBN SLdr
	SReu WOrn
'Guelder Rose' **new**	SLdr
§ 'Gumpo' (EA)	CMac EPot SLdr
'Gumpo Pink' (EA)	SLdr WBod
'Gumpo White' (EA)	MAsh WAbe WBod
'Gwenevere' (V) **new**	SFai
'Gwillt-king'	WCwm
'H.H. Hume' (EA)	CDoC IMGH SLdr
'H.O. Carre' (EA)	CMac
'H.Whitner'	NMun
habrotrichum	GGGa NMun
– F 15778	NMun
'Hachmann's Bananaflip'	LHyd
'Hachmann's Brasilia'	SBrw
'Hachmann's Charmant'	GGGa LMil
'Hachmann's Diadem'	LMil
'Hachmann's Feuerschein'	ENot LMil
'Hachmann's Kabarett' **new**	LMil
'Hachmann's Marlis' ♥ H4	ENot LHyd LMil SBrw SReu
§ 'Hachmann's Polaris' ♥ H4	LMil MAsh MBri MDun
'Hachmann's Porzellan'	LMil
§ 'Hachmann's Rokoko' (EA)	ECho GGGa LMil
'Hachmann's Belona' **new**	WWeb
haematodes	GGGa MDun NMun SRms
– AC 710	NMun
– Bu 290	GGGa
– CLD 1283	LMil
– 'Blood Red'	SLdr
§ – subsp. *chaetomallum*	GGGa LMil NMun SLdr
– – F 25601	NMun
– – JN 493	GGGa
– – R 18359	NMun
– – R 41	NMun
– subsp. *haemotodes*	NMun
F 6773	
– – McLaren S124A	NMun
– – SBEC 585	GGGa
'Haida Gold'	MGos MLea NMun SBrw SLdr
	SReu SSta
'Halfdan Lem'	CBcs CDoC CSam GGGa MAsh
	MBri MDun MGos MLea NMun
	SBrw SHBN SLdr SPer SReu SSta
	WOrn WWeb
'Hallelujah'	CWri MAsh
'Halton'	NMun
'Hamlet' (M)	LMil

'Hammondii' (Ad)	LKna
'Hana-asobi' (EA)	LHyd LRHS SCam SLdr
hanceanum	NMun WBod
– EN 2104	GGGa
– 'Canton Consul'	GGGa LHyd
– Nanum Group	GGGa WBod
– x *lutescens*	WBod
'Handsworth Scarlet'	SLdr
'Hansel'	MAsh SLdr
§ *haofui* Guiz 75	GGGa
Happy Group	GLbr SHBN
§ 'Hardijzer Beauty' (Ad)	LKna LRHS SLdr SReu WAbe
hardingii	see *R. annae* Hardingii Group
'Hardy Gardenia' (EA/d)	SBrw SReu
hardyi	see *R. augustinii* subsp. *hardyi*
'Harkwood Premiere'	GGGa LMil MGos SLdr
'Harkwood Red' (EA)	CTrh GQui SCam SLdr
'Harry Tagg'	CTrG GGGa SLdr
'Harvest Moon' (K)	LMil SCoo SReu
'Harvest Moon' (hybrid)	MBar MGos SBrw SLdr SReu
'Hatsugiri' (EA)	CMac ENot EPfP LHyd LKna LMil
	MBar SCam SLdr SReu
(Hawk Group) 'Crest'	see *R.* 'Crest'
– 'Hawk Buzzard'	SLdr
§ – 'Hawk Falcon'	SReu
– 'Jervis Bay'	see *R.* 'Jervis Bay'
'Haze'	SLdr
'Heather Macleod' (EA)	LHyd SLdr
heftii	NMun
'Helen Close' (EA)	CTrh SCam SLdr
'Helen Curtis' (EA)	SReu
'Helene Schiffner' ♥ H4	GGGa LMil NMun SReu
heliolepis	GGGa LMil
– AC 759	NMun
– SF 489	ISea
– SF 516	ISea
– var. *fumidum*	see *R. heliolepis* var. *heliolepis*
§ – var. *heliolepis*	LMil
– – CN&W 1038	ISea
– – F 6762	NMun
– – SSNY 66	NMun
x *hemigynum*	NMun
hemitrichotum	NMun
– F 30940	NMun
– KW 4050	NMun
hemsleyanum	GGGa LMil MDun NMun SLdr
– EN 2097	GGGa
aff. *hemsleyanum*	LMil
C&H 7189	
hemsleyanum x *ungernii*	GGGa
'Henry's Red' **new**	WWeb
heptamerum	see *R. degronianum* subsp.
	heptamerum
'Herbert' (EA)	CMac
§ 'Hexe' (EA)	WBod
hidakanum	SReu
'High Gold'	CWri
'High Summer'	LMil
'Hilda Margaret'	SReu
'Hille'[PBR] **new**	LMil
'Hino-crimson' (EA) ♥ H3-4	CDoC CMac CTrG CTrh CTri
	LKna LMil LRHS MAsh MBar
	MBri MGos SBrw SCam SLdr SPer
	SReu SSta WFar WLRN WStI
	WWeb
'Hinode-giri' (EA)	CBcs CDoC CMac CTrw ENot
	LHyd LKna NMun SCam SLdr
	SReu WPic
'Hinode-no-kumo' (EA)	NMun SLdr
N 'Hinomayo' (EA) ♥ H3-4	CBcs CMac CTrG EPfP GQui
	LHyd LKna LMil LRHS MBar
	NMun SCam SLdr SPer SReu SSta
	WBod WPic WStI

'Hino-scarlet'	see *R.* 'Campfire'
'Hino-tsukasa' (EA)	NMun SLdr
hippophaeoides	CDoC EPfP LMil MDun NMen
	NMun SLdr WFar
- F 22197a	SLdr
- Yu 13845	CDoC GGGa LMil MDun
- 'Bei-ma-shan'	see *R. hippophaeoides* 'Haba
	Shan'
§ - 'Haba Shan' ♀ H4	GGGa LMil MBri MDun
- 'Inshriach'	WBod
- var. *occidentale*	GGGa
C&Cu 9314	
hirsutum	GGGa LHyd LMil SLdr SReu
- f. *albiflorum*	GGGa
- 'Flore Pleno' (d)	ECho EPot GCrs GGGa MBar
	MDun MLea NLAp WAbe WBod
hirtipes	GGGa
- C&V 9546	GGGa
- KW 6223	NMun
- LS&T 3624	NMun
x ***hodconeri***	NMun
- 'pink'	NMun
hodgsonii	GGGa LMil LRHS MDun NHol
	NMun SLdr SReu
- B&SWJ 2656	WCru
- LS&H 21296	NMun
- TSS 9	NMun SLdr
- TSS 42A	NMun SLdr
- 'Poet's Lawn'	NMun
'Hojo-no-odorikarako' (EA)	NMun
'Hollandia' (hybrid)	SBrw SHBN
'Homebush' (K/d) ♀ H4	CBcs CDoC CMHG CWri ENot
	EPfP GGGa GKir GLbr LKna
	LMil MBar MBri MDun MHFa SLdr
	SPer SReu SSta WWcb
'Honey'	LKna NMun SBrw
'Honey Star' (V) **new**	SFai
'Honeydew'	SLdr
'Honeymoon'	MAsh NMun WLRN
'Honeysuckle' (K)	MBar SLdr SReu WBod
'Hong Kong'	MAsh
hongkongense	GGGa NMun
'Honourable	SBrw
John Boscawen'	
§ 'Ho-o' (EA)	CBcs SLdr
hookeri	CTrG LMil NMun SLdr SReu
- KW 8238	SLdr
- KW 13859	NMun
- Tigh-na-Rudha form	GGGa
'Hope Findlay'	LHyd
'Hoppy'	CDoC CSBt CWri ENot GKir GWCH
	LMil LRHS MAsh MDun MLea NBlu
	NMun SLdr SReu WCwm
'Horizon Lakeside'	GGGa LMil
'Horizon Monarch' ♀ H3-4	CWri GGGa LMil LRHS MDun
	SLdr WWeb
horlickianum	GGGa NMun
- KW 9403	NMun
'Hortulanus H. Witte' (M)	SLdr SReu WFar
'Hot Shot'	see *R.* 'Girard's Hot Shot'
'Hotei' ♀ H4	CBcs CDoC CSBt CSam CWri
	GGGa GKir LHyd LMil LRHS
	MAsh MBar MBri MDun MGos
	NMun NPri SBrw SHBN SLdr
	SReu SSta WWeb
Hotspur Group (K)	GGGa SCoo WLRN
'Hotspur' (K)	GKir MGos SLdr
'Hotspur Red' (K) ♀ H4	CDoC CSam GKir LKna LMil MBri
	SBrw SReu WOrn
'Hotspur Yellow' (K)	SReu
houlstonii	see *R. fortunei* subsp. *discolor*
	Houlstonii Group
huanum	LMil

- C&H 7073	GGGa
- EGM 316	LMil
'Hugh Koster'	CSBt LKna MGos NMun SBrw SLdr
'Humboldt' **new**	NBlu
Humming Bird Group	CMHG CSam EPot GGGa ISea
	LHyd LKna MBar MBri MDun
	MGos MLea NBlu NHol NMun
	SHBN SLdr SReu SRms WBod
hunnewellianum 'Crane'	GGGa SLdr
'Hurricane'	COtt MDun SBrw SLdr
'Hussar'	CWri
'Hyde and Seek'	GQui
'Hydie' (EA/d)	LMil MGos NPri
'Hydon Amethyst'	LHyd
'Hydon Ball'	LHyd
'Hydon Ben'	LHyd
'Hydon Comet'	LHyd
'Hydon Dawn' ♀ H4	CDoC COtt CWri GGGa GKir
	LHyd LMil LPan LRHS MAsh
	MDun MGos MLea NDlv NMun
	SBrw SLdr SReu SSta
'Hydon Glow'	LHyd NMun SLdr
'Hydon Gold'	LHyd
'Hydon Haley'	LHyd
'Hydon Hunter' ♀ H4	CBcs COtt ISea LHyd LMil LNet
	MAsh MBri NDlv NMun SBrw
	SLdr SPer SReu SSta
'Hydon Mist'	LHyd
'Hydon Pearl'	LHyd
'Hydon Rodney'	LHyd
'Hydon Salmon'	LHyd NMun
'Hydon Velvet'	LHyd SReu
hylaeum	NMun
- KW 6833	NMun
Hyperion Group	LKna LMil SBrw SReu SSta WFar
hyperythrum	GGGa LMil MDun NHol NMun
	SLdr
* - *album*	NMun
- pink-flowered	NMun
hypoglaucum	see *R. argyrophyllum* subsp.
	hypoglaucum
Ibex Group	NMun
'Ice Cream'	LKna
'Ice Cube'	MDun MGos MLea SLdr
'Ice Maiden'	SBrw SReu
'Iceberg'	see *R.* 'Lodauric Iceberg'
'Icecream Flavour'	see *R.* 'Flavour'
'Icecream Vanilla'	see *R.* 'Vanilla'
'Idealist'	SReu
Idealist Group	NMun
'Ightham Gold'	SReu
'Ightham Peach'	SReu
'Ightham Purple'	SReu
'Ightham Yellow'	NMun SLdr SReu
'Igneum Novum' (G)	SReu
'Ilam Louie Williams' (A)	SReu
§ 'Ilam Melford Lemon' (A)	LMil
§ 'Ilam Ming' (A)	LMil
§ 'Ilam Red Velvet'	SLdr
'Ilam Violet'	LKna
'Imago' (K/d)	CSdC LKna SLdr
'Ima-shojo' (EA/d)	LHyd LMil SCam SLdr WBod
§ 'Impala' (K)	LKna
impeditum	CBcs CDoC CSBt CWib EBee ENot
	GGGa GLbr ISea LHyd LKna MAsh
	MBar MDun MGos MLea NHar
	NHol NLAp NMen NMun NWea
	SBrw SLdr SReu SSta WBod WFar
	WWeb
- F 29268	GGGa NMun
- 'Blue Steel'	see *R. fastigiatum* 'Blue Steel'
- dark, compact	LKna
- 'Harry White's Purple'	see *R. fastigiatum* 'Harry White'

- 'Damio'	see *R. kaempferi* 'Mikado'
- 'Firefly'	see *R.* 'Hexe'
§ - 'Mikado' (EA)	LMil SBrw SReu SSta
'Kalinka'	GKir LHyd LMil LRHS MDun
	MGos NHol
'Kaponga'	CDoC MGos
'Karen Triplett'	LMil
'Karin'	COtt MDun SHBN SLdr
'Karin Seleger'	GGGa
'Kasane-kagaribi' (EA)	LHyd SLdr
'Kate Waterer' ♥ H4	CWri LKna MBar MGos NMun
	SBrw SReu
'Katharine Fortescue'	CWri
N 'Kathleen' (A)	SLdr
'Kathleen' rosy red (EA)	LKna WBod
* 'Katinka' (hybrid)	GGGa
'Katisha' (EA)	LHyd SLdr
'Katrina'	SLdr
'Katy Watson'	SReu
kawakamii (V)	GGGa
'Keija'	SReu
'Keinohana' (EA)	NMun
keiskei	CHig LHyd NMun SLdr
- compact	SLdr
- Cordifolium Group	GKev NHol WAbe
- 'Ebino'	GGGa NHol
- var. *ozawae*	GGGa ITim LMil LRHS MDun
'Yaku Fairy' ♥ H4	NHar SReu WAbe
- - - x *campylogynum*	NHol
var. *leucanthum*	
- - - x *lowndesii*	EPot
keleticum	see *R. calostrotum* subsp.
	keleticum
§ 'Ken Janeck'	GGGa
§ *kendrickii*	GGGa MDun NMun
- MR 62	GGGa
'Kenneth'	WBod
'Kentucky Colonel'	SLdr
'Kentucky Minstrel' (K)	SLdr
'Kermesinum' (EA)	COtt GGGa LMil MBar SLdr SPlb
	SReu WPat
I 'Kermesinum Album' (EA)	GGGa MBar MGos SReu
I 'Kermesinum Rosé' (EA)	LMil MBar MBri MDun NBlu SLdr
	SReu
kesangiae	MDun
- AC 110	NMun
- CH&M 3058	GGGa
- CH&M 3099	GGGa
- var. *kesangiae* KR 1136	NMun
aff. *kesangiae* KR 1640	GGGa MDun NMun
Kewense Group	see *R.* Loderi Group
keysii	CBcs GGGa LMil MDun NMun
- EGM 064	LMil
- KR 974	NMun
- KW 8101*	NMun
- 'Unicolor'	NMun
'Kilimanjaro'	GGGa SReu
Kilimanjaro Group	LMil NMun SBrw SSta
'Kimberly'	GGGa
'Kimbeth'	GGGa
'Kimigayo' (EA)	LHyd
'King Fisher'	NMun
'King George' Loder	see *R.* 'Loderi King George'
'King George' Van Nes	SReu
'King of Shrubs'	SLdr
kingianum	see *R. arboreum* subsp.
	zeylanicum
'King's Buff'	CWri
'Kingston'	MDun
§ 'Kirin' (EA/d)	CHig CMac CTrw LHyd LKna
	LRHS SLdr WBod
'Kirishima' (EA)	LKna SRms
'Kiritsubo' (EA)	LHyd SLdr

'Kisses' (V)	SFai
'Kitty Cole'	SLdr
kiusianum (EA) ♥ H4	GGGa LHyd NMun SReu SRms
	WAbe
- 'Album' (EA)	LHyd LMil SReu WAbe
- 'Amoenum'	see *R.* 'Amoenum'
- 'Ekubo' (EA)	SReu
- 'Hillier's Pink' (EA)	LMil
- var. *kiusianum*	LRHS
'Mountain Gem' (EA)	
'Kiwi Majic'	GGGa LMil MAsh MDun
'Klondyke' (K) ♥ H4	CBcs CTri ENot EPfP GGGa
	GKir LMil LRHS MAsh MBri
	MDun MGos MLea NPri SLdr
	SReu
'Kluis Sensation' ♥ H4	CBcs CSBt EBee ENot LHyd LKna
	MGos NMun NWea SBrw SHBN
	SLdr SReu
'Kluis Triumph'	LKna SBrw SReu
'Knap Hill Apricot' (K)	LKna LMil
'Knap Hill Red' (K)	CDoC LKna LMil SLdr
'Knap Hill White' (K)	CSdC
'Kobold' (EA)	NMun SLdr
'Koichiro Wada'	see *R. yakushimanum* 'Koichiro
	Wada'
'Kokardia'	CDoC SLdr
'Komurasaki' (EA)	NMun
kongboense	GGGa LMil
- C&V 9540	GGGa
- KR 5689	LMil
aff. *kongboense* KR 3725	LMil
§ 'Koningin Emma' (M)	LMil MBri NLar SLdr
§ 'Koningin Wilhelmina' (M)	CDoC SLdr WBod
konori var.	GGGa
phaeopeplum (V)	
'Koster's Brilliant Red' (M)	FNot LMil SLdr SReu
kotschyi	see *R. myrtifolium*
§ 'Kumo-no-ito' (EA)	SLdr
'Kupferberg'	SLdr
§ 'Kure-no-yuki' (EA/d)	CMac CTrG EPfP LHyd LKna LMil
	SCam
kyawii	NMun WPic
§ - Agapetum Group	NMun
lacteum	LMil MDun NMun SLdr
- AC 928	LMil
- CN&W 936	LMil
- EGM 356 from Wumenshan	LMil
- KR 2760	GGGa
- SBEC 345	GGGa
- SF 374	ISea
- bright yellow-flowered	NMun
'Lady Adam Gordon'	SLdr
'Lady Alice	CBcs CDoC CHig CMHG CTrG
Fitzwilliam' ♥ H2-3	CWri GGGa ISea LHyd LMil
	NMun SLdr WBod WGer
'Lady Annette de Trafford'	LKna
'Lady Armstrong'	CSBt
Lady Bessborough Group	SLdr
'Lady Bowes Lyon'	LHyd NMun SLdr
Lady Chamberlain Group	GGGa NMun SLdr
'Lady Chamberlain	see *R.* 'Salmon Trout'
Salmon Trout'	
'Lady Clairmont'	SBrw
'Lady Clementine	CDoC CSBt CWri EPfP GGGa
Mitford' ♥ H4	LHyd LKna LMil MGos MLea
	NMun NWea SBrw SHBN SLdr
	SPer SReu
'Lady Decies'	SReu
'Lady Digby'	CWri
'Lady Eleanor Cathcart'	CWri EPfP LKna MAsh NMun
	SBrw SLdr
'Lady Elphinstone' (EA)	SLdr
'Lady Grey Egerton'	LKna

'Lady Horlick' **new**   SLdr
'Lady Longman'   LHyd SBrw SSta
'Lady Louise' (EA)   SLdr
'Lady Primrose'   SLdr SReu
'Lady Robin' (EA)   SLdr
'Lady Romsey'   LMil
'Lady Rosebery' (K)   CSdC MBri MDun
Lady Rosebery Group   CSam MLea NMun
Ladybird Group   LMil SReu
laetum (V)   GGGa
Lamellen Group   LHyd SLdr
'Lampion'   ENot GGGa LHyd
'Lamplighter'   SReu
lanatoides   NMun
- C&C 7548   GGGa
- C&C 7574   GGGa
- C&C 7577   GGGa
- KW 5971   NMun
lanatum   LMil NMun
- B&SWJ 2464   WCru
- BB 185B   NMun
- dwarf, cream-flowered   GGGa
- Flinckii Group   see *R. flinckii*
'Langmans' (EA)   LKna
'Langworth'   CWri ECho LKna LMil MLea SBrw
   SReu WOrn
lanigerum   MDun NMun SReu
- C&V 9530   GGGa
- KW 8251   GGGa
- pink-flowered   NMun
- red-flowered   NMun
- 'Round Wood'   LHyd
lapponicum   GGGa
   Confertissimum Group
- Parvifolium Group   GGGa
   from Siberia
'Lapwing' (K)   LKna MBri SLdr
'Lascaux'   SReu
'Late Love' (EA)   CDoC MGos SSpi WGer
§ *latoucheae* (EA)   SSpi
- PW 86   GGGa
laudandum var.   GGGa
   temoense
Laura Aberconway Group   SLdr WBod
'Laura Morland' (EA)   LHyd
'Lava Flow'   LHyd NHol
'Lavender Brilliant'   CTrh
'Lavender Girl' ♀ H4   GGGa LHyd LKna LMil MGos
   NMun SBrw SLdr SReu SSta
'Lavender Lady' (EA)   CTrG
'Lavender Queen'   CWri MAsh NMun SLdr
'Lavendula'   GGGa LMil WWeb
'Le Progrès'   LMil SReu
'Lea Rainbow'   MLea
'Ledifolium'   see *R. x mucronatum*
'Ledifolium Album'   see *R. x mucronatum*
'Lee's Dark Purple'   CDoC CSBt CWri LMil MBar NBlu
   NMun NPri NWea SBrw SPer
   WFar
'Lee's Scarlet'   LKna LMil SLdr
'Lemon Cloud'   GGGa
* 'Lemon Drop' (A)   GGGa
'Lemon Grove'   SReu
'Lemon Lights' (A)   LMil
'Lemonora' (M)   LMil MBri SLdr
'Lem's 45'   MDun MLea SLdr
'Lem's Cameo' ♀ H3   GGGa LHyd LMil NMun SReu SSta
'Lem's Monarch' ♀ H4   CDoC CHig CWri GGGa LMil
   MAsh MDun MGos MLea SBrw
   SLdr SPoG SReu SSta WGer
'Lem's Tangerine'   LMil
'Lemur' (EA)   GGGa MBri MLea NHol SReu
   WPat

'Leni'   GKir LRHS MAsh
'Leny' (EA)   NHol
'Leo' (EA)   GQui LHyd LKna LRHS NMun
   SCam SLdr
'Leo' (hybrid)   EPfP LRHS NMun
'Leonardslee Giles'   SLdr
'Leonardslee Pink Bride'   SLdr
'Leonardslee Primrose'   SLdr
Leonore Group   NMun SReu
lepidostylum   CDoC CWri GGGa LHyd LMil
   LRHS MBar MBri MDun NHar
   NHol NMun SLdr SReu WAbe WFar
lepidotum   GGGa LHyd MDun NMun WAbe
- Elaeagnoides Group   GGGa
- 'Reuthe's Purple'   see *R.* 'Reuthe's Purple'
- yellow-flowered   ITim NMun
§ *leptocarpum*   GGGa LMil
- C&H 420   NMun
leptothrium   GGGa NMun
Letty Edwards Group   CSBt LKna NMun SBrw SLdr SReu
§ 'Leucanthum'   GGGa
leucaspis   CHig GGGa LHyd MDun NMun
   SLdr SReu
- KW 7171   NMun SLdr
'Leverett Richards'   SReu
levinei   GGGa
'Lila Pedigo'   COtt CWri GGGa LMil MAsh
   MDun MLea SBrw SLdr
'Lilac Time' (EA)   MBar SLdr
'Lilacinum' (EA)   WPic
liliiflorum Guiz 163   GGGa
'Lily Marleen' (EA)   CTri LRHS SCoo SLdr SReu
'Linda' ♀ H4   CSam CTri GGGa LMil LRHS
   MAsh MBar MBri MDun MGos
   SLdr SReu
'Linda Lee'   SLdr
lindleyi   GQui NMun
- L&S   GGGa
- 'Dame Edith Sitwell'   GGGa LMil
'Linearifolium'   see *R. stenopetalum* 'Linearifolium'
'Linnet' (K/d)   LKna
'Linwood Salmon' (EA/d)   SReu
Lionel's Triumph Group   LMil NMun SLdr
'Little Beauty' (EA)   SCam SLdr
'Little Ben'   ECho MBar MDun WBod
'Littlest Angel' (V)   SFai
'Loch Earn'   GGGa
'Loch Leven'   GGGa
'Loch o' the Lowes'   GGGa LHyd LMil MBri MDun
   MGos MLea WBVN
'Loch Rannoch'   GGGa GKir LMil MAsh NPri
'Loch Tummel'   GGGa
lochiae (V)   GGGa
'Lochinch Spinbur'   GQui
x *lochmium* **new**   GGGa
Lodauric Group   SReu
§ 'Lodauric Iceberg' ♀ H3-4   GGGa LKna LMil SBrw SLdr SReu
'Lodbrit'   SReu
§ Loderi Group   CBcs SLdr
'Loderi Fairy Queen'   NMun SLdr
'Loderi Fairyland'   LHyd NMun SLdr
§ 'Loderi Game   CBcs CWri LHyd LMil MLea
   Chick' ♀ H3-4   NMun SLdr SReu SSta
'Loderi Georgette'   NMun SLdr
'Loderi Helen'   NMun SLdr
§ 'Loderi Julie'   NMun SReu
§ 'Loderi King   CBcs CSBt CSam CWri GGGa ISea
   George' ♀ H3-4   LHyd LKna LMil MDun MLea
   NMun SHBN SLdr SReu SSta
   WBod WGer
'Loderi Patience'   LHyd NMun SLdr
'Loderi Pink   CWri LMil
   Diamond' ♀ H3-4

'Loderi Pink Topaz' ♀ H3-4 — LHyd LMil NMun SLdr
'Loderi Pretty Polly' — CWri NMun
'Loderi Princess Marina' — NMun SLdr
'Loderi Sir Edmund' — LHyd NMun SLdr
'Loderi Sir Joseph Hooker' — LHyd NMun SLdr
'Loderi Titan' — SReu
§ 'Loderi Venus' ♀ H3-4 — CDoC CWri GGGa LHyd LKna
　LMil LRHS MDun MLea NMun
　SHBN SLdr SReu SSta
'Loderi White Diamond' — LHyd NMun SLdr
'Loder's White' ♀ H3-4 — CDoC CWri ENot GGGa LHyd
　LKna LMil LRHS MDun MLea
　NMun SBrw SLdr SReu SSta
§ 'Logan Damaris' — LHyd NMun SLdr SReu
longesquamatum — GGGa LMil NMun SLdr
longipes EGM 336 — LMil
　- EGM 337 — LMil
　- var. *chienianum* — LMil
　- - EN 4074 — GGGa
　- var. *longipes* C&H 7072 — GGGa
　- - C&H 7113 — GGGa
longistylum — GGGa NMun
'Longworth' — NMun
'Looking Glass' — LRHS MAsh MDun SHBN
lopsangianum LS&T 5651 — NMun
'Lord Roberts' ♀ H4 — CBcs CHig CSam CTri CWri ENot
　GGGa GKir LKna LMil MAsh
　MBar MBri MGos MHFa MLea
　NBlu NMun SBrw SHBN SLdr
　SReu WFar WWeb
'Lord Swaythling' — LHyd SLdr
'Lori Eichelser' — CSam MDun MLea NDlv NHar
'Lorna' (FA) — ENot GQui LMil
'Louis Pasteur' — SBrw SReu
'Louisa' (EA) — SSpi
'Louise' (EA) — SLdr
'Louise Dowdle' (FA) — LMil SCam SLdr
'Love Song' (EA) — LRHS
'Lovely William' — LMil SLdr
lowndesii — WAbe
'Lucy Lou' — CSam GGGa
ludlowii — GGGa
　- x *viridescens* — NHol
ludwigianum — GGGa
§ *lukiangense* — NMun
　- R 72 — NMun
　- R 11275 — NMun
'Lullaby' (EA) — LKna SLdr
'Lunar Queen' — LHyd NMun SLdr
Luscombei Group — SLdr
'Luscombei Splendens' — SLdr
luteiflorum — LMil SLdr
　- KW 21040 — NMun
　- KW 21556 — GGGa
lutescens — CBcs CHig CWri ISea LMil MDun
　NMun SLdr SLon SReu SSta WAbe
　WBod
　- C&H 7124 — GGGa
　- Cox 5092 — NHol
　- Cox 5100 — NHol
　- 'Bagshot Sands' ♀ H3-4 — CDoC GGGa LHyd LMil LRHS
　SReu
§ *luteum* (A) ♀ H4 — CDoC CMHG CTrG CTri CWri
　EPfP GGGa GGar GLbr ISea LHyd
　LKna LMil LRHS MBar MBri MDun
　MGos MLea NBlu NMun SBrw
　SLdr SReu SRms SSta WBod WOrn
　WPic
　- 'Golden Comet' (A) — GGGa
§ *lyi* — NMun
　- KR 2861 — GGGa
　- KR 2932 — GGGa
　- KR 2962 — GGGa

---

* 'Mac Ovata' — CMac
macabeanum ♀ H3-4 — CBcs CDoC GGGa ICrw LMil
　LRHS MDun NMun SLdr SPer
　SReu SSpi SSta WGer WHer
　- KW 7724 — NMun
　- deep cream-flowered — CWri SLdr
　- DT 10 — GGGa
　- Reuthe's form — SReu
　- x *sinogrande* — SReu
macgregoriae (V) — GGGa
　Woods 2646
macranthum — see *R. indicum*
'Macranthum Roseum' (EA) — SReu
* *macrocarpum* new — CStu
macrophyllum — GGGa
macrosmithii — see *R. argipeplum*
'Macrostemon' — see *R.* (Obtusum Group)
'Macrostemon'
maculiferum — GGGa NMun SLdr
　- subsp. *anwheiense* — see *R. anwheiense*
'Madame Albert Moser' — LKna
'Madame de Bruin' — LKna SBrw SLdr
'Madame Ida Rubenstein' — SBrw
'Madame Masson' — CSam CWri GGGa GKir GWCH
　LMil LRHS MAsh MGos MLea
　NBlu NMun NPri SHBN SLdr
　SPer SReu SSta WBVN WFar
　WWeb
'Madame van Hecke' (EA) — COtt EPfP GKir LMil LRHS MAsh
　MBri NBlu SBrw SLdr SReu WFar
　WGor WWeb
maddenii — LMil NMun SLdr
§ - subsp. *crassum* — CTrw GGGa LMil NMun SLdr
　SReu WBod WPic
　- - AC 708 — NMun
§ - - Obtusifolium Group — NMun SLdr
§ - subsp. *maddenii* — NMun WAbe
　- - KR 2978 — LMil
§ - - Polyandrum Group — CBcs GQui ISea NMun SLdr
'Madcline's Yellow' — SLdr
'Mademoiselle Masson' — SBrw WFar
'Maestro' — LHyd
I 'Magic Flute' (V) — NPri
'Magnificum' (O) — LMil SLdr
magnificum — NMun SLdr SReu
'Maharani' — GGGa LMil LRHS MAsh SBrw
'Maja' (G) new — SLdr
§ *makinoi* ♀ H4 — CHig CWri GGGa LHyd LMil
　LRHS MDun NMun SLdr SReu
　SSpi SSta WGer
　- 'Fuju-kaku no matsu' — MGos
mallotum — CWri GGGa LHyd LMil MDun
　NMun SLdr SReu
　- Farrer 815 — GGGa
'Manda Sue' — MAsh SLdr WGor
Mandalay Group — SLdr
'Mandarin Lights' (A) — LMil LRHS MAsh MBri WWeb
'Manderley' — LMil SBrw
manipurense — see *R. maddenii* subsp. *crassum*
　Obtusifolium Group
'Manor Hill' — SLdr
'Marcel Ménard' — LMil SReu WFar WWeb
'Marchioness of Lansdowne' — CSBt SBrw
'Marcia' — SLdr
'Mardi Gras' — GGGa LMil MAsh NBlu
Margaret Dunn Group — CWri
'Margaret Falmouth' — SLdr SReu
'Margaret George' (EA) — LHyd
'Maria Derby' (EA) — SLdr
'Maricee' — GGGa SLdr WAbe
'Marie' (EA) — CMac
'Marie Curie' — SReu

'Marilee' (EA) — CDoC GKir LRHS MGos MOne SLdr
Mariloo Group — NMun SLdr
'Marinus Koster' — LKna MBri SLdr
'Marion' — LMil
'Marion Merriman' (K) — LKna
'Marion Street' ♀ H4 — LHyd LMil NMun SLdr SReu
'Mark Turner' — SReu
'Markeeta's Flame' — MDun
'Markeeta's Prize' ♀ H4 — CDoC CSam CWri GGGa LMil LRHS MAsh MBri MDun MGos MLea NBlu NMun SLdr WOrn WWeb
'Marley Hedges' — GGGa LMil
'Marlies' (A) — SLdr
'Marmot' (EA) — MLea
'Mars' — GGGa SLdr SReu
'Martha Hitchcock' (EA) — LKna SRms
'Martha Isaacson' (Ad) ♀ H4 — MGos SReu WCwm
'Martine' (Ad) — LKna MGos WBod
martinianum — NMun SLdr
aff. *martinianum* — GGGa
   KW 21557
'Maruschka' (EA) — GGGa
'Mary Drennen' — LMil
'Mary Fleming' — LHyd MDun NMun SLdr
'Mary Forte' — SBrw
'Mary Helen' (EA) — GKir LHyd LRHS MAsh SCoo SReu WPat
'Mary Meredith' (EA) — LHyd
'Mary Poppins' — GKir LMil LRHS NPri SCoo
'Maryke' — LMil
Matador Group — NMun SReu WBod
'Matador' — LHyd WBod
'Mauna Loa' (K) — LKna
'Maurice Skipworth' — CBcs
maximum — GGGa NMun SLdr
'Maxine Childers' — LMil
§ 'Maxwellii' (EA) — CMac WBod
May Day Group — CBcs CTrw CWri ISea LKna MDun MGos NMun SHBN SLdr SSta WBod
'May Day' ♀ H3-4 — CDoC LHyd SReu
'May Glow' — MGos
May Morn Group — SReu
'Mayor Johnstone' — CTri GKir LRHS MAsh NPri
'Mazurka' (K) — LKna
meddianum — GGGa NMun
 – var. *atrokermesinum* — NMun
  – – KW 2100a — GGGa
  – Harry White's form — SLdr
Medea Group — SLdr
Medusa Group — GGGa SReu
megacalyx — CBcs GGGa ISea
'Megan' (EA) — GGGa MAsh SLdr SReu WGwG
megaphyllum — see R. basilicum
megeratum — GGGa NMun SReu
 – R 18861 — SLdr
 – 'Bodnant' — WAbe WBod
mekongense — GGGa
 – var. *mekongense* — SReu
  – – KW 5829 — NMun
  – – Rubroluteum Group — see R. viridescens Rubroluteum Group
  – – Viridescens Group — see R. viridescens
§ – var. *melinanthum* — NMun
 – var. *rubrolineatum* — NMun
'Melford Lemon' — see R. 'Ilam Melford Lemon'
'Melidioso' **new** — LMil
'Melina' (EA/d) — GGGa
melinanthum — see R. mekongense var. melinanthum
'Merganser' ♀ H4 — GGGa LMil MDun MLea NHol NLAp SReu WAbe

'Merlin' (EA) — SLdr
Metis Group — WBod
metternichii — see R. degronianum subsp. heptamerum
 – var. *pentamerum* — see R. degronianum subsp. degronianum
'Mi Amor' — LMil
'Miami' (A) — SLdr
'Michael Hill' (EA) — CBcs CDoC COtt CTrh LHyd LMil MAsh SLdr SSpi
'Michael Waterer' — NMun SBrw SLdr
'Michael's Pride' — CBcs GQui NMun
micranthum — GGGa MDun NMun SLdr
microgynum — NMun
 – F 14242 — GGGa NMun
microleucum — see R. orthocladum var. microleucum
micromeres — see R. leptocarpum
microphyton — ISea
'Midnight Mystique' — GGGa
'Midori' (EA) — SLdr
'Midsummer' — SBrw
'Mikado' (EA) — see R. kaempferi 'Mikado'
mimetes — NMun SLdr
§ – var. *simulans* — NMun
  – – F 20428 — GGGa NMun SLdr
'Mimi' (EA) — CMac LHyd
'Mimra' — SLdr
'Mindy's Love' — LMil
'Ming' — see R. 'Ilam Ming'
'Minterne Cinnkeys' — MDun
minus — GQui
§ – var. *minus* — SLdr
§ – – Carolinianum Group — LMil
§ – – Punctatum Group — MBar
'Misomogiri' — CHig
'Miss Muffet' (EA) — SLdr
§ 'Moerheim' ♀ H4 — CWri EMil GKir LRHS MAsh MBar MGos MHFa MOne NHol NPri SLdr SReu SSta WStl
§ 'Moerheim's Pink' — LHyd LKna LMil MDun NHol SPer
'Moerheim's Scarlet' — LKna
'Moffat' — SReu
'Moidart' (Vs) — LMil
'Moira Salmon' (EA) — LHyd SLdr
'Molalla Red' (K) — LMil
§ *molle* subsp. *japonicum* (A) — GGGa SLdr
  – – JR 871 — GGGa
 – subsp. *molle* (A) C&H 7181 — GGGa
mollicomum — NMun
 – F 10347 — NMun
 – F 30940 — SLdr
'Mollie Coker' — CWri
Mollis orange (M) — MBar NBlu SRms
Mollis pink (M) — GGGa MBar NBlu SRms
Mollis red (M) — MBar NBlu SRms
Mollis salmon (M) — GGGa GQui
Mollis yellow (M) — GQui MBar NBlu SRms
'Molly Ann' — GGGa LRHS MAsh MDun SLdr SReu WGor
'Molten Gold' (v) — LRHS WWeb
monanthum CCH&H 8133 — GGGa
monosematum — see R. pachytrichum var. monosematum
montiganum — ISea
 – AC 2060 — LMil
montroseanum — LMil LRHS NMun SLdr SSpi WCru
* – 'Baravalla' — GGGa
 – 'Benmore' — NMun

'Moon Maiden' (EA) GQui MOne SLdr
Moonbeam Group LKna
'Moonshine' SReu
'Moonshine Bright' LHyd MDun SLdr SReu
'Moonshine Crescent' SLdr SReu
'Moonshine Supreme' LKna SReu
Moonstone Group MBar MDun MLea NMun SLdr
– pink-tipped NHol
'Moonstone Yellow' GGGa
'Moonwax' CBcs CSam CWri
§ 'Morgenrot' EMui GGGa LMil LRHS MAsh
MGos SReu WWeb
morii GGGa LHyd LMil MDun NMun
SLdr WGer
– W/A 10955 SLdr
'Morning Cloud' ♀ H4 CAbP GKir LHyd LMil LRHS MBar
MBri NDlv NMun SBrw SReu
WWeb
'Morning Magic' CWri LHyd NMun SLdr SReu
Morning Red see R. 'Morgenrot'
'Morvah' SLdr
'Moser's Maroon' CWri LKna LMil MGos NMun
SBrw SLdr
'Moser's Strawberry' LKna
'Motet' (K/d) CSdC LKna SLdr
'Moth' NHol
'Mother Greer' GGGa
'Mother of Pearl' LKna SBrw SLdr SReu
'Mother Theresa' LKna
'Mother's Day' (EA) ♀ H4 CDoC CMac CTrh EBre ENot EPfP
GKir GQui LHyd LKna LMil LRHS
MAsh MBar MBri MGos MLea
NBlu NMen NMun SBrw SCam
SLdr SReu SSta WBod WFar WLRN
WOrn WWeb
'Mount Everest' GGGa LHyd LMil SBrw SReu SSta
'Mount Rainier' (K) LMil SReu
'Mount Saint Helens' GGGa LMil MLea SLdr WWeb
'Mount Seven Star' see R. nakaharae 'Mount Seven
Star'
moupinense CBcs GGGa IDee LHyd NMun
SLdr SReu
– C&K 140 GGGa
– pink-flowered GGGa
'Mozart' (EA) WBod
'Mrs A.T. de la Mare' ♀ H4 CSBt CWri ENot GGGa LHyd
LKna LMil MBri MDun NMun
SBrw SLdr SReu SSta
'Mrs Anthony Waterer' (O) LKna
'Mrs Anthony Waterer' LKna SBrw
(hybrid)
'Mrs Ashley Slocock' SBrw SReu
'Mrs Betty Robertson' GWCH MDun MGos MLea NBlu
SLdr SReu
'Mrs C.B. van Nes' SBrw SReu
Mrs C. Whitner Group NMun
'Mrs Charles E. CBcs CSBt CWri ENot LHyd LKna
Pearson' ♀ H4 LMil NMun SBrw SHBN SLdr SPer
SReu
'Mrs Davies Evans' ♀ H4 CWri LHyd LKna MBar SBrw
SReu SSta
'Mrs Dick Thompson' SReu
'Mrs Donald Graham' SReu
'Mrs Doorenbos' CMac
'Mrs E.C. Stirling' LHyd LKna SBrw SRms
'Mrs Emil Hager' (EA) LHyd SLdr
'Mrs Furnivall' ♀ H4 CBcs CWri EPfP GBin GGGa
LHyd LKna MDun MGos MLea
SLdr SReu WWeb
'Mrs G.W. Leak' CSBt CSam CWri ENot EPfP
GGGa ISea LHyd LKna LMil
MDun MLea NMun SBrw SHBN
SLdr SPer SReu

'Mrs Helen Koster' LKna
'Mrs Henry Agnew' NMun SLdr
'Mrs J.C. Williams' ♀ H4 LKna LMil NMun SLdr
'Mrs J.G. Millais' LKna LMil MDun NMun SLdr
'Mrs James Horlick' NMun
'Mrs John Waterer' SBrw
'Mrs Lindsay Smith' LKna SBrw
'Mrs Lionel de MDun NMun SReu
Rothschild' ♀ H4
Mrs Lionel de Rothschild CWri LKna
Group
'Mrs P.D. Williams' LKna SBrw SReu
'Mrs Peter Koster' (M) SLdr WFar
'Mrs Philip Martineau' LKna
'Mrs R.S. Holford' ♀ H4 LKna NMun SBrw SLdr
'Mrs T.H. Lowinsky' ♀ H4 CSBt EPfP GGGa LKna LMil MAsh
MBri MDun MGos MHFa MLea
NMun NWea SBrw SLdr SPer
SReu SSta WWeb
'Mrs Tom Agnew' SBrw
'Mrs W.C. Slocock' LKna NMun SBrw SPer SReu SSta
'Mrs William Agnew' LKna
'Mrs William Watson' SBrw
§ × *mucronatum* (EA) CHig NMun SLdr SRms WPic
'Mucronatum' see R. × *mucronatum*
'Mucronatum
Amethystinum' see R. 'Amethystinum'
mucronulatum GGGa NMun
– B&SWJ 786 WCru
– pink-flowered WPGP
– var. *chejuense* see R. mucronulatum var. taquetii
– 'Cornell Pink' ♀ H4 GGGa LMil WFar
§ – var. *taquetii* GGGa
§ 'Multiflorum' SReu
'Muncaster Bells' NMun
'Muncaster Hybrid' NMun
'Muncaster Mist' NMun
'My Lady' GGGa
§ *myrtifolium* LMil MAsh SLdr
nakaharae (EA) NMun SLdr SReu
§ – 'Mariko' (EA) EPot GGGa LHyd MBar MBro
MGos NHol SLdr WAbe WPat
§ – 'Mount Seven Star' CDoC ECho GGGa LMil LRHS
(EA) ♀ H4 MBro NHol SLdr SReu WAbe
WPat
§ – orange-flowered (EA) GKir LMil LRHS MAsh MOne NPri
SBrw SHBN SReu SSta WWeb
– pink-flowered (EA) CHig GKir LHyd LMil LRHS NPri
SBrw SLdr SPer SReu SSta
– red-flowered (EA) SLdr
– 'Scree' (EA) SReu
'Nakahari Orange' see R. nakaharae orange-flowered
'Nakahari-mariko' see R. nakaharae 'Mariko'
nakotiltum NMun SLdr
'Nancy Evans' ♀ H3-4 CDoC COtt CSBt GGGa GKir
LHyd LMil LRHS MAsh MDun
MLea NPri SBrw SLdr SPer SReu
SSpi WGer WWeb
'Nancy Waterer' (G) ♀ H4 NLar SLdr SReu
'Nanki Poo' (EA) LHyd SLdr
Naomi Group CSam CWri LKna MLea SBrw
SReu
– 'Paris' see R. 'Paris'
'Naomi' (EA) GQui LKna LMil SCam SHBN SLdr
'Naomi Astarte' LKna MDun SBrw SLdr
'Naomi Early Dawn' NMun
'Naomi Hope' SLdr
'Naomi Nautilus' LMil
'Naomi Stella Maris' SLdr
'Narcissiflorum' CDoC ENot EPfP LHyd LKna LMil
(G/d) ♀ H4 LRHS NLar SPer SReu
'Naselle' GGGa LMil
'Ne Plus Ultra' (V) **new** SFai

	'Nelly de Bruin'	SBrw
	neriiflorum	GGGa ISea LMil MDun NMun SLdr SReu
	– Bu 287	GGGa
	– SF 366	ISea
	– subsp. *neriiflorum* L&S 1352	GGGa
§	– – Euchaites Group	NMun
§	– – Phoenicodum Group Farrer 877	NMun
§	– subsp. *phaedropum*	NMun
	– – C&H 422	NMun
	– – CCH&H 8125	GGGa
	– – KR 5593	LMil
	– – KW 6845*	NMun
	Neriihaem Group	NMun
	nervulosum (V)	GGGa
	'Nestor'	SReu
	'Netty Koster'	SBrw SLdr
	'New Comet'	LHyd NMun SLdr SReu
	'New Moon'	SReu
	'Newcomb's Sweetheart'	LMil MDun
	'Niagara' (EA) ♀ H3-4	CTrh ENot EPfP GQui LHyd LMil NMen SLdr WBod
	'Nichola' (EA)	SBrw SReu
	'Nico' (EA)	CMac GKir LRHS WBod WPat
	'Nicoletta'	GGGa LMil MAsh NBlu
	'Night Sky'	CDoC COtt GGGa LHyd LMil LRHS MAsh MBri MDun MGos MLea MOne NHol SLdr WOrn
	'Nightingale'	SBrw SReu
	nigroglandulosum	GGGa
	x *nikomontanum*	LMil
	nilagiricum	see *R. arboreum* subsp. *nilagiricum*
	'Nimbus'	LKna SLdr
	Nimrod Group	NMun SLdr
	'Nishiki' (EA)	CMac
	nitens	see *R. calostrotum* subsp. *riparium* Nitens Group
	nitidulum	NMun WAbe
	– var. *omeiense* KR 185	GGGa LMil NHol
	nivale subsp. *boreale* Ramosissimum Group	GGGa
§	– – Stictophyllum Group	GGGa
§	– subsp. *nivale*	GKev
	niveum ♀ H4	GGGa LMil LRHS MDun NMun SLdr SPoG SReu WGer
	– 'Clyne Castle'	SLdr
	– 'Nepal'	LHyd
	'Noble Mountain'	LMil
§	'Nobleanum Group	GGGa LHyd LKna LMil NMun SLdr SSta WBod
	'Nobleanum Album'	LHyd LKna LMil NMun SLdr SReu SSta WBod
	'Nobleanum Coccineum'	ISea NMun SReu
	'Nobleanum Venustum'	CSBt CWri LHyd LKna LMil SBrw SLdr SReu SSta WBod
	'Nofretete'	GGGa
	'Nora'	WPic
	'Nordlicht' (EA)	SLdr
	'Noriko' (EA) **new**	SLdr
N	'Norma' (R/d) ♀ H4	ENot LMil SReu
	Norman Shaw Group	LHyd
	'Northern Hi-Lights' (A)	GKir LMil LRHS MLea SLdr
	'Northern Starburst'	LMil MAsh
	'Nova Zembla'	EPfP GGGa GLbr ISea MAsh MBar MGos NBlu NPri SBrw SHBN SLdr SReu SSta WBVN WStl WWeb
	nudiflorum	see *R. periclymenoides*
	nudipes	LMil
	nuttallii	CBrd GGGa ISea LMil SLdr

	'Oban'	GGGa LMil LRHS MDun MLea NHol NLAp NMen WAbe
	Obtusum Group (EA)	LHyd
§	– 'Macrostemon' (EA)	WBod
	obtusum f. *amoenum*	see *R.* 'Amoenum'
	occidentale (A) ♀ H4	GGGa LMil LRHS SLdr SReu SSpi
	ochraceum	LMil
	– C&H 7052	GGGa
	– EGM 312	LMil
	'Odee Wright'	CDoC CTri CWri GGGa LRHS MAsh MLea NMun SLdr SReu
	'Odoratum' (Ad)	MLea
	'Oh-Too'	SBrw
	'Oi-no-mezame' (EA)	LHyd
	'Old Copper'	CWri LNet SBrw
	'Old Gold' (K)	SLdr SReu WWeb
	'Old Port' ♀ H4	LHyd LMil SBrw SHBN SReu
	Oldenburgh Group	SLdr
	oldhamii (EA)	NMun
	– ETOT 601	GGGa
	'Olga' ♀ H4	LHyd LKna LMil NMun SBrw SLdr SReu SSta
	'Olga Mezitt'	GGGa LHyd NHol
	'Olga Niblett' (EA)	SLdr
	oligocarpum	GGGa
	– Guiz 148*	GGGa
	'Olive'	LHyd LKna LMil WBod
	'Oliver Cromwell'	SBrw SReu
	Olympic Lady Group	LHyd SLdr
	Omar Group	MBar
§	'One Thousand Butterflies'	COtt GGGa MDun MLea NBlu SLdr WGer
N	'Ophelia'	SCam SLdr
	'Oporto'	SLdr
	'Orange Beauty' (EA) ♀ H3-4	CDoC CMac CTrh GGGa LHyd LKna LMil MAsh MBar MGos MHFa NMun SCam SLdr SReu SSta WBod WFar WGer WPic WWeb
	'Orange King' (EA)	WWeb
I	'Orange Queen' (V)	SFai
	'Orange Scout'	SLdr WGor WWal
	'Orange Splendour' (A)	LRHS WWeb
	'Orangengold'	MDun
	orbiculare ♀ H3-4	GGGa IDee LHyd LMil MDun NMun SLdr SSta WBod
	– C&K 230	GGGa
§	– subsp. *cardiobasis*	MDun NMun SLdr
	– subsp. *orbiculare* W/V 1519	NMun
	– Sandling Park form	SReu
	'Orchid Lights'	GKir LRHS SLdr
	'Oregon' (EA)	SLdr
	oreodoxa	LMil NMun SLdr SReu
§	– var. *fargesii* ♀ H4	GGGa LHyd LMil NMun
	– – Knott 348	NMun
§	– Erubescens Group	NMun
	– var. *oreodoxa*	LMil
	– – EN 4212	GGGa
	– – W/A 4245	NMun
	– var. *shensiense*	GGGa
	oreotrephes	CDoC LHyd LMil LRHS MDun NMun SLdr SReu
	– F 20489	NMun
	– F 20629	NMun
	– KW 9509	NMun
	– SF 640	ISea
§	– Exquisitum Group	ISea SReu WGwG
	– Timeteum Group	SReu
	aff. *oreotrephes* C&V 9557	GGGa
	Orestes Group	SLdr
	orthocladum	LMil MDun
§	– var. *microleucum*	GGGa ISea LMil NHol NMun

- var. **orthocladum**   GGGa NHol
  F 20488
'Oryx' (O)   CSdC LKna
'Osmar' ♀ H4   CBcs GGGa MGos
'Ostara'   CBcs COtt MGos
'Ostbo's Low Yellow'   SLdr
'Ouchiyama'   LKna
'Oudijk's Sensation'   CBcs CWri GGGa LKna MAsh
                               MGos MOne
(Our Kate Group)   SLdr
  'Our Kate'
'Ovation'   NHol
ovatum (EA)   CBcs NMun WBod
ovatum CN&W 548   ISea
- W/A 1391   NMun
'Oxydol' (K)   MBri
'P. den Ouden'   SBrw
  x **williamsianum**
§ **pachypodum**   GGGa
  pachysanthum ♀ H4   CDoC LHyd LMil MDun NMun
                               SLdr SReu SSpi
- RV 72/001   GGGa NMun SLdr
- 'Crosswater'   LMil LRHS MDun
- x **proteoides**   GGGa
  pachytrichum   GGGa NMun SLdr
§ - var. **monosematum**   ISea SLdr
- - CN&W 953   LMil
- - CN&W 956   GGGa
- - W/V 1522   NMun
- var. **pachytrichum**   NMun
  W/A 1203
- - 'Sesame'   LMil
'Palestrina' (EA) ♀ H3-4   CBcs CMac CTrh EPfP EPot LHyd
                               LKna LMil LRHS MGos NMun
                               SBrw SCam SLdr SPer SReu SSta
                               WBod WFar WGwG
'Pallas' (G)   SLdr SReu
paludosum   see R. **nivale** subsp. **nivale**
'Pamela Miles' (EA)   LHyd
'Pancake'   CMac
'Panda' (EA) ♀ H4   CDoC CMac GGGa LHyd LMil
                               LRHS MBar MBri MDun MLea
                               NDlv NPri SCoo SLdr SPer SPoG
                               SReu
panteumorphum   see R. x **erythrocalyx**
                               Panteumorphum Group
'Papaya Punch'   LMil MDun
papillatum   NMun
'Paprika Spiced'   CDoC COtt CWri LMil MAsh MBri
                               MDun MGos MLea SLdr WBVN
'Parade' (A)   LMil
'Paradise Pink' (EA)   ENot LMil
paradoxum C&K 228   GGGa
- CC&H 3906   GGGa
'Paramount' (K/d)   LKna
§ 'Paris'   LHyd
'Parkfeuer' (A) **new**   SLdr
parmulatum   LMil MDun NMun SLdr
- C&C 7538   GGGa
- KW 5875   NMun
- mauve-flowered   NMun SLdr
- 'Ocelot'   GGGa LHyd LMil MDun NMun
                               SLdr
- pink-flowered   GGGa NMun
parryae   GGGa
'Party Pink'   LMil
'Patty Bee' ♀ H4   CBcs CDoC CSBt CSam CWri
                               EPfP EPot GGGa GKir IMGH
                               LHyd LMil LRHS MAsh MBar MBri
                               MGos MLea NHar NHol NLAp
                               NMen SBod SReu SLdr SReu SSpi SSta
                               WAbe WFar
patulum   see R. **pemakoense** Patulum Group

'Pavane' (K)   LKna
'Peace'   GGGa NMun
'Peach Blossom'   see R. 'Saotome'
'Peach Lady'   SLdr
'Peaches and Cream'   SLdr
'Peep-bo' (EA)   LHyd SLdr
'Peeping Tom'   CDoC GKir LMil MAsh MDun
                               NMun SHBN SReu WGer WWeb
'Peggy Bannier'   SBrw
'Pelopidas'   SBrw
pemakoense   CSBt CTrG GGGa MAsh MBar
                               MGos NHol NMun SLdr SReu WAbe
§ - Patulum Group   MBar MBri NHol NLAp NMun
                               SLdr WPat
'Pemakofairy'   WAbe
pendulum CH&M 3094   GGGa
- LS&T 6660   GGGa
Penelope Group   SReu
'Penheale Blue' ♀ H4   CBcs CDoC CTrh GBin GGGa
                               LMil MAsh NDlv NHol SLdr
'Penjerrick Cream'   LHyd NMun SLdr
'Penjerrick Pink'   LHyd NMun SLdr
pennivenium   see R. **tanastylum** var. **pennivenium**
pentaphyllum (A)   LMil
'Percy Wiseman' ♀ H4   More than 30 suppliers
peregrinum   NMun SLdr
'Perfect Lady'   LMil
§ **periclymenoides** (A)   GGGa LMil LRHS SLdr
'Persil' (K) ♀ H4   CBcs CWri ENot EPfP GGGa
                               LHyd LKna LMil MAsh MBar MBri
                               MDun MGos MHFa MLea NBlu
                               SBrw SCoo SLdr SPer SReu WBod
                               WBrE WOrn
§ 'Persimmon'   LKna NMun
'Peste's Fire Light'   GGGa
'Peter Berg'   MGos
'Peter Gable' (EA)   SLdr
'Peter John Mezitt'   see R. (PJM Group) 'Peter John
                               Mezitt'
'Peter Koster' (hybrid)   CWri NMun SBrw SHBN SLdr WStI
petrocharis Guiz 120   GGGa
'Petrouchka' (K)   LKna MBri MDun
phaedropum   see R. **neriiflorum** subsp.
                               phaedropum
phaeochrysum   GGGa NMun SLdr
- USDAPI 59029/R11323   NMun
- var. **agglutinatum**   GGGa NMun
§ - var. **levistratum**   NMun SLdr SReu
- - AC 1757   WCwm
- McLaren cup winner   NMun
- var. **phaeochrysum**   NMun
  'Greenmantle'
'Phalarope'   CDoC CSam GGGa MAsh MBar
                               MGos NHol SReu WBod
'Pheasant Tail'   NMun SLdr
'Phoebe' (R/d)   SReu
phoenicodum   see R. **neriiflorum** subsp.
                               neriiflorum Phoenicodum Group
'Phyllis Korn'   CDoC CWri LHyd MAsh MDun
                               MHFa MLea NBlu NLar SLdr SPer
                               WBVN
'Piccolo' (K/d)   CSdC LKna
§ **piercei**   CWri GGGa LMil MDun NMun
- KW 11040   GGGa NMun
Pilgrim Group   LKna LMil NMun
pingianum   NMun SLdr
- EGM 304   LMil
- KR 150   NMun
- KR 184   GGGa
'Pink and Sweet' (A)   CDoC LMil
'Pink Bedspread'   SReu
'Pink Bountiful'   LKna
'Pink Bride'   SLdr

'Pink Cherub' ♀ H4 — CDoC EBee EMui ENot GLbr LHyd LRHS MAsh MBar MOne NMun SLdr SReu WOrn
'Pink Delight' — GLbr LKna WBod
'Pink Delight' (V) — SFai
'Pink Drift' — CDoC CSBt ENot ISea LKna LMil MAsh MBar MGos MOne NHar NHol NMun NWea SHBN SLdr
'Pink Ghost' — NMun SLdr
'Pink Gin' — LMil
'Pink Glory' — NMun
'Pink Leopard' — ISea LMil MAsh MLea NMun SLdr
'Pink Pancake' (EA) ♀ H4 — CBcs CTrh GQui LMil LRHS MGos SLdr SReu SSpi WGer
'Pink Pearl' (EA) — see R. 'Azuma-kagami' (EA)
'Pink Pearl' (hybrid) — CBcs CHig CSBt CTri ENot EPfP GGGa GKir ISea LKna LMil LRHS MAsh MBar MDun MGos NMun NWea SBrw SLdr SPer SReu SSta WBod WFar WMoo WOrn
'Pink Pebble' ♀ H3-4 — CTrw LHyd MDun MOne NMun SLdr SReu
'Pink Perfection' — MBar MGos NMun SBrw SLdr SReu WFar
'Pink Photo' — SLdr
'Pink Pillow' — SReu
'Pink Rosette' — LKna
N 'Pink Ruffles' — ENot WBod
'Pink Sensation' — MBri
'Pinkerton' — LHyd LKna
'Pintail' — GGGa LMil WAbe
'Pipaluk' — NMun
'Pipit' — GGGa WAbe
'Pippa' (EA) — CMac CTrG
PJM Group — MAsh MBri MDun MLea SSta
§ - 'Peter John Mezitt' ♀ H4 — LHyd LMil NMun SLdr SReu WBod
'PJM Elite' — GGGa LMil
'Pleasant White' (EA) new — NBlu
pocophorum — GGGa NMun SLdr
- var. hemidartum — GGGa NMun SLdr
- var. pocophorum — NMun
  USDAPI 59190/R11201
pogonostylum — see R. irroratum subsp. pogonostylum
'Point Defiance' — CWri GGGa LMil MDun SLdr
'Polar Bear' (EA) — LRHS MBar MDun MGos SLdr
'Polar Bear' ♀ H3-4 — GLbr LHyd LMil LRHS MAsh MGos SBrw SReu SSpi WBVN
Polar Bear Group — CDoC COtt CWri GGGa GKir ISea LMil MLea NMun SLdr
'Polar Haven' (EA) — LKna
'Polaris' — see Rhododendron 'Hachmann's Polaris'
'Polaris' (EA) — ENot MBri MGos SReu
§ poluninii — GGGa
polyandrum — see R. maddenii subsp. maddenii Polyandrum Group
§ polycladum — GKev LMil MLea
§ - Scintillans Group — GDra MBar MBri MDun MLea NHol NMun SLdr WPic
- - 'Policy' ♀ H4 — GGGa SReu
polylepis — GGGa NMun
- C&K 284 — GGGa
§ ponticum — CDoC CTri CWri GGGa LMil MBar MGos NWea SBrw SLdr SPer WFar
- AC&H 205 — GGGa
- 'Aureomarginatum' (v) — SBrw
- 'Cheiranthifolium' — NMun
- 'Foliis Purpureis' — CWri SReu
- 'Roseum' — SBrw
§ - 'Silver Edge' (v) — CDoC CSBt LMil SBrw SLdr SMur WWeb

- 'Variegatum' (v) — CBcs CDoC CHig EBee EBre ENot GGGa GKir ISea LRHS MAsh MBar MBri MDun MGos NBlu NMun NPri SPar SReu SRms SSta WFar WGer
'Pooh-Bah' (EA) — LHyd
'Pook' — LHyd
'Popacatapetl' — SLdr SReu
'Popcorn' (V) — GGGa SFai
'Port Knap' (EA) — LKna
'Port Wine' (EA) — LKna
'Potlatch' — GGGa
poukhanense — see R. yedoense var. poukhanense
§ 'Praecox' ♀ H4 — CBcs CSBt CSam CTrw EBee ENot EPfP GGGa ISea LHyd LKna LMil LRHS MAsh MBar MBri MGos NBlu NHol NMun NPri SBrw SHBN SLdr SPer SReu SSta WBod WFar
x praecox 'Emasculum' — see R. 'Emasculum'
praestans — GGGa LMil NMun SLdr
- Cox 6025A — GGGa
- KW 13369 — NMun
praevernum — GGGa LMil NMun SLdr
§ prattii — NMun SLdr
- 'Perry Wood' — LMil
'Prawn' — LKna SReu
Prelude Group — SLdr
preptum — GGGa SLdr
'President Roosevelt' (v) — CSBt GKir LKna LMil LNet LRHS MAsh MDun MGos NMun NPri SBrw SHBN SLdr SReu SSta WFar
'Pretty Girl' — LKna
'Pretty Woman' — GGGa LMil
'Pride of Leonardslee' — SLdr
'Pridenjoy' — LMil
'Prima Donna' — LMil SLdr SReu
primuliflorum — GGGa SLdr WAbe
- CN&W 1237 — ISea
- KW 4160 — NMun
- 'Doker-La' — LMil LRHS WAbe
- white-flowered Cox 6136 — GGGa
'Prince Camille de Rohan' — LMil SBrw
'Prince Henri de Pays Bas' (G) — CSdC LMil SLdr
'Prince of Wales' (EA) — SBrw
'Princess Alexandra' (V) — SFai
'Princess Alice' — CBcs CHig LHyd NMun SLdr WAbe WBod WPic
'Princess Anne' ♀ H4 — CMHG CSam EBee ENot GDra GGGa GKir LHyd LMil LRHS MAsh MBar MDun MGos MHFa MHdf MLea NLAp NMun NPri SBod SBrw SHBN SLdr SPer SReu SSta WAbe WBod
'Princess Galadriel' — SLdr
'Princess Ida' (EA) — LHyd SLdr
'Princess Juliana' — LMil WBod WGor
'Princess Margaret of Windsor' (K) — GQui LMil
'Princess Margaret Toth' — CSdC
principis — LMil NMun SLdr
- C&V 9547 — GGGa
- KR 3336 from Potrang Gyala — LMil
- KR 3844 from Pasum Tzo — LMil
- LS&E 15831 — NMun
- SF 95085 — ISea
- 'Lost Horizon' KW 5656 — LMil
§ - Vellereum Group — NMun SLdr
- - KW 5656 — NMun
§ prinophyllum (A) — LMil LRHS
'Prins Bernhard' (EA) — LKna SCam SLdr
'Prinses Juliana' (EA) — SLdr SReu WFar

'Professor Hugo de Vries' ♀ H4	LHyd LKna MGos SBrw SReu	
'Professor J.H. Zaayer'	MGos SBrw	
pronum	GGGa	
– R 151*	NMun	
– R.B. Cooke form	GGGa	
– Towercourt form	GGGa	
'Prostigiatum'	MGos	
prostratum	see *R. saluenense* subsp. *chameunum* Prostratum Group	
proteoides	GGGa	
– EGM 281	LMil	
– KGB 700	GGGa	
– R 151	NMun	
* – 'Ascrevie'	GGGa	
protistum	NMun SLdr	
– KR 1986	GGGa	
– KW 8069	NMun	
§ – var. *giganteum*	NMun SReu	
pruniflorum	GGGa NMun	
prunifolium (A)	GGGa LMil LRHS SLdr	
– 'Summer Sunset' (A)	NMun	
przewalskii	GGGa NMun SLdr	
– C&K 370	GGGa	
– Cox 5073	GGGa	
– subsp. *dabanshanense*	GGGa	
pseudochrysanthum ♀ H4	CDoC GGGa LHyd LMil LRHS NMun SLdr SReu SSta	
– ETE 442	GGGa	
– ETE 443	GGGa	
dwarf	WAbe	
Psyche Group	see *R.* Wega Group	
'Psyche' (EA)	MDun	
'Ptarmigan' ♀ H3-4	CBcs CDoC EPfP GGGa GLbr LHyd LMil MBar MGos MLca NHar NHol NLAp NMen NMun SLdr SPer SReu SSta WBod WFar	
pubescens	LMil SLdr	
– KW 3953	GGGa	
pubicostatum	LMil	
– AC 2051	LMil	
– CN&W 906	ISea	
§ 'Pucella' (G) ♀ H4	LMil NLar SLdr SReu	
pudorosum	NMun	
– L&S 2752	GGGa	
'Pulchrum Maxwellii'	see *R.* 'Maxwellii'	
pumilum	GCrs GDra GGGa MDun NMun WAbe	
* – 'Pink Baby'	NMen	
* – 'Pink Ban'	NMen	
'Puncta'	GGGa NHol	
punctatum	see *R. minus* var. *minus* Punctatum Group	
purdomii	GGGa SLdr	
'Purple Diamond'	see *R.* Diamant Group purple	
'Purple Emperor'	LKna	
'Purple Gem'	NHar NHol WWeb	
purple Glenn Dale (EA)	SLdr	
'Purple Heart'	ENot	
'Purple Splendor' (EA)	CMac CTrh LKna MGos SCam SLdr	
'Purple Splendour' ♀ H4	CBcs CSBt CWri ENot EPfP GGGa GLbr LHyd LKna LMil LRHS MAsh MBar MBri MDun MGos MLca NMun NWea SBrw SHBN SLdr SReu SSta WFar WGwG WMoo WWeb	
'Purple Triumph' (EA) ♀ H3	CBcs LKna LMil NMun SCam SLdr SReu SSta WBod	
'Purpurtraum' (EA) ♀ H4	GGGa	
'Quail'	GGGa	
Quaver Group	SRms	
'Queen Alice'	LRHS MDun	
'Queen Elizabeth II' ♀ H4	LHyd LMil SPer SReu SSta	
Queen Emma	see *R.* 'Koningin Emma'	
'Queen Mary'	MBar SBrw	
'Queen Mother'	see *R.* 'The Queen Mother'	
'Queen of England' (G)	CSdC	
Queen of Hearts Group	CWri NMun	
'Queen of Hearts'	LHyd	
'Queen Souriya'	SLdr SReu	
Queen Wilhelmina	see *Rhododendron* 'Königin Wilhelmina'	
'Queenswood Centenary'	LMil	
quinquefolium (A)	GGGa LMil NMun SLdr	
racemosum ♀ H4	LMil MBar MDun NMun SLdr SReu SSpi WWeb	
– AC 719	NMun	
– ACE 1367	WAbe	
– SF 365	ISea	
– SSNY 47	GGGa	
– 'Glendoick'	GGGa	
– 'Rock Rose' ♀ H3-4	MAsh WGer	
– – ex R 11265	CWri EPfP GGGa LHyd LMil MBri NMun	
– 'White Lace'	SReu	
– x *tephropeplum*	MBar	
– x *trichocladum* SBEC	NHol	
'Racil'	LKna MAsh MBar MDun MGos MLea	
'Racoon' (EA) ♀ H4	GGGa	
'Radiant' (M)	SLdr	
radicans	see *R. calostrotum* subsp. *keleticum* Radicans Group	
'Rainbow'	LKna NMun SLdr	
'Ramapo' ♀ H4	GGGa GKir GLbr LMil LRHS MAsh MBar MDun MGos MLea MOne NHar NHol NMen NPri SBrw SPer SReu SSta WBod WWeb	
ramsdenianum	GGGa LMil NMun SLdr	
– KR 5619	LMil	
'Rangoon'	MAsh NBlu	
'Raphael de Smet' (G/d)	LMil SReu	
'Rashomon' (EA)	LHyd SLdr SReu WBod	
'Raspberry Ripple'	LKna SReu	
ravum	see *R. cuneatum* Ravum Group	
'Razorbill' ♀ H4	CDoC EPot GGGa LHyd LMil LRHS MBri MGos MLca MOne NHar WAbe WBod WWeb	
recurvoides	GGGa LHyd LMil MDun NMun SReu	
– KW 7184	NMun SLdr	
– Keillour form	GGGa	
recurvum	see *R. roxieanum* var. *roxieanum*	
Red Admiral Group	NMun	
Red Argenteum Group	NMun	
'Red Arrow' **new**	LHyd	
'Red Carpet'	LMil NMun SLdr	
'Red Delicious'	CWri LMil	
'Red Diamond'	see *R.* Diamant Group red	
'Red Fountain' (EA)	LMil MAsh SLdr WPat	
'Red Glow'	LHyd NMun	
'Red Jack'	LMil	
'Red Riding Hood'	LKna	
I 'Red Rover' (V)	SFai	
'Red Sunset' (EA/d)	LRHS	
'Red Velvet'	see *R.* 'Ilam Red Velvet'	
'Red Walloper'	SBrw	
'Red Wood'	GGGa	
'Redpoll'	LHyd	
'Redwing' (EA)	CDoC MAsh SLdr SPer WWeb	
'Reich's Schneewittchen'	GGGa	
Remo Group	SLdr	
'Rendezvous' ♀ H4	ENot LMil SReu	
'Renoir' ♀ H4	CSBt LHyd LMil SLdr SReu	

reticulatum (A)	GGGa LMil NMun SLdr SReu
* - *leucanthum* (A)	GGGa
retusum (V)	GGGa
§ 'Reuthe's Purple'	GGGa NHol NMun SReu
'Rêve d'Amour' (Vs)	SLdr SReu SSta
'Rex' (EA)	MAsh SLdr
rex	CDoC COtt CWri GGGa IDee
	LHyd LMil LRHS MDun NMun
	SLdr
- EGM 295	LMil
- subsp. *arizelum*	see *R. arizelum*
§ - subsp. *fictolacteum*	CDoC GGGa LHyd LMil MDun
♀ H3-4	NMun SLdr SReu
- - SF 649	ISea
- - USDAPI 59104/R11043	NMun
- - 'Cherry Tip' R 11385	NMun
- - Hird 120	WPGP
- - Miniforme Group	LMil MDun
- - - F 25512	GGGa
- subsp. *gratum*	LMil
- - AC 3009 from Zibenshan	LMil
- yellow AC 2079	LMil
- x Sincerity Group	NMun SLdr
- - AC 901	MDun
rhabdotum	see *R. dalhousieae* var.
	rhabdotum
'Ria Hardijzer'	LKna MBri
rigidum	ISea LHyd NMun WAbe
* - *album*	NMun WBod
'Ring of Fire'	CDoC CWri LMil MAsh MDun
	MGos MHFa MLea SLdr SReu
	WGer
'Ripe Corn'	LHyd LKna NMun SLdr SReu
'Riplet'	GGGa MAsh MDun MLea NHar
'Ripples' (EA)	CTrh
ririei	GGGa LHyd NMun SLdr
- AC 2036	LMil
- W/V 1808	NMun
- W/V 5139	NMun SLdr
'Robert Croux'	SLdr
'Robert Keir'	NMun SLdr
'Robert Korn'	LMil MDun WWeb
'Robert Seleger'	GGGa LMil LRHS MAsh NHar
	WAbe WWeb
'Robert Whelan' (A)	MDun NLar SReu
'Robin Hill Frosty' (EA)	SLdr
Robin Hood Group	NMun
'Robin Redbreast'	NMun
'Robinette'	CBcs CWri MBri SLdr
'Rob's Favourite' (V)	SFai
'Rocket'	GKir LMil MAsh MBri NMun SLdr
	WBVN
'Rokoko'	see *R.* 'Hachmann's Rokoko'
Romany Chai Group	LHyd SLdr
'Romy'	NMun
'Rosa Marie'	SLdr
'Rosa Mundi'	CSBt EBee ENot
Rosalind Group	SLdr
'Rosata' (Vs) ♀ H4	MBri MDun SReu SSta
'Rose Bud'	MDun
'Rose Elf'	ECho NHar NHol
'Rose Glow' (A)	SReu
'Rose Gown'	SReu
'Rose Greeley' (EA)	CDoC CHig CTrh GQui LRHS
	SCam SLdr SPoG SReu WFar WLRN
'Rose Haze' (A)	SReu
'Rose Torch' (A)	SReu
roseatum F 17227	GGGa
'Rosebud' (EA/d) ♀ H3-4	CBcs CMac CTrh CTrw ECho GGGa
	LHyd LKna MBar MGos NMun
	SCam SLdr SReu WBod WLRN
'Rosemary Hyde' (EA)	SLdr
'Rosenkavalier'	LHyd

roseotinctum	see *R. sanguineum* subsp.
	sanguineum var. *didymoides*
	Roseotinctum Group
roseum	see *R. prinophyllum*
'Roseum Elegans'	CTri ECho LRHS MAsh MBar NBlu
	NMun NPri SBrw SLdr
'Rosiflorum'	see *R. indicum* 'Balsaminiflorum'
'Rosy Bell'	LKna
'Rosy Dream'	CAbP COtt CWri LMil MAsh MBri
	MHFa MLea SLdr
'Rosy Fire' (A)	SReu
'Rosy Lea'	MLea
'Rosy Lights' (A)	CTri MAsh MBri
'Rothenburg'	CSam CWri LHyd MDun SBrw
	SLdr SReu
rothschildii	GGGa LMil LRHS NMun
- AC 1868 from Dapo Shan	LMil
- C&Cu 9312	GGGa
roxieanum	CWri LHyd LMil NMun SLdr
	SReu
- R 25422	NMun
- USDAPI 59159/R11141	SLdr
§ - var. *cucullatum*	ISea LRHS MDun NMun
- - CN&W 680	GGGa
- - CN&W 690	LMil
- - CN&W 695	LMil
- - R 10920	NMun
- - SBEC 350	GGGa
- - SBEC 0345	NMun
- - dwarf Dawyck	GGGa
- var. *oreonastes* ♀ H4	CDoC GGGa LHyd LMil LRHS
	MDun NMun SLdr SSta
- - CN&W 307	GGGa
- - CN&W 740	GGGa
- - CN&W 743	GGGa
- - USDAPI 59222/R11312	GGGa NMun
- - Nymans form	SReu
- var. *parvum*	GGGa
§ - var. *roxieanum*	NMun
- - CN&W 727	GGGa
- - F 16508	NMun
'Royal Blood'	LHyd SLdr
'Royal Command' (K)	COtt GKir MBar SBrw SLdr
Royal Flush Group	ISea
'Royal Lodge' (K)	SLdr
'Royal Purple'	WBod
'Royal Ruby' (K)	CWri GLbr MBri SLdr
'Roza Stevenson'	LHyd NMun SBrw SLdr
'Rozanne Waterer' (K)/d	LKna
'Rubicon'	CWri LHyd MLea SLdr WBVN
rubiginosum	GGGa LHyd LMil NMun SLdr
	SReu
- SF 368	ISea
§ - Desquamatum Group	CBcs LHyd NMun SLdr
- pink	LMil
- white	LMil
'Rubinetta' (EA)	LMil LRHS MAsh SLdr WFar WWeb
rubroluteum	see *R. viridescens* Rubroluteum
	Group
'Ruby F. Bowman'	CWri MGos NMun SBrw SLdr SReu
'Ruby Hart'	CBcs GGGa MAsh MDun NHol
	SBrw SReu
Ruddigore Group	WBod
rude	see *R. glischrum* subsp. *rude*
'Ruffles and Frills'	ECho MAsh MDun SLdr
rufum	GGGa NMun SLdr
- Sich 155	GGGa
rugosum Sinclair 240 (V)	GGGa
'Rumba' (K)	LKna
rupicola	GDra LMil NMen NMun SLdr
§ - var. *chryseum*	GGGa LHyd NMun
- var. *muliense*	NMun
- - Yu 14042	GGGa

russatum ♀ H4	CBcs CSam EBee ENot EPot GDra GGGa LHyd LMil MDun NMun SLdr WAbe WPic
- C&Cu 9315	GGGa
- blue-black	LMil LRHS
- 'Purple Pillow'	CSBt NHar WWeb
* - 'Tower Court'	NMun
russotinctum	see *R. alutaceum* var. *russotinctum*
'Sacko'	CWri ECho GGGa GLbr LMil LTwo MAsh MDun MOne NHol SLdr WOrn
'Saffrano'	NBlu
'Saffron Queen'	CBcs CTrG CTrw WBod
'Sahara' (K)	CSdC LKna
'Saint Breward'	CTrG GGGa LHyd MDun MLea NHol SLdr WGer
'Saint Keverne'	SLdr
'Saint Merryn' ♀ H4	CDoC CTrG ENot GGGa LHyd MBri MHFa NHol NMun SLdr WBod
'Saint Michael'	SReu
'Saint Minver'	SLdr
'Saint Tudy'	CDoC EPfP LHyd LKna MDun NMun SLdr
'Saint Valentine' (V)	SFai
'Sakata Red' (EA)	WBod
'Sakon' (EA)	NMun SLdr
'Salmon Bedspread'	SReu
'Salmon Sander' (EA)	SLdr
§ 'Salmon Trout'	LMil
'Salmon's Leap' (EA/v)	CBcs COtt GQui LMil LRHS NPri SHBN SLdr SPer SReu WAbe WFar
saluenense	GGGa LMil NMun SLdr WAbe
- JN 260	GGGa
§ - subsp. *chameunum*	GGGa LMil NMun SLdr WAbe WGer
§ - - Prostratum Group	GGGa WAbe
- subsp. *riparioides*	see *R. calostrotum* subsp. *riparium* Rock's form
- subsp. *saluenense* F 19479	NMun
- =R 11005 Exbury form	LMil
'Sammetglut'	CWri SReu
'Samoa'	MAsh NBlu
'Sang de Gentbrugge' (G)	CSdC GGGa LMil SReu
sanguineum	GGGa LMil MDun NMun SLdr SReu
- Cox 6056	GGGa
§ - subsp. *didymum*	GGGa MDun NMun
- subsp. *sanguineum* var. *cloiophorum* R 10899	NMun
- - USDAPI 59553/R11212	NMun
- - var. *didymoides* Consanguineum Group	NMun
§ - - - Roseotinctum Group USDAPI 59038/R10903	GGGa NMun
- - var. *haemaleum*	GGGa LMil NMun
- - - F 21732	NMun
- - - F 21735	GGGa NMun
- - - R 31	GGGa
- - - USDAPI 59303/R10895	NMun
- - - USDAPI 59453/R10938	NMun
- - var. *sanguineum* F 25521	LMil
- - - R 10893	NMun
- - - USDAPI 59096/R11029	NMun
'Santa Maria'	COtt LRHS MHFa SLdr SReu SSta
§ 'Saotome' (EA)	LHyd SLdr
'Sapphire'	CSBt CTrG LKna MAsh MBar MDun SLdr SRms
'Sappho'	More than 30 suppliers
'Sapporo'	GGGa LMil MAsh

'Sarah Boscawen'	SReu
sargentianum	LMil MLea NMen NMun WAbe
- 'Whitebait'	GGGa NMun WAbe
'Sarled' ♀ H4	GGGa LMil NMen SReu
Sarled Group	GDra NHar NMun SPer SRms WAbe WBod
'Saroi' (EA)	NMun SLdr
'Sarsen' (K)	CSdC
'Saskia' (K)	LKna
'Satan' (K) ♀ H4	COtt LKna SLdr SReu
'Satschiko'	see *Rhododendron* 'Geisha Orange'
'Satsop Surprise'	GGGa
'Satsuki' (EA)	ECho LNet
'Saturne' (G) **new**	SLdr
'Saturnus' (M)	SLdr
'Saxon Dwarf' (V)	SFai
scabrifolium	CTrG NMun
§ - var. *spiciferum*	GGGa NMun SLdr WPic
- - SF 502	ISea
- - SF 534	ISea
'Scarlet Wonder' ♀ H4	More than 30 suppliers
schlippenbachii (A)	GGGa GIBF LHyd LMil NMun SLdr SReu SSpi
- 'Sid's Royal Pink' (A)	LMil MDun
'Schneeflöckchen'	GGGa
'Schneekrone'	GGGa MBri MDun NHol
'Schneeperle' (EA)	GGGa
'Schneespiegel'	ENot
'Schneewolke'	LMil
'Schubert' (EA)	MBar MGos SLdr WBod
scintillans	see *R. polycladum* Scintillans Group
'Scintillation'	CWri GGGa LMil MAsh MBar MDun MLea NMun SBrw SHBN SLdr WMoo WOrn WWeb
scopulorum	SLdr
- C&C 7571	GGGa
- KW 6354	GGGa
scottianum	see *R. pachypodum*
scyphocalyx	see *R. dichroanthum* subsp. *scyphocalyx*
Seagull Group	NMun SLdr
searsiae	NMun SLdr
'Sea-shell'	SLdr
'Seb'	SLdr
'Second Honeymoon'	CDoC CWri MLea SBrw SLdr SReu
'Seikai' (EA)	SLdr
seinghkuense CCH&H 8106	GGGa
- KW 9254	GGGa
selense	GGGa LMil NMun SLdr
- Cox 6041	GGGa
§ - subsp. *dasycladum*	NMun
- - F 11312	NMun
- - KW 7189	NMun
- - R 11269	NMun
- subsp. *jucundum*	GGGa LMil MDun NMun
- - KR 4051B	LMil
- - SF 660	ISea
- subsp. *selense* Cox 6024	GGGa
- - F 14458	NMun
§ - subsp. *setiferum*	NMun SLdr
semnoides	GGGa NMun SLdr
- F 21870	NMun
- F 25639	NMun
- R 25388	NMun
'Senator Henry Jackson'	GGGa LMil
'Sennocke'	LHyd
'September Song'	COtt CWri GGGa LMil MAsh MDun MGos MHFa MLea SLdr WBVN WGer
'Serendipity'	GGGa
serotinum	LMil NMun SLdr SReu

	– C&H 7189	GGGa
	– KR 4653	LMil
	– SEH 242	LMil
	serpyllifolium (A)	CBcs GGGa NMun SLdr
	'Sessostris' (G) **new**	CSdC
	'Sesterianum'	CMHG SLdr
	Seta Group	CBcs CHig NMun SLdr SReu
	setiferum	see *R. selense* subsp. *setiferum*
	setosum	GGGa LMil MDun NMun
	'Seven Stars'	CSBt NMun SLdr SReu
	'Shamrock'	CBcs CDoC CSam EPfP GCrs
		GEdr GKir ISea LRHS MAsh MBar
		MGos MLea NHar NHol NLAp
		SBrw SLdr SReu WBod WFar
		WWeb
	'Shantung Rose' (V)	SFai
	'Shanty' (K/d)	LKna
	'Sheila' (EA)	CDoC NPri
	shepherdii	see *R. kendrickii*
	sherriffii	GGGa MDun NMun SLdr
	– L&S 2751	NMun
	'Shiko' (EA)	MAsh
I	'Shiko Lavender' (A)	LMil
	Shilsonii Group	LHyd NMun SLdr SReu
	'Shinimiagagino' (EA)	NMun
	'Shi-no-noe' (EA)	NMun
	'Shintoki-no-hagasane' (EA)	LHyd
	'Shintsune' (EA)	NMun
	Shot Silk Group	NMun SLdr
	'Show Stopper' (V) **new**	SFai
	'Shrimp Girl'	EBee ENot LRHS MAsh MGos
		NMun SLdr SReu
	'Shukishima' (EA)	NMun
	shweliense	GGGa SReu
	sichotense	GGGa
	sidereum	GGGa NMun SLdr
	– AC 3056	WCwm
	– KW 6792	NMun
	– SF 314	ISea
	– SF 318	ISea
	siderophyllum	SLdr
	sikangense	NMun SLdr
	– C&K 246	GGGa
	– EGM 108	LMil
	– R 18142	NMun
§	– var. *cookeanum*	NMun
	Cookeanum Group	
	– var. *exquisitum*	MDun
	– – EGM 349 from	LMil
	Wumenshan	
	– var. *sikangense*	LMil
	– – Cox 5012	GGGa
	– – Cox 5105	GGGa NHol
*	*sikkimense* SD 1108	GGGa
§	'Silberwolke'	COtt EBee ENot LMil SBrw SReu
	'Silver Anniversary' **new**	MGos
	Silver Cloud	see *R.* 'Silberwolke'
	'Silver Edge'	see *R. ponticum* 'Silver Edge'
	'Silver Fountain' (EA)	LMil LRHS
	'Silver Glow' (EA)	CMac
	'Silver Jubilee'	LHyd LMil LRHS SLdr
	'Silver Moon' (EA)	NMun SCam SLdr SPer
	'Silver Queen' (A)	ECho
	'Silver Sixpence'	EBee ENot EPfP GKir LRHS MAsh
		MBar MDun MGos NMun NWea
		SHBN SLdr SReu
	'Silver Skies'	LMil
	'Silver Slipper' (K) ♀ H4	CDoC GKir LHyd LKna LMil LRHS
		MAsh MBar MBri MLea SLdr SPer
		SReu SSta WGer WGor
	'Silver Thimbles' (V) **new**	GGGa
	'Silverwood' (K)	LMil
	'Silvester' (EA)	COtt MBri SCam SLdr

	'Simona'	CWri LMil LRHS MAsh SPoG SReu
	simsii (EA)	CMac SLdr
	– SF 431	ISea
	simulans	see *R. mimetes* var. *simulans*
	sinofalconeri C&H 7183	GGGa
	– SEH 229	LMil
	sinogrande ♀ H3	CBcs CDoC CHEx CWri GGGa
		LMil LRHS MDun NMun SLdr SPer
		SPoG SSpi WBod WFar WGer WPic
	– AC 1888	WCwm
	– KR 4027	LMil
	– KW 21111	NMun SLdr
	– SF 350	ISea
	'Sir Charles Lemon' ♀ H3-4	CDoC CWri LMil LRHS MAsh
		MBri MDun MLea NMun SLdr
		SReu WCwm WGer
*	'Sir G.E. Simpson'	NMun
	'Sir George Sansom'	SLdr
	'Sir Robert' (EA)	SLdr
	'Sir William Lawrence' (EA)	LKna SReu
	'Skookum'	ECho GLbr MGos SLdr WBVN
	'Sleeping Beauty'	WAbe
	'Sleepy'	ENot GLbr MAsh NDlv NMun
		SLdr SPer SReu WLRN
	smirnowii	GGGa LMil LRHS NMun SLdr
		SReu
	smithii	see *R. argipeplum*
§	Smithii Group	CWri SReu
	smithii Argipeplum Group	see *R. argipeplum*
	'Sneezy'	CBcs CSBt ENot EPfP GGGa GKir
		LHyd LMil LRHS MAsh MBar
		MGos MOne NHol NMun SLdr
		SReu SSta WFar WOrn
	'Snipe'	CBcs CDoC ENot GGGa GKir
		GLbr LHyd LMil LRHS MAsh MBar
		MGos MOne NHar NHol NPri
		NWea SPer SReu
	'Snow' (EA)	CMac LRHS MBar SCam SLdr
	'Snow Crown'	NBlu SLdr
	(*lindleyi* hybrid)	
	'Snow Hill' (EA)	GQui LHyd LMil SLdr
	'Snow Lady'	CBcs EBee ENot EPfP GCrs GLbr
		LMil MAsh MBar MGos MLea
		MOne NHar NHol NLAp SLdr
		WGwG WOrn
	'Snow Queen'	SBrw SLdr
	Snow Queen Group	LKna LMil SReu
	Snow White Group	WWeb
	'Snowbird' (A)	GGGa LMil LRHS MAsh MMHG
		NPri WGer WWeb
	'Snowdrift' **new**	GGGa
	'Snowhite' (EA)	NPri
	'Snowstorm'	ECho MHFa SLdr WBVN
	'Soho' (EA)	CSdC GQui LNet SLdr
	'Soir de Paris' (Vs)	CDoC GGGa LHyd MAsh MBar
		MBri MLea NMun SLdr SReu SSta
		WBVN WBod WGer
	'Soldier Sam'	SReu SSta
	'Solidarity'	ECho GLbr MAsh MDun MLea
		SLdr WBVN
	'Solway' (Vs)	CSdC LMil
	'Sonata'	CWri GGGa MDun SReu
	'Sonatine'	LMil
	'Songbird'	GDra LHyd LKna LMil LRHS MAsh
		MBar MBri NMun SLdr SReu
		WBod WWeb
	'Sophie Hedges' (K/d)	LKna
	sororium (V) KR 3080	GGGa
	– KR 3085	LMil
	– var. *wumengense*	LMil
	CN&W 990	
	Souldis Group	LMil SLdr
	souliei	LMil NMun

– deep pink-flowered	GGGa
– white-flowered	GGGa
'Southern Cross'	CSam MLea NMun SLdr
'Souvenir de Congo'	SBrw
'Souvenir de D.A. Koster'	SLdr
'Souvenir de Doctor S. Endtz' ♀ H4	CSBt LKna MBar SBrw SLdr
'Souvenir du Président Carnot' (G/d)	LKna
'Souvenir of Anthony Waterer' ♀ H4	LKna SBrw SReu
'Souvenir of W.C. Slocock'	CSam LKna NMun SBrw SHBN SLdr SReu SSta
'Sparkler' (Vs)	GGGa
'Sparkler' (hybrid)	LRHS MGos
speciosum	see *R. flammeum*
'Spek's Brilliant' (M)	SReu
'Spek's Orange' (M) ♀ H4	MGos SReu
sperabile	NMun
– var. *weihsiense*	GGGa LMil NMun
– – AC 1915	LMil
– – CN&W 564	ISea
sperabiloides	GGGa NMun
– R 125	NMun
sphaeranthum	see *R. tricbostomum*
sphaeroblastum	GGGa SLdr
– KR 1481*	NMun
– var. *wumengense*	MDun
– – CN&W 510	ISea
– – CN&W 962	LMil
– – CN&W 968	GGGa
– – CN&W 1051	LMil
spiciferum	see *R. scabrifolium* var. *spiciferum*
spilotum	GGGa NMun SLdr
spinuliferum	GGGa NMun SLdr WBod
– SF 247	ISea
'Spitfire'	MGos SBrw SReu
'Splendens' (G)	CSdC
'Spoonbill' (K)	LKna
'Spring Beauty' (EA)	CMac NBlu SCam SLdr SReu
'Spring Magic'	LMil MAsh NMun SLdr
'Spring Pearl'	see *R.* 'Moerheim's Pink'
'Spring Rose'	MAsh NMun SLdr
'Spring Sunshine'	LMil
'Springbok'	LHyd
'Squirrel' (EA) ♀ H4	CDoC COtt GGGa GKir LHyd LMil LRHS MAsh MBri MDun MGos MLea NDlv SLdr SPer SReu WBod WGer
'Squirrel' tall (EA)	SLdr
'Staccato'	GGGa
Stadt Essen Group	CDoC LMil SLdr
stamineum	GGGa LMil NMun
– SF 417	ISea
– W/V 887	NMun
'Standishii'	SLdr
'Stanley Rivlin'	LHyd SLdr
§ 'Stanway'	LMil NMun
'Starbright Champagne'	LMil
'Starfish'	SBrw SReu
'Stella'	NMun
stenaulum	see *R. moulmainense*
§ *stenopetalum*	CMac ISea LMil NMun SLdr SReu
'Linearifolium' (A)	WAbe WPic
stewartianum	GGGa MDun NMun SLdr
– SF 370	ISea
'Stewartstonian' (EA)	CMac LHyd MBar MBri SReu SSta WBod WFar
stictophyllum	see *R. nivale* subsp. *boreale* Stictophyllum Group
'Stoat' (EA)	GQui MDun
'Stopham Girl' (A) **new**	LMil

'Stopham Lad' (A) **new**	LMil
'Stranraer'	MBri
'Strawberry Cream'	GGGa NHol
'Strawberry Ice' (K) ♀ H4	CBcs CDoC CMHG ENot EPfP GGGa GKir LHyd LKna LMil LRHS MAsh MBar MBri MDun MGos MHFa MLea MMHG NBlu NPri SLdr SPer SReu
'Streatley'	SLdr
strigillosum	GGGa MDun NMun SLdr
– C&H 7035	GGGa
– EGM 305	LMil
– EGM 338	LMil
– Reuthe's form	SReu
'Suave'	WBod
subansiriense C&H 418	GGGa NMun SLdr
suberosum	see *R. yunnanense* Suberosum Group
succothii	LHyd MDun
– BB 185a	NMun
– EGM 086	LMil
– LS&H 21295	NMun SLdr
'Suede'	MDun
'Sugar Pink'	LMil
'Sugared Almond' (K)	LMil
sulfureum	NMun
– SBEC 249	GGGa
'Sulphamer'	SLdr
'Summer Blaze' (A)	SReu
'Summer Flame'	SReu
'Summer Fragrance' (O) ♀ H4	LMil SReu SSta
'Sun Chariot' (K)	CBcs LHyd LKna MAsh MBri SLdr SReu
'Sunbeam' (hybrid)	LKna SBrw SReu
'Sunny' (V)	GGGa
(Sunrise Group) 'Sunrise'	SLdr
'Sunset Pink' (K)	LHyd SLdr
'Sunstruck'	GGGa
'Sunte Nectarine' (K) ♀ H4	GQui LHyd LMil MBri SCoo
superbum (V)	GGGa
'Superbum' (O)	SBrw SLdr SReu
'Surprise' (EA)	CDoC CTrh CTri LRHS NMun SCam SCoo SLdr
'Surrey Heath'	CBcs CMHG COtt CWri EBee ENot EPfP GKir LMil LNet LRHS MAsh MBar MBri MDun MGos MLea NBlu NDlv NMun SBrw SLdr SReu WOrn WWeb
'Susan' ♀ H4	CDoC CHig CSBt CSam CWri GGGa LHyd LKna LMil MAsh MBri MDun MLea NBlu NMun SBrw SLdr SPer SPoG SReu
'Susannah Hill' (EA)	CDoC CTrh MGos SLdr SReu
'Sussex Bonfire'	NMun SLdr
sutchuenense	GGGa IDee LMil MDun NMun SLdr
– var. *geraldii*	see *R.* x *geraldii*
'Swamp Beauty'	CWri LMil
'Swansong' (EA)	CMac
'Sweet Simplicity'	CSBt LKna SBrw
'Sweet Sixteen'	NMun SLdr
'Sweet Sue'	NBlu NMun SLdr SReu
'Swift'	CDoC GGGa GQui LRHS LTwo MAsh NHol SLdr WGer
'Sylphides' (K)	LKna MBri
'Sylvester'	CDoC MGos MHdf NBlu NMen SReu
'T.S. Black' (EA)	SLdr
taggianum 'Cliff Hanger' ex KW 8546	LMil

'Taka' (A)	SLdr	
'Takasago' (EA/d)	LHyd LMil	
'Talavera'	see *R.* (Golden Oriole Group) 'Talavera'	
taliense	GGGa LHyd LMil MDun NMun SLdr	
– F 6772	NMun SLdr	
– JN 782	GGGa	
– KR 2765	GGGa	
– KR 4056 from Cangshan	LMil	
– SSNY 352	GGGa	
'Tally Ho'	SLdr	
Tally Ho Group	NMun SLdr	
tamaense	see *R. cinnabarinum* subsp. *tamaense*	
'Tama-no-utena' (EA)	LHyd SLdr	
'Tamarindos'	LMil	
'Tanager' (EA)	CDoC CTrh LKna	
§ *tanastylum* var. *pennivenium*	NMun SLdr	
– – SF 593	ISea	
'Tangerine'	see *R.* 'Fabia Tangerine'	
tapetiforme	GGGa WAbe	
'Tarantella'	ENot LMil	
Tasco Group	SLdr	
tashiroi (EA)	NMun SLdr	
'Tatjana' ♀H4	ENot LMil LRHS	
tatsienense	GGGa	
'Taurus' ♀H4	CDoC COtt CWri GGGa LMil MAsh MDun MGos MLea WGer	
'Teal'	CSam MBar MDun MGos MLea NHol NMun SReu WWeb	
'Teddy Bear'	CDoC CWri GGGa LMil LRHS SLdr WAbe	
§ *telmateium*	NMun	
temenium	MDun	
– Cox 6037B	GGGa	
– R 10909	NMun	
– var. *dealbatum* Glaphyrum Group F 21902	NMun	
– var. *gilvum* 'Cruachan' R 22272	GGGa LMil NMun	
§ – var. *mesopolium* R 10950	NMun	
– var. *temenium* F 21734	NMun	
– – F 21809	NMun	
'Temple Belle'	CWri MDun	
Temple Belle Group	CSam LHyd LKna MLea NDlv NMun SLdr	
'Tender Heart' (K)	SLdr	
'Tensing'	SLdr	
§ *tephropeplum*	GGGa MDun NMun SLdr	
– KW 6303	NMun	
– SF 92069	ISea	
– USDAPQ 3914/R18408	GGGa	
– Deleiense Group	see *R. tephropeplum*	
'Tequila Sunrise'	LMil NMun	
'Terra-cotta'	LKna LMil	
'Terra-cotta Beauty' (EA)	CTrG WPat	
'Tessa'	CBcs MAsh SLdr	
Tessa Group	CDoC LKna LMil LRHS MGos	
'Tessa Bianca'	GGGa	
'Tessa Roza' ♀H4	GGGa GQui LHyd	
'Thai Gold' (V)	SFai	
thayerianum	GGGa NMun SLdr	
'The Dowager'	SLdr	
'The Freak'	SLdr	
§ 'The Hon. Jean Marie de Montague' ♀H4	CAbP CSam CWri EPfP LKna LMil MAsh MBri MDun MLea NMun SBrw SLdr SPoG WBVN WMoo WWeb	
'The Master' ♀H4	LHyd LKna LMil NMun SBrw SLdr SReu	
§ 'The Queen Mother'	LHyd	
'The Warrior'	SBrw	
thomsonii	GGGa LHyd LMil LRHS MDun NHol SLdr SReu	
– AC 113	NMun	
– B&SWJ 2638	WCru	
– Bu 270	GGGa	
– MH 70	GGGa	
– var. *candelabrum*	see *R.* x *candelabrum*	
§ – subsp. *lopsangianum*	GGGa	
– – LS&T 6561	NMun	
– subsp. *thomsonii* BL&M 228	NMun	
– – L&S 2847	GGGa	
Thor Group	GGGa SBrw SReu	
'Thousand Butterflies'	see *R.* 'One Thousand Butterflies'	
'Thunder'	MAsh MBri	
'Thunderstorm'	LHyd LKna SReu	
thymifolium	GGGa	
'Tiana'	GGGa	
'Tibet' ♀H3-4	GQui LMil MBar MDun NHar SHBN SLdr	
'Tidbit' ♀H4	GGGa LHyd LKna LMil MGos MLea NMun SLdr	
'Tilford Seedling'	LKna	
I 'Tilgates Peach'	CWri	
'Timothy James'	LRHS MAsh SReu	
'Tinkerbird'	GGGa	
'Tinsmith' (K)	SLdr	
'Tit Willow' (EA)	GKir LHyd LMil LRHS NPri SCoo SLdr	
'Titian Beauty'	CBcs COtt CSBt CWri EBee EPfP GBin GGGa GKir LHyd LMil LNet LRHS MAsh MBri MGos NBlu NDlv NMun NPri SBrw SLdr SPer WBrE WOrn WWeb	
'Titipu' (EA)	LHyd SLdr	
'Tolkien'	SReu	
'Tom Williams'	NMun SLdr	
'Too Bee'	GGGa NHol WAbe	
'Top Banana'	LRHS MDun SLdr	
'Topsvoort Pearl'	SReu	
'Torch'	LKna MGos	
'Toreador' (EA)	CTrG SCam SLdr	
'Torero'	GGGa LMil	
'Torridon' (Vs)	LMil	
'Tortoiseshell Champagne'	see *R.* 'Champagne'	
'Tortoiseshell Orange' ♀H3-4	CDoC CSBt LHyd LKna LMil MBri MDun SBrw SHBN SLdr SPer SPoG SReu SSta WGer WWeb	
'Tortoiseshell Salome'	LKna SBrw SReu	
'Tortoiseshell Scarlet'	NBlu SReu	
'Tortoiseshell Wonder' ♀H3-4	LKna LMil MAsh MGos NMun NPri SLdr SPer SReu	
'Totally Awesome' (K)	MAsh MLea WWeb	
'Toucan' (K)	MDun SLdr	
'Tow Head'	WWeb	
'Tower Beauty' (A)	LHyd	
'Tower Dainty' (A)	LHyd	
'Tower Daring' (A)	LHyd SLdr	
'Tower Dexter' (A)	LHyd	
'Tower Dragon' (A)	LHyd LMil	
'Trail Blazer'	GGGa	
traillianum	GGGa LMil NMun SLdr	
– CN&W 746	ISea	
– F 5881	NMun	
§ – var. *dictyotum*	NMun	
– – 'Kathmandu'	NMun SLdr	
Treasure Group	GDra LHyd SLdr	
'Trebah Gem'	NMun SLdr	
'Tregedna'	NMun SLdr	

'Tregedna Red'	SReu
'Trewithen Orange'	CDoC MBar MDun NMun SHBN SLdr
'Trewithen Purple'	CTrw
'Trianon'	NMun
trichanthum	CHig CPne GGGa LMil NMun
- 'Honey Wood'	LHyd LMil SLdr
trichocladum	NMun
- CN&W 880	ISea
- SF 661	ISea
- SF 96179	ISea
§ *trichostomum*	GGGa LRHS NMun SSpi WAbe WBod
- KW 4465	NMun
- Ledoides Group	MLea NMun SReu
- - 'Collingwood Ingram' ♥ H4	LMil SReu
triflorum	GGGa ISea MDun NMun
- C&V 9573	GGGa
- SF 95149	ISea
§ - var. *bauhiniiflorum*	CBcs NMun SLdr
- var. *triflorum* Mahogani Group	NMun
'Trilby'	SBrw SReu
'Trinidad'	MDun
triplonaevium	see *R. alutaceum* var. *russotinctum* Triplonaevium Group
'Troll' (EA)	SReu
'Tromba'	GGGa
'Troupial' (K)	LKna
'Trude Webster'	CHig GGGa MLea SReu
aff. *tsaii* H&M 1490	GGGa
tsangpoense	see *R. charitopes* subsp. *tsangpoense*
tsariense	GGGa LMil NHol NMun SLdr
- var. *magnum*	NMun
- Poluninii Group	see *R. poluninii*
- var. *trimoense*	GGGa LMil MDun NMun
- 'Yum Yum'	CWri GGGa NMun SLdr
aff. *tsariense*	LMil
tsariense × *proteoides*	GGGa
§ *tsusiophyllum*	GGGa WAbe
'Tsuta-momiji' (EA)	LHyd
tubiforme	see *R. glaucophyllum* subsp. *tubiforme*
'Tuffet'	ENeu
'Tulyar'	LKna
'Tunis' (K)	ECho
N 'Twilight' (EA)	MBri
'Twilight Pink'	NMun
'Twilight Sky' (A)	ENot SBrw SLdr
'Tyermannii'	LMil
'Ukamuse' (EA/d)	LHyd
'Umpqua Queen' (K)	MLea
Ungerio Group	NMun
ungernii	GGGa NMun SLdr
uniflorum	NHol NMun
§ - var. *imperator*	LMil
- - KW 6884	GGGa
- var. *uniflorum* KW 5876	NMun
'Unique' (G)	EPfP ISea LKna LRHS
'Unique' (*campylocarpum* hybrid) ♥ H4	CBcs CDoC CSam CWri GGGa GKir LHyd LKna LMil LNet LRHS MAsh MBri MDun NMun NPri SBrw SHBN SLdr SReu SSta
'Unique Marmalade'	LMil SLdr WBVN WWeb
'Unknown Warrior'	SBrw SReu
uvariifolium	GGGa NMun SLdr
- CN&W 127	ISea
- CN&W 382	CWri
- CN&W 1275	ISea
- Cox 6519	GGGa
- KR 4158 from Zhongdian,	LMil

Napa Hai	
- var. *griseum*	SLdr
- - C&C 7506	GGGa
- - KR 3423	LMil
- - KR 3428	LMil
- - KR 3774	LMil
- - KR 3782	LMil
- - SF 95184	ISea
- 'Reginald Childs'	LMil LRHS
- var. *uvariifolium* USDAPI 59623/R11391	NMun
- 'Yangtze Bend'	GGGa
vaccinioides (V) CCH&H 8051	GGGa
'Valentine' (EA)	GGGa
valentinianum	CBcs GGGa NMun SLdr WAbe WGer
- F 24347	NMun
- var. *oblongilobatum* C&H 7186	LMil
'Van'	LMil WWeb
'Van Nes Sensation'	LMil
'Van Weerden Poelman'	EMil SBrw
Vanessa Group	LMil SReu WBod
'Vanessa Pastel' ♥ H3-4	CDoC GGGa LHyd LMil MDun MLea NMun SLdr SReu
§ 'Vanilla'	LKna
vaseyi (A) ♥ H3-4	GGGa LMil SLdr
- white-flowered (A)	LMil
veitchianum	GGGa
§ - Cubittii Group	GGGa NMun SLdr
- - 'Ashcombe'	LHyd
- KNE Cox 9001	GGGa
vellereum	see *R. principis* Vellereum Group
'Velvet Gown' (EA)	ENot SReu
venator	GGGa MDun NMun
'Venetia' (K)	MBri
'Venetian Chimes'	EBee ENot ISea NMun SLdr SReu
vernicosum	GGGa LMil NMun
- F 5881	NMun
- JN 180	GGGa
- McLaren T 71	NMun
- SF 416	ISea
- Yu 13961	SLdr
- Yu 14694	SLdr
- Euanthum Group F 5880	NMun
'Veryan Bay'	CBcs
vesiculiferum	NMun
'Vespers' (EA)	MAsh
vialii (A)	GGGa
'Victoria Hallett'	SLdr SReu
'Vida Brown' (EA/d)	CMac ENot LKna MBri SLdr SReu SSta WPat
'Viennese Waltz'	GGGa
'Viking' (EA)	LHyd WBod
'Vincent van Gogh'	CDoC GGGa LMil
'Vinecourt Duke' (R/d)	CWri ECho GLbr MDun SLdr
'Vinecourt Troubador' (K/d)	CDoC ECho MDun SLdr
'Vineland Dream' (K/d)	ECho LRHS SLdr WCwm
'Vineland Fragrance'	MDun MHFa SLdr
I 'Vinestar' AM/T	SLdr
'Vintage Rosé' ♥ H4	CBcs LMil NMun SLdr SPoG SReu
'Violet Longhurst' (EA)	LHyd SLdr
'Violetta' (EA)	GGGa LRHS NMen SLdr
Virginia Richards Group	CWri GKir LHyd LRHS MAsh MGos NBlu NMun SBrw SLdr SReu SSta
§ *viridescens*	CSBt
- 'Doshong La'	LMil
§ - Rubroluteum Group	GGGa LMil

viscidifolium — GGGa NMun
'Viscosepalum' (G) — CSdC
viscosum (A) ♀ H4 — GGGa GIBF GQui LHyd LKna LMil LRHS MHdf SLdr SReu WBrE
- 'Antilope' — see *R.* 'Antilope'
- 'Arpege' — see *R.* 'Arpege'
- 'Grey Leaf' (Vs) — LMil
- var. *montanum* (A) — IBlr
- f. *rhodanthum* (A) — LMil
- 'Roseum' (Vs) — LMil
'Viscount Powerscourt' — ENot LMil SLdr
'Viscy' ♀ H4 — CDoC CWri ECho GGGa GQui LHyd LMil MAsh MDun MGos MLea SLdr WOrn

§ Volker Group — CWri LMil LRHS MAsh MBar MGos NDlv SReu SSta
- 'Babette' — LMil MBri
- 'Lackblatt' — CDoC LMil MAsh MBri MLea NBlu SLdr
- 'Vulcan' ♀ H4 — CBcs ENot EPfP GGGa LMil MAsh MLea SBrw SHBN SLdr
'Vulcan' x *yakushimanum* — SReu
'Vulcan's Flame' — CDoC
'Vuyk's Rosyred' (EA) ♀ H4 — CDoC CMac CTri ENot GQui LHyd LKna LMil LRHS MAsh MBar MBri MGos SBod SCam SLdr SPer SReu WBod WFar WStI
'Vuyk's Scarlet' (EA) ♀ H4 — CBcs CDoC CMac CTrh EPfP EPot GGGa GKir GQui LHyd LKna LMil LRHS MAsh MBar MBri MGos NMun NPri SBrw SCam SLdr SPer SPlb SReu SSta WBod WFar WWeb
'W.E. Gumbleton' (M) — SReu
'W.F.H.' ♀ H4 — CWri LMil NMun SLdr
'W. Leith' — SLdr
'Wagtail' — NHol WAbe
wallichii — GGGa MDun SLdr
- B&SWJ 2633 — WCru
- DM 21 — LMil
- LS&H 17527 — NMun
Walloper Group — NMun SReu
'Wallowa Red' (K) — ECho LHyd MAsh MBri MLea SLdr
'Wally Miller' — LMil MAsh MLea SReu SSta
walongense — NMun
aff. *walongense* C&H 373 — GGGa
'War Dance' — GGGa
wardii — GGGa IDee ISea LHyd LMil LRHS MDun NMun SLdr
- C&V 9558 — GGGa
- C&V 9606 — GGGa
- KR 3684 — LMil
- L&S — SReu
- SHEG 5672 — NMun
- var. *puralbum* — GGGa NMun
- - F 10616 — NMun
- 'Vibrant' — SLdr
- var. *wardii* — LMil
- - C&V 9548 — GGGa
- - F 21551 — NMun
- - KW 5736 — NMun
- - LS&E 15764 — NMun
- - LS&T 5679 — NMun
- - LS&T 5686 — NMun
- - LS&T 6591 — NMun
§ - - Litiense Group — NMun SLdr
- - CN&W 1079 — ISea
'Ward's Ruby' (EA) — CTrh CTrw SLdr
'Warrior' (EA) — SBrw
§ 'Washington State Centennial' (A) — GGGa MAsh
wasonii — GGGa LHyd LMil NMun
- f. *rhododactylum* — NMun SReu

- - KW 1876 — GGGa
- var. *wenchuanense* — GGGa NHol
- - C 5046 — GGGa
- white-flowered — SReu
'Waterfall' — WBod
watsonii — GGGa NMun SLdr SReu
- Cox 5075 — GGGa
'Waxbill' — GGGa
'Waxwing' — LKna
websterianum Cox 5123 — GGGa
- EGM 146 — LMil
'Wee Bee' ♀ H4 — CDoC EPot GCrs GGGa GKir LMil LTwo MAsh MDun MLea NDlv NHar NHol SReu WAbe WWeb
§ Wega Group — LHyd
'Welkin' — WBod
'Werei' — NMun
'Westminster' (O) — LKna LMil SPoG
'Weston's Pink Diamond' — GGGa LMil NHol
'Weybridge' — NMun SLdr
weyrichii (A) — GGGa
'Wheatear' — GGGa
'Whidbey Island' — LMil
'Whisperingrose' — CDoC LMil MGos MLea WWeb
'White Frills' (EA) — GLbr LHyd
White Glory Group — NMun SLdr
'White Gold' — GGGa MDun
'White Grandeur' (EA) — CTrh
'White Jade' (EA) — SLdr
'White Lady' (EA) — LKna LMil MBar SCam SLdr WGor
'White Lights' (A) ♀ H4 — LMil LRHS MAsh MBri SLdr WWeb
'White Olympic Lady' — LKna
'White Perfume' — SReu
'White Peter' — GGGa
'White Swan' (hybrid) — ENot LKna SBrw SReu
'White Wings' — GQui SLdr WPic
'Whitethroat' (K/d) ♀ H4 — CSdC CWri EPfP GKir GLbr GQui LKna LMil MAsh MBri SLdr
'Whitney's Dwarf Red' — SLdr
'Wigeon' — GGGa GKir LMil LRHS NHol
wightii — GGGa MDun NMun SLdr
'Wild Affair' — MDun
'Wilgen's Ruby' — CDoC CSBt LKna MBar MGos NWea SBrw SHBN SLdr WFar WStI WWeb
'Will Silent' (V) — SFai
'Willbrit' — CBcs CDoC CWri ECho LHyd MAsh MGos MHFa SLdr WGor WOrn
williamsianum ♀ H4 — CBcs CDoC CTrG CWri EPot GBin GGGa LHyd LMil LRHS MBar MDun MGos MLea NMun NWea SLdr SReu SRms SSpi WBod WPic
- Caerhays form — LMil MDun SLdr
- pink-flowered — CSBt
- 'Special' — GGGa
- white-flowered — NMun
'Willy' (EA) — CTrh SCam SLdr
wilsoniae — see *R. latoucheae*
Wilsonii Group — CTrG LKna
wiltonii ♀ H4 — GGGa LMil MDun NMun SLdr
- CC&H 3906 — GGGa
'Windlesham Scarlet' — EBee ENot LHyd SBrw SLdr
'Windsor Lad' — LKna SBrw SReu
'Windsor Peach Glow' (K) — LMil
'Winsome' (hybrid) ♀ H3 — CDoC GGGa LHyd LMil NPri WWeb
Winsome Group — CBcs CHig CTrw CWri GKir LKna LRHS MBar MDun NMun SBrw SLdr SSta WBod
'Winston Churchill' (M) — MBar SReu
I 'Wintergreen' (EA) — COtt CTrh
'Wishmoor' — NMun SLdr SReu
'Witch Doctor' — ECho LMil MDun MGos MLea SBrw SLdr WBVN

'Witchery'	GGGa	
'Wojnar's Purple'	LMil MAsh WWeb	
'Wombat' (EA) ♀ H4	CDoC COtt CTri EPot GGGa GKir	
	LHyd LMil LRHS MGos NHol SLdr	
	SReu	
'Wonderland'	LKna	
wongii	GGGa GQui LMil NMun SLdr	
'Woodcock'	LHyd WBod	
'Wren'	CSam GCrs GEdr GGGa LRHS	
	MAsh MBar MBri MDun MLea	
	MOne NHar NHol NLAp SLdr	
	SReu WAbe WWeb	
'Wryneck' (K)	CSdC LHyd LMil SLdr SReu	
'Wye' (K)	SLdr	
x *xanthanthum*	MLea	
xanthocodon	see *R. cinnabarinum* subsp.	
	xanthocodon	
xanthostephanum	NMun	
– CCH&H 8070	GGGa	
– KR 3095	LMil	
– KR 4462	LMil	
'Yaku Angel'	MDun	
'Yaku Incense'	MAsh MBri MDun MHFa WBVN	
'Yaku Prince'	CDoC MAsh MBri	
'Yaku Princess'	MAsh	
yakushimanum	CBcs CDoC CMHG CSam CWri	
	EPfP GGGa ISea LHyd LKna LMil	
	LPan LRHS MAsh MBar MBri	
	MDun MGos MLea NBlu NMun	
	NWea SBrw SLdr SPer SPlb SReu	
	SSta WAbe WGer	
I – 'Beefeater'	SLdr	
– 'Berg'	MAsh MDun	
– 'Edelweiss'	GGGa	
– 'Exbury form'	SReu	
– FCC form	see *R. yakushimanum* 'Koichiro	
	Wada'	
§ – 'Koichiro Wada' ♀ H4	CAbP EBee GGGa LHyd LMil	
	LRHS MAsh MGos NMun SBrw	
	SLdr SReu WAbe WGer	
– subsp. *makinoi*	see *R. makinoi*	
– 'Snow Mountain'	SReu	
I – 'Torch'	WBrE	
– subsp. *yakushimanum*	see *R.* 'Ken Janeck'	
'Ken Janeck'		
– x *bureavii*	SReu	
– x 'Coronation Day'	SLdr	
– x *decorum*	GGGa SLdr SReu	
– x 'Elizabeth'	GGGa	
– x 'Floriade'	SLdr	
– x *griersonianum*	SLdr	
– x *lunatum*	GGGa	
– x *pachysanthum*	GGGa SLdr SReu	
– x *proteoides*	GGGa	
– x *rex*	SReu	
– x *tsariense*	GGGa	
'Yaye' (EA)	CDoC SLdr	
§ *yedoense* var.	SLdr SReu	
poukhanense		
'Yellow Cloud' (K)	CDoC ECho LMil MBri WWeb	
'Yellow Hammer' ♀ H4	CDoC CSBt CTrG EPfP MDun	
	NWea SBrw WBVN WBrE	
Yellow Hammer Group	CBcs CHig CSam CWri GGGa	
	LKna LMil MBar MGos NMun	
	SHBN SLdr SReu SRms SSta	
	WBod	
'Yellow Petticoats'	MBri MLea	
'Yellow Rolls Royce'	MDun	
'Yoga' (K)	LKna	
'Yol'	SLdr	
I 'Yolanta'	WAbe	
'Youthful Sin'	ISea	
'Yo-zakura' (EA)	NMun	

yungningense	LMil MDun NMun	
yunnanense	GGGa ISea LHyd LMil MDun	
	NMun SLdr WPic	
– AC 751	MDun NMun	
– C&H 7145	GGGa	
– KGB 551	SReu	
– KGB 559	SReu	
– SF 379	ISea	
– SF 400	ISea	
– SF 96102	ISea	
– 'Openwood' ♀ H3-4	GGGa LMil	
– pink-flowered	GGGa	
– 'Red Throat'	SLdr	
§ – Suberosum Group	NMun	
– white-flowered	GGGa LMil WAbe	
'Yvonne Dawn'	NMun	
zaleucum	LMil MDun	
– AC 685	MDun NMun	
– F 15688	GGGa	
– F 27603	NMun	
– KR 2687	GGGa	
– KR 3979	LMil	
– SF 347	ISea	
– SF 578	ISea	
– Flaviflorum Group	NMun	
KW 20837		
Zelia Plumecocq Group	NMun SLdr	
zeylanicum	see *R. arboreum* subsp.	
	zeylanicum	
Zuiderzee Group	SBrw SLdr	

Rhodohypoxis (Hypoxidaceae)

'Albrighton'	CRDP EPot ERos EWes ITim	
	LAma NHol NMen SAga SBla SIng	
	WAbe WPat	
'Appleblossom'	EPot ERos EWes ITim NMen SCnR	
	SIng WAbe WOBN	
baurii ♀ H4	CElw CRDP EPot ETub GCrs	
	GEdr IKee IMGH ITim LRHS	
	MBro MTho NMen SAga SRms	
	WAbe WHil WWin	
– 'Alba'	CMea CRDP EDAr ITim MLLN	
	NMen	
– var. *baurii*	EPot EWes GCrs LBee SIng	
– 'Carina' **new**	EWes	
– var. *confecta*	EWes ITim SAga SBla SIng	
– 'Dulcie'	EWes ITim SCnR SIng SOkd	
– 'Lily Jean' (d)	ENot GEdr LRHS SIng WWeb	
– 'Pearl' **new**	ITim WHil	
– 'Perle'	EPot ERos EWes GEdr NJOw	
	NMen SCnR SIng WAbe	
– 'Pictus'	ITim	
– pink-flowered	ITim NLAp WCru	
– 'Pink Pearl'	EPot EWes ITim NHol	
– var. *platypetala*	CRDP EPot EWes ITim NHol	
	NMen SIng WAbe	
– – x *milloides*	LTwo	
– – Burtt 6981	EWes	
– red-flowered	NLAp SPlb	
– 'Red King' **new**	EWes	
– 'Susan Garnett-Botfield'	EPot EWes ITim NMen SIng	
	WAbe	
– white-flowered	ITim NLAp NMen WCru	
– x *ypoxis parvula*	see x *Rhodoxis hybrida*	
'Burgundy'	SIng	
'Candy Stripe' **new**	EWes LPan SIng	
'Confusion'	EWes WAbe	
'Dawn'	EPot EWes ITim LAma NHol	
	NLAp NMen SAga SBla SIng WAbe	
deflexa	CGra CLyd CRDP EWes GCrs	
	IMGH ITim NLAp SAga SCnR	
	SIng SMrm WAbe WOBN	
'Donald Mann'	EWes ITim NMen	

double, red-flowered	CRDP
'Douglas'	CRDP EPot ITim LAma NHol NMen SAga SBla SIng WAbe WLRN WPat
'Dusky'	EPot
'E.A. Bowles'	EWes GCrs ITim NMen SIng WAbe
'Emily Peel'	EWes WAbe
'Eva-Kate'	ERos EWes ITim LAma NHol SAga SBla SIng WPat
'Fred Broome'	EPot EWes ITim LAma NHol NMen SAga SBla SIng WAbe WPat
'Garnett'	EDAr EWes GCrs ITim NMen SBla WAbe WPat
'Great Scott'	ECho ERos EWes ITim SCnR SIng
'Harlequin'	EPot EWes ITim LAma NHol NMen SIng WAbe
'Hebron Farm Biscuit'	see *Hypoxis parvula* var. *albiflora* 'Hebron Farm Biscuit'
'Hebron Farm Cerise'	see x *Rhodoxis* 'Hebron Farm Cerise'
'Hebron Farm Pink'	see x *Rhodoxis hybrida* 'Hebron Farm Pink'
§ 'Helen'	EPot EWes ITim NHol SBla SIng WAbe
hybrids	ELan WOBN
'Kiwi Joy' (d)	CRDP SBla
'Knockdolian Red'	NHol
'Maddie's Blush' **new**	WOBN
'Margaret Rose'	EPot EWes GCrs NMen SIng WAbe
milloides	CPla CRDP EMlt EPot EWes GEdr GGar IKee IMGH ITim LBee LRHS NHol NLAp NMen NWCA SAga SBla SCnR SIng SSpi WAbe
– 'Claret'	CRDP CSam EWes LTwo SAga SBla SIng WAbe WOBN WPat
– 'Damask'	CRDP EWes SAga SBla
– giant	SMrm
– 'Monty'	EPot EWes GEdr SIng
'New Look'	ERos EWes ITim LTwo NMen SIng WAbe
'Picta' (v)	CRDP EPot EWes GCrs LAma NHol SAga SBla SSpi WAbe WOBN WPat
'Pinkeen'	EPot EWes GEdr ITim LTwo SIng WAbe
'Pintado'	EWes SBla
'Rosie Glow' **new**	WOBN
'Ruth'	EWes LAma NHol SBla SIng WAbe
'Shell Pink'	EWes ITim
'Starry Eyes' (d)	CRDP SBla
'Stella'	EPot ERos EWes GEdr ITim NHol NMen SAga SBla SIng WAbe WOBN
tetra **new**	ITim
'Tetra Pink'	EWes SIng WAbe
'Tetra Red'	EPot EWes ITim NHol NMen SIng WAbe WOBN WWin
'Tetra White'	see *R.* 'Helen'
thodiana	CRDP ERos EWes GEdr NMen SBla SCnR SIng SSpi WAbe
'Venetia'	SIng

Rhodophiala (Amaryllidaceae)

§ *advena*	WCot
bagnoldii F&W 8695 **new**	WCot
§ *bifida*	LBow
– *spathacea*	LBow
chilensis	CLAP
elwesii	EHyt
montana	NWoo

Rhodora see *Rhododendron*

Rhodothamnus (Ericaceae)

chamaecistus	GCrs WAbe

Rhodotypos (Rosaceae)

kerrioides	see *R. scandens*
§ *scandens*	CBcs CBot CPle CTri EBee EPfP EWTr GEil ICrw IMGH LHop SLon SMac SSpi WBod WCru WSHC WWin

x *Rhodoxis* (Hypoxidaceae)

'Aurora'	EWes
§ 'Hebron Farm Cerise'	EWes GEdr NMen SAga
§ *hybrida*	CRDP EWes NMen SIng SMrm WAbe
– 'Aya San'	EWes
§ – 'Hebron Farm Pink'	CBro EWes GEdr NMen SAga SBla SCnR SIng WAbe WOBN
– 'Hebron Farm Red Eye'	EWes SBla SCnR SIng WAbe
'Old Barn Pink' **new**	WOBN

Rhoeo see *Tradescantia*

Rhopalostylis (Arecaceae)

baueri	CBrP EAmu LPal
cheesemanii	CBrP
sapida	CAbb CBrP CTrC ECou LPal MPRe
– 'Chatham Island'	CBrP

rhubarb see *Rheum* x *hybridum*

Rhus (Anacardiaceae)

ambigua B&SWJ 3656	WCru
§ *aromatica*	CAgr CArn CFil CPle ELau EPfP IArd IDee WPGP
chinensis	CDoC EGFP EPfP MMat
copallina	ELan EPfP GIBF LRHS SMur
– red-leaved	WPat
coriaria	EPfP
cotinus	see *Cotinus coggygria*
glabra	CAgr CArn CBcs CDoC CLnd EPfP SPar SPer WDin
– 'Laciniata' misapplied	see *R.* x *pulvinata* Autumn Lace Group
N *hirta*	see *R. typhina*
incisa	SPlb
integrifolia	CArn CPle LRav
magalismontana **new**	EShb
potaninii	EPfP
§ x *pulvinata* Autumn Lace Group	CDoC ENot EPfP GKir MGos SDix SHBN SPar
– – 'Red Autumn Lace' ♀ H4	GKir LRHS MAsh MBlu MBri SPer
punjabensis var. *sinica*	CFee WPic
§ *radicans*	CArn COld CPlN GPoy
sylvestris	EPfP
toxicodendron	see *R. radicans*
trichocarpa	EPfP SSpi
trilobata	see *R. aromatica*
N *typhina* ♀ H4	More than 30 suppliers
§ – 'Dissecta' ♀ H4	CBcs CDoC CDul CLnd CSBt EBee ELan ENot EPfP GKir MAsh MBar MBri MGos MWat NBea NBlu SEND SPar SPer WDin WFar WOrn WTel
– 'Laciniata' hort.	see *R. typhina* 'Dissecta'
§ *verniciflua*	CFil CLnd CMCN EPfP GIBF IArd SSpi

Rhynchelytrum see *Melinis*

Rhynchosia (Papilionaceae)

cooperi **new**	GFai

Rhynchospora (Cyperaceae)

§ *colorata*	CRow NPer WDyG

Ribes ✿ (Grossulariaceae)

alpinum	ENot LBuc MRav NSti NWea SPer SRms WDin WGwG WRHF
- 'Aureum'	CMHG CSBt EHoe EPla NFor NPro WDin WSHC
- 'Schmidt'	MBar
americanum 'Variegatum' (v)	EHoe ELan EPla MRav NHol WPat
aureum hort.	see R. odoratum
* - 'Roxby Red'	MCoo
'Black Velvet' (F)	LRHS MBri MCoo
x **culverwellii** Jostaberry (F)	EMui GTwe LBuc LRHS SDea
diacanthum	CFil
dikuscha	IIve
divaricatum	CAgr
- 'Worcesterberry'	see Ribes 'Worcesterberry'
fragrans Pall. non Lodd.	IIve
gayanum	CPMA CPle NLar SLPl WHCG
x **gordonianum**	CDoC CMHG CPLG CPMA EBee EPfP EPla GBin GEil GKir LAst LHop LRHS MRav NSti SEND SLim SLon SSpi WCot WFar WHCG
laurifolium	CBcs CBot CFil CPLG CPla ELan SBrw SLim SPer WCru WDin WHCG WPGP WSHC WWal WWin
- (f)	CPMA EPfP GKir
- (m)	CHar CPMA EBee EPfP GKir WCFE WCot WPat
- 'Mrs Amy Doncaster'	EPla
- Rosemoor form	CSam EPfP SSpi WHCG
lobbii	EWes
nigrum 'Baldwin' (B)	CDoC CMac CWSG EPfP GBon LRHS MBri SDea SKee SPer WStI WWeb
- 'Ben Alder'[PBR] (B)	LRHS MBri SDea
- 'Ben Connan'[PBR] (B) ♀ H4	CDoC COtt EMui EPfP GTwe LRHS MBri MGos SCoo SDea WLRN WWeb
- 'Ben Lomond'[PBR] (B) ♀ H4	CSBt CTri EMui ENot GBon GKir GTwe LBuc LRHS MBri MGos MRav NBee NGHP NRog SDea SKee WStI WWeb
- 'Ben Loyal' (B)	GTwe
- 'Ben More' (B)	CSBt GKir GTwe LRHS MBri NBee SDea SPer WStI
- 'Ben Nevis' (B)	CSBt CTri GTwe SDea
- 'Ben Sarek'[PBR] (B) ♀ H4	CDoC CSBt CSam CSut CWSG EBre EMui ENot ERea GKir GTwe LBuc LRHS MBri MGos MRav NGHP NRog SDea SKee SPer WWeb
- 'Ben Tirran'[PBR] (B)	CDoC LBuc LRHS MBri MGos
- 'Black Reward' (B)	LRHS
- 'Blacksmith' (B)	MCoo
- 'Boskoop Giant' (B)	CMac GTwe LRHS NRog SPer
- 'Daniel's September' (B)	GTwe MCoo
- 'Farleigh' (B)	EMui
- 'Foxendown' (B)	EMui
* - 'Hystawneznaya' (B)	CAgr
- 'Jet' (B)	ENot GTwe LRHS NRog SPer
* - 'Kosmicheskaya' (B)	CAgr
- 'Laciniatum' (B)	EMon
- 'Laxton's Giant' (B)	GTwe
- 'Mendip Cross' (B)	GTwe
* - 'Robustum' **new**	WWeb
- 'Wellington XXX' (B)	CSBt ENot ERea GTwe LBuc LRHS MBri NBee NBlu NGHP NRog SKee WStI
- 'Westwick Choice' (B)	GTwe
§ **odoratum**	More than 30 suppliers
- 'Crandall'	ESim

praecox	CBcs SEND
- **rubrum** 'Blanka' (W)	CSut
- 'Fay's New Prolific' (R)	GTwe
- 'Gloire de Sablans' (R) **new**	WWeb
- 'Hollande Rose' (P)	GTwe
- 'Jonkheer van Tets' (R) ♀ H4	CSBt CWSG EMui GKir GTwe IArd LRHS MCoo SDea SKee
- 'Junifer' (R)	EMui GTwe
- 'Laxton's Number One' (R)	CSam CTri EBre EMui ENot GBon GTwe LRHS MBri MRav NGHP NRog SDea SPer WWeb
- 'Laxton's Perfection' (R)	MCoo
- 'October Currant' (P)	GTwe
- 'Raby Castle' (R)	GTwe
- 'Red Lake' (R) ♀ H4	CAgr CMac CSam CWSG EBre EPfP ERea GBon GTwe LBuc LRHS MBri MGos NBee NBlu NRog SDea SKee SPer WStI WWeb
- 'Redstart'[PBR] (R)	COtt CSBt GTwe LBuc LRHS MBri SDea SKee WWeb
- 'Rondom' (R)	SDea
- 'Rovada' (R)	CSut EMui GTwe
- 'Roxby Red' (R)	NGHP NRog
- 'Stanza' (R) ♀ H4	GTwe SDea
§ - 'Versailles Blanche' (W)	CMac CSBt CSam CTri EMui ENot EPfP GKir GTwe LBuc MBri MGos SDea SKee SPer
- 'White Dutch' (W)	MCoo
- 'White Grape' (W) ♀ H4	GTwe NRog
- 'White Pearl' (W)	CBcs SDea SKee
- 'White Transparent' (W)	GTwe
- White Versailles	see R. rubrum 'Versailles Blanche'
- 'Wilson's Long Bunch' (R)	GTwe
sanguineum	CSBt GKir MBar NLon WMoo WStI
- 'Albescens'	MWat SPer WBcn
- 'Brocklebankii'	CAbP CPLG EBee EPar EPfP EPla GKir LAst LRHS MGos MRav MWat NLon NPri NSti SBrw SHBN SLim SLon SPer SPla WAbe WEas WGwG WPen WSHC
- double	see R. sanguineum 'Plenum'
- 'Elk River Red'	GKir LRHS
- 'Flore Pleno'	see R. sanguineum 'Plenum'
- var. **glutinosum** 'Albidum'	SChu
- 'King Edward VII'	More than 30 suppliers
- 'Koja'	EBee LAst LRHS MBri NPro WBcn WWeb
- 'Lombartsii'	MRav
§ - 'Plenum' (d)	CBot MTed
- 'Poky's Pink'	EBre GKir GSki MGos MRav
- 'Pulborough Scarlet' ♀ H4	CBcs CChe CDoC CTri CWSG EBee ELan ENot EPfP EWTr GKir LRHS MAsh MGos MRav MWat NBee NBir SLim SMer SPer SPla SPlb SRms WFar WMoo WWeb
- 'Red Pimpernel'	CDoC CSBt EBee LAst MBNS MBri SCoo WBcn WFar
- 'Taff's Kim' (v)	EPla EVFa SMad
- 'Tydeman's White'	CChe CPLG CSBt ECtt ELan EPfP EVFa LAst MBar MHFa NLar NPri SSpi
- White Icicle = 'Ubric' ♀ H4	CBot CDoC CWSG CWib EBre ENot EPfP GKir GSki LRHS MBri MGos MRav NBir NPri NSti SLim SPer SPla
speciosum ♀ H3	More than 30 suppliers
uva-crispa var. **reclinatum** 'Achilles' (C/D)	GTwe
- var. **reclinatum** 'Admiral Beattie' (F)	GTwe NRog

- - 'Alma' (D)	NRog
- - 'Annelii' (F)	SDea
- - 'Aston Red'	see R. uva-crispa var. reclinatum 'Warrington'
- - 'Australia' (F)	NRog
- - 'Bedford Red' (D)	GTwe NRog
- - 'Bedford Yellow' (D)	GTwe
- - 'Beech Tree Nestling' (F)	GTwe
- - 'Bellona' (C)	NRog
- - 'Blucher' (F)	GTwe NRog
- - 'Bright Venus' (D)	GTwe
- - 'Broom Girl' (D)	GTwe NRog
- - 'Captivator' (F)	GTwe
- - 'Careless' (C) ♀ H4	CMac CSBt CSam EMui ENot ERea GBon GKir GTwe LRHS MBri MGos MRav NBee NRog SDea SKee SPer WStI
- - 'Champagne Red' (F)	GTwe
- - 'Clayton' (F)	NRog
- - 'Cook's Eagle' (C)	GTwe
- - 'Cousen's Seedling' (F)	GTwe
- - 'Criterion' (C)	GTwe NRog
- - 'Crown Bob' (C/D)	GTwe LRHS NRog
- - 'Dan's Mistake' (D)	GTwe LRHS NRog
- - 'Drill' (F)	GTwe
- - 'Early Sulphur' (D/C)	GTwe LRHS NRog SDea WStI
- - 'Edith Cavell' (F)	GTwe
- - 'Firbob' (D)	GTwe NRog
- - 'Forester' (D)	GTwe
- - 'Freedom' (C)	GTwe NRog
- - 'Gipsey Queen' (F)	GTwe
- - 'Glenton Green' (F)	GTwe
- - 'Golden Ball' (D)	SDea
- - 'Golden Drop' (D)	GTwe LRHS
- - 'Green Gem' (C/D)	GTwe NRog
- - 'Green Ocean' (F)	GTwe NRog
- - 'Greenfinch'PBR (F) ♀ H4	EMui GTwe LRHS MGos SDea
- - 'Greengage' (D)	NRog
- - 'Gretna Green' (F)	GTwe
- - 'Guido' (F)	GTwe NRog
- - 'Gunner' (D)	GTwe NRog
- - 'Heart of Oak' (F)	GTwe NRog
- - 'Hebburn Prolific' (D)	GTwe
- - 'Hedgehog' (D)	GTwe
- - 'Hero of the Nile' (C)	GTwe NRog
- - 'High Sheriff' (D)	GTwe NRog
- - 'Hinnonmäki' (F)	CAgr
- - 'Hinnonmäki Gul' (F)	ENot SDea
- - 'Hinnonmäki Röd' (F)	ENot GTwe MCoo SDea WWeb
- - 'Howard's Lancer' (C/D)	GTwe NRog SDea
- - 'Invicta'PBR (C) ♀ H4	CDoC CMac CSBt CSut CTri CWSG EBre EMui ENot EPfP GBon GKir LBuc LRHS MBri MGos SCoo SDea SKee SPer WStI WWeb
- - 'Ironmonger' (F)	GTwe LRHS NRog
- - 'Jubilee' (C/D)	COtt LBuc MBri MGos NRog
- - 'Keen's Seedling' (D)	GTwe
- - 'Keepsake' (C/D)	GTwe LRHS MRav NRog SDea
- - 'King of Trumps' (F)	GTwe LRHS NRog
- - 'Lancashire Lad' (C/D)	GTwe LRHS NRog
- - 'Langley Gage' (D)	GTwe LRHS NRog
- - 'Laxton's Amber' (D)	GTwe
- - 'Leveller' (D) ♀ H4	CMac CSBt CSut CTri EBre EMui ENot GBon GKir GTwe LBuc LRHS MBri MGos MRav NRog SDea SKee SPer WStI
- - 'London' (C/D)	GTwe LRHS NRog
- - 'Lord Derby' (C/D)	GTwe MBri NRog
- - 'Lord Kitchener' (F)	NRog
- - 'Macherauch's Seedling' (F)	NRog
- - 'Marigold' (F)	NRog

- - 'Martlet'PBR (F)	GTwe
- - 'Matchless' (D)	NRog
- - 'May Duke' (C/D)	LRHS NRog SDea
- - 'Mitre' (C)	GTwe
- - 'Pax'PBR (F)	CDoC CSBt EMui EPfP GTwe LBuc SDea SKee WLRN WWeb
- - 'Peru' (F)	GTwe NRog
- - 'Pitmaston Green Gage' (D)	GTwe
- - 'Plunder' (F)	GTwe NRog
- - 'Prince Charles' (F)	GTwe
- - 'Queen of Hearts' (F)	NRog
- - 'Queen of Trumps' (D)	GTwe NRog
- - 'Rifleman' (D)	GTwe
- - 'Rokula'PBR	CDoC EMui GTwe
- - 'Rosebery' (D)	GTwe
- - 'Scotch Red Rough' (D)	GTwe
- - 'Scottish Chieftan' (D)	GTwe
- - 'Sir George Brown' (D)	NRog
- - 'Snowdrop' (C)	GTwe
- - 'Speedwell' (F)	NRog
- - 'Spinefree' (F)	GTwe
- - 'Sultan Juror' (F)	NRog
- - 'Surprise' (C)	GTwe NRog
- - 'Suter Johnny' (F)	NRog
- - 'Telegraph' (F)	GTwe
- - 'The Leader' (F)	NRog
- - 'Tom Joiner' (F)	GTwe
- - 'Trumpeter' (C)	NRog
- - 'Victoria' (F)	GTwe NRog
§ - - 'Warrington' (D)	GTwe NRog
- - 'Whinham's Industry' (C/D) ♀ H4	CMac CSBt CSam CSut EMui ENot ERea GBon GKir GTwe LBuc MBri MGos MRav NBee NRog SDea SKee SPer WStI
- - 'White Eagle' (C)	NRog
- - 'White Lion' (C/D)	GTwe NRog
- - 'White Transparent' (C)	GTwe
- - 'Whitesmith' (C/D)	GTwe LRHS NBlu NRog SDea WStI WWeb
- - 'Woodpecker' (F)	GTwe LRHS NRog
- - 'Yellow Champagne' (F)	GTwe LRHS NRog
valdivianum	EPla
viburnifolium	CPle CSam LEdu SLon WPGP
§ 'Worcesterberry' (F)	EMui LRHS MBri MGos NRog SDea SPer

Richea (Epacridaceae)
dracophylla	SAPC

Ricinocarpos (Euphorbiaceae)
pinifolius new	ECou

Ricinus (Euphorbiaceae)
communis	CHEx CSpe SPar
- 'Carmencita' ♀ H3	LRav SPar
- 'Impala'	SPar
- 'Niger'	WMul
- 'Zanzibariensis'	WMul

Riocreuxia (Asclepiadaceae)
torulosa	SPlb

Robinia (Papilionaceae)
x ambigua	SSpi
boyntonii	CTho MGos
fertilis	EBee CLnd CTho CWib ECrN
hispida	CEnd CLnd CTho CWib ECrN ELan EPfP ICrw LNet MAsh MBlu SHBN SPer SSpi WDin WJas WOrn WSHC
- 'Macrophylla'	CEnd SSpi WPGP
N - 'Rosea'	CBcs CBot EBee ENot MGos WPGP

kelseyi	SPer
x *margaretta* Casque Rouge	see *R.* x *margaretta* 'Pink Cascade'
§ – 'Pink Cascade'	CDoC CDul CEnd CLnd CTho EBee ECrN EPfP EWTr LNet LPan LRHS MAsh MBlu MBri MGos SHBN SKee SPer SRPl SSpi WDin
neomexicana	CLnd
pseudoacacia	CCVT CLnd CWib ECrN ELan ENot EPfP LBuc LPan MCoo WDin WFar WNor
– 'Bessoniana'	CTho EBee ECrN ENot WDin
– 'Frisia' ♀ H4	More than 30 suppliers
– 'Inermis' hort.	see *R. pseudoacacia* 'Umbraculifera'
* – 'Mimosifolia'	MBri
– 'Rozynskiana'	CTho SFam
– 'Tortuosa'	CDul CEnd CLnd CTho EBee ECrN ELan EMil EPfP LPan LRHS MAsh MBlu MBri MGag MGos SLdr SPer SRPl WPGP
– Twisty Baby = 'Lace Lady'PBR	EBee ELan ENot EPfP LRHS MAsh MBri MGos MRav NLar SCoo SMad WWeb WWes
§ – 'Umbraculifera'	CLnd EBee ECrN EMil ENot LPan MGos SFam
– 'Unifoliola'	CTho
x *slavinii* 'Hillieri' ♀ H4	CDul CEnd CLnd CTho ECrN ELan EPfP EWTr LRHS MBlu SPer SPoG SSpi WPGP

Rochea see *Crassula*

Rodgersia ✿ (*Saxifragaceae*)

ACE 2303	GBuc
GLD 1329	NHol
CLD 1432	NHol
from Castlewellan	IBlr
red-flowered	WHil
aesculifolia ♀ H4	More than 30 suppliers
– green bud	IBlr
– pink-flowered	IBlr SSpi
– 'Red Dawn'	IBlr
aff. *aesculifolia* petaloid	IBlr
'Blickfang'	IBlr
'Die Anmutige'	CRow
'Die Schöne'	CLAP
'Elfenbeinturm'	EBee IBlr
henrici	CBct CRow EGle GKir IBlr LBuc MCCP NBro SLon SPer SWat WMoo WPnP WRus WTin
– 'Buckshaw White'	IBlr
– hybrid	EBee EMan NHol NLar SDes WAul WCru
'Herkules'	CBct EBee EMan GBin NLar SSpi WHil
'Irish Bronze' ♀ H4	EBee EBre EMan EPla GBin GKir IBlr LPio MCAu SSpi WMoo WPnP
'Koriata'	IBlr
'Kupfermond'	CRow IBlr
'Maigrün'	IBlr
nepalensis	CFil IBlr MDun
– EMAK 713	WCot
'Panache'	IBlr
'Parasol'	CBct CFil CHad CLAP EBee ELan GBuc IBlr NHol SSpi WPGP WPnP
pinnata	More than 30 suppliers
– L 1670	CLAP SSpi
– 'Alba'	EBee GKir IBlr LRHS MBri MLLN NHol WLin WPnP
– 'Buckland Beauty'	IBlr SBla SSpi

– 'Cally Salmon'	EGle GCal
– 'Crûg Cardinal'	WCru
– 'Elegans'	CBct CHEx CHad EBee EChP ELan EMan ENot EPar EPfP EPla GKir GMaP IBlr LAst LRHS MRav NHol NOrc SMad WCot WGer WPnP WWin
– from S W China **new**	GIBF
– 'Maurice Mason'	SDix SMHy
– 'Mont Blanc' **new**	IBlr
– Mount Stewart form	IBlr
– 'Perthshire Bronze'	IBlr
– 'Rosea'	IBlr
– 'Superba' ♀ H4	More than 30 suppliers
– white-flowered	GAbr GCal
podophylla ♀ H4	More than 30 suppliers
– 'Bronceblad'	IBlr
– Donard form	CFil IBlr MBri WCot
– 'Rotlaub'	CDes CRow EGle GCal IBlr LRHS MBri WCot WMoo
– 'Smaragd'	CLAP CRow EBee EGle GCal IBlr LRHS NLar
purdomii hort.	CDes EBee GCal GKir LRHS SOkh SSpi WCot
§ 'Reinecke Fuchs'	IBlr
'Rosenlicht'	CRow MTed
'Rosenzipfel'	IBlr
sambucifolia	CBcs CRow EBre EWTr GKir ITim LRHS MBri MFir NLar NSti SDes SMrm SPer SSpi WCot WCru WFar WGer WGwG WMoo
– dwarf pink-flowered	GKir IBlr
– dwarf white-flowered	IBlr
– large green-stemmed	IBlr
– large red-stemmed	IBlr
– 'Mountain Select'	WFar
x *pinnata*	IBlr
tabularis	see *Astilboides tabularis*

Rohdea ✿ (*Convallariaceae*)

japonica	CFil EBee LEur WCot WPGP
– 'Godaishu' (v) **new**	WCot
– 'Gunjaku' (v)	EMon WCot
– 'Lance Leaf'	EPla
– long-leaved	WCru WFar
– 'Talbot Manor' (v)	CFil EBee EPla SApp WCot WPGP
– 'Tama-jishi' (v)	WCot
– 'Tuneshige Rokujo' (v)	WCot
– variegated (v)	EBee WCot
watanabei B&SWJ 1911	WCru

Romanzoffia (*Hydrophyllaceae*)

§ *sitchensis*	CLyd CTri MAvo
suksdorfii E. Greene	see *R. sitchensis*
tracyi	CDes EBee GGar NRya WBor WCru
unalaschcensis	CNic GTou NWCA SRms WPer

Romneya (*Papaveraceae*)

coulteri ♀ H4	More than 30 suppliers
§ – var. *trichocalyx*	CFir EBee GMac IBlr SBrw SCro SPer SSpi WViv
§ – 'White Cloud' ♀ H4	EHol ENot ERea IBlr SMad SSpi
– 'White Sails'	IBlr
x *hybrida*	see *R. coulteri* 'White Cloud'
trichocalyx	see *R. coulteri* var. *trichocalyx*

Romulea (*Iridaceae*)

atrandra	EHyt WCot
bulbocodium	CBro CNic WFTG
– WM 9908	MPhe
– var. *clusiana* MS 239	EHyt
* – 'Knightshayes'	CLAP EHyt

- var. *leichtliniana* MS 784   EHyt
columnae   CNic
gigantea new   CStu
linaresii   CNic
longituba   see *R. macowanii*
§ **macowanii**   CPBP NMen
- var. *alticola*   EHyt
minutiflora   NRog
nivalis   LBow
ramiflora   EHyt
- subsp. *gaditana*   EHyt
requienii L 65   EHyt
rosea   NRog WCot
tempskyana   EHyt EPot
* **zahnii**   CNic

Rondeletia (*Rubiaceae*)
amoena   SOWG

Rorippa (*Brassicaceae*)
nasturtium-aquaticum WMAq

Rosa ✿ (*Rosaceae*)
ACE 241   CFee
CC 3306   GDrg
A Shropshire Lad =   CSam LRHS MAus MBri MJon
'Ausled'^PBR (S)   SWCr WWeb
Abbeyfield Rose =   SPer SWCr
'Cocbrose'^PBR
(HT) ♀ H4
§ 'Abbotswood'   EBls MAus
(*canina* hybrid)
Abigaile =   MJon NBat
'Tanelaigib'^PBR (F)
Abraham Darby =   CGro EBre EPfP GGre GKir LRHS
'Auscot'^PBR (S)   LStr MAsh MAus MFry MGan
   MJon MRav MWgw NPri SPer
   SRPl SSea SWCr WAct WHCG WStI
   WWeb
Acapulco =   IDic MFry
'Dicblender'^PBR (HT)
Ace of Hearts =   MBur SWCr
'Korred' (HT)
acicularis   GIBF
- var. *nipponensis*   EBls
'Adam' (ClT)   EBls
'Adam Messerich' (Bb)   EBee EBls ETWh MAus WHCG
'Adélaïde d'Orléans'   CRHN EBls ETWh LRHS MAus
(Ra) ♀ H4   MBri MRav SFam SPer SWCr WAct
   WHCG
Admirable =   MBur
'Searodney' (Min)
'Admiral Rodney' (HT)   MGan MJon NRog
Adriana = 'Frydesire' (HT)   MBri MFry
'Agatha' (G)   see *Rosa* x *francofurtana* 'Agatha'
Agatha Christie =   ENot MBri MJon MMat MRav
'Kormeita'^PBR   (ClF)SWCr
'Aglaia' (Ra)   MAus WHCG
'Agnes' (Ru) ♀ H4   EBls ECnt ENot EPfP GCoc IArd
   LRHS MAsh MAus MGan MMat
   MRav SPer SSea SWCr WAct
   WHCG WOVN
'Aimée Vibert' (Ra)   EBee EBls ETWh MAus MRav SPer
   SRPl SWCr WAct WHCG
'Alain Blanchard' (G)   EBls MAus WHCG
x *alba* (A)   EBls NRog
§ - 'Alba Maxima' (A)   EBls EMFP ENot GCoc LRHS
   MAus MMat MRav SFam SPer SRPl
   SSea SWCr WAct WHCG
§ - 'Alba Semiplena' (A) ♀ H4   CHad EBls EMFP LRHS MAus SPer
   SWCr WAct WHCG
- Celestial   see *R.* 'Céleste'
- 'Maxima'   see *R.* x *alba* 'Alba Maxima'

Alba Meidiland =   CBrm WOVN
'Meiflopan'^PBR (S/GC)
'Albéric Barbier' (Ra) ♀ H4   More than 30 suppliers
'Albertine' (Ra) ♀ H4   More than 30 suppliers
'Alchymist' (S/Cl)   CHad CPou EBee EBls ENot LRHS
   MAus MBNS MBri MGan MJon
   MMat MRav SFam SPer SWCr
   WAct WHCG WKif
Alec's Red = 'Cored' (HT)   CBcs CGro CSBt CWSG EBls ENot
   ESty GCoc GGre GKir LRHS LStr
   MAsh MAus MGan MJon MMat
   MRav NPri NRog SPer SWCr WWeb
Alexander = 'Harlex'   CGro CSBt EBls ENot GCoc GGre
(HT) ♀ H4   LGod LPlm LStr MAus MFry MGan
   MJon MMat MRav NRog SApu
   SPer SSea SWCr
'Alexander Hill Gray' (T)   EBls
'Alexander von   MGan
Humboldt' (Cl)
'Alexandre Girault' (Ra)   CRHN EBls EMFP ETWh LRHS
   MAus MBri SPer SWCr WAct WHCG
§ 'Alfred Colomb' (HP)   EBls
'Alfred de Dalmas'   see *R.* 'Mousseline'
misapplied
Alfresco = 'Chewcorpink'   CSBt LGod MJon SSea SWCr
(ClHT)
'Alida Lovett' (Ra)   EBls MAus
Alison = 'Coclibee'^PBR (F)   GCoc SApu SWCr
'Alison Wheatcroft' (F)   EBls
§ 'Alister Stella Gray' (N)   EBee EBls ETWh EWTr LRHS
   MAsh MAus MGan MRav NHaw
   SPer SSea SWCr WAct WHCG
'Allen Chandler' (ClHT)   EBls MAus
'Allgold' (F)   CBcs CGro EBls ENot GKir MGan
   MJon SWCr WStI
Alnwick Castle = 'Ausgrab'   MAus SWCr
(S) **new**
'Aloha' (ClHT) ♀ H4   CBcs CGro EBee EBls EBre ENot
   ESty GKir LRHS LStr MAus MBri
   MBur MFry MGan MJon MMat
   MRav NBat NRog SApu SChu SPer
   SSea SWCr WAct WHCG
alpina   see *R. pendulina*
'Alpine Sunset' (HT)   CTri EBls ECnt ENot ESty GGre
   GKir MAsh MGan MRav SPer SWCr
altaica hort.   see *R. pimpinellifolia* 'Grandiflora'
Altissimo = 'Delmur' (Cl)   CHad EBee EBls EMFP ENot MAus
   MGan MJon MMat SPer SSea
   SWCr WAct WGer
'Amadis' (Bs)   EBls MAus WHCG
Amanda = 'Beesian'^PBR (F)   MBri MJon SWCr
'Amazing Grace' (HT)   GCoc GGre SWCr
Amber Abundance =   SWCr
'Harfizz'^PBR (S) **new**
Amber Cover =   ECnt
'Poulbambe'^PBR
(GC) **new**
Amber Hit =   ECnt SWCr
'Poultrav'^PBR (Patio)
Amber Nectar =   MJon SWCr
'Mehamber'^PBR (F)
Amber Queen =   CGro CSBt EBee EBls ECnt ESty
'Harroony'^PBR (F) ♀ H4   GCoc GGre GKir IArd LGod LPlm
   LStr MAsh MAus MBri MBur MFry
   MGan MJon MRav NPri NRog
   SApu SPer SRPl SSea SWCr
Amber Star = 'Manstar'   NBat
(Min) **new**
Amber Sunset =   NBat
'Manamsun' (Min)
§ 'Ambossfunken' (HT)   MGan SWCr
Ambridge Rose =   LRHS MAus MJon SWCr
'Auswonder' (S)

'Amélia' — see R. 'Celsiana'
'American Pillar' (Ra) — CGro CRHN CSBt CSam CTri CWSG CWib EBls EBre ECnt ENot GKir ISea LRHS LStr MAsh MAus MGan MMat MRav NRog SApu SPer SSea SWCr WAct WHCG WWeb
'Amy Robsart' (RH) — EBls ETWh MAus SWCr
Anabell = 'Korbell' (F) — NBat
'Anaïs Ségalas' (G) — MAus
§ 'Andersonii' (*canina* hybrid) — EBls ISea MAus SWCr
§ 'Anemone' (Cl) — EBls MAus
anemoniflora — see R. x *beanii*
anemonoides — see R. 'Anemone'
- 'Ramona' — see R. 'Ramona'
'Angel Gates' **new** — WAct
Angela Rippon = 'Ocaru' (Min) — CSBt MFry MGan MJon SSea
'Angela's Choice' (F) — MGan SWCr
'Angèle Pernet' (HT) — EBls
'Angelina' (S) — EBls
Anisley Dickson = 'Dickimono'PBR (F) ♀ H4 — IDic LGod MGan NBat SApu SPer SWCr
'Ann Aberconway' (F) — MJon
Ann = 'Ausfete'PBR — LRHS MAus SWCr
'Anna de Diesbach' (HP) — EBls
Anna Ford = 'Harpiccolo'PBR (Min/Patio) ♀ H4 — CWSG LStr MAus MGan MJon SWCr WWeb
Anna Livia = 'Kormetter'PBR (F) ♀ H4 — MMat MRav
'Anna Olivier' (T) — EBls
'Anna Pavlova' (HT) — EBls SSea
Anne Boleyn = 'Ausecret' (S) — MAsh MAus SWCr
'Anne Cocker' (F) — GCoc MGan
'Anne Dakin' (ClHT) — MAus
Anne Harkness = 'Harkaramel'PBR (F) — CSBt MAus MGan MJon SSea
Anne Marie Laing = 'Jospink' (F) — EBls
'Anne of Geierstein' (RH) — EBls MAus MGan SWCr
'Anne Watkins' (HT) — EBls
Anneka = 'Harronver' (F/HT) — ENot
Annick = 'Fryfrenzy' **new** — MFry
'Anthony' **new** — EBls
Antique '89 = 'Kordalen'PBR (ClF) — EBee EBls ENot MBri MJon MMat MRav SWCr WGer
'Antoine Rivoire' (HT) — EBls
'Antonia d'Ormois' (G) — EBls
Anvil Sparks — see R. 'Ambossfunken'
Aperitif = 'Macwaira'PBR (HT) **new** — GCoc MJon
apothecary's rose — see R. *gallica* var. *officinalis*
'Apple Blossom' (Ra) — EBls SWCr WHCG
'Applejack' (S) — EBls
Apricot Ice = 'Dicyeti' (F) **new** — ESty IDic
'Apricot Nectar' (F) — CSBt MAus MGan SPer
'Apricot Silk' (HT) — CBcs CTri EBls GKir MAus MGan MRav NRog SPer SWCr
Apricot Spice = 'Sanspic' (HT) — MBur SWCr
Apricot Summer = 'Korpapiro'PBR (Patio) — ENot MAsh MBri MJon MMat SWCr WGer
Apricot Sunblaze = 'Savamark'PBR (Min) — CSBt EBls
'April Hamer' (HT) — NBat
Arc Angel = 'Fryorst' (HT) — MFry

Arcadian = 'Macnewye' (F) — MJon
'Archiduc Joseph' misapplied — see R. 'Général Schablikine'
'Archiduchesse Elisabeth d'Autriche' (HP) — EBls
'Ardoisée de Lyon' (HP) — EBls
Ards Beauty = 'Dicjoy' (F) — MGan SApu SPer
'Ards Rover' (ClHP) — EBls
'Arethusa' (Ch) — EBls EMFP ETWh SPla SWCr
'Arizona Sunset' (Min) — NBat
§ *arkansana* var. *suffulta* — EBls WHCG
Armada = 'Haruseful'PBR (S) — SApu SSea SWCr
'Arrillaga' (HP) — MAus
Artful Dodger = 'Sabbelief' (Patio) — MBur
'Arthur Bell' (F) ♀ H4 — CSBt CWSG EBls EBre ENot EPfP ESty GGre GKir IArd LPlm LStr MAsh MAus MBur MGan MMat MRav NPri NRog SApu SPer SRPl SSea SWCr WWeb
'Arthur de Sansal' (DPo) — EBls ETWh MAus WHCG
'Arthur Merril' (F) **new** — NBat
arvensis — CCVT CKin EBls LBuc MAus NWea WAct
§ 'Aschermittwoch' (Cl) — EBls MBur
Ascot Bonnet = 'Helbonnet' (F) — LStr
Ash Wednesday — see R. 'Aschermittwoch'
'Assemblage des Beautés' (G) — EBls MAus
'Astra Desmond' (Ra) — WTin
'Astrid Späth Striped' (F) — EBls
Atco Royale = 'Frywinner'PBR (F) — MFry
Atlantic Star = 'Fryworld'PBR (F) — MFry
Audrey Hepburn = 'Twodore' (HT) — MBur SWCr
Audrey Wilcox = 'Frywilrey' (HT) — CSBt MFry
'August Seebauer' (F) — EBls
'Auguste Gervais' (Ra) — EBls LRHS MAus SPer SWCr WHCG
'Augustine Guinoisseau' (HT) — EBls
'Augustine Halem' (HT) — EBls
Austrian copper rose — see R. *foetida* 'Bicolor'
Austrian yellow — see R. *foetida*
'Autumn' (HT) — NRog
'Autumn Delight' (HM) — EBls MAus WHCG
Autumn Fire — see R. 'Herbstfeuer'
'Autumn Sunlight' (ClF) — MGan SPer
'Autumn Sunset' (S) — EBls
'Autumnalis' — see R. 'Princesse de Nassau'
'Aviateur Blériot' (Ra) — EBls MAus
'Avignon' (F) — ECnt SWCr
Avocet = 'Harpluto' (F) — GGre SWCr
Avon = 'Poulmulti'PBR (GC) ♀ H4 — EBee ECnt ELan ENot ESty GCoc LGod MGan MJon MMat MRav SApu SPer SSea SWCr WHCG
Awakening = 'Probuzini' (Cl) — EBee EBls ETWh SWCr WHCG
Awareness = 'Frybingo'PBR (HT) — MFry
'Ayrshire Splendens' — see R. 'Splendens'
'Baby Bio' (F/Patio) — CBcs ESty MBri MGan NRog SWCr
'Baby Darling' (Min) — MGan SSea
'Baby Faurax' (Poly) — MAus
Baby Gold Star (Min) — see R. 'Estrellita de Oro'
'Baby Katie' (Min) — NBat
Baby Love = 'Scrivluv' (yellow) PBR (Min/Patio) ♀ H4 — ESty MAsh MAus MJon SWCr

Baby Masquerade = 'Tanba' (Min) — ENot MBur MGan MJon MMat NRog SWCr WStI WWeb

Baby Sunrise = 'Macparlez' (Min) — MJon SWCr

'Bad Neuenahr' (Cl) — MGan

'Ballerina' (HM/Poly) ♀ H4 — More than 30 suppliers

Ballindalloch Castle = 'Cocneel'PBR (F) — GCoc

'Baltimore Belle' (Ra) — CRHN EBls MAus SWCr WHCG

banksiae (Ra) — CWib GQui LPan SRms

- SF 96051 — ISea

- *alba* — see R. banksiae var. banksiae

§ - var. *banksiae* (Ra/d) — CBot CSBt EBee ELan EPfP ERea LStr MAus SBra SPer SSea WBcn WGer

- 'Lutea' (Ra/d) ♀ H3 — More than 30 suppliers

- 'Lutescens' (Ra) — CSBt

- var. *normalis* (Ra) — CBot CSBt LPhx MAus NSti WCot WHer WOut

'Bantry Bay' (ClHT) — CSBt EBls ELan LStr MGan MMat MRav SPer SPla SSea SWCr

Barbara Austin = 'Austop'PBR (S) — LRHS MAsh MAus SWCr

'Barbara Carrera' (F) — EBls

Barkarole = 'Tanelorak'PBR (HT) — CSBt LStr MJon SApu SSea SWCr

'Baron de Bonstetten' (HP) — EBls

'Baron de Wassenaer' (CeMo) — EBls MGan SWCr

'Baron Girod de l'Ain' (HP) — EBls MAus MRav SPer SPla SSea SWCr WGer WHCG

'Baroness Rothschild' (HP) — see R. 'Baronne Adolph de Rothschild'

§ 'Baronne Adolph de Rothschild' (HP) — EMFP MGan MRav MWgw SWCr WHCG

Baronne Edmond de Rothschild = 'Meigriso' (HT) — MAus SSea SWCr WAct

'Baronne Henriette de Snoy' (T) — EBls

'Baronne Prévost' (HP) — EBls MAus SFam WAct WHCG

Baroque = 'Harbaroque'PBR (GC/F/S) — SWCr

Barry Fearn = 'Korschwama'PBR (HT) — ENot MMat MRav

'Bashful' (Poly) — MGan

§ x *beanii* (Ra) — EPla SMad

'Beau Narcisse' (G) — MAus

'Beauté' (HT) — EBls MGan SWCr

Beautiful Britain = 'Dicfire'PBR (F) — CSBt CWSG EBls GGre IDic LStr MGan MJon MRav NRog SWCr

Beautiful Sunrise (Cl/Patio) **new** — ESty MJon SWCr

'Beauty of Rosemawr' (ClT) — EBls

Behold = 'Savahold' (Min) — NBat

'Bel Ange' (HT) — MGan

bella — LRHS MAsh

Bella = 'Pouljill'PBR (S) — SWCr

'Belle Amour' (AxD) — EBls MAus SWCr WHCG

'Belle Blonde' (HT) — MGan SPer

'Belle de Crécy' (G) ♀ H4 — CPou EBee EBls ENot GCoc GKir LStr MAsh MAus SFam SPer SSea SWCr WAct WHCG

'Belle des Jardins' misapplied — see R. 'Centifolia Variegata'

Belle Epoque = 'Fryyaboo'PBR (HT) — ENot GCoc LStr MAus MBur MFry MGan MJon MMat SApu SWCr

'Belle Isis' (G) — EBls MAus MRav SPer SWCr

'Belle Lyonnaise' (ClT) — EBls

'Belle Poitevine' (Ru) — EBls MAus

'Belle Portugaise' (ClT) — EBls MAus

Belle Story = 'Auselle' (S) — SPer

§ 'Belvedere' (Ra) — EBls MAus MBri SWCr WHCG

Benita = 'Dicquarrel'PBR (HT) — IDic MJon

Benjamin Britten = 'Ausencart' (S) **new** — MAsh MAus SWCr

Benson and Hedges Gold = 'Macgem'PBR (HT) — CWSG

Benson and Hedges Special = 'Macshana'PBR (Min) — ELan ENot ESty GGre MJon SWCr

Bering Rénaissance = 'Poulberin'PBR (S) **new** — ECnt

Berkshire = 'Korpinka'PBR (GC) ♀ H4 — ENot LStr MGan MJon MMat MRav SSea SWCr WOVN

Best of Friends = 'Pouldunk' (HT) — ECnt SWCr

Best Wishes = 'Chessnut'PBR (Cl/v) — COtt ENot GGre MBri MJon SSea SWCr

Bettina = 'Mepal' (HT) — MGan

Betty Boop = 'Wekplapic'PBR (F) — ECle GCoc MJon SWCr

Betty Driver = 'Gandri'PBR (F) — MGan SPer

Betty Harkness = 'Harette'PBR (F) — CSBt GCoc LStr SApu SWCr

'Betty Prior' (F) — GCoc MGan SWCr

'Betty Uprichard' (HT) — EBls

Bewitched = 'Poulbella'PBR (HT) — ECnt SWCr

'Beyreuth' (S) — MGan

Bianco = 'Cocblanco'PBR (Patio/Min) — GCoc MAus SWCr

Bibi Maizoon = 'Ausdimindo' (S) — SPer

Biddulph Grange = 'Frydarkeye' (S) — MFry

§ *biebersteinii* — EBls

'Big Chief' (HT) — MJon NRog SWCr

Big Purple = 'Stebigpu'PBR (HT) — ECnt MJon SApu SWCr

Birthday Girl = 'Meilasso'PBR (F) — GGre MJon MRav SApu SWCr WWeb

Birthday Wishes = 'Guesdelay' (HT) — ENot LPlm

Bishop Elphinstone = 'Cocjolly' (F) — GCoc

'Bit o' Sunshine' (Min) — MGan SWCr

'Black Beauty' (HT) — MAus MJon

'Black Ice' (F) — MGan SWCr

'Black Jack' (Ce) — see R. 'Tour de Malakoff'

Black Jack = 'Minkco' (Min/Patio) — NBat

Black Jade = 'Benblack' (Min/Patio) — MBur

'Black Prince' (HP) — EBls

'Blairii Number One' (Bb) — EBls

'Blairii Number Two' (ClBb) ♀ H4 — EBls ETWh LRHS MAus MRav SFam SPer SWCr WAct WHCG

'Blanche de Vibert' (DPo) — EBls ETWh MAus WHCG

'Blanche Double de Coubert' (Ru) ♀ H4 — EBee EBls ECnt ELan ENot EPfP GCoc LBuc LRHS LStr MAus MFry MGan MJon MMat MWgw NRog SApu SFam SPer SRPl SSea SWCr WAct WHCG WOVN

'Blanche Moreau' (CeMo) — EBls MAus MGan SPer WAct

'Blanchefleur' (CexG) — EBls ETWh MAus MRav SSea

blanda — EBls

Blenheim = 'Tanmurse'PBR (GC) — MBur MGan MJon MRav SApu

'Blessings' (HT) ♀ H4 — CBcs CGro CSBt EBls EBre ENot ESty GGre LPlm LStr MAsh MAus MBri MBur MFry MGan MJon

	MMat MRav NRog SApu SPer SRPl SSea SWCr
'Bleu Magenta' (Ra) ♀H4	EBee EBls ETWh IArd MAus MRav SWCr WAct WHCG WKif
'Bliss' (S)	EBls
'Bloomfield Abundance' (Poly)	CPou EBls ETWh MAus MRav SPer SWCr WHCG WHer
'Bloomfield Dainty' (HM)	EBls
Blooming Marvellous **new**	SWCr
'Blossomtime' (Cl)	NRog SPer
'Blue Diamond' (HT)	MGan SWCr
Blue Moon = 'Tannacht' (HT)	CGro EBls EBre ELan ENot EPfP GCoc GGre GKir LGod LPlm MAsh MBur MGan MJon MMat NBlu NPri NRog SApu SPer SWCr WWeb
Blue Parfum = 'Tanfifum' PBR	MJon SWCr
Blue Peter = 'Ruiblun' PBR (Min)	MFry MJon SApu SSea SWCr WWeb
'Blush Boursault' (Bs)	EBls
'Blush Damask' (D)	EBls SSea WHCG
'Blush Hip' (A) **new**	MAus
'Blush Noisette'	see R. 'Noisette Carnée'
'Blush Rambler' (Ra)	EBee EBls ETWh MAus SPer SPla SWCr WHCG
Blushing Bride = 'Harfling' (F)	MBur
'Blushing Lucy' (Ra)	LRHS MTPN SMrm SPer WAct WHCG
Blythe SpiritT?T = 'Auschool' PBR (S)	CSam MAus MBNS SWCr
Bob Greaves = 'Fryzippy' (F)	MFry
'Bob Woolley' (HT)	NBat
'Bobbie James' (Ra) ♀H4	CHad EBee EBls EBre ENot LRHS LStr MAus MBri MFry MGan MJon MRav NBat SFam SPer SSea SWCr WAct WHCG
'Bobby Charlton' (HT)	MFry MGan NRog
'Bobolink' (Min)	MGan SWCr
'Bon Silène' (T)	EBls
Bonbon Hit = 'Poulbon' PBR (Patio)	ECnt SWCr
'Bonfire Night' (F)	CGro ENot MBur MGan MMat MRav SWCr
Bonica = 'Meidomonac' PBR (GC) ♀H4	CBrm CSam CTri EBee EBls EBre ECnt ELan ENot EPfP GCoc LGod LRHS LStr MAus MBur MFry MGan MJon MMat MRav MWgw NBlu SApu SPer SSea SWCr WAct WHCG WOVN
'Bonn' (HM/S)	CBcs MGan NRog
'Bonne Nouvelle' (F)	SWCr
'Bonnie Scotland' (HT)	MGan
Bonsoir = 'Dicbo' (HT)	MGan
'Bottanix' (F)	MGan
'Botzaris' (D)	EBls SFam
'Boule de Nanteuil' (G)	EBls
'Boule de Neige' (Bb)	EBee EBls ECnt ENot EPfP GCoc LGod LRHS LStr MAus MMat MRav SFam SPer SPla SSea SWCr WAct WHCG WOVN
'Bouquet d'Or' (N)	EBls ETWh MAus SWCr WHCG
'Bouquet Tout Fait' (N)	WHCG
'Bouquet Tout Fait' misapplied	see R. 'Nastarana' (N)
'Bourbon Queen' (Bb)	EBls EMFP ETWh MAus SSea SWCr WHCG
Bow Bells = 'Ausbells' (S)	MAus
Boy O Boy = 'Dicuniform' PBR (GC)	IDic MJon SWCr
Boys' Brigade = 'Cocdinkum' PBR (Patio)	GCoc MGan SApu SWCr

§ *bracteata*	CHll CRHN EHol GQui MAus WAct WHCG
'Brandysnap' (F)	GKir
Brass Ring PBR	see R. Peek-a-boo = 'Dicgrow'
Brave Heart = 'Horbondsmile' (F)	GGre MAsh MAus MRav NBat SCoo SWCr
Breath of Life = 'Harquanne' PBR (ClHT)	CGro CSBt CSam CWSG EBls ELan ENot EPfP ESty GGre GKir LGod LRHS LStr MAsh MAus MBri MFry MGan MJon MRav NBat SApu SPer SSea SWCr
Bredon = 'Ausbred' (S)	MAus MBri
'Breeze Hill' (Ra)	EBls
§ 'Brenda Colvin' (Ra)	ISea MAus
'Brennus' (China hybrid)	EBls
Brian Rix = 'Harflipper' (S) **new**	SWCr
'Briarcliff' (HT)	EBls
Bridal Pink = 'Jacbri' (F)	MJon
Bride = 'Fryyearn' PBR (HT)	GCoc LStr MFry MJon MRav SApu
Bridge of Sighs = 'Harglow' (Cl)	ECnt LStr MBri SWCr
Bright Fire = 'Peaxi' PBR (Cl)	MJon SApu SWCr
Bright Smile = 'Dicdance' PBR (F/Patio)	GCoc IDic MAus MFry MGan MRav SPer SSea SWCr
Bright Spot	see R. Simply Sunblaze = 'Meidipser'
'Brindis' (ClF)	MGan
Britannia = 'Frycalm' PBR (HT)	ECnt ESty MAsh MFry MJon SWCr
Broadlands = 'Tanmirson' (GC)	LGod MBur MGan MJon MRav SApu SChu SRPl SWCr
Brother Cadfael = 'Ausglobe' PBR (S)	LRHS MAsh MAus MBri MJon SPer SWCr WWeb
Brown Velvet = 'Maccultra' PBR (F)	MJon SApu SWCr
'Brownie' (F)	MBur SWCr
§ *brunonii* (Ra)	CDoC CPLG EBls EWes MAus WLRN
- 'Betty Sherriff' (Ra)	CDoC SSpi
§ 'La Mortola' (Ra)	EBee EHol ETWh MAus MBri MRav SPer SWCr
Brush-strokes = 'Guescolour' (F)	LPlm
Bubbles = 'Frybubbly' PBR (GC)	MFry SWCr
Buck's Fizz = 'Poulgav' PBR (F)	MGan SWCr
'Buff Beauty' (HM) ♀H4	More than 30 suppliers
'Bullata'	see R. x *centifolia* 'Bullata'
§ 'Burgundiaca' (G)	EBee EBls ETWh LRHS MAus SSea SWCr WAct
Burgundian rose	see R. 'Burgundiaca'
'Burma Star' (F)	SWCr
burnet, double pink	see R. *pimpinellifolia* double pink
burnet, double white	see R. *pimpinellifolia* double white
Bush Baby = 'Peanob' PBR (Min)	LGod LStr SApu SPer SSea SWCr
Buttercup = 'Ausband' PBR (S)	LRHS MAus MBri SWCr WWeb
'Butterscotch Dream' (Patio) **new**	MAsh SWCr
Buxom Beauty = 'Korbilant' (HT)	ECnt ENot ESty MMat NBat WWeb
By Appointment = 'Harvolute' (F)	GGre
'C.F. Meyer'	see R. 'Conrad Ferdinand Meyer'
'Café' (F)	WBcn
'Caledonian' (HT)	NBat
californica (S)	GIBF MAus SSea
- 'Plena'	see R. *nutkana* 'Plena'

Calliope = 'Harfracas'PBR (F) **new** — SWCr

'Callisto' (HM) — EMFP ETWh MAus WHCG

Calypso = 'Poulclimb'PBR (Cl) — EBee ECle ECnt GGre MBri MBur SApu SSea SWCr

'Camaïeux' (G) — CPou EBee EBls ETWh IKee LRHS MAus SPer SSea SWCr WAct WHCG

Cambridgeshire = 'Korhaugen'PBR (GC) — ENot LGod LStr MAus MMat MRav SPer SSea SWCr

'Camélia Rose' (Ch) — EBls WHCG

'Cameo' (Poly) — EBls MAus MGan

'Canary Bird' — see R. xanthina 'Canary Bird'

Candle in the Wind = 'Mackincat' (S) **new** — MAsh SWCr

Candy Rose = 'Meiranovi' (S) — GGre

canina (S) — CArn CCVT CKin CLnd CTri ENot EPfP GIBF GKir LBuc MAus MRav NWea SRPl WMou

- 'Abbotswood' — see R. 'Abbotswood' (*canina* hybrid)

- 'Andersonii' — see R. 'Andersonii' (*canina* hybrid)

'Cantabrigiensis' (S) ♀ H4 — EBee EBls ENot ETWh MAus NRog SFam SPer SSea SWCr WAct WFar WHCG WOVN

Canterbury = 'Ausbury' (S) — MAus

'Capitaine Basroger' (CeMo) — EBls MAus

'Capitaine John Ingram' (CeMo) ♀ H4 — EBls ETWh MAus SPer SSea SWCr WHCG

'Captain Christy' (ClHT) — see R. 'Climbing Captain Christy'

'Captain Hayward' (HP) — EBls

'Cardinal de Richelieu' (G) ♀ H4 — CPou EBls ENot EPfP EWTr GCoc LRHS LStr MAsh MAus MFry MMat MRav SApu SFam SPer SSea SWCr WAct WHCG

Cardinal Hume = 'Harregale' (S) — EBls MGan SPer SWCr

'Care 2000' (S) — EBls

Carefree Days = 'Meirivouri' (Patio) — MAsh SWCr

'Caring' (Patio) **new** — SWCr

Caring for You = 'Coclust'PBR (HT) — GCoc

Caritas (HT) **new** — ECnt

'Carmen' (Ru) — EBls

§ 'Carmenetta' (S) — EBls MAus SWCr WAct

§ 'Carol' (Gn) — see R. 'Carol Amling'

§ 'Carol Amling' (Gn) — MJon SWCr

carolina — LHop SLPl WHCG

Caroline de Monaco = 'Meipierar' (HT) — MJon

'Caroline Testout' — see R. 'Madame Caroline Testout'

Cascade = 'Poulskab'PBR **new** — SWCr

Casino = 'Macca' (ClHT) — EBls ESty GCoc GKir LPlm MAsh MBur MFry MGan MJon MRav NBlu SWCr

Castle of Mey = 'Coclucid' (F) — GCoc MJon SWCr

Catherine Cookson = 'Noscook' (HT) — ENot NBat

'Catherine Mermet' (T) — EBls MAus

'Catherine Seyton' (RH) — EBls

§ 'Cécile Brünner' (Poly) ♀ H4 — EBls ECnt ELan EMFP ENot GCoc LStr MAus MGan MMat MRav NRog SPer SWCr WAct WHCG WOVN

'Cécile Brünner, White' — see R. 'White Cécile Brünner'

Cecily Gibson = 'Evebright' (F) — MJon SWCr

Celebration 2000 = 'Horcoffitup'PBR (S) — MAus

§ 'Céleste' (A) ♀ H4 — EBee EBls EMFP ENot GCoc LGod LStr MDun MFry MMat MRav SApu SFam SPer SSea SWCr WAct WGer WHCG WOVN

'Célina' (CeMo) — EBls MGan

'Céline Forestier' (N) ♀ H3 — EBee EBls EMFP ETWh MAus MRav SFam SPer SWCr WHCG

§ 'Celsiana' (D) — CSam EBls LRHS MAus SFam SPer SRPl SSea SWCr WAct WHCG

Centenaire de Lourdes = 'Delge' (F) — EBls

Centenary = 'Koreledas'PBR (F) ♀ H4 — ENot MMat MRav SPer SWCr

§ x *centifolia* (Ce) — EBls MAus MRav NRog SSea SWCr WAct WHCG

§ - 'Bullata' (Ce) — EBls MAus

§ - 'Cristata' (Ce) ♀ H4 — CSBt CSam EBls ECnt EMFP ENot EPfP LStr MAsh MMat MRav NRog SFam SPer SSea SWCr WAct WHCG

§ - 'Muscosa' (CeMo) — EBls ENot EWTr GCoc LRHS MAus MGan MMat MRav MWgw NRog SFam SSea SWCr WAct WHCG

- 'Muscosa Alba' **new** — WAct

- 'Parvifolia' — see R. 'Burgundiaca'

§ 'Centifolia Variegata' (Ce) — EBls ETWh MAus MGan

Centre Stage = 'Chewcreepy' (S/GC) **new** — MAsh MJon SWCr

Century Sunset = 'Tansaras'PBR (HT) — SApu SWCr

'Cerise Bouquet' (S) ♀ H4 — EBee EBls LRHS MAus MRav SPer SWCr WAct WHCG

Cha Cha = 'Cocarum' (Patio/Min) — SApu

Champagne Cocktail = 'Horflash'PBR (F) ♀ H4 — SWCr

Champagne = 'Korampa'PBR (F) — MJon

'Champneys' Pink Cluster' (China hybrid) — EBls MAus SFam

Champs Elysées = 'Meicarl' (HT) — MGan SWCr

'Chanelle' (F) — EBls GCoc MAus MGan NRog SPer SSea SWCr

Chapeau de Napoléon — see R. x *centifolia* 'Cristata'

'Chaplin's Pink Climber' (Cl) — EBls MGan NHaw SWCr

Chardonnay = 'Macrealea' (HT) — MJon SWCr

Charity = 'Auschar' (S) — LRHS MAus MBri SWCr WWeb

Charles Austin = 'Ausles' (S) — MAus MRav SWCr WHCG

Charles Aznavour = 'Meibeausai' (F) — SWCr

'Charles de Mills' (G) ♀ H4 — CHad EBee EBls ECnt ELan EMFP ENot EPfP EWTr LGod LRHS LStr MAsh MAus MFry MMat MRav SFam SPer SSea SWCr WAct WHCG

'Charles Gater' (HP) — EBls

'Charles Lefèbvre' (HP) — EBls

'Charles Mallerin' (HT) — EBls

Charles Notcutt = 'Korhassi'PBR (S) — ENot MMat SWCr

Charles Rennie Mackintosh = 'Ausren'PBR (S) — LRHS MAus MJon SWCr WWeb

Charleston = 'Meiridge' (F) — MGan

Charlie's Rose = 'Tanellepa' (HT) — SWCr

Charlotte = 'Auspoly'PBR (S) ♀ H4 — CAbP LRHS MAsh MAus MBri MJon NPri SApu SPer SSea SWCr WAct WWeb

Charmian = 'Ausmian' (S)   MAus
'Charter 700' (F)   MFry
'Château de   IArd
   Clos-Vougeot' (HT)
Chatsworth =   MGan MJon MRav SApu SCoo
   'Tanotax'PBR (Patio/F)   SPer SSea SWCr
Chaucer = 'Auscer' (S)   MAus
Chelsea Belle =   NBat
   'Talchelsea' (Min)
Chelsea Pensioner =   SApu
   'Mattche' (Min)
§ Cherry Brandy '85 =   CSBt MBur MGan MJon MRav
   'Tanryrandy'PBR (HT)   SWCr
'Cherryade' (S)   MGan
Cheshire = 'Fryelise' (HT)   MFry
Cheshire = 'Korkonopi'   ENot MAus MMat
   (County Rose Series) PBR
   (S)
'Cheshire Life' (HT)   MAus MBur MFry MGan MJon
      MRav NPri WStI
Chester Cathedral =   MJon SWCr
   'Franshine' (HT)
Chianti = 'Auswine' (S)   EBls MAus MBri MDun SWCr
      WAct WHCG
Chicago Peace =   EBls ESty GGre GKir LGod LPlm
   'Johnago' (HT)   MAsh MGan MJon NBlu NRog
      SWCr WStI
Childhood Memories =   MBri SWCr
   'Ferho' (HM/Cl)
Child's Play =   NBat
   'Savachild' (Min)
Chilterns =   ENot MMat MRav SWCr
   'Kortemma'PBR (GC)
'Chinatown' (F/S) ♀ H4   CBcs CGro CSBt EBls EBre ENot
      ESty GGre GKir LStr MAsh MAus
      MGan MJon MMat MRav NRog
      SApu SPer SSea SWCr
chinensis misapplied   see R. x odorata
chinensis 'Minima'   see R. 'Pompon de Paris' (MinCh)
   sensu stricto hort.
 - 'Mutabilis'   see R. x odorata 'Mutabilis'
 - 'Old Blush'   see R. x odorata 'Pallida'
Chloe = 'Poulen003' (S)   CPou ECnt SWCr
'Chloris' (A)   EBls SWCr
'Chorus Girl' (F)   MGan
Chris = 'Kirsan'PBR (Cl)   EBee ECnt ENot LStr MJon MMat
      SApu SSea SWCr WGor
Christian Dior =   EBls
   'Meilie' (HT)
'Christine Gandy' (F)   MGan
Christopher =   GCoc
   'Cocopher' (HT)
Christopher Columbus =   ENot IArd MBri MMat MRav SApu
   'Meinronsse' (HT)
§ 'Chromatella' (N)   EBls
'Chrysler Imperial' (HT)   EBls
Cider Cup =   ENot EPfP ESty GGre GKir IDic
   'Dicladida'PBR   LGod LStr MAsh MAus MBri
      MFry
   (Min/Patio) ♀ H4   MJon NBat SWCr
'Cinderella' (Min)   CSBt MGan
cinnamomea   see R. majalis
'Circus' (F)   MGan SWCr
City Lights =   CSBt MMat MRav
   'Poulgan'PBR (Patio)
City of Belfast = 'Macci' (F)   EBls ENot MAus
'City of Leeds' (F)   CWSG ENot GGre GKir MAsh
      MGan NRog SPer WStI
City of London =   CSBt EBls GGre LStr MBur MJon
   'Harukfore'PBR (F)   SApu SPer SWCr
'City of Portsmouth' (F)   CBcs MGan
City of York =   EBls
   'Direktör Benschop' (Cl)

Clair Matin =   CHad CPou EBls MAus SPer SWCr
   'Meimont' (ClS)   WAct
'Claire Jacquier' (N)   EBee EBls ETWh MAus SFam SPer
      SWCr WHCG
Claire Rayner =   LPlm MJon SWCr
   'Macpandem'PBR
   (F/Patio)
Claire Rose =   CGro EBee GKir LRHS MAus
   'Auslight'PBR (S)   MJon MRav NPri SPer SWCr
Clara = 'Poulen004' (S)   ECnt SWCr
'Clarence House' (Cl) new   EBls
Clarinda =   GCoc
   'Cocsummery' (F) new
'Clementina Carbonieri' (T)   EBls
Cleo = 'Beebop' (HT)   MJon SWCr
§ Cleopatra =   ENot MBur MMat MRav
   'Korverpea'PBR (HT)
'Cliff Richard' (F)   ESty MBur SWCr
'Climbing Alec's Red' (ClHT) SPer
'Climbing Allgold' (ClF)   EBls SSea SWCr
'Climbing Arthur Bell'PBR   CSBt CTri LPlm MAsh NRog SApu
   (ClF) ♀ H4   SPer SSea SWCr WWeb
'Climbing Ballerina' (Ra)   CSBt MGan SWCr
Climbing Bettina =   EBls
   'Mepalsar' (ClHT)
'Climbing Blessings' (ClHT) EBls
'Climbing Blue   MGan NPri SWCr
   Moon' (ClHT)
§ 'Climbing Captain   EBls MAus
   Christy' (ClHT)
'Climbing Cécile   CSBt EBee EBls ECnt EPfP ETWh
   Brünner' (ClPoly) ♀ H4   LGod LRHS LStr MAus MBur
      MRav MWgw SApu SFam SPer
      SSea SWCr WAct WHCG
'Climbing Château de   EBls MAus
   Clos-Vougcot' (ClHT)
'Climbing Cherryade'   MGan
   (ClHT)
'Climbing Christine' (ClHT)   MAus
§ 'Climbing Columbia' (ClHT)   ERca NRog SPer WHCG
'Climbing Comtesse
   Vandal' (ClHT)   EBls
'Climbing Crimson   EBls EMFP ETWh MAus MGan
   Glory' (ClHT)   NRog SWCr WStI
§ 'Climbing Devoniensis'   CPou EBls
   (ClT)
§ 'Climbing Ena Harkness'   CBcs CSam EBls GCoc GGre
   (ClHT)   MAus MBur MGan MRav NRog
      SPer SPla SWCr WWeb
'Climbing Ernest H. Morse' MGan
   (ClHT)
'Climbing Etoile de   CPou CRHN CSBt CTri CWSG
   Hollande' (ClHT) ♀ H4   EBls EBre EMFP EPfP GCoc GKir
      LRHS LStr MAus MGan MJon
      MRav NRog SApu SPer SSea SWCr
      WHCG WOVN WWeb
'Climbing Fashion' (ClF)   EBls
Climbing Fragrant Cloud   CBcs ELan MGan
   = 'Colfragrasar' (ClHT)
§ 'Climbing Frau Karl   EBls
   Druschki' (ClHP)
'Climbing General   EBls
   MacArthur' (ClHT)
§ Climbing Gold Bunny =
   'Meigro-Nurisar'PBR (ClF) MJon
'Climbing Grand-mère   EBls
   Jenny' (ClHT)
'Climbing Iceberg'   CGro CSBt EBee EBls EBre ELan
   (ClF) ♀ H4   ENot EPfP ESty GGre GKir IArd
      LPlm LStr MAus MBri MGan MJon
      MRav MWgw NRog SApu SPer
      SPla SRPl SSea SWCr WHCG
      WOVN WWeb

'Climbing Josephine Bruce' (ClHT) — LRHS MGan

'Climbing la France' (ClHT) — MAus MRav SWCr

§ 'Climbing Lady Hillingdon' (ClT) ♀ H3 — EBee EBls EBre EMFP EPfP ETWh LRHS MAus MGan MRav MWgw SApu SFam SPer SRPl SSea SWCr WAct WHCG

'Climbing Lady Sylvia' (ClHT) — CPou EBls EPfP ETWh LRHS MAsh MAus MGan NRog SPer SWCr

'Climbing Little White Pet' — see R. 'Félicité Perpétue'

'Climbing Madame Abel Chatenay' (ClHT) — EBls MAus

'Climbing Madame Butterfly' (ClHT) — EBls EBre EPfP LRHS MAus MGan SPer SWCr

'Climbing Madame Caroline Testout' (ClHT) — CPou EBls MAsh MAus NRog SPer SWCr WBcn

§ 'Climbing Madame Edouard Herriot' (ClHT) — EBls ETWh MAus MGan SPer SWCr

'Climbing Madame Henri Guillot' (ClHT) — EBls MAus

'Climbing Maman Cochet' (ClT) — EBls MAus

'Climbing Masquerade' (ClF) — EBls GGre GKir LPlm MAus MGan MJon MRav NRog SSea SWCr WStI WWeb

'Climbing McGredy's Yellow' (ClHT) — MGan

§ 'Climbing Mevrouw G.A. van Rossem' (ClHT) — EBls MAus

'Climbing Mrs Aaron Ward' (ClHT) — EBls MAus

'Climbing Mrs G.A. van Rossem' — see R. 'Climbing Mevrouw G.A. van Rossem'

'Climbing Mrs Herbert Stevens' (ClHT) — CPou EBee EBls LRHS MAsh MAus MRav NRog SPer SWCr WHCG

'Climbing Mrs Sam McGredy' (ClHT) ♀ H4 — CGro EBls MAus MBri MGan MJon NRog SWCr

'Climbing Niphetos' (ClT) — EBls MAus

'Climbing Ophelia' (ClHT) — EBee EBls MAus SPer SWCr

Climbing Orange Sunblaze = 'Meiji Katarsar'PBR (ClMin) — ENot MBri MJon SApu SPer SWCr

'Climbing Pascali' (ClHT) — CBcs MGan

§ 'Climbing Paul Lédé' (ClT) — EBee EBls EBre ETWh LRHS MAus SWCr WHCG

'Climbing Peace' (ClHT) — ETWh SWCr

'Climbing Picture' (ClHT) — EBls MAus MGan

§ 'Climbing Pompon de Paris' (ClMinCh) — CBot CRHN EBls LHop LRHS MAus MGan MRav SPer SRPl SWCr WHCG

'Climbing Regensberg' (ClF) **new** — SWCr

'Climbing Richmond' (ClHT) — EBls

'Climbing Roundelay' (Cl) — EBls

'Climbing Shot Silk' (ClHT) ♀ H4 — EBee EBls EMFP ETWh MGan SPer SWCr

§ 'Climbing Souvenir de la Malmaison' (ClBb) — CPou EBee EBls ETWh MAus SPer WAct WHCG

Climbing Super Star = 'Tangostar' (ClHT) — MAus

'Climbing Sutter's Gold' (ClHT) — MGan

'Climbing Talisman' (ClHT) — EBls

'Climbing the Doctor' (ClHT) — MGan

'Climbing The Queen Elizabeth' (ClF) — EBls

'Climbing Trumpeter' (ClF) — MAsh

Clodagh McGredy = 'Macswanle' (F) **new** — MJon SWCr

'Cloth of Gold' — see R. 'Chromatella'

Cocktail = 'Meimick' (S) — EBls MGan

Colchester Beauty = 'Cansend' (F) — ECnt SWCr

§ Colibri = 'Meimal' (Min) — MGan SPer

§ 'Colonel Fabvier' — EBls MAus SWCr

colonial white — see R. 'Sombreuil'

'Columbian' (ClHT) — see R. 'Climbing Columbia'

§ Colwyn Bay (F) — MJon SWCr

'Commandant Beaurepaire' (Bb) — EBls ETWh LRHS MAus

common moss — see R. x centifolia 'Muscosa'

Commonwealth Glory = 'Harclue'PBR (HT) — ESty SWCr

'Compassion' (ClHT) ♀ H4 — More than 30 suppliers

§ 'Complicata' (G) ♀ H4 — EBls ENot EPfP LRHS LStr MAus MGan MRav MWgw NRog SApu SFam SPer SSea SSpi SWCr WAct WHCG WOVN

N 'Comte de Chambord' misapplied — see R. 'Madame Knorr'

Comtes de Champagne = 'Ausufo' (S) **new** — MAsh MAus SWCr

'Comtesse Cécile de Chabrillant' (HP) — EBls MAus

'Comtesse de Lacépède' misapplied — see R. 'Du Maître d'Ecole'

§ 'Comtesse de Murinais' (DMo) — EBls MAus SFam SWCr

§ 'Comtesse du Caÿla' (Ch) — MAus SSea

'Condesa de Sástago' (HT) — EBls

§ 'Conditorum' (G) — EBls SFam SSea WAct

Congratulations = 'Korlift'PBR (HT) — CSBt EBee ECnt ENot GCoc IArd LGod LPlm LStr MAus MBri MFry MGan MJon MMat MRav NPri SApu SPer SSea SWCr WWeb

Conquest = 'Harbrill'PBR (F) — MRav SWCr

§ 'Conrad Ferdinand Meyer' (Ru) — CSBt EBls MAus MGan SPer

Conservation = 'Cocdimple'PBR (Min/Patio) — GCoc GGre LAst MBri SApu SSea SWCr

Constance Spry = 'Austance' (ClS) ♀ H4 — CGro CHad EBee EBls EBre ECnt ENot EPfP LRHS LStr MAus MGan MJon MMat MRav NPri SApu SFam SPer SSea SWCr WAct WGer WHCG WWeb

§ 'Cooperi' (Ra) — CWib EBls ETWh MAus SLon SPer SSea WAct WHCG

Cooper's Burmese — see R. 'Cooperi'

'Copenhagen' (ClHT) — EBls LRHS MAus

'Copper Delight' (F) — NRog

Copper Pot = 'Dicpe' (F) — MGan SPer

'Coral Cluster' (Poly) — EBls MAus MGan

'Coral Creeper' (ClHT) — EBls

'Coral Dawn' (ClHT) — EBls MFry MJon SWCr

Coral Reef = 'Cocdarlee'PBR (Min/Patio) — ESty GGre MBri SWCr

'Coral Satin' (Cl) — MGan

'Coralie' (D) — EBls

'Coralin' (Min) — MGan

Cordelia = 'Ausbottle' (S) — MAus MRav SWCr

Cordon Bleu = 'Harubasil' (HT) — MBur

'Cornelia' (HM) ♀ H4 — More than 30 suppliers

'Coronet' (F) — WHCG

Corvedale = 'Ausnetting' (S) **new** — MAus SWCr

'Coryana' — EBls

corymbifera — EBls

corymbulosa — EBls

'Cosimo Ridolfi' (G) — EBls
cottage maid — see R. 'Centifolia Variegata'
Cottage Rose = 'Ausglisten'PBR (S) — MAsh MAus MBri MJon MRav SWCr WWeb
Country Lady = 'Hartsam' (HT) — MBur
Country Living = 'Auscountry'PBR (S) — EBls LRHS
'Coupe d'Hébé' (Bb) — EBls MAus
§ Courage = 'Poulduf'PBR (HT) — EBee ECnt NEgg SWCr
'Cramoisi Picotée' (G) — EBls MAus
'Cramoisi Supérieur' (Ch) — EBls ETWh MAus WHCG
Crathes Castle = 'Cocathes' — GCoc
Crazy for You = 'Wekroalt'PBR (F) — ESty LGod MBur MJon SWCr
Cream Abundance = 'Harflax'PBR (F) **new** — GGre SWCr
Crème de la Crème = 'Gancre'PBR (Cl) — GCoc MBri MBur MGan SSea SWCr
'Crépuscule' (N) — EBls ETWh SSea WHCG
Cressida = 'Auscress' (S) — MAus
crested moss — see R. x centifolia 'Cristata'
Cricri = 'Meicri' (Min) — MAus MGan SWCr
Crimson Cascade = 'Fryclimbdown'PBR (Cl) — CSam ESty GKir MAsh MAus MBri MFry MRav NBat SApu SSea SWCr WHCG WWeb
'Crimson Conquest' (ClHT) — EBls
crimson damask — see R. gallica var. officinalis
'Crimson Descant' (Cl) — EBee ECnt SSea SWCr
Crimson Floorshow = 'Harglamour'PBR (GC) **new** — SWCr
'Crimson Gem' (Min) — MGan
'Crimson Globe' (Mo) — MGan
'Crimson Glory' (HT) — EBls MAsh MBur MGan SWCr
'Crimson Rambler' (Ra) — WBcn
'Crimson Shower' (Ra) ♥ H4 — EBre EMFP LPlm LRHS MAus MBur MGan MJon MMat MRav NRog SPer SWCr WGer WHCG WHer WStI
'Cristata' — see R. x centifolia 'Cristata'
Crocus Rose = 'Ausquest' (S) — ECnt MAus SWCr
Crown Princess Margareta = 'Auswinter' (S) — ECnt MAus MBri SCoo SWCr
Crowning Glory = 'Dicyardstick'PBR (S) — IDic
Crystal Palace = 'Poulrck'PBR (F/Patio) — EBee ECnt ENot MJon MMat SWCr
cuisse de nymphe — see R. 'Great Maiden's Blush'
'Cupid' (ClHT) — EBls EMFP ETWh MAus SPer
Curiosity = 'Cocty' (HT/v) — GGre MJon
§ Cymbeline = 'Auslean' (S) — SPer
'Cynthia Brooke' (HT) — EBls MBur
'D'Aguesseau' (G) — EBls ETWh MAus
'Daily Mail' — see R. 'Climbing Madame Edouard Herriot'
§ Daily Post = 'Frytrooper' (F) — MFry
Daily Sketch = 'Macai' (F) — MGan
'Dainty Bess' (HT) — EBls ETWh MAus SSea
Dainty Dinah = 'Cocamond' (Min/Patio) — SApu
'Dainty Maid' (F) — EBls MAus
'Daisy Hill' ('Macrantha' hybrid) — EBls
x damascena var. bifera — see R. x damascena var. semperflorens
§ - var. semperflorens (D) — EBls EMFP MAus MRav SSea SWCr WAct WHCG
N - 'Trigintipetala' misapplied — see R. 'Professeur Emile Perrot'

§ - var. versicolor (D) — EBls ENot ETWh MGan MMat SFam SPer SSea WAct WHCG
§ 'Dame de Coeur' (HT) — ENot
'Dame Edith Helen' (HT) — EBls
Dame Wendy = 'Canson'PBR (F) — MAus MGan SWCr
'Danaë' (HM) — CHad EBls EMFP ETWh MAus SWCr WHCG
Dancing Pink = 'Hendan' (F) — NBat
Danny Boy = 'Dicxcon'PBR (Patio) — GCoc IDic MBri MJon SWCr WGor
§ Danse des Sylphes = 'Malcair' (Cl) — EBls SWCr
'Danse du Feu' (Cl) — CBcs CGro CSBt CTri CWSG EBee EBls ELan ENot GCoc GGre GKir LGod LRHS LStr MAsh MAus MGan MJon MMat MRav NPri NRog SApu SMad SPer SSea SWCr WWeb
'Daphne Gandy' (F) — MGan SWCr
Dapple Dawn = 'Ausapple' (S) — MAus SPer SWCr
Darling Flame = 'Meilucca' (Min) — MGan MRav SApu SWCr
'Dart's Defender' — SLPl
David Whitfield = 'Gana'PBR (F) — MGan SWCr
davidii — EBls MAus SWCr
Dawn Chorus = 'Dicquasar'PBR (HT) ♥ H4 — CGro CSBt CWSG EBee EBre ECnt ENot EPfP ESty GCoc GGre IDic LGod LPlm LStr MAsh MAus MBri MFry MGan MJon MMat MRav SApu SPer SSea SWCr WWeb
'Day Dream' (HT) **new** — SWCr
'Daybreak' (HM) — EBls MAus NRog WAct WHCG
'Daydream' (F) **new** — GGre
§ 'De Meaux' (Ce) — EBls ENot ETWh MAus MRav SPer SRPl SSea SWCr WAct WHCG
'De Meaux, White' — see R. 'White de Meaux'
§ 'De Rescht' (DPo) ♥ H4 — CPou EBee EBls ENot EPfP LRHS MAsh MAus MBri MGan MJon MMat MRav MWgw SPer SPla SWCr WAct WGer WHCG
'Dearest' (F) — CBcs CSBt ESty GGre MGan MRav NPri NRog SPer SRPl SWCr WStI
§ Deborah Devonshire = 'Boscherrydrift'PBR (F) — GGre SWCr
Deb's Delight = 'Legsweet'PBR (F) — ELan MJon
'Debutante' (Ra) — CHad EBee EBls ETWh LRHS MAus SFam SWCr WHCG
'Deep Red Patio' (Patio) — SWCr
'Deep Secret' (HT) ♥ H4 — CGro CTri CWSG EBee EBre ECnt EPfP ESty GCoc GGre GKir LPlm MAsh MBur MFry MGan MJon MRav NBlu NRog SApu SPer SSea SWCr WWeb
'Delambre' (DPo) — EBls MAus MRav
'Delicata' (Ru) — MAus
Della Balfour = 'Harblend'PBR (Cl) **new** — GGre SWCr
'Dembrowski' (HP) — EBls
Denman = 'Landen' (HT) — SApu
'Dentelle de Malines' (S) — EBls LRHS MAus MBri WAct
'Deschamps' (N) — EBls
'Desprez à Fleurs Jaunes' (N) — CPou EBee EBls ETWh IArd LRHS MAus MRav SFam SPer SPla SWCr WHCG
'Deuil de Paul Fontaine' (Mo) — EBls
'Devon Maid' (Cl) — SWCr

'Devoniensis' (ClT) see *R.* 'Climbing Devoniensis'
Diadem = 'Tanmeda'^{PBR} (F) SWCr
Diamond Border = ECnt
 'Pouldiram'^{PBR} (S) **new**
'Diamond Jubilee' (HT) EBls SWCr
'Diana Armstrong' (HT) NBat
Diana, Princess of Wales IDic
 = 'Jacshaq' (HT)
Dick's Delight = IDic SWCr
 'Dicwhistle'^{PBR} (GC)
'Dickson's Flame' (F) MGan
Die Welt = 'Diekor' (HT) MBri NBat
'Diorama' (HT) ENot MAus MGan SWCr
'Directeur Alphand' (HP) EBls WHCG
Disco Dancer = IDic
 'Dicinfra'^{PBR} (F)
Dixieland Linda = EBls
 'Beadix' (ClHT)
Dizzy Heights = GCoc MBri MFry MJon SWCr
 'Fryblissful' (Cl)
Doc = 'Degenhard' (Poly) MGan
'Docteur Andry' (HP) EBls
'Docteur Grill' (T) EBls MAus
'Doctor A.J. Verhage' (HT) MGan
Doctor Dick = MBri NBat NRog
 'Cocbaden' (HT)
'Doctor Edward EBls
 Deacon' (HT)
§ Doctor Goldberg = MGan SWCr
 'Gandol' (HT)
Doctor Jackson = MAus
 'Ausdoctor' (S)
§ Doctor Jo = 'Fryatlanta' (F) MFry SWCr
'Doctor John Snow' (HT) MGan SWCr
Doctor McAlpine = MBri MJon SWCr
 'Peafirst'^{PBR} (F/Patio)
'Doctor W. Van Fleet' EBls MAus
 (Ra/Cl)
'Doktor Eckener' EBls MGan
'Don Charlton' (HT) NBat
'Don Juan' (Cl) MGan SWCr
§ 'Doncasteri' EBls
'Dopey' (Poly) MGan
'Doreen' (HT) NRog
'Doris Tysterman' (HT) CGro CSBt EBls EBre ESty GGre
 GKir LPlm LStr MAsh MAus MBri
 MGan MJon NBlu NRog SPer
 SWCr
'Dorothy Perkins' (Ra) CGro CRHN CSBt CTri EBls GCoc
 GGre LPlm LRHS MAus MGan
 MJon MMat MRav NPer NRog
 SApu SPer SRPl SSea SWCr
 WHCG
'Dorothy Wheatcroft' (F) MGan SWCr
'Dorothy Wilson' (F) EBls
'Dortmund' (ClHScB) ♀ ^{H4} EBls LGod LPlm LRHS MAus
 MGan SPer SWCr WAct WHCG
Double Delight = CGro CSBt ELan ESty GCoc GGre
 'Andeli' (HT) LPlm MBri MGan MJon MRav
 NRog SApu SPer SWCr
'Dream Girl' (Cl) MAus SFam
Dream Lover = GGre MAsh MRav SWCr
 'Peayetti'^{PBR} (Patio)
'Dreaming Spires' (Cl) CSBt ENot ESty MJon MMat MRav
 SApu SPer SSea SWCr
Dreamland = MFry MGan SWCr
 'Träumland' (F)
'Dresden Doll' (MinMo) EBls MAus SPer
Drummer Boy = SWCr
 'Harvacity'^{PBR} (F/Patio)
'Du Maître d'Ecole' (G) EBls ETWh MAus MRav SWCr
 WHCG
Dublin Bay = CSBt CTri EBee EBls EBre ECnt

'Macdub' (Cl) ♀ ^{H4} ELan ENot ESty GKir IArd LGod
 LPlm LStr MBri MBur MFry MGan
 MJon MMat MRav NRog SApu
 SPer SRPl SSea SWCr WGer
'Duc de Fitzjames' (G) EBls
'Duc de Guiche' (G) ♀ ^{H4} EBls ETWh MAus SFam SPer SSea
 SWCr WAct WHCG
'Duchess of Portland' see *R.* 'Portlandica'
'Duchesse d'Albe' (T) EBls
'Duchesse EBls MAus SFam SSea
 d'Angoulême' (G)
'Duchesse d'Auerstädt' (N) EBls
'Duchesse de EBls MAus MRav SWCr
 Buccleugh' (G)
§ 'Duchesse de EBee EBls ETWh LRHS MAus
 Montebello' (G) ♀ ^{H4} SFam SPer SWCr WAct WHCG
'Duchesse de EBls
 Rohan' (CexHP)
'Duchesse de EBls MAus SFam
 Verneuil' (CeMo)
Duke Meillandina = SApu SWCr
 'Meipinjid'^{PBR} (Min)
'Duke of Edinburgh' (HP) EBls MAus
'Duke of Wellington' (HP) EBee EBls ETWh SWCr WHCG
'Duke of Windsor' (HT) MGan SPer SWCr
'Duke of York' (Ch) EBls
'Dundee Rambler' (Ra) EBls MAus
'Dupontii' (S) EBee EBls ETWh LRHS MAus MRav
 SFam SPer SWCr WAct WOVN
'Dupuy Jamain' (HP) EBls WHCG
'Dusky Maiden' (F) EBls ETWh MAus MBri WHCG
'Dutch Gold' (HT) CGro CSBt CTri CWSG MAsh
 MAus MGan MRav NRog SPer
 SRPl SSea SWCr
Dwarf King see *R.* Zwergkönig '78 = 'Korkönig'
 (introduced 1978)
'E.H. Morse' see *R.* 'Ernest H. Morse'
'Easlea's Golden EBee EBls ETWh LRHS MAus
 Rambler' (Ra) ♀ ^{H4} MRav SWCr WAct WHCG
'Easter Morning' (Min) MGan MJon SPer SWCr
Easy Cover = ECnt
 'Pouleas'^{PBR} (GC) **new**
Easy Going = GCoc IArd
 'Harflow'^{PBR} (F)
'Eblouissant' (Poly) MGan MRav
ecae EBls LRHS MAus
– 'Helen Knight' see *R.* 'Helen Knight' (*ecae* hybrid)
'Eclair' (HP) EBls WHCG
'Eddie's Jewel' EBls MAus MGan
 (*moyesii* hybrid)
'Eden Rose' (HT) EBls MGan
Eden Rose '88 = MBri MJon SApu SPer SWCr
 'Meiviolin'^{PBR} (ClHT)
'Edith Bellenden' (RH) EBls
Edith Holden = MJon SApu
 'Chewlegacy'^{PBR} (F)
'Edward Hyams' **new** MAus
eglanteria see *R. rubiginosa*
Eglantyne = 'Ausmak'^{PBR} CAbP CSBt CSam EBre GCoc
 (S) ♀ ^{H4} LRHS LStr MAus MBri MJon MMat
 MRav MWgw SPer SWCr WWeb
Eleanor Annelise = GCoc
 'Cocslightly' (HT) **new**
'Elegance' (ClHT) EBls MAus MGan
§ *elegantula* 'Persetosa' (S) EBls ENot ETWh MAus SPer SWCr
 WAct WHCG
§ Elina = 'Dicjana'^{PBR} CSBt EBee ECnt ENot ESty GGre
 (HT) ♀ ^{H4} IDic LGod LPlm LStr MAus MBur
 MFry MGan MJon MMat MRav
 NBat NRog SApu SPer SWCr
 WHCG
'Eliza Boëlle' (HP) EBls
'Elizabeth Harkness' (HT) CWSG EBls MAus MBur MGan
 SPer SWCr

Elizabeth Heather Grierson = 'Mattnot' (CIHT)	MMat
Elizabeth of Glamis = 'Macel' (F)	CGro CWSG EBls EWTr GCoc MBri MGan NRog SPer SWCr
'Elizabeth Philp' (F)	LPlm
Elle = 'Meibdoros'[PBR] (HT)	SApu SWCr
Ellen = 'Auscup' (S)	MAus
'Ellen Poulsen' (Poly)	MGan
'Ellen Willmott' (HT)	EBee EBls EMFP ETWh MAus SWCr
'Elmshorn' (S)	CBcs MAsh MGan SWCr WHCG
'Else Poulsen' (Poly)	WHCG
Emanuel = 'Ausuel' (S)	MAus SPer
Emily = 'Ausburton' (S)	SApu
'Emily Gray' (Ra)	CGro CSBt EBee EBls EBre ECnt ENot GKir LRHS LStr MAsh MAus MBur MGan MJon MMat MRav NPri NRog SPer SSea SWCr WAct WHCG
'Emma Wright' (HT)	MAus
'Emmerdale' (F)	WStI
'Empereur du Maroc' (HP)	EBls EMFP ETWh MAus MRav SWCr WHCG
'Empress Josephine'	see R. x francofurtana
Empress Michiko = 'Dicnifty'[PBR] (HT)	GCoc IDic SApu
'Ena Harkness' (HT)	CGro EBls GGre MBur MGan NRog SWCr WStI
§ 'Enfant de France' (HP)	EBls
x engelmannii	EBls
England's Rose = 'Ausrace'[PBR] (S)	MAsh MAus SCoo SWCr
English Elegance = 'Ausleaf' (S)	MAus
English Garden = 'Ausbuff'[PBR] (S)	CGro EBee EBre EMFP ENot EPfP LRHS LStr MAus MMat MRav SApu SPer SSea SWCr WWeb
'English Miss' (F) ♀ H4	CSBt EBls ECnt ESty GKir LPlm LStr MAsh MAus MFry MGan MJon MRav SApu SPer SSea SWCr WStI
'Eos' (moyesii hybrid)	EBls SSea
'Erfurt' (HM)	EBls EMFP MAus MGan SWCr WHCG
§ 'Erinnerung an Brod' (S)	WHCG
§ 'Ernest H. Morse' (HT)	CSBt CTri CWSG EBls ESty GCoc GGre GKir MAsh MBur MGan MJon MRav NRog SPer SSea SWCr
'Ernest May' (HT)	SSea
Escapade = 'Harpade' (F) ♀ H4	EBls MAus MGan
Especially for You = 'Fryworthy'[PBR] (HT)	CSBt EBee ESty GCoc GGre LGod LStr MAsh MBur MFry SApu SCoo SSea WWeb
Essex = 'Poulnoz'[PBR] (GC)	EBre ENot MMat MRav SApu SPer SWCr WHCG
§ 'Estrellita de Oro' (Min)	LPlm MGan SPer SWCr
'Etain' (Ra)	ECnt SWCr
§ 'Etendard'	MRav SWCr WAct
Eternal Flame = 'Korassenet' (F) **new**	ECnt MMat
§ Eternally Yours = 'Macspeego'[PBR] (HT)	MJon SWCr
'Ethel' (Ra)	EBee EMFP ETWh
'Etoile de Hollande' (HT)	CHad EBee ELan ENot GKir MAsh MMat NPri SFam SSea
'Etoile de Lyon' (T)	EBls
'Eugène Fürst' (HP)	EBls
'Eugénie Guinoisseau' (Mo)	EBls WHCG
Euphoria = 'Intereup'[PBR] (GC/S)	GCoc IDic MJon SApu
Euphrates = 'Harunique' (persica hybrid)	MAus MGan WAct

'Europeana' (F)	MGan SWCr
'Eva' (HM)	EBls
'Evangeline' (Ra)	EBls EWTr MAus
Evelyn = 'Aussaucer'[PBR] (S) ♀ H4	CGro CSBt EBee EBre EMFP ENot EPfP GCoc GGre LGod LRHS LStr MAsh MAus MFry MJon MMat MRav MWgw SApu SChu SPer SPla SSea SWCr WWeb
§ Evelyn Fison = 'Macev' (F)	CSBt ELan ENot EPfP GGre GKir LPlm MAsh MAus MGan MJon MMat MRav NRog SPer SWCr
'Everest Double Fragrance' (F)	EBls
'Excelsa' (Ra)	CSBt CTri EBls EPfP GGre GKir IArd LGod MAsh MGan MJon MRav NRog NWea SSea SWCr WAct WStI
§ Exploit = 'Meilider'[PBR] (Cl)	GGre SWCr
§ Eye Paint = 'Maceye' (F)	MAus MGan MJon SMrm
'Eyecatcher' (F)	ECnt SWCr
Eyeopener = 'Interop'[PBR] (S/GC)	CGro EBls IDic MGan SWCr
'F.E. Lester'	see R. 'Francis E. Lester'
§ 'F.J. Grootendorst' (Ru)	EBls LGod LRHS MAus MGan MJon NRog SSea SWCr WAct
Fab = 'Bosconpea'[PBR] (F) **new**	GGre
'Fabvier'	see R. 'Colonel Fabvier'
Fairhope = 'Talfairhope' (Min)	NBat
§ Fairy Damsel = 'Harneatly' (Poly/GC)	EBls MBur SWCr
§ Fairy Prince = 'Harnougettc' (GC)	MAsh
Fairy Queen = 'Sperien' (Poly/GC)	IDic MAsh SSea SWCr
'Fairy Rose'	see R. 'The Fairy'
'Fairy Shell' (Patio)	MAsh
§ Fairy Snow = 'Holfairy' (S)	SWCr
§ Fairygold = 'Frygoldie'[PBR] (Patio)	MBri MFry
Fairyland = 'Harlayalong' (Poly)	EBls MAsh MBur SApu SWCr
Falstaff = 'Ausverse' (S)	ECnt MAsh MAus MBNS MBri SWCr
'Fantin-Latour' (centifolia hybrid) ♀ H4	CSam EBee EBls ECnt ELan ENot EPfP GCoc LGod LRHS LStr MAus MGan MMat MRav MWgw NRog SApu SFam SPer SRPl SSea SWCr WAct WGer WHCG
fargesii hort.	see R. moyesii var. fargesii
farreri var. persetosa	see R. elegantula 'Persetosa'
Fascination = 'Jacoyel' (HT)	ECle GKir LStr MBri SCoo
§ Fascination = 'Poulmax'[PBR] (F) ♀ H4	CSBt ECnt ENot EPfP GCoc LGod LPlm MAsh MAus MFry MGan MMat MRav SApu SPer SSea SWCr WWeb
'Fashion Flame' (Min)	SWCr
fedtschenkoana hort.	EBls LRHS MAus SPer WAct WHCG
fedtschenkoana Regel **new**	SLPl
'Felicia' (HM) ♀ H4	More than 30 suppliers
'Félicité Parmentier' (AxD) ♀ H4	EBls EMFP EWTr LRHS MAus MRav SFam SPer SWCr WAct WHCG
§ 'Félicité Perpétue' (Ra) ♀ H4	CBcs EBee EBls ELan ENot EPfP EWTr GCoc GKir ISea LRHS LStr MAsh MAus MBri MGan MMat MRav MWgw SApu SFam SPer SRPl SSea SWCr WAct WHCG
Felicity Kendal = 'Lanken' (HT)	MJon SWCr
'Fellemberg' (ClCh)	EBls MAus SWCr WHCG

Fellowship = 'Harwelcome'PBR (F) ♀ H4 | ECnt ENot ESty GCoc LGod LPlm LStr MAus MBur MFry MGan MJon MMat MRav SCoo SSea SWCr WGer
'Femina' (HT) | MGan
'Ferdinand Pichard' (Bb) ♀ H4 | CPou EBee EBls ECnt EMFP ENot EPfP EWTr LRHS MAus MBri MGan MJon MMat MRav MWgw SPer SSea SWCr WAct WFoF WGer WHCG WKif WOVN
§ Ferdy = 'Keitoli'PBR (GC) | EBls ENot MRav SApu SPer
Fergie = 'Ganfer'PBR (F/Patio) | MGan SWCr
Festival = 'Kordialo'PBR (Patio) | CGro ENot ESty LGod LPlm LStr MAus MGan MJon MMat MRav SApu SPer SSea SWCr WGer
Fiery Hit = 'Poulfiry'PBR (Min) | ECnt
Fiery Sunblaze = 'Meineyta'PBR (Min) | SWCr
Fiesta = 'Macfirinlin'PBR (Patio) | MBri MJon
Fifi = 'Hanfif' (F) | NBat
filipes **new** | GIBF
- 'Brenda Colvin' | see *R.* 'Brenda Colvin'
§ - 'Kiftsgate' (Ra) ♀ H4 | More than 30 suppliers
§ 'Fimbriata' (Ru) | CPou EBee EBls ETWh MAus MBri SPer SWCr WAct WHCG
Financial Times Centenary = 'Ausfin' (S) | MAus
Fiona = 'Meibeluxen'PBR (S/GC) | EBls GGre SWCr
'Fire Princess' (Min) | SWCr
'Firecracker' (F) | EBls
Firefly = 'Macfrabro' (Min) | MJon SWCr
Firestorm = 'Peazoe'PBR (Patio) **new** | SWCr
'First Love' (HT) | EBls MGan
'Fisher and Holmes' (HP) | EBls ETWh MAus WAct WHCG
Fisherman's Friend = 'Auschild'PBR (S) | MAus SPer
Flamenco = 'Poultika'PBR (Cl) | ECnt
'Fleur Cowles' (F) | MBur SWCr
'Flora' (Ra) | CRHN EBls MAus SFam
'Flora McIvor' (RH) | EBls MAus MGan
'Florence Mary Morse' (S) | SDix
Florence Nightingale = 'Ganflor'PBR (F) | MBur MGan SPer
Flower Carpet Red Velvet = 'Noare'PBR | ELan ENot MAsh MMat MRav SCoo WWeb
Flower Carpet Sunshine = 'Noason'PBR (GC) | ELan ENot EPfP LStr MAsh MMat MRav SCoo SWCr WWeb
§ Flower Carpet Twilight = 'Noatwi'PBR (GC) | LRHS MMat
Flower Carpet Velvet (GC/S) | EPfP
Flower Carpet White = 'Noaschnee'PBR (GC) ♀ H4 | CTri ELan ENot EPfP LRHS LStr MAsh MFry MGan MMat MRav SCoo SPer SSea SWCr WWeb
Flower Power = 'Frycassia'PBR (Patio) | CSBt ECnt ESty GCoc GGre GKir LStr MAsh MAus MBri MFry MJon MRav SApu SSea SWCr WWeb
§ *foetida* (S) | EBls MAus
§ - 'Bicolor' (S) | EBls ENot LRHS MAus MGan MMat NRog SPer SWCr WAct
§ - 'Persiana' (S) | EBls MAus MGan SPer
foliolosa | EBls SLPl WHCG
Fond Memories = 'Kirfelix'PBR (Patio) | GCoc LStr MJon SApu SWCr WWeb
'Fondant Cascade' (Patio/GC) | ESty SWCr

Forever Young = 'Jacimgol'PBR (F) | IDic MJon SWCr
forrestiana | EBls MAus SWCr WHCG
x *fortuneana* (Ra) | EBls WFar
Fortune's double yellow | see *R.* x *odorata* 'Pseudindica'
'Fountain' (HT/S) | EBls MAus MGan SPer SWCr
Fragrant Cloud = 'Tanellis' (HT) | CGro CWSG EBls EBre ECnt ENot EPfP ESty GCoc GGre GKir LPlm LStr MAsh MAus MBri MBur MFry MJon MMat MRav NRog SApu SPer SSea SWCr WWeb
'Fragrant Delight' (F) ♀ H4 | CSBt ECnt ESty GCoc GKir LPlm LStr MFry MGan MJon MRav SApu SPer SWCr SRPl SWCr WWeb
Fragrant Dream = 'Dicodour'PBR (HT) | CGro ESty IDic LStr MBri SWCr
Fragrant Gold = 'Tandugoft'PBR (HT) | SWCr
'Fragrant Hour' (HT) | MBur MGan SWCr
Fragrant Memories = 'Korpastato'PBR (HT/S) | ECle ENot ESty GCoc MAsh MMat
Frances Perry = 'Bosrexcity'PBR (F) | GGre SWCr
'Francesca' (HM) | EBls ETWh LRHS MAus MGan SFam SPer SWCr WAct WHCG
Francine Austin = 'Ausram'PBR (S/GC) | LRHS MAsh MAus MJon SPer SWCr WAct
'Francis Dubreuil' (T) | EBls
§ 'Francis E. Lester' (HM/Ra) ♀ H4 | CHad CRHN CSam EBee EBls EBre ETWh LRHS MAus MBri MJon SFam SPer SSea SWCr WAct WHCG
§ x *francofurtana* ♀ H4 | EBls ETWh MAus MRav SFam SSea SWCr WAct WHCG
- 'Agatha' | EBls
'François Juranville' (Ra) ♀ H4 | CHad CPou CRHN CSBt EBee EBls ENot ETWh LRHS LStr MAus MBri MGan MMat MRav NRog SApu SPer SRPl SWCr WAct
'Frau Astrid Späth' (F) | NRog
§ 'Frau Karl Druschki' (HP) | EBls ETWh MAus WAct
'Fräulein Octavia Hesse' (Ra) | EBls
'Fred Loads' (F/S) ♀ H4 | EBls MAus MGan MRav NBlu SApu SWCr
Freddie Mercury = 'Batmercury' (HT) | MBur MJon NBat
Free as Air = 'Mehbronze'PBR (Patio) | MBri
Freedom = 'Dicjem'PBR (HT) ♀ H4 | ECnt ENot GCoc GGre IDic LGod LPlm LStr MAus MBur MFry MGan MJon MMat MRav NBat NRog SApu SPer SSea SWCr WWeb
'Freiherr von Marschall' (T) | EBls
'Frensham' (F) | CBcs EBls ENot LStr MGan SSea SWCr
Fresh Pink (Min/Poly) | MGan
Friend for Life = 'Cocnanne'PBR (F) ♀ H4 | GCoc GGre MJon MRav SWCr
'Fringette' (Min) | MGan
'Fritz Nobis' (S) ♀ H4 | EBls EMil ENot GCoc LRHS LStr MAus MGan MMat MRav NHaw SPer SWCr WAct WHCG
Frothy = 'Macfrothy'PBR (Patio) | ECnt MJon SWCr
'Fru Dagmar Hastrup' (Ru) ♀ H4 | CHad CSBt CSam EBee EBls EBre ECnt ELan ENot EPfP GCoc GKir LBuc LStr MAus MFry MGan MJon MMat NRog SApu SPer SWCr WAct WHCG WOVN
'Frühlingsanfang' (PiH) | EBls MAus WAct WHCG
'Frühlingsduft' (PiH) | EBls ETWh NRog

'Frühlingsgold' (PiH) ♀ H4	CBcs CGro EBls EBre ELan ENot EPfP EWTr GCoc GKir LRHS LStr MAsh MAus MBri MFry MGan MMat MRav NRog NWea SApu SPer SSea SWCr WAct WHCG WOVN
'Frühlingsmorgen' (PiH)	EBls EBre ENot GCoc GKir LStr MAus MBri MGan MMat MRav NRog SApu SPer SSea SWCr WAct WHCG WOVN
'Frühlingsschnee' (PiH)	EBls
'Frühlingszauber' (PiH)	EBls
fuchianus **new**	GIBF
'Fulgens'	see *R.* 'Malton' (China hybrid)
Fulton Mackay = 'Cocdana'PBR (HT)	GCoc MFry MGan SApu SWCr
Fyvie Castle = 'Cocbamber' (HT)	GCoc MGan SWCr
'Gail Borden' (HT)	MGan SWCr
§ *gallica* (G)	EBls ENot SSea
- 'Complicata'	see *R.* 'Complicata'
- 'Conditorum'	see *R.* 'Conditorum'
§ - var. *officinalis* (G) ♀ H4	EBls ENot GCoc GKir GPoy LRHS MAsh MAus MJon MMat MRav NRog SApu SFam SPer SSea SWCr WAct WHCG
- *rubus*	WAct
- 'Velutiniflora' (G)	EBls SSea
§ - 'Versicolor' (G) ♀ H4	More than 30 suppliers
Galway Bay = 'Macba' (ClHT)	EBre ETWh GKir LRHS MAsh MGan MRav SPer SWCr
'Garden Beauty' (F)	SWCr
§ Garden News = 'Poulrim'PBR (HT)	ECnt ESty SWCr
Garden Party = 'Kormollis'PBR (F)	ENot MMat MRav SWCr
'Gardenia' (Ra)	EBee ETWh MAus SPer SWCr WHCG
'Gardiner's Pink' (Ra)	WHCG
'Garnette Carol'	see *R.* 'Carol Amling'
'Garnette Pink'	see *R.* 'Carol Amling'
'Gary Player' (HT)	NBat
'Général Galliéni' (T)	EBls
'Général Jacqueminot' (HP)	EBls MAus
'Général Kléber' (CeMo)	EBls MAus MRav SFam SPer SSea SWCr WAct WHCG
§ 'Général Schablikine' (T)	EBls EMFP ETWh MAus SWCr
N *gentiliana* (Ra)	EBls LRHS MAus WHCG
Gentle Touch = 'Diclulu'PBR (Min/Patio)	CGro CSBt CWSG EBls IDic MBri MFry MJon MMat MRav NRog SApu SPer SWCr
Geoff Hamilton = 'Ausham'PBR (S)	CSBt EBls ENot LRHS LStr MAsh MAus MBNS MBri MJon MMat SCoo SPer SWCr WWeb
'Georg Arends' (HP)	EBls MAus
'George Dickson' (HT)	EBls MAus
'George R. Hill' (HT)	NBat
'Georges Vibert' (G)	EBls ETWh MAus WHCG
Geraldine = 'Peahaze'PBR (F)	MGan
§ 'Geranium' (*moyesii* hybrid) ♀ H4	CBcs CGro EBee EBre ELan ENot EPfP GCoc GGre GKir IArd LGod LRHS LStr MAus MBri MDun MGan MJon MMat MRav SApu SPer SRPl SSea SWCr WAct WHCG WOVN
'Gerbe Rose' (Ra)	EBls MAus
Gertrude Jekyll = 'Ausbord'PBR (S) ♀ H4	More than 30 suppliers
'Ghislaine de Félligonde' (Ra/S)	CHad CPou EBee EBls EMFP ETWh EWTr LStr SMrm SSea SWCr WHCG

gigantea	EBls ISea
- 'Cooperi'	see *R.* 'Cooperi'
Ginger Syllabub = 'Harjolly' (Cl)	ESty GCoc LStr SWCr
§ Gingernut = 'Coccrazy'PBR (Patio)	GCoc GGre MBri SApu SWCr
Gipsy Boy	see *R.* 'Zigeunerknabe'
giraldii **new**	EBls
Glad Tidings = 'Tantide'PBR (F)	CGro CSBt CWSG LPlm MBri MBur MGan MRav NRog SApu SPer SWCr
Glamis Castle = 'Auslevel'PBR (S)	CBcs EBls EBre GKir LRHS LStr MAsh MAus MBNS MBri MJon MWgw SPer SWCr WWeb
§ *glauca* Pourr. (S) ♀ H4	More than 30 suppliers
'Glenfiddich' (F)	CGro CSBt CWSG GCoc GGre LPlm LStr MAus MBri MJon MRav NPri NRog NWea SPer SSea SWCr WStl WWeb
'Glenn Dale' (Cl)	EBee ETWh
Glenshane = 'Dicvood'PBR (GC/S)	ESty IDic MJon MRav SWCr
'Gloire de Bruxelles' (HP)	EBls
'Gloire de Dijon' (ClT)	More than 30 suppliers
'Gloire de Ducher' (HP)	ETWh MAus MGan MRav SWCr WAct WHCG
'Gloire de France' (G)	EBls ETWh MAus MRav SWCr
'Gloire de Guilan' (D)	EBls MAus SWCr WAct
'Gloire des Mousseuses' (CeMo)	EBls ETWh SFam SWCr WAct WHCG
'Gloire du Midi' (Poly)	MAus
'Gloire Lyonnaise' (HP)	EBee EBls ETWh SWCr WHCG
'Gloria Mundi' (Poly)	EBls MGan SWCr
Gloriana = 'Chewpope'PBR (ClMin)	ECle ESty MAus MBri MJon SSea SWCr
Glorious = 'Interictira'PBR (HT)	GCoc IDic MBri MJon SWCr
Glorious = 'Lcoglo' (HT)	NBat
Glowing Amber = 'Manglow'PBR (Min)	NBat
glutinosa	see *R.pulverulenta*
'Goethe' (CeMo)	EBls
Gold Bunny = 'Meifronuri' (F)	MBri MJon
Gold Crown	see *R.* 'Goldkrone'
'Goldbusch' (RH)	EBls MGan SSea WAct
'Golden Anniversary' (Patio)	ENot GCoc GGre LStr MAsh NEgg SPer SWCr
Golden Beryl = 'Manbcryl' (Min)	NBat
Golden Celebration = 'Ausgold'PBR (S) ♀ H4	CSBt CTri CWSG EBee EBre ECnt ENot GCoc GGre GKir LGod LRHS LStr MAsh MAus MBri MGan MJon MMat MRav NPri SApu SPer SWCr WGer WWeb
'Golden Chersonese' (S)	EBls MAus NRog SWCr
'Golden Dawn' (ClHT)	see *R.* 'Climbing Golden Dawn' (ClHT)
§ Golden Days = 'Rugolda'PBR (HT)	MBri
Golden Future = 'Horanymoll'PBR (Cl)	MBri SWCr
'Golden Glow' (Cl)	EBls MGan
Golden Hands = 'Chessupremo'PBR (Min/Patio)	SWCr
Golden Hope = 'Melpic'PBR (F)	MBri
§ Golden Jewel = 'Tanledolg'PBR (Patio)	ESty MAsh SApu SWCr
Golden Jubilee = 'Cocagold' (HT)	CGro GCoc GGre MRav SCoo SWCr

Golden Kiss = 'Dicalways' ECnt GCoc IDic NBat
(HT) **new**
Golden Melody =   EBls
'Irene Churruca' (HT)
Golden Mimi = 'Meispreyo' SWCr
(Patio)
Golden Moments =   MFry
'Frytranquil'PBR (HT)
'Golden Moss' (Mo)   EBls
Golden Oldie =   MFry
'Fryescape' (HT)
'Golden Ophelia' (HT)   EBls
§ Golden Penny =   EWTr MFry MGan MJon
'Rugul' (Min)
'Golden Rambler'   see R. 'Alister Stella Gray'
'Golden Salmon' (Poly)   MGan
'Golden Salmon   EBls
Supérieur' (Poly)
'Golden Shot' (F)   MGan
'Golden Showers' (Cl) ♀ H4 More than 30 suppliers
'Golden Slippers' (F)   CBcs MGan
'Golden Sunblaze'   see Rosa 'Rise 'n Shine'
§ Golden Symphonie =   MJon SWCr
'Meitoleil'PBR
(Min/Patio)
Golden Times   see R. Kordes' Golden Times =
'Kortime'
Golden Trust =   GGre LStr SWCr
'Hardish'PBR (Patio) **new**
Golden Wedding =   More than 30 suppliers
'Arokris'PBR (F/HT)
'Golden Wings' (S) ♀ H4 CHad EBls ECnt ENot EPfP EWTr
GCoc LPlm LRHS LStr MAsh MAus
MFry MGan MJon MMat MRav
SApu SPer SSea SWCr WAct
WHCG WOVN
Golden Years =   MAus SWCr
'Harween'PBR (F)
'Goldfinch' (Ra)   CHad EBee EBls EMFP GGre LRHS
LStr MAsh MAus MBri MRav SApu
SFam SPer SSea SWCr WAct
WHCG
Goldfinger = 'Pearoyal' (F) SWCr
'Goldilocks' (F)   NRog
§ Goldstar = 'Candide' (HT) ECnt MGan SApu SWCr
Good as Gold =   CSBt ECnt ESty LStr MBri MFry
'Chewsunbeam'PBR   MJon NPri SApu SWCr WGer
(ClMin)
Good Life =   GCoc GGre SWCr
'Cococircus'PBR (HT)
Good Luck = 'Burspec'PBR SPer SWCr
(F/Patio)
§ Gordon Snell =   IDic
'Dicwriter' (F)
Gordon's College =   GCoc MJon SApu
'Cocjabby'PBR (F) ♀ H4
Grace = 'Auskeppy' (S) **new** MAus
'Grace Darling' (T)   EBls
Grace de Monaco =   EBls MGan
'Meimit' (HT)
Gracious Queen =   GCoc GGre LRHS WWeb
'Bedqueen' **new**
Graham Thomas =   More than 30 suppliers
'Ausmas'PBR (S) ♀ H4
Granada (HT)   EBls
Grand Hotel =   ENot MBur MJon MMat SPer
'Mactel' (ClHT)
Grand-mère Jenny =   EBls MGan
'Grem' (HT)
'Grandpa Dickson' (HT) CSBt CWSG EBls EBre ESty GGre
GKir LGod LPlm MAsh MAus MBur
MGan MJon MRav NBat NBlu NPri
NRog SApu SPer SWCr WWeb

Granny's Favourite (F)   GGre SWCr
Great Expectations =   ENot LPlm MBur
'Jacdal' (F)
Great Expectations =   CBcs
'Lanican' (HT)
Great Expectations =   CGro CSBt ECnt EPfP GCoc GGre
'Mackalves'PBR (F)   IArd LGod LStr MAsh MBri MFry
MJon MMat SCoo SPer SWCr WWeb
§ 'Great Maiden's Blush' (A) EBls GCoc GGre MFry MRav
SFam SRPl WAct
'Great News' (F)   MAus
'Great Ormond Street' (F) EBls
'Great Western' (Bb)   EBls
'Green Diamond' (Min)   MJon
Greenall's Glory =   MAus MJon SSea SWCr
'Kirmac'PBR (F/Patio)
'Greenmantle' (RH)   EBls MAus MBri MGan
Greensleeves =   EBls SPer SWCr
'Harlenten' (F)
Greetings =   CSBt GGre IDic MAsh MRav
'Jacdreco'PBR (F)
Grenadine =   ECnt SWCr
'Poulgrena'PBR (HT)
'Grey Dawn' (F)   MBur SWCr
'Grimpant Cramoisi   EBls WHCG
Supérieur' (ClCh)
'Grootendorst'   see R. 'F.J. Grootendorst'
'Grootendorst   MAus SPer SWCr
Supreme' (Ru)
N 'Gros Choux de Hollande' EBls WHCG
hort. (Bb)
§ Grouse 2000 =   ENot
'Korteilhab'PBR (GC)
Grouse = 'Korimro'PBR   EBls ENot GCoc MAus MJon
(S/GC) ♀ H4   MMat MRav SApu WAct WOVN
§ Grumpy = 'Burkhardt' (Poly) MGan
'Gruss an Aachen' (Poly)   EBls EMFP EPfP EWTr LStr MAus
MGan SPer SWCr WAct WHCG
'Gruss an Teplitz'   CPou EBee EBls ETWh MAus SPer
(China hybrid)   SRPl WHCG
'Guinée' (ClHT)   CHad CSBt CTri EBee EBls EBre
ECnt ELan ENot EPfP EWTr GKir
LRHS LStr MAsh MAus MBur
MGan MMat MRav SChu SPer SPla
SSea SWCr WHCG
'Gustav Grünerwald' (HT) EBls MAus
Gwen Mayor =   GCoc
'Cocover'PBR (HT)
Gwent = 'Poulurt'PBR (GC) CSBt EBre ECnt ELan ENot GCoc
LGod LPlm LStr MAus MMat MRav
SApu SPer SSea SWCr WAct
WOVN WWeb
§ *gymnocarpa* var.   EBls ENot MGan SPer SSea SWCr
willmottiae   WAct WHCG
Gypsy Boy   see R. 'Zigeunerknabe'
'Gypsy Jewel' (Min)   SWCr
'Hadagni'PBR   see R. 'Smooth Angel'
'Hadvelvet'PBR   see R. 'Smooth Velvet'
'Hakuun' (F/Patio) ♀ H4 ESty MAsh MAus MGan SWCr
Hallé = 'Fryelectric' (HT) ECle ECnt MFry SWCr
'Hamburger Phönix' (Ra) CGro EBls MGan SPer SWCr WAct
Hampshire =   ENot MAus MGan MMat MRav
'Korhamp'PBR (GC)   SApu
Hampton Palace =   ECnt
'Poulgret'PBR (F) **new**
Hand in Hand =   MAsh MBri SWCr WWeb
'Haraztec'PBR
(Patio/Min)
Handel = 'Macha' (Cl) ♀ H4 CGro CSBt CTri CWSG EBls EBre
ELan ESty EWTr GGre GKir LGod
LPlm LRHS LStr MBri MBur MFry
MGan MJon MMat MRav NBlu
NRog SApu SPer SSea SWCr WWeb

	'Impulse' (Patio)	SWCr
	In the Pink = 'Peaverity'PBR (F)	GGre SWCr
	Indian Summer = 'Peaperfume'PBR (HT) ♀ H4	CSBt CWSG ESty GCoc LGod MBri MFry MJon MRav SWCr
	'Indigo' (DPo)	EBee EBls ETWh MAus WHCG
	Ingrid Bergman = 'Poulman'PBR (HT) ♀ H4	CSBt ECnt ENot GCoc GGre LGod LPlm LStr MAus MBur MFry MGan MJon MMat MRav SApu SWCr
§	Innocence = 'Cocoray'PBR (Patio)	GCoc SApu SWCr
	'Intermezzo' (HT)	MBur MGan SWCr
§	Intrigue = 'Korlech'PBR (F)	CSBt ENot LStr MBri MMat SSea SWCr
	Invincible = 'Runatru'PBR (F)	EBee ECnt MAus MFry MGan SWCr
	'Invitation' (HT)	MGan
	'Ipsilanté' (G)	EBls MAus WAct WHCG
	'Irene Av Danmark' (F)	EBls
	'Irène Watts' (Ch)	EBee EBls ECre EMFP EPfP ETWh EWTr MAus SPla SWCr WAct WHCG
	'Irene's Delight' (HT)	NRog
	'Iris Foster' new	NBat
	'Irish Elegance' (HT)	EBls
	Irish Eyes = 'Dicwitness'PBR (F)	CWSG ECle ECnt ENot EPfP GCoc GGre IArd IDic LGod LPlm LStr MAsh MBri MFry MJon MRav NPri SApu SCoo SPer SSea SWCr WWeb
	'Irish Fireflame' (HT)	EBls
	Irish Hope = 'Harexclaim'PBR (F) new	GGre SWCr
	Irresistible = 'Tinresist' (Min/Patio)	NBat
	Isabella = 'Poulisab'PBR (S)	CPou ECle ECnt GGre MAsh SWCr
	Isobel Derby = 'Horethel'PBR (HT)	GGre MJon
	'Ispahan' (D) ♀ H4	CHad EBls EPfP IKee LRHS MAus SApu SFam SPer SSea SWCr WAct WHCG
	'Ivory Fashion' (F)	EBls
	Jack Wood = 'Frydabble' (F)	MFry
	Jack's Wish (HT) new	MJon SWCr
§	x jacksonii 'Max Graf' (GC/Ru)	EBls ENot LRHS MAus MGan MRav NRog WAct WFar
§	- White Max Graf = 'Korgram'PBR (GC/Ru)	ENot MRav WAct
	Jacobite rose	see R. x alba 'Alba Maxima'
	'Jacpico'PBR	see R. 'Pristine'
	Jacqueline du Pré = 'Harwanna'PBR (S) ♀ H4	CSBt EBee ECnt ENot GCoc LRHS MAsh MAus MBri MGan MJon MMat MRav SApu SChu SPer SWCr WAct WGer WHCG
	Jacquenetta = 'Ausjac' (S)	MAus
N	'Jacques Cartier' hort.	see Rosa 'Marchesa Boccella'
	'James Bourgault' (HP)	EBls
	James Galway = 'Auscrystal' (S)	CSBt CWSG MAus SWCr
	'James Mason' (G)	EBls MAus
	'James Mitchell' (CeMo)	EBls MAus SWCr WHCG
	'James Veitch' (DPoMo)	EBls MAus WHCG
	'Jan Guest' (HT)	NRog
	Jane Asher = 'Peapeat'PBR (Min/Patio)	MBri MJon SWCr
	Jane Eyre = 'Mehpark'PBR (Cl)	COtt MGan MRav SApu SWCr
	'Janet's Pride' (RH)	EBls MAus
	Janina = 'Tanija' (HT)	MJon SWCr
§	'Japonica' (CeMo)	MAus

§	Jardins de Bagatelle = 'Meimafris'PBR (HT)	MBur MJon MRav SWCr
	Jayne Austin = 'Ausbreak'PBR (S)	CSBt CWSG EBre ENot LRHS MAus MJon NPri SApu SPer SWCr
	JazzPBR (Cl)	see R. That's Jazz = 'Poulnorm'
	Jean Kenneally = 'Tineally' (Min)	NBat
	'Jean Mermoz' (Poly)	MAus NRog SWCr WHCG
	'Jean Rosenkrantz' (HP)	EBls
	'Jean Sisley' (HT)	EBls
	'Jeanie Deans' (RH)	MAus
	'Jeanne de Montfort' (CeMo)	EBls MAus
	'Jelbar'PBR	see R. 'Wee Barbie'
§	Jemma Giblin = 'Horjemma' (Patio/F)	NBat
	Jenny Charlton = 'Simway' (HT)	NBat
	'Jenny Duval' misapplied	see R. 'Président de Sèze'
	'Jenny Wren' (F)	EBls MAus
	'Jenny's Dream' (HT)	LGod
	Jenny's Rose = 'Cansit' (F)	EBee ECnt SWCr
	'Jens Munk' (Ru)	WAct
	'Jersey Beauty' (Ra)	EBls
	'Jill Dando' (S)	EBls
	Jillian McGredy = 'Macarnhe' (F) new	MJon SWCr
	Jill's Rose = 'Ganjil'PBR (F)	MGan SWCr
	Jilly Jewel = 'Benmfig' (Min) new	NBat
	'Jiminy Cricket' (F)	EBls NRog
	'Jimmy Greaves' (HT)	MGan
	'Joan Bell' (HT)	NRog
	'Joanna Hill' (HT)	EBls
	'Joanna Lumley' (HT)	MBur
	'Joanne' (HT)	MJon NRog
	'Jocelyn' (F)	EBls
	'John Cabot' (S)	SSea
	John Clare = 'Auscent'PBR (S)	EBre LRHS MAus MBri SWCr
	'John Hopper' (HP)	EBls ETWh MAus SWCr
§	John Hughes = 'Sanphyllis' (F)	MBur
	John Keats = 'Meiroupis'PBR (S)	SApu SWCr
	Johnnie Walker = 'Frygran'PBR (HT)	ESty MFry
	José Carreras = 'Poulnew'PBR (HT)	ECnt SWCr
	'Josephine Bruce' (HT)	CBcs CSBt EBls LGod MBur MGan MRav NRog SWCr WStI
	'Josephine Wheatcroft'	see R. 'Rosina'
	'Joseph's Coat' (S/Cl)	ENot IArd LGod LStr MBri MFry MGan MMat MRav NBlu SSea SWCr
	'Journey's End' (HT)	MGan
	Jude the Obscure = 'Ausjo'PBR (S)	CAbP LRHS MAus MJon WWeb
§	Judi Dench = 'Peahunder' (F)	EPfP
	'Judy Fischer' (Min)	LGod SWCr
	'Julia Mannering' (RH)	MAus
	'Julia's Rose'PBR (HT)	CGro LStr MAus MBur MGan MJon SApu SPer SWCr
	'Juliet' (HP)	EBls
	jundzillii	CFee
	'Juno' (Ce)	EBls MAus WAct WHCG
	'Just for You' (F) new	GGre
	'Just Jenny' (Min)	NBat
	'Just Joey' (HT) ♀ H4	More than 30 suppliers
	Just Magic = 'Trobic' (Min)	MJon SWCr
	Just Reward = 'Guestall' (ClHT)	LPlm
	'Karl Foerster' (PiH)	EBls MAus

'Kassel' (S/Cl) — EBls

'Katharina Zeimet' (Poly) — EBls ETWh MAus MGan NRog WAct WHCG

Katherine Mansfield = 'Meilanein' (HT) — CSBt MBur

'Kathleen' (HM) — EBls

'Kathleen Ferrier' (F) — EBls MGan SWCr

'Kathleen Harrop' (Bb) — EBls ENot ETWh LRHS LStr MAus MBur MMat SFam SPer SRPl SWCr WAct WHCG

Kathleen Jane = 'Horcoed' (S/F) — GGre

Kathleen's Rose = 'Kirkitt' (F) — MJon

Kathryn McGredy = 'Macauclad'PBR (HT) — MJon SWCr

§ Kathryn Morley = 'Ausclub'PBR (F) — CAbP EBre LRHS MAus MJon MWgw SWCr

'Katie' (ClF) — MGan SWCr

Katie Crocker = 'Sabbrindley' (F) — MBur

'Kazanlik' misapplied — see R. 'Professeur Emile Perrot'

Keep in Touch = 'Hardrama'PBR (F) — GCoc SWCr

Keepsake = 'Kormalda' (HT) — ENot LPlm MGan MJon MMat

'Ken 'n' Norma Bright' (HT) **new** — NBat

Kent = 'Poulcov'PBR (S/GC) ♀ H4 — CSBt ECnt ELan ENot EPfP ESty GCoc LStr MAsh MJon MMat MRav SPer SPla SRPl SSea SWCr WAct WHCG WWeb

'Kew Rambler' (Ra) — CRHN EBee EBls ETWh MAus MRav SFam SPer SWCr WHCG

'Kiese' (*canina* hybrid) — MJon

'Kiftsgate' — see R. *filipes* 'Kiftsgate'

'Kilworth Gold' (HT) — MGan SWCr

'Kim' (Patio) — NRog

Kind Regards = 'Peatiger' (F) — ESty MBri SWCr

King's Macc = 'Frydisco' **new** — MFry

'King's Ransom' (HT) — CBcs CSBt EBls GGre MGan MJon MMat MRav SPer SWCr

'Kirsten Poulsen' (Poly) — EBls

Kiss 'n' Tell = 'Seakis' (Min) — MBur

'Kitty Hawk' (Min) — NBat

Knock Out = 'Dadler' (F) — ECle GCoc

x *kochiana* — EBls

'Köln am Rhein' (Cl) — MGan

§ 'Königin von Dänemark' (A) ♀ H4 — CHad EBee EBls EMFP ENot EPfP GCoc MAus MBri MJon MMat MRav MWgw SApu SPer SSea SWCr WAct WHCG

Korona = 'Kornita' (F) — MGan NRog

'Korresia' (F) — CSBt EBls ECnt EPfP ESty GCoc GGre GKir LGod LPlm LStr MAsh MAus MBri MBur MFry MGan MJon MMat MRav NRog SPer SWCr

§ Kristin = 'Benmagic' (Min) — NBat

Kronenbourg = 'Macbo' (HT) — EBls LPlm

'Kronprinzessin Viktoria' (Bb) — EBee EBls ETWh MAus WHCG

L.D. Braithwaite = 'Auscrim'PBR (S) ♀ H4 — CSam EBre ELan ENot EPfP GCoc LGod LPlm LRHS LStr MAsh MAus MFry MGan MJon MMat MRav NPri SApu SPer SRPl SSea SWCr WAct WHCG WWeb

'La Belle Distinguée' (RH) — EBls MAus WHCG

'La Belle Sultane' — see R. 'Violacea'

'La Follette' (Cl) — EBls

'La France' (HT) — EBls MAus MBur

'La Mortola' — see R. *brunonii* 'La Mortola'

'La Noblesse' (Ce) — EBls

'La Perle' (Ra) — CRHN MAus

'La Reine' (HP) — EBls

'La Reine Victoria' — see R. 'Reine Victoria'

'La Rubanée' — see R. 'Centifolia Variegata'

La Sévillana = 'Meigekanu'PBR (F/GC) — EBls ENot NHaw SApu SPer SWCr WOVN

'La Ville de Bruxelles' (D) ♀ H4 — EBls ETWh MAus MRav SFam SPer SWCr WAct WHCG

'Lady Alice Stanley' (HT) — EBls

'Lady Barnby' (HT) — EBls

'Lady Belper' (HT) — EBls

'Lady Curzon' (Ru) — EBls MAus SWCr

'Lady Forteviot' (HT) — EBls

'Lady Gay' (Ra) — EBee ETWh SWCr WHCG

'Lady Godiva' (Ra) — MAus

'Lady Hillingdon' (ClT) — see R. 'Climbing Lady Hillingdon'

'Lady Hillingdon' (T) — MAus

'Lady Iliffe' (HT) — MGan SWCr

Lady in Red = 'Sealady' (Min) — MBur

'Lady Love '95' (Patio) — ESty

Lady MacRobert = 'Coclent' (F) — GCoc

'Lady Mary Fitzwilliam' (HT) — EBls

Lady Mavis Pilkington = 'Kortlitse'PBR (HT) — MMat

Lady Penelope = 'Chewdor'PBR (ClHT) — CSBt MJon SSea SWCr

§ 'Lady Penzance' (RH) ♀ H4 — CBcs EBls MAus MFry MGan SApu SPer SWCr WAct

§ Lady Rachel = 'Candoodle' (F) — EBee ECnt SWCr

'Lady Romsey' (F) — EBls

Lady Rose = 'Korlady' (HT) — MAsh SWCr

'Lady Seton' (HT) — SPer

'Lady Sylvia' (HT) — CSBt CTri EBls MAus MGan NRog SPer SWCr

Lady Taylor = 'Smitling' (F/Patio) — MBur

'Lady Waterlow' (ClHT) — EBee EBls ETWh MAus SPer SWCr WHCG

laevigata (Ra) — EBls MAus SWCr

- 'Anemonoides' — see R. 'Anemone'

- 'Cooperi' — see R. 'Cooperi'

'Lafter' (S) — EBls

'Lagoon' (F) — EBls

L'Aimant = 'Harzola'PBR (F) ♀ H4 — CSBt ECle ENot ESty GCoc LGod LStr MAus MBur MFry MGan MJon MMat SApu SWCr

'Lamarque' (N) — MAus

'Laminuette' (F) — MJon

§ Lancashire = 'Korstesgli'PBR (GC) ♀ H4 — ECnt ENot ESty GCoc LStr MAus MMat MRav SWCr

Lancashire Life = 'Ruilanca'PBR (F) — MBri

§ 'Lanei' (CeMo) — EBls

Laura Anne = 'Cocclarion' (HT) — GCoc

§ Laura Ashley = 'Chewharla' (GC/ClMin) — CGro MAus SWCr

Laura Ford = 'Chewarvel'PBR (ClMin) ♀ H4 — CSBt CTri EBre ENot ESty GGre GKir LStr MAsh MAus MBri MGan MJon MMat MRav NBat NPri NRog SApu SSea SWCr WWeb

'Laura Jane' (HT) — MGan

'Laura Louisa' (Cl)　EBls
Laura = 'Meidragelac' (HT)　SWCr
§ 'Laure Davoust' (Ra)　EBee ETWh
'Lavender Jewel' (Min)　MAus MBur
'Lavender Lassie' (HM) ♀ H4　CPou EMFP ETWh MAus MFry MGan SPer SWCr WHCG
'Lavender Pinocchio' (F)　MAus
§ Lawinia = 'Tanklewi'PBR (ClHT) ♀ H4　CSBt GKir LRHS LStr MAsh MRav NPri SApu SPer SSea SWCr
'Lawrence Johnston' (Cl)　EBls LRHS MAus MJon SFam SPer SWCr WAct
Lazy Days (F) **new**　ECnt SWCr
'Le Havre' (HP)　EBls
'Le Rêve' (Cl)　EBls ETWh MAus SWCr
'Le Vésuve' (Ch)　EBls MAus
Leander = 'Auslea' (S)　MAus
Leaping Salmon = 'Peamight'PBR (ClHT)　CGro CSBt EBee ECnt ELan GCoc LGod MAus MBri MGan MJon MRav SApu SChu SPer SPla SSea SWCr WStI
'Leda' (D)　EBls EMFP MAus SFam SPer SSea SWCr WAct
Leeds Castle = 'Tanrupeza'PBR (GC) **new**　SWCr
'Lemon Pillar'　see R. 'Paul's Lemon Pillar'
Len Turner = 'Dicjeep' (F)　SApu
Léonardo de Vinci = 'Meideauri'PBR (F)　CSBt SApu
'Léonie Lamesch' (Poly)　EBls
'Léontine Gervais' (Ra)　CAbP CRHN LRHS MAus MBri SWCr WAct
Leslie's Dream = 'Dicjoon'PBR (HT)　IDic MJon SWCr
'Leverkusen' (Cl) ♀ H4　CHad EBee EBls EWTr LRHS MAus MGan MJon MRav SPer SPla SRPl SSea SWCr WAct WHCG
'Leveson-Gower' (Bb)　EBls
'Ley's Perpetual' (ClT)　EBee EBls ETWh SWCr WHCG
x *lheritieriana* (Bs)　EBee ETWh SWCr
§ Lichtkönigin Lucia = 'Korlillub' (S)　SSea
Life Begins at 49! (F) **new**　SWCr
'Lilac Charm' (F)　EBls
§ Lilac Rose = 'Auslilac' (S)　MAus
Lilian Austin = 'Ausli' (S)　MAus MBri
Lilian Baylis = 'Hardeluxe'PBR (F)　NBat
Liliana = 'Poulsyng'PBR (S)　ECle ECnt LPlm MAsh SWCr
§ Lilli Marlene = 'Korlima' (F)　CSBt CWSG EBls ENot GCoc MGan MMat NRog SPer SWCr
Lincoln Cathedral = 'Glanlin'PBR (HT)　MGan MJon SPer
Lincolnshire Poacher = 'Glareabit' (HT)　NBat
Lions International = 'Frycharm'PBR (HT)　MFry
Little Artist = 'Macmanly' (Min)　MJon SWCr
Little Bo-peep = 'Poullen'PBR (Min/Patio) ♀ H4　ENot MJon MRav SWCr
'Little Buckaroo' (Min)　LGod MGan SPer SWCr
'Little Dorrit' (Poly)　NRog
'Little Flirt' (Min)　MAus MGan SWCr
'Little Gem' (DPMo)　EBls MAus MGan
Little Jackie = 'Savor' (Min)　NBat
Little Muff = 'Horluisbond' (Min)　NBat
Little Rambler = 'Chewramb'PBR (MinRa) ♀ H4　CSBt ECnt ELan ENot MAus MJon MMat MRav SApu SWCr WGer

§ Little Rascal = 'Peaalamo'PBR (Patio/Min)　MAsh SWCr
Little Russell = 'Trobric' (Min)　MJon SWCr
'Little White Pet'　see R. 'White Pet'
Little Woman = 'Diclittle'PBR (Patio)　IDic LStr SWCr
'Liverpool Echo' (F)　LPlm MJon
§ Liverpool Remembers = 'Frystar'PBR (HT)　LGod MBur MFry SWCr
'Living Fire' (F)　MBur NRog
'Lollipop' (Min)　MGan
'Long John Silver' (Cl)　EBls MAus
longicuspis hort.　see R. *mulliganii*
longicuspis Bertoloni (Ra)　EBls SPla
- AC 2097　GGar
§ - var. *sinowilsonii* (Ra)　EBls GCal MAus
§ Lord Byron = 'Meitosier'PBR (ClHT)　LStr MBri MJon SApu SWCr
'Lord Louis' (HT)　MBur
'Lord Penzance' (RH)　EBls MGan MRav SPer SWCr WAct
L'Oréal Trophy = 'Harlexis' (HT)　MAus MJon SWCr
'Lorraine Lee' (T)　EBls
'Los Angeles' (HT)　EBls
'L'Ouche' misapplied　see R. 'Louise Odier'
'Louis Gimard' (CeMo)　EBls MAus SPer WAct WHCG
'Louis Philippe' (Ch)　EBls
'Louis XIV' (Ch)　CHad EBls WHCG
Louisa Stone = 'Harbadge' (S)　GGre SWCr
Louise Clements = 'Clelou' (S) **new**　EBls
§ 'Louise Odier' (Bb)　EBee EBls EBre ECnt EMFP ENot EPfP IArd LRHS LStr MAus MBri MDun MJon MRav MWgw SApu SFam SPer SPla SRPl SSea SWCr WAct WHCG WOVN
Love Knot = 'Chewglorious' (ClMin)　CSBt ECle ECnt MJon SWCr WGor
'Love Token' (F)　MBur SWCr
Lovely Fairy = 'Spevu'PBR (Poly/GC)　ECnt IDic MAsh SWCr WAct
Lovely Lady = 'Dicjubell'PBR (HT) ♀ H4　CSBt CTri EBee ECnt GGre IDic LPlm LStr MAsh MAus MGan MJon MRav NBlu SApu SWCr WWeb
'Lovers' Meeting'PBR (HT)　ESty GGre GKir LPlm MAsh MBur MGan MJon MRav NBlu NRog SPer SSea SWCr WStI
Loving Memory = 'Korgund'PBR (HT)　CGro CSBt CWSG EBee ECnt ENot GCoc GGre IArd LPlm LStr MBri MFry MGan MMat MRav NPri SPer SSea SWCr WWeb
Lucetta = 'Ausemi' (S)　MAus SPer
luciae　EBls
- var. *onoei*　CLyd EPot
'Lucilla' (Patio)　NBat
Lucky Duck = 'Diczest'PBR (Patio)　IDic MJon SWCr
'Lucy Ashton' (RH)　MAus
Luis Desamero = 'Tinluis' (Min)　NBat
'Lutea Maxima'　see R. x *harisonii* 'Lutea Maxima'
'Lykkefund' (Ra)　EBls MAus
'Lyon Rose' (HT)　EBls
'Ma Perkins' (F)　EBls SSea
'Ma Ponctuée' (DPMo)　EBls
'Mabel Morrison' (HP)　EBls MAus
Macartney rose　see R. *bracteata*
Macmillan Nurse = 'Beamac' (S)　EBls

'Macrantha' (Gallica hybrid) EBls LRHS MAus SPer WAct
x **macrantha** 'Raubritter'   see *R.* 'Raubritter' ('Macrantha' hybrid)
macrophylla   MAus SWCr
- B&SWJ 2603   WCru
- 'Doncasteri'   see *R.* 'Doncasteri'
§ - 'Master Hugh' ♀ H4   MBri
- - ex SS&W 7822   EBls MAus
Madam Speaker = 'Meizuzes'PBR (HT)   SApu SWCr
'Madame Abel Chatenay' (HT)   EBls MAus
'Madame Alfred Carrière' (N) ♀ H4   More than 30 suppliers
'Madame Alice Garnier' (Ra)   CPou EBee EBls ETWh SPer SWCr
'Madame Antoine Mari' (T)   EBls
'Madame Berkeley' (T)   EBls
'Madame Bravy' (T)   EBls MAus
'Madame Butterfly' (HT)   EBls MAus MBur MGan SApu SFam SPer SSea SWCr
§ 'Madame Caroline Testout' (HT)   EBee LRHS MRav SFam
'Madame Charles' (T)   EBls
'Madame d'Arblay' (Ra)   EBls
'Madame de Sancy de Parabère' (Bs)   EBls ETWh IArd MAus SFam SWCr WHCG
'Madame de Watteville' (T)   EBls
'Madame Delaroche-Lambert' (DPMo)   EBls ETWh MAus SWCr WAct WHCG
'Madame Driout' (CIT)   EBls WHCG
'Madame Eliza de Vilmorin' (HT)   EBls
'Madame Ernest Calvat' (Bb)   EBls ETWh MAus
'Madame Eugène Résal' misapplied   see *R.* 'Comtesse du Cayla'
'Madame Gabriel Luizet' (HP)   EBls
'Madame Georges Bruant' (Ru)   EBls MAus
§ 'Madame Grégoire Staechelin' (ClHT) ♀ H4   RHN CWSG EBee EBls EBre CECnt EMFP ENot LRHS LStr MAus MBri MGan MJon MMat MRav NBlu NRog SApu SChu SFam SPer SRPl SWCr WAct WHCG WOVN WWeb
'Madame Hardy' (CID) ♀ H4   CPou CSBt CSam EBee EBls ENot EPfP GCoc LGod LRHS LStr MAsh MAus MBri MGan MJon MMat MRav SApu SFam SPer SSea SWCr WAct WHCG WOVN
'Madame Isaac Pereire' (ClBb) ♀ H4   CHad EBee EBls EBre ECnt ENot EPfP GCoc LGod LRHS LStr MAus MBri MDun MFry MGan MJon MMat MRav NRog SApu SFam SMad SPer SSea SWCr WAct WHCG
'Madame Jules Gravereaux' (CIT)   EBls MAus
'Madame Jules Thibaud' (Poly)   MAus
§ 'Madame Knorr' (DPo) ♀ H4   CPou EBee EBls EMFP ENot EPfP MAsh MMat MRav MWgw SPer SSea SWCr WAct WOVN
'Madame Laurette Messimy' (Ch)   EBls ETWh MAus WHCG
'Madame Lauriol de Barny' (Bb)   EBls ETWh MAus MGan MRav SFam SWCr WHCG
'Madame Legras de Saint Germain' (AxN)   EBls LRHS MAus SFam SPer SWCr WAct WHCG
'Madame Lombard' (T)   EBls
'Madame Louis Laperrière' (HT)   EBls MAus MGan SPer SWCr

'Madame Louis Lévêque' (DPMo)   EBls SWCr WHCG
'Madame Pierre Oger' (Bb)   EBee EBls ECnt ENot LRHS LStr MAus MMat MRav SApu SPer SSea SWCr WAct WHCG
'Madame Plantier' (AxN)   EBee EBls LRHS MAus MRav SPer SSea SWCr WHCG WOVN
'Madame Scipion Cochet' (T)   EBls WHCG
'Madame Victor Verdier' (HP)   EBls
'Madame Wagram, Comtesse de Turenne' (T)   EBls
'Madame William Paul' (PoMo)   EBls
'Madame Zöetmans' (D)   EBls MAus
'Madeleine Selzer' (Ra)   EBls MGan SWCr
'Madge' (HM)   SDix
Madrigal = 'Harextra'PBR (S/F) **new**   GGre SWCr
'Magenta' (S/HT)   EBls MAus SPer SWCr
Magenta Floorshow = 'Harfloorshow'PBR (GC) **new**   SWCr
Magic Carpet = 'Jaclover'PBR (S/GC) ♀ H4   CSBt CWSG ECnt EPfP GCoc IDic LGod LPlm LRHS MAsh MAus MFry MGan MJon MMat MRav SApu SPer SRPl SSea
§ Magic Carrousel = 'Moorcar' (Min)   MAus
Magic Fire = 'Lapjaminal' (F)   GGre SWCr
'Magna Charta' (HP)   EBls
'Magnifica' (RH)   EBls MAus MGan
'Maid of Kent'PBR (Cl)   CSBt MGan MJon SCoo SPer SWCr
N 'Maiden's Blush' (A) ♀ H4   CSam CTri EBls EBre ELan EMFP ENot LRHS MAsh MAus MGan MMat MRav SApu SChu SFam SPer SSea SWCr WHCG
'Maiden's Blush, Great'   see *R.* 'Great Maiden's Blush'
'Maigold' (ClPiH) ♀ H4   More than 30 suppliers
§ **majalis**   EBls
Make a Wish = 'Mehpat'PBR (Min/Patio)   LStr MBri SWCr
'Malaga' (ClHT)   EBee ENot MMat
Malcolm Sargent = 'Harwharry' (HT)   SPer SWCr
Maltese rose   see *R.* 'Cécile Brünner'
§ 'Malton' (China hybrid)   EBls
Malvern Hills = 'Auscanary' (Ra)   MAus
Malverns = 'Kordehei' (GC)   ENot MMat
Mandarin = 'Korcelin'PBR (Min)   ESty LStr MAsh MJon MMat SSea WWeb
'Manettii' (N)   EBls
'Manning's Blush' (RH)   EBls MAus MRav SSea SWCr WAct
'Mannington Cascade' (Ra) **new**   EBls
'Mannington Mauve Rambler' (Ra) **new**   EBls
'Manuela' (HT)   MGan
'Manx Queen' (F)   MGan MJon SWCr
Many Happy Returns = 'Harwanted'PBR (S/F) ♀ H4   CGro CSBt CWSG EBee EBre ECnt ENot EPfP ESty GCoc GKir LGod LPlm LStr MAsh MBri MBur MFry MGan MJon MMat MRav SApu SPer SWCr WWeb
'Marbrée' (DPo)   EBls MAus
'Marcel Bourgouin' (G)   EBls
'Märchenland' (F/S)   EBls MAus

§ 'Marchesa Boccella' (DPo) ♀ H4 — CPou CSam EBee EBls EMFP ENot EPfP MAsh MAus MGan MMat MRav SPer SPla SSea SWCr WAct

'Marcie Gandy' (HT) — MGan SWCr

'Maréchal Davoust' (CeMo) — EBls MAus MRav SFam

'Maréchal Niel' (N) — CRHN EBls ERea ETWh MAus MGan SPer SWCr WHCG

'Margaret' (HT) — MBur MGan SWCr

Margaret Merril = 'Harkuly' (F/HT) ♀ H4 — More than 30 suppliers

§ Margaret Thatcher = 'Korflüg'PBR (HT) — MJon SWCr

'Margaret's Variegated Rose' — EVFa

Margaret's World = 'Kirbill' (F) — MJon

'Margo Koster' (Poly) — EBls MAus NRog SWCr

Marguerite Anne = 'Cocredward'PBR (F) — GCoc NBat SApu

'Marguérite Guillard' (HP) — EBls

'Marguerite Hilling' (S) ♀ H4 — EBls ENot GCoc GGre MAus MBri MGan MJon MMat MRav NRog SApu SPer SRPl SSea SWCr WAct WHCG WOVN

Maria McGredy = 'Macturang' new — MJon SWCr

x mariae-graebnerae — MAus SLPl WHCG

'Marie de Blois' (CeMo) — EBls

'Marie Louise' (D) — EBee EBls ETWh MAus SFam SWCr WAct WHCG

'Marie Pavič' (Poly) — EBls MAus WHCG

'Marie van Houtte' (T) — EBls MAus

'Marie-Jeanne' (Poly) — EBls MAus

'Marijke Koopman' (HT) — MFry

Marinette = 'Auscam'PBR (S) — MAus MJon SWCr

Marjorie Fair = 'Harhero' (Poly/S) ♀ H4 — EBls ECnt GGre LPlm MAsh MAus MGan MRav SWCr WAct WWeb

Marjorie May = 'Horsunpegy' (HT) — MJon

'Marlena' (F/Patio) — GCoc MAus MGan SWCr

Marry Me = 'Dicwonder'PBR (Patio) ♀ H4 — ECle ESty IDic MBri MJon SApu SWCr

'Martha' (Bb) — EBls MAus

'Martha's Choice' (HT) — NBat

'Martian Glow' (F/S) — MGan

'Martin Frobisher' (Ru) — EBls MAus

'Mary' (Poly) — LStr SWCr

Mary Donaldson = 'Canana' (HT) — MGan

§ Mary Gammon = 'Frysweetie' (Min/Patio) — MFry

Mary Magdalene = 'Ausjolly'PBR (S) — MAsh MAus SWCr

'Mary Manners' (Ru) — EBls SPer SWCr

Mary Pope = 'Korlasche' (HT) — ENot MMat MRav

Mary Rose = 'Ausmary'PBR (S) ♀ H4 — CGro CHad CSBt CSam CWSG EBee EBls EBre ELan ENot EPfP GCoc GGre GKir LGod LRHS LStr MAus MBri MFry MGan MJon MMat MRav SApu SPer SRPl SSea SWCr WOVN

'Mary Wallace' (Cl) — EBls MAus

Mary Webb = 'Auswebb' (S) — MAus MBri

'Masquerade' (F) — CBcs CGro CSBt CWSG EBls ENot LGod LStr MGan MJon MMat MRav NRog SSea SWCr WStI

'Master Hugh' — see R. macrophylla 'Master Hugh'

Matangi = 'Macman' (F) ♀ H4 — LGod LPlm MGan NRog

Matawhero MagicPBR — see Rosa Simply the Best = 'Macamster'

'Maude Elizabeth' (GC) new — EBls

'Maurice Bernardin' (HP) — EBls

'Max Graf' — see R. x jacksonii 'Max Graf'

'Maxima' — see R. x alba 'Alba Maxima'

maximowicziana — GIBF

'May Queen' (Ra) — CPou CRHN EBee EBls EMFP ETWh LRHS MAus MRav NLar SFam SPer SWCr WHCG

Mayor of Casterbridge = 'Ausbrid'PBR (S) — LRHS MAus MJon SWCr

'McGredy's Sunset' (HT) — NRog

'McGredy's Yellow' (HT) — EBls MBur MGan

'Meg' (ClHT) — CHad EBee EBls EWTr LRHS MAus MGan SPer SSea SWCr WAct WHCG

'Meg Merrilies' (RH) — EBls ETWh MAus MGan SSea SWCr WAct

'Megiddo' (F) — MGan

'Meicobius'PBR — see R. Terracotta = 'Meicobuis'

Meillandina = 'Meirov' (Min) — see R. Sir Harry Pilkington = 'Tanema'

Melina — see R. Sir Harry Pilkington = 'Tanema'

Melody Maker = 'Dicqueen'PBR (F) — CWSG IDic MGan

Memento = 'Dicbar'PBR (F) ♀ H4 — ENot IDic MGan

'Memoriam' (HT) — MBur MGan

Memory Lane = 'Peavoodoo'PBR (F) — GGre SWCr

Mercedes = 'Merkor' (F) — MJon

'Mermaid' (Cl) ♀ H3-4 — CBcs CGro CRHN CSBt CWSG EBls ECnt ENot EPfP EWTr GCoc GKir LHop LRHS LStr MAsh MAus MGan MJon MMat MRav NRog SApu SBra SPer SPla SSea SWCr WAct WHCG

'Merveille de Lyon' (HP) — EBls

§ Message = 'Meban' (HT) — MGan

'Meteor' (F/Patio) — MGan SWCr

§ 'Mevrouw Nathalie Nypels' (Poly) ♀ H4 — CHad EBls LRHS LStr MAus MRav SPer SWCr WAct WGer WKif WOVN

'Mexico' (Min) — LPlm

§ Michael Crawford = 'Poulvue'PBR (HT) — ECnt LGod SWCr

Michael Fish = 'Kirgale' (F) new — MJon SWCr

'Michèle Meilland' (HT) — EBls MAus MGan

x micrugosa — EBls MAus

– 'Alba' — EBls MAus

Middlesborough Football Club = 'Horflame' (HT) — NBat

Mike Thompson = 'Sherired' (HT) — NBat

'Millennium Rose 2000'PBR — see R. Rose 2000 = 'Cocquetrum'

Millionaire = 'Peazara'PBR (F) — GGre SApu SWCr

'Mills and Boon' (F) — MGan

Mimi = 'Meidesi' (Min) — MGan

Mini Metro = 'Rufin'PBR (Min) — MFry

Minilights = 'Dicmoppet' (Patio) — CGro

'Minnehaha' (Ra) — EBls EMFP LGod MAus SWCr

mirifica stellata — see R. stellata var. mirifica

Mischief = 'Macmi' (HT) — EBls GGre MGan NRog SPer SWCr

Miss Alice = 'Ausjake' (S) — MAsh MAus SWCr

§ Miss Dior = 'Harencens'PBR (S) — CSBt GGre

'Miss Edith Cavell' (Poly) — EBls MAus

Miss Flippins = 'Tuckflip' (Min) — NBat

Miss Harp = 'Tanolg' (HT) — MGan NRog

'Miss Lowe' (Ch) — EBls

§ 'Mister Lincoln' (HT) — EBls ESty LGod MGan SPer SWCr

Mistress Quickly = 'Ausky'PBR (S)	LRHS LStr MAus MJon SWCr WWeb	
'Mojave' (HT)	MGan SWCr	
'Moje Hammarberg' (Ru)	ENot MJon SWCr WAct	
§ Molineux = 'Ausmol'PBR (S) ♀ H4	CSBt CTri EBre ENot GCoc GKir LRHS MAsh MAus MBri MJon MMat SWCr WHCG WWeb	
'Mona Ruth' (Min)	MGan	
'Monique' (HT)	EBls MGan SWCr	
'Monsieur Tillier' (T)	EBls	
'Moonbeam = 'Ausbeam' (S)	MAus MRav	
'Moonlight' (HM)	CHad EBee EBls ECnt LRHS MAus MGan MRav NRog SPer SWCr WAct WHCG	
'Morgengruss' (Cl)	MGan SPer SWCr	
Moriah = 'Ganhol'PBR (HT)	MGan	
morlettii (Bs)	EBee EBls EHol ETWh MRav SWCr WHCG	
'Morning Jewel' (ClF) ♀ H4	GCoc LPlm MFry MGan MJon NRog SPer SWCr	
Morning Mist = 'Ausfire' (S)	LRHS MAus SWCr	
moschata (Ra)	EBls MAus MRav SSea SWCr WAct	
- 'Autumnalis'	see R. 'Princesse de Nassau'	
- var. nepalensis	see R. brunonii	
Mother's Day = 'Moersdag' (Poly/F)	GKir LStr MJon NEgg NPri SSea SWCr WWeb	
Mountain Snow = 'Aussnow' (Ra)	LRHS MAus MBri	
Mountbatten = 'Harmantelle'PBR (F) ♀ H4	CBcs CGro CWSG EBls EBre ELan ENot GGre GKir IFro LPlm LStr MAsh MAus MFry MGan MJon MMat MRav SApu SPer SRPl SSea SWCr	
§ 'Mousseline' (DPoMo)	EBls EMFP MAus MRav SPer SSea SWCr WAct WHCG	
'Mousseuse du Japon'	see R. 'Japonica'	
moyesii (S)	EBee EBls ELan ENot ISea MAus MFry MGan MJon MMat NRog NWea SPer SWCr WAct WOVN	
- 'Evesbatch' (S)	WAct	
§ - var. fargesii (S)	EBls	
- 'Geranium'	see R. 'Geranium' (moyesii hybrid)	
- 'Highdownensis'	see R. 'Highdownensis' (moyesii hybrid)	
- 'Hillieri'	see R. 'Hillieri'	
- holodonta	see R. moyesii f. rosea	
§ - f. rosea (S)	EBls ENot GCal	
- 'Sealing Wax'	see R. 'Sealing Wax' (moyesii hybrid)	
'Mozart' (HM)	MJon NLar SWCr WHCG	
'Mr Bluebird' (MinCh)	MAus MGan SWCr WStI	
'Mr Chips' (HT)	MBur SWCr	
'Mrs Anthony Waterer' (Ru)	EBls MAus SPer SWCr WAct WHCG	
'Mrs Arthur Curtiss James' (ClHT)	EBee ETWh SWCr	
'Mrs B.R. Cant' (T)	EBls	
'Mrs Doreen Pike = 'Ausdor'PBR (Ru)	LRHS MAus NHaw WAct	
'Mrs Eveline Gandy' (HT)	MGan	
'Mrs Foley Hobbs' (T)	EBls	
'Mrs Honey Dyson' (Ra)	CHad	
'Mrs John Laing' (HP)	EBee EBls EPfP LRHS MAus MRav SPer SWCr WHCG	
'Mrs Oakley Fisher' (HT)	CHad EBls EMFP ETWh MAus MBri SPer SWCr WAct	
'Mrs Paul' (Bb)	EBls MAus	
'Mrs Pierre S. duPont' (HT)	EBls	
'Mrs Sam McGredy' (HT)	CSBt MAus MGan	
'Mrs Walter Burns' (F/Patio)	MGan SWCr	
'Mullard Jubilee' (HT)	MGan SWCr	
§ mulliganii (Ra) ♀ H4	CDoC EBls EPfP MAus SPer SWCr WHCG	
multibracteata (S)	EBls MAus WHCG	
multiflora (Ra)	EBls GIBF IFro LBuc MAus WPic	
- 'Carnea' (Ra)	EBls	
- var. cathayensis (Ra)	EBls	
§ - 'Grevillei' (Ra)	EBee EBls EMFP ETWh MAus SPer SWCr	
- 'Platyphylla'	see R. multiflora 'Grevillei'	
- var. watsoniana	see R. watsoniana	
Mummy = 'Dicwhynot'PBR (Patio)	IDic	
'München' (HM)	MAus	
mundi	see R. gallica 'Versicolor'	
- 'Versicolor'	see R. gallica 'Versicolor'	
'Mutabilis'	see R. x odorata 'Mutabilis'	
'My Choice' (HT)	MGan SWCr	
'My Joy' (HT)	NBat	
'My Little Boy' (Min)	MBur	
My Love = 'Cogamo' (HT)	MBur MJon	
My Mum = 'Webmorrow' new	SWCr	
Myra = 'Battoo' (HT)	NBat	
Myriam = 'Cocgrand' (HT)	GCoc MJon SApu SWCr	
'Nan of Painswick' new	WAct	
'Nancy's Keepsake' (HT)	NBat	
'Narrow Water' (Ra)	EBee EBls ETWh SWCr WAct WHCG	
§ 'Nastarana' (N)	EBls	
'Nathalie Nypels'	see R. 'Mevrouw Nathalie Nypels'	
'National Trust' (HT)	CSBt EBls GGre IArd MAsh MGan MJon NBlu NRog SPer SWCr	
* 'Navie Viaud'	WAct	
'Nestor' (G)	EBls MAus	
'Nevada' (S) ♀ H1	More than 30 suppliers	
New Age = 'Wekbipuhit' (F) new	ESty GCoc MJon	
'New Arrival' (Patio/Min)	ESty GGre SWCr	
§ 'New Dawn' (Cl) ♀ H4	More than 30 suppliers	
New Fashion = 'Poulholm'PBR (Patio)	ENot	
'New Look' (F)	MGan SWCr	
'New Penny' (Min)	MGan MRav SWCr	
New Zealand = 'Macgenev'PBR (HT)	ESty MJon NBat SApu SWCr	
News = 'Legnews' (F)	MAus MGan SWCr	
Nice Day = 'Chewsea'PBR (ClMin) ♀ H4	CGro CSBt CWSG EBre ECnt ENot ESty GGre GKir LGod LStr MAsh MBri MBur MFry MJon MMat MRav SApu SSea SWCr WWeb	
'Nicola' (F)	MGan SWCr	
Nigel Hawthorne = 'Harquibbler' (S)	WAct	
Night Light = 'Poullight'PBR (Cl)	ECnt LPlm MBri MBur MFry MGan MJon SApu SWCr	
Nina = 'Mehnina'PBR (S) new	SWCr	
'Nina Weibull' (F)	ESty	
nitida	EBls ENot LRHS MAus NWea SPer SRPl SSea SWCr WAct WHCG WHer WOVN	
Noble Antony = 'Ausway'PBR (S)	ENot LRHS MAsh MAus MBri MJon MMat MWgw SCoo SWCr WWeb	
§ 'Noisette Carnée' (N)	CHad CSam EBee EBls EMFP EPfP ETWh MAus MDNS MBri MJon MRav MWgw SLPl SPer SSea SWCr WAct WHCG	
Norfolk = 'Poulfolk'PBR (GC)	EBls EBre ENot MGan MMat SApu SPer SPla SSea SWCr	
Northamptonshire = 'Mattdor'PBR (GC)	ENot LGod MGan MMat MRav SWCr	
'Northern Lights' (HT)	GCoc	
'Norwich Castle' (F)	EBls MBri	
Norwich Cathedral = 'Beacath' (HT)	EBls	
'Norwich Pink' (Cl)	MAus	
'Norwich Salmon' (Cl)	MAus	

'Norwich Union' (F) — EBls MBri

'Nostalgia' (Min) **new** — GGre

Nostalgie = 'Taneiglat'^{PBR} (HT) — ESty LStr MAsh MJon SCoo SWCr

'Nottingham Millennium' (F) — MGan

'Nova Zembla' (Ru) — EBls MAus

'Nozomi' (ClMin/GC) ♀ H4 — CGro CLyd EBls ECnt ENot ESty GCoc GGre MAus MGan MJon MRav MWgw NWCA SApu SMad SPer SSea SWCr WAct WHCG WOVN WWeb

'Nuits de Young' (CeMo) ♀ H4 — EBee EBls ENot GCoc MAus MMat SFam SSea SWCr WHCG

'Nur Mahal' (HM) — EBls ETWh MAus SWCr WHCG

nutkana (S) — EBls MAus

§ - var. *hispida* (S) — EBls

§ - 'Plena' (S) ♀ H4 — EBls ENot EPfP MAus MBri SFam SWCr WAct WGer WHCG

'Nymphenburg' (HM) — EBls ENot ETWh MAus SPer SWCr

'Nypels' Perfection' (Poly) — MAus

'Nyveldt's White' (Ru) — EBls MAus

Octavia Hill = 'Harzeal'^{PBR} (F/S) — CSBt MFry MJon MRav NPri SApu SPer SWCr

Oddball = 'Horodd' (F) — GGre SWCr

x *odorata* — GIBF

- 'Fortune's Double Yellow' — see R. x *odorata* 'Pseudindica'

§ - 'Mutabilis' (Ch) ♀ H3-4 — CHad CRHN EBls EHol EMFP ENot EPfP GCoc MAus MMat MRav SMad SMrm SPla SSea SWCr WAct WCFE WCot WHCG WOVN

§ - 'Ochroleuca' (Ch) — EBls ETWh

§ - 'Odorata' (Ch) — EBls

- old crimson China (Ch) — EBls WAct

§ - 'Pallida' (Ch) — CHad EBls EMFP EPfP GCoc LRHS MAus MRav SPla SSea SWCr WAct WHCG

§ - 'Pseudindica' (ClCh) — EBls MAus

§ - Sanguinea Group (Ch) — EBls WHCG

§ - 'Viridiflora' (Ch) — EBls ENot ETWh LRHS MAus MBur MMat SMad SPer SSea SWCr WAct WHCG

'Oeillet Flamand' — see R. 'Oeillet Parfait'

'Oeillet Panaché' (Mo) — WAct

§ 'Oeillet Parfait' (G) — EBls MAus

officinalis — see R. gallica var. officinalis

'Ohl' (G) — EBls

§ Ohshima Rose = 'Cochunter' (HT) — GCoc

'Oklahoma' (HT) — MGan SWCr

old blush China — see R. x *odorata* 'Pallida'

old cabbage — see R. x *centifolia*

Old John = 'Dicwillynily'^{PBR} (F) — ECle IDic MJon SWCr

Old Master = 'Macesp' (F) — MGan

old pink moss rose — see R. x centifolia 'Muscosa'

Old Port = 'Mackati'^{PBR} (F) — IArd MJon SApu SWCr

old red moss — see R. 'Henri Martin' , R. 'Lanei'

old velvet moss — see R. 'William Lobb'

old yellow Scotch (PiH) — see R. x harisonii 'Williams' Double Yellow'

Olde Romeo = 'Hadromeo' (HT) — SApu SWCr

Oliver Twist = 'Sabbyron' (Patio) — MBur

Olympic Palace = 'Poulymp'^{PBR} (Min) **new** — ECnt

'Omar Khayyám' (D) — EBls ENot MAus MMat MRav SWCr

§ 'Ombrée Parfaite' (G) — EBls

Open Arms = 'Chewpixcel'^{PBR} (ClMin) ♀ H4 — ENot LGod MAus MFry MJon MMat MRav SSea SWCr WGer

'Ophelia' (HT) — EBee EBls MAus MBur MGan SWCr

Orange Floorshow = 'Hargala'^{PBR} (GC) **new**

'Orange Honey' (Min) — MBur SWCr

§ 'Orange Sensation' (F) — CTri CWSG EBls ENot MAus MGan MRav NRog

§ Orange Sunblaze = 'Meijikatar'^{PBR} (Min) — CSBt EBls ENot MGan MJon MMat MRav SSea SWCr

'Orange Triumph' (Poly) — EBls

Orangeade (F) — MGan SWCr

§ Oranges and Lemons = 'Macoranlem'^{PBR} (S/F) — CGro ECnt ENot ESty GCoc GGre LGod LStr MAus MBri MBur MFry MGan MJon MMat MRav SApu SSea SWCr WWeb

'Oriana' (HT) — SWCr

'Orient Express' (HT) — CWSG MJon SWCr

'Orpheline de Juillet' — see R. 'Ombrée Parfaite'

Othello = 'Auslo'^{PBR} (S) — MAus SApu SPer WAct

Our George = 'Kirrush' (Patio) — MJon SWCr WGor

§ Our Jubilee = 'Coccages' (HT) — ESty

Our Love = 'Andour' (HT) — CWSG GGre SWCr

Our Molly = 'Dicreason'^{PBR} (GC/S) — IDic MGan MJon SApu SWCr

Owen's Pride = 'Kirpink' (F) — MJon

Oxfordshire = 'Korfullwind'^{PBR} (GC) ♀ H4 — ENot LStr MJon MMat MRav SSea SWCr

Paddy McGredy = 'Macpa' (F) — CGro MGan NRog SWCr

Paddy Stephens = 'Macclack'^{PBR} (HT) — MFry MJon

Painted Moon = 'Dicpaint'^{PBR} (HT) — ESty IDic

'Pam Ayres' — see R. Miss Pam Ayres = 'Kormarie'

Panache = 'Poultop'^{PBR} (Patio) — ECnt LStr MAsh SWCr

'Panorama Holiday' (F/HT) — MBur

'Papa Gontier' (T) — EBls MAus

'Papa Hémeray' (Ch) — EBls

Papa Meilland = 'Meisar' (HT) — CGro CSBt EBls MAus MGan MJon NRog SApu SPer SWCr

'Papillon' (CIT) — EBls

'Pâquerette' (Poly) — EBls

'Parade' (Cl) ♀ H4 — MAus MFry MRav SWCr WHCG

Paradise = 'Weizeip' (HT) — MGan SWCr

'Parkdirektor Riggers' (Cl) — CRHN CSam EBls ETWh LStr MAus MBri MGan MJon SPer SSea SWCr WHCG

Parks's yellow China — see R. x *odorata* 'Ochroleuca'

'Parkzierde' (Bb) — EBls

Parson's pink China — see R. x *odorata* 'Pallida'

Partridge = 'Korweirim'^{PBR} (GC) — EBls MAus MGan MJon MMat SApu SPer WAct WOVN

'Party Girl' (Min) — NBat

Party Trick = 'Dicparty'^{PBR} (F) — IDic MBri

parvifolia — see R. 'Burgundiaca'

Pas de Deux = 'Poulhult'^{PBR} (Cl) — ECnt SWCr

Pascali = 'Lenip' (HT) — EBls EBre ENot EPfP GCoc GGre GKir MAsh MAus MBur MGan MJon MMat MRav NBlu NRog SPer SRPl SSea SWCr

§ Pat Austin = 'Ausmum'^{PBR} (S) ♀ H4 — CSBt ENot LRHS MAsh MAus MBNS MJon MMat MRav SWCr WFoF WWeb

Pathfinder = 'Chewpobey'^{PBR} (GC) — CBrm MJon

Patricia = 'Korpatri' (F) — SWCr

'Paul Crampel' (Poly) — EBls MAus MGan NRog WAct

'Paul Lédé' (ClT)	see *R.* 'Climbing Paul Lédé'
'Paul Neyron' (HP)	EBls EMFP ETWh MAus MMat SPer SWCr WHCG
'Paul Ricault' (CexHP)	EBls MAus
Paul Shirville = 'Harqueterwife'PBR (HT) ♀ H4	CSBt ENot ESty GGre MAsh MAus MGan MMat MRav NRog SApu SPer SSea SWCr
'Paul Transon' (Ra) ♀ H4	CPou CRHN EBee EBls EMFP ETWh LRHS MAus MBri MBur SPer SWCr WOVN
'Paul Verdier' (Bb)	EBls
'Paula Louise' (F)	NBat
§ 'Paulii' (Ru)	EBls ENot MAus MMat WAct WHCG WOVN
'Paulii Alba'	see *R.* 'Paulii'
'Paulii Rosea' (Ru/Cl)	EBls MAus WAct WHCG
'Paul's Early Blush' (HP)	EBls
'Paul's Himalayan Musk' (Ra) ♀ H3-4	More than 30 suppliers
§ 'Paul's Lemon Pillar' (ClHT)	EBls EBre LRHS MAus MBNS NRog SMad SPer SSea SWCr
'Paul's Perpetual White' (Ra)	EBee EBls ETWh SWCr WHCG
'Paul's Scarlet Climber' (Cl/Ra)	CGro CSBt EBls ECnt ELan ENot EPfP GGre GKir LGod LRHS LStr MAsh MAus MGan MJon MMat MRav NPri SApu SPer SSea SWCr WWeb
Paws = 'Beapaw' (S)	EBls
'Pax' (HM)	CPou EBee EBls EMFP ETWh MAus SPer SRPl SWCr WHCG WKif
Peace = 'Madame A. Meilland' (HT) ♀ H4	CGro CSBt EBls ECnt ELan EPfP ESty GCoc GGre GKir LGod LPlm LStr MAsh MAus MBri MBur MFry MGan MJon MMat MRav NRog SApu SPer SRPl SSea SWCr WWeb
Peace Sunblaze (Min)	see *R.* Lady Meillandina = 'Meilarco' (Min)
Peacekeeper – 'Harbella'PBR (F)	CSBt MRav SWCr
Peach Blossom – 'Ausblossom'PBR (S)	LRHS MAus SWCr
'Peach Dream' (Patio)	ESty
§ Peach Sunblaze = 'Meixerul'PBR (Min)	MBri SApu SWCr
§ Pearl Anniversary = 'Whitston'PBR (Min/Patio)	GGre LStr MBri MRav SWCr
Pearl Drift = 'Leggab'PBR (S)	EBls MAus MJon SPer SWCr WHCG
§ Peek-a-boo – 'Dicgrow'PBR (Min/Patio)	ENot IDic MFry MGan SPer SWCr
§ Peer Gynt = 'Korol' (HT)	ENot MGan MMat NPri
Pegasus = 'Ausmoon'PBR (S)	LRHS LStr MAsh MAus MJon MWgw SSea SWCr WWeb
'Pélisson' (CeMo)	EBls
§ *pendulina*	EBls GIBF MAus WHCG
– 'Nana' **new**	NHol
'Penelope' (HM) ♀ H4	More than 30 suppliers
Penelope Keith = 'Macfreego'PBR (Min/Patio)	MJon SApu SWCr
'Penelope Plummer' (F)	EBls
Penny Lane = 'Hardwell'PBR (Cl) ♀ H4	CGro CSBt ECle ECnt ENot EPfP GCoc LGod LPlm LRHS LStr MAsh MAus MBri MBur MFry MGan MJon MMat MRav NBat NBlu NPri SApu SCoo SPer SSea SWCr WWeb
Pensioner's Voice = 'Fryrelax'PBR (F)	MFry SWCr
x *penzanceana*	see *R.* 'Lady Penzance'
Peppermint Ice = 'Bosgreen'PBR (F)	SApu

Perception = 'Harzippee'PBR (HT)	NBat SApu
Perdita = 'Ausperd' (S)	LRHS MAus MJon MRav SPer SRPl SWCr
§ Perestroika = 'Korhitom'PBR (F/Min)	ENot LStr MDun MJon MMat SApu SWCr
Perfect Day = 'Poulrem' (F)	ECnt SWCr
§ Perfecta = 'Koralu' (HT)	EBls MGan
'Perle des Jardins' (T)	EBls ENot MAus
'Perle des Panachées' (G)	EBls
§ 'Perle d'Or' (Poly) ♀ H4	CHad ECnt EMFP ENot EPfP EWTr GCoc LRHS MAus MMat NRog SChu SMad SPer SWCr WAct WHCG
'Perle von Hohenstein' (Poly)	EBls
'Pernille Poulsen' (F)	EBls
Perpetually Yours = 'Harfable'PBR (Cl)	GCoc LGod LStr MRav SApu SWCr
Persian yellow	see *R. foetida* 'Persiana'
Peter Beales = 'Cleexpert' (S) **new**	EBls
Peter Pan = 'Chewpan'PBR (Min)	MAsh MAus SSea SWCr
Peter Pan = 'Sunpete' (Patio)	MJon WWeb
Petit Four = 'Interfour' (Min/Patio)	SApu
'Petite de Hollande' (Ce)	EBls EMFP ETWh MAus SPer SWCr WAct WHCG
'Petite Lisette' (CexD)	EBls MAus WHCG
'Petite Orléannaise' (Ce)	EBls
Phab Gold = 'Frybountiful'PBR (F)	GCoc MFry
Phantom = 'Maccatsan' (S/GC)	MBur MJon SWCr
'Pharisäer' (HT)	EBls
§ Pheasant = 'Kordapt'PBR (GC)	ENot GCoc MAus MJon MMat SPer SWCr WAct WHCG WOVN
Phillipa = 'Poulheart'PBR (S)	ECnt SApu SWCr
Phoebe (Ru)	see *Rosa* 'Fimbriata'
phoenicia	EBls
'Phyllis Bide' (Ra) ♀ H4	EBee EBls EMFP EPfP ETWh IArd LRHS LStr MAus MGan MJon NHaw SApu SPer SRPl SSea SWCr WGer WHCG
Picasso = 'Macpic' (F)	EBls MGan
Piccadilly = 'Macar' (HT)	CGro CSBt EBls ENot GGre GKir MAsh MGan MJon MMat MRav NBlu NRog SPer SSea SWCr
Piccolo = 'Tanolokip'PBR (F/Patio)	ESty LStr MBri MFry MJon MRav SApu SSea SWCr
Pickwick = 'Sabclive' (Patio)	MBur
'Picture' (HT)	EBls MGan NRog SPer
'Pierre Notting' (HP)	EBls
Pigalle '84 = 'Meicloux' (F)	SWCr
§ *pimpinellifolia*	CKin EBls ECha ENot LBuc MAsh MAus MDun MGan MMat NWea SPer SSea SWCr WAct WBWf WHCG WOVN
– 'Altaica'	see *R. pimpinellifolia* 'Grandiflora'
§ – 'Andrewsii' ♀ H4	MAus MRav WAct
§ – double pink	EBls SWCr
§ – double white	CNat EBls GCoc IGor MAus SWCr WAct WBcn
– double yellow	see *R. x harisonii* 'Williams' Double Yellow'
§ – 'Dunwich Rose'	EBee EBls EBre ENot EPfP LRHS MAsh MAus MBri MGan MJon SPer SWCr WAct WHCG
– 'Falkland'	EBls ECha MAus
§ – 'Glory of Edzell'	EBls MAus
§ – 'Grandiflora'	EBls MAus SWCr

– – SF 18	ISea
– 'Harisonii'	see *R.* x *harisonii* 'Harison's Yellow'
– 'Irish Marbled'	EBls
– 'Lutea'	see *R.* x *harisonii* 'Lutea Maxima'
– 'Marbled Pink'	EBls MAus
– 'Mary, Queen of Scots'	EBls MAus SRms SWCr WAct
– 'Mrs Colville'	EBls MAus
– 'Ormiston Roy'	MAus
§ – 'Robbie'	WAct
– 'Single Cherry'	EBls MAus SSea
– 'Stanwell Perpetual'	see *R.* 'Stanwell Perpetual'
– 'Variegata' (v)	CArn
– 'William III'	EBls EWes MAus SLPl
– x *pendulina*	see *R.* x *reversa*
Pink Abundance = 'Harfrothy'PBR (F)	SWCr
Pink Bells = 'Poulbells'PBR (GC)	CGro EBls ENot GCoc MAus MMat SApu SPer WHCG
'Pink Bouquet' (Ra)	CRHN
Pink Drift = 'Poulcat'PBR (Min/GC)	ENot
'Pink Favorite' (HT)	CSBt MGan NRog SPer SWCr
Pink Fizz **new**	SWCr
§ Pink Flower Carpet = 'Noatraum'PBR (GC) ♀ H4	CSBt CTri EBre ELan ENot EPfP GGre GKir LRHS LStr MAsh MAus MFry MGan MMat MRav SCoo SPer SSea SWCr WWeb
'Pink Garnette'	see *R.* 'Carol Amling'
'Pink Grootendorst' (Ru) ♀ H4	EBls ENot EPfP LRHS LStr MAus MGan MJon MMat NRog SPer SSea SWCr WAct WHCG
§ Pink Hit = 'Poutipe'PBR (Min/Patio)	ECnt ENot MAsh MMat SWCr
Pink La Sevillana = 'Meigeroka'PBR (F/GC)	SWCr
Pink Meidiland = 'Meipoque'PBR (GC)	MGan
pink moss	see *R.* x *centifolia* 'Muscosa'
'Pink Parfait' (F)	EBls GCoc GGre MAus MGan NRog SPer SSea SWCr
Pink Peace = 'Meibil' (HT)	ESty GGre MRav SWCr
Pink Pearl = 'Kormasyl' (HT)	CSBt ENot MMat MRav SApu
'Pink Perpétué' (Cl)	CGro CSBt EBls EBre ECnt ELan ENot EPfP GCoc GGre GKir LPlm LRHS MAus MBri MBur MDun MGan MJon MMat MRav NBat NBlu NRog SApu SPer SRPl SSea SWCr WWeb
'Pink Petticoat' (Min)	SWCr
Pink Pirouette = 'Harboul'PBR (Patio) **new**	ESty
'Pink Prosperity' (HM)	EBls MAus
'Pink Showers' (ClHT)	WAct
§ Pink Sunblaze = 'Meijidiro' (Min/Patio)	SWCr
Pink Surprise = 'Lenbrac' (Ru)	MAus
Pinocchio = 'Rosenmärchen' (F)	EBls
'Pinta' (HT)	EBls
pisocarpa	EBls
Playtime = 'Morplati' (F)	ENot MAus MRav
Pleine de Grâce = 'Lengra' (S)	EBls LRHS MAus WAct
'Plentiful' (F)	EBls MBri
Poetry in Motion = 'Harelan'PBR (HT)	ESty GCoc GGre MBri MJon NBat SApu SWCr
Polar Star = 'Tanlarpost'PBR (HT)	CSBt EBls ECnt ENot GGre LGod LPlm LStr MFry MGan MRav NRog SPer SRPl SWCr
x *polliniana*	SLPl

'Polly' (HT)	EBls MGan NRog
polyantha grandiflora	see *R. gentiliana*
pomifera	see *R. villosa*
– 'Duplex'	see *R.* 'Wolley-Dod'
Pomona = 'Fryyeh'PBR (F)	CSBt MFry
'Pompon Blanc Parfait' (A)	EBls MAus
'Pompon de Bourgogne'	see *R.* 'Burgundiaca'
'Pompon de Paris' (ClMinCh)	see *R.* 'Climbing Pompon de Paris'
§ 'Pompon de Paris' (MinCh)	EBls
'Pompon Panaché' (G)	EBls MAus
'Porcellina' (F)	MJon SWCr
Portland rose	see *R.* 'Portlandica'
§ 'Portlandica'	EBls ETWh LRHS MAsh MAus SPer SSea SWCr WAct WHCG
Portmeirion = 'Ausguard'PBR (S)	MAus SCoo SWCr WWeb
Pot o' Gold = 'Dicdivine'PBR (HT)	CSBt IDic MAus MFry MGan MJon MRav SPer SWCr
'Poullack'PBR	see *R.* Lakeland Princess = 'Poullak'
Pour Toi = 'Para Ti' (Min)	ENot LPlm MAus MGan MJon MMat MRav NPri SPer SWCr
Powder Puff (F)	GGre SWCr
prairie rose	see *R. setigera*
Precious Moments = 'Lyopr' **new**	SWCr
'Precious Platinum' (HT)	LGod MJon MRav SPer SWCr
Preservation = 'Bosiljurika'PBR (S/F)	GGre SWCr
§ 'Président de Sèze' (G) ♀ H4	EBls ETWh MAus SFam SPer SWCr WAct WHCG
President Heidar Aliyev = 'Cocosimber'PBR (HT)	GCoc SWCr
'President Herbert Hoover' (HT)	EBls
'Prestige' (S)	NRog
Pretty in Pink = 'Dicumpteen'PBR (GC)	ECnt IDic MJon
Pretty Jessica = 'Ausjess' (S)	CTri GKir LRHS MAus MJon MRav SPer SWCr
Pretty Lady = 'Scrivo'PBR (F) ♀ H4	ECle LStr MAus MJon SWCr
Pretty Polly = 'Meitonje'PBR (Min) ♀ H4	CGro CTri ECnt EPfP ESty GKir LStr MAsh MBri MFry MGan MJon MMat MRav SApu SWCr WWeb
Pride of England = 'Harencore'PBR (HT)	GCoc GGre MBri MBur SWCr
'Prima Ballerina' (HT)	CGro CSBt CWSG EBls ENot ESty GCoc GGre GKir LAst LPlm LStr MAsh MGan MJon MMat MRav NBlu NRog SPer SSea SWCr
primula (S) ♀ H3-4	CHad EBls EMFP ENot MAus MJon MMat SPer SSea SWCr WAct WHCG
'Prince Camille de Rohan' (HP)	EBls MAus WHCG
'Prince Charles' (Bb)	EBls ETWh MAus SWCr WHCG
Prince Palace = 'Poulzin'PBR (F) **new**	ECnt
Prince Regent = 'Genpen' (S) **new**	SSea SWCr
Princess Alexandra = 'Pouldra'PBR (S)	ECle ECnt MAsh SWCr
Princess Alice = 'Hartanna' (F)	LGod MGan SWCr
Princess Michael of Kent = 'Harlightly' (F)	MGan
Princess Nobuko = 'Coclistine' (HT) **new**	GCoc
'Princess of Wales' (HP)	MMat

Princess of Wales = 'Hardinkum'PBR (F) ♀ H4 — CGro CSBt EBee ECle ECnt ENot ESty GCoc GGre LStr MAsh MBri MBur MGan MJon MRav NPri SApu SCoo SPer SWCr WWeb

Princess Royal = 'Dicroyal'PBR (HT) — GCoc IDic MBri

§ 'Princesse de Nassau' (Ra) — EBls MAus SWCr WAct WHCG

'Princesse Louise' (Ra) — CRHN MAus SFam

'Princesse Marie' misapplied — see R. 'Belvedere'

§ 'Pristine'PBR (HT) — IDic MAus MGan MJon SPer

N 'Professeur Emile Perrot' (D) — EBls ETWh SWCr WAct

'Prolifera de Redouté' misapplied — see R. 'Duchesse de Montebello'

'Prosperity' (HM) ♀ H4 — CBcs EBee EBls EMFP ENot EPfP GCoc LRHS MAus MFry MGan MJon MMat MRav MWgw NRog SPer SWCr WAct WHCG WOVN

Prospero = 'Auspero' (S) — EBee MAus MBri WAct

x pruhoniciana 'Hillieri' — see R. 'Hillieri'

pulverulenta — EBls

Pure Bliss = 'Dictator'PBR (HT) — ECnt GCoc IDic MJon SWCr

Pure Magic = 'Mattgrex' (Patio) — MAsh SWCr

'Purity' (Cl) — ETWh SWCr

'Purple Beauty' (HT) — MGan SWCr

Purple Tiger = 'Jacpurr'PBR (F) — ESty IDic MBur MJon SApu SWCr

'Purpurtraum' (Ru) — WHCG

Pzazz = 'Poulzazz'PBR (Min/Patio) — FCnt

Quaker Star = 'Dicperhaps' (F) — IDic

quatre saisons — see R x damascena var. semperflorens

'Quatre Saisons Blanche Mousseuse' (DMo) — EBls ETWh SWCr

Queen Elizabeth — see R. 'The Queen Elizabeth'

Queen Margarethe = 'Poulskov'PBR (F) new — ECnt

Queen Mother = 'Korquemu'PBR (Patio) ♀ H4 — CSBt EBls ELan ENot EPfP ESty GCoc LGod LRHS LStr MAsh MAus MBri MFry MGan MJon MMat MRav NPri SApu SPer SSca SWCr WWeb

'Queen of Bedders' (Bb) — EBls

Queen of Denmark — see R. 'Königin von Dänemark'

Queen of the Belgians — see R. 'Reine des Belges'

Queen's Palace = 'Poulelap'PBR (F) new — ECnt

Racy Lady = 'Dicwaffle'PBR (HT) — ECle IDic MJon NBat SWCr

Radio Times = 'Aussal'PBR (S) — MAus MJon SWCr

Rainbow Magic = 'Dicxplosion'PBR (Patio) — ESty IDic MAsh MJon SWCr

'Ralph Tizzard' (F) — SSea

'Rambling Rector' (Ra) ♀ H4 — More than 30 suppliers

§ 'Ramona' (Ra) — EBls ETWh MAus

§ 'Raubritter' ('Macrantha' hybrid) — EBls MAus MBri SPer SRPl SSea SWCr WAct WHCG

Ray of Hope = 'Cocnilly'PBR (F) — GCoc LGod NEgg

Ray of Sunshine = 'Cocclare'PBR (Patio) — GCoc MBri MFry

'Raymond Carver' (S) — EBls

'Raymond Chenault' (Cl) — MGan SWCr

Razzle Dazzle = 'Frybright'PBR (F) — MFry

'Rebecca Claire' (HT) — CSBt MJon SWCr

'Rebecca Kathleen' (F) — NBat

Reconciliation = 'Hartillery'PBR (HT) — CSBt ESty GGre SWCr

Red Ace = 'Amruda'PBR (Min) — MJon SWCr

Red Bells = 'Poulred'PBR (Min/GC) — CGro EBls ENot MAus MMat MRav SPer WHCG WOVN

Red Blanket = 'Intercell'PBR (S/GC) — CGro EBls ENot GCoc IDic MAus MGan MMat MRav SPer WAct WOVN

§ Red Coat = 'Auscoat' (F) — MAus SWCr

Red Dagmar = 'Speruge'PBR (S) — IDic LBuc

'Red Dandy' (F) — MGan

Red Devil = 'Dicam' (HT) — GGre LPlm MGan MJon MRav NBat NRog SWCr

'Red Garnette' — see R. 'Garnette'

'Red Grootendorst' — see R. 'F.J. Grootendorst'

Red Meidiland = 'Meineble'PBR (GC) — CBrm SWCr

red moss — see R. 'Henri Martin'

Red New Dawn — see R. 'Etendard'

Red Rascal = 'Jacbed'PBR (S/Patio) — CSBt ECnt IDic MBri MFry MJon SApu SWCr

red rose of Lancaster — see R. gallica var. officinalis

Red Splendour = 'Davona' (F) — NRog

§ Red Sunblaze = 'Meirutral'PBR (Min) — MJon WWeb

Red Trail = 'Interim'PBR (S/GC) — MJon

§ 'Red Wing' (S) — EBls MAus

§ Redgold = 'Dicor' (F) — GGre MGan SWCr

Redouté = 'Auspale'PBR (S) — CAbP EBre LRHS MAus SPer SWCr WWeb

Regensberg = 'Macyoumis'PBR (F/Patio) — ECnt ENot MAus MBri MFry MGan MJon MMat MRav NRog SApu SPer SSea SWCr

§ 'Reine des Belges' (Cl) — EBls

'Reine des Centifeuilles' (Ce) — EBls SFam

'Reine des Violettes' (HP) — CHad CPou EBls EPfP IArd LGod LRHS LStr MAsh MAus MDun MRav SApu SChu SPer SWCr WAct WHCG

'Reine Marie Henriette' (ClHT) — EBls

'Reine Olga de Wurtenburg' (N) new — EBls

§ 'Reine Victoria' (Bb) — EBee EBls EBre EMFP EPfP LRHS LStr MAsh MAus MGan MRav NHaw SPer SPla SWCr WAct WHCG

Remember Me = 'Cocdestin'PBR (HT) ♀ H4 — CWSG EBre FCnt ENot GCoc GGre IArd LGod LPlm LStr MAus MBri MFry MGan MJon MMat MRav NBat NRog SApu SPer SSea SWCr WWeb

Remembrance = 'Harxampton'PBR (F) ♀ H4 — ESty LGod LStr MAsh MBri MGan MRav SApu SPer SSea SWCr WWeb

Renaissance = 'Harzart'PBR (HT) — CSBt ECle ESty GCoc GGre LStr MBur MFry MJon MRav SSea SWCr

'René André' (Ra) — CRHN EBls EMFP ETWh MAus

'René d'Anjou' (CeMo) — EBls MAus

'Rescht' — see R. 'De Rescht'

Rest in Peace = 'Bedswap' (Patio/F) — GGre

'Rêve d'Or' (N) — EBls ETWh MAus SPer SWCr WHCG

'Réveil Dijonnais' (ClHT) — EBls MAus

'Reverend F. Page-Roberts' (HT) — EBls

Rhapsody in Blue = 'Frantasia' (S) new — ECle ESty SApu

Richard Buckley = 'Smitshort' (F) — MBur

§ x *richardii* — EBls MAus MRav SWCr WAct WHCG
Ring of Fire = — MAsh SWCr
'Morefire' (Patio)
§ 'Rise 'n' Shine' (Min) — LGod MGan SWCr
'Ritter von Barmstede' (Cl) — MGan
'Rival de Paestum' (T) — EBls MAus
'River Gardens' — NPer
Road to Freedom = — SWCr
'Franlac' (F)
'Rob Roy = 'Cocrob' (F) — GCoc GGre MBur MGan SPer SWCr
Robbie Burns = — MAus SWCr
'Ausburn' (PiH)
'Robert le Diable' (Ce) — CPou EBee EBls ETWh MAus SPer SWCr WAct WHCG
'Robert Léopold' (Mo) — EBls
'Robin Hood' (HM) — EBls ETWh SWCr
Robin Redbreast = — EBls IDic MJon SApu SWCr WGor
'Interrob'PBR (Min/GC)
§ Robusta = — EBls ECnt MAus MJon MMat SSea
'Korgosa'PBR (Ru) — SWCr
'Roger Lambelin' (HP) — EBls ENot MAus MMat SPer
Romance = — GGre MJon MRav WWeb
'Tanezamor'PBR (S)
Romantic Dreams = — SWCr
'Meilomit'PBR (F) **new**
§ Romantic Hedgerose = — ENot MMat
'Korworm' (F/S)
Romantic Palace = — ECnt
'Poulmanti'PBR (F) **new**
§ Rosabell = 'Cocceleste'PBR — ESty GCoc MFry SApu
(F/Patio)
Rosalie Coral = — ESty MJon SApu
'Chewallop'PBR (ClMin)
'Rosamini Gold' — see *R.* Golden Rosamini = 'Intergol'
Rosarium Uetersen = — MJon SWCr
'Kortersen' (ClHT)
§ Rose 2000 = — GCoc GKir NEgg
'Cocquetrum'PBR (F)
'Rose à Parfum — EBls
de l'Haÿ' (Ru)
§ 'Rose d'Amour' (S) ♥H4 — EBls ISea MAus WHCG
'Rose de Meaux' — see *R.* 'De Meaux'
'Rose de Meaux White' — see *R.* 'White de Meaux'
'Rose de Rescht' — see *R.* 'De Rescht'
'Rose des Maures'misapplied — see *R.* 'Sissinghurst Castle'
'Rose d'Hivers' (D) — EBls
'Rose d'Orsay' (S) — EBls
'Rose du Maître d'Ecole' — see *R.* 'Du Maître d'Ecole'
'Rose du Roi' (HP/DPo) — EBls ETWh MAus SWCr WAct WHCG
'Rose du Roi à Fleurs — EBls MAus
Pourpres' (HP)
'Rose Edouard' (Bb) — EBls
§ Rose Gaujard = — EBls ENot GGre GKir LGod LPlm
'Gaumo' (HT) — MAsh MBur MGan MMat MRav NBlu SWCr
§ Roselina = — ENot MMat SWCr
'Korsaku'PBR (GC/Ru)
§ 'Rose-Marie Viaud' (Ra) — CFee CPou EBee ETWh MAus SWCr WHCG
'Rosemary Foster' — SSpi
'Rosemary Gandy' (F) — MGan
Rosemary Harkness = — CSBt ESty LStr MJon MRav SApu
'Harrowbond'PBR (HT) — SPer SWCr
'Rosemary Rose' (F) — EBls NRog SPer
Rosenprofessor SieberPBR — see *R.* The Halcyon Days Rose = 'Korparesni'
'Roseraie de l'Haÿ' — More than 30 suppliers
(Ru) ♥H4
'Rosette Delizy' (T) — EBls
Rosie Larkin = — MFry
'Fryyippee' (S)

§ 'Rosina' (Min) — MGan
'Rosy Cheeks' (HT) — LPlm MBur MGan SWCr
Rosy Cushion = — ENot GCoc IDic MAus MGan
'Interall'PBR — MMat MRav SApu SPer SRPl SWCr
(S/GC) ♥H4 — WAct WHCG WOVN
Rosy Future = — CSBt ESty MBri SApu SWCr
'Harwaderox'PBR (F/Patio)
'Rosy Mantle' (Cl) — CBcs CSBt LPlm MGan SPer SWCr
§ Rote Max Graf = — EBls ENot MRav WAct
'Kormax'PBR (GC/Ru)
Roundelay' (HT) — EBls ETWh MAus SWCr
§ Roxburghe Rose = — GCoc
'Cocember' (HT)
roxburghii (S) — MBri SRPl SWCr WAct WHCG
- var. *hirtula* (S) **new** — CPLG
- f. *normalis* (S) — CFee EBls
- 'Plena' — see *R.* roxburghii f. roxburghii
§ - f. *roxburghii* (d/S) — MAus
'Royal Albert Hall' (HT) — EBls GCoc
Royal Flush = — MBri
'Peapatio' (F/Patio)
'Royal Gold' (ClHT) — EBls ENot ESty MBri MFry MGan MMat NRog SSea SWCr WStI
'Royal Highness' (HT) — EBls MGan NRog SWCr
'Royal Occasion' (F) — MRav SPer SWCr
Royal Philharmonic = — MBur
'Hardeed'PBR (HT)
Royal Salute = — ENot MJon MMat MRav NRog
'Macros' (Min)
'Royal Smile' (HT) — EBls
Royal Star and Garter = — MFry
'Frybizzy' (Cl)
Royal William = — CGro CSBt ECnt ELan ENot ESty
'Korzaun'PBR (HT) ♥H4 — GGre GKir LGod LPlm LStr MAsh MAus MBri MBur MGan MJon MMat MRav NPri NRog SApu SPer SRPl SWCr WWeb
Royal Worcester = — MJon SWCr
'Trobroy'PBR (S)
'Rubens' (HP) — EBls
§ *rubiginosa* — CCVT CKin EBls ENot EPfP GPoy IFro ILis LBuc MAsh MAus MHer MRav SFam SPer SWCr WAct WMou
rubra — see *R.* gallica
rubrifolia — see *R.* glauca
- 'Carmenetta' — see *R.* 'Carmenetta'
'Rubrotincta' — see *R.* 'Hebe's Lip'
rubus (Ra) — MAus MBNS
- SF 96062 — ISea
- *velutescens* — WAct
Ruby Anniversary = — CGro CSBt CWSG ESty LStr MFry
'Harbonny'PBR (Patio) — MRav SSea SWCr WWeb
Ruby Celebration = — CWSG MJon SWCr
'Peawinner'PBR (F)
'Ruby Wedding' (HT) — More than 30 suppliers
'Ruga' (Ra) — CWib EBls
rugosa (Ru) — CAgr CLnd CTri EBee ENot EPfP GKir LBuc MAus MBri MHer MRav NBlu NWea SPlb SWCr WStI
- 'Alba' (Ru) ♥H4 — CBcs CCVT CHad EBee EBls ECGP ECnt ELan ENot EPfP EWTr GBin GGre LBuc LRHS LStr MAsh MAus MBri MMat MRav NWea SPer SSea SWCr WAct WHen WOVN
- 'Rubra' (Ru) ♥H4 — CBcs CCVT CTri CWib ENot EPfP GGre LBuc MAsh MFry MMat SPer SWCr WAct WHen
- 'Scabrosa' — see *R.* 'Scabrosa'
'Rugosa Atropurpurea' (Ru) — NRog
'Rugspin' (Ru) — SWCr WAct

'Ruhm von Steinfurth' (HP) EBls

'Rumba' (F) SWCr

Running Maid = 'Lenramp' (S/GC) MAus

Rush = 'Lenmobri' (S) MAus

Rushing Stream = 'Austream'PBR (GC) MAus SWCr

'Ruskin' (HPxRu) EBls MAus SWCr

'Russelliana' (Ra) CRHN EBee EBls EMFP ETWh MAus SFam SSea SWCr WAct WHCG WRha

Rutland = 'Poulshine'PBR (Min/GC) ENot SRPl SWCr

'Sadler's Wells' (S) EBls

'Safrano' (T) EBls

Saint Boniface = 'Kormatt'PBR (F/Patio) CSBt ENot MMat

'Saint Catherine' (Ra) CFee

Saint Cecilia = 'Ausmit'PBR (S) LRHS MAus MJon MWgw SWCr

Saint Dunstan's Rose = 'Kirshru' (S) MBri MJon SApu SPer SWCr

Saint John = 'Harbillo'PBR (F) CSBt MRav SWCr

Saint John's rose see R. x richardii

Saint Mark's rose see R. 'Rose d'Amour'

'Saint Nicholas' (D) EBls MAus

'Saint Prist de Breuze' (Ch) EBls

Saint Swithun = 'Auswith'PBR (S) GQui LRHS MAus MJon SWCr

'Saint Wilfred's Hospice' SApu

'Salet' (DPMo) EBls ETWh MAus SWCr WHCG

Salita = 'Kormorlet' (Cl) MJon SWCr

'Sally Holmes'PBR (S) ♀ H4 CHad EBls ENot ETWh GCoc MAus MBri MFry MGan MJon MMat MRav SApu SPer SWCr WAct WHCG

Sally's Rose = 'Canrem' (HT) EBee ECnt SApu SWCr

Salmo = 'Poulnoev'PBR (Patio) ENot MBri MJon MMat MRav

§ Samaritan = 'Harverag'PBR (HT) CSBt ESty GGre MRav SApu SWCr

sancta see R. x richardii

'Sander's White Rambler' (Ra) ♀ H4 CHad CRHN EBee EBls EBre EMFP LRHS MAus MGan MJon MRav NPri NRog SMad SPer SRPl SSea SWCr WAct WHCG WWeb

'Sandringham Centenary'PBR (HT) EBls

'Sanguinea' see R. x odorata Sanguinea Group

§ Sarabande = 'Meihand' (F) MGan

'Sarah van Fleet' (Ru) CGro EBls EBre ENot EPfP GCoc IArd LBuc LRHS LStr MAus MFry MGan MMat MRav NRog SApu SFam SPer SPla SWCr WAct WOVN

Savoy Hotel = 'Harvintage'PBR (HT) ♀ H4 CGro CSBt ECnt EPfP GCoc GGre LGod LStr MAus MFry MGan MMat MRav SApu SPer SWCr

§ 'Scabrosa' (Ru) ♀ H4 EBee EBls ECnt EMFP GCoc LRHS MAsh MAus MGan MJon SPer SSea SWCr WAct WHCG WOVN

Scarlet Fire see R. 'Scharlachglut'

§ Scarlet Gem = 'Meido' (Min) MGan

Scarlet Glow see R. 'Scharlachglut'

Scarlet Meidiland = 'Meikrotal'PBR (S/GC) MGan SWCr

Scarlet Patio = 'Kortingle'PBR (Patio) ENot MAsh MMat

Scarlet Queen Elizabeth = 'Dicel' (F) CBcs CGro EBls GGre MAsh MBur MRav WStI

'Scarlet Showers' (Cl) MGan SWCr

'Scented Air' (F) MGan SPer

Scentimental = 'Wekplapep'PBR (F) MAsh MBri SWCr

§ Scent-sation = 'Fryromeo'PBR (HT) CWSG ESty GCoc MAsh MBur MFry MRav SApu SCoo SWCr

Scepter'd Isle = 'Ausland'PBR (S) ♀ H4 CAbP CSBt EBls ENot LRHS MAsh MAus MMat SCoo SPer SWCr WWeb

§ 'Scharlachglut' (ClS) ♀ H4 CPou EBls ENot LRHS MAus MBri MGan MMat MRav SApu SPer SWCr WAct WHCG WOVN

* schmidtiana CFee

'Schneelicht' (Ru) EBls MAus

§ 'Schneezwerg' (Ru) ♀ H4 EBls ENot GCoc MAus MBri MGan MJon MMat MRav SApu SPer SPla SRPl SSea SWCr WAct WHCG WOVN

'Schoolgirl' (Cl) CBcs CGro CSBt EBls EBre ELan ENot EPfP ESty GGre GKir LPlm LStr MAsh MBri MFry MGan MJon MMat MRav NBlu NRog SApu SPer SSea SWCr WWeb

'Scintillation' (S/GC) EBls MAus

Scotch rose see R. pimpinellifolia

Scotch yellow (PiH) see R. x harisonii 'Williams' Double Yellow' (PiH)

'Scotch Yellow' (HT) MJon SWCr

Scottish Special = 'Cocdapple' (Min/Patio) MBri

'Sea Pearl' (F) ENot MGan MMat MRav SWCr

§ 'Seagull' (Ra) ♀ H4 CGro CWSG EBee EBls ECnt EMFP GGre LGod LPlm LRHS LStr MAsh MGan MJon MRav NPri NRog NWea SPer SPla SRPl SSea SWCr WHCG

§ 'Sealing Wax' (moyesii hybrid) EBls LRHS MBri MJon WAct

Selfridges = 'Korpriwal'PBR (HT) MJon MMat NBat NRog

'Semiplena' see R. x alba 'Alba Semiplena'

'Sénateur Amic' (Cl) EBls

'Senator Burda' see R. Spirit of Youth = 'Meivestal'

sericea (S) CFee CPLG ITer MAus WHCG

- CC 3306 WRos

- SF 505 ISea

- SF 95049 ISea

- 'Heather Muir' see R. 'Heather Muir'

- subsp. omeiensis f. pteracantha (S) CHad EBee EBls ELan ENot EPfP ETWh MAus MGan MMat MRav NRog NWea SApu SMad SPer SSea SWCr WAct WOVN

- 'Red Wing' see R. 'Red Wing'

sertata GIBF

§ setigera EBls GIBF MAus

setipoda EBls MAus SWCr WAct WFar WHCG

'Seven Seas' (F) MBur

seven sisters rose see R. multiflora 'Grevillei'

Sexy Rexy = 'Macrexy'PBR (F) ♀ H4 CGro EBre EPfP ESty GCoc GGre GKir LStr MAsh MAus MBri MFry MGan MJon MRav NBat NRog SPer SSea SWCr WWeb

§ 'Shailer's White Moss' (CeMo) EBee EBls EMFP LRHS MAsh MAus MGan NRog SFam SWCr WHCG

Sharifa Asma = 'Ausreef'PBR (S) CSBt EBre ENot LRHS LStr MAus MJon MMat MRav SPer SWCr WAct WWeb

'Sheelagh Baird' (S/Poly) SWCr

Sheila's Perfume = 'Harsherry'PBR (HT/F) ECnt ESty GCoc GGre LPlm LStr MAsh MGan MJon MRav SApu SPer SWCr

'Shepherd's Delight' (F)   MGan SWCr

sherardii   WBWf

Shine On = 'Dictalent'[PBR]   CSBt ECnt IDic MAsh MBri MFry
(Patio) ♀ H4   MJon MRav SWCr WWeb

Shining Flare =   SWCr
'Hadflare' (HT) **new**

Shining Light =   GCoc
'Cocshimmer'[PBR] (Patio)

Shining Ruby =   SWCr
'Hadruby' (HT)

Shirley Spain =   GCoc
'Cocharod' (HT)

Shocking Blue =   CSBt ECnt ENot MAus MGan
'Korblue'[PBR] (F)   MJon MMat MRav SPer SWCr

Shona = 'Dicdrum' (F)   IDic

'Shot Silk' (HT)   CSBt EBee EBls MBur MGan SWCr

'Shropshire Lass' (S)   LRHS MAus MBri SPer

Sightsaver =   ESty MFry
'Fryaffair'[PBR] (HT)

§ Silver Anniversary =   CGro CSBt EBee ECnt ELan ENot
'Poulari'[PBR] (HT) ♀ H4   EPfP GCoc GGre GKir LGod LPlm
LRHS LStr MAsh MAus MFry
MGan MJon MMat MRav NEgg
NPri SApu SCoo SPer SSea SWCr
WWeb

'Silver Jubilee' (HT) ♀ H4   More than 30 suppliers

'Silver Lining' (HT)   EBls MBur SWCr

'Silver Moon' (Cl)   CRHN EBls

'Silver Wedding' (HT)   CGro CSBt CWSG EBls EBre ESty
GCoc GGre IArd LRHS MAus MBri
MBur MFry MGan MRav NBlu
NPri NRog SApu SPer SRPl SWCr

Silver Wedding   ESty GGre SWCr
Celebration (F)

§ Simba =   ENot MGan MMat
'Korbelma'[PBR] (HT)

Simon Robinson =   MJon SWCr
'Trobwich'[PBR] (Min/GC)

Simply Heaven =   EBee ECnt GCoc IDic MJon SWCr
'Diczombie'[PBR] (HT)

§ Simply Sunblaze =   SWCr
'Meidipser' (Min) **new**

§ Simply the Best =   CGro ECle ECnt ESty GCoc GGre
'Macmster'[PBR] (HT)   LGod LPlm LRHS LStr MAsh MBri
MMat SApu SCoo SWCr WWeb

§ Singin' in the Rain =   MJon SWCr
'Macivy'[PBR] (F)

sinowilsonii   see *R. longicuspis* var.
sinowilsonii

'Sir Cedric Morris' (Ra)   CRHN EBls SSea

Sir Clough =   MAus
'Ausclough' (S)

Sir Edward Elgar =   EBls EBre LStr MAus MRav SWCr
'Ausprima'[PBR] (S)

'Sir Frederick Ashton' (HT)   EBls

'Sir Joseph Paxton' (Bb)   MAus

Sir Neville Marriner =   NBat
'Glanmusic' (F)

§ Sir Walter Raleigh =   MAus MBri MRav SWCr
'Ausspry' (S)

Sir William Leech =   NBat
'Hortropic' (HT)

§ 'Sissinghurst Castle' (G)   EBls

'Sleepy' (Poly)   MGan

Smarty =   IDic MAus MGan MJon MRav
'Intersmart'[PBR] (S/GC)   SApu SPer SWCr WAct

§ 'Smooth Angel'[PBR] (HT)   LGod MGan NPri

Smooth Lady =   LGod MGan
'Hadlady' (HT)

Smooth Melody =   SPer
'Hadmelody'[PBR] (F)

Smooth Prince =   LGod MGan
'Hadprince'[PBR] (HT)

Smooth Romance =   MGan
'Hadromance'[PBR] (HT)

§ 'Smooth Velvet'[PBR] (HT)   LGod MGan SPer

'Sneezy' (Poly)   MGan

Snow Carpet =   CSBt EBls ENot GCoc MAus MFry
'Maccarpe'[PBR] (Min/GC)   MJon MMat WAct

'Snow Dwarf'   see *R.* 'Schneezwerg'

Snow Goose =   MAus MJon SPer SWCr
'Auspom'[PBR] (Cl/S)

Snow Hit =   ECnt SWCr
'Poulsnows'[PBR]
(Min/Patio)

'Snow Queen'   see *R.* 'Frau Karl Druschki'

§ Snow Sunblaze =   CSBt MRav SPer SWCr
'Meigovin'[PBR] (Min)

Snow White =   MJon
'Landisney' (HT)

Snowball = 'Macangeli'[PBR]   MJon SWCr
(Min/GC)

Snowcap = 'Harfleet'[PBR]   ESty
(Patio)

'Snowdon' (Ru)   EBls MAus

'Snowdrift'   WHCG

§ Snowdrop =   MFry
'Amoru' (Min/Patio)

'Snowflake' (Ra)   WHCG

'Snowline' (F)   SPer

'Soldier Boy' (Cl)   SWCr WHCG

§ Solitaire =   MBri MJon SWCr
'Macyefre'[PBR] (HT)

Solo Mio =   ECnt MAsh SWCr
'Poulen002'[PBR] (S)

§ 'Sombreuil' (ClT)   CHad EBee EBls EMFP EPfP ETWh
IArd LRHS MAus MRav SChu SFam
SPer SPla SWCr WAct WHCG

Someday Soon =   NBat
'Seasoon' (Min)

Something Special =   ECnt GCoc MJon
'Macwyo'[PBR] (HT)

'Sophie's Perpetual' (ClCh)   EBls ENot ETWh LRHS MAus
MGan MMat MRav NHaw SPer
SWCr WAct WHCG

Sophy's Rose =   MAsh MAus MBri MJon SWCr
'Auslot'[PBR] (S)   WWeb

soulieana (Ra/S) ♀ H3-4   CHad EBls MAus SWCr WAct WKif

'Soupert et Notting'   LRHS MAus MRav SPer SWCr
(DPoMo)

'Southampton' (F) ♀ H4   EBls ESty GGre LStr MAus MGan
MMat MRav NRog SApu SPer SSea
SWCr WBVN

'Souvenir d'Alphonse   EBls ENot WHCG
Lavallée' (ClHP)

'Souvenir de Brod'   see *R.* 'Erinnerung an Brod'

'Souvenir de Claudius   EBee EBls ETWh MAus NRog SPer
Denoyel' (ClHT)

'Souvenir de François   EBls
Gaulain' (T)

'Souvenir de Jeanne   EBls WHCG
Balandreau' (HP)

'Souvenir de la   see *R.* 'Climbing Souvenir de la
Malmaison' (ClBb)   Malmaison'

'Souvenir de la   EBls ECnt ENot GCoc LRHS MAus
Malmaison' (Bb)   MGan MMat MRav SPer SWCr
WAct

'Souvenir de Madame   CPou EBls EHol MAus MRav SWCr
Léonie Viennot' (ClT)

'Souvenir de Philémon   EBls MAus
Cochet' (Ru)

'Souvenir de Pierre   EBls
Vibert' (DPMo)

'Souvenir de Saint   CHad EBee EBls EMFP ETWh
Anne's' (Bb)   EWTr MAus SWCr WAct WHCG

'Souvenir d'Elise Vardon' (T)   EBls

'Souvenir di Castagneto' (HP)	MRav
'Souvenir du Docteur Jamain' (ClHP)	CHad CPou EBee EBls ENot LRHS LStr MAus SFam SMrm SPer SSea SWCr WAct WHCG WKif
'Souvenir du Président Carnot' (HT)	EBls
'Souvenir d'un Ami' (T)	EBls
spaldingii	see *R. nutkana* var. *hispida*
Spangles = 'Ganspa'PBR (F)	MBri MGan
'Spanish Beauty'	see *R.* 'Madame Grégoire Staechelin'
Sparkling Scarlet = 'Meihati' (ClF)	EBre ELan MAsh MGan SWCr
Sparkling Yellow = 'Poulgode'PBR (GC/S)	SWCr
'Special Anniversary' **new**	WWeb
Special Friend = 'Kirspec'PBR (Patio)	GCoc LStr MJon
Special Occasion = 'Fryyoung'PBR (HT)	ENot ESty GCoc GGre MFry MMat MRav SApu SWCr
'Spectabilis' (Ra)	EBls WHCG
'Spek's Yellow' (HT)	EBls
'Spencer' misapplied	see *R.* 'Enfant de France'
spinosissima	see *R. pimpinellifolia*
§ 'Splendens' (Ra)	EBls ETWh SLPl SSea SWCr WAct
'Spong' (G)	EBee EBls ETWh MAus SWCr WAct
St. Helena = 'Canlish' (F)	SWCr
St Piers = 'Harentrap'PBR (S)	GGre SWCr
§ St Tiggywinkle = 'Korbasren'PBR (GC)	ENot LGod MMat
Stacey's Star = 'Horstacey' (Patio)	NBat
§ 'Stanwell Perpetual' (PiH)	CTri EBls EMFP ENot EPfP GCoc LStr MBri MDun MMat MRav SApu SPer SSea SWCr WAct WHCG WOVN
'Star of Waltham' (HP)	WHCG
Star Performer = 'Chewpearl' (ClPatio) **new**	CSBt MJon SWCr
Stardust = 'Peavandyke'PBR (Patio/F)	ESty GGre MAsh MJon SWCr
Starina = 'Megabi' (Min)	MGan SWCr
Starlight Express = 'Trobstar'PBR (Cl)	GKir MAsh SCoo SPer SWCr
'Stars 'n' Stripes' (Min)	LGod LPlm MAus MFry SSea
Stella (HT)	EBls MGan SWCr
stellata	MAus
§ - var. *mirifica*	EBls MAus MGan
'Stephanie Diane' (HT)	LPlm
'Sterling Silver' (HT)	EBls LStr MGan SWCr
Strawberries and Cream = 'Geestraw' (Min/Patio)	ESty
Strawberry Fayre = 'Arowillip'PBR (Min/Patio)	EBre GKir MAsh MFry MRav SWCr WWeb
'Strawberry Ice' (F)	MJon SWCr
§ Sue Hipkin = 'Harzazz'PBR (HT)	CSBt ESty GGre MBur MRav SWCr
Sue Lawley = 'Macspash' (F)	MGan MJon SWCr
§ Suffolk = 'Kormixal'PBR (S/GC)	CGro CSBt EBre ELan ENot GCoc LPlm LStr MAus MGan MMat MRav SApu SPer SSea SWCr WAct WLRN WWeb
suffulta	see *R. arkansana* var. *suffulta*
Sugar and Spice = 'Peallure' (Patio)	SWCr
Sugar Baby = 'Tanabagus'PBR (Patio)	MAsh
Sugar 'n' Spice = 'Tinspice' (Min)	MAsh MRav
§ Suma = 'Harsuma'PBR (GC)	EPfP GCoc MJon SApu SWCr WAct
Summer Breeze = 'Korelasting'PBR (Cl)	ENot MMat MRav SWCr
Summer Dream = 'Frymaxicot'PBR (F)	CSBt LStr MFry SApu
§ Summer Fragrance = 'Tanfudermos'PBR (HT)	CSBt GCoc MRav SWCr
Summer Gold = 'Poulreb'PBR (F)	ECnt ENot MAsh MMat SApu SWCr WWeb
'Summer Holiday' (HT)	MBur SPer
Summer Lady = 'Tanydal'PBR (HT)	MBri MBur MJon SApu SWCr
Summer Love = 'Franluv' (F)	MJon SWCr
'Summer Magic' (Patio)	SWCr
Summer Palace = 'Poulcape'PBR (F/Patio)	ECle ECnt SWCr
Summer Snow = 'Weopop' (Patio)	MJon SWCr
'Summer Sunrise' (GC)	EBls
'Summer Sunset' (GC)	EBls
Summer Wine = 'Korizont'PBR (Cl) ♥ H4	CSBt EBee ECnt ENot MBri MGan MJon MMat SApu SPer SSea SWCr
§ Sun Hit = 'Poulsun'PBR (Patio)	CSBt ECnt ENot ESty GGre LGod MAsh MMat MRav SApu SWCr WWeb
Sunblest = 'Landora' (HT)	CGro ESty GGre LPlm MAsh MBur MFry MRav NBlu NRog SWCr
Sunderland Supreme = 'Nossun' (HT)	NBat
Sunrise = 'Kormarter'PBR (Cl)	ESty MBri MBur MFry MJon MMat MRav SApu SWCr WGer
§ Sunseeker = 'Dicracer'PBR (F/Patio)	EPfP ESty GGre IDic LGod MAsh MJon MRav SWCr WWeb
§ Sunset Boulevard = 'Harbabble'PBR (F) ♥ H4	CSBt ECnt ENot GGre GKir LGod LPlm LStr MAsh MAus MBri MFry MJon MMat MRav SApu SCoo SPer SSea SWCr WWeb
'Sunshine' (Poly)	MGan SPer
'Sunsilk' (F)	SWCr
Super Dorothy = 'Heldoro' (Ra)	MAus
Super Elfin = 'Helckleger'PBR (Ra) ♥ H4	ECnt ENot GGre LStr MGan MMat MRav SPer SSea SWCr
Super Excelsa = 'Helexa' (Ra)	ENot ESty GGre LStr MAsh MAus MGan MJon MMat MRav SSea SWCr
Super Fairy = 'Helsufair'PBR (Ra)	ECnt ENot GGre LStr MAus MGan MJon MMat MRav SPer SSea SWCr
§ Super Sparkle = 'Helfels'PBR (Ra)	EBee ECnt LStr MGan SApu SSea SWCr
§ Super Star = 'Tanorstar' (HT)	CTri EBls EBre ENot GKir LPlm LStr MAsh MGan MJon MRav SWCr WWeb
'Surpasse Tout' (G)	EBls MAus WHCG
§ 'Surpassing Beauty of Woolverstone' (ClHP)	EBls WHCG
§ Surrey = 'Korlanum'PBR (GC) ♥ H4	CSBt EBre ECnt ELan ENot ESty LGod LPlm LStr MAus MFry MGan MJon MMat MRav SApu SPer SPla SSea SWCr WAct
Susan Hampshire = 'Meinatac' (HT)	EBls MGan
Susan = 'Poulsue' (S)	EBee ECnt MAsh SWCr
Sussex = 'Poulave'PBR (GC)	CSBt EBre ECnt ENot GCoc LPlm LStr MBur MFry MGan MMat MRav SApu SPer SSea SWCr
'Sutter's Gold' (HT)	EBls MAus MBur MGan SWCr
Swan = 'Auswhite' (S)	GGre MAus MJon SWCr

Swan Lake = 'Macmed' (Cl)	EBee EBls EBre ECnt ELan ENot EPfP ESty GGre GKir LGod LRHS MAsh MBur MFry MGan MMat MRav NPri SPer SRPl SSea SWCr WWeb
Swany = 'Meiburenac' (Min/GC) ♀ H4	CGro EBls ESty MAus MGan SApu SPer SRPl SWCr WHCG
Sweet Bouquet = 'Sabchurchill' (HT)	MBur
Sweet Caroline = 'Micaroline' (Min) **new**	NBat
'Sweet Charity' (S)	GGre SWCr
Sweet Dream = 'Fryminicot'PBR (Patio) ♀ H4	CGro CSBt EBre ECnt ELan ENot EPfP ESty GCoc GGre LGod LPlm LStr MAus MBri MBur MFry MGan MJon MMat MRav NBat NRog SApu SPer SPla SSea SWCr WOVN WWeb
Sweet Fairy' (Min)	CSBt LPlm
Sweet Juliet = 'Ausleap'PBR (S)	CAbP CSBt CSam CWSG EBee EBls EBre GGre GKir LGod LPlm LRHS MAus MBri MJon NBat SApu SPer SWCr WWeb
Sweet Magic = 'Dicmagic'PBR (Min/Patio) ♀ H4	CGro CSBt EBre ECnt ENot EPfP ESty GGre IDic LGod LStr MAsh MBri MFry MGan MJon MMat MRav NBat SApu SPla SWCr WWeb
Sweet Memories = 'Whamemo' (Patio)	COtt CTri EBre ECnt EPfP ESty GCoc GKir LGod LStr MAsh MBur MJon MRav SCoo SPer SPla SSea SWCr WGer WWeb
§ Sweet Promise = 'Meihelvet' (GC)	MGan
'Sweet Repose' (F)	MGan SWCr
'Sweet Revelation'PBR	see *R.* Sue Hipkin = 'Harzazz'
§ Sweet Symphonie = 'Meibarke'PBR (Patio)	EBre ENot MBri MJon MMat MRav SWCr
'Sweet Thoughts' (Patio)	LPlm
'Sweet Velvet' (F)	MGan
'Sweet Wonder' (Patio)	COtt EPfP ESty GKir MAsh SWCr
N Sweetheart = 'Cocapeer'PBR (HT)	GCoc MGan SWCr
sweginzowii	GCal MAus
- 'Macrocarpa'	EBls
'Sydonie' (HP)	EBls WHCG
'Sympathie' (ClHT)	ENot LPlm MFry MGan MMat SPer SSea SWCr
Symphony = 'Auslett' (S)	MJon
taiwanensis	CFil
'Talisman' (HT)	EBls
Tall Story = 'Dickooky'PBR (F) ♀ H4	EBls IDic MJon SApu SWCr WHCG WOVN
'Tallyho' (HT)	EBls
Tamora = 'Austamora' (S)	MAus
§ Tango = 'Macfirwal' (F)	LPlm MBri MJon NRog
Tapis Jaune	see *R.* Golden Penny = 'Rugul'
Tatton = 'Fryentice' (F)	MBri MFry MJon SWCr
§ 'Tausendschön' (Ra)	EBls
'Tea Rambler' (Ra)	EBls
§ Tear Drop = 'Dicomo'PBR (Min/Patio)	IDic LStr MFry MGan MJon SApu SPer SWCr
§ Teasing Georgia = 'Ausbaker'PBR (S)	ECnt LRHS MAus MBri SWCr
Ted Gore = 'Hormislac' (F)	NBat
'Telstar' (F)	MGan SWCr
'Temple Bells' (ClMin/GC)	NRog
'Tenerife' (HT)	WStI
Tequila Sunrise = 'Dicobey'PBR (HT) ♀ H4	ECnt ENot ESty GGre GKir IDic LPlm LStr MAsh MAus MBri MFry MGan MJon MMat MRav NRog SApu SMrm SPer SSea SWCr WWeb
Tess of the D'Urbervilles = 'Ausmove'PBR (S)	MAus MBNS SWCr
'Texas Centennial' (HT)	EBls
§ Thaïs = 'Memaj' (HT)	EBls
Thank You = 'Chesdeep'PBR (Patio)	GCoc GGre MRav SWCr
Thanks a Million (HT)	GGre SWCr
§ That's Jazz = 'Poulnorm'PBR (ClF)	EBee ECnt LPlm MBur MJon SApu SWCr
§ The Alexandra Rose = 'Ausday'PBR (S)	LRHS MAus MWgw SWCr
'The Bishop' (CexG)	EBls MAus
'The Bride' (T)	EBls
The Cheshire Regiment = 'Fryzebedee' (HT)	MFry
§ The Children's Rose = 'Meilivar' (F)	SApu
'The Colwyn Rose'	see *R.* Colwyn Bay
The Compass Rose = 'Korwisco'PBR (S)	ENot MMat MRav SApu SPer SWCr
The Compassionate Friends = 'Harzodiac'PBR (F)	SWCr
§ The Countryman = 'Ausman'PBR (S)	EBre LRHS MAus MFry SWCr
§ The Daily Telegraph = 'Peahigh'PBR (F)	GGre MBri SWCr
The Dark Lady = 'Ausbloom'PBR (S)	CSam EBre LRHS MAus MBri MJon SWCr WWeb
The Didgemere Rose = 'Fertry' (S) **new**	SWCr
'The Doctor' (HT)	EBls MGan SSea SWCr
§ The Dove = 'Tanamola'PBR (F)	ECnt MGan SWCr
'The Ednaston Rose' (Cl)	SWCr WHCG
§ 'The Fairy' (Poly) ♀ H4	More than 30 suppliers
The Flower Arranger = 'Fryjam' (F)	LRHS
'The Garland' (Ra) ♀ H4	CRHN EBee EBls EMFP ETWh LRHS MAsh MAus SFam SPer SPla SWCr WAct WHCG
§ The Halcyon Days Rose = 'Korparesni'PBR (F)	ENot MMat
The Herbalist = 'Aussemi' (S)	LRHS MAus
The Jubilee Rose **new**	ECnt
The Lady = 'Fryjingo'PBR (S) ♀ H4	LPlm MAus MBur MFry MJon
The Maidstone Rose = 'Kordauerpa'PBR	ENot SWCr
The Mayflower = 'Austilly' (S) **new**	MAus SWCr
§ The McCartney Rose = 'Meizeli'PBR (HT)	GGre LStr MJon SApu SPer SWCr
'The New Dawn'	see *R.* 'New Dawn'
The Nun = 'Ausnun' (S)	MAus
The Painter = 'Mactemaik'PBR (F)	LStr MBur MFry MJon SApu SSea SWCr
The People's Princess = 'Geepeop'PBR (F) **new**	MAsh
§ The Pilgrim = 'Auswalker'PBR (S)	CAbP CHad CSBt EBee EBre ENot EPfP GKir LRHS MAus MBri MDun MJon MMat MRav SChu SPer SWCr WHCG WWeb
The Prince = 'Ausvelvet'PBR (S)	EBre LRHS LStr MAsh MAus MBNS MBri MJon SPer SWCr WWeb
The Prince's Trust = 'Harholding' (Cl) **new**	LStr
'The Prioress' (S)	MAus
§ The Pudsey Bear = 'Bedchild'PBR (HT)	GGre
§ 'The Queen Elizabeth' (F)	CBcs CGro CSBt CWSG EBls EBre ECnt ENot GCoc GKir LGod LPlm LStr MBri MBur MFry MGan

		MJon MMat MRav NRog SApu SPer SRPl SSea SWCr WWeb
	The Reeve = 'Ausreeve' (S)	MAus
	'The Rugby Rose' (HT)	MGan
	The Scotsman = 'Poulscots'PBR (HT)	ECnt GCoc GGre SWCr
	The Seckford Rose = 'Korpinrob' (S)	ENot MJon MMat MRav SWCr
§	The Squire = 'Ausquire' (S)	MAus
§	The Times Rose = 'Korpeahn'PBR (F) ♀ H4	ECnt ENot LGod LStr MAus MGan MJon MMat MRav SPer SRPl SSea SWCr
§	The Valois Rose = 'Kordadel'PBR (Min/Patio)	MMat
	'Thelma' (Ra)	EBls MAus
	Thelma Barlow = 'Fryforce' (HT)	MFry
	'Thérèse Bugnet' (Ru)	EBls MAus
	Thinking of You = 'Frydandy' (HT)	ECle ESty GCoc LGod LStr MAsh MBri MFry MJon SApu SWCr WWeb
	'Thisbe' (HM)	EBls MAus SPer SWCr WAct WHCG
§	Thomas Barton = 'Meihirvin' (HT)	LStr SApu
	Thousand Beauties	see R. 'Tausendschön'
	threepenny bit rose	see R. elegantula 'Persetosa'
	'Tiara' (RH)	SWCr
	Tiger Cub = 'Poulcub'PBR (Patio)	ENot MMat
	Tigris = 'Harprier' (persica hybrid) (S)	WAct
	'Till Uhlenspiegel' (RH)	EBls
	Times Past = 'Harhilt' (Cl)	ESty GCoc LStr SWCr
	'Tina Turner' (HT)	MBur MJon NBat SWCr
	Tintinara = 'Dicuptight'PBR (HT)	ECnt IDic MFry MGan
	Tip Top = 'Tanope' (F/Patio)	CBcs GKir MAsh MGan NRog SPer
	'Tipo Ideale'	see R. x odorata 'Mutabilis'
	'Tipsy Imperial Concubine' (T)	EBls
	Titanic = 'Macdako'PBR (F)	GCoc MJon SWCr
	Tivoli = 'Poulduce'PBR (HT)	ECnt ENot MAus
	'Toby Tristam' (Ra)	CRHN
	'Tom Foster' (HT)	NBat
	tomentosa	WBWf
	Too Hot to Handle = 'Macloupri'PBR (S/Cl)	MJon SApu SSea SWCr WGer
	Top Marks = 'Fryministar'PBR (Min/Patio)	CGro CSBt EBre ENot EPfP GCoc LGod LPlm LStr MAsh MBri MFry MGan MJon MMat MRav NRog SApu SCoo SPer SSea SWCr WStI WWeb
	'Top of the Bill' (Patio) **new**	GGre SWCr
	'Topeka' (F)	SWCr
	Topkapi Palace = 'Poulthe'PBR (F) **new**	ECnt
§	Toprose = 'Cocgold'PBR (F)	EBre GCoc GGre GKir MAsh SWCr
	'Topsi' (F/Patio)	NRog SPer
	Torvill and Dean = 'Lantor' (HT)	MJon SWCr
§	'Tour de Malakoff' (Ce)	CSBt EBls ETWh LRHS MAus MRav SFam SRPl SWCr WAct WHCG
	Tournament of Roses = 'Jacient' (HT)	MAus MJon SWCr
	Tower Bridge = 'Haravis' (HT)	GGre SWCr
§	Toynbee Hall = 'Korwonder'PBR (F)	ENot MMat
	'Trade Winds' (HT)	MGan SWCr
	Tradescant = 'Ausdir'PBR (S)	EBre LRHS MAus MBNS MGan SWCr
§	Tradition '95 = 'Korkeltin'PBR (Cl) ♀ H4	MBri MMat MRav SWCr
	Tranquility = 'Barout' (HT)	MBur SWCr
	'Treasure Trove' (Ra)	CRHN EBls EMFP LRHS MAus MBur SWCr WAct
	Trevor Griffiths = 'Ausold'PBR (S)	LRHS MAus
	'Tricolore de Flandre' (G)	EBls MAus
	'Trier' (Ra)	CPou EBee EBls ETWh MAus SWCr WHCG
	'Trigintipetala' misapplied	see R. 'Professeur Emile Perrot'
	'Triomphe de l'Exposition' (HP)	MAus
	'Triomphe du Luxembourg' (T)	EBls MAus
	triphylla	see R. x beanii
	Troika = 'Poumidor' (HT) ♀ H4	CSBt ENot ESty GGre GKir LStr MAsh MAus MBur MFry MGan MJon MMat MRav SPer SWCr
	Troilus = 'Ausoil' (S)	MAus
§	Tropico Sunblaze = 'Meiglassol'PBR (Min)	SWCr
	Trumpeter = 'Mactru' (F) ♀ H4	CSBt EBee ECnt ENot ESty IArd LGod LPlm LStr MAsh MAus MBri MBur MFry MGan MJon MMat MRav NBat SPer SSea SWCr WWeb
	Tumbling Waters = 'Poultumb'PBR (F/S)	ENot MMat MRav
	'Tuscany' (G)	GCoc MAus SPer WAct WHCG
	'Tuscany Superb' (G) ♀ H4	CHad CPou CSam EBee EBls EMFP ENot EPfP EWTr LRHS MAus MDun MMat MRav SPer SSea SWCr WAct WHCG WKif
	Twenty-fifth = 'Beatwe' (F)	EBls
§	Twenty-one Again! = 'Meinimo'PBR (HT)	MJon MRav SWCr
	Twist = 'Poulstri'PBR (Cl)	ECnt SWCr
	Tynwald = 'Mattwyt'PBR (HT)	CSBt ENot LStr MJon MMat SWCr
	'Typhoon' (HT)	MBur MJon
	'Tzigane' (HT)	SWCr
	'Ulrich Brünner Fils' (HP)	EBls MAus
	'Uncle Bill' (HT)	EBls
	Uncle Walter = 'Macon' (HT)	EBls
§	'Unique Blanche' (Ce)	EBls ETWh MAus SSea SWCr
§	Valencia = 'Korelia'PBR (HT) ♀ H4	CSBt ECnt ENot ESty LGod MAus MBur MJon MMat NBat
§	Valentine Heart = 'Dicogle'PBR (F) ♀ H4	CSBt ECnt ESty IArd IDic LGod MAsh MAus MFry MJon MRav SApu SWCr WWeb
	Valerie Sykes = 'Horflashrob' (F)	NBat
	Valiant Heart = 'Poulberg' (F)	ECnt SWCr
	'Vanguard' (Ru)	EBls
	'Vanity' (HM)	EBls MAus SPer
	'Variegata di Bologna' (Bb)	EBee EBls EMFP ETWh LRHS MAus MMat MRav SSea SWCr WAct
	Variety Club = 'Haredge' (Patio) **new**	LGod
	'Vatertag' (Min)	GGre MJon SWCr
	'Veilchenblau' (Ra) ♀ H4	CHad CRHN EBee EBls ECnt ELan ENot EPfP LGod LRHS LStr MAus MBri MBur MGan MRav MWgw NPri SApu SPer SSea SWCr WAct WHCG
	Velvet Fragrance = 'Fryperdee'PBR (HT)	CSBt EBee ECnt ESty GCoc MAus MBri MFry MJon MRav NBat SApu SWCr

Velvet Hit = 'Poulria'^PBR (Patio) — ENot MMat

'Venusta Pendula' (Ra) — EBls MAus

Versailles Palace = 'Poulsail'^PBR (F) **new** — SWCr

'Verschuren' (HT/v) — MJon

versicolor — see *R. gallica* 'Versicolor'

'Vick's Caprice' (HP) — EBls ETWh MAus

'Vicomtesse Pierre du Fou' (ClHT) — EBls MAus

Victor Hugo (HT) — see *R.* Spirit of Youth = 'Meivestal'

Vidal Sassoon = 'Macjuliat'^PBR (HT) — MBur MGan MJon MMat SApu SWCr

'Village Maid' — see *R.* 'Centifolia Variegata'

§ *villosa* L. — EBls ETWh MAus WAct

- 'Duplex' — see *R.* 'Wolley-Dod'

§ 'Violacea' (G) — EBee EBls ETWh MAus SSea SWCr WHCG

Violet Carson = 'Macio' (F) — MGan

'Violette' (Ra) — CPou CRHN EBee EBls ETWh MAus SPer SWCr WAct WHCG WHer

'Violinista Costa' (HT) — EBls

virginiana ♀ H4 — CPLG EBls ENot GCal GIBF MAus MGan MSte NWea SPer SRPl SWCr WAct WHCG WHen WOVN

- 'Plena' — see *R.* 'Rose d'Amour'

'Virgo' (HT) — EBls

'Viridiflora' — see *R.* x *odorata* 'Viridiflora'

Vital Spark = 'Cocacert' (F) — MGan SWCr

'Vivid' (Bourbon hybrid) — EBls

Voice of Thousands = 'Horsunsmile' (F) — NBat

'W.E. Lippiat' (HT) — EBls

Waltz = 'Poulkrid'^PBR (Cl) — ECnt SWCr

Wandering Minstrel = 'Harquince' (F) — SWCr

wardii var. *culta* — MAus

Warm Welcome = 'Chewizz'^PBR (ClMin) ♀ H4 — CGro EBre ECnt ENot EPfP ESty GGre GKir LGod LStr MAsh MAus MBri MFry MJon MMat MRav NBat NRog SMad SPer SSea SWCr WWeb

§ Warm Wishes = 'Fryxotic'^PBR (HT) ♀ H4 — CSBt EBee ECnt ENot ESty GCoc GGre GKir LGod LPlm LStr MAsh MAus MBri MBur MFry MGan MJon MMat SApu SWCr WWeb

'Warrior' (F) — MGan SPer

Warwick Castle = 'Auslian'^PBR (S) — MAus SPer

Warwickshire = 'Korkandel'^PBR (GC) — ENot MMat MRav SPer SWCr WOVN WWeb

§ *watsoniana* (Ra) — EBls

webbiana — EBls MAus SWCr WHCG

'Wedding Day' (Ra) — More than 30 suppliers

§ 'Wee Barbie'^PBR (Min) — SSea

Wee Cracker = 'Cocmarris'^PBR (Patio) — ENot ESty GCoc GGre LGod SWCr

Wee Jock = 'Cocabest'^PBR (F/Patio) — GCoc GKir MBri MRav SSea SWCr

'Weetwood' (Ra) — CRHN SPer

'Weisse aus Sparrieshoop' (S) — MGan

'Well Done' (Patio) — GGre SWCr

Welwyn Garden Glory = 'Harzumber'^PBR (HT) — ESty SWCr

'Wembley Stadium' (F/HT) — MGan

'Wendy Cussons' (HT) — CBcs CGro CWSG EBls GCoc GKir LPlm MAsh MBur MGan MJon MRav NRog SApu SPer SWCr

Wenlock = 'Auswen' (S) — EBre GGre MAus SPer SWCr

'West Country Millennium' (F) — MGan

§ Westerland = 'Korwest' (F/S) ♀ H4 — MGan MJon MMat MRav SWCr WGer

'Westfield Star' (HT) — MAus

§ Westminster Pink = 'Fryamour'^PBR (HT) — ECnt SWCr

Where the Heart Is = 'Cocoplan' (HT) **new** — GCoc

'Whisky Gill' (HT) — MGan SWCr

Whisky Mac = 'Tanky' (HT) — CBcs CGro CSBt CWSG EBls EBre ELan GCoc GGre MBri MBur MFry MGan MJon MRav NBlu NPri NRog SApu SPer SSea SWCr WWeb

'White Bath' — see *R.* 'Shailer's White Moss'

White Bells = 'Poulwhite'^PBR (Min/GC) — EBls ENot MMat MRav SPer SRPl WHCG WOVN

§ 'White Cécile Brünner' (Poly) — EBls MAus WHCG

'White Christmas' (HT) — MBur MGan SWCr

§ White Cloud = 'Korstacha'^PBR (S/ClHT) ♀ H4 — CSBt EBee ECnt ENot LGod LPlm MJon MMat MRav SWCr WHCG

White Cloud = 'Savacloud' (Min) — MBri MFry SApu

'White Cockade' (Cl) — EBls ETWh GCoc MFry MGan MRav SApu SPer SWCr

§ 'White de Meaux' (Ce) — EBls MAus

White Diamond = 'Interamon'^PBR (S) — ESty IDic MJon

White Floorshow (GC) **new** — SWCr

§ White Gold = 'Cocquiriam'^PBR (F) — GCoc GGre

'White Grootendorst' (Ru) — EBls MAus SSea WAct

White Knight (HT) — see *R.* Message = 'Meban' (HT)

White Knight = 'Poullaps' (ClHT/S) — EBee ECnt

White Meidiland = 'Meicoublan'^PBR (S/GC) — MGan SWCr

white moss — see *R.* 'Comtesse de Murinais' , *R.* 'Shailer's White Moss'

§ 'White Pet' (Poly) ♀ H4 — CHad CSBt EBee ECnt EMFP ENot EPfP ESty GCoc GGre LRHS LStr MAus MBri MGan MJon MMat MRav SApu SPer SPla SRPl SSea SWCr WAct

* 'White Pet' sport (Cl) — GCal

white Provence — see *R.* 'Unique Blanche'

'White Queen Elizabeth' (F) — EBls SRPl

white rose of York — see *R.* x *alba* 'Alba Semiplena'

'White Spray' (F) — EBls

'White Tausendschön' (Ra) — MAus

'White Wings' (HT) — CHad EBls ETWh MAus MGan SPer SWCr WAct WHCG

N *wichurana* (Ra) — EBls ETWh MAus SWCr WHCG

* - 'Nana' — MRav

- 'Variegata' (Ra/v) — CSWP EPot MCCP MJon SPar

* - 'Variegata Nana' (Ra/v) — MRav

'Wickwar' (Ra) — CSWP EBls EHol EPla GCal MSte SSpi SWCr WAct WHCG

§ Wife of Bath = 'Ausbath' (S) — MAus MBri

'Wilhelm' (HM) — EBls MAus MRav SWCr WHCG

'Will Scarlet' (HM) — MAus SWCr

'Willhire Country' (F) — EBls

'William Allen Richardson' (N) — EBls MAus SFam SWCr WHCG

'William and Mary' (S) — EBls

'William Cobbett' (F) — SSea

§ 'William Lobb' (CeMo) ♀ H4 — CHad CRHN CSBt EBls EBre ENot EPfP LGod LRHS LStr MAus MBri MDun MGan MMat MWgw SApu SChu SPer SSea SWCr WAct WHCG WKif

William Morris = 'Auswill'^{PBR} (S) — CSBt ECnt MAus MBri SWCr

William Quarrier = 'Coclager' (F) — GCoc

'William R. Smith' (T) — EBls

William Shakespeare 2000 = 'Ausromeo' (S) — CSBt MAus

William Shakespeare = 'Ausroyal'^{PBR} (S) — CSBt ENot GCoc GGre MBNS MBri NPri SPer SSea WStI

'William Tyndale' (Ra) — EBee ETWh WHCG

'Williams' Double Yellow' — see *R.* x *harisonii* 'Williams' Double Yellow'

willmottiae — see *R. gymnocarpa* var. *willmottiae*

Wiltshire = 'Kormuse'^{PBR} (S/GC) ♀ H4 — CSBt ECnt ENot ESty LPlm LStr MFry MJon MMat MRav SRPl SSea SWCr WOVN

Winchester Cathedral = 'Auscat'^{PBR} (S) — EBls EBre ECnt EMFP ENot EPfP GGre LGod LRHS LStr MAsh MAus MBri MJon MMat MRav MWgw NPri SApu SChu SPer SRPl SWCr WOVN WWeb

Windflower = 'Auscross' (S) — LRHS MAus

Windrush = 'Ausrush' (S) — MAus MJon SWCr WAct WHCG

Wine and Dine = 'Dicuncle'^{PBR} (GC) — IDic

Winter Magic = 'Foumagic' (Min) — MBur

x *wintoniensis* — WAct WHCG

Wise Portia = 'Ausport' (S) — MAus

Wishing = 'Dickerfuffle'^{PBR} (F/Patio) — IDic MAus MFry MJon SApu SPer SWCr

With Love = 'Andwit' (HT) — CSBt GGre MJon SApu SWCr

With Thanks = 'Fransmoov'^{PBR} (HT) **new** — MBri SWCr

'Woburn Abbey' (F) — CWSG EBls SSea

§ 'Wolley-Dod' (S) — EBls LRHS MAus MRav SWCr

§ Woman o'th' North = 'Kirlon' (T/Patio) — MJon

'Woman's Hour' (F/Patio) — EBls

§ *woodsii* — EBls IFro MAus WHCG

- var. *fendleri* — see *R. woodsii*

'Woolverstone Church Rose' — see *R.* 'Surpassing Beauty of Woolverstone'

Wor Jackie = 'Kirworjackie' (HT) — NBat

Worcestershire = 'Korlalon'^{PBR} (GC) — CSBt ENot ESty GCoc MAus MMat MRav SPer SWCr WWeb

World Peace 2000 = 'Peacycllow'^{PBR} (HT) — SWCr

§ *xanthina* 'Canary Bird' (S) ♀ H4 — More than 30 suppliers

§ - f. *hugonis* ♀ H4 — EBls MAus MGan NRog SPer SWCr WAct WHCG

- f. *spontanea* — CArn EBls MGan

'Xavier Olibo' (HP) — EBls

X-Rated = 'Tinx' (Min) **new** — NBat

Yellow Button = 'Auslow' (S) — MBri WAct

'Yellow Cécile Brunner' — see *R.* 'Perle d'Or'

Yellow Charles Austin = 'Ausyel' (S) — MAus

§ Yellow Dagmar Hastrup = 'Moryelrug'^{PBR} (Ru) — CBrm EBee ENot EPfP MAus MBri MGan MJon SApu SPer SWCr WAct WOVN

'Yellow Doll' (Min) — MAus SSea SWCr

'Yellow Dream' (Patio) — SWCr

'Yellow Patio' (Min/Patio) — LStr MAsh SSea SWCr

yellow Scotch — see *R.* x *harisonii* 'Williams' Double Yellow'

Yellow Sunblaze = 'Meitrisical'^{PBR} (Min) — CSBt SWCr

'Yesterday' (Poly/F/S) ♀ H4 — EBls GKir MAsh MAus MGan MRav SWCr

'Yolande d'Aragon' (HP) — EBls

York and Lancaster — see *R.* x *damascena* var. *versicolor*

Yorkshire Bank = 'Rutrulo'^{PBR} (HT) — MFry

Yorkshire = 'Korbarkeit'^{PBR} (GC) — ENot GCoc LStr MMat MRav SSea SWCr

'Yorkshire Lady' (HT) — NBat

Young Quinn = 'Macbern' (HT) — MBur

'Yvonne Rabier' (Poly) ♀ H4 — EBls LStr MAus MRav SPer SSea SWCr WAct WHCG

Zambra = 'Meicurbos' (F) — CBcs

'Zéphirine Drouhin' (Bb) — More than 30 suppliers

§ 'Zigeunerknabe' (S) — EBee EBls ECnt EMFP MAus MBri MRav SPer SSea SWCr WAct WHCG

'Zitronenfalter' (S) — MGan

'Zweibrücken' (Cl) — MGan

Roscoea ✿ (Zingiberaceae)

alpina — CBct CBro CLAP CPLG EBee EBre EChP EHrv EHyt EMar EPot ERos GDra GEdr GKir IBlr ITim MTho NLAp NWCA SRms WAbe WCru WLin WSan WViv

- CC 1820 — LEur WCot

- CC 3667 — GEdr GKev

- pink-flowered — WCom

auriculata — CAvo CBct CBro CFir CFwr CLAP CPne CRDP EBee EChP EHrv EMar EPot ERos ETub GCrs GEdr IBlr LEur MLLN MTho NHar SBla SCro SDes WCot WCru WFar WViv

- 'Floriade' — IBlr LEur

australis — CFir IBlr LEur SOkd WCru

'Beesiana' — CAvo CBro CFir CFwr CHEx CLAP CPLG CRDP EBee EChP EMan EMar ERos GBuc IBlr I Ama LEur MRav MTho NHar NHol SDes WAbe WCru WFar WHil WPnP WViv

'Beesiana' pale-flowered — IBlr LEur WPnP

'Beesiana' white-flowered — CBct CDes CFwr CLAP EBee EHrv EPfP GEdr IBlr LAst MBNS MMHG NBir WAbe WPnP

cautleyoides ♀ H4 — More than 30 suppliers

- Blackthorn strain — SBla

- var. *cautleyoides* **new** — EBee

- 'Early Purple' — CLAP

- hybrid — MLLN

- 'Jeffrey Thomas' — CBct CFwr CLAP EBee GEdr IBlr LEur

- 'Kew Beauty' ♀ H4 — CDes CFir CLAP CRDP GKir LEur MTed MTho

- 'Kew Beauty' seedlings — EGle EMan GCal

- mauve-flowered — SDes

- 'Purple Giant' — CLAP

- 'Reinier' — LEur

- x *humeana* — IBlr LEur

'Gestreept' — CLAP

humeana ♀ H4 — CBct CBro CLAP EBee EHyt ERos GBin GCrs GKev GMac LAma LRHS NHar SBla WCru WPrP

- f. *lutea* **new** — IBlr

- 'Purple Streaker' — CDes EBee WPGP

- f. *tyria* **new** — IBlr

kunmingensis var. *elongatobractea* **new** — LEur

'Monique' — CLAP LEur

procera — see *R. purpurea*

§ *purpurea*	More than 30 suppliers
– L&S 20845	IBlr
– 'Brown Peacock'	CLAP LEur
– var. *gigantea*	LEur
– – CC 1757	WCot
– 'Nico'	LEur
– pale-flowered **new**	EBla
– 'Peacock'	CLAP LEur
– 'Peacock Eye'	LEur WCot
– 'Polaris'	LEur
– var. *procera*	see *R. purpurea*
– short	CLAP
– tall	CLAP
§ *scillifolia*	CBro CDes CFir CFwr CPBP CRDP
	EBre EPot ERos GBuc GCal GEdr
	GKir IBlr LAma LEur LRHS MRHS
	MTho NBir NHar NMen NRog
	SUsu WCom WCot WCru WLin
– dark-flowered **new**	EHrv
– pink-flowered	CBct EBee EChP EHrv GEdr IBlr
	LEur WAbe WViv
tibetica	EBee EBre IBlr LEur NLAp WCru
	WOBN
– ACE 2539	EPot
– dark-flowered **new**	WWst
tumjensis	CLAP IBlr

Rosmarinus ✿ (*Lamiaceae*)

corsicus 'Prostratus'	see *R. officinalis* Prostratus Group
lavandulaceus hort.	see *R. officinalis* Prostratus Group
officinalis	More than 30 suppliers
– var. *albiflorus*	CArn CPrp CSev EBee ELau EPfP
	ESis GBar GPoy LRHS MBar
	MBow MChe MHer NChi NHHG
	NLon NSti SChu SDow SHDw
	SLim SMac SPer SPlb WCHb
	WHHs WWye
– – 'Lady in White'	CPrp CSBt EBee ELan EPfP LAst
	LRHS SDow SPer WHHs
– 'Alderney'	CPrp MHer SDow
§ – var. *angustissimus*	CMHG CSBt CSev CWib EBee
'Benenden Blue' ♀ H4	EGoo ELau GBar GPoy LHop
	LRHS MAsh MChe MHer MWgw
	NHHG SChu SDix SDow SMer
	SPar SPer SPlb STre WEas WHHs
	WWye
§ – – 'Corsican Blue'	CArn EPfP GBar GPoy MHer SCro
	SDow SHDw SIde WBrE WPer
– – 'Corsicus Prostratus'	CBcs ELau SMac
– 'Arta' **new**	SSpi
– 'Aureovariegatus'	see *R. officinalis* 'Aureus'
§ – 'Aureus' (v)	CMil CPla EVFa GBar IBlr NHHG
	SDry SMad WCHb WEas WHer
– 'Barbeque' **new**	CLvH
– 'Blue Boy' **new**	MHer
– 'Blue Lagoon' **new**	CLvH WJek
* – 'Boule'	CPrp WCHb
– 'Capercaillie'	SDow
– 'Collingwood Ingram'	see *R. officinalis* var.
	angustissimus 'Benenden Blue'
– dwarf, blue-flowered	ELau GBar
– 'Farinole' **new**	CPrp
– 'Fastigiatus'	see *R. officinalis* 'Miss Jessopp's
	Upright'
– 'Fota Blue'	CArn CBod CPlt CPrp CSev ELau
	EOHP GBar MHer NHHG NSti
	SAga SCro SDow SHDw SIde SPar
	WCHb WJek WWye
– 'Golden Rain'	see *R. officinalis* 'Joyce DeBaggio'
– 'Gorizia' **new**	SDow
– 'Green Ginger'	CPrp CSpe EChP EOHP GBin LHop
	MChe MHer NCot NPer SDow
	WBcn WBry WCHb WHHs WRus

– 'Guilded'	see *R. officinalis* 'Aureus'
– 'Gunnel's Upright'	GBar WRha
– 'Haifa' **new**	CLvH WCHb
– 'Heavenly Blue' **new**	GBar
– 'Henfield Blue'	SHDw
– 'Iden Blue'	SIde
– 'Iden Blue Boy'	SIde
– 'Iden Pillar'	SIde
§ – 'Joyce DeBaggio' (v)	MHer SDow
– 'Ken Taylor' **new**	LPhx
– 'Lady in Blue' **new**	WHHs
– *lavandulaceus*	see *R. officinalis* Prostratus Group
– 'Lilies Blue'	GPoy
– 'Lockwood Variety'	see *R. officinalis* (Prostratus
	Group) 'Lockwood de Forest'
– 'Majorca Pink'	CBcs CChe CPrp CSBt CSam EBee
	EGoo ELau GAbr GBar MBow
	MHer MRav NSti SDow SIde SLon
	SPar SPer SRms WCHb WHHs
	WPer WWye
– 'Maltese White'	CStr WCot
– 'McConnell's Blue' ♀ H4	CArn CDoC CPrp EBee EBre ELan
	ELau GAbr GBar LHop LRHS
	MAsh MBro MGos MRav MWat
	MWgw SDow SDry SHDw SPla
	SPlb WCHb WFar WHoo WPGP
	WPer WTel WWye
§ – 'Miss Jessopp's	More than 30 suppliers
Upright' ♀ H4	
§ – 'Mrs Harding'	CBod CPrp EBee MHer SDow
– 'Octopussy' **new**	WBry
– 'Pat Vlasto'	CStr
– 'Pointe du Raz' **new**	MRav
§ – 'Primley Blue'	CArn CBcs CBod CPrp CSam
	CSev CWSG EBee ECtt ELau GBar
	LRHS MChe MHer MRav NHHG
	NSti SChu SDow SIde SMer
	WCHb WHer WPer
§ – Prostratus Group	More than 30 suppliers
– – 'Capri' **new**	EOHP MRav
– – 'Gethsemane'	SIde
– – 'Jackman's Prostrate'	CBcs ECtt
§ – – 'Lockwood de Forest'	GBar SDow WPer
– f. *pyramidalis*	see *R. officinalis* 'Miss Jessopp's
	Upright'
* – 'Rampant Boule'	SDow
– *repens*	see *R. officinalis* Prostratus Group
– 'Roseus'	More than 30 suppliers
– 'Russell's Blue'	WFar
– 'Sea Level' **new**	WCHb
– 'Severn Sea' ♀ H4	More than 30 suppliers
– Silver Spires = 'Wolros'	LRav SIde
– 'Sissinghurst Blue' ♀ H4	CArn CBcs CSev EBee ELan ELau
	EMil EPfP GAbr GBar LAst LRHS
	MAsh MBow MRav NGHP SDow
	SIde SLim SPer SPlb SRms WCHb
	WCom WHHs WSel WWye
– 'Sissinghurst White'	WHHs
– 'South Downs Blue' **new**	SHDw
– 'Sudbury Blue'	EBee ELau GBar MChe MHer
	NHHG NLon NSti SDow SHDw
	WEas WJek
– 'Trusty'	ELan GBar LHop LRHS SDow
	WBcn WPer
– 'Tuscan Blue'	More than 30 suppliers
– 'Variegatus'	see *R. officinalis* 'Aureus'
– 'Vicomte de Noailles'	ERea
repens	see *R. officinalis* Prostratus Group

rosemary see *Rosmarinus officinalis*

Rostrinucula (*Lamiaceae*)

dependens Guiz 18	CBot

Rosularia ✿ (*Crassulaceae*)

	from Sandras Dag **new**	LBee
§	*aizoon*	ESis
	alba	see *R. sedoides*
§	*chrysantha*	EBur EMlt EPem ESis MHer NJOw NMen SIng SPlb WLow
	- number 1	CWil LBee
	crassipes	see *Rhodiola wallichiana*
§	*muratdaghensis*	EBur SChr SIng
	pallida A. Berger	see *R. chrysantha*
	pallida Stapf	see *R. aizoon*
	platyphylla hort.	see *R. muratdaghensis*
	rechingeri	CWil EPot
§	*sedoides*	CWil LRHS MBar SChu SIng WPer WWin
§	- var. *alba*	CTca CWil EDAr EHol EPot MBar NFla NLAp SChu WWin
	sempervivum	CWil EWes NMen SChr
§	- subsp. *glaucophylla*	CWil ETow NSla WAbe
	spatulata hort.	see *R. sempervivum* subsp. *glaucophylla*
	turkestanica	CWil

Rothmannia (*Rubiaceae*)

	capensis	EShb LRHS SOWG
§	*globosa*	ERea

Rubia (*Rubiaceae*)

manjith	GPoy
peregrina	CArn MSal
tinctorum	CArn ELau EOHP GBar GPoy GWCH MSal NCWG SWat WCHb WHer WWye

Rubus (*Rosaceae*)

	RCB/Eq C-1	WCot
	alceifolius Poiret	CFee CStr SDys SMac
	arcticus	EPPr GGar GIBF MBro MCCP NHar NLar SRms SRot WBea WCot WCru WFTG WPat
	- subsp. *stellarcticus*	ESim
	'Anna' (F)	
	- - 'Beata' (F)	ESim
	- - 'Linda' (F)	ESim
	'Sofia' (F)	ESim
	x *barkeri*	ECou WPGP
§	'Benenden' ♀ H4	More than 30 suppliers
	'Betty Ashburner'	CAgr CDoC EBee ENot EPfP EPla EWTr GQui LAst LBuc MGos MRav MWgw MWhi NArg SPer WDin WHCG
	biflorus ♀ H4	CBcs CFil EBee EMon EPfP EPla EWes LRHS MBlu SMac SSte
	'Boysenberry, Thornless' (F)	EMui GTwe LBuc LRHS SDea SPer
*	*buergeri* 'Variegatus' (v)	NHol WMoo
	caesius 'Sidings' (v)	CNat
	calophyllus	CFil WCot WPGP
	calycinoides Hayata	see *R. pentalobus*
	chamaemorus	GIBF GPoy
	cissoides	WCot
	cockburnianus (F)	CArn CBcs CPle CTri EBee EBre ELan ENot EPfP EWTr GKir LBuc LRHS MBlu MRav MWat NBea NHol NLon NSti NWea SPer SPlb SRms WDin WEas WFar
	- 'Goldenvale' PBR ♀ H4	CBcs CDoC CMHG CPle CWSG EBee EBre EHoe EMil ENot EPfP EPla GKir GQui LAst MBlu MRav MTis MWhi NEgg NHol NSti SLon SMad SPer SSpi WDin WWeb

	coreanus	CFil EPla
	crataegifolius	CBrd SMac SSte WPat
	'Emerald Spreader'	GKir LRHS MBri SBod WMoo
	flagelliflorus	MBar WHCG
	fockeanus hort.	see *R. pentalobus*
	formosensis B&SWJ 1798	WCru
	x *fraseri*	SSte
N	*fruticosus* agg.	CKin
	- 'Adrienne' (F)	Emui WWeb
	- 'Ashton Cross' (F)	EMui GTwe LBuc WWeb
	- 'Bedford Giant' (F)	CSBt ENot GTwe LRHS MGos MRav NRog SPer
	- 'Black Satin' (F)	LRHS MBri SDea SPer
	- 'Cook's Special' (F)	NRog
	- 'Cottenham Green'	EMon
	- 'Fantasia' PBR (F) ♀ H4	EMui
	- 'Godshill Goliath' (F)	SDea
	- 'Helen'	CSut EMui SDea
	- 'Himalayan Berry' **new**	ENot
	- 'Himalayan Giant' (F)	GTwe LRHS MRav NRog SDea SKee SPer
	- 'John Innes' (F)	CTri NRog
	- 'Loch Ness' PBR (F) ♀ H4	COtt CSBt EMui ENot GKir GTwe IArd LBuc LRHS MBri MGos SCoo SDea SPer
	- 'Merton Thornless' (F)	CSBt GTwe LRHS MGos NBee NRog WGwG
	- 'No Thorn' (F)	CAgr SDea
	- 'Oregon Thornless' (F)	CAgr CSBt EMui ENot GTwe MBri MRav SCoo SDea SKee SPer SRms
	- 'Pant Gwyn' (v)	CNat
	- 'Parsley Leaved' (F)	MRav NRog SDea
*	- 'Sylvan' (F)	LRHS MCoo MGos
	- 'Thornfree' (F)	SDea WWeb
	- 'Variegatus' (v)	CBot CRDP ITre MBlu NEgg NHol NSti SMad SSte WCot WPat
	- 'Veronique' (F)	EMui
	- 'Waldo'	COtt CSBt CSam EMui LBuc LRHS MGos SDea WWeb
	hakonensis B&SWJ 5555 **new**	WCru
	henryi	CBot EPfP EPla LRHS MRav NSti SLon SMac SSte WCot WFar WHCG
	var. *bambusarum*	CFil CMCN CPlN CWib LBee EMan EPar EPfP EPla MCCP SBra WCru WPat WTin
	hupehensis	SLPl
	ichangensis	CBot CMCN CPlN CPom CStr EPla LEdu
	idaeus	CKin
I	- 'Allgold'	see *R. idaeus* 'Fallgold'
	- 'Augusta' (F)	EMui
	- 'Aureus' (F)	ECha ELan EPla EVFa MRav NBid SDry SMac WCot WFar
	- 'Autumn Bliss' PBR (F) ♀ H4	CSBt CSam CSut CWSG EMui ENot EPfP GKir GTwe LBuc LRHS MBri MGos MRav NBee NRog SCoo SDea SKee SPer WWeb
§	- 'Fallgold' (F)	EMui EPfP LRHS WWeb
	- 'Galante' PBR (F)	EMui
	- 'Glen Ample' PBR (F) ♀ H4	CSBt CSut CWSG EMui GTwe LBuc LRHS MBri SCoo SDea SKee WWeb
	- 'Glen Clova' (F)	CSBt ENot EPfP GKir GTwe LRHS MRav NBee NBlu NRog SKee SPer WWeb
	- 'Glen Coe' (F)	GTwe
	- 'Glen Lyon' PBR (F)	GTwe LBuc LRHS MBri SCoo
	- 'Glen Magna' PBR (F)	CSBt CSut CWSG EMui GTwe LBuc LRHS MBri NRog SCoo SDea SKee

– 'Glen Moy'^{PBR} (F) ♀ H4	CSBt CSam EMui EPfP GKir GTwe LRHS MGos MRav NBee NRog SCoo SDea WWeb
– 'Glen Prosen'^{PBR} (F) ♀ H4	CSBt EMui ENot GKir GTwe LRHS MBri MRav NRog SCoo SDea SPer WWeb
– 'Glen Rosa'^{PBR} (F)	GTwe LRHS
– 'Glen Shee'^{PBR} (F)	GTwe
– 'Heritage' (F)	EMui LRHS MRav SCoo
– 'Julia' (F)	GTwe MCoo WWeb
– 'Leo'^{PBR} (F) ♀ H4	CSBt EMui GTwe MGos NRog SCoo WWeb
– 'Malling Admiral' (F) ♀ H4	COtt EMui ENot GKir GTwe LRHS NRog SCoo
– 'Malling Delight' (F) ♀ H4	CSBt GKir GTwe LRHS MRav SCoo
– 'Malling Jewel' (F) ♀ H4	COtt CSBt EMui ENot GKir GTwe LBuc LRHS NBee NRog SDea SPer
– 'Malling Joy' (F)	GTwe
– 'Malling Orion' (F)	MGos
– 'Redsetter' (F)	EMui
– 'Ruby' (F)	EMui
– 'Summer Gold' (F)	GTwe
– 'Terri-Louise' (F)	EMui
– 'Tulameen' (F)	EMui SCoo
– 'Zeva Herbsternte' (F)	GTwe
illecebrosus (F)	ITer SMac
irenaeus	CFil CPIN WPGP
Japanese wineberry	see *R. phoenicolasius*
'Kenneth Ashburner'	CDoC NLar SLPl WFar
'King's Acre Berry' (F)	EMui
laciniatus	EHol EPla
lambertianus	CFil
leucodermis	EPPr
NNS 00-663 **new**	
lineatus	CBot CBrd CDoC CMCo CPLG CPle EBee EPfP GEil GKir LRHS NSti SDix SDry SMac SMad WCru WDin WPGP WPat
x *loganobaccus*	EMui EPfP GTwe MRav NRog
'LY 59' (F) ♀ H4	SDea SPer SRms
– 'LY 654' (F) ♀ H4	CSam GKir GTwe LBuc LRHS MBri MGos SDea SPer WWeb
– thornless	CTri CWSG ECot GKir GTwe NRog SDea
'Margaret Gordon'	CPMA GKir MRav NPro WHCG
microphyllus	CRez EMan MGos WPat WWeb
'Variegatus' (v)	
§ *nepalensis*	CAgr CDoC GEdr GKir LEdu NHol NLAp
niveus	EPla
nutans	see *R. nepalensis*
odoratus	ELan EPfP MRav NPal SPer SSte WBor WCom WCot WHCG
palmatus	SLPl
var. *coptophyllus*	
parviflorus	CArn
– double (d)	EMon WCru
– 'Sunshine Spreader'	NPro WPat
parvus	ECou
pectinellus **new**	WBcn
– var. *trilobus*	CFee GMac MAvo MWhi SMac
– – B&SWJ 16698	NPro
– – B&SWJ 1669B	GSki LPio WCru WMoo
peltatus	CFil NLar WPGP
§ *pentalobus*	CRez CTri ELan EMan EPla MBar MWhi NFor SMac WFar WWin
– B&SWJ 3878	WCru
– 'Emerald Carpet'	CAgr ESim NLar SBod
§ *phoenicolasius*	EMui EPfP GEil GKir GTwe LRHS MBlu MBri MRav NRog NSti SDea SPer WAbb WCru WHCG

rolfei B&SWJ 3546	WCru
rosifolius **new**	CSpe
– 'Coronarius' (d)	CFee CHar CSpe ELan EMan EPPr LRHS MDun MRav MWhi NEgg NLon NPro NSti SPer WCot WFar WGwG WHil WOVN
sachalinensis	GIBF
saxatilis **new**	GIBF
setchuenensis	CMCN CSWP SSte
'Silvan' (F) ♀ H4	EMui GTwe
spectabilis	CPle CWib ELan EPla MRav NHol SBHF SRms SSte WCom WFar WRha
– 'Flore Pleno'	see *R. spectabilis* 'Olympic Double'
§ – 'Olympic Double' (d)	More than 30 suppliers
splendidissimus	WCru
B&SWJ 2361	
squarrosus	CPle ECou EHol EPla SMad
'Sunberry' (F)	GTwe SDea WWeb
swinhoei B&SWJ 1735	WCru
taiwanicola	GEdr NPSI SMac WWhi
– B&SWJ 317	NPro WCru
Tayberry Group (F) ♀ H4	CSam CTri EMui ENot GKir GTwe MBri MGos NRog SPer SRms WWeb
– 'Buckingham' (F)	CSut EMui GTwe LBuc LRHS WLRN WWeb
– 'Medana Tayberry' (F)	LRHS SDea SKee
§ *thibetanus* ♀ H4	More than 30 suppliers
– 'Silver Fern'	see *R. thibetanus*
tricolor	CAgr CBcs CChe CHEx CSBt CWib EBee ENot EPfP GBri GIBF GKir LGro MRav MTis MWhi NFor NHol SDix SHBN SLon SMac SPer SSte WBod WDin WHCG WWin
– 'Dart's Evergreen'	SLPl
– 'Ness'	SLPl
tridel 'Benenden'	see *R.* 'Benenden'
'Tummelberry' (F)	GTwe
ulmifolius	CBot CSev ENot EPla MBlu MRav NFor NLon NSti SChu SMac SPer WAbb WHal
'Bellidiflorus' (d)	
ursinus	LEdu
'Veitchberry' (F)	EMui GTwe
volkensii	SSpi
Walberton Red = 'Odel'	SPer
'Youngberry' (F)	SDea

Rudbeckia ✿ (*Asteraceae*)

Autumn Sun	see *R.* 'Herbstsonne'
californica	CSam MAnH MNrw WPer
deamii	see *R. fulgida* var. *deamii*
echinacea purpurea	see *Echinacea purpurea*
§ *fulgida* var. *deamii* ♀ H4	More than 30 suppliers
– var. *fulgida* **new**	WHil
§ – var. *speciosa*	CKno CM&M CMGP CSam ECha ELan EPfP ERou GAbr LRHS NGdn SPer SPlb SRms SWal WFar WMoo WPer WRHF WRus WTel WViv WWpP
– var. *sullivantii*	More than 30 suppliers
'Goldsturm' ♀ H4	
– Viette's Little Suzy = 'Blovi'^{PBR}	EBee EMan LRHS
glaucescens	WCot
NNS 00-667 **new**	
gloriosa	see *R. birta*
'Golden Jubilee' **new**	LRHS WWeb
'Goldquelle' (d) ♀ H4	More than 30 suppliers
§ 'Herbstsonne'	More than 30 suppliers
§ *hirta*	IIve
– 'Goldilocks' **new**	GWCH

– 'Irish Eyes'	LRHS LRav
– var. **pulcherrima**	EBee EFou
– 'Sonora'	COtt MBow
– 'Toto' ♀ H3	LPVe WHil
§ 'Juligold'	CPrp EBee EFou EMan LRHS
	NGdn NHlc SCro SHel SMrm SPla
	SPoG SSpe WFar
July Gold	see *R.* 'Juligold'
laciniata	CBrm CStr EBee ECGN EChP ELan
	EMan EMon EPPr EPfP GCal MFir
	NOrc NSti WCot WLRN WMoo
– 'Ampla' **new**	MDKP
– 'Golden Glow'	see *R. laciniata* 'Hortensia'
§ – 'Hortensia'	EMon EPla MFir SCro
maxima	CDes CFwr EBee EChP ECha EMan
	EMon LPhx LRHS MAnH MAvo MBri
	MCCP NLar NSti SChu SDix SMrm
	WAul WCot WFar WMoo WRus
– 'Brilliant'	SUsu
missouriensis	EBee
mollis	EBee
newmannii	see *R. fulgida* var. *speciosa*
nitida	WLin
occidentalis	EBlw EMar MLLN WFar WPer
– 'Black Beauty'PBR	EChP EMan EPfP IHMH MBNS
	MWrn NBhm NSti WMnd
– 'Green Wizard'	CKno CM&M CSam EBee ECtt
	EFou EHrv ELan EMan EPfP ERou
	EWTr MAnH MTis MWrn NDov
	NLar SMHy SPer SRms WFar
	WPGP WSan WWhi WWpP WWye
* **paniculata** **new**	EFou
purpurea	see *Echinacea purpurea*
speciosa	see *R. fulgida* var. *speciosa*
subtomentosa	CHor CPou EBee EFou EMan
	EMon GCal LRHS MAnH MAvo
	MCAu MDKP NSti WOld
'Sun Baby' **new**	CStr
'Takao' **new**	EBee MBri MLLN NPro SUsu
triloba	CFwr CMea CSam ECGN EFou
	EMan GBri MBri MCAu SCro
	WBea WFar WMoo WTin

rue see *Ruta graveolens*

Ruellia (Acanthaceae)

brittoniana 'Katie'	WCot
humilis	EBee EMan SCro SIgm WCot WHil
makoyana ♀ H1	CHal CSev IBlr MBri SMur SYvo
malacospermu **new**	WCot
'Mr Foster'	CHal
* **muralis** **new**	MAvo

Rumex (Polygonaceae)

§ **acetosa**	CArn CKin CSev ELau GBar GPoy
	GWCH LRHS MBow MChe MHer
	NBir NGHP NPri SIde SWal WHer
	WLHH WSel WWye
– 'Abundance'	ELau
– subsp. **acetosa**	EVFa WAlt
'Saucy' (v)	
– 'De Belleville' **new**	CPrp
– 'Profusion' **new**	GPoy
– subsp. **vinealis**	EMan
acetosella	CArn IIve MSal WSel
alpinus	WCot
flexuosus	CElw CRow EHoe EShb EVFa IBlr
	ITer NLar WWeb
hydrolapathum	CArn CHEx EMFW LPBA MSta
	SPlb WWpP
lunaria **new**	WHer
obtusifolius	CNat
'Golden My Foot' **new**	

sanguineus	EBlw EMan GGar IHMH LPBA
	MWgw NBlu SWal WCer WFar
	WMAq WMnd WWal
– var. **sanguineus**	CArn CBgR CElw CPrp CRow
	CSev EBee EHoe ELan EPar EPla
	LRHS MHer MNrw MTho NBro
	NHol SYvo WHer WLHH WPer
	WSel WWye
scutatus	CArn CPrp CSev ELau GPoy
	MChe MHer NBlu SIde WCer
	WHHs WHbs WHer WJek WLHH
	WWye
– 'Silver Shield'	CRDP CRow EBee ELau EMar
	EPPr EVFa IBlr NSti WCHb WJek
	WLHH
venosus	MSal

Rumohra (Davalliaceae)

adiantiformis ♀ H1	SEND

Rupicapnos (Papaveraceae)

africana	SBla

Ruschia (Aizoaceae)

karrooica	SChr
uncinata	SChr

Ruscus ✿ (Ruscaceae)

aculeatus	CArn EBee ENot EPfP GKir GPoy
	MRav NWea SAPC SArc SBrw
	SMad SPar SRms SSta WDin WHer
	WPGP WRHF WStI WWye
– (f)	WMou
– hermaphrodite	EPla EWes GCal SPer WGer
– (m)	WMou
– var. **aculeatus**	GCal MTcd
'Lanceolatus' (f)	
– var. **angustifolius** Boiss.	EPla
– – (f)	EPla
* – 'Wheeler's Variety' (f/m)	CPMA EBee
hypoglossum	EPla MTed SEND SLon WRHF
– WM 9804	MPhe
hypophyllum	MTed
racemosus	see *Danae racemosa*

Russelia (Scrophulariaceae)

§ **equisetiformis** ♀ H1	CHll SIgm SOWG WDyG
juncea	see *R. equisetiformis*

Ruta (Rutaceae)

chalepensis	CArn
§ – 'Dimension Two'	WHer
– prostrate	see *R. chalepensis* 'Dimension Two'
corsica	CArn
graveolens	CAgr CArn CPLG EFer GBar
	GPoy GWCH MChe NBlu NOak
	NPri SIde SPar SPet WHHs
	WHer WJek WPer WSHC
	WWye
– 'Jackman's Blue'	More than 30 suppliers
– 'Variegata' (v)	CBot ECha ELan EMan GBar GEil
	MChe NFor NPer SPer WBry
	WHer WJek WRHF
montana	EBee WCot
prostrata	see *R. chalepensis* 'Dimension Two'

Ruttya (Acanthaceae)

fruticosa 'Scholesii'	ERea

x *Ruttyruspolia* (Acanthaceae)

'Phyllis van Heerden'	GFai

S

Sabal (Arecaceae)

§	*bermudana*	CRoM EAmu LPal
	causiarum	CRoM
	domingensis **new**	CRoM
	etonia	LPal
§	*mexicana*	CRoM EAmu EPVP
	minor	CBrP CHEx CRoM EAmu EPVP
		LPal MPRe NPal WMul
	palmetto	CArn CDoC CRoM CTrC EAmu
		LPal MPRe WMul WNor
	princeps	see *S. bermudana*
	'Riverside'	CRoM
	rosei	LPal
	texana	see *S. mexicana*
	umbraculifera	MPRe
	uresana	LPal

Saccharum (Poaceae)

§	*baldwinii*	CBig
	brevibarbe	CBig EMan EPPr
	var. *contortum*	
	ravennae	CBig CCtw CPen EBee EHoe
		EMan EMon EWes GBin LRav
		MSte NSti SMad SPlb WFar
	rufipilum **new**	WCot
	strictum (Ell.) Ell. ex Nutt.	see *S. baldwinii*

sage see *Salvia officinalis*

sage, clary see *S. sclarea*

sage, pineapple see *S. elegans 'Scarlet Pineapple'*

Sageretia (Rhamnaceae)

§	*thea*	STre
	theezans	see *S. thea*

Sagina (Caryophyllaceae)

	boydii	EMNN EPot EWes NLAp
	subulata	IHMH SDes
§	- var. *glabrata* 'Aurea'	ECha ECtt EDAr EFer EMlt GKir
		LGro MBNS MOne MWhi NFla
		NHol SIng SRms WEas WHal
		WMoo WPer WWin WWpP

Sagittaria (Alismataceae)

	'Bloomin Babe'	CRow
	graminea	CRow
	'Crushed Ice' (v)	
	japonica	see *S. sagittifolia*
	latifolia	COld EMFW LMdh LPBA NPer
	- 'Flore Pleno' (d)	LMdh
*	*leucopetala*	NPer
	'Flore Pleno' (d)	
§	*sagittifolia*	CBen CRow EHon EMFW EPfP
		LMdh LPBA MSta NBlu SLon SWat
		WFar WMAq WWpP
	- 'Flore Pleno' (d)	CRow EMFW LMdh LPBA MSta
		SLon SWat WMAq
	- var. *leucopetala*	WMAq

Saintpaulia (Gesneriaceae)

	'Bob Serbin' (d)	WDib
	'Centenary'	WDib
	'Cherries 'n' Cream'	WDib
	'Chiffon Moonmoth' **new**	WDib
	'Chiffon Stardust' **new**	WDib
	'Halo's Aglitter'	WDib

	'Irish Flirt' (d)	WDib
	'Lemon Drop' **new**	WDib
	'Love Spots' **new**	WDib
	'Lucky Lee Ann' **new**	WDib
	'Mermaid' **new**	WDib
	'Midget Lillian' **new**	WDib
	'Powder Keg' **new**	WDib
	'Ramblin Magic' **new**	WDib
	'Rob's Dust Storm' (d)	WDib
	'Rob's Gundaroo' (d)	WDib
	'Rob's Ice Ripples' (d)	WDib
	'Rob's Mad Cat' **new**	WDib
	'Rob's Rinky Dink' (d)	WDib
	'Rob's Shadow Magic' (d)	WDib
	shumensis **new**	WDib
	'Sky Bandit' **new**	WDib
	'Tippy Toes' (d)	WDib

Salix ✿ (Salicaceae)

	acutifolia	ELan GIBF NSti SPla WDin
	- 'Blue Streak' (m) ♀ H4	CEnd CMHG CWiW EPfP EPla
		EWes MBlu MRav NBir SLon
		SMHy SWat WIvy
	aegyptiaca	CDoC CLnd MBlu NWea WMou
	alba	CAgr CCVT CKin CLnd CWiW
		ECrN ENot GKir LBuc NWea
		WDin WMou WOrn
	- f. *argentea*	see *S. alba* var. *sericea*
	- 'Aurea'	CLnd CTho MRav WIvy WMou
	- var. *caerulea*	CAgr CLnd ENot LBuc MRav
		NWea WMou
	- - 'Wantage Hall'	CWiW
	- 'Cardinalis' (f)	CWiW
	- 'Chermesina' hort.	see *S. alba* subsp. *vitellina* 'Britzensis'
	- 'Dart's Snake'	CEnd CTho EBee ELan ENot
		EPfP LRHS MRav SCoo SPer
		WBcn
	- 'Golden Ness'	MBri
	- 'Hutchinson's Yellow'	CDoC CTho MGos NWea WDin
	- 'Liempde' (m)	ENot MRav
	- 'Raesfeld'	CWiW
§	- var. *sericea* ♀ H4	CBcs CDoC CLnd CMHG CTho
		ECrN ENot EPfP GKir MBlu
		MRav NFor NLon NWea SHBN
		SMHy SPer WDin WGer WIvy
		WMou
	- 'Splendens'	see *S. alba* var. *sericea*
N	- 'Tristis'	CDul CLnd CTri CWSG ELan GKir
		LRHS MBri MGos NWea SKee
		SLim SRms WDin WHar
	- 'Tristis' misapplied	see *Salix* X *sepulcralis* var. *chrysocoma*
	- subsp. *vitellina* ♀ H4	CKin ENot EPfP EPla GKir LBuc
		MBNS MBrN NWea SLon SWat
		WDin WIvy WJas WMoo WPGP
§	- - 'Britzensis' (m) ♀ H4	More than 30 suppliers
	- - 'Vitellina Pendula'	see *S. alba* 'Tristis'
	- - 'Vitellina Tristis'	see *S. alba* 'Tristis'
§	*alpina*	CLyd GDra GIBF NBir NHol
	'Americana'	CWiW
	amplexicaulis 'Pescara'	CWiW
	amygdaloides	CWiW
	'Aokautere'	CWiW
	apoda (m)	ESis EWes GDra GIBF NBir NHar
		WPer
§	*arbuscula*	CBcs CNic GIBF NHar WDin
	arctica var. *petraea*	MBro NHol WIvy WPat
	arenaria	see *S. repens* var. *argentea*
	aurita	LRav NWea
	babylonica	CDul CEnd CTrG NBee SHBN
		WMou
	- 'Annularis'	see *S. babylonica* 'Crispa'

§ - 'Crispa' CFai ELan EPla LHop NBlu NPro
SHBN SMad SPla WBcn WLRN
- 'Pan Chih-kang' CWiW
§ - var. **pekinensis** CEnd
§ - - 'Tortuosa' ♀ H4 More than 30 suppliers
* - 'Tortuosa Aurea' MCCP WBrE
x **basaltica** (m) GIBF
bicolor (f) GIBF
- (m) GIBF
'Blackskin' CWiW
bockii GKir LRHS MBar NWCA WCFE
WFar
§ 'Bowles' Hybrid' CAgr LBuc MRav WMou
'Boydii' (f) ♀ H4 CFee EBee EPfP EPot GAbr GCrs
GDra GKir GTou ITim LPhx MAsh
MBri MBro MDun MGos NBir
NFor NHar NHol NLon NMen
NRya SBla SIng SPer SRms WAbe
WPat
§ 'Boyd's Pendulous' (m) CFee CLyd CWib EHyt MBar
brevipens EPfP
breviserrata CLyd GDra GIBF
caesia GIBF NWCA SRPl
candida GIBF
caprea CAgr CBcs CCVT CKin CLnd CTri
ECrN ENot EPfP GKir GTre LBuc
LHyr NWea WDin WMou
- 'Black Stem' CNat
- 'Curlilocks' COtt MBar
§ - 'Kilmarnock' (m) More than 30 suppliers
- - (m) see S. caprea 'Kilmarnock' (m)
cascadensis GIBF
cashmiriana CFai CLyd MBro NHol NWCA
WPat
* **caspica ruhra nana** SWat
x **cepusiensis** (f) GIBF
x **cernua** NWCA
'Chrysocoma' see S. x sepulcralis var.
chrysocoma
cinerea CAgr CBcs CDoC CDul CKin
ECrN ENot GKir GTre LBuc NWea
WDin
- 'Tricolor' (v) CArn SLim
commutata GIBF
§ **cordata** ECrN SLPl WDin
x **cottetii** EBee GIBF IArd MBar WDin
daphnoides CBrm CCVT CDoC CDul CLnd
CSam EBee ENot EPfP GKir MBrN
NSti NWea SHBN SPer SPla SRms
STre WDin WJas WMou
- 'Aglaia' (m) CBcs CTri ECrN WIvy WPGP
- 'Meikle' CAgr CWiW
- 'Netta Statham' CWiW
- 'Ovaru Udine' CWiW
- 'Oxford Violet' ECrN WIvy
- 'Sinker' WIvy
- 'Stewartstown' CWiW
'E.A. Bowles' see S. 'Bowles' Hybrid'
x **ehrhartiana** CNat
§ **elaeagnos** CAgr CCVT CDoC CLnd CTho
CTri EBee ENot EPfP GKir LRHS
MBlu MBrN MRav SLon SMHy
SPar SPer SWat WDin WFar WIvy
WMou
§ - subsp. **angustifolia** ♀ H4 CDul ELan MRav MTis NWea
SRms STre WWin
elbrusensis EPla
'Elegantissima' see S. x pendulina var.
elegantissima
eriocephala CWiW
'American Mackay'
- 'Kerksii' (m) CWiW
- 'Mawdesley' CWiW

- 'Russelliana' (f) CWiW
§ 'Erythroflexuosa' More than 30 suppliers
exigua More than 30 suppliers
fargesii CBot CDoC CEnd CFee CFil EBee
ELan EPfP GIBF GKir LEdu LHop
LRHS MBlu MDun MGos MRav
NHar NSti SBrw SDix SLim SPar
SSpi WCru WFar WPGP WPat
§ x **finnmarchica** EPot GEdr GIBF NWCA
foetida (f) GIBF
formosa see S. arbuscula
fragilis CCVT CDul CKin CLnd ECrN
GKir MRav NWea WDin WMou
- 'Legomey' WIvy
x **fruticosa** 'McElroy' CWiW
§ **fruticulosa** CTri EHyt GCrs GDra GKev GKir
GTou IKee NWCA SBla SMrm
WPat
'Fuiri-koriyanagi' see S. integra 'Hakuro-nishiki'
furcata see S. fruticulosa
glauca CNat
- subsp. **callicarpaea** (f) GIBF
glaucosericea EBee
'Golden Curls' see S. 'Erythroflexuosa'
gracilistyla CTho EPla NSti SLPl WMou
§ - 'Melanostachys' (m) More than 30 suppliers
x **grahamii** (f) GIBF
- 'Moorei' (f) NWCA
x **greyi** NPro
hastata (f) GIBF
- 'Wehrhahnii' (m) ♀ H4 More than 30 suppliers
helvetica ♀ H4 More than 30 suppliers
herbacea ESis GDra GIBF GTou NMen
hibernica see S. phylicifolia
hookeriana CLnd CMHG CTho EBee ELan
EPla MDlu MBrN MRav NHol SLPl
SSpi WCFE WIvy WMou
incana see S. elaeagnos
integra 'Albomaculata' see S. integra 'Hakuro-nishiki'
§ - 'Hakuro-nishiki' (v) More than 30 suppliers
- 'Pendula' (f) CEnd LRHS
irrorata CDul CLnd
'Jacquinii' see S. alpina
kinuyanagi (m) ELan EPla SMrm
§ **koriyanagi** CWiW WIvy
'Kumeti' CWiW
'Kuro-me' see S. gracilistyla
'Melanostachys'
x **laestadiana** GIBF
lanata ♀ H4 More than 30 suppliers
- 'Drake's Hybrid' NMcn
- hybrid WPat
- 'Mark Postill' see S. 'Mark Postill'
- 'Stuartii' see S. 'Stuartii'
lapponum ESis GIBF GKir MBro NHol
NWCA SRms
- (m) GIBF
- var. **daphneola** (f) GIBF
- - (m) GIBF
liliputa see S. turczaninowii
§ **lindleyana** CNic NBir NOak
lucida EBee ECrN
'Maerd Brno' (f) MBlu
magnifica ♀ H4 CEnd CFil CLnd CMCN EBee EMil
EPfP EPla GIBF GKir IDee MSte
NSti NWea SDry SKee SLim SMad
SSpi SWat WCru WDin WFar
WMou WPGP
- x **fargesii** new WPGP
§ 'Mark Postill' (f) CDoC CEbD EBee EMil LHop
LRHS MBNS SPla SPoG
matsudana 'Tortuosa' see S. babylonica var. pekinensis
'Tortuosa'

- 'Tortuosa Aureopendula'	see *S.* 'Erythroflexuosa'
'Melanostachys'	see *S. gracilistyla* 'Melanostachys'
x **meyeriana**	WIvy
- 'Lumley' (f)	CWiW
x **mollissima** var. **hippophaifolia** 'Jeffries'	CWiW
- var. **hippophaifolia**	CWiW
'Notts Spaniard' (f)	
- - 'Stinchcombe'	WIvy
- - 'Trustworthy' (f)	CWiW
- var. **undulata** 'Kottenheider Weide'	CWiW
moupinensis	EPfP
§ **myrsinifolia**	EPla MBlu
§ **myrsinites**	GIBF
- var. **jacquiniana**	see *S. alpina*
myrtilloides	CLyd
- 'Pink Tassels' (m)	NWCA SIng WPat
- x **repens**	see *S.* x *finnmarchica*
nakamurana var. **yezoalpina**	CFai CFee EPot GAbr GDra GEdr GIBF GKir LRHS MBro MRav NLAp NPro SLim WFar WIvy WPat
nepalensis	see *S. lindleyana*
nigricans	see *S. myrsinifolia*
nivalis	see *S. reticulata* subsp. *nivalis*
x **obtusifolia**	GIBF
onychiophylla (f)	GIBF
x **ovata**	CLyd GCrs NMen
§ x **pendulina** var. **elegantissima**	CTho
pentandra	CAgr CBot CDul CKin CLnd ECrN LRav NWea WDin WFar WMou
- 'Patent Lumley'	CWiW
'Philip's Fancy'	NWCA
§ **phylicifolia**	ECrN WMou
- 'Malham'	CWiW
polaris	CLyd GIBF
x **punctata**	GIBF
§ **purpurea**	CBcs CDul GIBF MBrN NWea SRms WDin WMou
- 'Abbeys'	WIvy
- 'Brittany Green' (f)	CWiW
- 'Continental Reeks'	CWiW WIvy
- 'Dark Dicks' (f)	CWiW WIvy
- 'Dicky Meadows'	CAgr CWiW WIvy
- 'Goldstones'	CAgr CWiW WIvy
- f. **gracilis**	see *S. purpurea* 'Nana'
- 'Green Dicks'	CAgr CWiW WIvy
- 'Helix'	see *S. purpurea*
- 'Howki' (m)	WMou
- 'Irette' (m)	CWiW
- 'Jagiellonka' (f)	CWiW WIvy
- var. **japonica**	see *S. koriyanagi*
- subsp. **lambertiana**	CWiW WIvy
- 'Lancashire Dicks' (m)	CWiW
- 'Leicestershire Dicks' (m)	CWiW
- 'Light Dicks'	CWiW
- 'Lincolnshire Dutch'	CWiW
§ - 'Nana'	CLyd EPfP EPla ESis MWhi SLPl SLon STre WAul WFar WMoo
- 'Nancy Saunders' (f)	CHad CTho CWiW EHoe EPPr EPla EVFa GBuc GGGa MBNS MBlu MBrN MBri MRav MSte NPro NSti SUsu WCot WIvy
- 'Pendula' ♀ H4	CEnd CTho CWib EBee ECrN ENot LRHS MAsh MBar MBri MRav NBlu NHol NWea SPoG WDin WStI
- 'Read'	CWiW
- 'Reeks'	CWiW
- 'Richartii' (f)	CWiW NSti WLRN
- 'Uralensis' (f)	CWiW

pyrenaica	CLyd EHyt GIBF NWCA
repens	GIBF GKir MBar SRms STre SWat WDin
§ - var. **argentea**	EBee ENot EPfP GDra GIBF MBar MRav MWgw MWhi NWCA NWea SLim SPer WDin WFar WWin
- from Saint Kilda	GKir
- 'Iona' (m)	CLyd WStI
- **pendula**	see *S.* 'Boyd's Pendulous' (m)
- 'Voorthuizen' (f)	EHol EHyt ESis MBar MGos WDin WGer WStI
reticulata ♀ H4	EPot GCrs GDra GIBF GKir GTou NBir NHar NMen NRya NSla NWoo WPat
§ - subsp. **nivalis**	EPot GDra GIBF
retusa	CTri GDra GIBF GKir GTou MBro NBir NHar WPat
- x **pyrenaica**	ECho
rosmarinifolia hort.	see *S. elaeagnos* subsp. *angustifolia*
x **rubens** 'Basfordiana' (m) **new**	CDoC CLnd CTho CWiW EPla EWes MBNS MRav NWea WLRN WMou
- 'Bouton Aigu'	CWiW
- 'Farndon'	CWiW
- 'Flanders Red'	CWiW
- 'Fransgeel Rood'	CWiW
- 'Glaucescens'	CWiW
- 'Golden Willow'	CWiW
- 'Jaune de Falaise'	CWiW
- 'Jaune Hâtive'	CWiW
- 'Laurina'	CWiW
- 'Natural Red'	CWiW
- 'Parsons'	CWiW
- 'Rouge Ardennais'	CWiW
- 'Rouge Folle'	CWiW
- 'Russet'	CWiW
x **rubra**	CWiW
- 'Abbey's Harrison'	CWiW
- 'Continental Osier'	CWiW
- 'Eugenei' (m)	CDul CTho ECrN EPla GQui MBlu SWat WBcn WIvy WMou WWin
- 'Fidkin'	CWiW
- 'Harrison's'	CWiW
- 'Harrison's Seedling A' (f)	CWiW
- 'Mawdesley'	CWiW
- 'Mawdesley Seedling A' (f)	CWiW
- 'Pyramidalis'	CWiW
'Scarlet Curls' **new**	WPat
x **sepulcralis**	NWea
- 'Caradoc'	CWiW
§ - var. **chrysocoma**	CDoC CSBt CWib EBee ECrN ENot EPfP GKir LBuc LPan LRHS MAsh MGos MWat NBea NBee NBlu SCoo SHBN SLim SPer SRPl WDin WLRN WOrn WWeb
serpyllifolia	CLyd CTri EHyt ESis GIBF MBro NHol NMen WPat
- x **retusa**	NWCA
serpyllum	see *S. fruticulosa*
'Setsuka'	see *S. udensis* 'Sekka'
x **simulatrix**	CLyd EBee EHyt GIBF MBar NWCA
x **sobrina**	GIBF
x **stipularis** (f)	CMHG CWib EPla NWea
§ 'Stuartii'	GAbr GIBF MBar NMen NWCA SRms
subopposita	CDul EBee ELan EWes MBNS MBar MBro NPro
x **tetrapla**	GIBF
thomasii	GIBF

'Tora'^{PBR} **new** — LRav

triandra — LRav WMou
- 'Black German' — CWiW
- 'Black Hollander' — CAgr CWiW WIvy
- 'Black Maul' — CAgr CWiW
- 'Grisette de Falaise' — CWiW
- 'Grisette Droda' — CWiW
- 'Long Bud' — CWiW
- 'Noir de Challans' — CWiW
- 'Noir de Touraine' — CWiW
- 'Noir de Villaines' — CWiW WIvy
- 'Rouge d'Orléans' — ECrN
- 'Sarda d'Anjou' — CWiW
- 'Semperflorens' (m) — CNat
- 'Whissander' — CAgr CWiW WIvy
x *tsugaluensis* — CDul CMHG SLPl
    'Ginme' (f)

§ *turczaninowii* (m) — GIBF
§ *udensis* 'Sekka' (m) — CLnd CMHG CTho EBee ECtt ELan EPar NBir NHol NWea STre SWat WFar WIvy WMou

uva-ursi — CLyd GIBF SLim
viminalis — CAgr CCVT CDul CKin CLnd EBee ENot LBuc NWea WDin WMou

- 'Bowles' Hybrid' — see S. 'Bowles' Hybrid'
- 'Brown Merrin' — CAgr WIvy
- 'Green Gotz' — CWiW WIvy
- 'Reader's Red' (m) — CAgr WIvy
- 'Riefenweide' — WIvy
- 'Yellow Osier' — CAgr WIvy
vitellina 'Pendula' — see S. alba 'Tristis'
§ *waldsteiniana* — GIBF MBar NWCA
x *wimmeriana* — EPot SRms
'Yelverton' — LRHS MBri MRav SWat WWes

Salvia ✿ (Lamiaceae)

CC&McK 77 — GTou
CD&R 3071 — CStr
acetabulosa — see S. multicaulis
✱ *aellamii* — CI'wr
aethiopis — CPle CSev CStr EBlw MLLN WPer WWyc
§ *africana* — CArn CDul CPle GGar LPio WDyG WWye
africana-caerulea — see S. africana
africana-lutea — see S. aurea
agnes — CStr LIck
albimaculata — SBla
amarissima — CPle CStr
'Amber' **new** — EBee SUsu
ambigens — see S. guaranitica 'Blue Enigma'
§ *amplexicaulis* — CPle MGol NLar SBod WPer WWye
angustifolia Mich. — see S. azurea
angustifolia Cav. — see S. reptans
apiana — CArn IIve MGol MHer MSal SAga SGar SIgm WCot
argentea ♀ H3 — More than 30 suppliers
arizonica — CPle CPom CStr EBee LIck MLLN MRod SDys
atrocyanea — CPle CStr GBri LIck MAsh MLLN MRod SDys WDyG WOut WWye
aucheri — CPle GBar GBuc GCal
§ *aurea* — CHal CHll CMil CPle CSev CStr CTCP ELan GGar LHop LPio MHFa MHar MIIcr MOak MRod MSte SAga SGar SSte WCot WDyG WPer
- 'Kirstenbosch' — CPle CStr EBee ECtt EPPr MAsh MLLN MRav MRod SDys WCot WOut WPer WWye

austriaca — CPle EBee GBri SHFr WPer
§ *azurea* — CArn CPle EBee LPhx LPio MAsh MNrw MRod MSte NPPs SAga SBod SMrm WOut WRha
- var. *grandiflora* — CStr MAsh
bacheriana — see S. buchananii
§ *barrelieri* — CPle CStr MRod SHFr
bertolonii — see S. pratensis Bertolonii Group
bicolor Des. — see S. barrelieri
blancoana — CArn CBot CPle CSLe CStr ECha ELau EMan GBar LEdu LHrt MAsh MHer MLLN MOak MSte NChi SAga SCro
blepharophylla — CPle CSpe CStr EBee ECtt EOrc GBri LHop LIck MAsh MBNS MHar MHer MSte MWat SAga WGwG WPen WWeb WWye
- 'Diablo' **new** — SDys
brachyantha — EBee
§ *buchananii* ♀ H1+3 — More than 30 suppliers
bulleyana misapplied — see S. flava var. megalantha
bulleyana — CBri EChP EMFP EMan EWes GBar LIck MHer MWrn NLar WCru WFar
cacaliifolia ♀ H1+3 — CPle CPne CRHN CSpe CStr EBlw EOrc GBar GBri MAsh MHar MHer MLLN MNrw MSte MWat MWgw SGar SHFr SPer SRkn SUsu WCom WOut WPPR WSHC WWye
caerulea hort. — see S. guaranitica 'Black and Blue'
caerulea L. — see S. africana
caespitosa — CPle EHyt SBla
campanulata — CPle CPom WCot
- CC&McK 1071 — CFir
canariensis — CFil CPle CStr EBee IGor MLLN MRod MSte SHFr WOut WSan WWye
candelabrum ♀ H3-4 — CArn CDes CMca CPle CPom EBee ECtt EMan EOrc EVFa GBri LPhx MAsh MHer MRod MWgw SAga SHFr WCHb WCot WHer WKif WSHC WWye
candidissima — WOut
canescens — CPom
cardinalis — see S. fulgens
castanea — CPle GBri MHar
§ *chamaedryoides* — CPle CSev CStr EBee LPhx MAsh MRod NDov SAga SChu SDys SSpi WCom WOut WPPR WSHC WWye
- var *isochroma* **new** — MAsh SDys
- silver — CStr LPhx MRod MSte SAga WOut
chamelaeagnea — CStr SDys
chapalensis — SAga
chiapensis — CPle EOrc IFro MRod WOut
chinensis — see S. japonica
'Christine Yeo' — CDes CDoC CPle EBee EPPr GAbr GBri GGar LIck MAsh MRod MSte SDys SGar SWal WOut WPGP WWye
cinnabarina — CPle
cleistogama misapplied — see S. glutinosa
cleistogama — MHer
    DeBary & Paul
clevelandii — CPle MGol MHer MRod WJek WOut
- 'Winnifred Gilman' **new** — SDys
coahuilensis — LPlix MRod NDov NPPs SAga SGar SMrm SOkh WSHC WWye
coccinea — CBot CDoC EOrc GBri MGol MHer MSte MWgw SHFr WPer WWye

- 'Brenthurst' **new**	CStr
- 'Coral Nymph'	EOrc LDai LIck LRHS MGol SChu SDys SWat WOut
- 'Indigo'	EPfP GBri MAsh WMnd WSan
- 'Lactea'	CBot
- 'Lady in Red' ♀ H3	CStr EOrc LIck SWat
* - 'Snow Nymph'	LIck
concolor hort.	see *S. guaranitica*
concolor Lamb.	CPle CStr GCal MAsh WDyG WOut WSHC
confertiflora	CDoC CPle CPom CSam CSpe CStr CTbh EBee EBlw ELan EMFP EOrc GBri IFro LIck MAsh MHar MLLN MLan MOak MSte MTis SAga SDys SGar WCom WDyG WOut WWye
corrugata	CDes CDoC CFwr CPle CPom CSpe CStr EBee ECtt EMan EOrc EPri GBri LHop LIck LPhx MAsh MLLN MRod MTis SAga SCro SDys SRkn SVen WCot WDyG WOut WPPR WWye
cyanescens	CPle EPot
cyclostegia **new**	EBee
darcyi	CHll CPle CStr EChP LIck LPhx MAsh MRod SAga SDys SIgm WOut WSHC WWye
davidsonii	CStr
'Dear Anja'	EFou EGle LHop LPhx NDov
dentata **new**	WCot
discolor ♀ H1	More than 30 suppliers
* - *nigra*	CMdw WDin
disermas	CPle CStr SPlb
divinorum	ELan EOHP GPoy MGol MSal
dolichantha	CHar EBee EShb EVFa MGol MWrn SBod WHil WLin WWye
dolomitica	CStr
dombeyi	CFir
dorisiana	CPle CPne CStr ELan EOHP MLLN MSte SDys WJek WOut WWye
§ *elegans*	CMHG CPle CSev CStr ELau EPri EWes LIck MAsh MSte NPPs SCro WCer WCom WFar WOut WPPR WWye
- 'Frieda Dixon'	EBee EOHP
- 'Honey Melon' **new**	EOHP
§ - 'Scarlet Pineapple'	More than 30 suppliers
* - 'Tangerine Sage'	CArn CBri CPrp ELau EOHP GBar GGar MBow MGol MHer NGHP SWal WBry WHHs
fallax	CStr
farinacea 'Alba'	LPVe
- 'Cirrus'	CFox
- 'Rhea'	LIck LRHS
- 'Strata'	ECtt LRHS
- 'Victoria' ♀ H3	ELau LPVe MHer MRod
§ *flava* var. *megalantha*	CFai CHea CPle ELan EOrc GBin LRHS MFir MNrw NChi NGdn NSti SHFr SSte WFar WPer WWin WWye
forreri	CDes EBee SDys SSpi WPGP
- CD&R 1269	CPle CStr GBri
§ *forsskaolii*	More than 30 suppliers
§ *fruticosa*	CArn CPle CStr ELau EOHP LRHS SIde
§ *fulgens* ♀ H3	CFwr CPle CStr IFro ILis MAsh MHer SAga SBri SGar SHFr SRkn WCHb WCom WFar WOut WRha WWhi WWye
gesneriiflora	CPle CStr MHer MSte WGwG WPer WWye
gilliesii	CStr
§ *glutinosa*	CArn CHad CPle CSam CSpe EOrc EPPr GCal LDai MAsh MCAu MNrw MWrn NBro NCWG NPPs SAga WOut WPer WWye
grahamii	see *S. microphylla* var. *microphylla*
greggii	CPle EBlw ECtt EWes LPio MAsh MHer MSte MTis SPar SPer SWat WOut WPer WWin
- CD&R 1148	CPle LIck SDys
- 'Alba'	CHal CPle EBee EOHP LIck MAsh NBur NGHP SDys WPPR WWol
- 'Blush Pink'	see *S. microphylla* 'Pink Blush'
- 'Caramba' (v)	CFwr CSpe MAsh NGHP SAga WWol
- 'Desert Blaze' (v)	CStr EMan EPPr LIck MAsh NDov NGHP SDys WCom WCot WHil
- 'Devon Cream'	see *S. greggii* 'Sungold'
- 'Forman's Red' **new**	EBee
- 'Keter's Red'	CPle EVFa MAsh MRod
§ - x *lycioides*	CPle EBee EMFP LPio MAsh MRod NPPs SBri SDys SGar SUsu WPPR WSHC WWye
- 'Magenta'	MDKP WHil
- 'Peach'	CDoC CPle CSpe EBee ELau EOrc EPfP EVFa LHop LPhx LPio LRHS MAsh MDKP MHer MLLN MSte NDov NGHP NPPs NPri SAga SGar SOkh SUsu SWal WPGP WPPR WWol
- 'Peach' misapplied	see *S. x jamensis* 'Pat Vlasto'
- 'Raspberry Royal'	see *S.* 'Raspberry Royale'
- 'Sierra San Antonio'	CSpe MAsh
- 'Stormy Pink' **new**	CSpe
- 'Sundown'	NGHP
§ - 'Sungold'	CPle CStr EBee EOrc EPfP LHop LIck LPhx LRHS MAsh SDys SWal WPPR WSan WWol
- yellow	LPio LRHS SSpi
§ *guaranitica*	CBot CFil CHEx CPle CPne EBre ECtt LPio MAsh MHer SAga SPer SRPl SRkn SUsu WCHb WPGP WSan WWye
- 'Argentine Skies'	CPle CStr EGle LIck LPhx LPio MAsh SAga SBla SChu SDys SMrm WDyG WOut WPGP WSHC WWye
§ - 'Black and Blue'	CFil CPle CRHN CSWP CSev CStr EBee EBlw EOHP GBri LIck LPhx MAsh MSte MWat SGar SMrm SVen WDyG WOut WPGP WPer WRha WWye
§ - 'Blue Enigma' ♀ H3-4	More than 30 suppliers
haematodes	see *S. pratensis* Haematodes Group
heldreichiana	CStr
heterochroa **new**	EBee
hians	CBrm CFir CPle EBee ECoo EOrc GBar GBri LPhx MBro MNrw SAga SBla SGar SMrm SRms SSte SSth WCer WCot WHoo WPer WWye
hierosolymitana	CPle CStr SHFr SUsu
hispanica hort.	see *S. lavandulifolia*
horminum	see *S. viridis* var. *comata*
hypargeia	CPle
indica	SRms
'Indigo Spires'	CHll CMdw CPle CPne CSpe CStr EBee EBlw ECtt EOrc EPPr EVFa GBri GMaP LPhx MAsh MHar MLLN MRod SBri SMrm SUsu WCom WDyG WOut WPPR WPen WSHC WWye

interrupta	CPle EHol EMan EOHP EWes LIck SAga SChu SHFr WCom WOut WPen		LPhx SAga SGar SSvw WHrl WPer WSan WWeb
involucrata ♀ H3	CFir CPle CSev CStr EOrc GCal GQui LPhx MAsh MHar MHer MRod NBro NBur NPPs SCro SDys SMrm SSte WOut WSHC	_macellaria_ misapplied	see _S. microphylla_
		macellaria	CSam
		macrophylla	WCra
		'Caramba' **new**	
– 'Bethellii' ♀ H3-4	More than 30 suppliers	_madrensis_	CStr LIck MOak MRod WCom
– 'Boutin' ♀ H3	CPle GBri MAsh MLLN SBri SDys	§ 'Maraschino'	CBri CStr EBee EMan MAsh WCot WMnd
§ – 'Hadspen'	CBot CFwr CHad CHll CSam CStr LIck MSte WCom WWye		
		mellifera	CPle
– 'Mrs Pope'	see _S. involucrata_ 'Hadspen'	_merjamie_	CPle CPom EBee SCro
– 'Mulberry Jam' **new**	MAsh	– 'Mint-sauce'	CPen CPla EMan EMar MCCP MNrw SHFr WBea WPer
I – var. _puberula_	CPle SDys		
iodantha	CPle WWye	_mexicana_	CDoC CPle GBri LIck SSpi WWye
x _jamensis_	CStr SDys	– T&K 550	CArn CBot
– CPN 5096	SAga	– 'Limelight'	CStr
– 'Cherry Queen'	CPle CStr MAsh SAga SDys WWye	– var. _minor_	CDoC CPle GBri MRod WPer
		§ _microphylla_	CArn CMHG CPle CPom EBlw ELau EOHP EOrc EWes GBar GGar LHop LHrt MBow MChe MHer NPPs NSti SHFr SSpi SYvo WCom WCru WHCG WHHs WPPR WPer
– 'Devantville'	CPle LPhx SAga		
– 'El Duranzo'	CPle LPio		
– 'Fuego'	LIck		
– 'James Compton'	EBee LIck LPio MSte SDys SGar SIgm	– CD&R 1495	MAsh
		– 'Cerro Potosi'	CBri CMdw CPle CStr EBee GBri MAsh MRod MSte SAga SDys SGar SHFr SMrm WPen WWeb WWye
– 'La Luna'	CPle CPom CSam CSev EBee ECtt EPfP EPri LPhx LPio MAsh MHar MHer MSte MUlv NDov NPPs SAga SBri SDys SGar SOkh SWal WCom WFar WPGP WPPR WPen WSHC WWye		
		– 'Elmar' **new**	EBee
		* – 'Huntingdon Red'	EOHP
		– 'Kew Red' ♀ H3-4	CDoC CPle CStr MAsh MBro SAga WHoo WPen
– 'La Siesta'	CPle LPio MAsh SDys	– 'Maraschino'	see _S._ 'Maraschino'
– 'La Tarde'	CPle LPio MAsh MRod MSte SAga SDys	§ – var. _microphylla_	More than 30 suppliers
		– – 'La Foux'	CHea CPle LPhx MAsh MRod SAga SDys SMrm SOkh
– 'Los Lirios' ♀ H3-4	CPle CStr EBee EOrc EPPr GBri LIck MSte SBri SDys SMrm WCom WOut WPen	– – 'Newby Hall' ♀ H3-4	CBrm CPle CStr EBee EOrc EWes LIck LPhx MAsh MSte SChu WPGP WPer
* – 'Mauve'	SDys	– var. _neurepia_	see _S. microphylla_ var. _microphylla_
– 'Moonlight Over Ashwood' (v) **new**	MAsh		
		– 'Oregon Peach'	LRHS MAsh
– 'Moonlight Serenade'	CPle CScv CStr EBlw EOrc GBri MAsh MRod SDys	– 'Oxford'	CPle CStr SDys
		§ – 'Pink Blush' ♀ H3-4	CAbP CBot CPle CPne EBee ELan EMan EOrc EPfP FPri FVFa GBri LRHS MAsh MLLN MMil MRod MSte NGHP SMrm SOkh SSpi SWal WCom WHil WSHC
§ – 'Pat Vlasto'	CPle CStr EBee GBri LIck MAsh SDys SMrm SWal WEas WPen WSHC WWye		
– pink seedling	WLin		
– 'Pleasant Pink'	CPle EBee LIck MAsh		
§ _japonica_	CArn CPle WWye	– 'Pleasant View' ♀ H3-4	CPle GBri MAsh
judaica	CPle CStr EBee EChP	– purple	EBee GCal WHHs
jurisicii	CArn CFir CPle CStr EBee EOrc SGar SHFr SIgm SScr WOut WWyc	§ – 'Ruth Stungo' (v)	CPle SAga
		– 'San Carlos Festival'	EBee MAsh SDys
		– 'Variegata' splashed	see _S. microphylla_ 'Ruth Stungo'
– pink-flowered **new**	CStr	– 'Wild Watermelon' **new**	MAsh
* _karvinskii_ **new**	CStr	§ – var. _wislizenii_	CDoC CPle CStr WPer
kuznetzovii	EBee	_miltiorhiza_	CArn EBee MSal
lanceolata	see _S. reflexa_	_miniata_	CPle CStr SDys WOut
§ _lavandulifolia_	More than 30 suppliers	_moorcroftiana_	MGol WPer
lemmonii	see _S. microphylla_ var. _wislizenii_	_muelleri_	CDes CMdw CSpe EBee WCom
leptophylla	see _S. reptans_	§ _multicaulis_ ♀ H4	CPle EBlw ECha EMan ETow MSte SHFr WPer WSHC
leucantha ♀ H1	More than 30 suppliers		
– 'Midnight' **new**	LIck	* _murrayi_	WCot
– 'Purple Velvet'	CPle GBri MAsh MRod SDys	_namaensis_ **new**	CStr
– 'Santa Barbara' **new**	MAsh	_napifolia_	CMea CStr EBee EPyc LPhx MGol MWrn NDov NGar SAga SBod WLin WOut
leucophylla	CStr MHer SIgm		
longispicata	MHFa		
lycioides hort.	see _S. greggii_ x _S. lycioides_	_nemorosa_	EBee EBre MWrn NLar SHFr SRms WOut
lycioides A. Gray	CHll CPle MAsh SDys SRkn WDyG		
lyrata	CPle EBee EMan EOHP GBri MDKP MGol MSal MSph SAga SGar SHFr SUsu WOut WWye	– 'Amethyst' ♀ H4	More than 30 suppliers
		– East Friesland	see _S. nemorosa_ 'Ostfriesland'
		– 'Lubecca' ♀ H4	EBee EBre ECtt EFou EGle EIIrv EMan EPfP EPla LRHS MCAu MCLN MLLN MWgw SMrm SPer WLRN WMnd WRus
– 'Burgundy Bliss'	SHar		
– 'Purple Knockout'	CFwr EBee EBlw EChP EMan EMar EPPr EVFa GSki LAst LPVe	– 'Midsummer' **new**	MGol

	- 'Negrito'	EGle
§	- 'Ostfriesland' ♀ H4	More than 30 suppliers
	- 'Phoenix Pink' **new**	LPhx
	- 'Plumosa'	see *S. nemorosa* 'Pusztaflamme'
§	- 'Pusztaflamme' ♀ H4	CPrp CPle CStr EBee EChP ECha EMan ENot EPfP LRHS MBri MBro MCAu MCLN MLLN MMHG NSti SAga SBla SCro SMrm SUsu WHoo WWeb WWye
	- 'Rose Queen'	CFwr CStr ECtt EMFP GKir NBir SPla WFar WHHs WRHF
	- 'Rosenwein'	CBri CMHG CSam EBee EMan GBuc LPVe LPhx MCAu SMrm
	- 'Royal Distinction' **new**	MUlv
	- 'Schwellenburg' **new**	EBee
§	- subsp. *tesquicola*	CPom EBee ECha EGle LPVe LPhx SAga SMrm
	- 'Wesuwe'	CPle EBee ECha EGle SCro
	neurepia	see *S. microphylla* var. *microphylla*
	nilotica	CArn CPle EBee EOrc EWll MGol SHFr WElm WHer WOut
	nipponica	CPle WPer
	- B&SWJ 5829	WCru
	- 'Fuji Snow' (v)	EBee EFou EMan EWes GBri MLLN
	nubicola	CPle CStr EMar GPoy LDai MWod WWye
	officinalis	More than 30 suppliers
	- 'Alba'	see *S. officinalis* 'Albiflora'
§	- 'Albiflora'	CBot EOHP GBar MHer MLLN NLon WCHb WJek WPer
N	- 'Aurea' ambig.	CWib EPar GPoy MBar MFir NPri SPar
	- 'Berggarten'	CArn EBee ECha EFou ELau EMan EMon EPfP EPri EWTr GBar GCal GKir LHop LPhx LPio MAnH MRav NSti SAga SChu SDes SDix SSvw WBry WCFE WHer WMnd
I	- 'Blackcurrant'	CHal WHHs
§	- broad-leaved	CBot CSWP ELau MHer SWat WHHs WJek WWye
	- 'Crispa'	WCHb
	- 'Extrakta'	EOHP
	- 'Herrenhausen'	MSte
§	- 'Icterina' (v) ♀ H4	More than 30 suppliers
	- 'Kew Gold'	ELau MRav WJek
	- *latifolia*	see *S. officinalis* broad-leaved
	- 'Minor'	EGoo WHer
*	- 'Nana' **new**	MAsh
	- narrow-leaved	see *S. lavandulifolia*
*	- 'Pink Splash' (v)	WCHb
	- *prostrata*	see *S. lavandulifolia*
	- 'Purpurascens' ♀ H4	More than 30 suppliers
	- 'Purpurascens Variegata' (v)	CStr GBar MAsh NChi NSti SPet WEas WJek
	- 'Robin Hill'	CBod GBar
	- 'Rosea'	CStr IIve WBcn WCHb WHer WOut
*	- tangerine	EDAr SPet
	- Tomentosa Group	CArn
	- 'Tricolor' (v)	More than 30 suppliers
	- 'Variegata'	see *S. officinalis* 'Icterina'
	- variegated (v) **new**	MAsh
	oppositiflora ♀ H1+3	CPle CStr EMan LIck MAsh MHer MRod SDys WPPR
	pachyphylla	SIgm
§	*patens* ♀ H3	More than 30 suppliers
	- 'Alba' misapplied	see *S. patens* 'White Trophy'
	- 'Blue Trophy'	LIck
	- 'Cambridge Blue' ♀ H3	More than 30 suppliers
	- 'Chilcombe'	CFai CPle CSam CStr EBee EBlw

		GBri LIck MAsh MHar MHer NGHP NPPs SAga SChu SDys SHFr SUsu WHoo WOut WPPR WSHC WWol WWye
	- 'Guanajuato'	CPle CPom CSam CSpe CStr EBee EVFa EWes IPot MAsh MHar MSte NPPs SAga SDys SRot SUsu WHil WPGP WPPR WSHC
	- 'Oxford Blue'	see *S. patens*
	- 'Royal Blue'	see *S. patens*
§	- 'White Trophy'	CHal CPle CPom CStr EBee EChP EOrc EPri ERou LDai LHop LIck LRHS MAsh MSte NGHP SCro SGar SWal WFar WPPR WSHC WWol WWye
	penstemonoides	EBee
	phlomoides	EBee MGol
	polystachya	CPle MRod WWye
	pratensis	CArn CFwr CKin CPle ECoo ELan EMon LPio MSal MWgw MWrn SGar WOut WPer WWye
	- 'Albiflora'	EMon LRHS
§	- Bertolonii Group	SEND
§	- Haematodes Group ♀ H4	CPle EBre EChP ECha ELan LDai MBro MNrw MWrn NDov NLar SBla SRms WHoo WPer WWye
	- 'Indigo' ♀ H4	CPlt EBee EBre EFou EMan EMar EPfP EWll LRHS MRav NDov NLar WAul WElm
	- Lapis Lazuli'	CDes CKno CPle CPlt CStr EBee EVFa LPhx
	- 'Rosea'	CBgR CPle EBre ECha LPhx LRHS WWye
	- 'Tenorei'	WPer
	przewalskii	CBel CDes CHar CPle CPom CStr EOrc GIBF IFro LPhx MGol MHer MNrw MSal MWgw MWrn NMRc SGar SHFr SMrm WOut WPer WWye
	- ACE 1157	EBee WCot WCru
	- DJH 210524	EPPr
	'Purple Majesty'	CHea CPle CStr EBee GBri LIck LPhx LPio MAsh MRod MSte SDys SMrm SSpi SUsu WCom WOut WSan WWye
	purpurea	CM&M CPle MGol
	'Raspberry Royale' ♀ H3-4	CDoC CFwr CPle CSev EBee EBlw ELan EPfP EPri EWoo LHop LIck LRHS MAsh MHer MSte NGHP NPPs SGar SMrm SUsu SWal SWat WCom WCra WPPR WPen WSHC WWol WWye
	recognita	CBot CPle LPhx
§	*reflexa*	LIck
	regeliana hort.	see *S. virgata* Jacq.
	regeliana Trautv.	CPle MLLN NBir WPer
	regla	CPle CStr MRod SDys
	repens	CPle CStr EBee IGor SDys WDyG WWye
§	*reptans*	CPle CSam CSpe CStr LHop LIck MAsh MHar SAga WDyG WOut WPer
	ringens	CPle
	riparia misapplied	see *S. rypara*
	roemeriana ♀ H3	CPle CStr EBee EOrc LIck MAsh MDKP NPPs NWCA SDys WCot WHil WOut WPGP
	rubescens **new**	CStr
	rutilans	see *S. elegans* 'Scarlet Pineapple'
	rypara	CPle CPom MLLN
	sagittata **new**	CStr MAsh

scabiosifolia	CPom ECoo MGol
scabra	CFir CPle CPle EChP MGol MRod
	MSte NPPs SDys WOut WWye
sclarea	CArn CPle EBee EBre ECtt EGoo
	ELau GPoy LRHS MChe MHer
	MWat NChi NGdn SIde WCHb
	WHHs WHer WHoo WPer WWye
§ - var. *sclarea*	CKno EWTr MAnH NSti SPet
	WCra WWeb WWpP
- var. *turkestanica* hort.	More than 30 suppliers
§ - 'Vatican White'	CPle EBee EMar GKir
- white-bracted	CBri CHar ECoo EFWa EOHP
	GMac LHop MAnH NLar SBod
	WCom WHHs WSHC
scutellarioides	CStr WOut
semiatrata hort.	see *S. chamaedryoides*
semiatrata Zucc.	CPle CSpe EOrc LIck LPhx MAsh
	SAga SDys WWye
'Silke's Dream' **new**	MAsh
sinaloensis	CFai CPle CSpe CTbh EBee MAsh
	MDKP MSte SDys WOut WRha
somalensis	CDoC CPle CStr MAsh WOut
spathacea ♀ H3-4	CPle CPom CStr EMan LHop LPhx
	SDys SIgm WWye
splendens	CStr
- peach-flowered **new**	CStr
§ - 'Van-Houttei' ♀ H3	CDoC CPle CStr LIck MAsh MLLN
	MRod SDys WCom WWye
sprucei	CStr
§ *staminea*	CPle CStr MGol MNrw SHFr
	WFlm WPer WSan WWye
stenophylla	CPle EBee EChP MGol SWal
	WGwG WOut WPer
x *superba* ♀ H4	CBot CSBt EBre ECtt ELan EOrc
	EPfP EWTr LEdu LRHS MBri MHer
	MMil MWat MWrn SCro SDes
	SDix SMrm SPer SRms SSpe SSvw
	WHoo WWhi WWye
- 'Adrian'	SChu
- 'Forncett Dawn'	EFou EGle SChu
- 'Rubin' ♀ H4	CDos EBee SChu SCro SMrm
- 'Superba'	CSev ECha EFou EHrv LPhx MHdf
	MRav NDov SCro
x *sylvestris*	More than 30 suppliers
'Blauhügel' ♀ H4	
§ - 'Blaukönigin'	CBri EBee EPfP ERou EWTr GKir
	IBal LPVe LRHS MWat MWrn
	NArg NLar NMir NOak NVic SDes
	SIgm SPet SPlb WBea WHil WPer
	WWeb
- Blue Queen	see *S.* x *sylvestris* 'Blaukönigin'
- 'Caradonna'	CFwr EBee SUsu
- 'Lye End'	ERou MRav WCot
§ - 'Mainacht' ♀ H4	More than 30 suppliers
- May Night	see *S.* x *sylvestris* 'Mainacht'
- 'Rose Queen'	More than 30 suppliers
- 'Rügen'	EBee EMan LBuc LRHS MBri
- 'Schneehügel'	EBee EChP ECha EGle EMan ENot
	EPfP GKir GMaP LPVe MBNS
	MCAu MMil NPri SBla SCro SPer
	WHil WLRN WMnd WWeb
- 'Tänzerin' ♀ H4	EFou EGle LPhx NDov SChu SCro
	SDys SMHy SMrm WCot
- 'Viola Klose'	CStr EBee EBre EFou EGle EMan
	EMar GCal GKir LPhx LRHS MBri
	MCAu NPPs SMrm
- 'Wissalink'	SUsu
tachiei hort.	see *S. forsskaolii*
taraxacifolia	CPle CStr
tesquicola	see *S. nemorosa* subsp. *tesquicola*
tiliifolia	EBee EOHP MGol SHFr SRms
tomentosa	CPle EBee ECoo MGol WOut
transcaucasica	see *S. staminea*

transsylvanica	CArn CBel CHea CPle EBee EChP
	EOrc EPfP EPPr EWTr LRHS MCAu
	MWgw MWrn SChu SCro SMrm
	STes SWat WCFE WCom WPer
'Trebah'	MAsh MRod NFla SCoo SDys SGar
	WWye
'Trelawney'	MAsh
'Trelissick'	IPot MAsh MRod NFla SAsh SDys
	WOut
'Trenance'	IPot MAsh MRod SDys SGar
'Trewithen'	MAsh MRod NFla SAsh SCoo SPoG
trijuga	WOut
triloba	see *S. fruticosa*
uliginosa ♀ H3-4	More than 30 suppliers
- 'African Skies'	SMrm WDyG
urica	SDys
'Van-Houttei'	see *S. splendens* 'Van-Houttei'
'Vatican City'	see *S. sclarea* 'Vatican White'
verbenaca	CArn CKin EOHP MHer MNrw
	MSal NMir NSco SHFr WOut WPer
	WWye
verticillata	CArn CPle CPlt CStr EBee ECha
	EGoo EHrv EPri LHrt LRHS MBro
	MCAu MGol MHer SDys WOut
	WPer WWye
- 'Alba'	CPle CSev EBee ECGN EGle
	EOrc EPfP ERou LRHS MAnH
	MCAu MRav MTis MWgw NGdn
	NSti SDes SRPl WHer WPer
	WRus
- 'Hannay's Blue'	EFou
- 'Hannay's Purple'	EFou
- 'Purple Rain'	More than 30 suppliers
- 'Smouldering Torches'	LPhx
- 'White Rain'	CAbP EFou LBBr
'Vicki Romo'	MRod
villicaulis	see *S. amplexicaulis*
§ *virgata* Jacq.	CHar CPle EBee MNrw MWrn
	WOut WPer WWye
§ *viridis* var. *comata*	CArn EMar EOHP MAsh MChe
	SIde WHHs WJek
- var. *viridis* **new**	SBod WHrl
viscosa Jacquin	CPle CStr WOut WWye
wagneriana	CStr
yunnanensis **new**	EBee
- B&SWJ 7874	WCru

Salvinia (*Salviniaceae*)

auriculata	WDyG

Sambucus ✿ (*Caprifoliaceae*)

adnata	EBee
- B&SWJ 2252	WCru
caerulea	see *S. nigra* subsp. *cerulea*
canadensis	NWea
chinensis	EBee
- B&SWJ 6542	WCru
coraensis	see *S. williamsii* subsp. *coreana*
ebulus	CKin LEdu NSti SMad
formosana	LEdu
- B&SWJ 1543	IFro WCru
§ *javanica* B&SWJ 4047	WCru
kamtschatica **new**	GIBF
nigra	CCVT CDul CKin ENot GKir GPoy
	GTre GWCH MBri MHer NWea
	SHFr SIde SMrm WDin WMou
- 'Albomarginata'	see *S. nigra* 'Marginata'
- 'Albovariegata' (v)	CDoC CDul EBee SSte WLRN
✿ - 'Ardwall'	GCal
N - 'Aurea' ♀ H4	CBcs CDul CLnd CSBt EBee ELan
	EMon ENot EPfP EWTr GKir MBar
	MRav NBee NLon NWea SPer
	WDin WFar WSHC

- 'Aureomarginata' (v) — EBee ELan EPfP MRav NFor NLon NSti SHBN SPar WCFE WFar
- Black Beauty = 'Gerda' ♀ H4 — More than 30 suppliers
- 'Black Lace' **new** — MBri
- 'Bradet' — CAgr
- 'Cae Rhos Lligwy' — WHer
- subsp. *canadensis* — CWib EVFa MBar NWea WHar
  'Aurea'
- - 'Maxima' — EPfP SMad SMrm
- - 'York' (F) — CAgr
- 'Cannop' — WAlt
- 'Castledean' — WAlt
§ - subsp. *cerulea* — EPfP
- 'Cool Head' — WAlt
- 'Frances' (v) — WBcn WCot
- 'Godshill' (F) — CAgr SDea
- 'Golden Locks' — MWgw
§ - 'Guincho Purple' — CBcs CDoC EBee EHoe ELan EPfP EWTr GAbr GCal ISea LRHS MAsh MBar MBlu MBri MDun MHer MRav NDov NFor NLon SLim SMrm SPer WCot WDin WFar WSHC
- 'Heterophylla' — see *S. nigra* 'Linearis'
- f. *laciniata* ♀ H4 — More than 30 suppliers
§ - 'Linearis' — CFai ELan EPla GEil MRav SPer
- 'Long Tooth' — CNat
- 'Luteovariegata' (v) — EVFa WBcn
- 'Madonna' (v) — CBcs CMHG EBee EPla EVFa EWTr LRHS MBri MGos MLLN MRav NBee SLim SMad SPer WCot
§ - 'Marginata' (v) — CMHG CPLG CWib EHoe GEil LRHS MBar MBri MGos MHer MLLN MRav NBid SDix SLon SPer SRPl WCot WDin WFar WHar WWin
- 'Marion Bull' (v) — CNat
- 'Plaque' (v) — CNat
- 'Plena' (d) — EMon EPla MInt SSte WCot
- 'Pulverulenta' (v) — CBgR CDoC EBee EPfP EPla GCal GKir LHop LRHS MAsh MLLN MRav NEgg SPar SPer WBcn WCot WSHC WWeb
- 'Purple Pete' — CNat
- 'Purpurea' — see *S. nigra* 'Guincho Purple'
- 'Pygmy' — EPla
- 'Pyramidalis' — CPMA EMon EPla MBlu WCot
- 'Robert Piggin' (v) — EVFa
- 'Sambu' (F) — CAgr
- 'Samdal' (F) — CAgr
- 'Samidan' (F) — CAgr
- 'Samnor' (F) — CAgr
- 'Samyl' (F) — CAgr
* - 'Tenuifolia' — MRav
- 'Thundercloud' — CMHG GKir LRHS MAsh MBri MTis NBee NChi NDov NPro SMad WBcn WCot WPat
- 'Variegata' — see *S. nigra* 'Marginata'
- f. *viridis* — CAgr CNat
racemosa — CAgr EPfP GIBF GWCH NWea WRha
- 'Aurea' — CLnd EHoe GKir
- 'Crûg Lace' **new** — WCru
- 'Goldenlocks' — EWes GKir MGos NLar NPro SPer WBcn
- 'Plumosa Aurea' — More than 30 suppliers
- 'Sutherland Gold' ♀ H4 — More than 30 suppliers
- 'Tenuifolia' — CMHG CPMA CSWP ELan EPfP LRHS NLar SMad SPer WCru WPat
wightiana — see *S. javanica*
§ *williamsii* — CMCN WFar
  subsp. *coreana*

Samolus (Primulaceae)
repens — CPBP ECou

Sanchezia (Acanthaceae)
nobilis hort. — see *S. speciosa*
§ *speciosa* — CHal

Sandersonia (Colchicaceae)
aurantiaca — CFwr EPot ETub LAma LBow LRHS NRog WViv

Sanguinaria (Papaveraceae)
canadensis — CArn CBct CBro EBee EHyt EPfP EPot ERos EWTr GBin GCrs GPoy IBlr IMGH LAma LRHS MCCP NDov NMen NRya SMad SPer WAbe WCru WPnP WShi WViv WWin
- f. *multiplex* (d) — CDes CLAP CRDP EMan EPPr GEdr GKir LRHS WPnP
- - 'Paint Creek Double' — SSpi
- - 'Plena' (d) ♀ H4 — CAvo CBct CBro CLyd CRDP EBee EHyt EPar EPot GCrs IMGH LAma NDov NGar NHar NLar NMen NRya SBla SIgm SIng SMac SSpi WAbe WEas WLin WPGP WSan WViv
- 'Peter Harrison' — LPhx

Sanguisorba (Rosaceae)
§ *albiflora* — CDes CRow EBee EBre EFou EGle ELan EMon ERou GBuc MCLN MRav NLar NPro SChu SMrm WBea WCot WFar WPGP WRus WWin
armena — SSvw WTin
benthamiana — CHEx
canadensis — CDes CKno CRow EBee EChP ECha EGle GAbr GCal GKir GPoy LPhx MCAu MFir MSte MWgw NCWG NVic SAga SPer WAul WBea WCot WCra WFar WOld WWye
* *caucasica* — EBee EWes LPhx WWye
hakusanensis — CDes EBee ECha MNrw NBir NBro NFla NPro WFar
magnifica — CDes
  Schischk. & Kom.
- *alba* — see *S. albiflora*
menziesii — CDes CHar CKno EBee EChP EGle EPPr GBin LPhx MCAu MCLN NLar NPro NSti SChu SUsu WCot WFar WPGP WPnP
§ *minor* — CAgr CArn CKin CPrp EBee ELau GBar GPoy MBar MBow MChe MDun MGas MHer NArg NBlu NBro NMir NPri SIde SPlb WBri WCHb WHHs WHbs WHer WMoo WPer WWye
- subsp. *muricata* — GWCH
obtusa — More than 30 suppliers
- var. *albiflora* — see *S. albiflora*
officinalis — CArn CKno EBee ECGN EHrv EPfP GBar GBin MBow MHer NMir NPPs NPro SWat WMoo WWye
- 'Arnhem' — EGle LPhx
- 'False Tanna' **new** — SMHy
- 'Pink Tanna' **new** — CBgR EMon EPPr
parviflora — see *S. tenuifolia* var. *parviflora*
pimpinella — see *S. minor*
'Pink Brushes' **new** — LHop
sitchensis — see *S. stipulata*
§ *stipulata* — CPlt ECGN GCal IBlr WCom
'Tanna' — CKno CPlt CPrp CRez EBee EGle EHoe EHrv EMon EPPr GBri GCal LHop LPhx NBir NDov NFla NPro

	SMrm SOkh SUsu WAul WCot
	WMaN WPrP WWhi
tenuifolia	CKno LPhx MCAu MSph NChi
	NLar WAul WBea WMoo WWhi
- 'Alba'	CDes CKno EBee GBuc GGar
	LPhx MBri MDun SAga WCot
	WFar WPGP
§ - var. *parviflora*	EBee
- - white **new**	WCot
- 'Pink Elephant'	EBee GBin NSti
- 'Purpurea'	EBee WCot WFar

Sanicula (*Apiaceae*)

europaea	EBee GBar GPoy MSal NSco WHer
	WWye

Sansevieria ✿ (*Dracaenaceae*)

trifasciata 'Golden	MBri
Hahnii' (v) ♀ H1	
- 'Laurentii' (v) ♀ H1	MBri

Santolina (*Asteraceae*)

§ *chamaecyparissus* ♀ H4	More than 30 suppliers
- var. *corsica*	see *S. chamaecyparissus* var. *nana*
- 'Double Lemon'	EBee EPfP SPar SPla WCot
- 'Lambrook Silver'	CDoC EBee ECtt EGoo ENot EPPr
	EPfP ESis GKir LRHS SCoo SKCG
	SLim SPar SPla WCra
- 'Lemon Queen'	CArn CBcs CDoC CSLe EGoo ELau
	EPfP GBar GKir LAst LRHS MAsh
	MBow MGos MHer NBir NPri SIde
	SPla SWat WCHb WFar WPer
§ - var. *nana* ♀ H4	CBcs CWib EBee ECha ENot EPfP
	GKir LRHS MBar MDun MHer
	MRav NFor SPer SRms SWat WPer
- 'Pretty Carol'	CAbP EBee EBre ELan EMil EPfP
	GBar GKir LPhx LRHS MAsh SAga
	SIde SLim SPla WWeb
- 'Small-Ness'	CDoC CLyd EBee EGoo EPfP ESis
	EWes GBar GEdr GKir LRHS
	MAsh MBro MHer MSte NMen
	SIng SLim SMrm SPar SPer STre
	WFar WPat WWeb
incana	see *S. chamaecyparissus*
'Oldfield Hybrid'	MLan WCot
pectinata	see *S. rosmarinifolia* subsp.
	canescens
§ *pinnata*	CArn CSLe CSev CTri MHer WPer
§ - subsp. *neapolitana* ♀ H4	CArn CSBt CSev CWib EBee ECha
	ELan ENot EPfP GBar LRHS MBri
	NFor NPri SDix SIde SPar WCom
	WEas WHCG WSel WWye
- - cream	see *S. pinnata* subsp.
	neapolitana 'Edward Bowles'
§ - - 'Edward Bowles'	More than 30 suppliers
- - 'Sulphurea'	CMea EGoo EPfP LPhx LRHS SPer
	WKif WPer WWhi WWpP
rosmarinifolia	CArn CDoC CHar ELau EWTr
	GWCH MHer MRav MWhi SLon
	SPar SPlb SRms WCHb WSel WWye
§ - subsp. *canescens*	EBee EPfP LRHS MRav WPer WWye
§ - subsp. *rosmarinifolia*	CChc CSev EBee ECha EGoo ELan
	ENot EPfP GBar GKir LRHS MHer
	MRav MWgw NSti SDix SIde SPer
	WBrE WCHb WDin WEas WFar
	WHoo WLin WSHC WTel WWin
	WWye
- - cream	NWoo
- - 'Primrose Gem' ♀ H4	CBcs CDoC CHar CSBt EBee ECha
	ELau EMil EPPr EPfP ESis GBar
	GKir LHop LRHS NPPs NPri NSti
	SBod SPar SPer SPla SRPl WCot
	WPer WWal WWye

tomentosa	see *S. pinnata* subsp. *neapolitana*
virens	see *S. rosmarinifolia* subsp.
	rosmarinifolia
viridis	see *S. rosmarinifolia* subsp.
	rosmarinifolia

Sanvitalia (*Asteraceae*)

'Little Sun'	CSpe LRHS NPri SPet
'Sunbini'	CSpe

Sapium (*Euphorbiaceae*)

japonicum	CFil CMCN WPGP

Saponaria (*Caryophyllaceae*)

'Bressingham' ♀ H4	EBre EDAr EPot LBee LRHS MTho
	NHar NMen SBla SBod SIng WAbe
	WPat WWin
caespitosa	EPot EWes GTou NJOw NMen
	WAbe
x *lempergii* 'Max Frei'	EBee GBuc LPhx LRHS MSte SAga
	SBla SCro SDix SHar SScr WCot
	WOVN
* 'Lilac Double'	MRav
lutea	CPBP NWCA
ocymoides ♀ H4	More than 30 suppliers
- 'Alba'	ECha WFar
- 'Rubra Compacta' ♀ H4	LRHS MTho
- 'Snow Tip'	EDAr ESis MWrn NDlv WGor WRHF
officinalis	CAgr CArn CBre CKin ELau GBar
	GPoy LEdu MChe MHer MSal
	NGHP NSti SIde SWal WFar WHHs
	WHer WMoo WPer WWal WWpP
	WWye
- 'Alba Plena' (d)	CRDP CSam EBee EBre ECha
	ECoo EMon GBar GKir GMac NSti
	WCHb WElm WFar WHer WPer
	WRha WWin
- 'Betty Arnold' (d)	WCot
§ - 'Dazzler' (v)	CRow ELau EMan GBar MRav
	NBir WCHb WHer
- 'Rosea Plena' (d)	More than 30 suppliers
- 'Rubra Plena' (d)	CBre CHad CRDP EBee ELan
	EMon MWhi NGHP NSti WCHb
	WCra WHer WRha
- 'Variegata'	see *S. officinalis* 'Dazzler'
x *olivana* ♀ H4	EDAr EMlt EPot ESis LBee MTho
	NMen SBla SIng WAbe WPat
	WWin
pamphylica	EBee MNrw
pulvinaris	see *S. pumilio*
§ *pumilio*	GTou
'Rosenteppich'	CGra SBla WLin WPat
zawadskii	see *Silene zawadskii*

Saposhnikovia (*Apiaceae*)

divaricata **new**	CArn MSal

Sarcococca ✿ (*Buxaceae*)

confusa ♀ H4	More than 30 suppliers
hookeriana ♀ H4	CTrG ECot EPfP GSki LAst MIdf
	SApp WBrE WFar WPGP
- B&SWJ 2585	WCru
- HWJCM 92	WCru
- Sch 2396	EPla
- var. *digyna* ♀ H4	More than 30 suppliers
I - - 'Schillingii' **new**	MAsh
- - 'Purple Stem'	CTri EHol EPfP EPla MGos MRav
	SDes WCru WDin WPGP
	WRHF
- var. *humilis*	More than 30 suppliers
orientalis	CFil CMCN CPMA ELan EPfP EPla
	LRHS MAsh MGos MLon SPla SSpi
	WFar WPGP

'Roy Lancaster'	see *S. ruscifolia* 'Dragon Gate'
ruscifolia	CBcs CPMA CPle CSBt EBee EBre
	ELan ENot EPfP EPla GEil GKir
	LRHS MAsh MGos MRav SDes
	SLim SLon SMac SPer SRms SSpi
	WCru WFar WPGP
– var. *chinensis* ♀ H4	CFil CPMA CSam EPfP EPla MRav
	WCru
– – L 713	EPla
§ – 'Dragon Gate'	CFil EPfP EPla LRHS MAsh SReu
	SSta WBcn WPGP
saligna	CBcs CFil CPMA EPfP WBcn
	WCru WPGP
wallichii B&SWJ 2291	WCru
– B&SWJ 7285	WCru

Sarmienta (Gesneriaceae)

repens ♀ H2	WAbe WCru

Sarothamnus see Cytisus

Sarracenia ✿ (Sarraceniaceae)

alata	CFwr CSWC GTro SHmp
– 'Copper Lid'	GTro
– heavily veined **new**	SHmp
– pubescent	CSWC
– purple lid	GTro
– 'Red Lid'	CSWC
– red x *purpurea*	CSWC
subsp. *venosa*	
– wavy lid **new**	SHmp
– x *flava* var. *maxima*	CSWC
x *areolata*	CSWC GTro
x *catesbyi* ♀ H1	CFil CSWC GTro
x *excellens* ♀ H1	CSWC GTro
– 'Judy'	GTro
flava ♀ H1	CFil CFwr CRDP CSWC GTro
	WPGP
– all green giant	see *S. flava* var. *maxima*
– 'Burgundy'	GTro
– var. *cuprea*	GTro
§ – var. *maxima*	CSWC WNor
– var. *ornata*	CSWC SHmp
– var. *rugelii* **new**	SHmp
– veinless	CSWC
x *harperi*	CSWC
leucophylla ♀ H1	CFwr CSWC GTro SHmp
'Lynda Butt' **new**	SHmp
x *melanorhoda*	GTro
x *miniata*	SHmp
minor	CSWC GTro SHmp
– 'Okee Giant'	CSWC LHew
– 'Okefenokee Giant'	see *S. minor* 'Okee Giant'
– x *oreophila*	CSWC
x *mitchelliana* ♀ H1	CFwr GTro
x *moorei*	GTro
– 'Brook's Hybrid'	CSWC GTro LHew
oreophila	CSWC GTro SHmp
– x *leucophylla*	CSWC
– x *minor*	CSWC
x *popei*	CSWC
psittacina	CSWC GTro SHmp
purpurea	CFil NWCA
– subsp. *purpurea*	CFwr CSWC GTro LEdu
– – f. *heterophylla*	CSWC
– subsp. *venosa*	CSWC GTro SHmp
– – var. *burkii*	CSWC
– – x *oreophila*	CSWC
x *readii*	GTro SHmp
– 'Farnhamii'	CSWC
x *rehderi*	SHmp
rubra	CSWC GTro
– subsp. *alabamensis*	CSWC SHmp

– subsp. *gulfensis*	CSWC SHmp
* – – f. *heterophylla*	CSWC
– subsp. *jonesii*	CSWC
* – – f. *heterophylla*	CSWC
– subsp. *rubra*	CSWC
– subsp. *wherryi*	CSWC
– – yellow flower	CSWC
x *swaniana*	GTro
x *wrigleyana* ♀ H1	GTro

Saruma (Aristolochiaceae)

henryi	EBee EMan LEur WCot

Sasa ✿ (Poaceae)

chrysantha hort.	see *Pleioblastus chino*
disticha 'Mirrezuzume'	see *Pleioblastus pygmaeus*
	'Mirrezuzume'
glabra f. *albostriata*	see *Sasaella masamuneana* f.
	albostriata
kagamiana **new**	EBee
kurilensis	EBee EPla LJus LPal MWht NMoo
	SDry WFar WJun
– 'Shimofuri' (v)	EPfP EPla ERod LJus SDry WJun
– short	EPla
megalophylla 'Nobilis'	SDry
nana	see *S. veitchii* f. *minor*
nipponica	CEnd SDry WJun
– 'Aureostriata'	SDry
oshidensis	EPla
§ *palmata*	CAbb CBcs CDul CHad COld
	CTrG CWib EBee EHoe ENot
	MCCP MGrG MWhi SPar WDin
	WFar WHer WPnP
– f. *nebulosa*	CBct CDDB CDoC CFir CHEx
	EBee EFul EHul ENot EPVP EPfP
	EPla EWes LJus MBrN MHdf
	MMoz MWht MWod NMoo SAPC
	SArc SDry WDyG WFar WJun
	WMoo
– 'Warley Place' (v)	SDry
quelpaertensis	EPla SDry
senanensis	SDry
tessellata	see *Indocalamus tessellatus*
tsuboiana	CBcs CDoC CFwr EBee EPla LPal
	MHdf MMoz MWgw MWht NGdn
	SDry WDyG WFar WMoo
§ *veitchii*	More than 30 suppliers
§ – f. *minor*	CBct EBee MCCP MMoz

Sasaella (Poaceae)

bitchuensis hort.	SDry
glabra	see *S. masamuneana*
§ *masamuneana*	CEnd EPla LAst
§ – f. *albostriata* (v)	CDoC CFil CMCo COtt CWib
	EBee EPPr EPla ERod EWsh LEdu
	LJus LPal MCCP MHdf MMoz
	MWgw MWht NGdn NMoo SDry
	WDyG WJun WMoo WPGP WViv
– f. *aureostriata* (v)	COtt EPla GCal LJus MMoz NPal
	SDry
§ *ramosa*	CFwr CHEx EBee EPVP EPla LAst
	LEdu LJus MCCP MMoz MWgw
	MWht NMoo NRya SDry WDin

Sassafras (Lauraceae)

albidum	CArn CBcs CFil CTho EPfP SSpi
	WPGP
tzumu	CFil

satsuma see Citrus unshiu

Satureja ✿ (Lamiaceae)

§ *coerulea* ♀ H4	EWes NBir NLAp

douglasii		CArn EOHP SHDw WJek
I	- 'Indian Mint'	NGHP WLHH
	hortensis	CBod GPoy ILis MChe MHer
		MLan WHHs WHer WJek WLHH
		WSel
	montana	CAgr CArn CPrp EEls ELau GPoy
		ILis LEdu LLWP MBri MChe MHer
		NMen SDix SIde SRms SRob
		WCHb WCer WHHs WHer WPer
		WWeb WWye
*	- *citriodora*	GPoy IIve MHer
	- 'Coerulea'	see *S. coerulea*
§	- subsp. *illyrica*	LLWP WJek
	- prostrate white	CRDP
	- 'Purple Mountain'	GPoy IIve LLWP MHer
	- *subspicata*	see *S. montana* subsp. *illyrica*
	parnassica	LLWP WPer
	repanda	see *S. spicigera*
	seleriana	NMen
§	*spicigera*	CArn CLyd CNic CPBP CPrp EBee
		EDAr ELau EPot GBar GEdr LLWP
		MHer NBir NPri WCHb WJek
		WLHH WSel WWin WWye
	thymbra	CArn EOHP LLWP SHDw WJek

Satyrium (Orchidaceae)

henryi **new**	WCot
nepalense	GGGa

Saurauia (Actinidiaceae)

subspinosa	CHEx

Sauromatum (Araceae)

	guttatum	see *S. venosum*
§	*venosum*	CHEx CKob CMea EBee EBot
		EMan ITer LAma LRHS MBri WCot
		WCru

Saururus (Saururaceae)

cernuus	CBen CHEx CRow CWat EBre
	EHon ELan EMFW EPfP LPBA MSta
	NBlu SLon SWat WMAq WWpP
chinensis	CRow EBee WCru

Saussurea (Asteraceae)

albescens	EBcc EMan WCot
auriculata HWJCM 490	WCru
grandiflora	EBee
hypoleuca	MNrw
obvallata **new**	GEdr
pulchella	EBee

savory, summer see *Satureja hortensis*

savory, winter see *Satureja montana*

Saxegothaea (Podocarpaceae)

conspicua	CBcs CDoC CMCN ECou EPla
	IDee LCon SMad WCwm

Saxifraga ✿ (Saxifragaceae)

	BM&W 118	GDra
	SEP 22	CLyd EHyt MWat
	McB 1397 from Nepal	CLyd
	'Ada' (x *petraschii*) (7) **new**	NMen
	'Aemula' (x *borisii*) (7)	NMen
§	'Afrodite'	CLyd EPot
	(*sempervivum*) (7)	
	aizoides	MBro
	var. *atrorubens* (9)	
	aizoon	see *S. paniculata*
	'Aladdin' (x *borisii*) (7)	NHol NMen
*	'Alan Hayhurst' (8)	WAbe

'Alan Martin'	CLyd EPot
(x *boydilacina*) (7)	
'Alba' (x *apiculata*) (7)	CSam ELan EMNN EMlt EPot
	GTou LRHS MBro MHer NHol
	NLAp NMen NSla SBla SChu SIng
	SPlb WCom WPat WWin
'Alba' (x *arco-valleyi*)	see *S.* 'Ophelia' (x *arco-valleyi*)
'Alba' (*oppositifolia*) (7)	CLyd ELan EMNN EWes GDra
	GKir GTou NHar NLAp NMen
	WAbe
'Albert Einstein'	NMen
(x *apiculata*) (7)	
§	'Albertii' (*callosa*) (8)	see *S.* 'Albida'
§	'Albida' (*callosa*) (8)	GTou LRHS SIng WAbe WCom
		WWin
'Aldebaran' (x *borisii*) (7)	EMNN NHar NMen
'Aldo Bacci' (7) **new**	NMen
'Alfons Mucha' (7)	CLyd EHyt MWat NMen
'Allendale Acclaim'	EHyt NDlv NMen
(x *lismorensis*) (7)	
'Allendale Accord'	EHyt NDlv NMen
(*diapensioides* x	
lilacina) (7)	
'Allendale Allure' (7) **new**	NMen
'Allendale Amber' (7) **new**	NMen
'Allendale Andante'	NMen
(x *arco-valleyi*) (7)	
'Allendale Angel' (7) **new**	EHyt NMen
'Allendale Argonaut' (7)	NDlv NMcn
'Allendale Ballad' (7)	NMen
'Allendale Ballet' (7)	CLyd EHyt NMen
'Allendale Bamby'	NMen
(x *lismorensis*) (7)	
'Allendale Banshee' (7) **new**	NMen
'Allendale Beau' (7) **new**	NMen
'Allendale Beauty' (7) **new**	NMen
'Allendale Betty' (7)	CLyd EHyt NMen
(x *lismorensis*) (7)	
'Allendale Billows' (7) **new**	NMen
'Allendale Bonny' (7) **new**	NMen
'Allendale Boon'	EHyt
(x *izari*) (7)	
'Allendale Bounty' (7)	NMen
'Allendale Bravo'	NMen
(x *lismorensis*) (7)	
'Allendale Cabal' (7)	NMen
'Allendale Celt'	NMen
(x *novacastelensis*) (7)	
'Allendale Charm' (7)	EHyt NMen
'Allendale Chick' (7)	NMen
'Allendale Comet' (7)	GCrs NMen
'Allendale Dance' (7) **new**	NMen
'Allendale Dream' (7)	NMen
'Allendale Duo' (7) **new**	NMen
'Allendale Garnet' (7)	NDlv NMen
'Allendale Joy'	NMen
(x *wendelacina*) (7)	
'Allendale Pearl'	CLyd EHyt NMen
(x *novacastelensis*) (7)	
'Allendale Ruby' (7)	NDlv NMen
'Allendale Snow'	NDlv
(x *rayei*) (7) **new**	
'Alpenglow' (7)	MWat NMen
alpigena (7)	CLyd WAbe
'Amitie' (x *gloriana*) (7)	NMen
andersonii (7)	CLyd EHyt EMNN MWat NMen
	NRya NWCA
- McB 1475	NHol
'Andrea della	NMen
Robbia' (7) **new**	
x *andrewsii* (8x11)	MDHE MTho WAbe
angustifolia Haw.	see *S. hypnoides*
'Anna' (7) **new**	NMen

'Anne Beddall'   CLyd MWat NMen
  (x *goringiana*) (7)

'Aphrodite'   see S. 'Afrodite'
  (*sempervivum*) (7)

x *apiculata*   see S. 'Gregor Mendel'
  sensu stricto hort.

'Apple Blossom' (15)   ECtt GTou MDHE MOne NFla
  NRya WGor

aquatica (15)   GKev NLAp

§ 'Arco' (x *arco-valleyi*) (7)   MWat NMen

x *arco-valleyi*   see S. 'Arco'
  sensu stricto hort.

x *arendsii* (15)   MDHE WEas
– purple (15) **new**   NBlu
– red (15) **new**   NBlu

§ 'Aretiastrum' (x *boydii*) (7)   CLyd NDlv NMen WOBN
aretioides (7)   NMen
'Ariel' (x *bornbrookii*) (7)   CLyd NMen
'Arthur' (x *anglica*) (7) **new**   NMen
'Assimilis' (x *petraschii*) (7)   CLyd WAbe
'August Hayek'   ITim MWat NMen
  (x *leyboldii*) (7)

'Aurea Maculata'   see S. 'Aureopunctata'
  (*cuneifolia*)

§ 'Aureopunctata'   COkL EBee EBre ECha EMan
  (x *urbium*) (11/v)   GBuc GCal MHer NHol NLon
  SMrm SPar SPer SPlb SRms
  WBro WCom WHen WMoo
  WWpP

'Baldensis'   see S. *paniculata* var. *baldensis*
'Ballawley Guardsman' (15)   ECho MBNS MDHE SIng

§ 'Beatrix Stanley'
  (x *anglica*) (7)   CLyd EMNN MHer NHar NHol
  NLAp NMen NRya

'Becky Foster' (x *borisii*) (7)   MWat NMen
'Beechcroft White' (15)   LRHS MDHE
'Bellisant'   CLyd NMen
  (x *bornibrookii*) (7)

'Berenika' (x *bertolonii*) (7)   NMen
'Beryl' (x *anglica*) (7) **new**   NMen
'Bettina' (x *paulinae*) (7)   NMen

x *biasolettoi*   see S. 'Phoenix'
  sensu stricto hort.

x *bilekii* (7)   CLyd
'Birch Baby' (15)   SIng
'Black Beauty' (15)   CBcs CMea ECho EMlt LRHS
  MDHE MHer

'Black Forest Gateaux'   CLAP
  (*fortunei*) (5)

'Black Ruby' (*fortunei*) (5)   More than 30 suppliers
'Blackberry and Apple   CBct CBos CElw CFai CLAP EBee
  Pie' (*fortunei*) (5)   EChP EMan GBin ITim MAvo
  MBrN MNrw MSte NCat NHol
  NPSI SDes SSpi WCot WFar
  WOBN WOld WWhi

'Blackberry'   NMen
  (*fortunei*) (5) **new**

'Blaník' (x *borisii*) (7)   CLyd NMen
'Blanka' (x *borisii*) (7)   NMen
'Blütenteppich' (15)   WPer
'Bob Hawkins' (15/v)   CLyd ELan GDra LRHS MDHE
  MHer NHar WWin

§ 'Bodensee'   WPat
  (x *hofmannii*) (7)

'Bohdalec'   NMen
  (x *megaseiflora*) (7)

'Bohemia' (7)   CGra CLyd EPot ITim NMen SBla
  WAbe

x *borisii* sensu stricto hort.   see S. 'Sofia'
'Bornmuelleri' (7)   NMen
'Boston Spa'   CLyd EMNN GCrs ITim LRHS
  (x *elisabethae*) (7)   MBro MHer NDlv NHol NMen
  SChu SIng SPlb WPat

'Brailes' (x *poluanglica*) (7)   ITim
'Bridget' (x *edithae*) (7)   CLyd CMea ESis GKir LRHS NDlv
  NHol NMen SIng WWin

'Brno' (x *elisabethae*) (7)   NHol NMen
bronchialis (10)   CLyd
– var. *vespertina*   see S. *vespertina*
'Brookside' (*burseriana*) (7)   CLyd EPot ITim NMen
brunoniana   see S. *brunonis*

§ *brunonis* (1)   GAbr WCru
– CC&McK 108   NWCA
bryoides (10)   GCrs GDra GTou NRya NWCA
x *burnatii* Sünd (8)   CLyd LRHS NDlv NMen NPro
  WGor

burseriana (7)   GKir MBro NLAp NRya WAbe
  WGor

'Buster' (x *hardingii*) (7)   NMen
'Buttercup' (x *kayei*) (7)   CLyd EPot GEdr GTou MBro
  MWat NHol NMen NWCA WHoo
  WPat

x *byam-groundsii* (7) **new**   CLyd
caesia L. (8)   SRms

§ *callosa* (8)   ♀ H4   EMlt GTou MBro MWat NHar
  NHol SBla WEas WPat WTin

– var. *bellardii*   see S. *callosa*
– subsp. *callosa* (8)   SOkd

§ – – var. *australis* (8)   EMlt EPot MDHE NBro NHol
  NMen WAbe

– – var. *callosa* (8)   MDHE
– var. *lantoscana*   see S. *callosa* subsp. *callosa* var.
  australis

– *lingulata*   see S. *callosa*
– x *cochlearis* (8)   see S. Silver Farreri Group
'Cambridge Seedling' (7)   MWat NMen
'Camyra' (7)   ITim MWat
canaliculata (15)   MDHE NMen
x *canis-dalmatica*   see S. x *gaudinii*

§ 'Carmen' (x *elisabethae*) (7)   EMNN GKir LRHS MBro MOne
  NDlv NLAp NMen NRya WAbe
  WOBN

§ 'Carniolica' (*paniculata*) (8)   CLyd LRHS MBar MDHE NBro
  NMen NWCA SBla WCom

'Carniolica'   MDHE WAbe
  (x *pectinata*) (8)

'Carnival' (15)   COkL
carolinica   see S. 'Carniolica' (*paniculata*)
'Castor' (x *bilekii*) (7)   MWat NMen
'Caterhamensis'
  (*cotyledon*) (8)   WEas
'Cathy Reed' (7) **new**   NMen
caucasica   see S. *desoulavyi*
  var. *desoulavyi*

cebennensis (15)   ♀ H2   CLyd ITim NMen NRya SIng
– dwarf (15)   WAbe
'Cecil Davies' (8)   MDHE
cespitosa (15)   GKir MDHE NWCA WAbe
'Chadov' **new**   NMen
'Chambers' Pink Pride'   see S. 'Miss Chambers'
'Charlecote'   ITim
  (x *poluanglica*) (7)

'Cheap Confections'   More than 30 suppliers
  (*fortunei*) (4)

§ *cherlerioides* (10)   ECtt MBNS NRya NVic WEas
'Cherry Pie'   EMan LHop NCat WCot
  (*fortunei*) (5) **new**
'Cherrytrees' (x *boydii*) (7)   NMen
'Chetwynd'   MWat NMen WAbe
  (*marginata*) (7)

'Chez Nous'   CLyd NMen
  (x *gloriana*) (7/v)

'Christine' (x *anglica*) (7)   CLyd MWat NHol NLAp NMen
cinerea (7)   NMen WAbe
'Cio-cio-san' (7) **new**   NMen
'Claire Felstead' (*cinerea*   GCrs

x *poluniniana*) **new**

'Clare' (x *anglica*) (7) — NMen

'Clare Island' (15) — MDHE SIng

§ 'Clarence Elliott' (*umbrosa*) (11) ♀ H4 — CLyd CMea CTri EWes GCal GKev GKir LRHS MHar MHer NFla NHol NRya NVic WAbe WCom WPat WWin

'Claudia' (x *borisii*) (7) — NMen

'Cleo' (x *boydii*) (7) — NMen

§ x *clibranii* (15) — MDHE SIng

§ 'Cloth of Gold' (*exarata* subsp. *moschata*) (15) — CLyd CMea ECha ECtt ELan EMlt GDra GTou LAst LBee LRHS MBar MHer NMen NRya SIng SPlb SRms WAbe WFar WWin

cochlearis (8) — CMea EHyt MDHE NJOw Nmen SIng WAbe

'Cockscomb' (*paniculata*) (8) — EPot MDHE NJOw NMen SIng WAbe

columnaris (7) — NSla

'Compacta' (*exarata* subsp. *moschata*) (15) — MBro

'Coolock Kate' **new** — NMen

'Cordata' (*burseriana*) (7) — NMen

'Corona' (x *boydii*) (7) — MWat NHol NMen

'Corrennie Claret' (15) — EWes GTou

I 'Correvoniana' hort. (*brevifolia*) (8) — ECtt ESis GKir LRHS MBro MHer MOne NDlv NRya SIng WCom WGor WWin

§ 'Corrie Fee' (*oppositifolia*) (7) — GCrs GKev GKir GTou NHar SIng

§ *cortusifolia* (5) — EBee NHar SSpi

- B&SWJ 5879 — WCru

- var. *fortunei* — see S. *fortunei*

- var. *stolonifera* (5) B&SWJ 6205 — WCru

'Cotton Crochet' (*fortunei*) (5/d) — EBee EMan MLLN NHol NPSI SMrm WCot WFTG WFar WOld

cotyledon (8) — GCrs GDra LBee LRHS NFor NHol SBla SIng WEas WPer

§ 'Cranbourne' (x *anglica*) (7) ♀ H4 — CLyd CMea EBre EMNN GCrs LRHS MBro MWat NHar NHol NLAp NMen SBla SIng WPat

'Cream Seedling' (x *elisabethae*) (7) — EBre ESis MWat NDlv NLAp NMen

'Crenata' (*burseriana*) (7) — CLyd EPot GCrs LRHS MBro MWat NDlv NHar NMen WAbe WHoo

'Crimson Rose' (*paniculata*) (8) — see S. 'Rosea'

§ *crustata* (8) — EHyt MDHE MDKP NHar NMen SIng WAbe

- var. *vochinensis* — see S. *crustata*

'Crystal Pink' (*fortunei*) (5/v) — CBct CMil EDec ElIrv EMil EVFa LAst LHop MBri MNrw MTis NCat NHar NMen NPSI SDes WCot WElm WFTG WFar WGor WOld

'Crystalie' (x *biasolettoi*) (7) — EPot LRHS MBro NMen NRya WPat

'Cultrata' (*paniculata*) (8) — NBro

§ 'Cumulus' (*iranica* hybrid) (7) ♀ H4 — CLyd CPBP EHyt GCrs ITim NLAp NMen SBla WAbe

cuneata (15) — GAbr NHol

§ *cuneifolia* (11) — CNic GDea GDra GGar IHMH LBee LRHS MHer MWat NDlv NFla NSti WRos

- var. *capillipes* — see S. *cuneifolia* subsp. *cuneifolia*

§ - subsp. *cuneifolia* (11) — ECtt

* - var. *subintegra* (11) — ECho

cuscutiformis (5) — see S. 'Cuscutiformis'

§ 'Cuscutiformis' (*stolonifera*) (5) — CHid EBee ETow GCal MRav SBla SRms WAbe WCru

cymbalaria (2) — EBur SIng

- var. *huetiana* (2) — CNic

dahurica — see S. *cuneifolia*

'Dainty Dame' (x *arco-valleyi*) (7) — CLyd LRHS MWat NDlv NMen

'Dana' (x *megaseiflora*) (7) — CLyd EMNN MWat NHol NMen

'Dartington Double' (15/d) — EBre EMlt EWes GDra GKir GTou LRHS MDHE NHar

'Dartington Double White' (15/d) — MDHE SDes WCom

'Dawn Frost' (7) — CLyd EHyt ITim NLAp NMen WAbe

'Delia' (x *hornibrookii*) (7) — CLyd EPot ITim NMen

§ 'Denisa' (x *pseudokotschyi*) (7) — NMen

densa — see S. *cherlerioides*

'Dentata' (x *geum*) — see S. 'Dentata' (x *polita*)

§ 'Dentata' (x *polita*) (11) — CMea ECha EPla GGar NVic SUsu WMoo

'Dentata' (x *urbium*) — see S. 'Dentata' (x *polita*)

derbeckii **new** — EBee

§ *desoulavyi* (7) — GTou NMen

diapensioides (7) — CLyd NMen WAbe

'Doctor Clay' (*paniculata*) (8) — LBee MDHE NLAp NMen NRya WAbe

'Doctor Ramsey' (8) — EHyt ESis EWes GTou LBee LRHS MBro NBro NDlv NMen SIng WGor

'Donald Mann' (15) — EWes

'Dorothy Milne' (7) — NMen

aff. *doyalana* (7) — CPBP

- - SEP 45 — EHyt

'Drakula' (*ferdinandi-coburgi*) (7) — CLyd LRHS MWat NDlv NMen SIng

'Dubarry' (15) — ECho EWes MDHE NRya

'Dulcimer' (x *petraschii*) (7) — NMen

'Duncan Lowe' (*andersonii*) (7) ♀ H4 — CLyd

'Dwight Ripley' (7) — NMen WOBN

'Edgar Irmscher' (7) — CLyd MWat NMen NWCA

'Edie Campbell' (15) — MDHE

'Edith' (x *edithae*) (7) — LRHS SIng

'Edward Elgar' (x *megaseiflora*) (7) — MWat NHol NMen

x *elegantissima* (15) — see S. x *clibranii*

'Elf' (7) — see S. 'Beatrix Stanley'

'Elf' (15) — ECtt EMNN LRHS NMen SIng SRms WGor

x *elisabethae* — see S. 'Carmen'

'Elizabeth Sinclair' (x *elisabethae*) (7) — NMen

'Ellie Brinckerhoff' (x *hornibrookii*) (7) — NMen

§ 'Ernst Heinrich' (x *heinrichii*) (7) — CLyd NMen NRya

'Esther' (x *burnatii*) (8) — CMea COkL EBre EHyt ESis GCrs GKir LBee LRHS NMen SBla SMer WAbc WHoo

§ 'Eulenspicgel' (x *geuderi*) (7) — CLyd EPot NMen

'Eva Hanzlikova' (7) **new** — CPBP

exarata (15) — LRHS WAbe

§ - subsp. *moschata* (15) — MDHE MWgw

fair maids of France — see S. 'Flore Pleno'

'Fairy' (*exarata* subsp. *moschata*) (15) — ECtt ELan EPot WCom

'Faldonside' (x *boydii*) (7) ♀ H4 — CLyd MBro MWat NDlv NHol NMen NRya SBla WHoo WPat

'Falstaff' (*burseriana*) (7) — CLyd MWat

x *farreri* hort. (8) — see S. Silver Farreri Group

'Faust' (x *borisii*) (7) — EMNN NMen WAbe

'Favorit' (x *bilekii*) (7) — EHyt

§ *federici-augusti* subsp.   CLyd GTou NSla WAbe
   grisebachii (7) ♀ H2-3
'Ferdinand'   NMen
  (x *bofmannii*) (7)
ferdinandi-   CLyd ECtt EPot ITim LRHS NDlv
  coburgi (7) ♀ H4   NRya NWCA WAbe WBrE
* - var. *rhodopea* (7)   CLyd EPot GKev LRHS NDlv
   NMen SIng
'Findling' (15)   EMlt EPot LGro LRHS NMen SIng
   WAbe WWin
§ *flagellaris* (1)   NMen WAbe
'Flavescens' misapplied   see *Saxifraga* 'Lutea' (*paniculata*)
'Flavescens'   NBro
  (*paniculata*) (8)
x *fleischeri* (7)   NMen
§ 'Flore Pleno'   CFir CRDP EBee EWes GEdr
  (*granulata*) (15/d)   MAvo NBir NHar NRya SIng
   WCom WFar
'Florissa' (*oppositifolia*) (7)   CLyd
florulenta Schott,   see *S. callosa*
  Nyman & Kotschy
'Flowers of Sulphur'   see *S.* 'Schwefelblüte'
§ *fortunei* (5) ♀ H4   CHEx EBee EBre EWTr GMaP
   ITim MRav NBir NHol SDes SIng
   SPer SRms SSpi WAbe WCru
   WMoo WWin
- f. *alpina* from   WCru
  Hokkaido **new**
- var. *incisolobata* (5)   SSpi
- var. *obtusocuneata* (5)   ECho EHyt LTwo NHar NMen
   WAbe
- f. *partita* **new**   WCru
- pink (5)   NPSI WAbe WFar WTMC
'Foster's Gold'   NMen
  (x *elisabethae*) (7)
'Four Winds' (15)   EWes LRHS NMen SIng WCom
   WGwG WMoo
'Francesco Redi' (7)   NMen
'Francis Cade' (8)   GAbr WAbe
'Franzii' (x *paulinae*) (7)   NMen
'Friar Tuck' (x *boydii*) (7)   MWat NMen
'Friesei' (x *salmonica*) (7)   CLyd EMNN EPot NHar NMen
x *fritschiana*   see *S.* 'Krain'
  sensu stricto hort. (8)
'Fumiko' (*fortunei*) (5)   WCru
  B&SWJ 6124
'Funkii' (x *petraschii*) (5)   MWat NMen
'Gaertneri' (*mariae-*   NMen
  theresiae) (7)
'Gaiety' (15)   ECho GDra MDHE NFla SIng
'Galaxie'   CLyd NDlv NHol NMen WOBN
  (x *megaseiflora*) (7)
'Ganymede'   NMen
  (*burseriana*) (7)
§ x *gaudinii* (8)   CLyd ECtt EMNN ESis GGar GTou
   LRHS NDlv NHar NMen SIng
   WGor WPer
'Gelber Findling' (7)   EPot LRHS MDHE
'Gem' (x *irvingii*) (7)   CLyd EMNN NHar NLAp NMen
'General Joffre' (15)   see *S.* 'Maréchal Joffre' (15)
georgei (7)   CLyd GCrs ITim NLAp NMen
- McB 1379   NHol
- hybrid (7)   GCrs
'Gertie Pritchard'   see *S.* 'Mrs Gertie Prichard'
  (x *megaseiflora*)
x *geuderi*   see *S.* 'Eulenspiegel'
  sensu stricto hort.
§ x *geum* (11)   CHid EBee EOrc MRav NWoo
   SMrm WFar WMoo
- Dixter form (11)   ECha SUsu WFar WWpP
'Glauca' (*paniculata* var.   see *S.* 'Labradorica'
  brevifolia)
'Gleborg' (15)   EWes MDHE

'Gloria'   CLyd EHyt LRHS MBro NHol
  (*burseriana*) (7) ♀ H4   NMen NSla SBla SIng WPat
x *gloriana* (7)   see *S.* 'Godiva'
'Gloriosa' (x *gloriana*) (7)   see *S.* 'Godiva'
§ 'Godiva' (x *gloriana*) (7)   CLyd EMNN ITim MWat NMen
   WAbe
'Gold Dust'   CLyd EMNN GCrs GTou MWat
  (x *eudoxiana*) (7)   NHar NJOw NLAp NMen NRya
   WWin
'Golden Falls' (15/v)   EMlt EWes GKir GTou LRHS
   MBNS MBro NHol NMen SPlb
   WCom WPat
Golden Prague   see *S.* 'Zlatá Praha'
  (x *pragensis*)
'Goring White' (7) **new**   NMen
'Gothenburg' (7)   CLyd EHyt NMen WAbe
'Grace' (x *arendsii*) (15/v)   see *S.* 'Seaspray'
'Grace Farwell'   CLyd CMea EMNN EMlt EPot
  (x *anglica*) (7)   GCrs LRHS MBar MBro NDlv
   NHol NMen NRya NWCA SBla
   WCom WHoo
'Grandiflora'   NHol
  (*burseriana*) (7)
granulata (15)   CNic NMen NRya NSco
'Gratoides' (x *grata*) (7)   NMen
§ 'Gregor Mendel'   CMea EMNN EMlt GDra GTou
  (x *apiculata*) (7) ♀ H4   ITim LRHS MBro NDlv NHol
   NLAp NMen SBla SRms WAbe
   WCom WHoo WTel
grisebachii   see *S. federici-augusti* subsp.
   grisebachii
'Haagii' (x *eudoxiana*) (7)   ELan EMNN GTou MBro NDlv
   NMen WTel
hallii see *S. marshallii*
'Hareknoll Beauty' **new**   NMen SOkd WAbe
'Harlow Car' (7)   CLyd NMen
'Harlow Car' x   CPBP
  poluniniana (7)
'Harold Bevington'   MDHE
  (*paniculata*) (8)
'Harry Marshall'   CLyd NMen
  (x *irvingii*) (7)
'Hartside Pink'   NWoo
  (*umbrosa*) (11)
'Hartswood White' (15)   MDHE MWat SIng
'Hedwig' (x *malbyana*) (7)   MWat NHol NMen
x *heinreichii*   see *S.* 'Ernst Heinrich'
  sensu stricto hort.
'Herbert Cuerden'   ITim
  (x *elisabethae*) (7)
'Hi-Ace' (15/v)   CLyd ECtt EMlt GTou MBro MHer
   NLAp SBla SPlb WAbe WFar
'Highdownensis' (8)   MDHE NDlv
'Hindhead Seedling'   CLyd EMNN ITim LRHS MWat
  (x *boydii*) (7)   NDlv NMen SIng
hirsuta (11)   EBre EMar GGar IFro MDHE NFla
   WCru
'Hirsuta' (x *geum*)   see *S.* x *geum*
'Hirtella' Ingwersen   MDHE
  (*paniculata*) (8)
'His Majesty' (x *irvingii*) (7)   EMNN NHar NMen WAbe
'Hocker Edge'   CLyd MWat NDlv NMen WAbe
  (x *arco-valleyi*) (7)
'Holden Seedling' (15)   ECtt EMNN EPot EWes MDHE
'Honnginton' **new**   ITim
x *hornibrookii* (7)   WPat
hostii (8)   CLyd GTou LBee LRHS SIng
   WTin
§ - subsp. *hostii* (8)   GEdr MDHE
- - var. *altissima* (8)   STre
- subsp. *rhaetica* (8)   MDHE NBro NDlv NMen WAbe
'Hsitou Silver' (*stolonifera*)   EVFa WCru
  (5) B&SWJ 1980

'Hunscote' **new**   ITim
hybrid JB 11   NMen
§ *hypnoides* (15)   MOne NHar
hypostoma (7)   CLyd
'Icelandica' (*cotyledon*) (8)   NHol
'Icicle' (x *elisabethae*) (7)   MWat NMen
'Ignaz Dörfler' (7) **new**   WAbe
imparilis **new**   WCru
'Ingeborg' (15)   ECha LBee LRHS MDHE SIng
iranica (7)   CLyd EMNN ITim MWat NMen
                                       WOBN
- pink (7)   CGra
'Irene Bacci' (x *baccii*) (7)   CLyd MWat NMen
'Iris Prichard'   CLyd ESis ITim MBro WAbe WHoo
    (x *hardingii*) (7)
'Irish' (15)   EPot MDHE
x *irvingii*   see S. 'Walter Irving'
    sensu stricto hort.
x *irvingii* (7) **new**   NDlv
'Ivana' (x *caroliquarti*) (7)   MWat
jacquemontiana (1) **new**   WAbe
'James Bremner' (15)   LRHS MDHE NBur NFla SIng
'Jan Palach' (x *krausii*) (7)   NMen
'Jason' (x *elisabethae*) (7)   MWat NMen
'Jenkinsiae' (x *irvingii*)   CFee CLyd EBre EMNN EMlt EPot
    (7) ♀ H4   ESis GKir GTou LRHS MBro NDlv
                                       NHol NLAp NMen NRya NWCA
                                       SBla SChu SMer WAbe WHoo
                                       WPat WWin
§ 'Johann Kellerer'   CLyd GCrs ITim NDlv NSla SBla
    (x *kellereri*) (7)   WAbe
'John Tomlinson'   CLyd NMen NSla WOBN
    (*burseriana*) (7)
'Josef Čapek'   CLyd EPot ITim NMen
    (x *megaseiflora*) (7)
'Josef Mánes' (x *borisii*) (7)   NMen
'Joy'   see S. 'Kaspar Maria Sternberg'
'Judith Shackleton'   CLyd EHyt MWat NMen WAbe
    (x *abingdonensis*) (7)
'Juliet'   see S. 'Riverslea'
§ *juniperifolia* (7)   CLyd EMNN GKir GTou LRHS
                                       MHer MWat NDlv NHar NLAp
                                       NWCA SChu SMer SRms
'Jupiter'   CLyd EMNN LRHS MWat NDlv
    (x *megaseiflora*) (7)   NHar NHol NMen
'Kampa' (7) **new**   CLyd
§ *karadzicensis* (7)   EMNN NMen
'Karasin' (7)   CLyd NMen
'Karel Čapek'   CLyd CMea EPot ITim MWat NDlv
    (x *megaseiflora*) (7)   NHol NRya
'Karel Stivín'   CLyd EMNN MWat NMen
    (x *editbae*) (7)
§ 'Kaspar Maria Sternberg'   CLyd EMNN MBro NHar NHol
    (x *petraschii*) (7)   NMen WPat
'Kath Dryden'   CLyd ITim NHol NLAp
    (x *anglica*) (7)
'Kathleen   CLyd EPot MBro MDHE NHar
    Pinsent' (8) ♀ H4   NWCA WAbe
'Kathleen'   CLyd NHol NLAp WOBN
    (x *polulacina*) (7)
x *kellereri*   see S. 'Johann Kellerer'
    sensu stricto hort.
'Kestoniensis'   MWat
    (x *salmonica*) (7)
'Kew Gem'   NMen
    (x *petraschii*) (7)
'Kewensis' (x *kellereri*) (7)   MWat NMen WAbe
'Kineton' (7)   ITim NMen
'King Lear'   ITim LRHS MWat NMen SBla SIng
    (x *bursiculata*) (7)
'Kingscote White' (15)   MDHE SIng
'Kinki Purple' (*stolonifera*)   WCru
    (5) B&SWJ 4972

'Knapton Pink' (15)   MDHE MOne NPri NRya SIng
                                       WAbe
'Knapton White' (15)   MDHE SIng
§ 'Kolbiana' (x *paulinae*) (7)   CLyd MWat
'Koprvnik' (*paniculata*) (8)   SIng WAbe
§ 'Krain' (x *fritschiana*)   NHol SIng SOkd
'Krákatit'   NMen WAbe
    (x *megaseiflora*) (7)
'Krasava'   CLyd CPBP EMNN EPot NHar
    (x *megaseiflora*) (7)   NHol NMen
kusnezowiana (7) **new**   SOkd
'Kyrillii' (x *borisii*) (7)   CLyd NMen
'Labe' (x *arco-valleyi*) (7)   CLyd EPot LRHS NMen SBla
                                       SIng
§ 'Labradorica'   MDHE
    (*paniculata*) (8)
'Lady Beatrix Stanley'   see S. 'Beatrix Stanley'
'Lagraveana'   NDlv NGar WWin
    (*paniculata*) (8)
x *landaueri*   see S. 'Leonore'
    sensu stricto hort.
'Latonica' (*callosa*) (8)   SOkd
'Lemon Hybrid'   NMen
    (x *boydii*) (7)
'Lemon Spires' (7)   NMen
'Lenka' (x *byam-*   EMNN NHar NMen
    groundsii) (7)
'Leo Gordon Godseff'   LRHS NMen SIng
    (x *elisabethae*) (7)
§ 'Leonore' (x *landaueri*) (7)   LRHS MWat SIng
'Letchworth Gem'   GCal
    (x *urbium*) (11)
x *leyboldii* (7)   GTou NMen
'Lidice' (7)   CLyd EMNN MBro NDlv NHar
                                       NMen WHoo
'Lilac Time'   NMen
    (x *youngiana*) (7) **new**
lilacina   CLyd EHyt EMNN NHar NHol
                                       NMen WPat
'Limelight' (*callosa*) (8)   MDHE
'Lindau' (7)   MWat
lingulata   see S. *callosa*
'Lismore Carmine'   CLyd GCrs ITim MWat NMen
    (x *lismorensis*) (7)
'Lismore Cherry' (7)   CLyd
'Lismore Gem'   NLAp NMen
    (x *lismorensis*) (7)
'Lismore Mist'   CLyd
    (x *lismorensis*) (7)
'Lismore Pink'   CLyd EPot MWat NLAp NMen
    (x *lismorensis*) (7)   NWCA WAbe
'Lohengrin'   MWat
    (x *boerbammeri*) (7)
'Lohmuelleri'   MWat
    (x *biasolettoi*) (7)
longifolia (8)   ELan NSla WGor
Love Me   see S. 'Miluj Mne'
lowndesii (7)   EHyt
'Ludmila Šubrová'   CLyd NMen
    (x *bertolonii*) (7)
'Lusanna' (x *irvingii*) (7)   CLyd NHol
'Luschtinetz' (15)   MDHE
'Lutea' (*diapensioides*)   see S. 'Wilhelm Tell', 'Primulina'
'Lutea' (*marginata*)   see S. 'Faust'
§ 'Lutea'   CNic ESis GDra GTou LBee
    (*paniculata*) (8) ♀ H4   LRHS MBro NBro NDlv NMen
                                       SChu
'Lužníce'   MWat NDlv NMen
    (x *poluluteopurpurea*) (7)
macedonica   see S. *juniperifolia*
x *macnabiana* (8)   WOBN
'Magdalena'   NMen
    (x *thomasiana*) (7)

'Major' (*cochlearis*) LRHS NMen WGor
  (8) ♀ H4
manshuriensis (4) EBee
§ 'Maréchal Joffre' (15) MDHE WCom
'Margarete' (x *borisii*) (7) CLyd MWat NMen
marginata (7) CLyd
- var. **balcanica** see *S. marginata* var. *rocheliana*
- var. **boryi** (7) CLyd EPot LRHS MWat NMen
  WAbe
- var. **coriophylla** (7) EPot GDra NMen NWCA
- var. **karadzicensis** see *S. karadzicensis*
§ - var. **rocheliana** (7) CLyd CPBP EPot LRHS NMen
'Maria Callas' CGra CLyd
  (x *poluanglica*) (7)
'Maria Luisa' GCrs MWat NDlv NMen
  (x *salmonica*) (7)
'Marianna' (x *borisii*) (7) CLyd CNic NDlv NMen NRya
'Marie Stivínová' MWat
  (x *borisii*) (7)
'Maroon Beauty' EBee ECtt EMan EMar MDKP
  (*stolonifera*) (5) MSPs WCot
'Mars' (x *elisabethae*) (7) MWat NMen
'Marshal Joffre' (15) see *S.* 'Maréchal Joffre' (15)
§ **marshallii** (4) WWin
§ 'Martha' (x *semmleri*) (7) CLyd EMNN NMen
'Mary Golds' (7) **new** CLyd
matta-florida (7) MWat NMen
'May Queen' (7) MWat NHol NMen
media (7) MWat
x **megaseiflora** see *S.* 'Robin Hood'
  sensu stricto hort.
'Melrose' (x *salmonica*) (7) NMen
mengtzeana 'Purple WCru
  Piggy' (*epiphylla*)
mertensiana (6) CLyd EBee GTou NBir WCru
- var. **bulbifera** (6) CNic
'Meteor' (7) NRya
micranthidifolia (4) CLAP EBee WPGP
'Millstream Cream' CLyd ITim MWat NMen
  (x *elisabethae*) (7)
§ 'Miluj Mne' EPot ITim NHar NLAp
  (x *poluanglica*) (7)
'Minnehaha' ITim WAbe
  (x *elisabethae*) (7)
'Minor' (*cochlearis*) EMNN ESis GTou LBee LRHS
  (8) ♀ H4 MBro NHol NMen NWCA SChu
  SIng WHoo WPat
'Minor Glauca' see *S.* 'Labradorica'
  (*paniculata*)
'Minor' (*paniculata*) see *S. paniculata* var. *brevifolia*
'Minutifolia' EPot LRHS MBro MDHE NDlv
  (*paniculata*) (8) NWCA WAbe WCom
§ 'Miss Chambers' CMea EBee EMan EMon SMHy
  (x *urbium*) (11) SUsu WCot WMoo WPen
'Mona Lisa' (x *borisii*) (7) CLyd MBro MWat NHol NMen
  WAbe WPat
§ 'Mondscheinsonate' NHol
  (x *boydii*) (7)
'Moonlight' see *S.* 'Sulphurea'
'Moonlight Sonata' see *S.* 'Mondscheinsonate'
  (x *boydii*)
moschata see *S. exarata* subsp. *moschata*
'Mossy Triumph' **new** GAbr
'Mother of Pearl' CLyd EMNN EPot NHar NLAp
  (x *irvingii*) (7) NMen WAbe
'Mother Queen' CLyd MBro NHol WHoo WPat
  (x *irvingii*) (7)
'Mount Nachi' CBct CDes CLyd CMGP CPLG
  (*fortunei*) (5) EBee EMan EWes GCal GMaP IPot
  ITim LRHS MBri MSte NBhm
  NHar NMen NPSI SDes SMad SPla
  SSpi WAbe WCot WFar WLin
  WOld WPGP WPer

'Mrs E. Piper' (15) COkL MDHE
§ 'Mrs Gertie Prichard' MWat NHol NMen
  (x *megaseiflora*) (7)
'Mrs Helen Terry' CLyd EPot ITim LRHS NDlv NMen
  (x *salmonica*) (7)
'Mrs Leng' MDKP NMen
  (x *elisabethae*) (7)
'Muffet' (*burseriana*) (7) NMen
mutata (8) CLyd SIng
'Myra' (x *anglica*) (7) CLyd EMNN LRHS MBro MWat
  NHol NMen NWCA WHoo WPat
'Myra Cambria' MWat NDlv NHol NMen WAbe
  (x *anglica*) (7)
'Myriad' (7) **new** CLyd
'Nancye' (x *goringiana*) (7) CLyd EHyt ITim NLAp NMen
  WOBN
§ **nelsoniana** (4) EBee NHol
nigroglandulifera new EBee
'Nimbus' (*iranica*) (7) EHyt NMen
'Niobe' (x *pulvilacina*) (7) CLyd EHyt NMen
nivalis (4) NHol
'Norvegica' (*cotyledon*) (8) GTou MDHE WWin
'Notata' (*paniculata*) (8) NLAp NMen
'Nottingham Gold' CLyd EPot MWat NHol NMen
  (x *boydii*) (7)
'Nugget' (7) NMen
'Obristii' (x *salmonica*) (7) ITim NDlv NHol NMen NRya
§ **obtusa** (7) NMen
'Ochroleuca' EMNN NMen
  (x *elisabethae*) (7)
odontophylla (13) **new** WAbe
'Odysseus' (*sancta*) (7) NMen
'Olymp' (*scardica*) (7) NMen
'Opalescent' (7) CLyd MWat NMen
§ 'Ophelia' (x *arco-* MWat NHol NMen
  valleyi) (7)
oppositifolia (7) GIBF GKir GTou MBNS MHer
  MOne NLAp NSla SIng SPlb SRms
  WAbe WWin
- 'Corrie Fee' see *S.* 'Corrie Fee'
- from Iceland (7) WAbe
* - subsp. **oppositifolia** CLyd EMNN GAbr GCrs GDra
  var. **latina** (7) GTou NHar NLAp
'Oriole' (x *boydii*) (7) NMen
'Oxhill' (7) ITim NMen
paniculata hort. subsp. see *S.* 'Labradorica'
  neogaea (8)
§ **paniculata** (8) CNic ESis GKir GTou LPVe LRHS
  MBro MDKP MHer MWat NDlv
  NLAp NMen NSla SAga SPlb SRms
  WHoo
- var. **baldensis** (8) CLyd EHyt EMlt GDra GKir GTou
  LRHS MBar MBro MWat NBro
  NDlv NHol NLAp NMen NRya
  SBla SPlb WWin
- var. **brevifolia** (8) SIng
§ - subsp. **cartilaginea** (8) NHol SBla
- subsp. **kolenatiana** see *S. paniculata* subsp.
  cartilaginea
paradoxa (15) EPot LRHS SBla WGor
'Parcevalis' CLyd
  (x *finnisiae*) (7x9)
'Parsee' NMen NRya
  (x *margoxiana*) (7)
x **patens** (8x9) NJOw
§ 'Paula' (x *paulinae*) (7) NMen
'Peach Blossom' (7) CLyd EPot GCrs LRHS MWat
  NMen NRya SBla
'Pearly Gates' CLyd GCrs MWat NMen
  (x *irvingii*) (7)
'Pearly Gold' (15) CMea LRHS NRya
'Pearly King' (15) CLyd ECho LRHS MHer NMen
  NPri WAbe WFar

'Pearly King' variegated (v) COkL

x **pectinata** Schott,   see S. 'Krain'
Nyman & Kotschy (8)

pedemontana (15)   MDHE WAbe

- from Mt. Kasbak (15) **new**   CLyd

'Penelope'   CLyd CMea EHyt EMlt EPot GCrs
(x *boydilacina*) (7)   LRHS MBro NHol NMen SBla SIng
    WAbe WHoo WPat

pensylvanica (4)   GCal

'Perikles' (7)   NMen

'Peter Burrow'   CLyd CPBP EHyt NHar NLAp
(x *poluanglica*)   NMen
(7) ♀ H4

'Peter Pan' (15)   EMNN EMlt EPot GDra GKir GTou
    LGro MBro MHer NFla NHol
    NMen NPri NPro NRya WPat

'Petra' (7)   CLyd EPot ITim MBro NHol NMen

x **petraschii** (7)   CLyd ITim

§ 'Phoenix' (x *biasolettoi*) (7)   CLyd EHyt ITim LRHS NMen SIng
    WOBN

'Pilatus' (x *boydii*) (7)   MWat NMen

'Pink Pearl' (7)   CMea NMen

'Pixie' (15)   CTri EBre ECtt EMNN GAbr GKir
    LBee LRHS MPWC MWat NFla
    NLAp NMen NPri SIng SRms

'Pixie Alba'   see S. 'White Pixie'

'Plena' (*granulata*)   see S. 'Flore Pleno'

'Pollux' (x *boydii*) (7)   EPot NHol NMen

x **poluanglica** (7)   NLAp

poluniniana (7)   CLyd EHyt EMNN NHar NHol
    NWCA

- x 'Winifred' **new**   CLyd

'Pompadour' (15)   LRHS MDHE

'Popelka' (*marginata*) (7)   CLyd

porophylla (7)   GDra NMen

- var. **thessalica**   see S. *sempervivum* f. *stenophylla*

aff. **porophylla** (7)   NWCA

'Portae' (x *fritschiana*) (8)   SIng

'Primrose Bee'   EPot
(x *apiculata*) (7)

'Primrose Dame'   EMNN ESis MDKP MWat NHol
(x *elisabethae*) (7)   NMen WAbe WCom

'Primulaize' (9x11)   CLyd MBro NCat NMen

'Primulaize Salmon' (9x11)   CMea LBee LBuc NDlv NHol
    NWoo WCom WHoo WPer

§ 'Primulina'   NDlv NMen WOBN
(x *malbyana*) (7)

primuloides   see S. 'Primuloides'

§ 'Primuloides'   MBro NPri SRms WEas
(*umbrosa*) (11) ♀ H4

'Prince Hal'   CLyd EMNN EPot ESis GCrs
(*burseriana*) (7)   LRHS NDlv NHar NLAp NMen
    SIng

'Princess' (*burseriana*) (7)   CLyd EHyt LRHS NMen SIng

'Probynii' (*cochlearis*) (8)   EPot MDHE MWat NDlv NMen

'Prometheus'   CLyd
(x *prossenii*) (7)

'Prospero' (x *petraschii*) (7)   MWat NMen

x **prossenii**   see S. 'Regina'
sensu stricto hort.

'Pseudofranzii'   NWCA
(x *paulinae*) (7)

x **pseudokotschyi**   see S. 'Denisa'
sensu stricto hort.

'Pseudoscardica'   MWat NMen
(x *wehrhahnii*) (7)

'Pseudovaldensis'   CNic MDHE WAbe
(*cochlearis*) (8)

pubescens   NLAp WAbe
subsp. **iratiana** (15)

punctata Sternbo. (4)   see S. *nelsoniana*

* **punctissima**   NHol

'Pungens' (x *apiculata*) (7)   NDlv NHol NMen

'Purpurea' (*fortunei*)   see S. 'Rubrifolia'

'Purpurteppich' (15)   MDHE WPer

§ 'Pygmalion' (x *webrii*) (7)   CLyd ESis NHol NMen WAbe
    WPat

'Pyramidalis'   EPfP SRms
(*cotyledon*) (8)

'Pyrenaica'   EMNN NHar NMen
(*oppositifolia*) (7)

quadrifaria (7)   NHol

'Quarry Wood'   CLyd ITim NHol NMen
(x *anglica*) (7)

'Rainsley Seedling' (8)   MDHE NBro NMen

ramsarica (7) **new**   CGra

ramulosa (7)   NMen

'Red Pixie'   COkL

'Red Poll'   CLyd EHyt ITim MWat NMen
(x *poluanglica*) (7)   NRya

'Regina' (x *prossenii*) (7)   CLyd ITim MHer NMen

retusa (7)   CLyd EMNN NMen NSla NWCA

'Rex' (*paniculata*) (8)   EHyt LBuc NHol NMen

§ 'Riverslea'   CPBP LRHS MBro MWat NHol
(x *hornibrookii*) (7)   NMen SIng WAbe WOBN WPat

§ 'Robin Hood'   CLyd EMNN LRHS MBro MWat
(x *megaseiflora*) (7)   NHar NHol NMen SBla WHoo
    WPat

'Rokujô' (*fortunei*) (5)   EBee GKir LRHS MBri NLar WCot
    WFar WTMC

'Romeo'   CLyd
(x *hornibrookii*) (7)

'Rosea' (*cortusifolia*) (5)   CLAP NHar WOBN

§ 'Rosea'   GDra GKir GTou LDce MBro
    NBro
(*paniculata*) (8) ♀ H4   NDlv NHol NSla SBla SRms WTel
    WWin

'Rosea' (x *stuartii*) (7)   NDlv NMen WAbe

'Rosemarie' (x *anglica*) (7)   CLyd NHol NMen

'Rosenzwerg' (15)   LRHS

'Rosina Sündermann'   EPot GDra NDlv
(x *rosinae*) (7)

rotundifolia (12)   CLyd EBee GBin NHol SSpi

§ - subsp. **chrysospleniifolia** WCru WPer
var. **rhodopea** (12)

'Roy Clutterbuck' (7)   NMen

'Rubella' (x *irvingii*) (7)   CLyd ITim MWat

§ 'Rubrifolia' (*fortunei*) (5)   CLAP EBee EBre EChP ECha EHoe
    EMan EVFa IBal NHar NMen SMad
    SSpi WAbe WCot WCru WFar WGer
    WLin WOld WSan WTMC WWeb

* 'Ruby Red'   NPro

rufescens 'Pink   WCru
Pagoda' (5) **new**

'Rusalka' (x *borisii*) (7)   CLyd NMen

'Russell Vincent Prichard'   NHol NMen
(x *irvingii*) (7)

'Ruth Draper'   EMNN NHar NLAp NWCA
(*oppositifolia*) (7)

'Ruth McConnell' (15)   CMea LRHS MDHE

'Sabrina'   CLyd MWat
(x *fallsvillagensis*) (7)

'Saint John's'   EBur MBro MDHE WAbe WWin
(x *fritschiana*) (8)

'Saint Kilda'   GCrs GTou
(*oppositifolia*) (7)

x **salmonica**   see S. 'Salomonii'
sensu stricto hort.

§ 'Salomonii'   CLyd ITim NDlv NMen SRms
(x *salmonica*) (7)

'Samo' (x *hertolonii*) (7)   CLyd NMen

sancta (7)   CLyd EPot LRHS NMen SRms

- subsp. **pseudosancta**   see S. *juniperifolia*
var. **macedonica**

'Sandpiper' (7) **new**   NHol

sanguinea (1)   MDHE

'Sanguinea Superba'   GDra MDHE SIng
  (× *arendsii*) (15) ♀ H4
sarmentosa   see *S. stolonifera*
'Sartorii'   see *S.* 'Pygmalion'
'Saturn' (× *megaseiflora*) (7) ITim MBro MWat NHol NMen
'Sázava'   CGra CLyd ITim MWat NMen
  (× *poluluteopurpurea*) (7)
scardica (7)   PBP EMNN MWat NBro NMen
- var. *dalmatica*   see *S. obtusa*
- f. *erythrantha* (7)   CLyd
- subsp. *korabensis* new   GCrs
- var. *obtusa*   see *S. obtusa*
§ 'Schelleri' (× *petraschii*) (7) EHyt NMen
'Schneeteppich' (15)   WCom WPer
§ 'Schwefelblüte' (15)   GTou LBee LRHS WCom WPat
scleropoda (7)   NMen
§ 'Seaspray' (× *arendsii*) EWes
  (15/v)
'Seissera' (*burseriana*) (7) ITim NHol NMen
× *semmleri* sensu   see *S.* 'Martha'
  stricto hort.
sempervivum (7)   CLyd NMen NSla NWCA WTin
- JCA 864.003   CPBP
§ - f. *stenophylla* (7)   GTou MHer
sendaica new   WCru
'Sendtneri' (8) new   WAbe
sibirica (14)   GTou
§ 'Silver Cushion' (15/v)   CMea ELan EPfP GDra GTou LAst
                             LRHS MBar NBlu SIng SMer SPlb
                             WAbe WCom WMoo
'Silver Edge' (× *arco-valleyi*) NMen WAbe
  (7)
Silver Farreri Group (8)   NDlv NGar
- 'Snowflake' (8)   CNic MDHE NDlv WAbe
'Silver Maid'   NMen SOkd
  (× *fritschiana*) (8)
'Silver Mound'   see *S.* 'Silver Cushion'
'Sir Douglas Haig' (15)   MDHE SIng
'Snowcap' (*pubescens*) (15) EHyt NDlv NWCA
'Snowdon' (*burseriana*) (7) MWat NMen
§ 'Sofia' (× *borisii*) (7) ITim
'Somerset Seedling' (8)   MDHE WGwG
'Sorrento' (*marginata*)   NMen
  (7) new
§ 'Southside Seedling'   More than 30 suppliers
  (8) ♀ H4
spathularis (11)   GKir MHar NCat WCom WCot
                             WEas WWin
'Speciosa' (*burseriana*) (7) NDlv
'Spinners Snow-storm'   SSpi
  (*fortunei*) (5)
'Splendens' (*oppositifolia*) ELan EMNN EPfP GKev NDlv
  (7) ♀ H4   NHol NLAp NMen SBla SMer
                             SRms WPat
'Spotted Dog' new   NHar
'Sprite' (15)   LRHS MDHE
spruneri (7)   LRHS NMen
- var. *deorum* (7)   NMen
'Stansfieldii' (*rosacea*) (15) EBre EMNN GKir LRHS MDHE
                             NMen SPlb
* 'Stansfieldii Rosea' (15) MDHE
§ 'Stella' (× *stormonthii*) (7) SBla
stellaris (4)   GTou
stenophylla   see *S. flagellaris*
  subsp. *stenophylla*
stolitzkae (7)   EMNN GCrs NLAp NMen NWCA
                             WAbe
§ *stolonifera* (5) ♀ H2   CArn CHEx CHal CPLG EBee
                             ECho GBin LDai MHar NBro SDix
                             SIng WEas WFar WMoo
- 'Hime' new   WCru
'Stormonth's Variety'   see *S.* 'Stella'
stribrnyi (7)   MWat NMen

- JCA 861-400   NWCA
'Sturmiana' (*paniculata*) (8) NMen SRms
aff. *subsessiliflora* (7)   NWCA
'Suendermannii'   ITim MWat NDlv SIng
  (× *kellereri*) (7)
'Suendermannii Major'   CLyd LRHS NRya
  (× *kellereri*) (7)
'Sugar Plum Fairy'   CLAP EBee EHrv EMan NCat
  (*fortunei*) (5)   NCot SPoG WCot WElm WTMC
§ 'Sulphurea' (× *boydii*) (7) CMea CPBP EMNN ESis LRHS
                             NHar NHol NMen NWCA SChu
                             SIng WAbe WCom WHoo WPat
'Sun Dance' (× *boydii*) (7) NHol
'Superba'   GCrs GDra GTou MBro MDHE
  (*callosa* var. *australis*) (8)
'Swan' (× *fallsvillagensis*) NMen
  (7) new
'Sylva' (× *elisabethae*) (7) MWat NMen
'Symons-Jeunei' (8)   MDHE WAbe
'Tábor' (× *schottii*) (7)   NMen
'Tamayura' (*fortunei*)   EMan NCat WCot
  (5) new
taygetea (12)   ETow
'Theoden' (*oppositifolia*) CLyd EMNN EWes GCrs GTou
  (7) ♀ H4   NHar NHol NLAp NWCA SBla
'Theresia' (× *mariae-theresiae*) NMen
  (7)
'Thorpei' (7)   NMen
'Timbalii' (× *gaudinii*) (8) SIng
'Timmy Foster' (× *irvingii*) CLyd NHol NMen
  (7)
tombeanensis (7)   CLyd NMen
'Tricolor' (*stolonifera*)   EBak LRHS WCru WFar
  (5) ♀ H2
'Triumph' (× *arendsii*) (15) ECtt EMNN GDra GTou LRHS
                             NPri NVic SBla
'Tully' (× *elisabethae*) (7) ESis NHol WPat
'Tumbling Waters'   EHyt EPot GAbr ITim LHop LRHS
  (8) ♀ H4   MBro NLAp NMen NSla NWCA
                             SIng SOkd WAbe WGor WPat
                             WWin
§ 'Tvůj Den'   NDlv NMen WAbe WOBN
  (× *poluanglica*) (7)
§ 'Tvůj Píseň'   CLyd EHyt ITim NDlv NLAp
  (× *poluanglica*) (7)
§ 'Tvůj Polibek'   EHyt EPot ITim MDKP NDlv
  (× *poluanglica*) (7)   NLAp NMen SBla
'Tvůj Přítel'   EMlt NDlv
  (× *poluanglica*) (7)
§ 'Tvůj Úsměv'   CLyd EHyt ITim MWat NDlv NLAp
  (× *poluanglica*) (7)   NMen
§ 'Tvůj Úspěch'   EHyt ITim NDlv NLAp NMen SBla
  (× *poluanglica*) (7)   SOkd WAbe
'Tycho Brahe'   CLyd NMen WAbe
  (× *doerfleri*) (7)
umbrosa (11)   COIW EBee EBre ECGP ENot
                             LRHS MRav SMac SPer SPlb SRms
                             WHen WMoo WWin
- 'Aurea'   see *S.* 'Aureopunctata'
- var. *primuloides*   see *S.* 'Primuloides'
- 'Unique'   see *S.* 'Bodensee'
× *urbium* (11) ♀ H4   CHEx EBee ELan ENot EPfP GDea
                             GKir LAst LEdu LGro MWgw NSti
                             SIng SPet WCFE WFar WPer
- *primuloides*   see *S.* 'Clarence Elliott'
  'Elliott's Variety'
'Vaccariana'   ECho
  (*oppositifolia*) (7)
'Václav Hollar'   MWat NMen
  (× *gusmusii*) (7)
'Vahlii' (× *smithii*) (7)   NMen WAbe
'Valborg'   see *S.* 'Cranbourne'

'Valentine'   see S. 'Cranbourne'
'Valerie Finnis'   see S. 'Aretiastrum'
I 'Variegata' (*cuneifolia*) (3/v) ECho ECtt EPfP ESis GGar IHMH
                                     MBar NBlu NPri NVic SHFr SIng
                                     SPet SPlb SWal WCom WMoo
                                     WPer WTel
'Variegata' (*umbrosa*)   see S. 'Aureopunctata'
I 'Variegata' (x *urbium*) (3/v)   EBee EPar EPfP GDra GGar GKir
                                     LAst LGro LRHS MRav MWrn
                                     NCat NFor NLar NSti NVic SRms
                                     WEas WWal WWin
   vayredana (15)   CLyd GCrs WAbe
   veitchiana (5)   EBee NBro NCat WCru
'Venetia' (*paniculata*) (8)   MDHE WAbe
'Vesna' (x *borisii*) (7)   CLyd EMNN MWat NHol NLAp
                                     NMen WWin
§ *vespertina* (10)   CGra
'Vincent van Gogh'   CLyd NHol NMen SRot WOBN
   (x *borisii*) (7)
'Vladana'   CLyd EMNN EPot NHar NHol
   (x *megaseiflora*) (7)   NMen NRya
'Vlasta' (7)   CLyd MWat NMen
'Vltava' (7)   NMen
'Volgeri' (x *hofmannii*) (7)   CLyd
'Wada' (*fortunei*) (5)   CBcs CBct CElw CLAP CSam
                                     EBee EChP ECtt EMan EPar LAst
                                     MDun MSte NBir NHar NPri SDes
                                     SMrm SPer SSpi WAbe WAul WBea
                                     WCot WFar WOld WTMC
§ 'Wallacei' (15)   ECho MDHE NMen
'Walpole's Variety' (15)   CBrm NHar WAbe WPer
§ 'Walter Ingwersen'   SIng SRms
   (*umbrosa*) (11)
'Walter Ingwersen'   see S. 'Walter Ingwersen'
   (*umbrosa*   (*umbrosa*)
   var. *primuloides*)
§ 'Walter Irving'   CLyd EMNN ITim LRHS NHar
   (x *irvingii*) (7)   NHol NMen WAbe
'Weisser Zwerg' (15)   MDHE WAbe
'Wellesbourne' (7) **now**   CLyd
'Welsh Dragon' (15)   MDHE WAbe
'Welsh Red' (15)   WAbe
'Welsh Rose' (15)   WAbe
   wendelboi (7)   CLyd FHyt EMNN MWat NMen
                                     WOBN
'Wendrush'   CLyd NMen
   (x *wendelacina*) (7)
'Wendy'   NMen WAbe
   (x *wendelacina*) (7)
'Wetterhorn'   CLyd
   (*oppositifolia*) (7)
'Wheatley Lion'   NMen
   (x *borisii*) (7)
'Wheatley Rose' (7)   CLyd ITim LRHS NHol
'White Cap' (x *boydii*) (7)   NHol NMen
'White Imp' (7)   CLyd
§ 'White Pixie' (15)   CLyd ECtt EMNN EMlt EPfP
                                     GDea GKir LBee LGro LRHS
                                     MHer NFla NLAp NPri NPro NRya
                                     SBla SRms
'White Star' (x *petraschii*)   see S. 'Schelleri'
'Whitehill' (8)   CLyd EBre EGoo ELan EMlt ESis
                                     GKir GTou LBee LRHS MBro
                                     NBro NEgg NHol NLAp NMen
                                     SIng SPet WAbe WCom WHoo
                                     WPat WPer WTin WWin
'Whitlavei Compacta'   NWoo
   (*hypnoides*) (15)
'Wilhelm Tell'   NMen WOBN
   (x *malbyana*) (7)
'William Boyd'   MWat
   (x *boydii*) (7)
'Winifred' (x *anglica*) (7)   CLyd GCrs ITim MWat NLAp NMen

'Winifred Bevington'   CLyd EBre EMNN EMlt EPot ESis
   (8x11)   GDra GEdr GTou ITim LBee LRHS
                                     MBro NBro NDlv NHar NLAp
                                     NMen NRya SIng WAbe WHoo
                                     WLin WPat WPer
'Winston Churchill' (15)   EPfP LBuc LRHS MBNS MDHE
                                     NPri SIng
'Winton' (x *paulinae*) (7)   NMen
'Wisley' (*federici-augusti*   MBro NHar NHol NMen NRya
   subsp. *grisebachii*)   WCom WHoo WPat
   (7) ♀ H2-3
'Wisley Primrose'   see S. 'Kolbiana'
'Yellow Rock' (7)   NRya
Your Day   see S. 'Tvuj Den'
Your Friend   see S. 'Tvuj Prítel'
Your Good Fortune   see S. 'Tvuj Uspech'
Your Kiss   see S. 'Tvuj Polibek'
Your Smile   see S. 'Tvuj Usmev'
Your Song   see S. 'Tvuj Písen'
Your Success   see S. 'Tvuj Uspech'
   x *zimmeteri* (8x11)   CLyd EWes
§ 'Zlatá Praha' (x *pragensis*)   CLyd CPBP NMen WAbe
   (7)
'Zlin' (7)   NMen

Scabiosa ✿ (Dipsacaceae)

   africana   CElw CHad GGar WCot
   alpina L.   see *Cephalaria alpina*
   atropurpurea   EBee EGoo SMrm
 - 'Ace of Spades'   CHad CSpe CWCL EBee EVFa
                                     GBri LPio LRHS MBri NDov NPPs
                                     SMad WCot WSan
§ - 'Chile Black'   More than 30 suppliers
§ - 'Chile Red'   ECoo GCal NPPs SAga
§ - 'Chile Sauce'   CFai CHar EMan LHop Llck MTis
                                     NPri WCra WWol
 - dark-flowered   CBri
 - 'Peter Ray'   ECtt EWes LRHS MBri
   banatica   see S. *columbaria*
   'Betsy Trotwood'   LPio
   'Burgundy Bonnets'   EBre LRHS
§ 'Butterfly Blue'   CMdw ENot EPfP EWTr GKir
                                     IHMH LRHS MBNS MBri MCAu
                                     MCLN MWgw NDov NLar SCoo
                                     SMrm SPer WFar WWeb
   caucasica   CSam EBot EPfP GKev LAst LRHS
                                     MBro NBlu NCat NChi NPPs
                                     WFTG WFar WHoo WWin
 - var. *alba*   CBot EHrv EPfP LRHS MBri NBlu
                                     WFar WHoo
 - 'Blausiegel'   CFir EBee EBre LRHS MBNS
                                     MCAu NGdn SPla
 - 'Bressingham White'   SAsh
 - 'Challenger'   SAsh
 - 'Clive Greaves' ♀ H4   More than 30 suppliers
 - 'Fama'   CMdw COIW CSpe EMan MBNS
                                     MHer NBir NLar SMrm SPlb SRms
                                     WBar WFar WHoo
 - 'Goldingensis'   EBee GKir GMac GWCH MBNS
                                     MHer NGdn NPri WPer
 - House's hybrids   CSBt LPVe NGdn NVic SMac
                                     SRms WHil WMoo
 - 'Isaac House'   MHdf
 - 'Kompliment'   ENot LRHS NLar
 - 'Miss Willmott' ♀ H4   CHad CM&M CSam CSev EBee
                                     ECha EFou EPfP ERou EWTr
                                     GKir LAst LHop LRHS MBro
                                     MCAu MHer NPPs SPer SPet SPla
                                     SUsu WAul WCot WFar WMnd
                                     WRus
 - 'Moerheim Blue'   EBee ECha ERou NGby
 - 'Mount Cook'   MWrn SAsh
 - 'Nachtfalter'   MBri

- Perfecta Series	CSpe EBee EChP GMaP LAst LBBr LPio LRHS NGdn NLar SMrm SWat
- - 'Perfecta Alba'	COlW CSpe EBee EChP EMan GKir GMaP LAst LPio MBro MPWC NChi NLar NOrc NPri SDes SMrm SWat WHil WWhi
- 'Stäfa'	CM&M EBee ERou LHop LRHS MBri MMHG MTis SAsh SBla SDes SMrm SPla SUsu WAul WFar WMnd
'Chile Black'	see *S. atropurpurea* 'Chile Black'
'Chile Pepper'	CFai CHar EMan LHop LIck MDKP MTis NPri SAga SPoG SUsu WWol
'Chile Red'	see *S. atropurpurea* 'Chile Red'
'Chile Sauce'	see *S. atropurpurea* 'Chile Sauce'
cinerea	WMoo WWin
§ *columbaria*	CBgR CKin EBee ECGP EWTr GDea MChe MLLN NLan NMir NPPs NSco NWCA SMrm SWal WHer WJek
- 'Nana'	EBee IBal LPVe NBir NGdn NLar NMen NPri WCFE WHil WSan
- subsp. *ochroleuca*	More than 30 suppliers
- - MESE 344	EBee
- var. *webbiana*	WLin
'Crimson Cushion'	CElw CSpe EBee ECtt MAnH WCra
drakensbergensis	EBee EMan GGar LPio MTPN MWrn
farinosa	CBot EBee MHar SAga SGar SMrm SUsu WPer
gigantea	see *Cephalaria gigantea*
graminifolia	EBre EDAr EMan GBuc LPio LRHS MDKP NBir NMen NPPs NWCA SRms
- 'Pinkushion'	CStr
- *rosea*	EWes
'Helen Dillon' **new**	EBee EMan SMrm
'House's Novelty Mix' **new**	SMac
'Irish Perpetual Flowering'	EMan NDov NPPs WCot
japonica	SMad WPer
- var. *acutiloba* **new**	NChi WHil
- var. *alpina*	CHar CSpe EBee EChP ECoo ESis GAbr GTou MBro MFir MLLN MWrn NGdn NLon NPPs SRot WBea WCot WHoo WLin WRha WSan
- 'Blue Diamonds' **new**	IBal WWeb
lucida	CHea EBee EChP EMan EPar EPfP GDra GTou LRHS MBro MCAu MRav NHol NPPs NPri SAga SBla WCot WEas WMnd WPGP WPat WPer
maritima	EBee
'Midnight'	CMea CSpe
'Miss Haversham'	CElw EBee LPio WCot WMaN WPGP
montana Mill.	see *Knautia arvensis*
montana (Bieb.) DC.	see *Knautia tatarica*
ochroleuca	see *S. columbaria* var. *ochroleuca*
parnassi	see *Pterocephalus perennis*
'Peggotty' **new**	EBee WCot
'Pink Buttons'	ECoo MWrn
'Pink Mist' PBR	EBee EPfP EWTr GKir LBBr LRHS MCAu MCLN NBir NLar SCoo SMrm SPer SRms WWeb
prolifera **new**	MWrn
pterocephala	see *Pterocephalus perennis*
'Rosie's Pink'	EMan SMrm
rumelica	see *Knautia macedonica*
'Satchmo'	see *S. atropurpurea* 'Chile Black'
songarica	EBee
JJ&JH 90/216 **new**	
succisa	see *Succisa pratensis*
tatarica	see *Cephalaria gigantea*
tenuis **new**	EChP EMan MWrn

'Tourbillon' **new**	WOut
triandra	EBee LHop
ucranica	MWrn WOut

Scadoxus (*Amaryllidaceae*)

multiflorus	LAma LRHS MBri NRog WCot
natalensis	see *S. puniceus*
§ *puniceus*	ERea NRog SYvo

Scaevola (*Goodeniaceae*)

aemula 'Blue Fan' PBR	see *S. aemula* 'Blue Wonder'
§ - 'Blue Wonder' PBR	CFox CSpe EMan LAst MOak NPer SHFr SMrm
- 'Petite'	CHal
Blauer Facher = 'Saphira' PBR	SMrm WWol
crassifolia	SPlb

Scandix (*Apiaceae*)

pecten-veneris	MSal

Schefflera (*Araliaceae*)

actinophylla ♀ H1	EBak SRms
arboricola ♀ H1	NBlo SEND XBlo
- B&SWJ 7040	WCru
- 'Compacta'	MBri
- 'Gold Capella' ♀ H1	LRHS MBri SEND
- 'Trinetta'	MBri
digitata	CTrC
elegantissima ♀ H1	EShb
microphylla B&SWJ 3872	WCru

Schima (*Theaceae*)

argentea	see *S. wallichii* subsp. *noronhae* var. *superba*
wallichii	CFil
subsp. *liukiuensis*	
§ - subsp. *noronhae* var. *superba*	CHEx ISea WBod
- subsp. *wallichii* var. *khasiana*	ISea
* *yunnanensis*	GGGa

Schinus (*Anacardiaceae*)

molle	IDee
polygamus	CBcs

Schisandra (*Schisandraceae*)

arisanensis B&SWJ 3050	WCru
chinensis	CArn CPIN EBee IIve WBVN WNor WSHC
- B&SWJ 4204	WCru
grandiflora	CDoC EBee ECot ELan EPfP LRHS MBlu SCoo SLim SSta
- B&SWJ 2245	WCru
- CC 3659	WCot
- var. *cathayensis*	see *S. sphaerandra*
henryi	CPIN
* *nigra* B&SWJ 5897	WCru
propinqua var. *sinensis*	CBot CSPN MBlu SBrw WCru WSHC
rubriflora	CFwr CHEx CRHN CSPN CTri CWSG CWib EBee EPfP IDee LRHS MBlu MDun MGos NRib NSti SBrw SHBN SPer SSpi WBod WWeb
- (f)	CBcs CPIN ELan MGos SBra WSHC
- (m)	CPIN EMil NHol
- x *grandiflora* **new**	WCru
§ *sphaerandra*	CPIN
sphenanthera	EBee ELan EMil EPfP GBin IMGH LRHS MDun SLim SRPl WSHC
verrucosa HWJ 664 **new**	WCru

Schivereckia (Brassicaceae)

doerfleri	CNic

Schizachyrium (Poaceae)

§ *scoparium*	CBri CBrm CFwr CKno EBee EBre EHoe EMan EMon EPPr EVFa EWes EWsh GSki LPVe SDes SUsu WDyG
- 'The Blues'	EPPr

Schizocentron see *Heterocentron*

Schizocodon see *Shortia*

Schizophragma (Hydrangeaceae)

corylifolium	WCru
hydrangeoides	CBcs CBrm CDoC CFil CPlN EBee EBre ELan EMil EPfP GKir LRHS MAsh MBlu MBri MDun MGos NPal SBra SBrw SLim SLon SMur SPer SSpi SSta WCru WDin WSHC
- 'Moonlight' (v)	CFil CFwr CSPN EBee ELan EPfP IMGH LRHS MAsh MBlu MBri NSti SBra SBrw SHGC SMur SPer SPla SSpi SSta WCru WFar WPGP WPat WSHC WWeb
* - f. *quelpartensis*	WCru
B&SWJ 1160	
- 'Roseum' ♀ H4	CAbP CBrm CDoC CFil CKno CMil CSPN EBee EPfP EWes IArd LAst LRHS MAsh MBlu MGrG MIlFa NPal NPri SBla SHGC SLim SPer SSpi WCot WCru WFar WPGP WSHC WWeb
integrifolium ♀ H4	CBcs CFil CMac CPlN EPfP LRHS MGos SBrw SDix SHBN SPer SSpi WSHC
- var. *fauriei*	WSHC
- - B&SWJ 1701	WCru
- var. *molle*	CPlN

Schizostachyum (Poaceae)

§ *funghomii*	EPla MMoz SDry WJun WPGP

Schizostylis ✿ (Iridaceae)

§ *coccinea*	More than 30 suppliers
- f. *alba*	More than 30 suppliers
- 'Anne'	WBro WHoo
- 'Ballyrogan Giant'	CDes CFir CLAP EBee EGle IBlr WPGP
- 'Cardinal'	MAvo WBro WFar
- 'Elburton Glow'	MAvo WFar
- 'Fenland Daybreak'	CHar CLAP EBlw EBre EChP EFou EGle GKir IBlr Lick LRHS MLan NGdn NHol NLar SGar SMrm SPet SSpe WBea WBro WFar WHoo WRus
- 'Gigantea'	see *S. coccinea* 'Major'
- 'Grandiflora'	see *S. coccinea* 'Major'
- 'Hilary Gould'	CLAP CRDP GBuc IBlr MAvo SChr SUsu WBea WBro WFar WHal WHil
- 'Hint of Pink'	MAvo MDKP
- 'Jennifer' ♀ H4	CAvo CBro CElw CFwr CHea CLAP CRDP CTri EFou ERos ERou GAbr IBlr LAst MAvo MBri MMil MRav NHol NMRc SApp SCro SPar SRms SUsu SVil WFar WHil WOld WWeb
- late-flowering	SIng
- 'Maiden's Blush'	CHar CSpe EBee ECGP EChP EGle EHrv GKir Lick LPio LRHS MAvo MSte NFla NLar WBro WFar WMoo WPnP
§ - 'Major' ♀ H4	More than 30 suppliers
* - 'Marietta'	CHid EBee WAul
- 'Molly Gould'	CDes EBee EGle MAvo WBro WHil
- 'Mrs Hegarty'	More than 30 suppliers
- 'November Cheer'	EBee EBre ECot GKir IBlr Lick LRHS MSte NBir NLar NLon SMrm SSpe WBro WFar
- 'Pallida'	CMil CSam EBee EBlw ECha EHrv ELan EMan GBuc IBlr MBct MRav NBir WFar
- 'Professor Barnard'	CFee CFwr CHar CPrp CSpe EBee GCal GMac IBlr LAst MBri MSte NBir NCot SPla WBro WFar WOld WPnn
- 'Red Dragon'	WFar
- 'Salmon Charm'	CLAP EBee EBre EFou IBlr LRHS MAvo WBro WFar
- 'Silver Pink'	IBlr
- 'Snow Maiden'	CAbP CFai CLAP CRDP LCTD LCaP LRHS MBNS WBro WLRN
- 'Strawberry' **new**	MAvo
§ - 'Sunrise' ♀ H4	More than 30 suppliers
- 'Sunset'	see *S. coccinea* 'Sunrise'
- 'Tambara'	CFwr CLAP CMHG CMdw CPou EBee EHrv EMan GMac IBlr LHop MAvo NGdn SApp WElm WFar WHil WPnP
- 'Viscountess Byng'	CBro CFwr CHea CPrp EBee EBlw EGle EPot ERou GAbr GCal IBlr LAst LRHS MAvo NPPs NRog SPar SPer WBea WCot WFar WHal WOld WPer
- 'Zeal Salmon'	CBro CFcc CFir CFwr CLAP CPou EBee ECha EGle GAbr IBlr LHop MAvo MRav NBir SApp SCro SSpi WBro WFar WHil WMoo

Schoenoplectus (Cyperaceae)

§ *lacustris*	EMFW IHMH NBlu SBHF
- subsp.	SLon
tabernaemontani	
- - 'Albescens' (v)	CWat EHon EMFW LPBA MSta SAWi SLon SWat WCot WDyG WHal WWpP
- - 'Zebrinus' (v)	CBen CBot CKno CWat EHon ELan EMFW EMan EPfP GBin LPBA MSta SLon SPlb SWat WCot WDyG WFar WHal WMAq WMoo WPrP WWeb WWpP
pungens	MSta

Schoenus (Cyperaceae)

pauciflorus	CFil CKno CWCL EBee ECou EHoc EMan EVFa EWes GOrn NBro SMrm WDyG WHal WMoo WPGP WPrP

Schotia (Caesalpiniaceae)

afra **new**	CKob
brachypetala	CKob SOWG

Schrebera (Oleaceae)

alata	CKob

Sciadopitys (Sciadopityaceae)

verticillata ♀ H4	CBcs CDoC CDul CKen CTho EHul GKir IDee ISea LBee LCon LLin LNet LPan LRHS MAsh MBar MBri MDun MGos NWea SLim SPar SSpi WDin WEve WNor WOrn
- 'Firework'	CKen
- 'Globe'	CKen
- 'Gold Star'	CKen

- 'Golden Rush' — CKen MGos
- 'Grüne Kugel' — CKen
- 'Jeddeloh Compact' — CKen
- 'Mecki' — CKen
- 'Picola' — CKen
- 'Pygmy' — CKen
- 'Shorty' — CKen
- 'Sternschnuppe' — CKen

Scilla (Hyacinthaceae)

adlamii	see Ledebouria cooperi
amethystina	see S. litardierei
amoena	WCot
autumnalis	CAvo CNic LAma LRHS WShi
bifolia ♀ H4	CAvo CBro EPar EPot LAma LRHS NRog WShi
- 'Alba'	EPot LRHS
- 'Rosea'	EPar EPot LAma LRHS NRog WPer
bithynica	NGar SSpi WShi
campanulata	see Hyacinthoides hispanica
chinensis	see S. scilloides
cilicica	CBro LAma
hohenackeri	ERos
- BSBE 811	WCot
hyacinthoides	CDes EHyt
italica	see Hyacinthoides italica
japonica	see S. scilloides
kraussii new	GIBF
libanotica	see Puschkinia scilloides var. libanotica
liliohyacinthus	CAvo CBro CRDP CRow IBlr MMHG SSpi
lingulata	CStu
- var. ciliolata	CBro
§ litardierei	CAvo CStu EPot ERos GIBF LAma LRHS MBri NGar NMen WCot
messeniaca	CPom GIBF SHel WCot
- 'Grecian Sky'	SIgm SUsu
§ mischtschenkoana	CAvo CBro EHyt EPar EPot ETub LAma LRHS MBri NRog WDav
- 'Tubergeniana' ♀ H4	CMea LPhx
monophyllos	CFil
morrisii	ERos
non-scripta	see Hyacinthoides non-scripta
nutans	see Hyacinthoides non-scripta
odorata new	EHyt
persica	ERos
peruviana	More than 30 suppliers
- SB&L 20/1	WCot
- 'Alba'	CBcs CSWP CSpe ECha LAma LPio MTho NRog SMrm
* - var. ciliata	WCot
S&L 311/2 new	
* - var. ifnense new	WCot
- var. venusta S&L 311/2	WCot
plumbea new	WCot
pratensis	see S. litardierei
puschkinioides	LAma
reverchonii	EHyt ERos
rosenii	EHyt GCrs
§ scilloides	CBrm CBro EPot ERos GIBF SCnR WCot
- MSF 782	SSpi
siberica ♀ H4	CAvo EPfP ETub LAma LRHS NCel NEgg NMen NRog WPer WShi
- 'Alba'	CBro EPar EPfP EPot ETub LAma LRHS NCel NEgg NRog WPer WShi
- subsp. armena	CHEx
- 'Spring Beauty'	CBro CMea EPar EPot LAma LRHS MBri NRog SRms
- var. taurica	ERos
tubergeniana	see S. mischtschenkoana 'Tubergeniana'
verna	CDes ERos WHer WShi
vicentina	see Hyacinthoides vicentina
violacea	see Ledebouria socialis

Scindapsus (Araceae)

aureus	see Epipremnum aureum
pictus (v)	LRHS MBri

Scirpoides (Cyperaceae)

§ holoschoenus	CBig

Scirpus (Cyperaceae)

cernuus	see Isolepis cernua
cyperinus	CBrm CFwr
holoschoenus	see Scirpoides holoschoenus
lacustris	see Schoenoplectus lacustris
- 'Spiralis'	see Juncus effusus f. spiralis
maritimus	see Bolboschoenus maritimus
sylvaticus	CKin MTed
tabernaemontani	see Schoenoplectus lacustris subsp. tabernaemontani

Scleranthus (Illecebraceae)

biflorus	CTrC EGle EMlt ESis EWes LJus NDlv NWCA SPlb WPer
brockiei	CTrC
singuliflorus	WPat
uniflorus	CLyd CTrC EWes GAbr NWCA SMad SPlb
- CC 466	NWCA

Scoliopus (Trilliaceae)

bigelowii	SBla SCnR SOkd WFar
hallii	SOkd WCru

Scolopendrium see Asplenium

Scolymus see Cynara

Scopolia (Solanaceae)

anomala	CPLG
carniolica	CAvo CFir COld EBee ECGN EChP EGle ELan EMon EPar GCal GDra GPoy IBlr LPhx MBlu MCCP MHar MSal MSte NChi NLar NSti SPlb WAul WCru WHil WPGP WPrP
- subsp. hladnikiana	CAvo EBre EPPr SDys WBcn WTin
- - WM 9811	MPhe
- 'Zwanenburg'	CAvo CMdw EBee EPar LEur WCot
lurida	MNrw MSal WWye
physaloides	MSal
sinensis	see Atropanthe sinensis

Scorzonera (Asteraceae)

hispanica	WCot
radiata	EBee
suberosa	EBee EHyt ETow
subsp. cariensis	

Scrophularia (Scrophulariaceae)

aquatica	see S. auriculata
§ auriculata	EFWa ELau MHer MSal NOrc NPer WHer WWpP WWye
§ - 'Variegata' (v)	CArn EChP ECtt EHoe ELan ENot EPfP ERou GKir LPBA LRHS MBri MDun MRav MSta MTis MWat SPer SPlb SRms WBea WCot WFar WHal WWin WWpP
buergeriana new	MSal
- 'Lemon and Lime' (v)	see Teucrium viscidum 'Lemon and Lime'
- 'Lemon and Lime' misapplied	see Teucrium viscidum 'Lemon and Lime'

§ *canina* subsp. *hoppii* <u>new</u>	EBee
grandiflora	EBee WFar WSan
juratensis	see *S. canina* subsp. *hoppii*
macrantha	WCot
marilandica <u>new</u>	EBee
nodosa	CArn CKin EBee ELau GDea
	MChe MSal NMir NSco WBri
	WHbs WHer WMoo WSel
- *tracheliodes*	CNat
- *variegata*	see *S. auriculata* 'Variegata'
scopolii	EBee
umbrosa	MSal
vernalis	EBee

Scutellaria ✿ (*Lamiaceae*)

albida	EBee GEdr
- subsp. *colchica* <u>new</u>	MSPs MWrn
§ *alpina*	CLyd CPBP CPlt EBre EMan ESis
	GCrs GEdr LBee LRHS SBla SPlb
	SRms SRot SUsu WGor WPer
- 'Arcobaleno'	CBrm ESis LPVe NLar
- 'Greencourt'	EBee
altissima	CArn EBee ELan EMan EMar
	GBuc MBro MOne MSal MWrn
	NBro NPPs SHel SPlb STes WBar
	WBea WCHb WHoo WMoo WPer
	WWin
amabilis <u>new</u>	EBee
'Amazing Grace' <u>new</u>	EWes
baicalensis	CArn EBee EMlt EWTr FWll
	GPoy IBlr MSal MWrn SBla SIgm
	WPer
barbata	MNrw MSal
canescens	see *S. incana*
columnae	IFro
diffusa	CPBP EBee EWTr WPer
galericulata	EBee GPoy GWCH MHer MSal NVic
	SHar WCHb WHer WJek WWye
hastata	see *S. hastifolia*
§ *hastifolia*	CTri EBee ECot ECtt EDAr EMNN
	EMar NFor NSti WPer
§ *incana*	CFwr CPlt EBee ECGN EFou EHrv
	ELan EMan EPPr EWTr LHop
	LPhx LRHS MNrw NSti SAga SDes
	SMrm SUsu WCot WMoo WWye
indica var. *japonica*	see *S. indica* var. *parvifolia*
§ - var. *parvifolia*	CLyd CPBP CPlt CStu EBee EBur
	EHyt EMan EWes LBee LRHS MTho
	NMen NWCA SBla SRot WPat
- - 'Alba'	CLyd CPBP EHyt EMan ETow
	LBee LRHS LTwo SBla WPat
lateriflora	CArn CBod EBee ELau EOHP
	GBar GPoy MChe MGol MSal NSti
	SPoG WCHb WCer WHbs WHer
	WJek WPer WSel WWye
nana var. *sapphirina*	NWCA
JJA 1840650	
novae-zelandiae	ECou EHyt LRHS MTho WAbc WCot
orientalis	CPBP EBee LBee LRHS SBla SScr
	WHoo WLin WPat WWin
- subsp. *carica*	WWye
- 'Eastern Star'	MWrn NArg SPet
- subsp. *pinnatifida*	EHyt EMlt ESis NWCA
pontica	ESis
prostrata	CMHG WPat WWin
scordiifolia	CLyd CMea CMil EBee ECha EMlt
	EPot GKir MBro MNrw NRya
	NWCA SBla SRms SUsu WCom
	WFar WHal WHoo WRus WWeb
	WWin WWye
- 'Seoul Sapphire'	EMan GCrs GDea SOkd WCot
supina	see *S. alpina*
tournefortii	EChP ECtt LLWP

seakale see *Crambe maritima*

Sebaea (*Gentianaceae*)

repens	SPlb
thomasii	GCrs SBla SOkd WAbe

Securigera see *Coronilla*

Securinega (*Euphorbiaceae*)

suffruticosa	IIve

Sedastrum see *Sedum*

Sedum ✿ (*Crassulaceae*)

B&SWJ 737	EGoo
§ 'Abbeydore'	CKno EBee EBre ECGP EFou
	EGle EGoo EMan EMon EVFa
	LRHS MAnH NSti SUsu WPGP
	WWeb
acre	CTri ECot EFer GPoy MBar MHer
	NBlu SPlb
- 'Aureum'	EDAr EMlt EPfP IHMH MBar
	MOne NBlu WFar WHoo WPat
- 'Elegans'	ECtt EDAr GDra GTou
§ - var. *majus*	CChe CNic
- 'Minus'	WFar
aggregatum	see *Orostachys aggregata*
§ *aizoon*	EPfP SBri SChu SIde SPlb WWal
- 'Aurantiacum'	see *S. aizoon* 'Euphorbioides'
§ - 'Euphorbioides'	EBee EDtc ECha ECtt EGoo FIan
	EMon LDai LRHS MHer MRav
	NPro SGar SPer WBea WCot WFar
albescens	see *S. rupestre* f. *purpureum*
aiboroseum	see *S. erythrostictum*
§ *album*	CHal IHMH MBNS NBro WPer
§ - 'Chloroticum'	EDAr
- 'Coral Carpet'	CNic CTca EDAr EPfP GAbr GDra
	IHMH MBar MRav MWat SChu
- var *micranthum*	see *S. album* 'Chloroticum'
§ - subsp. *teretifolium*	CTri MBar
'Murale'	
altissimum	see *S. sediforme*
altum	EMon LPhx WCot WFar WMoo
	WPer
amplexicaule	see *S. tenuifolium*
§ *anacampseros*	CHEx CNic EGoo NDov NHol WPer
anglicum	SChr
athoum	see *S. album*
atlanticum	see *S. dasyphyllum* subsp.
	dasyphyllum var. *mesatlanticum*
Autumn Joy	see *S.* 'Herbstfreude'
§ 'Bertram Anderson' ♀ H4	More than 30 suppliers
bithynicum 'Aureum'	see *S. hispanicum* var. *minus*
	'Aureum'
brevifolium	IHMH MDHE
bronze-leaved	WHil
caeruleum	WAbe
'Carl'	CKno EBee EBre EChP EFou EGle
	EGoo EMan EMon GMaP LHop
	LRHS MRav NBro NCat NSti SDes
	SUsu WCot WMnd
caucasicum	WAbb WEas
- DS&T 89001T	EMon
cauticola ♀ H4	CLyd CNic COkL EDAr EMan GCal
	GEdr MBrN MBro MHer MRav
	SDes SMrm SPar SRms SRot WElm
- from Lida	ECho
§ - 'Lidakense'	CMea CTri EBre ECtt EGle EMan
	EMlt GKir LRHS MBar MBri MBro
	MTis NHar NPPs NSla SBla SChu
	SIng SRot
- 'Robustum'	EBee EMon EWll

- x *tatarinowii*	EGoo EWes
confusum	EOas SChr SEND
'Coral Blush' **new**	EBee
'Coral Sunset'	EGoo
crassipes	see *Rhodiola wallichiana*
crassularia	see *Crassula milfordiae*
cryptomerioides	WCru
B&SWJ 054	
cyaneum hort. misapplied	see *S. takasui*
cyaneum Rudolph	NWCA
dasyphyllum	CNic CTca ESis GTou MBar MHer
	MOne MWat NHol NRya NWCA
	SRms
- subsp. *dasyphyllum*	CHEx CHal
var. *glanduliferum*	
- - 'Lilac Mound'	MDHE
§ - - var. *mesatlanticum*	CNic MDHE NBir
- *mucronatis*	see *S. dasyphyllum* subsp.
	dasyphyllum var. *mesatlanticum*
douglasii	see *S. stenopetalum* 'Douglasii'
drymarioides	EBee EFou
'Dudley Field'	MHer NPPs
'Eleanor Fisher'	see *S. telephium* subsp. *ruprechtii*
ellacombeanum	see *S. kamtschaticum* var.
	ellacombeanum
§ *erythrostictum*	MTho
- 'Frosty Morn' (v)	More than 30 suppliers
§ - 'Mediovariegatum' (v)	CBot COIW EBre EChP EGle
	EGoo ELan EMon EPfP ERou
	IFro LRHS MBri MHer MNrw
	MRav NEgg SAga SHBN SPar
	WBrE WFar WHil WMnd WMoo
	WPer WWal
§ *ewersii*	CHEx CNic CSLe CTca EBee EBre
	EDAr EMNN EMon GAbr GDea
	GTou LRHS MHer NBro SPlb
§ *fabaria*	EBee EMan WAbb WCot WEas
fastigiatum	see *Rhodiola fastigiata*
floriferum	see *S. kamtschaticum*
forsterianum	LGro SPlb
subsp. *elegans*	
frutescens	STre
furfuraceum	NMen
* 'Green Expectations'	EBee EChP EGle MSph NSti SDes
gypsicola	CHEx EBee WPer
'Harvest Moon'	EBur
§ 'Herbstfreude' ♀ H4	More than 30 suppliers
heterodontum	see *Rhodiola heterodonta*
hidakanum	CLyd ECtt EMFP GCrs GTou MBro
	NBro NHol NMen NPPs SUsu
	WHoo WPat
§ *hispanicum*	ECho SPlb
- 'Albescens'	CNic
- *glaucum*	see *S. hispanicum* var. *minus*
§ - var. *minus*	ECtt GTou MBar NPri NRya SChu
	SIng SPlb WMoo
§ - - 'Aureum'	ECha EDAr MBar NJOw WMoo
	WWpP
humifusum	CPBP EBur EHyt ETow NHol
	NMen SIng
hybridum	COkL
'Immergrünchen'	
integrifolium	see *Rhodiola integrifolia*
ishidae	see *Rhodiola ishidae*
'Joyce Henderson'	CStr EBee EChP ECtt EGle EMan
	EWTr LHop LPio MGrG MRav
	NLar SBla WCom WCot WEas
	WOld
§ *kamtschaticum* ♀ H4	ESis MBar MHer WBea WWpP
§ - var. *ellacombeanum*	CNic EDAr EGoo ESis MHer
♀ H4	NMen
§ - var. *floriferum*	More than 30 suppliers
'Weihenstephaner Gold'	
- var. *kamtschaticum*	CBrm CHEx CLyd COkL EBee
'Variegatum' (v) ♀ H4	ECtt EDAr EMlt EPfP ESis LBee
	MHer MWat SBla SIng SRms SRot
	WCot WEas WFar
- var. *middendorffianum*	see *S. middendorffianum*
kirilovii	see *Rhodiola kirilovii*
laxum subsp. *heckneri*	SSpi
lineare	CHEx
- 'Variegatum' (v)	MBri SChr
litorale	EBee
'Little Gem'	NMen
§ *lydium*	EMNN GTou MBar MHer MOne
	SPlb
- 'Aureum'	see *S. hispanicum* var. *minus*
	'Aureum'
- 'Bronze Queen'	see *S. lydium*
'Lynda Windsor'	CRDP MAsh SSpi
makinoi 'Variegatum' (v)	EBre
maweanum	see *S. acre* var. *majus*
maximowiczii	see *S. aizoon*
mexicanum	MBri
§ *middendorffianum*	CLyd ECho EDAr EGoo EMon
	GTou MBrN MDHE MHer MWat
	NMen SRms SRot WHoo WRHF
	WWin
monregalense	EDAr
'Moonglow'	ECtt NMen
moranense	CHal CNic ETow
morganianum ♀ H1	CHal EBak MBri
murale	see *S. album* subsp. *teretifolium*
	'Murale'
N *nevii* hort.	EGle SPlb
nicaeense	see *S. sediforme*
obcordatum	NMen
§ *obtusatum*	COkL ECtt EDAr MBro NBlu NBro
	NSla
§ - subsp. *retusum*	WCot
oppositifolium	see *S. spurium* var. *album*
§ *oreganum*	CTca ECha EDAr EMNN ESis
	GAbr GTou MBar MWat NMen
	SPlb SRms SRot WBea WPer
	WWin
- 'Procumbens'	see *S. oreganum* subsp. *tenue*
§ - subsp. *tenue*	CNic ESis MBro NHol NRya WPat
§ *oregonense*	CLyd EBur EOas GTou NMen
oryzifolium 'Minor'	EBur
oxypetalum	STre
pachyclados	see *Rhodiola pachyclados*
palmeri	CHEx CNic CSpe EMan EOas
	ETow NBir SChr SDix WWhi
pilosum	NMen NRya NWCA
§ *pluricaule*	EHyt SChu SPlb SRms SRot
populifolium	CMHG ECha GCal MHer NChi
	SDry STre WCom WPer
praealtum	EOas SChr SPar
primuloides	see *Rhodiola primuloides*
pruinosum	see *S. spatbulifolium* subsp.
	pruinosum
pulchellum	MSPs NWCA WCot
purdyi	NMen
'Purple Emperor'	More than 30 suppliers
'Purple Leaf'	NSti
'Red Admiral' **new**	CRDP
'Red Rum' **new**	LRHS
reflexum L.	see *S. rupestre* L.
reptans	NRya
retusum	see *S. obtusatum* subsp. *retusum*
rhodiola	see *Rhodiola rosea*
'Rose Carpet'	WWeb
'Rose Clair' **new**	WWeb
rosea	see *Rhodiola rosea*
rubroglaucum hort.	see *S. oregonense*
rubroglaucum Praeger	see *S. obtusatum*

x *rubrotinctum*	CHEx CHal SChr
§ 'Ruby Glow' ♀ H4	More than 30 suppliers
'Ruby Port' **new**	CSpe
§ *rupestre* L.	CAgr CNic CTca EPfP MBNS MBar
	MHer MWhi NBlu SChu SPlb
	WHer
- 'Angelina' C&K 38 **new**	EPPr EWes NBir SUsu
- 'Minus'	CNic
- 'Monstrosum Cristatum'	ITer NBir SMad WAlt
§ - f. *purpureum*	NRya
ruprechtii	see *S. telephium* subsp. *ruprechtii*
sarcocaule hort.	see *Crassula sarcocaulis*
§ *sediforme*	EDAr
- *nicaeense*	see *S. sediforme*
§ *selskianum*	COkL EBee GDra GTou IHMH
	MOne WFar
sexangulare	EDAr EMNN GAbr GDra IHMH
	MBar MHer MOne NBlu NRya
	SPlb SRms WBea WFar
sibiricum	WEas
§ *sieboldii*	CSam LGro MBri MBro MGGn
- 'Mediovariegatum' (v) ♀ H2-3	EBre EMan MHer WPer
'Silver Moon'	EBur ESis MDHE
spathulifolium	CAgr ECha EPot ESis GTou MDKP
	MOne SChu WEas
- 'Aureum'	EBur ECtt GKir GTou MBar MWat
	NRya
- 'Cape Blanco' ♀ H4	More than 30 suppliers
§ - subsp. *pruinosum*	MDHE
- 'Purpureum' ♀ H4	EBre EDAr EMNN EPfP GAbr
	GDra GKir GTou LBee LPVe LRHS
	MBar MBri MHer MWat NBlu
	NJOw NMen NRya SBla SMer SPlb
	WAbe WCom WFar WLin WPer
	WWin
§ *spectabile* ♀ H4	CArn CPrp EBee ELan EPfP GMaP
	LHrt LRHS MCAu MHer MRav
	NBee NCiC SHfr SPer SPlb SRms
	WDca WFar WTel WWin WWpP
- 'Abendrot'	EMon LRHS
- 'Album'	CHEx CWib WMoo WTin
- 'Brilliant' ♀ H4	More than 30 suppliers
- 'Brilliant Variegated' (v)	SDes
- 'Carmen'	WGwG WMoo
- 'Iceberg'	More than 30 suppliers
- 'Indian Chief'	CFwr CM&M CPrp EBee ECGN
	EChP EGle GKir GMaP LRHS SCro
	SPar SVil WCot WElm WFar WLRN
	WMnd WMoo WWpP
- 'Lisa'	EMon MTPN NLar
- 'Meteor'	CStr EBee MBNS MCAu MLLN
	MRav MWat SCro SMrm WBea
	WCot WPer
* - 'Mini'	ELan MRav
- 'Pink Fairy'	WHil
- 'Rosenteller'	EGle EMon SMrm
- September Glow	see *S. spectabile* 'Septemberglut'
§ - 'Septemberglut'	EBre EGoo EMan EMon GKir
	MCAu NSti WCot
- 'Stardust'	CFwr COIW CPrp EGle EGoo
	EMil EMon ENot EPfP ERou
	EWTr GLil GMaP LPVe LPio LRHS
	MBNS MCAu MHer MLLN SCro
	SPar SPer SPet WFar WGor WViv
	WWeb
- 'Variegatum'	see *S. erythrostictum* 'Mediovariegatum'
spinosum	see *Orostachys spinosa*
spurium	CHEx CWCL EGoo EWTr GAbr
	LGro MBNS NBlu SEND SRms
	WWpP
§ - var. *album*	EGoo ESis NRya

* - 'Atropurpureum'	CHar ECha NFor NLon
- 'Coccineum'	MBar MHer WBVN
- Dragon's Blood	see *S. spurium* 'Schorbuser Blut'
- 'Erdblut'	EBre GKir LRHS NFla NMen
- 'Fuldaglut'	CHal CNic COkL EBee EBre
	EDAr EHoe EMan EMlt ENot
	MBNS MWat NHar NRya SChu
	SIng SMrm WBea WMoo WPer
	WWin
- 'Green Mantle'	ECha SMer WWpP
- Purple Carpet	see *S. spurium* 'Purpurteppich'
- 'Purpureum'	EGoo GDra SIng SRms
§ - 'Purpurteppich'	COkL EBre ESis GKir LGro LRHS
	MRav NBro NHol SRms
- 'Roseum'	EWll SRms
- 'Ruby Mantle'	NPro WBVN
§ - 'Schorbuser Blut' ♀ H4	CMea EBee ECtt EPfP GKir MBNS
	MBro MWat NChi NRya NVic SPar
	SPlb SRms WEas WHoo WPat
	WRHF
I - 'Splendens Roseum'	LGro
- 'Summer Glory'	WBea
- 'Tricolor'	see *S. spurium* 'Variegatum'
I - 'Variegatum' (v)	CNic ECha EDAr EGoo EHoe EMlt
	ESis MBar MHer MRav NFla NRya
	SBod SIng SPla SPlb WBea WCot
	WEas WMoo WPat WWin
stefco	NRya
stenopetalum	CTca NMen SPlb
§ - 'Douglasii'	CNic MOne SRms
'Stewed Rhubarb Mountain'	CKno CPrp EBee EGGP ECtt EGle
	EMan EMon EPyc EVFa EWTr
	LDai LHop MBNS MRav NDov
	SChu WCom WCot WPGP
	WWeb
stoloniferum	
'Variegata' **new**	
'Strawberries and Cream'	CFwr EBee EChP EGle EMan
	EMon ERou GBin LAst LPhx
	LPio LRHS MBNS MBri MRav
	NBhm NDov NSti SChu WElm
	WWeb
stribrnyi	see *S. urvillei* Stribrnyi Group
'Sunset Cloud'	CMHG CSam EBee ECtt EGle
	EMon EWes GCal LRHS MRav
takasui	CLyd
§ *tatarinowii*	CLyd EDAr
§ *telephioides*	WCot
§ *telephium*	CAgr CArn CMea LHrt MBNS
	NBir SRms WWye
- 'Abbeydore'	see *S.* 'Abbeydore'
- 'Arthur Branch'	CElw CHar EPPr EVFa GBuc
	MNrw MSte MTho
- var. *borderei*	CElw EBee EGle EMan EMon
	LHop LRHS
- subsp. *fabaria*	see *S. fabaria*
* - 'Hester'	EBee SPar WWpP
- 'Jennifer'	EMan WCot
- 'Leonore Zuuntz'	WCot
- 'Matrona'	More than 30 suppliers
§ - subsp. *maximum*	CBrm SChu
- - 'Atropurpureum' ♀ H4	CBot CHad CMea CSpe EBee
	ECha ECoo EGle ELan EMan EMar
	EPfP EVFa LPVe MFir MRav SChu
	SDes SPar WEas WMoo WWeb
	WWin
- - 'Gooseberry Fool'	ECtt EGle EGoo EMan EMon
	ERou EVFa GMaP LPhx LPio
	MAnH MGrG SHar WCot WWeb
- 'Mohrchen' zur Linden	More than 30 suppliers
- 'Munstead Red'	More than 30 suppliers
- 'Roseovariegatum' (v)	EMon
§ - subsp. *ruprechtii*	More than 30 suppliers
- - 'Hab Gray'	EBee MSte NPPs WCot WWhi

– subsp. *telephium*	CKno CPlt CRDP EBee EGle EGoo
'Lynda et Rodney'	EMan EMon MSph WCot
– 'Variegatum' (v)	COtt ECoo LRHS SPar WHal WWin
– 'Veluwe se Wakel'	EBee
* – Washfield purple selection	EBee EVFa
§ *tenuifolium*	EBur
– subsp. *tenuifolium*	EBur
tetractinum	EFou
trollii	see *Rhodiola trollii*
§ *urvillei* Stribrnyi Group	CLyd
ussuriense	SUsu WFTG WOut
§ 'Vera Jameson' ♀ H4	More than 30 suppliers
'Weihenstephaner Gold'	see *S. kamtschaticum* var.
	floriferum 'Weihenstephaner Gold'
weinbergii	see *Graptopetalum paraguayense*
yezoense	see *S. pluricaule*

Seemannia see *Gloxinia*

Selaginella ✿ (*Selaginellaceae*)

apoda	MBri
braunii	NMar WCot
douglasii	NMar
emmeliana	see *S. pallescens*
helvetica	CStu
involvens	WRic
kraussiana ♀ H1	CHal MBri NMar NRya WRic
– 'Aurea'	CHal GGar MBri NMar SMad
– 'Brownii' ♀ H1	MBri NMar
– 'Variegata' (v) ♀ H1	MBri
martensii 'Watsoniana'	NMar
moellendorfii **new**	WRic
§ *pallescens*	NMar
– 'Aurea'	NMar
sanguinolenta	CStu SIng
uncinata ♀ H1	WRic
vogelii	NMar

Selinum (*Apiaceae*)

carvifolium	CPLG EMan MCAu
tenuifolium	see *S. wallichianum*
§ *wallichianum*	CHad CRow EGoo EMan EPla
	EWTr GBuc GGar LPhx LRHS
	MLLN NBid SIgm SMrm SPer SSpi
	WHer WPGP WWhi
– EMAK 886	CPou EBee GPoy MBri NSti SDix

Selliera (*Goodeniaceae*)

radicans	ECou GGar

Semele (*Ruscaceae*)

androgyna	CHEx CPlN CRHN

Semiaquilegia (*Ranunculaceae*)

§ *adoxoides*	EBee NPPs WPer
– B&SWJ 1190	WCru
'Early Dwarf'	EDif
§ *ecalcarata*	CBot CPlt EBee EMan GBin GIBF
	LDai LEur MNrw NHar NLar
	NOak NPPs NWCA SMrm SRms
	WCru WPGP WPer WPrP WSan
	WWhi WWin
* – f. *bicolor* **new**	WCru
– 'Flore Pleno' (d)	CBos EBee EChP EVFa
simulatrix	see *S. ecalcarata*

Semiarundinaria (*Poaceae*)

from Korea **new**	EPla
§ *fastuosa* ♀ H4	CAbb CBig CDDB CDoC CHEx
	CTrC EBee EFul EGln EPfP EPla
	ERod LJus LPal MHdf MMoz
	MWgw MWht NMoo NVic SAPC
	SArc SDix SDry SPlb WJun WMul

– var. *viridis*	CDDB EBee EPla ERod LPJP SDry
	WCru WJun
kagamiana	CDDB CDoC EBee EPla LJus
	MMoz MWht NMoo SDry WJun
§ *lubrica*	CFil WPGP
makinoi	CDDB EPla MWht WJun WPGP
nitida	see *Fargesia nitida*
§ *okuboi*	EPla ERod LPal MMoz MWht
	WJun
villosa	see *S. okuboi*
yamadorii	EPla ERod MMoz MWht SDry
	WJun
– 'Brimscombe'	EPla SDry
yashadake	EPla ERod SDry WJun
– *kimmei*	CAbb CDDB CDoC CFil EBee EPla
	ERod LJus MHdf MMoz MWht
	NMoo SDry WDyG WFar WJun
	WPGP

Sempervivella see *Rosularia*

Sempervivum ✿ (*Crassulaceae*)

from Sierra del Cadi	MOne NHol
from Sierra Nova	NDlv
'Aalrika'	CWil
'Abba'	MOne WHal WPer
acuminatum	see *S. tectorum* var. *glaucum*
'Adelaar'	CWil MApt
'Adelmoed'	CWil
'Adeltruid'	NHol
'Adlerhorst'	NHol
'Aglow'	CWil MHom MOne NMen
'Aladdin'	CWil MApt SRms
'Albertnellii'	NHol
'Alcithoë'	CWil MOne
'Aldo Moro'	CWil GAbr LBee MApt MHom
	MOne NMen
allionii	see *Jovibarba allionii*
'Allison'	CWil
'Alluring'	GAbr
'Alpha'	CWil EBee EMlt ESis LBee LRHS
	MApt MOne NHol NMen NPPs
	SIng SRms STre WHal WPer
altum	CWil MHom NMen
'Amanda'	CWil MApt MBro NMen SRms
	WHoo WPer
'Ambergreen'	NMen
'Andorra'	NHol
andreanum	CWil ESis MHom NBro NHol
	NMen SIng WTin
'Apache'	CWil NMen
'Apollo'	NHol
'Apple Blossom'	CWil GCrs MApt NMen
arachnoideum ♀ H4	More than 30 suppliers
– from Ararat	SDys
– 'Abruzzii'	GCrs SIng
– var. *bryoides*	CWil ESis MBro NMen SIng WLin
	WPer
– 'Clairchen'	MApt MBro NHol NMen NSla
– cristate	CWil
* – *densum*	EHyt EMlt ESis NRya
I – – 'Robin' **new**	LBee
– subsp. *doellianum*	see *S. arachnoideum* var.
	glabrescens
– from Fondo Majella, Italy	CWil
§ – var. *glabrescens*	EHyt NMen SDys
– – 'Album'	GCrs
– 'Gusseri'	SIng
– 'Kappa'	see *S.* 'Kappa'
– 'Laggeri'	see *S. arachnoideum* subsp.
	tomentosum
– 'Mole Harbord'	LRHS
– 'Peña Prieta'	NHol

I - 'Red Papaver' **new**   ECGP
   - 'Red Variety'   NMen
   - 'Rubrum'   COlW EPem EWTr LRHS MOne
                                    WLow
   - 'Sultan'   MApt MOne
   - subsp. *tomentosum*   see S. x *barbulatum* 'Hookeri'
     misapplied
§ - subsp. *tomentosum*   CHal CWil EBee EBre EMNN EMlt
     ♀ H4   EPot GKir LRHS MApt MBro
                                    MHer NHol NMen NPer NRya
                                    NWCA SChu SIng SRms WBrE
                                    WPer WWin
   - - 'Minor'   NHol NMen SIng
§ - - 'Stansfieldii'   GAbr SDys SIng STre WHal
   - x *calcareum*   CWil MBro NHol NMen WTin
   - x *grandiflorum*   SIng
   - x *montanum*   SIng
   - x *nevadense*   CWil SDys SIng
   - x *pittonii*   CWil MBro NHol NJOw NMen
   arenarium   see *Jovibarba arenaria*
   armenum   NMen
   'Aross'   CLyd GAbr NMen
   'Artist'   CWil
   arvernense   see S. *tectorum*
   'Ashes of Roses'   EGoo EPot ESis MBro MOne
                                    NMen WAbe WPer
   'Asteroid'   CWil NMen
   atlanticum   CWil GEdr MHom NDlv NMen
                                    NSla
   - from Atlas Mts, Morocco   CWil
   - from Oukaimaden   CWil MBro MOne NHol NMen
                                    WTin
   - 'Edward Balls'   CWil EPem MOne SDys
   'Atlantis'   NHol
   'Atropurpureum'   CHEx CWil GAbr MBro MOne
                                    SRms WGor WIvy WPer
   'Aurcum'   see *Greenovia aurea*
   balcanicum   MBro NMen
   ballsii   CWil NMen
   - from Kambecho   MHom
   - from Smólikas   CWil MApt MOne NMen
   - from Tschumba Petzi   CWil MApt SDys SIng
   'Banderi'   CWil MApt MOne
§ x *barbulatum*   MApt NMen SDys SIng WHoo WPer
§ - 'Hookeri'   CWil ESis MOne NMen SIng WAbe
                                    WPer
   'Bascour Zilver'   CWil GAbr SIng WHal
   'Bayan'   MTPN
* 'Beaute'   CWil
   'Bedazzled'   CWil
   'Bedivere'   CLyd CWil LBee MOne NMen SRms
* 'Bedivere Crested'   CWil
   'Bedley Hi'   MHom
   'Bella Donna'   CWil MApt MDHE MHom NHol
                                    NMen WPer
   'Bella Meade'   CWil EPem MOne NMen SRms WPer
   'Bellotts Pourpre'   CWil NHol
   'Bennerbroek'   MDHE
   'Benny Hill'   CWil
   'Bernstein'   MApt MBro MHer WHal
   'Beta'   MHom NHol NMen WAbe WCom
                                    WPer
   'Bethany'   CWil NHol NMen WHal
   'Bicolor'   EPfP
   'Big Mal'   NHol
   'Big Slipper'   EPem NHol
   'Binstead'   NHol
   'Black Beauty' **new**   MApt
   'Black Claret'   NHol
   'Black Knight'   EMlt ESis LBee LRHS SBla SRms
                                    WHal
   'Black Mini'   CWil EMlt ESis MApt MDKP
                                    MOne NBir NMen SRms

   'Black Mountain'   CWil LBee MOne
   'Black Prince'   CLyd CMil GCrs MApt
   'Black Velvet'   CWil MBro WCom WPer
   'Bladon'   WPer
   'Blood Tip'   CHEx CHal CLyd CWil EBee EGln
                                    EHyt EPot ESis GAbr GDea LBee
                                    LRHS MApt MBro MHer NHar
                                    NHol NMen SChu SRms WCom
                                    WGor WHal WHoo WLow
   'Blue Boy'   CWil EMlt ESis GAbr LBee MApt
                                    MOne NHol SIng SRms WCom
                                    WHoo WPer
   'Blue Moon'   CLyd MApt MOne NMen
   'Blue Time'   MApt MOne SChu WTin
   'Blush'   MApt
   'Boissieri'   see S. *tectorum* subsp. *tectorum*
                                    'Boissieri'
   'Booth's Red'   CLyd EPem MOne NMen SIng WGor
   borisii   see S. *ciliosum* var. *borisii*
   borissovae   CWil MHom NMen SDys
   'Boromir'   CWil MOne SChu
* 'Bowles' Variety'   WPer
   'Britta'   MOne SDys
   'Brock'   MHer NHol
   'Bronco'   CWil EBee LBee MApt MHom
                                    MOne NMen SChu SRms SUsu
                                    WLow
   'Bronze Pastel'   CLyd CWil MBro MHom MOne
                                    NMen SRms WTin
   'Bronze Tower'   NHol
   'Brown Owl'   CWil MOne NHol SRms
   'Brownii'   GAbr MOne NMen SBla WPer WTin
* 'Brunette'   GAbr
   'burgundy'   MOne
   'Burgundy Velvet'   MOne
   'Burnatii'   CWil MApt MOne NMen
   'Butterbur'   CWil
   'Café'   CWil EGoo ESis MBro NHol
                                    NMen SRms WPer
   'Cakor'   NHol
   x *calcaratum*   SIng SRms
   calcareum   CNic COlW CTca CWil EHyt EPot
                                    MBro MOne NBro NMen SPlb
                                    SRms WHoo WLow WPer
   - from Alps, France   CWil MOne
   - from Calde la Vanoise,   CWil MApt
     France
   - from Ceuze   CWil
   - from Col Bayard, France   CWil NMen
   - from Colle St Michael   CWil MOne NMen
   - from Gleize   CWil MOne NHol NMen
   - from Gorges du Cains   CWil MOne
   - from Guillaumes,   CWil MOne NMen
     Mont Ventoux, France
   - from Mont Ventoux, France   CWil MOne
   - from Queyras   CWil MOne NMen
   - from Route d'Annôt   CWil MOne
   - from Triora   CWil MBro MOne NHol NMen
* - 'Atropurpureum'   MBro SChu
   - 'Benz'   SDys
   - 'Extra'   CWil
   - 'Greenii'   CWil ESis MOne NDlv NHol
                                    NMen SIng
§ - 'Grigg's Surprise'   CWil EMlt ESis MApt MHer MOne
                                    NMen
   - 'Limelight'   CWil ESis MApt MBro NMen
                                    SChu SIng WHal WTin
   - 'Monstrosum'   see S. *calcareum* 'Grigg's
                                    Surprise'
   - 'Mrs Giuseppi'   CWil EBee EMlt ESis GAbr GDea
                                    LBee LRHS MBro MOne NMen
                                    NOak SBla SChu SIng SRms STre
                                    WAbe WPer

– 'Pink Pearl'	CWil EGoo MOne NMen SDys WTin
– 'Sir William Lawrence'	CPBP CWil EGln EPem ESis MApt MBro NMen SChu WHal WHoo
'Caldera'	NHol
* callosum barnesii **new**	GAbr
'Cameo'	NHol
'Canada Kate'	CWil MOne NHol WPer
'Candy Floss'	CWil MOne NMen
cantabricum	CWil MDHE NMen
– from Navafria	CWil NHol
– from Peña Prieta	NMen
– from Riaño, Spain	CWil GAbr
– from San Glorio	CWil GAbr MBro NMen
– from Santander, Spain	NHol
– from Sierra del Cadi, Spain	CLyd
– from Ticeros	CWil MApt MOne NMen
– from Valvernera	CWil
– subsp. cantabricum from Leitariegos	CWil ETow GAbr MOne NMen
* – subsp. guadaramense **new**	MApt NSla
– subsp. guadarramense from Lobo No. 1	CWil MBro MOne
– – from Lobo No. 2	MOne
– – from Navafria No. 1	WTin
– – from Valvanera No. 1	NMen
– subsp. urbionense	CLyd CWil SIng
– – from Picos de Urbión, Spain	MBro MOne NMen
– x montanum subsp. stiriacum	CWil WEas WTin
'Canth'	CWil NHol
* 'Carinal'	NBir
'Carluke'	MOne
'Carmen'	CHal CWil GAbr MApt MBro MOne
'Carneus'	MOne NHol
'Carnival'	CHal MApt MBro NMen WPer
caucasicum	CWil EHol MApt MHom MOne NMen SIng
– from Russia **new**	MApt
'Cavo Doro'	CWil MDHE
'Centennial'	MOne
charadzeae	CWil LBee NHol
'Cherry Frost'	CLyd MApt MOne WLRN
'Cherry Glow'	NHol
'Chocolate'	CWil MApt NHol
x christii	MOne NHol
'Christmas Time'	NHol
ciliosum ♀ H4	CPBP EGln ESis NMen SChu SIng WLow
– from Ali Botusch	SDys
§ – var. borisii	CNic EMlt ESis EWTr GCal GTou MBro NDlv NMen SChr WHal
– from Alí Butús	GCrs
* – from Gallica	CLyd
– from Ochrid	NMen
– var. galicicum 'Mali Hat'	GCrs NMen
– x ciliosum var. borisii	CHal NMen WTin
– x marmoreum	CWil MApt MBro NMen
'Cindy'	CWil MApt SRms
'Circlet'	CWil NHol
* cistaceum	WEas
'Clara Noyes'	WPer
'Clare'	CLyd EPem MApt MHer MOne
'Cleveland Morgan'	CWil EPem LRHS MHom NBro NHar NMen
'Climax'	EBee EPem EWll MHom NMen WRHF
'Cobweb Capers'	MHom MOne
'Cobweb Centre'	MOne NMen
'Collage'	CWil MApt NHol

'Collecteur Anchisi'	CWil MOne NHol SDys
'Commander Hay' ♀ H4	CHEx CLyd CWil EPfP ESis EWes GKev NFla NMen NPer SRms WEas WHal WLow WPer
'Comte de Congae'	MOne NMen
'Congo'	CWil MOne
'Conran'	NHol
'Cornstone'	NHol
'Corona'	CWil MApt MOne NHol SRms WPer
'Corsair'	CWil ESis MBro MOne NMen WGor WPer
'Crimson Velvet'	CHEx CWil EBee EDAr LBee MDHE MOne NHol WLin WPer
§ 'Crispyn'	CLyd CWil EHyt MApt MBro MOne NHol NMen WEas WPer
'Croton'	SIng WPer
'Cupream'	CWil MDHE NDlv SRms
'Dakota'	CWil NHol NMen
'Dallas'	CLyd CWil MApt MOne NHol NMen SRms
'Damask'	CWil LBee MApt MBro MDHE NMen WPer
'Dancer's Veil'	CWil
'Dark Beauty'	CLyd CWil EHyt MApt MBro MOne NMen WAbe WHal WLow
'Dark Cloud'	CWil GAbr LBee MOne WPer WTin
'Dark Point'	CWil MHom MOne NMen
'Darkie'	CWil WPer
davisii	CWil
'De Kardijk'	CWil
'Deebra'	CWil
'Deep Fire'	CWil MApt MOne NHol SRms WTin
x degenianum	GAbr MApt MBro WPer
'Delta'	MBro NMen WHoo WTin
densum	see S. tectorum
'Diane'	CWil
'Director Jacobs'	CWil EDAr GAbr MOne NHol NMen WEas WPer WWin
'Disco Dancer'	MApt
'Doctor Roberts'	NHol
dolomiticum	NMen
– x montanum	CWil MOne NBro NMen WTin
'Donarrose'	NHol
'Downland Queen'	CWil NHol
'Dragoness'	MApt MOne
'Duke of Windsor'	MApt MOne NMen
'Dusky'	CWil
'Dyke'	CTri CWil GAbr MBro NHol NMen WHal
dzhavachischvilii	MOne NMen
'Edge of Night'	CWil NHol SRms
'Eefje'	CWil
'El Toro'	MApt
'Elgar'	CWil MOne WPer
'Elizabeth'	WPer
'Elvis'	CLyd CWil GAbr MApt MBro NMen
'Emerald Giant'	CWil MOne NHol SRms WPer
'Emerson's Giant'	CWil MOne NMen
'Emma Jane'	MOne
'Emmchen'	CWil
'Engle's'	CLyd EBee EMlt LRHS MHer MOne NMen NPPs SChu SRms WHal WPer
'Engle's 13-2'	CWil MApt MOne NBro NHar NHol SChu
'Engle's No. 1'	MBro
'Engle's Rubrum'	CPBP ESis GAbr GTou LBee NHol NMen
erythraeum	CLyd NHol NMen WAbe WHal
– from Pirin, Bulgaria	NMen
– from Rila, Bulgaria	NMen
'Excalibur'	CLyd CWil MApt MBro NMen
'Exhibita'	CWil MApt MBro SDys SRms

'Nico'	CWil SRms
'Night Raven'	CLyd
'Nigrum'	see *S. tectorum* 'Nigrum'
'Niobe'	MOne
'Nixes 27'	MOne
'Noir'	CWil EWTr MOne NBro NMen SChu
'Norbert'	CWil MOne SRms
'Nortofts Beauty'	MOne
'Nouveau Pastel'	CWil MBro MOne NMen NPPs WHal
'Octet'	EPem MApt MOne NMen SIng
octopodes	CLyd ESis MDHE NBir
- var. *apetalum*	CWil EPem GAbr MOne NMen SIng SRms
'Oddity'	CPBP CWil MHer NMen WBea WCot WPer
'Ohio Burgundy'	CWil MApt MDHE MOne NDlv NMen WAbe WPer WTin
'Old Rose'	MOne
'Olga'	CWil
'Olivette'	MDHE NMen WPer WTin
'Omega'	MBro MOne WPer
'Opitz'	CLyd WPer
'Ornatum'	EPot MApt MHer MOne NMen WAbe WEas WHal
'Oscar'	CWil
ossetiense	CWil GAbr MOne NMen SIng
'Othello'	CHEx CHal CMil CTca CTri EBee EBre EMFP ESis GAbr GKev NBir STre WCot
'Packardian'	CWil MApt MOne NHol NMen
'Painted Lady'	CWil
'Palissander'	CWil GAbr MApt MBro MOne NMen
'Pam Wain'	MApt MHom NMen
'Paricutin'	CWil SDys
'Pastel'	CWil MApt MOne NMen SIng
patens	see *Jovibarba heuffelii*
'Patrician'	CWil EBre EMlt ESis LBee LRHS SRms
'Peach Blossom'	CWil
'Pekinese'	CLyd CTca CWil EMlt EPem EPot ESis GEdr MApt MBro NBro NHol NMen SIng SRms WCot WEas WPer WWin
'Peterson's Ornatum'	MOne SDys
'Petsy'	CWil SRms
'Pilatus'	CWil EWTr MOne SRms WTin
'Pink Astrid'	CWil
'Pink Cloud'	CWil MBro MOne SBla SRms
'Pink Dawn'	CWil MApt MOne
'Pink Lemonade'	MHom
* 'Pink Mist'	WPer
'Pink Puff'	CLyd CWil MApt MHom MOne NMen SRms
'Pinkie'	CWil
'Pippin'	CWil MApt MBro SRms WPer
'Piran'	CWil MApt MOne
pittonii	CHal CMea CWil EMlt EPot GAbr GCrs NMen WHal WLin
'Pixie'	CLyd CNic CWil GCrs MApt MOne NDlv NMen
'Plum Mist'	NHol
'Plumb Rose'	MApt MBro MOne NMen SChu
'Pluto'	CWil NHol
'Poke Eat'	MOne
'Polaris'	CLyd CWil MApt MHom
'Poldark'	MApt MOne
'Ponderosa'	CWil
'Pottsii'	CWil GAbr MHer MOne
'Prairie Sunset'	CWil GCrs MOne
'President Arsac'	MApt

'Procton'	MOne
'Proud Zelda'	CWil GAbr MOne NMen
'Pruhonice'	CWil MOne SRms
'Pseudo-ornatum'	EMlt EPfP LBee LRHS SChu SRms
'Pumaros'	NMen SDys
pumilum	CWil MBar NMen
- from Adyl Su No. 1	CWil
- from Armchi	CWil SDys
- from Armchi x *ingwersenii*	MOne NMen
- from El'brus No. 1	CWil
- from Techensis	CWil NMen
- x *arachnoideum*	GAbr
- x *ingwersenii*	CWil MBro WLow
'Purdy'	MApt MHom WAbe
'Purdy's 50-6'	CWil MApt
'Purdy's 90-1'	MOne
'Purple Beauty'	CLyd CWil MOne
'Purple King'	CWil MHom SDys
'Purple Passion'	MBro
'Purpurriese'	CWil
'Pygmalion'	GCrs MApt
'Queen Amalia'	see *S. reginae-amaliae*
'Quintessence'	CWil GCrs NHol SRms
'Racy'	CWil
'Radiant'	CWil
'Ragtime'	MOne
'Ramses'	MApt MOne SDys
'Raspberry Ice'	CLyd CWil EMlt EPot MApt MBro NBro NHol NMen WPer
'Rauer Kulm'	CWil
'Red Ace'	CWil ESis EWll GAbr NBro NMen SRms
'Red Beam'	CWil MDHE MOne
'Red Chips'	MHom
'Red Delta'	CWil MOne NBir NMen
'Red Devil'	CLyd CWil EHyt EMlt EPot ESis MBro MOne NMen
'Red Giant'	MOne
'Red Indian'	CWil MOne
'Red Lion'	CWil
'Red Lynn'	CWil
§ 'Red Mountain'	CHEx CHal CWil EBee EWll LBee LRHS MBro MOne MWat SRms WLRN
* 'Red Robin'	EBee EMlt MOne
'Red Rum'	WPer
'Red Shadows'	CWil ESis LBee WPer WTin
'Red Spider'	MHom NBro NMen
'Red Wings'	MOne NMen SRms
'Regal'	MApt MOne NMen
'Reggy'	CWil
'Regina'	NMen
reginae	see *S. reginae amaliae*
§ *reginae-amaliae*	NHol
- from Kambeecho No. 2	MDHE NMen SDys WTin
- from Mavri Petri	CLyd CWil MBro MOne SDys SIng
- from Peristéri, Greece	MBro
- from Sarpun	CWil MOne NMen SDys
- from Vardusa	SDys
§ 'Reginald Malby'	CTri LRHS MApt MDHE NMen SRms WTin
* *regis-fernandii*	
'Reinhard'	CTca CWil EMlt EPot GEdr MApt MBrN MHer MOne NMen NPPs SIng SRms WHal WPer
'Remus'	CWil MBro MOne NMen SDys SRms WGor
'Rex'	MOne NMen
'Rhone'	CWil MApt MBro MOne
* *richardii*	MBar
'Risque'	CWil MApt WPer

'Rita Jane' CLyd CWil MApt MHom MOne NMen WTin

'Robin' CLyd EPot NBro NHol SRms WTin

'Ronny' CWil

'Roosemaryn' MBro

'Rose Splendour' MOne

x **roseum** 'Fimbriatum' CWil GAbr LBee MBro NDlv NHol WEas

'Rosie' CLyd CMea CWil EMlt EPot GAbr MApt MBro MOne NHol NMen SIng SRms WHal WHoo WPer

'Rotkopf' CWil MApt MOne SChu SRms WLow

'Rotmantel' SDys WTin

'Rotund' CWil MApt

'Rouge' CWil NMen

'Royal Opera' CWil MOne

'Royal Ruby' CWil EMlt GAbr LBee LRHS MApt MOne SChu SRms

'Rubellum' MOne

'Rubin' ECGP EGoo EPfP ESis GAbr GEdr MApt MBro NBir NLAp NMen SRms WAbe WEas WHoo WPer

'Rubra Ash' **new** MApt

'Rubrum Ash' CWil EHyt EPem GAbr MBro MOne NMen WAbe

'Rubrum Ornatum' MHom

'Rubrum Ray' CWil MOne SRms

§ 'Ruby Glow' ESis

'Russian River' WHoo

'Rusty' CWil WFar

ruthenicum LRHS MHom

'Sabanum' CLyd MOne

'Safara' CWil

'Saffron' CWil MOne NMen

'Saga' EPem MOne

'Sanford's Hybrid' MOne

'Santis' MBro

'Sarah' MOne NMen

'Sassy Frass' CLyd MApt MOne NMen

'Saturn' CWil MApt MOne NMen

schlehanii see *S. marmoreum*

'Seminole' CWil MOne

'Shadri' MOne

'Sharon's Pencil' CWil

'Sheila' GAbr

'Shenoua Koula' SIng

'Shirley Moore' CWil MApt MOne

'Shirley's Joy' CHal GAbr NMen

'Sideshow' CWil MApt MOne

'Sigma' MOne

'Silberkarneol' see *S.* 'Silver Jubilee'

'Silberspitz' CWil MHer NBro NMen WPer

'Silver Cup' CWil

§ 'Silver Jubilee' CWil GAbr MDHE NBro NDlv SPlb SRms WLow

'Silver Queen' CWil

'Silver Spring' MOne

'Silver Thaw' CWil EMlt NMen SIng WCot

'Silverine' CWil

'Silvertone' CWil

'Simonkaianum' see *Jovibarba hirta*

'Sioux' CLyd CPBP CWil ESis EWll GAbr LBee MOne NMen NPPs SIng WPer

'Skrocki's Beauty' CWil

'Skrocki's Bronze' SChu WPer

'Skrocki's Purple Rose' CWil

'Slabber's Seedling' CWil MApt

'Smokey Jet' CWil

'Snowberger' CLyd CWil EGln EMlt EPem EPot ESis LRHS MApt MOne NHar NMen SRms WHal WPer

soboliferum see *Jovibarba sobolifera*

'Soothsayer' CWil MApt MOne NMen

'Sopa' CWil MOne NMen

sosnowskyi CWil MOne NMen

'Soul' CWil MApt

'Soul Sister' CWil

'Spanish Dancer' CWil MApt

'Spherette' CWil MApt MBro NMen WPer

'Spinnelli' MBro MOne WTin

'Spiver's Velvet' MOne

'Spring Mist' CWil MApt MBro MOne NHar SRms WGor WPer

'Sprite' CWil MApt MOne NMen SDys

stansfieldii see *S. arachnoideum* subsp. *tomentosum* 'Stansfieldii'

'Starburst' CWil

'Starion' CWil MApt MOne

'Starshine' MBro MHer MOne NHol NMen

'State Fair' CWil MBro NHol SIng WPer

* **stolonifera** **new** GAbr

'Strawberry Fields' CWil MOne

'Strider' MBro WTin

'Stuffed Olive' CWil ESis MOne SDys

'Sun Waves' CWil NHol SDys

'Sunrise' MOne

'Super Dome' CWil

'Superama' CWil MApt

'Syston Flame' CWil MOne NMen

'Tamberlane' CWil

'Tambimuttu' CWil MApt MOne

'Tarita' CWil

'Teck' CWil

§ **tectorum** ♀ H4 CArn CLyd COkL CPrp CSam CWil EBee ELan EPfP EWTr GPoy GTou LBee LRHS MApt MBar MDHE MHer NBlu NFla NLon NMen SIde SIng SPlb STre WAbe WJek WWye

– from Eporn CWil MOne NMen

– from Sierra del Cadi MApt

– subsp. **alpinum** CWil MBro NMen SIng

– 'Atropurpureum' ELan NHol WCom WTin

– 'Atrorubens' NHol

– 'Atroviolaceum' CWil ESis GCal NHol

– subsp. **cantalicum** MApt SRms

§ – var. **glaucum** CWil ESis EWTr NDlv WLow

§ – 'Nigrum' EHyt EMlt ESis LBee LRHS MApt MBro MHer MOne NBro NHol NMen SDys SRms

– 'Red Flush' CWil NHar NMen SDys WLin

– 'Royanum' ESis GAbr

– 'Sunset' CWil ESis GAbr NMen SDys SIng WHal

– subsp. **tectorum** MOne

§ – – 'Atropurpureum' CWil

§ – – 'Boissieri' CWil MApt MBro SRms

– – 'Triste' CWil EBee EMlt ESis LBee LRHS MBro MOne SRms WAbe

– 'Violaceum' CLyd MHom SIng SRms WAbe

'Telfan' MOne NMen

'Terlamen' CWil

'Terracotta Baby' CWil

'Thayne' NMen

'The Rocket' CWil

thompsonianum CWil ESis NDlv NHol NMen

'Thunder' CWil

'Tiffany' CBrm MOne NHol WPer

'Tiger Bay' NHol

'Tina' WPer

'Tip Top' CWil

'Titania' CWil EPem MApt MBro NBro NHar NMen WHal WTin

'Tombago' CWil MOne

'Topaz'	CWil EBee EMlt LBee LRHS MApt MOne NMen SBla SChu SRms
'Tordeur's Memory'	CWil LBee MApt MOne NMen
'Trail Walker'	CWil ESis LBee MOne SRms
transcaucasicum	CWil MOne
* 'Tree Beard'	CWil
'Tristesse'	CLyd CWil MApt MOne NMen WGor WGwG
'Truva'	MOne NMen
'Twilight Blues'	CWil
x *vaccarii*	NMen
'Vanbaelen'	CWil GAbr NMen SDys
'Vanessa'	CWil
'Vaughelen'	CWil MBro MOne
* *verschaffii*	EPem
x *versicolor*	NHol
'Veuchelen' **new**	MApt
vicentei	CWil MBro MHom NDlv NMen WTin
- from Gaton	LBee MApt MOne NMen
'Video'	CWil MApt MHom NMen
'Violet Queen'	CWil MApt
'Virgil'	CTca CWil GAbr MApt MBro NMen SDys SIng WCom WPer WTin
'Virginus'	CLyd CWil MApt MBro
'Vogro'	WTin
'Vulcano'	CWil
'Warners Pink'	MDKP
'Watermelon Rind'	MOne
webbianum	see *S. arachnoideum* subsp. *tomentosum*
'Webby Flame'	CWil
'Webby Ola'	MApt NMen
'Webby Ola'	CWil
'Wendy'	CLyd MOne NMen
'Westerlin'	CLyd CWil MOne NMen
'White Christmas'	CWil
'White Eyes'	SOkd
'Whitening'	GAbr NMen
x *widderi*	SIng
'Wollcott's Variety'	CWil EBee EPem GAbr LRHS MApt MDKP MOne NBir NHar NMen WPer
wulfenii	CWil NMen
'Zaza'	CWil
zeleborii	CHal SDys WHal
'Zenith'	CWil GAbr MApt SRms
I 'Zenobia'	MHom
'Zenocrate'	CWil WHal
'Zepherin'	CWil
'Zeppelin'	CWil MApt MBro
'Zilver Moon'	CWil
'Zircon'	NMen
'Zone'	CHEx CWil NMen
'Zorba' **new**	MApt
'Zulu'	CWil MApt

Senecio (Asteraceae)

§ *abrotanifolius*	EBee
- var. *tiroliensis*	see *S. abrotanifolius*
§ *articulatus*	CHal EShb
aschenbornianus	GCal
aureus	see *Packera aurea*
bicolor subsp. *cineraria*	see *S. cineraria*
bidwillii	see *Brachyglottis bidwillii*
buchananii	see *Brachyglottis buchananii*
candicans	see *S. cineraria*
cannabifolius	GCal
canus	WLin
chrysanthemoides	see *Euryops chrysanthemoides*
§ *cineraria*	IBlr NBlu

- 'Ramparts'	WEas
- 'Silver Dust' ♀ H3	CFox CSLe EPfP LRHS
- 'White Diamond'	ECha LGro
compactus	see *Brachyglottis compacta*
confusus	CPIN ELan ERea ESlt SOWG WMul
doria	LRHS SCro WCot WFar
doronicum	WCot
glastifolius	ERea GGar
'Gregynog Gold'	see *Ligularia* 'Gregynog Gold'
greyi hort.	see *Brachyglottis* (Dunedin Group) 'Sunshine'
greyi Hook.	see *Brachyglottis greyi*
heritieri DC.	see *Pericallis lanata*
hoffmannii	CPIN EShb
laxifolius hort.	see *Brachyglottis* (Dunedin Group) 'Sunshine'
'Leonard Cockayne'	see *Brachyglottis* 'Leonard Cockayne'
leucophyllus	SOkd
leucostachys	see *S. viravira*
macroglossus	CHll
- 'Variegatus' (v) ♀ H1	CHal CPIN ERea NBlu SMur
maritimus	see *S. cineraria*
monroi	see *Brachyglottis monroi*
petasitis	CHEx
polyodon	CSpe EBla EWes GBri MCCP MNrw SCro SUsu
- S&SH 29	CFir CPlt CRDP EBee
- subsp. *subglaber*	EMon IFro
przewalskii	see *Ligularia przewalskii*
pulcher	CDes CFil CSam EBee ETow GBri LEdu MAvo MNrw MTho SMrm SUsu WCru WPGP
reinholdii	see *Brachyglottis rotundifolia*
rowleyanus	EBak SMur
scandens	CMac CPIN ELan ERea MCCP MNrw MTho WCwm WHer WPGP
seminiveus	EBee
§ *serpens*	CHal CStu
§ *smithii*	CRDP CRow ELan GDea NBid NChi SAWi WBcn WCot WCru WFar
speciosus	NBir
spedenii	see *Brachyglottis spedenii*
squalidus	WHer
'Sunshine'	see *Brachyglottis* (Dunedin Group) 'Sunshine'
tamoides 'Variegatus' (v)	ERea
tanguticus	see *Sinacalia tangutica*
* *torputica*	SAWi
§ *viravira* ♀ H3-4	CSLe CSpe EDcc EGoo EHol ERca LIck MLLN MRav MWgw SLim SMac SMad SPer SRPl WCom WCot WEas WSHC

Senna (Caesalpiniaceae)

artemisioides ♀ H1	SOWG
§ *corymbosa*	CBot CHEx CRHN ERea LRHS SOWG SYvo
didymobotrya	SOWG
§ *marilandica*	EBee ELan ELau MSal SIgm
mexicana var. *chapmanii* **new**	SYvo
§ *obtusifolia*	MSal
retusa	CHEx
septemtrionalis	SBrw

Sequoia (Cupressaceae)

sempervirens ♀ H4	CBcs CDoC CDul CLnd CMCN CTho CTrG CWib ECrN EHul EPfP ERom GKir LCon LPan SKee SLon SPar WDin WEve WMou WNor

- 'Adpressa' — CDoC CMac CSli CTho EBre EHul EOrn EPla GKir LCon LLin MAsh MBar MBri MGos NWea SLim SPar WEve
- 'Prostrata' — CDoC CSli EBre EOrn EPla LLin MBar MBri

Sequoiadendron (Cupressaceae)

giganteum ♀ H4 — More than 30 suppliers
- 'Barabits Requiem' — MBlu MBri SMad
- 'Blue Iceberg' **new** — CKen
- 'Cannibal' **new** — MBlu
- 'Glaucum' — CDoC LCon LPan MBlu MBri NLar SMad
* - 'Glaucum Compactum' — MBri
- 'Greenpeace' **new** — MBlu
- 'Hazel Smith' — MBlu
- 'Pendulum' — CDoC CKen EPfP ERod LCon LPan MBlu
- 'Pygmaeum' **new** — MBlu
- 'Variegatum' (v) — CDoC EVFa LCon WBcn

Serapias (Orchidaceae)

lingua — CHdy EHyt LAma LEur SBla SCnR SSpi
- peach — LEur
parviflora **new** — WHer

Serenoa (Arecaceae)

repens — CBrP CRoM EPVP LPal

Seriphidium (Asteraceae)

caerulescens — EEls
  subsp. gallicum
§ canum — EBee EEls IIve MHer
§ ferganense — EEls
§ fragrans — EEls
§ maritimum — CArn GBar GGar ILis MHer NSti
- var. maritimum — EEls
nutans — CSLe EBee EEls MWat MWgw
§ tridentatum — CArn EBee MGol
- subsp. tridentatum — EEls
- subsp. wyomingense — EEls
tripartitum var. rupicola — EEls
§ vallesiacum ♀ H4 — ECGP EEls WEas
vaseyanaum — EEls

Serissa (Rubiaceae)

foetida — see S. japonica
§ japonica — STre
- rosea — STre
- 'Variegata' (v) — CHal STre

Serratula (Asteraceae)

coronata — EBre
* minor **new** — EBee
§ seoanei — CMea CRDP CTri EBee ECha EDAr EMan EMon LHop LPhx MHer MWat SAga SDix SIng SRms WCot WFar WPGP WPat WWhi WWin
shawii — see S. seoanei
tinctoria — CArn CKin ELau EMan GBar MSal NLar
- subsp. macrocephala — EBee
wolffii — EBee

Sesamum (Pedaliaceae)

indicum — CArn

Sesbania (Papilionaceae)

punicea — SOWG

Seseli (Apiaceae)

elatum subsp. osseum — CFil EBee ITer LPio SIgm
globiferum — LPhx SIgm
gummiferum — CArn CBot CFwr CSpe EMan EMar EMon ITer LEdu LPhx LPio SCro SIgm
hippomarathrum — SIgm
libanotis — LPhx LPio NDov NPPs SAga SIgm
montanum — ITer
pallasii — SIgm
rigidum — EBee
varium — LPio SIgm

Sesleria (Poaceae)

§ albicans — EPPr
§ argentea — CBrm GIBF
autumnalis — EPPr LBBr LPhx
caerulea — CSam EBee EBlw EChP EHoe ELan EMon LAst LBuc LPVe LPhx MBar MBri MLLN MMoz MWgw MWhi SDes SRGP SWal WWeb
- subsp. calcarea — see S. albicans
- 'Malvern Mop' **new** — CKno WPGP
* candida **new** — EPPr
cylindrica — see S. argentea
glauca — CRez EHoe NLar NOak NPro NSti SChu WPer
heufleriana — CElw CPlt ECGN EChP EHoe EMan EMon EPPr EPla MAvo SLPl SPlb WPrP
insularis — CSWP EMon EPPr LRHS WPrP
'Morning Dew' **new** — GCal
nitida — CBig CKno EBee EHoe EMan EMon EPPr LPhx LRHS MMoz WPGP
rigida — EHoe
sadleriana — EBee EPPr EWes

Setaria (Poaceae)

macrostachya ♀ H3 **new** — CKno LPhx
palmifolia — CHEx CRoM EPPr WDyG WHal WMul
viridis — NChi NSti WCot

Setcreasea see Tradescantia

Severinia (Rutaceae)

buxifolia — SCit

shaddock see Citrus maxima

Shepherdia (Elaeagnaceae)

argentea — CAgr CBcs CPle GIBF NLar
canadensis — CPle
rotundifolia **new** — GIBF

Sherardia (Rubiaceae)

arvensis — MSal

Shibataea (Poaceae)

chinensis — EPla
kumasasa — More than 30 suppliers
- f. aureostriata — EPla SDry
lancifolia — EPla SDry WJun

Shortia (Diapensiaceae)

galacifolia — IBlr
- brevistyla — IBlr
x interdexta 'Leona' — IBlr
soldanelloides — IBlr SSpi
- f. alpina — IBlr
- var. ilicifolia — IBlr SSpi
- - 'Askival' — IBlr

– var. **magna**	CDes IBlr
uniflora	IBlr WCru
* – var. **kamtchatica** <u>new</u>	WCru
– var. **kantoensis**	IBlr
* – var. **nana** <u>new</u>	WCru
– var. **orbicularis**	GCrs IBlr SSpi
'Grandiflora'	

Sibbaldia (*Rosaceae*)
procumbens	EBee GKir

Sibbaldiopsis (*Rosaceae*)
§ **tridentata**	EMar NChi
– 'Lemon Mac'	SIng SMac
– 'Nuuk'	MGos NBlu NHol NLon SMac

Sibiraea (*Rosaceae*)
altaiensis	see *S. laevigata*
§ **laevigata**	CFil

Sibthorpia (*Scrophulariaceae*)
europaea	CHEx CPLG

Sida (*Malvaceae*)
acuta <u>new</u>	MGol
hermaphrodita	EBee EMan EMon WCot

Sidalcea (*Malvaceae*)
'Brilliant'	CM&M EBee EChP EMan EPfP LCaP LRHS MMil MPWC NPPs NSti SPer WFar WLow WViv
candida	More than 30 suppliers
– 'Bianca'	CBot EBee EHrv ERou LAst LCaP LPVe MSte NLar NPri WFar WMoo WPer WWhi WWpP
'Crimson King'	WFar
'Croftway Red'	CBcs CFlr CMGP EBee ECGP ELan EMan EPfP GKir LRHS MFir MRav SAga SChu SCro SHel SLon SPer SPet WMaN WMoo WSan
cusickii	EBee
'Elsie Heugh' ♀ H4	More than 30 suppliers
hendersonii	EBee
hickmanii	EBee
subsp. **anomala**	
hirtipes	EBee
'Interlaken'	EBee EBre NOrc
'Jimmy Whittet' <u>new</u>	WBrE
'Little Princess'PBR	CFai EBee EMan GBri MBri MCLN NLar WWeb
'Loveliness'	CM&M CRDP EBee ELan EMan EVFa MAvo MRav NBro NCat NDov NGdn NLar SAga SVil WViv
malviflora	MFir NSti SChu SRms SYvo WWpP
– 'Alba'	WFar
'Mary Martin'	EMan
'Monarch'	MDKP
'Moorland Rose Coronet'	WMoo
'Mr Lindbergh'	EBee EMan EPfP ERou LRHS NHol SOkh SPer WFar
'Mrs Borrodaile'	CM&M CMGP EBee ECGN EMan GBuc LRHS MBNS MCAu MCLN MMil MRav NGdn NHol SChu SHel WElm WFar WMoo
'Mrs Galloway'	WFar
'Mrs T.Alderson'	EMan WFar WMoo
'My Love'	CFwr EBee EFou LPhx NCat NDov
neomexicana	EBee EMan GCal WBea WHil
'Oberon'	GBuc LPio WEas WFar WMoo
oregana	NBid NGdn WMoo
– 'Brilliant' <u>new</u>	IHMH
– subsp. **spicata**	EPPr WMoo

– – NNS 98-518	WCot
'Party Girl'	CBri CM&M CSBt EBre EChP ECot ECtt EFou GKir LPio LRHS MRav NCat NHol NLar NOrc NPPs NPri NVic SDes SPlb WBrE WFar WHil WMnd WMoo WPer WWeb
'Präriebrand'	LPhx SAga
'Purpurea'	EBee NChi STes WBea
reptans NNS 95-464 <u>new</u>	WCot
'Reverend Page Roberts'	MMHG MRav WCot WFar
'Rosaly'	EBee LPVe NCat NChi WGor
'Rosanna'	EChP LBuc LPVe NLar SWal WBea WWeb WWpP
'Rose Bouquet'	WLin
'Rose Queen'	EBee ECha ENot LHop LRHS MCAu MCLN MRav MTis MWgw SAga SChu SPer SRms WFar WMoo
'Rosy Gem'	EBre ECtt IHMH LCaP LRHS MBNS NCat WFar
Stark's hybrids	LRHS SRms WBea
'Sussex Beauty'	CMCo CRDP CSam EBee EFou EMan EWTr MArl MLLN MRav MSte NCat NCiC NDov NGdn NPPs SChu SPer SRkn WAul WCot WFar WLin WMoo
'Sweet Joy'	SMrm
'The Duchess'	WFar
'William Smith' ♀ H4	COtt CRDP CSam EBre ECtt EPfP EWes LAst LRHS MCLN MLLN MRav MWrn NCat NCiC NGdn NLon NOrc NPPs SPer SPla WFar
'Wine Red'	CPLG EBee ECGP ERou LHop MDKP MTis NCot SVil WHil

Sideritis (*Lamiaceae*)
syriaca	CBot EBee ECha EMan EOHP EWll IFro SGar SHFr SIgm SSvw

Sieversia (*Rosaceae*)
pentapetala	see *Geum pentapetalum*
§ **reptans**	CStu

Silaum (*Apiaceae*)
silaus	CKin WBWf

Silene (*Caryophyllaceae*)
acaulis	CBri EDAr EMlt ESis GTou LBee LRHS MTho NMen SBla SRms WAbe
§ – subsp. **acaulis**	CGra EPot GDra NCat SPlb SRms
– 'Alba'	CGra EPot EWes GDra LRHS NHar NLan SOkd WAbe
§ – subsp. **bryoides**	NWCA
– subsp. **elongata**	see *S. acaulis* subsp. *acaulis*
– subsp. **exscapa**	see *S. acaulis* subsp. *bryoides*
– 'Frances'	EPot GCrs GDra GTou NHar NMen NRya NSla NWCA WAbe
– 'Francis Copeland'	ECho NMen
– 'Helen's Double' (d)	EHyt EPot WAbe
* – **minima**	CLyd EPot
– 'Mount Snowdon'	EBre EDAr ELan EPfP EWes GDra LBee LRHS MTho NHar NMen NRya NWCA SRms WAbe WPat
– 'Pedunculata'	see *S. acaulis* subsp. *acaulis*
alba	see *S. latifolia*
alpestris	CM&M EBee EPfP ESis MBar MHer MNrw MTho NLon SRms SRot WBea WFar WMoo WOut
– 'Flore Pleno' (d) ♀ H4	CWCL ESis EWes LBee LRHS NFor NLon NSla WWin
* **andina** F&W 8174	NWCA

× *arkwrightii*	see *Lychnis* × *arkwrightii*
armeria	EBee WHer
asclepiadea <u>new</u>	GCrs
asterias	CElw CSam GBuc IFro IGor
	MBNS MNrw NBid NBro NSti
	WPer WWin
- MESE 429	EBee
atropurpurea	WAbe
MESE 66 <u>new</u>	
bellidioides	EBee WPGP
caroliniana	CBrm LPVe
subsp. *wherryi*	
chungtienensis	EBee
§ *compacta*	NLar SMrm WCot
aff. *delavayi* ACE 2466	EBee
§ *dioica*	CArn CKin EPfP GDea LHrt
	MBow MChe MHer NLan NLar
	NVic SRms SWat WFar WHen
	WHer WMoo WRos WShi
- 'Clifford Moor'^{PBR} (v)	EHoe LRHS NSti SCoo WCHb
- 'Compacta'	see *S. dioica* 'Minikin'
§ - 'Flore Pleno' (d)	CBgR EBee ECha LLWP MBct
	MNrw MRav MTho NBid NBro
	NGdn SMrm WEas WElm WFar
	WHoo WPer WWin
- golden-leaved	CRDP
§ - 'Graham's Delight' (v)	ECoo EMon WCHb WHer WMoo
- 'Inane'	CNat EBlw EMar MAvo MSph
	SHar WAlt WBea
- f. *lactea*	GDea MHer
§ - 'Minikin'	CBgR CLyd ECha EMon LRHS
	MAvo NCat SPer WAlt WBea WCot
	WTin
- 'Pat Clissold' (v)	WCHb
- 'Pembrokeshire Pastel' (v)	WAlt
- 'Richmond' (d)	GBuc MAvo MInt NCat
§ - 'Rosea Plena' (d)	CBre CM&M EMan EMon IKee
	MAnH MTho SChu SMrm WHer
	WPer
- 'Rubra Plena'	see *S. dioica* 'Flore Pleno'
- 'Thelma Kay' (d/v)	CFee CMil CSev EBee ECtt EMan
	EMon EWes GBuc NBid NLar
	WMoo WPGP
- 'Underdine'	EWes
- 'Variegata'	see *S. dioica* 'Graham's Delight'
§ *fimbriata*	CBre CHad CSpe EBee ECoo EEls
	EHrv ELan EPPr EPyc EWTr GCal
	MFir MMHG MRav MWat NGar
	NSti SBla SBri SChu SHel SMrm
	WAbb WCot WKif WRHF WWye
- 'Marianne'	EMon MNrw
gallica var.	SHFr
quinquevulnera <u>new</u>	
hookeri	MTho MWrn WCom
- Ingramii Group	CGra CPBP
inflata	see *S. vulgaris*
keiskei	ECha ETow WBVN WPer
- var. *minor*	EWes LRHS MDCh MTho MWrn
	WWin
latifolia	CArn MBow MGas NMir NSco
	WHen WHer
- subsp. *alba* <u>new</u>	GWCH
maritima	see *S. uniflora*
morrisonmontana	WCru
B&SWJ 3149	
multifida	see *S. fimbriata*
nutans	CArn MNrw SRms SSth WHer
* - var. *salmoniana*	WBWf
- var. *smithiana*	WBWf
orientalis	see *S. compacta*
petersonii	NWCA
- NNS 99-464	WCot
pusilla	CHal

regia	EBee LRav MNrw SSpi WCot WPGP
rubra	see *S. dioica*
schafta ♀ ^{H4}	CHal ECha ECtt EDAr EMNN EMlt
	EPfP GDra GKir LRHS MBro MFir
	MHdf MWat NBid NBlu NJOw
	NWCA SIng SPet SRms SWal WFar
	WHoo WPer WWin
- 'Abbotswood'	see *Lychnis* × *walkeri*
	'Abbotswood Rose'
- 'Robusta'	LRHS
§ - 'Shell Pink'	CNic EPot EWes LBee LRHS NBid
	NWCA WAbe WCom
schwarzenbergeri	GCrs
sieboldii	see *Lychnis coronata* var. *sieboldii*
'Snowflake'	COkL
suksdorfii	CLyd EPot WHoo
* *surortii*	WPer
tenuis	GBuc
- ACE 2429	GBuc
thessalonica	MCCP
§ *uniflora*	ECtt EGoo EMNN EMar EMlt EPfP
	GGar MFir MWat NBid NBlu NBro
	NDov NLon NOak NWoo SPlb
	SRms SWal WBar WHen WHer
	WLin WMoo WWeb
- 'Alba Plena'	see *S. uniflora* 'Robin Whitebreast'
I - 'Compacta'	CHid EMar LPVe NDlv WBea WMoo
§ - 'Druett's Variegated' (v)	CMHG EBre ECha ECtt EDAr EPot
	EWes GKir LBee LRHS MBar
	MHer NBid NMen NPri NVic SBla
	SIng SPet SPlb WBea WCom WCot
	WPat WWin
- 'Flore Pleno'	see *S. uniflora* 'Robin Whitebreast'
§ - 'Robin Whitebreast' (d)	CHar CNic CSLe EBee ECha ECtt
	GCal GKir GMaP LPVe MBar
	MHer MTho MWat MWgw NBid
	NBro NOak SRms SRot WCot
	WMoo WPer WWeb WWin
- 'Rosea'	CHar ECtt EMNN EMar LRHS
	MRav NFor NJOw SMrm SPlb
	SRot SUsu WPer
- 'Silver Lining' (v)	GBuc
- 'Swan Lake' (d) <u>new</u>	IHMH WCot
- 'Variegata'	see *S. uniflora* 'Druett's Variegated'
- Weisskehlchen	see *S. uniflora* 'Robin Whitebreast'
- 'White Bells'	CTri EBee ECtt EPfP SPet WBea
	WHoo WSHC
vallesia	WPer
virginica	CDes EBee
§ *vulgaris*	CKin MChe MGas MHer NLan
	NMir NSco
- SDR 1761	GKev
- subsp. *maritima*	see *S. uniflora*
waldsteinii <u>new</u>	SScr
wallichiana	see *S. vulgaris*
'Wisley Pink'	CHal ECtt
yunnanensis <u>new</u>	LPhx
§ *zawadskii*	GBuc MDKP MNrw SWal WPer

Silphium (Asteraceae)

gracile <u>new</u>	EBee
integrifolium	EBee IIve SAga WCot
laciniatum	CArn EBee EMan IIve WCot
perfoliatum	CArn EBee GPoy LRHS NLar NSti
	SDes SMad SMrm WCot WFar
terebinthinaceum	EBee LPhx SMad WCot

Silybum (Asteraceae)

marianum	CArn CSpe CTCP EBee ECoo EFer
	ELan EMan EPar EPfP GPoy MSal
	MWgw NArg NGHP SIde WCer
	WEas WFar WHer WWye
- 'Adriana'	ECoo EWll MSph NArg WBry

Simmondsia (Simmondsiaceae)
   chinensis   EOHP MSal

Sinacalia (Asteraceae)
§ tangutica   CHEx CRow CSam EBee ECha
                        EMan EPPr GGar MBNS NBro NSti
                        SDix SMrm WAbb WCot WCru WFar

Sinarundinaria (Poaceae)
   anceps   see Yushania anceps
   jaunsarensis   see Yushania anceps
   maling   see Yushania maling
   murieliae   see Fargesia murielae
   nitida   see Fargesia nitida

Sinningia (Gesneriaceae)
   'Arion'   NMos
   'Blanche de Méru' NMos
   'Blue Wonder'   MBri
   'Boonwood Yellow Bird' NMos
* caerulea new   WDib
   canescens ♀ H1   CHal
§ cardinalis   CHal EBak WDib
§ x cardosa   MBri
   'Cherry Belle'   NMos
   'Diego Rose'   MBri
   'Etoile de Feu'   LAma MBri NMos
   'Hollywood'   LAma NMos
   'Island Sunset'   NMos
   'Kaiser Friedrich' LAma MBri NMos
   'Kaiser Wilhelm' LAma MBri NMos
   leucotricha   ERea
   'Medusa'   NMos
   'Mont Blanc'   LAma MBri NMos
   nivalis new   WDib
   'Pegasus'   NMos
   Tigrina Group   NMos
   verticillata   CSpe
   'Violacea'   MBri NMos
   'Waterloo'   NMos

Sinobambusa (Poaceae)
   intermedia   EPla LJus
   orthotropa   CFil EPla WPGP
   rubroligula   CFil EPla NMoo WPGP
   tootsik   EPla SDry WJun
§ - f. albostriata   SDry
   - 'Variegata'   see S. tootsik f. albostriata

Sinocalycanthus (Calycanthaceae)
   chinensis   CBcs CMCN CPMA CPle CWib
                        EBee EPfP IDee LNet NPal SBrw
                        SMad SRPI SSpi WBod WFar WPGP

Sinofranchetia (Lardizabalaceae)
   sp.   CPlN GCal WCru

Sinojackia (Styracaceae)
   xylocarpa   EPfP SSpi WFar

Sinowilsonia (Hamamelidaceae)
   henryi   CBcs

Siphonochilus (Zingiberaceae)
   carsonii   CKob
   decorus   CKob

Sisymbrium (Brassicaceae)
§ luteum   SHar WHer

Sisyrinchium ✿ (Iridaceae)
   from Andes Mts   EWes

   from Tierra del Fuego CRow
   x anceps   see S. angustifolium
§ angustifolium   CMHG EBur ECha GKir MBNS
                        MBar MSal MWat NBir NBlu NLAp
                        SPlb SRms SYvo WPer
   - album   GKir GMaP MGGn NLar
§ arenarium   CPBP EBur EPot GEdr NMen
   atlanticum   ESis NBro SUsu WFTG WPer
   bellum hort.   see S. idahoense var. bellum
   bermudianum   see S. angustifolium
   - 'Album'   see S. graminoides 'Album'
   'Biscutella'   CHad CKno CLyd CTri EBur ECtt
                        EDAr EWTr ITer ITim LAst MHdf
                        NMen NPri SChu SIng SOkh SPar
                        SPla SPlb SWal WEas WGwG WHal
                        WMoo
* 'Blue Ice'   CKno CMea CPBP CSpe EBur
                        EDAr MAvo MBro NCat NHol
                        SMrm SPar WAbe WFar WHal
                        WHoo WMoo WPat WPer
   boreale   see S. californicum
   brachypus   see S. californicum Brachypus
                        Group
   'Californian Skies' More than 30 suppliers
§ californicum   CBen EBur EHon EPfP EShb EWTr
                        GAbr LPBA MBar MSta MWat
                        NBid NBro SWal WFar WMAq
                        WPer WWin WWpP WWye
§ - Brachypus Group CBro CHar ECtt EDAr EMlt EPot
                        GDra GGar GTou LPVe MBNS MHdf
                        MNrw MOne MWgw NBir NLAp
                        NLar NPri NVic SGar SPet SPlb SWat
                        WBrE WCer WElm WMoo WWpP
* capsicum   CPLG
§ chilense   ERos
   coeleste   EBur
   coeruleum   see Gelasine coerulea
   commutatum   CHar EDAr ERos GBuc MNrw
                        MWgw SGar SRot WBro
   convolutum   EChP EMan LRHS MSph NDov
                        NPPs SDri WCot
   cuspidatum   see S. arenarium
   'Deep Seas' new   SUsu
   demissum   CLyd CNic EBur
   depauperatum   CLyd EBur EMar ESis MNrw
                        NWCA WHer WMoo WPer
   'Devon Blue'   WFar
   'Devon Skies'   CHid CMCo CMHG CRez EBur
                        WAbe WFar WSan WWin
   douglasii   see Olsynium douglasii
   'Dragon's Eye'   MBrN SIng SRot SSth SSvw
                        SUsu
   'E.K. Balls'   More than 30 suppliers
   elmeri   EBur
   filifolium   see Olsynium filifolium
   graminoides   EBur NBro WPer
§ - 'Album'   CRez EBur EWTr LRHS NBro
                        WPer
   grandiflorum   see Olsynium douglasii
   'Hemswell Sky'   CLyd EBur EHoe LAst MDHE
                        MMil
   'Iceberg'   CRDP ITim NCat SMrm SUsu
   idahoense   ECha EDAr EMlt GAbr GEdr GGar
                        LBee LRHS MHer SPlb SRms
§ - 'Album' ♀ H4   More than 30 suppliers
§ - var. bellum   CBro CMHG EBre EBur ELan EPfP
                        GTou LRHS MBNS MNrw MWhi
                        NMen NPri NRya NWCA SGar
                        SIng SPet SRms WCom WHen
                        WMAq WPat WPer WWpP
   - - 'Pale Form' new SMHy
   - - 'Rocky Point'   CElw CLyd CMCo EBur MBro
                        SRot WCom WHoo WPat WWeb

- .blue	EGra
- var. **macounii** <u>new</u>	WFTG
iridifolium	see *S. micranthum*
junceum	see *Olsynium junceum*
littorale	CPLG EBur NLar WPer
macrocarpon ♀ H2-3	CFee CGra CLyd CPBP CStu EBur
	EHyt ERos ESis GTou ITim LBee
	LRHS MAvo MDKP NMen SBla
	SChr WLin WPer
'Marie'	EBur
'Marion'	CMil CRDP MAvo MSph NCat NHar
	SBla SRot SSth SSvw SUsu WWye
'May Snow'	see *S. idahoense* 'Album'
§ *micranthum*	CBro CPLG EBur
montanum	EBur ERos SSth SYvo
'Mrs Spivey'	EBur ECtt EMNN MBar MHer NBir
	NOak WRHF
'North Star'	see *S.* 'Pole Star'
nudicaule	EBur
- x *montanum*	CFee CMHG EBur EMNN ITim
	MDHE MNrw NHar NRya SRot WPer
palmifolium	CDes CFil
- JCA 2.880.010	WPGP
patagonicum	CPLG EBur EDAr ERos GBuc WPer
§ 'Pole Star'	CFee CLyd CNic CSpe EBur EChP
	EMar EMlt EPot EPyc GTou IBlr
	LRHS NHar NHol SRPl WFar WHal
	WMoo WPer
'Quaint and Queer'	CHea CM&M CMil CPLG EBur
	EChP ECha ECtt EMar ERou MBrN
	MRav MTho NBir NBro NChi
	SHBN WBea WCra WMoo WPer
	WRus WWhi WWin WWpP WWye
I 'Raspberry'	CMea EBur WAbe
scabrum	see *S. chilense*
'Sisland Blue'	EBur EWes
'Stars and Stripes'	LPBA
§ *striatum*	More than 30 suppliers
§ - 'Aunt May' (v)	More than 30 suppliers
- 'Variegatum'	see *S. striatum* 'Aunt May'

Sium (Apiaceae)

sisarum	ELau EOHP GBar GPoy MHer MSal

Skimmia ❀ (Rutaceae)

anquetilia	MBar WBod
arisanensis B&SWJ 7114	WCru
x *confusa*	EHol
- 'Isabella'	SPer
- 'Kew Green' (m) ♀ H4	More than 30 suppliers
§ *japonica*	CMHG CTrw CWib EBre EMil
	GKir GQui MGos NBlu SDes SRPl
	SReu SSta WDin WFar WGwG
	WHCG WStI
- (f)	CTrG CTri ElAn ENot EPfP SPer
	SRms
- B&SWJ 5053	WCru
- 'Alba'	see *S. japonica* 'Wakehurst White'
- 'Bowles' Dwarf Female' (f)	CHig CMHG EBee EPla LRHS
	MBar MBri MGos MRav NHol
	SDes SLim SPer WWeb
- 'Bowles' Dwarf Male' (m)	CMHG EBee EPla LRHS MBar
	MBri MHar SDes SLim WBod
- 'Bronze Knight' (m)	EBee ENot GBin LRHS MBar
	MGos MRav NHol SLim SSta
- 'Chameleon'	LAst MRav
- 'Claries Repens'	CDoC EPla LRHS
- 'Emerald King' (m)	LRHS MAsh MBar MBri MWgw
	WBcn WFar WWeb
N - 'Foremanii'	see *S. japonica* 'Veitchii'
§ - 'Fragrans' (m) ♀ H4	CDoC CHig CSBt CSam CTri
	CTrw EBee ENot EPfP GKir LRHS
	MBar MBlu MGos MRav SDes

	SHBN SLim SPer WBod WFar
	WGwG WWeb
- 'Fragrant Cloud'	see *S. japonica* 'Fragrans'
- 'Fragrantissima' (m)	LRHS MBri WBod
- 'Fructu Albo'	see *S. japonica* 'Wakehurst White'
- 'Highgrove Redbud' (f)	EBee LRHS MBar MGos SLim SSta
	WBcn WBod
- var. *intermedia* f. *repens*	WCru
B&SWJ 5560 <u>new</u>	
- 'Keessen' (f)	WFar
- 'Kew White' (f)	CAbP CBcs CDoC CSam EBee EBre
	EPfP GKir IArd MBri MGos MWat
	NHol SLon WHCG WLRN WPnP
- Luwian = 'Wanto'PBR	EBee LRHS NHol NPro SPar WFar
	WLRN
- 'Marlot'	EPfP MGos
- 'Nymans' (f) ♀ H4	CDoC CEnd CSam EBee EBre ElAn
	EPfP GKir LRHS MAsh MBar MBri
	MRav MWht NDlv NHol SDes
	SHBN SLim SMer SPer SPla SReu
	SSpi SSta WFar WStI WWal WWeb
- 'Oblata'	MBar SMer
- 'Obovata' (f)	EPla
- 'Pigmy' (f)	CPLG
- 'Red Princess' (f)	LAst MAsh MBri SDes WBcn
* - 'Red Riding Hood'	NHol
- 'Redruth' (f)	CBcs CDoC CSBt CSam EBee GKir
	LRHS MAsh MBar MGos MWat
	MWht NHol SLim SSta WBcn WWeb
§ - subsp. *reevesiana*	CDoC CMHG CRez CSBt CSam
	EBee EBre EPfP GKir GQui ISea
	LRHS MAsh MBar MBri MGos
	MRav NHol SDes SHBN SPer SReu
	SSpi SSta WBod WBrE WDin WFar
	WStI WWal
- - B&SWJ 3763	WCru
- - ETOT 182	WPGP
- - 'Chilan Choice'	EBee GKir LRHS MAsh SLim SPla
	SSta
- - 'Fata Morgana' (m)	MGos
- - var. *reevesiana*	WCru
B&SWJ 3544	
- - 'Robert Fortune'	MBar
§ - Rogersii Group	CTri MBar MWat
- - 'Dunwood'	MBar
- - 'George Gardner'	MBar
- - 'Helen Goodall' (f)	MBar
§ - - 'Nana Mascula' (m)	CTri
- - 'Rockyfield Green'	MBar
- - 'Snow Dwarf' (m)	LRHS MBar MBri
- 'Rubella' (m) ♀ H4	More than 30 suppliers
- 'Rubinetta' (m)	CChe EBee EPfP GKir IArd MAsh
	MBar MGos NHol SLim WFar
- 'Ruby Dome' (m)	LRHS MBar WBcn
- 'Ruby King' (m)	CDoC CSBt GKir IArd LRHS MAsh
	MBar MGos MWgw NHol SSta
- 'Scarlet Dwarf' (f)	EBee MBar
- 'Scarlet Queen' (f) <u>new</u>	CWib
- 'Stoneham Red'	MBri
- 'Tansley Gem' (f)	EPfP GKir LRHS MAsh MBar MBri
- 'Thelma King'	GKir LRHS WWeb
§ - 'Veitchii' (f)	CBcs CSBt CTri EBee ENot EPfP
	GKir IArd IMGH MAsh MBar MDun
	MGos MRav NHol SDes SEND
	SHBN SLim SPar SPer WBod WDin
	WPnP WStI WTel WWal WWeb
§ - 'Wakehurst White' (f)	CMHG CPle CSBt CTrw EBee
	EPfP GKir MBar MRav SHBN SLim
	SLon SPer SReu SSpi SSta WBod
	WCru WFar WWeb
- 'White Gerpa'PBR	MGos
- 'Winifred Crook' (f)	EPla GKir MBar MBri
- 'Winnie's Dwarf'	CHig

- 'Wisley Female' (f)	CDoC CTri ECtt EPla NHol SAga
laureola	CDoC CSam EBee ECot MRav NHol SDes SRms WFar WSHC
- 'Borde Hill' (f)	NPri
- subsp. *multinervia* Sch 2154	WPGP
'Olympic Flame'	EPfP GKir LRHS MGos NHol NPro SLim WFar WLRN
reevesiana	see *S. japonica* subsp. *reevesiana*
rogersii	see *S. japonica* Rogersii Group

Smallanthus (Asteraceae)

uvedalius	MSal

Smilacina (Convallariaceae)

atropurpurea	EBee WCru
dahurica **new**	EBee
formosana	WHil
- B&SWJ 349	WCru
forrestii	EBee LEur WCru
fusca	WCru
henryi	EBee LEur WCru
japonica	EBee LEur WCru WHil
- B&SWJ 1179	WCru
aff. *japonica* **new**	LEur
oleracea	EBee WCru
paniculata	EBee
purpurea	EBee SOkh
racemosa ♀ H4	More than 30 suppliers
- var. *amplexicaulis*	GCal MTed
- - 'Emily Moody'	SSpi
stellata	CAvo CBct CRDP CRow EBee EBre EPPr EPar EPla EPot LEur LHop MDun MLLN MRav NChi NFla NGar SIng SMac WAul WCru
szechuanica	LEur WCru
tatsiensis **new**	LEur
trifolia	EBee LEur
tubifera **new**	EBee

Smilax (Smilacaceae)

asparagoides 'Nanus'	see *Asparagus asparagoides* 'Myrtifolius'
aspera	CFil CPlN EBee LEdu SMur WCru WPGP
- 'Silver Shield' **new**	SSpi
china B&SWJ 4427	WCru
discotis	CBcs CPlN
glaucophylla B&SWJ 2971	WCru
nipponica	WCru
B&SWJ 4331 **new**	
rotundifolia	LEdu
sieboldii	CPlN MRav
- B&SWJ 744	WCru

Smithiantha (Gesneriaceae)

'Calder Girl'	NMos
'Carmel'	NMos
'Carmello'	NMos
'Castle Croft'	NMos
'Cinna Barino'	NMos
'Corney Fell'	NMos
'Dent View'	NMos
'Ehenside Lady'	NMos
'Harecroft'	NMos
'Little One'	NMos WDib
'Matins'	NMos
'Meadowcroft'	NMos
'Multiflora'	NMos
'New Yellow Hybrid'	NMos
'Orange King'	NMos
'Orangeade'	NMos

'Pink Lady'	NMos
'Sandybank'	NMos
'Santa Clara'	NMos
'Starling Castle'	NMos
'Summer Sunshine'	NMos
'Vespers'	NMos
'Zebrina Hybrid'	NMos

x *Smithicodonia* (Gesneriaceae)

§ 'Cerulean Mink'	NMos

Smyrnium (Apiaceae)

olusatrum	CArn CSev CSpe GBar LHrt MChe MGas MHer MSal SIde SWat WCer WHbs WHer WLHH WWye
perfoliatum	CRDP CSpe EHrv ELan EMar EOrc EPar EWes GBuc MFir NSti SDix WCot WEas
- subsp. *rotundifolium* MESE 337	EBee

Socratea (Arecaceae)

montana	LPal

Solandra (Solanaceae)

grandiflora Swartz	CPlN ERea WMul
hartwegii	see *S. maxima*
longiflora	ERea
§ *maxima*	ERea SVen WMul

Solanum (Solanaceae)

atropurpureum **new**	ITer
* *conchifolium*	SOkh WPat
crispum	EHol ISca WDin WStI
- 'Autumnale'	see *S. crispum* 'Glasnevin'
§ - 'Glasnevin' ♀ H3	More than 30 suppliers
- 'Variegatum' (v)	CWlb WGwG
dulcamara	CArn GPoy MGol
- 'Hullavington' (v)	CNat
- 'Variegatum' (v)	CBcs CMac EBee EHoe EPfP IBlr LRHS MAsh MBNS MBri NBlu NEgg NLon NSti SBra SPar SPet SRms WCot WFar WWeb
jasminoides	see *S. laxum*
laciniatum	CArn CBrm CDoC CFwr CHEx CSev CSpe CTrC EMan EMar EWes GDrg IBlr LHop MFir MLLN MTis SAPC SArc SGar SHFr SNew SYvo WHer
§ *laxum*	CBcs CDul CPlN EBee EPfP EShb LPan LRHS NSti SBra SCoo SPer SPet SPoG SRms WDin WFar WGwG WSHC WWeb
- 'Album' ♀ H5	More than 30 suppliers
- 'Album Variegatum' (v)	CFwr ELan EPfP GQui LAst LRHS MBNS NSti SBra WCot WSHC
* - 'Aureovariegatum' (v)	CTrC CWib EBee EPfP LRHS NBlu SCoo SLim SPar SPer SPla SPlb WBod WWeb
muricatum (F)	ESlt
- 'Quito' (F)	SSte
pseudocapsicum	MBri SYvo
- 'Ballon'	MBri
- variegated **new**	EShb
quitoense (F)	MGol SSte WMul
§ *rantonnetii*	CHll ELan EMan ERea IDee MOak SMrm SOWG
- 'Royal Robe'	CBcs CRHN GQui
* - 'Variegatum' (v)	ESlt WHil
seaforthianum	CPlN ESlt SOWG
valdiviense 'Variegatum' (v)	WDin
wendlandii	CPlN ERea EShb

Soldanella (Primulaceae)

alpina	EBee GCrs GTou ITim MTho MWat NHar NMen SBla SIng SRms WAbe WLin
austriaca	NLAp WAbe
carpatica	EDAr ETow GTou NCat NRya SIng WAbe
- 'Alba'	EDAr GKev ITim MDKP NHar NLAp NSla SBla WAbe WOBN
- × **pusilla**	CPBP NHar NRya SBla
- × **villosa**	MDKP
cyanaster	EBee EHyt NGar NRya SBla WAbe
dimoniei	CFee ITim NMen NSla NWCA SBla WAbe
§ **hungarica**	CLyd MTho WAbe WLin
minima	CLyd GCrs GGar NBro NDlv NGar NHar NMen NRya NSla SBla WAbe WLin WOBN
montana	CLAP CLyd CMea GCrs GTou MTho NGar NMen SIng WAbe WRha
- subsp. **hungarica**	see *S. hungarica*
pindicola	EBee EHyt EMan EWes MBro MOne NDlv NGar NHar NJOw NMen NWCA SIng WAbe WFar
pusilla	GDra GGar ITim NSla WAbe
villosa	CDes CLAP CRDP EBee GCrs GGar LRHS MTho NGar NHar NJOw NRya SAga SBla WAbe WFTG WFar WOBN WRus WSHC

Soleirolia (Urticaceae)

soleirolii	CHEx CHal CTri EPot LPBA LRHS MBri MCCP MWhi SHFr SIng STre WHer
- 'Argentea'	see *S. soleirolii* 'Variegata'
§ - 'Aurea'	CHal CTri EPot SIng STre
- 'Golden Queen'	see *S. soleirolii* 'Aurea'
- 'Silver Queen'	see *S. soleirolii* 'Variegata'
§ - 'Variegata' (v)	CHal

Solenomelus (Iridaceae)

chilensis	see *S. pedunculatus*
§ **pedunculatus**	CFee CFil EBee
- F&W 9606	CPBP WCot WPGP
sisyrinchium	CPBP ERos

Solenopsis (Campanulaceae)

axillaris	see *Isotoma axillaris*

Solenostemon ✿ (Lamiaceae)

'Anne Boleyn'	CHal MOak NHor
aromaticus	see *Plectranthus amboinicus*
'Autumn'	CHal MOak NHor
'Autumn Gold' **new**	NHor
'Barnum'	MOak
'Beauty' (v)	CHal MOak NHor
'Beauty of Lyons'	CHal MOak NHor
'Beckwith's Gem'	CHal NHor
'Bizarre Croton'	CHal MOak NHor
'Black Dragon'	CHal NHor
'Black Prince'	CHal MOak NHor WDib
'Blackheart'	MOak NHor
'Brightness' (v)	NHor
'Brilliant' (v)	MOak WDib
'Bronze Gloriosus'	MOak NHor
'Bronze Queen'	NHor
'Buttercup'	CHal NHor WDib
'Buttermilk' (v) ♀ H1	CHal MOak NHor
'Carnival' (v)	CHal MOak NHor WDib
'Carousel'	CHal MOak NHor
'Chamaeleon' (v)	CHal MOak NHor WDib

'City of Liverpool'	CHal NHor
'Combat'	CHal NHor
'Copper Sprite'	CHal MOak NHor
'Coppersmith'	NHor
'Crimson Ruffles' (v) ♀ H1	CHal MOak NHor WDib
'Crimson Velvet'	CHal MOak NHor
'Crinkly Bottom'	MOak NHor
'Crown of Bohemia' **new**	MOak
'Dairy Maid' (v)	CHal MOak NHor
'Dazzler' (v)	CHal MOak NHor
'Display'	CHal MOak NHor
'Dolly' (v)	MOak NHor
'Dracula'	CHal MOak NHor
'Emerald Forest'	MOak NHor
'Etna' (v)	CHal NHor
'Fire Fingers' **new**	MOak
'Firebrand' (v) ♀ H1	CHal MOak NHor
'Firedance'	MOak NHor
'Firefly'	CHal MOak NHor
'Freckles' (v)	CHal MOak NHor
'Funfair' (v)	CHal MOak NHor
'Gloriosus'	CHal MOak NHor
'Glory of Luxembourg' (v) ♀ H1	CHal MOak NHor
'Goldie'	CHal MOak NHor
'Green Mars' (v)	NHor
'Harvest Time'	MOak NHor
'Holly' (v)	MOak NHor
'Inky Fingers' (v)	CHal MOak NHor
'Jean' (v)	CHal MOak NHor
'Joseph's Coat' (v)	MOak NHor
'Juliet Quartermain'	CHal MOak NHor WDib
'Jupiter'	CHal MOak NHor
'Kentish Fire'	CHal MOak NHor
'Kiwi Fern' (v)	CHal MOak NHor WDib
'Klondike'	CHal MOak NHor
'Laing's Croton' (v)	CHal MOak NHor
'Lemon Dash'	MOak NHor
'Lemondrop'	CHal
'Leopard' (v)	MOak NHor
'Lord Falmouth' ♀ H1	CHal MOak NHor WDib
'Melody'	CHal MOak NHor
'Midas'	CHal MOak NHor
'Midnight'	MOak NHor
'Mission Gem' (v)	CHal MOak NHor WWol
'Molten Lava' (v)	MOak NHor
'Mrs Pilkington' (v)	MOak NHor
'Muriel Pedley' (v)	CHal MOak NHor
'Nettie' (v)	MOak NHor
'Ottoman'	CHal NHor
'Paisley Shawl' (v) ♀ H1	CHal NHor WDib
'Palisandra'	CSpe LHrt
pentheri	CHal NHor
'Percy Roots'	MOak NHor
'Peter's Wonder'	CHal NHor
'Phantom'	MOak
'Pheasant's Eye' (v)	NHor
'Picturatus' (v) ♀ H1	CHal NHor WDib
'Pineapple Beauty' (v) ♀ H1	CHal MOak NHor SSte WDib
'Pineapplette' ♀ H1	CHal MOak NHor SPoG WDib WWol
'Pink Devil' (v)	MOak NHor
'Pink Shawl'	MOak NHor
'Poyton' **new**	MOak
'Primrose Cloud'	MOak NHor
'Primrose Spire'	MOak NHor
'Purple Oak' **new**	CHal LAst NHor
'Raspberry Ripple'	CHal NHor
'Red Croton'	CHal MOak NHor
'Red Mars'	MOak NHor WDib
'Red Nettie' (v)	CHal MOak NHor
'Red Paisley Shawl' (v)	MOak NHor

'Red Rosie'	CHal
'Red Stinger'	CHal WWol
'Red Velvet'	CHal LHrt MOak NHor WWol
'Rob Roy' **new**	MOak
'Rose Blush' (v)	CHal LAst MOak NHor WDib WWol
'Rosie'	MOak NHor
'Roy Pedley'	CHal MOak NHor
'Royal Scot' (v) ♀ H1	CHal MOak NHor WDib
'Salmon Plumes' (v)	CHal MOak NHor
'Sam Cooke'	MOak
'Saturn'	NHor
'Scarlet Ribbons'	CHal MOak NHor
'Speckles'	CHal MOak NHor
'Spire'	MOak NHor
'Strawberry Jam' **new**	CHal MOak NHor
'Summer Wine' **new**	NHor
'Sunbeam' (v)	MOak NHor
thyrsoideus	see *Plectranthus thyrsoideus*
'Timotei' **new**	NHor
'Tom Cooke' **new**	MOak NHor
'Treales' (v)	CHal MOak NHor
'Vesuvius'	CHal MOak NHor
'Walter Turner' (v) ♀ H1	CHal MOak NHor WDib WWol
'White Gem' (v)	MOak NHor
'White Pheasant' (v)	MOak NHor
'Winsome' (v)	CHal MOak NHor WDib
'Winter Sun' (v)	CHal LHrt MOak NHor
'Wisley Flame'	NHor
'Wisley Tapestry' (v) ♀ H1	CHal MOak NHor WDib
'Yellow Croton'	MOak NHor

Solidago (Asteraceae)

Babygold	see *S.* 'Goldkind'
brachystachys	see *S. cutleri*
caesia	EBee ECha EMan EMon ERou
	EWcs MFir MStc NBir WCot
	WMoo WOld
canadensis	CAgr CTri ELan NNor SPlb WFar
	WHer
§ - var. *scabra*	WOld WTin
'Cloth of Gold'	CBcs COtt EBee GKir LRHS MBri
	MHFa NPro NSti SMer WLRN
	WMnd WOld
§ 'Crown of Rays'	CLyd EBee EBre ECtt EFou ERou
	LRHS MRav MWgw NArg SHar
	SMer WFar WMnd WWin
§ *cutleri*	CLyd EBee ELan EMon MBar MTho
	MWat NHol NJOw SBla SPlb SRms
	WFar WHoo WPat WPer WWin
- *nana*	EWes
'Dzintra'	EBee LBuc
'Early Bird'	FFou
§ *flexicaulis*	GMaP NLon
- 'All Gold'	WCot
§ - 'Variegata' (v)	CFwr EBee EChP ECoo ELan EMan
	EMar EMon EPPr EPfP GBin GMaP
	LRHS MHar NLar NSti SDes WCot
	WFar WHer WHil WOld WPer
'Gardone'	WFar
gigantea	EBee EMon EWTr WPer
glomerata	EMon WPer
Golden Baby	see *S.* 'Goldkind'
'Golden Crown'	WViv
§ 'Golden Dwarf'	EFou LRHS MCLN WWeb
'Golden Fleece'	see *S. sphacelata* 'Golden Fleece'
'Golden Rays'	see *S.* 'Goldstrahl'
'Golden Shower'	CSam MWat
'Golden Thumb'	see *S.* 'Queenie'
'Golden Wings'	CBre ERou MWat
'Goldenmosa' ♀ H4	CSBt CSam EBee EBre ECGN
	EMan ENot EPfP ERou EWTr
	GMaP LRHS MCLN MRav MWat
	SChu SPer WFar WOld

'Goldilocks'	LRHS NPri SRms
§ 'Goldkind'	CM&M COlW CSBt EBee ECtt
	EPfP ERou GKir MBow MBri MFir
	NArg NOak NOrc SDes SMac
	SMer SPet SWal WBea WFar
	WMoo WRHF WWeb WWpP
§ 'Goldstrahl'	LRHS
Goldzwerg	see *S.* 'Golden Dwarf'
graminifolia	SAga
hispida	EMon
hybrida	see x *Solidaster luteus*
'Inca Gold'	WViv
latifolia	see *S. flexicaulis*
'Laurin'	EBee EMil EPfP WHoo
'Ledsham'	EBee EMFP MMil WLRN WMnd
'Lemore'	see x *Solidaster luteus* 'Lemore'
'Leraft'	EBee LBuc
* *leuvalis*	CStr
'Linner Gold' zur Linden	EFou
'Monte d'Oro'	WViv
Monte Solo =	WViv
'Dansolmonte'PBR	
multiradiata	ESis
nemoralis	IIve
odora	MGol MSal
ohioensis	EBee IIve
* 'Peter Pan'	ERou WFar
§ 'Queenie'	ECha ESis LRHS MBri MHer NPro
	NVic SLon SPer SRms WGwG
	WLRN
rigida	LRHS MFir MRav WCot WPer
- JLS 88002WI	EMon
- subsp. *humilis*	EBee
rugosa	ECha LPhx MTed MWgw WCot
- var. *aspera*	EMon
'Fireworks'	CBre CPou CSam CStr EBee EFou
	EMan EPPr NCat NDov NPPs
	SUsu WCot WHoo WOld WTin
sempervirens	EBre EMon WCot
simplex var. *nana*	WPer
'Spätgold'	EFou
spathulata var. *nana*	NWCA
speciosa	IIve WPer
§ *sphacelata*	EBee LBuc LRHS WLRN WMnd
'Golden Fleece'	
spiraeifolia	IIve
Strahlenkrone	see *S.* 'Crown of Rays'
'Tom Thumb'	EGle MRav SRms WEas
ulmifolia	EBee IIve LRHS
virgaurea	CArn CBod CKin EBot GPoy
	GWCH IIve MHer NLar NSco
	WHHs WHer WJek WPer WSel
	WWye
- subsp. *alpestris*	CLyd NHol
var. *minutissima*	
- 'Praecox'	CM&M NHol
§ - 'Variegata' (v)	EHoe NPro WAlt WHHs
vulgaris 'Variegata'	see *S. virgaurea* 'Variegata'

x *Solidaster* (Asteraceae)

hybridus	see x *S. luteus*
§ *luteus*	CSBt CTri EBee EFou EWTr GBri
	GKir MBri MHar NGar SDes SRms
	WEas WFar WWin
§ - 'Lemore' ♀ H4	CElw EBee EBre ECGN ECha
	EFou ELan EMan ENot EPfP ERou
	GLil GMac LHrt LRHS MMil MRav
	MWat NPri NSti NVic SPer SUsu
	WCot WFar
'Super'	CStr EBee EFou LPhx WCot WFar

Sollya (Pittosporaceae)

fusiformis	see *S. heterophylla*

§ **heterophylla** ♀ H1	More than 30 suppliers
- 'Alba'	ELan SMrm
- mauve	ECou
- pink	CBcs CFRD CPlN CSPN EOrc SAdn
- 'Pink Charmer'	EBee EPfP ERea LRHS MAsh SBra
	SMrm SMur SPer WSHC

Sonchus (Asteraceae)

oleraceus 'Custard 'n'	WAlt
Green' (v)	
palustris	EMon

Sophora (Papilionaceae)

§ **davidii**	CWCL CWib ECou EPfP IDee MBlu
	MGos NPal SIgm SOWG WDin WPGP
flavescens	WCru
japonica ♀ H4	CAbP CAgr CBcs CDul CHEx
	CLnd CTho EBee EMil ENot EPfP
	EWTr MDun MGos MPEx MWhi
	SHBN SKee SPer SPlb WBod WDin
	WNor WOrn
- 'Pendula'	CBcs LRHS SCoo
- 'Regent'	LPan
§ 'Little Baby'	CBcs CFwr CWSG CWib EPfP ERea
	LAst MCCP MGos SHFr SMur WPat
macrocarpa	CFil GQui SBra
microphylla	CCtw CHEx CPle CTCP CTrC
	CWCL CWib EBee ECou GGar
	LHop SAPC SArc SEND SIgm SPar
	SVen WBod WCru WHer WOTO
- 'Dragon's Gold'	CTrC ECou ELan EPfP LRHS MAsh
	WDin
- 'Early Gold'	CBcs ERea GQui
- var. **fulvida**	ECou
- var. **longicarinata**	ECou
- Sun King =	LRHS MGos SCoo WWeb
'Hilsop' PBR ♀ H4	
prostrata misapplied	see S. 'Little Baby'
prostrata Buch.	CBcs CBot CTrC ECou
- Pukaki form	ECou
secundiflora	MGol SIgm
tetraptera ♀ H3	CAbP CBcs CCtw CLnd CMac
	CPne CTrC EBee ECou EPfP GQui
	ISea MLan NPSI SEND SGar SPer
	SRms WAbe WPGP
viciifolia	see S. **davidii**

Sorbaria (Rosaceae)

SF 95205	ISea
aitchisonii	see S. **tomentosa** var. **angustifolia**
arborea	see S. **kirilowii**
§ **kirilowii**	GIBF IFro NFor SLon SMad SPer
lindleyana	see S. **tomentosa**
rhoifolia	EPfP
sorbifolia	CAbP CBcs CMCo EBee EMil
	EWTr GEil GKir MBar MDun MTis
	MWhi NPro SEND SLPl SPar SPer
	WCot WDin WFar
- var. **stellipila**	CFil SLPl
- B&SWJ 776	WCru
§ **tomentosa**	CAbP EBre SHBN WHCG
§ - var. **angustifolia** ♀ H4	CDul CTri EBee ELan ENot EPfP
	GKir IMGH LRHS MDun MGos
	MRav SEND SLon SPar SPer SSta
	WCru WEas WFar WHer
* - 'Anthony Waterer' **new**	NPSI

x Sorbopyrus (Rosaceae)

auricularis 'Shipova' (F)	ESim

Sorbus ✿ (Rosaceae)

CLD 310	GIBF
Harry Smith 12732	GKir LRHS LSyl MDun

§ **alnifolia**	CLnd CTho EPfP GIBF MBlu
	SLPl
americana	CLnd GIBF NWea
- 'Belmonte'	GKir LRHS LSyl
- **erecta**	see S. **decora**
anglica	CDul CFox
'Apricot'	CEnd GKir
'Apricot Lady'	GKir LRHS LSyl MBri SSta WJas
'Apricot Queen'	CDul CLnd ECrN EMil GKir
aria	CCVT CDul CKin CLnd CSBt EBre
	EPfP GKir GTre LBuc LHyr MBar
	NBee NWea SKee WDin WMou
	WOrn WStI
- 'Aurea'	CLnd MBlu
- 'Chrysophylla'	CDul CLnd CSBt EBee GKir IMGH
	LRHS LSyl MBri MGos NWea SKee
	SLim SPer SPoG SRPl
- 'Decaisneana'	see S. **aria** 'Majestica'
- 'Gigantea'	CDul
- 'Lutescens' ♀ H4	More than 30 suppliers
- 'Magnifica'	CDoC CDul CTho EBee ELan
	ENot GTre LPan MAsh WDin WJas
§ - 'Majestica' ♀ H4	CDoC CDul CLnd CTho GIBF
	GKir GTre LPan LSyl MAsh NWea
	SPer WDin WJas WOrn
- 'Mitchellii'	see S. **thibetica** 'John Mitchell'
- var. **salicifolia**	see S. **rupicola**
* - 'Stangerii' **new**	CLnd
x **arnoldiana** '	GKir
Cerise Queen'	
aronioides misapplied	see S. **caloneura**
arranensis	GIBF
§ **aucuparia**	More than 30 suppliers
- 'Aspleniifolia'	CBcs CCVT CDul CLnd CSBt
	CTho EBee EBre ECrN ENot GKir
	GTre LPan LRHS MDun MGos
	NBea NWea SKee SPer WDin
	WFar WJas WOrn
§ - 'Beissneri'	CLnd EBee EMil GKir MGos NRog
	SKee
- 'Cardinal Royal'	EBee GQui LRHS WJas
- 'Dirkenii'	CDul CLnd COtt CWSG EBee
	GKir IMGH LSyl MAsh MDun
	SKee WDin WJas
- var. **edulis** (F)	CAgr CDul CLnd CTho LBuc
	MGos WDin
- - 'Rabina' (F)	ESim
- - 'Rosina' (F)	ESim
- - 'Rossica Major'	CDoC CDul CTho ECrN GQui LSyl
§ - 'Fastigiata'	CDoC CDul CEnd CSBt CTho CTri
	EBee ECrN EPfP GKir GTre LRHS
	MAsh MBri MGos MWat NBee
	NWea SHBN WDin WFar WStI
- 'Hilling's Spire'	CTho GKir LRHS MBri MLan
	NBea SLPl
- 'Pendula'	CDul EBee
- **pluripinnata**	see S. **scalaris**
- var. **rossica** Koehne	see S. **aucuparia** var. **edulis**
- 'Rossica Major'	see S. **aucuparia** var. **edulis**
	'Rossica Major'
- 'Rowancroft Coral Pink'	see Sorbus 'Rowancroft Coral Pink'
- 'Sheerwater Seedling'	CBcs CCVT CDoC CDul CLnd
♀ H4	CTho EBee EBre ECrN ELan ENot
	EPfP GKir LHyr LRHS MLan MRav
	NBee NBlu SCoo SLim SPer SSta
	WDin WOrn WStI
- 'Winterdown'	CNat
- 'Xanthocarpa'	see S. **aucuparia** var. **xanthocarpa**
- var. **xanthocarpa** ♀ H4	CLnd EBee ENot EPfP GTre MGos
	NBee WDin
'Bellona'	CDul LSyl WPat
bristoliensis	CDul LSyl
'Burka'	WPat

§ *caloneura*	CFil EPla LSyl WHCr
'Carpet of Gold'	CLnd LSyl NBea
cashmiriana	CLnd GKir LSyl SSpi
hort. pink-fruited	
cashmiriana Hedl. ♀ H4	More than 30 suppliers
- 'Rosiness'	GKir LRHS MBri MDun SCoo
	SKee SLim WHCr
chamaemespilus	GDra GIBF WPat
'Chamois Glow'	MAsh WJas
'Chinese Lace'	CDul CEnd CLnd CTho EBee
	ECot ECrN EPfP GKir LRHS LSyl
	MAsh MBri MDun MGos MLan
	MWat NBea SFam SHBN SKee
	SLim SMad SRPl SSpi WDin WGor
	WJas WOrn WWeb
§ *commixta*	CBcs CDul CEnd CLnd CMCN
	CTho EBee ECrN EPfP GIBF GKir
	GTre LRHS LSyl MBar MBri MGos
	MLan MRav NBea NBee SKee SPer
	WDin WJas WOrn WStI
* - 'Creamlace'	EBee GKir
- 'Embley' ♀ H4	CBcs CCVT CDul CLnd CMCN
	CSBt CSam CTho EBee ECrN ELan
	ENot EPfP GIBF GKir LRHS LSyl MBar
	MBri MGos MLan MRav NBee
	SSpi SSta WDin WOrn
- 'Jermyns'	GKir MBri
- var. *rufoferruginea*	GKir GQui LSyl
- - B&SWJ 6078	WCru
conradinae misapplied	see *S. pohuashanensis* (Hance)
	Hedlund
conradinae Koehne	see *S. esserteauana*
'Copper Kettle'	GKir MBri
'Coral Beauty'	CLnd
'Covert Gold' **new**	CEnd CLnd
croceocarpa	CDul CNat
cuspidata	see *S. vestita*
§ *decora* (Sarg.) C.K. Schneid.	CDul CTho GIBF LSyl SPer
* - 'Grootendorst'	CDul
- var. *nana*	see *S. aucuparia* 'Fastigiata'
devoniensis	CAgr CDul CNat CTho LSyl WMou
discolor misapplied	see *S. commixta*
discolor (Maxim.) Maxim.	CLnd EBee GKir MBri MGos
	MWat NWea WJas
domestica	CDul CLnd CMCN CTho ENot
	EPfP GTre LBuc NWea SLPl SPer
	WDin
- 'Maliformis'	see *S. domestica* f. *pomifera*
§ - f. *pomifera*	EHol GIBF
dumosa **new**	GIBF
'Eastern Promise'	CDul CWSG EMil GKir LRHS
	MAsh MBri MWat SCoo SKee SSta
	WDin WJas WWeb
eminens	CNat
§ *esserteauana*	CDoC CDul CLnd CTho EBee
	ENot LSyl
- 'Flava'	CTho GKir GTre LRHS LSyl
- x *scalaris*	LSyl
'Ethel's Gold'	LSyl
'Fastigiata'	see *S. aucuparia* 'Fastigiata', *S.* x
	thuringiaca 'Fastigiata'
folgneri	CDoC CEnd
- 'Emiel'	MBlu
- 'Lemon Drop'	CEnd CLnd GKir MBlu SCoo SKee
	SMad SSpi
§ *foliolosa*	GIBF LSyl MBlu MBri NWea
- 'Lowndes'	CLnd
forrestii	EBre EPfP GIBF GKir NBea SLPl
	SSpi
* *fortunei* **new**	CLnd
I *fruticosa* McAllister	CEnd CLnd COtt EBee EPfP GIBF
	GKir MBri NWea SSpi SSta WJas
	WPGP

- 'Koehneana'	see *S. koehneana*
'Ghose'	CEnd CLnd CTho GKir IMGH LRHS
	LSyl MBlu MBri SCoo SKee SPer SSpi
'Golden Wonder'	see *Sorbus* 'Lombarts Golden
	Wonder'
N *gonggashanica*	CLnd EGFP GKir
- L 1008	LSyl
* *gorrodini*	CLnd
§ *graeca*	CDul CMCN GIBF LSyl SEND
'Harvest Moon'	GKir GQui LRHS MBri
hedlundii	IBlr WWes
helenae	GGGa
hemsleyi	CLnd GIBF GKir MDun
x *hostii*	CLnd EBee ENot LRHS MRav SPer
§ *hupehensis* C.K. Schneid.	CBcs CDul CEnd CLnd CMCN
♀ H4	CTho EBee ECrN EPfP GIBF ISea
	LHyr MBar MRav NBee NWea
	SHBN SLPl SRPl SSpi SSta
	WCwm WDin WJas WNor
	WOrn
- SF 96268	ISea
- 'November Pink'	see *S. hupehensis* 'Pink Pagoda'
§ - var. *obtusa* ♀ H4	CDoC CLnd CMCN EPfP GIBF GKir
	MBlu MDun SFam SSpi SSta WDin
§ - 'Pink Pagoda'	CDoC CDul CLnd CWSG CWib
	EBee EMui EPfP GKir IArd IMGH
	LRHS MAsh MBri MGos MLan
	MWat NWea SCoo SKee SLim
	SLon SPer WDin WGer WWeb
- 'Rosea'	see *S. hupehensis* var. *obtusa*
* - *roseoalba*	GKir
hybrida hort.	see *S.* x *thuringiaca*
hybrida L.	NWea
- 'Gibbsii' ♀ H4	CDoC CLnd CTho ELan EPfP
	GKir LRHS LSyl MAsh
insignis	CDoC GIBF
intermedia	CBcs CDul CKin CLnd CSBt CTho
	CTri EBee ENot GIBF GKir GTrc
	LSyl MGos NBee NBlu NWea
	WDin WMou WStI
- 'Brouwers'	ELan NBee WMou
'Joseph Rock'	More than 30 suppliers
§ x *kewensis*	CDul CLnd GKir LSyl SPer SPlb WBrE
'Kirsten Pink'	CLnd CWib EBee GKir LSyl NEgg
§ *koehneana* C.K. Schneid.	CLnd GBin GCrs GGGa GKir
♀ H4	LRHS MDun NBlu NSla SHFr
	WTin
aff. *koehneana* Schneider	GKir
- - Harry Smith 12799	EPfP GKir LSyl MBri
'Kukula'	MDun
kurzii	GIBF
lanata hort	see *S. vestita*
lancastriensis	CDul CNat CTho GIBF LSyl
latifolia	CLnd CTho EBee ENot GIBF
	NWea WDin
laxiflora Koehne SF 96126	ISea
'Leonard Messel'	CTho GKir LRHS LSyl MBri NBea
'Leonard Springer'	EBee ENot EPfP GQui NWea SSta
leyana	WMou
§ 'Lombarts Golden Wonder'	CBcs CDoC CDul CLnd EBee
	GKir LPan LSyl NWea WJas
matsumurana hort.	see *S. commixta*
matsumurana	GKir
(Makino) Koehne	
megalocarpa	CDoC CFil CPMA EBee GKir
	WNor WPGP
meliosmifolia	LSyl
microphylla Yu 13815	LSyl
minima	CDul WMou
'Molly Sanderson'	IBlr SSta
monbeigii misapplied	LSyl
CLD 311	
monbeigii (Card.) Yü	CLnd GIBF

- CLD 237   LSyl
moravica 'Laciniata'   see *S. aucuparia* 'Beissneri'
mougeotii   GlBF GKir
multijuga   GlBF
§   *munda*   CMCN GBin GKir
N   *parva* L 937   LSyl
'Peachi-Ness'   CLnd LSyl
'Pearly King'   CBcs CSam CTho EBee GKir
   LRHS LSyl MAsh MBri NBea
   WJas
pekinensis   see *S. reticulata* subsp. *pekinensis*
§   'Pink Pearl'   GKir LRHS LSyl MDun
'Pink-Ness'   GKir LRHS MBri SKee
pogonopetala   LSyl
   misapplied Yu 14299
pogonopetala Koehne   GlBF
pohuashanensis hort.   see *S.* x *kewensis*
§   *pohuashanensis*   CSam CTho GKir WOTO
   (Hance) Hedlund
porrigentiformis   CDul CNat CTho
poteriifolia   GCrs NHar
prattii hort.   see *S. munda*
prattii Koehne   see *S. munda*
   var. *subarachnoidea*
pseudofennica   GlBF
N   *pseudovilmorinii*   EMon GKir
- MF 93044   SSpi
randaiensis   GlBF LSyl
- B&SWJ 3202   NHol SSpi WCru
'Ravensbill'   CTho GKir MBlu MBri
'Red Marbles'   LSyl
'Red Tip'   CDoC CDul CLnd LSyl MBar
   NEgg
reducta ♀ H4   CBcs CEnd CLyd CMCN CSWP
   EPfP GBin GDra GlBF GKir ISea
   ITim LRHS MBro NBlu NHar NHol
   NLAp NRya NWea SBrw SIng SMad
   SPer SSpi SSta WDin WFar WNor
- KGB 774   IDac
reflexipetala misapplied   see *S. commixta*
rehderiana misapplied   see *S. aucuparia*
rehderiana Koehne   CLnd GlBF GKir WNor
§   *reticulata*   LSyl
   subsp. *pekinensis*
rhamnoides SF 96227   ISea
'Rowancroft Coral Pink'   CTho LSyl MBar MGos
§   *rupicola*   CTho GlBF
'Salmon Queen'   CLnd
sambucifolia   GlBF
sargentiana ♀ H4   More than 30 suppliers
§   *scalaris* Koehne   CBcs CDul CEnd CTho CTri EBee
   EPfP GKir GTre IMGH LRHS
   MAsh MBri SKee SPer SPoG SSpi
   WDin WJas WOrn
'Schouten'   EBee ENot LRHS
scopulina hort.   see *S. aucuparia* 'Fastigiata'
setschwanensis   GGGa
sibirica   GlBF
'Signalman'   GKir LRHS MBri
'Sunshine'   CDoC GKir LRHS MAsh MBri
   WDin WJas
§   *thibetica* 'John Mitchell'   CDul CLnd CMCN CTho ECrN
   ♀ H4   ENot EPfP GKir GQui IMGH LPan
   LRHS MAsh MBlu MBri MGos MRav
   NBea NWea SLim WJas WOrn WPat
§   x *thuringiaca*   CSBt NBea WMou
§   - 'Fastigiata'   CBcs CDoC CDul CLnd EBee ENot
   GKir MGos NBee SKee WDin WJas
torminalis   CCVT CDul CKin CLnd CTho
   CTri EBee EPfP GKir GTre LBuc
   LRHS MBri MRav NWea SPer
   WDin WMou WOrn
umbellata   CMCN

- var. *cretica*   see *S. graeca*
ursina   see *S. foliolosa*
x *vagensis*   CLnd GlBF WMou
§   *vestita*   CLnd CMCN CTho LSyl
vexans   CDul CNat GlBF
vilmorinii ♀ H4   More than 30 suppliers
- 'Robusta'   see *S.* 'Pink Pearl'
wardii   CBcs CLnd CTho GKir LRHS
   MBlu MBri
'White Wax'   CDul CWSG EMui EPfP MAsh
   MDun MGos MLan NEgg WDin
'Wilfrid Fox'   CLnd SHBN SLPl
willmottiana   CDul
wilsoniana   CLnd
'Winter Cheer'   LSyl

Sorghastrum (*Poaceae*)

avenaceum   see *S. nutans*
§   *nutans*   CBig CBod CKno ECGN ECha
   EMan SMad WMoo
- 'Indian Steel'   CBig CBrm CFwr CKno CPen
   EBee EChP EMan EPPr LIck LPVe
   MAnH MCAu MSte SDes WHil

Sorghum (*Poaceae*)

halepense   MSte

sorrel, common see *Rumex acetosa*

sorrel, French see *R. scutatus*

Souliea see *Actaea*

soursop see *Annona muricata*

Sparaxis (*Iridaceae*)

bulbifera   EGrW LBow NRog SChr
elegans   EGrW EPot NRog
- 'Coccinea'   LBow WCot
grandiflora   NRog
   subsp. *acutiloba*
- subsp. *fimbriata*   LBow
- subsp. *grandiflora*   EGrW
hybrids   EGrW LAma
tricolor   CTbh EMui EPar MDun NRog
§   *variegata* (v)   LBow NRog

Sparganium (*Sparganiaceae*)

§   *erectum*   CRow ECoo EHon EMFW EMan
   LPBA MSta NPer SWat WFar WHer
   WMAq WWpP
ramosum   see *S. erectum*

Sparrmannia (*Tiliaceae*)

africana ♀ H1   CAbb CBcs CHEx CHll CKob
   CPLG CPle EAmu ERea EShb
   GQui MBri SAPC SArc SMur SYvo
- 'Variegata' (v)   ERea

Spartina (*Poaceae*)

patens   EHoe EPPr
pectinata   CBod CHEx EChP GBin GKir
   WFar
- 'Aureomarginata' (v)   More than 30 suppliers

Spartium (*Papilionaceae*)

junceum ♀ H4   More than 30 suppliers
- 'Brockhill Compact' **new**   LRHS

Spartocytisus see *Cytisus*

Spathantheum (*Araceae*)

orbignyanum   WCot

Spathipappus see *Tanacetum*

Spathiphyllum (Araceae)
'Viscount'	MBri
wallisii	CHal EOHP LRHS MBri

Speirantha (Convallariaceae)
§ **convallarioides**	CFil CLAP CRDP EBee ERos SOkd SSpi WCot WCru WPGP
gardenii	see *S. convallarioides*

Spergularia (Caryophyllaceae)
rupicola	CBrm MNrw

Sphacele see *Lepechinia*

Sphaeralcea (Malvaceae)
ambigua	EBee ELan
'Childerley'	EMan LHop SAga
coccinea	EMan SPlb
fendleri	CBcs CBot CHll CMHG CSam EOrc WWye
- subsp. **venusta**	EBee
'Hopleys Lavender'	EBee EMan LHop SAga
'Hyde Hall'	EBee MAvo MCCP MMil SMrm WBor WFTG
incana	CPne CPom CSev EBee NPPs SMrm
longisepala NNS 96-123	WCot
malviflora	WPer
miniata	CHll CMHG EBee ELan MLLN MOak SAga WCom WCot
munroana	CBot CBrm CMHG CSLe CSev CWCL EBee ELan EPPr LHop MOak SMrm WSHC
- 'Dixieland Pink'	WCom
- 'Manor Nursery' (v)	ECGP EMan EPPr EWes LHop WCot
- pale pink	CSpe ECtt EMan LPhx SAga SMrm WFTG
* - 'Shell Pink'	ECGP
'Newleaze Coral'	CSpe CWCL EMan LHop LLWP MAvo SAga
'Newleaze Pink'	LHop SAga
parvifolia	EBee
remota	CPLG EMan MNrw SPlb
rivularis	CPLG EBee EMan WMoo
umbellata	see *Phymosia umbellata*

Sphaeromeria (Asteraceae)
§ **capitata**	NWCA

Spigelia (Loganiaceae)
marilandica	CRDP EBee

Spilanthes (Asteraceae)
acmella	EOHP MSal
oleracea	MSal

Spiraea ✿ (Rosaceae)
CLD 138	EMon
'Abigail'	CDoC
albiflora	see *S. japonica* var. *albiflora*
arborea	see *Sorbaria kirilowii*
§ 'Arguta' ♀ H4	More than 30 suppliers
x **arguta** 'Bridal Wreath'	see *S.* 'Arguta'
- 'Compacta'	see *S.* x *cinerea*
- 'Nana'	see *S.* x *cinerea*
bella	WHCG
betulifolia	GEil MRav MWgw NLon SMac WHCG WPat
- var. **aemiliana**	CBot CWSG EBee EBre ECtt EPla ESis GKir MGos SLPl WFar

x **bumalda**	see *S. japonica* 'Bumalda'
- 'Wulfenii'	see *S. japonica* 'Walluf'
callosa 'Alba'	see *S. japonica* var. *albiflora*
§ **cantoniensis**	CPle MTed SLon
'Flore Pleno' (d)	
- 'Lanceata'	see *S. cantoniensis* 'Flore Pleno'
§ x **cinerea**	EPfP SSta
- 'Grefsheim' ♀ H4	CBcs CDoC COtt CSBt EBee ECtt EMil ENot GKir LRHS MBri MGos SLim SPer SPla SSta WCFE WDin WFar WWeb
crispifolia	see *S. japonica* 'Bullata'
decumbens	CPle
douglasii	MBar
- subsp. **menziesii**	NLon
formosana CC 1597	CPLG
§ x **foxii**	SLPl
fritschiana	SLPl SLon
hendersonii	see *Petrophytum hendersonii*
§ **japonica**	SBod SMer
- 'Alba'	see *S. japonica* var. *albiflora*
§ - var. **albiflora**	CEnd CPle ESis LRHS MBar MWat SPer SRms WHCG
- 'Allgold'	NBee
- 'Alpina'	see *S. japonica* 'Nana'
- 'Alpine Gold'	CFai NHol NPro WWeb
- 'Anthony Waterer' (v)	CBcs CChe CPle CSBt CWSG CWib EBee EBre ELan ENot EPfP GKir LRHS MBar MBri MGos MHer MRav NBee NWea SHBN SLim SPer SRms WBod WDin WTai WGwG WHar WTel
- 'Blenheim'	SRms
§ - 'Bullata'	CFee CMHG EPfP GEdr MBar NWCA SRms WAbe WBod WHCG
§ - 'Bumalda'	GKir WFar
- 'Candlelight' ♀ H4	CAbP CBcs CSBt CWSG EBee EBre EGra EPfP GKir LAst LRHS MAsh MGos NHol SCoo SLim SPer SPla WGwG
§ - 'Crispa'	CRez EBee EPfP LRHS MBar MTis NPro WFar WWeb
- 'Dart's Red' ♀ H4	GKir LRHS MBri SSta WWeb
- 'Firelight'	CAbP CBcs CChe CSBt EBee EBre ELan ENot EPfP GKir LHop LRHS MAsh MBri MGos MTis NHol SCoo SLim SPar SPer SPla SSta WBrE WGwG WLRN WStI
- var. **fortunei** 'Atrosanguinea'	WHCG
- 'Froebelii'	EWTr
- 'Glenroy Gold'	SLon WHen
- 'Gold Mound'	CMHG CSBt CWSG CWib EBee ELan ENot EPfP GKir LRHS MBar MBri MIcr MRav MWgw MWhi NBee NFor NLon SHBN SHFr SPer SPlb SRms SWal WDin WFar WHar WStI WWeb
- 'Gold Rush'	CMHG MBNS WHCG WRus
- Golden Princess = 'Lisp' PBR ♀ H4	CTri CWSG EBre EPfP GKir LAst LBuc LRHS MAsh MBar MGos MTis NBee NHol SLon SMer SPer SRPl SReu SRms SSta WCFE WDin WFar WStI WWeb
- 'Goldflame'	More than 30 suppliers
- 'Little Princess'	CBcs CBrm CWSG CWib EBee EMil ENot GKir LRHS MAsh MBar MBri MHdf MRav MWat MWhi NBee NBlu NHol SLim SPer SRms SSta WDin WFar WHar WWal WWeb
- Magic Carpet = 'Walbuma' PBR ♀ H4	LRHS MAsh SCoo WWeb

- 'Magnifica'	WHCG WPat
§ - 'Nana' ♀ H4	CMHG CSBt EBee EHyt ENot ESis MAsh MBar MRav MTho NHar NLon SRms WEas WHCG WLin WPat WPer
- 'Nyewoods'	see *S. japonica* 'Nana'
N - 'Shirobana'	More than 30 suppliers
- 'Snow Cap' **new**	CWib
§ - 'Walluf'	CFai COtt CPle CTri CWib GEil NFor NLon WHCG
- 'White Cloud' **new**	ELan
- 'White Gold' **new**	CAbP LRHS MAsh SPer WWeb
'Margaritae'	NPro SHBN SPer
nipponica	CBcs MBar
- 'Halward's Silver'	LRHS MRav NHol NPro SLPl WBcn WBod
- 'June Bride'	NBlu
- 'Rotundifolia'	GEil
§ - 'Snowmound' ♀ H4	More than 30 suppliers
- var. *tosaensis* hort.	see *S. nipponica* 'Snowmound'
- var. *tosaensis* (Yatabe) Makino	LHop MWat SReu
x *pachystachys*	GEil
palmata 'Elegans'	see *Filipendula purpurea* 'Elegans'
§ *prunifolia* (d)	CFai ELan EPla MBlu MRav SLon SPer WCom WHCG WTel WWin
- 'Plena'	see *S. prunifolia*
x *pseudosalicifolia* 'Triumphans'	GEil SHFr WWin
salicifolia	GEil WFar
stevenii	SPer
'Summersnow'	SLPl
'Superba'	see *S.* x *foxii*
thunbergii ♀ H4	CChe CSBt CTri CWib EBee ENot EPfP MRav NFor NLon NWea SCoo SLim SMer SPar SPer SRms WDin WGwG WHCG WWal
- 'Fujino Pink' **new**	WDin
* - 'Mellow Yellow'	WFar WPen
- 'Mount Fuji'	CAbP CWib EBre EHoe EPfP GSki LRHS MGos NPro SCoo WFar
* - *rosea*	WBcn
- 'Tickled Pink'	CAbP LRHS MTis NPro
ulmaria	see *Filipendula ulmaria*
x *vanhouttei*	CBcs CSBt CTri EBee ENot EPfP MBar MHer MRav NFor NLon SHBN SHFr SPer SRms WDin WFar WTel WWal
- 'Gold Fountain'	WBcn
- Pink Ice = 'Catpan' (v)	CAbP CBcs CDoC CMHG COtt CSLe CWib EBee EHoe EMil EPfP LAst LHop LRHS MAsh MGos MLLN MTis NLon SHBN SPar SPer SPlb SRPl WDin WFar WHar WTel WWeb
veitchii	MRav WBcn
venusta 'Magnifica'	see *Filipendula rubra* 'Venusta'

Spiranthes (Orchidaceae)

aestivalis	SSpi
cernua f. *odorata*	CBro CDes CFwr CSpe EBee EChP EHrv EMan EMar EWll GBri LAst LEur LHop LRHS MCCP MDun NHar NMen NSti SAga SMrm SPoG SUsu WCot WFTG WFar WPGP WWhi
'Chadd's Ford'	
spiralis	SSpi

Spirodela (Lemnaceae)

§ *polyrhiza*	EMFW MSta

Spodiopogon (Poaceae)

sibiricus	CBig CKno CWCL EBee ECGN EChP ECha EHoe EMan EMon EPPr LBBr LEdu MSte NFor WMoo WWeb

Sporobolus (Poaceae)

airoides **new**	EBee
asper **new**	EBee
cryptandrus	EBee EPPr
heterolepis	CBig EBee EHoe LHop LPhx MAvo MSPs WPrP
wrightii	EBee

Spraguea (Portulacaceae)

'Powder Puff'	LRHS

Sprekelia (Amaryllidaceae)

formosissima	CSpe CStu EBot LAma LRHS NRog

Stachys (Lamiaceae)

§ *affinis*	CArn CFir ELau GPoy Ilve LEdu
§ *albens* **new**	EOrc IFro
§ *albotomentosa*	CSpe EBee EMan LHop LPhx SHFr WCHb WCot
alopecuros	WWin
alpina	CNat EBee
x *ambigua*	NSti
atherocalyx	EBee MWod
balansae	NSti
betonica	see *S. officinalis*
§ *byzantina*	More than 30 suppliers
§ - 'Big Ears'	CMGP CWes EBee EBlw ECha EMan EMon ENot EWTr LHop MAnH MCAu MCLN MWat NDov SDes SMrm WCot WFar WMnd
§ - 'Cotton Boll'	CMGP COIW EBee ECha EFou GCal GMac LRHS MBct MCLN MHar MTho MWat SPer WCot WGwG WWal
- 'Countess Helen von Stein'	see *S. byzantina* 'Big Ears'
- gold-leaved[PBR]	see *S. byzantina* 'Primrose Heron'
- large-leaved	see *S. byzantina* 'Big Ears'
- 'Limelight'	EBee MGGn WCot
§ - 'Primrose Heron'[PBR]	COtt EBee ECha ECot EMan EPfP GMaP LRHS MAnH MCAu NDov NLar NOrc NSti SMer SPar SPer WBry
- 'Sheila McQueen'	see *S. byzantina* 'Cotton Boll'
- 'Silver Carpet'	More than 30 suppliers
- 'Striped Phantom' (v)	EMan MCAu WCHb WCot WEas
- 'Variegata'	see *S. byzantina* 'Striped Phantom'
candida	EBee EHyt
chrysantha	EHyt LPhx SAga
citrina	CMea GCal LRHS WCom
coccinea	CHar COIW CPla EBee ECGN EHrv EMan EOrc EWsh LLWP LRHS MCLN MHer MTis MUlv MWrn NBir NCot SHFr SPet STes SYvo WCHb WMoo WOut WPat WRos WSan WWin
- 'El Salto'	WCom
corsica	CDes EBee WPGP
cretica	EMan EOrc
densiflora	see *S. monieri*
§ *discolor*	EBee EChP EOrc EPPr MBri MBro MLLN SGar SMac WCot WCru WOut WPer WViv
dregeana **new**	SAga
germanica	CNat CPen EBee EMan NArg WBri WOut
- subsp. *bithynica*	SBla
grandiflora	see *S. macrantha*
heraclea	EBee
'Hidalgo'	see *S. albotomentosa*
iva	ESis ETow LPhx WLin

lanata	see *S. byzantina*	
lavandulifolia	EHyt WLin	
§ *macrantha*	CArn CHar CHea COIW ECha	
	ECoo GKir LAst LRHS MWgw	
	NChi NOak NOrc NSti SIng SMrm	
	SPet SRms STes WBea WCHb	
	WEas WFar WHil WViv WWin	
– 'Alba'	EBee ECha WMoo	
– 'Hummelo'	see *S. monieri* 'Hummelo'	
– 'Nivea'	EBee EHrv ELan EMan GCal	
	MMHG WPat WWal	
§ – 'Robusta' ♀ H4	CDes CStr EBee EBlw ELan GKir	
	MBri NBro NGdn SCro SHel SVal	
	WCot WRHF WWye	
– 'Rosea'	CBri CElw CMHG EBee EFou ELan	
	GMaP IKee MArl MCLN SCro SHel	
	SPlb WEas WPer WRha WWye	
– 'Superba'	CBri CRDP EBee EChP EPfP GKir	
	LRHS MBri MDun MGrG MMHG	
	MRav NCot SBla SDes SMrm SPer	
	WCHb WCom WCot WFar WMnd	
	WMoo WWeb	
– 'Violacea'	CDes CStr EBee MAvo WPGP	
marrubiifolia	EBee	
mexicana **new**	LPhx MDKP MSte	
§ *monieri*	CM&M CRDP EBee EChP EGle	
	EMan LRHS MAvo MCLN NLar	
	SMrm WCot WOBN WOut WPer	
	WViv	
§ – 'Hummelo'	EBee EFou EGle EMan ENot EPPr	
	EPfP LHop LPhx MCAu NCat	
	NDov SAga SMrm SUsu WWeb	
* – 'Rosea'	EBee NDov SBla	
– 'Saharan Pink' **new**	WElm	
– 'Spitzweg'	EPPr NDov SUsu	
nivea	see *S. discolor*	
§ *officinalis*	CArn CKin CSev CStr EBee EWTr	
	GBar GPoy MChe MGas MHer	
	MPEx MSal NLan NMir WBea	
	WHHs WHbs WHer WWye	
– 'Alba'	CArn CMGP CRDP EBee MCAu	
	MCLN NBro NRya WAlt WCHb	
	WCom WFar WHer WOut WRha	
	WWye	
– pale pink **new**	WFTG	
– 'Rosea'	CMea MCAu WCot	
– 'Rosea Superba'	CBgR EBee ECha MCLN MDKP	
	SIng WCot WFar WMoo	
olympica	see *S. byzantina*	
palustris	CKin LPBA MGas MSta NLan NSco	
	SHar WFar WOut	
plumosa	EBee	
setifera	EBee	
spicata	see *S. macrantha*	
sylvatica	CArn CKin EMan MGol NLan	
	NSco WBri WHer	
– 'Hoskin's Variegated' (v)	WAlt WCHb WWpP	
– 'Huskers' (v)	EBee EPPr ITer MCCP	
– 'Shade of Pale'	WAlt	
thirkei	EBee WRHF	
tuberifera	see *S. affinis*	

Stachytarpheta (Verbenaceae)
mutabilis	SOWG

Stachyurus (Stachyuraceae)
chinensis	CBcs CMCN CPMA CPle IArd
	IDee LRHS MBri MGos NLar SPoG
– 'Celina'	MBlu SSta
– 'Joy Forever' (v)	CEnd CMCN MBlu SRPl
himalaicus	CFil IArd IDee NLar WPGP
– HWJCM 009	WCru
leucotrichus	CPMA

'Magpie' (v)	CFil CPMA EPfP LRHS SLon SSpi	
	WCru WPGP	
praecox ♀ H4	More than 30 suppliers	
§ – var. *matsuzakii*	CFil NBhm WPGP	
– – B&SWJ 2817	WCru	
– – 'Scherzo' (v) **new**	WCru	
* – 'Rubriflora'	CPMA ELan EPfP LRHS MAsh	
	SSpi	
salicifolius	SLon	
sigeyosii B&SWJ 6915 **new**	WCru	
szechuanensis	CBcs	
yunnanensis	CFil WPGP	

Staphylea (Staphyleaceae)
bumalda	CBcs CMCN CPMA EPfP NLar	
	WPGP	
colchica	CBcs ELan EPfP SRPl WDin WSHC	
– 'Rosea' **new**	CBcs	
holocarpa	CBcs CPMA CPle EPfP MRav SSpi	
	WBVN WFar	
N – var. *rosea*	CPMA ENot EPfP	
N – 'Rosea'	CMCN MBlu MGos NLar SSpi WSHC	
pinnata	CBcs CPMA CWib EPfP LEdu	
	NLar WHCr WNor WPat	
trifolia	CAgr CBcs	

Statice see *Limonium*

Stauntonia (Lardizabalaceae)
hexaphylla	CBcs CDoC CHEx CPlN CSam	
	CTri EBee EHol EMan EPfP GQui	
	LRHS MDun SAdn SBra SHGC	
	SPer SReu SSpi SSta WBrE WPGP	
	WSHC	
– B&SWJ 4858	WCru	
purpurea B&SWJ 3690	WCru	

Stegnogramma (Thelypteridaceae)
pozoi	EFer EMon

Steirodiscus (Asteraceae)
tagetes **new**	WHer

Stellaria (Caryophyllaceae)
graminea	CKin NBid
holostea	CKin MChe NMir NSco WBri
	WHer WShi

Stenanthium (Melanthiaceae)
occidentale	SCnR
robustum	CRDP WPGP

Stenocarpus (Proteaceae)
sinuatus	CTrC

Stenochlaena (Blechnaceae)
palustris	MBri

Stenomesson (Amaryllidaceae)
§ *miniatum*	CStu

Stenotaphrum (Poaceae)
secundatum 'Variegatum'	CHal WDyG
(v) ♀ H1	

Stenotus (Asteraceae)
§ *acaulis*	WLin

Stephanandra (Rosaceae)
incisa	CBcs CPLG CPle WHCG WWal
§ – 'Crispa'	CDoC CPle CRez EBee ELan EMil
	ENot EPfP EWTr GEil GKir LAst
	LHop LRHS MBar MBlu MRav

	MWat MWgw MWhi NFor NHol SHBN SPer SPla WCFE WDin WFar WHCG WTel
- 'Dart's Horizon'	SLPl
- 'Prostrata'	see *S. incisa* 'Crispa'
tanakae	CBcs CDoC CPLG CPle ELan EPfP EWTr GKir IMGH LAst MBar MBlu MRav MWat NFor NLon SHBN SLPl SLon SPer SPla SRPl WDin WFar WHCG WPat

Stephania (Menispermaceae)

glandulifera	CPlN
japonica B&SWJ 2396	WCru
rotundifolia **new**	EBot

Stephanotis (Asclepiadaceae)

| *floribunda* ♀ H1 | CBcs CPlN EBak GQui LRHS MBri SMur SOWG |
| - *variegata* (v) | SMur |

Sternbergia (Amaryllidaceae)

candida	CBro EPot LAma
- JCA 933000	SSpi WCot
§ *clusiana*	EHyt LAma
colchiciflora	EHyt
fischeriana	CBro
greuteriana	EHyt SOkd
lutea	CBro CFwr CStu EBre EHyt EPot EWes LAma LRHS MRav MWat NMen NRog NWCA SDix SSpi WEas WLin
- Angustifolia Group	CBro EMon WCot
macrantha	see *S. clusiana*
sicula	CBro CFwr EHyt WCot
- var. *graeca*	EHyt EPot
- 'John Marr'	CDes

Stevia (Asteraceae)

| *rebaudiana* | EBee EOHP GPoy MSal WJek |

Stewartia ❀ (Theaceae)

gemmata	CFil MDun NLar WNor WPGP
'Korean Splendor'	see *S. pseudocamellia* Koreana Group
koreana	see *S. pseudocamellia* Koreana Group
malacodendron ♀ H4	EPfP LRHS MBri SSpi SSta
monadelpha	EPfP SSpi WBod WNor
ovata	CBcs SSpi SSta
N - var. *grandiflora*	GKir LRHS
pseudocamellia ♀ H4	More than 30 suppliers
- var. *koreana*	see *S. pseudocamellia* Koreana Group
§ - Koreana Group ♀ H4	CBcs CEnd CFil CMCN CTho EPfP MBri MDun NLar SPer SSpi WDin WFar WNor WPGP
- - B&SWJ 4630	WCru
pteropetiolata	CBcs
- var. *koreana*	LRHS
rostrata	CBcs CFil GIBF MBlu WNor WPGP
serrata	SSpi
sinensis ♀ H4	CFil CPMA EPfP MBlu MDun SBrw SSpi SSta WNor WPGP

Sticherus (Gleicheniaceae)

| *urceolatus* | WRic |

Stictocardia (Convolvulaceae)

| *beraviensis* | CPlN |

Stigmaphyllon (Malpighiaceae)

| *ciliatum* | CPlN |

Stipa (Poaceae)

B&SWJ 2302 from Sikkim	EBee WCru
§ *arundinacea*	More than 30 suppliers
- 'Autumn Tints'	EHoe
- 'Golden Hue' **new**	EHoe
barbata	CBrm CDes CKno CSpe EBee EBre ECGN EGle EHoe EMan EVFa EWes LPhx NOGN SMrm SPer WCom WCot WHal WHil WPGP WRos
- 'Silver Feather'	CBig EWsh LHrt LIck MAnH MWhi NGdn SMac
boysterica	CFee
brachytricha	see *Calamagrostis brachytricha*
§ *calamagrostis*	More than 30 suppliers
- 'Lemperg'	EMan EPPr
capillata	More than 30 suppliers
- 'Brautschleier'	GCal LHrt LIck SWal
* - 'Lace Veil'	CBig
chrysophylla **new**	CFil
- F&W 9321	WPGP
columbiana **new**	MLLN
comata	EBee IFro
elegantissima	CKno EHoe EVFa MGol SDes
extremiorientalis	CKno ECha EGle EPPr GIBF GSki LPhx NOGN SMad WHal WWpP
gigantea ♀ H4	More than 30 suppliers
- 'Gold Fontaene'	CDes CFir CKno EBee EFou EMon EPPr EWes LPhx MMoz MNrw SMad WCot WPGP
grandis	CBig CBrm CKno EBlw ECha EPPr GBin WHal WMoo WPer
joannis	EBee GCal WCot
lasiagrostis	see *S. calamagrostis*
lessingiana	CFil CM&M CPLG EBee EHul EPla GBin GIBF LHrt WPGP WPnP
neomexicana	EBee
offneri	CKno EBee EPPr EVFa EWes LPhx NDov SBla SIgm WCot
patens	EBee
pennata	CBcs CBig CKno EBee EHoe EMan EPPr GBin GCal GKir LPhx MFir NOak SMac SMad SMer WLRN
pulcherrima	CKno EMan EPPr EVFa GCal MAnH MAvo SIgm
- 'Windfeder'	CFir LPhx NChi SMrm WHil
robusta	EBee EPPr
spartea	CBrm
splendens misapplied	see *S. calamagrostis*
§ *splendens* Trin.	CBig ECoo EFou EHoe EMan EPPr EVFa LEdu LPhx MBrN WFoF
stenophylla	see *S. tirsa*
tenacissima	CSBt EBee ECha EFou EHoe EHul EMon EPla GSki WBro WDin WMoo
tenuifolia misapplied	see *S. tenuissima*
tenuifolia Steud.	More than 30 suppliers
§ *tenuissima*	More than 30 suppliers
- 'Pony Tails'	CBig EBee EPfP IBal LAst LRav MBNS MBar MLan MTis SCou STes WHil WMnd WWeb
§ *tirsa*	GBin
turkestanica	CKno EBee EVFa LPhx MAnH MMoz NDov SUsu SWat
ucrainica	EPPr LPhx MAnH

Stoebe (Asteraceae)

| *alopcuroides* **new** | SPlb |

Stokesia (Asteraceae)

| *cyanea* | see *S. laevis* |
| § *laevis* | CFwr CHea CPrp EBee EBlw ECGP ECha EGle EPfP EWTr GKir |

	GMac LAst LRHS MBro MCAu	
	NBro NFor NLar NLon SMrm SPet	
	WBrE WFar WPer WSan WWeb	
- 'Alba'	CHea CM&M CMGP COIW CPrp	
	CRDP EBee ECha EGle EHrv	
	EMan EPar EPfP ERou EWTr	
	GKir GMac LAst LPhx LRHS MBri	
	MRav NHol NPPs SChu SPer STes	
	WRus	
- 'Blue Star'	More than 30 suppliers	
- 'Mary Gregory'	More than 30 suppliers	
- mixed	CPou	
- 'Omega Skyrocket'	CBre CElw CFai CFwr CPou EBee	
	EChP EMan EMar ERou MLLN	
	MSPs NDov SMrm SOkh SUsu	
	WCot WFar WHil	
- 'Purple Parasols'	CElw CFai CFwr CM&M COtt CPrp	
	EBee EChP EGle EMan EMar EWll	
	GCal GMac LHop MSph NChi NPPs	
	NSti SAsh SHar SOkh STes SUsu	
	WAul WCot WCra WFar WWhi	
- 'Silver Moon'	CFwr CPrp CWes EBee EChP	
	EGle EMan EMar EMil EVFa GCal	
	LAst LBBr LBuc MGrG MTPN	
	MTis NBir NHaw NPri SHar SOkh	
	SVil WCot WFar	
- 'Träumerei'	CRDP EBee EChP EGle EMan	
	EMar ERou LAst LRHS MGrG MTis	
	NHol NPPs SLon SOkh SPet SWal	
	WMnd WMoo WWal	
- 'Wyoming'	ERou	

Stranvaesia see *Photinia*

x *Stranvinia* see *Photinia*

Stratiotes (Hydrocharitaceae)

aloides	CBen CWat ECoo EHon EMFW
	LMdh LPBA MSta SBHF SWat

strawberry see *Fragaria*

Strelitzia (Strelitziaceae)

alba	NBlo WMul XBlo
caudata	NBlo XBlo
nicolai	CAbb CHEx CRoM EAmu ESlt
	LPal NBlo SPar WMul XBlo
reginae ♀ H1	CAbb CBcs CBrP ELan ERea ESlb
	ESlt GQui LEur LPal LPan LRHS
	NBlo NPal SAPC SArc SPar SPlb
	SKms WMul XBlo
- 'Humilis'	NBlo XBlo
- 'Kirstenbosch Gold'	NBlo XBlo

Streptocarpella see *Streptocarpus*

Streptocarpus ✿ (Gesneriaceae)

'Albatross' ♀ H1	WDib
'Amanda' Dibley ♀ H1	WDib
'Anne'	CSpe WDib
'Athena'	WDib
baudertii	WDib
'Beryl'	WDib
'Bethan' ♀ H1	WDib
'Black Panther'	WDib
'Blue Gem'	WDib
'Blue Moon'	WDib
'Blue Nymph'	WDib
'Blushing Bride' (d)	WDib
* 'Boysenberry Delight'	WDib
'Branwen'	WDib
candidus	WDib
'Carol'	WDib

'Carys' ♀ H1	WDib
'Catrin' ♀ H1	WDib
caulescens	CHal WDib
* - 'Compactus'	CHal
- var. *pallescens*	WDib
'Charlotte' new	WDib
'Chorus Line' ♀ H1	WDib
'Clouds'	CSpe
'Concord Blue'	WDib
'Constant Nymph'	WDib
'Crystal Ice' PBR ♀ H1	WDib
cyaneus	WDib
- subsp. *polackii*	WDib
'Cynthia' ♀ H1	WDib
I 'Daphne' ♀ H1	WDib
'Diana'	WDib
dunnii	CFir WDib
'Elsi'	WDib
'Emily' new	WDib
'Emma'	WDib
'Falling Stars' ♀ H1	CSpe WDib
'Festival Wales'	WDib
'Fiona'	WDib
floribundus	WDib
gardenii	WDib
glandulosissimus ♀ H1	CHal EOHP SSte SVen WDib
'Gloria' ♀ H1	CSpe WDib
'Good Hope'	ERea
'Grape Slush'	WDib
'Happy Snappy' ♀ H1	WDib
'Heidi' ♀ H1	WDib
'Helen' ♀ H1	WDib
'Huge White'	CSpe
'Jennifer' ♀ H1	WDib
'Joanna'	WDib
johannis	WDib
'Julie'	WDib
'Karen'	WDib
kentaniensis	WDib
'Kim' ♀ H1	CSpe WDib
kirkii	WDib
'Laura' ♀ H1	WDib
'Little Gem'	CSpe
'Louise'	WDib
'Lynne'	WDib
'Maassen's White' ♀ H1	ERea WDib
'Mandy'	WDib
'Margaret' Gavin Brown	WDib
'Marie'	WDib
'Megan'	SPlb
'Melanie' ♀ H1	WDib
meyeri	WDib
'Midnight Flame'	WDib
'Mini Nymph'	WDib
modestus new	WDib
'Neptune'	WDib
'Nicola'	WDib
'Olga'	WDib
'Olwen' new	WDib
'Party Doll'	WDib
parviflorus	LEur
'Passion Pink'	WDib
'Paula' ♀ H1	WDib
pentherianus	WDib
'Pink Fondant'	CSpe
'Pink Souffle'	WDib
polyanthus subsp.	WDib
dracomontanus	
primulifolius	WDib
- subsp. *formosus*	WDib
prolixus	WDib
* 'Purple Passion'	CSpe
rexii	WDib

'Rhiannon'	WDib
'Rosebud'	WDib
'Rosemary' (d)	WDib
'Ruby' ♀ H1	WDib
'Ruffled Lilac'	CSpe
'Sally'	WDib
'Sandra'	WDib
'Sarah'	WDib
saxorum ♀ H1	CHal EGra EMan EOHP LIck MBri
	MOak NPPs SRms SSte WDib
	WFar WWol
– compact	EOHP WDib
'Sian'	WDib
'Snow White' ♀ H1	CSpe WDib
'Something Special'	WDib
'Sophie'	WDib
'Stella' ♀ H1	WDib
stomandrus	WDib
* 'Sugar Almond'	CSpe
'Susan' ♀ H1	WDib
'Terracotta' **new**	CSpe
'Tina' ♀ H1	WDib
'Tracey'	WDib
'Violet Lace'	CSpe
wendlandii	WDib
'Wendy'	WDib
'Wiesmoor Red'	WDib
'Winifred'	WDib

Streptolirion (Commelinaceae)
volubile	CPlN

Streptopus (Convallariaceae)
amplexifolius	EBee WCru
– M&PS 98/022	GCrs NLar
obtusatus **new**	EBee
roseus	EBee GCrs LAma
simplex	EBee

Streptosolen (Solanaceae)
jamesonii ♀ H1	CHal CHll CPlN CPle CSev EBak
	ELan EPfP ERea EShb MOak NRog
	SYvo WBod
– 'Fire Gold'	ERea

Strobilanthes (Acanthaceae)
anisophylla	CSpe WCot
atropurpurea misapplied	see *S. attenuata*
atropurpurea Nees	see *S. wallichii*
attenuata	More than 30 suppliers
– subsp. *nepalensis*	WWye
– – TSS from Nepal	EBee WRHF
– 'Out of the Ocean'	WOut
dyeriana (v) ♀ H1	CHal EBak EShb WCot WRha
flexicaulis	EBee
– B&SWJ 354	WCru
nutans	CDes EBee WCot
rankanensis	CDes EBee EDAr
– B&SWJ 1771	CPom WCru
violacea	CPrp ERea WPer
wallichii	CDes EBee NMRc SMHy

Stromanthe (Marantaceae)
amabilis	see *Ctenanthe amabilis*
sanguinea	CHal MBri
'Stripestar'	MBri

Strongylodon (Papilionaceae)
macrobotrys	SOWG

Strophanthus (Apocynaceae)
divaricatus	CPlN
kombe	CPlN MSal

Stuartia see *Stewartia*

Stylidium (Stylidiaceae)
affine **new**	SPlb
graminifolium	WCot
soboliferum **new**	ECou

Stylophorum (Papaveraceae)
diphyllum	CPBP CPou ECha EGle EMar EPar
	LAma MRav MSal WAul WCru WPnP
lasiocarpum	CPLG CPom EMan EMar EWTr
	GAbr MGrG NCat NDlv SGar
	WCot WCru WRos

Styphelia (Epacridaceae)
colensoi	see *Cyathodes colensoi*

Styrax (Styracaceae)
americanus	CBcs
formosanus	CFil WPGP
var. *formosanus*	
– – B&SWJ 3803	WCru
hemsleyanus ♀ H4	CAbP CBcs CEnd CFil CTho EPfP
	LRHS MBlu SPer SSpi WFar WNor
	WPGP
japonicus ♀ H4	More than 30 suppliers
§ – Benibana Group ♀ H4	SReu SSta
– – 'Pink Chimes'	CAbP CMCN CPLG CPMA ELan
	EPfP LRHS MAsh MBlu MBri
	MDun SKee SPer SSta
– 'Carillon'	LRHS
– 'Fargesii'	CFil EPfP GKir LRHS MAsh MBri
	SSpi SSta WFar
– 'Roseus'	see *S. japonicus* Benibana
	Group
obassia ♀ H4	CArn CBcs CMCN CPne CTho
	EPfP IMGH LPan LRHS MBlu SKee
	SSpi WBod WNor WPGP
– B&SWJ 6023	WCru
odoratissimus	CArn
serrulatus	CFil

Succisa (Dipsacaceae)
§ *pratensis*	CArn CKin CRDP EBee ECoo MBow
	MChe MHer NLan NLar NSco NWCA
	SMHy SSpi WGwG WHer WJek
– *alba*	EBee MDKP SSpi
– 'Buttermilk'	CPlt SSpi
– 'Corinne Tremaine' (v)	WHer
– dwarf	NGby NRya
– 'Peddar's Pink'	EWes WAlt
– *rosea*	SSpi

sunberry see *Rubus* 'Sunberry'

Sutera (Scrophulariaceae)
'Blizzard'PBR	SMrm WGor
cordata	LHop
– 'Pink Domino'PBR	ECtt
§ – 'Snowflake'	CFox CSpe ECtt LPVe MLan MOak
	NPri SCoo SMrm SPet WLRN
jurassica	see *Jamesbrittenia jurassica*
'Lavender Storm'	WWol
neglecta	EBee SPlb WPGP
Olympic Gold = 'Prosutv' (v)	ECtt NPri SCoo WWol
Sea Mist = 'Yagemil'PBR	NPri WGor

Sutherlandia (Papilionaceae)
frutescens	CAbb CArn GGar LRHS SPlb
	WCot WJek

- 'Prostrata'	EMan SIgm
montana	CFir SIgm

Swainsona (*Papilionaceae*)
galegifolia new	CHll
- 'Albiflora'	CSpe LPhx SBla SCro SOWG

Syagrus (*Arecaceae*)
§ **romanzoffiana**	CBrP CRoM EAmu LPJP LPal
	MPRe WMul

x Sycoparrotia (*Hamamelidaceae*)
semidecidua	CBcs CFil CPMA GKir LRHS MBlu
	SSta WPGP

Sycopsis (*Hamamelidaceae*)
sinensis	CMCN EPfP LRHS MBlu SMur
	SSpi WBcn WDin WFar
	WSHC

Symphoricarpos (*Caprifoliaceae*)
albus	CDul EBee ENot NWea WDin
- 'Constance Spry'	MTed SRms
§ - var. **laevigatus**	EBee ENot EPfP LBuc MBar
§ - 'Taff's White' (v)	WMoo
- 'Variegatus'	see *S. albus* 'Taff's White'
'Amethyst' **new**	EBee
x **chenaultii** 'Hancock'	CSBt EBee ELan ENot EPfP
	EWTr GEil MBar MRav MWat
	NLon NPro SHBN SPer WDin
	WFar
x **doorenbosii**	EBee ENot GKir LRHS MBar
	MRav
'Magic Berry'	NWea
- 'Mother of Pearl'	CDul EBee ELan ENot EPfP GKir
	LRHS MBar MGos MRav NWea
	SPer
- 'White Hedge'	CSBt ELan ENot LBuc LRHS MRav
	NWea SPer SPlb WTel
orbiculatus	CBrm IMGH LRHS WGwG
- 'Albovariegatus'	see *S. orbiculatus* 'Taff's Silver
	Edge'
- 'Argenteovariegatus'	see *S. orbiculatus* 'Taff's Silver
	Edge'
- 'Bowles' Golden Variegated'	see *S. orbiculatus* 'Foliis
	Variegatis'
§ - 'Foliis Variegatis' (v)	CSBt CTri EBee EHoe ENot EPfP
	EVFa GEil LRHS MGos MRav NPro
	NSti SHBN SPar SPer WDin WEas
	WFar WGwG WHCG WSHC WWal
	WWin
§ - 'Taff's Silver Edge' (v)	CBrm EBee EHoe LRHS MBar NSti
	SPar
- 'Variegatus'	see *S. orbiculatus* 'Foliis
	Variegatis'
rivularis	see *S. albus* var. *laevigatus*

Symphyandra (*Campanulaceae*)
	CDes EMon NLar
armena	EBee EBur ELan GBuc NLar
asiatica	WFar
cretica	EBee ECoo ETow MAvo MWrn
	NPPs
hofmannii	EBee EBur ELan EPyc MBro MTho
	MWrn NLar NPPs NPri SRms
	WFar WPer WRha WWin
§ **ossetica**	CElw EBee ELan EMan MWrn
	NCiC NWoo
§ **pendula**	CFir CTCP EBcc EChP EPfP EWTr
	EWes GBuc LPVe MBNS MLwd
	MWrn NJOw NLar WBar WFar
	WLin WPer WWeb
- **alba**	see *S. pendula*

wanneri	EBee EBur EChP EMan EPfP LRHS
	NLar WWin
zangezura	CNic CTCP EBee EBur EChP
	EMan MLwd MWrn

Symphyotrichum see Aster

Symphytum (*Boraginaceae*)
asperum	ECha ELan EMon MRav MSal
	MTed NCot NLar WCHb WCer
	WMoo WTMC
* **azureum**	EBee EBlw MBri MCAu MSte
	NLar SRPl WCHb WFar WMnd
	WTMC
'Belsay'	GBuc WHil
'Belsay Gold'	SDix
caucasicum ♀ H4	CElw CMHG CSam ECha ELau
	EPar GBar GPoy LEdu LRHS
	MAnH MBri MHar MRav NSti SIde
	SSvw WCHb WHer WHil WMoo
	WRha WWpP WWye
- 'Eminence'	CMCo CMdw CRDP EBee EGoo
	WCHb
- 'Norwich Sky'	CKno EBee EChP MMil NMir
	WCHb
cordatum MDM 94019	NGar
'Denford Variegated' (v)	CRow ITer MInt WBry WCot
§ 'Goldsmith' (v)	More than 30 suppliers
grandiflorum	EBee ENot GPoy WHHs
'Hidcote Blue'	More than 30 suppliers
§ 'Hidcote Pink'	COIW EBee EBlw EChP ECha
	ELau EPla EWsh LRHS MBow
	MRav MSte MWgw NBir NCot
	NSti SDes SLPl SRPl SUsu WCer
	WFar WMnd WMoo WPnP
	WTMC
'Hidcote Variegated' (v)	WCHb
ibericum	More than 30 suppliers
- 'All Gold'	CSpe ECha ECtt ELau MBri MRav
	SLon WCru WMoo WTMC
- 'Blaueglocken'	CBod CSev EBee EChP ECha
	NCat WMoo WPrP WSan
- dwarf	NPri WMoo
- 'Gold in Spring'	EBee EGoo GIBF NLar WCHb
	WCer WFar
- 'Jubilee'	see *S.* 'Goldsmith'
- 'Lilacinum'	EBee MBro WCer WHer
- 'Pink Robins'	WCHb
- variegated (v)	WCot
- 'Variegatum'	see *S.* 'Goldsmith'
- 'Wisley Blue'	EBee EPfP EWTr IHMH LRHS
	NCat NLar SDes WBan WCer
	WFar WMnd WMoo
'Lambrook Sunrise'	CBct CIAP EBee EPla LHop LRHS
	MAvo MBri MCAu MCLN MMil
	NBro NCot NGHP NSti SChu
	WCot WLRN WMoo WPnP WSan
	WTMC WWpP
'Langthorns Pink'	CPom ELan EMar GBar GBri GBuc
	GCal WCHb WCer
'Mereworth'	see *Symphytum* x *uplandicum*
	'Mereworth'
officinale	CAgr CArn CKin COld CSev GBar
	GPoy MChe MHer MNrw MSal
	NCWG NMir NPer SIde SRms
	SYvo WHer WWye
- 'Boraston White'	MHer WCHb
- var. **ochroleucum**	WHer WTMC
orientale	CAgr CPom EMon GCal STes
	WCHb
peregrinum	see *S.* x *uplandicum*
'Roseum'	see *S.* 'Hidcote Pink'
'Rotblum'	SDes

'Rubrum' CDes EBee EBlw ECot EHrv ELan ELau EPfP EVFa EWes LAst LRHS MCAu MCLN MHer MSte NCot NOrc SPer WCot WCru WHHs WSan WTMC

tuberosum CArn CBre CElw CMHG COld CRDP CSam EBlw ELau EOHP GPoy MBow MDun MFir MHer MSte NCat NHol NSti SMac WCHb WFar WHer WRha WTMC WWye

§ x **uplandicum** CSev CTri ELan ELau EMar GBar GWCH MHer MRav MSal SIde WCHb WCer WHHs WHbs WJek WWye

- 'Axminster Gold' (v) CBct CDes CHad CLAP CMea CPlt CRDP CRow EBee EMan EVFa IBlr ITer LHop LPhx NBid SAga SMrm SSpi WCot WFTG WPGP
- 'Bocking 14' CAgr CBod CPrp GBar IHMH SIde
- 'Lugh Samhoildánach' IIve
§ - 'Mereworth' (v) CBct EBee EVFa SMad WCHb
- 'Variegatum' (v) ♀ H4 More than 30 suppliers

Symplocarpus (Araceae)
foetidus EBee GIBF SSpi

Symplocos (Symplocaceae)
paniculata WWes
pyrifolia CFil

Syncarpha (Asteraceae)
eximia new SPlb

Syneilesis (Asteraceae)
aconitifolia EBee
- B&SWJ 879 WCru
palmata EBee WCot
- B&SWJ 1003 WCru
subglabrata B&SWJ 298 WCot WCru

Syngonium (Araceae)
'Maya Red' MBri
podophyllum ♀ H1 NBlo XBlo
- 'Emerald Gem' CHal
- 'Silver Knight' MBri
- 'Variegatum' (v) MBri
'White Butterfly' CHal MBri

Synnotia see Sparaxis

Synthyris (Scrophulariaceae)
laciniata ETow
- NNS 99-475 WCot
missurica ETow GBuc
- var. **stellata** CLAP CRDP EBee EBre EHrv GCal GGar SBla SSpi WFar WPGP
pinnatifida GBuc NWCA
reniformis GBuc IBlr

Synurus (Asteraceae)
deltoides new EBee

Syringa ✿ (Oleaceae)
afghanica misapplied see S. protolaciniata
amurensis see S. reticulata subsp. amurensis
x **chinensis** CTho WDin
- 'Saugeana' SPer
x **diversifolia** WBcn
'William H. Judd'
emodi CBot NEgg WHCG

- 'Aurea' IArd NLar
- 'Aureovariegata' (v) CBcs CEnd CPMA LRHS MAsh SSpi WDin
x **henryi** 'Alba' WBcn
x **hyacinthiflora** IArd
'Clarke's Giant'
- 'Esther Staley' ♀ H4 EBee ENot EPfP MRav
- 'Maiden's Blush' MBri
'Josee' EBee WFar WPat
x **josiflexa** 'Bellicent' ♀ H4 CEnd CLnd CPle EBee ELan ENot EPfP GKir ISea MAsh MBar MRav MTis NPri NSti SHBN SMur SPer SPlb SPoG SRms SSpi WDin WHCG WPat WPen WTel
- 'James MacFarlane' NRib
- 'Lynette' EPla NPro WBcn
§ - 'Royalty' COtt LBuc
josikaea CLnd CPle CSBt CTho LBuc MBar NLar SPer WHCG
komarovii GIBF
- L 490 GGGa
§ - subsp. **reflexa** CDul CTho EPfP LBuc MBar MGos MRav WDin WFar
§ x **laciniata** Mill. CBot CPMA EBee EHol EPfP GEil GKir LRHS MBri MRav NLar SMur SSpi WGor WHCG WPGP
§ **meyeri** var. **spontanea** More than 30 suppliers
'Palibin' ♀ H4
microphylla see S. pubescens subsp. microphylla
- 'Superba' see S. pubescens subsp. microphylla 'Superba'
'Minuet' MGos
oblata var. **alba** CPMA
palibiniana see S. meyeri var. spontanea 'Palibin'
patula hort. see S. meyeri var. spontanea 'Palibin'
patula (Palibin) Nakai see S. pubescens subsp. patula
pekinensis see S. reticulata subsp. pekinensis
x **persica** ♀ H4 CPLG CPMA EPfP EWTr GKir MGos MWat SLon SPer WTel
- 'Alba' ♀ H4 CBot CMil CPMA GQui WFar WHCG WPat
- var. **laciniata** see S. x laciniata
- 'Taff's Treasure' EMon
pinnatifolia CBot IArd WHCG WPGP
x **prestoniae** 'Agnes Smith' MGos
- 'Audrey' MGos
- 'Coral' COtt WFar
- 'Desdemona' SSpi
- 'Elinor' ♀ H4 CMHG CPle EBee ENot MRav NSti SPer
- 'Hiawatha' MGos WBcn
- 'Isabella' MGos SLdr
- 'Kim' CTho MRav
- 'Nocturne' LRHS MGos WFar
- 'Redwine' COtt LRHS MGos
- 'Royalty' see S. x josiflexa 'Royalty'
§ **protolaciniata** CMHG CPle EPla IDee SSta WAbe WFar WWeb
- 'Kabul' new EPfP NLar
§ **pubescens** SRkn
subsp. **microphylla**
§ - subsp. **microphylla** More than 30 suppliers
'Superba' ♀ H4
§ - subsp. **patula** CMac CSBt ELan EPfP GIBF LAst LNet MAsh MRav MWat NBee NWea SLon SPla SSta WFar WStI
§ - - 'Miss Kim' ♀ H4 CDoC CSBt CWSG EBee EBre ECle ENot EWTr GKir IArd LRHS MBri MBro MGos MRav NBlu

	NLon NPro SHBN SLim SSta WDin WHCG WPat WWeb
reflexa	see *S. komarovii* subsp. *reflexa*
reticulata	CPLG
§ - subsp. *amurensis*	CPle GIBF
- 'Ivory Silk'	CTho CWSG EPfP MAsh SKee
- var. *mandschurica*	see *S. reticulata* subsp. *amurensis*
§ - subsp. *pekinensis*	CBot CMCN CPle
- - 'Pendula'	IArd
x *swegiflexa*	CDul NLar
sweginzowii	CSam CTho EWTr LBuc SPer WFar
tomentella	CDul LBuc NWea SKee SRms
velutina	see *S. pubescens* subsp. *patula*
villosa	MWhi WBVN WDin
vulgaris	CLnd LBuc MBar NWea WBVN WBrE
- 'Agincourt Beauty'	MBri
- var. *alba*	MBar
- 'Albert F. Holden'	WBcn
§ - 'Andenken an Ludwig Späth' ♀ H4	CBcs CBot CDoC CDul CLnd CPMA CSBt CTho CTri EBee ENot EPfP GKir IArd LPan LRHS MBar MGos MRav NBlu NWea SHBN SKee SLim SLon SPer WBVN WFar WGwG WWeb
- 'Aurea'	CNat EPla MRav WBcn WWeb
- Beauty of Moscow	see *S. vulgaris* 'Krasavitsa Moskvy'
- 'Belle de Nancy' (d)	EBee ELan GKir MAsh MRav SHBN SLim WDin WGwG WLRN
- 'Charles Joly' (d) ♀ H4	More than 30 suppliers
- 'Condorcet' (d)	LNet
- 'Congo'	EBee ENot GKir MRav NMoo NPri SCoo SPer
- 'Edward J. Gardner' (d)	ENot LRHS MBri
- 'Firmament' ♀ H4	ELan ENot EPfP GKir MRav NLar SCoo SHBN SPer
- 'Glory'	MBri
- 'Katherine Havemeyer' (d) ♀ H4	More than 30 suppliers
§ - 'Krasavitsa Moskvy'	GKir LRHS MBri
- 'Madame Antoine Buchner' (d)	ENot GKir MRav
- 'Madame Florent Stepman'	LCaP
- 'Madame Lemoine' (d) ♀ H4	More than 30 suppliers
- 'Masséna'	EBee ENot MRav NPri SCoo SPer
- 'Maud Notcutt'	ENot GBin NPri SCoo SPer WLRN
- 'Michel Buchner' (d)	CBcs EBee ENot GKir MAsh MBar MHer MRav MWat NBee NBlu SKee SLim SPer
- 'Miss Ellen Willmott' (d)	MRav
- 'Mrs Edward Harding' (d) ♀ H4	EBee ENot EPfP GKir LBuc LNet MGos NPri NWea SLim WLRN
- 'Président Grévy' (d)	CDoC CLnd CMac EClc
- 'Primrose'	CBot CDoC CMac CSBt CTho EBee ELan ENot EPfP GBin GKir IArd LAst LRHS MAsh MDun MGos MRav SKee SPer SSta WDin WFar WLRN
- 'Rochester'	MBri
- 'Sensation'	CDoC CPle CSBt CWSG EBee ENot EPfP GBin GKir IArd LAst LRHS MAsh MDun MRav SCoo SHBN SKee SLdr SLim SPer SSta
- 'Souvenir d'Alice Harding' (d)	GKir LRHS
- 'Souvenir de Louis Spaeth'	see *S. vulgaris* 'Andenken an Ludwig Späth'
- variegated (v)	SLim
- variegated double (d/v)	EVFa MTed WBcn WWeb

- 'Vestale' ♀ H4	ENot MRav SCoo SDix
wolfii	CArn CPLG GIBF LBuc MCCP NLon WBVN
yunnanensis	CPLG CTho GIBF WDin WWin

Syringodea (Iridaceae)
luteo-nigra new	CStu

Syzygium (Myrtaceae)
paniculatum	CTrC

sweet cicely see *Myrrhis odorata*

T

Tabernaemontana (Apocynaceae)
coronaria	see *T. divaricata*
§ *divaricata*	ESlt SOWG

Tacitus see *Graptopetalum*

Tagetes (Asteraceae)
lucida	EOHP MSal WJek

Talbotia (Velloziaceae)
elegans	CSpe WCot

Talinum (Portulacaceae)
brevifolium new	CGra
calycinum	WDyG WMnd WSan
'Kingswood Gold' new	CPla
okanoganense	CGra ETow
'Zoe'	CGra

tamarillo see *Cyphomandra betacea*

tamarind see *Tamarindus indica*

Tamarindus (Caesalpiniaceae)
indica (F)	ELau NBlo SPlb XBlo

Tamarix (Tamaricaceae)
africana	WWin
gallica	CSBt EBee ENot NWea SAPC SArc WSHC
§ *parviflora*	EMil LRHS MGos
pentandra	see *T. ramosissima*
§ *ramosissima*	CTrC CTri EBee EBre ELan EPfP GEil MBar MWhi SEND SMrm SRms SSta WDin WSHC WWeh
- 'Pink Cascade'	CSBt EBee EMil ENot EPfP GKir LRHS MBri MGos MRav NBlu SPer WDin WGwG WStl WWal
- 'Rubra' ♀ H4	CChe CDoC EBee EMil ENot EPfP LRHS MBlu MGos MMHG SLon SPar WDin
- 'Summer Glow'	see *T. ramosissima* 'Rubra'
tetrandra ♀ H4	More than 30 suppliers
- var. *purpurea*	see *T. parviflora*

Tamus (Dioscoreaceae)
communis	CArn MSal

Tanacetum ✿ (Asteraceae)
CC&McK 460	GTou
§ *argenteum*	EBee MRav MTho SLon
- subsp. *canum*	EWes LRHS MAsh
§ *balsamita*	CArn CCge COld CPrp EBee ELan ELau EOHP GPoy MBri MHer

	MSal SWal WHbs WJek WLHH WPer WSel WWye
§ - subsp. **balsamita**	GPoy MSal SIde
§ - subsp. **balsamitoides**	CBod CPrp ELau GBar GWCH MChe MHer NPri SIde WJek WLHH WWye
- var. **tanacetoides**	see *T. balsamita* subsp. *balsamita*
- **tomentosum**	see *T. balsamita* subsp. *balsamitoides*
capitatum	see *Sphaeromeria capitata*
§ **cinerariifolium**	CArn CBod CPrp EChP EOHP GBar GPoy WPer
§ **coccineum**	GPoy MSal SGar SRms WFTG WFar WWin
- 'Aphrodite' (d)	EBee ECtt
- 'Bees' Jubilee'	ERou
- 'Brenda'	EBee LHop SPoG
- 'Duro'	CFir GBuc WHrl
- 'Eileen May Robinson' ♀ H4	CBcs EBee ECot EHol EMar ENot EPfP MCAu MWgw
- 'Evenglow'	EBee ECtt MCAu MRav MTis
- 'James Kelway' ♀ H4	EBee ECot ECtt EHol EMar EPfP EWll LRHS MBri MCAu MPWC MTis MWrn NBir SRms WHer WRHF
- 'King Size'	NMir WFar
- 'Laurin'	EBee
- 'Robinson's' **new**	CWib
- Robinson's giant-flowered	SRms WMoo
- 'Robinson's Pink'	EBee ELan ENot GKir GMaP LAst MWgw NOrc NPri SRms
- 'Robinson's Red'	CSBt CSam EBee EChP GKir GMaP IBal IHMH LAst LIck MWgw NOrc NPri NVic SRms WWeb
* - **rubrum** **new**	GWCH
- 'Sam Robinson'	WMoo
- 'Snow Cloud'	EBee ELan LRHS MCAu WMnd
§ **corymbosum**	EBee GCal NCat WCot
§ - subsp. **clusii**	EBee
- 'Festtafel'	ECha
densum	ECho EPot WCFE
- subsp. **amani**	EBee ECha EMFP ESis GBar GTou LBee LGro LRHS MHer MWat SEND SPer SRms WCom WLin WWin
§ **haradjanii**	CMea ECtt ELan EMNN EMlt MBro NFor NLAp NLon SBla SChu WEas WHer WSHC
herderi	see *Hippolytia herderi*
huronense	EBee
karelinii JJH 198 **new**	EBee
macrophyllum misapplied	see *Achillea grandifolia*
§ **macrophyllum** (Waldst. & Kit.) Sch.Bip.	EChP ECtt EMon EPPr GCal GKir LPhx WCot WPer
niveum	CArn EBee EOHP MFir MSal WBea WBri WBry WCot
- 'Jackpot'	EBee ENot EWes LRHS MWrn NCat SHar SPoG SSvw WWeb
§ **parthenium**	CAgr CArn CBod CKin CPrp ELau GBar GPoy MBow MChe MHer NCWG NPer SGar SIde SRms WBri WHHs WHer WWye
- 'Aureum'	CBod CHid CPrp CRow ECha ELan ELau GBar GPoy LGro MBow MBri MChe MHer NBlu NCWG SIng SPer SPlb SRms WCot WEas WHHs WHer WPer WWin WWpP
- double white (d)	CSWP GBar GPoy NPer SEND SRms
- 'Golden Ball'	ETow
- 'Golden Moss'	NVic
- 'Malmesbury'	CNat
- 'Minety'	CFox CNat
- 'Plenum' (d)	EHrv

§ - 'Rowallane' (d)	EBee EHol ELan GBuc GMac MAvo MBri MRav SUsu WCot LPVe
- 'Silver Ball'	
- 'Sissinghurst White'	see *T. parthenium* 'Rowallane'
- 'White Bonnet' (d)	EChP ERou WEas
§ **praeteritum**	LPhx
ptarmiciflorum 'Silver Feather'	ECha WJek
vulgare	CArn CBod CKin CPrp CSev EChP ECtt ELau GPoy MBow MChe MHar MHer MSal NSco SGar SIde SPar WMoo WWpP WWye
- var. **crispum**	CPrp EBee ELau EOHP EPla GBar GCal GPoy MBri MHer NCWG NLon NVic SIde WBea WCot WFar WHer WJek WRha WSel
- 'Golden Feather' **new**	EBee EOHP EWes SMad WCot
- 'Isla Gold' (v)	CBos CElw EBee EGle EMon EPPr EWes GCal MHar MMil NBid NSti SMad SUsu WBea WBry WCHb WCot WFar WMoo WRha WWye
- 'Silver Lace' (v)	CElw EChP EMon GBri ITer NCWG NGHP NSti SEND WBea WCHb WFar WHer WMoo

tangelo see *Citrus* X *tangelo*

tangerine see *Citrus reticulata*

tangor see *Citrus* X *nobilis* Tangor Group

Tanakaea (Saxifragaceae)

radicans	WCru

Tapeinochilos (Costaceae)

ananassae	MOak

Taraxacum (Asteraceae)

albidum	EBee
- DJH 452	CHid WCot
officinale sativum	IIve
- white-flowered	ITer
rubrifolium **new**	CSpe

Tarchonanthus (Asteraceae)

camphoratus	CTrC

tarragon see *Artemisia dracunculus*

Tasmannia see *Drimys*

Taxodium (Cupressaceae)

§ **distichum** ♀ H4	More than 30 suppliers
§ - var. **imbricatum**	CFil EPfP WPGP
- - 'Nutans' ♀ H4	CBcs CEnd CTho LCon LRHS MBlu MBri SKee SMad
- 'Secrest'	CBcs LRHS MBlu
mucronatum	CDoC CFil

Taxus ✿ (Taxaceae)

baccata ♀ H4	More than 30 suppliers
- 'Adpressa Aurea' (v)	CKen EPla GKir
- 'Adpressa Variegata' (m/v) ♀ H4	CDoC EHul LCon SLim
- 'Aldenham Gold'	CKen
- 'Amersfoort'	CDoC EOrn EPla LCon MDun WBcn
- 'Argentea Minor'	see *T. baccata* 'Dwarf White'
§ - Aurea Group	ENot SRms
I - 'Aurea Pendula'	EBre EOrn

I	- 'Aureomarginata' (v)	CBcs CSBt EOrn GKir LEar MAsh WStI
	- 'Autumn Shades'	CBcs
	- 'Cavendishii' (f)	ECho
	- 'Compacta'	EOrn EPla
	- 'Corleys Coppertip'	CKen CSam EHul EOrn GKir LCon LLin MAsh MBar MBri MOne SCoo WEve WLRN
	- 'Cristata'	CKen
	- 'David'	IArd NLar
	- 'Dovastoniana' (f) ♀ H4	CMac GKir LCon MBar NLar NWea WMou
	- 'Dovastonii Aurea' (m/v) ♀ H4	CMac EHul EOrn EPfP EPla GKir LBee LCon LPan LRHS MAsh MBar MBlu MBri NLar NWea SCoo SLim WCFE WDin
	- 'Drinkstone Gold' (v)	EHul WBcn
§	- 'Dwarf White' (v)	EOrn EPla LCon SCoo
	- 'Elegantissima' (f/v)	EHul EPfP LCon MTis SPoG
	- 'Erecta' (f)	EHul SHBN
§	- 'Fastigiata' (f) ♀ H4	More than 30 suppliers
	- Fastigiata Aurea Group	CKen CLnd CWib EHul EPfP IArd LAst LBuc LEar LLin LPan MGos NBee NBlu NRar SKee SRms WBrE WFar WHar WLRN
	- 'Fastigiata Aureomarginata' (m/v) ♀ H4	More than 30 suppliers
	- 'Fastigiata Robusta' (f)	EBre EPfP EPla GKir LCon LRHS MBar MBri SPoG WEve WFar WGer
	'Goud Elsje'	CKen EOrn WLRN
	- 'Green Column'	CKen MBlu
	- 'Green Diamond'	CKen WBcn
	- 'Hibernica'	see T. baccata 'Fastigiata'
	'Icicle'	CBcs EPla LCon LLin MGos NLar
	- 'Ivory Tower'	CBcs CKen LCon LLin MGos NLar WGor
	- 'Klitzeklein' **new**	CKen
	- 'Laurie' **new**	SPoG
	- 'Melfard'	CDoC EHul
	- 'Nutans'	CDoC CKen CNic CSBt EHul EOrn IMGH LCon LLin MBar MOne NDlv SCoo WLRN
	- 'Overeynderi'	EHul
	- 'Pendula'	MRav
	- 'Prostrata'	CMac
	- 'Pygmaea'	CKen
	- 'Repandens' (f) ♀ H4	CDoC EHul IArd LCon LPan MBar SHBN WCFE WDin WFar
I	'Repens Aurea' (v) ♀ H4	CDoC CKen CWib EHul EOrn EPfP LCon LLin LRHS MAsh MBar MBri MGos WDin WFar WStI
	- 'Semperaurea' (m) ♀ H4	CBcs CDoC CMac CSli EBre EHul EOrn GKir LBuc LCon LPan LRHS MAsh MBar MBri MGos NBee NWea SLim SPla WCFE WDin WFar
	- 'Silver Spire' (v)	CKen WBcn
	- 'Standishii' (f) ♀ H4	More than 30 suppliers
	- 'Summergold' (v)	CSli EBre EHul ELan ENot EPfP GKir LCon MAsh MBar MGos NBlu NHol SLim WDin WFar WStI
	- 'Washingtonii' (v)	IArd MBar SHBN
	- 'White Icicle' (v)	EOrn WGor
	brevifolia	EPla LCon
	cuspidata 'Aurescens' (v)	CKen EPla LCon SRms
	- var. **nana**	CNic EHul EOrn LCon MBar WWal
	- 'Robusta'	EHul LLin
	- 'Straight Hedge'	CDoC EHul IMGH LCon WGor WLRN
	x **media** 'Brownii'	EHul LBuc
	- 'Hicksii' (f) ♀ H4	EHul GKir IMGH LBuc MBar NWea SLim WFar WLRN

	- 'Hillii'	MBar
	- 'Lodi'	LBee
	- 'Viridis'	MGos

tayberry see *Rubus* Tayberry Group

Tecoma (Bignoniaceae)

	x **alata**	SOWG
	capensis ♀ H1	CHEx CPIN CSev CTCP EBak EShb LRHS SHFr SOWG SYvo
	- 'Aurea'	CSev SOWG
	- 'Lutea'	LRHS WMul
	'Orange Glow'	SOWG
	ricasoliana	see *Podranea ricasoliana*
	stans	SOWG

Tecomanthe (Bignoniaceae)

	dendrophila	CPIN
	speciosa	CPIN ECou SOWG

Tecomaria see *Tecoma*

Tecophilaea (Tecophilaeaceae)

	cyanocrocus ♀ H2	CAvo CBro EHyt EPot ETub GCrs LAma LRHS SBla SOkd WCom WCot
	- 'Leichtlinii' ♀ H2	CAvo CBro EHyt EPot ETub LAma LRHS SSpi
	- 'Purpurea'	see *T. cyanocrocus* 'Violacea'
	- Storm Cloud Group	GCrs
§	- 'Violacea'	CAvo CBro EHyt EPot GCrs LRHS
	violiflora	LAma

Tectaria (Dryopteridaceae)

	gemmifera	GQui NMar

Telanthophora (Asteraceae)

	grandifolia	CHEx SAPC SArc

Telekia (Asteraceae)

§	**speciosa**	More than 30 suppliers

Telesonix see *Boykinia*

Teline see *Genista*

Tellima (Saxifragaceae)

	grandiflora	More than 30 suppliers
	- 'Delphine' (v)	EPPr SAga SUsu WCot
	- 'Forest Frost'	EBee EMan NCat NGdn NLar NStI WCot WGor
	- Odorata Group	CBrc EChP ECha EGoo MRav NCat NStI WGwG WHrl WWal WWpP WWye
	- 'Purpurea'	see *T. grandiflora* Rubra Group
	- 'Purpurteppich'	EBee EBre ECha EGoo EHrv EMan EPPr GAbr GKir LHop LPio LRHS MLwd MRav MUlv NDov NGdn SChu WCot WElm WMnd WMoo WTMC
§	- Rubra Group	More than 30 suppliers

Telopea (Proteaceae)

	'Burgundy' **new**	CTrC
	oreades	CTrC
	speciosissima	CTrC SOWG SPlb SSpi
	truncata	CDoC CFil GGar ISea SSpi WPGP

Templetonia (Papilionaceae)

	retusa	ECou

Temu see *Blepharocalyx*

Tephroseris (Asteraceae)
   integrifolia — EBee WHer

Tephrosia (Papilionaceae)
   grandiflora new — GFai

Terminalia (Combretaceae)
   catappa (F) — NBlo XBlo

Ternstroemia (Theaceae)
   gymnanthera — see *T. japonica*
§   **japonica** — EPfP

Tetracentron (Tetracentraceae)
   sinense — CFil CMCN EPfP GQui IArd

Tetradenia (Lamiaceae)
   riparia new — EShb

Tetradium (Rutaceae)
§   **daniellii** — CFil CMCN EPfP GKir SSpi WPGP
§   - Hupehense Group — CBcs CMCN CPle EBee GKir MBri SSpi WDin
    glabrifolium — CFil EBee
    - B&SWJ 3541 — WCru
    - B&SWJ 6882 — WPGP
I   **velutinum** — CMCN

Tetragonolobus see *Lotus*

Tetraneuris (Asteraceae)
   brandegeei — WLin
§   **scaposa** — EPot LRHS

Tetrapanax (Araliaceae)
   CC 1925 **new** — CPLG
§   **papyrifer** ♀ H2-3 — CHEx CKob SAPC SArc
    - B&SWJ 7135 — WCru

Tetrapathaea see *Passiflora*

Tetrastigma (Vitaceae)
   voinierianum ♀ H1 — CPIN ESlt MBri SAPC SArc

Tetratheca (Tremandraceae)
   ciliata var. **alba** — SOWG
   thymifolia — ECou
    - pink-flowered **new** — SOWG

Teucrium (Lamiaceae)
*   **ackermannii** — CLyd EGoo LBee LRHS MBro NMen SBla SMac WAbe WHoo WPat
   aroanium — CLyd CMea EGle EPot LRHS MWat NMen NWCA SBla
   asiaticum — EGoo
   bicolor — CPle IFro WWye
   botrys — EGoo MHer MSal
   canadense — Ilve MSal
   chamaedrys hort. — see *T. x lucidrys*
   chamaedrys L. — CHal CPom CPrp CSam CWib EGoo EPot ESis GAbr LRHS NGHP NWCA SLim SRms STre SVen WCer WHbs WJek WSel WWeb
    - 'Nanum' — CLyd MBro WPat WWye
I   - 'Rose' **new** — NBlu
    - 'Rose Carpet' — CMGP EGoo EOrc WCom
    - subsp. **tauricola** — IDac
    - 'Variegatum' (v) — EGoo EMan GBar LLWP WCHb WCom WCot WPer WRha

§   **creticum** — WLin
   flavum — EChP WCHb WJek WPGP
    - subsp. **grandiflorum new** — WFTG
   fruticans — More than 30 suppliers
    - 'Azureum' ♀ H3 — CBcs CBot CHar CM&M CPle CWSG EBee LRHS MBro SBra SIgm SLim SPar SPer WBod WEas
    - 'Collingwood Ingram' — EBee
    - 'Compactum' — CDoC EBee EMan ENot ESis LRHS SLon SPer SPla WAbe
    - dark — SMrm
   hircanicum — More than 30 suppliers
    - 'Purple Tails' **new** — WGwG WHHs
§   x **lucidrys** — CArn CChe CMea CSev EChP ECha EGoo ELan ELau EPfP ERea GPoy LAst LPVe MChe MHer MRav MTis MWgw NGHP NPPs SGar SHFr SIde SPar SPer WEas WHHs WHoo WWin
   marum — CArn EOHP MSal NMen SBla SIgm WJek
   'Massif Central' — LRHS WWeb
   massiliense hort. — see *T. x lucidrys*
   massiliense L. — EGoo EMan EOrc WHer
   montanum — CMea GBar LPVe SCro
   musimonum — CLyd
   polium — CArn CLyd CPLG CWes ESis MBro MWat SIgm WJek WPat
    - subsp. **aureum** — NWCA SBla
   pyrenaicum — CHal CMea EHyt EMan EPot GCrs GEdr MBro MHer NSla NWCA SBla SIng WPat WWin WWye
   rosmarinifolium — see *T. creticum*
   rotundifolium — EBee
   scordium — CFox CNat
   scorodonia — CAgr CArn CKin COld CSev EGoo ELau GBar GPoy MChe MHer MSal MWrn NMir WHHs WHer WJek WLHH WSel WWye
    - 'Binsted Gold' — EBee EGoo EMan EMon EVFa LDai MHar SCro WAlt
    - 'Crispum' — CRez ELau EMar EOrc GBar MHar MHer MLLN MWat MWgw NBid NBro WBod WBrE WCHb WHoo WKif WMoo WPer WSel
*   - 'Crispum Aureomarginatum' — EBee
    - 'Crispum Marginatum' (v) — More than 30 suppliers
    - 'Winterdown' (v) — CMea EBee EGoo EMan EPPr EVFa LHop MBro SAga WCHb WHHs WHer WHil WHoo WLin
   scorodonium 'Pant Gwyn' (v) **new** — CNat
   subspinosum — CLyd CMea CStu LBee LRHS MBro NMen NWCA WHoo WPat
§   **viscidum** 'Lemon and Lime' — EBee ECtt EMan EMon EPPr LHop WCot WFTG WPGP
   webbianum — ECho

Thalia (Marantaceae)
   dealbata — CHEx GCal LEdu MSta SAWi SLon WDyG WMAq WMul WWpP

Thalictrum (Ranunculaceae)
   CC 3691 — ITer
   actaeifolium — EBee
   adiantifolium — see *T. minus* 'Adiantifolium'
   alpinum — EBee NRya
   angustifolium — see *T. lucidum*
   aquilegiifolium — More than 30 suppliers
    - var. **album** — CBos CBot CMil COIW EBee ECGN ECha EFou EGle ELan

		LHop LPhx LRHS MBri MBro
		MCAu MCLN MDun MNrw
		MWgw NBid NCot NPSI NSti SPer
		SPla SSpi WMnd WPer
*	- 'Hybridum'	CHad EBlw WFar WMoo WPer
	- Purple Cloud	see *T. aquilegiifolium*
		'Thundercloud'
	- 'Purpureum'	CSev EBee ECGN LPio MBro MDun
		MTis NLar NPSI SPla WCru WHoo
	- 'Roseum' **new**	WCot
§	- 'Thundercloud' ♀ H4	CFir EBee EBre ECtt EPfP GCal
		GKir LRHS MBri MCLN NLar
		WBrE WCra WWeb
	baicalense	EBee
§	*chelidonii*	EBre GKir
	- B&SWJ 2520	WCru
	clavatum	CDes EBee
	contortum	EBee SDys
	coreanum	see *T. ichangense*
	coriaceum	EBee
	cultratum	EChP
	- HWJCM 367	EBee NLar SSpi STes WCru
	dasycarpum	EBee EMan MLLN NLar
*	*decorum*	EVFa GMac LPio NCat WCru
§	*delavayi* ♀ H4	More than 30 suppliers
	- 'Album'	CRDP CSpe CWCL EBee EBre ECha
		EFou EGle LPhx LPio LRHS
		MBro MTis NOak WHoo WWhi
	- 'Hewitt's Double' (d) ♀ H4	More than 30 suppliers
	diffusiflorum	CDes CRDP GBri NHar SBla
		WSHC
	dioicum **new**	EBee
	dipterocarpum hort.	see *T. delavayi*
	dipterocarpum	CMil
	Franch. ACE 4.878.280	
	'Elin'	CBos CBre CDes CFir CSam CSpe
		EBee EBlw EChP EMan EMar
		ERou EVFa LHop LPhx NBir NCat
		NCot SMrm SOkh WCot WElm
		WPnP WRus
	fargesii **new**	EBee
	fendleri	GBin GBuc
	filamentosum	EMon
	- B&SWJ 777	WCru
	- CDC 185	CBos
*	- var. *tenuifolium*	
	'Heronswood' **new**	WCot
	aff. *finetii* DJHC 473 **new**	CDes
	flavum	EBee EDAr EFou GKir LPhx NBro
		SSpi SWat WBrE
§	- subsp. *glaucum* ♀ H4	More than 30 suppliers
	- 'Illuminator'	CHad CHid CKno CPar CSam
		EBre EGle EPPr EVFa GBri GKir
		LPio LRHS MArl MBri MCAu MMil
		MOne MRav NHol NPri SDes
		SMrm SPlb STes SUsu WCom
		WCot WCra WPnP
	flexuosum	see *T. minus* subsp. *minus*
	foetidum	EBee
	foliolosum B&SWJ 2705	WCru
	- S&SH 382	GBri
§	*ichangense*	EBee GBri GKir SAga
§	*isopyroides*	CPBP CSev EBlw EBre EChP ELan
		EPla EPot GBin GBuc GKir GTou
		LAst LPio LRHS MRav MTis
		MWgw NChi NGdn SLon SMac
		SRot WCot WCru WLRN
	kiusianum	CBos CHea CLyd CMGP ECha
		EDAr EGle EPot ESis EWes GAbr
		GBuc GEdr GMac LPhx LRHS
		MTho NBir NDov NHar NMGW
		NMen SRot WAbe WCom WCot
		WFar WLin WOVN

	- Kew form	SAga SRot
	koreanum	see *T. ichangense*
§	*lucidum*	CPou EBee ELan EMan LPhx
		MRav NLar NSti SHar SMHy
	minus	CAgr CMHG EBee ELan EMan
		EMon GBuc MNrw NOak NSti
		WPat WWye
§	- 'Adiantifolium'	EBee LPio LRHS MRav MWgw
		NChi NFla NOak SRms WFar
		WOut WPer
§	- subsp. *minus*	EBee
§	- subsp. *olympicum*	WPer
	- subsp. *saxatile*	see *T. minus* subsp. *olympicum*
	- var. *sipellatum*	CMil
	B&SWJ 5051 **new**	
	morisonii	EBee
	occidentale JLS 86255	MNrw
	orientale	EHyt SBla WPat
	polycarpum	NHol
	polygamum	see *T. pubescens*
§	*pubescens*	CBos EBee EBre ECha GBri LPhx
		MSal MTed WCot
	punctatum	MDun WCot WPnP
	- B&SWJ 1272	EMan GBin LPhx STes WCru
	reniforme	CFir CMil LPio
	- B&SWJ 2159	EMan
	- B&SWJ 2610	EBee WCru
	rhynchocarpum	CDes
	rochebruneanum	More than 30 suppliers
*	*rugosum*	GBuc
	rutaefolium **new**	EBee
	simplex	LPio NHol
	- var. *brevipes*	WCru
	B&SWJ 4794	
	sparsiflorum	WPrP
	speciosissimum	see *T. flavum* subsp. *glaucum*
	sphaerostachyum	CElw GDea GKir IFro LRHS MBri
		SMrm WGer
	squarrosum	EBee GMac LPio MTed NPPs
	tuberosum	CDes CElw CMea CPne CRDP
		EHyt EPot LPhx MLLN SBla 3Mrm
		WCot WPat
	uchiyamae	EBee EGle GBri NDov
	venulosum	EBee
	virgatum B&SWJ 2964	WCru

Thamnocalamus (Poaceae)

	aristatus	EPfP EPla LJus MHdf
	crassinodus	EPla SDry
	- dwarf	EPla
	- 'Kew Beauty'	EFul EPfP EPla ERod LJus
		MBrN MHdf MMoz SDry WJun
		WPGP
	- 'Lang Tang'	EFul EPla ERod WJun WPGP
	- 'Merlyn'	CHEx EPla ERod MMoz SDry
		WJun WPGP
	falcatus	see *Drepanostachyum falcatum*
	falconeri	see *Himalayacalamus falconeri*
	funghomii	see *Schizostachyum funghomii*
	khasianus	see *Drepanostachyum*
		khasianum
	maling	see *Yushania maling*
	spathaceus hort.	see *Fargesia murielae*
§	*spathiflorus*	CFil EFul EPla MHdf SDry WJun
	- subsp. *nepalensis*	EPla
§	*tessellatus*	CAbb EFul EPla LJus MMoz SDix
		SDry WJun

Thamnochortus (Restionaceae)

	cinereus	CBig CTrC
	insignis	CBig CCtw CTrC WNor WPrP
	lucens	CAbb CTrC
	spicigerus	CBig

Thapsia (Apiaceae)
decipiens	see *Melanoselinum decipiens*
garganica	CArn EBee EMan SIgm
maxima	SIgm
villosa	SIgm

Thea see *Camellia*

Thelypteris (Thelypteridaceae)
kunthii **new**	WRic
limbosperma	see *Oreopteris limbosperma*
palustris	CPLG EBee EBlw EFer EMon LEur MLan NHol NWoo SRms WFib WRic
phegopteris	see *Phegopteris connectilis*

Themeda (Poaceae)
japonica	CBrm EHoe EPPr GIBF SRGP
triandra	see *T. japonica*

Thermopsis (Papilionaceae)
caroliniana	see *T. villosa*
fabacea	see *T. lupinoides*
lanceolata	CHad CTri EBee ECGP EChP EMan GBin LRHS MBri MCAu MCLN MLLN MMil MTis NPri NSti SAga SMrm SOkh WAul WFar WPer WViv WWye
§ *lupinoides*	CPne EBee ECGP ECha EHrv EVFa EWTr GLil MWrn NOrc SMac SUsu WCot WCru WFar WPer
mollis	EBee NBid
montana	see *T. rhombifolia* var. *montana*
§ *rhombifolia* var. *montana*	CRDP EBee EFou ELan EPfP LHop MNrw NOrc NSti SGar SPer WAbb WBVN WGwG WLRN WPer WRus WWal
§ *villosa*	CPLG EBee EMan GIBF MLLN MRav MSte NDov NLar SBla SDix SPer WCom WCot WPGP WRus

Thevetia (Apocynaceae)
peruviana	LRHS MSal SOWG

Thladiantha (Cucurbitaceae)
dubia	CPIN SDix

Thlaspi (Brassicaceae)
alpinum	EPot MWat NJOw
bellidifolium	NBir
biebersteinii	see *Pachyphragma macrophyllum*
bulbosum	GEdr GTou
§ *cepaeifolium*	
subsp. *rotundifolium*	GTou NMen WBri
fendleri	MNrw
rotundifolium	see *T. cepaeifolium* subsp. *rotundifolium*

Thuja ✿ (Cupressaceae)
'Extra Gold'	see *T. plicata* 'Irish Gold'
§ *koraiensis*	IDee LCon MBar WCwm
occidentalis	LCon LLin SLim
'Amber Glow' **new**	
– Aurea Group	MBar
– 'Aureospicata'	EHul
– 'Autumn Glow'	WWeb
– 'Beaufort' (v)	CKen EHul LLin MBar
– 'Brabant'	LNet
– 'Caespitosa'	CKen CNic CSli LLin LRHS MOne NHol NLar SPoG WEve WGor
– 'Cristata Aurea'	CKen

– 'Danica' ♀ H4	CMac CSli EBre EHul ENot EOrn GKir LCon LLin MAsh MBar MGos NWea SBod SLim SMer SRms WCFE WEve WFar WStI WWeb
– 'Dicksonii'	EHul
– 'Douglasii Aurea' (v)	CKen
– 'Ellwangeriana Aurea'	MGos
– Emerald	see *T. occidentalis* 'Smaragd'
– 'Ericoides'	CDoC CTri EHul LRHS MBar SRms
– 'Europa Gold'	CDoC EHul GKir LBee MAsh MBar MGos SLim WLRN
– 'Fastigiata'	CDul MBar
– 'Filiformis'	CKen EPla
– 'Globosa'	CMac MBar SBod WGor
I – 'Globosa Variegata' (v)	CKen MBar WEve
– 'Gold Drop'	CKen
– 'Golden Globe'	CDoC CSli EHul ENot EOrn LLin LNet LPan MBar MGos NBlu SBod SCoo SLim SPla WDin WLRN
– 'Golden Minaret'	EHul
– 'Hetz Midget'	CKen EHul EOrn EPfP IMGH LLin MBar MOne NHol SCoo SLim SMer SPoG WDin WFar WLRN
– 'Holmstrup' ♀ H4	CDoC CMac CSBt CSli CWib EBre EHul ENot EOrn GKir LLin LRHS MAsh MBar NBee SLim SRms WCFE WDin WEve WFar WStI WTel WWeb
– 'Holmstrup's Yellow'	CDoC CKen EHul GKir LCon SCoo WCFE WEve WWeb
– 'Hoveyi'	CMac CTri EHul
– 'Linesville'	CKen
– 'Little Champion'	EHul
– 'Little Gem'	EHul GKir MGos NHol NPro SRms WDin WGor
– 'Lutea Nana' ♀ H4	CMac EHul EOrn MBar NDlv WCFE
– 'Malonyana'	LCon WCwm
– 'Marrisen's Sulphur'	CSli EHul EOrn SLim SPla WBcn WLRN
– 'Meineke's Zwerg' (v)	CKen
– 'Miky'	CKen WBcn
– 'Ohlendorffii'	CDoC CKen EHul EOrn LCon LLin MBar NHol
– 'Orientalis Semperaurescens'	see *Platycladus orientalis* 'Semperaurea'
I – 'Pumila Sudworth'	NHol
I – 'Pygmaea'	CKen MBar SLon
– 'Pyramidalis Aurea' **new**	ENot
– 'Pyramidalis Compacta'	EHul LNet WGor
– 'Recurva Nana'	EHul MBar NHol
– 'Rheingold' ♀ H4	More than 30 suppliers
§ – 'Smaragd' ♀ H4	CDoC CSBt CSli CWib EBre EHul ENot EOrn EPfP GKir LBuc LCon LLin LNet LPan LRHS MAsh MBar MGos NBlu SBod SPer SPla WCFE WEve WFar WOrn WStI
* – 'Smaragd Variegated' (v)	CKen
– 'Southport'	CKen MBri WEve
– 'Spaethii'	EHul EOrn
– 'Spiralis'	EHul IMGH MBar NLar WCFE
§ – 'Stolwijk' (v)	EHul EOrn LLin MBar MGos SLim WBcn WWeb
– 'Sunkist'	CKen CMac CSBt CSli CWib EBre EHul ENot EOrn GKir LNet LPan MAsh MBar MGos NHol SBod SLim SMer SPla SRPl WEve WFar WWeb
– 'Suzie'	LLin
– 'Teddy'	LCon LLin MAsh SLim WEve WFar
– 'Tiny Tim'	CDoC CMac CSBt CSli CWib EHul ENot ESis IMGH LCon LLin MAsh MBar MGos MOne WEve WGor WLRN WWeb

- 'Trompenburg'	CDoC ECho EHul EOrn MAsh WBcn
- 'Wansdyke Silver' (v)	CMac CSli EHul EOrn LCon MBar SLim SPla
- 'Wareana'	CMac
- 'Wareana Aurea'	see *T. occidentalis* 'Wareana Lutescens'
§ - 'Wareana Lutescens'	CSBt CWib EHul EOrn MBar WEve
- 'Woodwardii'	EHul MBar MOne SMer
- 'Yellow Ribbon'	CSBt CSli EBre EHul GKir LBee LCon LNet LRHS MBar SLim SMer SPla
orientalis	see *Platycladus orientalis*
plicata	CDul EHul GIBF LHyr MBar MGos NWea SLim SPer WDin WMou
- 'Atrovirens' ♀ H4	CTri EBre ENot GKir LBee LBuc LCon LPan LRHS MAsh MBar MBri MGos NBee NBlu SLim SMer SRPl SRms WDin WHar WWeb
* - 'Atrovirens Aurea'	WBcn
- 'Aurea' ♀ H4	EHul LBee LRHS MAsh SLim SRms
- 'Brooks Gold' **new**	CKen
- 'Can-can' (v)	GKir LCon
I - 'Cole's Variety'	CWib MBar SLim
- 'Collyer's Gold'	CBrm EHul SRms
- 'Copper Kettle'	CBrm CKen CNic CSli EGra EHul ENot GKir LCon MAsh MBar MBri NDlv NPro SCoo SLim WEve WGor WLRN
- 'Cuprea'	CKen EHul MBar
- 'Doone Valley'	CKen CSli EHul EOrn MBar NDlv NHol
'Fastigiata' ♀ H4	CMac LRHS WTel
- 'Gelderland'	EHul SCoo WEve
- 'Gracilis Aurea'	ECho EHul WBcn
- 'Grüne Kugel'	CDoC
- 'Hillieri'	MBar
§ - 'Irish Gold' (v) ♀ H4	CABP CMac EPla LCon LLin LRHS NPro SAga WBcn
- 'Rogersii'	CDoC CKen CMac CSli CTri EBre EHul EOrn EPfP GKir LCon LLin LRHS MAsh MBar MGos NBee NHol SLim SRms WTel
- 'Stolwijk's Gold'	see *T. occidentalis* 'Stolwijk'
- 'Stoneham Gold' ♀ H4	CDoC CKen CMac EBre EHul EOrn GKir LBee LCon LLin LRHS MAsh MBar MBri MGos NBee SBod SLim SMer SPer SRms WCFE WEve WTel
- 'Sunshine'	CKen
♣ - 'Windsor Gold'	EHul
- 'Winter Pink' (v)	CKen NLar
- 'Zebrina' (v)	CBcs CBrm CDoC CDul CMac CSBt CSli CWib EHul EOrn GKir LCon LLin MAsh MBar MGos MWat NBee NEgg NWea SLim SPer SRPl WCFE WDin WEve WFar WHar WTel WWin
- x *standishii*	WCwm
standishii	WCwm

Thujopsis (*Cupressaceae*)

dolabrata ♀ H4	CBcs CTho CTrG EHul GKir LBee MBar MMHG NDlv NEgg NLar NWea SHBN SPer WBrE WDin WFar
- 'Aurea' (v)	CDoC CKen EHul EOrn LCon LLin MBar MGos NLar SCoo SHBN SLim
- 'Laetevirens'	see *T. dolabrata* 'Nana'
§ - 'Nana'	CDoC CKen CMac EGra EHul EOrn IArd LCon LLin MBar SCoo SLim SRms STre WFar
- 'Variegata' (v)	CDoC CDul EHul EOrn LCon LLin MBar NDlv SCoo SHFr SLim SPoG WDin WEve WLRN
koraiensis	see *Thuja koraiensis*

Thunbergia (*Acanthaceae*)

alata	CPlN MBri SYvo
coccinea	CPlN LRHS
erecta	CKob CPlN ELan ERea ESlt LRHS SOWG
fragrans	CPlN ERea LRHS
grandiflora ♀ H1	CHll CPlN ELan EPfP ERea ESlt LRHS SOWG WMul
- 'Alba' ♀ H1+3	CHll CPlN WMul
gregorii ♀ H1+3	CHll CPlN CSpe LRHS SOWG
- 'Sun Lady' **new**	CSpe
laurifolia	CPlN
'Molly'	CPlN
mysorensis ♀ H1	CPlN ERea LRHS SOWG WMul
natalensis	CSpe
'Samantha' **new**	CSpe

thyme, caraway see *Thymus herba-barona*

thyme, garden see *T. vulgaris*

thyme, lemon see *T. x citriodorus*

thyme, wild see *T. serpyllum*

Thymus ✿ (*Lamiaceae*)

from Turkey	EWes LLWP SHDw
'Anderson's Gold'	see *T. pulegioides* 'Bertram Anderson'
azoricus	see *T. caespititius*
'Caborn Lilac Gem'	LLWP SHDw
§ **caespititius**	CArn CLyd ELau EPot GBar GDra GPoy LLWP MHer NCWG NMen NRya SPlb SRot WAbe WCHb WPer
caespitosus	GKir LLWP
camphoratus	CArn CBod ELau EOHP EWes GBar LLWP LPhx MHer MWat NCWG NGHP SHDw WAbe WHHs WJek
- 'A Touch of Frost'	SHDw
- 'Derry'	CSpe LLWP SHDw
capitatus new	CArn
carnosus misapplied	see *T. vulgaris* 'Erectus'
carnosus Boiss.	GBar
'Carol Ann' (v)	CBod CPrp ELau EWes GBar LLWP MBNS
cephalotos	EHyt WAbe
ciliatus	CArn CMea CPrp LLWP WPer
cilicicus Boiss. & Bail.	EHyt ETow EWes GBar MChe SBla WAbe WCHb WJek WWye
x *citriodorus*	CArn EDAr ELau GAbr GBar GPoy LGro LHrt LLWP MBow MBrN MChe MHer NBlu NCWG NOak SRms SWal WBrE WFar WHHs WHen WJek WPer WWye
- 'Archer's Gold'	see *T. pulegioides* 'Archer's Gold'
- 'Argenteus' (v)	LLWP MBro
- 'Aureus'	see *T. pulegioides* 'Aureus'
- 'Bertram Anderson'	see *T. pulegioides* 'Bertram Anderson'
§ - 'Golden King' (v)	CLyd EBre ECha EDAr ELan GBar LHop LLWP LRHS MBar MBri MBro MChe MHer NCWG NSti SPar WCHb WHoo WLin WPer WSel WStI

§ – 'Golden Lemon' (v) — CArn GPoy LLWP WJek WWpP WWye
  – 'Golden Lemon' misapplied — see *T. pulegioides* 'Aureus'
  – 'Golden Queen' (v) — CMea COlW EDAr EOHP EPot ESis GBar LBBr MBow MHer NBlu NPri SPar SPet SRms WWin
  – 'Lemon Supreme' **new** — LLWP
  – 'Lime' — LLWP
  – *repandus* — LLWP SIde
  – 'Silver King' (v) — LLWP
  – 'Silver Posie' — see *T. vulgaris* 'Silver Posie'
  – 'Silver Queen' (v) ♀ H4 — CBcs CHar CLyd CSam ECha EDAr ELan EMlt EOHP EWTr GBar GKir LRHS MBar MBro MChe MHer MWgw NBlu NCWG NLon NPPs SGar SPar SPlb WCom WFar WHoo WStI WWpP
* – 'Variegatus' (v) — GBar LHop MBri MChe NBlu WFar WWin
  – 'Variegatus' misapplied — see *T.* x *citriodorus* 'Golden King'
  – 'Villa Nova' (v) — LLWP
  'Coccineus' — see *T.* Coccineus Group
§ Coccineus Group ♀ H4 — More than 30 suppliers
§ – 'Atropurpureus' misapplied — LLWP SHDw
  – 'Hardstoft Red' (v) — GBar LLWP MChe
  – 'Purple Beauty' — LLWP
  – 'Purpurteppich' — LLWP
  – 'Red Elf' — GBar SHDw WJek
  comosus — EDAr GBar LLWP MChe WAbe WEas WPat WPer
  'Creeping Lemon' — ELau GBar LLWP MHer WHHs WJek
  'Creeping Mauve' **new** — LLWP
  'Creeping Orange' — LLWP
  'Dartmoor' — GBar GCal LLWP SIng
  'Desboro' — GBar LLWP MBNS MHer NCWG
  doerfleri — CLyd ECha EOHP LLWP WSel
  – 'Bressingham' — CArn CMea CPrp EBre ECtt EDAr ELau EMNN EMlt GBar GKir LBee LGro LLWP LRHS MBro MChe MHer MWgw NCWG SBla SIng SPlb SRms SWal WHHs WPat WPer WTel WWye
  'Doone Valley' (v) — More than 30 suppliers
  'E.B.Anderson' — see *T. pulegioides* 'Bertram Anderson'
  'Eastgrove Pink' — LLWP SHDw
  'Elf' — NLAp
  'Emma's Pink' — LLWP NCWG
  erectus — see *T. vulgaris* 'Erectus'
* *ericoides* — EPot MHer
  'Fragrantissimus' — CArn ELau EOHP GBar GPoy GWCH LLWP MChe MHer MWat NBlu NCWG NPri SIde SPlb WHHs WHen WJek WPer WWye
  'Hans Stam' **new** — LLWP
  'Hardstoft Red' — see *T.* (Coccineus Group) 'Hardstoft Red'
§ 'Hartington Silver' (v) — More than 30 suppliers
  herba-barona — CArn CNic CPrp CTri ECha EDAr ELau EOHP ESis GBar GDra GPoy LEdu LLWP MBow MHer NCWG NFor NHol NRya SIde SRms STre WHHs WPer WWye
  – 'Bob Flowerdew' — LLWP
  – *citrata* — see *T. herba-barona* 'Lemon-scented'
§ – 'Lemon-scented' — CArn ECha ELau GBar GPoy LLWP MHer MOne NCWG NLon SHDw SIde WCHb

  'Highdown' — SHDw
  'Highland Cream' — see *T.* 'Hartington Silver'
  hirsutus — NBir
  hyemalis — LLWP
  integer — SBla
  'Kurt' **new** — LLWP SHDw
  lanuginosus hort. — see *T. pseudolanuginosus*
§ 'Lavender Sea' — ELau EWes LLWP
  'Lemon Caraway' — see *T. herba-barona* 'Lemon-scented'
* 'Lemon Variegated' (v) — EDAr ELau GBar WHHs
  leucotrichus — MBro WCom WPat
  'Lilac Time' — EWes GBar LLWP MHer SHDw SPlb WCHb WHHs WJek
  longicaulis — CArn CLyd ECha EGoo ELau GBar LLWP MBNS NCWG WJek WWye
  longiflorus — IIve
  marschallianus — see *T. pannonicus*
  mastichina — CArn CMea GBar MChe SBla SChu WHHs WWye
  – 'Didi' — CArn LLWP MHer NCWG
  membranaceus — CLyd WAbe
  micans — see *T. caespititius*
  minus — see *Calamintha nepeta*
  montanus Waldst. & Kit. — see *T. pulegioides*
  neiceffii — CArn CLyd ECha ELau GBar LLWP NCWG NMen NWCA WWpP
* *nummularius* — ELau
  odoratissimus — see *T. pallasianus* subsp. *pallasianus*
  'Onyx' — NCWG
  'Orange Spice' **new** — LLWP SHDw
  pallasianus — ELau LLWP SHDw
§ – subsp. *pallasianus* — CBod GBar MHer
§ *pannonicus* — LLWP MHer NCWG WPer
  'Peter Davis' — CArn CBod EDAr EOHP ESis GBar LHop LLWP MBNS MBow MChe MHer NBir NCWG NLAp SBla SChu SIde WJek WLin WRHF
§ 'Pink Ripple' — CBod ELau EWes GBar LLWP MChe MHer SMHy WCHb WJek
§ *polytrichus* — CKin EEls EPot GPoy LLWP NSti
  subsp. *britannicus* — SPlb WJek WPer
  – – 'Minor' — EPot LLWP MHer SIde WPer
§ – – 'Thomas's White' ♀ H4 — LLWP MHer
  – – variegated (v) — WLin
  'Porlock' — CMea CSev EDAr ELau ESis GBar GPoy LLWP MChe MHer NCWG NRya SIde SRms STre WHoo WJek WLin WPer WWpP
  praecox — GBar LGro LLWP MHer NLan NSco WWol
  – subsp. *arcticus* — see *T. polytrichus* subsp. *britannicus*
  'Provence' — LLWP
§ *pseudolanuginosus* — More than 30 suppliers
  – 'Hall's Variety' — CHal ELau GBar
  – 'Mountain Select' — LLWP
§ *pulegioides* — CArn CBod CPrp ELau GBar GPoy LLWP MBow MBri MHer NBlu NCWG NPri NRya SHDw SIde WHHs WJek WPer WWpP WWye
§ – 'Archer's Gold' — More than 30 suppliers
§ – 'Aureus' ♀ H4 — EBre EDAr EMNN EMlt EWTr GBar GKir GTou LLWP LRHS MBar MBow MBri MBro MHer NBlu NWCA SBla SRms WFar WHen WHoo
§ – 'Bertram Anderson' ♀ H4 — More than 30 suppliers
  – 'Foxley' (v) — CBod CPrp EHoe ELau LLWP MChe NPro SHDw SPlb WCHb WJek WWpP

- 'Golden Dwarf'	LLWP	
§ - 'Goldentime'	GBar GKir LGro LLWP LRHS MChe SWal WJek WSel	
- 'Sir John Lawes'	LLWP SHDw	
- 'Tabor'	WJek	
- variegated	GBar	
'Redstart'	CBod CLyd ECha ELau EOHP EPot GBar LBee LLWP LRHS MChe NBlu MBow WCHb	
richardii subsp. *nitidus*	MHer STre WWye	
- subsp. *nitidus* 'Compactus Albus'	see *T. vulgaris* 'Snow White'	
'Rosalicht' **new**	LLWP	
'Rosedrift'	LLWP SHDw	
rotundifolius	ELau LLWP MHer SHDw	
§ 'Ruby Glow'	EBre ECGP ELau EWes LLWP MChe MRav NCWG SHDw WJek	
serpyllum	CArn ELau GKir LLWP MBri MChe NBlu NOak SIde SIng SPet SPlb SRms WBVN WJek WPer WWpP	
- var. *albus*	CHal ECha ELau EMNN ESis GDra GKir GPoy GTou LLWP MBow MBro NVic SBla SChu SIde SRms SWal WHHs WHoo WWye	
- 'Albus Variegatus'	see *T.* 'Hartington Silver'	
N - 'Annie Hall'	CHal EBre EDAr ELau EMNN EPot GBar LBee LGro LLWP LRHS MBow MChe MHer NCWG NFor SIde WHHs WPer WWye	
- 'Atropurpureus'	see *T.* (Coccineus Group) 'Atropurpureus'	
- 'Barwinnock Snowdrift' (v) **new**	GBar	
N - *coccineus* 'Major'	CMea EDAr GDra GKir LRHS MHer SIde WAbe WCom WJek	
N - - 'Minor'	CPrp EBre EDAr ELau GKir GTou LLWP MChe MHer SGar SRms WHHs WLin	
'Conwy Rose' **new**	WAbe	
N - 'East Lodge'	LLWP WWpP	
N - 'Elfin'	CArn CLyd EDAr EHyt EPot ESis EWes GTou LBee LRHS MBri MBro MHer SBla SIng SPlb WAbe WBea	
N - 'Flossy'	LLWP	
N - 'Fulney Red'	EWes LLWP	
N - 'Goldstream' (v)	CLyd CMea ELau EMNN ESis GBar LHop LLWP LRHS MBar MBri MChe MHer NGHP NRya NSti SPlb SRms WCHb WHHs WPer	
N - 'Iden'	SIde	
- subsp. *lanuginosus*	see *T. pseudolanuginosus*	
- 'Lavender Sea'	see *T.* 'Lavender Sea'	
N - 'Lemon Curd'	CBod CBrm CPrp ELau EOHP GBar LLWP MChe MHer NSti SHDw SIde SPlb WCHb WJek WRha WSel WWye	
N - 'Minimus'	CArn CBrm CHal CLyd ECha ELau EMlt ESis GBar LLWP LRHS MBow MBri MChe MHer NLap NSti SIde SPet SPlb SRot WBVN WCHb WHHs WHoo WPat WPer WRHF WSel WWye	
N - 'Minor'	CArn EMNN GBar GDra GWCH LBee MBro MChe NHol NMen NSla SBla WAbe WCom WLin WWin	
N - 'Minor Albus'	GBar	
- 'Minus'	see *T. serpyllum* 'Minor'	
N - 'Petite'	EOHP EWes LLWP	
N - 'Pink Chintz' ♀ H4	More than 30 suppliers	
- 'Pink Ripple'	see *T.* 'Pink Ripple'	
- subsp. *pulchellus*	LLWP	
- 'Purple Beauty'	see *Thymus* (Coccineus Group) 'Purple Beauty'	
- 'Purpurteppich'	see *Thymus* (Coccineus Group) 'Purpurteppich'	
N - 'Rainbow Falls' (v)	CBod GBar LLWP MBow MChe MHer NCWG NHol SHDw WBry WHHs	
- 'Red Elf'	see *Thymus* (Coccineus Group) 'Red Elf'	
N - 'Roseus'	EOHP GBar SIde	
N - 'Ruby Glow'	see *T.* 'Ruby Glow'	
N - 'Russetings'	CHal CLyd ECtt EDAr ELau EMNN EPot GBar LLWP MBar MChe MHer NCWG NHol NMen SIde SRms WWin WWpP WWye	
N - 'September'	LLWP MHer	
N - 'Snowdrift'	CArn CMea EDAr ELau EPot GBar LEdu MBar MBro MChe MHer NCWG NHol NRya NSti SIde SPlb WAbe WJek WPat WPer WRHF WWpP	
N - 'Splendens'	GMaP LLWP	
- 'Variegatus'	see *T.* 'Hartington Silver'	
N - 'Vey'	EWes GBar GMaP LLWP MChe MHer NCWG SHDw SIng WCHb	
sibthorpii	CArn	
N 'Silver Posie'	see *T. vulgaris* 'Silver Posie'	
* *taeniensis*	CArn	
* *valesiacus*	LLWP SHDw	
vulgaris	CAgr CArn CSam CSev ECha EDAr ELau GPoy LLWP MBar MBow MBri MChe MHer NBlu NCWG NVic SDix SPlb SWal WHHs WJek WPer	
- *albus*	GBar LLWP NCWG WHen	
- 'Aureus' hort.	see *T. pulegioides* 'Goldentime'	
* - 'Compactus'	LLWP	
- 'Diamantis' **new**	LLWP	
- 'Dorcas White'	LLWP WPer	
- 'English Winter'	GBar	
§ - 'Erectus'	CArn CLyd ETow GBar LLWP MHer WEas WPer WWyc	
- French	ELau LLWP SHDw SPlb	
- 'French Summer'	SIde	
- 'German Winter'	CArn	
- 'Golden Pins'	CArn GBar	
- 'Lemon Queen'	ELau	
- 'Lucy'	CPrp EOHP GBar LLWP	
- 'Pinewood'	GPoy LLWP MHer	
- pink	LLWP	
- 'Silver Pearl' (v)	LLWP	
§ - 'Silver Posie'	More than 30 suppliers	
§ - 'Snow White'	ELau EWes LLWP SHDw SWal WJek	
- 'Widecombe' (v)	LLWP SHDw	
zygis	CArn	

Tiarella (*Saxifragaceae*)

'April Rose'	NCat
'Black Snowflake' **new**	SHar
'Black Velvet'	EBee LIck SRot
collina	see *T. wherryi*
cordifolia ♀ H4	More than 30 suppliers
- 'Eco Red Heart'	SSpi
- 'Glossy'	EBee GBuc GKir SSpi WPGP
- 'Oakleaf'	CDes CLAP EBee EChP EMan EWTr GCal NBro NSti SOkh STcs WPnP
- 'Rosalie'	see x *Heucherella alba* 'Rosalie'
- 'Running Tapestry'	CLAP WMoo WPnP WPrP
- 'Slick Rock'	EBee ECha EPPr

'Cygnet'	CLAP EBee EMan SHar SRot WFar WMoo WPnP
'Dark Eyes'	NCat
'Dark Star'	ECtt EFou
'Dunvegan'	EBee SMad SSvw WMoo
'Elizabeth Oliver'	CDes CLAP WPnP WPrP
'Freckles'	MRav
'Heronswood Mist' (v) **new**	EBee NSti
'Inkblot'	CWes EBee EChP NBro SHar SYvo WFar WMoo WPnP
'Iron Butterfly'	CCol CHar CHea CLAP CWes EBee EFou EMan GBin LBBr NBro NPPs SHar SRot WBor WMoo
'Jeepers Creepers' **new**	MAvo SHar
* 'Laciniate Runner'	CLAP
'Martha Oliver'	CDes CLAP CPom CRez EBee GBuc WHal WPGP WPrP WTin
'Martha Roderick' **new**	CMea
'Mint Chocolate'	More than 30 suppliers
'Neon Lights'	NGdn SHar
§ 'Ninja'	More than 30 suppliers
'Petite Pink Bouquet' **new**	SOkh
'Pink Bouquet'	CLAP EBee EHoe EMan MLLN MSph SDes WFTG WFar WMoo
'Pink Skyrocket' **new**	SHar
'Pinwheel'	EBee ECha MRav NCat WTMC
polyphylla	EPPr EPar GAbr GBin LGro MLLN MRav MWod MWrn NOrc SMac WBea WCru WFar WMoo WPnP
- 'Filigran'	NLar
- 'Moorgrün'	GCal WFar
- pink	CLAP EHrv EPPr EPar EVFa
'Skeleton Key'	CLAP WCot
'Spring Symphony'	CCol CHar CLAP EBee GBin LIck NBir SHar WFar WMoo
'Starfish' **new**	SHar
'Tiger Stripe'	CHid CLAP COtt EBee ECha EMan ENot EPfP LRHS MRav NBro SPer SSvw WFar WMoo WPnP
trifoliata	ELan MRav NVic SBla WFar
unifoliata	CMCo MSal
§ *wherryi* ♀ H4	More than 30 suppliers
- 'Bronze Beauty'	More than 30 suppliers
- 'Green Velvet'	ECha
- 'Montrose'	CLAP EBee EVFa WPGP
- 'Skid's Variegated' (v)	CBct EBee EMan EVFa LBuc MAvo MSph WCot WMoo

Tibouchina (Melastomataceae)

graveolens	ERea
* *holosericea* 'Elsa'	ERea
'Jules'	ERea ESlt
organensis	CBcs CKno ERea GQui
paratropica	CPle CRHN SSpi
semidecandra hort.	see *T. urvilleana*
§ *urvilleana* ♀ H1	CBcs CDoC CHEx CKno CPLG CRHN CSpe CTbh EBak EBee EBot ECre ELan ERea ESlt ISea LPan LRHS MTis SAPC SArc SLon SOWG SPer SRms SYvo WMul
- 'Edwardsii'	CSev EMan MLan NPSI SUsu
- variegated (v) **new**	WCot

Tigridia ✿ (Iridaceae)

hybrids	SDeJ
lutea	SDeJ
multiflora	CFir
pavonia	CMdw CPLG CSpe EBot EDif EMui ERea LAma MBri NRog
- 'Aurea'	CFwr EBee
- 'Speciosa' **new**	CFwr EBee

Tilia ✿ (Tiliaceae)

americana	CDul CLnd CMCN EBee ENot NWea
- 'Dentata'	CDul
- 'Nova'	CDoC CTho
- 'Redmond'	CTho
amurensis	CMCN GIBF WMou
argentea	see *T. tomentosa*
begoniifolia	see *T. dasystyla*
'Blue Star' **new**	ENot
'Chelsea Sentinel'	CDul
chenmoui	MBlu WMou
chinensis	CMCN
chingiana	CDul CMCN GKir MBlu SBir SKee
cordata ♀ H4	CCVT CDul CKin CLnd CSBt CWib EBee ECrN ELan ENot EPfP GKir IMGH LBuc LHyr LPan NBee NWea SHBN SKee SPer WDin WMou WStI
§ - 'Böhlje'	CDul SLPl WMoo
- 'Dainty Leaf'	CDul
- 'Erecta'	see *T. cordata* 'Böhlje'
- 'Greenspire' ♀ H4	CDoC CDul CLnd CTho EBee ECrN ENot LPan LRHS NBee WMou
- 'Lico'	WMou
- 'Morden'	WMou
- 'Plymtree Gold'	CEnd CTho
- 'Swedish Upright'	CLnd CTho
- 'Winter Orange'	CDul CRez LRHS MBlu SBir SKee WMou
§ *dasystyla*	CLnd CMCN
x *euchlora* ♀ H4	CCVT CDoC CDul CLnd CMCN EBee ECrN ENot EPfP GKir LPan MBri MGos MWat NBee NWea SPer SSta WDin WFar WMou WOrn
x *europaea*	CDul CLnd ELan NWea WMou
- 'Pallida'	CDul CLnd CTho EBee SKee WMou
- 'Wratislaviensis' ♀ H4	CDoC CDul CLnd CTho EPfP MBlu NWea SMad WMou
x *flavescens* 'Glenleven'	CDul
'Hanwell' **new**	ENot
henryana	CDoC CDul CEnd CMCN CTho EBee EPfP ERod GKir LRHS MBlu SBir SMad WDin WMou WPGP
- var. *subglabra*	WMou
§ *heterophylla*	CMCN CTho
- var. *michauxii*	CLnd
insularis	CDul CMCN MBlu WMou
japonica	CDul CMCN WMou
kiusiana	CMCN GKir WMou
mandshurica	CMCN
maximowicziana	CDul SSta WPGP
mexicana	WMou
miqueliana	CMCN WMou
'Moltkei'	CLnd CMCN WPGP
mongolica	CDoC CDul CLnd CMCN CTho EBee ENot EPfP GKir WMou
monticola	see *T. heterophylla*
oliveri	CDul CMCN GKir MBlu NWea SBir SKee WMou WPGP
'Orbicularis'	WMou
'Palace Garden' **new**	ENot
paucicostata	CMCN
'Petiolaris' ♀ H4	CCVT CDoC CDul CEnd CLnd CMCN EBee ELan ENot EPfP GKir LRHS MBri NWea SHBN SKee SPer SSta WDin WMou
platyphyllos	CCVT CDoC CDul CKin CLnd CMCN CSBt CWib ECrN ENot

		EPfP GKir LBuc NBee NWea SCoo
		SKee SPer WDin WMou
	– 'Aurea'	CDul CTho ECrN MAsh MBlu
		WMou
	– 'Corallina'	see *T. platyphyllos* 'Rubra'
	– 'Erecta'	see *T. platyphyllos* 'Fastigiata'
§	– 'Fastigiata'	CDul CTho EBee ECrN ENot SLPl
	– 'Laciniata'	CDul CEnd CMCN CTho GKir
		WMou
	– 'Orebro'	SLPl
*	– 'Pendula'	CTho
§	– 'Rubra' ♀ H4	CDoC CDul CLnd CTho CWib
		EBee ECrN ENot EPfP GKir LBuc
		LHyr LRHS MBri MGos NBee
		NWea SLPl WDin WFar WMou
	– 'Tortuosa'	CDoC WMou
§	*tomentosa*	CDul CLnd CMCN CTho ECrN
		ELan ENot GKir IMGH NWea
		SEND WDin WMou
	– 'Brabant' ♀ H4	CDoC EBee ENot EPfP LPan NBee
	tuan	CMCN WMou
	x *vulgaris*	see *T.* x *europaea*

Tillaea see *Crassula*

Tillandsia (Bromeliaceae)

	argentea ♀ H1	MBri
	cyanea ♀ H1	LRHS MBri SMur
	usneoides	CHal SHmp

Tipularia (Orchidaceae)

	discolor **new**	CDes

Tithonia (Asteraceae)

	rotundifolia 'Torch'	SMrm

Tofieldia (Melanthiaceae)

	calyculata	NHol
	pusilla	ERos

Tolmiea (Saxifragaceae)

	menziesii	ECha LGro MBNS MBri MGww NHol
		NOrc WBrE WHrl WMoo WWpP
	– 'Goldsplash'	see *T. menziesii* 'Taff's Gold'
	– 'Maculata'	see *T. menziesii* 'Taff's Gold'
§	– 'Taff's Gold' (v) ♀ H4	CMHG CRow EBee ECha EHoe
		EMar EOHP EPar GAbr MBri
		MHer MGww NBid NGdn NHol
		NMRc NMir NSti NVic SPlb WBea
		WEas WHoo WWol WWpP WWye
	– 'Variegata'	see *T. menziesii* 'Taff's Gold'

Tonestus (Asteraceae)

§	*lyallii*	CNic WPer WWin
§	*pygmaeus*	NWCA WLin WPat

Toona (Meliaceae)

§	*sinensis*	CHEx CMCN CPle CTho CWib
		ECre EPfP EWTr IDee WBVN WPGP
	– 'Flamingo' (v)	CBcs

Torenia (Scrophulariaceae)

	Blue Moon =	WWol
	'Dantmoon' **new**	
	concolor var. *formosana*	MOak WCru
	B&SWJ 124	
	Summer Wave Series	SCoo
	– Summer Wave Blue =	WCot
	'Sunrenilabu'	
	'Tiger Moon' **new**	WWeb

Torreya (Taxaceae)

	grandis	EGFP

Tovara see *Persicaria*

Townsendia (Asteraceae)

	alpigena var. *alpigena*	CGra CPBP EHyt
	– var. *caelilinensis*	EHyt
	condensata	CGra CPBP NSla
	exscapa	EHyt
	florifera	EMan EMlt
	formosa	CMea CWes NBir WWin
	hookeri	CGra CPBP EHyt
	incana	CGra EHyt
	jonesii **new**	EHyt
	– var. *tumulosa*	ETow
	leptotes	CGra EHyt
	mensana	EHyt NMen
	montana	see *T. alpigena* var. *alpigena*
	nuttallii	CGra EHyt
§	*rothrockii*	CGra CPBP EHyt GMaP NMen
	spathulata	CGra CPBP EHyt
	wilcoxiana hort.	see *T. rothrockii*

Toxicodendron (Anacardiaceae)

	vernicifluum	see *Rhus verniciflua*

Trachelium (Campanulaceae)

§	*asperuloides*	EHyt
	caeruleum ♀ H1	ERea SGar WBrE WCot WHrl
	– 'Purple Umbrella'	CSam EMan
	– 'White Umbrella'	EMan
	jacquinii	MBro NWCA WCot WHoo WPat
	subsp. *rumelianum*	

Trachelospermum ✿ (Apocynaceae)

	from Naking, China	SLon
§	*asiaticum* ♀ H2-3	More than 30 suppliers
*	– 'Aureum'	LRHS
	– 'Golden Memories'	EPfP SMur SSpi
	– 'Goshiki' (v)	GQui MGos SSpi
	– var. *intermedium*	CFil WPGP
	– 'Nagaba' **now**	SSpi
	– 'Theta' **new**	SSpi
	jasminoides ♀ H2-3	More than 30 suppliers
§	– 'Japonicum'	CRHN CSPN GCal IArd LRHS SBra
		SLPl SLon SSpi
	– 'Major'	CSPN CTrG SSpi WBcn
*	– 'Oblanceolatum'	GCal
	– 'Tricolor' (v)	CRHN GCal IArd SSta
	– 'Variegatum' (v) ♀ H2-3	More than 30 suppliers
	– 'Waterwheel'	WBcn WSHC
	– 'Wilsonii'	EPfP GCal WBcn WCot
	W 776	CBot CMac CPIN CRHN CSPN
		CSam EBee EBre ELan EMil EPla
		GCal LRHS MCCP SAPC SArc
		SBrw SLim SPer SReu SSpi SSta
		WCru WHar WPGP
	majus hort.	see *T. jasminoides* 'Japonicum'
	majus Nakai	see *T. asiaticum*

Trachycarpus (Arecaceae)

§	*fortunei* ♀ H3-4	More than 30 suppliers
	– 'Nanus'	MGos
	latisectus	CBrP EAmu LPJP LPal NPal
		WMul
	martianus	CTrC EAmu EPVP LPJP LPal
		WMul
	nanus	LPal
	oreophilus	LPal
	takil	CBrP CRoM CTrC EAmu EPVP
		LPJP LPal NPal WMul
	wagnerianus	CBrP EAmu EGln EPVP EPla LPJP
		LPal NPal SDry SPar WMul
		WPGP

Trachystemon (*Boraginaceae*)

orientalis — CBre CBri CHEx CHid CPLG CRDP CSev EBee EChP ECha EGol ELan EPar EPfP MFir MHar MRav NBid NPSI SLon WCru WFar WHer WMoo WPnP WWal WWin WWye

Tradescantia ✿ (*Commelinaceae*)

albiflora	see *T. fluminensis*
x **andersoniana**	see *T.* Andersoniana Group
W. Ludwig & Rohw. nom. inval.	
§ Andersoniana Group	MSal NFor WEas WPer WWeb WWin WWpP
- 'Baby Doll'	EGle GKir
- 'Bilberry Ice'	More than 30 suppliers
- 'Blanca'	MWrn NChi
- 'Blue and Gold'	EBre EChP EMFW EPfP EPla ETub EVFa LAst LHop LRHS MBNS MCAu MMHG NGdn NPro NSti SDes SPer SPla STes WCot WCra WElm WHil WMnd WRus
- 'Blue Stone'	CMea EBlw ECha EFou LPVe MBNS NPri SOkh SRms WFar WMoo
- 'Blushing Bride'	EFou
- 'Bridal Veil'	CHll
- 'Caerulea Plena'	see *T. virginiana* 'Caerulea Plena'
- Carmine Glow	see *T.* (Andersoniana Group) 'Karminglut'
- 'Charlotte'	CFwr CStr EBee EChP EGle EMFW LCaP LRHS MCAu MGrG MHar MOne MWgw NBro NGdn SChu WLow WMnd WTMC
- 'Concord Grape'	More than 30 suppliers
- 'Croftway Blue'	SCro
- 'Danielle'	CRez EBee EChP EGle EPfP NGdn WLow WTMC
- 'David's Blaby Blue'	MTed
- 'Domaine de Courson'	EBee LPio
- 'Gisela' **new**	EFou
- 'In the Navy'	CFwr EBee
- 'Innocence'	More than 30 suppliers
- 'Iris Prichard'	CM&M CPrp EBee EChP ELan EPar EPfP EPla GMaP LHop LRHS NLar SCro WBor WFar WPnP WWal
- 'Isis' ♀ H4	CBcs CHar CMHG CPrp CSBt EBlw EChP ECtt EFou ELan EPar EPfP EPla GKir LRHS MRav MTis MWgw NBir NGdn NOrc SBod SChu SPar SPer SPla WCer WMnd WRus WWin
- 'J.C. Weguelin' ♀ H4	EBee EGle EMil EPfP EWTr GKir LCaP LRHS MBri NBir NDlv SDes SRms WMaN WMnd WPnP
§ - 'Karminglut' Foerster	CHar EBee EBlw EGle ELan EMan EPar EPfP GKir GMaP LLWP MAvo MBri MNrw MWrn NBir NGdn NOrc NVic SVil WCer WHil WHoo WWye
- 'Leonora'	COlW EBee ENot EPfP LRHS SRPl WPnP
- 'Little Doll'	CElw EBee ECtt EFou EGle EMan EWTr GBri GKir LAst MAvo MBri MDKP MGrG MHar MLLN MSph MTed NPri SOkh SVil WCot WFar WLin WMaN WRus WTMC WWhi
- 'Little White Doll'	CM&M CPrp CSpe EBee GMac LAst MSph MSte SOkh WCot WLin WWhi
- 'Mariella' **new**	EGle MCAu SVil
- 'Mrs Loewer' **new**	EMon
- 'Osprey' ♀ H4	More than 30 suppliers
- 'Pauline'	CHar EBee EBlw EChP ECtt EFou EMan EPla GKir LRHS MNrw MRav NBir NHol NLar SChu SMer WCer WFar WHil WHoo WTel WWal WWin
- 'Purewell Giant'	CSBt EBee ECot EMil LHop NBro NCat NDlv NLar SChu SPar SPer WGor WKif WMnd
- 'Purple Dome'	CHar CRDP EBee EBlw ECtt EFou EMFW EPla GKir GMaP LAst LRHS MHar MRav MWgw NBir NBro NCat NGdn SPar SPla STes WCer WMnd WWye
- 'Red Grape'	EBee EBre ECtt EFou GKir MAvo MBNS MCAu MUlv NSti SUsu WRus
- 'Rubra'	CMea COlW CPrp EBee EChP EPfP EWTr LPVe MOne MWgw NDlv NOrc NPri SBod SChu SCro SPar SRPl SRms WBar WMoo
- 'Sweet Kate'	CFwr MCCP SAga
- 'Sylvana' **new**	CM&M CRez EBee EGle MCAu SVil
- 'Valour'	EBee LRHS MAvo WFar WLin WPnP
- 'Zwanenburg Blue'	CM&M CMGP CRez ECGP EChP ECha EFou EMan EPyc GKir LRHS NBro SPlb WCom WLow WMnd WTel WWye
'Baerbel'	SBod
bracteata	EBee ETow
brevicaulis	EBee ECha EFou EMFP EPar EPla ERos GBuc GDra LRHS MHar MTho NBro NMen
'Bridesmaid'	MOak
canaliculata	see *T. ohiensis*
cerinthoides	CHal
fluminensis	SChr
- 'Albovittata'	CHal
- 'Aurea' ♀ H1	CHal MBri MOak
- 'Laekenensis' (v)	CHal MBri
- 'Maiden's Blush' (v)	CHal CSpe MOak SDes SGar SVen WFoF
- 'Quicksilver' (v) ♀ H1	CHal MBri
- 'Tricolor Minima' ♀ H1	CHal
multiflora	see *Tripogandra multiflora*
navicularis	see *Callisia navicularis*
occidentalis **new**	EBee
§ **ohiensis**	CFee EBee EMan LPBA
§ **pallida** ♀ H2-3	CHal IBlr
- 'Purpurea' ♀ H2-3	EShb MOak SVen
pendula	see *T. zebrina*
'Purple Sabre' **new**	LAst
purpurea	see *T. pallida* 'Purpurea'
sillamontana ♀ H1	CHal EOas MBri
spathacea 'Vittata' ♀ H1	CHal
'Tracey'	CM&M
tricolor	see *T. zebrina*
virginiana	CM&M EBot EFWa MWhi MWrn
- 'Alba'	EBot EWTr GCal WPer
§ - 'Caerulea Plena' (d)	CM&M CMGP CMHG EBee EChP EFou ELan EMan EPla LRHS MCLN MRav MUlv NChi SChu SRms WFar WWal
- 'Rubra'	CM&M LAst SPlb
§ **zebrina** ♀ H1	CHal SChr
- **discolor**	CHal
- **pendula**	see *T. zebrina*
- 'Purpusii' ♀ H1	CHal

- 'Quadricolor' (v) ♀ H1	CHal

Tragopogon (Asteraceae)

crocifolius	EMan WCot
porrifolius	ILis
pratensis	CArn CKin NMir

Trapa (Trapaceae)

natans	WFar

Trautvetteria (Ranunculaceae)

carolinensis	EBee WCru
var. ***japonica***	
- var. ***occidentalis***	GKir WCru

Trevesia (Araliaceae)

palmata	CKob

Trichopetalum (Anthericaceae)

§ ***plumosum***	CBro

Trichosanthes (Cucurbitaceae)

cucumerina	CPlN

Tricuspidaria see *Crinodendron*

Tricyrtis ✿ (Convallariaceae)

CC 3454	WCot
'Adbane'	CBct CLAP EBla ELan EMan EWTr EWes GKir LRHS MBri MMHG NLar WCot WFar WRha WViv
affinis	GBuc GGar WPnP
- B&SWJ 2804	WCru
- 'Variegata'	see *T.* 'Variegata' (*affinis* hybrid)
'Amanagowa'	CLAP WFar
bakeri	see *T. latifolia*
dilatata	see *T. macropoda*
'Eco Gold Spangles'	SSpi
flava	WCru
formosana ♀ H4	CAvo COlW CTbh EBre EChP ECha EHrv ELan EPfP GGar GKir GMac LAst LPVe LRHS MBri MCAu MNrw MTho MWrn SBla SDes SMac SMad SPet SRms WCot WEas WPnP WWal
- B&SWJ 306	CBct CLAP EBla WCot WCru WFar
- B&SWJ 355	CBct LEur WCru WFar
- B&SWJ 3635	WFar
- B&SWJ 3712	WCru WFar
- B&SWJ 6705	CLAP
- dark	GKir LEur WFar
'Dark Beauty'	CBos CLAP EBee EBlw EHrv EMan GSki LEur LRHS MBri MCLN SUsu WFar
- 'Lodge Farm' **new**	EBla
- pale	LRHS WFar
- 'Purple Beauty' **new**	CFwr
- 'Samurai' (v)	CLAP CMil EBee EMan EPPr LEur WCot
- 'Seiryu'	LEur
- 'Shelley's'	CBct CLAP ETow GCal LEur NBro WPrP
§ - Stolonifera Group	CAvo CBcs CBro CM&M CMHG EBee EBlw EHrv ELan EMan EMar EPfP LEur LHop LRHS MRav NGdn SCro SDix SPer WCom WFar WMnd WPnP WWeb WWin
- 'Variegata' (v)	EBee EBla LEur MLLN WCru WFar
'Harlequin'	LEur NLar
§ ***hirta***	CBcs CFwr CHid CPrp CSam EBre EFou EHrv EPfP GEdr GKir LPVe LPio LRHS MBri MCAu MTho NBro NGdn SDes SPer SPet WBea WCru WFar WGwG WHHs WPnP
§ - 'Alba'	CSam EHrv GEdr WFar WHil WWin
* - 'Albomarginata' (v)	CDes CPrp CRez EBee EBlw EChP EMar EPPr EPfP LBuc LEur MCAu SLon SSpi WMnd WPGP
- 'Golden Gleam'	CBct CHea EBla WCot WFar
- hybrids	CM&M MHer WCru WFar
- 'Kinkazan'	EBlw LEur WFar
- 'Makinoi Gold'	LEur WFar
- var. ***masamunei***	WCru
- 'Matsukaze'	CLAP WFar
- 'Miyazaki'	CFir CHea CHid EBee EBlw EFou EGle ELan EMan EPar GBuc LEur LRHS MNrw NLar SDes SMac SMad SMrm WBea WCot WFar
- 'Miyazaki Gold' (v)	EGle SDes
* - 'Nana'	WFar
- 'Silver Blue'	WFar
- 'Taiwan Atrianne'	CSam MBri SDes
- 'Variegata' (v)	CLAP CPlt EBlw EFou EMan EWes GBuc LEur LHop SDes SMad SUsu WCot WCru WFar WPnP WPrP
- 'White Flame' (v)	WCot
N Hototogisu	CBro CLAP CMea CPlt CPom CTbh EBee EBla EBlw EGle ELan EMan EMar EPar GMac LHop MCAu MTho MUlv NBir SUsu WCru WFar WHil WMnd WPnP WWin
ishiiana	CDes CLAP EBee LEur WCru WFar WPGP
- var. ***surugensis***	EBla LEur WCru WFar
'Ivory Queen'	WFar
japonica	see *T. hirta*
'Kohaku'	CBct CDes CLAP EBla ELan LEur WCot WCru WFar WPGP
lasiocarpa B&SWJ 3635	CLAP EBla WCru WFar
- B&SWJ 7013	WPrP
§ ***latifolia***	CBct EBlw ELan EMar EPPr EPot GEdr GGar GMaP LEur MHer MNrw NGdn NLar WAul WCru WFar WPnP WViv WWin
'Lemon Lime' (v)	CBct EMan LRHS MLLN MSph SUsu WFar
'Lilac Towers'	CBct EBre EPar GKir WCru WFar WKif
macrantha	GDra WWin
§ - subsp. ***macranthopsis***	CBct CBos CLAP EBla LEur SSpi WCot WCru WFar
macranthopsis	see *T. macrantha* subsp. *macranthopsis*
* ***macrocarpa***	WFar
N ***macropoda***	CBct CFwr CHid CSam EBee EBla ELan EMan EPar EPfP GAbr GBuc GMaP ITim LAst MCAu MCCP MGrG NGdn NWCA SDes SMad WFar WMnd WViv
- B&SWJ 1271	CBct EBla LEur WCru
- from Yungi Temple, China **new**	WCot
- variegated (v)	WCru
maculata	WViv
- HWJCM 470	WCru
nana	WCru
- 'Raven's Back' **new**	WCru
ohsumiensis	CBct CDes CLAP EBee EBlw ECha EMan EPot LEur MTho SUsu WCru WFar WPGP
perfoliata	LEur WCru WFar
'Shimone'	CHid CLAP CStu EBlw ECha ELan GBuc LEur LRHS WFar WKif WPrP

'Snow Fountain' **new**	EBee
stolonifera	see *T. formosana* Stolonifera Group
'Tojen'	CBct CLAP CMil EBee EBlw EChP ECha EGle EHrv ELan EMan EMar EPPr EPfP EWes GBuc GKir LAst LEur LRHS MBri MCAu MNrw MUlv NBir NBro SMrm SUsu WFar WPnP
'Toki-no-mai'	EBla
§ 'Variegata' (*affinis* hybrid) (v)	LEur WCru WFar WPnP
viridula **new**	LEur
'White Towers'	More than 30 suppliers
'White Towers' spotted	LEur SDys

Trientalis (*Primulaceae*)

europaea	SOkd
- rosea	CNat

Trifolium (*Papilionaceae*)

alpinum	EBee GDra WSan
badium	EBee
campestre	CKin
incarnatum	MHer WHer
ochroleucon	CFwr EBee EChP EHrv EMan EMar EShb GBri GLil LBuc LPhx MAvo NGHP SCro SMad SSvw WBry WHil WMoo WSan
pannonicum	CDes EBee EChP EHrv EMon EVFa GCal LPhx MLLN MSte NCot SEND SMrm SUsu WCot WFar WMoo WPGP WRus WSHC
pratense	MHer WHer
- 'Dolly North'	see *T. pratense* 'Susan Smith'
- 'Ice Cool'	see *T. repens* 'Green Ice'
- 'Nina'	EMan WAlt WCHb
- 'Speech House' (v)	WAlt
§ - 'Susan Smith' (v)	CElw CRow EBee ECha EMan EMar EMlt EPPr EShb EWes IBlr LRHS MGrG MHer MLLN MNrw MOak MTho NGHP WAlt WCHb WFar WWpP
repens	COld EHrv EWTr MCAu MWgw NCat NSco
- 'Douglas Dawson'	CBgR EMan LDai
- 'Gold Net'	see *T. pratense* 'Susan Smith'
- 'Good Luck'	CNat CRow MTho
§ - 'Green Ice'	CBre CMea CRow CSev EBee EChP EMan EMar EVFa MGrG MRav MTho NBir NSti WAlt WBea WCHb WCom WFar WHer WMoo WWye
- 'Harlequin' (v)	CBre EMlt WAlt WBea WCot WDyG WFar WMoo WPer
- 'Hiccups' (v)	WAlt
- pale pink	WAlt
- 'Pentaphyllum'	see *T. repens* 'Quinquefolium'
- 'Purp'	WAlt
- 'Purple Velvet'	EPPr
- 'Purpurascens'	CArn CBre EBee GCal GDra GGar GMac ILis LRHS MAvo MBNS MHer NHlc NSti WBea WHen WKif WMoo WWhi
§ - 'Purpurascens Quadrifolium'	CNic CStu EChP ECha EDAr EMar EWes NBid NChi NGHP NMir NPer SIde SIng SPer SPlb WAlt WCHb WFar WRHF WRus WWin WWpP WWye
- 'Quadrifolium'	EHoe EPar
§ - 'Quinquefolium'	EBee WPer
- 'Tetraphyllum Purpureum'	see *T. repens* 'Purpurascens Quadrifolium'

* - 'Velvet and Baize' (v)	CNat
- 'Wheatfen'	CBre CPlt CRow EBee EMan GAbr MAvo MRav MTho NCat NChi NDov NPer WAlt WBea WCHb WCom WCot WDyG WMoo
- 'William'	EMan MRav WAlt WCot
rubens	More than 30 suppliers
- 'Peach Pink'	CCol CSpe EChP EMan EMon LPhx MAvo MGrG MHar NCat STes SUsu WCot WRus
- 'Red Feathers' **new**	CFwr
- white-flowered **new**	LPhx MGrG
uniflorum	CDes

Trigonella (*Papilionaceae*)

foenum-graecum	CArn MSal SIde WLHH

Trigonotis (*Boraginaceae*)

rotundifolia	EBee EMan

Trillidium see *Trillium*

Trillium ❀ (*Trilliaceae*)

albidum	CLAP EHyt GBuc GCrs GKir NMen SSpi WCru
angustipetalum	CLAP
- hybrid **new**	SSpi
apetalon	EBee LAma WCru
camschatcense	CLAP EBee GKir LAma LEur SSpi WAbe WCru
§ *catesbyi*	CBro CLAP EBee EHrv EPot GCrs GEdr LAma SSpi WCru
cernuum	CLAP GCrs LAma WCru
chloropetalum	CBro EBee EBre EPar GAbr GDra GKir SBla SOkh SSpi WCru
§ - var. *giganteum* ♀ H4	NDov SSpi WAbe WCru
- 'Ice Creme'	SSpi
- var. *rubrum*	see *T. chloropetalum* var. *giganteum*
- 'Volcano'	SSpi
- white	ECha
cuneatum	CBcs CBro CFwr CLAP EBee ECha ELan EPar EPfP EPot GAbr GBuc GEdr GGar GMaP LAma LEur LRHS MDun MTho NMen SBod SPer SSpi WCru WFar
- x *luteum*	EPot LEur
- red	GCrs
decumbens	EPot
erectum ♀ H4	More than 30 suppliers
§ - f. *albiflorum*	CBro CFir CLAP CRDP EBee EBre EPot GKir LAma LEur SSpi WCru WPnP
- 'Beige'	GEdr GSki
- f. *luteum*	EPfP GCrs LAma SSpi WCru
flexipes	CBro CLAP EBee EPot GCrs GEdr GKir LAma LEur WCru
- x *erectum* **new**	GKir WCru
govanianum	EBee LAma SSpi WCru
grandiflorum ♀ H4	More than 30 suppliers
- 'Flore Pleno' (d) ♀ H4	EBre EPar EPot ETow GBuc GKir MTho NHar SOkd
- 'Jenny Rhodes' **new**	IBlr
- 'Snowbunting' (d)	SOkd
kurabayashii	CDes CFil CLAP GCrs LEur SSpi WPGP
§ *luteum* ♀ H4	CBcs CBro CFwr CHid CLAP EBee EHrv EPar EPot EWTr GAbr GBuc GEdr GKir GSki LAma MAvo MCAu MDun MUlv NHar NMen SPer SSpi WCru WFar WPnP WWst
nivale	EBee

ovatum	CLAP GCrs GDra GEdr GKir GNor LAma
- var. *hibbersonii*	CBro EHyt ETow GBuc GCrs GDra GEdr GMaP GNor LEur NHar NMen
- from Oregon **new**	CLAP
- 'Roy Elliott'	NBir NMen
parviflorum	GCrs SSpi
pusillum	CLAP EBee EPot GEdr GKev SSpi
- var. *pusillum*	EHyt GCrs NHar SBla
- var. *virginianum*	CBro LAma WCru
recurvatum	CBcs CPen EBee EHrv EPar EPot GAbr GKir GSki LAma LEur MDun NMen SPer WCru WFar WPnP
rivale ♀ H3	CBos CBro CElw CLAP EHrv EPot GCrs LAma NDov NGar NHar NMen SBla SOkd SSpi WAbe WFar
- 'Purple Heart'	EHyt EPot GCrs GEdr
rugelii	CLAP EBee GBuc GCrs GEdr GKir GMaP LAma LEur NMen SSpi WCru
- Askival hybrids	GBuc GCrs GKir NMen SSpi
- pink	GCrs
- x *vaseyi*	GCrs
sessile	CHid CLAP EBee EPot EWTr GAbr GBuc GEdr GKir GSki LAma MAvo MCAu NBir NHar NMen SPer SSpi WCot WCru WFar WPnP WSHC WShi
- var. *luteum*	see *T. luteum*
- purple	GKir
- 'Rubrum'	see *T. chloropetalum* var. *giganteum*
simile	CLAP EPot GEdr GKir
smallii	LAma WCru
stamineum	CLAP EBee GEdr
stylosum	see *T. catesbyi*
sulcatum	CBro CLAP CRDP EBee EPar EPot GBuc GCrs GDra GEdr GKir GMaP LEur NMen SSpi WCru WFar
tschonoskii	EBee LAma SSpi WCru
- var. *himalaicum*	LEur WCru
undulatum	EBee EPot GEdr LAma WCru
vaseyi	CBro CLAP CRDP EHyt EPot GBuc GCrs GEdr GKir LAma LEur NMen SSpi WCru
viride	CLAP NGby WCru WFar WPnP
viridescens	EBee GEdr LAma SSpi

Tripetaleia (Ericaceae)

§ *bracteata*	GKir

Tripogandra (Commelinaceae)

§ *multiflora*	CHal

Tripsacum (Poaceae)

dactyloides **new**	EPPr

Tripterospermum (Gentianaceae)

* aff. *chevalieri* B&SWJ 8359 **new**	WCru
cordifolium B&SWJ 081	WCru
fasciculatum B&SWJ 7197	WCru
japonicum	WAbe
- B&SWJ 1168	WCru
lanceolatum B&SWJ 085	WCru
taiwanense B&SWJ 1205	WCru

Tripterygium (Celastraceae)

regelii	CBcs CFil CPIN WPGP
wilfordii	CPIN

Trisetum (Poaceae)

distichophyllum	EHoe

flavescens	CKin
- 'Peter Hall' (v)	EPPr

Tristania (Myrtaceae)

laurina	see *Tristaniopsis laurina*

Tristaniopsis (Myrtaceae)

§ *laurina*	CTrC

Triteleia (Alliaceae)

californica	see *Brodiaea californica*
§ 'Corrina'	CAvo EBee MNrw WAul WCot
hyacinthina	EBee ERos ETub LAma LRHS WBea WHil
ixioides	CMea EBee ERos
- var. *scabra*	ETow
- - NNS 98-358	WCot
- 'Splendens'	EBee WCot
- 'Starlight'	CAvo EBee EPot
§ *laxa*	CAvo CMea EBee EPot EWTr LAma NRog WCom
- NNS 98-541	WCot
- NNS 98-544	WCot
- 'Allure' **new**	EBee
§ - 'Koningin Fabiola'	CFwr CTri EBee EMan EWTr LAma MBri NBir NRog WBea WBrE WCot WHil
- Queen Fabiola	see *T. laxa* 'Koningin Fabiola'
- 'Sierra Giant'	WCot
§ *peduncularis*	EBee LAma WCot
- NNS 95-499	WCot
x *tubergenii*	EBee LAma
uniflora	see *Ipheion uniflorum*

Trithrinax (Arecaceae)

acanthocoma	CBrP CRoM LPal
campestris	CBrP LPal

Tritoma see *Kniphofia*

Tritonia (Iridaceae)

bakeri	LBow
crocata ♀ H2-3	CPou EMui LBow NMen NRog WHer
- 'Pink Sensation'	CDes EBee
- 'Prince of Orange'	CPou
- 'Princess Beatrix'	EBee
deusta subsp. *miniata*	LBow
§ *disticha*	More than 30 suppliers
subsp. *rubrolucens*	
laxifolia	LBow
lineata	CDes CPou EBee
pallida **new**	SPlb
parvula	LBow
rosea	see *T. disticha* subsp. *rubrolucens*
securigera	GGar
squalida	LBow

Tritoniopsis (Iridaceae)

§ *pulchra*	CDes

Trochocarpa (Epacridaceae)

thymifolia	SOkd SReu WAbe

Trochodendron (Trochodendraceae)

aralioides	CBcs CDoC CFil CHEx CMCN CPLG CTho EPfP EPla GKir ICrw LRHS MGos SAPC SArc SBrw SHGC SLon SMad SPer SReu SSpi SSta WCot WCwm WDin
- from Japan B&SWJ 6080	WCru
- from Taiwan B&SWJ 6727	WCru

Trollius (*Ranunculaceae*)

ACE 1187 **new**	GEdr
acaulis	EBee EGle EPPr EWTr EWes GAbr GDra LEur MTho NRya WFar WPat
asiaticus	CRDP EBee GBuc GKir LBuc
§ *chinensis*	EBee ECha GCal LSyl NChi SRms SWat WBar
- 'Golden Queen' ♀ H4	More than 30 suppliers
- 'Imperial Orange'	WWal WWin
'Cressida'	EBee
× *cultorum* 'Alabaster'	CBos CDes CFir CLAP CMil CRDP CRow EBee EChP ECha EGle EMan EPfP GBuc GKir LAst MCLN MRav NLar SBla SMad SMrm WCFE WFar WPGP WTin WViv
- - seedlings	SSpi
- 'Baudirektor Linne'	MRav NGdn WFar
- 'Bressingham hybrids	EBre
- 'Byrne's Giant'	EBee WFar
- 'Canary Bird'	ELan EMil EPfP GBri NGdn SMur SRms
- 'Cheddar'	COtt CPen EBee EChP EGle ENot ERou MBri MCCP MCLN MRav NBro NGdn NLar NPro NSti SUsu WCra WFar WPnP
- 'Commander-in-chief'	CDes EBee WFar WPGP WPnP
- 'Earliest of All'	CSam EBee EGle EWTr GKir LRHS MBri NGdn SPer SRms WCra WFar WHoo
- 'Etna'	EBee EGle ERou GKir LRHS MBri WFar WLin WPnP WSan
§ - 'Feuertroll'	EBee ECha EMar MBNS MBri NPro SMur WCot WCra WFar WHoo WWeb
- Fireglobe	see *T.* × *cultorum* 'Feuertroll'
- 'Glory of Leiden'	EBee
- 'Golden Cup'	ECot NBir NGdn
- 'Golden Monarch'	EPar
- 'Goldquelle' ♀ H4	EHon SMur WWpP
- 'Goliath'	WFar
- 'Helios'	CSam EBee ECha
- 'Lemon Queen'	EBee EChP EMan EPar EPfP ERou GCal GKir LRHS LSyl MBri MRav NBlu NFor SDes SMrm SPer SWat WCra WFar WLin WPnP WRus WViv WWin
- 'Meteor'	WFar
- 'Orange Crest'	EBee EGle GCal WFar
- 'Orange Globe'	EBlw LBuc SMrm WFar WHil
- 'Orange Princess' ♀ H4	CSBt EBee ENot EPfP ERou GBin GKir LRHS LSyl NBro NLar NPri SDes SPer SRms WAul WCra WLin WPnP
- 'Prichard's Giant'	CM&M EBee EChP EGle ELan EMan NBro WCra WFar
- 'Salamander'	SMur
§ - 'Superbus' ♀ H4	CDes CM&M CMGP CMHG CRDP EBee EChP EFou EGle EHol ELan EPar EPfP GKir LAst MBNS NGdn SPer SSpi WFar WLin WPnP
- 'T. Smith'	EBee EGle LBuc MTis NBro WCot WFar
* - 'Taleggio'	NLar
- 'Yellow Beauty'	WFar
europaeus	CBot COlW CRow ECha EMFW ERou EWTr ITim LHop LPVe LRHS LSyl MBro MHer NGdn NMir NSti SAga SDes SMac SPet SRms SRot SWat WBrE WFar WHoo WPer WViv

- 'Superbus'	see *T.* × *cultorum* 'Superbus'
hondoensis	EBee EPPr GBin GIBF GKir LEur NLar NPro WElm
ircuticus **new**	EBee
laxus	EBee EWes
ledebourii hort.	see *T. chinensis*
papavereus	see *T. yunnanensis* var. *yunnanensis*
pulcher	ETow
pumilus	EBre ECha ELan EMlt GCrs ITim LBee LEur LRHS MBro MHer NChi NRya NWCA SPer SUsu WFar WPer WViv WWeb
- ACE 1818	GBuc WCot
- 'Wargrave'	EPot NMen
ranunculinus **new**	EBee
riederianus	EBee GKir
stenopetalus	EBee EChP ECha EWes GCal GKir MBri MRav WFar WPnP
yunnanensis	EBre GBuc GCrs GKir NBid NGby NWoo WPnP WWpP
- CD&R 2097	WCru
§ - var. *yunnanensis* **new**	EBee

Tropaeolum (*Tropaeolaceae*)

azureum	CPla WCot
- F&W 8667	WCot
brachyceras	NLar WCot
ciliatum ♀ H1	CBcs CBro CFil CFir CPlN CPla CPne CSam CStu EBee ELan EOrc EPot GCal LEur MPRe MTho NEgg NLar NSti SMrm WBor WCot WCru WFar WFoF WHer WNor WPGP WViv
* *hookerianum* subsp. *austropurpureum*	CFil EBee
- - F&W 9091	WCot
- subsp. *hookerianum*	EBee
- - F&W 8632	WCot
- - F&W 9467	WPGP
incisum	CFil SOkd
- F&W 9385	WPGP
lepidum	CPla WCot
* *lucidum* **new**	WCot
majus	WSel
- Alaska Series (v) ♀ H3	CBod CPrp SIde WJek WSel
* - 'Clive Innes'	ERea
- 'Crimson Beauty'	CSpe MLLN
§ - 'Darjeeling Double' (d)	LRHS NPri SMrm WCot WCru
- 'Darjeeling Gold' (d)	see *T. majus* 'Darjeeling Double'
- 'Empress of India'	CPrp LRHS WEas WJek
- 'Forest Flame'	LRHS
- 'Hermine Grashoff' (d) ♀ H2-3	CSWP CSpe ERea LRHS MLLN NPer SMrm WCot
- 'Margaret Long' (d)	CSpe GCal LRHS MLLN NPri SMrm WCot
* - 'Peaches and Cream'	WJek
- 'Red Wonder'	CHad CSWP CSpe LRHS NPri SMrm
- 'Ruffled Apricot' **new**	CSpe
- Tom Thumb mixed	WJek
- 'Wina'	WJek
pentaphyllum	CAvo CFil CSpe EBee ECha ELan GCal GCrs IBlr MTho WCot
peregrinum	LRHS
polyphyllum	CDes CFil CLAP CPlN EBee ECha EHyt GBuc GCrs SBla SMHy WCot WPGP WTre
speciosum ♀ H4	More than 30 suppliers
sylvestre	EBee WCru
tricolor ♀ H1	CAvo CFil CLAP CPlN EBee EHyt ELan EPot MTho SDix WBor WPat
tuberosum	CBcs CEnd ETub GPoy LRHS WBrE WPrP

- var. *lineamaculatum* 'Ken Aslet' ♀ H3	More than 30 suppliers
- var. *piliferum* 'Sidney'	CFil EBee IBlr WCru WPGP WWeb
- 'Salley Gardens'	IIve
- 'Ulrike'	IIve

Tsuga (Pinaceae)

canadensis	EHul LCon LPan MBar NBlu NWea SHBN WDin
- 'Abbott's Dwarf'	CKen LCon MGos
§ - 'Abbott's Pygmy'	CKen
- 'Albospica' (v)	CDoC EOrn LRHS WGor
- 'Armistice'	LCon
- 'Arnold Gold Weeper' **new**	CKen
- 'Aurea' (v)	LCon MBar WBcn
- 'Baldwin Dwarf Pyramid'	MBar
- 'Beehive' **new**	WGor
- 'Bennett'	EHul MBar
- 'Betty Rose' (v)	CKen
- 'Brandley'	CKen
§ - 'Branklyn'	CKen WBcn
- 'Cappy's Choice' **new**	CKen
- 'Cinnamonea'	CKen
- 'Coffin'	CKen
- 'Cole's Prostrate'	CDoC CKen EOrn GKir LCon LLin MAsh MBar NHol NLar SHBN
- 'Creamey' (v)	CKen
- 'Curley'	CKen
- 'Curtis Ideal'	CKen
* - 'Everitt's Dense Leaf'	CKen
- 'Everitt's Golden'	CKen
- 'Fantana'	CDoC EHul LBee LCon LLin LRHS MAsh MBar NLar SCoo SLim WLRN
- 'Gentsch White' (v)	LLin MGos
- 'Golden Splendor'	LLin
- 'Horsford'	CKen NLar
- 'Hussii'	CKen LCon NLar
- 'Jacqueline Verkade'	CKen
- 'Jeddeloh' ♀ H4	CDoC CMac CSli EBre EHul ENot EOrn GKir IMGH LCon LLin LRHS MAsh MBar MBri MGos SLim WDin WEve WStI
- 'Jervis'	CDoC CKen LCon NLar
- 'Julianne'	CKen
- 'Kingsville Spreader'	CKen
- 'Little Joe' **new**	CKen
I - 'Lutea'	CKen
- 'Many Cones'	CKen
- 'Minima'	CKen
- 'Minuta'	CDoC CKen EHul EOrn LBee LCon LLin LRHS MBar MGos SCoo SLon SPoG
- 'Nana'	CMac EHul WDin WLRN
- 'Palomino'	CDoC CKen MBar
- 'Pendula' ♀ H4	CDoC CKen EHul ENot EOrn LCon LRHS MBar MBri MOne NHol SLim WCwm WDin WEve WMou
- 'Pincushion'	CKen
- 'Prostrata'	see *T. canadensis* 'Branklyn'
- 'Pygmaea'	see *T. canadensis* 'Abbott's Pygmy'
- 'Rugg's Washington Dwarf'	CKen
- 'Snowflake'	CKen LCon MGos
- 'Stewart's Gem'	CKen
- 'Verkade Petite'	CKen
- 'Verkade Recurved'	CKen LCon MBar WBcn
- 'Von Helms' Dwarf'	CKen
- 'Warnham'	CKen ECho EOrn LBee LRHS MBri SCoo
caroliniana 'La Bar Weeping'	CKen

chinensis	GIBF
diversifolia 'Gotelli'	CKen
heterophylla ♀ H4	CDoC CDul CLnd ENot GKir LBuc LCon LRHS MBar NWea SHBN SMad SPer STre WDin WEve WFar
- 'Iron Springs'	CKen EOrn
- 'Laursen's Column'	CKen
menziesii	see *Pseudotsuga menziesii*
mertensiana	WCwm
- 'Blue Star'	CKen MGos
- 'Elizabeth'	CKen
I - 'Glauca Nana'	CKen
- 'Quartz Mountain'	CKen
sieboldii 'Baldwin' **new**	CKen
- 'Honeywell Estate'	CKen
- 'Nana'	CKen

Tsusiophyllum (Ericaceae)

tanakae	see *Rhododendron tsusiophyllum*

Tuberaria (Cistaceae)

guttata	WCru
lignosa	CMHG CMea EMan GEdr SGar WAbe WCot

Tulbaghia ✿ (Alliaceae)

	CFwr
acutiloba	CAvo ERos
alliacea	CAvo CFee ERos WCot
- x *violacea* **new**	LBee
capensis	CFee LPhx
cepacea	CStu NBir
§ - var. *maritima*	CAvo EBee ERos WCot
caddii	CAvo CFee LPhx WCot
- x *violacea*	CPne EBee
cominsii	CFil EBee SCnR
- x *violacea*	CAvo CFil EBee ERos WPrP
dregeana	WCot
'Fairy Star'	ERos WCot WOBN
fragrans	see *T. simmleri*
galpinii	CFil EBee ERos SChr WCot
'John May's Special'	CDes CKno EBee EMan MSph MSte WCot WPGP
'John Rider'	WPer
leucantha	CAvo CStu EBee ERos SBla WCot
maritima	see *T. cepacea* var. *maritima*
Marwood seedling	MTPN
natalensis	CAvo CPou EBee LPhx
- pink	ERos SOkh WCot
§ *simmleri*	CHar CPou EBee EBla EMar ERos EWes GSkt LAma LPio MSph MWrn SMrm WCot
- white	CPou
verdoornia **new**	WCot
violacea	CAvo CBcs CBro CCge CFil CFwr CMHG CPou CSev EBee ECha EHrv EMar ETub LAma LPan MTho SMrm SSpi SWat WCFE WCot WFar WHoo WPGP
* - 'Alba'	GSki LPio WFar
I - 'Fine Form' **new**	SMHy
* - *pallida*	CAvo CMdw CPou CRDP EBee WCot WPrP
§ - 'Silver Lace' (v)	More than 30 suppliers
- 'Variegata'	see *T. violacea* 'Silver Lace'

Tulipa ✿ (Liliaceae)

'Abba' (2)	NRog
'Abu Hassan' (3)	LAma
acuminata (15)	CBro LPhx LRHS WFTG
'Ad Rem' (4)	LAma NRog
'Addis' (14) ♀ H4	LAma

'African Queen' (3)	LAma
agenensis	WWst
aitchisonii	see *T. clusiana*
'Aladdin' (6)	LAma LRHS MWgw NRog
albertii (15)	LAma
'Albino' (3)	LAma
aleppensis (15)	LAma
'Alfred Cortot' (12) ♀ H4	LAma
'Ali Baba' (14) ♀ H4	MBri
'Allegretto' (11)	LAma NRog
altaica (15) ♀ H4	EPot LAma
amabilis	see *T. hoogiana*
'Ancilla' (12) ♀ H4	CBro LAma NRog
'Angélique' (11) ♀ H4	CAvo CMea ETub LAma LRHS MBri NBir NRog
'Anne Claire' (3)	LAma
'Apeldoorn' (4)	LAma LRHS MBri NRog
'Apeldoorn's Elite' (4) ♀ H4	LAma LRHS NRog
'Apricot Beauty' (1) ♀ H4	CHid ETub LAma LRHS MBri NBir NRog
'Apricot Jewel'	see *T. linifolia* (Batalinii Group) 'Apricot Jewel'
'Apricot Parrot' (10) ♀ H4	LAma NCel NRog
'Arabian Mystery' (3)	CAvo CMea ETub LAma NBir
'Aristocrat' (5) ♀ H4	LAma
'Artist' (8) ♀ H4	CAvo EChP LAma NBir
'Athleet' (3)	LAma LRHS
'Attila' (3)	ETub LAma LRHS NCel NRog
aucheriana (15) ♀ H4	CBro CMea EHyt EPot ERos LAma LRHS LTwo WWst
aximensis (15)	WWst
bakeri	see *T. saxatilis* Bakeri Group
'Ballade' (6) ♀ H4	LAma NCel NRog
'Ballerina' (6) ♀ H4	CAvo CMea ETub LAma MWgw NCel
batalinii	see *T. linifolia* Batalinii Group
'Beauty of Apeldoorn' (4)	LAma NCel NRog
Beauty Queen (1)	NRog
'Bellflower' (7)	LAma
'Bellona' (3)	LAma NRog
'Berlioz' (12)	LAma
'Bestseller' (1)	NRog
biebersteiniana (15)	LAma
§ *biflora* (15)	CBro EMar EPot LAma LRHS MBNS NRog
bifloriformis (15)	LRHS
'Big Chief' (4) ♀ H4	LAma MBri NRog
'Bing Crosby' (3)	ETub LAma
'Black Parrot' (10) ♀ H4	CAvo ETub LAma LRHS NCel NRog
'Blenda' (3)	ETub
'Bleu Aimable' (5)	ETub LAma LRHS
'Blue Heron' (7) ♀ H4	LAma NRog
'Blue Parrot' (10)	ETub LAma LRHS NCel NRog
'Blushing Lady' (5)	LAma
'Bonanza' (11)	LAma LRHS
'Boule de Neige' (2)	LAma
'Bravissimo' (2)	MBri
'Brilliant Star' (1)	LAma MBri NRog
'Burgundy' (6)	ETub LAma
'Burgundy Lace' (7)	LAma LRHS NRog
'Burns' (7)	LAma
butkovii (15)	LAma
I 'Calypso' (14) ♀ H4	ETub
'Candela' (13) ♀ H4	LAma NRog
'Cantata' (13)	CBro LAma
'Cantor' (5)	LAma
'Cape Cod' (14)	LAma NCel NRog
'Caprice' (10)	LAma
carinata (15)	LAma
'Carlton' (2)	LAma NRog
'Carnaval de Nice' (11/v) ♀ H4	EMar ETub LAma MBri NRog
'Cassini' (3)	LAma NCel
§ 'celsiana' (15)	LAma LRHS
'César Franck' (12)	LAma
'Charles' (3)	LAma NRog
'China Pink' (6) ♀ H4	CAvo CMea EPfP ETub LAma NCel NRog
'Chopin' (12)	LAma NCel NRog
'Christmas Dream' (1)	NRog
'Christmas Marvel' (1)	LAma LRHS NRog
chrysantha Boiss. ex Baker	see *T. montana*
'Clara Butt' (5)	LAma NRog
§ *clusiana* (15)	CAvo CBro CMea LAma
§ - var. *chrysantha* (15) ♀ H4	CAvo LAma LRHS NRog WFTG
- - 'Tubergen's Gem' (15)	LAma LRHS MBri
- 'Cynthia' (15) ♀ H4	CSWP EPot LAma LPhx LRHS NRog WFTG
§ - var. *stellata* (15)	LAma
'Concerto' (13)	CBro ETub LAma
'Cordell Hull' (5)	NRog
'Corona' (12)	NRog
'Corsage' (14) ♀ H4	LAma
'Couleur Cardinal' (3)	ETub LAma NRog
cretica (15)	EHyt
'Crystal Beauty' (7) ♀ H4	NRog
'Dancing Show' (8)	LAma
dasystemon (15)	EMar EPot LAma MBNS
'Daylight' (12)	NRog
'Diana' (1)	LAma NCel NRog
didieri	see *T. passeriniana*
'Dillenburg' (5)	LAma
'Diplomate' (4)	NRog
'Doll's Minuet' (8)	LAma
'Don Quichotte' (3) ♀ H4	LAma
'Donna Bella' (14) ♀ H4	EPfP LAma
'Douglas Bader' (5)	CAvo LAma LRHS NRog
'Dreaming Maid' (3)	LAma
'Dreamland' (5) ♀ H4	NRog
'Dutch Gold' (3)	LAma
'Dyanito' (6)	NRog
'Early Harvest' (12) ♀ H4	LAma NRog
'Easter Parade' (13)	LAma
'Easter Surprise' (14) ♀ H4	LAma
§ *edulis* (15)	EHyt LAma
eichleri	see *T. undulatifolia*
'Electra' (5)	LAma MBri NCel NRog
'Elegant Lady' (6)	ETub
'Elizabeth Arden' (4)	NRog
'Esperanto' (8/v) ♀ H4	EChP LAma NRog
'Estella Rijnveld' (10)	ETub LAma LRHS NBir NCel NRog
'Esther' (5)	NCel
'Fancy Frills' (7) ♀ H4	ETub LAma
'Fantasy' (10) ♀ H4	LAma LRHS NCel
'Fashion' (12)	LAma NRog
ferganica (15)	EPot LAma
'Fireside'	see *T. 'Vlammenspel'*
'First Lady' (3) ♀ H4	LAma
'Flair' (1)	LAma NRog
'Flaming Parrot' (10)	LAma NCel NRog
* 'Flowerdale'	CAvo
fosteriana (13)	MBri
'Franz Léhar' (12)	LAma
'Fresco' (14)	LAma
'Fringed Apeldoorn' (7)	NRog
'Fringed Beauty' (7) ♀ H4	MBri
'Fringed Elegance' (7) ♀ H4	LAma
'Fritz Kreisler' (12)	LAma LRHS
'Fulgens' (6)	LAma
'Gaiety' (12)	LAma LRHS
'Galata' (13)	LAma
galatica (15)	LAma
'Garden Party' (3) ♀ H4	LAma

'Gavota' (3)   LAma
'Generaal de Wet' (1)   ETub LAma MBri NCel NRog
'General Eisenhower' (4)   LAma
'Georgette' (5)   LAma MBri NRog
'Gerbrand Kieft' (11) ♀ H4   NRog
'Giuseppe Verdi' (12)   LAma LRHS MBri NCel NRog
'Glück' (12) ♀ H4   LAma NRog
'Gold Medal' (11)   LAma MBri
'Golden Apeldoorn' (4)   LAma LRHS MBri NCel NRog
'Golden Artist' (8)   LAma MBri NRog
'Golden Emperor' (13)   LAma LRHS
'Golden Melody' (3)   LAma NRog
'Golden Oxford' (4)   LAma NRog
'Golden Parade' (4)   LAma NRog
'Golden Springtime' (4)   LAma
'Gordon Cooper' (4)   LAma NRog
'Goudstuk' (12)   LAma
'Grand Prix' (13)   LAma
'Green Eyes' (8)   LAma
'Green Spot' (8)   LRHS
greigii (14)   CBro
grengiolensis (15)   LAma LRHS
'Greuze' (5)   LAma
'Groenland' (8)   LAma NCel NRog
'Gudoshnik' (4)   LAma NRog
hageri (15)   LAma
- 'Splendens' (15)   EChP EMar ETub LAma LRHS
                                      MBNS
'Halcro' (5) ♀ H4   ETub LAma
'Hamilton' (7) ♀ H4   EPfP LAma MBNS
'Hans Mayer' (4)   NRog
'Happy Family' (3)   LAma
'Havran'   LAma
'Heart's Delight' (12)   CBro ETub LAma LRHS NCel
                                      NRog
'Hit Parade' (13)   LAma
'Hoangho' (2)   LAma NRog
'Hollands Glorie' (4) ♀ H4   LAma
'Hollywood' (8)   LAma NRog
§ *hoogiana* (15)   EPot
§ *humilis* (15)   CBro EPar EWTr LAma MBri
                                      MWgw WShi
- 'Eastern Star' (15)   CMea LAma LRHS MBri MWgw
§ - 'Lilliput' (15)   CBro EPot LRHS
- 'Odalisque' (15)   EPot LAma LRHS
- 'Persian Pearl' (15)   EMar EPot GCrs LAma LRHS MBri
                                      NRog WFTG
- var. *pulchella*   GCrs
§ - - Albocaerulea Oculata   CMea EPot ETub LAma WFTG
  Group (15)
- 'Rosea'   GCrs
§ - Violacea Group (15)   CMea EChP EPar ETub LAma
                                      MBri
§ - - black base (15)   CBro GCrs LRHS
- - yellow base (15)   CBro GCrs LAma LRHS
'Humming Bird' (8)   LAma NRog
'Hytuna' (11)   LAma NRog
'Ibis' (1)   LAma
'Ile de France' (5)   LAma
iliensis (15)   EPot WWst
ingens (15)   LAma
'Inzell' (3)   ETub LAma
'Jacqueline' (6)   MWgw NRog
'Jeantine' (12) ♀ H4   MWgw
'Jewel of Spring' (4) ♀ H4   LAma
'Jimmy' (3)   NRog
'Jockey Cap' (14)   LAma
'Joffre' (1)   LAma MBri NRog
'Johann Strauss' (12)   CBro LAma MBri NCel NRog
'Juan' (13) ♀ H4   LAma MBri
'Kansas' (3)   LAma
'Karel Doorman' (10)   LAma
'Kareol' (2)   NRog

kaufmanniana (12)   CAvo CBro EPot EWTr MWgw
                                      NCel NRog
§ 'Kees Nelis' (3)   LAma MBri NRog
'Keizerskroon' (1) ♀ H4   LAma NRog
'Kleurenpracht'   see *T.* 'Princess Margaret Rose'
kolpakowskiana (15)   NRog
  ♀ H4
korolkowii **new**   WWst
kurdica (15)   LAma LRHS
* 'Lady Diana' (14)   MBri NCel
'Leen van der Mark' (3)   LAma NCel
'Lefeber's Favourite' (4)   LAma
'Libretto Parrot' (10)   LAma
'Lilac Time' (6)   LAma NCel
'Lilac Wonder'   see *T. saxatilis* (Bakeri Group)
                                      'Lilac Wonder'
'Lilliput'   see *T. humilis* 'Lilliput'
linifolia (15) ♀ H4   CAvo CMea EChP EHyt EPar EPfP
                                      EPot GIBF LAma LRHS NRog SSpi
                                      WFTG WShi
§ - Batalinii Group (15)   CBro LAma NRog WFTG
  ♀ H4
§ - - 'Apricot Jewel' (15)   CBro EPot
- - 'Bright Gem' (15) ♀ H4   CAvo CBro EPot LAma LRHS
                                      MBro NRog WCra WHoo
- - 'Bronze Charm' (15)   CAvo CBro CMea EPot LAma
                                      LPhx
- - 'Red Gem' (15)   CBro LAma
- - 'Yellow Jewel' (15)   EPot LAma
§ - Maximowiczii Group   CBro EPot LAma
'Little Beauty' (15)   WFTG
  ♀ H4 **new**
'London' (4)   LAma
'Lovely Surprise' (14)   ETub
'Lucky Strike' (3)   LAma
§ 'Lustige Witwe' (3)   LAma
'Lydia' (3)   LAma
§ 'Madame Lefeber' (13)   CBro MBri MWgw NRog
'Magier' (5)   LAma
'Maja' (7)   LAma
'Mamasa' (5)   LAma
'March of Time' (14)   MBri
'Maréchal Niel' (2)   LAma
'Mariette' (6)   CBro LAma LRHS MWgw
'Marilyn' (6)   ETub LAma LRHS NRog
'Marjolein' (6) ♀ H4   NRog
marjolletii (15)   CAvo CBro CMea LAma NRog
'Mary Ann' (14)   LAma
'Maureen' (5) ♀ H4   ETub LAma
mauritiana (15)   LAma
maximowiczii   see *T. linifolia* Maximowiczii
                                      Group
'Maytime' (6)   LAma MWgw NCel NRog
'Maywonder' (11) ♀ H4   LAma LRHS NCel NRog
'Menton' (5)   ETub
'Merry Christmas' (1)   NRog
Merry Widow   see *T.* 'Lustige Witwe'
'Mickey Mouse' (1)   NRog
'Minerva' (3)   NRog
'Miss Holland' (3)   MBri
'Mona Lisa' (6)   LAma NRog
§ *montana* (15)   CBro EPot GIBF LAma
'Monte Carlo' (2/d) ♀ H4   LAma LRHS NCel NRog
'Moonshine' (6)   NRog
'Mount Tacoma' (11)   CAvo ETub LAma MBri NCel
                                      NRog
'Mr Van der Hoef' (2)   LAma MBri NCel NRog
'Murillo' (2)   LAma
'My Lady' (4) ♀ H4   LAma
'Negrita' (3)   LAma NCel
neustruevae (15)   CBro CMea EPot GCrs
'New Design' (3/v)   EMar ETub LAma MBri NRog
'Orange Bouquet' (3) ♀ H4   LAma NRog

turkestanica (15) ♀ H4	CBro CSWP EChP EMar EPar EPfP EPot ETub EWTr LAma MBri MBro MWgw NPer NRog WBea WBrE WFTG WHoo
'Uncle Tom' (11)	LAma MBri
§ *undulatifolia* (15)	CBro LAma
'Union Jack' (5) ♀ H4	LAma
urumiensis (15) ♀ H4	CAvo CBro EPot LAma MBri MBro NRog WHoo
§ *urumoffii* (15)	LAma
'Valentine' (3) ♀ H4	LAma
'Van der Neer' (1)	LAma
'Varinas' (3)	LAma
'Veronique Sanson' new	ETub
violacea	see *T. humilis* Violacea Group
'Viridiflora' (8)	ETub NCel
'Vivaldi' (12)	LAma
'Vivex' (4) ♀ H4	LAma
§ 'Vlammenspel' (1)	LAma
'Vuurbaak' (2)	LAma
vvedenskyi (15)	EPot LAma NRog
- 'Tangerine Beauty' (15) ♀ H4	LRHS MBri
'West Point' (6) ♀ H4	CBro ETub LAma MWgw NCel NRog
* 'White Bouquet' (5)	NRog
'White Dream' (3)	ETub LAma LRHS NCel
'White Emperor'	see *T.* 'Purissima'
'White Parrot' (10)	CAvo LAma LRHS NCel NRog
'White Swallow' (3)	NRog
'White Triumphator' (6) ♀ H4	CAvo CBro CMea ETub LAma LRHS MWgw NBir NCel NRog
'White Virgin' (3)	LAma
whittallii	see *T. orphanidea* Whittallii Group
'Willem van Oranje' (2)	LAma NRog
'Willemsoord' (2)	ETub LAma LRHS MBri NCel NRog
wilsoniana	see *T. montana*
'Yellow Dawn' (14)	LAma LRHS NCel
'Yellow Emperor' (5)	MBri
'Yellow Empress' (13)	LAma
'Yellow Flight' (3)	LAma
'Yellow Parrot' (10)	NCel
'Yellow Present' (3)	LAma
'Yellow Purissima' (13) ♀ H4	NRog
'Yokohama' (3)	ETub LAma NRog
'Zampa' (14) ♀ H4	LAma
'Zombie' (13)	LAma

tummelberry see *Rubus* 'Tummelberry'

Tunica see *Petrorhagia*

Tupistra (Convallariaceae)

aurantiaca B&SWJ 2267	WCru
chinensis 'Eco China Ruffles' new	WCot
nutans	LEur

Turbina (Convolvulaceae)

corymbosa	MGol

Turnera (Turneraceae)

ulmifolia	MSal

Tussilago (Asteraceae)

farfara	CAgr CArn ELau GBar GPoy GWCH MHer MSal NSco WHer

Tutcheria (Theaceae)

§ *spectabilis*	EPfP

Tweedia (Asclepiadaceae)

§ *caerulea* ♀ H2	CM&M CSpe EMan ERea LLWP LPhx LPio SHFr SPar SPer SWal SYvo WEas WRos
- pink	LPio

Tylophora (Asclepiadaceae)

ovata	CPlN

Typha (Typhaceae)

angustifolia	CBen CKin CRow CWat EHon EMFW LPBA MSta NPer SBHF SPlb SWat WFar WWpP WWye
gracilis new	NBlu
latifolia	CAgr CBen CRow CWat EHon EMFW ENot LPBA MSta NPer SWal SWat WDyG WFar WHer WMAq WWpP WWye
- 'Variegata' (v)	CBen CRow CWat ELan EMFW LPBA MSta WCot WMAq
§ *laxmannii*	CBen CRow EHon EMFW LPBA MSta WWpP
minima	CBen CMHG CRDP CRow CWat EHoe EHon EMFW EPfP GBin LEdu LPBA MSta NPer SCoo SMad SWal SWat WFar WMAq WRos WWpP
- var. *gracilis*	ENot
shuttleworthii	CRow
stenophylla	see *T. laxmannii*

U

ugli see *Citrus* X *tangelo* 'Ugli'

Ugni (Myrtaceae)

candollei new	SSta
§ *molinae*	CDul CPLG CPle CSBt CTrC IDee ISea LEdu MDun SHFr SOWG WAbe WCHb WDin WGwG WJek WPlc WSHC WWal WWyc

Ulex (Papilionaceae)

europaeus	CCVT CDoC EBee EGoo ENot EPfP GWCH LBuc MCoo NWea WDin WHar WMou
§ - 'Flore Pleno' (d) ♀ H4	CBcs CBgR CDoC CSBt EBee EMon ENot EPfP EPla IArd MGos NLar NWea SHBN SPer WBcn WCot WFar
- 'Plenus'	see *U. europaeus* 'Flore Pleno'
- 'Prostratus'	MBar
gallii	WDin
- 'Mizen Head'	ESis GCal GGGa GSki MBlu MWhi SLon SMad WBcn
§ *minor*	EPla
nanus	see *U. minor*

Ullucus (Basellaceae)

tuberosus 'Humphrey Chadwick Earwicker' new	IIve
- 'Pica de Pulga'	IIve

Ulmus ❀ (Ulmaceae)

'Dodoens'	EBee IArd LBuc MGos
§ *glabra*	CDul ECrN GKir GTre NWea WDin

– 'Camperdownii'	CDoC CTho EBee ECrN ELan LPan NBee SPer
– 'Exoniensis'	CDul CTho SRPl
– 'Gittisham'	CTho
– 'Horizontalis'	see *U. glabra* 'Pendula'
– 'Lutescens'	CDoC CEnd CTho CTri LRHS SKee SLim
– 'Nana'	WPat
§ – 'Pendula'	LPan SLim
x *hollandica* 'Jacqueline Hillier'	EBre ELan EPfP EPla EWTr GDra GEdr GEil IMGH MBar MBro MHdf NBlu NHar NHol NWea SLon SPer SRms STre WAbe WCFE WDin WFar WOld WPGP WPat
– 'Lobel'	CDul CBee ENot MGos
– 'Wredei'	see *U. minor* 'Dampieri Aurea'
laevis new	CDul CTho EGFP
§ *minor* 'Dampieri Aurea'	CBot CDul CEnd CLnd CTho EBee ELan EPfP GKir LNet LRHS MAsh MBar MBlu MGos NBee NBlu SHBN SKee SLim SMad SPer WDin WPat
– 'Variegata' (v)	EPot SCoo
montana	see *U. glabra*
parvifolia	CMCN CTho ECrN NWea SMad STre WHCr WNor
– 'Frosty' (v)	ECho EPot
– 'Geisha' (v)	ELan MGos WBcn WPat
§ – 'Hokkaido'	ESis LBee LTwo MBro NHar NLar SBla WAbe WOBN WPat
– 'Pygmaea'	see *U. parvifolia* 'Hokkaido'
– 'Seiju'	SMad
– 'Yatsubusa'	CLyd EPot ESis EWes LTwo NLar SIng STre WPat
procera	CDul CTho LBuc WDin
– 'Argenteovariegata' (v)	CDul CTho MGos SMad
pumila	CAgr EPot WNor WOTO
rubra new	MSal
'Sapporo Autumn Gold'PBR	WDin

Umbellularia (*Lauraceae*)

californica	CAgr CArn CPne IArd SAPC SArc WSHC

Umbilicus (*Crassulaceae*)

erectus	see *U. luteus*
horizontalis new	Ilve
§ *luteus*	CRDP
rupestris	GDea GEdr Ilve NWCA SChr WBri WCot WCru WHer WShi WWye

Uncinia (*Cyperaceae*)

from Chile	EPla GCal
egmontiana	CBri CElw EBla EChP EHoe EMan EPPr EPyc GSki LRav MNrw MWrn NChi NHol SMac WCot WHrl WPnP WWeb
N *rubra*	More than 30 suppliers
uncinata	CFil CM&M ECha EMan GGar GSki LHop NHol SDix SGar
* – *rubra*	CFir CKno COIW CTrC CTri CWCL EAmu ECot EHol EHrv EPGN EVFa GSki IFro LRHS MCLN MMHG MNrw NGdn SDes SLim SPar STes WCom

Uniola (*Poaceae*)

latifolia	see *Chasmanthium latifolium*

Urceolina (*Amaryllidaceae*)

miniata	see *Stenomesson miniatum*
peruviana	see *Stenomesson miniatum*

Urechites see *Pentalinon*

Urginea (*Hyacinthaceae*)

macrocentra CD&R 218	WCot
maritima	EBee EBot ETub GPoy LAma MNrw MSal

Urospermum (*Asteraceae*)

dalechampii	CDes COtt CSam EBee EBre EMan GKir SAga WCot

Ursinia (*Asteraceae*)

alpina new	CPBP
montana	NWCA

Urtica (*Urticaceae*)

dioica 'Brightstone Bitch' (v)	WAlt
– 'Chedglow' (v)	CNat WAlt
– 'Dainty Danglers'	CNat
– 'Danae Johnston' (v)	WAlt
– 'Dusting' (v)	WAlt
– 'Dying for Attention'	WAlt
– 'Fearnvale Tigertooth' (v)	WAlt
– 'Good as Gold' (v)	WAlt
– subsp. *gracilis* var. *procera*	CNat
– 'Ingdust' (v)	WAlt
– OGG mutant	WAlt
– 'Spring Fever'	WAlt
– 'Worn Gilding' (v)	WAlt
galeopsifolia	CNat

Utricularia (*Lentibulariaceae*)

alpina	CSWC
australis	EFEx
biloba	GTro
bisquamata	CSWC GTro SHmp
blancheti	CSWC
calycifida	GTro SHmp
dichotoma	CSWC EFEx GTro
– var. *uniflora*	LHew
exoleta R. Brown	see *U. gibba*
§ *gibba*	EFEx
intermedia	EFEx
lateriflora	EFEx GTro
livida	CSWC EFEx GTro
longifolia	CSWC GTro
menziesii	EFEx GTro
monanthos	EFEx
nephrophylla	GTro SHmp
novae-zelandiae	GTro
ochroleuca	EFEx
praelonga	GTro SHmp
prehensilis	GTro
pubescens	LHew SHmp
reniformis	EFEx GTro SHmp
– *nana*	EFEx
sandersonii	GTro SHmp
– blue	GTro
subulata	EFEx
tricolor	GTro SHmp
vulgaris	CSWC EFEx

Uvularia (*Convallariaceae*)

§ *caroliniana*	IBlr
disporum	LAma
grandiflora ♀ H4	More than 30 suppliers
– dwarf	IBlr LEur
– 'Lynda Windsor' new	CRDP
– var. *pallida*	CAvo CBct CBos CDes CPom CRDP EBee ECha EGle EHrv

	EMan EPPr EPar GBri GBuc IBlr LEur LPhx MRav NDov SBla SMHy SUsu WCru
- 'Susie Lewis' **new**	WCru
- x *perfoliata*	IBlr
perfoliata	CBct CStu EBee ECha EDAr EGle EHyt EMan EPar EPfP EPla GBri GCrs IBlr LAma LEur MBro MRav NHar SIng SSpi WAbe WBrE WCru WHil WIvy WPGP
pudica	see *U. caroliniana*
sessilifolia	CBct CRDP EBee EPPr EPar EPot GCrs IBlr LAma NMen WCru WIvy

V

Vaccaria (Caryophyllaceae)
§ *hispanica*	MSal
segetalis	see *V. hispanica*

Vaccinium ✿ (Ericaceae)
from Bolivia **new**	EWes
arctostaphylos	SReu SSta
caespitosum	GDra SOkd
'Cinderella'	SSta
consanguineum	SReu
corymbosum (F) ♀ H4	CBcs ENot EPfP MBar MGos NBee SCoo SReu SSta WDin WGer
- 'Berkeley' (F)	CTrh GTwe LBuc LRHS SDea
- 'Blue Ray' (F)	CWib SCoo
- 'Bluecrop' (F)	CDoC CTrh CWib EMui EPfP GKir GTwe LBuc LRHS MAsh MBri MGos NBee SCoo SDea SKee SPer WWeb
- 'Bluegold' (F)	CTrh LRHS MAsh SCoo
- 'Bluejay' (F)	CTrh LRHS MAsh SCoo
- 'Bluetta' (F)	GTwe LRHS SCoo
- 'Collins' (F)	CTrh
- 'Concord' (F)	ENot SCoo
- 'Coville' (F)	EMui
- 'Duke' (F)	CTrh ELan EPfP GKir LRHS MAsh
'Earliblue' (F)	EMui LRHS MGos SDea
- 'Goldtraube' (F)	CDoC CTri CWSG GKir MBlu MBri MGos SDea SKee WStI
- 'Herbert' (F)	CTrh EMui GTwe MGos SCoo
- 'Ivanhoe' (F)	CTrh SCoo
- 'Jersey' (F)	GKir LRHS MAsh MGos SCoo SDea
- 'Nelson' (F)	CTrh SCoo
- 'Northland' (F)	GTwe SCoo SDea
- 'Patriot' (F)	CTrh GTwe LRHS MGos SCoo
- 'Pioneer' (F)	MBar
- 'Spartan' (F)	GTwe LRHS SCoo
- 'Sunrise' (F)	GTwe
- 'Top Hat' (F) **new**	LRHS MAsh
- 'Toro' (F)	GTwe LRHS
- 'Weymouth' (F)	SDea
crassifolium subsp. *sempervirens*	GKir LRHS MAsh
'Well's Delight' (F)	
cylindraceum ♀ H4	EPfP MBro SSta WAbe WFar WPat
- 'Tinkerbelle'	WAbe
- 'Tom Thumb'	WAbe
delavayi	GGar GKir LRHS MAsh MBar MDun NRya SReu SSpi SSta WAbe
donianum	see *V. sprengelii*

dunalianum	CBcs
- var. *caudatifolium* B&SWJ 1716	WCru
emarginatum	SSta
floribundum	CDoC CFil CMHG GDra GGar GKir GTou LRHS MAsh MDun SRPl SSpi SSta WAbe WPGP WPic
glaucoalbum ♀ H3-4	CAbP CDoC CPLG EPfP GGGa GKir LRHS MAsh MBar MRav SMad SPar SPer SReu SSpi SSta WBod WDin
griffithianum	SReu
§ *macrocarpon* (F)	ELan GKir GTwe LRHS MAsh MBar MBri NWCA SRms
- 'CN' (F)	ESim MGos
- 'Early Black' (F)	CBcs MGos SLdr
- 'Franklin' (F)	EPot ESim
- 'Hamilton' (F)	EPot GCrs ITim LTwo NHol WPat
- 'McFarlin' (F)	EMui
- 'Olson's Honkers' (F)	ESim
- 'Pilgrim' (F)	ESim
membranaceum	SSta
mortinia	NMen
moupinense	CDoC GKir IMGH LRHS MAsh WAbe
- 'Variegatum' (v)	LTwo
myrsinites	NLAp
myrtillus	GPoy IIve MBar WDin
'Nimo Pink'	MBar
nummularia	CNic EHyt EPot GDra GEdr GKir NHar NLAp SReu SSpi WAbe WPic
ovatum	CMHG GBin LRHS MBar MDun SSta WPic
- 'Thundercloud' **new**	CAbP LRHS MAsh
§ *oxycoccos* (F)	CArn GPoy WWes
padifolium	CFil WPGP
pallidum	IBlr
palustre	see *V. oxycoccos*
parvifolium	SReu
praestans	ESim GIBF NHol
retusum	CTrw ICrw WBod WDin WPic
sikkimense	GGGa
§ *sprengelii*	CBcs
uliginosum	GIBF
vitis-idaea	CNic EWTr GGar GPoy MBar MGos NLAp SReu SRot WFar
- 'Autumn Beauty'	NLar
- 'Compactum'	FWes NHar
- Koralle Group ♀ H4	EPfP MBar MBri MRav NHol SPar SPer WPat
- var. *minus*	EHyt GCrs GKir MAsh NMen SOkd WAbe
- 'Red Pearl'	CSBt EPfP LRHS MAsh MGos
* - 'Variegatum' (v)	EWes WPat

Valeriana (Valerianaceae)
'Alba'	see *Centranthus ruber* 'Albus'
alliariifolia	EMon GCal NBro NSti WCot
arizonica	CLyd EDAr MSte MTho NFla
'Coccinea'	see *Centranthus ruber*
coreana **new**	CFee
fedtschenkoi **new**	EBee
hardwickii	GPoy
- CC 2227	CPLG
jatamansii	CArn GPoy
montana	GTou NBro NRya SRms SWat
moyanoi **new**	CFil
officinalis	CAgr CArn CKin CRDP CSev EBee ECha ELau GBar GPoy ILis MAnH MBow MCAu MChe MHer NBro NLar SAga SCro SIde SRms SWat WAul WHer WMoo WPer WShi WWye

- subsp. *sambucifolia*	CFee SHar
* - 'Variegata' (v)	WCHb
phu 'Aurea'	More than 30 suppliers
* - 'Purpurea'	ECoo
pyrenaica	ECha EVFa SHar WCot WEas WFTG
saxatilis	NRya
supina	NWCA
tatamana	WEas
wallrothii	WCot

Valerianella (*Valerianaceae*)

§ *locusta*	GPoy
olitoria	see *V. locusta*

Vallea (*Elaeocarpaceae*)

stipularis	CDoC
- var. *pyrifolia*	CPLG CPle

Vallota see *Cyrtanthus*

Vancouveria (*Berberidaceae*)

chrysantha	CElw CFil EBee ECha EMan ERos EVFa GBuc GEil IBlr LEur LHop MNrw MRav NLar NRya NWCA SSpi WCru WSHC
hexandra	CElw CFil EBee ECGN EHrv EMan EMon EPar EPla ERos GBuc GCal GEil GKir IBlr LEur NRya NSti SSpi WAbe WBea WCru WWin
planipetala	IBlr LEur SSpi WCru

veitchberry see *Rubus* 'Veitchberry'

Veltheimia (*Hyacinthaceae*)

§ *bracteata* ♀ H1	CHal EBak IBlr LBow NRog SYvo WCot
- 'Yellow Flame'	CPne
§ *capensis* ♀ H1	CSev MTPN
viridifolia hort.	see *V. capensis*
viridifolia Jacq.	see *V. bracteata*

x *Venidioarctotis* see *Arctotis*

Venidium see *Arctotis*

Veratrum ❀ (*Melanthiaceae*)

album	CFil ECha GBuc GIBF LRHS MRav NLar SBla SChu SSpi WBrE WCot WCru WFar
- var. *flavum*	LPhx WCru
- var. *oxysepalum*	WCru
californicum	CFil IBlr
dolichopetalum B&SWJ 4416 **new**	WCru
formosanum	MNrw
- B&SWJ 1575	WCru
maackii var. *maackii* B&SWJ 5831	WCru
nigrum ♀ H4	CBct CBot CBro CFil CFir CPne EBee EMil EVFa GBuc GCal LPhx MMil MNrw NBhm NBir NBur NChi NGby NGdn NLar SChu SMad SMrm SPoG SSpi WCom WCot WFar WTin
stamineum	WCru
viride	EBee EBre IBlr NLar SBla SSpi

Verbascum ❀ (*Scrophulariaceae*)

acaule	NMen
adzharicum	EBee IFro MBro NBur WFTG WHoo WSan
- 'Charles Delight' **new**	MSph

Allestree hybrids	CFee EHol EHrv EMar
'Apricot Sunset'	ECoo LPhx
'Arctic Summer'	see *V. bombyciferum* 'Polarsommer'
arcturus	EBee WPer
* *bakerianum*	EBla ECtt MWrn WEas WHil WMoo
'Banana and Custard'	CFwr CWCL WSan
'Bill Bishop'	NHar SIng
blattaria	EBee EBot EHrv LIck LRHS MBow MNFA MWgw NBir SWat WEas WFar WHer WPer WRHF
- MESE 560	EBee
- f. *albiflorum*	CBri CNic CSpe EBee ECGN EChP EMar ERou LHop LLWP LPhx LRHS MBro MHer NDov NSti SGar WHer WPer WRus
- pink	CBri EBee EGoo NPPs STes
- yellow	CBri SWat WSan
* *boerhavii* bicolor	EWTr WElm WRos
§ *bombyciferum*	CBre CSev EBlw EChP ECha GMaP IIve MCLN NGdn NPSI NSti SGar SRms WCot WWeb
- BSSS 232	WCru
§ - 'Polarsommer'	COIW CSam CSpe EBre EPfP ERou GGar GKir LHrt LRHS MBri MLwd NBir NBlu NVic SPar SPer SPet SRms SWat WLow WViv WWeb
- 'Silver Lining'	NBur NPer WBry WMnd
'Brookside'	ECoo LPhx
'Broussa'	see *V. bombyciferum*
'Butterscotch'	MAnH MSph
Caribbean Crush Group **new**	CPen LBuc
- 'Mango' **new**	EBee ENot
chaixii	CHea CSam EBee EBlw ECha ECtt EHrv GAbr GBuc LHrt LRHS MMHG NBir SBla WAul WFar WMoo WPer
- 'Album' ♀ H4	More than 30 suppliers
chaixii x 'Wendy's Choice' **new**	MAvo
'Charles Harper' **new**	ECoo LPhx
(Cotswold Group) 'Cotswold Beauty' ♀ H4	More than 30 suppliers
- 'Cotswold Queen' ♀ H4	More than 30 suppliers
- 'Gainsborough' ♀ H4	More than 30 suppliers
- 'Mont Blanc'	EBee EBre EChP ECot EFou EHrv EMan EMar GMaP LAst LPio LRHS MAnH MCAu MLLN MNFA SChu SPer SPla SWat WRus WSan
- 'Pink Domino' ♀ H4	More than 30 suppliers
- 'Royal Highland'	More than 30 suppliers
- 'White Domino'	EBee ERou LCaP LRHS MBNS MCAu NPri SPar WViv
'Cotswold King'	CDes CSpe CWes EBee EChP EVFa EWTr LHop LPio MBri MSph NDov NPri WCot WPGP WSan
creticum	EBee EPri LPhx WPer
'Daisy Alice'	ECoo LPhx
§ *densiflorum*	CArn EBee EChP ECoo ERou ITer NFla SIde SPer WFar WPer WRHF
dumulosum ♀ H2-3	EDAr EHyt EPot NWCA WAbe WSan
'Ellenbank Rose'	MAnH
epixanthinum **new**	CPla EMan ITer MDKP SPoG
'Golden Wings' ♀ H2-3	CPBP CPla ECtt EPot ITim NMen WAbe WPat
'Helen Johnson'	More than 30 suppliers
I x *hybridum* 'Copper Rose' **new**	MWrn WHHs
- 'Snow Maiden'	CBri CPen WBry WFTG
'Jackie'	More than 30 suppliers
'Jolly Eyes'	CPen EBee EMan MAvo
'June Johnson' **new**	SHar
'Kynaston' **new**	SHar

'Letitia' ♀ H3	CPla EBee EBre ECtt EHyt ELan EMan EMlt EPot EWes GCal IMGH LBee LRHS MTho NMen NPri NWCA SBla SIng SRot WAbe WKif WPat WWin
longifolium	EBee LRHS WFar
- MESE 394	EBee
- var. *pannosum*	see *V. olympicum*
lychnitis	CArn LPhx WHer
macrurum	EBee
'Megan's Mauve'	CM&M CWCL EBee EBlw ECot EMan EMar EWll LAst NDov NPSI NSti SPer SUsu
'Monster' **new**	LPhx
nigrum	CArn COIW EBee EBot ECtt EPfP LHrt LRHS MBNS MCAu MChe MWrn NChi NSti SEND SMer SRob WCot WElm WFar WHer WHil WMoo WPer WWpP
- var. *album*	COIW EBee LPio MBri MCAu
'Norfolk Dawn'	ECoo LPhx
§ *olympicum*	CSam EBee EBlw ECtt EGoo ELan ENot EPfP GKir LHrt LPVE LRHS MBNS MWgw NBid NOak SDes SDix SEND SRob SWal WBry WCot WFar WPer
oreophilum	EBee
'Patricia'	ECoo LPhx
phoeniceum	CArn EBee EBot ECGN ELan EPfP LPVe LRHS MPWC MWgw MWrn NBro NOak NPPs SDes SGar SMer SPet SPlb WAul WEas WHen WPer WWeb WWin
* - 'Album'	CSpe EBee Llck SDes WBrE WOut
- 'Flush of Pink'	ECtt
- 'Flush of White'	CBot ECtt EGoo EMan ERou LAst LRHS MWrn NChi NPri SRob STes WGor WHen WHil WMoo WWhi WWpP
- hybrids	CBot COIW CSpe EGoo EMan MHer NBid NBlu NChi NGdn NVic SRms SWat WFar WGor WPer
- 'Violetta'	More than 30 suppliers
'Pink Ice'	MAvo
'Plum Pudding'	ECoo
'Primrose Cottage'	ECoo LPhx
'Primrose Skies'	ECoo
pulverulentum	CKin
pyramidatum	EBee WHer
'Raspberry Ripple'	CPcn EBee EMan EMar ENot EPfP MAnH MAvo NPSI SPer
'Raspberry Sorbet'	EMan
rorippifolium	EBee EMar EWll LPhx MCAu MSPs WCot WHil WSan
'Saffron Towers' **new**	WFTG
sinuatum	WCot
'Southern Charm'	CFwr CWCL EChP ECtt EMan ERou EWll LPVe LRHS MAnH MAvo MBri NChi STes WGor WHil WSan WWpP
* 'Spica'	EBee ERou WCot
spicatum	CBot GMac WFar WRus
spinosum	SBla
'Summer Sorbet'	CPcn EBee EMan ENot LBuc SPer
* 'Sunset shades'	MSph
thapsiforme	see *V. densiflorum*
thapsus	COld CScv EBee EBlw EBot GPoy GWCH MBow MChe MHer NFor NMir NSco SRob WHHs WSel WWye
'Tilney Moonbeam'	EMar
undulatum	CArn
'Valerie Grace'	ECoo LPhx
'Vernale'	CBot
wiedemannianum	EBee EWll SIgm WHer

Verbena (Verbenaceae)

'Adonis Light Blue' (G)	LRHS
'Apple Blossom' (G)	LRHS
'Aveyron' (G)	GBri SChu
* 'Batesville Rose' (G)	WCot
'Betty Lee' **new**	ECtt
'Blue Cascade' (G)	LPVe
'Blue Prince' (G)	CSpe
§ *bonariensis* ♀ H3-4	More than 30 suppliers
- variegated (v) **new**	ITer WCot
'Booty' (G)	SMrm
'Boughton House' (G)	CSpe MSte
bracteata **new**	GEil
canadensis	EBee
- 'Perfecta' (G)	MWrn
'Candy Carousel' (G)	CElw SPet
chamaedrifolia	see *V. peruviana*
'Claret' (G)	GBri WPen WViv
corymbosa	CBrm CHea CHll CM&M CPen CRez EBee EChP ECha EMan EPyc LHop LLWP NLar SBod SMrm WCom WCot WPer WWpP
- 'Gravetye'	CElw CHad GBuc GCal MOak NChi NGiC WFar
'Diamond Butterfly' (G)	NPri WWol
'Diamond Carousele' (G)	NPri
'Diamond Merci' (G)	Llck NPri WWol
'Diamond Rhodonit' (G)	WWol
'Diamond Topaz'	Llck WWol
'Edith Eddleman' (G)	EBee ECtt LRHS MGrG MNrw WCot
* 'Fiesta'	WCot
* 'Foxhunter' (G)	EMan
'Freefall'	GBri
hastata	More than 30 suppliers
- 'Alba'	CBri CHar EBee EMan EPyc EWTr GBar GBuc LDai MAnH MCCP MDKP MLLN STes WFTG WHrl WMoo WPer WTin WWpP
- 'Rosca'	More than 30 suppliers
'Hidcote Purple' (G)	MSte
hispida (G)	EBee
'Homestead Purple' (G)	CSev EBee EBur ECGP ECtt EMan EPfP LDai LHrt MWgw SAga SCoo SIng SMrm SUsu WGwG
'Huntsman' (G)	GBuc
'Imagination' (G)	CFox LRHS
incompta	EBee EMan
'Jenny's Wine' (G)	CElw
N 'Kemerton' (G)	EMan
'La France' (G)	CHea CSam ECha EMan EPfP GBri LPhx MAnH NDov SAga SChu SDix SMHy SMrm SOkh SUsu WHoo
(Lanai Series) 'Lanai Bright Pink' **new**	Llck
- 'Lanai Purple' **new**	SCoo
'Lawrence Johnston' (G) ♀ H3	WHen
litoralis	EBee
'Louis Ruby' **new**	SAga
'Loveliness' (G)	EMan IBlr LRHS SMer
macdougalii	EBee EChP EMan GEil IFro MGol STes WBVN WWpP
officinalis	CArn GBar GPoy MChe MGol MHer MSal SIde WHer WJek WLHH WPer WSel WWyc
patagonica	see *V. bonariensis*
'Peach Blossom' (G)	WCot
'Peaches and Cream' (G) ♀ H3	LRHS NPri

§ *peruviana* (G) — EBre EPfP MAsh MOak SChu SDix SIng SRms WWeb
'Pink Bouquet' — see *V.* 'Silver Anne'
'Pink Parfait' (G) — CHal CSpe ECtt ELan EMan EPfP LHrt MOak SMer SPet WWol
'Pink Pearl' (G) — ECtt
'Purple Sissinghurst' (G) — CSam
'Raspberry Crush' (G) — LRHS
'Red Cascade' — SPet
§ *rigida* ♀ H3 — More than 30 suppliers
- 'Polaris' — CHad CHar CStr EBee LHop LRHS SMrm STes SUsu WPen
* 'Royal Purple' — EMan
§ 'Silver Anne' (G) ♀ H3 — CSam EBee ECtt EMan LDai LHrt LRHS MOak NPri SChu SCro SDix SMer SRms SUsu WEas WHen
§ 'Sissinghurst' (G) ♀ H2-3 — CSam ECtt EMan MOak NPri SCro SIng SMrm SRms WEas WHen
* 'Snow Flurry' — WCot
(Splash Series) 'Splash Light Rose' **new** — WWol
- 'Splash Purple' — WWol
- 'Splash Rose' — WWol
- 'Splash Sky Blue' **new** — WWol
stricta — EBee EMan Iive
Tapien Pink = 'Sunver'PBR — WWol
Tapien Violet = 'Sunvop'PBR (G) — NPri
Temari Coral Pink = 'Sunmariripi'PBR — SCoo
Temari Scarlet = 'Sunmarisu'PBR (G) — NPri SCoo
Temari Violet Star (G) — NPri
Temari Violet = 'Sunmariba'PBR — NPri SCoo
'Tenerife' — see *V.* 'Sissinghurst'
tenuisecta (G) — WHil WMoo WPer
'Tortuga Peach' — LIck NPri
urticifolia — IIve
venosa — see *V. rigida*

Verbesina (Asteraceae)
alternifolia — CArn EMan
- 'Goldstrahl' **new** — MCAu
helianthoides **new** — CPLG EBee

Vernonia (Asteraceae)
crinita — EBee ECha EFou MWat NLar SIgm SMad
- 'Mammuth' — EMan LHop LPhx
fasciculata — EBee EMan Iive NLar SSvw WCot
noveboracensis — EBee ECGN SMrm WPer
- 'Albiflora' — NLar WPer

Veronica (Scrophulariaceae)
amethystina — see *V. spuria*
armena — CLyd ECGP EWes MHer MSte MWat NMen NRya SBla SRot WFar
§ *austriaca* — MLLN WMoo
- var. *dubia* — see *V. prostrata*
- 'Ionian Skies' — CLyd CMea CPBP CRDP CSpe CTri EBee EMan EOrc ESis EWes GBuc LBee LHop LPhx LRHS MHar MNrw NDov SBla SChu SHel SIgm SPer WCom WCru WFar WKif WPer
§ - subsp. *teucrium* — CArn EMan LAst LRHS NChi SChu SSpe WFar WOut WPer
- - 'Blue Blazer' — SCro
- - 'Blue Fountain' — LLWP
- - 'Crater Lake Blue' ♀ H4 — More than 30 suppliers

- - 'Kapitän' — ECha GBuc SMrm WFar WPer
- - 'Knallblau' — EBee EFou EMil GMac LRHS MBri SSvw WLRN
- - 'Königsblau' — EBee WBea
- - 'Royal Blue' ♀ H4 — EBee ECot EFou EMan EMlt EPfP GBuc LPio LRHS MArl MWrn NOak NSti WBea WFar WMnd WMoo
- - 'Shirley Blue' — see *V.* 'Shirley Blue'
beccabunga — CArn CBen CKin CWat EHon ELan EMFW GDea GPoy LPBA MGas MSta NMir NPer NSco SWat WFar WHer WMAq WWpP
bellidioides — GTou
'Bergen's Blue' **new** — EChP MBri WElm
Blue Bouquet — see *V. longifolia* 'Blaubündel'
'Blue Spire' — SWat WPer
bombycina — EHyt EPot ITim NWCA WLin
- subsp. *bolkardaghensis* — NMen
bonarota — see *Paederota bonarota*
caespitosa — CPBP MDHE
- subsp. *caespitosa* — CLyd EHyt NMen WAbe
candida — see *V. spicata* subsp. *incana*
x *cantiana* 'Kentish Pink' — CStr GBuc MBro MHer SHel SIng SPla WBea WPer
caucasica — CRDP EMon LPhx SAga WCru
chamaedrys — CKin IIve NMir
§ - 'Miffy Brute' (v) — EBee EPyc MDKP MHar NBir NFla NHol NPro WCom WHer
- 'Pam' (v) — CBre EPPr EVFa WAlt WCHb WWpP
- 'Variegata' — see *V. chamaedrys* 'Miffy Brute'
- 'Waterrow' — EMon WAlt
- 'Yorkley Wood' — WAlt
cinerea ♀ H4 — CLyd MBro SAga WEas WHoo
dabneyi — CDes
'Darwin's Blue' **new** — EChP MBNS MBri WGwG WHHs
'Ellen Mae' — EBee MCAu
exaltata — CWCL EBee ECGN EChP EMFP EMan GBuc LPhx MBct MSte NBur NChi SAga WCot WPer
'Fantasy' **new** — SMHy
filiformis — GWCH
- 'Fairyland' (v) — EMan EMon EWes WAlt WCHb
formosa — see *Parahebe formosa*
§ *fruticans* — GTou
fruticulosa — NWCA
gentianoides ♀ H4 — More than 30 suppliers
- 'Alba' — CMea CRDP EOrc GCal NBid NChi NSti SAga
- 'Barbara Sherwood' — EBee EBre GKir GMac MAnH MFir MLLN MNFA MTed WCot
- 'Lilacina' — EBee LRHS
- 'Nana' — EOrc MMil WBrE
- 'Pallida' — EBee EMan ENot EPfP IHMH LCaP LRHS MBrN MRav NPri SPlb WBor WFar
- 'Robusta' — EBee GMac LRHS MSph SPet WMnd
- 'Tissington White' — More than 30 suppliers
- 'Variegata' (v) — More than 30 suppliers
'Goodness Grows' — EMan LAst LRHS NChi SChu SSpe
grandis — CHar EBee EChP EMan EWll GAbr MHar MWhi MWrn NBur NPPs SPoG WMoo WOut
x *guthrieana* — CNic EMlt NMen SRms SRot WCru WFar WPer
'Heraud' **new** — MCAu
incana — see *V. spicata* subsp. *incana*
* - 'Candidissima' — GCal
'Inspiration' — EFou LPhx SMrm WFTG
* *keiskei* pink — ECtt
kellereri — see *V. spicata*
kiusiana — CPlt CRDP CStr EBee EBre EMan MTis SPoG

kotschyana	CPBP
liwanensis	EDAr NMen
- Mac&W 5936	EPot
longifolia	CSBt EBee ECha ELan EPfP EShb EWTr GWCH MBow MFir MHar NPPs SDes SMac SMrm STes WBea WCom WEas WLRN WMoo
- 'Alba'	CHea EBee EChP ELan EMan EPfP EWTr WBea WMoo
§ - 'Blaubündel'	EBee EFou ERou LPVe MPWC MWrn NGdn SMac WHil WWeb
- 'Blauer Sommer'	EBee EChP EFou EMan LRHS NGdn SPer WMnd
§ - 'Blauriesin'	CM&M COIW EBee ECGP EMil ERou GLil GMaP MBri NFla NSti SDes SMad SPer WFar
- Blue Giantess	see *V. longifolia* 'Blauriesin'
- 'Blue John' **new**	EBee MCAu
- 'Fascination'	MOne NGdn NPro SMrm WSan
- 'Foerster's Blue'	see *V. longifolia* 'Blauriesin'
- 'Joseph's Coat' (v)	EBee EGle EVFa
- 'Lila Karina'	EBee WCot WPer
- 'Lilac Fantasy' **new**	MCAu
- 'Oxford Blue'	LRHS WRHF
- 'Rose Tone'	ECha ERou MDKP WMoo
- 'Rosea'	EBee EChP ERou EWTr MGol MWgw MWrn SMac STes WBrE WPer
- 'Schneeriesin'	EBee ECGP ECha EHrv GMaP LRHS MBri MCAu NBir SChu SCro SPer
lyallii	see *Parahebe lyallii*
macrostachya	EBee
'Martje'	SMrm
montana	CKin
- 'Corinne Tremaine' (v)	EBee EMan EMar EMon EVFa IFro IHMH LHop MHar MLLN NBir SUsu WCot WHer WHrl
nipponica	SScr WPer
nummularia	NBur WPer
oenei **new**	CPBP
officinalis	CArn CKin Ilve WHbs
oltensis	CLyd CPBP EHyt EPot ESis EWes LTwo MHer NHol NMen WPat WWin
orchidea	EBee EBre SBri SRms
orientalis	EBee
- subsp. *orientalis*	NMen
ornata	EMan MGol WCot WPer
pectinata	ECtt ESis GDra NLon
- 'Rosea'	ECtt EWes GDra GKir WPer WWin
peduncularis	EOrc LRHS WEas
- 'Alba'	MHar WPer
§ - 'Georgia Blue'	More than 30 suppliers
- 'Oxford Blue'	see *V. peduncularis* 'Georgia Blue'
perfoliata	see *Parahebe perfoliata*
Pershore Gold = 'Perglow'	EGle WLRN
petraea 'Madame Mercier'	LHop LRHS MBri
'Pink Damask'	CHad CHar CSpe EBee EChP ECtt EFou EMan EMil ERou GLil GMaP LPVe LPhx LRHS MBri MUlv NDov NLar NPPs SCro SDes SMad SMrm SOkh SSvw SUsu WFar WMnd WRus
pinnata 'Blue Eyes'	ESis LBee LHop
prenja	see *V. austriaca*
§ *prostrata* ♀ H4	CAgr CLyd CSam CSpe EMNN EMlt ESis EWTr GDra GEdr GKir LBee LRHS MBro MWat NJOw SCro SHFr SRms WBea WCom WCru WEas WHoo WMoo WWin
- 'Alba'	CSpe MBro MWat WHoo WLin
§ - 'Blauspiegel'	CPBP SBla SIgm SMrm WCru
- 'Blue Ice'	GKir SMrm
- Blue Mirror	see *V. prostrata* 'Blauspiegel'
- 'Blue Sheen'	CBrm CSpe ECtt EMlt ESis GKir LPhx LRHS MBNS NBir SAga SChu SIng WFar WPer WWin
- 'Lilac Time' **new**	NBir SIng
- 'Loddon Blue'	GKir LRHS NVic SBla WCot WPer
- 'Miss Willmott'	see *V. prostrata* 'Warley Blue'
- 'Mrs Holt'	CHar CLyd CMea CPBP CSam CSpe EBre ECtt EMNN ESis GKir LPhx LRHS NBir NFor NMen SAga SBla SIng SRms WBea WCom WCru WWin
- 'Nana'	EMNN EPot ESis EWes MWat NMen
- 'Rosea'	ESis MWat SIgm WPer
- 'Silver Queen'	SRms
- 'Spode Blue' ♀ H4	CHar CMea COIW ECtt GMaP LHop LRHS MOne NWCA SBla SDes SIng SRms WLin
- 'Trehane'	CHea COIW EBre ECtt EDAr EMlt ESis LBee LGro LHop LRHS MBro MHer MWat NOak NRya SCro SDes SIng SPlb SRms SRot SWat WAbe
§ - 'Warley Blue'	CMGP
* *pseudolysimachion* **new**	WCot
repens	EWTr IHMH NBlu NNor NRya SPlb WPer
'Rosalinde'	CBot GBuc NCat WPer
'Royal Pink' **new**	CM&M
rupestris	see *V. prostrata*
saturejoides	CPBP SRms WPer
saxatilis	see *V. fruticans*
schmidtiana	GTou WPer
- 'Nana'	CPBP MBro WPat
selleri	see *V. wormskjoldii*
serpyllifolia	Ilve
§ 'Shirley Blue' ♀ H4	CPrp EBre EFou EPfP EWTr GKir MBNS MHer MWat NChi NMir SPer SRms WCFE WHen WMoo WPer WTel WWhi
sieboldiana	SMrm WCot
§ *spicata*	EBee EBot ELan LEdu LRHS MBNS MCAu MWgw NBId NBlu NFor NLon SDes SHel SMer SPet SRms WFar WPer WWye
- 'Alba'	EBee EMan EMil LPVe MBNS MRav SDes SRPl WBea WOut WPer
- 'Barcarolle'	EBee ELan MLLN
§ - 'Blaufuchs'	CMHG CSam ECtt WTel
- 'Blue Bouquet' **new**	IBal LPVe
- Blue Fox	see *V. spicata* 'Blaufuchs'
§ - 'Erika'	EBee ECha ECtt GBuc MLLN NArg NBir NOak SAga SDes SSte
- 'Heidekind'	More than 30 suppliers
- subsp. *hybrida*	WIlcr
§ - 'Icicle'	CM&M EBee EFou EOrc LRHS MBrN SUsu
§ - subsp. *incana*	More than 30 suppliers
- - 'Nana'	ECha ESis NBir SRms
- - 'Saraband'	WPer
- - 'Silbersee' **new**	LPVe
- - 'Silver Carpet'	EBee EFou EMan LRHS MRav MWgw NSti SChu SCoo SPer SPla WCom WMnd
- - 'Wendy'	CStr GCal
- 'Mori's Form'	EBot
- 'Nana Blauteppich'	EMan LPVe MBNS MPWC MWgw SDes WBar WBea WRHF WWeb
- 'Noah Williams' (v)	EBee EChP EGle EMan MBNS MCAu NPro SUsu WRus

- 'Pink Goblin' **new**	LPVe
- red	WBea
- Red Fox	see *V. spicata* 'Rotfuchs'
- 'Romiley Purple'	EBee ECGP ERou MBrN MBri
	MLLN MSte NSti SChu SHel SPer
	WCot WFar
- 'Rosalind'	NLar
- *rosea*	see *V. spicata* 'Erika'
- 'Rosenrot'	EMan LPVe NLAp WHHs
§ - 'Rotfuchs'	CPrp CStr EBee ECtt EFou ELan
	EMan EPar ERou EWTr EWsh GKir
	LAst LPVe MHdf MRav MWgw
	NBir NSti SCro SMrm SPer WBro
	WCot WFar WPer WTel WWin
- 'Royal Candles'	EBee EHan EPfP LBuc MBri WCot
	WWeb
- Royal Candles =	ENot GBri
'Glory'PBR **new**	
- 'Sahin's Early'	WCot
- 'Sightseeing'	ERou MGol MPWC NArg NBir
	SMac SRms
- *variegata* (v)	MLLN NBir
§ *spuria* L.	CStr EVFa GGar NBur WPer
stelleri	see *V. wormskjoldii*
subsessilis 'Blaue	WWeb
Pyramide'	
* - *hendersonii*	MTed MTis
'Sunny Border Blue'	CPrp CRez EBee EPfP GMac LCaP
	LPVe MBNS MNFA MSph NLar
	SDes SUsu WCot WFar WWeb
tauricola	MDHE WAbe WLin
- JJH 92101536	LPhx SAga
- MP 93236	IDac
- Mac&W 5835	EPot
telephiifolia	ECtt EGoo EHyt EMNN EMan
	EWes MDKP NMen NWCA WWin
teucrium	see *V. austriaca* subsp. *teucrium*
thessalica	EDAr EPot
thessalonica	EDAr
thymoides	NWCA
subsp. *pseudocinerea*	
- subsp. *thymoides*	ESis
virginica	see *Veronicastrum virginicum*
'Waterperry Blue'	GKir LRHS NWoo WPer
wherryi	WPer
'White Icicle'	see *V. spicata* 'Icicle'
'White Jolanda'	CMea EBee EChP LPVe LRHS NLar
	WWeb
'White Spire'	CBot
whitleyi	CLyd CNic GAbr WWin
§ *wormskjoldii*	EDAr EMlt ESis IHMH MBrN MBro
	NMen SBla SHel SRms WPer WWin
- 'Alba'	EMlt MDHE MDKP SCro WPer

Veronicastrum (Scrophulariaceae)

japonicum	ECGN
villosulum **new**	CPom EBee WCot WCru
§ *virginicum*	CArn CHea CRow EBee EChP
	ECha EFou EHrv GKir IKee MHdf
	NBir NSti SDes SRms WHHs
	WMoo WPer WWhi WWin
- 'Alboroseum'	ECGN EMan
- *album*	More than 30 suppliers
- 'Apollo'	CBre CMil EBee EChP EFou EGle
	EMan EPfP ERou GMac LAst LPhx
	LRHS MBri MWgw NBro NLar
	NSti SDes WFTG WHil WTMC
- 'Diane'	EBee EGle LPhx WFTG
- 'Fascination'	More than 30 suppliers
§ - var. *incarnatum*	CBri EBee ECGN EMan GKir
	GMaP LPhx LRHS MHdf MRav
	NBro NCiC NDov NFla SOkh SPer
	STes WFar

- 'Lavendelturm'	CPlt CRDP EBee ECha EGle EMil
	LPhx NDov SOkh WTMC
- mauve	EVFa
- 'Pink Glow'	COlW EBee EBre EFou EHoe
	EHrv ELan EMan EMil EPfP EWTr
	GAbr GKir LHop LPhx LRHS
	MCAu MTis NSti SAga SDes
	SMad SMrm SOkh SPla WFar
	WMnd
- 'Pointed Finger'	EFou SMrm SOkh
- *roseum*	see *V. virginicum* var.
	incarnatum
- 'Ruby Glow'	LCaP
- var. *sibiricum*	EBee ECha GCal MCAu NBid SDes
	SVal WHoo WMoo
- 'Spring Dew'	CBre CMGP EBee EChP EGle
	LPhx LRHS MCAu MWgw NDov
	NLar SOkh WFTG WMnd
- 'Temptation'	EBee EChP EFou EGle ERou LPhx
	MBri MCAu MTed NLar
'White Jolan' **new**	CFir

Verschaffeltia (Arecaceae)

splendida	NBlo XBlo

Verticordia (Myrtaceae)

plumosa	ECou
- purple	SOWG

Vestia (Solanaceae)

§ *foetida* ♀ H1	CBcs CPLG CPom CTCP CTrC
	CWib EChP EMan EPfP ERea MNrw
	SBrw SGar SHFr SOWG WCot
	WPGP WPer WPic WSHC WWye
lycioides	see *V. foetida*

Vetiveria (Poaceae)

zizanioides	MSal

Viburnum ✿ (Caprifoliaceae)

acerifolium	CFil CPle GIBF WBod WFar
	WHCG WPat
alnifolium	see *V. lantanoides*
atrocyaneum	CFil CPle ISea WFar WHCG WPGP
	WPat WWal
awabuki	CFil CHEx EBee EPfP NLar
	WPGP
betulifolium	CAbP CBrd CFil CMCN CPLG
	CPMA CPle CTrw EPfP EPla GIBF
	MBlu WHCG WPGP
bitchiuense	CPMA CPle ELan WWes
x *bodnantense*	CBot CTri CTrw CWSG EBee
	MDun MRav MWat NDlv NFor
	NLon WHar WStl WTel WWin
- 'Charles Lamont' ♀ H4	More than 30 suppliers
- 'Dawn' ♀ H4	More than 30 suppliers
- 'Deben' ♀ H4	CDoC EBee ENot EPfP GKir LRHS
	MBlu MBri MRav MWya SPer SSta
	WBod WCru WDin WFar
bracteatum	CFil CPle EPfP
buddlejifolium	GEil GKir SSpi WBcn WCru WFar
	WHCG
burejaeticum	GIBF
x *burkwoodii*	More than 30 suppliers
- 'Anne Russell' ♀ H4	CAbP CBcs CPMA CTri EBee EBre
	ELan ENot EPfP EWTr EWes GKir
	IArd LRHS MAsh MGos MRav
	NBee NHol NSti SHBN SLon SPer
	SPlb WDin WFar
- 'Chenaultii'	EPfP SRPl WCru WDin
- 'Compact Beauty'	EPfP
- 'Fulbrook' ♀ H4	CAbP CMHG EPfP LRHS MBri
	WDin WFar

- 'Mohawk'	CAbP CDoC CEnd CPMA ELan EPfP GKir LRHS MAsh MBri NLar SCoo SMur SPla SSpi WBcn WPat
- 'Park Farm Hybrid' ♀ H4	CAbP CDoC CPMA CSam CTri CWSG EBee EBre ELan ENot EPfP EPla GKir LRHS MAsh MBro MRav NBea NSti SLPl SPer SPla SRms WCru WPat WWeb
x *carlcephalum* ♀ H4	More than 30 suppliers
- 'Cayuga'	NLar
* - 'Variegatum' (v)	CPMA
carlesii	CBcs CWib EBee ENot EPfP GIBF GKir LRHS MBlu MRav NBlu NPri SCoo SLim SPer SRPl SReu WStd WTel
- 'Aurora' ♀ H4	More than 30 suppliers
- 'Charis'	CMHG CPMA CSBt LRHS NLar WBcn WBod
- 'Compactum'	CPMA
- 'Diana'	CEnd CMHG CPMA EPfP GKir LRHS MBro MWya NLar SSpi WPat WPen
- 'Marlou'	EPfP NLar
cassinoides	CPle EPfP GKir NMen WFar WPat
'Chesapeake'	CBrm CDoC CMHG CPMA EBee EWes LRHS NPro SEND WBcn WDin WWes
chingii	CFil CPMA CPle GGGa SLon WCru WPGP
cinnamomifolium ♀ H3	CAbP CBcs CFil CHEx CPLG CPle FPfP GKir lSea LNet LRHS MAsh NRib SAPC SArc SLon SPer SSpi WBod WFar WHCG WLRN WPGP WSHC
congestum	CPle
'Conoy'	CPMA
cotinifolium	CPle
cylindricum	CBot CFil CMCN CPle EPfP SMad SReu SSpi WBcn WCru WPGP
- B&SWJ 7239	WCru
dasyanthum	CPle EPfP GIBF GKir NLar
davidii ♀ H4	More than 30 suppliers
- ♀ H4 (f)	CBcs CBot CDoC CSBt ELan EPfP GIBF GKir MAsh MDun MGos SIIBN SPer SPla SReu SRms SSta WBod WPat
- ♀ H4 (m)	CBcs CBot CDoC CSBt CWSG ELan EPfP GIBF GKir MAsh MDun MGos MRav SPer SPla SReu SRms SSta WBod WPat
dentatum	EPfP WPGP
- var. *deamii* new	GIDF
§ - var. *pubescens*	CPle
dilatatum	CPne GIBF SSpi
- B&SWJ 4456	WCru
- 'Erie'	EPfP NLar
erubescens	CPMA WFar WWes
- var. *gracilipes*	CMdw CPle EPfP
'Eskimo'	CPMA CWSG EBee EPfP GKir LAst LRHS MAsh MBNS MBlu MBro MGos MRav NBlu NMoo SKee SLim SMur SReu SSpi WDin WFar WPat WWes
§ *farreri* ♀ H4	More than 30 suppliers
- 'Album'	see *V.farreri* 'Candidissimum'
§ - 'Candidissimum'	CBot CFil EBee ELan EPfP IArd IMGH LRHS MBri MMHG SPer SSpi WBcn WPat
- 'December Dwarf'	NLar
- 'Farrer's Pink'	CAbP CPMA NHol NLar
- 'Fioretta'	ENot NLar
- 'Nanum'	CFil CPMA EPfP MAsh MBar MBrN MRav NHol NLar SChu SSta WFar WHCG WPat
foetidum	CPle LBuc
- var. *rectangulatum*	WCru
B&SWJ 3637	
fragrans	see *V.farreri*
'Fragrant Cloud'	MGos
furcatum ♀ H4	EPfP GIBF IArd SSpi WHCG
- B&SWJ 5939	WCru
x *globosum* 'Jermyns Globe'	CAbP CBcs CDoC CEnd CFil CMHG CPle EBee EPla GKir MBar MGos MRav MSte SBrw SLon WBod WCru WDin WFar WHCG WPGP
grandiflorum	CPMA CSBt
- f. *foetens*	EPfP WBod
- 'Snow White'	ERea
harryanum	CFil CMHG CPle CPne EBee EPfP GKir LRHS MBNS SOWG WCru WPGP WSHC
henryi	CAbP CFil CPle EPfP LRHS NLar WDin WHCG WPat
x *hillieri*	CAbP CFil CPle GBin MRav MWhi NRib WBcn WFar WHCG WKif WPGP
- 'Winton' ♀ H4	CAbP CDoC EPfP EPla GKir LRHS MBri MTis NPro SHBN SLim SLon SOWG SSpi WBod WCru WDin WFar WWeb
ichangense	NLar
japonicum	CFil CHEx CPle CSam EPfP GKir SHBN WCru
x *juddii* ♀ H4	More than 30 suppliers
koreanum	WBod
- B&SWJ 4231	WCru
lantana	CBgR CCVT CKin CLnd CTri ECrN ENot EWTr GKir GWCH LBuc LHyr NWCa SPer WDin WFar WMou WStI
- 'Aureum'	ECtt EHoe EVFa MBlu NLar WBcn
- 'Mohican'	NPro WWes
- 'Variefolium' (v)	CPMA
§ *lantanoides*	EPfP GKir NLar SSpi
lentago	CAbP CPle
lobophyllum	CPle EPfP GIBF
luzonicum B&SWJ 3930	WCru
macrocephalum	CPMA WDin
- f. *keteleeri*	CPMA SSpi
mariesii	see *V.plicatum* 'Mariesii'
nervosum B&SWJ 2251a	WCru
nudum	CPle EBee EPfP GIBF NLar WWes
- var. *angustifolium* new	GIBF
- 'Pink Beauty'	CPMA LRHS MRav WFar WPGP
odoratissimum misapplied	CBcs CFil CPle EPfP IArd SHBN SSpi WSHC
odoratissimum	CHEx CPLG CSam
- B&SWJ 6913	WCru
- 'Emerald Lustre'	CHEx CSam EBee
- 'Oneida' new	NLar WDin
opulus	More than 30 suppliers
- 'Aureum'	CChe CHar CMHG CSam EBee EBre ECtt EHoe ELan EMil EPfP EWTr GKir LRHS MAsh MBar MGos MRav NHol NLon SHBN SPer SSta WDin WFar WHCG WPat WWeb
- 'Compactum' ♀ H4	More than 30 suppliers
- 'Flore Pleno' (d)	CHar
N - 'Fructu Luteo'	CHar ENot GKir
* - 'Harvest Gold'	EBee GKir SLim
- 'Nanum'	CAbP CPle EBee ELan EPla EPot ESis GKir MBar MRav NHol NMen NPro WDin WHCG WPGP WPat
- 'Notcutt's Variety' ♀ H4	CChe EBee ENot EPfP MGos SHBN SHFr SMur SRms WBcn
- 'Park Harvest'	GKir LRHS MBri NLar NSti SLPl WPat

§	- 'Roseum' ♀ H4	More than 30 suppliers
*	- 'Sterile'	see *V. opulus* 'Roseum'
*	- 'Sterile Compactum'	IMGH
N	- 'Xanthocarpum' ♀ H4	CBcs CDoC CDul CMHG CSam EBee EBre ELan EPfP GAbr GKir LAst LHop LRHS MBar MGos MRav MWat NHol SLPl SLon SPer SRms WBod WDin WFar WSHC WTel WWin
	- 'Xanthocarpum Compactum'	EMon
	parvifolium	NLar
N	*plicatum*	CTri CWib ENot IArd MBar WDin
	- 'Cascade'	EBee EWTr NLar SHBN SSpi WPnP
	- 'Dart's Red Robin'	ECtt LRHS MBri MGos NHol WBcn WPat
	- 'Grandiflorum'	CDoC CPle EPfP GKir LRHS MBar MBri SSta WBcn WHCG
	- 'Lanarth'	More than 30 suppliers
§	- 'Mariesii' ♀ H4	More than 30 suppliers
	- 'Nanum'	see *V. plicatum* 'Nanum Semperflorens'
	- 'Nanum Semperflorens'	CDoC EBee ECtt ESis IArd MBlu MBro MGos MRav MTis NBlu NHol SHBN WFar WHCG WPat WSHC WWal
	- 'Pink Beauty' ♀ H4	More than 30 suppliers
	- 'Popcorn'	CAbP GKir LRHS MAsh SReu SSpi SSta
*	- 'Prostratum'	ESis
	- 'Rosace'	MBlu
	- 'Rotundifolium'	IArd NHol NLar SHBN SRPl WPat
	- 'Rowallane'	EBee EPfP
	- 'Saint Keverne'	IArd SHBN SRob
	- 'Summer Snowflake'	CBrm CDoC CEnd CMHG CWSG EBee ENot EPfP EWTr GKir LRHS MBri MRav NHol SHBN SPer WDin WFar WHCG
	- f. *tomentosum*	EWTr WDin WHCG WStI
	- - 'Shasta'	NLar
	- 'Watanabe'	see *V. plicatum* 'Nanum Semperflorens'
	'Pragense' ♀ H4	CAbP CBcs CMCN CPle EBee EPfP EPla GKir MBar MGos MRav NBlu NHol NRib SLon SPer WBod WDin WFar WHCG WLRN WPat WPnP
	propinquum	CAbP
	- B&SWJ 4009	WCru
	pubescens	see *V. dentatum* var. *pubescens*
	x *rhytidophylloides*	GKir NFor WFar
	- 'Alleghany' **new**	NLar
	- 'Dart's Duke'	ENot GKir LRHS MBri SLPl
	rhytidophyllum	CDul CHEx CSBt EBee EBre ENot EPfP EWTr GKir LPan MBar MGos MRav NBlu NLon NWea SHBN SPar SPer SReu SRms SSpi WAul WBod WCFE WDin WFar WMoo WTel WWin
	- 'Holland'	EPla
	- 'Roseum'	CBot MRav SLPl
	- 'Variegatum' (v)	CPMA EVFa WBcn
	- 'Willowwood'	EBee LRHS MAsh SMad SPer WPat
§	*rigidum*	CFil WPGP
	sargentii	EPfP GBin GIBF
	- 'Onondaga' ♀ H4	More than 30 suppliers
	- 'Susquehanna'	EPfP
	semperflorens	see *V. plicatum* 'Nanum Semperflorens'
§	*setigerum*	CPle EPfP GIBF IArd NLar SLPl SMad SSpi
	- 'Aurantiacum'	EPfP

	'Shasta'	CMCN COtt EPfP LRHS MBri NHol SSpi WDin
	sieboldii	CBcs CPle GIBF
	- B&SWJ 2837	WCru
	- 'Seneca'	EPfP NLar
	suspensum	CBcs
	taiwanianum	WCru
	B&SWJ 3009	
	theiferum	see *V. setigerum*
	tinus	More than 30 suppliers
	- 'Bewley's Variegated' (v)	CBcs CDoC EBee EMil MGos MRav SCoo
I	- 'Compactum'	EBee SPoG
	- 'Eve Price' ♀ H4	More than 30 suppliers
	- 'French White' ♀ H4	CDoC CWSG EBee EPfP EPla LRHS MBri MRav SCoo SMac SPar WFar WGwG WPGP WWal WWeb
	- 'Gwenllian' ♀ H4	More than 30 suppliers
	- 'Israel'	EMil SMac SPer SPla WFar
	- 'Little Bognor'	LRHS MGos NPro
	- 'Lucidum'	CBcs CPle CSam MGos SHBN SPla WCFE WDin WFar
	- 'Lucidum Variegatum' (v)	CFil CPMA EHol SDry SLim WPGP
*	- 'Macrophyllum'	LPan WWeb
	- 'Magraf'	WBcn
*	- 'Pink Parfait'	MRav
	- 'Pink Prelude'	ENot MWya
	- 'Purpureum'	CBcs CSBt EBee EHoe EPfP EPla LRHS MAsh MRav SCoo SHBN SLPl SLim SPer SPoG WDin WFar WGwG WWal WWeb
	- subsp. *rigidum*	see *V. rigidum*
	- 'Spring Bouquet'	MGos MWya NBee
	- 'Variegatum' (v)	More than 30 suppliers
	tomentosum	see *V. plicatum*
	trilobum	GIBF
	urceolatum	WCru
	B&SWJ 6988 **new**	
	utile	CPle EPfP WFar WHCG WPGP WWes
	veitchii	CPle
	wrightii	CPle EPfP MBro WHCG WPat
	- var. *hessei*	EPfP LRHS NLar

Vicia (Papilionaceae)

	angustifolia	see *V. sativa* subsp. *nigra*
	cracca	CKin GWCH NLan NSco
§	*sativa* subsp. *nigra*	CKin
	sepium	CKin MGol
	sylvatica	CBgR

Victoria (Nymphaeaceae)

'Longwood Hybrid'	MSta

Vigna (Papilionaceae)

§	*caracalla*	CPlN

Villaresia see *Citronella*

Villarsia (Menyanthaceae)

bennettii	see *Nymphoides peltata* 'Bennettii'

Vinca ✿ (Apocynaceae)

	difformis ♀ H3-4	CHad CHar COIW CTri EBee ECha LLWP LRHS NCat SBri SDix SDry WHer WPic WWye
*	- 'Alba'	CPom WCom
	- subsp. *difformis*	CHid EMon
	- Greystone form	CDoC CHid EPPr EPfP EPla LHop MBNS SCoo SEND WPnP WRus
	- 'Jenny Pym'	CFwr CHid CPom EBee EPPr MAvo SMad WCom WOut WWeb

- 'Oxford'	SLPl
- 'Snowmound'	MRav
'Hidcote Purple'	see *V. major* var. *oxyloba*
major	CBcs CSBt CWib EBee ELan ENot
	EOrc EPfP GKir GPoy LBuc LRHS
	MBri MFir MGos MHer MWat NPri
	NWea SHBN SPer WDin WFar
	WGwG WMoo WStI WWeb
- 'Alba'	GBuc WEas
- 'Caucasian Blue'	CFil EBee WPGP
- 'Elegantissima'	see *V. major* 'Variegata'
- var. *hirsuta* hort.	see *V. major* var. *oxyloba*
§ - subsp. **hirsuta**	EMon WWye
(Boiss.) Stearn	
- 'Honeydew' (v)	EMon
§ - 'Jason Hill'	EMon
§ - 'Maculata' (v)	CDoC CSBt EBee EMar EMon ENot
	LHop LRHS MBar SDry SLim SPar
	SPer WCru WDin WMoo WWeb
§ - var. *oxyloba*	CFis CFwr CNic CoIW COld
	CPLG CTri EBee ECtt ELan EMon
	EOrc EPla GSki LHop MRav SLPl
	SLim SMac SRms WHen WPic
- var. *pubescens*	see *V. major* subsp. *hirsuta*
- 'Reticulata' (v)	ELan EMon
- 'Surrey Marble'	see *V. major* 'Maculata'
§ - 'Variegata' (v) ♀ H4	More than 30 suppliers
minor	CDoC CKin EBee EBlw ELan ENot
	EPar EPfP GAbr GKir GPoy MAsh
	MBar MBro MFir MHer MWat
	NBlu NPri NWea SHIr WDrE
	WDin WFar WStI WWye
- f *alba* ♀ H4	CBcs CBot CDoC EBee ECha
	EGoo EPfP GDra LAst LRHS
	MAsh MBar MGos MHer MWgw
	NBlu NOak NPri SHBN SMac SPer
	STre WCot WCru WStI WWpP
	WWye
- 'Alba Aureavariegata'	see *V. minor* 'Alba Variegata'
- f. *alba* 'Gertrude Jekyll'	CDoC CFwr CSBt EBee EBlw
♀ H4	ELan EMon ENot EPPr EPfP GKir
	ILis LRHS MBri MRav NHol NPri
	SChu SCoo SEND SLim SPer SPla
	SVil WDin WElm WGwG WHer
§ - 'Alba Variegata' (v)	EBre EHoe EPPr EPla GKir LAst
	MAsh MBar MFir MGos MHdf
	MHer NChi NHol NMRc NPri
	NPro SPer SRms STre WBod WCot
	WEas WFar WHer WTel
§ - 'Argenteovariegata' (v)	More than 30 suppliers
♀ H4	
§ - 'Atropurpurea' ♀ H4	More than 30 suppliers
- 'Aurea'	LBBr SPla WRHF
§ - 'Aureovariegata' (v)	CBcs CBot CChe GAbr GKir GPoy
	LAst LRHS MAsh MBar MFir MGos
	MRav NBlu NFor NHol NPri NVic
	SPer SPlb WFar WHen WTel WWye
- 'Azurea'	CHid
§ - 'Azurea Flore Pleno'	More than 30 suppliers
(d) ♀ H4	
* - 'Blue and Gold'	EGoo EMon MAvo
- 'Blue Cloud'	MLLN NHol
- 'Blue Drift'	EMon EWes MBNS MLLN NHol
- 'Blue Moon'	EBee ECtt NHol SPla WRHF
- 'Bowles' Blue'	see *V. minor* 'La Grave'
- 'Bowles' Variety'	see *V. minor* 'La Grave'
- 'Burgundy'	EPar LLWP MWgw SRms WWyc
- 'Caerulea Plena'	see *V. minor* 'Azurea Flore Pleno'
- 'Dartington Star'	see *V. major* var. *oxyloba*
- 'Double Burgundy'	see *V. minor* 'Multiplex'
- 'Garnet'	EWTr
- Green Carpet	see *V. minor* 'Grüner Teppich'
- 'Grüner Teppich'	EMon

- 'Illumination' (v)	CEnd COtt EHoe ELan EMan EPfP
	GBin LAst LHop LRHS MAsh MBri
	NPri SPer SPoG WWeb
§ - 'La Grave' ♀ H4	CChe CDoC CSBt CSev EBee
	EBlw ECGP ECha ELan ENot EPPr
	EPla EWTr GKir MBro MRav
	MWgw NBlu NHol SLim SPer SPla
	SRms SSvw STre WBod WCom
	WElm WWpP
- 'Maculata' (v)	EGoo ELan EPPr SCoo WBcn
- 'Marion Cran'	CEnd GSki
§ - 'Multiplex' (d)	CBgR EBee ECtt EMan EMon
	EOrc EPPr EPar EPla LBuc MAsh
	MBar MInt NHol NLon NPri SRms
	WCFE WCru WHrl WRHF
- 'Persian Carpet' (v)	EMon
- 'Purpurea'	see *V. minor* 'Atropurpurea'
- 'Rubra'	see *V. minor* 'Atropurpurea'
- 'Sabinka'	CHid EGoo EMon EPla
- 'Silver Service' (d/v)	CHid EMan EMon EPPr GBuc
	MInt MRav NHol WCot WHoo
- 'Variegata'	see *V. minor* 'Argenteovariegata'
- 'Variegata Aurea'	see *V. minor* 'Aureovariegata'
- 'White Gold'	CChe EBee NHol NPri NPro
sardoa new	EMon EPPr

Vincetoxicum (Asclepiadaceae)

forrestii ACE 1615	IDac
§ **hirundinaria**	CPLG EBee EEls GPoy
nigrum	EMon NBur NChi WCot WTin
officinale	see *V. hirundinaria*

Viola ✿ (Violaceae)

'Abigail' (Vtta)	LPVe
'Achilles' (Va)	LPVe
'Ada Jackson' (ExVa)	WOFF
'Adelina' (Va)	LPVe
'Admiral' (Va)	GMac MAnH WWhi
'Admiration' (Va)	GMac LPVe WBou
adunca	NWCA
- var. **minor**	see *V. labradorica* Schrank.
'Agnes Cochrane' (ExVa)	WOFF
'Agneta' (Va)	LPVe
'Alanta' (Va)	LPVe SAga WWhi
§ **alba**	EWes NHol NMen WBrE WWin
albanica	see *V. magellensis*
I 'Alcea' (Va)	LPVe
'Alethia' (Va)	LPVe
'Alex Blackwood' (SP) **new**	WOFF
'Alexander Rayfield' (Va)	LPVe
'Alexia' (Va)	LPVe
'Alice' **new**	CDev
'Alice Witter' (Vt)	CBre CDev CGro NChi SHar
'Alice Wood' (ExVa)	WOFF
'Alice Woodall' (Va)	LPVe
* 'Alison' (Va)	GMaP GMac WBou WWhi
'Alma' (Va)	WOFF
altaica	LPVe
'Alwyn' (Va)	LPVe
'Amelia' (Va)	GMac LPVe WBou WWhi
'Amethyst' (C)	EBee
§ 'Amiral Avellan' (Vt)	CDev CGro WHer
'Andrena' (Va)	LPVe
'Angela' (Va)	LPVe
'Anita' (Va)	LPVe
'Ann' (SP)	WOFF
'Ann Kean' (Vtta)	LPVe
'Ann Robb' (ExVa)	WOFF
'Anna' (Va)	LPVe
'Anna Leyns' (Va)	LPVe
'Annabelle' (Va)	LPVe
'Annaliese' (C)	LPVe
'Anne Mott' (Va)	LPVe

	'Annette Ross' (Va)	LPVe
I	'Annie' (Vt) **new**	CGro NCat
	'Annie Roberts' (FP) **new**	WOFF
I	'Annona' (Va)	LPVe
	'Anthea' (Va)	LPVe
	'Antique Lace' (Va)	GMac MHer
	'Aphrodite' (Va)	LPVe
	'Apollo' (Va)	LPVe
	'Arabella' (Va)	EBee LPVe LRHS SChu SMrm
		WBou WLRN
	arborescens	SSpi WCot
	'Ardross Gem' (Va)	CSam EBee ECtt EDAr GAbr GKir
		GMaP GMac LPVe LRHS MWgw
		NChi WBou WCom WEas WFar
		WKif WPer WWhi
	arenaria	see *V. rupestris*
	'Arkwright's Ruby' (Va)	LPVe LRHS SRms WWhi
	'Artemis' (Va)	LPVe
	'Ashvale Blue' (PVt) **new**	CGro
	'Aspasia' (Va) ♀ H4	GMac LBee LPVe LRHS WBou
		WWhi
	'Astrid' (Va)	LPVe
	'Atalanta' (Vtta)	LPVe LRHS
	'Athena' (Va)	LPVe
	athois	LPVe
	'Aurelia' (Va)	LPVe
	'Aurora' (Va)	LPVe
	'Avril' (Va)	LPVe
	'Avril Lawson' (Va)	CElw GMac MGrG WBou
	'Azurella'	LRHS
	'Baby Lucia' (Va)	CElw
	'Barbara' (Va)	LPVe WBou WOFF
	'Barbara Cawthorne' (C)	LPVe
	'Barnsdale Gem'	MBNS
	'Baroness de	WHer
	Rothschild' (Vt)	
	'Baronne Alice de	CDev
	Rothschild' (Vt)	
	'Beatrice' (Vtta)	WBou
	'Becka' (Va)	LPVe
	'Becky Groves' (Vt) **new**	CGro
*	*bella*	LPVe WEas
I	'Bella' (C) **new**	EBee
§	'Belmont Blue' (C)	CSpe EBre ECtt EWes GMaP
		GMac LBee LPVe LPhx LRHS
		MCLN MHer MRav NBir NChi
		NDov NPPs SAga SBla SChu SMrm
		SPer SRms WBou WCom WOut
	'Bernard Cox' (FP) **new**	WOFF
§	*bertolonii*	EBee LPVe WBou
	'Beshlie' (Va) ♀ H4	EBee ECtt GMac LPVe MBNS
		SChu WBou WEas WKif
	'Bessie Cawthorne' (C)	LPVe
	'Bessie Knight' (Va)	LPVe
	betonicifolia	LPVe
	'Bettina' (Va)	LPVe
	'Betty' (Va)	LPVe WOFF
	'Betty Dale' (ExVa)	WOFF
	'Bianca' (Vtta)	LPVe
	biflora	CMHG CPla EBlw EPar MTho
		NChi NRya
	'Bishop's Belle' (FP)	WOFF
	'Black Ace' (Va)	LPVe
	'Blackfaulds Gem' (SP) **new**	WOFF
	'Blue Bird' (Va)	GMac
	'Blue Butterfly' (C)	GMac MAnH
	'Blue Carpet' (Va)	GMac
	'Blue Cloud' (Va)	LPVe NChi
	'Blue Diamond'	EBee EFou
	'Blue Moon' (C)	SChu SDys WBou
	'Blue Moonlight' (C)	CBos CElw GBuc GMac LRHS
		NChi
	'Blue Perfection' (Va)	LRHS

	'Blue Tit' (Va)	SChu
	'Blueberry Cream'	NCat
	'Bonna Cawthorne' (Va)	LPVe
	bosniaca	see *V. elegantula bosniaca*
	'Boughton Blue'	see *V.* 'Belmont Blue'
	'Bournemouth Gem' (Vt)	CBre CDev CGro
§	'Bowles' Black' (T)	CArn CDev CSWP CSpe EBee
		ECha EDAr ELan EMlt EPfP EWTr
		LPVe LRHS MHer NBro SBla SRPl
		SRms WBea WBou WEas
	'Boy Blue' (Vtta)	LPVe
	'Brenda Hall' (Va)	LPVe
	'Bronwen' (Va)	LPVe
	'Bruneau' (dVt)	CGro EFou
*	'Bryony' (Vtta)	LPVe WBou
	bubanii	EBee GKev
	'Bullion' (Va)	LPVe WCot
	'Burncoose Yellow' **new**	WBou
	'Buttercup' (Vtta)	EBee GMaP GMac LBee LPVe
		NChi SChu SIng SMrm WBou
		WLRN WWhi
	'Butterpat' (C)	GMac MHer NHaw
	'Buxton Blue' (Va)	LPVe NCat
	calaminaria	LPVe
	'Calantha' (Vtta)	LPVe
	calcarata	LPVe
	'California' (Vt)	CDev
	'Callia' (Va)	LPVe
I	'Calliandra' (Vtta)	LPVe
I	'Calypso' (Va)	LPVe
	Can Can Series	WHer
	canadensis	CDes EBee
§	- var. *rugulosa*	CRDP
	'Candida' (Vtta)	LPVe
	canina	CKin IHMH NBro NPPs
*	- *alba*	CBre
	'Carberry Seedling' (Va)	LPVe
	'Carina' (Vtta)	LPVe
	'Carola' (Va)	LPVe
I	'Cassandra' (Vtta)	LPVe
	'Catforth Blue Ribbon'	CElw NCat
*	'Catforth Gold'	NCat
	'Catherine Williams' (ExVa)	WOFF
	'Cat's Whiskers'	CElw GMac
	cazorlensis	CPBP SBla
	'Chandler's Glory' (Va)	LPVe
	'Chantal' (Vtta)	LPVe
	'Chantreyland' (Va)	CFox NBir NFla
	'Charity' (Va)	LPVe
	'Charles William Groves'	CGro
	(Vt) **new**	
	'Charlotte'	CSam WBou
	'Charlotte Mott' (Va)	LPVe
	'Cherub'	GMac
	'Chloe' (Vtta)	LPVe
	'Christmas' (Vt)	CDev CGro LCaP
	'Christobel' (Va)	LPVe
	'Cinders' (Vtta)	GMac
	'Citrina' (Va)	LPVe
	'Claire' (Va)	LPVe
	'Clare Harrison' (Va)	LPVe
	'Cleeway Crimson'	WOFF
	(FP) **new**	
	'Clementina' (Va) ♀ H4	CElw LPVe MRav
	'Cleo' (Va)	EBee GMac WBou
	'Clive Groves' (Vt)	CBre CDev CGro CHid
	'Clodagh' (Va)	LPVe
	'Clover' (Va)	LPVe
	'Coconut Sorbet'	LRHS
	'Coeur d'Alsace' (Vt)	CBre CDev CNic CPBP EBee EFou
		EPar LPVe LPhx WCot WEas
		WWhi
	'Colette' (Va)	LPVe

'Colleen' (Vtta)	LPVe
'Columbine' (Va)	CBos CElw CGro CRDP CSam GKir GMaP GMac LBee LPVe LPhx LRHS MAnH MBow MHer NBir NWoo SAga SChu SIng SMrm SPer WBou WCom WCot WEas WLRN WWeb WWhi
§ 'Comte de Brazza' (dPVt)	CDev CGro CTri GMac WHer WRha
'Comte de Chambord' (dVt)	NChi WRha
'Connie' (Va)	LPVe
'Connigar'	CSam
'Connor Glendinning' (ExVa)	WOFF
'Coralie' (Vtta)	LPVe
'Cordelia' (Va)	EBee LPVe SBla
'Cornetto'	MBow MHer
* 'Cornish White'	CDev
cornuta ♀ H4	CAgr CElw CMea CPla EBee EOrc EPot GGar LPVe MBro MFir MWat NBir NBro NChi NWCA SMrm SPer SRms WBea WBou WFar WHen WHoo WRos WWpP
- Alba Group ♀ H4	More than 30 suppliers
§ - 'Alba Minor'	EBee ESis EWes GMac IGor LPVe MBNS MBro MCLN NBro NChi NPPs SChu WCom WFar
- blue	LPVe MHer
- 'Brimstone'	CHea GMac
- 'Cleopatra' (C)	GMac
- 'Clouded Yellow'	GMac MAnH
- 'Compton Lane'	WCom
- 'Eastgrove Blue Scented' (C)	see V. 'Eastgrove Blue Scented'
- 'Gypsy Moth' (C)	GMac
- 'Icy But Spicy'	EHrv
- Lilacina Group (C)	ECha GMac LPVe MBro MRav MSte NCat NChi NFla SChu SMrm SWat WFar
- 'Maiden's Blush'	EMan GMac NChi NPPs
- 'Minor' ♀ H4	CPla GMac LPVe LRHS MCLN NBro SBla WBou WCom
- 'Minor Alba'	see V. cornuta 'Alba Minor'
- pale blue	LRHS
* - 'Paris White'	EBee EPfP
- 'Purple Gem'	GMac
- Purpurea Group	CElw CMea ECha GBuc SRPl
- 'Rosea'	LPVe
- 'Spider'	GMac
- 'Variegata' (v)	LPVe
- 'Victoria's Blush'	CMea CSpe GMac MSte NBir NPPs SMrm WBou WWhi
- 'Violacea'	GMac LRHS
- 'Yellow King'	EBee EFou EHrv
corsica	EBee EMan LPVe SDys WOut
* 'Cottage Garden' (Va)	LRHS NHaw
'Countess of Shaftsbury' (dVt)	CDev
'Cox's Moseley' (ExVa)	WOFF
'Cressida' (Va)	LPVe
§ **cucullata** ♀ H4	SChu SRms WFar WPrP
§ - 'Alba' (Vt)	CBro CGro ECGP EPar EVFa LLWP NBir NChi SScr WEas
- **rosea**	EWes
* - 'Striata Alba'	LRHS MWgw NBro
curtisii	see V. tricolor subsp. curtisii
'Cuty' (Va)	LRHS
'Cyril Bell' (Va)	LPVe
I 'Czar'	see Viola 'The Czar'
'Czar Bleu' (Vt)	CDev
'Daena' (Vtta)	CBos LPVe

'Daisy Smith' (Va)	GMac NChi SChu WBou
'Dancing Geisha' (Vt)	CM&M EBee EMan LBuc MSph MTPN SHar WCot
'Dartington Hybrid' (Va)	LPVe
'Daveron' (C)	LPVe
'David Rhodes' (FP)	WOFF
'David Wheldon' (Va)	LPVe WOFF
'Davina' (Va)	LPVe SChu
'Dawn' (Vtta)	EBee GMaP LPVe SMrm WBou
'Deanna' (Va)	LPVe
'Decima' (Va)	LPVe
declinata	EBee
'Delia' (Va)	GMac LPVe WBou
'Delicia' (Vtta)	LPVe NChi WBou
'Delmonden' (Va)	CRDP SBla
delphinantha	CGra
'Delphine' (Va)	CElw LPVe MLLN MSte NChi NCiC SChu
'Demeter' (Va)	LPVe
'Desdemona' (Va)	EBee GMac LBee WBou
'Desmonda' (Va)	LPVe SChu
'Devon Cream' (Va)	GMac WBou
'Diana Groves' **new**	CGro
'Dimity' (Va)	LPVe
'Dione' (Vtta)	LPVe
I 'Diosma' (Va)	LPVe
§ **dissecta**	GBin WCot WPer
§ - var. **chaerophylloides** f. **eizanensis**	CGro MTho NWCA
- var. **sieboldiana**	CPMA CRDP
'Doctor Smart' (C)	LPVe
doerfleri	LPVe
'Dominique' (Va)	LPVe
'Dominy' (Vtta)	LPVe
'Donau' (Vt)	CDev CGro
'Double White' (dVt)	CGro
dubyana	EBee GBuc
'Duchesse de Parme' (dPVt)	CDev CGro GBar GMac IFro WHer
'D'Udine' (dPVt)	CDev CGro GMac WHer
'Dusk'	WBou
'E.A. Bowles'	see V. 'Bowles' Black'
'Eastgrove Blue Scented' (C)	EBee EMan GMac MCLN WBou WOutWCot WEas WIvy
'Eastgrove Elizabeth Booth'	WEas
'Eastgrove Ice Blue' (C)	WEas
'Eastgrove Twinkle' (C)	NCat WEas
eizanensis	see V. dissecta var. chaerophylloides f. eizanensis
'Elaine Cawthorne' (C)	LPVe
'Elaine Quin'	CBos EBee NCat NChi NCiC SChu SMrm WBou
§ **elatior**	CElw CMea CPla CSWP EBee EMon EPPr EPar GAbr GBri GBuc LPVe LRHS MHar MNrw NChi SChu WCom WCot WPer WWye
§ **elegantula**	EBee LPVe
§ - **bosniaca**	LPVe
'Elisha' (Va)	LPVe
'Elizabeth' (Va)	EBee LPVe NCat SChu SMrm WBou WLRN WWeb
'Elizabeth Cawthorne' (C)	LPVe
'Elizabeth Christie' (FP)	WOFF
'Elizabeth McCallum' (FP)	WOFF
'Elliot Adam' (Va)	EBee WBou WOut
'Elsie Coombs' (Vt)	CDev WPer
'Emily Mott' (Va)	LPVe
'Emma' (Va)	CMea LPVe
'Emma Cawthorne' (C)	LPVe
'Enterea' (Va)	LPVe
erecta	see V. elatior
'Eris' (Va)	LPVe NChi

	'Eros' (Va)	LPVe
	'Etain' (Va)	CBos COIW EBee ECha ELan
		EWes GBuc GMaP LPVe LPhx
		MSte NCiC NDov SMrm SUsu
		WBou WEas WLRN WWhi
	'Ethena' (Va)	LPVe
	'Etienne' (Va)	LPVe
	'Evelyn Cawthorne' (C)	LPVe
	'Evelyn Jackson' (Va)	WOFF
	'Fabiola' (Vtta)	GMac LBee LPVe NBir
*	'Fantasy'	WBou
	'Farewell' (ExVa) **new**	WOFF
	'Felicity' (Va)	LPVe
	'Finola Galway' (Va)	LPVe
	'Fiona' (Va)	GMaP GMac LPVe MSte NCat
		NChi SChu WBou WOut
	'Fiona Lawrenson' (Va)	LPVe
	flettii	NChi
	'Florence' (Va)	LPVe NChi
	'Foxbrook Cream' (C)	EMan GBuc GMac LPVe MHer
		NCiC NDov WBou WHoo WWhi
	'Frances' (Va)	LPVe
	'Frances Perry'	WWhi
	'Francesca' (Va)	LPVe
	'Freckles'	see *V. sororia* 'Freckles'
	'Frederica' **new**	CDev
	'Gary Caird' (FP) **new**	WOFF
	'Gatina' (Va)	LPVe
I	'Gazania' (Va)	LPVe WBou
	'Gazelle' (Vtta)	LPVe
	'George Carter' (FP) **new**	WOFF
	'George Hughes' (FP) **new**	WOFF
	'Georgina' (Va)	LPVe
	'Geraldine' (Vtta)	LPVe
	'Geraldine Cawthorne' (C)	LPVe NCat
*	'Gill Elwell'	WBou
	'Gina' (Vtta)	LPVe
	'Giselle' (Va)	LPVe
	'Gladys Findlay' (Va)	GMac LPVe WBou WOFF
	'Gladys Hughes' (FP)	WOFF
*	'Glenda'	WBou
	'Gloire de Verdon' (PVt)	CGro
	'Governor Herrick' (Vt)	CDev CGro WPer
§	*gracilis*	CElw ECha LPVe NBir WFar
	- 'Lutea'	CSam
*	- 'Magic'	SMrm
	- 'Major'	WBou
	gracilis x *cornuta*	LPVe
	'Green Jade' (v)	CPla EMan MBNS NBir
	'Greenroyd Fancy' (ExVa)	WOFF
	'Grey Owl' (Va)	CBos CMea EBee LBee LPVe LPhx
		LRHS SChu SMrm WBou WKif
		WPGP
	'Griselda' (Vtta)	LPVe
	'Grovemount Blue' (C)	CMea
§	*grypoceras* var. *exilis*	CNic EBee EBlw EMan EMlt EWll
		GBri SChu SMad WCom
	- 'Variegata' (v)	NBir
	'Gustav Wermig' (C)	GAbr LPVe NHaw WBou
	'Gwen Cawthorne' (C)	LPVe
	'H.H. Hodge' (ExVa)	WOFF
	'Hackpen'	CSam
	'Hadria Cawthorne' (C)	LPVe
	'Hansa' (C)	EBee NChi
	'Haslemere'	see *V.* 'Nellie Britton'
*	'Heaselands'	CBos SMHy SMrm SUsu
I	'Hebe' (Vtta)	LPVe
§	*hederacea*	CDev CMHG ECou GMaP GQui
		LPVe MNrw NBro NOak SAga
		SRms WWye
	- blue	CFee WPer
	- 'Putty'	ECou EWes
	'Helen W. Cochrane' (ExVa)	WOFF

	'Helena' (Va)	LPVe SChu
	'Hera' (Va)	LPVe
	'Hespera' (Va)	LPVe
I	'Hesperis' (Va)	LPVe
	heterophylla	see *V. bertolonii*
	subsp. *epirota*	
*	'Hetty Gatenby'	WBou WOFF
	'Hextable' (C)	LPVe
	hirsutula **new**	EBla
	hirta	CKin
	hispida	EBee LPVe
	'Hudsons Blue'	CElw WEas
	'Hugh Campbell' (ExVa)	WOFF
	'Huntercombe Purple'	CElw LBee LHop LPVe LRHS
	(Va) ♀ H4	MWat NBir SBla SChu SRms SUsu
		WBou WCom WKif
	'Hyperion' (Va)	LPVe
	'I.G. Sherwood' (FP)	WOFF
	'Iantha' (Vtta)	LPVe
	'Icy But Spicy' (C)	EBee GKir SMrm SSvw
	'Iden Gem' (Va)	LPVe WBou
	'Inverurie Beauty' (Va)	GKir GMaP GMac LPVe MFir NCat
	♀ H4	NDov SChu WBou WKif WPen
	'Inverurie Mauve' (Va)	LPVe
	'Iona' (Va)	LPVe
	'Irene Hastings' (ExVa) **new**	WOFF
	'Irina' (Va)	LPVe
	'Irish Elegance' (Vt)	CDev SChu
	'Irish Mary' (Va)	LPVe SChu
	'Irish Molly' (Va)	CBot CElw CSpe EBee ECha ELan
		GKir GMaP GMac LPVe LPhx
		LRHS MHer NChi NPri SBla SChu
		SIng SMrm SPer SRms WBou WEas
		WHer WRus WWhi WWin
	'Isata' (Vtta)	LPVe
	'Isla' (Vtta)	LPVe
	'Ita' (Va)	LPVe
	'Iver Grove' (Va)	LPVe
	'Ivory'	NPri
	'Ivory Queen' (Va)	CBos GMaP GMac LPVe MWgw
		WBou
	'Ivory White' (Va)	CDev LPVe
	'Jack Frost' (FP)	WOFF
*	'Jack Sampson'	CDev
	'Jackanapes' (Va) ♀ H4	CElw EBee ECha EHyt ELan GKir
		GMac LHop LPVe LRHS NChi
		SChu SDes SIng SMrm SPer
		SRms WBou WFar WWeb WWhi
		WWin
	'Jacqueline Snocken'	WOFF
	(ExVa)	
	'James'	EWes
	'Jane Askew' (Va)	LPVe
	'Jane Mott' (Va)	LPVe
	'Janet' (Va)	EBee LPVe SMrm WWol
	'Janine' (Vtta)	LPVe
	'Janna' (Va)	LPVe
	'Jean Arnot'	WHer
	'Jeannie Bellew' (Va)	EBee GMac IHMH LPVe MMil SChu
		SPer SRms WBou WFar WLRN
	'Jemma' (Va)	LPVe
	'Jenelle' (Vtta)	LPVe
	'Jennifer Andrews' (Va) **new**	WOFF
	'Jenny' (Vtta)	LPVe
	'Jersey Gem' (Va)	GMac LPVe
	'Jessica' (Va)	LPVe
	'Jessie' (SP)	WOFF
	'Jessie East'	WEas
	'Jessie Taylor' (FP)	WOFF
	'Jimmy's Dark' (ExVa)	WOFF
	'Joan Christie' (FP)	WOFF
	'Joanna' (Va)	WBou
I	'Jocunda' (Va)	LPVe

'Joella' (Va)	LPVe	
'John Goddard' (FP)	WOFF	
'John Powell' (FP)	WOFF	
'John Raddenbury' (Vt)	CDev SHar	
'John Rodger' (SP)	WOFF	
'John Yelmark' (Va)	EBee LPVe	
'John Zanini' (Vtta)	LPVe	
'Johnny Jump Up' (T)	LRHS	
jooi	CPBP EBee EVFa GTou NBir NBro NChi NMen SBla WRha	
jordanii	EBee LPVe	
'Jordieland Gem' (c)	EMan GMac	
'Josie' (Va)	LPVe	
'Joyce Gray' (Va)	GMac WBou	
'Judy Goring' (Va)	LPVe	
'Julia' (Va)	LPVe	
'Julian' (Va)	CElw GMac SAga SBla SRms WBou WIvy	
'Juno' (Va)	GMac LPVe	
'Jupiter' (Va)	EBee LPVe SMrm	
'Karen' (Va)	WCom	
'Kate' (Va)	CElw	
'Katerina' (Va)	LPVe	
'Kathleen Hoyle' (ExVa)	WOFF	
'Kathy' (Vtta)	LPVe	
'Katie Grayson' (C)	LPVe	
'Katinka' (Va)	LPVe	
'Kerrie' (Va)	LPVe	
'Kiki McDonough' (C)	LPVe SChu	
'Kiluna' (Va)	LPVe	
'Kim' **new**	CDev	
'King of the Blues' (Va)	LPVe	
'King of the Violets' **new**	SHar	
'Kinvarna' (Va)	LPVe	
'Kirsty' (Va)	LPVe	
'Kitten'	EBee EMan EWll GMaP GMac LRHS MSte NCat NChi SAga SChu WBou	
I 'Kitty' **new**	CCge	
'Kitty White' (Va)	LPVe	
koreana	see *V. grypoceras* var. *exilis*	
- 'Sylettas' **new**	CGro SPoG	
'La France' (Vt)	SBla	
N *labradorica* hort.	see *V. riviniana* Purpurea Group	
§ *labradorica* Schrank.	CHar EBlw EMil GLil LRHS LSyl MRav NPri SHFr SMer STre WCra WFar	
N - *purpurea* misapplied	see *V. riviniana* Purpurea Group	
'Lady Finnyoon' (Va)	WOFF	
'Lady Hume Campbell' (PVt)	CBre CGro WHer	
'Lady Saville'	see *V.* 'Sissinghurst'	
'Lady Tennyson' (Va)	GMac LPVe SBla WOFF	
'Lamorna' (Vtta)	LPVe	
lanceolata	SSpi	
'Larissa' (Va)	LPVe	
'Latona' (Va)	LPVe	
'Laura' (C)	GBuc IHMH	
'Laura Cawthorne'	EBee NDov	
'Lavender Lady' (Vt)	CBre CGro	
'Laverna' (Va)	LPVe	
'Lavinia' (Va)	EBee LBee LPVe LRHS	
'Leander' (Va)	LPVe	
'Leda' (Va)	LPVe	
'Lemon Sorbet'	GBuc NCat	
'Leora' (Vtta)	LPVe	
'Leora Hamilton' (C)	LPVe	
'Lerosa' (Vtta)	LPVe	
'Lesley Keay' (ExVa)	WOFF	
'Leta' (Vtta)	LPVe	

'Letitia' (Va)	CBos EBee EFou GMaP GMac LPVe SMrm SPer WBou WFar WLRN WWol	
'Leto' (Va)	LPVe	
'Lewisa' (Va)	LPVe	
'Lianne' (Vt)	CDev CGro WPer	
'Lilac Rose' (Va)	WBou	
'Liliana' (Va)	LPVe	
'Lindsay' **new**	CBos	
'Liriopa' (Va)	LPVe	
'Lisa Cawthorne' (C)	LPVe	
'Little David' (Vtta) ♀ H4	CBos CSam EBee GMac LPVe MHer NChi SRms WBou WOut WPGP WWhi	
'Livia' (Vtta)	LPVe	
'Lola' (Va)	LPVe	
'Lord Nelson' (Va)	EBee LPVe	
'Lord Plunket' (Va)	LPVe WBou WOFF	
'Lorna' (Va) ♀ H4	LPVe WOFF	
'Lorna Cawthorne' (C)	CElw LPVe MSte NCat WOut	
'Lorna Moakes' (Va)	LPVe SAga	
'Louisa' (Va)	GMac LPVe SChu	
'Louise Gemmell' (Va)	LPVe NHaw SChu	
'Love Duet'	NBir	
'Luca' (Va)	LPVe	
'Lucinda' (Va)	LPVe	
'Lucy' (Va)	LPVe	
'Ludy May' (Va)	LPVe	
'Luna' (Vtta)	LPVe	
§ *lutea*	GKev LPVe WBou WOut	
- subsp. *elegans*	see *V. lutea*	
'Luxonne' (Vt)	CBre CGro	
'Lydia' (Va)	LPVe SChu WBou	
'Lydia Groves' (Vt)	CDev CGro	
'Lynn' (Va)	LPVe	
'Lysander' (Va)	LPVe	
macedonica	see *V. tricolor* subsp. *macedonica*	
macloskeyi var. *pallens*	WLRN	
'Madame Armandine Pagès' (Vt)	CBre CDev EBee	
'Madclainc' (Va)	LPVe	
'Madge' (Va)	LPVe	
'Maera' (Vtta)	LPVe	
§ *magellensis*	NChi	
'Maggie' (Va)	LPVe	
'Maggie Mott' (Va) ♀ H4	CElw CSam EBee ECha EDAr EOrc GBuc GKir GMaP GMac LBee LHop LPVe LRHS MBri MCLN MHer NChi SBla SPer WBou WEas WFar WKif WRus WTel WWhi WWin	
'Magic'	GMaP GMac LBee SChu WBou	
'Magnifico'	LRHS	
'Majella' (Vtta)	LPVe	
'Malise' (Vtta)	LPVe	
'Malvena' (Vtta)	LPVe	
mandshurica	LPVe NWCA	
- 'Fuji Dawn' (v)	CGro CPla CRez EMan ITer LRHS MAvo MCCP MWod MWrn SPoG WOut	
'Margaret' (Va)	WBou	
'Margaret Cawthorne' (C)	LPVe	
'Marian' (Va)	LPVe	
'Marie-Louise' (dPVt)	CDev CGro CTri EPar	
'Marika' (Va)	LPVe	
'Mars' (Va)	EBee LPVe SHar	
'Marsland's Yellow' (Vtta)	LPVe	
'Martin' (Va) ♀ H4	CSam EBee ECha EShb EWes GMaP GMac LBee LPVe MMil MRav NDov SAga SChu SMrm WBou WCom WFar WIvy WKif WWin WWol	
'Mary Cawthorne' (C)	LPVe	

'Mauve Beauty' (Va)	LPVe	
'Mauve Haze' (Va)	GMac MSte WBou WEas	
'Mauve Radiance' (Va)	GMac LPVe NVic WBou	
'May Mott' (Va)	CBos EBee GMaP GMac SMrm WBou	
'Mayfly' (Va)	GMac MSte WBou	
'Meena' (Vtta)	LPVe	
'Megumi' (Va)	LPVe	
'Melinda' (Vtta)	LPVe WBou	
* 'Melissa' (Va)	LPVe SChu	
'Mercury' (Va)	LPVe WBou	
'Merry Cheer' (C)	LPhx SUsu	
'Midnight Turk' (Va)	GBuc	
'Milkmaid' (Va)	EBee EFou EWll LBee NBir NHaw WKif WWhi	
'Mina Walker' (ExVa)	WOFF	
'Minerva' (Va)	LPVe	
'Miranda' (Vtta)	LPVe	
'Miss Brookes' (Va)	LPVe WBou WOFF	
'Mistral' (Va)	LPVe	
'Misty Guy' (Vtta)	NChi WBou	
'Mitzel' (Vtta)	LPVe	
'Molly Sanderson' (Va) ♀ H4	More than 30 suppliers	
I 'Mona' (Va)	LPVe	
'Monica' (Va)	LPVe SChu	
'Moonlight' (Va) ♀ H4	EBee ECha EDAr ELan EVFa GMaP GMac LBee LHop LPVe MHer NDov SBla SChu WBou WCom WWhi	
'Moonraker'	GMaP NBir NCat	
'Moonstone'	GMac	
'Morvana' (Va)	LPVe	
'Morwenna' (Va)	LPVe WCom WWhi	
'Moscaria' (Va)	LPVe	
'Moseley Ideal' (ExVa)	WOFF	
'Moseley Perfection' (Va)	LPVe	
'Mrs C.M. Snocken' (FP)	WOFF	
'Mrs Chichester' (Va)	GMac LPVe WBou WOFF	
'Mrs Cotterell'	EBee GBuc NCat	
'Mrs David Lloyd George' (dVt)	CDev WHer	
'Mrs G. Robb' (ExVa)	WOFF	
'Mrs Lancaster' (Va)	CHid EBee EWes GMaP GMac LPVe NBir NChi SChu SRms WBou WLRN	
'Mrs M.B. Wallace' (ExVa)	WOFF	
'Mrs R. Barton' (Vt)	CDev CGro	
'Mrs Staples'	EBee	
'Myfawnny' (Va)	CBos CElw CMea EBee EDAr ELan EWes GDra GMac LBee LPVe LRHS NCiC NPri SChu SMrm SRms WBou WFar WHil WKif WLRN WWhi	
'Mylene' (Va)	LPVe	
'Myntha' (Vtta)	LPVe	
'Nadia' (Va)	LPVe	
'Naomi' (Va)	LPVe	
'Natasha' (Va)	LPVe	
'Neapolitan'	see V. 'Pallida Plena'	
§ 'Nellie Britton' (Va) ♀ H4	EBee GDra GMac LPVe SChu WWhi WWin	
'Nemesis' (Va)	LPVe	
nemorosa 'Viola Close' new	WCot	
'Neptune' (Va)	LPVe	
'Nerena' (Vtta)	LPVe	
'Nesta' (Vtta)	LPVe	
'Netta Statham'	see V. 'Belmont Blue'	
'Nicole' (Va)	LPVe	
'Nigra' (Va)	EWTr LPVe	
'Nina' (Va)	LPVe	
'Nona' (Va)	LPVe	
'Nora'	WBou	

'Norah Church' (Vt)	CDev CGro EBee SBla	
'Norah Leigh' (Va)	ELau WBou WBro	
obliqua	see V. cucullata	
'Octavia' (Va)	LPVe	
'Odile' (Va)	LPVe	
odorata	CAgr CArn CBcs CDev CKin CPrp CSWP EBee EBlw EGoo EPar EPfP EWTr GBar GMac GPoy LPVe LRHS MRav MWat SIde STes WCom WCot WWye	
- 'Alba'	CBre CDev CKin CPom CSWP EBee EBlw EFou ELan EMan EPar EWTr GBar ILis LAst MHer NCat NOak NPri SIde WMoo WWhi WWye	
- 'Alba Plena' (d)	EPar NChi SBla WHer	
- apricot	see V. 'Sulphurea'	
- var. dumetorum	see V. alba	
- flore-pleno (d)	EPar	
- 'Forncett Mavis'	EFou	
- pink	EPar EVFa	
I - 'Rosea' (Vt) new	CGro	
- rosea	CDes EBlw GBar GMac MRav WCot WWhi	
- 'Sisters'	CGro	
- 'Sulphurea'	see V. 'Sulphurea'	
'Olive Edmonds' (Va)	LPVe	
'Olwyn' (Va)	LPVe	
'Opéra' (Vt)	CGro	
'Orchid Pink' (Vt)	SHar	
oreades	ETow LPVe	
'Oriana' (Va)	LPVe	
orphanidis	LPVe	
ossea	LPVe	
'Painted Lady' (Va)	GMac	
§ 'Pallida Plena' (dPVt)	CDev CGro WHer	
palmata	LPVe	
'Palmer's White' (Va)	LPVe WBou	
palustris	CKin ELau WHer WShi	
'Pamela Zambra' (Vt)	CDev	
'Pandora' (Va)	LPVe	
papilionacea	see V. sororia	
'Parme de Toulouse' (dPVt)	CBre CDev CGro EBee	
'Pat Creasy' (Va)	CBos GMac WBou	
'Pat Kavanagh' (C)	CMea GMac LPVe MLLN MWat NChi NDov SMrm WBou	
'Patricia Brookes' (Va)	LPVe	
patrinii	EBee	
pedata	CBro CFai EBee EBot EMan EPot LRHS NHar SPer SSpi WAbe WCot WHil WPer	
- 'Bicolor'	EBee WAbe	
pedatifida	CFai CSpe EMan EVFa MBNS MBro MTho WCom WLin	
- white-flowered new	CFai	
'Peggy Brookes' (FP)	WOFF	
'Peppered-palms'	CPla EBee LRHS	
'Perle Rose' (Vt)	CDev CGro SBla	
'Perry's Pride' new	CBos	
'Pete'	SChu	
'Petra' (Vtta)	LPVe	
'Philippa Cawthorne' (C)	LPVe	
'Phoebe' (Va)	LPVe	
'Phyllida' (Va)	LPVe	
'Phyllis Dove'	CGro	
'Pickering Blue' (Va)	LPVe WBou	
'Pilar' (Va)	LPVe SChu	
'Pippa' (Vtta)	LPVe	
'Poppy' (Va)	LPVe	
'Priam' (Va)	LPVe	
'Primrose Cream' (Va)	LPVe	
'Primrose Dame' (Va)	EBee LPVe MHer WBou	
'Primrose Pixie' (Va)	WBou	

'Prince Henry' (T)	LPVe NBlu
'Prince John' (T)	LPVe LRHS NBlu
'Princess Mab' (Vtta)	LPVe WBou
'Princess of Prussia' (Vt)	CBre CDev EBee WHer
'Princess of Wales'	see V. 'Princesse de Galles'
'Princess Yellow'	CFox
(Princess Series)	
§ 'Princesse de Galles' (Vt)	CDev CGro CM&M CTri EPar NSti
	WRus
pumila	NChi
'Purity' (Vtta)	LPVe
'Purple Wings' (Va)	CBos WBou
'Putty'	WCru
'Queen Charlotte' (Vt)	CDev CGro CM&M EBee EShb
	GMac ILis MHer MWgw NChi
	NWCA WCot WFTG WMoo WPnP
	WRHF
'Queen Disa' (Vtta)	LPVe
'Queen Victoria'	see V. 'Victoria Regina'
'R.N. Denby' (ExVa)	WOFF
'Ramona' (Va)	LPVe
'Raven'	GMac LPhx NCat NDov SChu
	WBou
'Ravenna' (Va)	LPVe
'Rawson's White' (Vt)	CGro SHar
'Rebecca' (Vtta)	More than 30 suppliers
'Rebecca Cawthorne' (C)	LPVe
'Red Charm' (Vt)	CM&M EBee MWgw NCat WElm
	WLRN
'Red Giant' (Vt)	CGro SHar
'Red Lion'	CDev
'Red Queen' (Vt)	NSti
reichenbachiana	EPar
'Reine des Blanches' (dVt)	EFou
'Remora' (Vtta)	LPVe
reniforme	see V. hederacea
'Rhoda' (Va)	LPVe
'Richard Vivian' (Va)	LPVe
'Richard's Yellow' (Va)	LPVe
riviniana	CArn CKin GWCH MBow MGas
	MHer NSco WHer WJek WShi
- 'Ed's Variegated' (v)	EBee EPPr WCot
§ - Purpurea Group	More than 30 suppliers
- white	EWes NWoo
'Rob Roy'	GMac
'Rodney Davey' (Vt/v)	CPla EMan EVFa IFro MDCh NBir
	NBro WElm WLRN WPnP
'Rodney Fuller' (FP)	WOFF
'Rodney Marsh'	NBir
'Romilly' (Va)	LPVe
'Rosalie' (Va)	LPVe
* 'Rosanna'	CDev
'Roscastle Black'	CElw CPlt EBee GMaP GMac
	LRHS MAnH SMrm WBou WCot
	WPGP WWhi
'Rosemary Cawthorne' (C)	LPVe
rotundifolia **new**	EBee
'Rowan Hood' (ExVa)	WOFF
'Rowena' (Va)	LPVe
* 'Royal Elk'	CGro
'Royal Robe' (VT)	CDev
'Rubin' **new**	NFla
'Rubra' (Vt)	WPer
rugulosa	see V. canadensis var. rugulosa
§ *rupestris*	SHar
* - *rosea*	CDev CNic CPla EBee EDAr EWTr
	GAbr IFro LLWP MBct MHer
	MNrw MWgw NCat NSti NWCA
	STre WEas WGwG WHHs
'Russian Superb' (Vt)	CDev
'Ruth Blackall' (Va)	LPVe
'Ruth Elkans' (Va)	GMac LPVe
* 'Ruth Elkins'	WBou WOFF

'Saint Helena' (Vt)	CBre CDev
'Sally' (Vtta)	LPVe
'Samantha' (Vtta)	LPVe
'Sandra Louise' (C)	LPVe
'Sarah Binnie' (ExVa) **new**	WOFF
'Saughton Blue' (Va)	LPVe
selkirkii	CDev CNic CPla EHyt ITer LPVe
	MDCh MWod NBro NWCA
- 'Variegata' (v)	CGro EVFa GBri GBuc NBir WOut
septentrionalis	CRDP ECha ELau EMan MNrw
	MOne MRav NBro NRya WPen
- *alba*	CHid CM&M CMHG CSWP EBee
	EChP EFou MRav WFar WLRN
	WPer
'Septima' (Va)	LPVe
'Serena' (Va)	LPVe WBou
'Sheila' (Va)	WBou
'Sherbet Dip' **new**	WBou
'Shirobana' **new**	WCru
'Sidborough Poppet'	EGoo EWes NHar WPer
'Sigrid' (Va)	LPVe
'Sir Fred Warner' (Va)	LPVe
§ 'Sissinghurst' (Va)	GMac LPVe NBir
'Sky Blue' (Va)	LPVe
'Smugglers' Moon'	MSte SChu
'Snow Queen' (Va)	WWhi
'Sophie' (Vtta)	LPVe SChu
§ *sororia*	EBee EPPr GSki LPVe LRHS
	MWgw WLRN WWal
- 'Albiflora'	CBre CSpe EBee EDAr EMil EPPr
	EPar EPfP GEdr GMaP GSki IHMH
	LRHS MBNS MSph NHar NPro
	WPer WRus
§ - 'Freckles'	More than 30 suppliers
- 'Freckles' dark	LHop
- 'Priceana'	CBre CCge CDev CElw CM&M
	EBee FMan EOrc EWTr NCat NChi
	NGiC SMrm WElm WLRN WPGP
	WWal
- 'Speckles' (v)	EMon
'Soula' (Vtta)	LPVe
* 'Spencer's Cottage'	WBou
* 'Stacey Proud' (v)	NPro
'Steyning' (Va)	LPVe WBou
stojanowii	CGro SBla WEas
'Sugar Plum' (Va)	GMac
§ 'Sulphurea' (Vt)	CDev CGro CPBP CPMA CSWP
	EPar EVFa LPVe MHar MHer
	MMHG MRav NPPs SUsu WCom
	WCot WPer WWhi
'Susanah' (Vtta)	LPVe
'Susie' (Va)	FWll WBou
'Swanley White'	see V. 'Comte de Brazza'
'Sylvia Hart'	MTho
'Talitha' (Va)	GMac LPVe MAnH
'Tamsin' (Va)	LPVe
'Tanith' (Vt)	CBre CDev EBee
'Tara' (Va)	LPVe
'Thalia' (Vtta)	LPVe WBou
§ 'The Czar' (Vt)	CBre CGro ILis
'Thea' (Va)	LPVe
'Thelma' (Va)	LPVe
'Thetis' (Va)	LPVe
'Thierry' (Va)	LPVe
'Tiffany' (Va)	LPVe
'Tiger Eyes' **new**	EBla SWal
'Tina' (Va)	LPVe WOFF
'Titania' (Va)	CGro LPVe
'Tom' (SP)	WOFF
'Tom Tit' (Va)	LPVe WBou
'Tony Venison' (C/v)	CElw EBee EDAr EHoe EMan
	GDra MTho NHaw WBou WCom
	WFTG

	'Toulouse'	WHer
	tricolor	CKin CPrp EFer GBar GPoy GWCH MHer NGHP NSco SIde SPlb WHHs WHer WJek WSel
§	- subsp. *curtisii*	LPVe
§	- subsp. *macedonica*	LPVe
	- 'Sawyer's Blue'	WPer
	- subsp. *saxatilis*	see *V. tricolor* subsp. *macedonica*
	'Tullia' (Vtta)	LPVe
	'Una' (Va)	LPVe
	'Unity' (Vtta)	LPVe
	'Velleda' (Vtta)	LPVe
	velutina	see *V. gracilis*
	'Venetia' (Va)	LPVe
	'Venus' (Va)	LPVe
	verecunda B&SWJ 604a	WCru
§	- var. *yakusimana*	CRDP ESis GDra WOBN
	'Victoria'	see *V.* 'Czar Bleu'
	'Victoria Cawthorne' (C)	CElw CMea EBee EMan GBuc GMac LPVe LPhx MBro MHer MOne MSte NDov NPPs SBla SChu WBou WCom WEas WHoo WWhi
§	'Victoria Regina' (Vt)	CBre CDev
	'Victoria's Blush' (C)	CBos CSpe EBee ECtt GBuc GMaP MHer MMil NChi WCom
	'Violacea' (C)	LPVe
	'Virginia' (Va)	GMac LPVe SChu WBou
	'Virgo' (Va)	LPVe
	'Vita' (Va)	GBuc GMac LPVe MBNS SBla SChu SMrm WBou WIvy WWhi
	vourinensis	LPVe
	'Wanda' (Va)	LPVe
	'Wasp' (Va)	GMac
	'Wendy' (SP)	LPVe
	'White Ladies'	see *V. cucullata* 'Alba'
	'White Pearl' (Va)	GBuc GMac LPhx MLLN WBou
	'White Perfection'	LRHS MBNS
	'White Superior'	CBcs NCat
	'White Swan' (Va)	GMac LPVe NChi
	'William Fife' (ExVa)	WOFF
	'William Snocken' (FP)	WOFF
	'William Wallace' (Va)	LPVe
	'Windward' (Vt)	NCat
	'Winifred Jones' (Va)	WBou
	'Winifred Warden' (Va)	MBNS
	'Winifred Wargent' (Va)	LPVe
	'Winona' (Vtta)	LPVe
	'Winona Cawthorne' (C)	GMac LPVe NChi NDov NHaw NPPs WBou WWhi
	'Wisley White'	EBee WFar
	'Woodlands Cream' (Va)	GMac MAnH MHer NCiC WBou WOFF
	'Woodlands Lilac' (Va)	LPVe SChu WBou WOFF
	'Woodlands White' (Va)	LPVe WBou WOFF
	'Xantha' (Va)	LPVe
	yakusimana	see *V. verecunda* var. *yakusimana*
	'Zalea' (Va)	LPVe
	'Zara' (Va)	GMaP WBou
	'Zenobia' (Vtta)	LPVe
	'Zepherine' (Va)	LPVe
	'Zeta' (Va)	LPVe
	'Ziglana' (Va)	LPVe
	'Zoe' (Vtta)	EBee LPVe NPri SMrm WBou WWol
	'Zona' (Va)	LPVe

Viscaria (Caryophyllaceae)

	vulgaris	see *Lychnis viscaria*

Vitaliana (Primulaceae)

§	*primuliflora*	CLyd ETow GCrs GDra GKir GTou ITim MBro NLAp NMen NRya NSla

	- subsp. *praetutiana*	EHyt EPot MBro NHar NHol NMen NWCA SBla WAbe WFar WLin WPat
	- subsp. *tridentata*	NMen

Vitex (Verbenaceae)

	agnus-castus	CAgr CArn CBcs CPLG CSpe EBee EDAr EEls ELan ELau EShb GPoy LEdu LRHS MCCP MHer SIgm SLon SMad SPer SRPl WDin WFar WHer WSHC WWye
	- 'Blue Spire'	CFwr
	- var. *latifolia*	EBee LRHS MAsh NPSl WDin
	incisa	see *V. negundo* var. *heterophylla*
	negundo	CArn EOHP EWTr
§	- var. *heterophylla*	CPle

Vitis ✿ (Vitaceae)

	'Abundante' (F)	WSuV
	aestivalis new	CBcs
	'Alden' (O/W)	WSuV
	amurensis	CPIN EBee EPfP EPla GIBF LRHS
	- B&SWJ 4138	WCru
	'Aurore' Seibel 5279 (W)	WSuV
	'Baco Noir' (O/B)	GTwe SDea WSuV
	Black Hamburgh	see *V. vinifera* 'Schiava Grossa'
	'Black Strawberry' (B)	WSuV
§	'Boskoop Glory' (F)	CMac EMil GTwe LBuc NBlu SCoo SDea SEND WSuV
	'Brant' (O/B) ♀ H4	More than 30 suppliers
	'Brilliant' (B) new	WSuV
	'Buffalo' (B) new	WSuV
	californica (F)	ERea
	'Canadice' (O/R/S)	SDea WSuV
	'Cascade' (O/B)	see *V.* Seibel 13053
	Castel 19637 (B)	WSuV
	'Chambourcin' (B)	WSuV
	coignetiae ♀ H4	More than 30 suppliers
	- B&SWJ 4744	WCru
	- Claret Cloak = 'Frovit' PBR	EBee ELan ENot EPfP LRHS MAsh MRav NEgg SBrw SMur SPar SPer SSpi WPGP WPat WWeb
	- B&SWJ 4550 from Korea	WCru
*	- 'Rubescens'	CPIN
	'Dalkauer' (W)	WSuV
I	'Diamond' (B) new	WSuV
	'Einset' (B/S) new	WSuV
	ficifolia	see *V. thunbergii*
	flexuosa B&SWJ 5568	WCru
	- var. *choii* B&SWJ 4101	WCru
§	'Fragola' (O/R)	CMac CPIN EBee EBre EPfP EPla ERea EWTr GTwe MRav NVne SDea SEND SPer SRms WCom WSuV
	'Gagarin Blue' (O/B)	ERea GTwe NPer NVne SDea WSuV
	'Glenora' (F/B/S)	WSuV
	henryana	see *Parthenocissus henryana*
	'Himrod' (O/W/S)	ERea GTwe SDea WSuV
	inconstans	see *Parthenocissus tricuspidata*
	'Interlaken' (G/W)	ERea WSuV
	'Kempsey Black' (B)	WSuV
	'Kuibishevski' (O/R)	WSuV
	labrusca	CPIN
	- 'Concord' (O/B)	ERea
	Landot 244 (O/B)	WSuV
	'Léon Millot' (O/G/B)	EMui ERea NVne SDea WSuV
	'Maréchal Foch' (O/B)	WSuV
	'Maréchal Joffre' (O/B)	GTwe NVne WSuV
	'Muscat Bleu' (O/B)	ERea WSuV
	Oberlin 595 (O/B)	WSuV

'Orion'	EMui NVne WSuV WWeb
palmata	WCru
parsley-leaved	see *V. vinifera* 'Ciotat'
parvifolia	CPlN WPat
'Phönix' (O/W)	GTwe NVne SKee WSuV
piasezkii	WCru
– B&SWJ 5236	WCru
* 'Pink Strawberry' (O)	WSuV
'Pirovano 14' (O/B)	ERea GTwe SDea WSuV
§ 'Plantet' (O/B)	WSuV
* 'Poloske Muscat' (W)	WSuV
pseudoreticulata	CFil CPlN WPGP
* 'Queen of Esher'	GTwe
quinquefolia	see *Parthenocissus quinquefolia*
Ravat 51 (O/W)	WSuV
'Regent'PBR	CWSG GTwe MCoo MGos NVne SKee WOrn WSuV WWeb
'Rembrant' (R)	WSuV
riparia	CPlN WCru
'Rondo' EM 6494-5 (O/B)	EMui NVne WSuV WWeb
'Schuyler' (O/B)	ESim WSuV
Seibel (F)	EMui GTwe SDea
§ Seibel 13053 (O/B)	ERea LRHS MAsh SDea WSuV
Seibel 138315 (R)	WSuV
Seibel 5409 (W)	WSuV
Seibel 5455	see *V.* 'Plantet'
Seibel 7053	WSuV
Seibel 9549	WSuV
'Seneca' (W)	WSuV
§ 'Seyval Blanc' (O/W)	CAgr ERea GTwe NVne SDea WSuV
Seyve Villard 12.375	see *V.* 'Villard Blanc'
Seyve Villard 20.473 (F)	MAsh WSuV
Seyve Villard 5276	see *V.* 'Seyval Blanc'
'Suffolk Seedless' (B/S) **new**	WSuV
'Tereshkova' (O/B)	ERea SDea WSuV
'Thornton' (F/S)	WSuV
§ *thunbergii* B&SWJ 4702	WCru
'Triomphe d'Alsace' (O/B)	LRHS MAsh NPer SDea WSuV
'Trollinger'	see *V. vinifera* 'Schiava Grossa'
'Vanessa' (O/R/S)	ERea
§ 'Villard Blanc' (O/W)	WSuV
vinifera	NVne
– EM 323158B	WSuV
– 'Abouriou' (O/B)	WSuV
– 'Adelheidtraube' (F) **new**	WSuV
– 'Albalonga' (W)	WSuV
§ – 'Alicante' (G/B)	ERea GTwe NVne SDea WSuV
– 'Apiifolia'	see *V. vinifera* 'Ciotat'
– 'Appley Towers' (G/B)	ERea
– 'Augusta Louise' (O/W) **new**	WSuV
– 'Auxerrois' (O/W)	WSuV
– 'Bacchus' (O/W)	EPla NVne SDea WSuV
– 'Black Alicante'	see *V. vinifera* 'Alicante'
– 'Black Corinth' (G/B/S)	ERea
– 'Black Frontignan' (G/O/B)	ERea WSuV
– Black Hamburgh	see *V. vinifera* 'Schiava Grossa'
– 'Black Monukka' (G/B/S)	ERea WSuV
– 'Black Prince' (G/B)	WSuV
– 'Blauburger' (O/B)	WCru
– 'Blue Portuguese'	see *V. vinifera* 'Portugieser'
§ – 'Bouvier' (W)	WSuV
– 'Bouviertraube'	see *V. vinifera* 'Bouvier'
– 'Buckland Sweetwater' (G/W)	ERea GTwe MBri MGos NVne SDea WSuV
– 'Cabernet Sauvignon' (O/B)	MAsh SDea WSuV
– 'Canners' (F/S)	ERea
– 'Canon Hall Muscat' (G/W)	ERea NVne

– 'Cardinal' (O/R)	ERea WSuV
– 'Chaouch' (G/W)	ERea
– 'Chardonnay' (O/W)	MAsh NPer NVne SDea SPer WSuV
§ – 'Chasselas' (G/O/W)	EMui ERea LRHS MAsh NVne SDea WSuV WWeb
– 'Chasselas de Fontainebleau' (F) **new**	EMil
– 'Chasselas de Tramontaner' (F) **new**	EMil
– 'Chasselas d'Or'	see *V. vinifera* 'Chasselas'
– 'Chasselas Rosé' (G/R)	ERea WSuV
– 'Chasselas Vibert' (G/W)	ERea WSuV
– 'Chenin Blanc' (O/W)	WSuV
§ – 'Ciotat' (F)	EPla ERea NVne SDea WCru WSuV
§ – 'Cot' (O/B)	WSuV
– 'Crimson Seedless' (R/S)	ERea
– 'Csabyongye' (W)	WSuV
– 'Dattier de Beyrouth' (W)	WSuV
– 'Dornfelder' (O/R)	EBee NVne SKee SLim WSuV
– 'Dunkelfelder' (O/R)	NVne WSuV
– 'Early Van der Laan' (F)	EMil NBlu
– 'Ehrenfelser' (O/W)	WSuV
– 'Elbling' (O/W)	WSuV
– 'Excelsior' (W)	WSuV
– 'Faber' (O/W)	WSuV
– 'Ferdinand de Lesseps'	ERea
– 'Fiesta' (F/W/S)	WSuV
– 'Findling' (W)	NVne WSuV
– 'Flame' **new**	ESim
– 'Flame Seedless' (B/S) **new**	WSuV
– 'Forta' (O/W)	WSuV
– 'Foster's Seedling' (G/W)	ERea GTwe SDea WSuV
– 'Gamay Hatif' (O/B)	ERea
– 'Gamay Hatif des Vosges'	WSuV
– 'Gamay Noir' (O/B)	WSuV
– Gamay Teinturier Group (O/B)	WSuV
– 'Gewürztraminer' (O/R)	LRHS MAsh SDea WSuV
– 'Glory of Boskoop'	see *V.* 'Boskoop Glory'
– 'Golden Champion' (G/W) **new**	WSuV
– 'Golden Chasselas'	see *V. vinifera* 'Chasselas'
– 'Golden Queen' (G/W)	kRea
– 'Goldriesling' (O/W)	NVne WSuV
– 'Gros Colmar' (G/B)	ERea
– 'Gros Maroc' (G/B)	ERea
– 'Grüner Veltliner' (O/W)	WSuV
– 'Gutenborner' (O/W)	WSuV
– 'Helfensteiner' (O/R)	WSuV
– 'Huxelrebe' (O/W)	NVne WSuV
– 'Incana' (O/B)	CPlN EBee EPfP EPla MRav WCFE WCom WCot WCru WSHC
– 'Juliaumsrebe' (O/W)	WSuV
– 'Kanzler' (O/W)	WSuV
– 'Kerner' (O/W)	NVne WSuV
– 'Kernling' (F)	NVne WSuV
– 'King's Ruby' (F/S)	ERea
– 'Lady Downe's Seedling' (G/B)	ERea
– 'Lady Hastings' (G/B)	ERea
– 'Lady Hutt' (G/W)	ERea
– 'Lakemont' (O/W/S)	ERea
– 'Madeleine Angevine' (O/W)	EMui ERea GTwe LRHS MAsh MGos NVne SDea SLim WSuV
– 'Madeleine Celine' (F) **new**	WSuV
– 'Madeleine Noire'	NVne
– 'Madeleine Royale' (G/W)	ERea WSuV
– 'Madeleine Silvaner' (O/W)	EMui ERea GTwe LRHS MAsh MGos NPer NVne SDea SPer WSuV

- 'Madresfield Court' (G/B)   ERea GTwe NVne WSuV
- 'Malbec'   see *V. vinifera* 'Cot'
- 'Merlot' (G/B)   NVne SDea WSuV
- 'Mireille' (F)   GTwe SDea WSuV
- 'Morio Muscat' (O/W)   WSuV
- 'Mrs Pearson' (G/W)   ERea
- 'Mrs Pince's Black   ERea NVne
  Muscat' (G/B)
§ - 'Müller-Thurgau' (O/W)   EMui ERea GKir GTwe LRHS
     MAsh MBri MGos SDea SLim SPer
     WSuV WWeb
- 'Muscat Blanc à Petits   WSuV
  Grains' (O/W)
- 'Muscat Champion' (G/R)   ERea
- 'Muscat de Saumur'   WSuV
  (O/W)
- 'Muscat Hamburg' (G/B)   EMil EMui ERea MAsh MGos
     NVne SDea WSuV
- 'Muscat of Alexandria'   CBcs CMac CRHN CSam EHol
  (G/W)   EMui ERea NVne SDea SLim SRPl
- 'Muscat of Hungary'   ERea
  (G/W)
- 'Muscat Ottonel' (O/W)   WSuV
- 'Muscat St Laurent'   WSuV
  (W) **new**
- 'New York Muscat' (O/B)   ERea WSuV
- 'No. 69' (W)   WSuV
- 'Noir Hatif de Marseilles'   ERea WSuV
  (O/B)
- 'Oliver Irsay' (O/W)   ERea WSuV
- 'Optima' (O/W)   WSuV
- 'Ortega' (O/W)   NVne WSuV
- 'Perle' (O/W)   WSuV
- 'Perle de Czaba' (G/O/W)   EMil ERea WSuV
- 'Perlette' (O/W/S)   ERea WSuV
- 'Petit Rouge' (B) **new**   WSuV
- 'Pinot Blanc' (O/W)   LRHS MAsh WSuV
- 'Pinot Gris' (O/B)   SDea WSuV
- 'Pinot Noir' (O/B)   NVne WSuV
- 'Plavač Mali' (B)   WSuV
§ - 'Portugieser' (O/B)   WSuV
- 'Précoce de Bousquet'   WSuV
  (O/W)
- 'Précoce de Malingre'   ERea SDea
  (O/W)
- 'Primavis Frontignan'   WSuV
  (G/yd)
- 'Prince of Wales' (G/B)   ERea
- 'Purpurea' (O/B) ♀ H4   More than 30 suppliers
- 'Regner' (O/W)   MGos
- 'Reichensteiner' (O/G/W)   SDea WSuV
- 'Reine Olga' (O/R)   ERea
- 'Reliance' (O/R/S)   ERea WSuV
- 'Riesling' (O/W)   LRHS MAsh WSuV
- Riesling-Silvaner   see *V. vinifera* 'Müller-Thurgau'
- 'Rish Baba'   ERea
- 'Royal Muscadine'   EPla NVne WSuV
  (G/O/W)
- 'Saint Laurent' (G/O/W)   ERea WSuV
- 'Sauvignon Blanc' (O/W)   NVne WSuV
- 'Scheurebe' (O/W)   WSuV
§ - 'Schiava Grossa' (G/B/D)   More than 30 suppliers
- 'Schönburger' (O/W)   NVne SDea WSuV
- 'Schwartz Reisling'   WSuV
  (B) **new**
- 'Sémillon'   MAsh
- 'Septimer' (O/W)   WSuV
- 'Shiraz' (B)   WSuV
- 'Siegerrebe' (O/W/D)   EMui ERea GTwe LRHS MAsh
     NVne SDea WSuV WWeb
- 'Silvaner' (O/W)   WSuV
- 'Spetchley Red'   EBee WCru WPat
- strawberry grape   see *V.* 'Fragola'

- 'Suffolk Red' (G/R/S)   ERea
§ - 'Sultana' (W/S)   EMui ERea GTwe NVne SDea WSuV
- 'Syrian' (G/W)   ERea
- Teinturier Group (F)   ERea
- 'Thompson Seedless'   see *V. vinifera* 'Sultana'
- 'Trebbiano' (G/W)   ERea
* - 'Triomphe' (O/B)   EMui NVne
- 'Triomphrebe' (W) **new**   WSuV
- 'Vitalis Gold' **new**   WWeb
- 'Vitalis Ruby'   WWeb
- 'Wrotham Pinot' (O/B)   EWTr NVne SDea WSuV
- 'Würzer' (O/W)   WSuV
- 'Zweigeltrebe' (O/B)   WSuV
* 'White Strawberry' (O/W)   WSuV
'Zalagyongye' (W) **new**   WSuV

Vriesea (Bromeliaceae)

carinata	MBri
hieroglyphica	MBri
x **poelmanii**	MBri
x **polonia**	MBri
saundersii ♀ H1	MBri
splendens ♀ H1	MBri
'Vulkana'	MBri

W

Wachendorfia (Haemodoraceae)

brachyandra	WCot
thyrsiflora	CDes CFir CHEx CMCo CPLG CTrC EBee IBlr WCot WDyG WFar WPGP

Wahlenbergia (Campanulaceae)

	ECou
albomarginata	ECou EMan GTou LRHS NHar NLAp
- 'Blue Mist'	ECou
congesta	CPBP EHyt EPot LRHS
gloriosa	CSpe GCrs GKev LBee LRHS MBro NLAp NMen WFar WWin
pumilio	see *Edraianthus pumilio*
pygmaea	MBro WHoo
§ **saxicola**	CLyd CRow EHyt EMan EPot GEdr GTou MWrn WPer
serpyllifolia	see *Edraianthus serpyllifolius*
simpsonii	GTou
tasmanica	see *W. saxicola*
undulata	CSpe

Waldsteinia (Rosaceae)

fragarioides	EBee SMac WPer
geoides	EBee EMan EPPr EPfP LRHS NPro SPer WCom WLRN
ternata	More than 30 suppliers
§ - 'Mozaick' (v)	GKir IBlr NBir NPro WCom
- 'Variegata'	see *W. ternata* 'Mozaick'

Wallichia (Arecaceae)

densiflora	CBrP CRoM LPal
disticha	LPal

walnut see *Juglans*

Wasabia (Brassicaceae)

japonica	CArn GPoy

Washingtonia (Arecaceae)

filifera ♀ H1	CAbb CBrP CDoC CRoM CTbh CTrC EAmu EPVP LPal MBri

	MPRe SAPC SArc SEND SMad SPar SPlb WMul
robusta	CRoM CTrC EAmu EPVP LPal SChr SMad SPar SPlb WMul

Watsonia (Iridaceae)

aletroides	CCtw CDes EBee ITer LPio LRHS SIgm WCot WHil
angusta	CDes CPLG CPne IBlr IKee ITer WPrP
- JCA 3.950.409	WCot
ardernei	see *W. borbonica* subsp. *ardernei* 'Arderne's White'
beatricis	see *W. pillansii*
I 'Best Red'	GCal LPio
§ *borbonica*	CCtw CPne CPou CWCL IBlr ITer LPio SAga SWat WCot
- subsp. *ardernei* hort.	see *W. borbonica* subsp. *ardernei* 'Arderne's White'
§ - subsp. *ardernei* (Pourr.) Goldblatt 'Arderne's White'	CDes CLAP EBee ERos GCal MSte SBla WHil WPGP
- subsp. *borbonica*	CDes CLAP EBee WPGP
brevifolia	see *W. laccata*
coccinea	CDes EBee ITer WPGP
densiflora	CBcs CFil CPou CTrC EBee ITer MSte WCot
fourcadei	CPne EBee ITer WPGP
- S&SH 89	CDes
fulgens	CPne LEdu MSte
galpinii	CFir IBlr
gladioloides	CFil
§ *humilis*	CDes CFil CStu ITer SSpi WPGP
knysnana **new**	ITer
§ *laccata*	CPou EBee ITer SWat WCot
lepida	CFil CPou ITer
- JCA 3.192.800	SSpi
x *longifolia* **new**	ITer
marginata	CPou ITer SWat WCot WHil
- 'Star Spike' **new**	WCot
marlothii	CFil
meriania	CFil CPou EBee GCal GSki IBlr WCot WHil
- var. *bulbillifera*	CFwr EBee GAbr GMac IBlr LPio LRHS
* 'Mount Congreve'	SVen
§ *pillansii*	CCtw CFil CHEx CLAP CPou EBee EBre EMan ERos GMac GSki IBlr ITer SBla SIgm SMrm SWat WCot
pink	CDes EBee
pulchra **new**	ITer
pyramidata	see *W. borbonica*
roseoalba	see *W. humilis*
'Stanford Scarlet'	CDes CLAP CPou EBee IBlr SBla SChr WPGP WSHC
stenosiphon	CPou EBee IBlr
strubeniae	IBlr
tabularis	IBlr ITer SWat WCot
'Tresco Dwarf Pink'	CDes CLAP CPou EBee EMan GAbr GCal LPio NGby WCot WPGP
vanderspuyae	CCtw CPou EBee IBlr ITer
watsonioides	WCot
wilmaniae	CFil CPou IBlr ITer
- JCA 3.955.200	SSpi
wordsworthiana	CPou
zeyheri **new**	ITer

Wattakaka see *Dregea*

Wedelia (Asteraceae)

§ *texana* **new**	EBee

Weigela ✿ (*Caprifoliaceae*)

CC 1231	CPLG
'Abel Carrière'	CMac CTri EBee ECtt EPfP GEil NWea SEND WCFE WFar WLRN WTel
'Avalanche' hort.	see *W.* 'Candida'
'Avalanche' Lemoine	see *W. praecox* 'Avalanche'
'Boskoop Glory'	GQui SPer
Briant Rubidor = 'Olympiade' (v)	CDoC CFwr CSBt CWSG EBee ECtt EHoe ENot EPfP GKir LRHS MAsh MBNS MBar MGos MRav MWhi NBee NFor NHol SEND SLim SPar SPer SPlb SWal WBod WFar WStI WWeb
'Bristol Ruby'	More than 30 suppliers
§ 'Candida'	CTri ELan EWes GEil GSki LRHS MBar MRav NBlu NHol SPer WTel
Carnaval = 'Courtalor'[PBR]	COtt CSBt CWib GKir LPan LRHS MBri WLRN WStI
'Conquête'	GEil GKir LAst
coraeensis	CHll IArd MBlu
- 'Alba'	GEil
'Davnik'	MTPN
decora	GQui
'Emerald Edge'	WBcn
'Eva Rathke'	CTri GKir NWea SCoo WFar WTel
'Evita'	MBar MGos WFar
floribunda **new**	GEil
florida	CTrw EPfP MBar MHdf MWat SMer
- f. *alba*	CBcs WFar
* - 'Albovariegata' (v)	WBrE
- 'Bicolor'	CMac ELan
- 'Bristol Snowflake'	CSWP EPfP GKir MBNS MBar MGos MHer NLar WBod WLRN
- 'Foliis Purpureis' ♀ [H4]	More than 30 suppliers
- 'Java Red'	LRHS
- 'Langtrees Variegated' (v)	EVFa
'Pink Princess'	WWeb
- 'Samabor'	WFar
'Sunny Princess'	NHol
- 'Suzanne' (v)	CBcs EVFa LAst LRHS MGos NPro WWeb
- 'Tango'	CPMA ECtt LRHS MAsh MBri MWya NPro WBcn WWeb
- var. *venusta*	GEil
- 'Versicolor'	CMHG CMac CPLG CWib GQui SLon SMrm WFar
- Wine and Roses = 'Alexandra'	CAbP CBcs CDoC EBee ELan FNot EPfP LAst MAsh NPri NPro NSti
'Florida Variegata' (v) ♀ [H4]	More than 30 suppliers
'Gustave Malet'	GEil GQui
hortensis	GIBF
- 'Nivea'	CPle MBri NPro
- var. *rubra* **new**	GEil
japonica	GEil
- 'Dart's Colourdream'	CFwr EBee ECtt EWes GKir MGos MRav SCoo SLPl SLim SMer WDVN
- 'Variegated Dart's Colourdream' (v)	EVFa
'Jean's Gold'	ELan MGos MRav NPri
'Kosteriana Variegata' (v)	CFwr CSLe EBee LRHS MAsh SLon WFar WLRN
'Le Printemps' **new**	GEil
'Looymansii Aurea'	CMHG CTri ELan EPfP EVFa GEil GKir LAst LRHS MRav NHol SLon SPar SPer WBod WDin WFar WHar WPen WWal WWin
Lucifer = 'Courtared'[PBR]	CDoC CSBt EBee NHol WLRN

'Marjorie'	IMGH WLRN
maximowiczii	CPLG CPle GQui GSki WLRN
§ *middendorffiana*	More than 30 suppliers
'Minuet'	EBee EPfP GSki MBar MGos MRav NPro SPla WWeb
'Mme. le Couturier' **new**	GEil
'Mont Blanc'	CBot CDul MMHG
Nain Rouge = 'Courtanin'^{PBR}	CBcs EBee LRHS NHol WLRN
'Nana Variegata' (v)	CPLG LRHS MBar MBri NBee NHol
'Newport Red'	EBee ENot GEil GKir LRHS MBNS MRav MWat NWea SMer WFar WGwG WLRN WWal
'Pink Poppet'	LAst LRHS MAsh NPro SCoo SPoG WWeb
praecox	GIBF
§ – 'Avalanche'	ECtt MRav WStI
'Praecox Variegata' (v) ♀ H4	CChe CTri EBee ELan EPfP GKir MAsh MBri MRav SMac SPar SPer SPla SRPl SReu SRms WCFE WCru WFar WHCG WSHC
'Red Prince' ♀ H4	EBee ELan GWCH LAst LRHS MBri MGos WBod
'Ruby Queen'^{PBR}	CDoC EPfP LRHS
'Rumba'	EMil GSki MBri MMHG MRav NPro
'Samba'	LRHS MBri
'Snowflake'	EBee ECtt NLon NPri NPro SRms WDin WFar
'Styriaca' **new**	GEil
subsessilis B&SWJ 1056	WCru
'Victoria'	CDoC CMHG CWib EBee EBre ECtt ELan EPfP LAst LRHS MAsh MBri SCoo SPar SPer SPla WBrE WGor WHar WLRN WWeb
'Wessex Gold' (v)	CFai WHCG

Weinmannia (*Cunoniaceae*)

racemosa 'Kamahi'	CTrC
trichosperma	IBlr ISea SAPC SArc

Weldenia (*Commelinaceae*)

candida	EHyt LTwo NHar NMen SIng SOkd WAbe

Westringia (*Lamiaceae*)

angustifolia	ECou
brevifolia	ECou
– Raleighii Group	ECou
§ *fruticosa* ♀ H1	CBcs CPle ECou WJek
– 'Variegata' (v)	CPle GQui WJek
– 'Wynyabbie Gem'	EMan
longifolia	ECou
rigida 'Morning Light' (v)	EMan WCot
rosmariniformis	see *W. fruticosa*

Wettinia (*Arecaceae*)

maynensis	LPal

whitecurrant see *Ribes rubrum* (W)

Widdringtonia (*Cupressaceae*)

cedarbergensis	GGar
cupressoides	see *W. nodiflora*
§ *nodiflora*	GGar
schwarzii	GGar

Wigandia (*Hydrophyllaceae*)

caracasana	CKob

Wikstroemia (*Thymelaeaceae*)

gemmata	SSta
kudoi **new**	WCru

wineberry see *Rubus phoenicolasius*

Wisteria ✿ (*Papilionaceae*)

§ *brachybotrys*	CMCN LNet SLim
§ – Murasaki-kapitan	CEnd LNet
§ – 'Okayama'	LNet
§ – 'Shiro-kapitan'	CEnd CPMA CSPN CTri EBee ENot EPfP EPla LNet LRHS MAsh MBri MGag MGos NHol SBra SHBN SLim SLon SPar SPer WPGP WWeb
* – 'White Silk'	CEnd CPMA LNet MGos
§ – 'Burford'	CEnd CSPN EMui LNet LRHS MAsh MBri MGag MWat NBea NHol NRib SCoo SKee SLim WHar
– 'Caroline'	CBcs CDoC CEnd CSBt CSPN EBee EPfP ERea GKir LNet LRHS MBlu MGag MGos NBea NBee SBrw SPar SPer SSpi
floribunda	CBcs CRHN CRez CWib ELan EPla LPan LRHS MAsh SBra SBrw SHBN WDin WNor
§ – 'Alba' ♀ H4	More than 30 suppliers
§ – 'Asagi'	LNet MGag
– 'Black Dragon'	see *W.* x *formosa* 'Yae-kokuryû' (d)
* – 'Blue Pacific'	LNet
– 'Bonzai Pink' **new**	LNet
– 'Burford'	see *W.* 'Burford'
– 'Cannington'	SCoo SLim
* – 'Cascade'	LNet MGos
§ – 'Domino'	CBcs CEnd EBee EPfP EPla GKir LNet LPan LRHS MBar MGag MGos NBea NEgg NHol SBra SBrw SLim SPer SSta WSHC WWeb
– 'Fragrantissima'	see *W. sinensis* 'Jako'
– 'Geisha'	LNet
* – 'Harlequin'	CBcs CHad CSPN EBee LNet LRHS MBro MGos WPat
– 'Hichirimen'	see *W. floribunda* 'Asagi'
– 'Hon-beni'	see *W. floribunda* 'Rosea'
– 'Honey Bee Pink'	see *W. floribunda* 'Rosea'
– 'Honko'	see *W. floribunda* 'Rosea'
– 'Issai Perfect'	LNet SKee
§ – 'Kuchi-beni'	CBcs CSBt CSPN EBee ELan EPfP GKir LNet LRHS MGag MGos SBra SBrw SLim SPar WWeb
– 'Lavender Lace'	see *W.* 'Lavender Lace'
– 'Lawrence'	CSPN LNet LRHS NBee
– 'Lipstick'	see *W. floribunda* 'Kuchi-beni'
– 'Longissima'	see *W. floribunda* 'Multijuga'
– 'Longissima Alba'	see *W. floribunda* 'Alba'
– 'Macrobotrys'	see *W. floribunda* 'Multijuga'
– 'Magenta'	LNet LRHS SBrw
§ – 'Multijuga' ♀ H4	More than 30 suppliers
– 'Murasaki-naga'	see *W. floribunda* 'Purple Patches'
– 'Murasaki-noda'	MGos
– 'Nana Richin's Purple'	CEnd LNet LRHS
– 'Peaches and Cream'	see *W. floribunda* 'Kuchi-beni'
– 'Pink Ice'	see *W. floribunda* 'Rosea'
§ – 'Purple Patches'	EBee GKir LNet LRHS MGag MGos MWat NPri SLim SPer
* – 'Purple Tassle'	LNet
– Reindeer	see *W. sinensis* 'Jako'
§ – 'Rosea' ♀ H4	More than 30 suppliers
– 'Royal Purple'	ERea LNet LRHS MGag WGor
– 'Russelliana'	EBee SLim
– 'Shiro-naga'	see *W. floribunda* 'Alba'
– 'Shiro-noda'	see *W. floribunda* 'Alba'
– 'Sky Blue' **new**	LNet
– 'Snow Showers'	see *W. floribunda* 'Alba'

- 'Violacea Plena' (d)	CDoC EBee LNet LPan LRHS MGag MGos MRav NPri SHBN SPar SPer WDin WWeb
x *formosa*	LNet SLim
- 'Black Dragon' (d)	see *W.* x *formosa* 'Yae-kokuryû' (d)
- 'Domino'	see *W. floribunda* 'Domino'
- 'Issai' Wada pro parte	see *W. floribunda* 'Domino'
- 'Kokuryû' (d)	see *W.* x *formosa* 'Yae-kokuryû' (d)
§ - 'Yae-kokuryû' (d)	CBcs CEnd CSBt CSPN EBee EPfP EPla GKir LNet LPan LRHS MAsh MGag MGos NBlu NHol SBra SBrw SHBN SKee SLim SMad SPar SReu SSpi SSta WGor WWeb
frutescens	WNor
- 'Alba'	see *W. frutescens* 'Nivea'
- 'Amethyst Falls'	LNet
- 'Magnifica'	see *W. macrostachya* 'Magnifica'
§ - 'Nivea'	LNet
- 'Swartley Purple'	LNet
Kapitan-fuji	see *W. brachybotrys*
'Kofuji'	see *Millettia japonica*
§ 'Lavender Lace'	EPfP LNet LRHS
macrostachya	LNet
'Bayou Two o'Clock'	
- 'Clara Mack'	LNet
§ - 'Magnifica'	EBee LNet
- 'Pondside Blue'	LNet
maerostachya	LNet
'Abbeville Blue' **new**	
multijuga 'Alba'	see *W. floribunda* 'Alba'
'Showa-beni'	CEnd LNet LRHS SCoo SLim
sinensis ♀ H4	More than 30 suppliers
- 'Alba' ♀ H4	CBcs CDoC CWib EBee ELan ENot EPfP LBuc LNet LPan LRHS MBar MGag MWat SBra SBrw SLim SPar SPer SPla WDin WFar
- 'Amethyst'	CSBt CSPN EBee EPfP ERea LRHS MGos MRav NSti SBra SBrw SPla SReu
- 'Blue Sapphire'	CHad CSPN EBee LNet LRHS SBra SBrw WBod
- 'Consequa'	see *W. sinensis* 'Prolific'
- 'Cooke's Special'	LNet
- from Beijing	LNet
§ - 'Jako'	CEnd LBuc LNet NHol SBra
- 'Larry's White'	LNet
- 'Oosthoek's Variety'	see *W. sinensis* 'Prolific'
- 'Prematura'	see *W. floribunda* 'Domino'
- 'Prematura Alba'	see *W. brachybotrys* 'Shiro-kapitan'
§ - 'Prolific'	CHad CPIN CSBt CSam CTri EBee ELan EPfP LBuc LNet LPan LRHS MBri MGag MGos NBlu SBra SBrw SKee SPar SPer SPla SSpi WPat WWeb
- 'Rosea'	LPan SKee
venusta	see *W. brachybotrys* 'Shiro-kapitan'
- var. *violacea* hort.	see *W. brachybotrys* Murasaki-kapitan
- var. *violacea* Rehder	see *W. brachybotrys* Murasaki-kapitan
villosa	WNor

Withania (Solanaceae)

somnifera	CArn EOHP GPoy MSal SHDw

Wittsteinia (Alseuosmiaceae)

vacciniacea	EBee GEil WCru WWes

Wodyetia (Arecaceae)

bifurcata	EAmu LPal

Woodsia (Woodsiaceae)

intermedia	NBro
obtusa	CLAP EBee EBlw EFer GCal LAst LRHS NHar NSti WRic
polystichoides ♀ H4	GQui NHar

Woodwardia ✿ (Blechnaceae)

from Emei Shan, China	CLAP
blechnoides **new**	NMar
fimbriata	CHid CLAP EBee GCal MAvo NBlu NWCA SSpi WCot WPGP
martinezii	CFil
orientalis	WPic
- var. *formosana*	NMar
- - B&SWJ 6865	WCru
radicans ♀ H3	CAbb CFil CHEx CLAP EBee GQui ISea NMar SAPC SArc SMad WAbe WCot WPic
unigemmata	CHEx CLAP EDAr SSpi WAbe WHal

worcesterberry see *Ribes divaricatum*

Wulfenia (Scrophulariaceae)

amherstiana	GCed SOkd
blechicii subsp. *rohlenae* **new**	GIBF
carinthiaca	CNic EBee GAbr GEdr GIBF MMHG MOne NBir NLAp

Wyethia (Asteraceae)

helianthoides	EBee EMan
scabra **new**	EBee

X

Xanthoceras (Sapindaceae)

sorbifolium ♀ H3-4	CAgr CBcs CBot CFil CLnd CMCN CTho CWib EBee ECrN ELan EPfP GKir IArd IDee MBlu MRav NPSI SBrw SMad SPar SSpi WDin WFar WLRN WNor WPGP

Xanthophthalmum (Asteraceae)

coronarium	CArn
§ *segetum*	GWCH MBow WHer

Xanthorhiza (Ranunculaceae)

simplicissima	CBcs CFil CRow EBee EPfP GCal LEdu NLar SBrw SDys SMad SSpi WPGP

Xanthorrhoea (Xanthorrhoeaceae)

australis	CPLG SPlb WGer
johnsonii	CTrC MGos NRog SHmp
preisii	LPan

Xanthosoma (Araceae)

sagittifolium	WMul
violaceum	WMul

Xerochrysum (Asteraceae)

bracteatum 'Coco'	CMHG EMan GMac WCot
- 'Dargan Hill Monarch'	CHll CMHG CSev CSpe SRms WEas
- 'Eastgrove Sherbert'	WEas
- 'Skynet'	CSev GCal GMac

Xerophyllum (*Melanthiaceae*)

tenax   CFir GBuc GIBF WLin

Xylorhiza see *Machaeranthera*

Xyris (*Xyridaceae*)

juncea   ECou

Y

youngberry see *Rubus* 'Youngberry'

Ypsilandra (*Melanthiaceae*)

thibetica   EBee LEur NGar WCru

Yucca ✿ (*Agavaceae*)

aloifolia	CHEx CTrC EOas LRHS MGos MPRe SAPC SArc SNew SPar SPlb WMul
- 'Marginata' (v)	MPRe
- 'Purpurea'	SPlb
- 'Tricolor'	MPRe
- 'Variegata' (v)	LPal LPan SAPC SArc SPar
angustifolia	see *Y. glauca*
angustissima	GCal
- NNS 99-509	WCot
arizonica	GCal
baccata	CTrC EOas GCal SPar WCot
- NNS 99-510	WCot
brevifolia	CRoM CTrC EOas
carnerosana	CTrC
§ *elata*	CTrC
§ *elephantipes* ♀ H1	LRHS MBri SEND SMur SPar
- 'Jewel' (v)	SEND SPar
faxoniana	EOas
filamentosa ♀ H4	More than 30 suppliers
- 'Bright Edge' (v) ♀ H3	CDoC CMHG CSBt CSpe EBee EBre ECtt ELan ENot EPfP EPla GKir LEdu LPan LRHS MAsh MBri MCCP MGos MRav MTis MWat MWgw NCot SHBN SLim SPar SPer WCot WPat
- 'Color Guard' (v)	NCot WCot
- 'Variegata' (v) ♀ H3	CBcs CBot CSBt EPfP LRHS MGos SAga SPar SPer SRms WDin WFar WGer
filifera **new**	EOas
flaccida	EBot NBee SDix SEND SPar
- 'Golden Sword' (v) ♀ H3	CAbb CBrm CDoC CMHG CSBt CTrC CWSG EBee EBre ELan EPfP EVFa GKir LPio LRHS MAsh MBri MCCP MRav NBir NCot NMoo SLim SPar SPer WCot WPat WWeb WWhi
- 'Ivory' ♀ H3-4	CDoC CEnd CHar EBee ECtt ELan ENot EPfP GAbr GCal GKir GMaP LRHS MAsh MBlu MBri MGos MRav SLPl SMad SPar SPer SRms SSta STre WCot WLeb WPic WWeb
x *floribunda*	SAPC SArc SPar
'Garland's Gold' (v)	CBcs CDoC GQui LRHS MBri MDun MGos SPar WBod WFar WPat
§ *glauca*	CAbb CBcs CBrP CMHG CTrC EBot EPfP GCal LRHS MBri SAPC SEND WBod
- NNS 99-511	WCot
- var. *radiosa* **new**	CTrC

gloriosa ♀ H4	CBcs CDoC CHEx CTri ENot EOas EPla EWTr LAst LNet LPan LRHS MPRe NBlu NPal SAPC SArc SEND SHBN SMad SPar SSpi WBrE WStI
- 'Aureovariegata'	see *Y. gloriosa* 'Variegata'
- 'Nobilis'	SDix
§ - 'Variegata' (v) ♀ H4	More than 30 suppliers
guatemalensis	see *Y. elephantipes*
harrimaniae	GCal SIgm
kanabensis	GCal
radiosa	see *Y. elata*
recurvifolia ♀ H4	CHEx EOas EPfP SAPC SArc SPar
rigida	CBrP CTrC
rostrata	CAbb CBrP CTrC EOas LPal SAPC SArc WMul
schidigera	GCal WCot
schottii	CBrP GCal WCot
thompsoniana	CTrC GCal
torreyi	CTrC GCal WCot
'Vittorio Emanuele II'	MTed
whipplei	CAbb CBot CBrP CCtw CDoC CFil CRoM EBee EBot EOas GCal LEdu LRHS SAPC SPar SSpi WBrE WPGP
- subsp. *parishii*	SIgm

Yushania (*Poaceae*)

§ *anceps*	CAbb CBcs CDoC CFil CHEx CHad EBee EFul EPfP EPla GBin LJus MGos MHdf MMoz MWht NVic SAPC SArc SDry SPer SPla WBrE WCru WDin WFar WMoo WPGP
§ - 'Pitt White'	CFil EBee EPla SDry WJun
- 'Pitt White Rejuvenated'	ERod
chungii	CFil EPla WPGP
maculata	EPla ERod LJus MMoz SDry WJun
§ *maling*	EPfP EPla ERod MMoz SDry WJun

Z

Zaluzianskya (*Scrophulariaceae*)

JCA 15665	WAbe
imported from USA	SSpi
capensis	CPLG
- 'Midnight Candy'	EMan
'Katherine'	EMan SIng SRot SScr
ovata	CPLG EHyt EPot GBri LPio MAvo MTho NBir NBur NJOw SAga SBla SMrm WAbe WCom
* cf. *rostrata* DBG 219	ETow
'Semonkong'	CMdw GCal LPio MSte

Zamia (*Zamiaceae*)

fischeri **new**	NRog
floridana	CRoM LPal
furfuracea	CBrP EAmu LPal
muricata	LPal NRog
pumila	CBrP NRog
roezlii	CBrP
skinneri	LPal
standleyi	CBrP
vazquezii	CBrP

Zamioculcas (*Araceae*)

zamiifolia   ESlt

Zantedeschia (*Araceae*)

§ *aethiopica* ♀ H3	More than 30 suppliers
- 'Apple Court Babe'	CElw CRDP CRow CStu GCal MNrw SApp

- 'Childsiana' — CRDP SApp
- 'Crowborough' ♀ H3 — More than 30 suppliers
- 'Glow' — MNrw WCot
- 'Green Goddess' ♀ H3 — More than 30 suppliers
- 'Little Gem' — ECha LPio
- 'Mr Martin' — CDes EBee EMan MNrw WCot WFTG WPGP
- 'Mr Sam' — CLAP
- 'Pershore Fantasia' (v) — EBee EVFa MAvo MNrw WCot WFar WPnP
- 'Whipped Cream' new — MNrw
- 'White Gnome' — EBee WFar
- 'White Pixie' new — COtt ENot
- 'White Sail' — CLAP EBee EMan EMar GCal LBuc MRav WFib

albomaculata — CSut CTrC EBee LAma LCaP NRog
'Anneke' new — WBrE WViv
'Apricot Glow' — CHll WViv
'Aztec Gold' — CHEx
'Best Gold' — see *Zantedeschia* 'Florex Gold'
black new — CSut
'Black Eyed Beauty' — CStu EMui IHMH LAma NRog
'Black Magic' — LAma WFar WViv
'Black Pearl' new — LAma
'Bridal Blush' — LAma
'Cameo' — CSut EMui LAma MNrw WFar WViv
'Carmine Red' — EPot MNrw WBrE
'Celeste' — WViv
'Chianti' new — MNrw WViv
'Crystal Blush' new — LAma
elliottiana ♀ H1 — CBcs CFir CHal GQui ITer LAma MNrw NRog SYvo WPnn WViv
'Flame' — EMui
§ 'Florex Gold' — CSut LAma NRog WViv
'Galaxy' — WViv
'Golden Sun' — WViv
'Harvest Moon' — LAma
'Helen O'Connor' — SYvo
'Hot Shot' new — WViv
'Kiwi Blush' — CAbP CBcs CFir CHEx CLAP CRow CSpe EBee ELan EMan ERou LRHS MAvo MCCP NPal SAWi SApp SEND SPar SSpi SVil WCot WFTG WFar WPnP WPnn WSan
'Lavender Petite' — LAma NRog
'Lime Lady' — ECha
'Little Suzie' — WViv
'Majestic Red' — EMui NBlu WCot WViv
'Mango' — EMui EPot ETub IHMH LAma MNrw WCot WPnP WPnn WViv
'Maroon Dainty' — LAma NRog
orange new — IHMH
'Pink Mist' new — EMar LAma MNrw WAbe
'Pink Persuasion' — EMui EPot LAma MNrw WFar WViv
'Purple Haze' PBR new — WViv
red new — IHMH
rehmannii ♀ H1 — CStu GQui IHMH LAma LCaP MCCP MNrw NLar SRms SYvo WViv
- 'Little Dream' — WViv
* 'Romeo' — SYvo
'Schwarzwalder' PBR new — ETub IHMH WViv
'Sensation' new — IHMH
'Shell Pink' — NRog
'Silver Lining' new — LAma
'Solfatare' — LAma LCaP MNrw
'Treasure' — WCot WViv
yellow new — IHMH
'Yellow Queen' new — WViv

Zanthorhiza see *Xanthorhiza*

Zanthoxylum (Rutaceae)
ailanthoides — CFil EPfP

- from Japan — WPGP
americanum — CBcs CFil ELan
armatum — CAgr CFil WPGP
bungeanum — CAgr CFil WPGP
coreanum — CFil WPGP
oxyphyllum — CFil WPGP
piasezkii new — CBcs
piperitum — CFil EBee SMad WOTO WPGP
- purple-leaved — CFil
planispinum — LEdu MRav
schinifolium — CAgr CBcs
- B&SWJ 1245 — WCru
simulans — CBcs CLnd CPLG MBlu
stenophyllum new — CBcs

Zauschneria (Onagraceae)
arizonica — see *Z. californica* subsp. *latifolia*
§ *californica* — CBcs CBri CBrm CHll CMHG EBee EPfP GQui MCCP NBur NMen SLon WHrl WPnn WWeb
- 'Albiflora' — EOrc EPot WAbe
§ - subsp. *cana* — CSam ECGP ECha MHar SChu SIgm
- - 'Sir Cedric Morris' — EPfP LRHS MAsh SMur
- 'Clover Dale' — EWes
§ - 'Dublin' ♀ H3 — More than 30 suppliers
- 'Ed Carman' — EBee EMan SMrm
§ - subsp. *garrettii* — NWCA SDys SIgm
- 'Glasnevin' — see *Z. californica* 'Dublin'
§ - subsp. *latifolia* — MBro SIgm WPnn
- - NNS 95-512 — NWCA
- - 'Sally Walker' — EWes SMrm
§ - subsp. *mexicana* — CWib EPot MHer NCat SRms WAbe
- 'Olbrich Silver' — CWCL EBee ECha EMan EWes LHop MBro NWCA SUsu WAbe WCom WCot WHil WHoo WPat WWin
- 'Solidarity Pink' — CSpe MTho NWCA WKif WPat
- 'Western Hills' ♀ H4 — CBri CFir CLyd CSpe EBee LHop LPhx MRav NWCA SAga SBla SIgm SIng WAbe WHoo WPGP
cana villosa — see *Z. californica* subsp. *mexicana*
'Copton Ash Pink' new — SIgm
I 'Pumilio' new — NMcn
§ *septentrionalis* — ETow SBla SIgm

Zea (Poaceae)
mays 'Quadricolor' (v) new — NGHP

Zebrina see *Tradescantia*

Zelkova ✿ (Ulmaceae)
carpinifolia — CDoC CDul CLnd CMCN CTho LRHS MAsh STre WDin WNor
serrata ♀ H4 — CBcs CDul CLnd CMCN CTho EBee ECrN ELan EPfP EWTr GKir IArd MBar NBea NHol NPSl NPal NWea SBir SPer SRPl STre WBod WCru WDin WFar WMou WNor WPGP
- 'Goblin' — CLnd MBro SSta WPat
- 'Green Vase' — LPan LRHS MBlu SCoo SLim
- 'Variegata' (v) — CPMA MBlu MGos WBcn
- 'Yatsubusa' — STre
- 'Yrban Ruby' — MGos SSta
sinica — CBcs CLnd CMCN WNor
x *verschaffeltii* — GKir

Zenobia (Ericaceae)
pulverulenta — CAbP CBcs CDoC CSBt CTrG ELan EPfP EWTr GKir GQui ICrw

	LRHS MBar MBlu MBri SBod
	SHBN SLon SPer SReu SSpi SSta
	WBod WDin WFar WNor WPGP
	WPat WPic WSHC
- 'Blue Sky'	EPfP NLar SSpi

Zephyranthes ✿ (*Amaryllidaceae*)

atamasca	CStu ERos
brazosensis **new**	CStu
candida	CAvo CBro CStu EBee EMan
	EMon EPot EPyc ERea ERos ITim
	LAma LEur LRHS NMen NRog
	SDeJ SDix
citrina	EBee EHyt ERos LAma NMen
	NRog WCot
drummondii	EBee WCot
flavissima	CBro EBee WCot WPrP
'Grandjax'	WCot
'La Buffa Rose'	WCot
lindleyana **new**	WCot
macrosiphon	EBee
mexicana **new**	ERos
minima **new**	CStu
'Prairie Sunset'	WCot
robusta	see *Habranthus robustus*
rosea	EBee EPot LAma
sulphurea	LAma
verecunda	CStu

Zexmenia (*Asteraceae*)

| *hispida* | see *Wedelia texana* |

Zigadenus (*Melanthiaceae*)

| *elegans* | CSam EBee EBre ECha EHyt EMan |

	EPar ERos LRHS NWCA SMad SSpi
	WCom WWin
fremontii	CStu EBee EBla WCot
glaberrimus	SSpi
nuttallii	EBee EMan ERos MDKP
	WCot
venenosus	EBee

Zingiber (*Zingiberaceae*)

chrysanthum	CKob LEur WMul
clarkei	CKob LEur WMul
'Midnight' **new**	CKob
mioga	CKob GPoy LEur MSal WMul
officinale	CKob GPoy MSal NCWG
purpureum	CKob
rubens	CKob
zerumbet	CKob EBot GPoy LEur WMul
- 'Darceyi' (v)	CKob

Zinnia (*Asteraceae*)

| *grandiflora* | EBee |

Zizia (*Apiaceae*)

| *aptera* | EBee EMan EMar LPhx |
| *aurea* | EBee LPhx WTin |

Ziziphora (*Lamiaceae*)

| *clinopodioides* **new** | EBee |

Ziziphus (*Rhamnaceae*)

§ *jujuba* (F)	CAgr CGOG LEdu LPan
- 'Lang' (F)	CBcs ERea
- 'Li' (F)	LPan
sativa	see *Z. jujuba*

SUPPLEMENTARY KEYS TO THE DIRECTORY

NOMENCLATURE NOTES

These notes refer to plants in the main Plant Directory that are marked with a 'N'. 'Bean Supplement' refers to W.J. Bean *Trees & Shrubs Hardy in the British Isles* (Supplement to the 8th edition) edited by D L Clarke 1988.

Acer palmatum var. *coreanum*
This includes, but is not synonymous with, the plant sold by Hilliers as *A. palmatum* 'Koreanum', now named *A. palmatum* var. *coreanum* 'Korean Gem'.

Acer palmatum 'Sango-kaku'/ 'Senkaki'
Two or more clones are offered under these names. *A. palmatum* 'Eddisbury' is similar with brighter coral stems.

Acer pseudoplatanus 'Leopoldii'
True 'Leopoldii' has leaves stained with yellowish pink and purple. Plants are often *A. pseudoplatanus* f. *variegatum*.

Acer pseudoplatanus 'Spaethii'
The true cultivar has large leaves with light yellow specks.

Achillea ptarmica The Pearl Group/ *A. ptarmica* (The Pearl Group) 'Boule de Neige' / *A. ptarmica* (The Pearl Group) 'The Pearl'
In the recent trial of achilleas at Wisley, only one of the several stocks submitted as 'The Pearl' matched the original appearance of this plant according to Graham Stuart Thomas, this being from Wisley's own stock. At rather less than 60cm (2ft), this needed little support, being the shortest of the plants bearing this name, with slightly grey, not glossy dark green, leaves and a non-invasive habit. This has been designated as the type for this cultivar and only this clone should bear the cultivar name 'The Pearl'. The Pearl Group covers all other double-flowered clones of this species, including seed-raised plants which are markedly inferior, sometimes scarcely double, often invasive and usually needing careful staking. It has been claimed that 'The Pearl' was a re-naming of Lemoine's 'Boule de Neige' but not all authorities agree: all plants submitted to the Wisley trial as 'Boule de Neige' were different from each other, not the same clone as Wisley's 'The Pearl' and referrable to The Pearl Group.

Aconitum autumnale
A synonym of *A. napellus* and *A. carmichaelii* Wilsonii Group.

Anemone magellanica
According to *European Garden Flora*, this is a variant of the very variable *A. multifida*.

Anemone nemorosa 'Alba Plena'
This name is used for several double white forms including *A. nemorosa* 'Flore Pleno' and *A. nemorosa* 'Vestal'.

Artemisia granatensis hort.
Possibly a variant of *A. absinthium*.

Artemisia ludoviciana var. *latiloba* / *A. ludoviciana* 'Valerie Finnis'
Leaves of the former are glabrous at maturity, those of the latter are not.

Artemisia stelleriana 'Boughton Silver'
This was thought to be the first validly published name for this plant, 'Silver Brocade' having been published earlier but invalidly in an undated publication. However, an earlier valid publication for the cultivar name 'Mori' has subsequently been found for the same plant. A proposal to conserve 'Boughton Silver' has been tabled because of its more widespread use.

Aster amellus Violet Queen
It is probable that more than one cultivar is sold under this name.

Aster dumosus
Many of the asters listed under *A. novi-belgii* contain varying amounts of *A. dumosus* blood in their parentage. It is not possible to allocate these to one species or the other and they are therefore listed under *A. novi-belgii*.

Aster × *frikartii* 'Mönch'
The true plant is very rare in British gardens. Most plants are another form of *A.* × *frikartii*, usually 'Wunder von Stäfa'.

Aster novi-belgii
See note under *A. dumosus*. *A. laevis* is also involved in the parentage of most cultivars.

Azara paraguayensis
This is an unpublished name for what seems to be a hybrid between *A. serrata* and *A. lanceolata*.

Berberis aristata
Plants so named may be either *B. chitria* or *B. floribunda*.

Berberis buxifolia 'Nana'/ 'Pygmaea'
See explanation in Bean Supplement.

Berberis stenophylla 'Lemon Queen'
This sport from 'Pink Pearl' was first named in 1982. The same mutation occurred again and was named 'Cream Showers'. The older name has priority.

Bergenia **Ballawley hybrids**
The name 'Ballawley' refers only to plants vegetatively propagated from the original clone. Seed-raised plants, which may differ considerably, should be called Ballawley hybrids.

Betula pendula 'Dalecarlica'
The true plant of this name is rare in cultivation in the British Isles and is probably not available from nurseries.

Betula utilis var. *jacquemontii*
Plants are often the clones *B. utilis* var. *jacquemontii* 'Inverleith' or *B. utilis* var. *jacquemontii* 'Doorenbos'

Blechnum chilense/B. tabulare
The true *B. tabulare* has an AGM and is grown in the British Isles but is probably not presently offered by nurseries. This name is often misapplied to *B. chilense*.

Brachyscome
Originally published as *Brachyscome* by Cassini who later revised his spelling to *Brachycome*. The original spelling has been internationally adopted.

Brachyglottis greyi and *laxifolia*
Both these species are extremely rare in cultivation, plants under these names usually being *B.* 'Sunshine'.

Calamagrostis × *acutiflora* 'Karl Foerster'
C. × *acutiflora* 'Stricta' differs in being 15cm taller, 10-15 days earlier flowering with a less fluffy inflorescence.

Caltha polypetala
This name is often applied to a large-flowered variant of *C. palustris*. The true species has more (7-10) petals.

Camassia leichtlinii 'Alba'
The true cultivar has blueish-white, not cream flowers.

Camassia leichtlinii 'Plena'
This has starry, transparent green-white flowers; creamy-white 'Semiplena' is sometimes offered under this name.

Camellia japonica 'Campbellii'
This name is used for five cultivars including 'Margherita Coleoni' but applies correctly to Guichard's 1894 cultivar, single to semi-double full rose pink.

Campanula lactiflora 'Alba'
This refers to the pure white flowered clone, not to blueish- or greyish-white flowered plants, nor to seed-raised plants.

Campanula persicifolia
Plants under "cup and saucer white" are not definitely ascribed to a particular cultivar. 'White Cup and Saucer' is a cultivar named by Margery Fish.

Carex morrowii 'Variegata'
C. oshimensis 'Evergold' is sometimes sold under this name.

Carya illinoinensis
The correct spelling of this name is discussed in *Baileya*, **10**(1) (1962).

Cassinia retorta
Now included within *C. leptophylla*. A valid infra-specific epithet has yet to be published.

Ceanothus 'Italian Skies'
Many plants under this name are not true to name.

Chamaecyparis lawsoniana 'Columnaris Glauca'
Plants under this name might be *C. lawsoniana* 'Columnaris' or a new invalidly named cultivar.

Chamaecyparis lawsoniana 'Elegantissima'
This name has been applied to two cultivars, 'Elegantissima' of Schelle and subsequently (invalidly) 'Elegantissima' of Hillier.

Chamaecyparis pisifera 'Squarrosa Argentea'
There are two plants of this name, one (valid) with variegated foliage, the other (invalid) with silvery foliage.

Chrysanthemum 'Anastasia Variegated'
Despite its name, this seems to be derived from 'Mei-kyo', not 'Anastasia'.

Cistus 'Silver Pink'
Plants under this name are not usually true to type. *C.* 'Grayswood Pink' (most commonly), *C.* × *argenteus* 'Peggy Sammons' and *C.* × *skanbergii* are often offered under this name.

Clematis chrysocoma
The true *C. chrysocoma* is a non-climbing erect plant with dense yellow down on the young growth, still uncommon in cultivation.

Clematis 'Jackmanii Superba'
Plants under this name are usually *C.* 'Gipsy Queen'.

Clematis montana
This name should be used for the typical white-flowered variety only. Pink-flowered variants are referable to *C. montana* var. *rubens*.

Clematis 'Victoria'
There is also a Latvian cultivar of this name with petals with a central white bar.

Colchicum 'Autumn Queen'
Entries here might refer to the slightly different *C.* 'Prinses Astrid'.

Cornus 'Norman Hadden'
See note in Bean Supplement, p.184.

Cotoneaster dammeri
Plants sold under this name are usually *C. dammeri* 'Major'.

Cotoneaster frigidus 'Cornubia'
According to Hylmø this cultivar, like all other variants of this species, is fully deciduous. Several evergreen cotoneasters are also grown under this name, most are clones of *C.* × *watereri* or *C. salicifolius*.

Crataegus coccinea
C. intricata, *C. pedicellata* and *C. biltmoreana* are occasionally supplied under this name.

Crocus cartwrightianus 'Albus'
The plant offered is the true cultivar and not *C. hadriaticus*.

Dianthus fringed pink
D. 'Old Fringed Pink' and *D.* 'Old Fringed White' are also sometimes sold under this name.

Dianthus 'Musgrave's Pink' (p)
This is the registered name of this white-flowered cultivar.

Elymus magellanicus
Although this is a valid name, Roger Grounds has suggested that many plants might belong to a different, perhaps unnamed species.

Epilobium glabellum hort.
Plants under this name are not *E. glabellum* but are close to *E. wilsonii* Petrie or perhaps a hybrid of it.

Erodium glandulosum
Plants under this name are often hybrids.

Erodium guttatum
Doubtfully in commerce; plants under this name are usually *E. heteradenum*, *E. cheilanthifolium* or hybrids.

Erysimum cheiri 'Baden-Powell'
Plant of uncertain origin differing from *E. cheiri* 'Harpur Crewe' only in its shorter stature.

Erysimum 'Variegatum'
This name might refer to any of the variegated cultivars of *Erysimum*.

Eucryphia 'Penwith'
The cultivar name 'Penwith' was originally given to a hybrid of *E. cordifolia* × *E. lucida*, not *E.* × *hillieri*, though plants under this name are often clones of the latter species.

Fagus sylvatica **Cuprea Group/Atropurpurea Group**
It is desirable to provide a name, Cuprea Group, for less richly coloured forms, used in historic landscapes before the purple clones appeared.

Fagus sylvatica 'Pendula'
This name refers to the Knap Hill clone, the most common weeping form in English gardens. Other clones occur, particularly in Cornwall and Ireland.

Forsythia 'Beatrix Farrand'
The true plant might not be in cultivation.

Fragaria chiloensis 'Variegata', *F. vesca* 'Variegata'
Most, possibly all, plants under these names are *F.* × *ananassa* 'Variegata'.

Fuchsia loxensis
For a comparison of the true species with the hybrids 'Speciosa' and 'Loxensis' commonly grown under this name, see Boullemier's Check List (2nd ed.) p.268.

Gentiana cachemirica
Most plants sold are not true to type.

Geum 'Borisii'
This name refers to cultivars of *G. coccineum* Sibthorp & Smith, especially *G.* 'Werner Arends' and not to *G.* × *borisii* Kelleper.

Halimium alyssoides and *H. halimifolium*
Plants under these names are sometimes *H.* × *pauanum* or *H.* × *santae*.

Hebe 'C.P. Raffill'
See note in Bean Supplement, p.265.

Hebe 'Carl Teschner'
See note in Bean Supplement, p.264.

Hebe glaucophylla
A green reversion of the hybrid *H.* 'Glaucophylla Variegata' is often sold under this name.

Hedera helix 'Caenwoodiana' / 'Pedata'
Some authorities consider these to be distinct cultivars while others think them different morphological forms of the same unstable clone.

Hedera helix 'Oro di Bogliasco'
Priority between this name and 'Jubiläum Goldherz' and 'Goldheart' has yet to be finally resolved.

Helleborus × *hybridus* / *H. orientalis* hort.
The name *H.* × *hybridus* for acaulescent hellebore hybrids does not seem to follow the *International Code of Botanical Nomenclature* Article H.3.2 requiring one of the parent species to be designated and does not seem to have been typified, contrary to Article 7 of the Code. However, the illustration accompanying the original description in Vilmorin's *Blumengärtnerei* 3(1): 27 (1894) shows that one parent of the cross must have been *H. guttatus*, now treated as part of *H. orientalis*. Taking this illustration as the type for this hybrid species makes it possible to retain *H.* × *hybridus* formally as a hybrid binomial (rather than *H. hybridus* as in our last edition), as the Code's requirement to distinguish one parent is now met.

Hemerocallis fulva 'Kwanso', 'Kwanso Variegata', 'Flore Pleno' and 'Green Kwanso'
For a discussion of these plants see *The Plantsman* 7(2).

Heuchera micrantha var. *diversifolia* 'Palace Purple'
This cultivar name refers only to plants with deep purple-red foliage. Seed-raised plants of inferior colouring should not be offered under this name.

Hosta 'Marginata Alba'
This name is wrongly used both for *H. crispula* and, more commonly, for *H. fortunei* 'Albomarginata'.

Hosta montana
This name refers only to plants long grown in Europe, which differ from *H. elata*.

Hydrangea macrophylla **Teller Series**
This is used both as a descriptive common name for Lacecap hydrangeas (German *teller* = plate, referring to the more or less flat inflorescence) and for the series of hybrids raised by Wädenswill in Switzerland bearing German names of birds. It is not generally possible to link a hydrangea described by the series name plus a colour description (e.g. Teller Blau, Teller Rosa, Teller Rot) to a single cultivar.

Hypericum fragile
The true *H. fragile* is probably not available from British nurseries.

Hypericum 'Gemo'
Either a selection of *H. prolificum* or *H. prolificum* × *H. densiflorum*.

Ilex × *altaclerensis*
The argument for this spelling is given by Susyn Andrews, *The Plantsman*, 5(2) and is not superceded by the more recent comments in the Supplement to Bean's Trees and Shrubs.

Iris
Apart from those noted below, cultivar names marked 'N' are not registered. The majority of those marked 'I' have been previously used for a different cultivar.

Iris histrioides 'Major'
Two clones are offered under this name, the true one pale blue with darker spotting on the falls, the incorrect one violet-blue with almost horizontal falls.

Iris pallida 'Variegata'
The white-variegated *I. pallida* 'Argentea Variegata' is sometimes wrongly supplied under this name, which refers only to the gold-variegated cultivar.

Juniperus × *media*
This name is illegitimate if applied to hybrids of *J. chinensis* × *J. sabina*, having been previously used for a different hybrid (P.A. Schmidt, *IDS Yearbook 1993*, 47-48). Because of its importance to gardeners, a proposal to conserve its present use was tabled but subsequently rejected.

Lamium maculatum 'Chequers'
This name refers to two plants; the first, validly named, is a large and vigorous form of *L. maculatum* with a stripe down the centre of the leaf; the second is silver-leaved and very similar to *L. maculatum* 'Beacon Silver'.

Lavandula 'Alba'
Might be either *L. angustifolia* 'Alba' or *L.* × *intermedia* 'Alba'

Lavandula angustifolia 'Lavender Lady' / *L.* 'Cambridge Lady'
Might be synonyms of *L. angustifolia* 'Lady'.

Lavandula × *intermedia* 'Arabian Night'
Plants under this name might be *L.* × *intermedia* 'Impress Purple'.

Lavandula spica
This name is classed as a name to be rejected (*nomen rejiciendum*) by the *International Code of Botanical Nomenclature*.

Lavandula 'Twickel Purple'
Two cultivars are sold under this name, one a form of *L.* × *intermedia*, the other of *L. angustifolia*.

Lavatera olbia and *L. thuringiaca*
Although *L. olbia* is usually shrubby and *L. thuringiaca* usually herbaceous, both species are very variable. Cultivars formally ascribed to one species or the other have been shown to be hybrids and are referable to the recently-named hybrid species *L.* × *clementii*.

Lobelia 'Russian Princess'
This has green, not purple, leaves and rich pink, not purple, flowers.

Lonicera × *americana*
Most plants offered by nurseries under this name are correctly *L.* × *italica*. The true *L.* × *americana* is still widely grown but is slow to propagate. See *The Plantsman*, 12(2).

Lonicera × *brownii* 'Fuchsioides'
Plants under this name are usually *L.* × *brownii* 'Dropmore Scarlet'.

Lonicera × *heckrotii* 'Gold Flame'
This name applies to the original clone. Many plants under this name are a different clone for which the name 'American Beauty' has been proposed.

Lonicera periclymenum 'Serotina'
See note in Bean Supplement, p.315.

Lonicera sempervirens f. *sulphurea*
Plants in the British Isles usually a yellow-flowered form of *L. periclymenum*.

Magnolia × *highdownensis*.
Believed to fall within the range of variation of *M. wilsonii*.

Mahonia pinnata
Most plants in cultivation under this name are believed to be *M.* × *wagneri* 'Pinnacle'.

Malus domestica 'Dummellor's Seedling'
The phonetic spelling 'Dumelow's Seedling' contravenes the ICBN ruling on orthography, i.e. that, except for intentional latinizations, commemorative names should be based on the original spelling of the person's name (Article 60.11). The spelling adopted here is that used on the gravestone of the raiser in Leicestershire.

Meconopsis **Fertile Blue Group**
This cultivar-group comprises seed-raised and intrinsically perennial tall blue poppies of as yet indeterminate origin (i.e. fertile forms other than the species *M. betonicifolia*, *M. grandis* and

M. simplicifolia). The only cultivar so far established is *M.* 'Lingholm' (syns 'Blue Ice' and 'Correnie'). The bulk of seed-raised plants in cultivation and offered for sale are very likely to be *M.* 'Lingholm', although sometimes poorly selected. Many of these plants are currently being distributed erroneously as *M.* × *sheldonii* and as *M. grandis*.

Meconopsis George Sherriff Group
This cultivar-group comprises a number of sterile (almost invariably) clones of large blue poppies previously (and erroneously) known collectively as *M. grandis* GS600.

Meconopsis grandis ambig.
See note under *M.* Fertile Blue Group. The true species might still be in cultivation in the British Isles but, if it is, is rare.

Meconopsis Infertile Blue Group
This cultivar-group comprises long-established sterile (almost invariably) clones of large blue poppies other than George Sherriff Group and often given the epithet × *sheldonii*.

Meconopsis × sheldonii ambig.
See notes for *M.* Fertile Blue Group and *M.* Infertile Blue Group.

Melissa officinalis 'Variegata'
The true cultivar of this name was striped with white.

Narcissus poeticus 'Plenus'
A name of uncertain application used for *N. poeticus* 'Spalding Double White' and *N. poeticus* 'Tamar Double White'.

Nemesia caerulea 'Joan Wilder'
The lavender blue clone 'Joan Wilder', described and illustrated in *The Hardy Plant*, 14(1), 11-14, does not come true from seed; it may only be propagated from cuttings.

Osmanthus heterophyllus 'Gulftide'
Probably correctly *O.* × *fortunei* 'Gulftide'.

Papaver orientale agg.
Plants listed as *P. orientale* agg. (i.e. aggregate) or as one of its cultivars may be *P. orientale* L., *P. pseudo-orientale* or *P. bracteatum* or hybrids between them.

Papaver orientale 'Flore Pleno'
P. 'Fireball' is sometimes offered under this name and possibly also *P. orientale* 'May Queen' and *P. orientale* 'Olympia'.

Passiflora antioquiensis
According to National Collection holder John Vanderplank, the true species is not in cultivation in the British Isles. Plants under this name are likely to be clones of *P.* × *exoniensis*.

Pelargonium 'Beauty of Eastbourne'
This should not be confused with *P.* 'Eastbourne Beauty', a different cultivar.

Pelargonium 'Lass o' Gowrie'
The American plant of this name has pointed, not rounded leaf lobes.

Pelargonium quercifolium
Plants under this name are mainly hybrids. The true species has pointed, not rounded leaf lobes.

Penstemon 'Taoensis'
This name for a small-flowered cultivar or hybrid of *P. isophyllus* originally appeared as 'Taoense' but must be corrected to agree in gender with *Penstemon* (masculine). Presumably an invalid name (published in Latin form since 1958), it is not synonymous with *P. crandallii* subsp. *glabrescens* var. *taosensis*.

Pernettya
Botanists now consider that *Pernettya* (fruit a berry) is not separable from *Gaultheria* (fruit a capsule) because in some species the fruit is intermediate between a berry and a capsule. For a fuller explanation see D. Middleton, *The Plantsman*, 12(3).

Picea pungens 'Glauca Pendula'
This name is used for several different glaucous cultivars.

Pinus ayacahuite
P. ayacahuite var. *veitchii* (syn. *P. veitchii*) is occasionally sold under this name.

Pinus montezumae
Plants propagated from mature trees in British gardens are mostly an unnamed long-needled variety of *P. rudis*.

Pinus nigra 'Cebennensis Nana'
A doubtful name, possibly a synonym for *P. nigra* 'Nana'.

Polystichum setiferum 'Wollaston'
Incomplete name which may refer to either of two cultivars.

Populus nigra 'Italica'
See note in Bean Supplement, p.393.

Prunus laurocerasus 'Castlewellan'
We are grateful to Dr Charles Nelson for informing us that the name 'Marbled White' is not valid because although it has priority of publication it does not have the approval of the originator who asked for it to be called 'Castlewellan'.

Prunus laurocerasus 'Variegata'
The true 'Variegata', (marginal variegation), dates from 1811 but this name is also used for the relatively recent cultivar *P. laurocerasus* 'Castlewellan'.

Prunus serrulata var. pubescens
See note in Bean Supplement, p.398.

Prunus × subhirtella 'Rosea'
Might be *P. pendula* var. *ascendens* 'Rosea', *P. pendula* 'Pendula Rosea', or *P.* × *subhirtella* 'Autumnalis Rosea'.

Rheum × cultorum
The name *R.* × *cultorum* was published without adequate description and must be abandoned in favour of the validly published *R.* × *hybridum*.

Rhododendron (azaleas)
All names marked 'N', except for the following, refer to more than one cultivar.

Rhododendron 'Hinomayo'
This name is based on a faulty transliteration (should be 'Hinamoyo') but the spelling 'Hinomayo' is retained in the interests of stability.

Rhus typhina
Linnaeus published both *R. typhina* and *R. hirta* as names for the same species. Though *R. hirta* has priority, it has been proposed that the name *R. typhina* should be conserved.

Robinia hispida 'Rosea'
This name is applied to *R. hispida* (young shoots with bristles), *R. elliottii* (young shoots with grey down) and *R. boyntonii* (young shoots smooth).

Rosa × *damascena* 'Trigintipetala'
The true cultivar of this name is probably not in cultivation in the British Isles.

Rosa gentiliana
Plants under this name are usually the cultivar 'Polyantha Grandiflora' but might otherwise be *R. multiflora* 'Wilsonii', *R. multiflora* var. *cathayensis*, *R. henryi* or another hybrid.

Rosa 'Gros Choux de Hollande' hort. (Bb)
It is doubtful if this name is correctly applied.

Rosa 'Jacques Cartier' hort.
For a discussion on the correct identity of this rose see *Heritage Rose Foundation News*, Oct. 1989 & Jan. 1990.

Rosa 'Maiden's Blush'
R. 'Great Maiden's Blush' may be supplied under this name.

Rosa 'Professeur Emile Perrot'
For a discussion on the correct identity of this rose see *Heritage Roses*, Nov. 1991.

Rosa Sweetheart
This is not the same as the Sweetheart Rose, a common name for *R.* 'Cécile Brünner'.

Rosa wichurana
This is the correct spelling according to the ICBN 1994 Article 60.11 (which enforces Recommendation 60C.1c) and not *wichuraiana* for this rose commemorating Max Wichura.

Rubus fruticosus L. agg.
Though some cultivated blackberries do belong to *Rubus fruticosus* L. *sensu stricto*, others are more correctly ascribed to other species of *Rubus* section *Glandulosus* (including *R. armeniacus, R. laciniatus* or *R. ulmifolius)* or are hybrids of species within this section. Because it is almost impossible to ascribe every cultivar to a single species or hybrid, they are listed under *R. fruticosus* L. agg. (i.e. aggregate) for convenience.

Salix alba 'Tristis'
This cultivar should not be confused with *S. tristis*, which is now correctly *S. humilis*. Although this cultivar is distinct in European gardens, most plants under this name in the British Isles are *S.* × *sepulcralis* var. *chrysocoma*.

Salvia microphylla var. *neurepia*
The type of this variety is referable to the typical variety, *S. microphylla* var. *microphylla*.

Salvia officinalis 'Aurea'
S. officinalis var. *aurea* is a rare variant of the common sage with leaves entirely of gold. It is represented in cultivation by the cultivar 'Kew Gold'. The plant usually offered as *S. officinalis* 'Aurea' is the gold variegated sage *S. officinalis* 'Icterina'.

Sambucus nigra 'Aurea'
Plants under this name are usually not *S. nigra*.

Sedum nevii
The true species is not in cultivation. Plants under this name are usually either *S. glaucophyllum* or occasionally *S. beyrichianum*.

Senna corymbosa
Some plants sold as *S. corymbosa* are *S.* × *floribunda*.

Skimmia japonica 'Foremanii'
The true cultivar, which belongs to *S. japonica* Rogersii Group, is believed to be lost to cultivation. Plants offered under this name are usually *S. japonica* 'Veitchii'.

Sorbus
Except for the following, *Sorbus* species marked N refer to names proposed by Dr Hugh McAllister for apomictic microspecies but not yet published.

Sorbus multijuga Sch 1132
Though this is an accepted name, this collection was obtained from outside the usual range of this species.

Spiraea japonica 'Shirobana'
Shirobana-shimotsuke is the common name for *S. japonica* var. *albiflora*. Shirobana means white-flowered and does not apply to the two-coloured form.

Staphylea holocarpa var. *rosea*
This botanical variety has woolly leaves. The cultivar 'Rosea', with which it is often confused, does not.

Stewartia ovata var. *grandiflora*.
Most, possibly all, plants available from British nurseries under this name are not true to name but are derived from the improved Nymans form.

Thymus serpyllum cultivars
Most cultivars are probably correctly cultivars of *T. polytrichus* or hybrids though they will remain listed under *T. serpyllum* pending further research.

Thymus 'Silver Posie'
The cultivar name 'Silver Posie' is applied to several different plants, not all of them *T. vulgaris*.

Tricyrtis Hototogisu
This is the common name applied generally to all Japanese *Tricyrtis* and specifically to *T. hirta*.

Tricyrtis macropoda
This name has been used for at least five different species.

Uncinia rubra
This name is also misapplied to *U. egmontiana* and *U. uncinata*.

Verbena
Entries marked (G) are considered by some botanists to belong to a separate genus, *Glandularia*. The principal differences are that verbenas have quadrangular, upright stems and terminal (rarely axillary) flowers in spikes or panicles of spikes; glandularias have cylindrical, creeping or semi-erect stems and flowers in terminal and axillary heads, sometimes elongating with age.

Verbena 'Kemerton'
Origin unknown, not from Kemerton.

Viburnum opulus 'Fructu Luteo'
See note below.

Viburnum opulus 'Xanthocarpum'
Some entries under this name might be the less compact *V. opulus* 'Fructu Luteo'.

Viburnum plicatum
Entries may include the 'snowball' form, *V. plicatum* 'Sterile'.

Viola labradorica
See Note in *The Garden*, 110(2): 96.

COLLECTORS' REFERENCES

Abbreviations following a plant name, refer to the collector(s) of the plant. These abbreviations are expanded below, with a collector's name or expedition title. For a fuller explanation, turn to p.13.

A&JW	A. & J. Watson, S America
A&L	Ala & Lancaster expedition, N Iran, 1972
AB&S	Archibald, Blanchard & Salmon, Morocco 1980s
AC	Alan Clark, Kaiyuan/Kunming Yunnan Expedition, China, 1995
AC&H	Apold, Cox & Hutchinson, NE Turkey, 1962
AC&W	Albury, Cheese & Watson
ACE	Alpine Garden Society expedition, China, 1994
ACL	A.C. Leslie
AGS/ES	Alpine Garden Society expedition, Sikkim, 1983
AGSJ	Alpine Garden Society expedition, Japan, 1988
Airth	Murray Airth
Akagi	Akagi Botanical Garden
AL&JS	Leslie & Sharman, Yugoslavia, 1990
Argent	Argent, G
B	Beer, Nepal, 1975
B&L	Brickell & Leslie, China
B&M	C.D. Brickell & B. Mathew
B&S	P. Bird & M. Salmon
B&SWJ	B. & S. Wynn-Jones
BB	B. Bartholomew, Bhutan, 1974
BC	B. Chudziak, Kanchenjunga, Nepal, 1993
BC&W	Beckett, Cheese & Watson
BL&M	Beer, Lancaster & Morris, E Nepal, 1971
BM	B. Mathew
BM&W	Binns, Mason & Wright, Nepal, 1978
BS	Basil Smith

BSBE	Bowles Scholarship Botanical Expedition
BSSS	Crûg Expedition, Jordan, 1991
Bu	S. Bubert
Burtt	Burtt, B.L.
C	Cole, Desmond T.
C&C	P.A. & K.N.E. Cox, SE Tibet, 1996
C&Cu	K.N.E. Cox & J. Cubey
C&H	P.A. Cox & P.C. Hutchison, Assam, NE Frontier & N Bengal, 1965; Sichuan & Yunnan, China, 1995
C&K	Chamberlain & Knott
C&R	Christian & Roderick, California, Oregon, Washington
C&S	A. Clark & I. Sinclair, Bhutan, 1994
C&V	K.N.E. Cox & S. Vergera, SE Tibet, China, 1995
C&W	M. Cheese & J. Watson
CC	C. Chadwell
CC&H	D.F. Chamberlain, P.A. Cox & P.C. Hutchison, Sichuan, China, 1989
CC&McK	Chadwell & McKelvie, Nepal, West Himalaya, 1990-92
CC&MR	C. Chadwell & M. Ramsey, Kashmir, 1985; Himachal Pradesh & W Himalaya, 1989
CCH&H	Chamberlain, Cox, Hootman & Hutchison
CD&R	J. Compton, J. D'Arcy & E.M. Rix, China, Drakensburg, Mexico & Korea
CDB	C.D. Brickell
CDC	Coode & Dockrill
CDC&C	Compton, D'Arcy, Christopher & Coke
CDPR	Compton, D'Arcy, Pope & Rix
CE&H	Christian, Elliott & Hoog, Yugoslavia & Greece, 1982
CEE	Chengdu Edinburgh Expedition, Sichuan, China, 1991

CER   Cox, Evans & Richardson, Tsari, S.E. Tibet, 1999

CGW   C. Grey-Wilson

CH&M   P.A. Cox, P.C. Hutchinson & D.M. McDonald, Sichuan & Yunnan, China, 1986; Bhutan, 1988

CHP&W   Chadwell, Howard, Powell & Wright, Kashmir, 1983

CL   C. Lovell

CLD   Kew, Edinburgh & RHS Expedition, Zhongdian (Chungtien), Lijiang & Dali, China, 1990

CM&W   M. Cheese, A.R. Mitchell & J. Watson

CN&W   A. Clark, J. Nielson & R. J Wilson, W. China

CNDS   Nelson, C. & Sayers, D.

Cooper   R.E. Cooper (1890-1962), Bhutan, 1914 & '15; Punjab, India, 1916; NE Burma

Cox   Cox, P

CPC   Cobbleswood Plant Collection

CSE   Cyclamen Society Expedition

CT   Carla Teune

DBG   Denver Botanic Garden, Colorado

DC   Cheshire, David

DF   Derek Fox

DJH   Dan Hinkley

DJHC   Dan Hinkley, China

DM   David Millais

Doleshy   Doleshy, F.L.

DS&T   Drake, Sharman & Thompson, Turkey, 1989

DWD   Rose, D.

ECN   E. Charles Nelson

EDHCH   Eric D. Hammond (for Heronswood Nursery) China, 1997

EGM   E.G. Millais, Bhutan, 1988 (with others); Sichuan & Yunnan, China, 1995

EKB   E.K. Balls

EM   East Malling Research Station clonal selection scheme

EMAK   Edinburgh Makalu Expedition, Nepal, 1991

EMR   E.M. Rix

EN   Edward Needham

ENF   E. Nigel Fuller

ETE   Edinburgh Expedition, Taiwan, 1993

ETOT   M. Flanagan & T. Kirkham, Taiwan, 1992

F   George Forrest (1873-1932)

F&W   A. Flores & J. Watson, Chile, 1992

Farrer   Reginald Farrer (1880-1920)

FK   Fergus W. Kinmonth, China; Nepal; Bhutan, 1990; Vietnam, 1991

FMB   F.M. Bailey

G   M.F. Gardner

G&K   M.F. Gardner & S.G. Knees

G&P   M.F. Gardner & C. Page, Chile, 1992

GG   George Gusman

G-W&P   Grey-Wilson & Phillips

GS   George Sherriff (1898-1967)

Guitt   G.G. Guittonneau

Guiz   J.B. Simmons, H. Fliegner & J. Russell, Guizhou, China, 1985

H   Paul Huggins. Oxford University Expedition, Tehri Garhwal, C Himalaya

H&B   O. Hilliard & B.L. Burtt

H&D   Howick & Darby

H&M   Howick & McNamara

H&W   Hedge & Wendelbo, Afghanistan, 1969

Harry Smith   Karl August Harald Smith (1889-1971)

Hartside   Hartside Nursery, breeder's number

HCM   Heronswood Expedition to Chile, 1998

HH&K   S. & S. Hannay & N. Kingsbury, Bulgaria, 1995

HLMS   L.S. Springate on Reading/Islamabad Expedition, NE Pakistan, 1994

HM&S   B. Halliwell, M. Mason & P. Smallcombe

HOA   Hoog, A.

Hummel   D. Hummel, China, 1950

HW&E   Hedge, Wendelbo & Ekberg, Afghanistan, 1982

HWEL   J.M. Hirst & D. Webster, Lesotho

HWJ/HWJCM   Crûg Heronswood expedition, E Nepal, 1995

HZ   Henrik Zetterlund

IDS   International Dendrological Society

J&JA   J.C. & J. Archibald

JCA   J.C. Archibald

JE   Jack Elliott

JJ   John Jackson

JJ&JH   Josef J. & Jarmila Halda

JJH   Josef J. Halda

J.Jurasek   Jurasek, J.

JLS   J.L. Sharman, USA, 1988

JMT   J. Mann Taylor

JN   Jens Nielson

JR   J. Russell

JRM   J.R. Marr, Greece & Turkey, 1975

JW   J. Watson

K   G. Kirkpatrick

K&E   Kew & Edinburgh Expedition, China, 1989

K&LG   K.D. & L.M. Gillanders, Ecuador, 1994; Yunnan, China, 1993, '94, '96; Vietnam, 1992; Tibet, 1995

K&Mc   G. Kirkpatrick & R. McBeath.

K&T   Kurashige, Y. & Tsukie

KEKE   Kew/Edinburgh Kanchenjunga Expedition, NE Nepal, 1989

KGB   Kunming-Gothenburg Expedition, NW Yunnan, China, 1993

KR   K. Rushforth

KRW   K.R. Wooster, breeder's number

KW   Frank Kingdon-Ward (1885-1958)

L   Roy Lancaster

L&S   F. Ludlow (1885-1972) & G. Sherriff (1898-1967)

LA	Long Ashton Research Station clonal selection scheme.
LEG	Lesotho, Edinburgh, Gothenburg Expedition
Lismore	Lismore Nursery, breeder's number
LM&S	Leslie, Mattern & Sharman, Bulgaria, 1994
LP	Hon. W.J.L. Palmer (1894-1971)
LS&E	F. Ludlow, G. Sherriff & H. Elliot
LS&H	F. Ludlow, G. Sherriff & Hicks, Bhutan, 1949
LS&T	F. Ludlow, G. Sherriff & G. Taylor, SE Tibet, 1938
M&PS	Mike and Polly Stone, Gravelly Range MT 1993
M&T	B. Mathew & J. Tomlinson
Mac&W	MacPhail & Watson
McB	Ron McBeath, Nepal, 1981, '83 & '90
McLaren	Henry McLaren, 2nd Baron Aberconway (1879-1953)
MDM	Myers, Michael D.
MESE	AGS Expedition, Greece, 1999
MF	Maurice Foster, Yunnan, China, 1993 & '96
MH	M. Heasman, Bhutan, 1992
MK	Michael Kammerlander
MP	Mojmir Pavelka, Euroseeds, Czech Republic
MPF	M.P. Frankis
MS	M. Salmon
MSF	M.S. Fillan, Tenerife, 1988; S Korca, 1989
MS&CL	M. Salmon & C. Lovell
NJM	N.J. Macer, Mallorca, 1993; W Canada, 1994
NNS	Northwest Native Seeds (R. Ratko), Seattle.
NS	Nick Turland (Northside Seeds)
Og	Mikinori Ogisu
P&C	D.S. Paterson & S. Clarke, Western USA, 1991
P&W	Polastri & Watson, Chile
PB	Peter Bird
PC&H	G. Pattison, P. Catt & M. Hickson, Mexico, 1994
PD	Peter Davis
PF	Paul Furse
PJC	P.J. Christian
PJC&AH	P.J. Christian & A. Hoog, Greece & Yugoslavia, 1985
Polunin	Polunin, O.
Pras	Milan Prasil
PS&W	Polunin, Sykes & Williams, W Nepal, 1952
PW	Peter Wharton, Guizhou, China, 1994
R	J.F.C. Rock (1884-1962)
RB	Ray Brown (Plant World, Devon), Chile, 1994
RCB/Eq	Robert Brown, Ecuador, 1998
RH	R. Hancock
RMRP	Rocky Mountain Rare Plants, Denver, Colorado
RS	Reinhart Suckow
RV	Richard Valder
S&B	M. Salmon & J. Blanchard
S&F	Salmon & Fillan, Spain & Morocco
S&L	I. Sinclair & D. Long, Bhutan, 1984
S&SH	Sheilah & Spencer Hannay, Lesotho, NE Cape Province, 1989 & '91; C Nepal, 1993
Sandham	Sandham, J.
SB&L	Salmon, Bird & Lovell, Jordan &Morocco
SBEC	Sino-British Expedition, Cangshan, SW China, 1981
SBEL	Sino-British Expedition, Lijiang, Yunnan, China, 1987
SBQE	Sino-British Qinghai Expedition, Royal Botanic Garden, Edinburgh, 1998
Sch	A.D. Schilling, Nepal, 1975, '76, '77, '78, '83; Bhutan, 1988
SD	Sashal Dayal
SDR	Stella & David Rankin
SEH	Steve Hootman
SEP	Swedish Expedition to Pakistan
SF	P. Forde (Seaforde Gardens), Bhutan, 1990
SG	Salmon, M. & Guy, P
SH	Spencer Hannay
Sich	Simmons, Erskine, Howick & McNamara, Sichuan, China, 1988
SOJA	Kew Expedition to Southern Japan, 1989
SS&W	Stainton, Sykes & Williams, C Nepal, 1954
SSNY	Sino-Scottish Expedition, NW Yunnan, China, 1992
T	Nigel P. Taylor
T&K	N.P. Taylor & S. Knees
TS&BC	T. Smythe & B. Cherry, Yunnan, China, 1994
TSS	T. Spring-Smyth, E Nepal, 1961-62, '70
TW	Tony Weston (with A.D. Schilling), Nepal, 1985; (with K. Rushforth) SW Yunnan, China 1993
USDAPI	US Dept of Agriculture Plant Index Number
USDAPQ	US Dept of Agriculture Plant Quarantine Number
USNA	United States National Arboretum
VHH	Vernon H. Heywood
W	E.H. Wilson (1876-1930)
W/A	E.H. Wilson, for Arnold Arboretum, 1906-19
W/V	E.H. Wilson, for Veitch, 1899-1905
WM	Will McLewin
Woods	Paddy Woods
Wr	David & Anke Wraight
Yu	Tse Tsun Yu (1908-86)

CLASSIFICATION OF GENERA

Genera including a large number of species or with many cultivars are often subdivided into groups. Please turn to p.13 for a fuller explanation.

ACTINIDIA

(s-p)   Self-pollinating

BEGONIA

(C)   Cane
(R)   Rex
(S)   Semperflorens Cultorum
(T)   × *tuberhybrida* (Tuberous)

CHRYSANTHEMUM

(By the National Chrysanthemum Society)
(1)   Indoor Large (Exhibition)
(2)   Indoor Medium (Exhibition)
(3a)   Indoor Incurved: Large-flowered
(3b)   Indoor Incurved: Medium-flowered
(3c)   Indoor Incurved: Small-flowered
(4a)   Indoor Reflexed: Large-flowered
(4b)   Indoor Reflexed: Medium-flowered
(4c)   Indoor Reflexed: Small-flowered
(5a)   Indoor Intermediate: Large-flowered
(5b)   Indoor Intermediate: Medium-flowered
(5c)   Indoor Intermediate: Small-flowered (6a)
Indoor Anemone: Large-flowered
(6b)   Indoor Anemone: Medium-flowered
(6c)   Indoor Anemone: Small-flowered
(7a)   Indoor Single: Large-flowered
(7b)   Indoor Single: Medium-flowered
(7c)   Indoor Single: Small-flowered
(8a)   Indoor True Pompon
(8b)   Indoor Semi-pompon
(9a)   Indoor Spray: Anemone
(9b)   Indoor Spray: Pompon
(9c)   Indoor Spray: Reflexed
(9d)   Indoor Spray: Single
(9e)   Indoor Spray: Intermediate
(9f)   Indoor Spray: Spider, Quill, Spoon or Any Other Type
(10a)   Indoor, Spider
(10b)   Indoor, Quill
(10c)   Indoor, Spoon
(11)   Any Other Indoor Type
(12a)   Indoor, Charm
(12b)   Indoor, Cascade
(13a)   October-flowering Incurved: Large-flowered
(13b)   October-flowering Incurved: Medium-flowered

(13c)   October-flowering Incurved: Small-flowered
(14a)   October-flowering Reflexed: Large-flowered
(14b)   October-flowering Reflexed: Medium-flowered
(14c)   October-flowering Reflexed: Small-flowered
(15a)   October-flowering Intermediate: Large-flowered
(15b)   October-flowering Intermediate: Medium-flowered
(15c)   October-flowered Intermediate: Small-flowered
(16)   October-flowering Large
(17a)   October-flowering Single: Large-flowered
(17b)   October-flowering Single: Medium-flowered
(17c)   October-flowering Single: Small-flowered
(18a)   October-flowering Pompon: True Pompon
(18b)   October-flowering Pompon: Semi-pompon
(19a)   October-flowering Spray: Anemone
(19b)   October-flowering Spray: Pompon
(19c)   October-flowering Spray: Reflexed
(19d)   October-flowering Spray: Single
(19e)   October-flowering Spray: Intermediate
(19f)   October-flowering Spray: Spider, Quill, Spoon or Any Other Type
(20)   Any Other October-flowering Type
(22a)   Charm: Anemone
(22b)   Charm: Pompon
(22c)   Charm: Reflexed
(22d)   Charm: Single
(22e)   Charm: Intermediate
(22f)   Charm: Spider, Quill, Spoon or Any Other Type
(23a)   Early-flowering Outdoor Incurved: Large-flowered
(23b)   Early-flowering Outdoor Incurved: Medium-flowered
(23c)   Early-flowering Outdoor Incurved: Small-flowered
(24a)   Early-flowering Outdoor Reflexed: Large-flowered
(24b)   Early-flowering Outdoor Reflexed: Medium-flowered
(24c)   Early-flowering Outdoor Reflexed: Small-flowered
(25a)   Early-flowering Outdoor Intermediate: Large-flowered

(25b)	Early-flowering Outdoor Intermediate: Medium-flowered
(25c)	Early-flowering Outdoor Intermediate: Small-flowered
(26a)	Early-flowering Outdoor Anemone: Large-flowered
(26b)	Early-flowering Outdoor Anemone: Medium-flowered
(27a)	Early-flowering Outdoor Single: Large-flowered
(27b)	Early-flowering Outdoor Single: Medium-flowered
(28a)	Early-flowering Outdoor Pompon: True Pompon
(28b)	Early-flowering Outdoor Pompon: Semi-pompon
(29a)	Early-flowering Outdoor Spray: Anemone
(29b)	Early-flowering Outdoor Spray: Pompon
(29c)	Early-flowering Outdoor Spray: Reflexed
(29d)	Early-flowering Outdoor Spray: Single
(29e)	Early-flowering Outdoor Spray: Intermediate
(29f)	Early-flowering Outdoor Spray: Spider, Quill, Spoon or Any Other Type
(29K)	Early-flowering Outdoor Spray: Korean
(29Rub)	Early-flowering Outdoor Spray: Rubellum
(30)	Any Other Early-flowering Outdoor Type

CLEMATIS

(A)	Alpina Group (Section Atragene)
(D)	Diversifolia Group
(Fl)	Florida Group (double-flowered)
(Fo)	Forsteri Group
(H)	Heraclcifolia Group
(I)	Integrifolia Group
(J)	Jackmanii Group
(L)	Lanuginosa Group
(P)	Patens Group
(T)	Texensis Group
(Ta)	Tangutica Group
(Vt)	Viticella Group

DAHLIA

(By the National Dahlia Society with corresponding numerical classification according to the Royal Horticultural Society's International Register)

(Sin)	1 Single
(Anem)	2 Anemone-flowered
(Col)	3 Collerette
(WL)	4 Waterlily (unassigned)
(LWL)	4B Waterlily, Large
(MWL)	4C Waterlily, Medium
(SWL)	4D Waterlily, Small
(MinWL)	4E Waterlily, Miniature
(D)	5 Decorative (unassigned)
(GD)	5A Decorative, Giant
(LD)	5B Decorative, Large
(MD)	5C Decorative, Medium
(SD)	5D Decorative, Small
(MinD)	5E Decorative, Miniature
(SBa)	6A Small Ball
(MinBa)	6B Miniature Ball
(Pom)	7 Pompon
(C)	8 Cactus (unassigned)
(GC)	8A Cactus, Giant
(LC)	8B Cactus, Large
(MC)	8C Cactus, Medium
(SC)	8D Cactus, Small
(MinC)	8E Cactus, Miniature
(S-c)	9 Semi-cactus (unassigned)
(GS-c)	9A Semi-cactus, Giant
(LS-c)	9B Semi-cactus, Large
(MS-c)	9C Semi-cactus, Medium
(SS-c)	9D Semi-cactus, Small
(MinS-c)	9E Semi-cactus, Miniature
(Misc)	10 Miscellaneous
(O)	Orchid-flowering (in combination)
(B)	Botanical (in combination)
(DwB)	Dwarf Bedding (in combination)
(Fim)	Fimbriated (in combination)
(Lil)	Lilliput (in combination)

DIANTHUS

(By the Royal Horticultural Society)

(p)	Pink
(p,a)	Annual Pink
(pf)	Perpetual-flowering Carnation
(b)	Border Carnation
(M)	Malmaison Carnation

FRUIT

(B)	Black (*Vitis*), Blackcurrant (*Ribes*)
(Ball)	Ballerina (*Malus*)
(C)	Culinary (*Malus, Prunus, Pyrus, Ribes*)
(Cider)	Cider (*Malus*)
(D)	Dessert (*Malus, Prunus, Pyrus, Ribes*)
(F)	Fruit
(G)	Glasshouse (*Vitis*)
(O)	Outdoor (*Vitis*)
(P)	Pinkcurrant (*Ribes*)
(Perry)	Perry (*Pyrus*)
(R)	Red (*Vitis*), Redcurrant (*Ribes*)

| (S) | Seedless (*Citrus, Vitis*) |
| (W) | White (*Vitis*), Whitecurrant (*Ribes*) |

GLADIOLUS

(B)	Butterfly
(E)	Exotic
(G)	Giant
(L)	Large
(M)	Medium
(Min)	Miniature
(N)	Nanus
(P)	Primulinus
(S)	Small
(Tub)	Tubergenii

HYDRANGEA MACROPHYLLA

| (H) | Hortensia |
| (L) | Lacecap |

IRIS

(By the American Iris Society)

(AB)	Arilbred
(BB)	Border Bearded
(Cal-Sib)	Series *Californicae* × Series *Sibiricae*
(CH)	Californian Hybrid
(DB)	Dwarf Bearded (not assigned)
(Dut)	Dutch
(IB)	Intermediate Bearded
(La)	Louisiana Hybrid
(MDB)	Miniature Dwarf Bearded
(MTB)	Miniature Tall Bearded
(SDB)	Standard Dwarf Bearded
(Sino-Sib)	Series *Sibiricae*, chromosome number 2n=40
(Spuria)	Spuria
(TB)	Tall Bearded

LILIUM

(Classification according to *The International Lily Register* (ed. 3, 1982) with amendments from Supp. 10 (1992), Royal Horticultural Society)

(I)	Early-flowering Asiatic Hybrids derived from *L. amabile*, *L. bulbiferum*, *L. cernuum*, *L. concolor*, *L. davidii*, *L.* × *hollandicum*, *L. lancifolium*, *L. leichtlinii*, *L.* × *maculatum* and *L. pumilum*
(Ia)	Upright flowers, borne singly or in an umbel
(Ib)	Outward-facing flowers
(Ic)	Pendant flowers
(II)	Hybrids of Martagon type, one parent having been a form of *L. hansonii* or *L. martagon*
(III)	Hybrids from *L. candidum*, *L. chalcedonicum* and other related European species (excluding *L. martagon*)
(IV)	Hybrids of American species
(V)	Hybrids derived from *L. formosanum* and *L. longiflorum*
(VI)	Hybrid Trumpet Lilies and Aurelian hybrids from Asiatic species, including *L. henryi* but excluding those from *L. auratum*, *L. japonicum*, *L. rubellum* and *L. speciosum*.
(VIa)	Plants with trumpet-shaped flowers
(VIb)	Plants with bowl-shaped flowers
(VIc)	Plants with flat flowers (or only the tips recurved)
(VId)	Plants with recurved flowers
(VII)	Hybrids of Far Eastern species as *L auratum*, *L. japonicum*, *L. rubellum* and *L. speciosum* (Oriental Hybrids)
(VIIa)	Plants with trumpet-shaped flowers
(VIIb)	Plants with bowl-shaped flowers
(VIIc)	Plants with flat flowers
(VIId)	Plants with recurved flowers
(VIII)	All hybrids not in another division
(IX)	All species and their varieties and forms

MALUS *SEE* FRUIT

NARCISSUS

(By the Royal Horticultural Society, revised 1998)

(1)	Trumpet
(2)	Large-cupped
(3)	Small-cupped
(4)	Double
(5)	Triandrus
(6)	Cyclamineus
(7)	Jonquilla and Apodanthus
(8)	Tazetta
(9)	Poeticus
(10)	Bulbocodium
(11a)	Split-corona: Collar
(11b)	Split-corona: Papillon
(12)	Miscellaneous
(13)	Species

NYMPHAEA

(H)	Hardy
(D)	Day-blooming
(N)	Night-blooming
(T)	Tropical

PAEONIA

| (S) | Shrubby |

PELARGONIUM

(A)	Angel
(C)	Coloured Foliage (in combination)
(Ca)	Cactus (in combination)
(d)	Double (in combination)
(Dec)	Decorative
(Dw)	Dwarf
(DwI)	Dwarf Ivy-leaved
(Fr)	Frutetorum
(I)	Ivy-leaved
(Min)	Miniature
(MinI)	Miniature Ivy-leaved
(R)	Regal
(Sc)	Scented-leaved
(St)	Stellar (in combination)
(T)	Tulip (in combination)
(U)	Unique
(Z)	Zonal

PRIMULA

(Classification as per W.W. Smith & Forrest (1928) and W.W. Smith & Fletcher (1941-49))

(1)	Amethystina
(2)	Auricula
(3)	Bullatae
(4)	Candelabra
(5)	Capitatae
(6)	Carolinella
(7)	Cortusoides
(8)	Cuneifolia
(9)	Denticulata
(10)	Dryadifolia
(11)	Farinosae
(12)	Floribundae
(13)	Grandis
(14)	Malacoides
(15)	Malvacca
(16)	Minutissimae
(17)	Muscarioides
(18)	Nivales
(19)	Obconica
(20)	Parryi
(21)	Petiolares
(22)	Pinnatae
(23)	Pycnoloba
(24)	Reinii
(25)	Rotundifolia
(26)	Sikkimensis
(27)	Sinenses
(28)	Soldanelloideae
(29)	Souliei
(30)	Vernales
(A)	Alpine Auricula
(B)	Border Auricula
(Poly)	Polyanthus
(Prim)	Primrose
(S)	Show Auricula
(St)	Striped Auricula

PRUNUS *SEE* FRUIT

PYRUS *SEE* FRUIT

RHODODENDRON

(A)	Azalea (deciduous, species or unclassified hybrid)
(Ad)	Azaleodendron
(EA)	Evergreen azalea
(G)	Ghent azalea (deciduous)
(K)	Knap Hill or Exbury azalea (deciduous)
(M)	Mollis azalea (deciduous)
(O)	Occidentalis azalea (deciduous)
(R)	Rustica azalea (deciduous)
(V)	Vireya rhododendron
(Vs)	Viscosa azalea (deciduous)

RIBES *SEE* FRUIT

ROSA

(A)	Alba
(Bb)	Bourbon
(Bs)	Boursault
(Ce)	Centifolia
(Ch)	China
(Cl)	Climbing (in combination)
(D)	Damask
(DPo)	Damask Portland
(F)	Floribunda or Cluster-flowered
(G)	Gallica
(Ga)	Garnette
(GC)	Ground Cover
(HM)	Hybrid Musk
(HP)	Hybrid Perpetual
(HT)	Hybrid Tea or Large-flowered
(Min)	Miniature
(Mo)	Moss (in combination)
(N)	Noisette
(Patio)	Patio, Miniature Floribunda or Dwarf Cluster-flowered
(Poly)	Polyantha
(PiH)	Pimpinellifolia hybrid (Hybrid Scots Briar)
(Ra)	Rambler
(RH)	Rubiginosa hybrid (Hybrid Sweet Briar)
(Ru)	Rugosa
(S)	Shrub
(T)	Tea

SAXIFRAGA

(Classification from Gornall, R.J. (1987). *Botanical Journal of the Linnean Society*, **95**(4): 273-292)
(1)   Ciliatae
(2)   Cymbalaria
(3)   Merkianae
(4)   Micranthes
(5)   Irregulares
(6)   Heterisia
(7)   Porphyrion
(8)   Ligulatae
(9)   Xanthizoon
(10)   Trachyphyllum
(11)   Gymnopera
(12)   Cotylea
(13)   Odontophyllae
(14)   Mesogyne
(15)   Saxifraga

TULIPA

(Classification from *Classified List and International Register of Tulip Names* by Koninklijke Algemeene Vereening voor Bloembollenculture 1996)
(1)   Single Early Group
(2)   Double Early Group
(3)   Triumph Group
(4)   Darwinhybrid Group
(5)   Single Late Group (including Darwin Group and Cottage Group)
(6)   Lily-flowered Group
(7)   Fringed Group
(8)   Viridiflora Group
(9)   Rembrandt Group
(10)   Parrot Group
(11)   Double Late Group
(12)   Kaufmanniana Group
(13)   Fosteriana Group
(14)   Greigii Group
(15)   Miscellaneous

VERBENA

(G)   Species and hybrids considered by some botanists to belong to the separate genus *Glandularia*.

VIOLA

(C)   Cornuta Hybrid
(dVt)   Double Violet
(ExVa) Exhibition Viola
(FP)   Fancy Pansy
(PVt)   Parma Violet
(SP)   Show Pansy
(T)   Tricolor
(Va)   Viola
(Vt)   Violet
(Vtta) Violetta

VITIS *SEE* FRUIT

REVERSE SYNONYMS

The following list of reverse synonyms is intended to help users find from which genus an unfamiliar plant name has been cross-referred. For a fuller explanation see p.13.

Acacia – Racosperma
Acanthocalyx – Morina
Acca – Feijoa
x Achicodonia – Eucodonia
Achillea – Anthemis
Acinos – Calamintha
Acinos – Micromeria
Actaea – Cimicifuga
Aethionema – Eunomia
Agapetes – Pentapterygium
Agarista – Leucothoe
Agastache – Cedronella
Aichryson – Aeonium
Ajania – Chrysanthemum
Ajania – Eupatorium
Albizia – Acacia
Alcea – Althaea
Allardia – Waldheimia
Allocasuarina – Casuarina
Aloysia – Lippia
Althaea – Malva
Alyogyne – Hibiscus
Alyssum – Ptilotrichum
x Amarygia – Amaryllis
Amaryllis – Brunsvigia
Amomyrtus – Myrtus
Amsonia – Rhazya
Anaphalis – Gnaphalium
Anchusa – Lycopsis
Androsace – Douglasia
Anemone – Eriocapitella
Anisodontea – Malvastrum
Anomatheca – Lapeirousia
Anredera – Boussingaultia
Antirrhinum – Asarina
Aphanes – Alchemilla
Arctanthemum – Chrysanthemum
Arctostaphylos – Arbutus
Arctotis – x Venidioarctotis
Arctotis – Venidium
Arenga – Didymosperma
Argyranthemum – Anthemis
Argyranthemum – Chrysanthemum
Armoracia – Cochlearia
Arundinaria – Pseudosasa
Asarina – Antirrhinum
Asarum – Hexastylis

Asclepias – Gomphocarpus
Asparagus – Smilax
Asperula – Galium
Asphodeline – Asphodelus
Asplenium – Camptosorus
Asplenium – Ceterach
Asplenium – Phyllitis
Asplenium – Scolopendrium
Aster – Crinitaria
Aster – Doellingeria
Aster – Microglossa
Asteriscus – Pallenis
Astilboides – Rodgersia
Atropanthe – Scopolia
Aurinia – Alyssum
Austrocedrus – Libocedrus
Azorella – Bolax
Azorina – Campanula

Bambusa – Arundinaria
Bashania – Arundinaria
Bellevalia – Muscari
Bellis – Erigeron
Besseya – Veronica
Blechnum – Lomaria
Bolax – Azorella
Bolboschoenus – Scirpus
Borago – Anchusa
Borinda – Fargesia
Bothriochloa – Andropogon
Boykinia – Telesonix
Brachyglottis – Senecio
Bracteantha – Helichrysum
Brimeura – Hyacinthus
Brugmansia – Datura
Brunnera – Anchusa
Buglossoides – Lithospermum
Bulbine – Bulbinopsis
Buphthalmum – Inula

Cacalia – Adenostyles
Caiophora – Loasa
Caladium – Xanthosoma
Calamagrostis – Agrostis
Calamagrostis – Stipa
Calamintha – Clinopodium
Calliergon – Acrocladium
Callisia – Phyodina
Callisia – Tradescantia
Calocedrus – Libocedrus
Calocephalus – Leucophyta
Calomeria – Humea
Caloscordum – Nothoscordum
Calytrix – Lhotzkya

Camellia – Thea
Cardamine – Dentaria
Carpobrotus – Lampranthus
Cassiope – Harrimanella
Catapodium – Desmazeria
Cayratia – Parthenocissus
Centaurium – Erythraea
Centella – Hydrocotyle
Centranthus – Kentranthus
Centranthus – Valeriana
Cephalaria – Scabiosa
Ceratostigma – Plumbago
Cercestis – Rhektophyllum
Cestrum – Iochroma
Chaenomeles – Cydonia
Chaenorhinum – Linaria
Chamaecyparis – Cupressus
Chamaecytisus – Cytisus
Chamaedaphne – Cassandra
Chamaemelum – Anthemis
Chasmanthium – Uniola
Cheilanthes – Notholaena
Chiastophyllum – Cotyledon
Chimonobambusa – Arundinaria
Chimonobambusa – Gelidocalamus
Chimonobambusa – Quiongzhuea
Chionohebe – Pygmea
x Chionoscilla – Scilla
Chlorophytum – Diuranthera
Chondrosum – Bouteloua
Chrysanthemum – Dendranthema
Cicerbita – Lactuca
Cionura – Marsdenia
Cissus – Ampelopsis
Cissus – Parthenocissus
x Citrofortunella – Citrus
Citronella – Villaresia
Clarkia – Eucharidium
Clarkia – Godetia
Clavinodum – Arundinaria
Claytonia – Calandrinia
Claytonia – Montia
Clematis – Atragene
Cleyera – Eurya
Clinopodium – Acinos
Clinopodium – Calamintha
Clytostoma – Bignonia
Clytostoma – Pandorea
Cnicus – Carduus
Codonopsis – Campanumoea
Colobanthus – Arenaria
Consolida – Delphinium
x Coralia – Carmichaelia x
   Corallospartium

Cordyline – Dracaena
Cornus – Chamaepericlymenum
Cornus – Dendrobenthamia
Coronilla – Securigera
Cortaderia – Gynerium
Corydalis – Fumaria
Corydalis – Pseudofumaria
Cosmos – Bidens
Cotinus – Rhus
Cotula – Leptinella
Crassula – Rochea
Crassula – Sedum
Crassula – Tillaea
Cremanthodium – Ligularia
Crinodendron – Tricuspidaria
Crocosmia – Antholyza
Crocosmia – Curtonus
Crocosmia – Montbretia
Cruciata – Galium
Ctenanthe – Calathea
Ctenanthe – Stromanthe
× Cupressocyparis –
    Chamaecyparis
Cyathodes – Leucopogon
Cyathodes – Styphelia
Cyclosorus – Pneumatopteris
Cymbalaria – Linaria
Cynara – Scolymus
Cyperus – Mariscus
Cypripedium – Criogenes
Cyrtanthus – Anoiganthus
Cyrtanthus – Vallota
Cyrtomium – Phanerophlebia
Cyrtomium – Polystichum
Cytisus – Argyrocytisus
Cytisus – Genista
Cytisus – Lembotropis
Cytisus – Spartocytisus

Daboecia – Menziesia
Dacrycarpus – Podocarpus
Dactylorhiza – Orchis
Danae – Ruscus
Darmera – Peltiphyllum
Dasypyrum – Haynaldia
Datura – Brugmansia
Davallia – Humata
Delairea – Senecio
Delosperma – Lampranthus
Delosperma – Mesembryanthemum
Dendrocalamus – Bambusa
Derwentia – Hebe
Desmodium – Lespedeza
Dichelostemma – Brodiaea
Dicliptera – Barleria
Dicliptera – Justicia
Diervilla – Weigela
Dietes – Moraea

Diplazium – Athyrium
Disporopsis – Polygonatum
Distictis – Phaedranthus
Distylium – Sycopsis
Dolichothrix – Helichrysum
Dracaena – Pleomele
Dracunculus – Arum
Dregea – Wattakaka
Drepanostachyum – Arundinaria
Drepanostachyum –
    Thamnocalamus
Drepanostachyum –
    Chimonobambusa
Drimys – Tasmannia
Duchesnea – Fragaria
Dunalia – Acnistus
Dypsis – Chrysalidocarpus
Dypsis – Neodypsis

Echeveria – Cotyledon
Echinacea – Rudbeckia
Edraianthus – Wahlenbergia
Egeria – Elodea
Elatostema – Pellionia
Eleutherococcus – Acanthopanax
Elliottia – Botryostege
Elliottia – Cladothamnus
Elymus – Agropyron
Elymus – Leymus
Ensete – Musa
Epilobium – Chamaenerion
Epipremnum – Philodendron
Epipremnum – Scindapsus
Episcia – Alsobia
Eranthis – Aconitum
Erigeron – Aster
Erigeron – Haplopappus
Erysimum – Cheiranthus
Eucodonia – Achimenes
Eupatorium – Ageratina
Eupatorium – Ajania
Eupatorium – Ayapana
Eupatorium – Bartlettina
Euphorbia – Poinsettia
Euryops – Senecio

Fallopia – Bilderdykia
Fallopia – Polygonum
Fallopia – Reynoutria
Farfugium – Ligularia
Fargesia – Arundinaria
Fargesia – Sinarundinaria
Fargesia – Thamnocalamus
Fatsia – Aralia
Felicia – Agathaea
Felicia – Aster
Fibigia – Farsetia
Filipendula – Spiraea

Foeniculum – Ferula
Fortunella – Citrus
Furcraea – Agave

Galium – Asperula
Galtonia – Hyacinthus
Gaultheria – Chiogenes
Gaultheria – × Gaulnettya
Gaultheria – Pernettya
Gelasine – Sisyrinchium
Genista – Chamaespartium
Genista – Cytisus
Genista – Echinospartum
Genista – Teline
Gentianopsis – Gentiana
Gerbera – Leibnitzia
Gladiolus – Acidanthera
Gladiolus – Anomalesia
Gladiolus – Homoglossum
Gladiolus – Petamenes
Glechoma – Nepeta
Gloxinia – Seemannia
Gomphocarpus – Asclepias
Goniolimon – Limonium
Graptopetalum – Sedum
Graptopetalum – Tacitus
Greenovia – Sempervivum
Gymnospermium – Leontice

Habranthus – Zephyranthes
Hacquetia – Dondia
× Halimiocistus – Cistus
× Halimiocistus – Halimium
Halimione – Atriplex
Halimium – Cistus
Halimium – × Halimiocistus
Halimium – Helianthemum
Halocarpus – Dacrydium
Haplopappus – Aster
Hechtia – Dyckia
Hedychium – Brachychilum
Hedyscepe – Kentia
Helianthella – Helianthus
Helianthemum – Cistus
Helianthus – Heliopsis
Helichrysum – Gnaphalium
Helictotrichon – Avena
Helictotrichon – Avenula
Heliopsis – Helianthus
Hepatica – Anemone
Herbertia – Alophia
Hermodactylus – Iris
Heterocentron – Schizocentron
Heterotheca – Chrysopsis
Hibbertia – Candollea
Hieracium – Andryala
Himalayacalamus –
    Arundinaria

Himalayacalamus –
   Drepanostachyum
Hippocrepis – *Coronilla*
Hippolytia – *Achillea*
Hippolytia – *Tanacetum*
Hoheria – *Plagianthus*
Homalocladium –
   Muehlenbeckia
Howea – *Kentia*
Hyacinthoides – *Endymion*
Hyacinthoides – *Scilla*
Hymenocallis – *Elisena*
Hymenocallis – *Ismene*
Hyophorbe – *Mascarena*
Hypochaeris – *Hieracium*
Hypoxis – *Rhodohypoxis*

Incarvillea – *Amphicome*
Indocalamus – *Sasa*
Iochroma – *Acnistus*
Iochroma – *Cestrum*
Iochroma – *Dunalia*
Ipheion – *Tristagma*
Ipheion – *Triteleia*
Ipomoea – *Mina*
Ipomoea – *Pharbitis*
Ipomopsis – *Gilia*
Ischyrolepis – *Restio*
Ismelia – *Chrysanthemum*
Isolepis – *Scirpus*

Jamesbrittenia – *Sutera*
Jeffersonia – *Plagiorhegma*
Jovibarba – *Sempervivum*
Juncus – *Scirpus*
Jurinea – *Jurinella*
Justicia – *Beloperone*
Justicia – *Jacobinia*
Justicia – *Libonia*

Kalanchoe – *Bryophyllum*
Kalanchoe – *Kitchingia*
Kalimeris – *Aster*
Kalimeris – *Asteromoea*
Kalimeris – *Boltonia*
Kalopanax – *Eleutherococcus*
Keckiella – *Penstemon*
Knautia – *Scabiosa*
Kniphofia – *Tritoma*
Kohleria – *Isoloma*
Kunzea – *Leptospermum*

Lablab – *Dolichos*
Lagarosiphon – *Elodea*
Lagarostrobos – *Dacrydium*
Lallemantia – *Dracocephalum*
Lamium – *Galeobdolon*
Lamium – *Lamiastrum*

Lampranthus –
   Mesembryanthemum
Lampranthus – *Oscularia*
Laurentia – *Hippobroma*
Lavatera – *Malva*
Ledebouria – *Scilla*
× *Ledodendron* – *Rhododendron*
Lepechinia – *Sphacele*
Lepidothamnus – *Dacrydium*
Leptinella – *Cotula*
Leptodactylon – *Gilia*
Leucanthemella –
   Chrysanthemum
Leucanthemella – *Leucanthemum*
Leucanthemopsis –
   Chrysanthemum
Leucanthemopsis – *Tanacetum*
Leucanthemum –
   Chrysanthemum
Leucochrysum – *Helipterum*
Leucophyta – *Calocephalus*
Leucopogon – *Cyathodes*
× *Leucoraoulia* – *Raoulia*
Leuzea – *Centaurea*
Leymus – *Elymus*
Ligularia – *Senecio*
Ligustrum – *Parasyringa*
Lilium – *Nomocharis*
Limonium – *Statice*
Linanthus – *Linanthastrum*
Lindelofia – *Adelocaryum*
Lindera – *Parabenzoin*
Liriope – *Ophiopogon*
Lithocarpus – *Quercus*
Lithodora – *Lithospermum*
Littorella – *Plantago*
Lophomyrtus – *Myrtus*
Lophomyrtus – *Myrtus*
Lophospermum – *Asarina*
Lophospermum – *Maurandya*
Lophostemon – *Tristania*
Lotus – *Dorycnium*
Lotus – *Tetragonolobus*
Ludwigia – *Jussiaea*
Luma – *Myrtus*
× *Lycene* – *Lychnis*
Lychnis – *Agrostemma*
Lychnis – *Silene*
Lychnis – *Viscaria*
Lycianthes – *Solanum*
Lytocaryum – *Cocos*
Lytocaryum – *Microcoelum*

Macfadyena – *Bignonia*
Macfadyena – *Doxantha*
Machaeranthera – *Xylorhiza*
Mackaya – *Asystasia*
Macleaya – *Bocconia*

Mahonia – *Berberis*
Mandevilla – *Dipladenia*
Mandragora – *Atropa*
Marrubium – *Ballota*
Matricaria – *Chamomilla*
Matricaria – *Tripleurospermum*
Maurandella – *Asarina*
Maurandella – *Maurandya*
Maurandya – *Asarina*
Melicytus – *Hymenanthera*
Melinis – *Rhynchelytrum*
Mentha – *Preslia*
Merremia – *Ipomoea*
Millettia – *Wisteria*
Mimulus – *Diplacus*
Minuartia – *Arenaria*
Modiolastrum – *Malvastrum*
Moltkia – *Lithodora*
Moltkia – *Lithospermum*
Morina – *Acanthocalyx*
Mukdenia – *Aceriphyllum*
Muscari – *Hyacinthus*
Muscari – *Leopoldia*
Muscari – *Leopoldia*
Muscari – *Muscarimia*
Muscari – *Pseudomuscari*
Myricaria – *Tamarix*
Myrteola – *Myrtus*

Naiocrene – *Claytonia*
Naiocrene – *Montia*
Nassella – *Stipa*
Nectaroscordum – *Allium*
Nematanthus – *Hypocyrta*
Nemesia – *Diascia*
Neopaxia – *Claytonia*
Neopaxia – *Montia*
Neoregelia – *Guzmania*
Neoregelia – *Nidularium*
Nepeta – *Dracocephalum*
Nepeta – *Origanum*
Nephrophyllidium – *Fauria*
Nertera – *Coprosma*
Nipponanthemum –
   Chrysanthemum
Nipponanthemum –
   Leucanthemum
Nymphoides – *Villarsia*

Oemleria – *Osmaronia*
Oenothera – *Chamissonia*
Olearia – *Pachystegia*
Olsynium – *Phaiophleps*
Olsynium – *Sisyrinchium*
Onixotis – *Dipidax*
Ophiopogon – *Convallaria*
Orchis – *Dactylorhiza*
Oreopteris – *Thelypteris*

Orostachys – Sedum
Osmanthus – × Osmarea
Osmanthus – Phillyrea
Osteospermum – Dimorphotheca
Othonna – Hertia
Othonna – Othonnopsis
Ozothamnus – Helichrysum

Pachyphragma – Cardamine
Packera – Senecio
Paederota – Veronica
Papaver – Meconopsis
Parahebe – Derwentia
Parahebe – Hebe
Parahebe – Veronica
Paraserianthes – Albizia
Paris – Daiswa
Parthenocissus – Ampelopsis
Parthenocissus – Vitis
Passiflora – Tetrapathaea
Paxistima – Pachystema
Pecteilis – Habenaria
Pelargonium – Geranium
Peltoboykinia – Boykinia
Penstemon – Chelone
Pentaglottis – Anchusa
Pentalinon – Urechites
Pericallis – Senecio
Persea – Machilus
Persicaria – Aconogonon
Persicaria – Bistorta
Persicaria – Polygonum
Persicaria – Tovara
Petrocoptis – Lychnis
Petrophytum – Spiraea
Petrorhagia – Tunica
Petroselinum – Carum
Phegopteris – Thelypteris
Phoenicaulis – Parrya
Photinia – Heteromeles
Photinia – Stransvaesia
Photinia – × Stravinia
Phuopsis – Crucianella
Phyla – Lippia
Phymosia – Sphaeralcea
Physoplexis – Phyteuma
Physostegia – Dracocephalum
Pieris – Arcterica
Pilosella – Hieracium
Piper – Macropiper
Pisonia – Heimerliodendron
Plagiomnium – Mnium
Plecostachys – Helichrysum
Plectranthus – Solenostemon
Pleioblastus – Arundinaria
Pleioblastus – Sasa
Podranea – Tecoma
Polianthes – Bravoa

Polygonum – Persicaria
Polypodium – Phlebodium
Polystichum – Phanerophlebia
Poncirus – Aegle
Potentilla – Comarum
Pratia – Lobelia
Prumnopitys – Podocarpus
Prunus – Amygdalus
Pseudocydonia – Chaenomeles
Pseudopanax – Metapanax
Pseudopanax – Neopanax
Pseudopanax – Nothopanax
Pseudosasa – Arundinaria
Pseudotsuga – Tsuga
Pseudowintera – Drimys
Pterocephalus – Scabiosa
Ptilostemon – Cirsium
Pulicaria – Inula
Pulsatilla – Anemone
Pushkinia – Scilla
Pyrethropsis – Argyranthemum
Pyrethropsis – Chrysanthemum
Pyrethropsis – Leucanthemopsis
Pyrethropsis – Leucanthemum
Pyrrocoma – Haplopappus

Reineckea – Liriope
Retama – Genista
Rhapis – Chamaerops
Rhodanthe – Helipterum
Rhodanthemum –
   Chrysanthemopsis
Rhodanthemum –
   Chrysanthemum
Rhodanthemum –
   Leucanthemopsis
Rhodanthemum – Leucanthemum
Rhodanthemum – Pyrethropsis
Rhodiola – Clementsia
Rhodiola – Rosularia
Rhodiola – Sedum
Rhododendron – Azalea
Rhododendron – Azaleodendron
Rhododendron – Rhodora
Rhodophiala – Hippeastrum
× Rhodoxis – Hypoxis ×
   Rhodohypoxis
× Rhodoxis – Rhodohypoxis
Rosularia – Cotyledon
Rosularia – Sempervivella
Rothmannia – Gardenia
Ruellia – Dipteracanthus
Ruschia –
   Mesembryanthemum
Rytidosperma – Merxmuellera

Saccharum – Erianthus
Sagina – Minuartia

Salvia – Salvia
Sanguisorba – Dendriopoterium
Sanguisorba – Poterium
Sasa – Arundinaria
Sasa – Pleioblastus
Sasaella – Arundinaria
Sasaella – Pleioblastus
Sasaella – Sasa
Sasamorpha – Sasa
Satureja – Micromeria
Sauromatum – Arum
Saussurea – Jurinea
Scadoxus – Haemanthus
Schefflera – Brassaia
Schefflera – Dizygotheca
Schefflera – Heptapleurum
Schizachyrium – Andropogon
Schizostachyum – Arundinaria
Schizostachyum – Thamnocalamus
Schoenoplectus – Scirpus
Scirpoides – Scirpus
Scirpus – Eriophorum
Sedum – Hylotelephium
Sedum – Rhodiola
Sedum – Sedastrum
Sedum – Villadia
Semiaquilegia – Aquilegia
Semiaquilegia – Paraquilegia
Semiarundinaria – Arundinaria
Semiarundinaria – Oligostachyum
Senecio – Cineraria
Senecio – Kleinia
Senecio – Ligularia
Senna – Cassia
Seriphidium – Artemisia
Shortia – Schizocodon
Sibbaldiopsis – Potentilla
Sieversia – Geum
Silene – Lychnis
Silene – Melandrium
Silene – Saponaria
Sinacalia – Ligularia
Sinacalia – Senecio
Sinarundinaria –
   Semiarundinaria
Sinningia – Gesneria
Sinningia – Rechsteineria
Sisymbrium – Hesperis
Sisyrinchium – Phaiophleps
× Smithicodonia –
   × Achimenantha
Solanum – Lycianthes
Soleirolia – Helxine
Solenopsis, – Isotoma
Solenostemon, – Coleus
× Solidaster – Aster
× Solidaster – Solidago
Sorbaria – Spiraea

Sparaxis – Synnotia
Sphaeralcea – Iliamna
Sphaeromeria – Tanacetum
Spirodela – Lemna
Spraguea – Calyptridium
Stachys – Betonica
Steirodiscus – Gamolepis
Stenomesson – Urceolina
Stenotus – Haplopappus
Steptocarpus – Streptocarpella
Stewartia – Stuartia
Stipa – Achnatherum
Stipa – Lasiagrostis
Stipa – Oryzopsis
Strobilanthes – Pteracanthus
Succisa – Scabiosa
Sutera – Bacopa
Syagrus – Arecastrum
Syagrus – Cocos

Tanacetum – Achillea
Tanacetum – Balsamita
Tanacetum – Chrysanthemum
Tanacetum – Matricaria
Tanacetum – Pyrethrum
Tanacetum – Spathipappus
Tanacetum – Sphaeromeria
Tecoma – Tecomaria
Tecomaria – Tecoma
Telekia – Buphthalmum
Tephroseris – Senecio
Tetradium – Euodia
Tetraneuris – Actinella
Tetraneuris – Hymenoxys

Tetrapanax – Fatsia
Thamnocalamus – Arundinaria
Thamnocalamus –
  Sinarundinaria
Thlaspi – Hutchinsia
Thlaspi – Noccaea
Thuja – Platycladus
Thuja – Thujopsis
Thymus – Origanum
Tiarella – × Heucherella
Tonestus – Haplopappus
Toona – Cedrela
Trachelium – Diosphaera
Trachycarpus – Chamaerops
Tradescantia – Rhoeo
Tradescantia – Setcreasea
Tradescantia – Tradescantia
Tradescantia – Zebrina
Trichopetalum – Anthericum
Trichophorum – Scirpus
Tripetaleia – Elliottia
Tripleurospermum – Matricaria
Tripogandra – Tradescantia
Tristagma – Beauverdia
Tristaniopsis – Tristania
Triteleia – Brodiaea
Tritonia – Crocosmia
Tropaeolum – Nasturtium hort.
Tuberaria – Helianthemum
Tulipa – Amana
Tweedia – Oxypetalum

Ugni – Myrtus
Ullucus – Anredera

Ursinia – Euryops
Uvularia – Oakesiella

Vaccinium – Oxycoccus
Verbascum – Celsia
Verbascum –
  × Celsioverbascum
Verbena – Glandularia
Verbena – Lippia
Veronicastrum – Veronica
Vigna – Phaseolus
Villadia – Sedum
Viola – Erpetion
Vitaliana – Androsace
Vitaliana – Douglasia

Weigela – Diervilla
Weigela – Macrodiervilla

Xanthophthalmum –
  Chrysanthemum
Xanthorhiza – Zanthorhiza

Yushania – Arundinaria
Yushania – Sinarundinaria
Yushania – Thamnocalamus

Zantedeschia – Calla
Zauschneria – Epilobium
Zephyranthes – × Cooperanthes
Zephyranthes – Cooperia
Zephyranthes – Habranthus

THE NAMING OF PLANTS

To make the best use of the *RHS Plant Finder*, it is helpful to understand some of the complexities of botanical names.

COMMON NAMES VS BOTANICAL NAMES

Common Names

The most common question asked by gardeners is 'Why can't we just use common names?'. While, on the face of it, this is an attractive proposition, there are several factors that make this impractical for garden plants. The main hurdle is that plants are introduced from all over the world and therefore do not have common names in the language of the recipient country. Although common names could be introduced along with the plant, in whatever language, experience teaches us that acceptance of such names is likely to be resisted, and the possible need to transliterate the names from non-Roman scripts, such as Japanese or Hebrew, is a further complication. Additionally, there will often be more than one name available and there is no system to decide which one to use. Many plants attract a plethora of common names of very local usage, even within a small country and, of course, widespread plants have common names in many languages. Also, there will be plants that do not have a common name in any language if they have never been found to be useful to man.

It would naturally be possible to invent common names in suitable languages for recipient countries. In fact this is already done extensively in the United States, but with no system to regulate or standardise names, confusion can easily arise through 'common' names having no regard for the relationships between plants. For example, fragrant Himalayan champaca, banana shrub and Jack Fogg michelia are common names listed in a recent catalogue for *Michelia champaca, Michelia figo* and *Michelia × foggii* 'Jack Fogg' respectively. These are three closely related plants whose botanical names identify them precisely *and* reveal their relatedness. With no other point of reference, the common names chosen are forced to draw upon unrelated elements of the botanical names and can end up as more complex constructions without conveying as much information. The 'common' names do not show that these are similar plants yet do not avoid 'difficult' botanical elements. An added problem in an alphabetical list like the *RHS Plant Finder* is that common names of related plants would appear in different parts of the book.

On a slightly different but related tack, familiar and well-loved common names tend to get used for more than one plant. A classic example in the English-speaking world is bluebell, referring to *Hyacinthoides non-scripta* in England, *Campanula rotundifolia* in Scotland, *Sollya heterophylla* in Australia and species of *Mertensia* in North America. The scope for confusion is enormous.

Botanical Names

Most people do not think twice about using rhododendron, chrysanthemum or fuchsia as the common names for three large, popular groups of plants, but these are also their botanical names. The fact that they have passed into common usage demonstrates the great strength of botanical names – they are intended to be universal. The aim of the botanical naming system is to provide each different plant with a single name which can be recognised by anyone, whatever their own language.

Botanical names are often referred to as Latin names, but this is slightly misleading. While it is true that the rules governing the formation and spelling of names are based on Latin, any word, in any language, can form the basis of a plant name. Thus many plant names commemorate people and places or are derived from common names used in the country of origin. These are indiscriminately mixed with Latin and Greek words, all of them 'latinized' by following the rules of Latin grammar.

WHAT BOTANICAL NAMES REPRESENT

To understand how botanical names are applied, it is necessary briefly to describe how plants are classified, since the units into which they are separated determine the structure of names.

Species

The basic unit of plant classification is the **species** (not 'specie' – species is both singular and plural in biology) which can be defined as a group of interbreeding individuals producing more-or-less similar offspring and differing from other similar groups by a number of key characters.

Genera

Species which share a number of significant features are grouped together to form a **genus** (plural **genera**). The characteristics of a genus are often quite easy to recognise, making this perhaps the most generally useful level at which plants can be identified for practical purposes. It is common for a plant to be referred to as, for instance, *Malva* sp., the **sp.** being an abbreviation of species and indicating an unidentified species of a particular genus. Genera can vary in size from a single species to over a thousand, depending on their distinctive characteristics. Compare *Rhodochiton* with *Rhododendron* in this book, for example.

Families

Genera are grouped into larger entities called **families**, some of which are easily recognised, others less so. Although families may appear at first to be of only academic interest, knowledge of the family to which an unknown plant belongs is the springboard to identifying it, and for the gardener, it can give an indication of the conditions required for successful cultivation.

The majority of families have always had names ending with the same group of letters, *-aceae*, and based on a genus within the family. This neatly distinguishes family names from genera and other plant groups. However, there are eight families with very well-known names which do not conform to this pattern. While it is perfectly acceptable to continue to use these names, the modern trend is to use alternative names with *-aceae* endings and this is what has been adopted in the *RHS Plant Finder*. The families are *Compositae* (*Asteraceae*), *Cruciferae* (*Brassicaceae*), *Gramineae* (*Poaceae*), *Guttiferae* (*Clusiaceae*), *Labiatae* (*Lamiaceae*), *Leguminosae* (split into three families based on well-known sub-families: *Caesalpiniaceae*, *Mimosaceae* and *Papilionaceae*), *Palmae* (*Arecaceae*) and *Umbelliferae* (*Apiaceae*). Also, the traditionally large family *Liliaceae* is split into a number of smaller, more natural families that may be unfamiliar to readers.

HOW NAMES WORK

At higher levels: genus, species and family

The name of a species is made up of two elements and is known as a **binomen** or **binominal name**, commonly referred to as a **binomial**. First comes the name of the genus, for example, *Malva*. Added to this is the **specific epithet**, for example, *moschata*. Put together, they form the name of a species, *Malva moschata*, which is in the family *Malvaceae*. To make them stand out in text, plant names are printed in italics (or underlined in handwriting) and the genus and family start with capital letters. Each species in a genus is given a different specific epithet, for example, *Malva verticillata* and *M. sylvestris* (abbreviation of a genus name to a single letter, once established in a piece of text, is perfectly acceptable). While genus names are uniquely associated with related plants, specific epithets can each be used once in as many genera as botanists decide appropriate. Repetition of an epithet within a genus would naturally cause confusion and is not allowed.

At lower levels: subspecies, variety and form

Things start to get complicated when variation within species needs recognition by use of further names. When plants have a wide distribution in the wild, natural selection and evolution work at different rates in different areas, especially if populations become geographically isolated. Such populations are often distinguished as **subspecies** (abbreviated to **subsp.** or occasionally **ssp.** but this can easily be confused with **spp.**, the abbreviation for species plural, so is not recommended), easily attributable to the species but differing in significant characters. Once a particular population is recognised as a subspecies and given a name, plants typical of the species automatically become a subspecies bearing the name of the species. Thus *Malva sylvestris* subsp. *mauritanica* differs from the typical subsp. *sylvestris* in having a more robust habit and larger, deeper purple flowers with darker veins.

Populations and individuals that exhibit less striking differences are named as varieties and forms (technically **varietas** and **forma**, abbreviated to **var.** and **f.** respectively). Their designation as a varietas or forma relates partly to the degree of difference exhibited and partly to the botanical tradition of the country in which a botanist was trained. So *Malva alcea* var. *fastigiata* differs from typical plants in having an upright habit (although other characters may vary too) and *M. moschata* f. *alba* simply has white rather than mauve flowers. Botanically, these are not very significant differences, but in the garden they can be crucial to achieving the desired effect.

Although subspecies, varietas and forma tend to be used somewhat erratically and interchangeably, they are technically ranked in order of difference and one plant can have a name at each rank – for example, the diminutive daffodil *Narcissus romieuxii* subsp. *albidus* var. *zaianicus* f. *lutescens*.

As can be seen, there are five ranked elements to this name which, when fully presented, gives a very precise idea to the daffodil enthusiast as to the characters of the plant in question. Mercifully, this situation is rare! Such complex names are rarely used and indeed are not really essential from a naming point of view – the trinomen *N. romieuxii* f. *lutescens* provides a perfectly precise name for the plant. Where cultivars are derived from such a plant, it is not generally necessary to cite every rank but simply sufficient to add the cultivar name to the species binomial (or even just the genus). In this book, all ranks are given where known to emphasise the relationships of the plants listed.

Sometimes, a second epithet is quoted without indication of rank, an invalid construction known as an **unranked trinomen** or **trinomial**. In these cases, either the rank is not known or it is unclear whether or not the name should be treated as a cultivar. This is an unsatisfactory situation but requires considerable research to resolve.

Hybrids

Some plant species, when grown together, either in the wild or in gardens, are found to interbreed. The resulting offspring are known as **hybrids** and the majority occur between species within a single genus. For example, hybrids between *Erica ciliaris* and *E. tetralix* have been given the hybrid name *Erica* × *watsonii*, the multiplication sign denoting hybrid origin. Some hybrids have not been given a hybrid name but are referred to by quoting the parent species linked by a multiplication sign, for instance *Drosera pulchella* × *D. nitidula*. This is termed a **hybrid formula**. Hybrids between different genera are given a new hybrid genus name and the different combinations of species are treated as species in their own right. Thus the hybrid *Mahonia aquifolium* × *Berberis sargentiana* has been named × *Mahoberberis aquisargentii* and *M. aquifolium* × *B. julianae* is × *Mahoberberis meithkeana*.

There are also a few special-case hybrids called graft hybrids, where the tissues of two plants are physically rather than genetically mixed. These are indicated by an addition rather than a multiplication sign, so *Laburnum* + *Cytisus* becomes + *Laburnocytisus*.

Cultivars

In cultivation, variation within species and that generated by hybridisation is particularly valued. Plants exhibiting desirable characteristics of flower colour, habit, size, variegation, fruit colour, flavour etc. are often given names. These are termed **cultivar** names (from <u>culti</u>vated <u>var</u>iety) and can be added to a binomial or simply a generic name. To make them stand out from the purely botanical part of a name, they are enclosed in single quotation marks and are not written in italics, resulting in names like *Malva sylvestris* 'Primley Blue' and + *Laburnocytisus* 'Adamii'. Additionally, new cultivar names coined since 1959 should follow international rules and be in a modern language — i.e., they should not be Latin or latinized, as many were in the past – to make them stand out even more clearly. As with specific epithets, cultivar names should not be repeated within a genus, although it is easy to find historical examples where this has occurred.

Cultivars are often popularly referred to as varieties, which is fine if they have names like 'Mavoureen Nesmith' or 'Techny Spider', but could be confused with a botanical varietas if they are older, latinized names. Consistent use of the term cultivar is therefore helpful in promoting clarity when using plant names.

Group, Grex and Series

When dealing with some genera where there are a lot of cultivars or where a well-known cultivar becomes variable through poor selection of propagation material or gives rise to a lot of new ones through breeding work, it has been found useful to use a collective name, the **cultivar-group name**, to identify them. Such a name always includes the word Group and, when used in conjunction with a cultivar name, is enclosed in round brackets (never single quotation marks). For example, *Actaea simplex* (Atropurpurea Group) 'Brunette' is a distinct cultivar within a group of purple-leaved cultivars. It is also possible to recognise as a cultivar-group a species, subspecies or varietas no longer felt by botanists to be worthy of recognition as a separate entity when the whole range of variation in related plants is considered. Such a species becomes part of another species, and botanically its name becomes a synonym. However, its characteristics are often horticulturally significant and the transfer of its name to a cultivar-group is useful to gardeners. For example, while *Rhododendron scintillans* is no longer recognised as a separate species and is botanically 'sunk' into *R. polycladum*, it is recognised horticulturally as *R. polycladum* Scintillans Group.

In some plant groups, notably within orchids, where complex hybrid parentages are carefully recorded, the group system is further refined. Each hybrid is given a **grex** name (Latin for flock) which covers all offspring from that particular cross, however different they may be from one another. Individual cultivars may then be named and propagated by division or micropropagation. Although a grex is similar to a botanical hybrid in principal, backcrossing a member of a grex with one of its parents results in a new grex, with a new name, whereas backcrossing a hybrid makes no difference to the hybrid name. In contrast to groups, with grex names no brackets are used and grex is abbreviated to **g.** – for example, *Pleione* Shantung g. is a popular grex of hardy ground-living orchids while *P.* Shantung g. 'Muriel Harberd' is a particularly good cultivar, selected from the grex.

With seed-raised plants, particularly F1 hybrid flowers, **series** have become increasingly popular. A series is like a group in that it contains a number of similar cultivars, but it differs in being created specifically as a marketing device, with cultivars added to create a range of flower colours on plants of similar habit. The identities of individual cultivars are often undisclosed, and the individual colour elements may be represented by slightly different cultivars over the years. Series names are treated similarly to group names. Unfortunately, the term series also has a precise botanical usage, but one that is unlikely to affect gardeners.

Synonyms

Although the ideal is for each species or cultivar to have only one name, anyone dealing with plants soon comes across a situation where one plant has received two or more names, or two plants have received the same name. In each case, only one name and application, for reasons of precision and stability, can be regarded as correct. Additional names are known as **synonyms**, constant thorns in the sides of gardeners! Two major factors leading to name changes and the creation of synonyms are rarely understood and require some explanation. Firstly, in the past and during the 19th century in particular, when a huge amount of botanical exploration was taking place, it was possible for botanists to be beavering away describing and naming plants in different parts of the world, blissfully unaware that they were duplicating someone else's work. This is perhaps difficult to understand in these days of instant global communication, but it led to many cases of a single species with two or more names or two or more species with the same name. The simplest way to resolve the problem of duplicated and superfluous names is to invoke a rule of **priority** – the earliest name correctly published wins and new names are therefore needed for some plants with later, incorrect names. This is a basically sound idea but has led to changes of some very familiar, yet incorrect names due to the discovery of earlier, correct ones in very obscure texts. This can have a destabilising effect, contrary to the intention of the rule of priority, so there is now a much more pragmatic view being taken, with some of the more destabilising proposed name changes vetted by an international panel and often rejected if the

technically wrong name is widely known. For example, the popular heather, *Erica carnea* was saved from a change to *E. herbacea*. An even more dramatic example was the retention of the genus name *Freesia* instead of the technically correct *Anomatheca*.

Cultivars acquire extra names in similar ways to wild plants and also through deliberate re-naming when the original name is felt not to promote good sales. The same principle of priority applies for cultivars as for wild plants so there are always cases where correction is needed. However, it is not always appropriate to provide a new, unique name for a cultivar which has been given the same name as an existing plant. Where there are large groups of cultivars, such as in *Fuchsia* and *Pelargonium*, repetition of cultivar names has proved difficult to avoid. In these cases, names can be qualified with the name of the raiser, the date of introduction or the plant type to help pinpoint their identity.

The second factor leading to name changes is misidentification. In gardens, many plants are distributed with the wrong name, usually through simple error, and it is important that these mistakes are corrected so that the plant you buy agrees with the description that goes with the name.

In the case of wild plants, correct identification and naming relies on knowing what species exist and how they are related. We have by no means discovered every plant species on the planet, and every discovery sheds new light on plant relationships. Add to this the increasingly reliable evidence of evolutionary trends provided by DNA and molecular studies and the fact that, for better or worse, the naming system aims to reflect the classification and therefore relationships, and it can be seen that some changes are inevitable. The most obvious results of new knowledge are changes to the membership of genera, some being split, with new ones created, others amalgamated – 'lumped' or 'sunk' in botanical slang. However, the closer we get to cataloguing the whole plant kingdom, the fewer new changes should occur.

Authorities

In the light of the problems raised by the existence of synonyms, and in order that plant names can be used with precision within the scientific world, there is a system whereby the name of the person who coined the name of a plant species (its **author** or **authority**) is added to the plant name, often in abbreviated form. For instance, *Malva moschata* L. was named by the prolific botanist Linnaeus, whose own name is abbreviated by international convention to **L.** Most of the time, this information is irrelevant to the gardener, except in cases where the same name has been given to two different plants. Although only one usage is correct, both may be encountered in books and catalogues, so indicating the author is the only way to be certain about which plant is being referred to. The same can happen with cultivars and, although authors are not routinely attached to cultivar names, this is sometimes the only way to be certain which plant, with the desired characteristics, you are dealing with.

Trade Designations and Trade Marks

Until fairly recently, cultivars, grexes and groups were the end of the story with regard to garden plant names. However, the expanding use of Plant Breeders' Rights (PBR) has resulted in an increasing number of additional names known as **trade designations**, and the marketing of plants using trade marks has also added confusion.

To obtain PBR protection, a new plant must be registered and pass tests for distinctness, uniformity and stability under an approved name. The approved name is its cultivar name, which should be unique to that plant within the genus and must, by law, be used on labels at point-of-sale. However, it has become common practice for the names registered for PBR to be code or nonsense names which do nothing to promote healthy sales. An additional selling name is therefore given (or perhaps several, covering different countries in which the plant is sold) and this is the **trade designation**. It looks like a cultivar name and is often presented as such, but should not be enclosed in single quotation marks and should be printed in a contrasting typeface to the cultivar name. Rose growers started the trend for code names, but with the rapid expansion of PBR they can now be found attached to almost any plant. *Choisya ternata* Sundance is a good example of a common garden centre plant with both a trade designation and a coded cultivar name, *C. ternata* 'Lich'. In the Plant Directory section of this book, trade designations are linked to cultivar names by an equals sign (Sundance = 'Lich') for clarity.

There is a second category of trade designation, involving cultivar names originating in foreign languages. In many countries there is resistance to using foreign cultivar names which can easily be translated or given an alternative name. For the sake of stability, the correct form of a cultivar name is taken, with certain provisos, as that in which it was originally published, in a nursery catalogue or elsewhere. Translations are therefore classified as trade designations. In the *RHS Plant Finder*, translations are cross-referenced to their correct cultivar names, in the same way as synonyms.

Trade marks used in conjunction with, or apparently *as* cultivar names cause particular problems when assessing which words constitute a cultivar name and which are a marketing device. It seems that trade mark law is regularly misinterpreted when it comes to plants, since a trade mark is a device to identify goods from a particular source and cannot be used to identify a particular plant. However, the way names are presented on labels and in catalogues often leaves this as the only possible interpretation. Care is therefore needed when quoting trade marks alongside plant names. They are best treated as trade designations, i.e. printed in a different typeface but with the appropriate ™ or ® suffix.

USING COMMON NAMES

Having begun with a section on common names and why they are not the best way to communicate information about plants, let's end with one celebrating them. They are, after all, often charmingly descriptive and contribute richly to our vocabulary. In a context where their meaning is clear, there is nothing wrong with using common names. To refer to gardener's garters rather than *Phalaris arundinacea* var. *picta* and King Edward potatoes instead of *Solanum tuberosum* 'King Edward' is usually the only sensible option. The same is true when we talk about wallflowers, daffodils, pansies and other common garden plants, either among our friends or for an audience sharing the same language and gardening experience. Only when communicating with a large audience, as books and magazines must do, is it necessary to think more carefully about using precise botanical names. Or, perhaps, when ordering the latest introduction from a far-flung corner of the world, its common name (or names) might be even more difficult to get to grips with than, for instance, *Xysmalobium stockenstroemense* or *Romanzoffia unalaschcensis* – or would it?

Adrian Whiteley
March 2001

A QUESTION OF NOMENCLATURE

Though Adrian Whiteley's succinct and elegant explanation of the naming of plants sets out the general principles of plant nomenclature we use, it helps to explain how we have interpreted and applied some of the other rules of nomenclature required by the two Codes (the *International Code of Botanical Nomenclature 2000* (the Saint Louis Code or ICBN) and the *International Code of Nomenclature of Cultivated Plants 1995* (ICNCP)). Our aim has been to make plant names in *The RHS Plant Finder* as consistent, reliable and stable as possible, and acceptable to gardeners and botanists alike, not only in the British Isles but around the world.

Cases in which the most correct name or the interpretation of the codes is debatable are referred to the RHS's Advisory Panel on Nomenclature and Taxonomy. The Panel looks at all recent and current proposals to change or correct names and strives for a balance between the stability of well-known names and botanical and taxonomic correctness according to the codes of nomenclature. Unlike the independent Horticultural Taxonomy Group (Hortax), its aim is to consider individual problems of plant nomenclature rather than general principles. Chaired by Chris Brickell, the panel includes Susyn

> '*The question of nomenclature is always a vexed one. The only thing certain is, that it is impossible to please everyone.*'
>
> W.J. BEAN - PREFACE TO FIRST EDITION OF *Trees & Shrubs Hardy in the British Isles.*

Andrews (Kew), Dr James Compton (University of Reading), Dr Christopher Grey-Wilson, Dr Stephen Jury (University of Reading), Sabina Knees (Edinburgh), Dr Alan Leslie (RHS), Tony Lord, Dr Simon Thornton-Wood (RHS), Piers Trehane (Index Hortensis) and Adrian Whiteley (RHS).

Many name changes proposed by nurseries and Plant Finder users over the past year have been adopted but others have yet to be considered and approved by the Panel. We hope that all those who have generously told us about wrong names will be patient if the corrections they suggest are not immediately made: all such opinions are much valued but the volume of information is great and

must be thoroughly checked before we make changes.

Families and genera used in *The RHS Plant Finder* are almost always those given in Brummitt's *Vascular Plant Families and Genera*. For spellings and genders of generic names, Greuter's *Names in Current Use for Extant Plant Genera* is being followed; there are rare cases in which this disagrees with some prominent recent publications such as its use of the spelling *Diplarrhena* as opposed to *Diplarrena* in the current *Flora of Australia*. However, the general effect will be to keep names in exactly the same form as they are already known to gardeners.

In some cases the Panel feels that the conflicting views about the naming of some groups of plants will not be easily resolved. Our policy is to wait until an absolutely clear consensus is reached, not to rush to rename plants only to have to change names a second time when opinions have shifted yet again.

This edition contains few major changes to plant names. One has been the addition of both species and genome group to each edible banana cultivar. Thus a triploid cultivar such as 'Silk' belonging to AAB Group has two sets of chromosomes from *Musa acuminata* (A) and one set from *M. balbisiana* (B), making it botanically a clone of *M. ? paradisiaca*; here it is found under *Musa ? paradisiaca* 'Silk' (AAB Group). The big perennial blue poppies have been placed in Cultivar-groups following the treatment devised by the Meconopsis Group (discussed in *The New Plantsman*) and there has been a thorough revision of names of the taller *Phlox* cultivars.

Once again, the Internet has proved a great boon in the checking of plant names and carries searchable sources of information in ever increasing number on both wild species and cultivated plants. The most extensive and reliable websites giving information on plant names are included in our Bibliography, though many of the addresses have changed in the last year.

All of us involved in the publication of *The RHS Plant Finder* remain committed to the use of plant names that are as correct as possible. As before, gardeners and nurserymen may still choose to differ and use what names they want, many preferring a more conservative and a few a more radical approach to naming. Except for those names in which we have made corrections of a couple of letters to bring them in line with the codes of nomenclature, we are responsible for none of the name changes in this or any other edition of *The RHS Plant Finder.*

RULES OF NOMENCLATURE

Throughout *The RHS Plant Finder* we try to follow the codes of nomenclature rigorously. Plant names that are clearly not permissible under these and for which there seems to be no valid alternative are marked I (for invalid), even if they have been accepted by the appropriate International Cultivar Registrar. The commonest sorts of invalid names seem to be those that are wholly or partly in Latin (not permissible since 1959, e.g. 'Pixie Alba', 'Superba', 'Variegata') and those which use a Latin generic name as a cultivar name (e.g. *Rosa* 'Corylus', *Viola* 'Gazania').

Apart from being discourteous to the plants' originators and their countries, the translating of foreign plant names into English is a bad and insular practice that is likely to cause confusion; it is also contrary to Article 28 of the 1995 ICNCP. The Code requires that such translations be considered trade designations and not cultivar names and so should be presented in a different font (here sans serif) and not in quotes. It may be years yet before we make sense of the host of German names and apparent English translations for a genus such as *Coreopsis*, many of which must be synonyms. Throughout *The RHS Plant Finder*, we have tried to give preference to the original name in every case, although English translations are also given as trade designations where they are in general use.

The substitution of slick selling names by nurseries which do not like, or have not bothered to find out, the correct names of the plants they sell is sharp practice not expected of any reputable nursery; it is also a probable breach of the Trades Description Act.

The publication of the ICNCP has done a great deal to clarify nomenclature without generally introducing rules that cause destabilising name changes. However, it significantly alters the sort of plant names that are allowed since 1 January 1996: nurseries that name plants are strongly urged to check that the names they want to use are acceptable under the new Code.

One Article of the 1995 Code that affects names published since 1995, is Art. 17.13, dealing in part with the use of botanical or common generic names within a cultivar or group name. This bans names in which the last word of the cultivar name is the common or botanical name of a genus or species. Two sorts of such names are commonly found: those based on colours (ending Lilac, Lavender, Rose, Rosa, Apricot, Peach, Mauve (French for *Malva*)) and those based on personal names (Rosemary, Hazel). These will be marked I in The RHS Plant Finder if known to have been published after 1995 or marked with an asterisk if their date of publication is unknown.

This rule does not preclude cultivar epithets ending with common names which apply to only part of a genus such as Cerise, Cherry, Lemon, Lime, Orange, Pink, or Violet, each of which refers to more than one species and/or their hybrids.

An Article of the new Code which the Panel has agreed it cannot implement is Art. 17.11, banning cultivar names consisting of solely adjectival words in a modern language, unless one of these words may be considered a substantive or unless the epithet is the recognized name of a colour. As this rule is retroactive, applying to all cultivar names whenever they were published, if applied strictly it could require rejection of several hundred cultivar names in *The RHS Plant Finder*, many of them very well known and widely used. Furthermore, it is difficult to apply: many adjectives also have substantive meanings, albeit sometimes obscure ones, that might or might not justify acceptance of the names; it is not easy to decide which names of colours are accepted and which are not. Our Panel's judgement is that, as currently worded, this Article is unintentionally restrictive and potentially destabilizing; a future edition of the Code is unlikely to be so proscriptive. So for the time being we will not use this Article as a basis for making changes, nor for declaring already established names unacceptable.

ORTHOGRAPHY

One of the most striking changes in the new Saint Louis edition of the *International Code of Botanical Nomenclature* is its clarification of what orthographic (spelling) corrections should be made to commemorative plant names. In the previous (Tokyo 1994) edition of the ICBN, this proved the most difficult part of the code to implement because of its ambiguous phrasing and aroused a great deal of debate at our Panel meetings. The present code rules that such epithets as *alcoquiana*, *glaziovii*, *bigelovii* and *bureavii*, commemorating Alcock, Glaziou, Bigelow and Bureau, are intentional and acceptable latinizations that do not affect merely the terminations of the names. However, we are now told that in *fortuni*, *billardierii* and *backhousii*, only the termination is affected so these must be corrected to *fortunei*, *billardierei* and *backhousei* respectively. Though this makes the permitted spelling clear in a number of cases, many other cases seem still to be debatable. Though some such names have been changed to accord with the new edition of the code where the code's intention is clear, we have not had time to make all such corrections. In other cases where the code is less clear, our Panel will have to deliberate carefully, only making changes if the intention of the code is certain.

VERIFICATION OF NAMES

Although we try to verify every name that appears in these pages, the amount of time that can be allotted to checking each of over 70,000 entries must be limited. There is always a proportion that does not appear in any of the reference sources used and those unverified names for which there may be scope for error are marked with an asterisk. Such errors may occur with species we cannot find listed (possibly synonyms for more recent and better known names) or may include misspellings (particularly of names transliterated from Japanese or Chinese, or commemorating a person). We are especially circumspect about names not known to the International Cultivar Registrar for a particular genus. We are always grateful to receive information about the naming and origin of any asterisked plant and once we feel reassured about the plant's pedigree, the asterisk will be removed. Of course, many such names will prove to be absolutely correct and buyers can be reassured if they know that the selling nursery takes great care with the naming of its plants. However, although we are able to check that names are valid, correctly styled and spelt, we have no means of checking that nurseries are applying them to the right plant; caveat emptor!

For *Hosta*, *Juniperus* and *Saxifraga*, gardeners and nurseries are often unfamiliar with the species to which a particular cultivar belongs and so these are listed by cultivar first, giving the species in parentheses.

ADJECTIVAL NAMES

Latin adjectival names, whether for species, subspecies, cultivar etc., must agree in gender with the genus, not with the specific name if the latter is a noun (as for *Styrax obassia*, *Lonicera caprifolium* etc.). Thus azaleas have to agree with *Rhododendron*, their true genus (neuter), rather than *Azalea* (feminine). For French cultivar names, adjectives should agree with whatever is being described; for roses, this is almost always la rose (feminine) but on rare occasions le rosier (when describing vegetative characteristics such as climbing forms), *l'oeillet* or *le pompon* (all masculine).

It is often the case that gardeners consider two plants to be distinct but botanists, who know of a whole range of intermediates linking the two, consider them to be the same species. The most notable example is for the rhododendrons, many species of which were 'sunk' in Cullen and Chamberlain's revision. In such cases we have always tried to provide names that retain important horticultural entities, even if not botanically distinct, often by calling the sunk species by a Cultivar-group name, such as *Rhododendron rubiginosum* Desquamatum Group. Cultivar-group names are also used for swarms of hybrids with the same parentage. These were formerly treated as grex names, a term now only used for orchids; thus grex names for lilies, bromeliads and begonias are now styled as Groups. A single clone from the Group may be given the same cultivar name, e.g. 'Polar Bear'. In many cases nursery catalogues do not specify whether the named clone is being offered or other selections from the hybrid swarm and entries are therefore given as e.g. *Rhododendron* Polar Bear Group & cl.

One requirement of the 1995 ICNCP is that cultivar-group names used after 1 January 1996 must have been validly published with a description or reference to a previously published description. Such publication is beyond the scope and purpose of *The RHS Plant Finder*. As principal editor, I may not style the more variable taxa that appear in this and subsequent editions as cultivar-groups unless they have been published elsewhere as Groups. Nevertheless, I still feel it is helpful to gardeners and other plant users to use cultivar names only for those plants that fulfil the Code's requirement that a cultivar be distinct, uniform and stable in its narrow sense. This applies particularly to mixtures and races of seed-raised plants that embrace significant variation, are often not distinct from similar named selections and may be changed in character from year to year. Any new entries that are of this nature are here styled neither as cultivars nor as cultivar-groups but simply as epithets or descriptions, without quotation marks and thus beyond the scope of the new Code. This applies especially to plants described as 'strains' or 'hybrids', though the latter term is sometimes merely a provenance rather than a sign of common parentage. Thus plants here appearing as cultivars with their names in quotes have, as far as I can tell, uniform and predictable characteristics. There are a few cases in which it is difficult to tell whether a 'sunk' species remains horticulturally distinct enough to merit a group name, as for many of the rhododendrons; we would be grateful if users would let us know of any plants that we have 'sunk' in synonymy but which still need to be distinguished by a separate name. In many cases, the plants gardeners grow will be the most extreme variants of a species; although one 'end' of the species will seem to be quite a different plant from the other 'end' to the gardener, the botanist will see them as the outer limits of a continuous range of variation and will give them the same species name. We often hear gardeners complain 'How can these two plants have the same name? They are different!' In such cases, although the botanist may have to 'lump' them under the same name, we will always try to provide an acceptable name to distinguish an important horticultural entity, even if it is not botanically distinct.

TAXONOMIC RANK

The ICBN requires the rank of each infraspecific botanical epithet to be given. In many cases, it is not at all clear whether a colour form shown as, say, alba is a true botanical forma or a cultivar of garden origin. Our inclination here is not to treat such plants as cultivars if they are recorded as being naturally occurring, nor if they embrace considerable variation: forma *alba* would be preferred if a valid publication is recorded, otherwise a previously-published Group name or a simple description such as "white-flowered". In the absence of conclusive evidence we will leave such names styled as they are at present and so some ranks remain to be added in future editions. In many cases, *alba* is assumed without any proof to be the correct name for a white-flowered variant though research often shows that the validly published name is something quite different such as *albiflora, leucantha* or *nivea*.

AUTHOR CITATIONS

Adrian Whiteley has explained the need to cite the author of a particular name if it has been used twice or more by different authors for different plants. This applies equally to botanical epithets and to cultivars, for instance of some fuchsias. Generally the more recent name will be invalid and may be cross-referenced to the plant's first validly published name. Author's names appear directly after the species name and if abbreviated follow Brummitt and Powell's *Authors of Plant Names*; abbreviations are also listed in e.g. Mabberley's *The Plant-Book*. Such names appear in a smaller typeface, and neither in quotes nor in sans serif font, so should not be confused with cultivar names or trade designations.

HYPHENATION

The ICBN ruling on hyphenation (Article 60.9) forbids the use of hyphens after a 'compounding form' (i.e. *albo, pseudo, aureo, neo*). Hyphens are still permitted to divide separate words such as *novae-angliae* or *uva-crispa* and following the Tokyo Congress (1993), after a vowel terminating a compounding form when followed by the same vowel (e.g. *Gaultheria semi-infera, Gentiana sino-ornata*).

TERMINATIONS OF COMMEMORATIVE NAMES

According to Article 60.11 (referring to Recommendation 60C.1) of ICNCP, the genitive form of commemorative names ending in -a is always *-ae*, even if a man is being commemorated (as for *Picea koyamae*). This same article requires that the well known *Crocosmia* be spelt *masoniorum* and not *masonorum* and that *Rosa wichurana* be spelt thus and not *wichuraiana*. However, corrections do not have to be made to epithets derived from personal names already in Greek or Latin or possessing a well-established latinized form. The new edition of the code gives *edithae* (for Editha or Edith) and *murielae* (for Muriela or Muriel) as examples of this category.

The RHS Plant Finder is useful not only as a directory of plant sources but as a 'menu' of plants grown by British gardeners. Such a list is of great value not only to private gardeners; landscapers can use it to check the range of plants they can incorporate in designs; gardeners in countries of the European Union can check which plants they can import by Mail Order; botanists can discover the species grown in Britain, some of them from recorded natural sources; nurserymen can use it to select for propagation first-rate plants that are still not readily available; horticultural authors, who often only want to write about plants the public are able to buy, will find it invaluable. For all such users, *The RHS Plant Finder* can be recommended as a source of standard, up-to-date and reliable nomenclature.

Tony Lord
March 2002

BIBLIOGRAPHY

This is by no means exhaustive but lists some of the more useful works used in the preparation of the *RHS Plant Finder*. Included are websites, all of which were available on line in February/March 2002. The websites of raisers of new plants (not listed here) are also an invaluable source of information. The PBR grant holder will be found in the appropriate PBR source listed below.

GENERAL

Allan, H.H., et al. 2000. *Flora of New Zealand*. Wellington. (5 vols).

Altwegg, A., G. Fortgens & E. Siebler (eds.). 1996. *ISU Yearbook 1965-95*. Windisch, Germany: Internationale Stauden-Union.

Bailey, L.H. & E.Z. Bailey, et al. 1976. *Hortus Third*. New York: Macmillan.

Bean, W.J. 1988. *Trees and Shrubs Hardy in the British Isles*. (8th edn ed George Taylor & D.L. Clarke & Supp. ed. D.L. Clarke). London: John Murray.

Beckett, K (ed.) 1994. *Alpine Garden Society Encyclopaedia of Alpines*. Pershore, Worcs. AGS (2 vols).

Brickell, C. & P. Trehane. 1997. 'The RHS Advisory Panel on Nomenclature and Taxonomy'. *The New Plantsman* 4(2): 115-119.

Brickell, C. (ed.). 1996. *The Royal Horticultural Society A-Z Encyclopedia of Garden Plants*. London: Dorling Kindersley.

Brickell, C. (ed.). 1999. *The RHS New Encyclopedia of Plants and Flowers*. London: Dorling Kindersley.

Brummitt, R.K. (comp.). 1992. *Vascular Plant Families and Genera*. Kew: RBG.

Brummitt, R.K. & C.E. Powell (eds.). 1992. *Authors of Plant Names*. Kew: RBG.

Cave, Y. & V. Paddison. 1999. *The Gardener's Encyclopaedia of New Zealand Native Plants*. Auckland: Godwit.

Chittenden, F.J. & P.M. Synge (eds.). 1956. *The Royal Horticultural Society Dictionary of Gardening*. (2nd ed.). Oxford: Clarendon Press. (4 vols + Supp.).

Clement, E.J. & M.C. Foster. 1994. *Alien Plants of the British Isles*. London: Botanical Society of the British Isles.

Cullen, J. (ed.). 2001. *Handbook of North European Garden Plants*. Cambridge University Press.

Erhardt, W., E. Götz, N. Bödeker & S. Seybold (eds.). 2000. Zander. *Handwörterbuch der Pflanzennamen* (Dictionary of Plant Names). Stuttgart: Ulmer. (16th edn)

Forrest, M. (comp.) & E.C. Nelson (ed.). 1985. *Trees and Shrubs Cultivated in Ireland*. Dublin: Boethius Press for An Taisce.

Goldblatt, P. & J. Manning. 2000. *Cape Plants. A Conspectus of the Cape Flora of South Africa*. South Africa/USA: Nat. Bot. Inst. South Africa/Missouri Bot. Gard.

Graf, A.B. 1963. *Exotica 3. Pictorial Cyclopedia of Exotic Plants*. (3rd ed.). New Jersey: Roehrs.

Graf, A.B. 1986. *Tropica. Color Cyclopedia of Exotic Plants and Trees*. (3rd ed.). New Jersey: Roehrs.

Greuter, W., et al. (eds.). 2000. *International Code of Botanical Nomenclature* (Saint Louis Code). Königstein, Germany: Koeltz Scientific Books.

Greuter, W., R.K. Brummitt, E. Farr, N. Kilian, P.M. Kirk & P.C. Silva (comps.). 1993. NCU-3. *Names in Current Use for Extant Plant Genera*. Königstein, Germany: Koeltz Scientific Books.

Grierson, A.J.C., D.G. Long & H.J. Noltie, et al. (eds.). 2001. *Flora of Bhutan*. Edinburgh: RBG.

Griffiths, M. (ed.). 1994. *The New RHS Dictionary Index of Garden Plants*. London: Macmillan.

Harkness, M.G. 1993. *The Bernard E. Harkness Seedlist Handbook*. (2nd edn). London: Batsford.

Hickman, J.C. (ed.). 1993. *The Jepson Manual. Higher Plants of California*. Berkeley & Los Angeles: Univ. California Press.

'The Hillier Arboretum'. 1978. *The Garden (RHS)* 103: 181.

Hillier Nurseries, (comp.). 1991. *The Hillier Manual of Trees & Shrubs*. (6th ed.). Newton Abbot, Devon: David & Charles.

Hirose, Y. & M. Yokoi. 1998. *Variegated Plants in Colour*. Iwakuni, Japan: Varie Nine.

Hirose, Y. & M. Yokoi. 2001. *Variegated Plants in Colour*. Volume 2. Iwakuni, Japan: Varie Nine Ltd.

Huxley, A., M. Griffiths & M. Levy (eds.). 1992. *The New RHS Dictionary of Gardening*. London: Macmillan.

Jacobsen, H. 1973. *Lexicon of Succulent Plants*. London: Blandford.

Jellitto, L. & W. Schacht. 1990. *Hardy Herbaceous Perennials*. Portland, Oregon: Timber Press. (2 vols).

Krüssmann, G. & M.E. Epp (trans.). 1986. *Manual of Cultivated Broad-leaved Trees and Shrubs*. London: Batsford. (3 vols).

Leslie, A. 1997. 'The RHS Advisory Panel on Nomenclature and Taxonomy: part 2'. *The New Plantsman* 4(3): 170-174.

Leslie, A.C. & J.L. Sharman. 1999. *Monksilver Nursery*.

Leslie, A.C. (trans.). *New Cultivars of Herbaceous Perennial Plants 1985-1990*. Hardy Plant Society.

Mabberley, D.J. 1997. *The Plant-Book. A Portable Dictionary of the Vascular Plants*. (2nd ed.). Cambridge: Cambridge Univ. Press.

Metcalf, L.J. 1987. *The Cultivation of New Zealand Trees and Shrubs*. Auckland: Reed Methuen.

Phillips, R. & M. Rix. 1989. *Shrubs*. London: Pan.

Phillips, R. & M. Rix. 1993. *Perennials*. London: Pan. (2 vols).

Phillips, R. & M. Rix. 1997. *Conservatory and Indoor Plants*. London: Macmillan. (2 vols).

Platt, Karen (comp.). 2000. *The Seed Search*. (4th Edition). Sheffield.

Rehder, A. 1940. *Manual of Cultivated Trees and Shrubs Hardy in North America*. (2nd ed.). New York: Macmillan.

Royal Botanic Gardens Kew. 1997. *Index Kewensis* CD-ROM. Version 2.0. Oxford: Oxford Univ. Press.

Stace, C. 1997. *New Flora of the British Isles*. (2nd ed.). Cambridge: Cambridge University Press.

Stearn, W.T. 1992. *Botanical Latin*. (4th ed.). Newton Abbot, Devon: David & Charles.

Stearn, W.T. 1996. *Stearn's Dictionary of Plant Names for Gardeners*. London: Cassell.

Thomas, G.S. 1990. *Perennial Garden Plants. A Modern Florilegium*. (3rd ed.). London: Dent.

Thomas, G.S. 1992. *Ornamental Shrubs, Climbers & Bamboos*. London: John Murray.

Trehane, P. (comp.). 1989. *Index Hortensis. Volume 1: Perennials*. Wimborne: Quarterjack Publishing.

Trehane, P., et al. 1995. *International Code of Nomenclature for Cultivated Plants*. Wimborne, UK: Quarterjack Publishing.

Tutin, T.G., et al. (ed.). 1993. *Flora Europaea. Volume 1. Psilotaceae to Platanaceae*. (2nd edn). Cambridge Univ. Press.

Tutin, T.G., et al. 1964. *Flora Europaea*. Cambridge University Press. Vols 1-5.

van de Laar, H.J. & P.C. de Jong. 1995. *Naamlijst van Houtige Gewassen*. (List of Names of Woody Plants). Boskoop, Netherlands: Proefstation Voor de Boomkwekerij.

van de Laar, H.J., G. Fortgens, M.H.A. Hoffman & P.C. de Jong. 1995. *Naamlijst van Vaste Planten*. (List of Names of Perennials). Boskoop, Netherlands: Proefstation Voor de Boomkwekerij.

Walter, K.S. & H.J. Gillett (eds.). 1998. 1997 *IUCN Red List of Threatened Plants*. Gland, Switzerland and Cambridge, UK: IUCN.

Walters, S.M. & J. Cullen, et al. (eds.). 2000. *The European Garden Flora*. Cambridge: Cambridge University Press. (6 vols).

GENERAL PERIODICALS

Aquilegia Publishing. *Plants, New, Rare and Unusual. The Hardy Plant*.

Internationale Stauden-Union. *ISU Yearbook*.

Royal Horticultural Society. *The Garden*.

Royal Horticultural Society. *The Plantsman*.

Royal Horticultural Society. *The New Plantsman. The Sport*.

GENERAL WEBSITES

IOPI Provisional Global Plant Checklist. www.bgbm.fu-berlin.de/iopi/gpc/query.htm

Australian Cultivar Registration Authority www.anbg.gov.au/acra/

Australian National Botanic Gardens, (comp.). Australian Plant Names Index. www.anbg.gov.au/anbg/names.html

Australian Plant Breeders' Rights List 2002. www.affa.gov.au

BIOTA of North America Program. 1998. A Synonymized Checklist of the Vascular Flora of the United States, Puerto Rico and the Virgin Isles. www.csdl.tamu.edu/FLORA/b98/check98.htm

Community Plant Variety Office List of Grants and Applications for Plant Variety Rights 2001. www.cpvo.fr/en/default.html

International Plant Names Index. http://www.ipni.org/

Missouri Botanical Garden. Flora Mesoamericana Internet Version (W^3FM) www.mobot.org/fm/intro.html

Morin, N.R. (ed) et al. Flora of North America 2000 http://hua.huh.harvard.edu/fna/index.html

New Ornamentals Database. http://members.tripod.com.~HatchL/nosdex.html

US Patent and Trademark Office. US Patent Full-Text Database www.uspto.gov/patft/index.html

USDA, NRCS. 2001 The Plants Database. Version 3.1 http://plants.usda.gov/

VAST. TROPICOS Database 2002. Missouri Botanical Garden. http://mobot.mobot.org/W3T/Search/vast.html

GENERA

Acacia

Beckett, K.A. 1993. 'Some Australian Wattles in Cultivation'. *The Plantsman* 15(3): 131-47.

Simmons, M.H. 1987. *Acacias of Australia*. (2nd ed.). Melbourne: Nelson.

Acaena

Yeo, P.F. 1973. pp. 193-221 in Green, P.S. (ed.). *Plants: Wild and Cultivated. A Conference on Horticulture and Field Botany*. Middlesex: E.W. Classey.

Acer

Harris, J.G.S. 2000. *The Gardener's Guide to Growing Maples*. Newton Abbot, Devon: David & Charles.

Van Gelderen, C.J. & D.M. Van Gelderen. 1999. *Maples for Gardens. A Color Encyclopaedia*. Portland, Oregon: Timber Press.

Vertrees, J.D. 2001. *Japanese Maples. Momiji and Kaede*. (3rd ed.). Portland, Oregon: Timber Press.

Achillea

Thornton-Wood, S.P. 1999. 'Colour on a Plate'. *The Garden (RHS)* 124(6): 442-447.

Actaea (syn. *Cimicifuga*)
Compton, J. 1992. '*Cimicifuga L. Ranunculaceae.*' *The Plantsman* 14(2): 99-115.
Compton, J. 1992. '*Cimicifuga.* A Bane of a Name for a Fine Plant'. *The Garden (RHS)* 117(11): 504-506.
Compton, J.A. & A. Culham. 2000. 'The Name is the Game'. *The Garden (RHS)* 125(1): 48-52.
Compton, J.A., A. Culham & S.L. Jury. 1998. 'Reclassification of *Actaea* to Include *Cimicifuga* and *Souliea (Ranunculaceae)*'. *Taxon* 47:593-634.
Adiantum
Goudey, C.J. 1985. *Maidenhair Ferns in Cultivation.* Melbourne: Lothian.
Agapanthus
Snoeijer, W. 1998. *Agapanthus. A Review.* Gouda: Wim Snoeijer.
Agapetes
Argent, G.C.G. & P.J.B. Woods. 1986. '*Agapetes (Ericaceae)* in Cultivation'. *The Plantsman* 8(2): 65-85.
Agavaceae
Irish, M. & G. Irish. 2000. *Agaves, Yuccas and Related Plants. A Gardener's Guide.* Portland, Oregon: Timber Press.
Aizoaceae
Burgoyne, P., H. Hartmann, S. Hammer, P. Chesselet, E. van Jaarsveld, C. Klak, G. Smith, B. van Wyk & H. Kurzweil. 1998. *Mesembs of the World.* South Africa: Briza Publications.
Ajuga
Adam, C.G. 1982. 'Ajugas'. *Bull. Alpine Gard. Soc. Gr. Brit.* 50(1):82-84.
Allium
Dadd, R. 1997. 'RHS Trials: Grand Alliums'. *The Garden (RHS)* 122(9): 658-661.
Davies, D. 1992. *Alliums. The Ornamental Onions.* London: Batsford.
Gregory, M., et al. 1998. *Nomenclator Alliorum.* London: RBG, Kew.
Mathew, B. 1996. *A Review of Allium section Allium.* London: RBG, Kew.
Alnus
Ashburner, K. 1986. '*Alnus -* A Survey'. *The Plantsman* 8(3): 170-188.
Androsace
Smith, G. & D. Lowe. 1997. *The Genus Androsace.* Pershore, Worcs.: AGS.
Anemone
Toubøl, U. 1981. 'Clonal Variation in *Anemone nemorosa*'. *The Plantsman* 3(3): 167-174.
Anemone, Japanese
McKendrick, M. 1990. 'Autumn Flowering Anemones'. *The Plantsman* 12(3): 140-151.
McKendrick, M. 1998. 'Japanese Anemones'. *The Garden (RHS)* 123(9): 628-633.
Anthemis
Leslie, A. 1997. 'Focus on Plants: *Anthemis tinctoria*'. *The Garden (RHS)* 122(8): 552-555.

Apiaceae (Umbelliferae)
Ingram, T. 1993. *Umbellifers.* Pershore, Worcs. Hardy Plant Society.
Pimenov, M.G. & M.V. Leonov. 1993. *The Genera of the Umbelliferae.* London: RBG, Kew.
Aquilegia
Munz, P.A. 1946. '*Aquilegia*: the Cultivated and Wild Columbines'. *Gentes Herb.* 7(1): 1-150.
Arecaceae (Palmae, palms)
Jones, D.L. 1995. *Palms Throughout the World.* Chatswood, NSW: Reed Books.
Uhl, N.W. & J. Dransfield. 1987. *Genera Palmarum.* Lawrence, Kansas: Allen Press.
Argyranthemum
Cheek, R. 1993. 'La Belle Marguerite'. *The Garden (RHS)* 118(8): 350-355.
Humphries, C.J. 1976. 'A Revision of the Macaronesian Genus *Argyranthemum*'. *Bull. Brit. Mus. Nat. Hist., Bot.* 5(4): 145-240.
Arisaema
Mayo, S.J. 1982. 'A Survey of the Cultivated Species of *Arisaema*'. *The Plantsman* 3(4): 193-209.
Pradhan, U.C. 1997. *Himalayan Cobra Lilies.* (2nd edn). Kalimpong, West Bengal, India: Primulaceae Books.
Arum
Bown, D. 2000. *Plants of the Arum Family.* (2nd ed.). Portland, Oregon: Timber Press.
Boyce, P. 1993. *The Genus Arum.* London: HMSO.
Asplenium
Rickard, M. 1997. '*Asplenium scolopendrium*'. *The Garden (RHS)* 122(2): 86-89.
Aster
Picton, P. 1999. *The Gardener's Guide to Growing Asters.* Newton Abbott: David & Charles.
Ranson, E.R. 1946. *Michaelmas Daisies and Other Garden Asters.* London: John Gifford.
Astilbe
Noblett, H. 2001. *Astilbe.* Cumbria: Henry Noblett.
Astrantia
Bishop, K. 2000. 'Into the Limelight'. *The Garden (RHS)* 125(5): 350-353.
Auricula
Baker, G. & P. Ward. 1995. *Auriculas.* London: Batsford.
Bamboo
Bell, M. 2000. *The Gardener's Guide to Growing Bamboos.* Newton Abbot: David & Charles.
Chao, C.S. 1989. *A Guide to Bamboos Grown in Britain.* RBG, Kew.
Ohrnberger, D. 1999. *The Bamboos of the World. Annotated Nomenclature and Literature of the Species and the Higher and Lower Taxa.* Amsterdam: Elsevier.
Begonia
Ingles, J. 1990. *American Begonia Society listing of Begonia cultivars.* Revised Edition Buxton Checklist. American Begonia Soc.
Thompson, M.L. & E.J. Thompson. 1981. *Begonias. The Complete Reference Guide.* New York: Times Books.

Betula

Ashburner, K. & T. Schilling. 1985. '*Betula utilis* and its Varieties'. *The Plantsman* 7(2): 116-125.

Ashburner, K.B. 1980. '*Betula* - A Survey'. *The Plantsman* 2(1): 31-53.

Hunt, D. (ed.). 1993. *Betula: Proceedings of the IDS* Betula *Symposium 1992*. Richmond, Surrey: International Dendrology Society.

Bougainvillea

Choudhury, B. & B. Singh (comps.). 1981. *The International Bougainvillea Check List*. New Delhi: Indian Agricultural Research Institute.

Iredell, J. 1990. *The Bougainvillea Grower's Handbook*. Brookvale, Australia: Simon & Schuster.

Iredell, J. 1994. *Growing Bougainvilleas*. London: Cassell.

MacDaniels, L.H. 1981. 'A study of cultivars in *Bougainvillea* (*Nyctaginaceae*)'. *Baileya* 21(2):77-100.

Singh, B., R.S. Panwar, S.R. Voleti, V.K. Sharma & S. Thakur. 1999. *The New International Bougainvillea Check List*. (2nd ed.). New Delhi: Indian Agricultural Research Institute.

Swithinbank, A. 1995. '*Bougainvillea*'. *The Garden* (*RHS*) 120(10): 634-637.

Bromeliaceae

Beadle, D.A. (comp.). 1998. *The Bromeliad Cultivar Registry*. The Bromeliad Society International.

Luther, H.E. & E. Sieff. 1991. *An Alphabetical List of Bromeliad Binomials*. Orlando, Florida: Bromeliad Society.

Rauh, W. 1979. *Bromeliads for Home, Garden and Greenhouse*. Blandford, Dorset: Blandford Press.

Brugmansia

Shaw, J.M.H. 1998. 'Variation in *Brugmansia sanguinea*'. *The New Plantsman* 5(1): 48-60.

Shaw, J.M.H. 1999. 'Nomenclature Notes on *Brugmansia*'. *The New Plantsman* 6(3): 148-151.

Buddleja

Maunder, M. 1987. 'Notes on Tender Species of *Buddleja*'. *The Plantsman* 9(2): 65-80.

Bulbs

Bryan, J.E. 1989. *Bulbs* Vols 1 & 2. Bromley, Kent: Christopher Helm.

Du Plessis, N. & G. Duncan. 1989. *Bulbous Plants of Southern Africa*. Cape Town: Tafelberg.

Grey-Wilson, C. & B. Mathew. 1981. *Bulbs*. London: Collins.

Leeds, R. 2000. *The Plantfinder's Guide to Early Bulbs*. Newton Abbot, Devon: David & Charles.

Phillips, R., M. Rix & B. Mathew (ed.). 1981. *The Bulb Book*. London: Ward Lock Ltd.

Royal General Bulbgrowers Association. 1991. *International Checklist for Hyacinths and Miscellaneous Bulbs*. Hillegom, The Netherlands: KAVB.

Buxus

Batdorf, L.R. 1995. *Boxwood Handbook*. Boyce, VA. The American Boxwood Society.

Braimbridge, E. 1994. 'Some Boxwoods in Cultivation'. *The Plantsman* 15: 236-254.

Callistemon

Mitchem, C.M. 1993. 'The Beautiful Bottlebrushes'. *The Plantsman* 15(1): 29-41.

Calluna see **Heathers**

Calochortus

Martinelli, S. 1995. 'Kaleidoscopic *Calochortus*'. *Bull. Alpine Gard. Soc. Gr. Brit.* 63(1): 71-92.

Martinelli, S. 1995. 'Kaleidoscopic *Calochortus*'. *Bull. Alpine Gard. Soc. Gr. Brit.* 63(2):180-199.

Camellia

Savige, T.J. (comp.). 1993. *The International Camellia Register* (2 vols + 1997 Suppl.). The Int. Camellia Soc.

Campanula

Lewis, P. & M. Lynch. 1998. *Campanulas. A Gardeners Guide*. (2nd edn) London. Batsford.

Canna

Cooke, I. 2001. *The Plantfinder's Guide to Cannas*. Newton Abbot, Devon: David & Charles.

Cooke, I. 1999. 'Psychedelic Wonders'. *The Garden* (*RHS*) 124(5): 364-369.

Hayward, K. 2000. *Canna Handbook*. Farnborough, Hants: Hart Canna.

Carnivorous Plants

D'Amato, P. 1998. *The Savage Garden*. Berkeley, USA: Ten Speed Press.

Pietropaulo, J. & P. Pietropaulo. 1986. *Carnivorous Plants of the World*. Oregon, USA: Timber Press.

Schlauer, J. (comp.). *Carnivorous Plant Database. 2001* www2.labs.agilent.com/bot/cp_home

Slack, A. 1988. *Carnivorous Plants*. (Revd edn). Sherborne, Dorset: Alphabooks.

Carpinus

Rushforth, K. 1985. 'Hornbeams and Hop Hornbeams'. *The Plantsman* 7(3): 173-191.

Rushforth, K. 1986. 'Keys to *Carpinus* and *Ostrya*'. *The Plantsman* 8(4): 249-256.

Wright, D. 1985. 'Notes on *Carpinus* and *Ostrya*'. *The Plantsman* 7(4): 212-216.

Caryopteris

Pattison, G. 1989. '*Caryopteris* x *clandonensis*'. *The Plantsman* 11(1): 16-19.

Cassiope

Blake, F.S. 1985. 'Cassiopes for Everyone'. *Bull. Alpine Gard. Soc. Gr. Brit.* 53(1): 61-65.

Starling, B. 1989. 'Cassiopes'. *The Plantsman* 11(2): 106-116.

Stone, M. 1998. 'The Askival Hybrid Cassiopes'. *Bull. Alpine Gard. Soc. Gr. Brit.* 66(4): 484-492.

Ceanothus

Gardiner, J.M. 1997. '*Ceanothus*'. *The Garden* (*RHS*) 122(5): 308-311.

Cercidiphyllum

Dosmann, M.S. 1999. 'Katsura a Review of *Cercidiphyllum* in Cultivation and in the Wild'. *The New Plantsman* 6(1): 52-62.

Cestrum

Beckett, K.A. 1987. '*Cestrum* in Cultivation'. *The Plantsman* 9(3): 129-132.

Chaenomeles
Jewell, D. 1998. 'Fiery Flowers of Spring'. *The Garden (RHS)* 123(2): 90-93.
Weber, C. 1963. 'Cultivars in the Genus *Chaenomeles*'. *Arnoldia (Jamaica Plain)* 23(3): 17-75.
Chrysanthemum (Dendranthema)
Brummitt, D. 1997. '*Chrysanthemum* once again'. *The Garden (RHS)* 122(9): 662-663.
Gosling, S.G. (ed.). 1964. *British National Register of Chrysanthemums*. Whetstone, London: Nat. Chrysanthemum Soc.
British National Register of Names of Chrysanthemums Amalgamated Edition 1964-1996 & Supp. 1996-2000. Tamworth, Staffordshire: National Chrysanthemum Soc.
Cimicifuga see *Actaea*
Cistus
Page, R.G. 1991. '*Cistus* Notes'. *The Plantsman* 13(3): 143-156.
Page, R.G. 1998. 'The *Cistus* and *Halimium* Hybrids of Eric Sammons'. *The New Plantsman* 5(4):219-229.
Page, R.G. 2000. 'Sun Worshippers'. *The Garden (RHS)* 125(6): 458-463.
Citrus
Davies, F.S. & L.G. Albrigo. 1994. *Citrus*. Wallingford, Oxon: Cab International.
Saunt, J. 1990. *Citrus Varieties of the World*. Norwich: Sinclair.
Cladrastis
Spongberg, S. & J. Ma. 1997. *Cladrastis: a Historic and Taxonomic Overview*. IDS Yearbook 1996.
Clematis
Evison, R. 1998. *The Gardener's Guide to Growing Clematis*. Newton Abbot: David & Charles.
Fisk, J. 1989. *Clematis, the Queen of Climbers*. London: Cassell.
Fretwell, B. 1989. *Clematis*. London: Collins.
Grey-Wilson, C. 2000. *Clematis the Genus*. London: Batsford.
Johnson, M. 2001. *The Genus Clematis*. Södertälje, Sweden: Magnus Johnsons Plantskola AB of Bengt Sundström.
Lloyd, C. & T. Bennett. 1989. *Clematis*. (Revd edn). London: Viking.
Snoeijer, W. (comp.). 1991. *The Clematis Index*. Boskoop, Netherlands: Fopma.
Snoeijer, W. 1996. *Checklist of Clematis Grown in Holland*. Boskoop, Netherlands: Fopma.
Codonopsis
Grey-Wilson, C. 1990. 'A Survey of *Codonopsis* in Cultivation'. *The Plantsman* 12(2): 65-99.
Grey-Wilson, C. 1995. '*Codonopsis convolvulacea* and its Allies'. *The New Plantsman* 2(4): 213-225.
Matthews, Y.S. 1980. 'The Genus *Codonopsis*'. *Bull. Alpine Gard. Soc. Gr. Brit.* 48: 96-108.
Conifers
den Ouden, P. & B.K. Boom. 1965. *Manual of Cultivated Conifers*. The Hague: Martinus Nijhof.

Farjon, A. 1998. *World Checklist and Bibliography of Conifers*. London: RBG, Kew.
Krüssmann, G. & M.E. Epp (trans.). 1985. *Manual of Cultivated Conifers*. London: Batsford.
Lewis, J. & A.C. Leslie. 1987. *The International Conifer Register*. Part 1. *Abies* to *Austrotaxus*. 1989 Part 2. *Belis* to *Pherosphaera*, Excluding the Cypresses. 1992 Part 3. The Cypresses. 1998 Part 4 *Juniperus*. London. RHS.
Welch, H.J. 1979. *Manual of Dwarf Conifers*. New York: Theophrastus.
Welch, H.J. 1991. *The Conifer Manual*. Volume 1. Dordrecht, The Netherlands: Kluwer Academic Publishers.
Welch, H.J. 1993. *The World Checklist of Conifers*. Bromyard, Herefordshire: Landsman's Bookshops Ltd.
Coprosma
Hutchins, G. 1995. 'Notes on Cultivated Australian and New Zealand Coprosmas'. *The New Plantsman* 2(1): 12-37.
Cornus
Flanagan, M. 1998. 'The Dogwood Days of Winter'. *The Garden (RHS)* 123(1): 16-19.
Howard, R.A. 1961. 'Registration Lists of Cultivar Names in *Cornus* L. *Arnoldia (Jamaica Plain)* 21(2): 9-18.
Corokia
Hutchins, G. 1994. 'The Genus *Corokia*'. *The Plantsman* 15(4): 225-235.
Corydalis
Lidén, M. & H. Zetterlund. 1997. *Corydalis*. Worcs. AGS.
Mathew, B. 2001. RHS trials: Earning their Spurs (*Corydalis*). *The Garden (RHS)* 126(3): 184-187.
Rix, E.M. 1993. *The Plantsman* 15(3): 129-30.
Corylopsis
Wright, D. 1982. '*Hamamelidaceae*: a Survey of the Genera in Cultivation'. *The Plantsman* 4(1): 29-53.
Corylus
Crawford, M.1995. *Hazelnuts: Production and Culture*. Dartington, Devon: Agroforestry Research Trust.
Game, M. 1995. 'Champion of the Cobnut'. *The Garden (RHS)* 120(11): 674-677.
Cotoneaster
Fryer, J. & B. Hylmö. 1998. 'Seven New Species of *Cotoneaster* in Cultivation'. *The New Plantsman* 5(3): 132-144.
Fryer, J. & B. Hylmö. 2001. 'Captivating Cotoneasters'. *The New Plantsman* 8(4): 227-238.
Fryer, J. 1996. 'Undervalued Versatility. *Cotoneaster*'. *The Garden (RHS)* 121(11): 709-715.
Crassulaceae
Eggli, U. & H. Hart. 1995. *Evolution and Systematics of the Crassulaceae*. Leiden, Netherlands: Backhuys.
Crocosmia
Dunlop, G. 1999. 'Bright Sparks'. *The Garden (RHS)* 124(8): 599-605.
Kostelijk, P.J. 1984. '*Crocosmia* in Gardens'. *The Plantsman* 5(4): 246-253.

Crocus
Jacobsen, N., J. van Scheepen & M. Ørgaard. 1997. 'The *Crocus chrysanthus - biflorus* Cultivars'. *The New Plantsman* 4(1): 6-38.
Mathew, B. 1982. *The Crocus. A Review of the Genus Crocus (Iridaceae)*. London: Batsford.

Cyclamen
Grey-Wilson, C. 1997. *Cyclamen. A Guide for Gardeners, Horticulturists & Botanists*. London: Batsford.

Cypripedium
Cribb, P. 1997. *The Genus Cypripedium*. Portland, Oregon: Timber Press.

Cyrtanthus
Holford, F. 1989. '*Cyrtanthus* in the Cool Greenhouse'. *The Plantsman* 11(2): 170-175.

Dahlia
RHS & R. Hedge (comps.). 1969. *Tentative Classified List and International Register of Dahlia Names 1969*, and Supp. 1-12. London: RHS.

Daphne
Brickell, C. & R. White. 2000. 'A Quartet of New Daphnes'. *The New Plantsman* 7(1): 6-18.
Brickell, C. 2000. '*Daphne*. Part 2: Henderson's Daphne'. *The New Plantsman* 7(2): 114-122.
Brickell, C.D. & B. Mathew. 1976. *Daphne. The Genus in the Wild and in Cultivation*. Woking, Surrey: Alpine Garden Society.
Grey-Wilson, C. (ed.). 2001. *The Smaller Daphnes*. Pershore, Worcs. AGS.

Daphniphyllum
Boyce, P. 1999. '*Daphniphyllum*'. *Curtis's Botanical Magazine* 16(4): 267-272.

Delphinium
A Tentative Checklist of Delphinium Names. 1949. London: RHS.
A Tentative Check-List of Delphinium Names. Addendum to the 1949 Tentative Check-list of Delphinium Names. 1970. London: RHS.
Leslie, A.C. *The International Delphinium Register Supplement 1993-94* (1995), *1994-95* (1996), *1996-97* (1998), *1997-98* (1999), *1998-99* (2000). The Delphinium Society Year Book 1995-2000. London: RHS.
Leslie, A.C. 1996. *The International Delphinium Register Cumulative Supplement 1970 - 1995*. London: RHS.

Dendranthema see **Chrysanthemum**

Dianthus
Bird, R. 1994. *Border Pinks*. London: Batsford.
Galbally, J. & E. Galbally. 1997. *Carnations and Pinks for Garden and Greenhouse*. Portland, Oregon: Timber Press.
Leslie, A.C. *The International Dianthus Register 1983-2000*. (2nd edn & Supps 1-17). London: RHS.

Diascia
Benham, S. 1987. '*Diascia*: A survey of the species in cultivation'. *The Plantsman* 9(1): 1-17.
Harrison, H. 1996. '*Diascia* (*Scrophulariaceae*)'. *Hardy Plant* 18(1): 41-47.

Lord, T. 1996. '*Diascia* on trial'. *The Garden* (*RHS*) 121(4): 192-194.

Dierama
Hilliard, O.M. & B.L. Burtt. 1990. '*Dierama*, a neglected genus'. *The Plantsman* 12(2): 106-12.
Hilliard, O.M. & B.L. Burtt. 1991. *Dierama. The Harebells of Africa*. Johannesburg; London: Acorn.

Dionysia
Grey-Wilson, C. 1989. *The Genus Dionysia*. Woking, Surrey: AGS.

Dodecatheon
Mitchem, C. 1991. 'A review of the genus *Dodecatheon*'. *The Plantsman* 13(3): 157-170.

Douglasia
Mitchell, B. 1999. 'Celebrating the Bicentenary of David Douglas: a Review of *Douglasia* in Cultivation'. *The New Plantsman* 6(2): 101-108.

Dracaena
Bos, J.J., P. Graven, W.L.A. Hetterscheid & J.J. van de Wege. 1992. 'Wild and Cultivated *Dracaena fragrans*'. *Edinburgh Journal of Botany* 49(3): 311-331.

Echinacea
Vernon, J. 1999. 'Power Flowers'. *The Garden* (*RHS*) 124(8): 588-593.

Epimedium (**Berberidaceae**)
Barker, D.G. 1996. *Epimediums and Other Herbaceous Berberidaceae*. Pershore, Worcs. The Hardy Plant Society.
Stearn, W.T. 1937. '*Epimedium* & *Vancouveria*, A Monograph'. *J. Linn. Soc., Bot.* 51: 409-535.
White, R. 1996. '*Epimedium*: Dawning of a New Area'. *The Garden* (*RHS*) 121(4): 208-214.

Episcia
Dates, J.D. 1993. *The Gesneriad Register 1993. Check List of Names with Descriptions of Cultivated Plants in the Genera Episcia & Alsobia*. Galesburg, Illinois: American Gloxinia & Gesneriad Soc.

Erica see also **Heathers**
Baker, H.A. & E.G.H. Oliver. 1967. *Heathers in Southern Africa*. Cape Town: Purnell.
Schumann, D., G. Kirsten & E.G.H. Oliver. 1992. *Ericas of South Africa*. Vlaeberg, S. Africa: Fernwood Press.

Erodium
Bacon, L. 1990. *Bull. Alpine Gard. Soc. Gr. Brit.* 58(1): 65-83.
Clifton, R. 1994. *Geranium Family Species Checklist. Part 1 Erodium.* (4th ed.). The Geraniaceae Group.
Leslie, A.C. 1980. 'The Hybrid of *Erodium corsicum* With *Erodium reichardii*'. *The Plantsman* 2:117-126.
Victor, D.X. (comp.). 2000. *Erodium Register of Cultivar Names*. The Geraniaceae Group.

Eryngium
Grant, M. 2000. 'Showing their Metal'. *The Garden* (*RHS*) 125(7): 534-539.

Erythronium
Mathew, B. 1992. 'A Taxonomic and Horticultural

Review of *Erythronium* L. (*Liliaceae*)'. *J. Linn. Soc., Bot.* 109: 453-471.

Mathew, B. 1998. 'The genus *Erythronium*'. *Bull. Alpine Gard. Soc. Gr. Brit.* 66(3): 308-321.

Eucalyptus

Kelly, S. 1989. *Eucalyptus*. (3rd edn, 2 vols). South Yarra, Australia: Viking O'Neil.

Eucomis

Compton, J. 1990. '*Eucomis* L'Heritier'. *The Plantsman* 12(3): 129-139.

Eucryphia

Wright, D. 1983. '*Eucryphia, Hoheria* and *Plagianthus*. A review of the genus'. *The Plantsman* 5(3): 167-185.

Euonymus

Brown, N. 1996. 'Notes on cultivated species of *Euonymus*'. *The New Plantsman* 3(4): 238-243.

Lancaster, C.R. 1982. '*Euonymus* in Cultivation - Addendum'. *The Plantsman* 4: 61-64, 253-254.

Lancaster, R. 1981. 'An Account of *Euonymus* in Cultivation and its Availability in Commerce'. *The Plantsman* 3(3): 133-166.

Euphorbia

Turner, R. 1995. *Euphorbias. A Gardeners Guide*. London: Batsford.

Witton, D. 2000. *Euphorbias*. Pershore, Worcs: Hardy Plant Society.

Fagus

Dönig, G. 1994. *Die Park-und Gartenformen der Rotbuche Fagus sylvatica* L. Erlangen, Germany: Verlag Gartenbild Heinz Hansmann.

Wyman, D. 1964. *Registration List of Cultivar Names of Fagus* L. *J. Arnold Arbor.* 24(1): 1-8.

Fascicularia

Nelson, E.C. & G. Zizka. 1997. '*Fascicularia* (*Bromeliaceae*): Which Species are Cultivated and Naturalized in Northwestern Europe'. *The New Plantsman* 4(4): 232-239.

Nelson, E.C., G. Zizka, R. Horres & K. Weising. 1999. 'Revision of the Genus *Fascicularia* Mez (*Bromeliaceae*)'. *Botanical Journal of the Linnean Society* 129(4): 315-332.

Ferns

Checklist of World Ferns. 2001. http://homepages.caverock.net.nz/~bj/fern/

Johns, R.J. 1996. *Index Filicum. Supplementum Sextum pro Annis 1976-1990*. RBG, Kew.

Johns, R.J. 1997. *Index Filicum. Supplementum Septimum pro Annis 1991-1995*. RBG, Kew.

Jones, D.L. 1987. *Encyclopaedia of Ferns*. Melbourne: Lothian.

Kaye, R. 1968. *Hardy Ferns*. London: Faber and Faber.

Rickard, M.H. 2000. *The Plantfinder's Guide to Garden Ferns*. Newton Abbot, Devon: David and Charles.

Rush, R. 1984. *A Guide to Hardy Ferns*. London: British Pteridological Society.

Ficus carica

Hendy, J. 1997. 'A Taste of Paradise'. *The Garden (RHS)* 122(9): 636-640.

Filipendula

Barnes, P.G. 1998. 'Confusion in Cultivated Meadowsweets' (*Filipendula* Miller). *The New Plantsman* 5(3): 145-153.

Fragaria

Day, D. (ed.). 1993. *Grower Digest 3: Strawberries*. (Revd edn). London: Nexus.

Fremontodendron

McMillan-Browse, P. 1992. 'Fremontias. California's finest Shrubs?' *The Plantsman* 14(1): 41-44.

Fritillaria

Mathew, B., et al. 2000. '*Fritillaria* issue'. *Bot. Mag.* 17(3): 145-185.

Pratt, K. & M. Jefferson-Brown. 1997. *The Gardener's Guide to Growing Fritillaries*. Newton Abbot: David & Charles.

Turrill, W.B. & J.R. Sealy. 1980. 'Studies in the Genus *Fritillaria* (*Liliaceae*)'. *Hooker's Icones Plantarum* Vol 39 (1 & 2). RBG, Kew.

Fruit

Catalogue of Cultivars in the United Kingdom National Fruit Collection. 1997. Kent, UK: Brogdale Horticultural Trust.

Index of the Bush Fruit Collection at the National Fruit Trials 1987. Faversham, Kent: MAFF.

Bowling, B.L. 2000. *The Berry Grower's Companion*. Portland, Oregon: Timber Press.

Hogg, R. 1884. *The Fruit Manual*. (5th Ed.) London: Journal of Horticulture Office.

Fuchsia

Bartlett, G. 1996. *Fuchsias - A Colour Guide*. Marlborough, Wilts: Crowood Press.

Boullemier, Leo.B. (comp.). 1991. *The Checklist of Species, Hybrids and Cultivars of the Genus Fuchsia*. London, New York, Sydney: Blandford Press.

Boullemier, Leo.B. (comp.). 1995. *Addendum No. 1 to the 1991 Checklist of Species, Hybrids and Cultivars of the Genus Fuchsia*. Dyfed, Wales: British Fuchsia Soc.

Goulding, E. 1995. *Fuchsias: The Complete Guide*. London: Batsford.

Johns, E.A. 1997. *Fuchsias of the 19th and early 20th century*. Kidderminster, Worcs: British Fuchsia Soc.

Nijhuis, M. 1994. 1000 *Fuchsias*. London: Batsford.

Nijhuis, M. 1996. 500 *More Fuchsias*. London: Batsford.

Van Veen, G. *2002 Gelderse Fuchsia Info-site*. http://home-1.worldonline.nl/~veenvang/A-homepage.htm

Galanthus

Davis, A.P., B. Mathew (ed.) & C. King (ill.). 1999. *The Genus Galanthus. A Botanical Magazine Monograph*. Oregon: Timber Press.

Gaultheria (incl. Pernettya)

Middleton, D.J. 1990. '*Pernettya* or *Gaultheria*?' *The Plantsman* 12.

Middleton, D.J. 1991. 'Infrageneric Classification of Genus *Gaultheria*'. *J. Linn. Soc., Bot.* 106(3): 229-258.

Middleton, D.J. 1991. '*Pernettya* or *Gaultheria*'. *The Plantsman* 13.

Gentiana

Bartlett, M. 1975. *Gentians*. Dorset: Blandford Press.

Halda, J.J. 1996. *The Genus Gentiana*. Dobr,: Sen.

Wilkie, D. 1950. *Gentians*. (2nd ed Rev). London: Country Life.

Geranium

Bath, T. & J. Jones. 1994. *The Gardener's Guide to Growing Hardy Geraniums*. Newton Abbot, Devon: David & Charles.

Clifton, R.T.F. 1995. *Geranium Family Species Check List* Part 2. *Geranium*. (4th Edition, issue 2). Dover: The Geraniaceae Group.

Jones, J., et al. 2001. *Hardy Geraniums for the Garden*. (3rd Edition, Revd and Enlarged). Pershore, Worcs: Hardy Plant Society.

Victor, D.X. 2000. *Geranium. Register of Cultivar Names*. The Geraniaceae Group. www.hardygeraniums.com/register_of_cultivar_names

Yeo, P.F. 1992. *Hardy Geraniums*. (2nd ed.). Kent: Croom Helm.

Gesneriaceae

Dates, J.D. 1986. *The Gesneriad Register 1986. Check List of Names with Descriptions of Intergeneric Hybrids in the Tribe Gloxinieae*. Sugar Grove, Illinois: American Gloxinia & Gesneriad Soc.

Dates, J.D. 1987. *The Gesneriad Register 1987. Check List of Names with Descriptions of Cultivated Plants in the Genera Bucinellina, Columnea, Dalbergaria, Pentadenia, Trichantha also Intergeneric Hybrids*. Galesburg, Illinois: American Gloxinia & Gesneriad Soc.

Dates, J.D. 1990. *The Gesneriad Register 1990. Check List of Names with Descriptions of Cultivated Plants in the Genus Aeschynanthus*. Galesburg, Illinois: American Gloxinia & Gesneriad Soc.

Gladiolus

British Gladiolus Society List of Cultivars Classified for Show Purposes 1994. Mayfield, Derbyshire: British Gladiolus Society.

British Gladiolus Society List of European Cultivars Classified for Exhibition Purposes 1997 & 1998. Mayfield, Derbyshire: British Gladiolus Society.

British Gladiolus Society List of New Zealand Cultivars Classified for Exhibition Purposes 1997 & 1998. Mayfield, Derbyshire: British Gladiolus Society.

British Gladiolus Society List of North American Cultivars Classified for Exhibition Purposes 1997 & 1998. Mayfield, Derbyshire: British Gladiolus Society.

Goldblatt, P. & J. Manning. 1998. *Gladiolus in Southern Africa*. Vlaeberg, South Africa: Fernwood Press.

Goldblatt, P. 1996. *Gladiolus in Tropical Africa*. Oregon: Timber Press.

Gleditsia

Santamour, F.S. & A.J. McArdle. 1983. 'Checklist of Cultivars of Honeylocust (*Gleditsia triacanthos* L.)'. *Journal of Arboriculture* 9: 271-276.

Gramineae see **Poaceae**

Grevillea

Olde, P. & N. Marriott. 1995. *The Grevillea Book* (3). Kenthurst, NSW: Kangaroo Press.

Haemanthus

Snijman, D. 1984. 'A Revision of the Genus *Haemanthus*'. *J. S. African Bot.* (Supp) 12:

Hamamelis

Coombes, A.J. 1996. 'Winter Magic. Introduction to Witch Hazels'. *The Garden* (*RHS*) 121(1): 28-33.

Lane, C. 1998. '*Hamamelis* in Small Spaces'. *The Garden* (*RHS*) 123(1): 38-41.

Strand, C. 1998. 'Asian Witch Hazels and their Hybrids: A History of *Hamamelis* in Cultivation'. *The New Plantsman* 5(4): 231-245.

Heathers see also **Calluna, Erica**

Nelson, E.C. & D.J. Small (eds.). 2000. *International Register of Heather Names. Volume 1 Hardy Cultivars & European Species.* Parts 1-4. The Heather Society.

Small, D. & A. Small (comps.). 1992. *Handy Guide to Heathers. Descriptions and Suppliers of Over 1000 Varieties*. Denbeigh Heather Nurseries.

Underhill, T. 1990. *Heaths & Heathers. The Grower's Encyclopedia*. Newton Abbot: David & Charles.

Hebe

Chalk, D. 1988. *Hebes & Parahebes*. Bromley, Kent: Christopher Helm.

Hutchins, G. 1997. *Hebes: Here and There. A monograph on the Genus Hebe*. Caversham, Berks: Hutchins & Davies.

Hedera

McAllister, H. 1988. 'Canary & Algerian Ivies'. *The Plantsman* 10(1): 27-29.

McAllister, H.A. & A. Rutherford. 1990. '*Hedera helix & H. hibernica* in the British Isles'. *Watsonia* 18:7-15.

Rose, P.Q. 1996. *The Gardener's Guide to Growing Ivies*. David & Charles.

Rutherford, A., H. McAllister & R.R. Mill. 1993. 'New Ivies from the Mediterranean Area and Macaronesia'. *The Plantsman* 15(2): 115-128.

Hedychium

Schilling, T. 1982. 'A Survey of Cultivated Himalayan and Sino-Himalayan *Hedychium* Species'. *The Plantsman* 4: 129-149.

Spencer-Mills, L. 1996. 'Glorious *Hedychium*'. *The Garden (RHS)* 121(12): 754-759.

Helichrysum

Hilliard, O.M. & B.L. Burtt. 1987. *The Garden* (*RHS*) 112(6):276-77.

Heliconia

Berry, F. & W.J. Kress. 1991. *Heliconia. An Identification Guide*. Washington: Smithsonian Institution Press.

Helleborus
Mathew, B. 1989. *Hellebores.* Woking: AGS.
Rice, G. & E. Strangman. 1993. *The Gardener's Guide to Growing Hellebores.* Newton Abbot, Devon: David and Charles.

Hemerocallis
Erhardt, W. 1988. *Hemerocallis Daylilies.* London: Batsford.
Grenfell, D. 1998. *The Gardener's Guide to Growing Daylilies.* Newton Abbot: David & Charles.
Kitchingman, R.M. 1985. 'Some Species and Cultivars of *Hemerocallis*'. *The Plantsman* 7(2):68-89.
Monroe, W.E. (comp.). 1973. *Hemerocallis Check List July 1 1957 to July 1 1973.*
1983. *Hemerocallis Check List July 1 1973 to July 1 1983.* American Hemerocallis Soc.
Munson, R.W. 1993. *Hemerocallis - The Daylily.* Timber Press.
Petit, T.L. & J.P. Peat. 2000. *The Color Encyclopaedia of Daylilies.* Portland, Oregon: Timber Press.
Shield, J. 1997. *Daylily Database.* http://galagarden.com/release31.html
Webber, S. (ed.). 1988. *Daylily Encyclopaedia.* Damascus, Maryland: Webber Gardens.

Herbs see also *Lavandula, Origanum*
Page, M. & W. Stearn. *Culinary Herbs. A Wisley Handbook.*
Phillips, R. & N. Foy. 1990. *Herbs.* London: Pan.

Hibiscus
Beers, L. & J. Howie. 1990. *Growing Hibiscus.* (2nd edn). Kenthurst, Australia: Kangaroo Press.
Chin, H.F. 1986. *The Hibiscus: Queen of Tropical Flowers.* Kuala Lumpur: Tropical Press Sdn. Bhd.
Segall, B. 1995. '*Hibiscus syriacus*'. *The Garden (RHS)* 120(8): 487-491.
Walker, J. 1999. *Hibiscus.* London: Casell.

Hippeastrum
KAVB. 1980. *Alfabetische Lijst van de in Nederland in Cultuur Zijnde Amaryllis (Hippeastrum) Cultivars.* Hillegom, Netherlands: Koninklijke Algemeene Vereeniging Voor Bloembollencultur.
Read, V.M. 1998. 'Blooming Bold'. *The Garden (RHS)* 123(10): 734-737.

Hosta
Grenfell, D. 1990. *Hosta.* London: Batsford.
Grenfell, D. 1993. *Hostas.* Pershore, Worcs: Hardy Plant Society.
Grenfell, D. 1996. *The Gardener's Guide to Growing Hostas.* Newton Abbot: David & Charles.
Hammelman, T. *2002 Giboshi.com Hosta Database.* www.giboshi.com
Schmid, W.G. 1991. *The Genus Hosta.* London: Batsford.

Hoya
Innes, C. 1988. 'The Genus *Hoya*'. *The Plantsman* 10(3): 129-40.

Hyacinthus
Clark, T. 2000. 'Focus on Plants: Treasures of the East (Hyacinths)'. *The Garden (RHS)* 125(9): 672-675.
Stebbings, G. 1996. 'Heaven Scent'. *The Garden (RHS)* 121(2): 68-72.

Hydrangea
Church, G. 1999. *Hydrangeas.* London: Cassell.
Haworth-Booth, M. 1975. *The Hydrangeas.* London: Garden Book Club.
Lawson-Hall, T. & R. Brian. 1995. *Hydrangeas. A Gardener's Guide.* London: Batsford.
Mallet, C. 1992 & 1994. *Hydrangeas. Species and Cultivars.* Vols 1&2. Varengeville Sur Mer: Centre d'Art Floral.

Hypericum
Lancaster, R. & N. Robson. 1997. 'Focus on Plants. Bowls of Beauty'. *The Garden (RHS)* 122(8): 566-571.

Ilex
Andrews, S. 1983. 'Notes on some *Ilex × altaclerensis* clones'. *The Plantsman* 5(2): 65-81, and 1984 'More notes on clones of *Ilex × altaclerensis*.' *The Plantsman* 6(3): 157-166. Erratum vol.6 p.256.
Andrews, S. 1985. 'Holly berries of a varied hue'. *The Garden (RHS)* 110(11): 518-522.
Andrews, S. 1994. 'Hollies with a difference'. *The Garden (RHS)* 119(12): 580-583.
Dudley, T.R. & G.K. Eisenbeiss. 1992. *International Checklist of cultivated Ilex.* Part 1 *Ilex opaca.* 1992 Part 2 *Ilex crenata.* Washington: US Dept. of Agriculture.
Galle, F.C. 1997. *Hollies: the genus Ilex.* Portland, Oregan: Timber Press.

Impatiens
Grey-Wilson, C. 1983. 'A survey on *Impatiens* in cultivation'. *The Plantsman* 5: 86-102.
Grey-Wilson, C. 1997. 'Focus on plants. Impetuous balsams'. *The Garden (RHS)* 122(8): 583-587.

Incarvillea
Grey-Wilson, C. 1994. 'A survey of *Incarvillea* in cultivation'. *The New Plantsman* 1(1): 36-52.
Grey-Wilson, C. 1998. 'A new look at *Incarvillea* subgenus *Pteroscleris*'. *The New Plantsman* 5(2): 76-98.

Iochroma
Shaw, J.M.H. 1998. 'A review of *Iochroma* in cultivation'. *The New Plantsman* 5(3): 154-192.

Iridaceae
Innes, C. 1985. *The World of Iridaceae. A comprehensive record.* Ashington, Sussex: Holly Gate.

Iris
American Iris Society Database 2000. www.irisregister.com/
Hoog, M.H. 1980. 'Bulbous irises (sect. *Reticulata, Juno, Xiphium*)'. *The Plantsman* 2(3): 141-64
Mathew, B. 1981. *The Iris.* London: Batsford.
Mathew, B. 1993. 'The Spuria Irises'. *The Plantsman* 15(1): 14-25.
Service, N. 1990. '*Iris unguicularis*'. *The Plantsman* 12(1): 1-9.

Stebbings, G. 1997. *The Gardener's Guide to Growing Iris*. Newton Abbot: David & Charles.

The Species Group of the British Iris Society, (ed.). 1997. *A Guide to Species Irises. their Identification and Cultivation*. Cambridge: Cambridge Univ. Press.

Kalmia

Jaynes, R.A. 1997. *Kalmia. Mountain Laurel and Related Species*. Oregon: Timber Press.

Pullen, A. 1997. '*Kalmia latifolia*'. *The Garden* (*RHS*) 122(6): 400-403.

Kniphofia

Grant-Downton, R. 1997. 'Notes on *Kniphofia thomsonii* in Cultivation and in the Wild'. *The New Plantsman* 4(3): 148-156.

Taylor, J. 1985. '*Kniphofia* - A Survey'. *The Plantsman* 7(3): 129-160.

Kohleria

Dates, J.D. (ed.) & F.N. Batcheller (comp.). 1985. *The Gesneriad Register 1985. Check List of Names with Descriptions of Cultivated Plants in the Genus Kohleria*. Lincoln Acres, California: American Gloxinia and Gesneriad Soc.

Lachenalia

Duncan, G.D. 1988. *The Lachenalia Hand Book*.

Lantana

Howard, R.A. 1969. 'A Check List of Names Used in the Genus *Lantana*'. *J. Arnold Arbor.* 29(11): 73-109.

Larix

Horsman, J. 1988. 'A Survey of the Species of *Larix*'. *The Plantsman* 10(37):

Lathyrus

Norton, S. 1994. 'All the Colours of the Rainbow'. *The Garden (RHS)* 119(5): 216-221.

Norton, S. 1994. 'Some Observations on *Lathyrus rotundifolius*'. *The New Plantsman* 1(2): 78-83.

Norton, S. 1996. 'National Collection of *Lathyrus*'. The National Plant Collections Directory 1996: 41-43.

Lavandula

McNaughton, V. 2000. *Lavender. the Grower's Guide*. Woodbridge, Suffolk: Garden Art Press.

Tucker, A.O. & K.J.W. Hensen. 1985. 'The Cultivars of Lavender and Lavandin (*Labiatae*)'. *Baileya* 22(4): 168-177.

Upson, T. 1999. 'Deep Purple'. *The Garden* (*RHS*) 124(7): 524-529.

Lavatera

Miller, D.M. 1999. 'Mallow Moments'. *The Garden* (*RHS*) 124(9): 676-679.

Legumes

ILDIS. *International Legume Database and Information Service*. Version 5.0, 2000. www.ildis.org

Lewis, G.P. 1987. *Legumes of Bahia*. London: RBG, Kew.

Lock, J.M. & J. Heald. 1994. *Legumes of Indo-China*. London: RGB, Kew.

Lock, J.M. & K. Simpson. 1991. *Legumes of West Asia*. London: RGB Kew.

Lock, J.M. 1989. *Legumes of Africa: A Checklist*. London: RGB, Kew.

Roskov, Yu.R., A.K. Sytin & G.P. Yakovlev. 1996. *Legumes of Northern Eurasia*. London: RGB, Kew.

Leptospermum

1963. 'Check List of *Leptospermum* Cultivars'. Journal of the Royal New Zealand Inst. of Hort. 5(5): 224-30.

Dawson, M. 1997. 'A History of *Leptospermum scoparium* in Cultivation - Discoveries from the Wild'. *The New Plantsman* 4(1): 51-59.

Dawson, M. 1997. 'A History of *Leptospermum scoparium* in Cultivation - Garden Selections'. *The New Plantsman* 4(2): 67-78.

Leucojum

Elliott, J. 1992. '*Leucojum*'. *The Plantsman* 14(2): 70-79.

Lewsia

Davidson, B.L.R. 2000. *Lewisias*. Portland, Oregon: Timber Press.

Elliott, R. 1978. *Lewisias*. Woking: AGS.

Mathew, B. 1989. *The Genus Lewisia*. Bromley, Kent: Christopher Helm.

Liliaceae sensu lato

Mathew, B. 1989. 'Splitting the *Liliaceae*'. *The Plantsman* 11(2): 89-105.

Lilium

Leslie, A.C. *The International Lily Register 1982-2000*. (3rd Ed & Supps 1-18). London: RHS.

Liriodendron

Andrews, S. 1992. *IDS Year Book 1992*: 15-19. London.

Lonicera

Bradshaw, D. 1991. 'Climbing Honeysuckles (*Lonicera*)'. *The Plantsman* 13(2): 106-110.

Bradshaw, D. 1995. 'Know your Honeysuckles'. *The Garden* (*RHS*) 120(7): 406-411.

Wright, D. 1983. 'Climbing Honeysuckles'. *The Plantsman* 4(4): 236-252.

Magnolia

Callaway, D.J. 1994. *Magnolias*. London: B.T. Batsford Ltd.

Frodin, D.G. & R. Govaerts. 1996. *World Checklist and Bibliography of Magnoliaceae*. London: RBG, Kew.

Gardiner, J. 2000. *Magnolias. A Gardeners' Guide*. Portland, Oregon: Timber Press.

Hunt, D. (ed.). 1998. *Magnolias and their allies*. IDS and The Magnolia Society.

Langford, L.W. (ed.). 1994. *Check List of the Cultivated Magnolias*. The Magnolia Soc.

Malus

Crawford, M. 1994. *Directory of Apple Cultivars*. Devon: Agroforestry Research Trust.

Fiala, J.L. 1994. *Flowering Crabapples. The Genus Malus*. Portland, Oregon: Timber Press.

Morgan, J. & A. Richards. 1993. *The Book of Apples*. London: Ebury Press.

Parfitt, B. 1965. *Index of the Apple Collection at the National Fruit Trials*. Faversham, Kent: MAFF.

Rouèche, A. 2000. *Les Crets Fruits et Pomologie.*
  http://perso.club-internet.fr/lescrets/index2
Spiers, V. 1996. *Burcombes, Queenies and Colloggetts.*
  St Dominic, Cornwall: West Brendon.
Taylor, H.V. 1948. *The Apples of England.* London:
  Crosby Lockwood.
Meconopsis
Cobb, J.L.S. 1989. *Meconopsis.* Bromley, Kent:
  Christopher Helm.
Cox, P. 1996. 'Further Notes on *Meconopsis
  integrifolia* and its Allies'. *The New Plantsman* 3(2):
  80-83.
Grey-Wilson, C. 1992. 'A Survey of the Genus
  Meconopsis in cultivation'. *The Plantsman* 14(1): 1-33.
Grey-Wilson, C. 1996. '*Meconopsis integrifolia,* the
  Yellow Poppywort and its Allies'. *The New
  Plantsman* 3(1):22-39.
Mimulus
Silverside, A.J. 1994. *Mimulus: 180 Years of
  Confusion in The Common Ground of Wild &
  Cultivated Plants* (Perry & Ellis). Cardiff: Nat.
  Mus. of Wales.
Moraea
Goldblatt, P. 1986. *The Moraeas of Southern Africa.*
  Kirstenbosch: Nat. Bot. Gards.
Narcissus
Blanchard, J.W. 1990. *Narcissus - a Guide to Wild
  Daffodils.* Woking, Surrey: AGS.
Kington, S. (comp.). 1998. *The International
  Daffodil Register and Classified List 1998* (3rd edn
  & Supp. 1-3, 1998-2000). London: RHS.
  www.rhs.org.uk/research.
Throckmorton, T.D. (ed.). 1985. *Daffodils to Show
  & Grow and Abridged Classified List of Daffodil
  Names.* Hernando, Mississippi: RHS and
  American Daffodil Soc.
Nematanthus
Arnold, P. 1978. *The Gesneriad Register 1978. Check
  List of Nematanthus.* American Gloxinia and
  Gesneriad Soc.
Nerium
Pagen, F.J.J. 1987. *Oleanders. Nerium L. and the
  Oleander Cultivars* Agricultural Univ Wageningen
  Papers.
Toogood, A. 1997. '*Nerium oleander'. The Garden
  (RHS)* 122(7): 488-491.
Nothofagus
Hill, R.S. & J. Read. 1991. 'A Revised Infrageneric
  Classification of *Nothofagus* (*Fagaceae*)'. *Botanical
  Journal of the Linnean Society* 105(1): 37-72.
Nymphaea
International Water Lily Society. 1993. *Identification
  of Hardy Nymphaea.* Stapely Water Gardens Ltd.
Knotts, K. & R. Sacher (comps.). 2000. *Provisional
  Check List of Names/Epithets of Nymphaea L.*
  International Waterlily & Water Gardening
  Society. Cocoa Beach, Florida.
Swindells, P. 1983. *Waterlilies.* London: Croom Helm.

Olearia
Heads, M. 1998. 'Biodiversity in the New Zealand
  divaricating tree daisies: *Olearia* sect. nov.
  (*Compositae*)'. *Botanical Journal of the Linnean
  Society* 127(3): 239-285.
Orchidaceae
Cribb, P. & C. Bailes. 1989. *Hardy Orchids.* Bromley,
  Kent: Christopher Helm.
Hunt, P.F. & D.B. Hunt. 1996. *Sander's List of
  Orchid Hybrids: Addendum 1991-1995.* London:
  RHS.
The International Orchid Register.
  http://www.rhs.org.uk/research
Origanum (herbs)
Paton, A. 1994. 'Three membranous-bracted species
  of *Origanum'. The Kew Magazine* 11(3): 109-117.
White, S. 1998. *Origanum. The herb marjoram and
  its relatives.* Surrey: NCCPG.
Osteospermum
Cheek, R. 1997. '*Osteospermum'. The Garden (RHS)*
  122(7): 506-511, 511.
Oxalis
Erskine, P. 1998. '*Oxalis enneaphylla* and its cousins'.
  Bull. Alpine Gard. Soc. Gr. Brit. 66(3): 345-352.
Paeonia
Harding, A. & R.G. Klehm. 1993. *The Peony.*
  London: Batsford.
Haw, S.G. 1991. *The Plantsman* 13(2): 94-97.
Haworth-Booth, M. 1963. *The Moutan or Tree
  Peony.* London: Garden Book Club.
Kessenich, G.M. 1976. *Peonies.* (Variety Check List
  Pts 1-3). American Peony Society.
Osti, G.L. 1999. *The Book of Tree Paeonies.* Turin:
  Umberto Allemandi & C.
Page, M. 2000. 'A cultural revolution'. *The Garden
  (RHS)* 125(5): 336-339.
Rogers, A. 1995. *Peonies.* Portland, Oregon: Timber
  Press.
Wang, L., et al. 1998. *Chinese Tree Peony.* Beijing:
  China Forestry Publishing House.
Palmae, palms (see *Arecaceae*)
Papaver
Grey-Wilson, C. 1998. 'Oriental glories' *The Garden
  (RHS)* 123(5): 320-325.
Grey-Wilson, C. 2000. *Poppies. The poppy family in
  the wild and in cultivation.* London: Batsford.
Parahebe
Heads, M. 1994. *Botanical Journal of the Linnean
  Society* 115(1): 65-89.
Passiflora
Vanderplank, J. 1996. *Passion Flowers.* (2nd ed.).
  London, England: Cassell.
Pelargonium
Anon. 1978. *A checklist and register of Pelargonium
  cultivar names.* Part one A-B. Australian
  Pelargonium Society.
Abbott, P.G. 1994. *A Guide to Scented Geraniaceae.*
  Angmering, West Sussex: Hill Publicity Services.

Bagust, H. 1988. *Miniature and Dwarf Geraniums.* London: Christopher Helm.

Clifford, D. 1958. *Pelargoniums.* London: Blandford Press.

Key, H. 2000. *1001 Pelargoniums.* London: Batsford.

Miller, D. 1996. *Pelargonium. A gardener's guide to the species and cultivars and hybrids.* London: Batsford.

Van der Walt, J.J.A., et al. 1977. *Pelargoniums of South Africa.* (1-3). Kistenbosch: Nat Bot Gards.

Penstemon

Elliott, J. & S. Thornton-Wood. 1997. 'Dwarf Penstemon'. *The Garden (RHS)* 122(9): 652-655.

Lindgren, D.T. & B. Davenport. 1992. *List and description of named cultivars in the genus Penstemon* (1992). University of Nebraska.

Lord, T. 1994. 'Peerless penstemons'. *The Garden (RHS)* 119(7): 304-309.

Nold, R. 1999. *Penstemons.* Portland, Oregon: Timber Press.

Way, D. & P. James. 1998. *The Gardener's Guide to Growing Penstemons.* Newton Abbott: David & Charles.

Philadelphus

Wright, D. 1980. '*Philadelphus*'. *The Plantsman* 2(2): 104-116.

Phlomis

Mann Taylor, J. 1998. *Phlomis. The Neglected Genus.* Wisley: NCCPG.

Phlox

Stebbings, G. 1999. 'Simply Charming'. *The Garden (RHS)* 124(7):518-521.

Wherry, E.T. 1955. *The Genus Phlox.* Morris Arboretum Monographs III.

Phormium

Heenan, P.B. 1991. *Checklist of Phormium Cultivars.* Royal New Zealand Inst. of Hort.

McBride-Whitehead, V. 1998. 'Phormiums of the Future'. *The Garden (RHS)* 123(1): 42-45.

Phygelius

Coombes, A.J. 1988. '*Phygelius* Cultivars'. *The Plantsman* 9(4): 233-246.

Pieris

Bond, J. 1982. '*Pieris* - A Survey'. *The Plantsman* 4(2): 65-75.

Wagenknecht, B.L. 1961. 'Registration Lists of Cultivar Names in the Genus *Pieris* D. Don'. *Arnoldia (Jamaica Plain)* 21(8): 47-50.

Pinus

Muir, N. 1992. 'Some Notes on Nut Pines'. *The Plantsman* 14(2): 80-98.

Plectranthus

Miller, D. & N. Morgan. 2000. 'Focus on Plants: a New Leaf'. *The Garden (RHS)* 125(11): 842-845.

Shaw, J.M.H. 1999. 'Notes on the Identity of Swedish Ivy and Other Cultivated *Plectranthus*'. *The New Plantsman* 6(2): 71-74.

Pleione

Cribb, P. & I. Butterfield. 1999. *The Genus Pleione.* (2nd edn). London: RBG Kew.

Poaceae (Gramineae, grasses)

Clayton, W.D. & S.A. Renvoize. 1986. *Genera Graminum. Grasses of the World.* London: HMSO.

Darke, R. 1999. *The Colour Encyclopedia of Ornamental Grasses.* London: Weidenfeld & Nicolson.

Grounds, R. 1998. *The Plantfinder's Guide to Ornamental Grasses.* Newton Abott, Devon: David & Charles.

Ryves, T.B., E.J. Clement & M.C. Foster. 1996. *Alien Grasses of the British Isles.* London: Botanical Society of the British Isles.

Podocarpus

Hutchins, G. 1991. 'New Zealand and Australian *Podocarpus*'. *The Plantsman* 13(2): 98-105.

Podophyllum

Shaw, J.M.H. 1999. 'New Taxa, Combinations and Taxonomic Notes on *Podophyllum*'. *The New Plantsman* 6(3): 158-165.

Shaw, J.M.H. 2000. 'A Taxonomic Revision of *Podophyllum* in the Wild and in Cultivation'. Part 1, *The New Plantsman* 7(1): 30-41. Part 2, *The New Plantsman* 7(2): 103-113. Part 3, *The New Plantsman* 7(3): 142-159. Part 4, *The New Plantsman* 7(4): 220-235.

Polemonium

Nichol-Brown, D. 1997. *Polemonium.* Teeside: Trimdon.

Polypodium

Leslie, A.C. 1993. '*Polypodium vulgare*'. *The Garden (RHS)* 118(10): 450-452.

Potentilla

Brearley, C. 1987. 'The Shrubby Potentillas'. *The Plantsman* 9(2): 90-109.

Brearley, C. 1991. 'Herbaceous Potentillas'. *The Plantsman* 13(1): 42-53.

Brearley, C. 1992. 'Potentillas, a Survey'. *Bull. Alpine Gard. Soc. Gr. Brit.* 60(3), 60(4): 321-328, 428-435.

Davidson, C.G. & L.M. Lenz. 1989. 'Experimental Taxonomy of *Potentilla fruticosa*'. *Canadian Journal of Botany* 67(12): 3520-3528.

Davidson, C.G., R.J. Enns & S. Gobin. 1994. *A Checklist of Potentilla fruticosa: the Shrubby Potentillas.* Morden, Manitoba: Agriculture & Agri-Food Canada Research Centre.

Primula

Fenderson, G.K. 1986. *A Synoptic Guide to the Genus Primula.* Lawrence, Kansas: Allen Press.

Green, R. 1976. *Asiatic Primulas.* Woking: AGS.]

Halda, J.J. 1992. *The Genus Primula in Cultivation and the Wild.* Denver, Colorado: Tethys Books.

Hecker, W.R. 1971. *Auriculas & Primroses.* London: Batsford.

Richards, J. 1993. *Primula.* Batsford.

Smith, G.F., B. Burrow & D.B. Lowe. 1984. *Primulas of Europe and America.* Woking: AGS.

Wemyss-Cooke, T.J. 1986. *Primulas Old and New.* Newton Abbot: David & Charles.

Primula allionii

Archdale, B. & D. Richards. 1997. *Primula allionii Forms and Hybrids.* Nat. Auricula & Primula Soc.

Primula auricula hort.

Baker, G. *Double Auriculas.* Nat. Auricula & Primula Soc.

Hawkes, A. 1995. *Striped Auriculas.* National Auricula & Primula Society, Midland & West Section.

Nicholle, G. 1996. *Border Auriculas.* National Auricula & Primula Soc.

Robinson, M.A. 2000. *Auriculas for Everyone.* Lewes: Guild of Master Craftsmen Publications.

Telford, D. 1993. *Alpine Auriculas.* Nat. Auricula & Primula Soc., Midland & West.

Ward, P. 1991. *Show Auriculas.* Nat. Auricula & Primula Soc., Midland & West.

Proteaceae

Rebelo, T. 1995. *Proteas. A field guide to the Proteas of Southern Africa.* Vlaeberg: Fernwood Press/Nat. Bot. Inst.

Prunus

1986. *Index of the Cherry Collection at the National Fruit Trials 1986.* Faversham, Kent: MAFF.

Bultitude, J. *Index of the Plum Collection at the National Fruit Trials.* Faversham, Kent: MAFF.

Crawford, M. 1996. *Plums.* Dartington, Devon: Agroforestry Research Trust.

Crawford, M. 1997. *Cherries: Production and Culture.* Dartington, Devon: Agroforestry Research Trust.

Grubb, N.H. 1949. *Cherries.* London: Crosby Lockwood.

Jacobsen, A.L. 1992. *Purpleleaf Plums.* Portland, Oregon: Timber Press.

Jefferson, R.M. & K.K. Wain. 1984. *The Nomenclature of Cultivated Flowering Cherries (Prunus), The Satu-Zakura Group.* Washington: USDA.

Kuitert, W. 1999. *Japanese Flowering Cherries.* Oregon: Timber Press.

Smith, M.W.G. 1978. *Catalogue of the Plums at the National Fruit Trials.* Faversham, Kent: MAFF.

Taylor, H.V. 1949. *The Plums of England.* London: Crosby Lockwood.

Pulmonaria

Hewitt, J. 1994. *Pulmonarias.* Pershore, Worcs: The Hardy Plant Society.

Hewitt, J. 1999. 'Well spotted'. *The Garden (RHS)* 124(2):98 - 103.

Pyracantha

Egolf, D.R. & A.O. Andrick. 1995. *A Checklist of Pyracantha Cultivars.* Agricultural Research Service.

Pyrus

Crawford, M. 1996. *Directory of Pear Cultivars.* Totnes, Devon: Agroforestry Research Institute. 100 pp.

Parfitt, B. 1981. *Index of the Pear Collection at the National Fruit Trials.* Faversham, Kent: MAFF.

Smith, M.W.G. 1976. *Catalogue of the British Pear.* Faversham, Kent: MAFF.

Quercus

Avalos, S.V. 1995. *Contribución al concimiento del género* Quercus (Fagaceae) *en el estado de Guerrero, Mexico.* Mexico City: Facultad de Ciencias, UNAM.

Miller, H.A. & S.H. Lamb. 1985. *Oaks of North America.* Happy Camp, California: Naturegraph.

Mitchell, A. 1994. 'The Lucombe Oaks'. *The Plantsman* 15(4):216-224.

Ranunculus

Carter, J.R.L. 1996. 'Bright as a Buttercup'. *The Garden (RHS)* 121(2): 90-95.

Raoulia

Hutchins, G. 1980. 'Raoulias'. *The Plantsman* (2):100-103.

Rhododendron

Argent, G., G. Fairweather & K. Walter. 1996. *Accepted Names in Rhododendron Section Vireya.* RBG, Edinburgh.

Argent, G., J. Bond, D. Chamberlain, P. Cox & A. Hardy. 1997. *The Rhododendron Handbook 1998. Rhododendron Species in Cultivation.* London: RHS.

Chamberlain, D.F. & S.J. Rae. 1990. 'A Revision of *Rhododendron* IV. Subgenus *Tsutsusi*'. *Edinburgh Journal of Botany* 47(2).

Chamberlain, D.F. 1982. 'A revision of *Rhododendron* II. Subgenus *Hymenanthes*'. *Notes Roy. Bot. Gard. Edinburgh* 39(2).

Cox, P. & K. Cox. 1988. *Encyclopedia of Rhododendron hybrids.* London: Batsford.

Cullen, J. 1980. 'A revision of *Rhododendron* I. Subgenus *Rhododendron* sections *Rhododendron* and *Pogonanthum*'. *Notes Roy. Bot. Gard. Edinburgh* 39(1).

Davidian, H.H. 1982-1992. *The Rhododendron Species* Vols I-IV. London: Batsford.

Galle, F.C. 1985. *Azaleas.* Portland, Oregon: Timber Press.

Lee, F.P. 1958. *The Azalea Book.* New York: D. Van Nostrand.

Leslie, A. (comp.). 1980. *The Rhododendron Handbook 1980.* London: RHS.

Leslie, A. *The International Rhododendron Register. Checklist of Rhododendron Names Registered 1989 1994.* (& Supps 28-39). London: RHS.

Salley, H.E. & H.E. Greer. 1986. *Rhododendron Hybrids. A guide to their origins.* London: Batsford.

Tamura, T. (ed.). 1989. *Azaleas in Kurume.* Kurume, Japan: International Azalea Festival '89.

Rhus

Coombes, A.J. 1994. 'Cut-leaved sumachs'. *The New Plantsman* 1(2): 107-113.

Ribes

Crawford, M. 1997. *Currants and Gooseberries: Production and Culture.* Dartington, Devon: Agroforestry Research Trust.

Romneya

McMillan Browse, P. 1989. '*Romneya*'. *The Plantsman* 11(2):121-24

Rosa

Austin, D. 1996. *English Roses.* (2nd Ed). London: Conran Octopus.

Beales, P. 1992. *Roses.* London: Harvill.

Beales, P., T. Cairns, W. Duncan, G. Fagan, W. Grant, K. Grapes, P. Harkness, K. Hughes, J. Mattock & D. Ruston. 1998. *Botanica's Roses. The Encyclopedia of Roses.* UK: Grange Books.

Cairns, T. (ed.). 2000. *Modern Roses XI. The World Encyclopedia of Roses.* London: Academic Press.

Dickerson, B.C. 1992. *The Old Rose Advisor.* Portland, Oregon: Timber Press.

Dobson, B.R. & P. Schneider (comps.). 1996. *Combined Rose List.* Ohio, USA

Haw, S.G. 1996. 'Notes on Some Chinese and Himalayan Rose Species of Section *Pimpinellifoliae'. The New Plantsman* 3(3):143-146.

Help Me Find Roses www.helpmefind.com/sites/rrr/rosetest.

McCann, S. 1985. *Miniature Roses.* Newton Abbot: David & Charles.

Phillips, R. & M. Rix. 1988. *Roses.* London: Macmillan.

Phillips, R. & M. Rix. 1993. *The Quest for the Rose.* London: BBC Books.

Thomas, G.S. 1995. *The Graham Stuart Thomas Rose Book.* London: John Murray.

Verrier, S. 1996. *Rosa gallica.* Balmain, NSW: Florilegium.

Rosaceae

Phipps, J.B., K.R. Robertson, P.G. Smith & J.R. Rohrer. 1990. 'A Checklist of the Subfamily *Maloideae* (*Rosaceae*)'. *Canadian Journal of Botany* 68: 2209-2269.

Rosularia

Eggli, U. 1988. 'A Monographic Study of the Genus *Rosularia'. Bradleya* (Suppl.) 6: 1-118.

Saintpaulia

Moore, H.E. 1957. *African Violets, Gloxinias and their Relatives. A Guide to the Cultivated Gesneriads.* New York: Macmillan.

Salix

Newsholme, C. 1992. *Willows. The Genus Salix.* London: Batsford.

Salvia

Clebsch, B. 1997. *A Book of Salvias.* Oregon: Timber Press.

Compton, J. 1994. 'Mexican Salvias in Cultivation'. *The Plantsman* 15(4):193-215.

Saxifraga

Bland, B. 2000. *Silver Saxifrages.* Pershore, Worcs: AGS.

Horný, R., K.M. Webr, J. Byam-Grounds & E. Zoulova (ill.). 1986. *Porophyllum Saxifrages.* Stamford, Lincolnshire: Byam-Grounds Publications.

Kohlein, F. 1984. *Saxifrages and Related Genera.* London: Batsford.

McGregor, M. (ed.). 2000. *Saxifrage 2000.* Driffield, E. Yorks: Saxifrage Society.

McGregor, M. 1995. *Saxifrages: The Complete Cultivars & Hybrids.* (1st ed.).

McGregor, M. & W. Harding (comps.). 1998. *Saxifrages: The Complete List of Species.* Driffield, E Yorks.: The Saxifrage Society.

Stocks, A. 1995. *Saxifragaceae.* Hardy Plant Society.

Webb, D.A. & R.J. Gornall. 1989. *Saxifrages of Europe.* Bromley, Kent: Christopher Helm.

Schisandra

Whiteley, A.C. 1997. 'The Genus *Schisandra* in Cultivation'. *The New Plantsman* 4(2):88-97.

Sedum

Evans, R.L. 1983. *Handbook of Cultivated Sedums.* Motcombe, Dorset: Ivory Head Press.

Stephenson, R. 1994. *Sedum. The Cultivated Stonecrops.* Portland, Oregon: Timber Press.

Sempervivum

Miklánek, M. *List of Cultivars* v15.1. *Sempervivum* and *Jovibarba.* 2002. http://miklanek.tripod.com/MCS

Mitchell, P.J. (comp.). 1985. *International Cultivar Register for Jovibarba, Rosularia, Sempervivum.* Volume One. Burgess Hill: Sempervivum Soc.

Shortia

Barnes, P.G. 1990. 'A Summary of the Genus *Shortia'. The Plantsman* 12(1): 23-34, 34.

Sinningia

Dates, J.D. 1988. *The Gesneriad Register 1988. Check List of Names with Descriptions of Cultivated Plants in the Genus Sinningia.* Galesburg, Illinois: American Gloxinia and Gesneriad Society, Inc.

Skimmia

Brown, P.D. 1980. 'The Genus *Skimmia* as Found in Cultivation'. *The Plantsman* 1(4): 224-259.

Solenostemon

Pedley, W.K. & R. Pedley. 1974. *Coleus - A Guide to Cultivation and Identification.* Edinburgh: Bartholemew.

Sophora

Hutchins, G. 1993. 'The New Zealand Sophoras'. *The Plantsman* 15(1): 1-13.

Sorbus

McAllister, H. 1984. 'The Aucuparia Section of *Sorbus'. The Plantsman* 6(4): 248-255.

McAllister, H. 1996. '*Sorbus*: Mountain Ash and its Relatives'. *The Garden* (*RHS*) 121(9): 561-567.

Snyers d'Attenhoven, C. 1999. '*Sorbus* Lombart hybrids'. pp. 76-81 in *Belgische Dendrologie.* Belgium.

Wright, D. 1981. '*Sorbus* - A Gardener's Evaluation'. *The Plantsman* 3(2): 65-98.

Streptocalyx

Innes, C. 1993. *The Plantsman* 15(2): 73-81.

Streptocarpus

Arnold, P. 1979. *The Gesneriad Register 1979: Check List of Streptocarpus.* Binghamton, New York: American Gloxinia & Gesneriad Soc.

Succulents
Eggli, U. & N. Taylor. 1994. *List of Names of Succulent Plants other than Cacti Published 1950-92.* London: RBG, Kew.
Grantham, K. & P. Klaassen. 1999. *The Plantfinder's Guide to Cacti and Other Succulents.* Newton Abbot, Devon: David & Charles.
Syringa
Fiala, J.L. 1988. *Lilacs. The Genus Syringa.* London: Christopher Helm.
Vrugtman, F. 2000. *International Register of Cultivar Names in the Genus Syringa L.* (Oleaceae). Hamilton, Ontario: RBG
Tilia
Muir, N. 1983. 'A Survey of the Genus *Tilia*'. *The Plantsman* 5(4): 206-242.
Muir, N. 1988. 'Additional Notes on Hybrid Limes (*Tilia*)'. *The Plantsman* 10(2): 104-127.
Tillandsia
Kiff, L.F. 1991. *A Distributional Checklist of the Genus Tillandsia.* Encino, California: Botanical Diversions.
Tricyrtis
Mathew, B. 1984. 'A Review of the Genus *Tricyrtis*'. *The Plantsman* 6(4): 193-224.
Trillium
Case, F.W.J. & R.B. Case. 1997. *Trilliums.* Portland, Oregon: Timber Press.
Jacobs, D.L. & R.L. Jacobs. 1997. *American Treasures. Trilliums in Woodland Garden.* Eco-Gardens. Decatur, Georgia.
Tulbaghia
Benham, S. 1993. '*Tulbaghia.* A Survey of the Species in Cultivation'. *The Plantsman* 15(?): 89-110.
Tulipa
van Scheepen, J. (ed.). 1996. *Classified List and International Register of Tulip Names.* Hillegom, The Netherlands: Koninklijke Algemeene Vereeniging Voor Bloembollencultuur.
Ulmus
Green, P.S. 1964. 'Registratration of Cultivar Names in *Ulmus*'. *Arnoldia* (*Jamaica Plain*) 24: 41-80.
Umbelliferae see **Apiaceae**
Vegetables
Official Journal of the EC. Common Catalogue of Varieties of Vegetable Species C167A. 1999 (21st edn). Luxembourg: Office for Official Publications of the EC.

Phillips, R. & M. Rix. 1993. *Vegetables.* London: Pan.
Veratrum
Mathew, B. 1989. 'A Review of *Veratrum*'. *The Plantsman* 11(1): 34-61.
Verbascum
Johnstone, V. & C. Wilson. 2000. 'Dreaming Spires'. *The Garden* (*RHS*) 125(8): 608-613.
Viola
Coombes, R.E. 1981. *Violets.* London: Croom Helm.
Farrar, R. 1989. *Pansies, Violas & Sweet Violets.* Reading: Hurst Village Publishing.
Fuller, R. 1990. *Pansies, Violas & Violettas. The Complete Guide.* Marlborough: The Crowood Press.
Perfect, E.J. 1996. *Armand Millet and his Violets.* High Wycombe: Park Farm Press.
Zambra, G.L. 1950. *Violets for Garden and Market.* (2nd Ed). London: Collingridge.
Vitis
Pearkes, G. 1989. *Vine Growing in Britain.* London: Dent.
Robinson, J. 1989. *Vines, Grapes and Wines.* London: Mitchell Beazley.
Watsonia
Goldblatt, P. 1989. *The Genus Watsonia.* South Africa: Nat. Bot. Gards.
Weigela
Howard, R.A. 1965. 'A Check List of Cultivar Names in *Weigela*'. *Arnoldia* (*Jamaica Plain*) 25: 49-69.
Wisteria
Valder, P. 1995. *Wisterias. A Comprehensive Guide.* Australia: Florilegium.
Zantedeschia
Toogood, A. & A. Mattin. 1998. 'Variations on a Theme'. *The Garden* (*RHS*) 123(3): 176-179.
Zauschneria
Raven, P.H. 1977. 'Generic and Sectional Delimitation in *Onagraceae*, Tribe *Epilobieae*'. *Ann. Missouri Bot. Gard.* 63(2): 326-340.
Robinson, A. 2000. 'Focus on Plants: Piping Hot'. *The Garden* (*RHS*) 125(9): 698-699.
Zelkova
Ainsworth, P. 1989. 'The Genus *Zelkova*'. *The Plantsman* 11(?): 80-86.
Hunt, D. (ed.). 1995. *International Dendrology Society Yearbook 1994.*
Muir, N. 1991. 'The Genus *Zelkova* - Extra Notes'. *The Plantsman* 13(2): 125-126.

INTERNATIONAL PLANT FINDERS

GERMANY

Erhardt, A. & W. (comp.). (4th ed. 2000). *PPP-Index, The European Plant Finder.* ISBN-3-8001-3183-8. 100,000 plants and seeds available from 2,000 European retail and wholesale nurseries. CD-ROM only. Orders: The Plant Press, 10 Market Street, Lewes, East Sussex, BN7 2NB, UK. T (01273) 476151. E-mail john@plantpress.com £39.99. Or Verlag Eugen Ulmer, PO Box 70 05 61, D-70574 Stuttgart. T +49 711-4507-121. E-mail: info@ulmer.de DM 98. Website: www.ulmer.de

ITALY

Feroni, F. C., & Volta, T. (comp.) & Mondadori, G. (ed.). (1996). *Il Cercapiante.* ISBN 88-374-1366-1. 15,000 plants from 400 nurseries including 100 specialist suppliers; 100 European nurseries; all Italian botanical and professional Associations, all Italian Garden Clubs, wide Bibligraphy. Orders: Corso Magenta 55, 20123 Milano. T. +39 (02) 4331 3367. F +39 (02) 460 823. E-mail: gardenia@edgm.it

NETHERLANDS

Terra (2000/2001). *Plantenvinder voor de lage landen.* ISBN 90-6255-936-0. Approx. 50,000 plants and 150 nurseries. Orders: Uitgeverij Terra, POB 1080, 7230 AB Warnsveld, Netherlands. T +31 (575) 581310. F +31 (575) 525242. E-mail: info@terraboek.nl; website: www.terraboek.nl. €11.30.

NEW ZEALAND

Gaddum, M. (comp). (1999). *Gaddum's Plant Finder 2000.* ISBN 0 473 06210 0. 30,000 plants and seeds from 200 nurseries with retail outlets. Common names included and indexed. Additional plants sourced at the website. NZ$ 39.95 plus postage overseas.

Gaddum M. (comp.) (2001). *The Trade Plant Finder 2001.* No ISBN. 35,000 plants and seeds from 310 nurseries. Wholesale nurseries easily identified. NZ$ 85 + postage overseas.

Orders: New Zealand Plant Finder, PO Box 2237, Gisborne, NZ. F +64 (6) 862 3111 or email meg@plantfinder.co.nz

Gaddum, M. (comp.). (est. 1998). www.plantfinder.co.nz Adjusted monthly, this searchable database contains the plant finder data. Access mainly by subscription.

UNITED KINGDOM

Pawsey, A (ed.). (20th ed. 2002-2003). *Find that Rose!* Covers autumn 2002-spring 2003. Lists over 3,100 varieties available in the UK with basic type, colour and fragrance codes. New varieties highlighted. Details of approx. 60 growers. How to find a rose with a particular Christian name or to celebrate a special event and where to see roses in bloom. For further information send an SAE to: The Editor, 303 Mile End Road, Colchester, Essex CO4 5EA. To order, send a cheque for £3 made out to *Find That Rose!* to the above address.

USA

Hill, Susan & Narizny, Susan (comp.) (2000). *The Pacific North West Plant Locator 2000/2001.* ISBN 0-967 4907-1-5. Directory of sources for plants (no seeds) available at retail and mail order nurseries in Oregon, Washington and Idaho; complete nursery information, how to contact nurseries and purchase plants. Includes a common name/botanical name index. Orders: Black-Eyed Susans Press, PMB 227, 6327-C, SW Capitol Highway, Portland, OR 97201-1937, USA. Email: susans@blackeyedsusanspress.com Price US$20 plus $4 p+p (USA) or $10 (outside USA). Website: www.blackeyedsusanspress.com

Burch, Derek (comp.) & Galletta, Kay (ed.). *PlantFinder.* A monthly magazine produced for the wholesale nursery and landscape industry to provide current listings of plants and plant-related materials in the southern United States. Orders: Betrock Information Systems Inc., 7770 Davie Road Extension, Hollywood, Florida 33024-2516. Subscription cost US$69.95 (double for foreign mail subscriptions). Email: betrock@betrock.com Website: www.hortworld.com

Hutchinson, B. & A. (comp.). *The Plant & Supply Locator.* A monthly magazine produced for the wholesale nursery and landscape industry giving current listings of plants in the southeastern United States. Orders: Hutchinson Publishing Corp., 102 East Lee Road, Taylors, South Carolina 29687. T +1 (864) 292 9490.

Nurseries

THE FOLLOWING NURSERIES STOCK BETWEEN THEM
AN UNRIVALLED CHOICE OF PLANTS BUT BEFORE MAKING
A VISIT, PLEASE REMEMBER TO CHECK WITH THE NURSERY
THAT THE PLANT YOU SEEK IS CURRENTLY AVAILABLE.

NURSERY CODES AND SYMBOLS

The first letter of each nursery code represents the area of the country in which the nursery is situated.

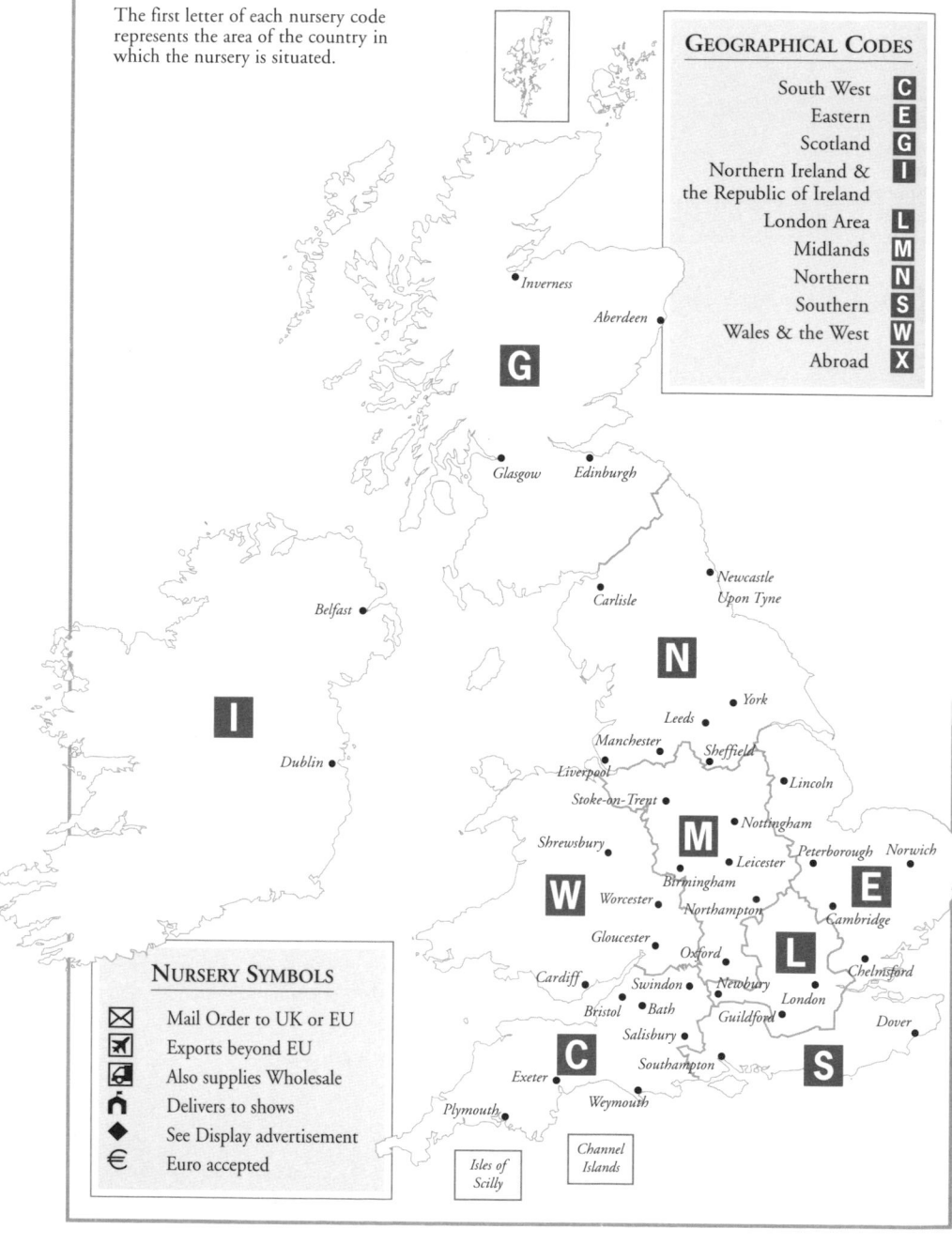

GEOGRAPHICAL CODES

South West	**C**
Eastern	**E**
Scotland	**G**
Northern Ireland & the Republic of Ireland	**I**
London Area	**L**
Midlands	**M**
Northern	**N**
Southern	**S**
Wales & the West	**W**
Abroad	**X**

NURSERY SYMBOLS

⊠	Mail Order to UK or EU
✈	Exports beyond EU
▣	Also supplies Wholesale
ń	Delivers to shows
◆	See Display advertisement
€	Euro accepted

USING THE THREE NURSERY LISTINGS

Your first reference from the Plant Directory is the Nursery Details by Code listing, which includes all relevant information for each nursery in order of nursery code. The Nursery Index by Name is an alphabetical list for those who know a nursery's name but not its code and wish to check its details in the main list. The Specialist Nurseries index is to aid those searching for a particular plant group.

1 NURSERY DETAILS BY CODE

Once you have found your plant in the Plant Directory, turn to this list to find out the name, address, opening times and other details of the nurseries whose codes accompany the plant.

> **KEY**
> ☒ Mail order to UK or EU   ♞ Delivers to shows
> ✠ Exports beyond EU   € Euro accepted
> ☑ Also supplies Wholesale   ◆ See Display advertisement

A geographical code is followed by three letters reflecting the nursery's name

LLin

LINCLUDEN NURSERY ☑ ☒ EU ☑ ♞ € ◆
Bisley Green, Bisley, Woking, Surrey GU24 9EN
☎ (01483) 797005   **Fax:** (01483) 474015
Email: sales@lincludennursery.co.uk
Website: www.lincludennursery.co.uk
Contact: Mr & Mrs J A Tilbury
Opening Times: 0930-1630 Mon-Sat all year excl. B/hols. Closed Chelsea week & Xmas.
Min Mail Order UK: No minimum charge
Min Mail Order EU: Nmc
Cat. Cost: 3 x 1st class
Credit Cards: Visa, MasterCard, Solo, Switch
Specialities: Dwarf, slow-growing & unusual conifers.
Map Ref: L, C3
OS Grid Ref: SU94/596

Refer to the box at the base of each right-hand page for a key to the symbols

A brief summary of the plants available plus any other special characteristics of the nursery

The map letter is followed by the map square in which the nursery is located

The Ordnance Survey national grid reference for use with OS maps

2 NURSERY INDEX BY NAME

If you seek a particular nursery, look it up in this alphabetical index. Note its code and turn to the Nursery Details by Code list for full information.

Leba Orchard - Green's Leaves	WLeb
Lilliesleaf Nursery	GLil
Lime Cross Nursery	SLim
Lincluden Nursery	LLin
Linden Farm Nurseries	**SLFN**
Lingen Nursery and Garden	WLin
Linward Hardy Plants	MLwd
Liscahane Nursery	ILsc

3 SPECIALIST NURSERIES

A list of 28 categories under which nurseries have classified themselves if they exclusively, or predominantly, supply this range of plants.

CONIFERS

CKen CLnd CTho EGlv
EHul EOrn GTre LBee
LCon LLin LPan MAsh
MBar NBee NLar SCoo
SCrf SLim WEve WGor
WHar

How to Use the Nursery Listings

The details given for each nursery have been compiled from information supplied to us in answer to a questionnaire. In some cases, because of constraints of space, the entries have been slightly abbreviated.

Nurseries are not charged for their entries, and inclusion in no way implies a value judgement.

Nursery Details by Code (*page 772*)

Each nursery is allocated a code, for example SLan. The first letter of each code indicates the main area of the country in which the nursery is situated. In this example, S=Southern England. The remaining three letters reflect the nursery's name, in this case Langley Boxwood Nursery in Hampshire.

In this main listing the nurseries are given in alphabetical order of codes for quick reference from the Plant Directory. All of the nurseries' details, such as address, opening times, mail order service etc., will be found here.

Opening Times

Although opening times have been published as submitted and where applicable, it is always advisable, especially if travelling a long distance, to check with the nursery first. The initials NGS indicate that the nursery is open under the National Gardens Scheme.

Mail Order - ⊠ UK or EU

Many nurseries provide a mail order service which, in many cases, now extends to all members of the European Union. Where 'No minimum charge' (Nmc) is shown please note that to send even one plant may involve the nursery in substantial postage and packing costs. Even so, some nurseries may not be prepared to send tender or bulky plants.

Export ⊠

Export refers to mail order beyond the European Union. Nurseries that are prepared to consider exporting are indicated. However, there is usually a substantial minimum charge and, in addition, all the costs of Phytosanitary Certificates and Customs have to be met by the purchaser.

Catalogue Cost

Some nurseries offer their catalogue free, or for a few stamps (the odd value quoted can usually be made up from a combination of first or second class stamps), but a large (at least A5) stamped addressed envelope is always appreciated as well. Overseas customers should use an equivalent number of International Reply Coupons (IRCs) in place of stamps.

Wholesale or Retail ⊡

All nurseries listed in the *RHS Plant Finder* provide a retail service. Many retailers also have a wholesale trade and would frequently be prepared to offer discounts for large single orders.

Specialities

Nurseries list here the plants or genera that they supply, together with other features about their service. Some hold National Collections of plants to which they may or may not charge an entry fee. Please enquire before visiting a Collection.

Delivery to Shows ⋔

Many nurseries will deliver pre-ordered plants to flower shows for collection by customers. These are indicated by a marquee symbol. Contact the nursery for details of shows they attend.

Payment in Euros €

All Republic of Ireland nurseries will, of course, accept Euro payments.

A number of UK nurseries have indicated that they will accept payment in Euros. You should, however, check with the nursery concerned before making such a payment, as some will only accept cash and some only cheques, whilst others will expect the purchaser to pay bank charges.

Maps

If you wish to visit any of the nurseries you can find its approximate location on the relevant map (following p.921), unless the nursery has requested this is not shown (this usually applies to mail order only nurseries). Some of the more difficult-to-find nurseries also provide their Ordnance Survey national grid reference for use with OS publications such as the Land Ranger series.

Nursery Index by Name (*page 911*)

For convenience, an alphabetical index of nurseries is included on p.911. This gives the names of all nurseries listed in the book in alphabetical order of nursery name together with their code.

Specialist Nurseries (*page 919*)

This list of nurseries has been introduced to help those with an interest in finding specialist categories of plant. Nurseries have been asked to classify themselves under one or more headings where this represents the type of plant they *predominantly* or *exclusively* have in stock. For example, if you wish to find a nursery specialising in ornamental grasses, look up 'Grasses' in the listing where you will find a list of nursery codes. Then turn to the Nursery Details by Code, for details of the nurseries.

Please note that not all nurseries shown here will have plants listed in the Plant Directory. This may be their choice or because the *RHS Plant Finder* does not list seeds or annuals and only terrestrial orchids and hardy cacti. For space reasons, it is rare to find a nursery's full catalogue listed in the Plant Directory.

In all cases, please ensure you ring to confirm the range available before embarking on a journey to the nursery.

The specialist plant groups listed in this edition are:

Acid-loving	Ferns
Alpines/rock	Fruit
Aquatics/marginals	Grasses
Bamboos	Hedging
British Wild flowers	Herbs
Bulbous plants	Orchids
Cacti & succulents	Organic
Carnivorous	Ornamental trees
Chalk-loving	Peat-free
Climbers	Period plants
Coastal	Propagate to order
Conifers	Seeds
Conservatory	Specimen-sized plants
Drought-tolerant	Topiary

Perennials and shrubs have been omitted as these are considered to be too general and serviced by a great proportion of the nurseries.

Deleted Nurseries

Every year a few nurseries ask to be deleted. This may be because they are about to move or close, or they are changing the way in which they trade. A small number do not reply and, as we have no current information concerning them, they are deleted.

Please, never use an old edition

NURSERY DETAILS BY CODE

Please note that all these nurseries are listed in alphabetical order by their code. All nurseries are listed in alphabetical order by their name in the **Nursery Index by Name** on page 911.

SOUTH WEST

CAbb **ABBOTSBURY SUB-TROPICAL GARDENS** ⊠ EU
Abbotsbury, Nr Weymouth, Dorset DT3 4LA
☎ (01305) 871344
Fax: (01305) 871344
Email: gardens@abbotsbury.co.uk
Contact: David Sutton
Opening Times: 1000-1800 daily mid Mar-1st Nov. 1000-1500 Nov-mid Mar.
Min Mail Order UK: £10.00 + p&p
Min Mail Order EU: £20.00 + p&p
Cat. Cost: £2 + A4 Sae + 42p stamp
Credit Cards: Access, Visa, MasterCard, Switch
Specialities: Less common & tender shrubs incl. palms, tree ferns, bamboos & plants from Australia, New Zealand & S. Africa.
Map Ref: C, C5

CAbP **ABBEY PLANTS**
Chaffeymoor, Bourton, Gillingham, Dorset SP8 5BY
☎ (01747) 840841
Contact: K Potts
Opening Times: 1000-1300 & 1400-1700 Tue-Sat Mar-Nov. Dec-Feb by appt.
Cat. Cost: 2 x 2nd class
Credit Cards: None
Specialities: Flowering trees & shrubs. Shrub roses incl. many unusual varieties.
Map Ref: C, B5

CAbx **ABRAXAS GARDENS** ⊠ EU 🛈
7 Little Keyford Lane, Frome, Somerset BA11 5BB
☎ (01373) 472879
Website: www.abraxasgardens.co.uk
Contact: Duncan Skene
Opening Times: By appt. and NGS days.
Min Mail Order UK: No minimum charge
Min Mail Order EU: £100 plant value
Cat. Cost: Free
Credit Cards: None
Specialities: *Aster, Crocosmia, Iris sibirica, Hemerocallis* (spiders, spider variants & unusual forms). Many recent introductions available only in small numbers.
Map Ref: C, B5
OS Grid Ref: ST775465

CAgr **AGROFORESTRY RESEARCH TRUST** ⊠ UK
46 Hunters Moon, Dartington, Totnes, Devon TQ9 6JT
☎ (01803) 840776
Fax: (01803) 840776
Email: mail@agroforestry.co.uk
Website: www.agroforestry.co.uk
Contact: Martin Crawford
Opening Times: Not open, mail order only.
Min Mail Order UK: No minimum charge
Cat. Cost: 4 x 1st class
Credit Cards: MasterCard, Visa
Specialities: Mostly trees, shrubs & perennials. *Alnus, Berberis, Amelanchier, Carya, Elaeagnus, Juglans, Pinus, Quercus* & *Salix.* Also seeds. Some plants in small quantities only.

CArn **ARNE HERBS** 🖥 ⊠ EU 🖂 €
Limeburn Nurseries, Limeburn Hill, Chew Magna, Bristol BS40 8QW
☎ (01275) 333399
Fax: (01275) 333399
Email: lyman@lyman-dixon.freeserve.co.uk
Website: www.arneherbs.co.uk
Contact: A Lyman-Dixon & Jenny Thomas
Opening Times: Most times, please check first.

Min Mail Order UK: No minimum charge
Min Mail Order EU: Nmc
Cat. Cost: £2.75 UK, 8 x IRC refundable on
first order.
Credit Cards: None
Specialities: Herbs, wild flowers & cottage
flowers. A few plants limited, please see
catalogue for details. Will deliver to Farmers'
Markets.
Map Ref: C, A5
OS Grid Ref: ST563638

CAvo AVON BULBS ⊠ EU ♙
Burnt House Farm, Mid-Lambrook, South
Petherton, Somerset TA13 5HE
☎ (01460) 242177
Fax: (01460) 242177
Email: info@avonbulbs.co.uk
Website: www.avonbulbs.co.uk
Contact: C Ireland-Jones
Opening Times: Thu, Fri, Sat mid Sep-end
Oct & mid Feb-end Mar for collection of
pre-booked orders.
Min Mail Order UK: £10.00 + p&p
Min Mail Order EU: £20.00 + p&p
Cat. Cost: 4 x 2nd class
Credit Cards: Visa, Access, Switch
Specialities: Mail order supply of a very wide
range of smaller, often unusual bulbs.
Map Ref: C, B5

CBcs BURNCOOSE NURSERIES 🔲 ⊠ EU 🔲 ♙
Gwennap, Redruth, Cornwall TR16 6BJ
☎ (01209) 860316
Fax: (01209) 860011
Email: burncoose@eclipse.co.uk
Website: www.burncoose.co.uk
Contact: C H Williams
Opening Times: 0830-1700 Mon-Sat &
1100-1700 Sun.
Min Mail Order UK: No minimum charge
Min Mail Order EU: Nmc*
Cat. Cost: £1.50 incl. p&p
Credit Cards: Visa, Access, Switch
Specialities: Extensive range of over 3000
ornamental trees & shrubs and herbaceous.
Rare & unusual *Magnolia, Rhododendron*.
Conservatory plants. 30 acre garden.
*Note: individual quotations for EU sales.
Map Ref: C, D1
OS Grid Ref: SW742395

CBct BARRACOTT PLANTS 🔲 ⊠ UK ♙ €
Old Orchard, Calstock Road, Gunnislake,
Cornwall PL18 9AA
Email: GEOFF@geoff63.freeserve.co.uk

Contact: Geoff Turner, Thelma Watson
Opening Times: 0900-1700 Thu-Sat, Mar-
end Jul. Sep or other times by appt.
Min Mail Order UK: £10.00
Cat. Cost: 2 x 1st class
Specialities: Herbaceous plants: shade-loving,
foliage & form. *Acanthus, Astrantia, Bergenia,
Convallaria, Ligularia, Liriope, Smilacina,
Symphytum & Tricyrtis*.
Map Ref: C, C3
OS Grid Ref: SX436702

CBdn ANN & ROGER BOWDEN ⊠ EU 🔲 € ◆
Cleave House, Sticklepath, Okehampton,
Devon EX20 2NL
☎ (01837) 840481
Fax: (01837) 840482
Email: bowdenshosta@eclipse.co.uk
Website: www.hostas-uk.com
Contact: Ann & Roger Bowden
Opening Times: By appt. only.
Min Mail Order UK: No minimum charge
Min Mail Order EU: Nmc
Cat. Cost: 3 x 1st class
Credit Cards: Visa, Access, EuroCard, Switch
Specialities: *Hosta* only. National Collection
of modern hybrid *Hosta*.
Map Ref: C, C3

CBel BELMONT HOUSE NURSERY ⊠ UK €
Little Horton, Devizes, Wilts SN10 3LJ
☎ (01380) 860510
Contact: Gordon Cottis
Opening Times: By appt. Please phone.
Min Mail Order UK: Please enquire*
Cat. Cost: 2 x 2nd class
Credit Cards: None
Specialities: *Helleborus* hybrids & true
species, *Galanthus, Digitalis, Geranium,
Pulmonaria*, other hardy perennials.
*Note: mail order of *Cyclamen & Galanthus*
only, Nov-Feb. *Galanthus* stock limited &
variable. Other plants may be available in
small quantities.
Map Ref: C, A6

CBen BENNETT'S WATER LILY FARM 🔲 ⊠ EU
Putton Lane, Chickerell, Weymouth,
Dorset DT3 4AF
☎ (01305) 785150
Fax: (01305) 781619

C

Email: JB@waterlily.co.uk
Website: www.waterlily.co.uk
Contact: J Bennett
Opening Times: Tue-Sun Apr-Aug, Tue-Sat Sept & Mar.
Min Mail Order UK: £25.00 + p&p*
Min Mail Order EU: £25.00 + p&p
Cat. Cost: Sae for price list
Credit Cards: Visa, Access, MasterCard, Switch
Specialities: Aquatic plants. National Collection of water lilies.
*Note: mail order Apr-Sep only.
Map Ref: C, C5
OS Grid Ref: SY651797

CBgR BEGGAR'S ROOST PLANTS ♠
Lilstock, Bridgwater, Somerset TA5 1SU
☎ (01278) 741519
Fax: (01278) 741519
Contact: Rosemary FitzGerald, Kate Harris
Opening Times: By appt. only.
Credit Cards: None
Specialities: British native plants & their garden-worthy varieties. Hardy ferns. Classic perennials, incl. *Salvia, Penstenmon*. Available in small quantities only.
Map Ref: C, B4
OS Grid Ref: ST168450

CBHf BLOOMS OF BRESSINGHAM ⊠ UK ◆
Bath Road, Haresfield, Nr Stonehouse, Glos GL10 3DP
☎ (01452) 721081
Fax: (01452) 724919
Email: j3@jardinerie.co.uk
Website: www.bloomsofbressingham.co.uk
Contact: Mike O'Nions
Opening Times: 0900-1700 1st Nov-31st Mar, 0900-1800 1st Apr-31st Oct, 7 days. Closed Xmas, Boxing Day & Easter Sun.
Min Mail Order UK: £4.35
Cat. Cost: None issued.
Credit Cards: Visa, Delta, Switch, MasterCard
Specialities: Wide general range. Many own varieties. Focus on hardy ornamental plants & grasses. Perennials. Plants listed against nursery code EBre.
Map Ref: W, D5

CBig THE BIG GRASS CO. ▦ ⊠ EU ▨ ♠ €
Hookhill Plantation, Woolfardisworthy East, Black Dog, Nr Crediton, Devon EX17 4RX
☎ (01363) 866146
Fax: (01363) 866146

Email: alison@big-grass-co.co.uk
Website: www.big-grass-co.co.uk
Contact: Alison & Scott Evans
Opening Times: By appt. only.
Min Mail Order UK: Nmc
Min Mail Order EU: Nmc
Cat. Cost: 2 x 1st class
Credit Cards: None
Specialities: Grasses.
Map Ref: C, B3

CBla BLACKMORE & LANGDON LTD ⊠ EU ▨
Pensford, Bristol BS39 4JL
☎ (01275) 332300
Fax: (01275) 332300/(01275) 331207
Email: plants@blackmore-langdon.com
Website: www.blackmore-langdon.com
Contact: J S Langdon
Opening Times: 0900-1700 Mon-Fri, 1000-1600 Sat & Sun.
Min Mail Order UK: Nmc
Min Mail Order EU: Nmc
Cat. Cost: Sae 2 x 2nd class
Credit Cards: MasterCard, Visa, Switch
Specialities: *Phlox, Delphinium* & *Begonia*. Also seeds.
Map Ref: C, A5

CBod BODMIN PLANT AND HERB NURSERY
Laveddon Mill, Laninval Hill, Bodmin, Cornwall PL30 5JU
☎ (01208) 72837
Fax: (01208) 76491
Email: CHYROSE44@aol.com
Contact: Mark Lawlor
Opening Times: 0900-1800 (or dusk) 7 days.
Cat. Cost: 2 x 1st class
Credit Cards: MasterCard, Visa, Switch, Solo
Specialities: Herbs, herbaceous & grasses, aquatic, marginal & bog plants, plus interesting range of shrubs. Wide range of fruit & ornamental trees. New range of coastal, patio & conservatory plants.
Map Ref: C, C2
OS Grid Ref: SX053659

CBos BOSVIGO PLANTS
Bosvigo House, Bosvigo Lane, Truro, Cornwall TR1 3NH
☎ (01872) 275774
Fax: (01872) 275774
Email: bosvigo.plants@virgin.net
Website: www.bosvigo.com
Contact: Wendy Perry

Opening Times: 1100-1800 Thu-Sat Mar-end Sep.
Cat. Cost: 4 x 1st class
Credit Cards: None
Specialities: Rare & unusual herbaceous.
Map Ref: C, D2
OS Grid Ref: SW815452

CBot   THE BOTANIC NURSERY ⊠ EU ⋔ €
(Office) Bath Road, Atworth, Nr Melksham,
Wilts SN12 8NU
☎ mobile 07850 328756
Fax: (01225) 700953
Email: infobotanic@aol.com
Website: www.TheBotanicNursery.com
Contact: T & M Baker
Opening Times: 1000-1700 Fri & Sat +
themed openings - send for details. Closed
Nov-Feb.
Min Mail Order UK: 30p Sae for mail
order lists.
Cat. Cost: £1.00 coin
Credit Cards: Visa, Access
Specialities: Rare hardy shrubs & perennials
for lime soils. *Eryngium, Papaver orientale*
cultivars, *Delphinium*. National Collection of
Digitalis. Note: nursery & plant sales at
Cottles Lane, nr. Stonar School, Atworth,
nr. Melksham.
Map Ref: C, A5

CBrd   BROADLEAS GARDENS LTD
Broadleas, Devizes, Wilts SN10 5JQ
☎ (01380) 722035
Fax: (01380) 722035
Contact: Lady Anne Cowdray
Opening Times: 1400-1800 Wed, Thu &
Sun Apr-Oct.
Cat. Cost: 1 x 1st class
Credit Cards: None
Specialities: General range.
Map Ref: C, A6

CBre   BREGOVER PLANTS ⊠ EU ⋔
Hillbrooke, Middlewood, North Hill,
Nr Launceston, Cornwall PL15 7NN
☎ (01566) 782661
Contact: Jennifer Bousfield
Opening Times: 1100-1700 Wed-Fri
Mar-mid Oct and by appt.
Min Mail Order UK: No minimum charge
Min Mail Order EU: Nmc
Cat. Cost: 2 x 1st class
Credit Cards: None
Specialities: Unusual hardy perennials grown
in small garden nursery. Note: limited stocks,

mail order Oct-Mar only.
Map Ref: C, C2
OS Grid Ref: SX273752

CBri   BRIDGEMAN & KENT
Plumtree Cottage, Bottlesford, Pewsey,
Wiltshire SN9 6LW
☎ (01672) 851845
Fax: (01672) 851845
Email: anduff@bridgeman-kent.co.uk
Contact: Andrew Duff
Opening Times: By appt. only Mar-late Oct.
Cat. Cost: None issued
Credit Cards: None
Specialities: Herbaceous & bulbous
perennials. Limted numbers as wide range.
Map Ref: C, B6
OS Grid Ref: SU110590

**CBrm   BRAMLEY LODGE GARDEN
NURSERY** ⋔ €
Beech Tree Lane, Ipplepen, Newton Abbot,
Devon TQ12 5TW
☎ (01803) 813265
Email: bramleylodge@btinternet.com
Website: www.bramleylodge-nursery.co.uk
Contact: Susan Young
Opening Times: 1000-1600 Thu-Sun Mar-
Oct, 1000-1600 Sun Nov-Feb.
Cat. Cost: 3 x 1st class
Credit Cards: None
Specialities: Grasses. Also trees, shrubs &
perennials. Several small model themed
gardens.
Map Ref: C, C3

CBro   BROADLEIGH GARDENS ⊠ EU ⋔
Bishops Hull, Taunton,
Somerset TA4 1AE
☎ (01823) 286231
Fax: (01823) 323646
Email: info@broadleighbulbs.co.uk
Website: www.broadleighbulbs.co.uk
Contact: Lady Skelmersdale
Opening Times: 0900-1600 Mon-Fri for
viewing only. Orders collected if notice given.
Min Mail Order UK: No minimum charge
Min Mail Order EU: Nmc
Cat. Cost: 2 x 1st class
Credit Cards: Visa, MasterCard
Specialities: Jan catalogue: bulbs in growth

⊠ Mail order to UK or EU   ⋔ Delivers to shows
▣ Exports beyond EU   € Euro accepted
▣ Also supplies Wholesale   ◆ See Display advertisement

C

(*Galanthus, Cyclamen* etc.) & herbaceous.
June catalogue: dwarf & unusual bulbs.
National Collection of Alec Grey hybrid
daffodils.
Map Ref: C, B4

CBrP   BROOKLANDS PLANTS ▦ ⊠ EU
25 Treves Road, Dorchester,
Dorset DT1 2HE
☎ (01305) 265846
Email: IanWatt@quicklink.freeserve.co.uk
Contact: Ian Watt
Opening Times: By appt. for collection of
plants only.
Min Mail Order UK: £25.00 + p&p
Min Mail Order EU: £25.00 + p&p
Cat. Cost: 2 x 2nd class
Credit Cards: None
Specialities: Palms & cycads. Over 100
species from seedling to specimen size. Other
plants grown incl. *Agave, Yucca, Dasylirion,
Cordyline, Puya, Restio* & bamboo.
Map Ref: C, C5

CBSw   BLOOMS OF BRESSINGHAM ⊠ UK ◆
Hay Lane, Nr Wroughton, Swindon,
Wiltshire SN4 9QT
☎ (01793) 852736
Fax: (01793) 852746
Email: j7@jardinerie.co.uk
Website: www.bloomsofbressingham.co.uk
Contact: Bob Sawyer
Opening Times: 0900-1700 1st Nov-31st
Mar, 0900-1800 1st Apr-31st Oct, 7 days.
Closed Xmas, Boxing Day & Easter Sun.
Min Mail Order UK: £4.35
Cat. Cost: None issued.
Credit Cards: Visa, Delta, Switch, MasterCard
Specialities: Wide general range. Many own
varieties. Focus on hardy ornamental plants
& grasses. Perennials. Plants listed against
nursery code EBre.
Map Ref: C, A6

CBur   BURNHAM NURSERIES ▦ ⊠ EU ▨ ⋔
Forches Cross, Newton Abbot,
Devon TQ12 6PZ
☎ (01626) 352233
Fax: (01626) 362167
Email: mail@burnhamnurseries.co.uk
Website: www.orchids.uk.com
Contact: Sara Rittershausen
Opening Times: 1000-1600 Mon-Sun.
Min Mail Order UK: No minimum charge
Min Mail Order EU: £100.00 + p&p
Cat. Cost: Large Sae + 40p stamp

Credit Cards: Visa, Switch, American
Express, MasterCard
Specialities: All types of orchid except British
native types. Note: please ask for details on
export beyond EU.
Map Ref: C, C4

CCAT   CIDER APPLE TREES ▦ ⊠ EU €
Kerian, Corkscrew Lane, Woolston,
Nr North Cadbury, Somerset BA22 7BP
☎ (01963) 441101
Contact: Mr J Dennis
Opening Times: By appt. only.
Min Mail Order UK: £6.50 + p&p
Min Mail Order EU: £6.50 + p&p
Cat. Cost: Free
Credit Cards: None
Specialities: *Malus* (speciality standard
trees).
Map Ref: C, B5

**CCge   COTTAGE GARDEN PLANTS
AND HERBS** ⋔
North Lodge, Canonteign, Christow,
Exeter EX6 7NS
☎ (01647) 252950
Contact: Shirley Bennett
Opening Times: 1000-1700 w/ends &
B/hols Easter-Sep. Ring for private visit at
other times.
Specialities: Cottage garden plants, herbs and
esp. hardy geraniums (over 200 kinds
available).
Map Ref: C, C3
OS Grid Ref: SX836829

CCha   CHAPEL FARM HOUSE NURSERY €
Halwill Junction, Beaworthy,
Devon EX21 5UF
☎ (01409) 221594
Fax: (01409) 221594
Contact: Robin or Toshie Hull
Opening Times: 0900-1700 Tue-Sat,
1000-1600 Sun & B/hol Mons.
Cat. Cost: None issued.
Credit Cards: None
Specialities: Plants from Japan. Also
herbaceous. Japanese garden design service
offered.
Map Ref: C, C3

CChe   CHERRY TREE NURSERY ▦
(Sheltered Work Opportunities), off New
Road Roundabout, Northbourne,
Bournemouth, Dorset BH10 7DA
☎ (01202) 593537, (01202) 590840

Fax: (01202) 590626
Contact: Stephen Jailler
Opening Times: 0830-1530 Mon-Fri, 0900-1200 most Sats.
Cat. Cost: A4 Sae + 54p stamps
Credit Cards: None
Specialities: Hardy shrubs.
Map Ref: C, C6

CCol   COLD HARBOUR NURSERY ⊠ UK ♁
(Office) 28 Moor Road, Swanage,
Dorset BH19 1RG
☎ (01929) 423520 evenings
Email: coldharbournursery@hotmail.com
Website: www.dorset-perennials.co.uk
Contact: Steve Saunders
Opening Times: 1000-1700 Tue-Fri & most w/ends 1st Mar-end Oct. Other times by appt.
Min Mail Order UK: £6.00 + p&p
Cat. Cost: 3 x 2nd class
Credit Cards: None
Specialities: Unusual herbaceous perennials incl. hardy *Geranium*, daylilies & grasses.
Note: nursery is at Bere Road (opp. Silent Woman Inn), Wareham.
Map Ref: C, C5

CCtw   CHURCHTOWN NURSERIES ⊠ UK ♁
Gulval, Penzance, Cornwall TR18 3BE
☎ (01736) 362626
Fax: (01736) 362626
Contact: C Osborne
Opening Times: 1000-1700 Apr-Sep, 1000-1600 Oct-Mar or by appt.
Min Mail Order UK: £25.00 + p&p
Cat. Cost: 1 x 1st class Sae for list.
Credit Cards: None
Specialities: Good, ever-increasing, range of shrubs, herbaceous & tender perennials & ornamental grasses incl. some more unusual.
Map Ref: C, D1
OS Grid Ref: SW486317

CCVT   CHEW VALLEY TREES ▣ ⊠ UK
Winford Road, Chew Magna,
Bristol BS40 8QE
☎ (01275) 333752
Fax: (01275) 333746
Email: enquiries@chewvalleytreesandlandscapes.co.uk
Website: www.chewvalleytreesandlandscapes.co.uk
Contact: J Scarth
Opening Times: 0800-1700 Mon-Fri all year. 0900-1600 7th Sep-25th May.

Min Mail Order UK: No minimum charge*
Cat. Cost: Free
Credit Cards: Visa, MasterCard, Switch
Specialities: Native British & ornamental trees, shrubs, apple trees & hedging.
*Note: max. plant height for mail order 2.7m.
Map Ref: C, A5
OS Grid Ref: ST558635

**CDDB   DEVON & DORSET
BAMBOO ⊠ UK ♁ € ◆**
(Office) 13 Morley Road, Exeter,
Devon EX4 7BD
☎ (01392) 422853
Fax: (01392) 422853
Email: tgard@devondorsetbamboo.fsnet.co.uk
Website: www.devondorsetbamboo.com
Contact: Tom Gard
Opening Times: 1000-1730 Mon-Sat. Phone first to ensure someone at nursery.
Min Mail Order UK: £15.00 + p&p
Cat. Cost: 1 x 1st or 2nd class
Credit Cards: Not for mail orders
Specialities: Bamboo. Note: nursery is at Teign Valley Nursery, Bridford, nr. Exeter.
Map Ref: C, C4

CDes   DESIRABLE PLANTS ⊠ UK
Pentamar, Crosspark, Totnes,
Devon TQ9 5BQ
☎ (01803) 864489
Email: sutton.totnes@lineone.net
Contact: Dr J J & Mrs S A Sutton
Opening Times: Not open, mail order only.
Min Mail Order UK: Nmc
Cat. Cost: 3 x 1st class
Credit Cards: None
Specialities: Choice & interesting herbaceous plants by mail order. Cat. available May for autumn dispatch. *Watsonia* & other S. hemisphere *Iridaceae, Anemone, Crinum, Arisaema, Thalictrum* & *Pulmonaria*.
Note: nursery not at this address.

CDev   DEVON VIOLET NURSERY ▣ ⊠ EU ▣ €
Rattery, South Brent, Devon TQ10 9LG
☎ (01364) 643033
Fax: (01364) 643033
Email: virgin.violets@virgin.net
Website: www.sweetviolets.co.uk

C

Contact: Robert Sidol, Sarah Bunting
Opening Times: All year round. Please ring first.
Min Mail Order UK: 4 plants
Min Mail Order EU: 4 plants
Cat. Cost: 1 x 1st class
Credit Cards: None
Specialities: Violets & Parma violets. National Collection of *Viola odorata*.
Map Ref: C, C3
OS Grid Ref: SX747620

CDob　Samuel Dobie & Son ⊠ UK
Long Road, Paignton, Devon TQ4 7SX
☎ (01803) 696411
Fax: (01803) 696450
Website: www.dobies.co.uk
Contact: Customer Services
Opening Times: 0830-1700 Mon-Fri (office). Also answerphone.
Min Mail Order UK: No minimum charge*
Cat. Cost: Free
Credit Cards: Visa, MasterCard, Switch, Delta
Specialities: Wide selection of popular flower & vegetable seeds. Also includes young plants, summer flowering bulbs & garden sundries.
*Note: mail order to UK & Rep. of Ireland only.

CDoC　Duchy of Cornwall ⊠ UK ◆
Cott Road, Lostwithiel, Cornwall PL22 0HW
☎ (01208) 872668
Fax: (01208) 872835
Email: sales@duchynursery.co.uk
Website: www.duchyofcornwallnursery.co.uk
Contact: Tracy Wilson
Opening Times: 0900-1700 Mon-Sat, 1000-1700 Sun & B/hols.
Min Mail Order UK: Nmc
Cat. Cost: Cat £2.00 (stamps or cheque)
Credit Cards: Visa, American Express, Access, Switch, Delta
Specialities: Very wide range of garden plants incl. trees, shrubs, conifers, roses, perennials, fruit & half-hardy exotics.
Map Ref: C, C2

CDul　Dulford Nurseries ▣ ⊠ EU
Cullompton, Devon EX15 2DG
☎ (01884) 266361
Fax: (01884) 266663
Email: dulford.nurseries@virgin.net

Website: www.dulford-nurseries.co.uk
Contact: David & Mary Barrow
Opening Times: 0730-1630 Mon-Fri.
Min Mail Order UK: Nmc
Min Mail Order EU: Nmc
Cat. Cost: Free
Credit Cards: None
Specialities: Native, ornamental & unusual trees & shrubs incl. oaks, maples, beech, birch, chestnut, ash, lime, *Sorbus* & pines.
Map Ref: C, C4
OS Grid Ref: SY062062

CEbD　Ebberly Down Nursery ⊠ UK ♠ €
Ebberly Cross Nr Torrington, Devon EX38 7JT
☎ (01769) 560398
Contact: M & K Jones
Opening Times: 1000-1700 Apr-Dec.
Min Mail Order UK: £10.00
Cat. Cost: 4 x 1st class
Credit Cards: None
Specialities: Bamboos, hardy palms, ferns, hostas, unusual grasses, shrubs & perennials.
Map Ref: C, B3

CEgg　Eggesford Gardens & Country Centre Ltd ⊠ EU
Eggesford, Chulmleigh, Devon EX18 7QU
☎ (01769) 580250
Fax: (01769) 581041
Contact: Jonathon Parish
Opening Times: 0900-1700 7 days excl. Xmas, Boxing & New Year's Day.
Min Mail Order UK: £15.00 + p&p
Min Mail Order EU: £20.00 + p&p
Cat. Cost: None issued.
Credit Cards: MasterCard, Visa, Switch, Delta, American Express
Specialities: Wide general range. Strong in shrubs, herbaceous, roses, & *Clematis*.
Map Ref: C, B3

CElm　Elm Tree Nursery ⊠ UK
Court Farm, Sidbury, Sidmouth, Devon EX10 0QG
☎ (01395) 597790
Contact: M Saunders
Opening Times: Not open, mail order only.
Min Mail Order UK: £10.00 + p&p
Cat. Cost: 1 x 1st class
Specialities: Hardy *Cyclamen*. Rarest cultivars only available in small quantities.

C

CElw **ELWORTHY COTTAGE PLANTS** ⋔
Elworthy Cottage, Elworthy, Lydeard St
Lawrence, Taunton, Somerset TA4 3PX
☎ (01984) 656427
Email: mike@elworthy-cottage.co.uk
Website: www.elworthy-cottage.co.uk
Contact: Mrs J M Spiller
Opening Times: 1000-1600 Tue, Thu & Fri
mid Mar-end Sep & by appt.
Cat. Cost: 3 x 2nd class
Credit Cards: None
Specialities: *Clematis* & unusual herbaceous
plants esp. hardy *Geranium, Geum*, grasses,
Campanula, Crocosmia, Pulmonaria, Astrantia
& *Viola*. Note: nursery on B3188, 5 miles
north of Wiveliscombe.
Map Ref: C, B4
OS Grid Ref: ST084349

CEnd **ENDSLEIGH GARDENS** 🖾 ⊠ UK ◆
Milton Abbot, Tavistock,
Devon PL19 0PG
☎ (01822) 870235
Fax: (01822) 870513
Email: Treemail@endsleigh-gardens.com
Website: www.endsleigh-gardens.com
Contact: Michael Taylor
Opening Times: 0800-1700 Mon-Sat.
1000-1700 Sun (closed Sun Dec & Jan).
Min Mail Order UK: £12.00 + p&p
Cat. Cost: 2 x 1st class
Credit Cards: Visa, Access, Switch,
MasterCard
Specialities: Choice & unusual trees &
shrubs incl. *Acer* & *Cornus* cvs. Old apples &
cherries. *Wisteria*. Grafting service.
Map Ref: C, C3

CFai **FAIRHAVEN NURSERY** ⊠ UK ⋔
Clapworthy Cross, Chittlehampton,
Umberleigh, Devon EX37 9QT
☎ (01769) 540528
Email: fairhavennursery@hotmail.com
Contact: Derek & Pauline Burdett
Opening Times: 1000-1600 all year, but
please check first.
Min Mail Order UK: £10.00 + p&p
Cat. Cost: 2 x 1st class
Credit Cards: None
Specialities: Propagate & grow wide selection
of more unusual varieties of hardy trees,
shrubs & perennials. Many grown in small
batches that may not be ready for despatch
on request. Orders taken for delivery when
available.
Map Ref: C, B3

CFee **FEEBERS HARDY PLANTS** ⊠ EU ◆
1 Feeber Cottage, Westwood, Broadclyst,
Nr Exeter, Devon EX5 3DQ
☎ (01404) 822118
Contact: Mrs E Squires
Opening Times: 1000-1700 Wed Mar-Jul &
Sep-Oct. Sat & Sun by prior appt.
Min Mail Order UK: No minimum charge*
Min Mail Order EU: Nmc
Cat. Cost: Sae + 36p stamp
Credit Cards: None
Specialities: Plants for wet clay soils, alpines
& hardy perennials incl. those raised by
Amos Perry.
*Note: mail order limited. Plants held in
small quantities unless grown from seed.
Map Ref: C, C4

CFil **FILLAN'S PLANTS** 🖾 ⊠ UK
Tuckermarsh Gardens, Tamar Lane,
Bere Alston, Devon PL20 7HN
☎ (01822) 840721
Fax: (01822) 841551
Email: fillansplants@yahoo.co.uk
Contact: Mark Fillan
Opening Times: 1000-1700 Sat Mar-Sep &
by appt. any other time.
Min Mail Order UK: £20.00 + p&p
Cat. Cost: 3 x 1st class
Credit Cards: None
Specialities: Bamboos, *Hydrangea* & unusual
woody plants.
Map Ref: C, C3
OS Grid Ref: SX444678

CFir **FIR TREE FARM NURSERY** ⊠ EU €
Tresahor, Constantine, Falmouth,
Cornwall TR11 5PL
☎ (01326) 340593
Email: ftfnur@aol.com
Website: www.cornwallgardens.com,
www.members.aol.com/ftfnur
Contact: Jim Cave
Opening Times: 1000-1700 Thu-Sun
1st Mar-30th Sep.
Min Mail Order UK: £25.00 + p&p
Min Mail Order EU: £40.00 + p&p
Cat. Cost: 6 x 1st class or cheque for
£1.60
Credit Cards: Visa, Access, Delta, Switch
Specialities: Over 3500 varieties of cottage

K E Y	⊠ Mail order to UK or EU	⋔ Delivers to shows
	🗷 Exports beyond EU	€ Euro accepted
	🖾 Also supplies Wholesale	◆ See Display advertisement

C

garden & rare perennials & 100 types of *Clematis*.
Map Ref: C, D1

CFis   **MARGERY FISH GARDENS €**
East Lambrook Manor, East Lambrook,
South Petherton, Somerset TA13 5HL
☎ (01460) 240328
Fax: (01460) 242344
Email: enquiries@eastlambrook.com
Website: www.eastlambrook.com
Contact: Mark Stainer
Opening Times: 1000-1700 1st Feb-31st
Oct 7 days.
Credit Cards: Visa, Switch, MasterCard
Specialities: Hardy *Geranium, Euphorbia,
Helleborus* & herbaceous. National
Collection of hardy *Geranium* on site.
Map Ref: C, B5

CFox   **FOXLEY ROAD NURSERIES**
Foxley Road, Malmesbury,
Wilts SN16 0JQ
☎ (01666) 822171
Email: carol@foxleyroadnurseries.co.uk
Website: www.foxleyroadnurseries.co.uk
Contact: Carol Hinwood
Opening Times: 1000-1600 Mon-Sat Feb,
Mar, Jul-Dec. 0900-1700 Mon-Sat & 1000-
1600 Sun Apr, May & Jun.
Cat. Cost: Sae
Credit Cards: Visa, MasterCard, Switch
Specialities: Wide general range of shrubs &
herbaceous perennials, patio & hanging
basket plants, vegetables, herbs, unusual wild
flowers.
Map Ref: C, A5
OS Grid Ref: ST915865

CFRD   **FORD NURSERY** 🖳 ♀
The Willows, Broom Lane, Oake,
Taunton, Somerset TA4 1BE
☎ (01823) 461961
Fax: (018230) 461961
Contact: Mr P F Dunn
Opening Times: 0900-1300 & 1400-1700
Mon-Fri. Sat & Sun by appt. only.
Cat. Cost: 3 x 2nd class
Map Ref: C, B4
OS Grid Ref: ST160244

CFul   **RODNEY FULLER** ✉ UK
Coachman's Cottage, Higher Bratton,
Seymour, Wincanton, Somerset BA9 8DA
☎ (01963) 34480
Email: coachmans@tinyworld.co.uk

Contact: Rodney Fuller
Opening Times: By appt. only.
Min Mail Order UK: £18.00 incl.
Cat. Cost: 2 x 1st class
Credit Cards: None
Specialities: *Helianthemum*.
Map Ref: C, B5

CFwr   **THE FLOWER BOWER** ✉ EU ♀
Woodlands, Shurton, Stogursey,
Nr Bridgwater, Somerset TA5 1QE
☎ (01278) 732134
Fax: (01278) 732134
Email: flower.bower@virgin.net
Contact: Sheila Tucker
Opening Times: Open most days mid-Mar-
31st Oct, please phone first.
Min Mail Order UK: £10.00 + p&p*
Min Mail Order EU: £20.00 + p&p
Cat. Cost: 4 x 1st class
Credit Cards: None
Specialities: Unusual perennials. Crocosmias,
kniphofias, hardy geraniums, *Phlox*, grasses,
bamboos, ferns & bulbs.
*Note: mail order Oct-end Mar only.
Map Ref: C, B4

CGOG   **GLOBAL ORANGE
GROVES UK** 🖳 ✉ EU 🖳 ♀
Horton Road, Horton Heath,
Wimborne, Dorset BH21 7JN
☎ (01202) 826244
Fax: (01202) 814651
Contact: P K Oliver
Opening Times: 1030-1700 7 days, unless
exhibiting.
Min Mail Order UK: Nmc
Min Mail Order EU: Nmc
Cat. Cost: Sae
Credit Cards: None
Specialities: Citrus trees, citrus fertiliser &
book *Success with Citrus*. Peaches, apricots,
nectarines, mangoes, avocados,
pomegranates, figs, persimmon, Ziziphus
jujube.
Map Ref: C, B6

CGra   **GRAHAM'S HARDY PLANTS** ✉ EU ♀
Southcroft, North Road, Timsbury,
Bath BA2 0JN
☎ (01761) 472187
Email: graplant@aol.com
Website: www.members.aol.com/graplant
Contact: Graham Nicholls
Opening Times: Not open to the public for
the near future.

C

Min Mail Order UK: £2.00 + p&p
Min Mail Order EU: £2.00 + p&p
Cat. Cost: 2 x 1st class or 2 x IRC
Credit Cards: None
Specialities: North American alpines
especially *Lewisia, Eriogonum, Penstemon,
Campanula, Kelseya, Phlox.*
Map Ref: C, B5

CGro   C W GROVES & SON ⊠ EU ▣
West Bay Road, Bridport,
Dorset DT6 4BA
☎ (01308) 422654
Fax: (01308) 420888
Email: c.w.grovesandson@zetnet.co.uk
Website:
www.users.zetnet.co.uk/c.w.grovesandson/
Contact: C W Groves
Opening Times: 0830-1700 Mon-Sat,
1030-1630 Sun.
Min Mail Order UK: No minimum charge*
Min Mail Order EU: £15.00 + p&p
Cat. Cost: 1 x 1st class
Credit Cards: Access, Visa, Switch, Delta,
MasterCard
Specialities: Nursery & garden centre
specialising in Parma & hardy *Viola.*
*Note: mainly violets by mail order.
Map Ref: C, C5

CGsR   GRASS ROOTS NURSERY ń
Fox Cottage, 24 Spirthill, Nr Calne,
Wilts SN11 9HP
☎ (01249) 760383
Contact: Jenny Bartlett
Opening Times: By appt. only. Please
phone.
Credit Cards: None
Specialities: Grasses. Large range but some
only available in small numbers. Hardy
perennials & herbs.
Map Ref: C, A6

CHad   HADSPEN GARDEN & NURSERY €
Hadspen House, Castle Cary,
Somerset BA7 7NG
☎ (01749) 813707
Fax: (01749) 813707
Email: pope@hadspengarden.co.uk
Website: www.hadspengarden.co.uk
Contact: N & S Pope
Opening Times: 1000-1700 Thu-Sun &
B/hols. 1st Mar-1st Oct. Garden open at the
same time.
Cat. Cost: 4 x 1st class
Credit Cards: None

Specialities: Large-leaved herbaceous.
Old fashioned and shrub roses.
Map Ref: C, B5

CHal   HALSWAY NURSERY ⊠ UK
Halsway, Nr Crowcombe, Taunton,
Somerset TA4 4BB
☎ (01984) 618243
Contact: T A & D J Bushen
Opening Times: Most days, please phone
first.
Min Mail Order UK: £2.00 + p&p
Cat. Cost: 2 x 1st class*
Credit Cards: None
Specialities: *Coleus* & *Begonia* (excl. tuberous
& winter flowering). Good range of
greenhouse & garden plants.
*Note: list for *Coleus* & *Begonia* only, no
nursery list.
Map Ref: C, B4

**CHar   WEST HARPTREE
NURSERY ▣ ń**
Bristol Road, West Harptree, Bath and
North East Somerset BS40 6HG
☎ (01761) 221370
Fax: (01761) 221989
Email: harptreenursery@supanet.com
Website: www.herbaceousperennials.co.uk
Contact: Bryn & Helene Bowles
Opening Times: From 1000 Tue-Sun
1st Mar-30th Nov.
Cat. Cost: Large Sae for free names list.
Credit Cards: MasterCard, Switch, Visa
Specialities: Unusual herbaceous perennials
& shrubs. Lilies, bulbs & grasses.
Map Ref: C, B5

CHdy   HARDY ORCHIDS ⊠ EU ▣
New Gate Farm, Scotchey Lane,
Stour Provost, Gillingham,
Dorset SP8 5LT
☎ (01747) 838368
Fax: (01747) 838308
Email: hardyorchids@supanet.com
Website: www.hardyorchids.supanet.com
Contact: N J Heywood
Opening Times: By appt. only.
Min Mail Order UK: £10.00 + p&p
Min Mail Order EU: £10.00 + p&p
Cat. Cost: 2 x 1st class

C

Credit Cards: None
Specialities: Hardy orchids - *Cypripedium, Dactylorhiza* & *Pleione*.
Map Ref: C, B5
OS Grid Ref: ST778217

CHea   HEATHER BANK NURSERY ⊠ UK n̂
Woodlands, 1 High Street,
Littleton Panell, Devizes,
Wiltshire SN10 4EL
☎ (01380) 812739
Email: mullanhbn.fsnet.co.uk
Contact: Mrs B Mullan
Opening Times: 1000-1500 Mon, Tue & Fri & w/ends. Other times by appt.
Min Mail Order UK: £10.00 + p&p
Cat. Cost: 3 x 1st class
Credit Cards: None
Specialities: *Campanula, Polemonium* & cottage garden plants.
Map Ref: C, B6

CHEx   HARDY EXOTICS ⊠ EU
Gilly Lane, Whitecross, Penzance,
Cornwall TR20 8BZ
☎ (01736) 740660
Fax: (01736) 741101
Website: www.hardyexotics.co.uk
Contact: C Shilton/J Smith
Opening Times: 1000-1700 Mon-Sat 1100-1700 Sun Apr-Oct, 1000-1700 Mon-Sat closed Sun Nov-Mar. Please phone first in winter months if travelling a long way.
Min Mail Order UK: £50.00 + carriage
Min Mail Order EU: £100.00
Cat. Cost: £1.00 postal order or 4 x 1st class (no cheques)
Credit Cards: Visa, Access, MasterCard, Connect, Delta
Specialities: Largest collection in the UK of trees, shrubs & herbaceous plants for tropical & desert effects. Hardy & half-hardy plants for gardens, patios & conservatories.
Map Ref: C, D1
OS Grid Ref: SW524345

CHid   HIDDEN VALLEY NURSERY ⊠ UK n̂ €
Umberleigh, Devon EX37 9BU
☎ (01769) 560567
Email: hiddenvalleynursery@email.com
Website: www.pelindley@lineone.net
Contact: Linda & Peter Lindley
Opening Times: Daylight hours, but please phone first.

Min Mail Order UK: No minimum charge*
Cat. Cost: 2 x 1st class
Credit Cards: None
Specialities: Hardy perennials especially shade lovers.
*Note: mail order during Mar only.
Map Ref: C B3
OS Grid Ref: SS567205

CHig   THE HIGH GARDEN ▣ ⊠ UK
Courtwood, Newton Ferrers,
South Devon PL8 1BW
☎ (01752) 872528
Contact: F Bennett
Opening Times: By appt.
Min Mail Order UK: £20.00 + p&p
Cat. Cost: 2 x 1st class
Credit Cards: None
Specialities: *Pieris* & *Rhododendron*.
Map Ref: C, D3

CHll   HILL HOUSE NURSERY & GARDENS €
Landscove, Nr Ashburton,
Devon TQ13 7LY
☎ (01803) 762273
Fax: (01803) 762273
Email: sacha@garden.demon.co.uk
Website: www.garden.demon.co.uk
Contact: Raymond, Sacha & Matthew Hubbard
Opening Times: 1100-1700 7 days, all year. Open all B/hols incl. Easter Sun. Tearoom open 1st Mar-30th Sep.
Cat. Cost: None issued.
Credit Cards: Delta, MasterCard, Switch, Visa
Specialities: 3000+ varieties of plants, most propagated on premises, many rare or unusual. The garden, open to the public, was laid out by Edward Hyams. Pioneers of glasshouse pest control by beneficial insects.
Map Ref: C, C3

CHor   HORTON VALE NURSERY
Horton Heath, Wimborne,
Dorset BH21 7JN
☎ (01202) 813473
Contact: David Wright
Opening Times: 0900-1700 open 6 days, closed Wed, Feb-Nov.
Cat. Cost: None issued
Credit Cards: None
Specialities: Perennials.
Map Ref: C, C6

CJas **JASMINE COTTAGE GARDENS** ✉ UK
26 Channel Road, Walton St Mary,
Clevedon, Somerset BS21 7BY
☎ (01275) 871850
Email: margaret@bologrew.demon.co.uk
Website: www.bologrew.pwp.blueyonder.co.uk
Contact: Mr & Mrs M Redgrave
Opening Times: May to Sep, daily by appt.
Min Mail Order UK: No minimum charge*
Cat. Cost: None issued
Credit Cards: None
Specialities: *Rhodochiton, Asarina,
Maurandya, Dicentra macrocapnos, Salvia,
Solenopsis, Isotoma*, half-hardy geraniums.
*Note: mail order seed only.
Map Ref: C, A4

CKel **KELWAYS LTD** ▣ ✉ EU ▣ ň €
Langport, Somerset TA10 9EZ
☎ (01458) 250521
Fax: (01458) 253351
Email: sales@kelways.co.uk
Website: www.kelways.co.uk
Contact: Mr David Root
Opening Times: 0900-1700 Mon-Fri,
1000-1700 Sat, 1000-1600 Sun.
Min Mail Order UK: £4.00 + p&p*
Min Mail Order EU: £8.00 + p&p
Cat. Cost: Free
Credit Cards: Visa, Access
Specialities: *Paeonia, Iris, Hemerocallis* &
herbaceous perennials. National Collection
of *Paeonia lactiflora*.
*Note: mail order for *Paeonia, Iris* &
Hemerocallis only.
Map Ref: C, B5

CKen **KENWITH NURSERY (GORDON
HADDOW)** ✉ EU ▣ € ◆
Blinsham, Nr Torrington, Beaford,
Winkleigh, Devon EX19 8NT
☎ (01805) 603274
Fax: (01805) 603663
Email: conifers@kenwith63.freeserve.co.uk
Website: www.kenwithnursery.co.uk
Contact: Gordon Haddow
Opening Times: 1000-1630 Wed-Sat Nov-
Feb & by appt. 1000-1630 7 days Mar-Oct.
Min Mail Order UK: £10.00 + p&p
Min Mail Order EU: £50.00 + p&p
Cat. Cost: 3 x 1st class
Credit Cards: Visa, MasterCard, EuroCard
Specialities: All conifer genera. Grafting a
speciality. Many new introductions to UK.
National Collection of dwarf conifers.
Map Ref: C, B3

CKin **KINGSFIELD CONSERVATION
NURSERY** ▣ ✉ UK
YSJ Seeds, Broadenham Lane, Winsham,
Chard, Somerset TA20 4JF
☎ (01460) 30070
Fax: (01460) 30070
Email: ysjseeds@aol.com
Contact: Melissa Boles
Opening Times: Please phone for details.
Min Mail Order UK: Nmc
Cat. Cost: 31p stamps
Credit Cards: None
Specialities: Native trees, shrubs, wild flowers
& wild flower seeds, bulbs & associated
British native species.
Map Ref: C, C4

CKno **KNOLL GARDENS** ✉ UK ň
Hampreston, Stapehill, Nr Wimborne,
Dorset BH21 7ND
☎ (01202) 873931
Fax: (01202) 870842
Email: enquiries@knollgardens.co.uk
Website: www.knollgardens.co.uk
Contact: N R Lucas
Opening Times: 1000-1700 7 days Apr-Sep,
1000-1600 Sun-Thu Oct-Mar.
Closed Xmas period.
Min Mail Order UK: No minimum charge
Cat. Cost: 6 x 1st class or on web.*
Credit Cards: Visa, MasterCard
Specialities: Grasses (main specialism).
Select perennials (select list).
*Note: catalogue available from Chelsea on.
Map Ref: C, C6

CKob **KOBAKOBA** ✉ EU ▣ ň
2 High Street, Ashcott, Bridgwater,
Somerset TA7 9PL
☎ (01458) 210700
mobile 07870 624969
Fax: (01458) 210650
Email: plants@kobakoba.co.uk
Website: www.kobakoba.co.uk
Contact: Christine Smithee & David
Constantine
Opening Times: Please phone for opening
times.
Min Mail Order UK: No minimum charge
Min Mail Order EU: Nmc
Cat. Cost: 4 x 1st class/4 x IRC

KEY		
✉ Mail order to UK or EU		ň Delivers to shows
▣ Exports beyond EU		€ Euro accepted
▣ Also supplies Wholesale		◆ See Display advertisement

C

Credit Cards: Visa, MasterCard, Delta
Specialities: Plants for tropical effect incl. *Ensete, Musa, Hedychium* & other *Zingiberaceae*. Conservatory & greenhouse plants.
Map Ref: C, B5
OS Grid Ref: ST4237

CLAP   LONG ACRE PLANTS ⊠ EU ń
South Marsh, Charlton Musgrove,
Nr Wincanton, Somerset BA9 8EX
☎ (01963) 32802
Fax: (01963) 32802
Email:
LongAcrePlants@woodlanders.fsnet.co.uk
Contact: Nigel & Michelle Rowland
Opening Times: 1000-1700 Thu-Fri,
Feb-Jul & Sep.
Min Mail Order UK: £10.00 + p&p
Min Mail Order EU: £20.00 + p&p
Cat. Cost: 3 x 1st class
Credit Cards: MasterCard, Visa
Specialities: Ferns, lilies, woodland bulbs & perennials. National Collection of *Asarum*.
Map Ref: C, B5

CLCN   LITTLE CREEK NURSERY ⊠ EU ◪ ń
39 Moor Road, Banwell, Weston-super-
Mare, Somerset BS29 6EF
☎ (01934) 823739
Fax: (01934) 823739
Contact: Rhys & Julie Adams
Opening Times: By appt only.
Min Mail Order UK: No minimum charge
Min Mail Order EU: Nmc
Cat. Cost: 3 x 1st class
Credit Cards: None
Specialities: Species *Cyclamen* (from seed), *Helleborus, Agapanthus* & *Schizostylis*.
Map Ref: C, B4

CLnd   LANDFORD TREES ◧ ⊠ EU €
Landford Lodge, Landford, Salisbury,
Wiltshire SP5 2EH
☎ (01794) 390808
Fax: (01794) 390037
Email: sales@landfordtrees.co.uk
Website: www.landfordtrees.co.uk
Contact: C D Pilkington
Opening Times: 0800-1700 Mon-Fri.
Min Mail Order UK: Please enquire
Min Mail Order EU: Please enquire
Cat. Cost: Free
Credit Cards: None
Specialities: Deciduous ornamental trees.
Map Ref: C, B6   OS Grid Ref: SU247201

CLoc   C S LOCKYER ◧ ⊠ EU ń € ◆
Lansbury, 70 Henfield Road, Coalpit Heath,
Bristol BS36 2UZ
☎ (01454) 772219
Fax: (01454) 772219
Email: sales@lockyerfuchsias.co.uk
Website: www.lockyerfuchsias.co.uk
Contact: C S Lockyer
Opening Times: 1000-1300, 1430-1700 most days, please ring. Many open days & coach parties.
Min Mail Order UK: 6 plants + p&p
Min Mail Order EU: £12.00 + p&p
Cat. Cost: 4 x 1st class
Credit Cards: None
Specialities: *Fuchsia*.
Map Ref: C, A5

CLvH   DEVONSHIRE LAVENDERS & HERBS ◧ ⊠ UK
Exmouth Road, West Hill, Ottery St Mary,
Devon EX11 1JZ
☎ (01404) 823221
Fax: (01404) 823335
Email: sales@lavenders.net
Website: www.lavenders.net
Contact: Owen Lane
Opening Times: 0900-1700 Mon-Fri,
1000-1600 Sat & Sun.
Min Mail Order UK: £10.00*
Cat. Cost: 2 x 1st class
Credit Cards: Visa, MasterCard, Solo, JCB, Switch
Specialities: *Lavandula* & all herbs.
*Note: mail order lavenders all year, herbs spring/summer only.
Map Ref: C, C4
OS Grid Ref: SY062949

CLyd   LYDFORD ALPINE NURSERY ⊠ UK ń
2 Southern Cottages, Lydford, Okehampton,
Devon EX20 4BL
☎ (01822) 820398
Contact: Julie & David Hatchett
Opening Times: 1000-1700 Tue & Thu
Apr-Oct & by appt. Nov-Mar by appt. only.
Closed 8th-14th Jul.
Min Mail Order UK: £10.00 + p&p*
Cat. Cost: Sae for saxifrage list.
Credit Cards: None
Specialities: *Saxifraga*. Very wide range of choice & unusual alpines in small quantities.
*Note: mail order *Saxifraga* only.
Map Ref: C, C3
OS Grid Ref: SX504830

CM&M **M & M Plants** ń
Lloret, Chittlehamholt, Umberleigh,
Devon EX37 9PD
☎ (01769) 540448
Contact: Mr M Thorne
Opening Times: 0930-1730 Tue-Sat
Apr-Oct & 1000-1600 Tue-Sat Nov-Mar,
& B/hols.
Cat. Cost: 4 x 1st class
Credit Cards: None
Specialities: Perennials. Also carry a good
range of alpines, shrubs, trees & roses.
Map Ref: C, B3

CMac **Macpennys Nurseries** ⊠ UK
154 Burley Road, Bransgore, Christchurch,
Dorset BH23 8DB
☎ (01425) 672348
Fax: (01425) 673945
Contact: T & V Lowndes
Opening Times: 0800-1700 Mon-Fri,
0900-1700 Sat 1400-1700 Sun. Closed
Xmas & New Year.
Min Mail Order UK: Nmc
Cat. Cost: A4 Sae with 4 x 1st class
Credit Cards: Access, American Express,
Delta, Access, EuroCard, MasterCard, Visa,
Switch, Solo
Specialities: General
Map Ref: C, C6

CMCN **Mallet Court
Nursery** ▣ ⊠ EU ▣ ń €
Curry Mallet, Taunton,
Somerset TA3 6SY
☎ (01823) 481493
Fax: (01823) 481493
Email: harris@malletcourt.freeserve.co.uk
Website: www.malletcourt.co.uk
Contact: J G S & P M E Harris F.L.S.
Opening Times: 0900-1700 Mon-Fri. Sat &
Sun by appt.
Min Mail Order UK: No minimum charge*
Min Mail Order EU: Nmc
Cat. Cost: £1.50
Credit Cards: MasterCard, Visa
Specialities: Maples, oaks, *Magnolia*, hollies
& other rare and unusual plants including
those from China & South Korea.
*Note: mail order Oct-Mar only.
Map Ref: C, B4

CMCo **Meadow Cottage Plants** ▣ ń €
Pitt Hill, Ivybridge, Devon PL21 0JJ
☎ (01752) 894532
Contact: Mrs L P Hunt

Opening Times: By appt. only.
Cat. Cost: 2 x 2nd class
Credit Cards: None
Specialities: Hardy *Geranium* & other hardy
perennials.
Map Ref: C, D3

CMdw **Meadows Nursery** ▣ ń €
5 Rectory Cottages, Mells, Frome,
Somerset BA11 3PA
☎ (01373) 813025
Fax: (01373) 813025
Contact: Sue Lees & Eddie Wheatley
Opening Times: 1000-1800 Wed-Sun
1st Feb-31st Oct & B/hols.
Cat. Cost: 4 x 1st class
Credit Cards: None
Specialities: Hardy perennials, shrubs &
some conservatory plants.
Map Ref: C, B5

CMea **The Mead Nursery** ń
Brokerswood, Nr Westbury,
Wilts BA13 4EG
☎ (01373) 859990
Contact: Steve & Emma Lewis-Dale
Opening Times: 0900-1700 Wed-Sat &
B/hols, 1200-1700 Sun, 1st Feb-10th Oct.
Closed Easter Sun.
Cat. Cost: 5 x 1st class
Credit Cards: None
Specialities: Perennials, alpines, pot grown
bulbs and grasses.
Map Ref: C, B5
OS Grid Ref: ST833517

CMGP **Milton Garden Plants** €
Milton-on-Stour, Gillingham,
Dorset SP8 5PX
☎ (01747) 822484
Fax: (01747) 822484
Email: r.w.r.cumming@btinternet.co
Website: www.miltongardenplants.co.uk
Contact: Sue Hardy & Richard Cumming
Opening Times: 0900-1700 Tue-Sat &
B/hol Mons, 1000-1630 Sun. Closed Jan.
Cat. Cost: 3 x 1st class for plant list
Credit Cards: Visa, Access, Switch, Delta
Specialities: Very wide range of perennials.
Ever changing selection of trees, shrubs,
conifers, alpines & herbs. Emphasis on good

C

information with display gardens alongside.
Map Ref: C, B5
OS Grid Ref: ST797280

CMHG MARWOOD HILL GARDENS
Barnstaple, Devon, EX31 4EB
☎ (01271) 342528
Website: www.marwoodhillgardens.co.uk
Contact: Malcolm Pharoah
Opening Times: 1100-1700 7 days.
Cat. Cost: 5 x 2nd class
Credit Cards: Visa, Delta, MasterCard,
Switch, Solo
Specialities: Large range of unusual trees &
shrubs. *Eucalyptus*, alpines, *Camellia*, *Astilbe*,
bog plants & perennials. National
Collections of *Astilbe*, *Tulbaghia* & *Iris ensata*.
Map Ref: C, B3

CMil MILL COTTAGE PLANTS ⊠ EU ♙
The Mill, Henley Lane, Wookey,
Somerset BA5 1AP
☎ (01749) 676966
Email: mcp@tinyworld.co.uk
Contact: Sally Gregson
Opening Times: 1000-1800 Wed Mar-Sep
or by appt. Phone for directions.
Min Mail Order UK: £5.00 + p&p
Min Mail Order EU: £10.00 + p&p
Cat. Cost: 4 x 1st class
Credit Cards: None
Specialities: Unusual & period cottage plants
esp. *Dierama*, *Papaver orientale*, hardy
Geranium, *Euphorbia*, ferns, *Pulmonaria*
& grasses. Also *Hydrangea aspera* &
H. serrata cultivars.
Map Ref: C, B5

CNat NATURAL SELECTION ⊠ UK ♙ €
1 Station Cottages, Hullavington,
Chippenham, Wilts SN14 6ET
☎ (01666) 837369
Email: martin@worldmutation.demon.co.uk
Website: www.worldmutation.demon.co.uk
Contact: Martin Cragg-Barber
Opening Times: Please phone first.
Min Mail Order UK: £9.00 + p&p
Cat. Cost: £1.00 or 5 x 2nd class
Credit Cards: None
Specialities: Unusual British natives &
others. Also seed.
Map Ref: C, A5

CNCN NAKED CROSS NURSERIES ▣ ⊠ UK
Waterloo Road, Corfe Mullen,
Wimborne, Dorset BH21 3SR

☎ (01202) 693256
Fax: (01202) 693259
Contact: Peter French
Opening Times: 0900-1700 7 days.
Min Mail Order UK: 10 heathers
Cat. Cost: 2 x 1st class
Credit Cards: Visa, Access, American
Express, Switch, Not for mail orders
Specialities: Heathers.
Map Ref: C, C6

CNic NICKY'S ROCK GARDEN NURSERY ♙
Broadhayes, Stockland, Honiton,
Devon EX14 9EH
☎ (01404) 881213
Email: Dianabob.Dark@nickys.sagehost.co.uk
Contact: Diana & Bob Dark
Opening Times: 0900-dusk 7 days. Please
phone first to check & for directions.
Cat. Cost: 3 x 1st class
Credit Cards: None
Specialities: Plants for rock gardens, scree,
troughs, banks, walls & front of border &
dwarf shrubs. Many unusual. Plants
propagated in small numbers. Ring to check
availability before travelling.
Map Ref: C, C4
OS Grid Ref: ST236027

CNMi NEWPORT MILLS NURSERY ⊠ EU ♙ €
Wrantage, Taunton,
Somerset TA3 6DJ
☎ (01823) 490231
mobile 07950 035668
Contact: John Barrington, Rachel Pettitt
Opening Times: By appt. only.
Min Mail Order UK: No minimum charge
Min Mail Order EU: Nmc
Cat. Cost: Free
Credit Cards: None
Specialities: *Delphinium*. Mail order Apr-Sep
for young delphiniums in 7cm pots.
Dormant plants can be sent out in
autumn/winter if requested.
Map Ref: C, B4

COkL OAK LEAF NURSERIES ▣ ⊠ ♙
24 Crantock Drive, Almondsbury, Bristol
BS32 4HG
☎ (01454) 620180
mobile 07718 667940
Contact: David Price
Opening Times: Not open, mail order only.
Min Mail Order UK: £10.00 + p&p
Cat. Cost: 2 x 1st class
Credit Cards: None

Specialities: Wide range of rock & herbaceous plants, some unusual, incl. *Dianthus, Helianthemum, Lavandula, Hebe* & *Saxifraga*. Shrubs also a speciality.
Map Ref: C, A5

COld   THE OLD MILL HERBARY
Helland Bridge, Bodmin,
Cornwall PL30 4QR
☎ (01208) 841206
Fax: (01208) 841206
Email: enquiries@oldmillherbary.co.uk
Website: www.oldmillherbary.co.uk
Contact: Mrs B Whurr
Opening Times: 1000-1700 Thu-Tue Apr-30th Sep.
Cat. Cost: 6 x 1st class
Credit Cards: None
Specialities: Culinary, medicinal & aromatic herbs, shrubs, climbing & herbaceous plants.
Map Ref: C, C2
OS Grid Ref: SX065717

COlW   THE OLD WITHY GARDEN NURSERY ✉ UK
The Grange, Gweek, Helston,
Cornwall TR12 6BE
☎ (01326) 221171
Email: WithyNursery@fsbdial.co.uk
Contact: Sheila Chandler or Nick Chandler
Opening Times: 1000-1700 Wed-Mon mid Feb-end Oct.
Min Mail Order UK: Nmc
Cat. Cost: 4 x 1st class
Credit Cards: MasterCard, Visa, Delta, Switch, American Express
Specialities: Cottage garden plants, perennials, biennials & grasses.
Map Ref: C, D1

COtt   OTTER NURSERIES LTD
Gosford Road, Ottery St. Mary,
Devon EX11 1LZ
☎ (01404) 815815
Fax: (01404) 815816
Email: otter@otternurseries.co.uk
Contact: Mrs Pam Poole
Opening Times: 0800-1730 Mon-Sat, 1030-1630 Sun. Closed Xmas, Boxing Day & Easter Sun.
Cat. Cost: None issued
Credit Cards: Visa, Access, American Express, Diners, Switch
Specialities: Large garden centre & nursery

with extensive range of trees, shrubs, conifers, climbers, roses, fruit & hardy perennials.
Map Ref: C, C4

CPar   PARKS PERENNIALS
242 Wallisdown Road, Wallisdown,
Bournemouth BH10 4HZ
☎ (01202) 524464
Contact: S Parks
Opening Times: Apr-Oct most days, please phone first.
Cat. Cost: None issued.
Credit Cards: None
Specialities: Hardy herbaceous perennials.
Map Ref: C, C6

CPas   PASSIFLORA (NATIONAL COLLECTION)
▣ ✉ EU ▣ ♂ €
Lampley Road, Kingston Seymour,
Clevedon, North Somerset BS21 6XS
☎ (01934) 833350
Fax: (01934) 877255
Email: greenhelm@lineone.net
Contact: John Vanderplank or Jane Lindsay
Opening Times: 0900-1300 & 1400-1700 Mon-Sat, May-Sep.
Min Mail Order UK: £20.00 + p&p
Min Mail Order EU: £30.00 + p&p
Cat. Cost: 3 x 1st class
Credit Cards: Visa, Access, EuroCard, MasterCard
Specialities: *Passiflora*. National Collection of over 200 species & varieties.
Note: retail nursery now at Kingston Seymour.
Map Ref: C, A4

CPBP   PARHAM BUNGALOW PLANTS ✉ EU ♂ €
Parham Lane, Market Lavington, Devizes,
Wilts SN10 4QA
☎ (01380) 812605
Email: jjs@pbplants.freeserve.co.uk
Contact: Mrs D E Sample
Opening Times: Please ring first.
Min Mail Order UK: Nmc
Min Mail Order EU: Nmc
Cat. Cost: Sae
Credit Cards: None
Specialities: Alpines & dwarf shrubs.
Map Ref: C, B6

C

CPen   **Pennard Plants** ✉ EU ⋒ €
3 The Gardens, East Pennard,
Shepton Mallet,
Somerset BA4 6TU
☎ (01749) 860039
mobile 07702 579627
Fax: (01749) 860232
Email: sales@pennardplants.com
Website: pennardplants.com
Contact: Chris Smith
Opening Times: By appt. only.
Min Mail Order UK: Nmc
Min Mail Order EU: Nmc
Cat. Cost: 2 x 1st class
Credit Cards: None
Specialities: Ornamental grasses, *Agapanthus,
Crocosmis, Dahlia* & *Phlox.*
Note: nursery at The Walled Garden at East
Pennard.
Map Ref: C, B5

CPev   **Peveril Clematis Nursery** €
Christow, Exeter EX6 7NG
☎ (01647) 252937
Contact: Barry Fretwell
Opening Times: 1000-1300 & 1400-1730
Fri-Wed, 1000-1300 Sun. Dec-Mar by
appointment.
Cat. Cost: 2 x 1st class
Credit Cards: None
Specialities: *Clematis.*
Map Ref: C, C3

CPhi   **Alan Phipps Cacti** ✉ EU €
62 Samuel White Road, Hanham,
Bristol BS15 3LX
☎ (0117) 9607591
Contact: A Phipps
Opening Times: All times, but prior phone
call essential to ensure a greeting.
Min Mail Order UK: £5.00 + p&p
Min Mail Order EU: £20.00 + p&p
Cat. Cost: Sae or 2 x IRC (EC only)
Credit Cards: None
Specialities: *Mammillaria, Astrophytum* &
Ariocarpus. Species & varieties will change
with times. Ample quantities exist in spring.
Limited range of *Agave.*
Note: Euro accepted as cash only.
Map Ref: C, A5

CPla   **Plant World Botanic
Gardens** ▣ ✉ EU ▣ ◆
St Marychurch Road, Newton Abbot,
South Devon TQ12 4SE
☎ (01803) 872939

Fax: (01803) 875018
Contact: Ray Brown
Opening Times: 0930-1700 7 days a week,
Apr (Easter if earlier)-Oct.
Min Mail Order UK: £8.00*
Min Mail Order EU: £20.00
Cat. Cost: 3 x 1st class or 2 x IRC.
Credit Cards: Visa, Access, EuroCard,
MasterCard
Specialities: Alpines & unusual herbaceous
plants. 4 acre garden correctly planted out
as the map of the world. National Collection
of *Primula.*
*Note: mail order for seed only.
Map Ref: C, C3

CPle   **Pleasant View Nursery** ✉ EU
Two Mile Oak, Nr Denbury,
Newton Abbot,
Devon TQ12 6DG
☎ (01803) 813388 answerphone
Contact: Mrs B D Yeo
Opening Times: Nursery open 1000-1700
Wed-Fri mid Mar-end Sep (closed for lunch
1245-1330).
Min Mail Order UK: £20.00 + p&p
Min Mail Order EU: £20.00 + p&p (Salvias
only)
Cat. Cost: 3 x 2nd class or 2 x IRC
Credit Cards: None
Specialities: *Salvia* & unusual shrubs for
garden & conservatory. National Collections
of *Salvia* & *Abelia.* Nursery off A381 at Two
Mile Oak Cross towards Denbury.
Map Ref: C, C3

CPLG   **Pine Lodge Gardens
& Nursery**
Cuddra, Holmbush, St Austell,
Cornwall PL25 3RQ
☎ (01726) 73500
Fax: (01726) 73500
Email: sclemo@talk21.com
Website: www.pine-lodge.co.uk
Contact: Ray & Shirley Clemo
Opening Times: 1000-1700 7 days
25th Mar-31st Oct.
Cat. Cost: 5 x 2nd class
Credit Cards: None
Specialities: Rare & unusual shrubs &
herbaceous, some from seed collected on
plant expeditions each year. National
Collection of *Grevillea.* Limited stocks of
all plants.
Map Ref: C, D2
OS Grid Ref: SX045527

CPlN   THE PLANTSMAN NURSERY ⊠ EU ☑ ◆
North Wonson Farm, Throwleigh,
Okehampton, Devon EX20 2JA
☎ (01647) 231699 office
☎ (01647) 231618 nursery
Fax: (01647) 231157
Email: pnursery@aol.com
Website: www.plantsman.com
Contact: Guy & Emma Sisson
Opening Times: Mail order & strictly by
appt.
Min Mail Order UK: £25.00 + p&p
Min Mail Order EU: £45.00 + p&p
Cat. Cost: £2.00*
Credit Cards: MasterCard, Access,
American Express, Delta, Diners, EuroCard,
Switch, Visa
Specialities: Unusual hardy & tender
climbers. Seeds for non-EU countries.
*Note: seed list available for non-EU
countries.
Map Ref: C, C3

CPlt   PLANTAHOLICS
Hillside, Coombe Street, Penselwood,
Wincanton, Somerset BA9 8NF
☎ (01747) 840852
Contact: Jane Edmonds
Opening Times: Usually 1000-1600 Thu,
Fri & Sat, 18th Apr-28th Sep 2002, 17th
Apr-27th Sep 2003. Please phone first.
Cat. Cost: 3 x 1st class (Feb-Jul only)
Credit Cards: None
Specialities: Small nursery concentrating
mainly on high performance perennials for
various situations. Many unusual & most
propagated on the nursery.
Map Ref: C, B5

CPMA   P M A PLANT SPECIALITIES ☑ ⊠ EU ☑
Lower Mead, West Hatch, Taunton,
Somerset TA3 5RN
☎ (01823) 480774
Fax: (01823) 481046
Email: karan@junker.net
Website: www.junker.net
Contact: Karan or Nick Junker
Opening Times: Strictly by appt. only.
Min Mail Order UK: Nmc
Min Mail Order EU: Nmc
Cat. Cost: 5 x 2nd class
Credit Cards: None
Specialities: Choice & unusual shrubs incl.
grafted *Acer palmatum, Cornus, Magnolia* & a
wide range of *Daphne*. Limited numbers of
some hard to propagate plants, esp. daphnes.

Reserve orders accepted.
Map Ref: C, B4

CPne   PINE COTTAGE PLANTS ☑ ⊠ EU ☑ ♠ €
Pine Cottage, Fourways, Eggesford,
Chulmleigh, Devon EX18 7QZ
☎ (01769) 580076
Fax: (01769) 581427
Email: pcplants@supanet.com
Contact: Dick Fulcher
Opening Times: By appt. only. Special open
weeks for *Agapanthus*, 1000-1800 daily excl.
Sun mornings, 22nd Jul-10th Aug 2002 &
21st Jul-9th Aug 2003.
Min Mail Order UK: £15.00 + p&p
Min Mail Order EU: £20.00 + p&p
Cat. Cost: 4 x 1st class
Credit Cards: None
Specialities: National Collection of
Agapanthus.
Note: mail order *Agapanthus* from Oct-Jun.
Some cvs available in small quantities only.
Map Ref: C, B3

CPom   POMEROY PLANTS
Tower House, Pomeroy Lane, Wingfield,
Trowbridge, Wilts BA14 9LJ
☎ (01225) 769551
Contact: Simon Young
Opening Times: Mar-Nov. Please phone
first.
Cat. Cost: None issued
Credit Cards: None
Specialities: Hardy, mainly species,
herbaceous perennials. Many unusual and
often small numbers. Specialities *Allium*,
Salvia & shade-lovers, esp. *Epimedium*.
Map Ref: C, B5
OS Grid Ref: ST817569

CPou   POUNSLEY PLANTS ☑ ⊠ EU ♠ €
Poundsley Combe, Spriddlestone, Brixton,
Plymouth PL9 0DW
☎ (01752) 402873
Fax: (01752) 402873
Email: pou.599@aol.com
Website: www.tripod.co.uk/pounsley
Contact: Mrs Jane Hollow
Opening Times: Normally 1000-1700 Mon-
Sat but please phone first.
Min Mail Order UK: £10.00 + p&p*

C

Min Mail Order EU: £20.00 + p&p
Cat. Cost: 2 x 1st class
Credit Cards: None
Specialities: Unusual herbaceous perennials
& cottage plants. Selection of *Clematis* & old
roses. Large selection of South African
monocots.
*Note: mail order Nov-Feb only.
Map Ref: C, D3
OS Grid Ref: SX521538

CPrp PROPERPLANTS.COM ⊠ UK ń
15 Grass Valley Park, Bodmin,
Cornwall PL31 1DN
☎ (01208) 269330
Fax: (01208) 269330
Email: info@Properplants.com
Website: www.ProperPlants.com
Contact: Sarah Wilks
Opening Times: Not open.
Min Mail Order UK: Nmc
Cat. Cost: 4 x 1st class
Credit Cards: Visa, MasterCard, Switch,
Delta
Specialities: Culinary, medicinal, aromatic &
decorative herbs. Wide range of unusual
& easy herbaceous perennials.

CQua QUALITY DAFFODILS ▣ ⊠ EU ▣ € ◆
14 Roscarrack Close, Falmouth,
Cornwall TR11 4PJ
☎ (01326) 317959
Fax: (01326) 317959
Email: RAScamp@daffodils.uk.com
Website: www.daffodils.uk.com
Contact: R A Scamp
Opening Times: Not open, mail order
only.
Min Mail Order UK: No minimum charge
Min Mail Order EU: Nmc
Cat. Cost: 3 x 1st class
Credit Cards: None
Specialities: *Narcissus* hybrids & species.
Map Ref: C, D1

CRde ROWDE MILL NURSERY €
Rowde, Devizes, Wilts SN10 1SZ
☎ (01380) 723016
Fax: (01380) 723016
Email: cholmeley@supanet.com
Contact: Mrs J Cholmeley
Opening Times: 1000-1700 Thu-Sun &
B/hol Mon Apr-Sep.
Cat. Cost: None issued
Credit Cards: None
Specialities: Wide range of hardy perennials,

all grown on the nursery. Plants offered in
pots or lifted from stockbeds.
Map Ref: C, A6

CRDP R D PLANTS ▣
Homelea Farm, Chard Road, Tytherleigh,
Axminster, Devon EX13 7BG
☎ (01460) 220206 between 0830-0930
only.
Contact: Rodney Davey & Lynda Windsor
Opening Times: 0900-1300 & 1400-1700
Tue-Sun 1st Mar-30th Jun. Please check first.
Feb by appt. for hellebores.
Cat. Cost: 4 x loose 2nd class
Credit Cards: None
Specialities: Choice & unusual herbaceous,
shade & woodland plants, *Helleborus*, plus
rarities.
Map Ref: C, C4
OS Grid Ref: ST3203

CRea REALLY WILD FLOWERS ▣ ⊠ EU ▣ ń €
H V Horticulture Ltd,
Spring Mead, Bedchester,
Shaftesbury, Dorset SP7 0JU
☎ (01747) 811778
Fax: (01747) 811499
Email: rwflowers@aol.com
Website: www.reallywildflowers.co.uk
Contact: Grahame Dixie
Opening Times: Not open to public.
Min Mail Order UK: £40.00 + p&p
Min Mail Order EU: £100.00 + p&p
Cat. Cost: 3 x 1st class
Credit Cards: None
Specialities: Wild flowers for grasslands,
woodlands, wetlands & heaths. Seeds,
orchids. Advisory & soil analysis services.
Map Ref: C, B5

CRez REZARE NURSERIES
Rezare, Nr Treburley, Launceston,
Cornwall PL15 9NX
☎ (01579) 370969
Email: REZARENURSERIES@aol.com
Contact: Kym & Rick Finney/Mel & Jim
Gearing
Opening Times: 1000-1730, 7 days
1st Mar-end Oct. Other times by appt.
Cat. Cost: None issued
Credit Cards: MasterCard, Visa
Specialities: Growers of a full & varied range
of choice & unusual plants of the highest
quality, incl. a good selection of herbaceous
perennials, shrubs & trees.
Map Ref: C, C2

CRHN ROSELAND HOUSE NURSERY ⊠ UK ♄
Chacewater, Truro, Cornwall TR4 8QB
☎ (01872) 560451
Email: clematis@roselandhouse.co.uk
Website: www.roselandhouse.co.uk
Contact: C R Pridham
Opening Times: 1200-1800 Mon, Tue &
Wed Mar-Sep.
Min Mail Order UK: No minimum charge
Cat. Cost: 2 x 1st class
Credit Cards: None
Specialities: Climbing & conservatory plants.
Map Ref: C, D1

CRoM ROSEDOWN MILL PALMS AND
EXOTICS ▣ ⊠ EU
Hartland, Bideford, Devon EX39 6AH
☎ (01237) 441527
Email: huwcol@aol.com
Website: www.rosedownmill.co.uk
Contact: Huw Collingbourne
Opening Times: By appt. only.
Min Mail Order UK: £25.00
Min Mail Order EU: £25.00
Cat. Cost: Sae for list
Credit Cards: None
Specialities: Palms, cycads, pachypodiums.
Map Ref: C, B2
OS Grid Ref: SS276248

CRow ROWDEN GARDENS ▣ ⊠ EU ▣
Brentor, Nr Tavistock, Devon PL19 0NG
☎ (01822) 810275
Fax: (01822) 810275
Email: rowdengardens@btopenworld.com
Contact: John R L Carter
Opening Times: 1000-1700 Sat, Sun &
B/hols 26th Mar-end Sep. Other times in
2002 & all of 2003 by appt only.
Min Mail Order UK: Nmc
Min Mail Order EU: Nmc
Cat. Cost: 6 x 1st class
Credit Cards: None
Specialities: Aquatics, damp loving &
associated plants incl. rare & unusual
varieties. National Collections of *Polygonum*
& *Ranunculus ficaria*. National Collections of
Caltha & water iris applied for.
Map Ref: C, C3

CRsw ROSEWARNE COLLECTIONS ⊠ UK
Duchy College, Rosewarne, Camborne,
Cornwall TR14 0AB
☎ (01209) 722100
Fax: (01209) 722159
Email: r.smith@cornwall.ac.uk

Contact: Ros Smith or Marshall Hutchens
Opening Times: By appt. only.
Min Mail Order UK: £10.00 + p&p
Cat. Cost: 2 x 1st class
Credit Cards: None
Specialities: *Escallonia* species & hybrids.
National Collection of *Escallonia*.
Map Ref: C, D1

CRWN THE REALLY WILD
NURSERY ▣ ⊠ UK ♄ €
19 Hoopers Way, Torrington,
Devon EX38 7NS
☎ (01805) 624739
Email: thereallywildnursery@hotmail.com
Website: www.thereallywildnurserydevon.biz
Contact: Kathryn Moore
Opening Times: Not open.
Min Mail Order UK: £10.00 + p&p*
Cat. Cost: 3 x 1st class
Credit Cards: None
Specialities: Wild flowers, bulbs & seeds.
*Note: mail order Apr-Oct only, grown to
order (plants in pots or plugs).

CSam SAMPFORD SHRUBS ⊠ UK €
Sampford Peverell, Tiverton,
Devon EX16 7EN
☎ (01884) 821164
Email: martin@samshrub.co.uk
Website: www.samshrub.co.uk
Contact: M Hughes-Jones & S Proud
Opening Times: 0900-1700 7 days Mar-Jun.
0900-1700 Thu-Sat & 1000-1600 Sun
during Feb & Jul-Nov. Mail order Oct-mid
Mar.
Min Mail Order UK: £15.00 + p&p*
Cat. Cost: Sae
Credit Cards: MasterCard, Switch, Solo,
Delta, Electron, Maestro, Visa
Specialities: Propagate an extensive range of
garden-worthy common and uncommon
plants. National Collection of *Helenium*.
Pulmonaria & *Crocosmia* displays.
*Note: mail order Oct-mid Mar only.
Map Ref: C, B4
OS Grid Ref: ST043153

CSBt ST BRIDGET NURSERIES LTD ▣ ⊠ UK
Old Rydon Lane, Exeter EX2 7JY
☎ (01392) 873672/3/4

KEY		
⊠ Mail order to UK or EU	♄ Delivers to shows	
▣ Exports beyond EU	€ Euro accepted	
▣ Also supplies Wholesale	◆ See Display advertisement	

C

Fax: (01392) 876710
Website: www.stbridgetnurseries.co.uk
Contact: Garden Centre Plant Advice
Opening Times: 0800-1700 Mon-Sat,
1030-1630 Sun, 0800-1700 Bank Hols.
Min Mail Order UK: Nmc
Cat. Cost: Free
Credit Cards: Visa, MasterCard, Switch,
Solo
Specialities: Large general nursery, with two
garden centres.
Map Ref: C, C4
OS Grid Ref: SX955905

CSdC SHERWOOD COTTAGE ▣ €
Newton St Cyres, Exeter EX5 5BT
☎ (01392) 851589
Email: vaughan.gallavan@connectfree.co.uk
Contact: Vaughan Gallavan
Opening Times: By appt. only.
Cat. Cost: 2 x 1st class
Credit Cards: None
Specialities: Magnolias, trees & shrubs.
National Collection of Knap Hill azaleas.
Ghent & species deciduous azaleas.
Map Ref: C, C3

CSev LOWER SEVERALLS NURSERY ⊠ UK
Crewkerne, Somerset TA18 7NX
☎ (01460) 73234
Fax: (01460) 76105
Email: mary@lowerseveralls.co.uk
Website: www.lowerseveralls.co.uk
Contact: Mary R Pring
Opening Times: 1000-1700 Fri-Wed
1st Mar-20th Oct & Sun 1400-1700
May & Jun.
Min Mail Order UK: £20.00*
Cat. Cost: 4 x 1st class
Credit Cards: None
Specialities: Herbs, herbaceous &
conservatory plants.
*Note: Mail order perennials only.
Map Ref: C, B5
OS Grid Ref: ST457111

CSil SILVER DALE NURSERIES ⊠ EU € ◆
Shute Lane, Combe Martin,
Devon EX34 0HT
☎ (01271) 882539
Email: silverdale.nurseries@virgin.net
Contact: Roger Gilbert
Opening Times: 1000-1800 7 days.
Min Mail Order UK: Nmc
Min Mail Order EU: Nmc
Cat. Cost: 4 x 1st class

Credit Cards: Visa, MasterCard, EuroCard
Specialities: National Collection of *Fuchsia*.
Hardy fuchsias (cultivars and species).
Map Ref: C, B3

CSLe SILVER LEAF NURSERIES ▣ ⊠ UK ♠ ◆
Charmouth Road, Lyme Regis,
Dorset DT7 3HF
☎ (01297) 444655
Fax: (01297) 444655
Email: woodberry@fsbdial.co.uk
Website: www.woodbury@fsbdial.co.uk
Contact: Chris Hughes
Opening Times: 1000-1700 Fri-Mon, or by
appointment
Min Mail Order UK: £25.00
Cat. Cost: 4 x 1st class
Credit Cards: None
Specialities: Silver- & grey-leafed plants, incl.
many lavenders. Will propagate to order.
Map Ref: C, C4
OS Grid Ref: ST932343

CSli SLIPPS GARDEN CENTRE
Butts Hill, Frome, Somerset BA11 1HR
☎ (01373) 467013
Fax: (01373) 467013
Contact: James Hall
Opening Times: 0900-1730 Mon-Sat,
1000-1630 Sun.
Cat. Cost: None issued
Credit Cards: Visa, Access, MasterCard,
Delta, Switch
Specialities: Conifers. *Achillea*.
Map Ref: C, B5

CSpe SPECIAL PLANTS ⊠ EU ♠ €
Hill Farm Barn, Greenways Lane, Cold
Ashton, Chippenham, Wilts SN14 8LA
☎ (01225) 891686
Email: specialplants@bigfoot.com
Website: www.specialplants.net
Contact: Derry Watkins
Opening Times: 1030-1630 7 days Mar-
Sept. Other times please ring first to check.
Min Mail Order UK: £10.00 + p&p*
Min Mail Order EU: £10.00 + p&p
Cat. Cost: 5 x 2nd class (sae only for seed
list)
Credit Cards: MasterCard, Visa, Delta,
Switch, Electron, Maestro
Specialities: Tender perennials, *Felicia,
Diascia, Mimulus, Pelargonium, Salvia,
Streptocarpus*, hardy geraniums. Many
varieties propagated in small numbers.
New introductions of S. African plants.

C

*Note: mail order Sep-Mar only.
Map Ref: C, A5
OS Grid Ref: ST749726

**CSPN SHERSTON PARVA NURSERY
LTD** ⊠ EU ⊠ ♠ €
Malmesbury Road, Sherston,
Wilts SN16 0NX
☎ (01666) 841066
Fax: (01666) 841132
Email: sales@sherstonparva.com
Website: www.sherstonparva.com
Contact: Martin Rea
Opening Times: 1000-1700 7 days
1st Feb-31th Dec. Closed Jan.
Min Mail Order UK: No minimum charge
Min Mail Order EU: Nmc
Cat. Cost: Free
Credit Cards: MasterCard, Delta, Visa,
Switch
Specialities: *Clematis*, wall shrubs &
climbers.
Map Ref: C, A5

CStu STONE LANE GARDENS ⊠ ⊠ UK
Stone Farm, Chagford, Devon TQ13 8JU
☎ (01647) 231311   **Fax:** (01647) 231311
Email: kenneth_ashburner@talk21.com
Website:
www.mythicgarden.users.btopenworld.com
Contact: Kenneth Ashburner
Opening Times: By appt. only.
Min Mail Order UK: No minimum charge
Cat. Cost: £3.00 for descriptive catalogue
Specialities: Wide range of wild provenance
Betula & *Alnus*. Interesting varieties of
Rubus, Sorbus etc.

CStr SUE STRICKLAND PLANTS ⊠ UK ♠
The Poplars, Isle Brewers, Taunton,
Somerset TA3 6QN
☎ (01460) 281454
Fax: (01460) 281454
Email: sue@stricklandc.freeserve.co.uk
Contact: Sue Strickland
Opening Times: 0930-1430 Mon-Wed
Apr-Jul & Sep and some Sun, please phone
first. Other times by appt.
Min Mail Order UK: No minimum charge*
Cat. Cost: 2 x 1st class
Credit Cards: None
Specialities: *Salvia* & unusual herbaceous
perennials incl. *Nepeta, Helianthus,
Origanum* & *Monarda*.
*Note: mail order for *Salvia* only.
Map Ref: C, B4

CStu STUCKEY'S ALPINES ♠
38 Phillipps Avenue, Exmouth,
Devon EX8 3HZ
☎ (01395) 273636
Email: stuckeysalpines@aol.com
Contact: Roger & Brenda Stuckey
Opening Times: As NGS dates or by
appointment.
Cat. Cost: None issued
Credit Cards: None
Specialities: National Collection of dwarf
Helichrysum. Alpines in general. *Primula*
especially *allionii* forms & show auriculas.
Map Ref: C, C4

CSut SUTTONS SEEDS ⊠ UK
Woodview Road, Paignton,
Devon TQ4 7NG
☎ (01803) 696321
Fax: (01803) 696345
Website: www.suttons-seeds.co.uk
Contact: Customer Services
Opening Times: (Office) 0830-1700
Mon-Fri. Also answerphone.
Min Mail Order UK: No minimum charge
Cat. Cost: Free
Credit Cards: Visa, MasterCard, Switch,
Delta
Specialities: Over 1,000 varieties of flower &
vegetable seed, bulbs, plants & sundries.

**CSWC SOUTH WEST CARNIVOROUS
PLANTS** ⊠ EU ♠
2 Rose Cottages, Culmstock, Cullompton,
Devon EX15 3JJ
☎ (01884) 841549
Fax: (01884) 841549
Email: flytraps@littleshopofhorrors.co.uk
Website: www.littleshopofhorrors.co.uk
Contact: Jenny Pearce & Alistair Pearce
Opening Times: By appt.
Min Mail Order UK: £10.00 + p&p
Min Mail Order EU: £20.00 + p&p
Cat. Cost: 3 x 2nd class
Credit Cards: MasterCard, Visa, Switch,
Delta
Specialities: *Cephalotus, Nepenthes, Dionea,
Drosera, Darlingtonia, Sarracenia, Pinguicula*
& *Utricularia*. Specialists in hardy
carnivorous plants & *Dionea muscipula* cvs.
Map Ref: C, B4

C

CSWP   SONIA WRIGHT PLANTS ⊠ EU ▣
Buckerfields Nursery, Ogbourne St George,
Marlborough, Wilts SN8 1SG
☎ (01672) 841065
Fax: (01672) 541047
Contact: Anyas Simon, Sonia Wright
Opening Times: 1000-1800 Thu-Sat Mar-
Oct. 1000-1600 Thu-Sat Nov-Feb. 1200-
1600 Sun Apr-Jun.
Min Mail Order UK: £15 Primulas only*
Min Mail Order EU: £15 Primulas only
Cat. Cost: 4 x 1st class
Credit Cards: None
Specialities: Barnhaven polyanthus &
primroses. Grasses, grey-leaved plants, *Iris*,
Euphorbia, *Penstemon*, old roses.
*Note: mail order primroses only despatched
autumn. Nursery has moved to above
address.
Map Ref: C, A6

CTbh   TREBAH ENTERPRISES LTD
Trebah, Mawnan Smith, Falmouth,
Cornwall TR11 5JZ
☎ (01326) 250448
Fax: (01326) 250781
Email: mail@trebah-garden.co.uk
Website: www.trebah-garden.co.uk
Contact: Plant Sales Staff
Opening Times: 1030-1700 all year.
Cat. Cost: None issued
Credit Cards: Visa, Access, EuroCard,
American Express, Switch, Delta, Electron,
MasterCard, Solo
Specialities: Tree ferns, *Camellia, Gunnera*
& conservatory climbers.
Map Ref: C, D1
OS Grid Ref: SW770276

CTca   TRECANNA NURSERY ⋔
Rose Farm, Latchley, Nr Gunnislake,
Cornwall PL18 9AX
☎ (01822) 834680
Fax: (01822) 834680
Email: mark@trecanna.com
Website: www.trecanna.com
Contact: Mark Wash
Opening Times: 1000-1700 Fri, Sat &
B/hols, 29th Mar-19th Oct 2002 &
21st Mar-18th Oct 2003.
Cat. Cost: 2 x 1st class
Credit Cards: None
Specialities: Fragrant & collectable plants.
Wide choice of *Crocosmia, Helianthemum,
Sempervivum* & unusual perennials.
Note: mail order will be available from

spring 2003, ring for details.
Map Ref: C, C3
OS Grid Ref: SX247733

CTCP   TURNPIKE COTTAGE PLANTS ⊠ EU ▣ ⋔
(office) Turnpike Cottage, Trow, Salcombe
Regis, Sidmouth, Devon EX10 0PB
☎ (01395) 515265, mobile 07870 389889
Fax: (01395) 515265
Email: plants@turnpike.fsbusiness.co.uk
Website: www.echiums.com
Contact: Mike Burgess
Opening Times: 0900-1700 Mon-Sat,
1000-1600 Sun.
Min Mail Order UK: £5.00*
Min Mail Order EU: £5.00
Credit Cards: all major credit/debit cards
Specialities: *Echium*. *Note: mail order seeds
only. Nursery at Sidmouth Garden Centre,
Stowford, Sidmouth, Devon.
Map Ref: C, C4

CTho   THORNHAYES NURSERY ▣ ⊠ EU
St Andrews Wood, Dulford, Cullompton,
Devon EX15 2DF
☎ (01884) 266746
Fax: (01884) 266739
Email: trees@thornhayes.demon.co.uk
Website: www.thornhayes-nursery.co.uk
Contact: K D Croucher
Opening Times: 0800-1600 Mon-Fri.
Min Mail Order UK: No minimum charge
Min Mail Order EU: Nmc
Cat. Cost: 5 x 1st class
Credit Cards: None
Specialities: A broad range of forms of
ornamental, amenity & fruit trees incl.
West Country apple varieties.
Map Ref: C, C4

CTrC   TREVENA CROSS NURSERIES ▣ ⊠ UK €
Breage, Helston, Cornwall TR13 9PS
☎ (01736) 763880
Fax: (01736) 762828
Email: sales@trevenacross.co.uk
Website: www.trevenacross.co.uk
Contact: Graham Jeffery, John Eddy
Opening Times: 0900-1700 Mon-Sat,
1030-1630 Sun.
Min Mail Order UK: No minimum charge*
Cat. Cost: A5 Sae with 2 x 1st class
Credit Cards: Access, Visa, Switch
Specialities: South African, Australian &
New Zealand plants, incl. *Aloe, Protea*, tree
ferns, palms, *Restio*, hardy succulents & wide
range of other exotics.

*Note: mail order to EU by negotiation.
Map Ref: C, D1

CTre TREWIDDEN NURSERY 🔲 ⊠ EU ☝
Trereife, Penzance, Cornwall TR20 8TT
☎ (01736) 362087
Fax: (01736) 3331470
Email: trewiddennursery@excite.co.uk
Website: www.trewidden-nursery.co.uk
Contact: John Ashton
Opening Times: By appt. only.
Min Mail Order UK: £6.00
Min Mail Order EU: No minimum charge
Cat. Cost: 2 x 1st class
Credit Cards: None
Specialities: *Camellia* & unusual shrubs,
bamboos, ferns, grasses, bananas &
ornamentals.
Map Ref: C, D1

CTrF TRESIDDER FARM PLANTS 🔲 ⊠ EU
Tresidder Farm, St Buryan, Penzance,
Cornwall TR19 6EZ
☎ (01736) 810656
Contact: N Milligan
Opening Times: By appt. Please phone.
Min Mail Order UK: £15.00 + p&p
Min Mail Order EU: £15.00 + p&p
Cat. Cost: 2 x 1st class for plant & seed lists.
Credit Cards: None
Specialities: *Proteaceae, Aloeaceae,* large *Aloe*
collection, unusual succulents.
Map Ref: C, D1

CTrG TREGOTHNAN NURSERY 🔲 ⊠ EU ▧ €
Estate Office, Tregothnan, Truro,
Cornwall TR2 4AN
☎ (01872) 520325
Fax: (01872) 520291
Email: bigplants@tregothnan.co.uk
Website: www.tregothnan.com
Contact: Jonathon Jones
Opening Times: By appt. for collection only.
Min Mail Order UK: £2.50
Min Mail Order EU: £5.00
Cat. Cost: On web.
Credit Cards: MasterCard, Visa, Delta,
EuroCard
Specialities: Unusual & rare plants from own
stock. Extra large specimens available for
instant effect. Known wild origin plants.

CTrh TREHANE CAMELLIA
NURSERY 🔲 ⊠ EU ▧ ☝ €
J Trehane & Sons Ltd, Stapehill Road,
Hampreston, Wimborne, Dorset BH21 7ND

☎ (01202) 873490
Fax: (01202) 873490
Contact: Lorraine or Jeanette
Opening Times: 0900-1630 Mon-Fri all
year (excl. Xmas & New Year). 1000-1600
Sat-Sun in spring & by special appt.
Min Mail Order UK: No minimum charge
Min Mail Order EU: Nmc
Cat. Cost: £1.70 cat./book
Credit Cards: Visa, Access, MasterCard
Specialities: Extensive range of *Camellia*
species, cultivars & hybrids. Many new
introductions. Evergreen azaleas, *Pieris,*
Magnolia & blueberries.
Map Ref: C, C6

CTri TRISCOMBE NURSERIES ⊠ UK ◆
West Bagborough, Nr Taunton,
Somerset TA4 3HG
☎ (01984) 618267
Email: triscombe.nurseries2000@virgin.net
Contact: S Parkman
Opening Times: 0900-1300 & 1400-1730
Mon-Sat. 1400-1730 Sun & B/hols.
Min Mail Order UK: No minimum charge
Cat. Cost: 2 x 1st class
Credit Cards: None
Specialities: Trees, shrubs, roses, fruit,
Clematis, herbaceous & rock plants.
Map Ref: C, B4

CTrw TREWITHEN NURSERIES 🔲 ⊠ UK €
Grampound Road, Truro,
Cornwall TR2 4DD
☎ (01726) 882764
Fax: (01726) 882301
Email: gardens@trewithen-estate.demon.co.uk
Website: www.trewithengardens.co.uk
Contact: M Taylor
Opening Times: 0800-1630 Mon-Fri.
Min Mail Order UK: No minimum charge
Cat. Cost: £1.25
Specialities: Shrubs, especially *Camellia* &
Rhododendron.
Map Ref: C, D2

CTuc EDWIN TUCKER & SONS ⊠ EU
Brewery Meadow, Stonepark, Ashburton,
Newton Abbot, Devon TQ13 7DG
☎ (01364) 652403
Fax: (01364) 654300

C

Contact: Geoff Penton
Opening Times: 0800-1700 Mon-Fri,
0800-1600 Sat.
Min Mail Order UK: No minimum charge
Min Mail Order EU: Nmc
Cat. Cost: Free
Credit Cards: Visa, MasterCard, Switch
Specialities: Over 100 varieties of seed
potatoes. Wide range of vegetables, flowers,
green manures & sprouting seeds in packets.
All not treated. Over 200 varieties of
organically produced seeds.
Map Ref: C, C3

CVer   VERYANS PLANTS ▣ ⊠ UK
The Glebe, Coryton, Okehampton,
Devon EX20 4PA
☎ (01822) 860302
Contact: T J Millar
Opening Times: Essential to phone first
for appointment.
Min Mail Order UK: No minimum charge
Cat. Cost: None issued
Credit Cards: None
Specialities: Range of hardy perennials
including. *Aster*, ornamental grasses,
Geranium, Epimedium & large selection of
primroses, many rare.
Map Ref: C, C3

CWat   THE WATER GARDEN ⊠ UK
Hinton Parva, Swindon,
Wilts SN4 0DH
☎ (01793) 790558
Fax: (01793) 791298
Email: watergarden@supanet.com
Contact: Mike & Anne Newman
Opening Times: 1000-1700 Wed-Sun.
Min Mail Order UK: £10.00 + p&p
Cat. Cost: 4 x 1st class
Credit Cards: Visa, Access, Switch
Specialities: Water lilies, marginal &
moisture plants, oxygenators & alpines.
Map Ref: C, A6

CWCL   WESTCOUNTRY NURSERIES (INC.
WESTCOUNTRY LUPINS) ▣ ⊠ EU ♫ € ◆
Ford Hill Forge, Hartland, Bideford,
Devon EX39 6EE
☎ (01237) 441208
Fax: (01237) 441208
Email: SarahConibear@westcountry-
nurseries.co.uk
Website: www.westcountry-nurseries.co.uk
Contact: Sarah Conibear
Opening Times: By appt. only.

Min Mail Order UK: £15.00
Min Mail Order EU: £25.00
Cat. Cost: 2 x 1st class + A5 Sae for full
colour cat.
Credit Cards: None
Specialities: *Lupinus, Lewisia, Hellebore,*
gentians, cyclamen, lavender, select
perennials & grasses.

CWDa   WESTDALE NURSERIES ▣ ⊠ EU ▣ ♫
Holt Road, Bradford-on-Avon,
Wilts BA15 1TS
☎ (01225) 863258
Fax: (01225) 863258
Email: westdale.nurseries@talk21.com
Website: www.westdalenurseries.co.uk
Contact: Louisa Bernal
Opening Times: 0900-1800 7 days.
Min Mail Order UK: £10.00 + p&p
Min Mail Order EU: £10.00 + p&p
Cat. Cost: 4 x 1st class
Credit Cards: MasterCard, Visa
Specialities: *Bougainvillea, Geranium,*
conservatory plants.
Note: export beyond EU by arrangement.
Map Ref: C, A5

CWdb   WOODBOROUGH GARDEN CENTRE
Nursery Farm, Woodborough, Nr Pewsey,
Wilts SN9 5PF
☎ (01672) 851249
Fax: (01672) 851249
Contact: Els M Brewin
Opening Times: 0900-1700 Mon-Sat,
1100-1700 Sun.
Cat. Cost: None issued
Credit Cards: Access, Diners, EuroCard,
MasterCard, Switch, Visa
Specialities: Wide range of shrubs, trees,
herbaceous, alpines & herbs. Large selection
of climbers esp. *Clematis,* & spring bulbs.
Map Ref: C, A6

CWes   WEST KINGTON NURSERIES
LTD. ▣ ⊠ ♫
Pound Hill, West Kington, Nr Chippenham,
Wilts SN14 7JG
☎ (01249) 782822
Fax: (01249) 782953
Email: sales@westkingtonnurseries.co.uk
Contact: Jennie Hughes/Phil Walker
Opening Times: 1000-1700 7 days, incl.
B/hols Feb-Dec.
Cat. Cost: Free
Credit Cards: MasterCard, Visa
Specialities: Herbaceous, alpines, *Buxus* &

topiary. Herbaceous liners.
Map Ref: C, A5

CWGr   WINCHESTER GROWERS
LTD. 🛒 ✉ EU 🗹 ⋔
Varfell Farm, Long Rock, Penzance,
Cornwall TR20 8AQ
☎ (01736) 851033
Fax: (01736) 851033
Email: dahlias@wgltd.co.uk
Website: www.wgltd.co.uk
Contact: Sarah Thomas
Opening Times: 31st Aug & 1st Sep 2002.
Other times by appt.
Min Mail Order UK: No minimum charge
Min Mail Order EU: Nmc
Cat. Cost: Free
Credit Cards: Visa, Delta, MasterCard,
Switch
Specialities: National Collection of *Dahlia*.
Due to large number of varieties, stock of
some is limited.
Map Ref: C, D1

CWhi   WHITEHOUSE IVIES 🛒 ✉ EU 🗹 ⋔ €
Fishleigh Down, Sanctuary Lane,
Hatherleigh, Devon EX20 3LH
☎ (01837) 810753
Fax: (01837) 810753
Email: whitehouseivies@sanctuary30.fsnet.co.uk
Contact: Gail Haddow
Opening Times: 0900-1700 Mon-Sat by
appt.
Min Mail Order UK: £17.70 + p&p
Min Mail Order EU: £17.70 + p&p
Cat. Cost: £1.50 or 6 x 1st class
Credit Cards: Visa, MasterCard, EuroCard
Specialities: Ivy, over 350 varieties.
Map Ref: C, C3

CWib   WIBBLE FARM NURSERIES 🛒 ✉ EU 🗹 ⋔
Wibble Farm, West Quantoxhead,
Nr Taunton, Somerset TA4 4DD
☎ (01984) 632303
Fax: (01984) 633168
Email: wibblefarmnurseries@hotmail.com
Contact: Mrs M L Francis
Opening Times: 0800-1700 Mon-Fri,
1000-1600 Sat. All year excl. B/hols.
Min Mail Order UK: No minimum charge
Min Mail Order EU: Nmc
Cat. Cost: 2 x 1st class
Credit Cards: MasterCard, Switch, Visa
Specialities: Growers of a wide range of
hardy plants, many rare & unusual.
Map Ref: C, B4

CWil   FERNWOOD NURSERY ✉ EU 🗹 €
Peters Marland,
Torrington,
Devon EX38 8QG
☎ (01805) 601446
Email: hw@fernwood-nursery.co.uk
Website: www.fernwood-nursery.co.uk
Contact: Howard Wills & Sally Wills
Opening Times: Any time by appt. Please
phone first.
Min Mail Order UK: No minimum charge
Min Mail Order EU: Nmc
Cat. Cost: Sae for list or £1.50 for
Houseleeks booklet
Credit Cards: None
Specialities: National Collections of
Sempervivum, Jovibarba, Rosularia &
Phormium.
Map Ref: C, C3
OS Grid Ref: SS479133

CWin   WINFRITH HOSTAS 🛒 ✉ UK €
5 Knoll Park, Gatemore Road,
Winfrith, Newburgh, Dorchester,
Dorset DT2 8LD
☎ (01305) 852935
Website: www.winfrithhostas.co.uk
Contact: John Ledbury
Opening Times: By appt.
Min Mail Order UK: No minimum charge*
Cat. Cost: 2 x 1st class
Credit Cards: None
Specialities: *Hosta*.
*Note: available from Oct-Mar only.
Map Ref: C, C5

CWiW   WINDRUSH WILLOW 🛒 ✉ EU 🗹 €
Higher Barn, Sidmouth Road,
Aylesbeare, Exeter EX5 2JJ
☎ (01395) 233669
Fax: (01395) 233669
Email: windrushw@aol.com
Website: www.windrushwillow.com
Contact: Richard Kerwood
Opening Times: By appt.
Min Mail Order UK: No minimum charge
Min Mail Order EU: Nmc
Cat. Cost: 2 x 1st class
Credit Cards: None
Specialities: *Salix*. Unrooted cuttings
available Dec-Mar.

C

CWoo   IAN AND ROSEMARY WOOD ✉ EU
Newlands, 28 Furland Road, Crewkerne,
Somerset TA18 8DD
☎ (01460) 74630
Email: ianwood@ukgateway.net
Contact: Ian and Rosemary Wood
Opening Times: By appt. only. Primarily
mail order service.
Min Mail Order UK: No minimum charge
Min Mail Order EU: £20.00 + p&p
Cat. Cost: 2 x 1st class
Credit Cards: None
Specialities: *Erythronium, Cyclamen* species
& dwarf *Narcissus* species.
Map Ref: C, B5

CWri   NIGEL WRIGHT RHODODENDRONS ▣
The Old Glebe, Eggesford, Chulmleigh,
Devon EX18 7QU
☎ (01769) 580632
Contact: Nigel Wright
Opening Times: By appt. only.
Cat. Cost: 2 x 1st class
Credit Cards: None
Specialities: *Rhododendron* only. 200 varieties
field grown. Root-balled, not potted. For
collection only. Specialist grower.
Map Ref: C, B3

**CWSG   WEST SOMERSET GARDEN
CENTRE** ✉ UK
Mart Road, Minehead, Somerset TA24 5BJ
☎ (01643) 703812
Fax: (01643) 706470
Email: wsgardencentre@compuserve.com
Website: www.westsomersetgardencentre.co.uk
Contact: Mrs J K Shoulders
Opening Times: 0800-1700 Mon-Sat,
1000-1600 Sun.
Min Mail Order UK: No minimum charge
Cat. Cost: Phone for availability.
Credit Cards: Access, Visa, Switch, Solo
Specialities: Wide general range.
Ceanothus.
Map Ref: C, B4

EASTERN

EAmu   AMULREE EXOTICS ▣ ✉ UK ♫
(Office) Katonia Avenue, Maylandsea,
Essex CM3 6AD
☎ (01245) 425255
Fax: (01245) 425255
Email: SDG@exotica.fsbusiness.co.uk
Website: www.turn-it-tropical.co.uk
Contact: S Gridley

Opening Times: 0930-1730 7 days spring-
autumn, 1000-1630 7 days autumn-
spring.
Min Mail Order UK: No minimum charge
Cat. Cost: 2 x 2nd class
Credit Cards: Visa, MasterCard, Electron,
Solo, Switch
Specialities: Hardy & half-hardy plants for
home, garden & conservatory. Palms,
bamboos, bananas, tree ferns, cannas, gingers
& much more.
Note: nursery is at Tropical Wings, Wickford
Road, South Woodham Ferrers.
Map Ref: E, D2

EAsh   ASHPOND PLANTS
Ashpond House, Oxborough Road,
Stoke Ferry, Norfolk PE33 9TA
☎ (01366) 500447
Contact: Claire Smith
Opening Times: 1200-1700 Fri & Sat
1st Apr-30th Sep (incl.)
Cat. Cost: None issued.
Credit Cards: None
Specialities: Cottage garden & unusual hardy
perennials. Some plants available in limited
quantities. Garden open.
Map Ref: E, B1
OS Grid Ref: TF708001

EBak   B & H M BAKER ▣
Bourne Brook Nurseries, Greenstead Green,
Halstead, Essex CO9 1RJ
☎ (01787) 472900/476369
Contact: B, HM and C Baker
Opening Times: 0800-1630 Mon-Fri,
0900-1200 & 1400-1630 Sat & Sun.
Cat. Cost: 2 x 1st class + 33p
Credit Cards: MasterCard, Delta, Visa,
Switch
Specialities: *Fuchsia* & conservatory plants.
Map Ref: E, C2

EBee   BEECHES NURSERY ✉ EU ♫
Village Centre, Ashdon, Saffron Walden,
Essex CB10 2HB
☎ (01799) 584362
Fax: (01799) 584362
Email: sales@beechesnursery.co.uk
Website: www.beechesnursery.co.uk
Contact: Alan Bidwell/Kevin Marsh
Opening Times: 0830-1700 Mon-Sat,
1000-1700 Sun & B/hols.
Min Mail Order UK: £10.00*
Min Mail Order EU: £20.00
Cat. Cost: 6 x 2nd class

Credit Cards: Visa, Access, MasterCard, EuroCard, Switch
Specialities: Herbaceous specialists & extensive range of other garden plants.
*Note: mail order generally from Oct-Feb, Mar-Sep where conditions permit. Trees NOT available by mail order.
Map Ref: E, C2

EBla   BLACKSMITHS COTTAGE NURSERY 🔲 ń
Langmere Green Road, Langmere, Diss Norfolk IP21 4QA
☎ (01379) 740982
(01379) 741917 (nursery)
Fax: (01379) 741917
Email: Blackcottnursery@aol.com
Contact: Ben or Jill Potterton
Opening Times: 1000-1700 Fri-Sun Mar-Oct & B/hols, or by appt.
Cat. Cost: 2 x 1st class
Credit Cards: None
Specialities: Hardy *Geranium, Digitalis, Heuchera, Crocosmia, Polygonatum, Tricyrtis* & Siberian *Iris.* Over 1000 species grown. Large selection of shade plants.
Map Ref: E, C3

EBls   PETER BEALES ROSES ⊠ EU 🔲
London Road, Attleborough, Norfolk NR17 1AY
☎ (01953) 454707
Fax: (01953) 456845
Email: sales@classicroses.co.uk
Website: www.classicroses.co.uk
Contact: Simon White
Opening Times: 0900-1700 Mon-Fri, 0900-1630 Sat, 1000-1600 Sun & B/hols.
Min Mail Order UK: No minimum charge
Min Mail Order EU: Nmc
Cat. Cost: Free
Credit Cards: Visa, MasterCard, Access, Switch, Solo, Delta, JCB
Specialities: Old fashioned roses & classic roses. National Collection of Species Roses.
Map Ref: E, C3

EBlw   BLACKWATER PLANTS ⊠ UK ń
Knowles Farm, Wycke Hill (A414), Maldon, Essex CM9 6SH
☎ mobile 07931 311108
Email: blackwaterplants@ukonline.co.uk
Contact: Kirsty Bishop & Fiona Mildren
Opening Times: 1000-1700 Wed-Sat Mar-Oct & by appt.

Min Mail Order UK: £10.00
Cat. Cost: 2 x 1st class
Credit Cards: None
Specialities: Wide range of plants, many for shade and moist soils, incl. grasses, bamboos, ferns, palms & perennials. Peat free & organic. National Collection of *Astrantia.*
Map Ref: E, D2

EBot   BOTANICUS ⊠ EU
The Nurseries, Ringland Lane, Old Costessey, Norwich, Norfolk NR8 5BG
☎ (01603) 742063
Website: www.urbanjungle.uk.com
Contact: Anthony Murphy
Opening Times: 1000-1700 Tue-Sun & B/hol Mons. Late opening Thu 1000-2000 May-Sep.
Min Mail Order UK: £15.00 + p&p*
Min Mail Order EU: £50.00 + p&p
Cat. Cost: 6 x 1st class
Credit Cards: None
Specialities: Historic garden plants grown in Britain from Roman times to 1900, particularly bulbs, herbaceous perennials & shrubs.
*Note: mail order for bulbs, corms, tubers & rhizomes only.
Map Ref: E, B3

EBre   BLOOMS OF BRESSINGHAM ⊠ UK ♦
Bressingham, Diss, Norfolk IP22 2AB
☎ (01379) 688480
Fax: (01379) 688340
Email: bressingham@blooms-uk.com
Website: www.bloomsofbressingham.co.uk
Contact: Martin Cotterill
Opening Times: 0900-1700 1st Nov-31st Mar, 0900-1800 1st Apr-31st Oct, 7 days. Closed Xmas, Boxing Day & Easter Sun.
Min Mail Order UK: £4.35
Cat. Cost: None issued
Credit Cards: Visa, Delta, Switch, MasterCard
Specialities: Wide general range. Many own varieties. Focus on hardy ornamental plants & grasses. Perennials. Plants for all Blooms of Bressingham nurseries are listed against this nursery's code.
Map Ref: E, C3

E

EBrP   **BLOOMS OF BRESSINGHAM** ⊠ UK ◆
Elton Hall, Elton,
Peterborough PE8 6SH
☎ (01832) 280058
Fax: (01832) 280081
Email: ELTON@blooms-uk.com
Website: www.bloomsofbressingham.co.uk
Contact: Tom Green
Opening Times: 0900-1700 1st Nov-31st
Mar, 0900-1800 1st Apr-31st Oct, 7 days.
Closed Xmas, Boxing Day & Easter Sun.
Min Mail Order UK: £4.35
Cat. Cost: None issued
Credit Cards: Delta, Switch, MasterCard,
Visa
Specialities: Wide general range. Many own
varieties. Focus on hardy ornamental plants
& grasses. Perennials. Plants listed against
nursery code EBre.
Map Ref: E, C1

EBur   **JENNY BURGESS** ⊠ EU ☒ ń €
Alpine Nursery, Sisland,
Norwich NR14 6EF
☎ (01508) 520724
Contact: Jenny Burgess
Opening Times: Any time by appt.
Min Mail Order UK: £5.00 + p&p*
Min Mail Order EU: £10.00 + p&p
Cat. Cost: 3 x 1st class
Credit Cards: None
Specialities: Alpines, *Sisyrinchium* &
Campanula. National Collection of
Sisyrinchium.
*Note: *Sisyrinchium* only by mail order.
Map Ref: E, B3

ECGN   **THE CONTENTED GARDENER
NURSERY** ⊠ UK ń
The Garden House, 42 Wragby Road,
Bardney, Lincs LN3 5XL
☎ (01526) 397307
Fax: (01526) 397280
Email: maryleeheykoop@aol.com
Website: www.leeheykoop.co.uk
Contact: Lee Heykoop
Opening Times: Please phone to arrange a
visit.
Min Mail Order UK: £25.00 + £12.00
p&p
Cat. Cost: A4 Sae + 4 x 1st class
Credit Cards: None
Specialities: Perennials & grasses for
naturalistic planting in dry and damp and
woodland edge.
Map Ref: E, B1

ECGP   **CAMBRIDGE GARDEN PLANTS** ń
The Lodge, Clayhithe Road, Horningsea,
Cambs CB5 9JD
☎ (01223) 861370
Contact: Mrs Nancy Buchdahl
Opening Times: 1100-1730 Thu-Sun
mid Mar-31st Oct. Other times by appt.
Cat. Cost: 4 x 1st class
Credit Cards: None
Specialities: Hardy perennials incl. wide
range of *Geranium, Allium, Euphorbia,
Penstemon, Digitalis*. Some shrubs, roses &
Clematis.
Map Ref: E, C2
OS Grid Ref: TL497637

ECha   **THE BETH CHATTO
GARDENS LTD** ⊠ EU
Elmstead Market, Colchester,
Essex CO7 7DB
☎ (01206) 822007
Fax: (01206) 825933
Email: info@bethchatto.fsnet.co.uk
Website: www.bethchatto.co.uk
Contact: Beth Chatto
Opening Times: 0900-1700 Mon-Sat
1st Mar-31st Oct. 0900-1600 Mon-Fri
1st Nov-1st Mar. Closed Sun & B/hols.
Min Mail Order UK: £20.00
Min Mail Order EU: Ask for details
Cat. Cost: £3.00 incl. p&p
Credit Cards: Visa, Switch, MasterCard
Specialities: Predominantly herbaceous.
Many unusual for special situations.
Map Ref: E, D3

ECho   **CHOICE LANDSCAPES** ⊠ EU ☒ ń €
Priory Farm, 101 Salts Road,
West Walton, Wisbech,
Cambridgeshire PE14 7EF
☎ (01945) 585051
Fax: (01945) 580053
Website: www.ChoiceLandscapes.com
Contact: Michael Agg & Jillian Agg
Opening Times: 1000-1700 Wed-Sat
5th Mar-31st Oct 2002 & 1st Mar-1st Nov
2003. Other times by appt.
Min Mail Order UK: Nmc
Min Mail Order EU: £10.00 + p&p
Cat. Cost: 4 x 1st class or 4 IRC
Credit Cards: Visa, MasterCard, Switch,
Solo
Specialities: Dwarf conifers, alpines, acers,
rhododendrons, hostas, bulbs, pines &
lilies.
Map Ref: E, B1

E

EChP **CHOICE PLANTS** ⊠ UK ∱ € ◆
83 Halton Road, Spilsby,
Lincolnshire PE23 5LD
☎ (01790) 752361
mobile 07887 913704
Fax: (01790) 752524
Email: jgunson@spilsby94.fsnet.co.uk
Contact: Joan Gunson
Opening Times: 1000-1700 Wed-Sun &
B/hol Mon Mar-Oct.
Min Mail Order UK: £10.00 + p&p*
Cat. Cost: 2 x 1st class
Credit Cards: None
Specialities: Hardy *Geranium*, *Crocosmia*,
Hemerocallis, *Iris* & a good selection of
unusual hardy perennials.
*Note: mail order Feb-May & Sep-Nov
only.
Map Ref: E, B1

ECle **CLEY NURSERIES LTD** ⊠ UK €
Holt Road, Cley-next-the-Sea, Holt,
Norfolk NR25 7TX
☎ (01263) 740892
Fax: (01263) 741138
Website: www.cleynurseries.co.uk
Contact: Alec or Gill Mellor
Opening Times: 1000-1600 7 days.
Min Mail Order UK: £10.00 + p&p
Cat. Cost: List 2 x 1st class
Credit Cards: Visa, Access, Switch
Specialities: Roses.
Map Ref: E, B3

ECnt **CANTS OF COLCHESTER** ⊠ EU ⊠
Nayland Road, Mile End,
Colchester,
Essex CO4 5EB
☎ (01206) 844008
Fax: (01206) 855371
Email: finder@cantsroses.co.uk
Website: www.cantsroses.co.uk
Contact: Angela Pawsey
Opening Times: 0900-1300, 1400-1630
Mon-Fri. Sat varied, please phone first. Sun
closed.
Min Mail Order UK: No minimum charge*
Min Mail Order EU: Nmc
Cat. Cost: Free
Credit Cards: Visa, MasterCard, Delta, Solo,
Switch
Specialities: Roses. Unstaffed rose field can
be viewed dawn-dusk every day from end
Jun-end Sep.
*Note: mail order end Oct-end Mar only.
Map Ref: E, C3

ECoo **PATRICIA COOPER**
Magpies, Green Lane, Mundford,
Norfolk IP26 5HS
☎ (01842) 878496
Contact: Patricia Cooper
Opening Times: 0900-1700 Mon, Tue, Thu
& Fri 1200-1700 Sat & Sun.
Cat. Cost: Free
Credit Cards: None
Specialities: Unusual hardy perennials,
grasses & foliage plants.
Map Ref: E, C2

ECot **THE COTTAGE GARDEN**
Langham Road, Boxted, Colchester,
Essex CO4 5HU
☎ (01206) 272269
Email: enquiries@thecottage-garden.co.uk
Website: www.thecottage-garden.co.uk
Contact: Alison Smith
Opening Times: 0800-1700 7 days spring &
summer. 0800-1700 Thu-Mon Sep-Feb.
Cat. Cost: Free leaflet
Credit Cards: Visa, Access, Connect, Switch,
Delta
Specialities: 400 varieties of shrubs, 390
varieties of herbaceous. Huge range of trees,
shrubs, alpines, herbs, hedging, all home
grown. Garden antiques.
Map Ref: E, C3
OS Grid Ref: TM003299

ECou **COUNTY PARK NURSERY**
Essex Gardens, Hornchurch, Essex RM11 3BU
☎ (01708) 445205
Contact: G Hutchins
Opening Times: 0900-dusk Mon-Sat excl.
Wed, 1000-1700 Sun Mar-Oct. Nov-Feb
by appt. only.
Cat. Cost: 3 x 1st class
Credit Cards: None
Specialities: Alpines & rare and unusual
plants from New Zealand, Tasmania &
Falklands. National Collection of *Coprosma*
& *Parahebe*. Many plants limited in quantity.
Map Ref: E, D2

ECre **CREAKE PLANT CENTRE**
Nursery View, Leicester Road, South Creake,
Fakenham, Norfolk NR21 9PW
☎ (01328) 823018

KEY		
⊠ Mail order to UK or EU	∱ Delivers to shows	
⊠ Exports beyond EU	€ Euro accepted	
⊠ Also supplies Wholesale	◆ See Display advertisement	

E

Contact: Mr T Harrison
Opening Times: 1000-1300 & 1400-1730
7 days excl. Xmas.
Cat. Cost: None issued
Credit Cards: None
Specialities: Unusual shrubs, herbaceous, conservatory plants. Huge selection of hardy *Geranium*.
Map Ref: E, B1

ECri   Crin Gardens 🖾 ⊠ UK
79 Partons Road, Kings Heath,
Birmingham B14 6TD
☎ 0121 443 3815
Fax: 0121 443 3815
Contact: M Milinkovic
Opening Times: Not open.
Min Mail Order UK: No minimum charge
Cat. Cost: 2 x 1st class
Credit Cards: None
Specialities: Lilies. Limited stock available on first come, first served basis.

ECrN   Crown Nursery 🖾 ⊠ UK ń
High Street, Ufford, Woodbridge,
Suffolk IP13 6EL
☎ (01394) 460755
Fax: (01394) 460142
Email: enquiries@crown-nursery.co.uk
Website: www.crown-nursery.co.uk
Contact: Jill Proctor
Opening Times: 0900-1700 (or dusk if sooner) Mon-Sat.
Min Mail Order UK: Nmc
Cat. Cost: 2 x 1st class
Credit Cards: Visa, Delta, MasterCard, EuroCard, JCB, Switch
Specialities: Mature & semi-mature native, ornamental & fruit trees.
Map Ref: E, C3   **OS Grid Ref:** TM292528

ECtt   Cottage Nurseries 🖾 ⊠ UK
Thoresthorpe, Alford,
Lincolnshire LN13 0HX
☎ (01507) 466968
Fax: (01507) 463409
Email: cottagenurseries@freewire.co.uk
Website: members.tripod.co.uk/cottagenurseries
Contact: W H Denbigh
Opening Times: 0900-1700 7 days 1st Mar-31st Oct, 1000-1600 Thu-Sun Nov-Feb.
Min Mail Order UK: No minimum charge
Cat. Cost: 3 x 1st class
Credit Cards: None
Specialities: Wide general range.
Map Ref: E, A2

EDAr   D'Arcy & Everest 🖾 ⊠ EU ń €
(Office) PO Box 78, St Ives, Huntingdon,
Cambridgeshire PE27 4UQ
☎ (01480) 497672,
mobile 07715 374440/1
Fax: (01480) 466042
Email: richard@darcyeverest.fsnet.co.uk
Contact: Angela Whiting, Richard Oliver
Opening Times: By appt. only.
Min Mail Order UK: £10.00 + p&p
Min Mail Order EU: £50.00 + p&p
Cat. Cost: 6 x 1st class
Credit Cards: None
Specialities: Alpines, herbs & selected perennials.
Note: nursery is at Pidley Sheep Lane (B1040), Somersham, Huntingdon.
Map Ref: E, C2

EDif   Different Plants ń
The Mellis Stud, Gate Farm, Cranley Green,
Eye, Suffolk IP23 7NX
☎ (01379) 870291
Contact: Fleur Waters
Opening Times: Sat-Thu by appt. only, closed Fri. Plant stall Diss market Friday May-Sep.
Cat. Cost: 4 x 1st class
Credit Cards: None
Specialities: *Mimulus aurantiacus* & hybrids, *Arctotis* named & selected seed strains, half-hardy bulbous/cormous perennials incl. *Dietes, Aristea, Cypella, Tigridia* & *Anomatheca laxa.* Stocks of bulbs may be limited in numbers.
Map Ref: E, C3

EDsa   Darasina Nursery 🖾
Ingatestone Hall, Hall Lane, Ingatestone,
Essex CM4 9NR
☎ (01277) 353235
Contact: Stephen Nelson
Opening Times: 1130-1730 Sat, Sun & B/Hol, Easter Sat-end Sep. Other times by appt.
Cat. Cost: Free list
Credit Cards: None
Specialities: Courtyard style & container planting. Hardy & half-hardy shrubs incl. figs, *Pittosporum, Melianthus.* Many uncommon perennials, ferns, herbs & vegetable plants.
Map Ref: E, D2

EEls   Elsworth Herbs
Avenue Farm Cottage, 31 Smith Street,
Elsworth, Cambridgeshire CB3 8HY

E

☎ (01954) 267414
Fax: (01954) 267414
Email: john.twibell@talk21.com
Contact: Drs J D & J M Twibell
Opening Times: By appt. only.
Cat. Cost: 3 x 1st class
Credit Cards: None
Specialities: National Collections of
Artemisia & *Nerium oleander*. Wide range of
Artemisia & *Seriphidium*, *Nerium oleander*.
Limited stocks. Orders may require
propagation from Collection material, for
which we are the primary reference source.
Map Ref: E, C2

EFam   FAMECHECK SPECIAL PLANTS ⊠ UK
Hilltrees, Wandlebury Hill (A1307),
Cambridge, Cambridgeshire CB2 4AD
☎ (01223) 243734 long ring or after dark
Contact: Miss F Cook N.D.H.
Opening Times: 1000-1700 except Tue,
Wed & Sat, all year unless frost. Other times
by appt.
Min Mail Order UK: £5.00 + p&p
Cat. Cost: 2 x 1st class for list.
Credit Cards: None
Specialities: Daffodils, long-lasting &
weatherproof cut-flower varieties. Bearded
Iris & orange violets. Some only available in
small quantities. About 1000 modern
varieties, mostly imported. National
Collection Holder status applied for
daffodils & *Iris*.
Map Ref: E, C2

EFer   THE FERN NURSERY ▨ ⊠ EU ń
Grimsby Road, Binbrook,
Lincolnshire LN8 6DH
☎ (01472) 398092
Email: timm@fernnursery.fsnet.co.uk
Contact: R N Timm
Opening Times: 0900-1700 Sat & Sun
Apr-Oct or by appt.
Min Mail Order UK: No minimum charge
Min Mail Order EU: Nmc
Cat. Cost: 2 x 1st class
Credit Cards: None
Specialities: Ferns & hardy perennials. Please
note only plants listed in the mail order part
of the catalogue will be sent mail order.
Map Ref: E, A1
OS Grid Ref: TF212942

EFEx   FLORA EXOTICA ⊠ EU ▨ €
Pasadena, South-Green, Fingringhoe,
Colchester, Essex CO5 7DR

☎ (01206) 729414
Contact: J Beddoes
Opening Times: Not open, mail order only.
Min Mail Order UK: No minimum charge
Min Mail Order EU: Nmc
Cat. Cost: 4 x 1st class
Credit Cards: None
Specialities: Exotica flora incl. orchids.

EFou   FOUR SEASONS ⊠ UK €
Forncett St Mary, Norwich,
Norfolk NR16 1JT
☎ (01508) 488344
Fax: (01508) 488478
Email: mail@fsperennials.co.uk
Website: www.fsperennials.co.uk
Contact: J P Metcalf & R W Ball
Opening Times: Not open, mail order only.
Min Mail Order UK: £15.00 + p&p
Cat. Cost: Free
Credit Cards: Visa, MasterCard, Switch
Specialities: Herbaceous perennials.
*Anemone, Aster, Campanula, Chrysanthemum,
Digitalis, Erigeron, Geranium, Helenium, Iris,
Salvia* & grasses.

EFpt   FILLPOTS NURSERY ▨ ⊠ UK ń
52 Straight Road, Boxted, Colchester,
Essex CO4 5RB
☎ (01206) 272389
Fax: (01206) 272389
Email: plants@fillpots.fsnet.co.uk
Contact: Richard, Mary or Les Brann
Opening Times: 0900-1700 Mon-Sat,
1000-1600 Sun.
Min Mail Order UK: £4.50 + p&p
Cat. Cost: 3 x 1st class
Credit Cards: Switch, Solo, MasterCard, Visa
Specialities: *Fuchsia, Buddleja, Hydrangea,
Phygellus* & bedding plants.
Map Ref: E, C3
OS Grid Ref: 337997

EFul   FULBROOKE NURSERY ⊠ EU ń
Home Farm, Westley Waterless, Newmarket,
Suffolk CB8 0RG
☎ (01638) 507124
Fax: (01638) 507124
Email: fulbrook@clara.net
Website: www.fulbrooke.co.uk
Contact: Paul Lazard

KEY		
⊠ Mail order to UK or EU	ń Delivers to shows	
▨ Exports beyond EU	€ Euro accepted	
▨ Also supplies Wholesale	◆ See Display advertisement	

E

Opening Times: By appt. most times incl. w/ends.
Min Mail Order UK: £5.50 + p&p
Min Mail Order EU: £6.00 + p&p
Cat. Cost: 3 x 1st class
Credit Cards: None
Specialities: Bamboos & grasses.
Map Ref: E, C2

EFWa **FOUR WAYS GARDEN & NURSERY**
Duffins Farm, Cross Roads, Lotts Bridge,
Three Holes, Wisbech,
Cambridgeshire PE14 9JG
☎ (01354) 638315
Email: vsteele@duffinsfarm.free-online.co.uk
Website: www. duffins.free-online.co.uk
Contact: Miss Verity Steele, Mr Barry Weekes
Opening Times: 1000-1600 1st & 3rd Sat-Sun, Mon-Fri by appt & invitation.
Cat. Cost: 1 x 1st class
Credit Cards: None
Specialities: Hardy perennials, native plants, grasses, oenotheras.
Map Ref: E, B1
OS Grid Ref: TL512986

EGFP **GRANGE FARM PLANTS** ⊠ UK
Grange Farm, 38 Fishergate Road,
Sutton St James, Spalding,
Lincolnshire PE12 0EZ
☎ (01945) 440240 mobile 07751 532795
Fax: (01945) 440355
Email: ellis.family@tinyonline.co.uk
Contact: M C Ellis
Opening Times: By appt. only.
Min Mail Order UK: Nmc
Cat. Cost: 1 x 1st class
Credit Cards: None
Specialities: Rare trees & shrubs, especially *Juglans, Fraxinus*. Some species in limited supply.
Map Ref: E, B2
OS Grid Ref: TF3818

EGle **GLEN CHANTRY** €
Ishams Chase, Wickham Bishops,
Essex CM8 3LG
☎ (01621) 891342
Fax: (01621) 891342
Contact: Sue Staines & Wol Staines
Opening Times: 1000-1600 Fri & Sat from 6th Apr-28th Sep. Also Sun & Mon on NGS open days. Sae for details.
Cat. Cost: 4 x 1st class
Credit Cards: None

Specialities: A wide & increasing range of perennials & alpines, many unusual.
Map Ref: E, D2

EGln **GLENHIRST CACTUS NURSERY** ⊠ EU 🖾
Station Road, Swineshead, Nr Boston,
Lincolnshire PE20 3NX
☎ (01205) 820314
Fax: (01205) 820614
Email: sabell@glenhirstcactiandpalms.co.uk
Website: www.glenhirstcactiandpalms.co.uk
Contact: N C & S A Bell
Opening Times: 1000-1700 Thu-Sun & B/hols 1st Apr-30th Sep, other times please phone first to check. Mail order all year.
Min Mail Order UK: No minimum charge
Min Mail Order EU: Nmc
Cat. Cost: 2 x 1st class
Credit Cards: Visa, MasterCard, Switch, Solo, Electron
Specialities: Extensive range of cacti & succulent plants & seeds, incl. Christmas cacti & orchid cacti. Hardy & half-hardy desert plants. Display gardens. Palms, *Cordyline, Bamboo*, tree ferns, *Phormium* & other hardy architectural plants.
Map Ref: E, B1
OS Grid Ref: TF245408

EGlv **GLENVILLE NURSERIES** 🖾 ⊠ EU ◆
King John Bank, Walpole St Andrew,
Wisbech, Cambridgeshire PE14 7LD
☎ (01945) 780020
Fax: (01945) 780078
Email: btowler@netcomuk.co.uk
Website: www.glenvillenurseries.co.uk
Contact: B R Towler
Opening Times: 1000-1600 Mon-Fri, Sat by arrangement, closed Sun.
Min Mail Order UK: £6.00 + p&p
Min Mail Order EU: £30.00 + p&p
Cat. Cost: 2 x 2nd class
Credit Cards: MasterCard, Switch, Delta, Visa
Specialities: Young flowering, ornamental & climbing shrubs. Also conifers.
Map Ref: E, B1
OS Grid Ref: TF487188

EGol **GOLDBROOK PLANTS** ⊠ EU 🖾
Hoxne, Eye, Suffolk IP21 5AN
☎ (01379) 668770
Fax: (01379) 668770
Contact: Sandra Bond
Opening Times: 1000-1700 or dusk if earlier, Thu-Sun Apr-Sep, Sat & Sun

Oct-Mar or by appt. Closed during Jan,
Chelsea & Hampton Court Shows.
Min Mail Order UK: £15.00 + p&p
Min Mail Order EU: £100.00 + p&p
Cat. Cost: 4 x 1st class
Credit Cards: None
Specialities: Very large range of *Hosta*
(over 900), *Hemerocallis* & bog *Iris*.
Map Ref: E, C3

EGoo ELISABETH GOODWIN NURSERIES ň
Elm Tree Farm, 1 Beeches Road, West Row,
Bury St Edmunds, Suffolk IP28 8NP
☎ (01638) 713050
Email: elisabeth.goodwin@bushinternet.com
Contact: Elisabeth Goodwin
Opening Times: Any time by prior
arrangement. Open days to be confirmed.
Cat. Cost: Sae or email for list
Credit Cards: None
Specialities: Drought tolerant plants for both
sun & shade esp. *Dianthus, Helianthemum,
Sedum, Teucrium, Vinca*, grasses, *Aquilegia,
Digitalis, Achillea, Agastache* & *Onosma*.
Some plants grown in limited quantities.
Map Ref: E, C2

EGra GRASMERE PLANTS ⊠ UK
Grasmere, School Road, Terrington St John,
Wisbech, Cambridgeshire PE14 7SE
☎ (01945) 880514
Contact: Angela Fleming
Opening Times: 1000-1700 Thu-Tue
Apr-Jul & Sep. 1000-1700 Sat & Sun Oct,
Nov, Feb & Mar. Other times by appt.
Garden open.
Min Mail Order UK: £10.00 + p&p*
Cat. Cost: 2 x 2nd class
Credit Cards: None
Specialities: Hardy perennials incl. *Geranium*
& grasses, shrubs & dwarf conifers.
*Note: mail order perennials only.
Map Ref: E, B1

EGrW THE GREAT WESTERN GLADIOLUS
NURSERY ▣ ⊠ EU € ◆
PO Box 147, Shipdham, Thetford,
Norfolk IP25 7BR
☎ (01362) 820870
Fax: (01362) 820870
Email: gladioli@aol.com
Website: www.greatwesternglads.co.uk
Contact: Frank Hartnell
Opening Times: By appt. only.
Min Mail Order UK: Nmc
Min Mail Order EU: Nmc

Cat. Cost: 4 x 1st class (2 catalogues)
Credit Cards: None
Specialities: *Gladiolus* species & hybrids,
corms & seeds. Other South African bulbous
plants.

EHan HANGING GARDENS NURSERIES LTD
Ongar Road West, A414, Writtle,
Chelmsford, Essex CM1 3NT
☎ (01245) 421020
Fax: (01245) 422293
Email: @hanginggardens.co.uk
Website: www.hanginggardens.co.uk
Contact: Jim Drake & Bob Teasell
Opening Times: 0900-1800 Apr-Nov,
0900-1700 Dec-Mar, 7 days.
Cat. Cost: None issued
Credit Cards: Access, American Express,
Delta, EuroCard, MasterCard, Switch, Visa
Specialities: *Clematis*, David Austin roses,
basket & patio plants, excellent range of
hardy nursery stock.
Note: (office) 15 Further Meadow, Writtle,
Chelmsford CM1 3LE.
Map Ref: E, D2

EHea THE HEATHER SOCIETY ⊠ EU €
Denbeigh, All Saints Road, Creeting St.
Mary, Ipswich, Suffolk IP6 8PJ
☎ (01449) 711220
Fax: (01449) 711220
Email: heathers@zetnet.co.uk
Website: www.heathersociety.org.uk
Contact: David & Anne Small
Opening Times: Not open.
Min Mail Order UK: Nmc for members.
£11.50 (incl. 1 yr membership)
Min Mail Order EU: Nmc for members,
£12.50 (incl. 1 yr membership).
Cat. Cost: 1 x 1st class
Credit Cards: Visa, MasterCard
Specialities: Heathers. Mail order for
Heather Society members within the EU.
Apr only.

EHoe HOECROFT PLANTS ⊠ EU ň € ◆
Severals Grange, Holt Road, Wood Norton,
Dereham, Norfolk NR20 5BL
☎ (01362) 684206
Fax: (01362) 684206
Email: hoecroft@acedial.co.uk

K E Y		
⊠ Mail order to UK or EU	ň Delivers to shows	
▣ Exports beyond EU	€ Euro accepted	
▣ Also supplies Wholesale	◆ See Display advertisement	

E

Website: www.hoecroft.co.uk
Contact: Jane Lister
Opening Times: 1000-1600 Thu-Sun
1st Apr-1st Oct or by appt.
Min Mail Order UK: No minimum charge
Min Mail Order EU: Nmc
Cat. Cost: 5 x 2nd class/£1coin
Credit Cards: None
Specialities: 240 varieties of variegated and
300 varieties of coloured-leaved plants in all
species. 270 grasses.
Note: nursery 2 miles north of Guist
on B1110
Map Ref: E, B3

EHof   HOFFLANDS DAFFODILS ⊠ EU ✉
Little Totham Road, Goldhanger,
Maldon, Essex CM9 8AP
☎ (01621) 788678
Fax: (01621) 788445
Email: Hofflands@care4free.net
Contact: John Pearson
Opening Times: By appt. only. Normally
mail order only.
Min Mail Order UK: No minimum charge
Min Mail Order EU: Nmc
Cat. Cost: Free
Credit Cards: MasterCard, Visa
Specialities: *Narcissus.*

EHol   HOLKHAM GARDENS
Holkham Park, Wells-next-the-Sea,
Norfolk NR23 1AB
☎ (01328) 711636
Email: info@holkhamgardens.com
Contact: Peter Gill, Trevor Gill
Opening Times: 1000-1700 7 days Mar-
Oct. 1100-dusk 7 days Nov-Feb. Closed mid
Dec-early Jan.
Cat. Cost: 3 x 1st class
Credit Cards: Access, Visa, Switch, MasterCard
Specialities: Wide range of shrubs,
herbaceous perennials, alpines, wall plants,
climbers, roses, conservatory plants and
herbs, both common & unusual. Some
plants in limited supply.
Map Ref: E, B1

**EHon   HONEYSOME AQUATIC
NURSERY** ▣ ⊠ UK
The Row, Sutton, Nr Ely,
Cambridgeshire CB6 2PF
☎ (01353) 778889
Contact: Mrs L S Bond
Opening Times: At all times by
appointment only.

Min Mail Order UK: No minimum charge
Cat. Cost: 2 x 1st class
Credit Cards: None
Specialities: Hardy aquatic, bog & marginal.
Map Ref: E, C2

EHrv   HARVEYS GARDEN PLANTS ⊠ EU ✉ ♠ €
Mulberry Cottage, Bradfield St George,
Bury St Edmunds, Suffolk IP30 0AY
☎ (01284) 386777
Fax: (01284) 386777 & answerphone
Email: roger@harveysgardenplants.co.uk
Website: www.harveysgardenplants.co.uk
www.hellebore.co.uk
Contact: Roger Harvey
Opening Times: 15th Jan-30th Jun &
1st Sep-31st Oct.
Min Mail Order UK: £15.00 + p&p
Min Mail Order EU: Please enquire
Cat. Cost: 5 x 1st class
Credit Cards: None
Specialities: *Helleborus, Anemone,
Epimedium, Euphorbia, Eryngium, Astrantia,
Pulmonaria* & other herbaceous perennials.
Woodland plants, heleniums. National
Collection of *Helenium* being set up with
NCCPG.
Map Ref: E, C2

EHul   HULL FARM ▣ ⊠ UK
Spring Valley Lane, Ardleigh, Colchester,
Essex CO7 7SA
☎ (01206) 230045
Fax: (01206) 230820
Contact: J Fryer & Sons
Opening Times: 1000-1600 7 days excl.
Xmas.
Min Mail Order UK: £30.00 + p&p
Cat. Cost: 5 x 2nd class
Credit Cards: MasterCard, Visa
Specialities: Conifers, grasses.
Map Ref: E, C3
OS Grid Ref: GR043274

EHyt   HYTHE ALPINES ⊠ EU ♠
Methwold Hythe, Thetford,
Norfolk IP26 4QH
☎ (01366) 728543
Fax: (01366) 728543
Contact: Mike Smith
Opening Times: 1000-1700 Tue & Wed
Mar-Oct.
Min Mail Order UK: No minimum charge
Min Mail Order EU: Nmc
Cat. Cost: 6 x 1st class, 4 x IRCs
Credit Cards: None

E

Specialities: Rare & unusual alpines, rock
garden plants & bulbs for enthusiasts &
exhibitors.
Map Ref: E, C2

EJWh   JILL WHITE ⊠ UK ṅ €
'St Davids', Recreation Way, Brightlingsea,
Essex CO7 ONJ
☎ (01206) 303547
Contact: Jill White
Opening Times: By appt. only.
Min Mail Order UK: Nmc
Cat. Cost: Sae
Credit Cards: None
Specialities: *Cyclamen* species especially
Cyclamen parviflorum. Also seed.
Map Ref: E, D3

EKMF   KATHLEEN MUNCASTER FUCHSIAS ṅ
18 Field Lane, Morton, Gainsborough,
Lincolnshire DN21 3BY
☎ (01427) 612329
Email: jim@smuncaster.freeserve.co.uk
Website:
www.kathleenmuncasterfuchsias.co.uk
Contact: Kathleen Muncaster
Opening Times: 1000-dusk Thu-Mon. After
mid Jun please phone to check.
Cat. Cost: 2 x 1st class
Credit Cards: None
Specialities: *Fuchsia.* National Collection of
hardy *Fuchsia* (full status).
Map Ref: E, A1

ELan   LANGTHORNS PLANTERY
High Cross Lane West, Little Canfield,
Dunmow, Essex CM6 1TD
☎ (01371) 872611
Fax: (01371) 872611
Contact: E Cannon, P Seymour
Opening Times: 1000-1700 or dusk (if
earlier) 7 days excl. Xmas fortnight & Easter
Sun.
Cat. Cost: £1.50
Credit Cards: Visa, Access, Switch,
MasterCard, Delta
Specialities: Wide general range with many
unusual plants.
Map Ref: E, D2

ELau   LAUREL FARM HERBS ⊠ EU
Main Road, Kelsale, Saxmundham,
Suffolk IP13 2RG
☎ (01728) 668223
Email: seagontheherbman@aol.com
Website: www.theherbfarm.co.uk

Contact: Chris Seagon
Opening Times: 1000-1700 Wed-Mon 1st
Mar-31st Oct. 1000-1500 Wed-Fri 1st Nov-
28th Feb.
Min Mail Order UK: 6 plants
Min Mail Order EU: 12 plants
Cat. Cost: £5.00* or free on web.
Credit Cards: Visa, MasterCard, Switch,
Delta
Specialities: Herbs esp. rosemary, thyme,
lavender, mint, comfrey & sage.
*Note: mail order from 1st Apr. Cat. cost
refunded on first order over £25.00. Credit
cards only accepted for internet orders.
Map Ref: E, C3

EMan   MANOR NURSERY ⊠ UK
Thaxted Road, Wimbish, Saffron Walden,
Essex CB10 2UT
☎ (01799) 513481
Fax: (01799) 513481
Email: flora@gardenplants.co.uk
Website: www.gardenplants.co.uk
Contact: William Lyall
Opening Times: 0900-1700 summer.
0900-1600 winter. Closed Xmas.
Min Mail Order UK: 10 plants
Cat. Cost: 4 x 2nd class
Credit Cards: Visa, Access, Switch,
EuroCard, MasterCard
Specialities: Uncommon perennials,
grasses, hardy *Geranium, Sedum* & cottage
garden plants. Variegated & coloured
foliage plants. Many newly introduced
cultivars.
Map Ref: E, C2

EMar   LESLEY MARSHALL ⊠ UK
Uncommon Garden Plants, Islington Lodge
Cottage, Tilney All Saints, King's Lynn,
Norfolk PE34 4SF
☎ (01553) 765103
Email: lesley.marshall@amserve.net
Contact: Lesley & Peter Marshall
Opening Times: 0930-1800 Mon, Wed,
Fri-Sun Mar-Oct.
Min Mail Order UK: 6 plants*
Cat. Cost: £1 refundable. £1 coin/4 x 1st
class
Credit Cards: None
Specialities: Uncommon garden plants,

KEY		
⊠ Mail order to UK or EU	ṅ Delivers to shows	
⊠ Exports beyond EU	€ Euro accepted	
⊠ Also supplies Wholesale	◆ See Display advertisement	

E

hardy perennials & plants for foliage effect. *Hemerocallis*. Choice seed list. Some plants available in limited quantities.
*Note: mail order Feb-Apr (spring list) & Sep-Nov (autumn list).
Map Ref: E, B1

EMcA S M McARD (SEEDS) ◧✉ EU
39 West Road, Pointon Sleaford, Lincolnshire NG34 0NA
☎ (01529) 240765
Fax: (01529) 240765
Email: seeds@smmcard.com
Website: www.smmcard.com
Contact: Susan McArd
Opening Times: Not open, mail order only.
Min Mail Order UK: Nmc
Min Mail Order EU: Nmc
Cat. Cost: 2 x 2nd class
Credit Cards: None
Specialities: Unusual & giant vegetables especially tree (Egyptian) onion. Seeds & plants.

EMFP MILLS' FARM PLANTS & GARDENS ✉ EU
Norwich Road, Mendlesham, Suffolk IP14 5NQ
☎ (01449) 766425
Fax: (01449) 766425
Email: sue@millsfarmplants.co.uk
Website: www.millsfarmplants.co.uk
Contact: Peter & Susan Russell
Opening Times: 0900-1730 Wed-Sun Mar-Dec & B/hol Mon.
Min Mail Order UK: No minimum charge*
Min Mail Order EU: Nmc
Cat. Cost: 5 x 2nd class
Credit Cards: Access, Visa, Switch, MasterCard, Delta, Solo
Specialities: Pinks, old roses, wide general range.
*Note: mail order for pinks & roses only.
Map Ref: E, C3
OS Grid Ref: TM119650

EMFW MICKFIELD WATERGARDEN CENTRE LTD ◧✉ EU ◧€
Debenham Road, Mickfield, Stowmarket, Suffolk IP14 5LP
☎ (01449) 711336
Fax: (01449) 711018
Email: mike@mickfield.co.uk
Website: www.watergardenshop.co.uk
Contact: Mike & Yvonne Burch
Opening Times: 0930-1700 7 days.
Min Mail Order UK: No minimum charge

Min Mail Order EU: £25.00 + p&p
Cat. Cost: £1.00
Credit Cards: Visa, Access, MasterCard, Switch
Specialities: Hardy aquatics, *Nymphaea* & moisture lovers.
Map Ref: E, C3

EMic MICKFIELD HOSTAS ✉ EU ⋔€
The Poplars, Mickfield, Stowmarket, Suffolk IP14 5LH
☎ (01449) 711576
Fax: (01449) 711576
Email: mickfieldhostas@btconnect.com
Website: www.mickfieldhostas.co.uk
Contact: Mr & Mrs R L C Milton
Opening Times: By appt. only. See catalogue or website.
Min Mail Order UK: See cat. for details
Min Mail Order EU: See cat.
Cat. Cost: 4 x 1st class*
Credit Cards: See catalogue for details
Specialities: *Hosta*, over 600 varieties (subject to availability) mostly from USA. New varieties become available during the season.
*Note: catalogue cost refunded on order.
Map Ref: E, C3

EMil MILL RACE NURSERY ◧€
New Road, Aldham, Colchester, Essex CO6 3QT
☎ (01206) 242521
Fax: (01206) 241616
Email: admin@millracenursery.co.uk
Website: www.millracenursery.co.uk
Contact: Bill Mathews
Opening Times: 0900-1730 7 days.
Cat. Cost: Sae + 2 x 1st class
Credit Cards: Access, Visa, Diners, Switch
Specialities: Over 400 varieties of herbaceous & many unusual trees, shrubs & climbers.
Map Ref: E, C2

EMlt MALLETTS NURSERIES ◧✉ UK
Home Farm, Dell Corner Lane, N Burlingham, Norwich, Norfolk NR13 4SX
☎ (01603) 713676
Email: peter@mallettsnurseries.co.uk
Website: www.mallettsnurseries.co.uk
Contact: Peter Mallett
Opening Times:
Min Mail Order UK: Nmc
Cat. Cost: 4 x 1st class
Credit Cards: None

E

Specialities: Alpines.
Map Ref: E, B3
OS Grid Ref: TG362103

EMNN MARTIN NEST
NURSERIES 🖾 ⊠ EU 🏛
Grange Cottage, Harpswell Lane,
Hemswell, Gainsborough,
Lincolnshire DN21 5UP
☎ (01427) 668369
Fax: (01427) 668080
Contact: M Robinson and J Shardlow
Opening Times: 1000-1600 7 days.
Min Mail Order UK: No minimum charge
Min Mail Order EU: £30.00 + p&p
Cat. Cost: 3 x 2nd class
Credit Cards: Visa, Access, Switch,
MasterCard, American Express
Specialities: Alpines esp. *Primula*, auriculas
& *Saxifraga*. National Collection of show &
alpine Auriculas.
Map Ref: E, A1

EMon MONKSILVER NURSERY ⊠ EU €
Oakington Road, Cottenham,
Cambridgeshire CB4 8TW
☎ (01954) 251555
Fax: (01223) 502887
Email: plants@monksilver.com
Website: www.monksilver.com
Contact: Joe Sharman & Alan Leslie
Opening Times: 1000-1600 Fri & Sat
1 Mar-30 Jun, 22 Sep + Fri & Sat Oct 2002.
Min Mail Order UK: £15.00 + p&p
Min Mail Order EU: £30.00 + p&p
Cat. Cost: 8 x 1st class
Credit Cards: None
Specialities: Herbaceous plants, grasses,
*Anthemis, Arum, Helianthus, Lamium,
Nepeta, Monarda, Salvia, Vinca*, sedges &
variegated plants. Many NCCPG 'Pink
Sheet' plants. Ferns.
Map Ref: E, C2

EMor JOHN MORLEY ⊠ EU
North Green Only, Stoven, Beccles,
Suffolk NR34 8DG
Contact: John Morley
Opening Times: By appt. only.
Min Mail Order UK: Details in cat.
Min Mail Order EU: Details in cat.
Cat. Cost: 6 x 1st class
Credit Cards: Visa, MasterCard, Switch,
Delta
Specialities: *Galanthus*, a comprehensive
range of cultivars.

EMui KEN MUIR LTD 🖾 ⊠ UK
Honeypot Farm, Rectory Road,
Weeley Heath,
Essex CO16 9BJ
☎ 0870 7479111
Fax: (01255) 831534
Email: info@kenmuir.co.uk
Website: www.kenmuir.co.uk
Contact: Ming Yang, Claire Higgins
Opening Times: 1000-1600.
Min Mail Order UK: Nmc
Cat. Cost: Free
Credit Cards: Visa, Access, Switch
Specialities: Fruit.
Map Ref: E, D3

ENor NORFOLK LAVENDER ⊠ EU 🏛
Caley Mill, Heacham, King's Lynn,
Norfolk PE31 7JE
☎ (01485) 570384
Fax: (01485) 571176
Email: admin@norfolk-lavender.co.uk
Website: www.norfolk-lavender.co.uk
Contact: Henry Head
Opening Times: 0930-1700 7 days.
Min Mail Order UK: £15.00 + p&p
Min Mail Order EU: £15.00 + p&p
Cat. Cost: 2 x 1st class
Credit Cards: Visa, Access, Switch
Specialities: National Collection of
Lavandula.
Map Ref: E, B1

ENot NOTCUTTS NURSERIES 🖾 ⊠ EU 🏛 €
Woodbridge, Suffolk IP12 4AF
☎ (01394) 383344
Fax: (01394) 445440
Email: sales@notcutts.co.uk
Website: www.notcutts.co.uk
Contact: Plant Adviser
Opening Times: Garden centres 0900-1800
Mon-Sat & 1030-1630 Sun.
Min Mail Order UK: £200.00 + p&p
Min Mail Order EU: £500.00 + p&p
Cat. Cost: £5.00 + £1.25
Credit Cards: Visa, Access, Switch, Connect
Specialities: Wide general range. Specialist
list of *Syringa*. National Collection of
Hibiscus.
Map Ref: E, C3
OS Grid Ref: TM268487

K E Y	⊠ Mail order to UK or EU	🦶 Delivers to shows
	🏛 Exports beyond EU	€ Euro accepted
	🖾 Also supplies Wholesale	◆ See Display advertisement

E

EOas   OASIS ⊠ EU
42 Greenwood Avenue,
South Benfleet, Essex SS7 1LD
☎ (01268) 757666
Fax: (01268) 795646
Email: paul@oasisdesigns.co.uk
Website: www.oasisdesigns.co.uk
Contact: Paul Spracklin
Opening Times: Strictly by appt. only.
Min Mail Order UK: No minimum charge
Min Mail Order EU: £75
Cat. Cost: 2 x 1st class
Credit Cards: None
Specialities: Small nursery offering a range of
hardy & half-hardy exotic succulent plants
incl. *Agave, Aloe, Beschorneria, Dasylirion,
Nolina, Yucca* & cacti.
Note: most items held in limited quanitites.
Map Ref: E, D2

EOHP   OLD HALL PLANTS ⊠ EU €
1 The Old Hall, Barsham, Beccles,
Suffolk NR34 8HB
☎ (01502) 717475
Email: info@oldhallplants.co.uk
Website: www.oldhallplants.co.uk
Contact: Janet Elliott
Opening Times: By appt. most days, please
phone first.
Min Mail Order UK: Nmc
Min Mail Order EU: Nmc
Cat. Cost: 4 x 1st class
Credit Cards: None
Specialities: Herbs, over 600 varieties
grown.
Map Ref: E, C3
OS Grid Ref: TM395904

EOrc   ORCHARD NURSERIES ⊠ UK ń
Tow Lane, Foston, Grantham,
Lincolnshire NG32 2LE
☎ (01400) 281354
Fax: (01400) 281354
Email: orchnurs@lineone.net
Contact: Margaret Rose
Opening Times: 1000-1800 Wed-Mon
1st Feb-30th Sept. Other times by appt.
Min Mail Order UK: No minimum
charge
Cat. Cost: 5 x 2nd class
Credit Cards: None
Specialities: Small flowered *Clematis*,
unusual herbaceous esp. *Geranium,
Helleborus, Hosta, Salvia*. Sae for seed list,
mainly *Helleborus*.
Map Ref: E, B1

EOrn   ORNAMENTAL CONIFERS ◆
22 Chapel Road, Terrington St Clement,
Kings Lynn, Norfolk PE34 4ND
☎ (01553) 828874
Fax: (01553) 828874
Contact: Peter Rotchell
Opening Times: 0930-1700 6 days, closed
Wed, 2nd Feb-18th Dec.
Credit Cards: None
Specialities: Conifers.
Map Ref: E, B1

EPar   PARADISE CENTRE ⊠ EU ⊠ ń €
Twinstead Road, Lamarsh, Bures,
Suffolk CO8 5EX
☎ (01787) 269449
Fax: (01787) 269449
Email: hedy@paradisecentre.com
Website: www.paradisecentre.com
Contact: Cees & Hedy Stapel-Valk
Opening Times: 1000-1700 Sat-Sun &
B/hols or by appt. Easter-1st Nov.
Min Mail Order UK: £7.50 + p&p
Min Mail Order EU: £25.00 + p&p
Cat. Cost: 5 x 1st class
Credit Cards: Visa, Access, Diners
Specialities: Unusual bulbous & tuberous
plants including shade & bog varieties.
Some seeds.
Map Ref: E, C2

EPem   PEMBROKE FARM NURSERY ń €
Pembroke Farm, Barway, Ely,
Cambridgeshire CB7 5UB
☎ (01353) 722903
Fax: (01353) 722903
Email: Pemcacti@aol.com
Website: www.cactiandsucculents.co.uk
Contact: Richard & Sheena Drane
Opening Times: 1000-1800 Thu-Sat
Apr-Oct. Other times by appt.
Cat. Cost: None issued
Credit Cards: None
Specialities: Cacti & succulents including
Agave, Aloe & *Sempervivum*. Please send sae
for shows to be attended in 2002.
Map Ref: E, C2

EPfP   THE PLACE FOR PLANTS ń
East Bergholt Place, East Bergholt,
Suffolk CO7 6UP
☎ (01206) 299224
Fax: (01206) 299224
Email: sales@placeforplants.co.uk
Contact: Rupert & Sara Eley
Opening Times: 1000-1700 (or dusk if

E

earlier) 7 days. Closed Xmas fortnight &
Easter Sun. Garden open Mar-Oct.
Cat. Cost: 2 x 1st class
Credit Cards: Visa, Access, MasterCard,
EuroCard, Delta, Switch
Specialities: Wide range of specialist &
popular plants. 15 acre mature garden.
Map Ref: E, C3

EPGN PARK GREEN NURSERIES ⊠ EU ▣ ń
Wetheringsett, Stowmarket, Suffolk IP14 5QH
☎ (01728) 860139
Fax: (01728) 861277
Email: nurseries@parkgreen.fsnet.co.uk
Website: www.parkgreen.co.uk
Contact: Richard & Mary Ford
Opening Times: 1000-1600 Mon-Fri &
1000-1300 Sat, 1 Mar-22 Sep.
Min Mail Order UK: Nmc
Min Mail Order EU: Nmc
Cat. Cost: 4 x 1st class
Credit Cards: Visa, MasterCard, Delta,
Switch
Specialities: *Hosta, Astilbe,* ornamental
grasses & herbaceous.
Map Ref: E, C3
OS Grid Ref: TM136644

EPla P W PLANTS ⊠ EU ń ◆
Sunnyside, Heath Road, Kenninghall
Norfolk NR16 2DS
☎ (01953) 888212
Fax: (01953) 888212
Email: pw.plants@paston.co.uk
Contact: Paul Whittaker
Opening Times: Every Fri & last Sat in
every month, plus all Sats Apr-Sep.
Min Mail Order UK: No minimum charge
Min Mail Order EU: Nmc
Cat. Cost: 5 x 1st class
Credit Cards: Visa, MasterCard, Switch,
JCB, Solo
Specialities: Bamboos, grasses, choice
shrubs & perennials, climbers (incl. wide
selection of *Hedera*) Note: does not deliver
to Chelsea Show.
Map Ref: E, C3

EPln THE PLANT LOVERS ▣ ń
Candlesby House, Candlesby, Spilsby,
Lincolnshire PE23 5RU
☎ (01754) 890256
Fax: (01754) 890594
Contact: Tim Wilson
Opening Times: Daily but please phone first.
Cat. Cost: None issued

Credit Cards: None
Specialities: A wide range of cacti and other
succulents also *Sempervivum* (houseleeks).
Map Ref: E, B1

EPot POTTERTON & MARTIN ▣ ⊠ EU ▣ ń €
Moortown Road, Nettleton, Caistor,
Lincolnshire LN7 6HX
☎ (01472) 851714
Fax: (01472) 852580
Email: pottin@globalnet.co.uk
Website: www.users.globalnet.co.uk/~pottin
Contact: Robert Potterton
Opening Times: 0900-1630 7 days.
Min Mail Order UK: Nmc
Min Mail Order EU: Nmc
Cat. Cost: £1 in stamps
Credit Cards: Electron, MasterCard, Delta,
Switch, Solo, JCB, Maestro, Visa
Specialities: Alpines, dwarf bulbs, conifers &
shrubs. Hardy orchids & *Pleione*. Seed list
sent out in Nov.
Map Ref: E, A1

**EPPr THE PLANTSMAN'S
PREFERENCE** ⊠ EU ń
(Office) Lynwood, Hopton Road,
Garboldisham, Diss, Norfolk IP22 2QN
☎ (01953) 681439 (office)
☎ (07799) 855559 (nursery)
Email: plantpref@aol.com
Website: www.plantpref.co.uk
Contact: Jenny & Tim Fuller
Opening Times: 0930-1700 Fri, Sat & Sun
Mar-Oct. Other times by appt.
Min Mail Order UK: No minimum charge
Min Mail Order EU: Nmc
Cat. Cost: 4 x 1st class
Credit Cards: None
Specialities: Hardy *Geranium* (450),
grasses & sedges (600+). Unusual &
interesting perennials.
Note: nursery is at Hall Farm, Church Road,
South Lopham, Diss.
Map Ref: E, C3
OS Grid Ref: TM041819

EPri PRIORY PLANTS ⊠ UK
1 Covey Cottage, Hintlesham,
Nr Ipswich, Suffolk IP8 3NY
☎ (01473) 652656

Y	⊠ Mail order to UK or EU	ń Delivers to shows
E	▣ Exports beyond EU	€ Euro accepted
K	▣ Also supplies Wholesale	◆ See Display advertisement

E

Fax: (01473) 652656
Contact: Sue Mann
Opening Times: By appt. only. Please ring first to avoid disappointment.
Min Mail Order UK: £15.00 + p&p
Cat. Cost: 3 x 1st class
Credit Cards: None
Specialities: *Penstemon*, hardy *Geranium*, *Euphorbia*, *Campanula*, *Salvia* & grasses. Cottage garden perennials.
Map Ref: E, C3

EPts POTASH NURSERY ⊠ UK ň
Cow Green, Bacton, Stowmarket,
Suffolk IP14 4HJ
☎ (01449) 781671
Email: enquiries@potashnursery.co.uk
Website: www.potashnursery.co.uk
Contact: M W Clare
Opening Times: 1000-1700 Fri-Sun & B/hol Mons mid Feb-end Jun.
Min Mail Order UK: £12.50
Cat. Cost: 4 x 1st class
Credit Cards: Visa, Delta, MasterCard
Specialities: *Fuchsia*.
Map Ref: E, C3

EPVP PALM VIEW PLANTS ▣ ⊠ UK
10 Milden Road, Ipswich,
Suffolk IP2 0LB
☎ (01473) 402747
Email: palmview@ntworld.co.uk
Contact: Robert Gooding
Opening Times: By appt. only.
Min Mail Order UK: Nmc
Cat. Cost: 3 x 1st class
Specialities: cold hardy palms & exotics.
Map Ref: E, C3

EPyc PENNYCROSS PLANTS ▣
Earith Road, Colne,
Huntingdon, Cambridgeshire
PE28 3NL
☎ (01487) 841520
Email: plants@pennycross99.freeserve.co.uk
Contact: Janet M Buist
Opening Times: 0900-dusk Thu, 1400-dusk Fri, 1st Mar-31st Oct. Other times by appointment.
Cat. Cost: 4 x 2nd class
Credit Cards: None
Specialities: Hardy perennials. Grasses. Some plants available in limited quantities only.
Map Ref: E, C2
OS Grid Ref: TL378759

ER&R RHODES & ROCKLIFFE ⊠ EU ▣ ň
2 Nursery Road, Nazeing,
Essex EN9 2JE
☎ (01992) 451598 (office hours)
Fax: (01992) 440673
Email: RRBegonias@aol.com
Contact: David Rhodes or John Rockliffe
Opening Times: By appt.
Min Mail Order UK: £2.50 + p&p*
Min Mail Order EU: £5.00 + p&p
Cat. Cost: 2 x 1st class
Credit Cards: None
Specialities: *Begonia* species & hybrids. National Collection of *Begonia*. Plants propagated to order.
*Note: mail order Apr-Sep only.
Map Ref: E, D2

ERea READS NURSERY ⊠ EU ▣
Hales Hall, Loddon,
Norfolk NR14 6QW
☎ (01508) 548395
Fax: (01508) 548040
Email: plants@readsnursery.co.uk
Website: www.readsnursery.co.uk
Contact: Stephen Read
Opening Times: 1000-1700 (dusk if earlier) Tue-Sat, 1100-1600 Sun & B/hols Easter-end Sep & by appt.
Min Mail Order UK: £10.00 + p&p
Min Mail Order EU: £10.00 + p&p
Cat. Cost: 4 x 1st class
Credit Cards: Visa, Access, Diners, Switch
Specialities: Conservatory plants, vines, *Citrus*, figs & unusual fruits & nuts. Wall shrubs & climbers. Scented & aromatic hardy plants. Box & yew hedging & topiary. UK grown. National Collections of *Citrus*, figs, vines.
Map Ref: E, B3

ERob ROBIN SAVILL CLEMATIS
SPECIALIST ▣ ⊠ EU ▣
(Office) 2 Bury Cottages, Bury Road,
Pleshey, Chelmsford, Essex CM3 1HB
☎ (01245) 237380
Fax: (01245) 603882
Email: clematis@madasafish.com
Contact: Robin Savill
Opening Times: Mail order only. Visitors by appt. only.
Min Mail Order UK: 1 plant + p&p
Min Mail Order EU: 1 plant + p&p
Cat. Cost: £2.50 or 10 x 1st class
Credit Cards: None
Specialities: Over 800 varieties of *Clematis*

incl. many unusual species & cvs from around the world. National Collection of *Clematis viticella*.
Map Ref: E, D2

ERod   THE RODINGS PLANTERY ⊠ EU ◨ ⋔ €
Anchor Lane, Abbess Roding,
Essex CM5 0JW
☎ (01279) 876421
Email: andy@bamboo100.fsnet.co.uk
Contact: Jane & Andy Mogridge
Opening Times: By appointment only. Occasional open days, please phone for details.
Min Mail Order UK: £15.00 + p&p
Min Mail Order EU: £500.00 + p&p
Cat. Cost: 3 x 1st class
Credit Cards: None
Specialities: *Bamboo.* Rare & unusual trees.
Map Ref: E, D2

ERom   THE ROMANTIC GARDEN ◨ ⊠ EU ◨ ⋔ € ◆
Swannington, Norwich,
Norfolk NR9 5NW
☎ (01603) 261488
Fax: (01603) 864231
Email: enquiries@romantic-garden-nursery.co.uk
Website: www.romantic-garden-nursery.co.uk
Contact: John Powles
Opening Times: 1000-1700 Wed Fri & Sat all year.
Min Mail Order UK: £5.00 + p&p
Min Mail Order EU: £30.00 + p&p
Cat. Cost: 4 x 1st class
Credit Cards: Visa, Access, American Express
Specialities: Half-hardy & conservatory. *Buxus* topiary, ornamental standards, large specimens.
Map Ref: E, B3

ERos   ROSEHOLME NURSERY ◨ ⊠ EU ◨
Roseholme Farm, Howsham, Market Rasen, Lincolnshire LN7 6JZ
☎ (01652) 678661
Fax: (01472) 852450
Email: Pbcenterpr@aol/com
Contact: P B Clayton
Opening Times: By appt. for collection of orders.
Min Mail Order UK: Nmc
Min Mail Order EU: Nmc
Cat. Cost: 2 x 2nd class
Credit Cards: None

Specialities: Underground lines - bulbs, corms, rhizomes & tubers (esp. *Crocus, Iris*).
Map Ref: E, A1

ERou   ROUGHAM HALL NURSERIES ◨ ⊠ EU ◨ ⋔ € ◆
Ipswich Road, Rougham, Bury St Edmunds, Suffolk IP30 9LZ
☎ 0800 970 7516
Fax: (01359) 271149
Email: hardyperennials@aol.com
Website: www.roughamhallnurseries.co.uk
Contact: A A & K G Harbutt
Opening Times: 1000-1600 Thu-Mon Easter-31st Oct.
Min Mail Order UK: Nmc
Min Mail Order EU: Nmc
Cat. Cost: 5 x 1st class
Credit Cards: MasterCard, Visa
Specialities: Hardy perennials especially *Aster* (n-a, n-b & species), *Delphinium, Hemerocallis, Iris, Kniphofia, Papaver* & *Phlox.* National Collections of *Delphinium* & gooseberry. Please note delphiniums for collection only, no mail order.
Map Ref: E, C2

ERsn   SUE ROBINSON
21 Bederic Close, Bury St Edmunds, Suffolk IP32 7DN
☎ (01284) 764310
Fax: (01284) 764310
Contact: Sue Robinson
Opening Times: By appt. only.
Cat. Cost: None issued
Credit Cards: None
Specialities: Variegated & foliage plants. Garden open. Lectures at clubs & societies, group bookings welcome.

ESCh   SHEILA CHAPMAN CLEMATIS ⋔
Crowther Nurseries, Ongar Road, Abridge, Romford, Essex RM4 1AA
☎ (01708) 688090
Fax: (01708) 688677
Contact: Sheila Chapman
Opening Times: 0930-1700 (or dusk in winter) all year excl. Xmas week.
Cat. Cost: 4 x 1st class
Credit Cards: Visa, Access, Switch, Connect, Delta, Discover, EuroCard, Electron, JCB,

E

KEY		
⊠ Mail order to UK or EU	⋔ Delivers to shows	
◨ Exports beyond EU	€ Euro accepted	
◨ Also supplies Wholesale	◆ See Display advertisement	

E

Laser, MasterCard
Specialities: Over 600 varieties of *Clematis*.
Map Ref: E, D2

ESgl   SEAGATE IRISES ✉ EU €
A17 Long Sutton By-Pass, Long Sutton,
Lincolnshire PE12 9RX
☎ (01406) 365138
Fax: (01406) 365447
Email: Sales@irises.co.uk
Website: www.irises.co.uk
Contact: Julian Browse or Wendy Browse
Opening Times: 1000-1800 daily May-Sep.
Please phone for appt. Oct-Apr.
Min Mail Order UK: Nmc
Min Mail Order EU: Nmc carriage at cost.
Cat. Cost: £2.50, no stamps please.
Credit Cards: Visa, Access, MasterCard,
Switch
Specialities: Bearded *Iris*, over 400 varieties,
modern & historic tall bearded, medians &
dwarfs. Many container grown available.
Map Ref: E, B1
OS Grid Ref: TF437218

EShb   SHRUBLAND PARK
NURSERIES ✉ UK ♙ €
Coddenham, Ipswich, Suffolk IP6 9QJ
☎ (01473) 833187, mobile 07890 527744
Fax: (01473) 832838
Email: gill.stitt@btinternet.com
Website: www.shrublandparknurseries.co.uk
Contact: Gill Stitt
Opening Times: 0900-1700 (dusk if earlier)
Sat, Sun & Wed. Other times by prior appt.
Please ring to check during the 2 weeks
either side of Xmas & for directions before
visiting.
Min Mail Order UK: £10.00*
Cat. Cost: Free
Credit Cards: Visa, MasterCard, Delta,
Switch, Solo, JCB, Electron, Maestro
Specialities: A new nursery offering an
increasing range of plants for the
conservatory & sheltered outdoor locations.
Some hardy plants.
*Note: mail order limited at present, but
expanding.
Map Ref: E, C3

ESim   CLIVE SIMMS ✉ UK
Woodhurst, Essendine, Stamford,
Lincolnshire PE9 4LQ
☎ (01780) 755615
Email: clive_simms@lineone.net
Website: www.clivesimms.com

Contact: Clive & Kathryn Simms
Opening Times: By apptointment for
collection only.
Min Mail Order UK: No minimum charge
Cat. Cost: 2 x 1st class
Specialities: Uncommon nut trees & unusual
fruiting plants.

ESis   SISKIN PLANTS ✉ EU
April House, Davey Lane,
Charsfield, Woodbridge,
Suffolk IP13 7QG
☎ (01473) 737567
Fax: (01473) 737567
Email: info@siskinplants.co.uk
Website: www.siskinplants.co.uk
Contact: Chris & Valerie Wheeler
Opening Times: Not open. Mail order only.
Min Mail Order UK: Nmc
Min Mail Order EU: Nmc
Cat. Cost: 4 x 1st class
Credit Cards: Visa, MasterCard, Switch,
Solo
Specialities: Alpines, sempervivums, small
perennials, grasses & dwarf shrubs especially
plants for troughs. National Collection of
dwarf *Hebe*.
Map Ref: E, C3

ESlt   SCARLETTS QUALITY
PLANTS ▣ ✉ EU ▣ ♙ €
Nayland Road, West Bergholt, Colchester,
Essex CO6 3DH
☎ (01206) 242533
Fax: (01206) 242530
Email: info@scarletts.co.uk
Website: www.scarletts.org
Contact: Kate Backhouse
Opening Times: By appt. only.
Min Mail Order UK: No minimum charge
Min Mail Order EU: Nmc
Cat. Cost: Free list
Credit Cards: MasterCard, EuroCard, Visa,
Delta
Specialities: Conservatory plants. *Citrus*.
Map Ref: E, C2

ESou   SOUTHFIELD NURSERIES ▣ ✉ EU ♙ ◆
Bourne Road, Morton, Nr Bourne,
Lincolnshire PE10 0RH
☎ (01778) 570168
Contact: Mr & Mrs B Goodey
Opening Times: 1000-1215 & 1315-1600
7 days. Nov-Jan by appt. only.
Min Mail Order UK: Nmc
Min Mail Order EU: Nmc

E

Cat. Cost: 3 x 1st class
Credit Cards: None
Specialities: A wide range of cacti &
succulents incl. some of the rarer varieties,
all grown on our own nursery.
Map Ref: E, B1

ESty STYLE ROSES 🔲 ⊠ EU 🗹 ń
10 Meridian Walk, Holbeach, Spalding,
Lincolnsire PE12 7NR
☎ (01406) 424089,
mobile 07932 044093
Fax: (01406) 424089
Email: styleroses@aol.com
Website: www.styleroses.co.uk
Contact: Chris Styles
Opening Times: Vary, please phone.
Min Mail Order UK: No minimum charge
Min Mail Order EU: Nmc
Cat. Cost: Free
Credit Cards: None
Specialities: Roses: standard & bush roses.
Note: export beyond EU subject to countries'
plant health requirements, carriage & export
certificates where required charged at cost.
Map Ref: E, B1

ESul BRIAN & PEARL SULMAN ⊠ EU ń
54 Kingsway, Mildenhall, Bury St Edmunds,
Suffolk IP28 7HR
☎ (01638) 712297
Fax: (01638) 712297
Email: pearl@sulmanspelargoniums.co.uk
Website: www.sulmanspelargoniums.co.uk
Contact: Pearl Sulman
Opening Times: Not open, mail order only.
Open w/end 1st/2nd Jun 2002, early Jun
2003 (phone for confirmation of dates).
Min Mail Order UK: £18.00
Min Mail Order EU: £18.00 + p&p
Cat. Cost: 4 x 1st class
Credit Cards: Visa, MasterCard
Specialities: *Pelargonium.*
Map Ref: E, C2

ETho THORNCROFT CLEMATIS
NURSERY ⊠ EU 🗹 ń €
The Lings, Reymerston, Norwich,
Norfolk NR9 4QG
☎ (01953) 850407
Fax: (01953) 851788
Email: sales@thorncroft.co.uk
Website: www.thorncroft.co.uk
Contact: Ruth P Gooch
Opening Times: 1000-1630 Thu-Tue,
Mar-Oct, 1000-1500 Mon-Fri, Nov-Feb.

Min Mail Order UK: Nmc
Min Mail Order EU: Nmc
Cat. Cost: 5 x 2nd class
Credit Cards: MasterCard, Solo, Visa, Delta,
Switch
Specialities: *Clematis.* Note: does not export
to USA, Canada or Australia. Accepts euros
only as cash not cheques.
Map Ref: E, B3
OS Grid Ref: TG039062

ETow TOWN FARM NURSERY ⊠ EU
Street House, The Street, Metfield,
Harleston, Norfolk IP20 0LA
☎ (01379) 586189
Email: david.baker@themail.co.uk
Website: www.alpinemeadow.co.uk
Contact: F D Baker
Opening Times: Feb-Oct by appt. only.
Min Mail Order UK: £5.00 + p&p
Min Mail Order EU: £20.00 + p&p
Cat. Cost: Sae
Credit Cards: None
Specialities: Unusual alpines, border
perennials. Also seed.
Map Ref: E, C3

ETub VAN TUBERGEN UK LTD 🔲 ⊠ EU
Four Winds, Low Road, Bressingham, Diss,
Norfolk IP22 2AG
☎ (01379) 688282
Fax: (01379) 687227
Email: van.tubergen@tesco.net
Website: www.vantubergen.co.uk
Contact: General Manager
Opening Times: Not open, mail order only.
Min Mail Order UK: Nmc
Min Mail Order EU: Nmc
Cat. Cost: Free
Credit Cards: Visa, Access, MasterCard,
Switch
Specialities: Bulbs.

ETWh TREVOR WHITE OLD
FASHIONED ROSES 🔲 ⊠ EU
Bennetts Brier, The Street, Felthorpe,
Norwich, Norfolk NR10 4AB
☎ (01603) 755135
Fax: (01603) 755135
Email: trevor@oldfashionedroses.freeserve.co.uk
Contact: Mr T A & Mrs V J White

E

Opening Times: 0900-1700 by appt only.
Min Mail Order UK: Nmc
Min Mail Order EU: £100 + p&p
Cat. Cost: Free
Credit Cards:
Specialities: Old-fashioned, shrub, climbing
& rambling roses.
Map Ref: E, B3

EVFa   VALLEY FARM PLANTS n̂
Hillington, Kings Lynn, Norfolk PE31 6DW
☎ (01485) 600288
Fax: (01485) 601211
Email: olineave@freeuk.co.uk
Contact: Oliver Neave
Opening Times: 1000-1700 Wed-Sun
second week Mar-3rd week Oct.
Specialities: Variegated & interesting foliage
plants. Mainly perennials, shrubs & grasses.
Map Ref: E, B1

EWes   WEST ACRE GARDENS ✉ UK n̂
West Acre, Kings Lynn, Norfolk PE32 1UJ
☎ (01760) 755562
Contact: J J Tuite
Opening Times: 1000-1700 7 days 1st Feb-
30th Nov. Other times by appt.
Min Mail Order UK: Nmc
Cat. Cost: 4 x 1st class
Credit Cards: Visa, MasterCard, Delta,
Switch
Specialities: Unusual shrubs, herbaceous
& alpines. Large selection of *Rhodohypoxis* &
grasses.
Map Ref: E, B1

EWll   THE WALLED GARDEN ◆
Park Road, Benhall, Saxmundham,
Suffolk IP17 1JB
☎ (01728) 602510
Fax: (01728) 602510
Email: jim@thewalledgarden.co.uk
Website: www.thewalledgarden.co.uk
Contact: J R Mountain
Opening Times: 0930-1700 Tue-Sun Mar-
Oct, Tue-Sat Nov-Feb.
Cat. Cost: 2 x 1st class
Credit Cards: Visa, MasterCard, Switch
Specialities: Tender & hardy perennials &
wall shrubs.
Map Ref: E, C3
OS Grid Ref: TM371613

EWoo   WOOTTEN'S PLANTS ✉ EU
Wenhaston, Blackheath, Halesworth,
Suffolk IP19 9HD

☎ (01502) 478258
Fax: (01502) 478258
Email: sales@woottensplants.co.uk
Website: www.woottensplants.co.uk
Contact: M Loftus
Opening Times: 0930-1700 7 days.
Min Mail Order UK: No minimum charge
Min Mail Order EU: Nmc
Cat. Cost: £2.50 illus. + £1.50 p&p
Credit Cards: Access, Visa, American
Express, Switch
Specialities: *Pelargonium, Penstemon, Salvia,
Hemerocallis, Hosta* & *Iris*. Grasses.
Map Ref: E, C3

EWsh   WESTSHORES NURSERIES
82 West Street, Winterton,
Lincolnshire DN15 9QF
☎ (01724) 733940
Fax: (01724) 733940
Email: westshnur@aol.com
Contact: Gail & John Summerfield
Opening Times: 0930-1800 (or dusk) Wed-
Mon 1st Mar-mid Nov.
Cat. Cost: 2 x 1st class
Credit Cards: None
Specialities: Ornamental grasses &
herbaceous perennials.
Map Ref: E, A1

**EWTr   WALNUT TREE GARDEN
NURSERY** ✉ UK €
Flymoor Lane, Rocklands,
Attleborough, Norfolk
NR17 1BP
☎ (01953) 488163
Fax: (01953) 483187
Email: jimnclare@aol.com
Website: www.walnut-tree-garden-
nursery.co.uk
Contact: Jim Paine & Clare Billington
Opening Times: 0900-1800 Tue-Sun Feb-
Nov & B/hols.
Min Mail Order UK: £30.00
Cat. Cost: 4 x 1st class
Credit Cards: Visa, MasterCard, Switch,
Solo
Map Ref: E, B1

SCOTLAND

GAbr   ABRIACHAN NURSERIES ✉ EU
Loch Ness Side, Inverness, Invernesshire,
Scotland IV3 8LA
☎ (01463) 861232
Fax: (01463) 861232

G

Contact: Mr & Mrs D Davidson
Opening Times: 0900-1900 daily (dusk if earlier) Feb-Nov.
Min Mail Order UK: No minimum charge
Min Mail Order EU: Nmc
Cat. Cost: 4 x 1st class
Credit Cards: None
Specialities: Herbaceous, *Primula*, *Helianthemum*, hardy *Geranium* & *Sempervivum*.
Map Ref: G, B2

GBar   **BARWINNOCK HERBS** ⊠ EU €
Barrhill by Girvan, Ayrshire,
Scotland KA26 0RB
☎ (01465) 821338
Fax: (01465) 821338
Email: herbs.scotland@barwinnock.com
Website: www.barwinnock.com
Contact: Dave & Mon Holtom
Opening Times: 1000-1700 7 days 1st Apr-31st Oct.
Min Mail Order UK: No minimum charge
Min Mail Order EU: Nmc
Cat. Cost: Free
Credit Cards: Visa, MasterCard, Delta, Switch, Solo
Specialities: Culinary, medicinal, fragrant-leaved plants & wildflowers organically grown.
Map Ref: G, D2

GBin   **BINNY PLANTS** ⊠ EU ń €
West Lodge, Binny Estate, Ecclesmachen Road, Nr Broxbourn, West Lothian, Scotland EH52 6NL
☎ (01506) 858931
Fax: (01506) 858155
Email: binnyplants@aol.com
Contact: Billy Carruthers
Opening Times: 1000-1700 Thu-Mon 14 Mar-31 Oct.
Min Mail Order UK: No minimum charge*
Min Mail Order EU: £25.00
Cat. Cost: 3 x 1st class
Credit Cards: Visa, MasterCard, EuroCard
Specialities: Perennials incl. *Euphorbia*, *Geranium*, *Hosta*. Plus large selection of grasses & ferns.
*Note: Mail order Oct-Mar only.
Map Ref: G, C3

GBon   **BONHARD NURSERY**
Murrayshall Road, Scone, Perth, Tayside, Scotland PH2 7PQ
☎ (01738) 552791

Fax: (01738) 552939
Contact: Mr & Mrs Hickman
Opening Times: 0900-1700, or dusk if earlier, 7 days.
Cat. Cost: Free (fruit trees & roses)
Credit Cards: Access, EuroCard, MasterCard, Switch, Visa
Specialities: Herbaceous, conifers & alpines. Fruit & ornamental trees. Shrub & species roses.
Map Ref: G, C3

GBri   **BRIDGE END NURSERIES** ń
Gretna Green, Dumfries & Galloway, Scotland DG16 5HN
☎ (01461) 800612
Fax: (01461) 800612
Contact: R Bird
Opening Times: 0930-1700 all year. Evenings by appt.
Cat. Cost: None issued
Credit Cards: None
Specialities: Hardy cottage garden perennials. Many unusual & interesting varieties.
Map Ref: G, D3

GBuc   **BUCKLAND PLANTS** ⊠ EU €
Whinnieliggate, Kirkcudbright, Scotland DG6 4XP
☎ (01557) 331323
Fax: (01557) 331323
Website: www.bucklandplants.co.uk
Contact: Rob or Dina Asbridge
Opening Times: 1000-1700 Thu-Sun 1st Mar-1st Nov.
Min Mail Order UK: £15.00 + p&p
Min Mail Order EU: £50.00 + p&p
Cat. Cost: 3 x 1st class
Credit Cards: None
Specialities: A very wide range of scarce herbaceous & woodland plants incl. *Anemone, Cardamine, Crocosmia, Erythronium, Helleborus, Lilium, Meconopsis, Primula, Tricyrtis* & *Trillium*.
Map Ref: G, D2

GCal   **CALLY GARDENS** ▣ ⊠ UK
Gatehouse of Fleet, Castle Douglas, Scotland DG7 2DJ
Fax: (01557) 815029. Also information line.

⊠ Mail order to UK or EU	ń Delivers to shows
⊠ Exports beyond EU	€ Euro accepted
▣ Also supplies Wholesale	◆ See Display advertisement

KEY

G

Contact: Michael Wickenden
Opening Times: 1000-1730 Sat-Sun,
1400-1730 Tue-Fri. Easter Sat-last Sun in
Sept.
Min Mail Order UK: £15.00 + p&p
Cat. Cost: 3 x 1st class
Credit Cards: None
Specialities: Unusual perennials. *Agapanthus,
Crocosmia, Eryngium, Euphorbia,* hardy
Geranium & grasses. Some rare shrubs,
climbers & conservatory plants.
Map Ref: G, D2

GCed   Cedar Cottage Plants ⊠ UK
Aberfoyle Road, Balfron Station, Glasgow,
Scotland G63 0SQ
☎ (01360) 440701
Fax: (01360) 440933
Email: rkpgreen@cs.com
Website: www.ourworld.cs.com/cedarcott
Contact: Richard Green
Opening Times: By appt. only. Please
phone.
Min Mail Order UK: No minimum charge
Cat. Cost: 3 x 1st class
Credit Cards: None
Specialities: Herbaceous perennials.
Map Ref: G, C2
OS Grid Ref: NS532918

GCoc   James Cocker & Sons 🖰 ⊠ EU €
Whitemyres, Lang Stracht, Aberdeen,
Scotland AB15 6XH
☎ (01224) 313261
Fax: (01224) 312531
Email: sales@roses.uk.com
Website: www.roses.uk.com
Contact: Alec Cocker
Opening Times: 0900-1730 7 days.
Min Mail Order UK: No minimum charge
Min Mail Order EU: £4.55 + p&p
Cat. Cost: Free
Credit Cards: Visa, MasterCard, Delta,
Switch
Specialities: Roses.
Map Ref: G, B3

GCrs   Christie's Nursery ⊠ EU 🖰 🛉 € ◆
Downfield, Westmuir, Kirriemui,r Angus,
Scotland DD8 5LP
☎ (01575) 572977
Fax: (01575) 572977
Email: ianchristie@btconnect.com
Website: www.christiealpines.co.uk
Contact: Ian & Ann Christie
Opening Times: 1000-1700 Mon,

Wed-Sat & Sun 1st Mar-31st Oct. Closed
Tue & Sun.
Min Mail Order UK: 5 plants + p&p
Min Mail Order EU: On request
Cat. Cost: 2 x 1st class
Credit Cards: Access, Delta, EuroCard, JCB,
MasterCard, Switch, Visa
Specialities: Alpines, esp. gentians, *Cassiope,
Primula, Lewisia,* orchids, *Trillium* &
ericaceous.
Map Ref: G, B3

GDea   Deanston Nursery ⊠ EU 🖰 €
Deanston Farm, Lochfoot, Dumfries &
Galloway, Scotland DG2 8QX
☎ (01556) 690519
Fax: (01566) 690641
Email: info@deanstonnursery.co.uk
Website: www.deanstonnursery.co.uk
Contact: Susan McClelland
Opening Times: 1000-1800 (closed Mon &
Tue) 1st Apr-1st Oct. Other times by
appointment.
Min Mail Order UK: No minimum charge
Min Mail Order EU: Nmc
Cat. Cost: 3 x 1st class
Credit Cards: MasterCard, Visa, Switch,
Solo, JCB
Specialities: Wide and eclectic selection of
unusual & interesting hardy plants, some
only available in small numbers.
Map Ref: G, D2
OS Grid Ref: NX860718

GDra   Drake's Alpines
Inshriach Alpine Nursery, Aviemore,
Invernesshire, Scotland PH22 1QS
☎ (01540) 651287
Fax: (01540) 651656
Email: drakes.alpines@virgin.net
Website: www.kincraig.com/drakesalpines
Contact: John Borrowman
Opening Times: 0900-1700 Mon-Fri,
1000-1600 Sat & Sun 1st Mar-31st Oct.
Credit Cards: Visa, MasterCard, Switch,
JCB, Delta
Specialities: Rare and unusual alpines & rock
plants. Especially *Primula, Meconopsis,
Gentian.*
Map Ref: G, B2

GDrg   Dragoons Pool Nursery ⊠ UK
Beattock, Moffat, Dumfries & Galloway,
Scotland DG10 9TT
☎ mobile 07776 430527
Email: bill@chudziak.fsnet.co.uk

Contact: Bill Chudziak
Opening Times: 1100-1800 Wed-Sun & all
B/hols 25th Mar-30th Sep.
Min Mail Order UK: £10.00 + p&p
Cat. Cost: 3 x 1st class
Credit Cards: None
Specialities: *Meconopsis*, *Primula* & plants of
Himalyan origin.
Note: nursery is 200 yds N. of J15, M74;
proceed to B7076, next to ambulance
depot.
Map Ref: G, D3

GEdr   EDROM NURSERIES ⊠ EU ⋔
Coldingham, Eyemouth,
Berwickshire Scotland TD14 5TZ
☎ (01890) 771386
Fax: (01890) 771386
Email: info@edromnurseries.co.uk
Website: www.edromnurseries.co.uk
Contact: Mr Terry Hunt
Opening Times: 0900-1700 Mon-Sun,
1st Mar-30th Sep. Other times by appt.
Min Mail Order UK: Nmc
Min Mail Order EU: £20.00
Cat. Cost: 3 x 2nd class
Credit Cards: Visa, MasterCard
Specialities: *Trillium, Arisaema, Primula,
Gentiana, Meconopsis, Anemone* & other
alpines.

GEil   EILDON PLANTS ▣
Lowood Nurseries, Melrose,
Roxburghshire, Scotland TD6 9BJ
☎ (01896) 755530
Fax: (01896) 755530
Email: sales@eildonplants.co.uk
Contact: R Sinclair
Opening Times: 1000-1700 7 days
Mar-Oct.
Cat. Cost: 2 x 1st class
Credit Cards: None
Specialities: Specialist propagators of a wide
range of shrubs for sale as pot liners or
finished plants. Unusual shrubs & old
roses.
Map Ref: G, C3

GEve   EVELIX DAFFODILS ⊠ EU €
Aird Asaig, Evelix,
Dornoch, Sutherland, Highland,
Scotland IV25 3NG
☎ (01862) 810715
Email: dugaldmacarthur@lineone.net
Contact: D C MacArthur
Opening Times: By appt. only.

Min Mail Order UK: Nmc
Min Mail Order EU: Nmc
Cat. Cost: 3 x 1st class, available July.
Specialities: New *Narcissus* cultivars for
garden display & exhibition. Many cultivars
are in limited supply.
Map Ref: G, A2

GFai   FAIRHOLM PLANTS ⊠ UK
Fairholm, Larkhall, Lanarkshire,
Scotland ML9 2UQ
☎ (01698) 881671
Fax: (01698) 888135
Email: sh.fairholm@virgin.net
Contact: Mrs J M Hamilton
Opening Times: Apr-Oct by appt.
Min Mail Order UK: No minimum charge*
Cat. Cost: 1 x 2nd class for descriptive list.
Specialities: *Abutilon* & unusual half hardy
perennials especially South African. National
Collection of *Abutilon* cultivars.
*Note: mail order for young/small plants.
Map Ref: G, C2
OS Grid Ref: NS754515

GFle   FLEURS PLANTS ⊠ EU ⋔ €
2 Castlehill Lane, Abington Road,
Symington, Biggar, Scotland ML12 6SJ
☎ (01899) 308528
Contact: Jim Elliott
Opening Times: Please phone to arrange a
visit.
Min Mail Order UK: £8.00 + p&p
Min Mail Order EU: £20.00 + p&p
Cat. Cost: Sae
Credit Cards: None
Specialities: *Primula, Meconopsis.*
Map Ref: G, C3

**GGar   GARDEN COTTAGE
NURSERY** ⊠ UK
Tournaig, Poolewe, Achnasheen,
Highland, Scotland IV22 2LH
☎ (01445) 781777
Fax: (01445) 781777
Email: sales@gcnursery.co.uk
Website: www.gcnursery.co.uk
Contact: Ben Rushbrooke
Opening Times: 1030-1800 Mon-Sat mid
Mar-mid Oct or by appt.
Min Mail Order UK: £10.00 + p&p

G

G

Cat. Cost: 4 x 2nd class
Credit Cards: None
Specialities: A wide range of plants especially those from the southern hemisphere, Asiatic primulas & plants for coastal gardens.
Map Ref: G, A2
OS Grid Ref: NG878835

GGGa GLENDOICK GARDENS
LTD ▣ ⊠ EU ▣
Glencarse, Perth, Scotland PH2 7NS
☎ (01738) 860205
Fax: (01738) 860630
Email: sales@glendoick.com
Website: www.glendoick.com
Contact: P A, E P & K N E Cox
Opening Times: By appt. only. 1400-1700, 1st & 3rd Sun in May. Garden centre open 7 days.
Min Mail Order UK: £35.00 + p&p
Min Mail Order EU: £100.00 + p&p
Cat. Cost: £2.00 or £1.50 stamps
Credit Cards: Visa, MasterCard, Delta, Switch, JCB
Specialities: Rhododendrons, azaleas and ericaceous, *Primula* & *Meconopsis*. Plants from wild seed. Many catalogue plants available at garden centre.
Map Ref: G, C3

GGre GREENHEAD ROSES ▣ ⊠ EU
Greenhead Nursery, Old Greenock Road, Inchinnan, Renfrew, Scotland PA4 9PH
☎ (0141) 812 0121
Fax: (0141) 812 0121
Email: greenheadnursery.aol.com
Contact: C N Urquhart
Opening Times: 1000-1700 7 days.
Min Mail Order UK: No minimum charge*
Min Mail Order EU: Nmc
Cat. Cost: Sae
Credit Cards: Visa, Switch
Specialities: Roses. Wide general range, dwarf conifers, trees, heathers, rhododendrons & azaleas, shrubs, alpines, fruit, hardy herbaceous & spring & summer bedding.
*Note: mail order for bush roses only, Oct-Mar.
Map Ref: G, C2

GIBF IAIN BRODIE OF FALSYDE ⊠ EU
(Office) Cuilalunn, Kinchurdy Road, Boat of Garten, Invernesshire, Scotland PH24 3BP
☎ (01479) 831464

Fax: (01479) 831672
Email: plants&seeds@falsyde.sol.co.uk
Contact: Iain Brodie of Falsyde
Opening Times: Please phone first.
Min Mail Order UK: £20
Min Mail Order EU: £30
Cat. Cost: 3 x 1st class
Credit Cards: None
Specialities: *Betulaceae, Rosaceae* & *Ericaceae*.
Note: nursery is at Auchgourish Gardens, Boat of Garten.
Map Ref: G, B2

GKev KEVOCK GARDEN PLANTS &
FLOWERS ▣ ⊠ EU €
16 Kevock Road, Lasswade, Midlothian, Scotland EH18 1HT
☎ (0131) 663 2089,
mobile 07811 321585
Email: kevockgarden@postmaster.co.uk
Website: www.kevockgarden.co.uk
Contact: Stella Rankin
Opening Times: Not open.
Min Mail Order UK: No minimum charge
Min Mail Order EU: Nmc
Cat. Cost: 4 x 1st class
Credit Cards: Visa, MasterCard, Switch
Specialities: Chinese & Himalayan plants.

GKir KIRKDALE NURSERY ⊠ UK
Daviot, Nr Inverurie, Aberdeenshire, Scotland AB51 0JL
☎ (01467) 671264
Fax: (01467) 671282
Email: info@kirkdalenursery.co.uk
Website: www.kirkdalenursery.co.uk
Contact: Geoff or Alistair
Opening Times: 1000-1700 7 days (summer), 1000-1600 7 days (winter).
Min Mail Order UK: £20.00 + p&p*
Credit Cards: Visa, Access, Switch
Specialities: Trees, herbaceous, grasses.
*Note: mail order strictly mid-Oct to mid-Mar, carriage at cost.
Map Ref: G, B3

GLbr LADYBRAE FARM NURSERY ▣ ⊠ UK ◆
Ladybrae Farm, Ladysbridge, Banff, Scotland AB45 2JR
☎ (01261) 861259 (after 1800)
Email: fbeasley@lineone.net
Website: www.ladybraefarmnursery.co.uk
Contact: Frances Beasley
Opening Times: 1000-1800 Sat-Thu, closed Fri.
Min Mail Order UK: No minimum charge*

Cat. Cost: 2 x 1st class
Credit Cards: None
Specialities: Hardy ornamentals, esp. hardy geraniums, hebes, acid lovers, *Daphne*.
*Note: mail order Nov-Mar.
Map Ref: G, B3

GLil   LILLIESLEAF NURSERY ⬛⬛ ✉ EU €
Garden Cottage, Linthill, Melrose,
Roxburghshire, Scotland TD6 9HU
☎ (01835) 870415
Fax: (01835) 870415
Email: lleafnursery@aol.com
Contact: Teyl de Bordes
Opening Times: 0900-1700 Mon-Sat,
1000-1600 Sun. Dec-Feb, please phone first.
Min Mail Order UK: Nmc*
Min Mail Order EU: Nmc
Cat. Cost: 2 x 1st class
Credit Cards: Visa, Access
Specialities: *Epimedium* & wide range of common & uncommon plants. National Collection of *Epimedium*.
*Note: mail order of *Epimedium* only.
Map Ref: G, C3

GMac   ELIZABETH MACGREGOR ✉ EU ⬛
Ellenbank, Tongland Road, Kirkcudbright,
Scotland DG6 4UU
☎ (01557) 330620
Fax: (01557) 330620
Email: elizabeth@violas.abel.co.uk
Contact: Elizabeth MacGregor
Opening Times: 1000-1700 Mon, Fri & Sat May-Sep, or please phone.
Min Mail Order UK: 6 plants £12.60 + p&p
Min Mail Order EU: £50.00 + p&p
Cat. Cost: 4 x 1st class or 5 x 2nd class
Credit Cards: Visa, MasterCard
Specialities: Violets, violas & violettas, old and new varieties. *Campanula, Geranium, Penstemon, Aster, Primula, Iris* & other unusual herbaceous.
Map Ref: G, D2

GMaP   MACPLANTS ⬛ ♠
Berrybank Nursery, 5 Boggs Holdings,
Pencaitland, E Lothian,
Scotland EH34 5BA
☎ (01875) 341179
Fax: (01875) 340842
Email: sales@macplants.co.uk
Contact: Claire McNaughton
Opening Times: 1030-1700 7 days

mid Mar-end Sept.
Cat. Cost: 4 x 2nd class
Credit Cards: MasterCard, Switch, Visa
Specialities: Herbaceous perennials, alpines, hardy ferns, violas & grasses.
Map Ref: G, C3

GNor   SHEILA NORTHWAY AURICULAS ✉ EU
Balmaclellan, Castle Douglas,
Kirkcudbrightshire, Scotland DG7 3QR
☎ (01644) 420661
Contact: Sheila Northway & M Northway
Opening Times: Mail order (Feb-Nov) & by appt. only.
Min Mail Order UK: £10.00 + p&p
Min Mail Order EU: £10.00 + p&p
(normally 48 hr priority rate).
Cat. Cost: A4 Sae + 2 x 2nd class
Credit Cards: None
Specialities: *Primula allionii, P. auricula* plus a few other *Primula*.
Map Ref: G, D2

GOrn   ORNAMENTAL GRASSES ✉ EU
14 Meadowside of Cruigmyle, Kemnay,
Inverurie, Aberdeenshire,
Scotland AB51 5LZ
☎ (01467) 643544
Contact: John & Lois Frew
Opening Times: By appt.
Min Mail Order UK: No minimum charge
Min Mail Order EU: Nmc
Cat. Cost: 3 x 1st class
Credit Cards: None
Specialities: Ornamental grasses.
Map Ref: G, B3

GPlc   PLANTIECRUB GROWERS LTD ⬛⬛ ✉ EU
Gott, Shetland, Scotland ZE2 9SH
☎ (01595) 840600
Fax: (01595) 840600
Contact: Olaf Isbister
Opening Times: 0900-1700 Mon-Wed Fri & Sat, 0900-1800 Thurs, 1400-1700 Sun.
Min Mail Order UK: No minimum charge
Min Mail Order EU: Nmc
Cat. Cost: 1 x 1st class
Credit Cards: Visa, Delta, MasterCard, Switch
Specialities: Bedding, perennials, basket &

G

patio plants, indoor plants, glasshouse fruits & salads.
Map Ref: G, A3

GPoy **POYNTZFIELD HERB NURSERY** ✉ EU 🖾 €
Nr Balblair, Black Isle, Dingwall, Ross & Cromarty, Highland, Scotland IV7 8LX
☎ (01381) 610352*
Fax: (01381) 610352
Email: info@poyntzfieldherbs.co.uk
Website: www.poyntzfieldherbs.co.uk
Contact: Duncan Ross
Opening Times: 1300-1700 Mon-Sat 1st Mar-30th Sep, 1300-1700 Sun May-Aug.
Min Mail Order UK: £5.00 + p&p
Min Mail Order EU: £10.00 + p&p
Cat. Cost: 4 x 1st class
Credit Cards: Visa, Switch, all major credit/debit cards
Specialities: Over 400 popular, unusual & rare herbs esp. medicinal. Also seeds.
*Note: phone between 1200-1300 & 1800-1900 only.
Map Ref: G, B2
OS Grid Ref: NH711642

GQui **QUINISH GARDEN NURSERY** 🖾 ✉ EU
Dervaig, Isle of Mull Argyll, Scotland PA75 6QL
☎ (01688) 400344
Fax: (01688) 400344
Contact: Nicholas Reed
Opening Times: By appt. only.
Min Mail Order UK: Nmc
Min Mail Order EU: Nmc
Cat. Cost: 2 x 1st class
Credit Cards: None
Specialities: Specialist garden shrubs & conservatory plants.
Map Ref: G, C1

GSki **SKIPNESS PLANTS** 🖾 ✉ EU 🖎
The Gardens, Skipness, Nr Tarbert Argyll, Scotland PA29 6XU
☎ (01880) 760201
Fax: (01880) 760201
Email: bill@skipnessplants.freeserve.co.uk
Website: www.plants-scotland.co.uk
Contact: Bill & Joan McHugh
Opening Times: 0900-1800 Mon-Fri, 0900-1600 Sat-Sun end Mar-Oct.
Min Mail Order UK: No minimum charge
Min Mail Order EU: Nmc
Cat. Cost: £1.00*
Credit Cards: Visa, MasterCard, Delta

Specialities: Unusual herbaceous perennials, shrubs, climbers & grasses.
*Note: Catalogue cost refunded on first order.
Map Ref: G, C2

GTou **TOUGH ALPINE NURSERY** 🖾 ✉ EU 🖾
Westhaybogs, Tough Alford, Aberdeenshire, Scotland AB33 8DU
☎ (01975) 562783
Fax: (01975) 563561
Email: fred@alpines.co.uk
Website: www.alpines.co.uk
Contact: Fred & Monika Carrie
Opening Times: 1st Mar-31st Oct. Please check first.
Min Mail Order UK: Nmc
Min Mail Order EU: Nmc
Cat. Cost: 3 x 2nd class
Credit Cards: MasterCard, Access, Switch, Delta, Visa
Specialities: Alpines.
Map Ref: G, B3

GTre **TREEPAC** 🖾 ✉ EU 🖾 €
(Office) PO Box 11440, Ellon, Scotland AB41 7YD
☎ (01358) 761473
Fax: (01358) 761473
Email: steve_f_tate@hotmail.com
Website: www.treepac.fsnet.co.uk
Contact: Mrs Eleanor Tate
Opening Times: Please phone for appt. or to place an order.
Min Mail Order UK: £4.95
Min Mail Order EU: £24.95
Cat. Cost: 4 x 1st class
Credit Cards: Visa
Specialities: Scottish native species & their cultivars, eg *Sorbus*, *Prunus*.
Note: nursery is at the Tanglandford Triangle, Methlick, Aberdeenshire.
Map Ref: G, B3

GTro **TROPIC HOUSE** 🖾 ✉ EU 🖾 🖎
Langford Nursery, Carty Port, Newton Stewart, Wigtownshire, Scotland DG8 6AY
☎ (01671) 402485, (01671) 404050
Email: ian@bookcorner.co.uk
Contact: Mrs A F Langford
Opening Times: 1000-1700 7 days Easter-end Sep. Other times by appt.
Min Mail Order UK: Nmc
Min Mail Order EU: £20.00 + p&p
Cat. Cost: 1 x 1st class

Credit Cards: Switch, Solo, MasterCard,
Visa, JCB, Maestro, Electron
Specialities: Carnivorous.
Map Ref: G, D2

GTwe J TWEEDIE FRUIT TREES ⊠ UK ◆
Maryfield Road Nursery,
Nr Terregles, Dumfries,
Scotland DG2 9TH
☎ (01387) 720880
Contact: John Tweedie
Opening Times: Please ring for times.
Collections by appt.
Min Mail Order UK: Nmc
Cat. Cost: Sae
Credit Cards: None
Specialities: Fruit trees & bushes. A wide
range of old & new varieties.
Map Ref: G, D2

GUzu UZUMARA ORCHIDS ⊠ EU ◪ €
9 Port Henderson, Gairloch,
Rosshire, Scotland IV21 2AS
☎ (01445) 741228
Fax: (01445) 741228
Email: i.la_croix@virgin.net
Website: www.uzumaraorchids.com
Contact: Mrs I F La Croix
Opening Times: By appt only.
Min Mail Order UK: Nmc
Min Mail Order EU: Nmc
Cat. Cost: Sae
Credit Cards: None
Specialities: African & Madagascan
orchids.

GWCH WOODSIDE COTTAGE HERBS ⊠ UK €
Woodside Cottage, Longriggend,
Airdrie, Lanarkshire,
Scotland ML6 7RU
☎ (01236) 843826
Fax: (01236) 842545
Email: mail@herbscents.co.uk
Website: herbscents.co.uk
Contact: Brenda Brown
Opening Times: 1400-1800 Fri-Mon,
May-Sep.
Min Mail Order UK: Nmc
Cat. Cost: 4 x 1st class
Credit Cards: Visa, MasterCard, Switch,
Solo
Specialities: Herbs, wild flowers & hardy
plants incl. shrubs, grasses & cottage garden
flowers.
Map Ref: G, C2
OS Grid Ref: NS824708

N. IRELAND & REPUBLIC

IArd ARDCARNE GARDEN CENTRE €
Ardcarne, Boyle,
Co. Roscommon,
Republic of Ireland
☎ 00 353 (0)79 67091
Fax: 00 353 (0)79 67341
Email: ardcarne@indigo.ie
Website: www.ardcarnegc.com
Contact: James Wickham, Mary Frances
Dwyer, Kirsty Ainge
Opening Times: 0900-1800 Mon-Sat,
1400-1800 Sun & B/hols.
Credit Cards: Access, Visa, American Express
Specialities: Coastal plants, native & unusual
trees, specimen plants & semi-mature trees.
Wide general range.
Note: Euro accepted from Jan 2002.
Map Ref: I, B1

IBal BALI-HAI NURSERY ◪ ⊠ EU ◪ €
42 Largy Road, Carnlough, Ballymena,
Co. Antrim, N. Ireland BT44 0EZ
☎ 028 2888 5289
Fax: 028 2888 5289
Email: ian_w_scroggy@btinternet.com
Website: www.balihainursery.com
Contact: Mrs M E Scroggy
Opening Times: Mon-Sat by appointment
only.
Min Mail Order UK: Nmc
Min Mail Order EU: Nmc
Cat. Cost: £1.50
Credit Cards:
Specialities: *Hosta, Phormium.*
Note: euro only accepted as cheques. Export
beyond EU restricted to bare root perennials.
Map Ref: I, A3

IBlr BALLYROGAN NURSERIES ◪ ⊠ EU ◪
The Grange, Ballyrogan, Newtownards,
Co. Down, N. Ireland BT23 4SD
☎ (028) 9181 0451 (evenings)
Email: gary.dunlop@btinternet.com
Contact: Gary Dunlop
Opening Times: Only open by appt.
Min Mail Order UK: £10.00 + p&p
Min Mail Order EU: £20.00 + p&p
Cat. Cost: 2 x 1st class
Credit Cards: None

KEY		
⊠ Mail order to UK or EU		♖ Delivers to shows
◪ Exports beyond EU		€ Euro accepted
◪ Also supplies Wholesale		◆ See Display advertisement

Specialities: Choice herbaceous. *Agapanthus, Celmisia, Crocosmia, Euphorbia, Meconopsis, Rodgersia, Iris, Dierama* & *Phormium.*
Note: Limited exports beyond EU.
Map Ref: I, B3

IBro   BROOKWOOD NURSERIES ⊠ EU €
18 Tonlegee Road, Coolock, Dublin 5,
Republic of Ireland
☎ 00 353 (0)18 473298
Contact: Jim Maher
Opening Times: For collection only. 1st Feb-30th Apr.
Min Mail Order UK: £5.00 + p&p
Min Mail Order EU: £5.00 + p&p
Cat. Cost: 2 x 1st class
Credit Cards: None
Specialities: Hybrid *Crocosmia* rarities & hardy *Cyclamen.* Note: mail order 1st Feb-20th Apr & 1st Sep-31th Oct.
Map Ref: I, C3

ICar   CARNCAIRN DAFFODILS BROUGHSHANE 🖾 ⊠ EU 🖾
Broughshane, Ballymena, Co. Antrim,
N. Ireland BT43 7HF
☎ (028) 2586 1216
Fax: (028) 2586 2842
Contact: Mr & Mrs R H Reade
Opening Times: 1000-1700 Mon-Fri. Please phone in advance.
Min Mail Order UK: Nmc
Min Mail Order EU: Nmc
Cat. Cost: Free
Credit Cards: None
Specialities: Old & new *Narcissus* cultivars, mainly for show.
Map Ref: I, A3

IClo   CLONMEL GARDEN CENTRE 🖾 €
Glenconnor House, Clonmel, Co. Tipperary,
Republic of Ireland
☎ 00 353 (0)52 23294
Fax: 00 353 (0)52 29196
Email: clonmelgc@eircom.net
Contact: Beth, Terry or Chris Hanna
Opening Times: 0900-1800 Mon-Sat, 1200-1800 Sun, 1000-1800 B/hols.
Credit Cards: Visa, Access, MasterCard, Laser
Specialities: Wide range of plants including many less common varieties. The garden centre is situated in the grounds of a Georgian country house with extensive gardens.
Map Ref: I, D2

ICro   CROCKNAFEOLA NURSERY €
Killybegs, Co. Donegal,
Republic of Ireland
☎ 00 353 (0)73 51018
Fax: 00 353 (0)73 51018
Email: crocknafeola@hotmail.com
Contact: Andy McKenna
Opening Times: 0900-1800 Mon-Sat & 1200-1800 Sun in summer, until dusk in winter. Closed Oct-Feb.
Cat. Cost: None issued
Credit Cards: None
Specialities: Bedding plants, herbaceous perennials, rhododendrons, plants for containers, roses, plus shrubs & hedging for coastal areas.
Map Ref: I, D2

ICrw   CAREWSWOOD GARDEN CENTRE ⊠ EU 🖾 ♠ € ◆
Carewswood House,
Castlemartyr, Co. Cork,
Republic of Ireland
☎ 00 353 (0)21 4667283
Fax: 00 353 (0)21 4667637
Email: sales@carewswoodgardencentre.com
Website: www.carewswoodgardencentre.com
Contact: Gillian Hornibrook
Opening Times: 0900-1800 Mon-Sat & 1200-1800 Sun.
Min Mail Order UK: No minimum charge*
Min Mail Order EU: Nmc
Cat. Cost: on website
Credit Cards: Visa, Access, American Express, MasterCard
Specialities: Rare & unusual shrubs, alpines & herbaceous plants.
Note: mail order of small plants only.
Map Ref: I, D2

IDac   DACUS PLANTS ⊠ EU 🖾 €
PO Box No. 5326, Dunlaoghaire,
Co. Dublin, Republic of Ireland
☎ mobile 0868 920859
Fax: 00 353 (0)1 2809602
Email: dacusc@indigo.ie
Contact: Carl Dacus
Opening Times: Not open to public.
Min Mail Order UK: €20.00 + p&p
Min Mail Order EU: €20.00 + p&p
Cat. Cost: 2 x 1st class
Credit Cards: None
Specialities: Alpines, perennials & shrubs, many rare & unusual, from collected seed. North American, South American & South African plants.

IDee   **DEELISH GARDEN CENTRE** ⊠ EU €
Skibbereen, Co. Cork, Republic of Ireland
☎ 00 353 (0)28 21374
Fax: 00 353 (0)28 21374
Email: deel@eircom.net
Contact: Bill & Rain Chase
Opening Times: 1000-1300 & 1400-1800
Mon-Sat, 1400-1800 Sun.
Min Mail Order UK: IR£50.00 + p&p
Min Mail Order EU: IR£100.00 + p&p
Cat. Cost: Sae
Credit Cards: Visa, Access
Specialities: Unusual plants for the mild
coastal climate of Ireland. Conservatory plants.
Sole Irish agents for Chase Organic Seeds.

IDic   **DICKSON NURSERIES LTD** 🖪 ⊠ EU 🖾
Milecross Road, Newtownards, Co. Down,
N. Ireland BT23 4SS
☎ (028) 9181 2206
Fax: (028) 9181 3366
Email: mail@dickson-roses.co.uk
Website: www.dickson-roses.co.uk
Contact: A P C Dickson OBE,
Linda Stewart
Opening Times: 0800-1230 & 1300-1700
Mon-Thu. 0800-1230 Fri. Closes at 1600
Mon-Thu Dec-Jan.
Min Mail Order UK: One plant
Min Mail Order EU: £25.00 + p&p
Cat. Cost: Free
Credit Cards: None
Specialities: Roses especially modern
Dickson varieties.
Map Ref: I, B3

IFro   **FROGSWELL NURSERY** ⊠ EU €
Cloonconlon, Straide, Foxford, Co. Mayo,
Republic of Ireland
☎ 00 353 (0)94 31420
Fax: 00 353 (0)94 31420
Email: jane@frogswell.com
Website: www.frogswell.com
Contact: Jane Stanley
Opening Times: Please phone first. Garden
open by appointment, group bookings
welcome.
Min Mail Order UK: No minimum charge*
Min Mail Order EU: Nmc
Cat. Cost: 3 x 1st class
Credit Cards: None
Specialities: A small nursery growing unusual
perennials & shrubs, many from seed sourced
in Japan & South America, often in small
quantities. *Note: mail order available Sep-Apr.
Map Ref: I, B1

IGor   **GORTKELLY CASTLE NURSERY** ⊠ EU €
Upperchurch, Thurles, Co. Tipperary,
Republic of Ireland
☎ 00 353 (0) 504 54441
Contact: Clare Beumer
Opening Times: Open by appointment
only.
Min Mail Order UK: No minimum charge
Min Mail Order EU: Nmc
Cat. Cost: 5 x 1st class (UK), 5 x 30p (Rep.
of Ireland)
Credit Cards: None
Specialities: Choice perennials.
Map Ref: I, C2

IHMH   **HUBERT MCHALE** 🖪 ⊠ EU €
Foghill, Carrowmore-Lacken, Ballina,
Co. Mayo, Republic of Ireland
☎ 00 353 (0)96 34996
Email: hubertmchale@eircom.net
Contact: Hubert McHale
Opening Times: By appt. only.
Min Mail Order UK: No minimum charge
Min Mail Order EU: Nmc
Cat. Cost: 2 x IRC
Credit Cards: None
Specialities: Perennial herbs, aquatics, foliage
& rockery plants.
Map Ref: I, B1

IIve   **IVERNA HERBS** ⊠ EU 🖾 ṅ €
Glenmalure, Rathdrum, Co. Wicklow,
Republic of Ireland
Contact: Peter O'Neill
Opening Times: Mail order, or write for
appt.
Min Mail Order UK: No minimum charge
Min Mail Order EU: Nmc
Cat. Cost: £3.00 cheque
Credit Cards: None
Specialities: Over 600 herbs, wildflowers &
unusual edibles. Many rare introductions.
Stocks are limited but larger quantities will
be propagated to order.
Map Ref: I, C3

IKee   **KEENAN'S NURSERY & GASH
GARDENS** 🖪 ṅ €
Gash, Castletown, Portlaoise, Co. Laoise,
Republic of Ireland
☎ 00 353 (0) 502 32247

KEY		
⊠ Mail order to UK or EU	ṅ Delivers to shows	
🖾 Exports beyond EU	€ Euro accepted	
🖪 Also supplies Wholesale	◆ See Display advertisement	

Fax: 00 353 (0) 502 32857
Email: gashgardens@eircom.net
Contact: Mary Keenan
Opening Times: Nursery: 1000-1700
Mon-Sat, 1400-1700 Sun, all year.
Gardens: 1st May-30th Sep.
Cat. Cost: Free
Credit Cards: None
Specialities: Extensive range of herbaceous
perennials & a select range of unusual
shrubs.
Map Ref: I, C2

ILis   **LISDOONAN HERBS** ⊠ EU ♙ €
98 Belfast Road, Saintfield, Co. Down,
N. Ireland BT24 7HF
☎ (028) 9081 3624
Email: b.pilcher@pop.dial.pipex.com
Contact: Barbara Pilcher
Opening Times: Wed & Sat am. For other
times, please phone to check.
Min Mail Order UK: Nmc
Min Mail Order EU: Nmc
Cat. Cost: 2 x 1st class
Credit Cards: None
Specialities: Aromatics, herbs, kitchen garden
plants, period plants, some native species.
Freshly cut herbs & salads.
Map Ref: I, B3
OS Grid Ref: J390624

ILsc   **LISCAHANE NURSERY** €
Ardfert, Tralee, Co. Kerry,
Republic of Ireland
☎ 00 353 (0)667 134222
Fax: 00 353 (0)667 134600
Contact: Dan Nolan/Bill Cooley
Opening Times: 1000-1800 Tue-Sat
(summer), 1000-1700 Thu-Sat (winter).
Sun please phone. Closed Mon.
Cat. Cost: None issued
Credit Cards: Visa, Access, Laser
Specialities: Coastal shelter plants,
Eucalyptus.
Map Ref: I, D1

IMGH   **M G H NURSERIES** ♙ €
50 Tullyhenan Road, Banbridge, Co. Down,
N. Ireland BT32 4EY
☎ (028) 4062 2795
Fax: (028) 4062 2795
Contact: Miss M G Heslip
Opening Times: 1000-1800 Tue-Fri &
1000-1700 Sat, Apr-Sep. 1230-dusk Tue-Fri
& 1000-dusk Sat, Oct-Mar
Cat. Cost: 3 x 1st class

Credit Cards: None
Specialities: Grafted conifers, holly, Japanese
maples, box, ornamental trees & flowering
shrubs.
Map Ref: I, B3

IOrc   **ORCHARDSTOWN
NURSERIES** ⊠ EU ☒ €
4 Miles Out, Cork Road, Waterford,
Republic of Ireland
☎ 00 353 (0)513 84273
Fax: 00 353 (0)513 84422
Contact: Ron Dool
Opening Times: 0900-1800 Mon-Sat,
1400-1800 Sun.
Min Mail Order UK: No minimum charge*
Min Mail Order EU: Nmc
Cat. Cost: None issued
Credit Cards: Visa, MasterCard
Specialities: Unusual hardy plants incl.
shrubs, shrub roses, trees, climbers,
Rhododendron species & water plants.
*Note: only some plants mail order.
Map Ref: I, D2

IPot   **THE POTTING SHED** ⊠ EU €
Bolinaspick, Camolin, Enniscorthy,
Co. Wexford, Republic of Ireland
☎ 00 353 (0)548 3629
Fax: 00 353 (0)548 3540
Email: sricher@iol.ie
Website: www.camolinpottingshed.com
Contact: Susan Carrick
Opening Times: 1100-1800 Wed-Sat, 1300-
1800 Sun, 17th Apr-29th Sep 2002. Other
times by appt.
Min Mail Order UK: No minimum charge
Min Mail Order EU: Nmc
Cat. Cost: 3 x 1st class
Credit Cards: MasterCard, Visa
Specialities: Herbaceous & ornamental
grasses.
Map Ref: I, C3

IRhd   **RINGHADDY DAFFODILS** ⊠ EU ☒ €
Ringhaddy Road, Killinchy, Newtownards,
Co. Down, N. Ireland BT23 6TU
☎ (028) 9754 1007
Fax: (028) 9754 2276
Email: ringdaff@nireland.com
Contact: Nial Watson
Opening Times: Not open.
Min Mail Order UK: £20.00 + p&p
Min Mail Order EU: £30.00 + p&p
Cat. Cost: £2.00*
Credit Cards: None

Specialities: New daffodil varieties for exhibitors and hybridisers.
*Note: catalogue cost redeemable on order.

IRya   RYANS NURSERIES €
Lissivigeen, Killarney, Co. Kerry,
Republic of Ireland
☎ 00 353 (0)64 33507
Fax: 00 353 (0)64 37520
Email: tlryan@eircom.net
Website: www.ryansnurseries.com
Contact: Mr T Ryan
Opening Times: 0900-1800 Mon-Sat
1400-1800 Sun.
Cat. Cost: None issued
Credit Cards: Visa, Laser, MasterCard
Specialities: *Camellia, Pieris, Acacia, Eucalyptus, Dicksonia,* azaleas & many tender and rare plants.
Map Ref: I, D1

ISea   SEAFORDE GARDENS 🔲⊠ EU 🔲ή €
Seaforde, Co. Down, N. Ireland BT30 8PG
☎ (028) 4481 1225
Fax: (028) 4481 1370
Email: plants@seafordegardens.com
Website: www.seafordegardens.com
Contact: P Forde
Opening Times: 1000-1700 Mon-Fri all year. 1000-1700 Sat & 1300-1800 Sun mid Feb end Oct.
Min Mail Order UK: No minimum charge
Min Mail Order EU: Nmc
Cat. Cost: Free
Credit Cards: None
Specialities: Over 700 varieties of self-propagated trees & shrubs. National Collection of *Eucryphia.*
Map Ref: I, B3

ISsi   SEASIDE NURSERY 🔲⊠ EU €
Claddaghduff, Co. Galway,
Republic of Ireland
☎ 00 353 (0)95 44687
Fax: 00 353 (0)95 44761
Email: seaside@anu.ie
Website: www.anu.ie/seaside/
Contact: Tom Dyck
Opening Times: 0900-1300 & 1400-1800 Mon-Sat, 1400-1800 Sun.
Min Mail Order UK: No minimum charge
Min Mail Order EU: Nmc
Cat. Cost: £3.00
Credit Cards: Visa
Specialities: Plants & hedging suitable for seaside locations. Rare plants originating

from Australia & New Zealand especially *Phormium, Astelia.*
Map Ref: I, B1

ITer   TERRA NOVA PLANTS ⊠ EU 🔲 €
Dromin, Kilmallock, Co. Limerick,
Republic of Ireland
☎ 00 353 (0)63 90744
Email: terranovaplants@eircom.net
Website: homepage.eircom.net/~terranovaplants
Contact: Deborah Begley
Opening Times: Garden & nursery open by appt.
Min Mail Order UK: No minimum charge
Min Mail Order EU: Nmc
Cat. Cost: 6 x IRC
Credit Cards: None
Specialities: Bulbous aroids, variegated plants, unusual plants grown from seed. Large seedlist in autumn.
*Note: dormant bulbs & seeds only.
Map Ref: I, C2

ITim   TIMPANY NURSERIES & GARDENS 🔲⊠ EU 🔲ή €
77 Magheratimpany Road, Ballynahinch,
Co. Down, N. Ireland BT24 8PA
☎ (028) 9756 2812
Fax: (028) 9756 2812
Email: timpany@alpines.freeserve.co.uk
Website: www.alpines.freeserve.co.uk
Contact: Susan Tindall
Opening Times: 1030-1730 Tue-Sat, Sun by appointment. Closed Mon excluding B/hols.
Min Mail Order UK: Nmc
Min Mail Order EU: £30.00 + p&p
Cat. Cost: £1.50
Credit Cards: Visa, Access, MasterCard
Specialities: *Celmisia, Androsace, Primula, Saxifraga, Helichrysum, Dianthus, Meconopsis, Primula auricula* & *Cassiope.*
Map Ref: I, B3

LONDON AREA

LAco   ACORN NURSERIES ⊠ UK
Quainton, Aylesbury,
Buckinghamshire HP22 4BX
☎ (01296) 655305
Fax: (01296) 655305

Email: robertstalloaks@aol.com
Contact: Alun Roberts
Opening Times: 0900-1700 7 days, Mar-Oct.
Min Mail Order UK: No minimum charge
Cat. Cost: 4 x 1st class
Credit Cards:
Specialities: Hardy perennials, *Fuchsia*, *Dianthus*.
Map Ref: L, A2

Cat. Cost: Free
Credit Cards: MasterCard, Switch, Visa, Connect
Specialities: *Dahlia*. Note: trial grounds at Bowmans Farm nr. Jct. 22 M25, at MacDonalds roundabout take B556 to Colney Heath on left hand side 500m.
Map Ref: L, B3
OS Grid Ref: TL169049

L

LAma   JACQUES AMAND ▣ ⊠ EU ▣ €
The Nurseries, 145 Clamp Hill, Stanmore, Middlesex HA7 3JS
☎ (020) 8420 7110
Fax: (020) 8954 6784
Email: bulbs@jacquesamand.co.uk
Contact: Stuart Chapman & John Amand
Opening Times: 0900-1700 Mon-Fri, 1000-1400 Sat-Sun. Limited Sun opening in Dec & Jan.
Min Mail Order UK: No minimum charge
Min Mail Order EU: Nmc
Cat. Cost: 1 x 1st class
Credit Cards: Visa, Access
Specialities: Rare and unusual species bulbs esp. *Arisaema*, *Trillium*, *Fritillaria*, tulips.
Map Ref: L, B3

LAst   ASTERBY & CHALKCROFT NURSERIES ▣ ◆
The Ridgeway, Blunham, Nr Sandy, Bedfordshire MK44 3PH
☎ (01767) 640148
Fax: (01767) 640217
Email: sales@asterbyplants.co.uk
Website: www.asterbyplants.co.uk
Contact: Simon & Elizabeth Aldridge
Opening Times: 1000-1700 7 days. Closed Xmas & Jan.
Cat. Cost: 2 x 1st class
Credit Cards: Visa, MasterCard, Switch
Specialities: Hardy shrubs & herbaceous. *Clematis* & trees.
Map Ref: L, A3
OS Grid Ref: TL151497

LAyl   AYLETT NURSERIES LTD ▣
North Orbital Road, London Colney, St Albans, Hertfordshire AL2 1DH
☎ (01727) 822255
Fax: (01727) 823024
Email: Aylett_Nurseries@compuserve.com
Website: www.martex.co.uk/hta/aylett
Contact: Roger S Aylett
Opening Times: 0830-1730 Mon-Fri, 0830-1700 Sat, 1030-1630 Sun.

LBBr   BELL BAR NURSERY ▣ ń
Bulls Lane, Bell Bar, Nr Hatfield, Hertfordshire AL9 7BB
☎ (01707) 650007
Fax: (01707) 650008
Email: swener@globalnet.co.uk
Contact: S Wener
Opening Times: 0900-1630 Fri & Sat Mar-Nov. Other times by appt.
Cat. Cost: 2 x 1st class
Credit Cards: None
Specialities: Hardy perennials, grasses, ferns & bamboo. *Euphorbia*, *Geranium*, *Carex* & *Salvia*.
Map Ref: L, B4
OS Grid Ref: TL243053

LBCl   BLOOMS OF BRESSINGHAM ⊠ UK ◆
Clandon Park, West Clandon Guildford Surrey GU4 7RQ
☎ (01483) 222925   Fax: (01483) 211903
Email: clandon@blooms-uk.com
Website: www.bloomsofbressingham.co.uk
Contact: Steven Rivers
Opening Times: 0900-1700 1st Nov-31st Mar, 0900-1800 1st Apr-31st Oct, 7 days. Closed Xmas, Boxing Day & Easter Sun.
Min Mail Order UK: £4.35
Cat. Cost: None issued.
Credit Cards: Visa, Delta, Switch, MasterCard
Specialities: Wide general range. Many own varieties. Focus on hardy ornamental plants & grasses. Perennials. Plants listed against nursery code EBre.
Map Ref: L, C3

LBee   BEECHCROFT NURSERY ▣
127 Reigate Road, Ewell, Surrey KT17 3DE
☎ (020) 8393 4265
Fax: (020) 8393 4265
Contact: C Kimber
Opening Times: 1000-1600 Mon-Sat, 1000-1400 Sun from Mar-Nov incl. Closed Sun Dec-Feb incl. & Xmas-New Year week.
Cat. Cost: 10 x 1st class

Credit Cards: Visa, Switch, MasterCard
Specialities: Conifers & alpines.
Map Ref: L, C3

LBHW BLOOMS OF BRESSINGHAM ⊠ UK ◆
Studley Green, Stokenchurch, High
Wycombe, Buckinghamshire HP14 3UX
☎ (01494) 483761
Fax: (01494) 482675
Email: j6@jardinerie.co.uk
Website: www.bloomsofbressingham.co.uk
Contact: Mike Green
Opening Times: 0900-1700 1st Nov-31st
Mar, 0900-1800 1st Apr-31st Oct, 7 days.
Closed Xmas, Boxing Day & Easter Sun.
Min Mail Order UK: £4.35
Cat. Cost: none issued
Credit Cards: Visa, Delta, Switch,
MasterCard
Specialities: Wide general range. Many own
varieties. Focus on hardy ornamental plants
& grasses. Perennials. Plants listed against
nursery code EBre.
Map Ref: L, B2

LBow RUPERT BOWLBY ⊠ EU
Gutton, Reigate, Surrey RH2 0TA
☎ (01737) 642221
Fax: (01737) 642221
Email: Rupert.Bowlby@care4free.net
Website: www.rupert.bowlby.care4free.net
Contact: Rupert Bowlby
Opening Times: Sat & Sun pm in Mar & Sep.
Min Mail Order UK: No minimum charge
Min Mail Order EU: Nmc
Cat. Cost: 2 x 2nd class
Credit Cards: None
Specialities: South African bulbs & corms.
Map Ref: L, C4

LBre BLOOMS OF BRESSINGHAM ⊠ UK ◆
Dorney Court, Dorney, Windsor,
Buckinghamshire SL4 6QP
☎ (01628) 669999
Fax: (01628) 669693
Email: dorney.court@blooms-uk.com
Website: www.bloomsofbressingham.co.uk
Contact: Peter Freeman
Opening Times: 0900-1700 1st Nov-31st
Mar, 0900-1800 1st Apr-31st Oct, 7 days.
Closed Xmas, Boxing Day & Easter Sun.
Min Mail Order UK: £4.35
Cat. Cost: None issued
Credit Cards: Delta, Switch, MasterCard,
Visa
Specialities: Wide general range. Many own

varieties. Focus on hardy ornamental plants
& grasses. Perennials. Plants listed against
nursery code EBre.
Map Ref: L, B3

LBSe BLOOMS OF BRESSINGHAM ⊠ UK ◆
Station Road, Betchworth,
Reigate, Surrey RH3 7LX
☎ (01737) 842099
Fax: (01737) 843829
Email: reigate@blooms-uk.com
Website: www.bloomsofbressingham.co.uk
Contact: Nathan Berrisford
Opening Times: 0900-1700 1st Nov-31st
Mar, 0900-1800 1st Apr-31st Oct, 7 days.
Closed Xmas, Boxing Day & Easter Sun.
Min Mail Order UK: £4.35
Cat. Cost: None issued.
Credit Cards: Visa, Delta, Switch,
MasterCard
Specialities: Wide general range. Many own
varieties. Focus on hardy ornamental plants
& grasses. Perennials. Plants listed against
nursery code EBre.
Map Ref: L, C3

LBuc BUCKINGHAM
NURSERIES ⊠ EU ▣ ♠ € ◆
14 Tingewick Road, Buckingham,
Buckinghamshire MK18 4AE
☎ (01280) 822133
Fax: (01280) 815491
Email: enquiries@buckingham-nurseries.co.uk
Website: www.buckingham-nurseries.co.uk
Contact: R J & P L Brown
Opening Times: 0830-1730 (1800 in
summer) Mon-Fri, 1000-1600 Sun. Late
night opening Thu 1930 (2000 in summer).
Min Mail Order UK: No minimum charge
Min Mail Order EU: Nmc
Cat. Cost: Free
Credit Cards: Visa, MasterCard, Switch
Specialities: Bare rooted and container
grown hedging. Trees, shrubs, herbaceous
perennials, alpines, grasses & ferns.
Map Ref: L, A2

LBut BUTTERFIELDS NURSERY ▣ ⊠ EU ▣
Harvest Hill, Bourne End,
Buckinghamshire SL8 5JJ
☎ (01628) 525455

⊠ Mail order to UK or EU	♠ Delivers to shows	
▣ Exports beyond EU	€ Euro accepted	
▣ Also supplies Wholesale	◆ See Display advertisement	

KEY

Contact: I Butterfield
Opening Times: 0900-1300 & 1400-1700.
Please phone beforehand in case we are
attending shows.
Min Mail Order UK: Nmc*
Min Mail Order EU: £30.00 + p&p
Cat. Cost: 2 x 2nd class
Credit Cards: None
Specialities: National Collection of *Pleione*.
Dahlia for collection. Scientific Award 1999.
*Note: only *Pleione* by mail order.
Map Ref: L, B3

LCaP   CARPENDERS PARK NURSERY 🖾 ń
Little Oxhey Lane, Watford,
Hertfordshire WD1 5BA
☎ (020) 8420 1959
Fax: (020) 8420 1958
Email: enquiries@carpenders.co.uk
Website: www.carpenders.co.uk
Contact: Mark Sage
Opening Times: 0830-1830 Mon-Sat,
0930-1830 Sun.
Cat. Cost: None issued
Credit Cards: Visa, MasterCard, Switch,
Delta, American Express, Solo
Specialities: Herbaceous perennials incl.
many unusual varieties. Large range of
unusual hostas. Over 500 ornamental &
fruit trees in stock incl. specimens.
Map Ref: L, B3

LCha   CHASE ORGANICS (GB) LTD 🖾 EU 🖾
Riverdene Business Park, Molesey Road,
Hersham, Surrey KT12 4RG
☎ (01932) 253666
Fax: (01932) 252707
Email: chaseorg@aol.com
Website: www.organiccatalog.com
Contact: S Bossard
Opening Times: 0930-1630 Mon-Fri.
Min Mail Order UK: 80p p&p under
£17.50*
Min Mail Order EU: No minimum charge
(seed only)*.
Cat. Cost: Free
Credit Cards: Visa, Access, Switch,
MasterCard
Specialities: 'The Organic Gardening
Catalogue' offers vegetable, herb & flower
seeds & garden sundries especially for
organic gardeners.
*Note: mail order plants only to UK, seeds
to EU. Outside EU by arrangement.
Map Ref: L, C3

LChG   THE CHELSEA GARDENER
125 Sydney Street, London SW3 6NT
☎ (020) 7352 5656
Fax: (020) 7352 9809
Email: plants@chelseagardener.co.uk
Website: www.chelseagardener.com
Contact: Nicole Coleman, Elmarie Benson
Opening Times: 1030-1800 Mon-Fri, 0900-
1800 Sat, 1200-1800 Sun, all year excl.
25th Dec-1st Jan 2002.
Credit Cards: MasterCard, Visa, American
Express
Specialities: Architectural & large specimen
plants & topiary. A good range of
conservatory & house plants. Supplied from
a prominent central London location.
Map Ref: L, B3
OS Grid Ref: TQ272782

LChw   CHADWELL SEEDS 🖾 EU 🖾
81 Parlaunt Road, Slough,
Berkshire SL3 8BE
☎ (01753) 542823
Fax: (01753) 542823
Contact: Chris Chadwell
Min Mail Order UK: Nmc
Min Mail Order EU: Nmc
Cat. Cost: 3 x 2nd class
Credit Cards: None
Specialities: Seed collecting expedition to
the Himalayas. Separate general seed list of
Japanese, N. American & Himalayan
plants.

LCla   CLAY LANE NURSERY ń
3 Clay Lane, South Nutfield, Nr Redhill,
Surrey RH1 4EG
☎ (01737) 823307
Email: ken.claylane@talk21.com
Contact: K W Belton
Opening Times: 1000-1700 Tue-Sun
1st Feb-31st Aug. Other times by appt.
Please phone before travelling.
Cat. Cost: 3 x 1st class
Credit Cards: None
Specialities: *Fuchsia*.
Map Ref: L, C4

LCon   THE CONIFER GARDEN 🖾 UK ń
Hare Lane Nursery, Little Kingshill, Great
Missenden, Buckinghamshire HP16 0EF
☎ (01494) 862086 (0900-1800 hrs)
Fax: (01494) 862086
Email: info@conifer garden.co.uk
Website: www.conifergarden.co.uk
Contact: Mr & Mrs M P S Powell

Opening Times: Usually 1100-1600 Tue-Wed, Fri & Sat (1100-1300 Dec-Jan & Jul-Aug.) Please phone first.
Min Mail Order UK: No minimum charge*
Cat. Cost: 2 x 1st class for list only
Credit Cards: None
Specialities: Conifers only, over 500 varieties always in stock.
*Note: mail order to UK only, by overnight carrier.
Map Ref: L, B3

LCTD   CTDA ⊠ EU ☒
174 Cambridge Street, London SW1V 4QE
☎ (020) 7976 5115
Contact: Basil Smith
Opening Times: Not open.
Min Mail Order UK: £15.00 + p&p
Min Mail Order EU: £15.00 + p&p
Cat. Cost: Free
Credit Cards: None
Specialities: Hardy *Cyclamen* for the garden, named *Helleborus, Dierama, Schizostylis* & *Aquilegia* species. Also seeds.

LCtg   COTTAGE GARDEN NURSERY ◆
Barnet Road, Arkley, Barnet, Hertfordshire EN5 3JX
☎ (020) 8441 8829
Fax: (020) 8531 3178
Email: nurseryinfo@cottagegardennursery-barnet.co.uk
Website: www.cottagegardennursery-barnet.co.uk
Contact: David and Wendy Spicer
Opening Times: 0930-1700 Tue-Sat Mar-Oct, 0930-1600 Tue-Sat Nov-Feb, 1000-1600 Sun & B/hol Mon all year.
Cat. Cost: None issued.
Credit Cards: Visa, Access, MasterCard, Switch, Solo, Delta
Specialities: General range of hardy shrubs, trees & perennials. Architectural & exotics, *Fuchsia*, seasonal bedding, patio plants.
Map Ref: L, B3

LDai   DAISY ROOTS ⊠ UK ⋔
8 Gosselin Road, Bengeo, Hertford, Hertfordshire SG14 3LG
☎ (01992) 582401
Email: dayzroots@aol.com
Website: www.plantpotty.net
Contact: Anne Godfrey
Opening Times: By appointment only & as NGS.
Min Mail Order UK: No minimum charge

Cat. Cost: 3 x 1st class
Credit Cards: None
Specialities: Ever-increasing range of choice & unusual perennials, particularly *Agastache, Anthemis, Digitalis, Erysimum, Salvia* & *Sedum*.
Map Ref: L, B4

LDea   DEREK LLOYD DEAN ⊠ EU ☒ ⋔
8 Lynwood Close, South Harrow, Middlesex HA2 9PR
☎ (020) 8864 0899
Website: www.dereklloyddean.com
Contact: Derek Lloyd Dean
Opening Times: Not open, mail order only.
Min Mail Order UK: £2.50 + p&p
Min Mail Order EU: £2.50 + p&p
Cat. Cost: 2 x 1st class
Credit Cards: None
Specialities: Regal, angel, ivy & scented leaf *Pelargonium*. National Collection of Angel *Pelargonium*.

LEar   EARLSTONE NURSERY ☒ ⊠ UK
Earlstone Manor Farm, Burghclere, Newbury, Berkshire RG20 9NG
☎ (01635) 278648
Fax: (01635) 278672
Email: earlstonenursery@wistbray.com
Contact: B C Ginsberg or J Wallis
Opening Times: By appt.
Min Mail Order UK: £30.00 + p&p
Cat. Cost: Free
Credit Cards: None
Specialities: All varieties of *Buxus*. Topiary. *Taxus baccata* & other varieties of *Taxus*. Various varieties of *Ilex*.
Map Ref: L, C2

LEdu   EDULIS ☒ ⊠ EU ⋔ €
1 Flowers Piece, Ashampstead, Berkshire RG8 8SG
☎ (01635) 578113
Fax: (01635) 578113
Email: edulis.2000@virgin.net
Website: www.edulis.co.uk
Contact: Paul Barney
Opening Times: By appt. only.
Min Mail Order UK: £30.00 + p&p
Min Mail Order EU: £50.00 + p&p
Cat. Cost: 6 x 1st class

KEY		
⊠ Mail order to UK or EU	⋔ Delivers to shows	
☒ Exports beyond EU	€ Euro accepted	
☒ Also supplies Wholesale	◆ See Display advertisement	

Credit Cards: None
Specialities: Unusual edibles, architectural plants, permaculture plants.
Map Ref: L, B2

LEur   THE EUROPA NURSERY ✉ EU ✉ ň
PO Box 17589, London E1 4YN
☎ (020) 7265 8131
Fax: (020) 7366 9892
Email: europanurs@aol.com
Website: www.europa-nursery.co.uk
Contact: Tim Branney & Adam Draper
Opening Times: Not open, mail order only.
Min Mail Order UK: No minimum charge
Min Mail Order EU: Nmc
Cat. Cost: 3 x 1st class
Credit Cards: None
Specialities: Woodland & shade-loving perennials, incl. rare & new introductions. *Arisaema, Arum, Disporum, Epimedium, Hedychium, Lilium* species, *Paris, Polygonatum, Smilacina, Tricyrtis,* hardy ferns & hardy orchids.

LFol   FOLIAGE SCENTED & HERB PLANTS
Walton Poor, Crocknorth Road, Ranmore Common, Dorking, Surrey RH5 6SX
☎ (01483) 282273
Fax: (01483) 282273
Contact: Mrs Prudence Calvert
Opening Times: 1000-1700 Wed-Sun Apr-Sep & B/hols. 1000-1700 Thu & Fri or by appt. remainder of year. Please phone for appt. if possible.
Cat. Cost: 3 x 2nd class
Credit Cards: None
Specialities: Herbs, aromatic & scented plants.

LGod   GODLY'S ROSES ◻ ✉ EU
Redbourn, St Albans, Hertfordshire AL3 7PS
☎ (01582) 792255
Fax: (01582) 794267
Contact: Colin Godly
Opening Times: 0900-1900 summer, 0900-dusk winter, Mon-Fri. 0900-1800 Sat & Sun.
Min Mail Order UK: £4.50 + p&p
Min Mail Order EU: £50.00 + p&p
Cat. Cost: Free
Credit Cards: Visa, Access, American Express, Switch
Specialities: Roses.
Map Ref: L, B3

LGro   GROWING CARPETS ✉ UK ň € ♦
Christmas Tree House, High Street, Guilden Morden, Nr Royston, Hertfordshire SG8 0JP
☎ (01763) 852705
Contact: Mrs E E Moore
Opening Times: 1100-1700 Thu-Sat 16th Mar-26th Oct 2002 (closed Jul & Aug).
Min Mail Order UK: Nmc*
Cat. Cost: 5 x 2nd class
Credit Cards: None
Specialities: Wide range of ground-covering plants.
*Note: in order to avoid bad weather conditions, plants are only dispatched in Apr, Sep & Oct on a first-come first-served basis.
Map Ref: L, A4

LHew   HEWITT-COOPER CARNIVOROUS PLANTS ✉ UK ň
76 Courtney Crescent, Carshalton-on-the Hill, Surrey SM5 4NB
☎ (020) 8643 9307
Email: nigel@nigelandpolly.fsnet.co.uk
Website: www.hccarnivorousplants.co.uk
Contact: Nigel Hewitt-Cooper
Opening Times: By appt.
Min Mail Order UK: £10.00 + p&p*
Cat. Cost: 1 x 1st class
Credit Cards: None
Specialities: Carnivorous plants. Some species limited.
*Note: mail order May-Nov.
Map Ref: L, C4

LHop   HOPLEYS PLANTS LTD ◻ ✉ UK ň ♦
High Street, Much Hadham, Hertfordshire SG10 6BU
☎ (01279) 842509
Fax: (01279) 843784
Email: sales@hopleys.co.uk
Website: www.hopleys.co.uk
Contact: Aubrey Barker
Opening Times: 0900-1700 Mon & Wed-Sat, 1400-1700 Sun. Closed Jan & Feb.
Min Mail Order UK: No minimum charge
Cat. Cost: 5 x 1st class
Credit Cards: Visa, Access, Switch
Specialities: Wide range of hardy & half-hardy shrubs & perennials.
Map Ref: L, A4
OS Grid Ref: TL428196

LHrt   HORTUS NURSERY ✉ UK ň
80 Old Charlton Road, Shepperton, Middlesex TW17 8BS
☎ (01932) 242216

Fax: (01932) 241694
Contact: Marie-Elaine Houghton
Opening Times: 1000-1700 every Fri
Mar-Oct or by appt. at other times. Please
phone first to check.
Cat. Cost: 2 x 1st class
Credit Cards: None
Specialities: Ornamental grasses &
perennials, particularly *Carex, Aster, Digitalis,
Euphorbia* & *Penstemon.* Garden featured in
RHS 'The Garden'. Open as nursery. Garden
design & planting service.
Map Ref: L, C3

LHyd   HYDON NURSERIES ⬛⊠ EU € ◆
Clock Barn Lane, Hydon Heath,
Godalming, Surrey GU8 4AZ
☎ (01483) 860252
Fax: (01483) 419937
Contact: A F George, Rodney Longhurst &
Mrs A M George
Opening Times: 0800-1245 & 1400-1700
Mon-Sat. Sun during May & by appt.
Open B/hols.
Min Mail Order UK: No minimum charge
Min Mail Order EU: £25.00 + p&p
Cat. Cost: £1.50 or 6 x 1st class or 8 x 2nd
class
Credit Cards: None
Specialities: Large and dwarf *Rhododendron,
yakushimanum* hybrids, azaleas (deciduous &
evergreen), *Camellia* & other trees & shrubs.
Specimen *Rhododendrons.*
Map Ref: L, C3

LHyr   HYRONS TREES ⬛⊠ UK
The Green, Sarratt, Nr Rickmansworth,
Hertfordshire WD3 6BL
☎ (01923) 263000
Fax: (01923) 270625
Email: peiser@hyronstrees.co.uk
Website: www.hyronstrees.co.uk
Contact: Graham Peiser
Opening Times: By appt. only.
Min Mail Order UK: £30.00*
Specialities: Broadleaved trees, topiary &
hedging. All available in containers.
*Note: mail order only for topiary.
Map Ref: L, B3

**LIck   LOWER ICKNIELD FARM
NURSERIES** ⊠ UK ◆
Lower Icknield Way, Great Kimble,
Aylesbury, Buckinghamshire HP17 9TX
☎ (01844) 343436
mobile 07803 979993

Fax: (01844) 343436
Email: lowericknield@waitrose.com
Contact: S Baldwin, D Baldwin
Opening Times: 0900-1730 7 days excl.
Xmas-New Year.
Min Mail Order UK: £14.00*
Cat. Cost: 3 x 1st class. Argyranthemums
only
Credit Cards: None
Specialities: National Collection of
Argyranthemum. Patio & basket plants.
Tender & hardy perennials. Salvias. Grasses.
*Note: mail order argyranthemums.
Map Ref: L, B3
OS Grid Ref: SP814058

LIri   THE IRIS GARDEN ⊠ EU € ◆
47 Station Road, Barnet,
Hertfordshire EN5 1PR
☎ (020) 8441 1300
Fax: (020) 8441 1300
Email: theirisgarden@aol.com
Website: www.theirisgarden.co.uk
Contact: Clive Russell
Opening Times: Nursery not open. Visit our
iris exhibits at shows. Please phone for show
details.
Min Mail Order UK: £15.00 + p&p
Min Mail Order EU: £25.00 + p&p
Cat. Cost: 8 x 1st class.
Credit Cards: None
Specialities: Modern tall bearded *Iris* from
breeders in UK, USA, France & Australia.
Note: Orders must be received by end Jun.

LJus   JUST BAMBOO LTD ⬛⊠ EU ⬛♫ €
109 Hayes Lane, Bromley, Kent BR2 9EF
☎ (020) 8462 1800
mobile 07071 226266
Fax: (020) 8462 1800
Email: mikejames@justbamboo.com
Website: www.justbamboo.com
Contact: Mike James
Opening Times: By appt. only 1400-1800
Tue-Fri, 1000-1700 Sat, 1000-1300 Sun.
Min Mail Order UK: £20.00 + p&p
Min Mail Order EU: £60.00 + p&p
Cat. Cost: Sae + 2 x 1st class
Credit Cards: None
Specialities: *Bamboo,* ferns & grasses.
Note: some species are only available in small

KEY		
⊠ Mail order to UK or EU	♫ Delivers to shows	
⬛ Exports beyond EU	€ Euro accepted	
⬛ Also supplies Wholesale	◆ See Display advertisement	

L

numbers. Please ring and order for propagation.
Map Ref: L, B4

LKna   **KNAP HILL & SLOCOCK NURSERIES** 🖥 ⊠ EU 🖾
Barrs Lane, Knaphill, Woking, Surrey GU21 2JW
☎ (01483) 481214/5
Fax: (01483) 797261
Website: www.knaphillrhododendrons.co.uk
Contact: Mrs Joy West
Opening Times: 0900-1700 Mon-Fri by appointment only.
Min Mail Order UK: No minimum charge
Min Mail Order EU: Nmc
Cat. Cost: 3 x 1st class
Credit Cards: Visa, Access, MasterCard
Specialities: Wide variety of rhododendrons & azaleas.
Map Ref: L, C3

LLin   **LINCLUDEN NURSERY** 🖥 ⊠ EU 🖾 ń € ◆
Bisley Green, Bisley, Woking, Surrey GU24 9EN
☎ (01483) 797005
Fax: (01483) 474015
Email: sales@lincludennursery.co.uk
Website: www.lincludennursery.co.uk
Contact: Mr & Mrs J A Tilbury
Opening Times: 0930-1630 Mon-Sat all year excl. B/hols. Closed Chelsea week & Xmas.
Min Mail Order UK: No minimum charge
Min Mail Order EU: Nmc
Cat. Cost: 3 x 1st class
Credit Cards: Visa, MasterCard, Solo, Switch
Specialities: Dwarf, slow-growing & unusual conifers.
Map Ref: L, C3
OS Grid Ref: SU947596

LLWP   **L W PLANTS** ⊠ UK ń
23 Wroxham Way, Harpenden, Hertfordshire AL5 4PP
☎ (01582) 768467
Email: lwplants@waitrose.com
Website: www.thymus.co.uk
Contact: Mrs M Easter
Opening Times: 1000-1700 most days, but please phone first.
Min Mail Order UK: £15.00 + p&p*
Cat. Cost: A5 Sae + 5 x 2nd class
Credit Cards: None
Specialities: Unusual hardy perennials &

herbs esp. *Geranium, Penstemon* & *Thymus*. National Collections of *Thymus, Hyssopus* & *Satureja*.
*Note: mail order late Sep-Apr, *Thymus* all year round & no minimum charge.
Map Ref: L, B3

LMdh   **MAIDENHEAD AQUATICS**
Wyevale Garden Centre, Forest Road, Binfield, Bracknell, Berkshire RG42 4HA
☎ (01344) 453666
Fax: (01344) 459111
Website: www.fishkeeper.co.uk
Contact: Thomas Talfan Williams
Opening Times: 0900-1800 Mon-Sat, 1100-1700 Sun.
Credit Cards: Visa, MasterCard, Switch, Solo
Specialities: Large selection of aquatic, marginal & bog plants. Please phone to check current availability.
Map Ref: L, B3

LMil   **MILLAIS NURSERIES** 🖥 ⊠ EU 🖾 ń ◆
Crosswater Lane, Churt, Farnham, Surrey GU10 2JN
☎ (01252) 792698
Fax: (01252) 792526
Email: sales@rhododendrons.co.uk
Website: www.rhododendrons.co.uk
Contact: David Millais
Opening Times: 1000-1300 & 1400-1700 Mon-Fri. Sat spring & autumn. Daily in May and early Jun.
Min Mail Order UK: £25.00 + p&p*
Min Mail Order EU: £60.00 + p&p
Cat. Cost: 4 x 1st class
Credit Cards: Visa, Switch, Delta, MasterCard
Specialities: Rhododendrons & azaleas.
*Note: mail order Oct-Apr only.
Map Ref: L, C3
OS Grid Ref: SU856397

LMor   **MOREHAVENS** 🖥 ⊠ EU
Sandpit Hill, Buckland Common, Tring, Hertfordshire HP23 6NG
☎ (01494) 758642
Fax: (01494) 758642
Website: www.camomilelawns.co.uk
Contact: B Farmer
Opening Times: Only for collection.
Min Mail Order UK: £12.50 incl. p&p
Min Mail Order EU: £12.50
Cat. Cost: Free

Credit Cards: None
Specialities: *Camomile* 'Treneague'.
Map Ref: L, B3

LNet   NETTLETONS NURSERY 🔳 ⊠ EU ⌷ € ◆
Ivy Mill Lane, Godstone,
Surrey RH9 8NF
☎ (01883) 742426
mobile 07710 810074
Fax: (01883) 742426
Email: johnathan.nettleton@ntlworld.com
Contact: Jonathan Nettleton
Opening Times: 0900-1300 & 1400-1700
Mon Tue Fri & Sat summer. In winter please
phone first. Closed Sun, Wed & Thu.
Min Mail Order UK: Wisterias from
£12.00
Min Mail Order EU: £25.00
Cat. Cost: 3 x 1st class
Credit Cards: Visa, Access
Specialities: 40 cvs of Japanese, Chinese &
American *Wisteria*. 100 cvs of Japanese,
Oriental & European *Acer*. Good stocks of
Camellia, ericaceous shrubs & general
nursery stock.
Map Ref: L, C4

LPal   THE PALM CENTRE 🔳 ⊠ EU ⌷ ń €
Ham Central Nursery, opposite Riverside
Drive, Ham Street, Ham, Richmond,
Surrey TW10 7HA
☎ (020) 8255 6191
Fax: (020) 8255 6192
Email: mail@palmcentre.co.uk
Website: www.palmcentre.co.uk
Contact: Martin Gibbons
Opening Times: 0900-1700 (dusk in winter)
7 days. Admin & Order Dept. 0900-1700
Mon-Fri.
Min Mail Order UK: £10.00 + p&p
Min Mail Order EU: £10.00 + p&p
Cat. Cost: Free
Credit Cards: Visa, MasterCard, Switch
Specialities: Palms & cycads, exotic & sub-
tropical, hardy, half-hardy & tropical.
Seedlings to mature trees. Also bamboos, tree
ferns & other exotics.
Map Ref: L, B3

**LPan   PANTILES PLANT & GARDEN
CENTRE** 🔳 ⊠ EU ⌷ ń ◆
Almners Road, Lyne, Chertsey,
Surrey KT16 0BJ
☎ (01932) 872195
Fax: (01932) 874030
Email: pantiles@telinco.co.uk

Website: www.pantiles-nurseries.co.uk
Contact: Andy Horn
Opening Times: 0900-1800 Mon-Sat,
1100-1700 Sun summer. 0900-1700
Mon-Sat, 1000-1600 Sun winter.
Min Mail Order UK: £100.00 + p&p
Min Mail Order EU: £100.00 + p&p
Cat. Cost: Free
Credit Cards: Visa, Switch, MasterCard
Specialities: Large trees, shrubs, conifers &
climbers in containers. Australasian & other
unusual plants. Selection of tree ferns from
New Zealand & Australia.
Map Ref: L, C3

LPBA   PAUL BROMFIELD - AQUATICS
🔳 ⊠ EU ⌷ €
Maydencroft Lane, Gosmore,
Hitchin, Hertfordshire
SG4 7QD
☎ (01462) 457399
mobile 07801 656848
Fax: (01462) 422652
Email: info@bromfieldaquatics.co.uk
Website: www.bromfieldaquatics.co.uk
Contact: P Bromfield
Opening Times: 1000-1730 Mon-Sat
Feb-Oct. Please ring first. Order online at
website.
Min Mail Order UK: £15.00 incl.
Min Mail Order EU: £100.00 incl.
Cat. Cost: 2 x 1st class
Credit Cards: Visa, MasterCard, Delta,
JCB, Switch
Specialities: Water lilies, marginals & bog.
Map Ref: L, A3

LPen   PENSTEMONS BY COLOUR 🔳 ⊠ EU
76 Grove Avenue, Hanwell,
London W7 3ES
☎ (020) 8840 3199
Fax: (020) 8840 6415
Email: debra.hughes1@virgin.net
Contact: Debra Hughes
Opening Times: Any time by appt.
Min Mail Order UK: £5.00 + p&p
Min Mail Order EU: £10.00 + p&p
Cat. Cost: Free
Credit Cards: None
Specialities: *Penstemon*.
Map Ref: L, B3

KEY		
⊠ Mail order to UK or EU	ń Delivers to shows	
⌷ Exports beyond EU	€ Euro accepted	
🔳 Also supplies Wholesale	◆ See Display advertisement	

L

LPhx   PHOENIX PERENNIAL PLANTS
Paice Lane, Medstead, Alton,
Hampshire GU34 5PR
☎ (01420) 560695
Fax: (01420) 563640
Email: GreenFarmPlants.Marina.Christopher
@Care4free.net
Contact: M Christopher
Opening Times: 1000-1800 Thu-Sat,
21st Mar-26th Oct 2002 & 20th Mar-25th
Oct 2003.
Cat. Cost: 4 x 1st class
Credit Cards: Visa, MasterCard, JCB,
Switch, Visa, Delta, Electron, Solo, American
Express
Specialities: Small shrubs, sub-shrubs &
perennials, many uncommon. *Cistus,
Prostanthera, Achillea, Eryngium, Monarda,
Phlox, Verbascum,* bulbs & grasses.
Note: formerly Green Farm Plants, co-located
with Select Seeds LSss.
Map Ref: L, C2

LPio   PIONEER NURSERY ▣ ⊠ EU ⋔ €
Baldock Lane, Willian, Letchworth,
Hertfordshire SG6 2AE
☎ (01462) 675858
Email: milly@pioneerplants.com
Website: www.pioneerplants.com
Contact: Nick Downing
Opening Times: 0930-1730 Tue-Sun Mar-
Oct, 1000-16000 Tue-Sat Nov, Dec & Feb.
Min Mail Order UK: £15.00 + p&p
Min Mail Order EU: €30
Cat. Cost: Free
Credit Cards: MasterCard, Visa
Specialities: *Salvia,* tender perennials.
Wide range of hard-to-find perennials &
bulbs.
Map Ref: L, A3

LPJP   PJ'S PALMS AND
EXOTICS ⊠ EU €
41 Salcombe Road, Ashford,
Middlesex TW15 3BS
☎ (01784) 250181
Contact: Peter Jenkins
Opening Times: Mail order only 1st Mar-
30th Nov. Visits by arrangement.
Min Mail Order UK: No minimum charge
Min Mail Order EU: Nmc
Cat. Cost: 2 x 1st class
Credit Cards: None
Specialities: Palms, bananas & other exotic
foliage plants, hardy & half-hardy.
Map Ref: L, B3

LPlm   A J PALMER & SON ▣ ⊠ EU
Denham Court Nursery, Denham Court
Drive, Denham, Uxbridge,
Middlesex UB9 5PG
☎ (01895) 832035
Fax: (01895) 832035
Email: sheila@palmersroses.co.uk
Website: www.palmersroses.co.uk
Contact: Sheila Palmer
Opening Times: 0900-dusk 7 days Jul-Oct,
rose field viewing. 0900-1700 Mon-Sat,
1000-1300 Sun Nov. Dec-Jun phone.
Min Mail Order UK: No minimum charge
Min Mail Order EU: Nmc
Cat. Cost: Free
Credit Cards: None
Specialities: Roses.
Note: main showfield on the A40 near
Denham Roundabout (junction 1 M40)
unstaffed.
Map Ref: L, B3

LPVe   PLANTA VERA ▣ ⊠ UK
Lyne Hill Nursery, Farm Close, Lyne
Crossing Road, Chertsey, Surrey KT16 0AT
☎ (01932) 563011
Fax: (01932) 563011
Email: PlantaVera@mmay45.fsnet.co.uk
Contact: Morris May
Opening Times: Not open.
Min Mail Order UK: £24.00 (12 plants)
Cat. Cost: Free availability list in Autumn
Credit Cards: None
Specialities: 415 named violas & violettas.
Note: mail order collection by arrangement.
Map Ref: L, C3

LRav   RAVEN VALLEY PLANT
NURSERY
(Office) 3 Fairoaks Park,
Aldershot Road, Worplesdon,
Guildford, Surrey GU3 3HG
☎ (01483) 234605
mobile 07887 925945, 07984 706638
Email: ravenvalley@aol.com
Website: www.plantzalive.com
Contact: Maria & Terry Milton
Opening Times: 1000-1300 & 1400-1600
(1700 in summer), Sat, Sun & B/hols only.
Closed Jan & Feb.
Cat. Cost: 2 x 1st class or on web.
Credit Cards: None
Specialities: *Eucalyptus,* grasses. Note:
nursery is at Raven Valley, Mayfields,
Woking.
Map Ref: L, C3

LRHS **WISLEY PLANT CENTRE (RHS)** ◆
RHS Garden, Wisley, Woking,
Surrey GU23 6QB
☎ (01483) 211113
Fax: (01483) 212372
Email: wisleyplantcentre@rhs.org.uk
Opening Times: 1000-1800 Mon-Sat
1100-1700 Sun summer, 1000-1730
Mon-Sat 1000-1600 Sun winter. Closed
25-27 Dec & Easter Sun.
Cat. Cost: None issued
Credit Cards: MasterCard, Access, American
Express, Switch, Visa
Specialities: Very wide range, many rare &
unusual.
Map Ref: L, C3

LSde **SLADE PARK PLANTS** ⊠ EU
Old Slade Lane, Iver,
Buckinghamshire SL0 9DX
☎ (01753) 650287
Fax: (01753) 650287
Email: dayvidslilies@aol.com
Website: www.sladepark.co.uk
Contact: David Hughes
Opening Times: By appt. only.
Min Mail Order UK: No minimum charge
Min Mail Order EU: £25.00
Cat. Cost: 2 x 1st class
Credit Cards: None
Specialities: *Hemerocallis* cvs, specifically
recent American introductions.
Map Ref: L, B3

LSee **SEEDS BY SIZE** ⊠ EU ☒ €
45 Crouchfield, Boxmoor, Hemel
Hempstead, Hertfordshire HP1 1PA
☎ (01442) 251458
Email: john-robert-size@seeds-by-size.co.uk
Website: www.seeds-by-size.co.uk
Contact: Mr John Robert Size
Opening Times: Not open, mail order only.
Min Mail Order UK: No minimum charge
Min Mail Order EU: Nmc
Cat. Cost: 2 x 1st class
Credit Cards: None
Specialities: Flowers & vegetables. 1,400
varieties of vegetable, (175 cabbage, 99
cauliflower, 70 onion, 100 tomatoes) & 4,900
flowers such as 291 varieties of sweet pea,
100 herbs. Note: cash only euro payments.

LSiH **SINO-HIMALAYAN PLANT
ASSOCIATION** ⊠ UK ☒
81 Parlaunt Road, Slough,
Berkshire SL3 8BE

☎ (01753) 542823
Fax: (01753) 542823
Contact: Chris Chadwell
Min Mail Order UK: No minimum charge
Cat. Cost: None issued
Credit Cards: None
Specialities: Seed available for exchange to
members. Please apply for membership.

LSss **SELECT SEEDS** ⊠ UK ḣ
Paice Lane, Medstead, Nr Alton,
Hampshire GU34 5PR
☎ (01420) 560695
Fax: (01420) 563640
Email: GreenFarmPlants.Marina.Christopher
@Care4free.net
Contact: Marina Christopher
Opening Times: Not open. Mail order only.
Min Mail Order UK: £10.00
Cat. Cost: 3 x 1st class
Credit Cards: Visa, MasterCard, JCB,
Switch, Delta, Electron, Solo, American
Express
Specialities: Seeds. *Aconitum, Eryngium,
Thalictrum, Sanguisorba & Angelica.*
Note: co-located with Phoenix Perennial
Plants LPhx.
Map Ref: L, C2

LStr **HENRY STREET
NURSERY** ☒ ⊠ EU
Swallowfield Road, Arborfield,
Reading, Berkshire RG2 9JY
☎ (0118) 9761223
Fax: (0118) 9761417
Email: info@henrystreet.co.uk
Website: www.henrystreet.co.uk
Contact: Mr M C Goold
Opening Times: 0900-1730 Mon-Sat, 1000-
1600 Sun.
Min Mail Order UK: No minimum charge
Min Mail Order EU: Nmc
Cat. Cost: Free
Credit Cards: Visa, Access, Switch
Specialities: Roses.
Map Ref: L, C3

LSyl **SYLVATICA NURSERY** ⊠ EU ḣ €
Crosswater Farm, Crosswater Lane,
Churt, Farnham, Surrey GU10 2JN
☎ (01252) 792775

KEY		
⊠ Mail order to UK or EU	ḣ Delivers to shows	
☒ Exports beyond EU	€ Euro accepted	
☒ Also supplies Wholesale	◆ See Display advertisement	

Fax: (01252) 792526
Email: johnmillais@sylvatica.fsnet.co.uk
Contact: John Millais
Opening Times: By appt.
Min Mail Order UK: No minimum charge
Min Mail Order EU: Nmc
Cat. Cost: 4 x 1st class
Credit Cards: None
Specialities: *Sorbus* & woodland perennials.
Note: mail order outside the EU by
arrangement
Map Ref: L, C3

L

LTOO   TOOBEES EXOTICS ⊠ EU ⊠ n̂ €
(Office) 20 Inglewood, St Johns,
Woking Surrey GU21 3HX*
☎ (01483) 797534 (nursery)
(01483) 722600 (evenings)
Fax: (01483) 751995
Email: bbpotter@compuserve.com
Website: www.toobees-exotics.com
Contact: Bob Potter
Opening Times: 1000-1700 Thu-Sun &
B/hol Mons 18 Apr-29 Sep 2002, 17 Apr-
28 Sep 2003. Other times by appointment.
Min Mail Order UK: No minimum charge
Min Mail Order EU: Nmc
Cat. Cost: Sae
Credit Cards: MasterCard, Visa, Delta, Switch
Specialities: South African & Madagascan
succulents, many rare & unusual species.
Palms, tree ferns, air plants, carnivorous
plants, *Euphorbia*, *Pachypodium*.
Note: nursery is at Blackhorse Road, Woking.
Map Ref: L, C3

LTWO   TWO JAYS ALPINES n̂ ◆
(Office) 35 Greenways, Luton,
Bedfordshire LU2 8BL
☎ (01442) 864951
Fax: (01442) 864951
Email: john.spokes@talk21.com
Contact: John Spokes
Opening Times: 0930-1730 or dusk if
earlier, 7 days.
Cat. Cost: 3 x 2nd class
Specialities: Alpines. Note: nursery is at
Little Heath Farm, Little Heath Lane, Potten
End, Berkhamstead.
Map Ref: L, A3

LVER   THE VERNON GERANIUM
NURSERY ⊠ EU
Cuddington Way, Cheam,
Sutton, Surrey SM2 7JB
☎ (020) 8393 7616

Fax: (020) 8786 7437
Email: mrgeranium@aol.com
Website: www.geraniumsuk.com
Contact: Philip James & Liz Sims
Opening Times: 0930-1730 Mon-Sat,
1000-1600 Sun, 1st Mar-31st Jul.
Min Mail Order UK: No minimum charge
Min Mail Order EU: Nmc
Cat. Cost: £2.00 UK, £2.50 EU
Credit Cards: Visa, MasterCard, Switch
Specialities: *Pelargonium* & *Fuchsia*.
Map Ref: L, C4

MIDLANDS

MAAq   AVON AQUATICS ⊠ ⊠ UK
Ilmington Road, Wimpstone, Stratford-
upon-Avon, Warwickshire CV37 8NR
☎ (01789) 450638
Fax: (01789) 450967
Email: avonaquatics@btinternet.com
Website: www.avonaquatics.com
Contact: Rebecca Morgan & Richard
Morgan
Opening Times: 0900-1700 Mon-Sat
1000-1600 Sun.
Min Mail Order UK: £50.00 + p&p
Credit Cards: Visa, MasterCard, Switch,
Solo
Specialities: Water lilies (70 varieties of
Nymphaea), marginals (native), oxygenators
& bog plants.
Map Ref: M, C2

MAln   L A ALLEN ⊠ ⊠ EU
178 Hill Village Road, Four Oaks, Sutton
Coldfield, West Midlands B75 5JG
☎ (0121) 308 0697
Email: www.fidalgo.freeserve.co.uk
Contact: L A Allen
Opening Times: By prior appt.
Min Mail Order UK: No minimum charge
Min Mail Order EU: Nmc
Cat. Cost: 3 x 1st class
Credit Cards: None
Specialities: National Collection of *Primula
auricula*. Type: alpine auriculas, show edged,
show self, doubles, stripes. Surplus plants
from the Collection, so limited in numbers.

MAnH   ARN HILL PLANTS n̂ €
62 West Lockinge, Wantage,
Oxfordshire OX12 8QE
☎ (01235) 834312
mobile 07879 862749
Fax: (01235) 862361

Email: sally@arnhillplants.com
Website: www.arnhillplants.com
Contact: Sally Hall
Opening Times: 1000-1600 Thu-Sat,
4th Apr-12th Oct 2002 & Apr-Oct 2003.
Closed 1st 2 weeks of Aug.
Cat. Cost: 4 x 1st class
Credit Cards:
Specialities: Unusual & traditional hardy
perennials. *Campanula, Adenphora, Monarda,
Lobelia* & grasses.
Note: nursery has moved to above address.
Map Ref: M, D2
OS Grid Ref: SU423878

**MApt   APPLETREE COTTAGE
PLANTS** 🖸 ⊠ EU 🖾
51 Shearing Hill, Gedling,
Nottinghamshire NG4 3GY
☎ (0115) 9616534
Email: JANY@time-designs.co.uk
Website: www.time-designs.co.uk
Contact: Jany Sefyllian
Opening Times: 1000-1700 Mon-Fri, please
ring first. W/ends by appt.
Min Mail Order UK: £6.00
Min Mail Order EU: £10.00
Cat. Cost: 2 x 1st class
Credit Cards: Visa, Access, MasterCard,
Solo, Switch, Delta, Electron
Specialities: *Sempervivum, Fuchsia*, herbs,
alpines, hardy plants. Small, new nursery,
limited but increasing stock.
Map Ref: M, B3

MArl   ARLEY HALL NURSERY
Arley Hall Nursery, Northwich,
Cheshire CW9 6NA
☎ (01565) 777479/777231
Fax: (01565) 777465
Email: janefoster@btinternet.com
Contact: Jane Foster
Opening Times: 1200-1730 Tue-Sun
Easter-end Sep. Also B/hol Mons.
Cat. Cost: 4 x 1st class
Credit Cards: Visa, Switch, MasterCard,
Delta, Solo, Electron, Maestro
Specialities: Wide range of herbaceous incl.
many unusual varieties.
Map Ref: M, A1

**MAsh   ASHWOOD NURSERIES
LTD** 🖸 ⊠ EU 🛉
Greensforge, Kingswinford,
West Midlands DY6 0AE
☎ (01384) 401996

Fax: (01384) 401108
Email: ashwoodnurs@hotmail.com
Website: www.ashwood-nurseries.co.uk
Contact: John Massey & Philip Baulk
Opening Times: 0900-1800 Mon-Sat &
1100-1700 Sun excl. Xmas & Boxing Day.
Min Mail Order UK: No minimum charge*
Min Mail Order EU: Nmc
Cat. Cost: 6 x 1st class
Credit Cards: Visa, Access, MasterCard
Specialities: Large range of hardy plants
& dwarf conifers. National Collections of
Lewisia & *Cyclamen* species. Hellebores,
Hepatica. *Note: mail order for seeds &
special offers only.
Map Ref: M, C2

**MAus   DAVID AUSTIN ROSES
LTD** 🖸 ⊠ EU 🖾 €
Bowling Green Lane, Albrighton
Wolverhampton WV7 3HB
☎ (01902) 376377
Fax: (01902) 372142
Email: retail@davidaustinroses.co.uk
Website: www.davidaustinroses.com
Contact: Retail Dept
Opening Times: 0900-1700 Mon-Fri,
1000-1800 Sat, Sun & B/hols. Until dusk
Nov-Mar.
Min Mail Order UK: No minimum charge
Min Mail Order EU: Nmc
Cat. Cost: Free
Credit Cards: Access, Switch, Visa
Specialities: Roses. National Collection of
English Roses.
Map Ref: M, B1

MAvo   AVONDALE NURSERY 🛉
(Office) 3 Avondale Road, Earlsdon,
Coventry, Warwickshire CV5 6DZ
☎ (024) 766 73662
mobile 07979 093096
Fax: (024) /66 73662
Email: enquiries@avondalenursery.co.uk
Website: www.avondalenursery.co.uk
Contact: Brian Ellis
Opening Times: 1000-1230, 1400-1700
7 days 1st Mar-15th Oct. Closed Sun pm
Jul-Aug. Other times by appt.
Cat. Cost: 4 x 1st class
Credit Cards: None

M

Specialities: Rare & unusual perennials esp. *Campanula, Eryngium, Leucanthemum, Geum, Crocosmia, Pulmonaria* & grasses. Note: nursery is at Smith's Nursery, 3 Stoneleigh Road, Baginton, Nr Coventry.
Map Ref: M, C2

MBar **BARNCROFT NURSERIES** ▣ ⊠ UK
Dunwood Lane, Longsdon, Nr Leek, Stoke-on-Trent, Staffordshire ST9 9QW
☎ (01538) 384310
Fax: (01538) 384310
Website: www.barncroftnurseries.co.uk
Contact: S Warner
Opening Times: 0930-1730 or dusk if earlier Fri-Sun all year, plus Mon-Thu 0930-1730 Mar-Dec.
Min Mail Order UK: £10.00 + p&p
Cat. Cost: £2.50 incl. p&p
Credit Cards: None
Specialities: Extensive range of over 2000 heathers, conifers, shrubs, trees, climbers, dwarf grasses & rhododendrons. Display garden containing 400 heather cultivars.
Map Ref: M, B1

MBct **BARCOTE GARDEN HERBACEOUS PLANTS**
Barcote Garden, Faringdon, Oxfordshire SN7 8PP
☎ (01367) 870600
Email: garden@barcote.free-online.co.uk
Contact: Christine Smith
Opening Times: By arrangement Mar-Sep. Closed Oct-Feb.
Cat. Cost: Sae for plant list.
Credit Cards: None
Specialities: Herbaceous perennials. Small quantities of all plants listed.
Map Ref: M, D2
OS Grid Ref: SU322977

MBlm **BLOOMS OF BRESSINGHAM** ⊠ UK ◆
Oxford Road, Bicester, Oxfordshire OX6 8NY
☎ (01869) 242248
Fax: (01869) 252114
Email: bicester@blooms-uk.com
Website: www.bloomsofbressingham.co.uk
Contact: Lee Tudge
Opening Times: 0900-1700 1st Nov-31st Mar, 0900-1800 1st Apr-31st Oct, 7 days. Closed Xmas, Boxing Day & Easter Sun.
Min Mail Order UK: £4.35
Cat. Cost: None issued
Credit Cards: Delta, Switch, MasterCard, Visa

Specialities: Wide general range. Many own varieties. Focus on hardy ornamental plants & grasses. Perennials. Plants listed against nursery code EBre.
Map Ref: M, D3

MBlu **BLUEBELL NURSERY & ARBORETUM** ⊠ EU ♠ €
Annwell Lane, Smisby, Nr Ashby de la Zouch, Derbyshire LE65 2TA
☎ (01530) 413700
Fax: (01530) 417600
Email: sales@bluebellnursery.com
Website: www.bluebellnursery.com
Contact: Robert & Suzette Vernon
Opening Times: 0900-1700 Mon-Sat & 1030-1630 Sun Mar-Oct, 0900-1600 Mon-Sat (not Sun) Nov-Feb. Closed 24th Dec-4th Jan. Closed Easter Sun.
Min Mail Order UK: No minimum charge
Min Mail Order EU: Nmc
Cat. Cost: £1.30 + 2 x 1st class
Credit Cards: Visa, Access, Switch
Specialities: Uncommon trees & shrubs. Display garden & arboretum.
Map Ref: M, B1

MBNS **BARNSDALE GARDENS** ♠
Exton Avenue, Exton, Oakham, Rutland LE15 8AH
☎ (01572) 813200
Fax: (01572) 813346
Email: office@barnsdalegardens.co.uk
Website: www.barnsdalegardens.co.uk
Contact: Nick or Sue Hamilton
Opening Times: 0900-1700 Mar-May & Sep-Oct, 0900-1900 Jun-Aug, 1000-1600 Nov-Feb, 7 days. Closed 20th & 25th Dec.
Cat. Cost: A5 + 5 x 2nd class
Credit Cards: Visa, Access, MasterCard, Switch, Delta, American Express
Specialities: Choice & unusual garden plants. Over 70 varieties of *Penstemon*, large collection of *Hemerocallis*.
Map Ref: M, B3

MBow **BOWDEN HALL NURSERY** ⊠ UK
(Office) Malcoff Farmhouse, Malcoff, Chapel-en-le-Frith, High Peak, Derbyshire SK23 0QR
☎ (01663) 751969
mobile 07867 502775
Fax: (01663) 751469 (phone first)
Email: info@bowdenhallnursery.co.uk
Website: www.bowdenhallnursery.co.uk

Contact: Julie Norfolk
Opening Times: 1030-1700 Thu-Sun &
B/hols from 1st Mar. Other times by
appointment
Min Mail Order UK: £10.00 + p&p*
Cat. Cost: 5 x 1st class or £1.50 (cat. also
growing guide)
Credit Cards: None
Specialities: Herbs, wild flowers & hardy
cottage garden plants & some old roses.
Plants grown in peat-free compost using
organic fertilisers. *Note: mail order excl.
roses. Nursery at Bowden Hall, Bowden,
Chapel-en-le-Frith, High Peak.
Map Ref: M, A2
OS Grid Ref: SK065817

MBre   BRETBY NURSERIES ◆
Bretby Lane, Burton-on-Trent,
Staffordshire DE15 0QS
☎ (01283) 703355
Fax: (01283) 704035
Email: info@bretbynurseries.co.uk
Website: www.bretbynurseries.co.uk
Contact: Mrs S Lord
Opening Times: 0900-1700 Mon-Sat,
1030-1630 Sun.
Cat. Cost: Info. on request
Credit Cards: Visa, Diners, EuroCard,
Switch, Delta, Electron
Specialities: Wide range of shrubs.
Map Ref: M, B1

MBri   BRIDGEMERE NURSERIES
Bridgemere, Nr Nantwich,
Cheshire CW5 7QB
☎ (01270) 521100
Fax: (01270) 520215
Email: info@bridgemere.co.uk
Website: www.bridgemere.co.uk
Contact: Keith Atkey, Nigel Snow
Opening Times: 0900-2000 Mon-Sat,
1000-1900 Sun summer, 0900-1800 winter.
Cat. Cost: None issued
Credit Cards: Visa, Access, MasterCard,
Switch
Specialities: Perennials, shrubs, trees, roses,
climbers, rhododendrons & azaleas, alpines,
heathers, bamboos, ferns, grasses, aquatics,
houseplants.
Map Ref: M, B1

MBrN   BRIDGE NURSERY 🟦 €
Tomlow Road, Napton-on-the-hill,
Nr Rugby, Warwickshire CV47 8HX
☎ (01926) 812737

Website: www.BridgeNursery.co.uk
Contact: Christine Dakin & Philip Martino
Opening Times: 1000-1600 Fri-Sun
Apr-Oct. Other times by appt.
Cat. Cost: 4 x 1st class
Credit Cards: None
Specialities: Ornamental grasses, sedges
& bamboos. Also range of shrubs &
perennials.
Map Ref: M, C2
OS Grid Ref: SP463625

MBro   BROADSTONE NURSERIES
13 The Nursery, High Street,
Sutton Courtenay, Abingdon,
Oxfordshire OX14 4UA
☎ (01235) 847557 (evenings preferred)
Contact: J Shackleton
Opening Times: 1400-1700 Tue, 1400-1800
Sat (except show days). By appointment on
other days/times.
Cat. Cost: 3 x 1st class
Credit Cards: None
Specialities: Plants for rock garden, scree,
troughs & borders. Lime tolerant hardy
alpines, perennials & unusual plants. Small
selection choice shrubs.
Map Ref: M, D3

**MBSH   BRITISH SEED HOUSES
LTD 🟦 ⊠ EU 🟥 €**
Camp Road, Witham St Hughs, Lincoln,
Lincolnshire LN6 9QJ
☎ (01522) 868714
Fax: (01522) 868095
Email: seeds@bshlincoln.co.uk
Website: www.britishseedhouses.com
Contact: Simon Taylor
Opening Times: 0800-1730 Mon-Fri excl.
B/hols.
Min Mail Order UK: £50.00 + p&p
Min Mail Order EU: £50.00 + p&p
Cat. Cost: 2 x 1st class
Credit Cards: MasterCard, Visa
Specialities: Seed.

MBSo   BLOOMS OF BRESSINGHAM ⊠ UK ◆
Kenilworth Road, Hampton in Arden,
Solihull B92 0LP
☎ (01675) 442866
Fax: (01675) 443326

KEY		
⊠ Mail order to UK or EU	ň Delivers to shows	
🟥 Exports beyond EU	€ Euro accepted	
🟦 Also supplies Wholesale	◆ See Display advertisement	

M

M

Email: j4@jardinerie.co.uk
Website: www.bloomsofbressingham.co.uk
Contact: Brian O'Callaghan
Opening Times: 0900-1700 1st Nov-31st
Mar, 0900-1800 1st Apr-31st Oct, 7 days.
Closed Xmas, Boxing Day & Easter Sun.
Min Mail Order UK: £4.35
Cat. Cost: None issued.
Credit Cards: Visa, Delta, Switch,
MasterCard
Specialities: Wide general range. Many own
varieties. Focus on hardy ornamental plants
& grasses. Perennials. Plants listed against
nursery code EBre.
Map Ref: M, C3

MBur BURROWS ROSES ⊠ EU ⋔
Meadow Croft, Spondon Road, Dale Abbey,
Derby, Derbyshire DE7 4PQ
☎ (01332) 668289
Fax: (01332) 668289
Contact: Stuart & Diane Burrows
Opening Times: Not open, mail order only.
Min Mail Order UK: No minimum order,
up to 3 plants £2.00 p&p
Min Mail Order EU: £4.00 + p&p
Cat. Cost: 2 x 1st class
Credit Cards: None
Specialities: Roses only.

MCad CADDICK'S CLEMATIS
NURSERY ⊠ EU € ◆
Lymm Road, Thelwall, Warrington,
Cheshire WA13 0UF
☎ (01925) 757196
Fax: (01925) 268357
Website: www.caddicksclematis.co.uk
Contact: Mrs D Caddick
Opening Times: 1000-1700 Tue-Sat
8th Feb-31st Oct, 1100-1600 Sun. Nov by
arrangement. 1100-1600 B/hols. Closed
Dec & Jan.
Min Mail Order UK: £13.90 + p&p
Min Mail Order EU: £13.90 + p&p
Cat. Cost: 4 x 1st class UK, £2.00 or credit
card EU & Eire.
Credit Cards: Visa, Access, MasterCard,
Switch
Specialities: *Clematis.*
Map Ref: M, A1

MCAu CLAIRE AUSTIN HARDY
PLANTS ⊠ EU
The Stone House, Cramp Pool, Shifnal,
Shropshire TF11 8PE
☎ (01952) 463700

Fax: (01952) 463111
Email: enquiries@claireaustin-hardyplants.
co.uk
Website: www.claireaustin-hardyplants.co.uk
Contact: Claire Austin
Opening Times: 0900-1700 Mon-Fri.
Min Mail Order UK: No minimum charge
Min Mail Order EU: £50.00 + p&p
Cat. Cost: Free
Credit Cards: MasterCard, Visa, Switch
Specialities: *Paeonia, Iris, Hemerocallis* &
hardy plants.
Map Ref: M, B2

MCCP COLLECTORS CORNER
PLANTS ⊠ UK ⋔
33 Rugby Road, Clifton-upon-Dunsmore,
Rugby, Warwickshire CV23 0DE
☎ (01788) 571881
Contact: Pat Neesam
Opening Times: By appt. only.
Min Mail Order UK: £10.00
Cat. Cost: 6 x 1st class
Credit Cards: None
Specialities: General range of choice
herbaceous perennials, grasses, shrubs, palms,
ferns & bamboos.
Map Ref: M, C3

MChe CHESHIRE HERBS ⊠ EU ⋔ € ◆
Fourfields, Forest Road, Nr Tarporley,
Cheshire CW6 9ES
☎ (01829) 760578
Fax: (01829) 760354
Email: info@cheshireherbs.com
Website: www.cheshireherbs.com
Contact: Mr & Mrs Ted Riddell
Opening Times: 1000-1700 7 days
3rd Jan-24th Dec.
Min Mail Order UK: No minimum charge
Min Mail Order EU: Nmc
Cat. Cost: 2 x 1st class
Credit Cards: Access, Visa, Switch
Specialities: Display herb garden &
Elizabethan knot garden.
*Note: mail order seeds only (not plants).
Map Ref: M, B1
OS Grid Ref: SJ580673

MCLN COUNTRY LADY NURSERY
Lilac Cottage, Chapel Lane, Gentleshaw,
Nr Rugeley, Staffordshire WS15 4ND
☎ (01543) 675520
Fax: (01543) 675520
Website: www.countryladynursery.co.uk
Contact: Mrs Sylvia Nunn

Opening Times: 1000-1700 Thu-Sun &
B/hol Mons Mar-end Sep. Other times by
appt.
Cat. Cost: 4 x 1st class
Credit Cards: None
Specialities: Wide range of unusual
perennials incl. hardy *Geranium*, *Heuchera*,
Penstemon, *Hosta*, *Hemerocallis*, *Achillea*,
Phlox & *Papaver*. 1 acre show garden.
Map Ref: M, B1

MCls JAMES COLES & SONS (NURSERIES)
LTD 🖩 🛉
Coles Plant Centre, 624 Uppingham Road,
Thurnby, Leicestershire LE7 9QB
☎ (0116) 241 8394
Fax: (0116) 243 2311
Email: retail@james-coles-nurseries.co.uk
Website: www.james-coles-nurseries.co.uk
Contact: Mark Goddard
Opening Times: 0800-1700 Mon-Fri,
0900-1700 Sat & Sun.
Credit Cards: MasterCard, Switch
Specialities: Fruit, ornamental trees &
shrubs.
Map Ref: M, B3

MCoo COOL TEMPERATE 🖩 ⊠ EU 🛉
5 Colville Villas, Nottingham,
Nottinghamshire NG1 4HN
☎ (0115) 947 4977
Fax: (0115) 947 4977
Email: philcorbett53@hotmail.com
Website: www.cooltemperate.co.uk
Contact: Phil Corbett
Opening Times: Not open, mail order
only.
Min Mail Order UK: No minimum charge
Min Mail Order EU: Nmc
Cat. Cost: 2 x 1st class
Credit Cards: None
Specialities: Tree fruit, soft fruit, nitrogen-
fixers, hedging, own-root fruit trees.

MCre CRESCENT PLANTS 🖩 ⊠ EU 🛉
34 The Crescent, Cradley Heath,
West Midlands B64 7JS
☎ (0121) 550 2628
Fax: (0121) 550 2732
Email: ian@auriculas.co.uk
Website: www.auriculas.co.uk
Contact: Ian Goddard
Opening Times:
Min Mail Order UK: No minimum charge
Min Mail Order EU: Nmc
Cat. Cost: 2 x 1st class

Credit Cards: None
Specialities: Named varieties of *Primula
Auricula* incl. show, alpine, double, striped
& border types. Also seed.

MDCh DAVID CHESHIRE SEEDS AND
PLANTS 🖩 ⊠ EU 🖾 🛉
85 Grasmere Crescent, Nuneaton,
Warwickshire CV11 6EB
☎ mobile 07866 687198
Email: david@david-cheshire-seeds.co.uk
Website: www.david-cheshire-seeds.co.uk
Contact: David Cheshire
Opening Times: Mail order only, or by
appointment.
Min Mail Order UK: £5.00
Min Mail Order EU: £5.00
Cat. Cost: 2 x 1st class
Credit Cards:
Specialities: Seeds. Rare plants. Perennials,
grasses, bamboos, unusual trees,
specimens.

MDHE D H E PLANTS ⊠ UK
(Office) Rose Lea, Darley House Estate,
Darley Dale, Matlock, Derbyshire
DE4 2QH
☎ (01629) 732512
Contact: Peter M Smith
Opening Times: 1000-1700 Tue-Sat,
1030-1630 Sun. Please phone first as nursery
may move.
Min Mail Order UK: No minimum charge*
Cat. Cost: 2 x 1st class
Credit Cards: None
Specialities: Alpines esp *Erodium* (70+),
Helianthemum & *Saxifraga*.
*Note: mail order Oct-Mar only. Nursery
stock is at Robert Young Floral Centre,
Bakewell Rd, Matlock.
Map Ref: M, B1

MDKP D K PLANTS 🛉
(Office) 19 Harbourne Road, Cheadle, Stoke
on Trent, Staffordshire ST10 1JU
☎ (01538) 754460
mobile 07779 545015
Contact: Dave Knox
Opening Times: 0900-2000 (or dusk if
earlier) Mon-Tue. Other times by appt.
Cat. Cost: 4 x 1st + A4 Sae

M

Credit Cards: None
Specialities: Unusual hardy alpines & perennials. All grown on the nursery.
Note: nursery is at new roundabout across from Queen's Arms pub, Freehay Crossroads, Cheadle.
Map Ref: M, B1

MDun   **DUNGE VALLEY GARDENS** ▤ €
Windgather Rocks, Kettleshulme,
High Peak SK23 7RF
☎ (01663) 733787
Fax: (01663) 733787
Email: enquiries@dungevalley.co.uk
Website: www.dungevalley.co.uk
Contact: David Ketley
Opening Times: 1030-1700 1st Apr-31st Aug or by appt. Closed Mon except B/Hols. Open w/ends Mar.
Cat. Cost: A5 Sae
Credit Cards: MasterCard, Visa
Specialities: *Rhododendron* species & hybrids. Magnolias, trees, shrubs & perennials, some rare & wild collected. *Meconopsis, Trillium,* acers & bamboos.
Map Ref: M, A2
OS Grid Ref: SJ989777

MEHN   **ELIZABETH HOUSE NURSERY** ▤ ♁ €
Weedon Lois, Towcester,
Northamptonshire NN12 8PN
☎ (01327) 860056
Fax: (01327) 860779
Contact: Lindsey Cartwright
Opening Times: 1000-1700 Thu-Sat, Mar-Oct. Closed Aug.
Cat. Cost: 2 x 1st class
Credit Cards:
Specialities: Wide range of hardy perennials.
Map Ref: M, C3
OS Grid Ref: SP604472

MFie   **FIELD HOUSE NURSERIES** ⊠ EU
Leake Road, Gotham,
Nottinghamshire NG11 0JN
☎ (0115) 9830278
Fax: (0115) 9831486
Email: dlvwjw@field-house-alpines.fsbusiness.co.uk
Contact: Doug Lochhead & Valerie A Woolley
Opening Times: 0900-1700 Fri-Wed or by appt.
Min Mail Order UK: Min. order 4 plants*
Min Mail Order EU: £30.00

Cat. Cost: 4 x 1st or 4 x IRCs
Credit Cards: Visa, Access
Specialities: *Primula*, auriculas, alpines & rock plants. 3 National Collections of *Primula* and *P. auricula*.
*Note: mail order for *Primula*, auriculas & seeds only.
Map Ref: M, B3

MFir   **THE FIRS NURSERY** ⊠ UK ♁
Chelford Road, Henbury, Macclesfield,
Cheshire SK10 3LH
☎ (01625) 426422
Fax: (01625) 426422
Contact: Fay J Bowling
Opening Times: 1000-1700 Mon/Tue Thu/Sat Mar-Jun. Tue, Thu-Sat Jul-Sep.
Min Mail Order UK: £10.00 + p&p
Cat. Cost: 2 x 1st class
Credit Cards: None
Specialities: Wide range of herbaceous perennials, many unusual.
Map Ref: M, A2
OS Grid Ref: SJ885735

MFOX   **FOX COTTAGE PLANTS** ♁
Yew Tree Farm, Thatchers Lane, Tansley,
Matlock, Derbyshire DE4 5FD
☎ (01629) 57493
mobile 07787 963966
Fax: (01629) 57493
Contact: Mrs Avril Buckley
Opening Times: 1200-1700 daily Feb-Oct. Nov-Jan by appt. Please ring to confirm.
Cat. Cost: 2 x 1st class
Credit Cards: None
Specialities: Unusual hardy & tender perennials.
Map Ref: M, C2
OS Grid Ref: SK324594

MFry   **FRYER'S NURSERIES LTD** ▤ ⊠ EU ▨ €
Manchester Road, Knutsford,
Cheshire WA16 0SX
☎ (01565) 755455
Fax: (01565) 653755
Email: garethfryer@fryers-roses.co.uk
Website: www.fryers-roses.co.uk
Contact: Gareth Fryer
Opening Times: 0900-1730 Mon-Sat & 1030-1630 Sun & 1000-1730 B/hols.
Min Mail Order UK: No minimum charge
Min Mail Order EU: Nmc
Cat. Cost: Free
Credit Cards: Visa, Access, Switch
Specialities: Extensive rose nursery & garden

centre producing over half a million bushes annually. Rose fields in bloom June-October.
Map Ref: M, A1

MGag **GAGGINI'S PLANT CENTRE** 🖾 ⊠ UK 🗷
Glebe House, Glebe Road, Mears Ashby, Northamptonshire NN6 0DL
☎ (01604) 812371/811811
Fax: (01604) 812353
Email: 106612.1047@compuserve.com
Contact: John B & Mrs J E Gaggini
Opening Times: 0800-1730 Mon-Fri. 0900-1730 Sat & Sun.
Min Mail Order UK: £8.00 + p&p*
Cat. Cost: £1.00 (please state retail)
Credit Cards: Visa, Access, Switch, MasterCard
Specialities: Specialist growers of container trees, shrubs, conifers & fruit, esp. *Wisteria.*
*Note: mail order for *Wisteria* only.
Map Ref: M, C3

MGan **GANDY'S (ROSES) LTD** 🖾 ⊠ EU
North Kilworth, Nr Lutterworth, Leicestershire LE17 6HZ
☎ (01858) 880398
Fax: (01858) 880433
Contact: Miss R D Gandy
Opening Times: 0900-1700 Mon-Sat & 1400-1700 Sun.
Min Mail Order UK: No minimum charge
Min Mail Order EU: £25.00 + p&p
Cat. Cost: Free
Credit Cards: None
Specialities: 580 rose varieties.
Map Ref: M, C3

MGas **LINDA GASCOIGNE WILD FLOWERS** ⊠ UK 🗈
17 Imperial Road, Kibworth, Beauchamp, Leicestershire LE8 0HR
☎ (0116) 2793959
Contact: Linda Gascoigne
Opening Times: By appt. only.
Min Mail Order UK: £5.00 + p&p
Cat. Cost: 3 x 1st class
Credit Cards: None
Specialities: Wide range of wild flowers & plants to attract wildlife. No peat used.
Map Ref: M, C3

MGGn **THE GREEN GARDEN** ⊠ UK 🗈
Dewsnaps, Chinley, High Peak, Derbyshire SK23 6AW
☎ (01663) 751175

Fax: (01663) 751332
Email: Sally@TheGreenGarden.co.uk
Website: www.TheGreenGarden.co.uk
Contact: Sally Williams
Opening Times: Please phone for appt.
Min Mail Order UK: No minimum charge
Cat. Cost: 4 x 1st class
Credit Cards: None
Specialities: Unusual perennials & grasses. National Collection of *Ballota.*
Map Ref: M, A2

MGol **GOLDEN COTTAGE PLANTS** ⊠ EU 🗷 🗈
Golden Cottage, Scarcliffe Lanes, Upper Langwith, Mansfield Nottinghamshire NG20 9RQ
☎ (07971) 743567
Contact: C Coleman
Opening Times: By appt. only.
Min Mail Order UK: No minimum charge
Min Mail Order EU: Nmc
Cat. Cost: 1 x 1st class
Credit Cards: None
Specialities: Ethnobotanical plants and seeds. Hardy, tropical & sub-tropical. All plants & seeds only available in limited quantity ie 2 plants/person/species.

MGos **GOSCOTE NURSERIES LTD** ⊠ EU € ◆
Syston Road, Cossington, Leicestershire LE7 4UZ
☎ (01509) 812121
Fax: (01509) 814231
Email: sales@goscote.co.uk
Website: www.goscote.co.uk
Contact: Derek Cox, James Toone
Opening Times: 7 days, closed between Xmas & New Year.
Min Mail Order UK: £50.00 + p&p
Min Mail Order EU: £150.00 + p&p
Cat. Cost: 5 x 1st class
Credit Cards: Visa, Access, MasterCard, Delta, Switch
Specialities: Japanese maples, rhododendrons & azaleas, *Magnolia, Camellia, Pieris* & other *Ericaceae.* Ornamental trees & shrubs, conifers, fruit, heathers, alpines, *Clematis* & unusual climbers. Show Garden to visit.
Map Ref: M, B3

Ⓨ	⊠ Mail order to UK or EU	🗈 Delivers to shows
Ⓔ	🗷 Exports beyond EU	€ Euro accepted
Ⓚ	🖾 Also supplies Wholesale	◆ See Display advertisement

M

MGrG GRANBY GARDENS NURSERY ⊠ UK
Granby House, 8 Long Acre, Bingham,
Nottinghamshire NG13 8BG
☎ (01949) 837696
mobile 07984 625557
Email: mojoflo@amserve.net
Contact: Maureen & John Gladwin
Opening Times: By appointment only.
Closed Aug.
Min Mail Order UK: No minimum charge
Cat. Cost: None issued
Credit Cards: None
Specialities: A wide range of herbaceous
perennials, shrubs & climbers. Some rare
& unusual.
Map Ref: M, B3

MHar HARTS GREEN NURSERY
89 Harts Green Road, Harborne,
Birmingham B17 9TZ
☎ (0121) 427 5200
Contact: B Richardson
Opening Times: 1400-1730 Wed Apr-Jul
& Sep. Other times, excl. Aug, by
appointment.
Cat. Cost: None issued.
Credit Cards: None
Specialities: Hardy perennials. Some in small
quantities only.
Map Ref: M, C2

MHdf HARDIFOLIA
Fieldcrest, Thornton Common Road,
Wirral, CH63 0LT
☎ (0151) 334 8878
Contact: Cindy Barrett
Opening Times: 1000-1730 Tue-Sat Apr-
Oct, 1000-1430 Fri-Sat Nov-Mar.
Cat. Cost: 2 x 1st class
Specialities: Unusual hardy plants, bamboos
& grasses at a small nursery.

MHer THE HERB NURSERY ◆
Thistleton, Oakham,
Rutland LE15 7RE
☎ (01572) 767658
Fax: (01572) 768021
Contact: Peter Bench
Opening Times: 0900-1800 (or dusk) 7 days
excl. Xmas-New Year.
Cat. Cost: A5 Sae.
Credit Cards: None
Specialities: Herbs, wild flowers, cottage
garden plants, scented-leaf pelargoniums.
Map Ref: M, B3

MHFa HIGH FARM NURSERIES 🆒 ⊠ UK
Nobut Lane, Leigh, Stoke-on-Trent,
Staffordshire ST10 4QH
☎ (01889) 502252
Fax: (01889) 502621
Website: www.highfarmnurseries.fsnet.co.uk
Contact: Jason or Simon Nash
Opening Times: 0900-1700 Mon-Sun
Mar-Nov. Please phone first.
Min Mail Order UK: £20.00
Cat. Cost: 2 x 1st class
Credit Cards: None
Specialities: Family run nursery growing a
large number of rare & unusual plants incl.
herbaceous perennials, grasses, bamboos,
Daphne & rhododendrons. Many plants in
limited numbers, order early to avoid
disappointment.
Map Ref: M, B1

MHom HOMESTEAD PLANTS ⊠ UK
The Homestead, Normanton, Bottesford,
Nottingham, Nottinghamshire NG13 0EP
☎ (01949) 842745
Fax: (01949) 842745
Contact: Mrs S Palmer
Opening Times: By appt.
Min Mail Order UK: No minimum charge*
Cat. Cost: 4 x 2nd class
Credit Cards: None
Specialities: *Helleborus* species, *Hosta*,
Jovibarba & *Sempervivum* & *Paeonia* species.
Other herbaceous perennials in small
numbers.
*Note: mail order for *Hosta*, *Jovibarba*,
Sempervivum & *Paeonia* only.
Map Ref: M, B3

MHrb THE HERB GARDEN
Kingston House Estate, Race Farm
Lane, Kingston Bagpuize,
Oxfordshire OX13 5AU
☎ (01865) 820159
Fax: (01865) 820159
Email: vcjw37@yahoo.com
Website: www.KingstonHerbGarden.co.uk
Contact: Val Williams
Opening Times: As for Kingston House
Open Days or phone for appt. Sae for
details.
Cat. Cost: 2 x 1st class
Credit Cards: None
Specialities: Herbs, dye plants & lavenders in
a walled garden setting. Check website for
availability.
Map Ref: M, D2

MIDC   IAN AND DEBORAH
COPPACK 🖾 ⊠ UK € ◆
Woodside, Langley Road, Langley,
Macclesfield, Cheshire SK11 0DG
☎ (01260) 253308
Fax: (01260) 253308
Email: coppack@coppack.worldonline.co.uk
Contact: Ian & Deborah Coppack
Opening Times: 0900-1700.
Min Mail Order UK: No minimum charge
Cat. Cost: 1 x 1st class
Credit Cards: None
Specialities: *Hosta.*
Map Ref: M, A2
OS Grid Ref: 938715

MInt   INTAKES FARM
Sandy Lane, Longsdon, Stoke-on-Trent,
Staffordshire ST9 9QQ
☎ (01538) 398452
Contact: Mrs Kathleen Inman
Opening Times: By appt. only.
Cat. Cost: None issued
Credit Cards: None
Specialities: Double, variegated & unusual
forms of British native & cottage garden
plants.
Map Ref: M, B1

MJac   JACKSON'S NURSERIES 🖾
Clifton Campville, Nr Tamworth,
Staffordshire B79 0AP
☎ (01827) 373307
Fax: (01827) 373307
Contact: N Jackson
Opening Times: 0900-1800 Mon Wed-Sat,
1000-1700 Sun.
Cat. Cost: 2 x 1st class
Credit Cards: None
Specialities: *Fuchsia.*
Map Ref: M, B1

MJon   C & K JONES 🖾 ⊠ EU 🖾 ń €
Golden Fields Nurseries, Barrow Lane,
Tarvin Cheshire CH3 8JF
☎ (01829) 740663
Fax: (01829) 741877
Email: keith@ckjones.freeserve.co.uk
Website: www.jonestherose.co.uk
Contact: Keith Jones/P Woolley
Opening Times: 0900-1630 Mon-Fri.
Closed Sat & Sun.
Min Mail Order UK: 1 plant + p&p
Min Mail Order EU: 1 plant + p&p
Cat. Cost: £1.00
Credit Cards: MasterCard, Delta, Switch, Visa

Specialities: Roses.
Map Ref: M, B1

MKay   KAYES GARDEN NURSERY
1700 Melton Road, Rearsby,
Leicestershire LE7 4YR
☎ (01664) 424578
Contact: Hazel Kaye
Opening Times: 1000-1700 Tue-Sat &
B/hols 1000-1200 Sun Mar-Oct. By appt.
Nov, Dec & Feb. Closed Jan.
Cat. Cost: 2 x 1st class
Credit Cards: None
Specialities: Herbaceous, climbers &
aquatic plants. Grasses.
Map Ref: M, B3
OS Grid Ref: SK648140

MLan   LANE END NURSERY
Old Cherry Lane, Lymm, Cheshire WA13 0TA
☎ (01925) 752618
Email: sawyer@laneend.u-net.com
Website: www.laneend.u-net.com
Contact: I Sawyer
Opening Times: 0930-1730 Thu Tue
Feb-Dec.
Cat. Cost: None issued
Credit Cards: None
Specialities: Award of Garden Merit plants
with a wide range of choice & unusual
shrubs, trees, perennials & ferns.
Map Ref: M, A1

MLea   LEA RHODODENDRON GARDENS
LTD ⊠ EU 🖾
Lea, Matlock, Derbyshire DE4 5GH
☎ (01629) 534380/534260
Fax: (01629) 534260
Contact: Peter Tye
Opening Times: 1000-1730 7 days 20 Mar-
30 Jun. Out of season by appt.
Min Mail Order UK: £15.00 + p&p
Min Mail Order EU: £15.00 + p&p
Cat. Cost: 30p + Sae
Specialities: Rhododendrons & azaleas.
Map Ref: M, B1

MLLN   LODGE LANE NURSERY & GARDENS ń
Lodge Lane, Dutton, Nr Warrington,
Cheshire WA4 4HP
☎ (01928) 713718

M

M

Fax: (01928) 713718
Email: rod@lodgelanenursery.co.uk
Website: www.lodgelanenursery.co.uk
Contact: Rod or Diane Casey
Opening Times: 1000-1700 Wed-Sun &
B/hols, mid Mar-mid Sep. By appointment
outside these dates.
Cat. Cost: 3 x 1st class
Credit Cards: None
Specialities: Unusual perennials & shrubs
incl. *Achillea, Allium, Aster, Campanula,
Crocosmia, Digitalis, Nepeta, Penstemon,
Salvia, Euphorbia, Geranium, Heuchera, Inula,
Kniphofia* & ornamental grasses. National
Collection of *Inula* from Tatton Park.
Map Ref: M, A1
OS Grid Ref: SJ586779

MLwd LINWARD HARDY PLANTS ✉ UK 🛉
17 Roland Avenue, Nuthall, Nottingham,
Nottinghamshire NG16 1BB
☎ (0115) 854 5283
Email: Edds@ntlworld.com
Website: www.linwardhardyplants.co.uk
Contact: Edward Seeley & Linda Scott
Opening Times: By prior arrangement only.
Min Mail Order UK: No minimum charge
Cat. Cost: 50p coin
Credit Cards: None
Specialities: Hardy *Geranium, Digitalis* &
unusual hardy perennials. Some stock in
limited quantities. Enquiries always welcome.
Map Ref: M, B3
OS Grid Ref: SK522438

MMat MATTOCK'S ROSES 📧✉ EU 🗺
Freepost, The Rose Nurseries, Nuneham
Courtenay Oxford OX44 9PY
☎ 08457 585652
Fax: (01865) 343166
Email: roses@mattocks.co.uk
Website: www.mattocks.co.uk
Contact: Sales Office
Opening Times: 0900-1730 Mon-Sat
(closes 1700 Nov-Feb), 1100-1700 Sun.
Min Mail Order UK: No minimum charge
Min Mail Order EU: Nmc
Cat. Cost: Free
Credit Cards: Visa, MasterCard
Specialities: Roses.
Map Ref: M, D3

MMHG MORTON HALL GARDENS ✉ UK 🛉
Morton Hall, Ranby, Retford,
Nottinghamshire DN22 8HW
☎ (01777) 702530

Email: mortonhall@business77.freeserve. co.uk
Contact: Gill McMaster
Opening Times: 0900-1600 Mon-Fri,
1400-1700 Sat, Sun & B/hols Mar-Nov.
Min Mail Order UK: £5.00 + p&p
Cat. Cost: 3 x 1st class
Credit Cards: None
Specialities: Shrubs & perennials.
Map Ref: M, A3

MMil MILL HILL PLANTS ◆
Mill Hill House, Elston Lane, East Stoke,
Newark, Nottinghamshire NG23 5QJ
☎ (01636) 525460
mobile 07713 176507
Email: millhill@talk21.com
Website:
http://come.to/mill.hill.plants&garden
Contact: G M Gregory
Opening Times: 1000-1730 Fri-Sun &
B/hols Mar-Oct & by appt.
Cat. Cost: none issued
Credit Cards: None
Specialities: Hardy perennials, many
unusual, & bearded *Iris*. National Collection
of *Berberis*.
Map Ref: M, B3

**MMoz MOZART HOUSE NURSERY
GARDEN** ✉ UK 🛉
84 Central Avenue, Wigston,
Leicestershire LE18 2AA
☎ (0116) 288 9548
Contact: Des Martin
Opening Times: By appointment only.
Min Mail Order UK: £20.00 + p&p*
Cat. Cost: 5 x 1st class
Credit Cards: None
Specialities: Bamboo, ornamental grasses,
rushes & sedges, ferns.
*Note: mail order to UK & Ireland only.
Map Ref: M, C3

MNes NESS GARDENS
Univ. of Liverpool Botanic Gdns.,
Ness, Neston, South Wirral,
Cheshire CH64 4AY
☎ (0151) 353 0123
Fax: (0151) 353 1004
Email: peter.cunnington@liverpool.ac.uk
Website:
www.merseyworld.com/nessgardens/
Contact: D Maher
Opening Times: 0930-1700 7 days Apr-Oct,
1000-1600 7 days Nov-Mar.
Cat. Cost: None issued

Credit Cards: Delta, Switch, Visa
Specialities: *Rhododendron, Primula, Meconopsis, Penstemon* & *Camellia.*
Map Ref: M, A1

MNew NEWINGTON NURSERIES €
Newington, Wallingford,
Oxfordshire OX10 7AW
☎ (01865) 400533
Fax: (01865) 891766
Email: newington@connectfree.co.uk
Website: www.newington-nurseries.co.uk
Contact: Mrs A T Hendry
Opening Times: 1000-1700 Tues-Sun
Mar-Oct, 1000-1600 Tues-Sun Nov-Feb.
Cat. Cost: 4 x 1st class & A4 sae
Credit Cards: Access, MasterCard, Visa, Switch
Specialities: Unusual cottage garden plants,
old-fashioned roses, conservatory plants &
herbs. National Collection of *Alocasia*
(*Araceae*).
Map Ref: M, D3

**MNFA THE NURSERY FURTHER
AFIELD** ⊠ EU €
Evenley Road, Mixbury, Nr Brackley,
Northamptonshire NN13 5YR
☎ (01280) 848808
Fax: (01280) 848864
Email:
sinclair@nurseryfurtherafield.freeserve.co.uk
Contact: Gerald Sinclair
Opening Times: 1000-1300 & 1400-1700
Wed-Sat mid Mar-early Oct. Closed Aug.
Special open days as advertised. By appt. for
collection of orders.
Min Mail Order UK: £15.00 + p&p*
Min Mail Order EU: £25.00 + p&p
Cat. Cost: A5 Sae
Credit Cards: None
Specialities: Hardy perennials, many
unusual, including *Anemone nemorosa, Aster, Geranium, Hemerocallis* & *Iris sibirica.*
National Collection of *Hemerocallis.*
*Note: mail order for *Hemerocallis* only.
Map Ref: M, C3

MNrw NORWELL NURSERIES 🟦⊠ UK 🐾◆
Woodhouse Road, Norwell, Newark,
Nottinghamshire NG23 6JX
☎ (01636) 636337
Email: wardha@aol.com
Contact: Dr Andrew Ward
Opening Times: 1000-1700 Mon, Wed-Fri
& Sun (Wed-Mon May & Jun). By appt.
Aug & 20th Oct-1st Mar.

Min Mail Order UK: £12.00 + p&p
Cat. Cost: 3 x 1st class
Credit Cards: None
Specialities: A large collection of unusual &
choice herbaceous perennials & alpines
especially *Penstemon*, hardy *Geranium, Geum*,
summer bulbs, grasses & woodland plants.
Gardens open.
Map Ref: M, B3

MOak OAKLAND NURSERIES 🟦⊠ EU 🟥🐾
147 Melton Road, Burton-on-the-Wolds,
Loughborough, Leicestershire LE12 5TQ
☎ (01509) 880646
Fax: (01509) 889294
Email: tim@joakland.freeserve.co.uk
Website: www.oaklandnurseries.co.uk
Contact: Tim & John Oakland
Opening Times: Strictly by appt. Apr-Sep.
Min Mail Order UK: £15.00 + p&p
Min Mail Order EU: £15.00 + p&p
Cat. Cost: 4 x 1st class
Credit Cards: MasterCard, Visa
Specialities: Tender perennials, *Canna, Coleus, Caladium, Abutilon*, conservatory &
exotic plants. Some *Canna* limited quantity,
Coleus propagate to order.
Note: export *Canna* and *Caladium* only as
dormant plants.
Map Ref: M, B3
OS Grid Ref: SK615214

MOke OKELL'S NURSERIES 🟦🐾
Duddon Heath, Nr Tarporley,
Cheshire CW6 0EP
☎ (01829) 741512
Fax: (01829) 741587
Email: sales@okellsnurseries.co.uk
Website: www.okellsnurseries.co.uk
Contact: Tim Okell, Rosemary Lambert
Opening Times: 0900-1700 7 days (retail)
0830-1700 5 days (wholesale).
Cat. Cost: Free
Credit Cards: Visa, Access, Switch, MasterCard
Specialities: Heathers & alpines.
Map Ref: M, B1

MOne ONE HOUSE NURSERY ⊠ UK 🐾◆
Buxton New Road, Macclesfield,
Cheshire SK11 0AD
☎ (01625) 427087

M

M

Contact: Miss J L Baylis
Opening Times: 1000-1700 Tue-Sun &
B/hol Mons Mar-Oct, Nov-Feb ring for
opening times.
Min Mail Order UK: No minimum charge*
Cat. Cost: 3 x 1st class
Credit Cards: None
Specialities: Alpines & perennials. Good
range of *Primula, Sempervivum*, dwarf
Rhododendron, dwarf conifers, bulbs &
gentians.
*Note: mail order for *Sempervivum* & double
primroses only.
Map Ref: M, A2

MPet **PETER GRAYSON (SWEET PEA
SEEDSMAN)** 📇 ✉ EU 📧
34 Glenthorne Close, Brampton,
Chesterfield, Derbyshire S40 3AR
☎ (01246) 278503
Fax: (01246) 278503
Contact: Peter Grayson
Opening Times: Not open, mail order
only.
Min Mail Order UK: No minimum charge
Min Mail Order EU: Nmc
Cat. Cost: C5 Sae, 1 x 2nd class
Credit Cards: None
Specialities: *Lathyrus* species & cutivars.
Large collection of old-fashioned sweet peas
& over 100 Spencer sweet peas incl. own
cultivars and collection of old-fashioned
cottage garden annuals & perennials.

MPEx **PLANTA EXOTICA** ✉ EU
11 Heath Close, Banbury,
Oxfordshire OX15 4RZ
☎ (01295) 721989
Fax: (01295) 721989
Contact: Mrs M Hill
Opening Times:
Min Mail Order UK: £3.95 + p&p
Min Mail Order EU: £3.95 + p&p
Cat. Cost: 2 x 1st class
Specialities: Landscaping.
Map Ref: M, C2

MPhe **PHEDAR NURSERY** 📇 ✉ EU 📧 €
Bunkers Hill, Romiley, Stockport,
Cheshire SK6 3DS
☎ (0161) 430 3772
Fax: (0161) 430 3772
Contact: Will McLewin
Opening Times: Frequent especially in
spring but very irregular. Please phone to
arrange appointment.

Min Mail Order UK: No minimum charge
Min Mail Order EU: Nmc
Cat. Cost: 2 x A5 AE or address labels +
4 x 1st class
Credit Cards: None
Specialities: *Helleborus, Paeonia*.
Note: non-EU exports subject to destination
& on an ad hoc basic only. Please contact
nursery for details. Limited stock of some
rare items.
Map Ref: M, A2
OS Grid Ref: SJ936897

MPRe **PLANTS FOR ALL
REASONS** 📇 ✉ UK
Woodshoot Nurseries, King's Bromley,
Burton-upon-Trent, Staffordshire
DE13 7HN
☎ (01543) 472233
Fax: (01543) 472115
Email: sales@plants-for-all-reasons.com
Website: www.plants-for-all-reasons.com
Contact: Janice Rea
Opening Times: Retail by appt. Wholesale
on site, please phone for details.
Min Mail Order UK: £20 + p&p
Cat. Cost: 2 x 1st class
Credit Cards: None
Specialities: *Phormium, Pittosporum,
Tropaeolum*, daphnes, palms, agaves.
Map Ref: M, B2
OS Grid Ref: SK127164

MPWC **PARSLEY WOODS COTTAGE
GARDEN NURSERY**
Tattenhall Road, Newton-by-Tattenhall,
Chester, CH3 9BD
☎ (01829) 771282
mobile 07773 648144
Fax: (01829) 771282
Email: parsley_woods@hotmail.com
Contact: Hilary Scarratt
Opening Times: 1000-1700 Fri-Tue (closed
Wed & Thu) Apr-Sep. Other times by
appointment only.
Cat. Cost: 2 x 2nd class
Specialities: Cottage garden perennials.
Map Ref: M, B1
OS Grid Ref: ST492602

MRav **RAVENSTHORPE NURSERY** ✉ EU
6 East Haddon Road, Ravensthorpe,
Northamptonshire NN6 8ES
☎ (01604) 770548
Fax: (01604) 770548
Email: Plants@6ravensthorpe.freeserve.co.uk

M

Contact: Jean & Richard Wiseman
Opening Times: 1000-1800 (dusk if earlier)
Tue-Sun. Also B/hol Mons.
Min Mail Order UK: No minimum charge
Min Mail Order EU: Nmc
Cat. Cost: None issued.
Credit Cards: Visa, MasterCard
Specialities: Over 2,600 different trees,
shrubs & perennials with many unusual
varieties. Search & delivery service for large
orders, winter months only.
Map Ref: M, C3
OS Grid Ref: SP665699

MRod **RODBASTON COLLEGE** 🖾 ⊠ EU
Rodbaston, Penkridge,
Staffordshire ST19 5PH
☎ (01785) 712209
Fax: (01785) 715701
Email: rodenenquiries@rodbaston.ac.uk
Contact: Yoke van der Meer
Opening Times: By appt.
Min Mail Order UK: £10.00
Min Mail Order EU: £15.00
Cat. Cost: 2 x 1st class
Credit Cards: None
Specialities: Salvias. National Collection of
'New World' *Salvia*.
Map Ref: M, B1

MS&S **S & S PERENNIALS** ⊠ UK ⋔
24 Main Street, Normanton Le Heath,
Leicestershire LE67 2TB
☎ (01530) 262250
Contact: Shirley Pierce
Opening Times: Afternoons only, otherwise
please phone.
Min Mail Order UK: No minimum charge
Cat. Cost: 2 x 1st class
Credit Cards: None
Specialities: *Erythronium, Fritillaria*, hardy
Cyclamen, dwarf *Narcissus, Hepatica* &
Anemone.
Map Ref: M, B1

MSal **SALLEY GARDENS** ⊠ EU 🖾 €
32 Lansdowne Drive, West Bridgford,
Nottinghamshire NG2 7FJ
☎ (0115) 9233878 evenings
Contact: Richard Lewin
Opening Times: By appt.
Min Mail Order UK: No minimum charge
Min Mail Order EU: Nmc
Cat. Cost: Sae
Credit Cards: None
Specialities: Medicinal plants especially from

North America & China. Dye plants, herbs,
spices, seeds.
Map Ref: M, B3

MSGs **SHOWGLADS** ⊠ UK
105 Derby Road, Bramcote, Nottingham,
Nottinghamshire NG9 3GZ
☎ (0115) 925 5498
Email: rogerbb@lineone.net
Contact: Roger Braithwaite
Opening Times: Not open.
Min Mail Order UK: £3.25
Cat. Cost: 2 x 1st class
Credit Cards: None
Specialities: *Gladiolus*.

MSph **SPRINGHILL PLANTS**
(Office) 18 Westfields Abingdon,
Oxfordshire OX14 1BA
☎ (01235) 530889 after 1800
mobile 07790 863378.
Contact: Caroline Cox
Opening Times: Apr-Sep by appointment
only. Please phone first.
Cat. Cost: 75p or 3 x 1st class
Credit Cards: None
Specialities: Small nursery offering a wide
range of unusual & garden worthy perennials
& shrubs. Many AGM & rare plants
available.
Note: nursery is at Buildings Farm, Gozzard's
Ford, Nr. Marcham, Abingdon.
Map Ref: M, D2

MSPs **STRACHAN'S PLANTS** 🖾 ⊠ UK ⋔
(Office) 4 Staple Hall Road, Northfield,
Birmingham B31 3TH
☎ (0121) 478 1038 (1800-2100 hrs)
mobile 07960 340396 (day)
Email: andy.strachan@care4free.net
Contact: Julie Dyhouse or Andy Strachan
Opening Times: 0900-1700 most days Mar-
Oct, but please phone first to confirm as
attend a lot of shows.
Min Mail Order UK: No minimum charge
Cat. Cost: 2 x 1st class + A5 sae to office
address for list.
Credit Cards: None
Specialities: Small nursery specialising in rare
& unusual perennials & old favourites.
Note: nursery is at CLM, Newtown,

K E Y	⊠ Mail order to UK or EU	⋔ Delivers to shows
	🖾 Exports beyond EU	€ Euro accepted
	🖾 Also supplies Wholesale	◆ See Display advertisement

Offenham, Evesham, Worcs. WR11 5RZ.
Map Ref: W, C5

M

MSta   **Stapeley Water Gardens Ltd** ▣ ⊠ EU ▣
London Road, Stapeley, Nantwich,
Cheshire CW5 7LH
☎ (01270) 623868
Fax: (01270) 624919
Email: stapeleywg@btinternet.com
Website: www.stapeleywatergardens.co.uk
Contact: Mr Dean Barratt
Opening Times: From 0900 Mon-Fri, 1000
Sat, Sun & B/hols all year excl. Xmas Day.
Please check closing times.
Min Mail Order UK: No minimum charge
Min Mail Order EU: Nmc
Cat. Cost: £2.00 handbook, price list free
Credit Cards: Visa, Access, MasterCard,
Switch
Specialities: World's largest water garden
centre. Full range of hardy water lilies,
aquatic, bog & poolside plants. National
Collection of *Nymphaea* (UK & France).
Map Ref: M, B1

MSte   **Steventon Road Nurseries** ▣ €
Steventon Road, East Hanney, Wantage,
Oxfordshire OX12 0HS
☎ (01235) 868828
Fax: (01235) 763670
Email: JohnGraham.SteventonRoadNursery
@virgin.net
Website: www.steventonroadnurseries.co.uk
Contact: John Graham
Opening Times: 0900-1700 Mon-Fri,
1000-1700 Sat & Sun Mar-Nov, Mon, Wed,
Fri Dec-Feb.
Cat. Cost: 4 x 1st class
Credit Cards: None
Specialities: Tender & hardy perennials.
Map Ref: M, D2

MTed   **Ted Brown Unusual Plants** ▣ €
1 Croftway, Markfield, Leicester,
Leicestershire LE67 9UG
☎ (01530) 244517
Contact: Ted Brown
Opening Times: From 1000 Sat, Sun &
B/hols Mar-Nov. Other times by appt.
Cat. Cost: None issued
Credit Cards: None
Specialities: Mainly herbaceous, many
unusual. Bamboos.
Map Ref: M, B3

MTho   **A & A Thorp** ♙
Bungalow No 5, Main Street,
Theddingworth,
Leicestershire LE17 6QZ
☎ (01858) 880496
Contact: Anita & Andrew Thorp
Opening Times: 1000-1700.
Cat. Cost: 50p + Sae
Credit Cards: None
Specialities: Unusual plants or those in short
supply.
Map Ref: M, C3

MTis   **Tissington Nursery** ♙
Tissington, Nr Ashbourne,
Derbyshire DE6 1RA
☎ (01335) 390650
Fax: (01335) 390693
Email: info@tissingtonnursery.co.uk
Website: www.tissingtonnursery.co.uk
Contact: Mrs Sue Watkins
Opening Times: 1000-1800 daily 1st Mar-
30th Sep incl. Easter Sun & B/hols.
Cat. Cost: 3 x 1st class
Credit Cards: Visa, MasterCard
Specialities: Perennials, shrubs & climbers
incl. unusual varieties. Some available only in
very limited numbers.
Map Ref: M, B1
OS Grid Ref: SK176521

MTPN   **The Plant Nursery** ⊠ UK ♙
Sandy Hill Lane, Off Overstone Road,
Moulton, Northampton NN3 7JB
☎ (01604) 454106, (01933) 275765
Contact: Stuart Smart, Louise Ozier
Opening Times: 1000-1700 Fri-Sun, Mar-
Oct. By appt. Sun only, Oct-Mar.
Min Mail Order UK: No minimum charge*
Cat. Cost: 3 x 1st class
Credit Cards: None
Specialities: Wide range of herbaceous,
alpines, shrubs, grasses, hardy *Geranium*,
Sempervivum & succulents.
*Note: mail order of *Sempervivum*, succulents
only.
Map Ref: M, C3

MUlv   **Ulverscroft Grange Nursery**
Priory Lane, Ulverscroft Markfield,
Leicestershire LE67 9PB
☎ (01530) 243635
Fax: (01530) 243635
Contact: Susan Gill
Opening Times: 1000-1700 Tue-Sun
Mar-Nov. Other times by appt.

M

Cat. Cost: Sae for list.
Credit Cards: Visa, Switch, MasterCard,
American Express
Specialities: Herbaceous perennials.
Map Ref: M, B3

MWar WARD FUCHSIAS ⊠ UK
5 Pollen Close, Sale, Cheshire M33 3LS
☎ (0161) 282 7434
Contact: K Ward
Opening Times: 0930-1700 Tue-Sun
Feb-Jun incl. B/hols.
Min Mail Order UK: No minimum charge
Cat. Cost: Free
Credit Cards: None
Specialities: *Fuchsia*.
Map Ref: M, A2

MWat WATERPERRY GARDENS LTD ⊠ UK
Waterperry, Nr Wheatley,
Oxfordshire OX33 1JZ
☎ (01844) 339226/254
Fax: (01844) 339883
Email: office@waterperrygardens.fsnet.co.uk
Website: www.waterperrygardens.co.uk
Contact: Mr R Jacobs
Opening Times: 0900-1730 Mon-Fri,
0900-1800 Sat & Sun summer. 0900-1700
winter.
Min Mail Order UK: No minimum charge*
Cat. Cost: 75p
Credit Cards: Visa, MasterCard, Switch,
American Express
Specialities: General, plus National
Collection of *Saxifraga* (*Porophyllum*).
*Note: Limited mail order, please phone for
information.
Map Ref: M, D3
OS Grid Ref: SP630064

MWgw WINGWELL NURSERY ⊠ UK
Top Street, Wing, Oakham,
Rutland LE15 8SE
☎ (01572) 737727
Fax: (01572) 737788
Email: dejardin.design@btinternet.com
Contact: Rose Dejardin
Opening Times: 1000-1700 daily (except
Easter Sun) Mar-Dec.
Min Mail Order UK: No minimum charge
Cat. Cost: £1 for descriptive catalogue
Credit Cards: None
Specialities: Herbaceous perennials.
*Note: mail order Oct-Mar for herbaceous
plants, grasses & ferns only.
Map Ref: M, B3

MWhe A D & N WHEELER ⋔
Pye Court, Willoughby, Rugby,
Warwickshire CV23 8BZ
☎ (01788) 890341
Fax: (01788) 890341
Contact: Mrs N Wheeler
Opening Times: 1000-1630 7 days mid
Feb-late Jun. Other times please phone for
appointment.
Cat. Cost: 3 x 1st class
Credit Cards: None
Specialities: *Fuchsia*, *Pelargonium* &
hardy *Geranium*.
Map Ref: M, C3

MWhi WHITEHILL FARM
NURSERY ⊠ EU €
Whitehill Farm, Burford,
Oxfordshire OX18 4DT
☎ (01993) 823218
Fax: (01993) 822894
Contact: P J M Youngson
Opening Times: 0900-1800 (or dusk if
earlier) 7 days.
Min Mail Order UK: £5.00 + p&p
Min Mail Order EU: £5.00 + p&p
Cat. Cost: 4 x 1st class*
Credit Cards: None
Specialities: Grasses & bamboos, less
common shrubs, perennials & trees.
*Note: £1.00 of catalogue cost refunded on
first order.
Map Ref: M, D2
OS Grid Ref: SP268113

MWht WHITELEA NURSERY ⊠ UK
Whitelea Lane, Tansley, Matlock,
Derbyshire DE4 5FL
☎ (01629) 55010
Email: whitelea@nursery-stock.freeserve.co.uk
Website: www.nursery-stock.freeserve.co.uk
Contact: David Wilson
Opening Times: By appt.
Min Mail Order UK: No minimum
charge
Cat. Cost: 2 x 1st class
Credit Cards: None
Specialities: *Bamboo*, ivies. Substantial
quantities of 30 cvs & species of bamboo,
remainder stocked in small numbers only.
Map Ref: M, B1

M

MWod   WOODLANDS GRANGE ♠
Plantation Lane, Hopwas,
Nr Tamworth Staffordshire B78 3AS
☎ (01827) 311567
Fax: (01827) 54144
Email: enquiries@woodlandsgrange.co.uk
Website: www.woodlandsgrange.co.uk
Contact: Sean Bradnack, Jim Bliss
Opening Times: 0830-1700 Mon-Sat,
1030-1630 Sun. Late night opening during
season, please phone for details.
Specialities: Rare & unusual herbaceous.
Bamboo and grasses.
Map Ref: M, B1

MWoo   WOODFIELDS ⊠ UK
Wood End, Clifford Chambers,
Stratford-on-Avon, Warwickshire
CV37 8HR
☎ (01789) 205618
Contact: M Woodfield
Opening Times: 1000-1630 Mon-Fri,
1000-1600 Sat & 0900-1200 Sun for plant
collection only.
Min Mail Order UK: See catalogue for details*
Cat. Cost: Sae
Credit Cards: None
Specialities: Lupins & *Delphinium*, plants
& seeds.
*Note: mail order for carnations only.
Map Ref: M, C2

MWrn   WARREN HILLS NURSERY ⊠ UK ♠
Warren Hills Cottage, Warren Hills Road,
Coalville, Leicestershire LE67 4UY
☎ (01530) 812350
Email: warrenhills@tinyworld.co.uk
Contact: Penny Waters or Bob Taylor
Opening Times: By appt. only.
Min Mail Order UK: £10.00 + p&p
Cat. Cost: 2 x 1st class
Credit Cards: None
Specialities: *Astrantia, Campanula, Dierama,
Penstemon, Salvia, Heuchera, Nepeta.*
National Collection of *Astrantia.*
Map Ref: M, B1

MWya   WYATTS ♠ €
Hill Barn Farm, Great Rollright, Chipping
Norton, Oxfordshire OX7 5SH
☎ (01608) 684835, (01608) 684990
Fax: (01608) 684990
Email: wyatts@callnetuk.com
Website: www.cotswoldgardenplants.co.uk
Contact: John Wyatt or Dawn Whittaker
Opening Times: 0930-1700 7 days 21st

Oct-1st Mar, 0930-1800 2nd Mar-20th Oct.
Cat. Cost: 2 x 1st class
Credit Cards: MasterCard, Switch, Delta,
Visa
Specialities: Many unusual & rare plants,
shrubs & trees incl. *Daphne, Euonymus,
Viburnum, Clematis, Cornus* & *Acer.* Alpines,
fruit trees & cane fruit. Please check
availability list.
Map Ref: M, C2
OS Grid Ref: SP317313

NORTHERN

**NABC   ASKHAM BRYAN COLLEGE
NURSERY ⊠ UK**
Askham Bryan, York,
Yorkshire YO23 3FR
☎ (01904) 772277
Fax: (01904) 772288
Website: www.askham-bryan.ac.uk
Contact: Jacqueline McKenna
Opening Times: 1000-1500 Fri.
Min Mail Order UK: No minimum charge
Cat. Cost: Free
Credit Cards: None
Specialities: Hardy shrubs, perennials,
especially *Daphne, Hosta.* National
Collection of *Spiraea.*
Map Ref: N, C2
OS Grid Ref: SE553476

NArg   ARGHAM VILLAGE NURSERY ⊠ UK
Argham Grange, Grindale, Bridlington,
East Yorkshire YO16 4XZ
☎ (01723) 892141
Fax: (01723) 892141
Email: geoffpickering@arghamvillage.co.uk
Website: www.arghamvillage.co.uk
Contact: Geoff Pickering
Opening Times: 1000-1700 Mar-Oct,
1130-1500 Nov-Feb, 7 days.
Min Mail Order UK: £50.00 + p&p
Cat. Cost: 4 x 1st class
Credit Cards: Visa, MasterCard, Delta
Specialities: Herbaceous perennials.
Aquatic plants, marginals, bog, alpines,
rock plants.
Map Ref: N, C3

NAsh   ASHTONS NURSERY GARDENS ▣ ⊠ UK
Mythop Road, Lytham, Lytham St Annes,
Lancashire FY8 4JP
☎ (01253) 736627/794808
Fax: (01253) 735311
Email: info@ashtons-lytham.co.uk

Website: www.ashtons-lytham.co.uk
Contact: T M Ashton
Opening Times: 0900-1700 daily.
Min Mail Order UK: No minimum charge
Cat. Cost: None issued
Credit Cards: MasterCard, Visa, Switch,
Delta, American Express
Specialities: Herbaceous plants. Hardy
shrubs.
Map Ref: N, D1

NBat BATTERSBY ROSES ⊠ EU €
Peartree Cottage, Old Battersby,
Great Ayton, Cleveland TS9 6LU
☎ (01642) 723402
Email: battersbyroses@lineone.net
Website: www.battersbyroses.8m.com
Contact: Eric & Avril Stainthorpe
Opening Times: 1000-dusk most days.
Min Mail Order UK: No minimum charge
Min Mail Order EU: Nmc
Cat. Cost: Sae
Credit Cards: None
Specialities: Exhibition roses including some
American miniatures.
Map Ref: N, C2

NBea BEAMISH CLEMATIS NURSERY €
Burntwood Cottage, Stoney Lane,
Beamish, County Durham DH9 0SJ
☎ (0191) 370 0202
Fax: (0191) 370 0202
Contact: Colin Brown or Jan Wilson
Opening Times: 0900-1700 7 days Feb-Nov.
0900-dusk Dec & Jan.
Cat. Cost: 3 x 1st class
Credit Cards: None
Specialities: *Clematis*, climbers, shrubs &
ornamental trees.
Map Ref: N, B2

NBee BEECHCROFT NURSERIES ⊠ UK
Bongate, Appleby-in-Westmorland,
Cumbria CA16 6UE
☎ (01768) 351201
Fax: (01768) 351201
Contact: Roger Brown
Opening Times: 0900-1700 Tue-Sun, closed
Mon.
Min Mail Order UK: No minimum charge*
Cat. Cost: Sae for tree list.
Credit Cards: None
Specialities: Hardy field-grown trees &
shrubs.
*Note: mail order trees Nov-Mar only.
Map Ref: N, C1

NBhm BEETHAM NURSERIES
Pool Darkin Lane, Beetham,
Nr Milnthorpe, Cumbria LA7 7AP
☎ (01539) 563630
Fax: (01539) 564487
Contact: S & L Abbit
Opening Times: 0900-1800 Summer,
0900-dusk Winter.
Cat. Cost: None issued
Credit Cards: Visa, American Express, Switch
Specialities: Comprehensive range of trees,
shrubs & herbaceous plants. Many unusual
varieties.
Map Ref: N, C1

**NBid BIDE-A-WEE COTTAGE
GARDENS ⊠ UK**
Stanton, Netherwitton Morpeth
Northumberland NE65 8PR
☎ (01670) 772262
Email: bideaweecg@aol.com
Contact: Mark Robson
Opening Times: 1330-1700 Sat & Wed,
27th Apr-7th Sep 2002.
Min Mail Order UK: No minimum charge
Cat. Cost: 3 x 1st class
Credit Cards: None
Specialities: Unusual herbaceous perennials,
Primula, grasses.
Map Ref: N, B2

**NBir BIRKHEADS COTTAGE GARDEN
NURSERY ⊠ UK ♦**
Nr Causey Arch, Sunniside,
Newcastle upon Tyne,
Tyne & Wear NE16 5EL
☎ (01207) 232262
mobile 07778 447920
Fax: (01207) 232262
Email: birkheads.nursery@virgin.net
Website: www.birkheadscottagenursery.co.uk
Contact: Mrs Christine Liddle
Opening Times: 1000-1700 every day Mar-
end Oct. Winter opening Nov-Feb (please
phone first). Groups by appt.
Min Mail Order UK: £30.00*
Cat. Cost: None issued
Credit Cards: None
Specialities: Hardy herbaceous perennials,
grasses, bulbs & herbs. *Allium, Campanula,
Digitalis, Euphorbia, Geranium, Primula.*

N

KEY		
⊠ Mail order to UK or EU	♦ Delivers to shows	
☒ Exports beyond EU	€ Euro accepted	
☒ Also supplies Wholesale	♦ See Display advertisement	

Max. 30 of any plant propagated each year.
*Note: mail order Nov-Feb only. Orders
taken all year for winter deliveries
Map Ref: N, B2
OS Grid Ref: NZ220569

NBlo   TABLE BAY VIEW NURSERY ⊠ EU ⊠
29 Curlew Drive, Irlam,
Manchester M44 6HZ
☎ (0161) 776 1686
Fax: (0161) 776 1686
Contact: Tony Hopkinson, Cath Moony
Opening Times: Not open, mail order only.
Min Mail Order UK: £15.00 + p&p
Min Mail Order EU: £15.00
Cat. Cost: £3.30 incl p&p.*
Credit Cards: None
Specialities: Tropical, sub-tropical,
ornamental & fruiting plants.
*Note: UK customers may contact the UK
appointed agents or Cape Town office direct.
For catalogue, send cheque/postal order to
Cape Town office. See entry XBlo.

NBlu   BLUNDELL'S NURSERIES ⊡
68 Southport New Road, Tarleton, Preston,
Lancashire PR4 6HY
☎ (01772) 815442
Email: jerplusjeff@netscapeonline.co.uk
Contact: Any member of staff
Opening Times: 0900-1700 daily excl.
Weds. Closed Dec-Feb.
Cat. Cost: None issued
Credit Cards: None
Specialities: Trees, shrubs, incl. topiary &
large specimens, conifers. *Clematis* & other
climbers, perennials, alpines, ferns, heathers,
herbs, hanging basket, bedding, conservatory
plants, aquatics, hedging, roses. Garden
design service available.
Map Ref: N, D1

NBrk   T H BARKER & SONS ⊠ EU ♦
Baines Paddock Nursery, Haverthwaite,
Ulverston, Cumbria LA12 8PF
☎ (015395) 58236
Email: rachel@thbarker.demon.co.uk
Website: www.ukclematis.co.uk
Contact: W E Thornley
Opening Times: 0930-1730 Wed-Mon
1st Feb-30th Nov. Closed Tue.
Min Mail Order UK: 2 plants + p&p
Min Mail Order EU: 6 plants + p&p
Cat. Cost: £1.00 (Clematis & Climbers)
Credit Cards: None
Specialities: *Clematis, Lonicera* & other

climbers. Cottage garden plants esp. hardy
Geranium, Aster, Ranunculus, Iris & *Viola*.
Many rare. Most stock grown on the nursery.
Map Ref: N, C1

NBro   BROWNTHWAITE HARDY PLANTS
Fell Yeat, Casterton, Kirkby Lonsdale,
Lancashire LA6 2JW
☎ (015242) 71340 (after 1800).
Contact: Chris Benson
Opening Times: Tue-Sun 1st Apr-30th Sep.
Cat. Cost: 3 x 1st class
Credit Cards: None
Specialities: Herbaceous perennials & grasses
incl. *Geranium, Campanula, Iris*, especially
*Iris ensata, Primula auricula, Primula
sieboldii* & *Penstemon*. National Collection
of *Ligularia*.
Map Ref: N, C1

NBtw   BRAITHWELL NURSERIES €
2 Holywell Cottages, Braithwell, Rotherham,
South Yorkshire S66 7AB
☎ (01709) 812093
Contact: Philip Yardley
Opening Times: 1000-1800 Mar-Nov,
times vary Dec-Feb, please phone first.
Closed Xmas & New Year.
Cat. Cost: None issued
Credit Cards: None
Specialities: Wide range incl. shrubs,
perennials, grasses, climbers, alpines,
bamboos, palms, agave. Many seasonal
plants. Small stocks of some.
Note: nursery on B6427 between Braithwell
& Maltby.
Map Ref: N, D2

NBur   BURTON AGNES HALL NURSERY ⊠ EU
Burton Agnes Hall Preservation Trust Ltd,
Estate Office, Burton Agnes, Driffield,
East Yorkshire YO25 0ND
☎ (01262) 490324
Fax: (01262) 490513
Email: burton.agnes@farmline.com
Website: www.burton-agnes.com
Contact: Mrs S Cunliffe-Lister
Opening Times: 1100-1700 Apr-Oct.
Min Mail Order UK: £15.00 + p&p*
Min Mail Order EU: £15.00 + p&p
Cat. Cost: 4 x 1st class
Credit Cards: None
Specialities: Large range perennials &
alpines. Many unusual varieties esp.
*Penstemon, Osteospermum, Digitalis, Anemone,
Geranium*. National Collection of *Campanula*.

*Note: mail order Nov-Mar only.
Map Ref: N, C3

NCat **CATFORTH GARDENS**
Cherry Tree Lodge Nursery, Roots Lane,
Catforth, Preston, Lancashire PR4 0JB
☎ (01772) 690561
Contact: Judith & Tony Bradshaw
Opening Times: 1030-1700 16 Mar-end
Aug 2002, Thu-Sun & B/hols or by appt.
Cat. Cost: 5 x 1st class
Credit Cards: None
Specialities: National Collection of Hardy
Geranium (full status). Garden open at same
times as nursery. Over 1500 varieties of
herbaceous plants.
Map Ref: N, D1

NCel **CELEBRATIONS NURSERY** 🖾 ⊠ UK 🕯
19 Sycamore Centre, Eastwood Trading
Estate, Rotherham, South Yorkshire S65 1EN
☎ (01709) 769860
Fax: (01709) 769860
Contact: Tony Parks
Opening Times: By appt. only.
Min Mail Order UK: £10.00
Cat. Cost: 2 x 2nd class
Credit Cards: Visa, MasterCard
Specialities: Bulbous plants.

NChi **CHIPCHASE CASTLE NURSERY** 🕯
Chipchase Castle, Wark, Hexham,
Northumberland NE48 3NT
☎ (01434) 230083
Website: www.northernperennials.co.uk
Contact: Suzanne Newell & Janet Beakes
Opening Times: 1000-1700 Thu-Sun &
B/hol Mons Easter (or 1st Apr)-mid Oct.
Cat. Cost: A5 sae for list
Credit Cards: None
Specialities: Unusual herbaceous especially
Erodium, Eryngium, Geranium, Penstemon &
Viola.
Map Ref: N, B2

NChl **CHILTERN SEEDS** ⊠ EU 🖾 ◆
Bortree Stile, Ulverston, Cumbria LA12 7PB
☎ (01229) 581137 (24 hrs)
Fax: (01229) 584549
Email: info@chilternseeds.co.uk
Website: www.chilternseeds.co.uk
Opening Times: Normal office hours, Mon-Fri.
Min Mail Order UK: No minimum charge
Min Mail Order EU: Nmc
Cat. Cost: 3 x 2nd class
Credit Cards: Visa, Access, American

Express, Switch, MasterCard, EuroCard
Specialities: Over 4,600 items of all kinds -
wild flowers, trees, shrubs, cacti, annuals,
houseplants, vegetables & herbs.

NCiC **CICELY'S COTTAGE GARDEN
PLANTS** 🕯
43 Elmers Green, Skelmersdale,
Lancashire WN8 6SG
☎ (01695) 720790
Email: maureen.duncan@ic.24net
Contact: Maureen Duncan
Opening Times: Please phone to avoid
disappointment as opening times vary.
Cat. Cost: Free plant list
Credit Cards: None
Specialities: Shrubs, hardy, half-hardy &
tender perennials incl. *Penstemon.* Traditional
& unusual cottage garden plants.
Map Ref: N, D1

NCot **COTTAGE GARDEN PLANTS** ⊠ UK
1 Sycamore Close, Whitehaven,
Cumbria CA28 6LE
☎ (01946) 695831
Email: jnprkss@aol.com
Website: www.cottagegardenplants.com
Contact: Mrs J Purkiss
Opening Times: By appt. only. For garden
see NGS handbook.
Min Mail Order UK: No minimum charge
Cat. Cost: 3 x 1st class sae
Credit Cards: None
Specialities: Hardy perennials including
*Corydalis, Dicentra, Geranium, Polemonium,
Primula* & *Pulmonaria.*
Map Ref: N, C1

NCro **CROSTON CACTUS** ⊠ EU 🕯
43 Southport Road, Eccleston, Chorley,
Lancashire PR7 6ET
☎ (01257) 452555
Email: desert.plants@lineone.net
Website: www.croston-cactus.co.uk
Contact: John Henshaw
Opening Times: 0930-1700 Wed-Sat & by
appt.
Min Mail Order UK: £5.00 + p&p
Min Mail Order EU: £10.00 + p&p
Cat. Cost: 2 x 1st or 2 x IRCs
Credit Cards: None

Specialities: Mexican cacti, *Echeveria* hybrids & some bromeliads & *Tillandsia*.
Map Ref: N, D1

NCWG **CHESTERS WALLED GARDEN**
Chollerford, Hexham,
Northumberland NE46 4BQ
☎ (01434) 681483
Contact: Susie White
Opening Times: 1000-1700 7 days Mar-end Oct. Please phone for winter times.
Cat. Cost: None issued.
Credit Cards: None
Specialities: Extensive range of herbs. National Collection of *Thymus* & *Origanum*. Wild flowers, grasses & unusual perennials esp. *Geranium*, *Epilobium* & variegated plants. Note: nursery formerly known as Hexham Herbs.
Map Ref: N, B2

NDlv **DALESVIEW NURSERY** ▣ ⊠ EU ▣
24 Braithwaite Edge Road, Keighley,
West Yorkshire BD22 6RA
☎ (01535) 606531
Contact: David Ellis & Eileen Morgan
Opening Times: 1000-1700 Wed-Sun & B/hols.
Min Mail Order UK: No minimum charge
Min Mail Order EU: Nmc
Cat. Cost: 4 x 1st class
Specialities: Dwarf *Hebe*, *Saxifraga*, *Primula*, *Rhododendron*, *Fuchsia* & conifers.
Map Ref: N, C2

NDov **DOVE COTTAGE NURSERY**
23 Shibden Hall Road, Halifax,
West Yorkshire HX3 9XA
☎ (01422) 203553
Email: dovecottage.nursery
Website: www.dovecottagenursery.co.uk
Contact: Stephen & Kim Rogers
Opening Times: 1000-1800 Wed-Sun & B/hols Feb-Sep.
Cat. Cost: 4 x 1st class
Credit Cards: Switch, Solo, Delta, Electron, Visa, MasterCard
Specialities: *Helleborus* & selected perennials & grasses for naturalistic planting.
Map Ref: N, D2

NEgg **EGGLESTON HALL** ▣ ⊠ EU ▣ ń €
Garden Cottage, Eggleston, Barnard Castle,
County Durham DL12 0AG
☎ (01833) 650115
Fax: (01833) 650971

Email: mbhock@btinternet.com
Contact: Malcolm Hockham, Gordon Long
Opening Times: 1000-1700 7 days.
Min Mail Order UK: £12.95*
Min Mail Order EU: £15.95
Cat. Cost: £2.00 + Sae
Credit Cards: EuroCard, Maestro, Visa, Electron, Switch, Solo, JCB
Specialities: Rare & unusual plants with particular emphasis on flower arranging. *Note: mail order *Celmisia spectabilis* Oct-Mar only.
Map Ref: N, C2
OS Grid Ref: NY997233

NEqu **EQUATORIAL PLANT CO.** ▣ ⊠ EU ▣ ń €
7 Gray Lane, Barnard Castle,
County Durham DL12 8PD
☎ (01833) 690519
Fax: (01833) 690519
Email: equatorialplants@teesdaleonline.co.uk
Contact: Dr Richard Warren
Opening Times: By appt. only.
Min Mail Order UK: No minimum charge
Min Mail Order EU: Nmc
Cat. Cost: Free
Credit Cards: Visa, Access
Specialities: Laboratory raised orchids only.

NFir **FIR TREES PELARGONIUM NURSERY** ⊠ UK ń
Stokesley, Middlesbrough,
Cleveland TS9 5LD
☎ (01642) 713066
Fax: (01642) 713066
Website: www.firtreespelargoniums.co.uk
Contact: Helen Bainbridge
Opening Times: 1000-1600 7 days 15th Mar-30th Sep, 1000-1600 Mon-Fri 1st Oct-15th Mar.
Min Mail Order UK: £2.50 + p&p
Cat. Cost: 4 x 1st class
Credit Cards: MasterCard, Visa, Switch
Specialities: All types of *Pelargonium* - fancy leaf, regal, decorative regal, oriental regal, angel, miniature, zonal, ivy leaf, stellar, scented, dwarf, unique, golden stellar & species.
Map Ref: N, C2

NFla **FLAXTON HOUSE NURSERY**
Flaxton, York, North Yorkshire Y060 7RJ
☎ (01904) 468753
Contact: Mrs H Williams
Opening Times: 1000-1700 Tue-Sun

1st Mar-31st Oct.
Cat. Cost: 2 x 1st class
Credit Cards: None
Specialities: Wide general range of herbaceous & alpines with many unusual plants. Selection of climbers & shrubs. Limited quantities so phone before travelling.
Map Ref: N, C2
OS Grid Ref: 467462

NFor   FORD NURSERY   ⊠ UK ◆
Castle Gardens, Ford,
Berwick-upon-Tweed TD15 2PZ
☎ (01890) 820379
Fax: (01890) 820594
Email: Ford.nursery@which.net
Website: www.FordNursery.co.uk
Contact: Marjorie Spark & Roy Harmeston
Opening Times: 1000-1730 7 days
Mar-Oct, 1000-1630 Mon-Fri Nov-Feb.
Min Mail Order UK: No minimum charge
Cat. Cost: Free
Credit Cards: Visa, Access, Switch
Specialities: Over 1200 different species of container grown hardy ornamental shrubs, perennials, trees & herbs, climbers & grasses.
Map Ref: N, A2

NGar   GARDENSCAPE   ⊠ EU 🏃€
Fairview, Smelthouses, Summerbridge
Harrogate, North Yorkshire HG3 4DH
☎ (01423) 780291
mobile 07801 232024
Fax: (01423) 780291
Email: mdmyers@gardenscape.co.uk
Website: www.gardenscape.co.uk
Contact: Michael D Myers
Opening Times: By appt.
Min Mail Order UK: £10.00 + p&p
Min Mail Order EU: £30.00
Cat. Cost: 3 x 1st class
Credit Cards: None
Specialities: Woodland plants & alpines, snowdrops. National Collections of *Anemone nemorosa, Hepatica* & *Primula marginata*.
Map Ref: N, C2
OS Grid Ref: SE195644

NGby   GILBEY'S PLANTS   🖾 ⊠ EU 🏃€
(office) 42 Park Street, Masham, Ripon
North Yorkshire HG4 4HN
☎ (01765) 689927
Fax: (01765) 689927
Email: gilbeyplants@aol.com
Contact: Giles N Gilbey
Opening Times: 1000-1700 Mon-Sat,

1400-1700 Sun, 1st Mar-1st Oct. Winter by appointment only.
Min Mail Order UK: No minimum charge
Min Mail Order EU: Nmc
Cat. Cost: 4 x 1st class
Credit Cards: None
Specialities: Unusual hardy perennials & ferns. *Note: mail order Oct-Mar only.
Nursery at The Walled Garden, Cemetery Road, Thirsk YO7 4DL.
Map Ref: N, C2

NGCt   GARTH COTTAGE NURSERY   🖾 ⊠ UK
Garth Cottage, Newby Wiske, Northallerton, North Yorkshire DL7 9ET
☎ (01609) 777233 incl. answerphone.
Fax: (01609) 775777
Email: pturner@garth-cottage.fsnet.co.uk
Contact: Paul & Christine Turner
Opening Times: At present by prior arrangement only.
Min Mail Order UK: No minimum charge
Cat. Cost: 3 x 1st class for each of 2 (herbs & lavenders, ivies).
Credit Cards: None
Specialities: 300+ varieties of herbs, with emphasis on culinary incl. 50 mint, 30 rosemary, 20 sage, 15 basil, 15 oregano & 50+ thyme. 100 varieties of lavender & 300 varieties of ivy.

NGdn   GARDEN HOUSE NURSERIES
The Square, Dalston, Carlisle, CA5 7LL
☎ (01228) 710297
Email: david@gardenhousenursery.co.uk
Website: www.gardenhousenursery.co.uk
Contact: David Hickson
Opening Times: 0900-1700 7 days
Mar-Oct.
Cat. Cost: None issued, plant list on web
Credit Cards: None
Specialities: *Geranium, Hosta, Hemerocallis, Iris,* grasses, bamboos & *Penstemon.*
Map Ref: N, B1

NGHP   GREEN GARDEN HERBS &
PLANTS   🖾🏃
(Office) 73 Alma Road, Leeds,
Yorkshire LS6 2AH
☎ (0113) 274 7940
mobile 07949 906290

Contact: Sarah Clark, Stefan Vida
Opening Times: Please phone for details.
Cat. Cost: 2 x 2nd class
Credit Cards: Visa
Specialities: Herbs.
Note: nursery is at Greenscapes Horticultural Centre, Brandon Crescent, Shadwell, Leeds.
Map Ref: N, D2

NHal   HALLS OF HEDDON 🖼 ⊠ EU 🖼
(Office) West Heddon Nurseries, Heddon-on-the-wall, Northumberland NE15 0JS
☎ (01661) 852445
Fax: (01661) 852398
Email: hallsofheddon@breathemail.net
Website: www.hallsofheddon.co.uk
Contact: Judith Lockey
Opening Times: 0900-1700 Mon-Sat 1000-1700 Sun.
Min Mail Order UK: No minimum charge
Min Mail Order EU: £25.00 + p&p*
Cat. Cost: 3 x 2nd class
Credit Cards: None
Specialities: *Chrysanthemum* & *Dahlia*. Wide range of herbaceous.
*Note: mail order *Dahlia* & *Chrysanthemum* only. EU & export *Dahlia* tubers only.
Map Ref: N, B2

NHar   HARTSIDE NURSERY GARDEN ⊠ EU 🖼 🔨
Nr Alston, Cumbria CA9 3BL
☎ (01434) 381372
Fax: (01434) 381372
Email: Hartside@macunlimited.net
Contact: S L & N Huntley
Opening Times: 0930-1630 Mon-Fri, 1230-1600 Sat, Sun & B/hols, mid Mar-31st Oct. By appt. 1st Nov-mid Mar.
Min Mail Order UK: No minimum charge
Min Mail Order EU: £50.00 + p&p
Cat. Cost: 4 x 1st class or 3 x IRC
Credit Cards: Visa, Access, Switch
Specialities: Alpines grown at altitude of 1100 feet in Pennines. *Primula*, ferns, *Gentian* & *Meconopsis*.
Map Ref: N, B1

NHaw   THE HAWTHORNES NURSERY ⊠ UK
Marsh Road, Hesketh Bank, Nr Preston, Lancashire PR4 6XT
☎ (01772) 812379
Website: www.hawthornes-nursery.co.uk
Contact: Irene & Richard Hodson
Opening Times: 0900-1800 7 days 1st Mar-30th Jun, Thu-Sun July-Oct. Gardens open for NGS.

Min Mail Order UK: £10.00
Cat. Cost: 5 x 1st class
Credit Cards: None
Specialities: *Clematis*, honeysuckle, choice selection of shrub & climbing roses, extensive range of perennials, mostly on display in the garden.
Map Ref: N, D1

NHer   HERTERTON HOUSE GARDEN NURSERY
Hartington, Cambo, Morpeth, Northumberland NE61 4BN
☎ (01670) 774278
Contact: Mrs M Lawley & Mr Frank Lawley
Opening Times: 1330-1730 Mon, Wed, Fri-Sun 1st Apr-end Sep. (Earlier or later in the year weather permitting.)
Cat. Cost: None issued
Credit Cards: None
Specialities: Country garden flowers.
Map Ref: N, B2

NHHG   HARDSTOFT HERB GARDEN 🖼
Hall View Cottage, Hardstoft, Pilsley, Nr Chesterfield, Derbyshire S45 8AH
☎ (01246) 854268
Contact: Lynne & Steve Raynor
Opening Times: 1000-1700 daily 15th Mar-15th Sep. Closed Tue excl. Easter & B/hol weeks.
Cat. Cost: Free
Credit Cards: MasterCard, Switch, Delta, Visa
Specialities: Wide range of herbs. Over 40 lavenders & 12 rosemary. Scented pelargoniums. National Collection of *Echinacea*.
Map Ref: N, D2

NHlc   HALECAT NURSERIES
Witherslack, Grange over Sands, Cumbria LA11 6RU
☎ (01539) 52536
Fax: (01539) 52215
Email: theyard@halecat.fsnet.co.uk
Website: www.halecat.co.uk
Contact: Graham Nunn
Opening Times: 0900-1630 Mon-Sat, 1230-1630 Sun. Closed w/ends 31st Oct-31st Mar. Parties by appt.
Cat. Cost: None issued
Credit Cards: None
Specialities: *Hosta, Hydrangea, Euphorbia*, grey foliage and perennial border plants.
Map Ref: N, C1

NHol HOLDEN CLOUGH
NURSERY 🖾 ⊠ EU 🖾 ň ◆
Holden, Bolton-by-Bowland, Clitheroe
Lancashire BB7 4PF
☎ (01200) 447615
Fax: (01200) 447615
Email: enquiries@holdencloughnursery.co.uk
Website: www.holdencloughnursery.co.uk
Contact: P J Foley
Opening Times: 0900-1630 Mon-Sat all
year & B/hol Mons, 1300-1630 Easter Sun +
Sun May & Jun B/hol w/ends. Closed 25th
Dec-2nd Jan 2003 & Good Fri. Please phone
first to check opening times.
Min Mail Order UK: No minimum charge
Min Mail Order EU: Nmc
Cat. Cost: £1.40
Credit Cards: MasterCard, Visa, Delta
Specialities: Large general list incl. *Primula*,
Saxifraga, *Sempervivum*, *Pulmonaria*, *Astilbe*,
grasses, *Hosta*, heathers & *Rhododendron*.
*Note: seasonal mail order on some items.
Map Ref: N, C2
OS Grid Ref: SD773496

NHor HORN'S GARDEN CENTRE ⊠ EU €
Dixon Estate, Shotton Colliery,
County Durham DH6 2PX
☎ (0191) 526 2987
Fax: (0191) 526 2889
Contact: G Horn & Theresa Horn
Opening Times: 0900-1730 Mon-Sat 1000-
1600 Sun, all year excl. Easter Mon.
Min Mail Order UK: £6.80 + p&p
Min Mail Order EU: £6.80 + p&p
Cat. Cost: 3 x 1st class
Credit Cards: Visa, EuroCard, MasterCard,
Access, Switch, American Express, Delta
Specialities: National Collection of *Coleus*
(*Solenostemon*).
Map Ref: N, B2

NJOw JOHN OWEN NURSERIES 🖾
20 West Bank, Carlton, Nr Goole,
East Yorkshire DN14 9PZ
☎ (01405) 861415, mobile 07762 650131
Fax: (01405) 861415
Contact: John D W Owen
Opening Times: 1000-1700 Thu-Sat,
1st Mar-31st Oct & B/hols.
Cat. Cost: 3 x 2nd class
Map Ref: N, D3   OS Grid Ref: SE629243

NLan LANDLIFE WILDFLOWERS LTD 🖾⊠UK ň
National Wildflower Centre, Court Hey
Park, Liverpool, Merseyside L16 3NA

☎ (0151) 737 1819
Fax: (0151) 737 1820
Email: gill@landlife.org.uk
Website: www.wildflower.org.uk
Contact: Gillian Watson
Opening Times: 1100-1600 Wed-Sun
1st Apr-30 Sep.
Min Mail Order UK: £30.00 (plants), no
min. for seeds.
Cat. Cost: Sae + 2 x 2nd class
Credit Cards: Visa, Delta, Access, Switch,
Solo
Specialities: Wild herbaceous plants & seeds.
Cafe & shop. Visitor centre, admission
charge.
Map Ref: N, D1

NLAp LANESIDE ALPINES ň
74 Croston Road, Garstang, Preston,
Lancashire PR3 1HR
☎ (01995) 605537
mobile 0794 6659661
Email: jcrhutch@aol.com
Contact: Jeff Hutchings
Opening Times: By appt. only.
Cat. Cost: Sae
Specialities: Alpines, incl. gentians,
Penstemon species, primulas, show auriculas,
Saxifraga, *Sisyrinchium*, dwarf evergreen
shrubs, planted bowls & planted tufa.
Note: mail order from autumn 2002.
Map Ref: N, D1

NLar LARCH COTTAGE NURSERIES ⊠ EU € ◆
Melkinthorpe, Penrith,
Cumbria CA10 2DR
☎ (01931) 712404
Fax: (01931) 712727
Email: plants@larchcottage.freeserve.co.uk
Website: www.larchcottagenurseries.com
Contact: Joanne McCullock
Opening Times: Daily from 1000-1730.
Min Mail Order UK: No minimum charge
Min Mail Order EU: Nmc
Cat. Cost: £2.00
Credit Cards: Visa, Access, Switch, Delta,
Solo
Specialities: Unusual & old fashioned
perennials. Rare & dwarf conifers. Unusual
shrubs & trees.
Map Ref: N, C1

N

	KEY		
⊠	Mail order to UK or EU	ň	Delivers to shows
🖾	Exports beyond EU	€	Euro accepted
🖾	Also supplies Wholesale	◆	See Display advertisement

N

NLon   **The Longframlington Centre for Plants & Gardens** 🖥 ⊠ UK ◆
Swarland Road, Longframlington, Morpeth,
Northumberland NE65 8DB
☎ (01665) 570382
Fax: (01665) 570382
Email: info@tlcfp.fsbusiness.co.uk
Website: www.longframlingtongardens.co.uk
Contact: Hazel Huddleston
Opening Times: 0900-1900 (or dusk) 7 days
all year, or by appt.
Min Mail Order UK: No minimum charge
Cat. Cost: £2.50 incl.
Credit Cards: Access, Visa
Specialities: Hardy ornamental trees, shrubs,
perennials, herbs, ground cover & alpines.
Map Ref: N, B2
OS Grid Ref: 145008

NLRH   **Little Red Hen Nurseries** 🖥 ⊠ UK
91 Denholme Road, Oxenhope, Keighley,
West Yorkshire BD22 9SJ
☎ (01535) 643786
Email: louise@redhens.co.uk
Website: www.redhens.co.uk
Contact: Louise Harris
Opening Times: Please phone first.
Min Mail Order UK: No minimum charge
Cat. Cost: Free
Credit Cards: None
Specialities: Small nursery with limited
stock. Details in catalogue or on website.
Map Ref: N, D2

NMar   **J & D Marston** ⊠ EU ◆
Culag, Green Lane, Nafferton, Driffield,
East Yorkshire YO25 0LF
☎ (01377) 254487
Fax: (01377) 254487
Contact: J & D & Mrs J K Marston
Opening Times: 1350-1700 Sat & Sun
Easter-mid Sep. Other times by appt.
Min Mail Order UK: £15.00 + p&p
Min Mail Order EU: £60.00 + carriage
Cat. Cost: 4 x 1st class
Credit Cards: None
Specialities: Hardy & greenhouse ferns only.
Map Ref: N, C3

NMen   **Mendle Nursery** ⊠ EU 🖘
Holme, Scunthorpe,
Lincolnshire DN16 3RF
☎ (01724) 850864
Email: annearnshaw@lineone.net
Website: www.mendlenursery.com
Contact: Mrs A Earnshaw

Opening Times: 1000-1600 Tue-Sun.
Min Mail Order UK: No minimum charge
Min Mail Order EU: Nmc
Cat. Cost: 3 x 1st class
Credit Cards: None
Specialities: Many unusual alpines especially
Saxifraga & *Sempervivum*.
Map Ref: N, D3
OS Grid Ref: SE925070

NMGW   **M G W Plants** ⊠ UK 🖘
45 Potovens Lane, Lofthouse Gate,
Wakefield, West Yorkshire WF3 3JE
☎ (01924) 820096
Email: mgwplants@btinternet.co.uk
Contact: Michael G Wilson
Opening Times: 1000-1800 Wed-Sat
1st Feb-31st Oct.
Min Mail Order UK: £10.00 + p&p
Cat. Cost: 1 x 1st class
Credit Cards: None
Specialities: Alpines incl. *Campanula* &
Geranium. Bulbs incl. *Colchicum* & *Crocus*.
Herbaceous incl. *Geranium* & *Iris*.
Map Ref: N, D2

NMir   **Mires Beck Nursery** 🖥 ⊠ EU
Low Mill Lane, North Cave, Brough,
North Humberside HU15 2NR
☎ (01430) 421543
Contact: Irene Tinklin & Martin Rowland
Opening Times: 1000-1600 Thu-Sat
1st Mar-30th Sep. 1000-1500 Thu-Fri
1st Oct-30th Nov & by appt.
Min Mail Order UK: No minimum charge*
Min Mail Order EU: Nmc
Cat. Cost: 3 x 1st class
Credit Cards: None
Specialities: Wild flower plants of Yorkshire
provenance.
*Note: Mail order for wild flower plants,
plugs & seeds only.
Map Ref: N, D3

NMoo   **Moor Monkton Nurseries** ⊠ UK
Moor Monkton, Nr York,
North Yorkshire YO25 8JJ
☎ (01904) 738770
Fax: (01904) 738770
Email: sales@bamboo-uk.co.uk
Website: www.bamboo-uk.co.uk
Contact: Peter Owen
Opening Times: 0900-1700.
Min Mail Order UK: No minimum charge*
Cat. Cost: 5 x 2nd class or email for details.
Credit Cards: None

Specialities: Bamboos, palms, unusual trees, shrubs & perennials.
*Note: Mail order for bamboo only.
Map Ref: N, C2

NMos STANLEY MOSSOP ▨ ▧ EU ▨
Boonwood Garden Centre, Gosforth, Seascale, Cumbria CA20 1BP
☎ (01946) 725330
Fax: (01946) 725330
Email: www.mossop@boonwood.fsnet.co.uk
Contact: Stanley, Gary & Kay Mossop.
Opening Times: 1000-1700 7 days.
Min Mail Order UK: No minimum charge
Min Mail Order EU: £50.00 + p&p
Cat. Cost: Free
Credit Cards: None
Specialities: *Achimenes, Achimenantha, Eucodonia, Gloxinia* (including species) & *Smithiantha.*
Map Ref: N, C1

NMRc MILLRACE NURSERY
84 Selby Road, Garforth Leeds LS25 1LP
☎ (0113) 286 9233
Fax: (0113) 286 9908
Contact: C Carthy
Opening Times: 1000-1700 Tue, Thu-Sat & B/hols Apr-mid Oct, 1100-1600 Sun May-Jun.
Cat. Cost: 2 x 1st class
Credit Cards: None
Specialities: Unusual perennials, especially drought-resistant, incl. hardy geraniums, alliums, campanulas, penstemnons, potentillas & veronicas. Some plants in small numbers only.
Map Ref: N, D2

NMun PENTON MILL ▨ EU ▨
Penton, Carlisle, Cumbria CA6 5QU
☎ (01228) 577336
Fax: (01228) 577336
Email: acrhodos@onetel.net.uk
Contact: Alan J Clark
Opening Times: 1000-1700 7 days 1st Apr-31st Oct. All other times by appt.
Min Mail Order UK: £20.00 + p&p
Min Mail Order EU: £50.00 + p&p
Cat. Cost: 6 x 2nd class
Credit Cards: Access, Visa, Not for telephone orders
Specialities: Rhododendrons & azaleas & moisture loving primulas. Note: nursery formerly Muncastle Castle.
Map Ref: N, B1

NMyG MARY GREEN HOSTAS & HARDY PERENNIALS ▨ UK ♌
27 Park Avenue, Euxton, Nr Chorley, Lancashire PR7 6JQ
☎ (01257) 270821, mobile 07778 910348
Fax: (01257) 270821
Email: Marygreenplants@aol.com
Contact: Mary Green
Opening Times: By appt. only.
Min Mail Order UK: £10.00
Cat. Cost: 3 x 1st class
Credit Cards: None
Specialities: Choice herbaceous perennials, incl. hostas, astilbes & geraniums.
Note: nursery is at The Walled Garden, Hornby, Lancaster.
Map Ref: N, D1

NNew NEWTON HILL ALPINES ▨ ♌ €
335 Leeds Road, Newton Hill, Wakefield, West Yorkshire WF1 2JH
☎ (01924) 377056
Email: s.vigors@nmsi.ac.uk
Contact: Sheena Vigors
Opening Times: 0900-1700 Fri-Wed all year. Closed Thu. Please phone first.
Cat. Cost: 2 x 1st class
Credit Cards: None
Specialities: Alpines esp. *Saxifraga*, also *Erica*, conifers & dwarf shrubs.
Map Ref: N, D2

NNEX NORTHERN EXOTICS ▨ ♌ €
Darlington Back Lane, Whinney Hill, Stockton, TS21 1BQ
☎ (01642) 582906
Contact: Martin Haliwell
Opening Times: By appt. only.
Specialities: *Cordyline australis, Trachycarpus fortunei, Chamaerops humilis, Fatsia japonica, Acacia dealbata, Callistemon, Eucalyptus, Phyllostachys, Pinus greggii* & *Pinus michoacana*
Map Ref: N, C2
OS Grid Ref: NZ391191

NNor NORCROFT NURSERIES ▨ ▨ UK
Roadends, Intack, Southwaite, Carlisle Cumbria CA4 0LH
☎ (016974) 73933, mobile 07887 781555
Fax: (016974) 73969

N

Email: stellaandkeithbell@sbell44.fsnet.co.uk
Contact: Keith Bell
Opening Times: Every afternoon excl. Mon but open B/hols.
Min Mail Order UK: No minimum charge
Cat. Cost: 2 x 2nd class
Credit Cards: None
Specialities: Hardy herbaceous, ornamental grasses, hostas, *Lilium*, acquatics.
Map Ref: N, B1
OS Grid Ref: NY474433

NOaD OAK DENE NURSERIES ▣ ⊠ UK
10 Back Lane West, Royston, Barnsley, South Yorkshire S71 4SB
☎ (01226) 722253
Fax: (01226) 722253
Contact: J Foster or G Foster
Opening Times: 0900-1800 1st Apr-30th Sep, 1000-1600 1st Oct-31st Mar. (Closed 1230-1330.)
Min Mail Order UK: Please phone for further information.
Cat. Cost: None issued.
Credit Cards: None
Specialities: Cacti, succulents & South African *Lachenalia* bulbs.
Map Ref: N, D2

NOak OAK TREE NURSERY ⊠ UK ♠
Mill Lane, Barlow, Selbly, North Yorkshire YO8 8EY
☎ (01757) 618409
Contact: Gill Plowes
Opening Times: By appt. only.
Min Mail Order UK: £10.00 + p&p
Cat. Cost: 2 x 1st class
Credit Cards: None
Specialities: Cottage garden plants, grasses & ferns.
Map Ref: N, D3

NOGN THE ORNAMENTAL GRASS NURSERY ⊠ UK ♠
Church Farm, Westgate, Rillington, Malton, North Yorkshire YO17 8LN
☎ (01944) 758247
mobile 07813 327886
Fax: (01944) 758247
Email: sales@ornamentalgrass.co.uk
Website: www.ornamentalgrass.co.uk
Contact: Angela Kilby
Opening Times: 0930-1600 Tue, Wed & Thu 1st May-mid Oct.
Min Mail Order UK: No minimum charge
Cat. Cost: 4 x 1st class

Credit Cards: None
Specialities: Ornamental grasses, bamboos, ferns & hostas.
Map Ref: N, C3

NOrc ORCHARD HOUSE NURSERY ▣
Orchard House, Wormald Green, Nr Harrogate, North Yorkshire HG3 3PX
☎ (01765) 677541
Fax: (01765) 677541
Contact: Mr B M Corner
Opening Times: 0800-1630 Mon-Fri.
Cat. Cost: 4 x 1st class
Credit Cards: None
Specialities: Herbaceous perennials, ferns, grasses, water plants & unusual cottage garden plants.
Map Ref: N, C2

NPal THE PALM FARM ▣ ⊠ EU ▣ €
Thornton Hall Gardens, Station Road, Thornton Curtis, Nr Ulceby, Humberside DN39 6XF
☎ (01469) 531232
Fax: (01469) 531232
Website: www.thepalmfarm.com
Contact: W W Spink
Opening Times: 1400-1700 7 days in summer. Please phone for winter times.
Min Mail Order UK: £11.00 + p&p
Min Mail Order EU: £25.00 + p&p
Cat. Cost: 1 x 2nd class
Credit Cards: None
Specialities: Hardy & half-hardy palms, unusual trees, shrubs & conservatory plants.
Note: some plants available only in small quantities. Payment in euros accepted only if purchaser pays bank commission.
Map Ref: N, D3

NPar GERRY PARKER PLANTS ⊠ EU ♠ €
9 Cotherstone Road, Newton Hall, Durham DH1 5YN
☎ (0191) 386 8749
Email: Gerryparker@btinternet.com
Contact: G Parker
Opening Times: Open by appt.
Min Mail Order UK: No minimum charge
Min Mail Order EU: Nmc
Cat. Cost: 3 x 1st class
Credit Cards: None
Specialities: Woodland plants, bulbs, border plants, all suited to clay soils. Many in small quantities.
Map Ref: N, B2

NPer **PERRY'S PLANTS**
The River Garden, Sleights, Whitby,
North Yorkshire YO21 1RR
☎ (01947) 810329
Fax: (01947) 810940
Email: perry@rivergardens.fsnet.co.uk
Contact: Pat & Richard Perry
Opening Times: 1000-1700 mid-March to
Oct.
Cat. Cost: Large (A4) Sae
Credit Cards: None
Specialities: *Lavatera, Malva, Erysimum,*
Euphorbia, Anthemis, Osteospermum & *Hebe.*
Uncommon hardy & container plants &
aquatic plants.
Map Ref: N, C3
OS Grid Ref: NZ869082

NPoe **POETS COTTAGE SHRUB NURSERY**
Lealholm, Whitby,
North Yorkshire YO21 2AQ
☎ (01947) 897424
Contact: Hilda Rees
Opening Times: 0900-1700 Mar-Christmas,
1300-1530 Jan & Feb, 7 days.
Cat. Cost: None issued.
Credit Cards: None
Specialities: Dwarf conifers, *Acer* &
herbaceous.
Map Ref: N, C3

NPol **POLEMONIUM PLANTERY** ▧ ⊠ UK ♠
28 Sunnyside Terrace, Trimdon Grange,
Trimdon Station, Co. Durham TS29 6HF
☎ (01429) 881529
Email: polemoniumpc@aol.com
Website:
www.geocities.com/polemonium_plantery
Contact: David or Dianne Nichol-Brown
Opening Times: Red Cross & NGS, 4th
Sun in May & 3rd Sun in July & Sep. Also
by appt.
Min Mail Order UK: £10.00
Cat. Cost: Sae for list or £4.50 for full
colour booklet
Credit Cards: None
Specialities: National Collection of
Polemonium & related genera, plus some
rare North American plants.
Map Ref: N, B2

NPPs **PENNINE PERENNIALS** ♠
15 Mount View, Uppermill, Saddleworth,
Manchester OL3 6DB
☎ (01457) 872494/873110
Email: pennineperennials@btinternet.com

Contact: Sarah Crawcour, Helen Grainger
Opening Times: Mar-Oct by appt. only.
Cat. Cost: A5 sae for plant list
Credit Cards: None
Specialities: Unusual hardy perennials,
particularly those suitable for Pennine areas.
Note: nursery at different address in same
village.
Map Ref: N, D2

NPri **PRIMROSE COTTAGE NURSERY** ◆
Ringway Road, Moss Nook, Wythenshawe,
Manchester M22 5WF
☎ (0161) 437 1557
Email: info@primrosecottagenursery.co.uk
Website: www.primrosecottagenursery.co.uk
Contact: Caroline Dumville
Opening Times: 0815-1730 Mon-Sat, 0930-
1730 Sun (summer). 0815-1700 Mon-Sat,
0930-1700 Sun (winter).
Cat. Cost: 1 x 1st class
Credit Cards: Visa, Access, Switch,
MasterCard, Solo
Specialities: Hardy herbaceous perennials,
alpines, herbs, roses, patio & hanging basket
plants. Shrubs.
Map Ref: N, D2

NPro **PROUDPLANTS** ♠
East of Eden Nurseries, Ainstable, Carlisle,
Cumbria CA4 9QN
☎ (01768) 896604
Fax: (01768) 896604
Contact: Roger Proud
Opening Times: 0900-1800 7 days Mar-
Nov. Other times by appt.
Cat. Cost: None issued
Credit Cards: None
Specialities: Interesting & unusual shrubs &
perennials esp. dwarf & ground cover plants.
Map Ref: N, B1

NPSI **PLANTS OF SPECIAL INTEREST** ◆
4 High Street, Braithwell, Nr Rotherham,
South Yorkshire S66 7AL
☎ (01709) 790642
Fax: (01709) 790342
Email: info@psinursery.co.uk
Website: www.psinursery.co.uk
Contact: Rita Ann Dunstan
Opening Times: 1000-1700 Tue-Sun

N

⊠ Mail order to UK or EU	♠ Delivers to shows	
▣ Exports beyond EU	€ Euro accepted	
▧ Also supplies Wholesale	◆ See Display advertisement	

Jan-Dec, & B/hol Mons. Closed Xmas.
Cat. Cost: None issue
Credit Cards: Access, Switch, Visa, MasterCard
Specialities: Selection of herbaceous plants esp. *Zantedeschia* & grasses. Specimen shrubs, semi-mature trees & architectural plants. Note: nursery in centre of Braithwell opp. Red Lion public house.
Map Ref: N, D2

NRar   Rarer Plants
Ashfield House, Austfield Lane, Monk Fryston, Leeds, North Yorkshire LS25 5EH
☎ (01977) 682263
Contact: Anne Watson
Opening Times: 1000-1600 Sat & Sun 20th Feb-1st Apr.
Cat. Cost: Sae
Credit Cards: None
Specialities: *Helleborus* & *Galanthus*.
Map Ref: N, D2

NRib   Ribblesdale Nurseries 🖻 🏠 €
Newsham Hall Lane, Woodplumpton, Preston, Lancashire PR4 0AS
☎ (01772) 863081
Email: ribblesdale99@hotmail.com
Contact: James Hart
Opening Times: 0900-1730 daily. 0900-1900 Thu Apr-Jul. Closed Mon Aug-Easter.
Credit Cards: Visa, MasterCard, Delta, Switch
Specialities: Trees, shrubs & perennials. Conifers, hedging, alpines, fruit, climbers, herbs, aquatics, ferns & conservatory plants.
Map Ref: N, D1
OS Grid Ref: SD515351

NRob   W Robinson & Sons Ltd 🖻 ✉ EU 🖻 €
Sunny Bank, Forton, Nr Preston, Lancashire PR3 0BN
☎ (01524) 791210
Fax: (01524) 791933
Email: info@mammothonion.co.uk
Website: www.mammothonion.co.uk
Contact: Miss Robinson
Opening Times: 0900-1700 7 days Mar-Jun, 0800-1700 Mon-Fri Jul-Feb.
Min Mail Order UK: No minimum charge
Min Mail Order EU: Nmc
Cat. Cost: Free
Credit Cards: Visa, Access, American Express, Switch
Specialities: Mammoth vegetable seed. Onions, leeks, tomatoes & beans. Range of vegetable plants in the spring.

NRog   R V Roger Ltd 🖻 ✉ EU 🖻
The Nurseries, Malton Road (A169), Pickering. North Yorkshire YO18 7HG
☎ (01751) 472226
Fax: (01751) 476749
Email: ian@clivia.demon.co.uk
Website: www.ian@clivia.demon.co.uk
Contact: I M Roger, G Dawson, S Murfitt, N Perkins
Opening Times: 0900-1700 Mon-Sat, 1300-1700 Sun. Closed 25th Dec-2nd Jan.
Min Mail Order UK: No minimum charge
Min Mail Order EU: Nmc
Cat. Cost: £1.50
Credit Cards: Visa, Access, Switch, MasterCard
Specialities: General list, hardy in north of England.
Map Ref: N, C3
OS Grid Ref: SE801827

NRya   Ryal Nursery 🖻 ✉ EU 🏠
East Farm Cottage, Ryal, Northumberland NE20 0SA
☎ (01661) 886562
Fax: (01661) 886918
Email: alpines@ryal.freeserve.co.uk
Contact: R F Hadden
Opening Times: Mar-Jul 1300-1600 Mon-Tue but please phone first, 1000-1600 Sun & other times by appt.
Min Mail Order UK: £5.00 + p&p
Min Mail Order EU: £5.00 + p&p
Cat. Cost: Sae
Credit Cards: None
Specialities: Alpine & woodland plants.
Map Ref: N, B2
OS Grid Ref: NZ015744

NSco   Scott's Wildflowers 🖻 ✉ UK
Swallow Hill Barn, 31 Common Side, Distington, Workington, Cumbria CA14 4PU
☎ (01946) 830486
Email: wildflowers@btinternet.com
Website: www.scottswildflowers.co.uk
Contact: Ted Scott
Opening Times: 1000-1600 Mar-Oct, 1130-1500 Nov-Feb, 7 days.
Min Mail Order UK: £6.00 + p&p
Cat. Cost: 2 x 1st class
Credit Cards:
Specialities: Native British wildflowers.
Map Ref: N, C1

NShi SHIRLEY'S PLANTS ⊠ UK ♐
6 Sandheys Drive, Church Town, Southport,
Merseyside PR9 9PQ
☎ (01704) 213048
Website: www.stbegonias.com
Contact: Shirley & Terry Tasker
Opening Times: By appt. only.
Min Mail Order UK: No minimum charge
Cat. Cost: 2 x 1st class
Credit Cards: None
Specialities: National Collection of *Begonia*
species & hybrids.
Map Ref: N, D1
OS Grid Ref: SD355183

NSla SLACK TOP ALPINES ▣ ⊠ UK ♐ €
Hebden Bridge, West Yorkshire HX7 7HA
☎ (01422) 845348
Contact: M R or R Mitchell
Opening Times: 1000-1700 Wed-Sun &
B/hol Mons 1st Mar-31st Oct.
Min Mail Order UK: £10.00
Cat. Cost: Sae
Credit Cards: None
Specialities: Alpine & rockery plants. *Gentiana,
Saxifraga, Primulas, Hepatica* & *Pulsatilla.*
Map Ref: N, D2
OS Grid Ref: SD977286

NSpr SPRINGWOOD PLEIONES ⊠ EU ♐
35 Heathfield, Leeds, West Yorkshire LS16 7AB
☎ (0113) 261 1781
Email: ken@pleiones.com
Website: www.pleiones.com
Contact: Ken Redshaw
Opening Times: By appt. only.
Min Mail Order UK: £3.00 + p&p
Min Mail Order EU: £3.00 + p&p
Cat. Cost: 1 x 1st class
Credit Cards: None
Specialities: *Pleione.*
Map Ref: N, D2
OS Grid Ref: SE265400

NSti STILLINGFLEET LODGE
NURSERIES ⊠ UK
Stillingfleet, North Yorkshire YO19 6HP
☎ (01904) 728506
Fax: (01904) 728506
Email: vanessa.cook@still-lodge.freeserve.co.uk
Website: www.stillingfleetlodgenurseries.co.uk
Contact: Vanessa Cook
Opening Times: 1000-1600 Tue Wed Fri &
Sat 1st Apr-18th Oct.
Min Mail Order UK: No minimum charge*
Cat. Cost: 8 x 2nd class

Credit Cards: None
Specialities: Foliage & unusual perennials.
Hardy *Geranium, Pulmonaria*, variegated
plants & grasses. National Collection of
Pulmonaria.
*Note: mail order Nov-mid Mar only.
Map Ref: N, C2

NTay TAYLORS NURSERIES ⊠ UK ♐ ♦
Sutton Road, Sutton, Doncaster,
South Yorkshire DN6 9JZ
☎ (01302) 700716
Fax: (01302) 708415
Email: tayclem@easicom.com
Contact: Julie Taylor
Opening Times: 0900-1700 daily. Closed
Xmas & Boxing Day & New Year's Day.
Min Mail Order UK: 1 plant + p&p
Cat. Cost: 6 x 1st class
Credit Cards: Visa, Access, MasterCard,
Delta, Switch, Solo
Specialities: *Clematis* (over 300 varieties).
Map Ref: N, D2

NTHB TAVISTOCK HERB NURSERY ▣ ⊠ UK ♐
Tavistock, Preston Old Road, Clifton,
Lancashire PR4 0ZA
☎ (01772) 683505
Fax: (01772) 683505
Email: tavistockherbs@themail.co.uk
Contact: Mrs C Jones
Opening Times: By appt. only.
Min Mail Order UK: No minimum charge
Cat. Cost: 2 x 1st class stamps
Credit Cards: None
Specialities: Herbs. *Mentha* & *Thymus*
species. Note: main nursery at Monteagle
Drive, Hornby, Nr. Lancaster.
Map Ref: N, D1

NVic THE VICARAGE GARDEN ⊠ EU
Carrington, Urmston, Manchester M31 4AG
☎ (0161) 775 2750
Fax: (0161) 775 3679
Email: info@vicaragebotanicalgardens.co.uk
Website: www.vicaragebotanicalgardens.co.uk
Contact: Paul Haine
Opening Times: 0900-1700 Mon-Sat, closed
Thu. 1000-1630 Sun all year.
Min Mail Order UK: £10.00 + p&p
Min Mail Order EU: £25.00 + p&p

KEY		
⊠ Mail order to UK or EU	♐ Delivers to shows	
▣ Exports beyond EU	€ Euro accepted	
▣ Also supplies Wholesale	♦ See Display advertisement	

Cat. Cost: 5 x 1st class or 2 x 2nd class for list
Credit Cards: Visa, MasterCard
Specialities: Herbaceous, alpines, grasses, ferns. Free admission to 7 acre gardens.
Map Ref: N, D2
OS Grid Ref: SJ729926

NVne   THE VINE HOUSE 🖼✉ UK 🛉
3 Elm Street, Skelmanthorpe, Huddersfield, West Yorkshire HD8 9BH
☎ (01484) 865964
Email: sales@thevinehouse.co.uk
Website: www.thevinehouse.co.uk
Contact: Stuart Smith
Opening Times: Visitors by arrangement.
Min Mail Order UK: No minimum charge
Cat. Cost: Large Sae
Credit Cards: None
Specialities: *Vitis*, mostly *Vitis vinifera*.
Map Ref: N, D2

NWCA   WHITE COTTAGE ALPINES ✉ EU 🛉€
Sunnyside Nurseries, Hornsea Road, Sigglesthorne, East Yorkshire HU11 5QL
☎ (01964) 542692
Fax: (01964) 542692
Email: NWCA@whitecottalpines.demon.co.uk
Website: www.whitecottalpines.demon.co.uk
Contact: Sally E Cummins
Opening Times: 1000-1700 (or dusk) Thu-Sun & B/hol Mon 1 Mar-30 Sep. If travelling far, please phone first.
Min Mail Order UK: £7.50 + p&p
Min Mail Order EU: £15.00 + p&p
Cat. Cost: 4 x 1st class
Credit Cards: Visa, MasterCard, Switch, JCB
Specialities: Alpines & rock plants. 500+ species incl. American, dwarf *Salix* & *Helichrysum*. Note: euro payments cash only.
Map Ref: N, C3

NWea   WEASDALE NURSERIES ✉ EU €
Newbiggin-on-Lune, Kirkby Stephen, Cumbria CA17 4LX
☎ (01539) 623246
Fax: (01539) 623277
Email: sales@weasdale.com
Website: www.weasdale.com
Contact: Andrew Forsyth
Opening Times: 0830-1730 Mon-Fri. Closed w/ends, B/hols, Xmas-New Year.
Min Mail Order UK: No minimum charge
Min Mail Order EU: Nmc
Cat. Cost: £1.50 or 6 x 1st class, £2 by credit/debit card
Credit Cards: Visa, MasterCard, Switch,

Delta, Access, Solo
Specialities: Hardy forest trees, hedging, broadleaved & conifers. Specimen trees & shrubs grown at 850 feet. Mail order a speciality.
*Note: mail order Nov-Apr only.
Map Ref: N, C1

NWit   D S WITTON ✉ UK
26 Casson Drive, Harthill, Sheffield, South Yorkshire S26 7WA
☎ (01909) 771366
Fax: (01909) 771366
Email: donshardyeuphorbias@btopenworld.com
Website: www.donshardyeuphorbias.btinternet.co.uk
Contact: Don Witton
Opening Times: By appt. only.
Min Mail Order UK: No minimum charge*
Cat. Cost: 1 x 1st class + sae
Credit Cards:
Specialities: National Collection of hardy *Euphorbia*. Over 130 varieties.
*Note: mail order *Euphorbia* seed only.
Map Ref: N, D2
OS Grid Ref: SK494812

NWoo   WOODLANDS COTTAGE NURSERY
Summerbridge Harrogate N Yorks HG3 4BT
☎ (01423) 780765
Email: annstark@btinternet.com
Website: www.woodlandscottagegarden.co.uk
Contact: Mrs Ann Stark
Opening Times: By appt. only, mid Mar-mid Sep.
Cat. Cost: 2 x 1st class
Credit Cards: None
Specialities: Herbs, plants for shade & hardy perennials.
Map Ref: N, C2
OS Grid Ref: SE195631

NYoL   YORKSHIRE LAVENDER ✉ UK
The Yorkshire Lavender Farm, Terrington, York, North Yorkshire YO60 6QB
☎ (01653) 648430, (01653) 648008
Fax: (01653) 648430
Email: albayork@netscapeonline.co.uk
Website: www.lavenderworld.com
Contact: Nigel W B Goodwill
Opening Times: 1030-1630 7 days Easter-30th Sep.
Min Mail Order UK: £10.00
Cat. Cost: None issued
Credit Cards: None

Specialities: *Lavandula*. Herbs.
Map Ref: N, C3

NZep   ZEPHYRWUDE IRISES ⊠ EU
48 Blacker Lane, Crigglestone, Wakefield,
West Yorkshire WF4 3EW
☎ (01924) 252101, mobile 07813 978165
Contact: Richard L Brook
Opening Times: Mail order only. Viewing
by appt. 0900-dusk most days May-early
June, peak late May. Phone 0900-2300.
Min Mail Order UK: £15.00 + p&p
Min Mail Order EU: £15.00 + p&p
Cat. Cost: 1 x 1st class
Credit Cards: None
Specialities: Bearded *Iris*, 1970s-80s hybrids
only. Mainly 12in. dwarf & intermediate, a
few tall. Catalogue available Apr-Sep.
Delivery Aug-Oct only.
Map Ref: N, D2
OS Grid Ref: SE302161

SOUTHERN

SAdn   ASHDOWN FOREST GARDEN CENTRE
& NURSERY
Duddleswell, Ashdown Forest, Nr Uckfield,
East Sussex TN22 3JP
☎ (01825) 712300
Fax: (01825) 712175
Contact: Victoria Tolton
Opening Times: 0900-1730 winter,
0900-1900 summer.
Credit Cards: all major credit/debit cards
Specialities: *Lavandula*.
Map Ref: S, C4

SAft   AFTON PARK NURSERY ń
Newport Road, Afton, Freshwater,
Isle of Wight PO40 9XR
☎ (01983) 755774, mobile 09665 43031
Email: Chris@skyroots.demon.co.uk
Website: www.skyroots.demon.co.uk
Contact: Chris Barnes
Opening Times: 0930-1700 7 days Mar-end
Oct. Winter, please phone first.
Cat. Cost: 4 x 1st class
Credit Cards: Visa, MasterCard
Specialities: Wide general range, emphasis on
unusual perennials, grasses, coastal shrubs &
plants for Mediterranean gardens.
Map Ref: S, D2

SAga   AGAR'S NURSERY €
Agars Lane, Hordle, Lymington,
Hampshire SO41 0FL

☎ (01590) 683703
Contact: Diana Tombs, Debbie Ursell
Opening Times: 1000-1700 Fri-Wed Mar-
Oct, 1000-1600 Fri-Wed Nov, Dec & Feb.
Cat. Cost: None issued
Credit Cards: None
Specialities: *Penstemon* & *Salvia*. Also wide
range of hardy plants incl. shrubs, climbers
& herbaceous.
Map Ref: S, D2

SAll   ALLWOOD BROS ⊠ EU
London Road, Hassocks,
West Sussex BN6 9NB
☎ (01273) 844229
Fax: (01273) 846022
Contact: David James
Opening Times: 0900-1600 Mon-Fri.
Min Mail Order UK: No minimum charge*
Min Mail Order EU: Nmc
Cat. Cost: 2 x 1st class
Credit Cards: Access, Visa, MasterCard,
Switch
Specialities: *Dianthus* incl. hardy border
carnations, pinks, perpetual & *Allwoodii*,
some available as seed.
*Note: exports seed only.
Map Ref: S, D4

SAPC   ARCHITECTURAL PLANTS
(CHICHESTER) LTD 🖼 ⊠ EU 🖾 ń € ◆
Lidsey Road Nursery, Westergate,
Nr Chichester, West Sussex PO20 6SU
☎ (01243) 545008
Fax: (01243) 545009
Email: enquiries@architecturalplants.com
Website: members.aol.com/gshaw29868/
archplnt.htm, www.architecturalplants.com
Contact: Christine Shaw
Opening Times: 1000-1600 Sun-Fri all year.
Closed Sat.
Min Mail Order UK: No minimum charge
Min Mail Order EU: £150.00 + p&p
Cat. Cost: Free
Credit Cards: Visa, Access, EuroCard,
Switch, Delta, Electron, JCB, MasterCard,
American Express
Specialities: Architectural plants & hardy
exotics esp. evergreen broadleaved trees &
seaside exotics, trees & spiky plants,
yuccas/agaves.

KEY		
⊠ Mail order to UK or EU	ń Delivers to shows	
🖾 Exports beyond EU	€ Euro accepted	
🖼 Also supplies Wholesale	◆ See Display advertisement	

Note: second nursery near Horsham, Code SArc.
Map Ref: S, D3

SApp APPLE COURT ⊠ EU € ◆
Hordle Lane, Hordle, Lymington,
Hampshire SO41 0HU
☎ (01590) 642130
Fax: (01590) 644220
Email: applecourt@btinternet.com
Website: www.applecourt.com
Contact: Diana Grenfell, Roger Grounds, Jenny.
Opening Times: 1000-1700 (closed 1300-1400) daily excl. Wed Mar-Sep. Closed Oct-Feb.
Min Mail Order UK: £15.00 + p&p
Min Mail Order EU: £50.00 + p&p
Cat. Cost: 4 x 1st class
Credit Cards: None
Specialities: *Hosta*, grasses, ferns, *Hemerocallis*. National Collection of *Woodwardia, Rohdea,* & *Hosta*.
Map Ref: S, D2

SApu APULDRAM ROSES ⊠ EU €
Apuldram Lane, Dell Quay Chichester,
West Sussex PO20 7EF
☎ (01243) 785769
Fax: (01243) 536973
Email: enquiries@apuldramroses.co.uk
Website: www.apuldramroses.co.uk
Contact: Mrs Sawday
Opening Times: Not open.
Min Mail Order UK: £4.50 + p&p*
Min Mail Order EU: £4.50 + p&p
Cat. Cost: Free
Credit Cards: Switch, MasterCard, Visa, Delta, Solo
Specialities: Roses.
*Note: mail order Nov-Mar.

SArc ARCHITECTURAL
PLANTS ⊠ EU ⩗ ⋔ € ◆
Cooks Farm, Nuthurst, Horsham,
West Sussex RH13 6LH
☎ (01403) 891772
Fax: (01403) 891056
Email: enquiries@architecturalplants.com
Website: www.architecturalplants.com
Contact: Sarah Chandler & Rachel Hannibal
Opening Times: 0900-1700 Mon-Sat, closed Sun.
Min Mail Order UK: No minimum charge
Min Mail Order EU: £150.00 + p&p
Cat. Cost: Free
Credit Cards: American Express, Access,

EuroCard, Switch, Delta, Electron, JCB, Visa
Specialities: Architectural plants & hardy exotics. Note: second nursery near Chichester, code SAPC.
Map Ref: S, C3

SAsh ASHENDEN NURSERY ⋔
Cranbrook Road, Benenden Cranbrook,
Kent TN17 4ET
☎ (01580) 241792
Fax: (01580) 241792
Contact: Kevin McGarry
Opening Times: By appt. Please phone.
Cat. Cost: 1 x 1st class Sae
Credit Cards: None
Specialities: Rock garden plants, perennials & ornamental grasses.
Map Ref: S, C5

SAWi ANTHONY ARCHER-WILLS
LTD ⩗ ⊠ UK ⋔
Broadford Bridge Road, West Chiltington,
West Sussex RH20 2LF
☎ (01798) 813204
Fax: (01798) 815080
Email: aawltd.fsnet.co.uk
Contact: Anthony Archer-Wills
Opening Times: 0900-1600. Please phone first.
Min Mail Order UK: £15.00 + p&p
Cat. Cost: £1.00 + 2 x 2nd class
Credit Cards: None
Specialities: Ponds, lakes & water garden plants.

SBai STEVEN BAILEY LTD ⩗ ⊠ EU ⋔
Silver Street, Sway, Lymington,
Hampshire SO41 6ZA
☎ (01590) 682227
Fax: (01590) 683765
Contact: Fiona Whittles
Opening Times: 1000-1300 & 1400-1630 Mon-Fri all year. 1000-1300 & 1400-1600 Sat Mar-Jun excl. B/hols.
Min Mail Order UK: Quote
Min Mail Order EU: Quote
Cat. Cost: 2 x 2nd class
Credit Cards: Visa, MasterCard, Switch
Specialities: Carnations, pinks, *Alstroemeria* & penstemons.
Map Ref: S, D2

SBdl BROGDALE HORTICULTURAL
TRUST ⩗ ⊠ EU ⩗ €
Brogdale Orchards, Faversham,
Kent ME13 8XZ

☎ (01795) 591491
Fax: (01795) 531710
Contact: Nick Wiles
Opening Times:
Min Mail Order UK: No minimum charge
Min Mail Order EU: Nmc
Cat. Cost: £4.95
Credit Cards: Visa, MasterCard, Switch
Specialities: Over 5000 fruit varieties, most of which can be propagated to order. Holders of several National Collections of fruit.
Map Ref: S, C5

SBHF BREWERS HALL FARM COTTAGE PLANTS ⊠ EU ☒ ♠ €
Tonbridge Road, Mereworth,
Kent ME18 5JD
☎ (01622) 815523
Email: watergardenin4U@aol.com
Website: www.pondplants-direct.co.uk
Contact: Mrs A Sleeman
Opening Times: Phone lines open 0900-2100.
Min Mail Order UK: No minimum charge
Min Mail Order EU: Nmc
Cat. Cost: Available on web only.
Credit Cards: Visa, MasterCard
Specialities: Water lilies, aquatic & moisture-loving plants.

SBir BIRCHFLEET NURSERY ☒
Nyewood, Petersfield,
Hampshire GU31 5JQ
☎ (01730) 821636
Fax: (01730) 821636
Email: gammoak@aol.com
Contact: John & Daphne Gammon
Opening Times: By appt. only. Please phone.
Cat. Cost: 2 x 1st class
Credit Cards: None
Specialities: Oaks. Beech. National Collection of *Liquidambar*.
Map Ref: S, C3

SBla BLACKTHORN NURSERY €
Kilmeston, Alresford, Hampshire SO24 0NL
☎ (01962) 771796
Fax: (01962) 771071
Contact: A R & S B White, M Ellis
Opening Times: 0900-1700 Fri & Sat only 1st Mar-29th Jun 2002. 0900-1700 Fri & Sat only 7th Mar-30th Jun & 5th-27th Sep 2003. Hellebore Days 0900-1600 Fri 14th & Sat 15th Feb 2003.
Cat. Cost: Plant list for 3 x 1st class
Credit Cards: None

Specialities: Choice perennials & alpines, esp. *Daphne, Epimedium, Helleborus* & *Hepatica.*
Map Ref: S, C2

SBod BODIAM NURSERY
Cowfield Cottage, Bodiam, Robertsbridge, East Sussex TN32 5RA
☎ (01580) 830811, mobile 07881 578713
Fax: (01424) 870832
Email: bodiam@sedlescombe.12.freeserve.co.uk
Contact: Tracey Pearman
Opening Times: 0900-1700 or by appt.
Cat. Cost: 4 x 1st class
Credit Cards: Visa, MasterCard, Solo, JCB
Specialities: Herbaceous perennials, grasses, conifers, *Camellia* & climbers.
Map Ref: S, C5

SBra J BRADSHAW & SON ☒ ⊠ UK ♠ ◆
Busheyfield Nursery, Herne, Herne Bay, Kent CT6 7LJ
☎ (01227) 375415
Fax: (01227) 375415
Contact: D J Bradshaw & Martin Bradshaw
Opening Times: 1000-1700 Tue-Sat 1st Mar-31st Oct & B/hol Mons. Other times by appt. only.
Min Mail Order UK: 2 plants + p&p
Cat. Cost: Sae + 2 x 1st class
Credit Cards: None
Specialities: *Clematis, Lonicera,* other climbers & wall shrubs.
Map Ref: S, C5
OS Grid Ref: TR174646

SBri BRICKWALL COTTAGE NURSERY
1 Brickwall Cottages, Frittenden, Cranbrook Kent TN17 2DH
☎ (01580) 852425
Contact: Sue Martin
Opening Times: 1000-1700 Sun 14th Apr 2002, Sun 2nd Jun 2002, Sun 8th Sep 2002 or by appt.
Cat. Cost: 2 x 1st class
Credit Cards: None
Specialities: Hardy perennials. Stock limited in quantity. *Geum, Potentilla,* herbaceous.
Map Ref: S, C5
OS Grid Ref: TQ815410

S

SBrk BROOKSIDE NURSERY 🔲⊠ EU 🔲ń €
Elderberry Farm, Bognor Road,
Rowhook, Horsham,
West Sussex RH12 3PS
☎ (01403) 790996
Fax: (01403) 790195
Email: alanbutler1@compuserve.com
Website: www.brookside-nursery.com
Contact: A J Butler
Opening Times: 1000-1700 Thu-Sun &
B/hol Mons. Please phone first.
Min Mail Order UK: No minimum charge
Min Mail Order EU: Nmc
Cat. Cost: 1 x 1st class
Credit Cards: Visa, MasterCard, Switch
Specialities: Cacti & succulent plants.
National Collection of *Sansevieria*.
Map Ref: S, C3

S

SBrw BROADWATER PLANTS
(Office) Coblands Nursery,
Trench Road, Tonbridge,
Kent TN10 3HQ
☎ (01892) 534760
Fax: (01892) 534760
Email: broadwater@coblands.co.uk
Website: www.coblands.co.uk,
www.broadwaterplants.co.uk
Contact: John Moaby
Opening Times: 0900-1630 Mon-Fri,
0900-1600 Sat 1st Mar-30th Jun.
Cat. Cost: 3 x 1st class
Credit Cards: MasterCard, Visa
Specialities: *Rhododendron*, *Camellia* &
ericaceous. Field grown *Rhododendron* (hardy
hybrids) specimen sizes. Limited stocks of
some varieties. Please check before travelling.
Note: nursery is at Fairview Lane, Tunbridge
Wells.
Map Ref: S, C4

**SCam CAMELLIA GROVE
NURSERY** 🔲⊠ EU 🔲ń €
Market Garden, Lower Beeding,
West Sussex RH13 6PX
☎ (01403) 891143
Fax: (01403) 891336
Email: rhs20@camellia-grove.com
Website: www.camellia-grove.com
Contact: Chris Loder
Opening Times: 7 days, by appt. only. This
is so we can give you our undivided
attention.
Min Mail Order UK: No minimum charge
Min Mail Order EU: £100.00 +p&p
Cat. Cost: 2 x 1st class

Specialities: Camellias & azaleas.
Map Ref: S, C3

SChr JOHN CHURCHER ⊠ EU 🔲
47 Grove Avenue, Portchester, Fareham,
Hampshire PO16 9EZ
☎ (023) 9232 6740
Email: John@plants-palms.freeserve.co.uk
Contact: John Churcher
Opening Times: By appt. only. Please phone.
Min Mail Order UK: No minimum charge
Min Mail Order EU: Nmc
Cat. Cost: 4 x 1st class
Credit Cards: None
Specialities: Hardy *Opuntia*, *Agave*, *Aloe*,
succulents, palms, tree ferns, plus small
general range of attractive species, hardy &
half-hardy.
Map Ref: S, D2
OS Grid Ref: SU614047

**SChu CHURCH HILL COTTAGE
GARDENS** ⊠ UK €
Charing Heath, Ashford, Kent TN27 0BU
☎ (01233) 712522
Fax: (01233) 712522
Contact: Mr M & J & Mrs M Metianu
Opening Times: 1000-1700 1st Feb-30th Nov
Tue-Sun & B/hol Mons. Other times by appt.
Min Mail Order UK: £10.00 + p&p
Cat. Cost: 4 x 1st class
Credit Cards: None
Specialities: Unusual hardy plants, *Dianthus*,
Hosta, ferns & *Viola*, alpines & shrubs.
Map Ref: S, C5

SCit THE CITRUS CENTRE 🔲⊠ EU
West Mare Lane, Marehill, Pulborough,
West Sussex RH20 2EA
☎ (01798) 872786
Fax: (01798) 874880
Email: enquiries@citruscentre.co.uk
Website: www.citruscentre.co.uk
Contact: Amanda & Chris Dennis
Opening Times: 0930-1730 Wed-Sun.
Phone for Xmas & B/hol opening times.
Min Mail Order UK: No minimum charge
Min Mail Order EU: Nmc
Cat. Cost: Sae
Credit Cards: Visa, Access
Specialities: *Citrus* & *Citrus* relatives.
Map Ref: S, D3

SCko COOKOO BOX NURSERY 🔲⊠ EU 🔲ń
Longfield, 63 Charlesford Avenue,
Kingswood, Maidstone, Kent ME17 3PH

☎ (01622) 844866
Contact: Mr P Cook
Opening Times: By appt. only.
Min Mail Order UK: No minimum charge
Min Mail Order EU: Nmc
Cat. Cost: 2 x 1st class
Credit Cards: None
Specialities: A family run nursery with an increasing range of grasses, cottage garden perennials, *Salvia, Phlox, Hosta, Penstemon* (some unusual) & spring, summer & autumn bedding.
Map Ref: S, C5

SCnR **COLIN ROBERTS** ⊠ UK
Tragumna, Morgay Wood Lane, Three Oaks, Guestling, East Sussex TN35 4NF
☎ mobile 07718 029909
Fax: (01424) 814308
Contact: Colin Roberts
Opening Times: Not open.
Min Mail Order UK: £20.00
Cat. Cost: 2 x 1st class
Credit Cards: None
Specialities: Dwarf bulbs & woodland plants incl. many rare & unusual, in small numbers.

SCog **COGHURST NURSERY** 🖪⊠ EU 🛉 €
Ivy House Lane, Near Three Oaks, Hastings, East Sussex TN35 4NP
☎ (01424) 756228
Fax: (01424) 428944
Email: rotherview@btinternet.com
Contact: R Bates & W Bates
Opening Times: 0930-1600 7 days.
Min Mail Order UK: No minimum charge
Min Mail Order EU: Nmc
Cat. Cost: 4 x 1st class
Credit Cards: all major credit/debit cards
Specialities: *Camellia.* Note: nursery is on the same site as Rotherview Nursery.
Map Ref: S, D5

SCon **CONNOISSEURS' CACTI** 🖪⊠ EU 🖪 €
(Office) 51 Chelsfield Lane, Orpington, Kent BR5 4HG
☎ (01689) 837781
Email: Jp@connoisseurs-cacti.fsnet.co.uk
Contact: John Pilbeam
Opening Times: 1030-1330 but please phone first.
Min Mail Order UK: No minimum charge
Min Mail Order EU: Nmc
Cat. Cost: Sae or IRC
Credit Cards: None
Specialities: *Mammillaria, Sulcorebutia,*

Gymnocalycium, Rebutia, Haworthia, Lithops. Note: no phytosanitary certificate supplied with mail order beyond EC. Nursery at Woodlands Farm, Shire Lane, Nr Farnborough, Kent.

SCoo **COOLING'S NURSERIES LTD**
Rushmore Hill, Knockholt, Sevenoaks, Kent TN14 7NN
☎ (01959) 532269
Fax: (01959) 534092
Email: Plantfinder@coolings.co.uk
Website: www.coolings.co.uk
Contact: Mark Hooker & Gary Carvosso
Opening Times: 0900-1700 Mon-Sat & 1000-1630 Sun.
Cat. Cost: None issued
Credit Cards: Visa, Access, Switch, Electron, Delta, MasterCard
Specialities: Large range of perennials, conifers & bedding plants. Some unusual shrubs.
Map Ref: S, C4

SCou **COOMBLAND GARDENS** ⊠ EU 🖪
Coombland, Coneyhurst, Billingshurst, West Sussex RH14 9DG
☎ (01403) 741727   **Fax:** (01403) 741079
Email: coombland@lineone.net
Website: www.coombland.co.uk
Contact: David Browne
Opening Times: 1400-1600 Mon-Fri Mar-end Oct. B/hols & other times by appt. only.
Min Mail Order UK: £20.00 + p&p
Min Mail Order EU: 8 plants + p&p*
Cat. Cost: 5 x 1st class
Credit Cards: Visa, MasterCard, Delta
Specialities: National Collection of Hardy *Geranium.* Choice herbaceous. Seeds.
*Note: hardy geraniums only to EU.
Map Ref: S, C3

SCrf **CROFTERS NURSERIES** €
Church Hill, Charing Heath, Nr Ashford, Kent TN27 0BU
☎ (01233) 712798
Fax: (01233) 712798
Email: croftersch@hotmail.com
Contact: John & Sue Webb
Opening Times: 1000-1700. Closed Sun-Tue. Please check first.

S

Cat. Cost: 3 x 1st class
Credit Cards: None
Specialities: Fruit, ornamental trees &
conifers. Old apple varieties. Small number
of *Prunus serrula* with grafted ornamental
heads.
Map Ref: S, C5

SCro   CROFTWAY NURSERY 🔲 ⊠ EU 𝗻 €
Yapton Road, Barnham. Bognor Regis.
West Sussex PO22 0BH
☎ (01243) 552121
Fax: (01243) 552125
Email: sales@croftway.co.uk
Website: www.croftway.co.uk
Contact: Graham Spencer
Opening Times: 0900-1700 Mon-Sat, 1000-
1600 Sun. Closed 1st Dec-28th Feb except
by appt.
Min Mail Order UK: No minimum charge
Min Mail Order EU: Nmc
Cat. Cost: Free
Credit Cards: Visa, Access, Switch, American
Express, MasterCard
Specialities: Wide general range, emphasis on
perennials. Specialists in *Iris* & hardy
Geranium.
Map Ref: S, D3

SDay   A LA CARTE DAYLILIES ⊠ EU € ◆
Little Hermitage, St Catherine's Down, Nr
Ventnor, Isle of Wight PO38 2PD
☎ (01983) 730512
Email: andy@ukdaylilies.com
Website: www.ukdaylilies.com
Contact: Jan & Andy Wyers
Opening Times: By appt. only.
Min Mail Order UK: No minimum charge
Min Mail Order EU: Nmc
Cat. Cost: 3 x 1st class
Credit Cards: None
Specialities: *Hemerocallis.* National
Collections of Miniature & Small Flowered
Hemerocallis & Large Flowered *Hemerocallis*
(post-1960 award-winning cultivars).
Map Ref: S, D2

SDea   DEACON'S NURSERY 🔲 ⊠ EU 🗹 € ◆
Moor View, Godshill,
Isle of Wight PO38 3HW
☎ (01983) 840750 (24 hrs), (01983) 522243
Fax: (01983) 523575
Email: deacons.nursery@btopenworld.com
Website: www.deaconsnurseryfruits.co.uk
Contact: G D & B H W Deacon
Opening Times: 0800-1600 Mon-Fri May-

Sep, 0800-1700 Mon-Fri 0800-1200 Sat
Oct-Apr.
Min Mail Order UK: No minimum charge
Min Mail Order EU: Nmc
Cat. Cost: Free
Credit Cards: Visa, Access, Switch
Specialities: Over 300 varieties of apple, old
& new, pears, plums, gages, damsons,
cherries. Modern soft fruit, grapes, hops,
nuts & family trees.
Map Ref: S, D2

SDeJ   DE JAGER & SONS 🔲 ⊠ EU 🗹
The Nurseries, Marden, Kent TN12 9BP
☎ (01622) 831235
Fax: (01622) 832416
Email: PdeJag@aol.com
Contact: Mrs B Pavey
Opening Times: 0900-1700 Mon-Fri
Min Mail Order UK: £15.00 + p&p
Min Mail Order EU: £15.00 + p&p
Cat. Cost: Free
Credit Cards: Visa, Access
Specialities: Wide general range esp. bulbs.
Lilium, Tulipa, Narcissus species &
miscellaneous. Large range of perennials.
Map Ref: S, C4

SDes   DESIGNER PLANTS 🔲
Back Lane, Ightham, Sevenoaks,
Kent TN15 9AU
☎ (01732) 885700
Fax: (01732) 882497
Email: dp@coblands.co.uk
Website: www.plants4designers.co.uk
Contact: Nigel Gibson
Opening Times: 0900-1600 Mon-Fri. Sat by
appt.
Cat. Cost: W/Sale Cat. only
Credit Cards: Visa, MasterCard
Specialities: General range esp. herbaceous,
common & unusual, many in large
quantities. Grasses & ferns.
Map Ref: S, C4

SDix   GREAT DIXTER NURSERIES ⊠ EU
Northiam, Rye, East Sussex TN31 6PH
☎ (01797) 253107
Fax: (01797) 252879
Email: nursery@greatdixter.co.uk
Website: www.greatdixter.co.uk
Contact: K Leighton
Opening Times: 0900-1230 & 1330-1700
Mon-Fri, 0900-1200 Sat all year. Also 1400-
1700 Sat, Sun & B/hols Apr-Oct.
Min Mail Order UK: £15.00 + p&p

Min Mail Order EU: £15.00 + p&p
Cat. Cost: 4 x 1st class
Credit Cards: Access, Switch, Visa,
MasterCard, Solo, Delta
Specialities: *Clematis*, shrubs and plants.
Gardens open.
Note: plants dispatched Sep-Mar only.
Map Ref: S, C5

SDow DOWNDERRY NURSERY ▣ ⊠ EU ▣ ∩ €
Pillar Box Lane, Hadlow, Nr Tonbridge,
Kent TN11 9SW
☎ (01732) 810081
Fax: (01732) 811398
Email: simon@downderry-nursery.co.uk
Website: www.downderry-nursery.co.uk
Contact: Dr S J Charlesworth
Opening Times: 1000-1700 1st May-31 Oct
& by appt.
Min Mail Order UK: No minimum charge
Min Mail Order EU: Nmc
Cat. Cost: 3 x 1st class
Credit Cards: Delta, MasterCard, Switch, Visa
Specialties: National Collections of
Lavandula and *Rosmarinus*.
Map Ref: S, C4

SDry DRYSDALE GARDEN EXOTICS ⊠ EU
Bowerwood Road, Fordingbridge,
Hampshire SP6 1BN
☎ (01425) 653010
Contact: David Crampton
Opening Times: 0930-1730 Wed-Fri,
1000-1730 Sun. Closed 24th Dec-2nd Jan
inclusive.
Min Mail Order UK: £10.00 + p&p
Min Mail Order EU: £15.00 + p&p
Cat. Cost: 3 x 1st class
Credit Cards: None
Specialities: Plants for exotic & foliage effect.
Plants for Mediterranean gardens. National
Collection of Bamboos.
Map Ref: S, D1

SDys DYSONS NURSERIES ▣ ⊠ UK ∩
Great Comp Garden, Platt, Sevenoaks,
Kent TN15 8QS
☎ (01732) 886154
Email: william.dyson@ukgateway.net
Website: www.greatcomp.co.uk
Contact: William T Dyson
Opening Times: 1100-1800 7 days
1st Apr-31st Oct. Other times by appt.
Min Mail Order UK: £9.00 + p&p
Cat. Cost: 4 x 1st class
Credit Cards: None

Specialities: Wide range of choice & unusual
plants especially *Salvia*, *Sempervivum* &
Crocosmia.
Map Ref: S, C4

SEND EAST NORTHDOWN FARM ▣ ⊠ UK ◆
Margate, Kent CT9 3TS
☎ (01843) 862060
Fax: (01843) 860206
Email: friend.northdown@ukonline.co.uk
Website: www.botanyplants.co.uk
Contact: Louise & William Friend
Opening Times: 0900-1700 Mon-Sat,
1000-1700 Sun all year. Closed Xmas week
& Easter Sun.
Min Mail Order UK: £15.00
Cat. Cost: None issued.
Credit Cards: Visa, Switch, MasterCard
Specialities: Chalk & coast-loving plants.
Map Ref: S, B6

SFai FAIRWEATHER'S GARDEN
CENTRE ▣ ⊠ EU ▣ €
High Street, Beaulieu,
Hampshire SO42 7YB
☎ (01590) 612113
Fax: (01590) 612615
Email: plantdoc@martex.co.uk
Website: www.fairweathers.co.uk
Contact: Christopher Fairweather
Opening Times: 0930-1700 7 days.
Min Mail Order UK: No minimum charge
Min Mail Order EU: Nmc
Cat. Cost: 2 x 1st class
Credit Cards: Visa, MasterCard
Specialities: National Collection of Vireya
Rhododendrons. Our main collection, at
local nursery, can be viewed by appt.
Map Ref: S, D2

SFam FAMILY TREES ⊠ EU ◆
Sandy Lane, Shedfield,
Hampshire SO32 2HQ
☎ (01329) 834812
Contact: Philip House
Opening Times: 0930-1230 Wed & Sat
mid Oct-end May (& Easter Mon).
Min Mail Order UK: No minimum charge
Min Mail Order EU: Nmc
Cat. Cost: Free
Credit Cards: None

S

Specialities: Fruit & ornamental trees. Trained fruit tree specialists: standards; espaliers; cordons. Other trees, old- fashioned & climbing roses, evergreens. Trees, except evergreens, sold bare rooted. Large specimens in pots.
Map Ref: S, D2

SGar   GARDEN PLANTS 🖼️ 🗽
Windy Ridge, Victory Road, St Margarets-at-Cliffe, Dover, Kent CT15 6HF
☎ (01304) 853225
Email:
GardenPlants@GardenPlants-nursery.co.uk
Website: www.GardenPlants-nursery.co.uk
Contact: Teresa Ryder & David Ryder
Opening Times: 1000-1700 (closed Wed).
Cat. Cost: 2 x 1st class + A5 sae
Credit Cards: None
Specialities: Unusual perennials, *Penstemon*, *Salvia* & *Diascia*. Plantsman's garden open to view. Map essential for first visit.
Map Ref: S, C6
OS Grid Ref: TR358464

SGrm   GRIMSDYKE HOUSE 🖼️ ✉️ EU 🗽
12 Southcourt Avenue, Bexhill-on-Sea, East Sussex TN39 3AR
☎ (01424) 221452
Fax: (01424) 221452
Email: bougainvilleaplants@grimsdykehouse. freeserve.co.uk
Website: www.bougainvilleaplants.com
www.bougainvilleaplants.co.uk
Contact: A P Hamilton
Opening Times: 0900-1700 Mon-Fri, 0900-1200 Sat & Sun.
Min Mail Order UK: £6.00
Min Mail Order EU: £6.00
Cat. Cost: 3 x 1st class
Credit Cards: None
Specialities: *Bougainvillea*.
Note: export only express airmail & phyto certificate, all costed individually. Nursery open for pre-arranged collection only.
Map Ref: S, D5

SHar   HARDY'S COTTAGE GARDEN PLANTS 🖼️ ✉️ EU 🗽
Freefolk Priors, Freefolk, Whitchurch, Hampshire RG28 7NJ
☎ (01256) 896533
Fax: (01256) 896572
Email:
hardy@cottagegardenplants.fsnet.co.uk
Website: www.hardys-plants.co.uk
Contact: Rosy Hardy

Opening Times: 1000-1700 7 days 1st Mar-31st Oct.
Min Mail Order UK: No minimum charge
Min Mail Order EU: Nmc
Cat. Cost: 8 x 1st class
Credit Cards: Visa, Access, Electron, Switch, Solo
Specialities: Hardy *Geranium* & other herbaceous both old & new. Collection of *Viola odorata* & Parma violets now available.
Map Ref: S, C2

SHay   HAYWARD'S CARNATIONS 🖼️ ✉️ EU
The Chace Gardens, Stakes Road, Purbrook, Waterlooville, Hampshire PO7 5PL
☎ (023) 9226 3047
Fax: (023) 9226 3047
Contact: A N Hayward
Opening Times: 0930-1700 Mon-Fri.
Min Mail Order UK: £10.00 + p&p
Min Mail Order EU: £50.00 + p&p
Cat. Cost: 1 x 1st class
Credit Cards: None
Specialities: Hardy pinks & border carnations (*Dianthus*). Greenhouse perpetual carnations.
Map Ref: S, D2

SHBN   HIGH BANKS NURSERIES 🖼️ 🗽
Slip Mill Road, Hawkhurst, Kent TN18 5AD
☎ (01580) 754492
Fax: (01580) 754450
Contact: Jeremy Homewood
Opening Times: 0800-1700 (1630 in winter) daily.
Cat. Cost: £1.50 (stamps) + A4 Sae
Credit Cards: Access, Visa, Switch, Delta
Specialities: Wide general range with many unusual plants. Minimum of 250,000 plants on site at any one time. Many unusual plants. Open ground stock limited between Nov and Feb.
Map Ref: S, C5

SHDw   HIGHDOWN NURSERY 🖼️ ✉️ EU 🗽 🗽 €
New Hall Lane, Small Dole, Nr Henfield, West Sussex BN5 9YH
☎ (01273) 492976
Fax: (01273) 492976
Email: highdown.herbs@btinternet.com
Contact: A G & J H Shearing
Opening Times: 0900-1700 7 days.
Min Mail Order UK: £10.00 + p&p
Min Mail Order EU: £10.00 + p&p
Cat. Cost: 3 x 1st class

S

Credit Cards: Visa, MasterCard, Delta, JCB, EuroCard
Specialities: Herbs.
Map Ref: S, D3

SHel   **HELLYER'S GARDEN PLANTS** ⊠ UK ♦
Orchards, off Wallage Lane*, Rowfant, Nr Crawley, West Sussex RH10 4NJ
☎ (01342) 718280
Fax: (01342) 718280
Email: penelope.hellyer@hellyers.co.uk
Website: www.hellyers.co.uk
Contact: Penelope Hellyer
Opening Times: 1000-1700 Wed-Sat Mar-Oct & by prior appt.
Min Mail Order UK: No minimum charge
Cat. Cost: 4 x 1st + A5 Sae (1st class).
Credit Cards: None
Specialities: Hardy plants for sun/shade. Small selection of climbers & shrubs. 100+ varieties of hardy *Geranium*. Some stock in limited quantity; small numbers available through propagation service.
*Note: Wallage Lane is off the B2028 between Crawley Down & Turners Hill.
Map Ref: S, C4
OS Grid Ref: TQ334373

SHFr   **SUE HARTFREE** ⊠ EU
25 Crouch Hill Court, Lower Halstow, Nr Sittingbourne, Kent ME9 7EJ
☎ (01795) 842426
Contact: Sue Hartfree
Opening Times: Any time by appt. Please phone first.
Min Mail Order UK: £15.00 + p&p
Min Mail Order EU: £20.00 + p&p
Cat. Cost: A5 Sae + 4 x 1st class
Credit Cards: None
Specialities: Rare & unusual shrubs & perennials (hardy & tender) incl. *Salvia, Penstemon, Lysimachia* & *Impatiens*. Mature specimens can be seen growing in the garden.
Map Ref: S, C5

SHGC   **HAMBROOKS GROWING CONCERN** ▣ ⊠ EU ▣ ∩
Wangfield Lane, Curdridge, Southampton, Hampshire SO32 2DA
☎ (01489) 780505/797771
Fax: (01489) 785396
Email: steveharding@hambrooks.co.uk
Website: www.hambrooks.co.uk
Contact: Stephen Harding
Opening Times: 0730-1800 Mon-Fri.
Min Mail Order UK: No minimum charge

Min Mail Order EU: Nmc
Cat. Cost: 2 x 1st class
Credit Cards: Visa, MasterCard, Switch, Electron
Specialities: Specimen stock, herbaceous, conifers, shrubs, grasses, climbers & hedging.
Map Ref: S, D2

SHHo   **HIGHFIELD HOLLIES** ⊠ EU ▣ ♦
Highfield Farm, Hatch Lane, Liss, Hampshire GU33 7NH
☎ (01730) 892372
Fax: (01730) 894853
Email: louise@bendall.prestel.co.uk
Website: www.commercepark.co.uk/bendall/
Contact: Mrs Louise Bendall
Opening Times: By appt.
Min Mail Order UK: No minimum charge
Min Mail Order EU: £500 + p&p
Cat. Cost: £2.00 for illustrated cat.
Credit Cards: None
Specialities: 100+ species & cultivars *Ilex* incl. specimen trees, hedging & topiary. Some in short supply.
Map Ref: S, C3
OS Grid Ref: SU787276

SHmp   **HAMPSHIRE CARNIVOROUS PLANTS** ▣ ⊠ EU ▣ ∩ €
Ya-Mayla, Allington Lane, West End, Southampton SO30 3HQ
☎ (023) 8047 3314, mobile 07703 258296
Fax: (023) 8047 3314
Email: matthew@msoper.freesave.co.uk
Website: www.hampshire-carnivorous.co.uk
Contact: Matthew Soper
Opening Times: By appt. only.
Min Mail Order UK: No minimum charge
Min Mail Order EU: £50.00 + p&p
Cat. Cost: 2 x 2nd class
Credit Cards: Visa, MasterCard
Specialities: Carnivorous plants esp. *Nepenthes, Heliamphora, Sarracenia Pinguicula* & *Utricularia*.

SHol   **HOLLY GATE CACTUS NURSERY** ▣ ⊠ EU €
Billingshurst Road, Ashington, West Sussex RH20 3BB
☎ (01903) 892 930
Email: hollygate@tmh.globalnet.co.uk

S

Website: www.hollygatecactus.co.uk
Contact: Mr T M Hewitt
Opening Times: 0900-1700 7 days Feb-Oct, 0900-1600 Nov-Jan.
Min Mail Order UK: £5.00 + p&p
Min Mail Order EU: £10.00 + p&p
Cat. Cost: 2 x 1st class
Credit Cards: None
Specialities: Cacti & succulents, plants & seeds. World famous cactus garden.
Map Ref: S, D3

SHom   HOME PLANTS
52 Dorman Ave North, Aylesham, Canterbury, Kent CT3 3BW
☎ (01304) 841746
Contact: Stuart & Sue Roycroft
Opening Times: By appt. only, please phone first.
Cat. Cost: SAE for list
Credit Cards: None
Specialities: *Phygelius*. National Collection Holder status applied for. Limited stock, please phone first.

SHvs   HARVEST NURSERIES ✉ EU €
Harvest Cottage, Boonshill Farm, Iden, Nr Rye, East Sussex TN31 7QA
☎ (01797) 230583
Email: derek@harvest99.freeserve.co.uk
Contact: D A Smith
Opening Times: Not open, mail order only.
Min Mail Order UK: No minimum charge
Min Mail Order EU: £20.00 + p&p
Cat. Cost: 2 x 1st class
Credit Cards: None
Specialities: *Epiphyllum* & wide range of succulents. Descriptive catalogue.

SIde   IDEN CROFT HERBS ✉ EU ☒ ◆
Frittenden Road, Staplehurst, Kent TN12 0DH
☎ (01580) 891432
Fax: (01580) 892416
Email: idencroft.herbs@dial.pipex.com
Website: www.herbs-uk.com
Contact: Rosemary & D Titterington
Opening Times: 0900-1700 Mon-Sat all year. 1100-1700 Sun & B/hols 1st Mar-30th Sep.
Min Mail Order UK: No minimum charge*
Min Mail Order EU: Nmc
Cat. Cost: 2 x 1st class for descriptive list.
Credit Cards: Visa, Access, Delta, JCB, EuroCard, Switch

Specialities: Herbs, aromatic & wild flower plants & plants for bees & butterflies. National Collections of *Mentha* & *Origanum*. *Note: exports seed only.
Map Ref: S, C5

SIgm   TIM INGRAM 🜨 €
Copton Ash, 105 Ashford Road, Faversham, Kent ME13 8XW
☎ (01795) 535919
Contact: Dr T J Ingram
Opening Times: 1400-1800 Tue-Fri & Sat-Sun Mar-Oct. Nov-Feb by appt.
Cat. Cost: 4 x 1st class
Credit Cards: None
Specialities: Unusual perennials, alpines & plants from Mediterranean-type climates incl. *Lupinus, Penstemon, Salvia* & umbellifers. Limited stock of some rarer plants .
Map Ref: S, C5
OS Grid Ref: TR015598

SIng   W E TH. INGWERSEN LTD 🜨
Birch Farm Nursery, Gravetye, East Grinstead, West Sussex RH19 4LE
☎ (01342) 810236
Email: info@ingwersen.co.uk
Website: www.ingwersen.co.uk
Contact: M P & M R Ingwersen
Opening Times: 0900-1600 daily excl. Sun & B/hols, Mar-Sep. 0900-1600 Mon-Fri Oct-Feb.
Cat. Cost: 2 x 1st class
Credit Cards: None
Specialities: Very wide range of hardy plants mostly alpines. Also seed.
Map Ref: S, C4

SIri   IRIS OF SISSINGHURST ✉ EU € ◆
Plummers Farmhouse, Biddenden Road, Sissinghurst, Kent TN17 2JP
☎ (01580) 715137
Email: irisofs@aol.com
Contact: Margaret Roberts
Opening Times: 1000-1700 following w/ends: 4th-5th, 11th-12th May, 8th-9th, 15th-16th Jun, 31st Aug-1st Sep 2002. Other times by appt.
Min Mail Order UK: No minimum charge
Min Mail Order EU: Nmc
Cat. Cost: 2 x 1st class
Credit Cards: None
Specialities: *Iris*, short, intermediate & tall bearded, *Sibirica* & many species.
Map Ref: S, C5

SKCa **KENT CACTI** ⊠ EU
(Office) 35 Rutland Way, Orpington,
Kent BR5 4DY
☎ (01689) 836249,
mobile 07767 881981
Fax: (01689) 830157
Contact: Mr D Sizmur
Opening Times: 1000-1700 most days.
Please phone first.
Min Mail Order UK: No minimum charge
Min Mail Order EU: Nmc
Cat. Cost: A5 Sae. No list for carnivorous
plants.
Credit Cards: None
Specialities: *Agave, Astrophytum, Conophytum,*
Crassula, Echeveria, small *Opuntia,*
Mammillaria. Note: nursery is at Woodlands
Farm, Shire Lane, Farnborough, Kent.
Map Ref: S, C4
OS Grid Ref: TQ432635

SKCG **KERRY'S COTTAGE GARDEN PLANTS**
83 Middle Mead, Hook,
Hampshire RG27 9TE
☎ (01256) 764916
Contact: Kerry Leach
Opening Times: Apr-Oct by appt. only.
Cat. Cost: Free
Credit Cards: None
Specialities: *Penstemon.* Small garden nursery
with plants propagated in small numbers.
Please ring to check availability before travelling.
Map Ref: S, C2

SKee **KEEPERS NURSERY** ⊠ UK
Gallants Court, Gallants Lane, East Farleigh,
Maidstone, Kent ME15 0LE
☎ (01622) 726465
Fax: (01622) 726465
Email: info@keepers-nursery.co.uk
Website: www.keepers-nursery.co.uk
Contact: Hamid Habibi
Opening Times: All reasonable hours by
appt.
Min Mail Order UK: £10.00 + p&p
Cat. Cost: 2 x 1st class. Free by email.
Credit Cards: Visa, MasterCard, American
Express, Switch, Solo
Specialities: Old & unusual top fruit
varieties. Top fruit propagated to order.
Map Ref: S, C4

SKen **KENT STREET NURSERIES** ▣ ⊠ EU €
Sedlescombe, Battle, East Sussex TN33 0SF
☎ (01424) 751134
Fax: (01424) 751499

Email: peter@1066-countryplants.co.uk
Website: www.1066-countryplants.co.uk
Contact: P Stapley
Opening Times: 0900-1800 7 days.
Min Mail Order UK: £6.50
Min Mail Order EU: Nmc
Cat. Cost: 2 x 1st class, email, or on web
Credit Cards: MasterCard, Visa
Specialities: *Pelargonium,* bedding &
perennials.
Map Ref: S, D5
OS Grid Ref: 790155

SLan **LANGLEY BOXWOOD**
NURSERY ▣ ⊠ EU ▣ ṅ € ◆
Rake, Nr Liss, Hampshire GU33 7JL
☎ (01730) 894467
Fax: (01730) 894703
Email: langbox@msn.com
Website: www.boxwood.co.uk
Contact: Elizabeth Braimbridge
Opening Times: 0900-1630 Mon-Fri, 1000-
1600 Sat. Please phone for directions.
Min Mail Order UK: £20.00 + p&p
Min Mail Order EU: £100.00 + p&p
Cat. Cost: 4 x 1st class
Credit Cards: MasterCard, Visa
Specialities: *Buxus* species, cultivars &
hedging. Good range of topiary, *Taxus,* and
'character-pruned' specimens. National
Collection of *Buxus.* Evergreen topiary &
hedging.
Map Ref: S, C3
OS Grid Ref: SU812290

SLau **THE LAURELS NURSERY** ▣ ṅ €
Benenden, Cranbrook, Kent TN17 4JU
☎ (01580) 240463
Fax: (01580) 240463
Email: PeterKellett@Thelaurelsnursery.co.uk
Website: www.thelaurelsnursery.co.uk
Contact: Peter or Sylvia Kellett
Opening Times: 0800-1700 Mon-Thu, 0800-
1600 Fri, 0900-1200 Sat, Sun by appt. only.
Cat. Cost: Free
Credit Cards: None
Specialities: Open ground & container
ornamental trees, shrubs & climbers incl.
flowering cherries, birch & *Wisteria.*
Map Ref: S, C5
OS Grid Ref: TQ815313

S

Y	⊠ Mail order to UK or EU ṅ Delivers to shows
E	▣ Exports beyond EU € Euro accepted
K	▣ Also supplies Wholesale ◆ See Display advertisement

SLay **LAYHAM GARDEN CENTRE & NURSERY** ▣ ⊠ EU
Lower Road, Staple, Nr Canterbury,
Kent CT3 1LH
☎ (01304) 813267
Fax: (01304) 814007
Email: layham@gestaple.fsnet.co.uk
Contact: Ellen Wessel
Opening Times: 0900-1700 Mon-Sat 0900-1700 Sun.
Min Mail Order UK: No minimum charge
Min Mail Order EU: £25.00 + p&p
Cat. Cost: Free
Credit Cards: Visa, American Express, Switch
Specialities: Roses, herbaceous, shrubs, trees & hedging plants.
Map Ref: S, C6
OS Grid Ref: TR276567

S

SLBF **LITTLE BROOK FUCHSIAS** ▣
Ash Green Lane West, Ash Green,
Nr Aldershot, Hampshire GU12 6HL
☎ (01252) 329731
Email: carol.gubler@business.ntl.com
Website: www.littlebrookfuchsias.co.uk
Contact: Carol Gubler
Opening Times: 0900-1700 Wed-Sun 1st Jan-7th Jul.
Cat. Cost: 50p + Sae
Credit Cards: None
Specialities: Fuchsias, old & new.
Map Ref: S, C3

SLdr **LODER PLANTS** ▣ ⊠ EU ▣ ♠ €
Market Garden, Lower Beeding,
West Sussex RH13 6PX
☎ (01403) 891412
Fax: (01403) 891336
Email: rhspf@rhododendrons.com
Website: www.rhododendrons.com
Contact: Chris Loder
Opening Times: 7 days, by appt. only so we can give you our undivided attention.
Min Mail Order UK: No minimum charge
Min Mail Order EU: £100.00 + p&p
Cat. Cost: 2 x 1st class
Credit Cards: Visa, Access
Specialities: Rhododendrons & azaleas in all sizes. *Camellia, Acer.*
Map Ref: S, C3

SLFN **LINDEN FARM NURSERIES** ▣ ⊠ UK €
Stockett Lane, E. Farleigh, Maidstone,
Kent ME15 0QD
☎ (01622) 745413

Fax: (01622) 745946
Email: linfarnur@cs.com
Website: www.lfgardendesign.co.uk
Contact: Andrew Rankin
Opening Times: 1000-1500 winter, 0900-1700 summer (closed Mon).
Min Mail Order UK: £25.00
Cat. Cost: Free
Credit Cards: MasterCard, Visa, Switch
Specialities: Hebes, conifers, herbaceous.
Map Ref: S, C4
OS Grid Ref: TQ742516

SLim **LIME CROSS NURSERY** ▣ ⊠ ♦
Herstmonceux, Hailsham,
East Sussex BN27 4RS
☎ (01323) 833229
Fax: (01323) 833944
Email: LimeCross@aol.com
Contact: J A Tate, Mrs A Green
Opening Times: 0830-1700 Mon-Sat & 1000-1600 Sun.
Cat. Cost: 5 x 2nd class
Credit Cards: Visa, MasterCard, Delta, Switch
Specialities: Conifers, trees & shrubs, climbers.
Map Ref: S, D4

SLon **LONGSTOCK PARK NURSERY** ⊠ UK
Longstock, Stockbridge,
Hampshire SO20 6EH
☎ (01264) 810894
Fax: (01264) 810924
Email: longstocknursery@leckfordestate.co.uk
Website: www.longstocknursery.co.uk
Contact: Peter Moore
Opening Times: 0830-1630 Mon-Sat all year excl. Xmas & New Year, & 1100-1700 Sun Mar-Oct.
Min Mail Order UK: No minimum charge
Cat. Cost: £2 cheque incl. p&p
Credit Cards: Visa, Access, Switch, MasterCard
Specialities: A wide range, over 2000 varieties, of trees, shrubs, perennials, climbers, aquatics & ferns. National Collection of *Buddleja* & *Clematis viticella.*
Map Ref: S, C2

SLPl **LANDSCAPE PLANTS** ▣ ⊠ EU ▣
Cattamount, Grafty Green, Maidstone,
Kent ME17 2AP
☎ (01622) 850245
Fax: (01622) 858063
Email: tomladell@aol.com
Contact: Tom La Dell
Opening Times: By appt. only.
Min Mail Order UK: £100.00 + p&p

Min Mail Order EU: £200.00 + p&p
Cat. Cost: 2 x 1st class
Credit Cards: None
Specialities: Garden & landscape shrubs & perennials.
Map Ref: S, C5
OS Grid Ref: TQ772468

SMac MacGregors Plants for Shade 🔲 ⊠ UK 🔥
Carters Clay Road,
Lockerley, Romsey,
Hampshire SO51 0GL
☎ (01794) 340256
Fax: (01794) 341828
Email: bowrons@macgregorsplants.demon.co.uk
Website: www.macgregors-shadeplants.co.uk
Contact: Irene & Stuart Bowron
Opening Times: 1000-1600 most days, or by appt. Please phone before travelling.
Min Mail Order UK: No minimum charge
Cat. Cost: 3 x 1st class
Credit Cards: MasterCard, Visa
Specialities: Plants for shade & other less common shrubs & perennials. Limited stock of rarer plants (may be reserved prior to propagation). National Collection of *Phygelius*. Note: mail order restricted to small numbers of mature plants sent by 24hr carrier.
Map Ref: S, C2
OS Grid Ref: SU308239

SMad Madrona Nursery ⊠ UK 🔥 €
Pluckley Road, Bethersden,
Kent TN26 3DD
☎ (01233) 820100
Fax: (01233) 820091
Contact: Liam MacKenzie
Opening Times: 1000-1700 Sat-Tue 16th Mar-29th Oct. Closed 7th-21th Aug.
Min Mail Order UK: No minimum charge
Cat. Cost: Free
Credit Cards: Visa, MasterCard, American Express, JCB, Switch
Specialities: Unusual shrubs, conifers & perennials.
Map Ref: S, C5
OS Grid Ref: TQ918419

SMer Merryfield Nurseries (Canterbury) Ltd ⊠ UK
Stodmarsh Road, Canterbury,
Kent CT3 4AP
☎ (01227) 462602
Email: merry-field@tinyonline.co.uk
Contact: Mrs A Downs

Opening Times: 1000-1600 Mon, 0900-1730 Tue-Sat, 1000-1700 Sun B/hol Mons.
Min Mail Order UK: £10.00 + p&p
Cat. Cost: None issued
Credit Cards: Access, Visa, Switch
Specialities: Wide range of shrubs, conifers, herbaceous, many unusual.
Map Ref: S, C5

SMHT Mount Harry Trees ◆
Offham, Lewes, East Sussex BN7 3QW
☎ (01273) 474456
Fax: (01273) 474266
Contact: A Renton
Opening Times: By appt.
Cat. Cost: 2 x 1st class
Credit Cards: None
Specialities: Deciduous trees, specialising in heavy-standard to semi-mature sizes, incl. *Sophora japonica*, *Aesculus indica*, *Tilia mongolica*, *Paulownia tomentosa*, *Sorbus* varieties & *Cercidiphyllum japonicum*.
Map Ref: S, D4

SMHy Marchants Hardy Plants 🔥
2 Marchants Cottages, Ripe Road,
Laughton, East Sussex BN8 6AJ
☎ (01323) 811737
Fax: (01323) 811737
Contact: Graham Gough
Opening Times: mid-Mar-Oct, or by appointment.
Cat. Cost: 4 x 1st class
Specialities: Uncommon herbaceous perennials. *Agapanthus*, *Kniphofia*, *Sedum*, choice grasses, *Miscanthus*, *Molinia*.
Map Ref: S, D4
OS Grid Ref: TQ506119

SMrm Merriments Gardens €
Hawkhurst Road, Hurst Green,
East Sussex TN19 7RA
☎ (01580) 860666
Fax: (01580) 860324
Email: markbuchele@beeb.net
Website: www.merriments.co.uk
Contact: Mark & Amanda Buchele
Opening Times: 0930-1730 Mon-Sat, 1030-1730 Sun (or dusk in winter).
Cat. Cost: £1.00 + 2 x 1st class
Credit Cards: Visa, Access, American Express

S

K E Y ⊠ Mail order to UK or EU 🔥 Delivers to shows
🗷 Exports beyond EU € Euro accepted
🔲 Also supplies Wholesale ◆ See Display advertisement

Specialities: Unusual shrubs. Tender & hardy perennials.
Map Ref: S, C4

SMur   **Murrells Plant & Garden Centre**
Broomers Hill, Lane Pulborough,
West Sussex RH20 2DU
☎ (01798) 875508
Fax: (01798) 872695
Contact: Clive Mellor
Opening Times: 0900-1730 summer, 0900-1700 winter, 1000-1600 Sun.
Cat. Cost: 3 x 1st class
Credit Cards: Switch, MasterCard, Visa, Solo
Specialities: Shrubs, trees & herbaceous plants incl. many rare & unusual varieties.
Map Ref: S, D3

SNew   **New Forest Palms & Exotics** 🖾
Hollybush Cottage, Pauls Lane, Sway,
Lymington, Hampshire SO41 6BR
☎ (01590) 683864
mobile 07870 483972
Fax: (01590) 683864
Email: Paulsnursery@farmersweekly.net
Website: www.newforestpalms.co.uk
Contact: F R Toyne
Opening Times: 1000-1700 Tue-Sun Mar-Oct. 1000-1500 Tue-Sun Nov-Feb. Closed Mon.
Cat. Cost: 2 x 1st class
Credit Cards: Visa, MasterCard
Specialities: Ornamental grasses & plants for the Mediterranean look. Note: nursery 300 yards down lane from the cottage.
Map Ref: S, D2
OS Grid Ref: SZ292978

SNut   **Nutlin Nursery** ń
Crowborough Road, Nutley, Nr Uckfield,
East Sussex TN22 3HU
☎ (01825) 712670
Fax: (01825) 712670
Contact: Mrs Morven Cox
Opening Times: Phone in evening (before 2100) before visiting.
Cat. Cost: 1 x 1st class
Credit Cards: None
Specialities: *Hydrangea*, *Wisteria*, hardy ferns.
Map Ref: S, C4

SOkd   **Oakdene Nursery** ⊠ EU 🖾 ń
Street End Lane, Broad Oak, Heathfield,
East Sussex TN21 8TU
☎ (01435) 864382

Contact: David Sampson
Opening Times: 0900-1700 Wed-Sat excl. B/hols. Sun by appt.
Min Mail Order UK: £10.00
Min Mail Order EU: £25.00
Cat. Cost: 3 x 2nd class
Credit Cards: None
Specialities: Rare & unusual alpines. Woodland plants.
Map Ref: S, C4

SOkh   **Oakhurst Nursery** ń
Mardens Hill, Crowborough,
East Sussex TN6 1XL
☎ (01892) 653273
Fax: (01892) 653273
Email: sandy.colton@tesco.net
Contact: Stephanie Colton
Opening Times: 1100-1700 most days mid Apr-mid Sep. Other times &, if travelling, please phone first esp. at w/ends.
Cat. Cost: 2 x 1st class
Credit Cards: None
Specialities: Common & uncommon herbaceous perennials in small quantities to enable as wide a range as possible.
Map Ref: S, C4

SOWG   **The Old Walled Garden** 🖾 ⊠ UK ń €
Oxonhoath, Hadlow, Kent TN11 9SS
☎ (01732) 810012
Fax: (01732) 810856
Email: amyrtle@aol.com
Contact: John & Heather Angrave
Opening Times: 0900-1700 Mon-Fri. W/ends by appt.
Min Mail Order UK: No minimum charge
Cat. Cost: 2 x 1st class
Credit Cards: None
Specialities: Many rare & unusual shrubs. Wide range of conservatory plants esp. Australian. National Collection of *Callistemon*.
Map Ref: S, C4

SPar   **The Paradise Garden** 🖾 ń
19 Cootham Green, Storrington,
West Sussex RH20 4EE
☎ mobile 07960 358445
Email: Clive@theparadisegarden.co.uk
Website: www.theparadisegarden.co.uk
Contact: Clive Parker
Opening Times: At time of going to press, nursery in process of moving site. Please contact by email or mobile phone for new address.

Cat. Cost: None issued
Specialities: Architectural & foliage plants.
Over 50 named varieties of *Canna*.

SPer   PERRYHILL NURSERIES LTD ń
Hartfield, East Sussex TN7 4JP
☎ (01892) 770377
Fax: (01892) 770929
Email: sales@perryhillnurseries.co.uk
Website: www.perryhillnurseries.co.uk
Contact: P J Chapman
Opening Times: 0900-1700 7 days 1st Mar-
31st Oct. 0900-1630 1st Nov-28th Feb.
Cat. Cost: £2.00 or on web
Credit Cards: Visa, Access, MasterCard,
EuroCard, Switch
Specialities: Wide range of trees, shrubs,
conifers, *Rhododendron* etc. Over 1300
herbaceous varieties, over 500 rose varieties
Map Ref: S, C4

SPet   PETTET'S NURSERY ◪ń€
Poison Cross, Eastry, Sandwich,
Kent CT13 0EA
☎ (01304) 613869
Fax: (01304) 613869
Email: terry@pettetsnursery.fsnet.co.uk
Contact: T & E H P Pettet
Opening Times: 0900-1700 daily Mar-Jun.
1000-1600 daily Jul-Nov.
Credit Cards: None
Specialities: Climbers, shrubs, herbaceous
perennials, alpines, pelargoniums, fuchsias.
Map Ref: S, C6

SPla   PLAXTOL NURSERIES ✉ EU
The Spoute, Plaxtol, Sevenoaks,
Kent TN15 0QR
☎ (01732) 810550
Fax: (01732) 810149
Email: info@plaxtol-nurseries.co.uk
Website: www.plaxtol-nurseries.co.uk
Contact: Tessa, Donald & Jenny Forbes
Opening Times: 1000-1700 7 days. Closed
2 weeks from Xmas Eve.
Min Mail Order UK: £10.00 + p&p*
Min Mail Order EU: £30.00 + p&p
Cat. Cost: 2 x 1st class
Credit Cards: Visa, American Express,
MasterCard
Specialities: Hardy shrubs & herbaceous esp.
for flower arrangers. Old-fashioned roses,
ferns & climbers.
*Note: mail order Nov-Mar only.
Map Ref: S, C4
OS Grid Ref: TQ611535

SPlb   PLANTBASE €
Lamberhurst Vineyard, Lamberhurst Down,
Lamberhurst, Kent TN3 8ER
☎ (01892) 891453
Fax: (01892) 891453
Email: graham@plantbase.freeserve.co.uk
Contact: Graham Blunt
Opening Times: 1000-1700 7 days Mar-Oct.
Cat. Cost: 2 x 1st class
Credit Cards: Visa, Switch, Access,
MasterCard, Delta
Specialities: Wide range of alpines,
perennials, shrubs, climbers, waterside plants,
herbs, Australasian shrubs & South African
plants. Second plant centre at Tenterden
Vineyard.
Map Ref: S, C5

SPLN   POUND LANE NURSERIES ◪€
Ampfield, Romsey,
Hampshire SO51 9BL
☎ (02380) 739685
Fax: (02380) 740300
Contact: Mr T A Holmes
Opening Times: 0830-1730 Mon-Fri &
0930-1700 Sat & Sun.
Credit Cards: None
Specialities: Wide general range of trees,
shrubs, conifers, rhododendrons & azaleas.
Larger range of kalmias & *Daphne*.
Map Ref: S, C2
OS Grid Ref: SU401218

SPoG   THE POTTED GARDEN NURSERY
Ashford Road, Bearsted,
Maidstone, Kent ME14 4NH
☎ (01622) 737801
Fax: (01622) 632459
Email: sales@pottedgarden.fsnet.co.uk
Contact: Robert Brookman
Opening Times: 0900-1730 (dusk in winter)
7 days. Closed Xmas, Boxing Day & New
Year's Day
Credit Cards: Visa, MasterCard, Switch,
Electron, Delta, Solo
Map Ref: S, C5

SPop   POPS PLANTS ✉ EU ◪ń€
Pops Cottage, Barford Lane, Downton,
Salisbury, Wiltshire SP5 3PZ
☎ (01725) 511421

K E Y		
✉ Mail order to UK or EU	ń Delivers to shows	
▣ Exports beyond EU	€ Euro accepted	
◪ Also supplies Wholesale	♦ See Display advertisement	

Fax: (01425) 653472
Email: mail@popsplants
Website: www.popsplants.com
Contact: G Dawson or L Roberts
Opening Times: Strictly by appt. only.
Min Mail Order UK: No minimum charge
Min Mail Order EU: Nmc
Cat. Cost: 1 x 1st class
Specialities: *Primula auricula*. Some varieties in limited numbers.

SRat UNUSUAL PLANTS AT RATSBURY €
Smallhythe Road, Tenterden,
Kent TN30 7LU
☎ (01580) 762066
Email: Ratsbury@aol.com
Contact: Jane Kirk
Opening Times: Daily except Wed,
Apr-Jun, w/ends only mid-Jun-end Sep,
closed Aug.
Credit Cards: None
Specialities: Unusual and traditional cottage garden plants.
Map Ref: S, C5
OS Grid Ref: TQ887322

SReu G REUTHE LTD ✉ EU
Crown Point Nursery, Sevenoaks Road,
Ightham, Nr Sevenoaks, Kent TN15 0HB
☎ (01732) 810694
Fax: (01732) 862166
Contact: C & P Tomlin
Opening Times: 0900-1630 Mon-Sat
(closed Wed). 1000-1630 Sun & B/hols Apr
& May only, occasionally in Jun, please
check. Closed Jan, Jul & Aug.
Min Mail Order UK: £30.00 + p&p
Min Mail Order EU: £500.00*
Cat. Cost: £2.00
Credit Cards: Visa, Access
Specialities: Rhododendrons & azaleas, trees, shrubs & climbers.
*Note: mail order certain plants only to EU.
Map Ref: S, C4

SRGP ROSIES' GARDEN PLANTS ✉ EU ☑ ♁
Rochester Road Aylesford Kent ME20 7EB
☎ (01622) 715777
Fax: (01622) 715777
Email: JCAviolet@aol.com
Website: www.rosiesgardenplants.com
Contact: J C A'violét
Opening Times: 1000-1700 Thu-Sat 7th
Mar-5th Oct 2002.
Min Mail Order UK: No minimum charge
Min Mail Order EU: Nmc

Cat. Cost: 2 x 1st class
Credit Cards: Visa, MasterCard, Switch
Specialities: Hardy *Geranium*, *Buddleja* & grasses.
Map Ref: S, C4

SRiv RIVER GARDEN NURSERIES ☑ ✉ EU ♁ €
Troutbeck, Otford, Sevenoaks,
Kent TN14 5PH
☎ (01959) 525588
Fax: (01959) 525810
Email: box@river-garden.co.uk
Website: www.river-garden.co.uk
Contact: Jenny Alban Davies
Opening Times: By appt. only.
Min Mail Order UK: £10.00 + p&p
Min Mail Order EU: £50.00 + p&p
Cat. Cost: 2 x 1st class
Credit Cards: Visa, MasterCard, Access,
Switch, Solo, American Express, JCB
Specialities: *Buxus* species, cultivars &
hedging. *Buxus* topiary.
Map Ref: S, C4
OS Grid Ref: TQ523593

SRkn RAPKYNS NURSERY ☑ ♁
Scotsford Farm, Street End Lane, Broad Oak
Heathfield, East Sussex TN21 8UB
☎ (01892) 652071
mobile 07771 916933
Fax: (01892) 652071
Contact: Fiona Moore, Steven Moore
Opening Times: 1000-1700 Tue & Fri,
Mar-Oct.
Cat. Cost: 2 x 1st class
Credit Cards: None
Specialities: Azaleas, Campanulas, *Ceanothus*,
geraniums, lavenders, lobelias, *Clematis*,
penstemons, salvias & grasses. Unusual
shrubs & perennials.
Map Ref: S, C4
OS Grid Ref: TQ604248

SRms RUMSEY GARDENS ✉ UK ◆
117 Drift Road, Clanfield, Waterlooville,
Hampshire PO8 0PD
☎ (023) 9259 3367
Email: info@rumsey-gardens.co.uk
Website: www.rumsey-gardens.co.uk
Contact: Mr N R Giles
Opening Times: 0900-1700 Mon-Sat & 1000-
1700 Sun & B/hols. Closed Sun Nov-Feb.
Min Mail Order UK: No minimum charge
Cat. Cost: On web
Credit Cards: Visa, MasterCard, Switch
Specialities: Wide general range. National

Collection of *Cotoneaster*.
Map Ref: S, D2

SRob   ROBINS NURSERY
Coldharbour Road, Upper Dicker, Hailsham,
East Sussex BN27 3PY
☎ mobile 07798 527634
Email: robnurse@robnurse.free-online.co.uk
Website: www.robnurse.free-online.co.uk
Contact: Stuart Dye
Opening Times: 1100-1700 Sat & Sun,
Mar-Oct.
Cat. Cost: Free
Credit Cards: None
Specialities: Small retail nursery specialising
in herbaceous plants.
Map Ref: S, D4
OS Grid Ref: TQ561109

SRos   ROSEWOOD DAYLILIES ⊠ UK
70 Deansway Avenue, Sturry,
Nr Canterbury, Kent CT2 0NN
☎ (01227) 711071
Fax: (01227) 711071
Email: Rosewoodgdns@aol.com
Contact: Chris Searle
Opening Times: By appt. only. Please phone
Min Mail Order UK: No minimum charge
Cat. Cost: 2 x 1st class
Credit Cards: None
Specialities: *Hemerocallis*, mainly newer
American varieties. *Agapanthus*.
Map Ref: S, C5

SRot   ROTHERVIEW NURSERY ▣ ⊠ EU ♠ €
Ivy House Lane, Three Oaks, Hastings,
East Sussex TN35 4NP
☎ (01424) 756228
Fax: (01424) 428944
Email: rotherview@btinternet.com
Contact: Ray Bates
Opening Times: 1000-1700 Mar-Oct,
1000-1530 Nov-Feb, 7 days.
Min Mail Order UK: £10.00 + p&p
Min Mail Order EU: £20.00 + p&p
Cat. Cost: 2 x 1st class
Credit Cards: all major credit/debit cards
Specialities: Alpines.
Note: nursery is on same site as Coghurst
Camellias.
Map Ref: S, D5

**SRPl   ROGER PLATTS GARDEN
DESIGN & NURSERIES**
Stick Hill, Edenbridge, Kent TN8 5NH
☎ (01732) 863318

Fax: (01732) 863318
Email: plattsgdn@aol.com
Contact: Roger Platts
Opening Times: 0900-1700 7 days.
Cat. Cost: Available shortly
Credit Cards: Access, Visa, Switch
Specialities: Perennials, roses, shrubs,
specimen sized plants.
Map Ref: S, C4

SScr   SCREE GARDENS €
56 Valley Drive, Loose, Maidstone,
Kent ME15 9TL
☎ (01622) 746941
Contact: Michael Brett
Opening Times: 1000-1700 Sat & Sun
Apr-Aug. Garden open under NGS.
Please phone first.
Cat. Cost: 1 x 2nd class for list
Credit Cards: None
Specialities: Rock garden, scree, trough &
herbaceous plants.
Map Ref: S, C5

SSea   SEALE NURSERIES ⊠ UK ◆
Seale Lane, Seale, Farnham,
Surrey GU10 1LD
☎ (01252) 782410
Email: plants@sealesuperroses.com
Website: www.sealesuperroses.com
Contact: David & Catherine May
Opening Times: 7 days. Closed 25th Dec-
3rd Jan.
Min Mail Order UK: £10.00 + p&p
Credit Cards: Visa, Switch, Access, Delta
Specialities: Roses, *Pelargonium, Fuchsia.*
Some varieties in short supply, please phone
first.
Map Ref: S, C3

SSpe   SPELDHURST NURSERIES
Langton Road, Speldhurst, Tunbridge Wells,
Kent TN3 0NR
☎ (01892) 862682
Fax: (01892) 862682
Email: VistasLtd@aol.com
Contact: Christine & Stephen Lee
Opening Times: 1000-1700 Wed-Sat excl.
Jan. 1000-1600 Sun Mar-Jul & Sep-Oct.
Cat. Cost: 4 x 1st class for list.
Credit Cards: MasterCard, Visa, Switch, Delta

S

KEY		
⊠ Mail order to UK or EU	♠ Delivers to shows	
▣ Exports beyond EU	€ Euro accepted	
▣ Also supplies Wholesale	◆ See Display advertisement	

Specialities: Herbaceous.
Map Ref: S, C4

SSpi   SPINNERS GARDEN €
School Lane, Boldre, Lymington,
Hampshire SO41 5QE
☎ (01590) 673347
Fax: (01590) 679506
Email: kevin@hughes83.fsnet.co.uk
Contact: Peter Chappell & Kevin Hughes
Opening Times: 1000-1700 Tue-Sat. Sun &
Mon by appt. only.
Cat. Cost: 3 x 1st class
Credit Cards: None
Specialities: Less common trees & shrubs
esp. *Acer, Magnolia*, species & lace-cap
Hydrangea. Woodland & bog plants.
National Collection of *Trillium*.
Map Ref: S, D2

**SSpr   SPRINGBANK
        NURSERIES** ▣ ⊠ EU ▣
Winford Road, Newchurch, Sandown,
Isle of Wight PO36 0JX
☎ (01983) 865444
Fax: (01983) 868670
Contact: K Hall
Opening Times: 7 days Sep-Oct.
Collections by appt. Specific open days to be
advertised.
Min Mail Order UK: £10.00 + p&p
Min Mail Order EU: £25.00 + p&p
Cat. Cost: 6 x 1st class
Credit Cards: None
Specialities: *Nerine sarniensis* hybrids (over
600 varieties) & some species. National
Collection of *Nerine sarniensis*.
Map Ref: S, D2

SSta   STARBOROUGH NURSERY ⊠ EU
Starborough Road, Marsh Green,
Edenbridge, Kent TN8 5RB
☎ (01732) 865614
Fax: (01732) 862166
Contact: C & P Tomlin
Opening Times: 0900-1600 Thu-Sat, or by
appt. Closed Jan, Jul & Aug.
Min Mail Order UK: £30.00 + p&p
Min Mail Order EU: £500.00*
Cat. Cost: £2.00
Credit Cards: Visa, Access
Specialities: Rare and unusual shrubs
especially *Daphne, Acer*, rhododendrons &
azaleas, *Magnolia* & *Hamamelis*.
*Note: certain plants only to EU.
Map Ref: S, C4

SSte   STENBURY NURSERY ⊠ EU ♠ €
Smarts Cross, Southford, Nr Whitwell,
Isle of Wight PO38 2AG
☎ mobile 07909 525343
Email: stenburynursery@netscapeonline.co.uk
Contact: Mr B Clarke
Opening Times: 1000-1600 Sat & Sun 21st
Mar-1st Oct.
Min Mail Order UK: No minimum charge
Min Mail Order EU: Nmc
Cat. Cost: 2 x 1st class
Credit Cards: None
Specialities: *Passiflora, Melaleuca,
Callistemon* & other Australian plants,
*Solanum, Aquilegia, Digitalis, Salvia,
Asclepias, Lobelia* & *Rubus*.
Note: mail order Apr-Sep only.
Map Ref: S, D2

SSth   SOUTHEASE PLANTS €
Corner Cottage, Southease, Nr Lewes,
East Sussex BN7 3HX
☎ (01273) 513681
Fax: (01273) 513681
Contact: Adrian Orchard
Opening Times: 1100-1700 Wed-Sat,
1400-1700 Sun & by appt.
Cat. Cost: 2 x 1st class
Credit Cards: None
Specialities: A small nursery concentrating
on hellebores, with a small range of
herbaceous perennials, biennials & annuals
in limited quantities.
Map Ref: S, D4
OS Grid Ref: TQ422052

SSvw   SOUTHVIEW NURSERIES ▣ ⊠ UK ♠ € ◆
Chequers Lane, Eversley Cross, Hook,
Hampshire RG27 0NT
☎ (0118) 9732206
Contact: Mark & Elaine Trenear
Opening Times: Mail order only. Orders for
collection by prior arrangement.
Min Mail Order UK: No minimum charge
Cat. Cost: Free
Credit Cards: None
Specialities: Unusual hardy plants,
specialising in old fashioned pinks & period
plants. National Collection of Old Pinks.
Orders by prior arrangement only.
Map Ref: S, C3

STes   TEST VALLEY NURSERY ♠ €
Stockbridge Road, Timsbury, Romsey,
Hampshire SO51 0NG
☎ (01794) 368881

Fax: (01794) 368493
Email: jbenn@onetel.net.uk
Contact: Julia Benn
Opening Times: 1000-1600 Tue-Sun Mar-
Oct & B/hol Mons, or by appt.
Cat. Cost: 3 x 2nd class
Credit Cards: None
Specialities: Small nursery with range of
herbaceous perennials, specialising in
unusual & new varieties. Limited quantities
of some varieties. Phone first to avoid
disappointment.
Map Ref: S, C2

STil   TILE BARN NURSERY ▨ ⊠ EU ▨ €
Standen Street, Iden Green, Benenden,
Kent TN17 4LB
☎ (01580) 240221
Fax: (01580) 240221
Email: tilebarn.nursery@virgin.net
Website: www.tilebarn-cyclamen.co.uk
Contact: Peter Moore
Opening Times: 0900-1700 Wed-Sat.
Min Mail Order UK: £10.00 + p&p
Min Mail Order EU: £25.00 + p&p
Cat. Cost: Sae
Credit Cards: None
Specialities: *Cyclamen* species.
Map Ref: S, C5
OS Grid Ref: TQ805301

STop   SUSSEX TOPIARY ⊠ UK ♠ ◆
(Office) Sante Fe, Rectory Drive,
Bidborough, Tunbridge Wells,
Kent TN3 0UN
☎ (01403) 823131, (01273) 452519
Fax: (01273) 452519
Email: sussextopiary@zoom.co.uk
Contact: Denis De Ambrosi
Opening Times: 1000-1700 Tue-Sun,
closed Mon.
Min Mail Order UK: No minimum charge
Cat. Cost: 2 x 1st class
Credit Cards: None
Specialities: Specimen plants, trainers,
hedging, box species.
Note: nursery is at Naldretts Lane, Bucks
Green, Horsham, West Sussex.
Map Ref: S, C4
OS Grid Ref: TQ082329

STre   PETER TRENEAR ⊠ UK
Chantreyland, Chequers Lane, Eversley
Cross, Hampshire RG27 0NX
☎ (0118) 9732300
Email: peter@babytrees.co.uk

Website: www.babytrees.co.uk
Contact: Peter Trenear
Opening Times: 0900-1630 Mon-Sat.
Min Mail Order UK: £5.00 + p&p
Cat. Cost: 1 x 1st class
Credit Cards: None
Specialities: Trees, shrubs, conifers & *Pinus*.
Map Ref: S, C3
OS Grid Ref: SU795612

SUsu   USUAL & UNUSUAL PLANTS ♠ €
Onslow House, Magham Down, Hailsham,
East Sussex BN27 1PL
☎ (01323) 840967
Fax: (01323) 844725
Email: jennie@onslow.clara.net
Contact: Jennie Maillard
Opening Times: 0930-1730 Wed-Sat &
B/hol Mons 1 Mar-31 Oct.
Cat. Cost: Sae + 75p
Credit Cards: None
Specialities: Small quantities of a wide
variety of unusual perennials esp. *Diascia*,
Erysimum, *Euphorbia*, hardy *Geranium*,
Salvia & grasses.
Map Ref: S, D4
OS Grid Ref: TQ607113

SVal   VALE NURSERY ⊠ UK
Heath Cottage, Hayes Lane, Stockbury
Valley, Sittingbourne, Kent ME9 7QH
☎ (01795) 844004
Fax: (01795) 842991
Email: info@valenursery.co.uk
Website: www.valenursery.co.uk
Contact: Anthony Clarke
Opening Times: Not open, mail order only.
Min Mail Order UK: £10.00
Cat. Cost: Free
Specialities: Herbaceous perennials. Limited
quantities of some stock.

SVen   VENTNOR BOTANIC GARDEN
Undercliff Drive, Ventnor,
Isle of Wight PO38 1UL
☎ (01983) 855397
Fax: (01983) 856756
Email: simon@vbg1.demon.co.uk
Website: http://botanic.co.uk
Contact: Simon Goodenough & Jan Wyers
Opening Times: 1000-1700 7 days Mar-Oct.

Cat. Cost: None issued
Credit Cards: MasterCard, Visa
Map Ref: S, D2

SVil   THE VILLAGE NURSERIES ⋔ € ◆
Sinnocks, West Chiltington,
Pulborough West Sussex RH20 2JX
☎ (01798) 813040   **Fax:** (01798) 817240
Email: petermanfield@aol.com
Website: www.village-nurseries.co.uk
Contact: Peter Manfield
Opening Times: 0900-1800 or dusk, 7 days.
Cat. Cost: None issued
Credit Cards: Visa, Delta, MasterCard,
Switch, Solo
Specialities: Wide range of hardy perennials
& grasses, incl. many new varieties. Selected
shrubs, conifers, climbers & trees.
Map Ref: S, D3

SWal   WALLACE PLANTS ⋔
Lewes Road Nursery, Lewes Road,
Laughton, East Sussex BN8 6BN
☎ (01323) 811729
Email: sjk@wallaceplants.fsnet.co.uk
Contact: Simon Wallace
Opening Times: 0930-1800 or dusk 7 days
incl B/hols.
Cat. Cost: 3 x 1st class
Credit Cards: None
Specialities: Ornamental grasses, hebes,
fuchsias, hardy geraniums, salvias,
penstemons, some unusual plants.
Map Ref: S, D4

SWat   WATER MEADOW
NURSERY ▣ ⊠ EU ▣ ⋔ €
Cheriton, Nr Alresford,
Hampshire SO24 0QB
☎ (01962) 771895
Fax: (01962) 771895
Email: plantaholic@onetel.net.uk
Website: www.plantaholic.co.uk
Contact: Mrs Sandy Worth
Opening Times: 1000-1700 Wed-Sat
Mar-Jul or by appt.
Min Mail Order UK: £10.00 + p&p
Min Mail Order EU: £50.00 + p&p
Cat. Cost: 6 x 1st class or £1.50 cheque
Credit Cards: Visa, MasterCard
Specialities: Water lilies, extensive water
garden plants, unusual herbaceous
perennials, aromatic herbs & wildflowers.
National Collection of *Papaver orientale*
group.
Map Ref: S, C2

SWCr   WYCH CROSS NURSERIES
Wych Cross, Forest Row,
East Sussex RH18 5JW
☎ (01342) 822705
Fax: (01342) 825329
Email: roses@wychcross.co.uk
Website: www.wychcross.co.uk
Contact: J Paisley
Opening Times: 0900-1730 Mon-Sat.
Cat. Cost: Free
Credit Cards: Visa, MasterCard, Delta,
Switch
Specialities: Roses.
Map Ref: S, C4

SYvo   YVONNE'S PLANTS
66 The Ridgway, Woodingdean, Brighton,
East Sussex BN2 6PD
☎ (01273) 300883
Email: yvonnesplants@cdlaw.freeserve.co.uk
Website:
www.cdlaw.freeserve.co.uk/yvonnesplants
Contact: Mrs Yvonne Law
Opening Times: Mar-Oct by appt. only.
Cat. Cost: None issued, plant list on web
Credit Cards: None
Specialities: Conservatory, tender &
herbaceous perennials, incl. *Cestrum,
Agapanthus, Canna, Fuchsia, Hedychium* &
grasses.
Map Ref: S, D4
OS Grid Ref: TQ360056

WALES AND THE WEST

WAba   ABACUS NURSERIES ▣ ⊠ EU ⋔
Drummau Road, Skewen, Neath,
Wales SA10 6NW
☎ (01792) 817994 (evenings)
Email: plants@abacus-nurseries.co.uk
Website: www.abacus-nurseries.co.uk
Contact: David Hill
Opening Times: Not open to the public.
Collection by arrangement.
Min Mail Order UK: No minimum charge
Min Mail Order EU: Nmc
Cat. Cost: 1 x 2nd class
Credit Cards: None
Specialities: *Dahlia.*
Map Ref: W, D3

WAbb   ABBEY DORE GARDEN
Abbey Dore Court, Abbey Dore,
Nr Hereford, Herefordshire HR2 0AD
☎ (01981) 240419
Fax: (01981) 240419

Contact: Mrs C Ward
Opening Times: 1100-1730 31st Mar-30th
Sep. Closed Mon & Wed.
Cat. Cost: None issued
Credit Cards: None
Specialities: Shrubs & hardy perennials,
many unusual, which may be seen growing
in the garden.
Map Ref: W, C4

WAbe ABERCONWY NURSERY ♙
Graig, Glan Conwy, Colwyn Bay, Conwy,
Wales LL28 5TL
☎ (01492) 580875
Contact: Dr & Mrs K G Lever
Opening Times: 1000-1700 Tue-Sun
Feb-Oct.
Cat. Cost: 2 x 2nd class
Credit Cards: Visa, MasterCard
Specialities: Alpines, including specialist
varieties, esp. autumn gentians, *Saxifraga* &
dwarf ericaceous. Shrubs, incl. large range of
Cistus, & woodland plants incl. *Helleborus*
& *Epimedium*.
Map Ref: W, A3
OS Grid Ref: SH799744

WAct ACTON BEAUCHAMP
ROSES ⊠ EU ▣
Acton Beauchamp, Worcester,
Worcestershire WR6 5AE
☎ (01531) 640433
Fax: (01531) 640802
Contact: Lindsay Bousfield
Opening Times: 1400-1700 Wed-Sun Feb-
Oct, 1000-1700 B/hol Mon. Also by appt.
Note: Nov-Mar mail order only.
Min Mail Order UK: No minimum charge
Min Mail Order EU: Nmc
Cat. Cost: 3 x 1st class
Credit Cards: Visa, MasterCard
Specialities: Species roses, old roses, modern
shrub, English, climbers, ramblers &
ground-cover roses.
Map Ref: W, C4
OS Grid Ref: SO683492

WAlt ALTERNATIVES ⊠ UK
The Brackens, Yorkley Wood, Nr Lydney
Gloucestershire GL15 4TU
☎ (01594) 562457
Email: altern@lineone.net
Website: website.lineone.net/~altern/
Contact: Mrs Rosemary Castle
Opening Times: Mail order only.
Min Mail Order UK: £8.00

Cat. Cost: 3 x 1st class
Credit Cards: None
Specialities: Unusual & ornamental forms of
common British wildflowers.
Note: small stocks, mainly spring/autumn
supply.

WAul AULDEN FARM ♙
Aulden, Leominster,
Herefordshire HR6 0JT
☎ (01568) 720129
Email: pf@auldenfarm.co.uk
Website: www.auldenfarm.co.uk
Contact: Alun & Jill Whitehead
Opening Times: 1000-1700 Tue & Thu
Apr-Aug.
Cat. Cost: 2 x 1st class
Credit Cards: None
Specialities: Hardy herbaceous perennials,
with a special interest in *Hemerocallis* &
Iris ensata.
Map Ref: W, C4

WBad BADSEY LAVENDER
FIELDS ▣ ♙
Badsey Fields Lane, Evesham,
Worcestershire WR11 5EX
☎ (01386) 832124
Fax: (01386) 832124
Contact: Phil Hodgetts
Opening Times: 0900-1800 7 days excl.
Xmas week.
Cat. Cost: 2 x 1st class
Credit Cards: None
Specialities: Lavenders.
Map Ref: W, C5

WBaG BALMER GROVE PLANTS
Welshampton, Ellesmere,
Shropshire SY12 0PP
☎ (01948) 710403
Contact: Nick & Gill Eleftheriou
Opening Times: 0930-1800 Fri-Mon
Mar-Oct. Closed Thu. Please ring to visit on
other days.
Cat. Cost: None issued
Credit Cards: None
Specialities: Selected unusual hardy garden
plants, mainly herbaceous perennials, all
home grown in loam-based compost.
Map Ref: W, B4

W

WBan   **The Garden at the Bannut**
Bringsty, Herefordshire WR6 5TA
☎ (01885) 482206
Fax: (01885) 482206
Email: everettbannut@zetnet.co.uk
Website: www.bannut.co.uk
Contact: Daphne Everett
Opening Times: 1400-1700 Wed, Sat, Sun
& B/hols Easter-end Sep & by appt.
Specialities: *Penstemon, Calluna, Erica* &
Daboecia.
Map Ref: W, C4
OS Grid Ref: SO691546

WBar   **Barncroft Nurseries** ▨
Olden Lane, Ruyton-xi-Towns, Shrewsbury,
Shropshire SY4 1JD
☎ (01939) 261619
Contact: Mrs R E Eccleston
Opening Times: 1000-1730 Tue-Sat
1000-1600 Sun. Closed throughout Jan.
Open B/hols.
Cat. Cost: 4 x 1st class
Credit Cards: None
Specialities: Wide range of unusual
herbaceous plants, shrubs, water plants,
water lily ponds & ferns, as well as cottage
garden favourites.
Map Ref: W, B4

WBCf   **Blooms of Bressingham** ✉ UK ◆
Newport Road, St Mellons,
Cardiff CF3 2WJ
☎ (02920) 777977
Fax: (02920) 793351
Email: j8@jardinerie.co.uk
Website: www.bloomsofbressingham.co.uk
Contact: Malcolm James
Opening Times: 0900-1700 1st Nov-31st
Mar, 0900-1800 1st Apr-31st Oct, 7 days.
Closed Xmas, Boxing Day & Easter Sun.
Min Mail Order UK: £4.35
Cat. Cost: None issued
Credit Cards: Visa, Delta, Switch,
MasterCard
Specialities: Wide general range. Many own
varieties. Focus on hardy ornamental plants
& grasses. Perennials. Plants listed against
nursery code EBre.
Map Ref: W, D4

WBCh   **Blooms of Bressingham** ✉ UK ◆
Evesham Road, Cheltenham,
Gloucestershire GL50 4SJ
☎ (01242) 672560/672153
Fax: (01242) 676135

Email: j2@jardinerie.co.uk
Website: www.bloomsofbressingham.co.uk
Contact: Peter Ulyatt
Opening Times: 0900-1700 1st Nov-31st
Mar, 0900-1800 1st Apr-31st Oct, 7 days.
Closed Xmas, Boxing Day & Easter Sun.
Min Mail Order UK: £4.35
Cat. Cost: None issued.
Credit Cards: Visa, Delta, Switch,
MasterCard
Specialities: Wide general range. Many own
varieties. Focus on hardy ornamental plants
& grasses. Perennials. Plants listed against
nursery code EBre.
Map Ref: W, C5

WBcn   **Beacon's Nurseries** ▨
Tewkesbury Road, Eckington, Nr Pershore,
Worcestershire WR10 3DE
☎ (01386) 750359
Contact: Jonathan Beacon
Opening Times: 0900-1300 & 1400-1700
Mon-Sat & 1400-1700 Sun. (Closed 25th
Dec-1st Jan.)
Cat. Cost: 2 x 1st class
Credit Cards: None
Specialities: Shrubs, camellias, herbaceous,
aquatics, conifers, climbing plants & hollies.
Map Ref: W, C5

WBea   **Beacons' Botanicals** ✉ UK ⚲
Banc-y-Felin, Carregsawdde, Llangadog,
Carmarthenshire, Wales SA19 9DA
☎ (01550) 777992
Email: chrisandsuewill@bushinternet.com
Contact: Mrs S H Williams
Opening Times: Most weekdays, please
phone first.
Min Mail Order UK: £10.00 + p&p
Cat. Cost: 2 x 1st class
Credit Cards: None
Specialities: Hardy *Geranium, Allium,
Campanula, Persicaria*, unusual mints &
hardy bulbs, *Veronica*. Extensive range of
rare & unusual herbaceous plants.
Map Ref: W, C3

WBod   **Bodnant Garden Nursery
Ltd** ✉ EU ▨
Tal-y-Cafn Colwyn Bay Clwyd,
Wales LL28 5RE
☎ (01492) 650731
Fax: (01492) 650863
Email: sales@bodnant.co.uk
Website: www.bodnant.co.uk
Contact: Sian Grindley

Opening Times: All year.
Min Mail Order UK: No minimum charge
Min Mail Order EU: Nmc
Cat. Cost: £2*
Credit Cards: Visa, MasterCard, Switch, Connect, American Express
Specialities: *Rhododendron, Camellia, Magnolia.* Wide range of unusual trees and shrubs.
*Note: catalogue cost refundable with 1st order.
Map Ref: W, A3

WBor   BORDERVALE PLANTS 🛆
Nantyderi, Sandy Lane, Ystradowen, Cowbridge, Vale of Glamorgan, Wales CF71 7SX
☎ (01446) 774036
Email: nyd@btopenworld.com
Website: www.bordervale.co.uk
Contact: Claire E Jenkins
Opening Times: 1000-1700 Fri-Sun & B/hols mid Mar-mid Oct. Other times by appointment.
Cat. Cost: 1st class Sae.
Credit Cards: None
Specialities: Unusual herbaceous perennials & shrubs, as well as cottage garden plants, many displayed in the 2 acre garden.
Map Ref: W, D3
OS Grid Ref: ST022776

WBou   BOUTS COTTAGE NURSERIES ✉ EU 🛆
Bouts Lane, Inkberrow, Worcestershire WR7 4HP
☎ (01386) 792923
Website: www.boutsviolas.co.uk
Contact: M & S Roberts
Opening Times: Not open to the public.
Min Mail Order UK: No minimum charge
Min Mail Order EU: Nmc
Cat. Cost: Sae
Credit Cards: None
Specialities: *Viola.*

WBrE   BRON EIFION NURSERY ✉ UK
Bron Eifion, Criccieth, Gwynedd, Wales LL52 0SA
☎ (01766) 522890
Email: Stress2k@btinternet.com
Contact: Suzanne Evans
Opening Times: 1000-dusk 7 days 1st Mar-31st Oct. 1st Nov-29th Feb by apptointment only.
Min Mail Order UK: £30.00 + p&p

Min Mail Order EU: £50.00 + p&p
Cat. Cost: 4 x 2nd class
Credit Cards: None
Specialities: *Kalmia, Daphne, Embothrium,* plants for coastal regions & wide range of hardy plants.
Map Ref: W, B2

WBri   BRINGSTY NURSERY ✉ EU
Bringsty Common, Nr Bromyard, Worcestershire WR6 5UW
☎ (01886) 821482
Email: jennifer@bringstyherbs.fsnet.co.uk
Contact: Ms J M Powles
Opening Times: 1000-1700 Wed-Sun 1 Apr-30 Sep.
Min Mail Order UK: £10.00
Min Mail Order EU: £20.00
Cat. Cost: 3 x 1st class
Credit Cards: None
Specialities: Over 350 varieties of container grown medicinal, decorative & culinary herbs. Rockery & cottage garden plants. Wild flowers.
Note: Some stock is limited where hard to raise.
Map Ref: W, C4

WBro   BROOK FARM PLANTS ✉ UK
Boulsdon Lane, Newent, Gloucestershire GL18 1JH
☎ (01531) 822534
Email: sally@brookfarmplants.co.uk
Website: www.brookfarmplants.co.uk
Contact: Mrs S E Keene
Opening Times: Visitors welcome most times by appt.
Min Mail Order UK: No minimum charge
Cat. Cost: 3 x 2nd class
Credit Cards: None
Specialities: *Digitalis, Papaver, Schizostylis* & other unusual perennials. Some stock may be limited availability, but can be grown to order.
Map Ref: W, C4

WBry   JULIA'S GARDEN 🛆 €
Bryn Ffynnon Fields Nursery, Bontuchel, Ruthin, Wales LL15 2BL
☎ mobile 07977 549767

W

Email: jon@juliasgarden.fsbusiness.co.uk
Contact: Julia White
Opening Times: 1000-1600 Sat & Sun only
4th May-8th Sep 2002 & by appt.
Cat. Cost: 2 x 1st class
Credit Cards: Visa, MasterCard
Specialities: Traditional cottage plants &
herbs incl. *Alcea, Mentha, Origanum,
Digitalis* & *Angelica.*
Map Ref: W, A3

WBuc   **BUCKNELL NURSERIES** 🖼️✉️ UK
Bucknell, Shropshire SY7 0EL
☎ (01547) 530606
Fax: (01547) 530699
Contact: A N Coull
Opening Times: 0800-1700 Mon-Fri &
1000-1300 Sat.
Min Mail Order UK: No minimum charge
Cat. Cost: Free
Credit Cards: None
Specialities: Bare rooted hedging conifers &
forest trees.
Map Ref: W, C4
OS Grid Ref: 737355

WBVN   **BANWY VALLEY NURSERY**
Foel, Llangadfan, Nr Welshpool, Powys,
Wales SY21 0PT
☎ (01938) 820281
Fax: (01938) 820281
Email: banwy.valley@virgin.net
Contact: Syd Luck
Opening Times: 1000-1700 Tue-Sun.
Open B/hols.
Cat. Cost: 2 x 1st class
Credit Cards: None
Specialities: Perennials, shrubs, incl.
climbers, ornamental & fruit trees.
Ever expanding range of magnolias &
rhododendrons. All grown on the nursery.
Map Ref: W, B3
OS Grid Ref: SH993107

WBWf   **BRITISH WILDFLOWERS** ✉️ UK
Marked Ash Cottage, Rushbury, Church
Stretton, Shropshire SY6 7EL
☎ (01584) 841539
Contact: Spencer Stoves
Opening Times: By appt. only.
Min Mail Order UK: No minimum charge
Cat. Cost: 1 x 1st class stamp
Credit Cards: None
Specialities: British wild flowers of known
British origin only.
Map Ref: W, B4

WCel   **CELYN VALE EUCALYPTUS
NURSERIES** 🖼️✉️ EU 🖼️ € ◆
Carrog, Corwen, Clwyd, Wales LL21 9LD
☎ (01490) 430671
Fax: (01490) 430671
Email: info@eucalyptus.co.uk
Website: www.eucalyptus.co.uk
Contact: Andrew McConnell & Paul Yoxall
Opening Times: 0900-1600 Mon-Fri Jan-
Nov. Please phone first outside these days.
Min Mail Order UK: 3 plants + p&p
Min Mail Order EU: 3 plants + p&p
Cat. Cost: 2 x 1st class
Credit Cards: Switch, Delta, Solo, Electron,
MasterCard, Visa
Specialities: Hardy *Eucalyptus* & *Acacia.*
Map Ref: W, A3

WCer   **CERNEY HOUSE GARDENS**
North Cerney, Cirencester,
Gloucesershire GL7 7BX
☎ (01285) 831205
Fax: (01285) 831676
Email: cerneygardens@hotmail.com
Contact: Barbara Johnson
Opening Times: Tue Wed & Fri Apr-Sep,
or by appt.
Cat. Cost: None issued
Credit Cards: None
Specialities: Herbs, hardy *Geranium, Ajuga,
Pulmonaria, Vinca, Tradescantia, Symphytum,
Papaver orientale* & *Helleborus.* National
Collection of *Tradescantia.*
Map Ref: W, D5

WCFE   **CHARLES F ELLIS** €
(Office) Barn House, Wormington,
Nr Broadway, Worcestershire WR12 7NL
☎ (01386) 584077 (nursery)
Fax: (01386) 584077
Contact: Charles Ellis
Opening Times: 1000-1600 7 days 1st Apr-
30th Sep.
Cat. Cost: None issued.
Credit Cards: None
Specialities: Wide range of more unusual
shrubs, conifers & climbers.
Note: Nursery is at Oak Piece Farm Nursery,
Stanton, Broadway.
Map Ref: W, C5

WCGr   **CARROB GROWERS** ✉️ EU €
Llangunville, Llanrothal, Nr Monmouth
Monmouthshire NP25 5QL
☎ (01600) 714529
Contact: R & C Boyle

Opening Times: By appt. only, Oct-Mar.
Min Mail Order UK: No minimum charge*
Min Mail Order EU: Nmc
Cat. Cost: 1 x 1st class
Credit Cards: None
Specialities: Old & modern varieties of peonies of particular garden-worthiness.
*Note: mail order available Oct-Mar. Some stock available in limited numbers.
Map Ref: W, D4
OS Grid Ref: SO490166

WCHb   THE COTTAGE HERBERY 𝐧
Mill House, Boraston,
Nr Tenbury, Wells,
Worcestershire WR15 8LZ
☎ (01584) 781575
Fax: (01584) 781483
Contact: K & R Hurst
Opening Times: 1000-1800 Sun and by appt, May-end Jun.
Cat. Cost: 4 x 1st class
Credit Cards: None
Specialities: Over 600 varieties of herbs. Aromatic & scented foliage plants, esp *Symphytum, Lamium, Monarda, Ajuga, Salvia, Lobelia* & *Crocosmia*. Seeds.
Map Ref: W, C4

WChG   CHENNELS GATE GARDENS & NURSERY
Eardisley, Herefordshire HR3 6LT
☎ (01544) 327288
Contact: Mark Dawson
Opening Times: 1000-1700 7 days Mar-Dec.
Cat. Cost: 2 x 2nd class
Credit Cards: None
Specialities: Interesting & unusual cottage garden plants, grasses, hedging & shrubs.
Map Ref: W, C4

WCom   COMPTON LANE NURSERIES ▣ ⊠ UK 𝐧
Little Compton, Moreton-in-Marsh,
Gloucestershire GL56 0SJ
☎ (01608) 674578
Fax: (01608) 674877
Contact: Chris Brown
Opening Times: 1000-1700 Tue-Sat Feb-Oct.
Min Mail Order UK: £15.00 + p&p*
Cat. Cost: 5 x 1st class, sae for separate mail order list.
Credit Cards: None
Specialities: Mainly alpines/herbaceous & a few unusual shrubs. *Saxifraga, Primula,*

Cyclamen, Viola, Philadelphus, Hebe.
*Note: mail order Oct-Mar.
Map Ref: W, C5

WCot   COTSWOLD GARDEN FLOWERS ▣ ⊠ EU ☑ 𝐧 €
Sands Lane, Badsey, Evesham,
Worcestershire WR11 5EZ
☎ (01386) 422829 mail order (01386) 422829
Fax: (01386) 49844
Email: info@cgf.net
Website: www.cgf.net
Contact: Bob Brown/Vicky Parkhouse/Gareth Miller (mail order)
Opening Times: 0900-1730 Mon-Fri all year. 1000-1730 Sat & Sun Mar-Sep, Sat & Sun Oct-Feb by appt.
Min Mail Order UK: No minimum charge
Min Mail Order EU: Nmc
Cat. Cost: Free
Credit Cards: MasterCard, Access, Diners, Visa, Switch
Specialities: A very wide range of easy & unusual perennials. National Collection of *Lysimachia.*
Map Ref: W, C5   **OS Grid Ref:** SP077426

WCra   CRANESBILL NURSERY ⊠ EU
White Cottage, Stock Green, Nr Redditch
Worcestershire B96 6SZ
☎ (01386) 792414
Fax: (01386) 792280
Email: smandjbates@aol.com
Contact: Mrs S M Bates
Opening Times: 1000-1700 19th Mar-30th Sep. Closed Wed & Thu. Aug by appt. only. Please contact for w/end opening.
Min Mail Order UK: No minimum charge
Min Mail Order EU: Nmc
Cat. Cost: 4 x 1st class
Credit Cards: None
Specialities: Hardy geraniums & other herbaceous plants.
Map Ref: W, C5

WCru   CRÛG FARM PLANTS ▣ ◆
Griffith's Crossing, Nr Caernarfon,
Gwynedd, Wales LL55 1TU
☎ (01248) 670232
Email: bleddyn&sue@crug-farm.co.uk

K E Y
⊠ Mail order to UK or EU   𝐧 Delivers to shows
☑ Exports beyond EU   € Euro accepted
▣ Also supplies Wholesale   ◆ See Display advertisement

Website: www.crug-farm.co.uk
Contact: Mr B and Mrs S Wynn-Jones
Opening Times: 1000-1800 Thu-Sun last
Sat Feb-last Sun Sep, plus B/hols.
Cat. Cost: 3 x 2nd class
Credit Cards: Visa, Access, Delta,
MasterCard
Specialities: Shade plants, climbers, hardy
Geranium, Pulmonaria, rare shrubs,
Tropaeolum, herbaceous & bulbous incl. self-
collected new introductions from the Far
East. National Collections of *Coriaria, Paris*
& *Polygonatum.*
Map Ref: W, A2
OS Grid Ref: SH509652

WCwm **CWMRHAIADR NURSERY** ⊠ UK
Glaspwll, Machynlleth, Powys,
Wales SY20 8UB
☎ (01654) 702223
Fax: (01654) 702223
Email: glynne.jones@btinternet.com
Contact: Glynne Jones
Opening Times: By apptointment only.
Please phone.
Min Mail Order UK: £10.00*
Cat. Cost: 2 x 1st class
Credit Cards: None
Specialities: Trees & shrubs for autumn
colour. Camellias, rhododendrons &
magnolias. Rarer conifer species & clones.
*Note: mail order Nov & Mar only.
Map Ref: W, B3

WDav **MARTIN DAVIS PLANTS** ⊠ EU ♘ €
Osric, 115 Calton Road, Gloucester,
Gloucestershire GL1 5ES
☎ (01452) 539749
Email: martin@osrics.freeserve.co.uk
Contact: Martin Davis
Opening Times: By appt. only.
Min Mail Order UK: No minimum charge*
Min Mail Order EU: Nmc
Cat. Cost: 4 x 1st class
Credit Cards: None
Specialities: *Allium, Lilium, Canna,* dwarf
bearded *Iris* & other bulbous/rhizomatous
subjects.
*Note: mail order for bulbs Oct-Jan, for
plants Mar-May, limited stock.
Map Ref: W, D5

WDib **DIBLEY'S NURSERIES** ▣ ⊠ EU ♘ ◆
Llanelidan, Ruthin,
Denbighshire LL15 2LG
☎ (01978) 790677

Fax: (01978) 790668
Email: sales@dibleys.com
Website: www.dibleys.com
Contact: R Dibley
Opening Times: 1000-1700 7 days
Mar-Oct.
Min Mail Order UK: No minimum charge
Min Mail Order EU: Nmc
Cat. Cost: Free
Credit Cards: Visa, Access, Switch, Electron,
Solo
Specialities: *Streptocarpus, Columnea,
Solenostemon* & other gesneriads & *Begonia.*
National Collection of *Streptocarpus.*
Map Ref: W, A3

WDin **DINGLE NURSERIES** ▣ €
Welshpool, Powys,
Wales SY21 9JD
☎ (01938) 555145
Fax: (01938) 555778
Email: kerry@dinglenurseries.co.uk
Website: www.dinglenurseries.co.uk
Contact: Kerry Hamer
Opening Times: 0900-1700 Wed-Mon.
Cat. Cost: Free plant list
Credit Cards: MasterCard, Switch,
EuroCard, Delta, Visa
Specialities: Largest range of trees &
shrubs in Wales. Wide seasonal selection
of garden plants incl. roses, herbaceous
perennials, conifers & bare rooted forestry,
hedging & fruit. All sizes incl. many mature
specimens.
Map Ref: W, B4

WDyf **DYFFRYN NURSERIES** ▣ ⊠ EU €
Home Farm, Dyffryn,
Cardiff,
Wales CF5 6JU
☎ (02920) 592085
Fax: (02920) 593462
Email: dyffrynnurseries@daiatlas.co.uk
Website: www.dyffryn-nurseries.co.uk
Contact: Victoria Hardaker
Opening Times: 0800-1600 Mon-Fri,
1100-1600 Sat & Sun.
Min Mail Order UK: £25.00
Min Mail Order EU: £25.00
Cat. Cost: None issued.
Credit Cards: MasterCard, Access, Switch,
Delta, Visa
Specialities: Plants with architectural forms
incl. large specimens & also aesthetic natural
landscaping products.
Map Ref: W, D3

WDyG DYFFRYN GWYDDNO NURSERY ✉ UK 🙆 ◆
Dyffryn Farm, Lampeter Velfrey, Narberth
Pembrokeshire, Wales SA67 8UN
☎ (01834) 861684
Email: sally.polson@virgin.net
Website: www.pembrokeshireplants.co.uk
Contact: Mrs S L Polson
Opening Times: 1000-1700 Mon-Thu Apr-
Oct & many Sun. Phone for details or an
appt. for other times.
Min Mail Order UK: No minimum charge*
Cat. Cost: 2 x 2nd class
Credit Cards:
Specialities: Eclectic, yet wide-ranging, from
tender salvias & grasses to bog. Peat free &
principled.
*Note: mail order via web site.
Map Ref: W, D2
OS Grid Ref: SR138148

WEas EASTGROVE COTTAGE GARDEN NURSERY
Sankyns Green, Little Witley,
Worcestershire WR6 6LQ
☎ (01299) 896389
Website: www.eastgrove.co.uk
Contact: Malcolm & Carol Skinner
Opening Times: 1400-1700 Thu-Sun
1st Apr-28th Jul & B/hol Mons. Closed
Aug. 1400-1700 Thu-Sat 5th Sep-
12th Oct.
Cat. Cost: On web
Credit Cards: None
Specialities: Unique cottage garden &
arboretum. Many varieties of *Viola*, *Iris*,
Dianthus & *Aquilegia*, plus a wide range of
old favourites & many unusual plants.
Map Ref: W, C5
OS Grid Ref: SO795644

WEll ELLWOOD PENSTEMONS ✉ UK
Ellwood House, Fern Road,
Ellwood, Coleford, Forest of Dean,
Gloucestershire GL16 7LY
☎ (01594) 833839
Contact: Yvonne Shorthouse
Opening Times: Most times Mon-Sat
Apr-Oct by appt. only, please phone first.
Min Mail Order UK: No minimum charge
Cat. Cost: 3 x 1st class
Credit Cards: None
Specialities: Penstemons. Will propagate to
order. Stock limited as propagated on site.
Map Ref: W, D4
OS Grid Ref: SO591082

WElm THE GARDEN AT THE ELMS NURSERY 🙆
Frenchlands Lane, Lower Broadheath,
Worcestershire WR2 6QU
☎ (01905) 640841
Fax: (01905) 640675
Email: msharthill@aol.com
Contact: Emma Stewart
Opening Times: Sat only 1st Apr-30th Sep
and by appt.
Cat. Cost: 3 x 1st class (plant list)
Credit Cards: None
Specialities: Unusual hardy plants & cottage
garden favourites, particularly *Achillea*,
Geranium, *Iris*, *Kniphofia* & *Papaver* grown
in small quantities & on view in old
farmhouse garden, open by appt.
Map Ref: W, C5
OS Grid Ref: SO791571

WEve EVERGREEN CONIFER CENTRE 🔲 ✉ UK ◆
Tenbury Road, Rock, Nr Kidderminster,
Worcestershire DY14 9RB
☎ (01299) 266581
Fax: (01299) 266755
Email: brian@evergreen-conifers.co.uk
Website: www.evergreen-conifers.co.uk
Contact: Mr B Warrington
Opening Times: 0900-1700 (dusk in
winter) Mon-Sat.
Min Mail Order UK: No minimum charge*
Cat. Cost: 4 x 1st class for list
Credit Cards: Electron, Visa, MasterCard,
Switch, Solo
Specialities: Conifers mainly but also acers,
heathers, trees, evergreen shrubs.
*Note: mail order small conifers only.
Map Ref: W, C4

WFar FARMYARD NURSERIES 🔲 ✉ EU 🔳 ◆
Llandysul, Dyfed, Wales SA44 4RL
☎ (01559) 363389, (01267) 220259
Fax: (01559) 362200
Email: richard@farmyardnurseries.co.uk
Website: www.farmyardnurseries.co.uk
Contact: Richard Bramley
Opening Times: 1000-1700 7 days excl.
Xmas, Boxing & New Year's Day.
Min Mail Order UK: No minimum charge
Min Mail Order EU: £50.00 + p&p

W

KEY		
✉ Mail order to UK or EU	🙆 Delivers to shows	
🔳 Exports beyond EU	€ Euro accepted	
🔲 Also supplies Wholesale	◆ See Display advertisement	

Cat. Cost: 4 x 1st class
Credit Cards: Visa, Switch, MasterCard
Specialities: Excellent general range especially *Helleborus, Hosta, Tricyrtis* & *Schizostylis*, plus shrubs, trees, climbers, alpines & esp. herbaceous. National Collection of *Tricyrtis*.
Map Ref: W, C2

WFib   FIBREX NURSERIES LTD ▣ ⊠ EU ☑ ♠
Honeybourne Road, Pebworth, Stratford-on-Avon, Warwickshire CV37 8XP
☎ (01789) 720788
Fax: (01789) 721162
Email: sales@fibrex.co.uk
Website: www.fibrex.co.uk
Contact: U Key-Davis & R L Godard-Key
Opening Times: 1030-1700 Mon-Fri, 1200-1700 Sat & Sun Mar-Jul. 1030-1600 Mon-Fri Aug-Feb. Office hours 0930-1700 Mon-Fri all year excl. last 2 wks Dec/1st wk Jan.
Min Mail Order UK: £10.00 + p&p
Min Mail Order EU: £20.00 + p&p
Cat. Cost: 2 x 2nd class
Credit Cards: MasterCard, Visa
Specialities: *Hedera*, ferns, *Pelargonium* & *Helleborus*. Plant collections subject to time of year, please check by phone. National Collections of *Pelargonium* & *Hedera*.
Map Ref: W, C5

WFoF   FLOWERS OF THE FIELD ▣
Field Farm, Weobley, Herefordshire HR4 8QJ
☎ (01544) 318262
Fax: (01544) 318262
Email: floweroffthefield@tesco.net
Contact: Kathy Davies
Opening Times: 0900-1900 7 days.
Cat. Cost: 2 x 1st class
Credit Cards: None
Specialities: Cut flowers eg lilies, chrysanthemums, carnations, freesias & gladioli. Traditional, unusual perennials & grasses, shrubs, trees, herbs. Summer & winter hanging baskets, bedding.
Map Ref: W, C4

WFTG   FROM THE GARDEN ⊠ UK ♠
Little Freeth, Thornbury, Nr Bromyard, Herefordshire HR7 4NW
☎ (01885) 482808
Email: linda@plantsfromthegarden.com
Website: www.plantsfromthegarden.com
Contact: Mrs L Waight

Opening Times: 1000-1800 Tue & Wed 1st Mar-31st Oct or by appt. Phone for directions.
Min Mail Order UK: No minimum charge
Cat. Cost: 2 x 2nd class
Credit Cards: None
Specialities: Unusual, rare & traditional garden-worthy herbaceous perennials, mostly hardy. Small selection of bulbs. Limited stock of some items.
Map Ref: W, C4

WGei   W G GEISSLER
Winsford, Kingston Road, Slimbridge, Gloucestershire GL2 7BW
☎ (01453) 890340
Fax: (01453) 890340
Email: w.geissler@virgin.net
Website: www.t.mann.taylor.clara.net/ptero.html
Contact: W G Geissler
Opening Times: 0900-1700 (2000 in summer) Mar-Nov.
Cat. Cost: None issued.
Credit Cards: None
Specialities: Hardy cacti & succulents & related books. National Collections of *Opuntia* (sect. *Tephrocactus*) & *Pterocactus*.
Map Ref: W, D4

WGer   FRON GOCH GARDEN CENTRE
Pant Road, Llanfaglan, Caernarfon, Gwynedd, Wales LL54 5RL
☎ (01286) 672212
Fax: (01286) 678912
Email: info@frongoch-gardencentre.co.uk
Website: www.frongoch-gardencentre.co.uk
Contact: R A & Mrs V Williams
Opening Times: 0900-1800 Mon-Sat, 1030-1630 Sun all year.
Cat. Cost: None issued
Credit Cards: MasterCard, Switch, Visa
Specialities: Wide range of trees, shrubs, conifers & herbaceous perennials, ferns & grasses; emphasis on plants for coastal & damp sites.
Map Ref: W, A2

WGor   GORDON'S NURSERY ⊠ UK ♠
1 Cefnpennar Cottages, Cefnpennar, Mountain Ash, Mid Glamorgan, Wales CF45 4EE
☎ (01443) 474593
Fax: (01443) 475835
Email: gordonsnursery@compuserve.com
Website: http:\\ourworld.compuserve.com/

homepages/gordonsnursery
Contact: D A Gordon
Opening Times: 1000-1800 7 days
1st Mar-31st Oct. 1100-1600 Sat & Sun
1st Nov-28th Feb.
Min Mail Order UK: No minimum charge*
Cat. Cost: 3 x 1st class
Credit Cards: Visa, MasterCard, Switch,
Solo, Electron
Specialities: Shrubs, perennials, alpines &
dwarf conifers.
*Note: mail order only available in some
cases, please check for conditions in
catalogue.
Map Ref: W, D3
OS Grid Ref: SO037012

WGwG   GWYNFOR GROWERS ⊠ UK €
Gwynfor, Pontgarreg, Llangranog,
Llandysul, Ceredigion Wales SA44 6AU
☎ (01239) 654151
Fax: (01239) 654152
Email: anne@gwynfor-growers.freeserve.co.uk
Contact: Anne & Bob Seaman
Opening Times: 1000-1600 Wed-Sun
winter, 1000-1800 Tue-Sun rest of year.
Min Mail Order UK: £30.00 + p&p
Cat. Cost: 4 x 1st class
Credit Cards: None
Specialities: Good general range specialising
in herbaceous plants & *Fuchsia*.
Map Ref: W, C2

WGWT   GRAFTED WALNUT TREES 🔲⊠ UK €
The Manse, Catel Isaac, Llandeilo,
Camarthenshire, Wales SA19 7TN
☎ (01558) 669043
Email: gary@bitenet.co.uk
Website: www.graftedwalnuts.co.uk
Contact: Gary Wignall
Opening Times: 0900-1800 Mon-Fri.
Min Mail Order UK: No minimum charge
Cat. Cost: 3 x 1st class
Credit Cards: None
Specialities: Grafted walnut trees including
nut-bearing varieties of English walnut,
ornamental forms of English & black
walnut, minor species & hybrids.
Note new address of nursery.

WHal   HALL FARM NURSERY ♠€
Vicarage Lane, Kinnerley, Nr Oswestry,
Shropshire SY10 8DH
☎ (01691) 682135
Fax: (01691) 682135
Email: hallfarmnursery@ukonline.co.uk

Website: www.hallfarmnursery.co.uk
Contact: Christine & Nick Ffoulkes-Jones
Opening Times: 1000-1700 Tue-Sat 1st
Mar-12th Oct 2002. 2003 may differ.
Cat. Cost: 4 x 1st class
Credit Cards: None
Specialities: Unusual herbaceous plants incl.
hardy *Geranium*, *Pulmonaria*, grasses, bog
plants & pool marginals, late-flowering
perennials, foliage plants.
Map Ref: W, B4
OS Grid Ref: SJ333209

WHar   HARLEY NURSERY
Harley, Shropshire SY5 6LP
☎ (01952) 510241
Fax: (01952) 510222
Email: Harleynurseries@farmersweekly.net
Contact: Duncan Murphy, Moira
Murphy, Michael Birt
Opening Times: 0900-1730 Mon-Sat,
1000-1750 Sun & B/hols. Winter hours
1000-1600 Sun & B/hols.
Cat. Cost: 2 x 1st class
Credit Cards: Visa, Access
Specialities: Wide range of ornamental &
fruit trees. Own grown shrubs, climbers,
wide range of hedging plants year round.
Conservation & wildlife plants & native
trees a speciality.
Map Ref: W, B4

WHbs   HERBS AT MYDDFAI
Beiliglas, Myddfai, Nr Llandovery,
Carmarthenshire, Wales SA20 0QB
☎ (01550) 720494
Fax: (01550) 720628
Email: gill@myddfai.com
Contact: Gill Swan
Opening Times: 1400-1800 Tue-Sat
Apr-Oct, or by appt.
Cat. Cost: 2 x 1st class
Credit Cards: None
Specialities: Herbs & wild flowers. Organic.
Map Ref: W, C3
OS Grid Ref: SN781310

WHCG   HUNTS COURT GARDEN & NURSERY
North Nibley, Dursley,
Gloucestershire GL11 6DZ
☎ (01453) 547440

W

Fax: (01453) 549944
Email: keith@huntscourt.fsnet.co.uk
Contact: T K & M M Marshall
Opening Times: Nursery & garden
0900-1700 Tue-Sat excl. Aug. Also by appt.
See NGS for Sun openings.
Cat. Cost: 5 x 2nd class
Credit Cards: None
Specialities: Old roses species & climbers.
Hardy *Geranium, Penstemon* & unusual
shrubs.
Map Ref: W, D4

WHCr HERGEST CROFT GARDENS
Kington, Herefordshire
HR5 3EG
☎ (01544) 230160
Fax: (01544) 232031
Email: banks@hergest.kc3.co.uk
Contact: Stephen Lloyd
Opening Times: 1330-1830 7 days Apr-Oct.
Cat. Cost: None issued
Credit Cards: None
Specialities: *Acer, Betula* & unusual woody
plants.
Map Ref: W, C4

WHen HENLLYS LODGE PLANTS
Henllys Lodge, Beaumaris, Anglesey,
Gwynedd, Wales LL58 8HU
☎ (01248) 810106
Email: cranesbill@hugheslane.freeserve.co.uk
Contact: Mrs E Lane
Opening Times: 1100-1700 Mon Wed Fri
Sat Sun & by appt. Apr-Oct.
Cat. Cost: 2 x 1st class
Credit Cards: None
Specialities: Hardy *Geranium*, ground cover
& cottage style perennials.
Map Ref: W, A3
OS Grid Ref: SH601773

**WHer THE HERB GARDEN & HISTORICAL
PLANT NURSERY** ⊠ EU ♠
Pentre Berw, Gaerwen, Angleseyy,
Wales LL60 6LF
☎ (01248) 422208, mobile 07751 583958
Email: The_Herb-Garden@hotmail.com
Contact: Corinne & David Tremaine-
Stevenson
Opening Times: 1000-1700 7 days excl.
Tue. Open all B/hols.
Min Mail Order UK: £15.00 + p&p
Min Mail Order EU: £50.00 + p&p
Cat. Cost: List £2.00 in stamps
Credit Cards: None

Specialities: Wide range of herbs, rare
natives & wild flowers; rare & unusual
perennials & old roses.
Map Ref: W, A2

WHHs HERITAGE HERBS ▨ ⊠ EU ♠
Gwynfor, Pontgarreg, Ceredigion,
Wales SA44 6AU
☎ (01239) 654151
Fax: (01239) 654152
Email: info@heritageherbs.co.uk
Contact: Anne & Bob Seaman
Opening Times: 1000-1700 Tues-Sun,
summer. 1000-1600 Wed-Sun, winter.
Min Mail Order UK: £30.00
Min Mail Order EU: £30.00
Cat. Cost: 4 x 1st class
Credit Cards: None
Specialities: Herbs
Map Ref: W, C2

**WHil HILLVIEW HARDY
PLANTS** ▨ ⊠ EU ▨ ♠ € ◆
(off B4176), Worfield, Nr Bridgnorth,
Shropshire WV15 5NT
☎ (01746) 716454
Fax: (01746) 716454
Email: hillview@themutual.net
Website: www.hillviewhardyplants.com
Contact: Ingrid Millington, John Millington
Opening Times: 0900-1700 Mon-Sat Mar-
mid Oct. At other times, please phone first.
Min Mail Order UK: £10.00 + p&p
Min Mail Order EU: £10.00 + p&p
Cat. Cost: 4 x 2nd class
Credit Cards: MasterCard, Visa
Specialities: Choice herbaceous perennials
incl. *Aquilegia, Astrantia, Auricula, Primula,
Monarda, Dierama, Crocosmia, Watsonia,
Eucomis, Phlox, Schizostylis, Verbascum,*
grasses & ferns.
Map Ref: W, B4
OS Grid Ref: SO772969

WHoo HOO HOUSE NURSERY ▨ € ◆
Hoo House, Gloucester Road, Tewkesbury,
Gloucestershire GL20 7DA
☎ (01684) 293389
Fax: (01684) 293389
Email: nursery@hoohouse.co.uk
Contact: Robin & Julie Ritchie
Opening Times: 1400-1700 Mon-Sat.
Cat. Cost: 3 x 1st class
Credit Cards: None
Specialities: Wide range of herbaceous &
alpines - many unusual, incl. *Campanula,*

W

Geranium & *Penstemon*. National Collections
of *Platycodon* & *Gentiana asclepiadea* cultivars.
Map Ref: W, C5
OS Grid Ref: SO893293

WHrl   HARRELLS HARDY PLANTS
(Office) 15 Coxlea Close, Evesham,
Worcestershire WR11 4JS
☎ (01386) 443077
Fax: (01386) 443852
Email: enicklin@evesham11.fsnet.co.uk
Website: http://mysite.freeserve.com/harrell
shardyplants
Contact: Liz Nicklin & Kate Phillips
Opening Times: By appt. only this year.
Please phone before visiting.
Cat. Cost: 3 x 1st class
Credit Cards: None
Specialities: A developing nursery offering
wide range of hardy plants, new & old,
many unusual. Note: nursery located off
Rudge Rd, Evesham. Please phone for
directions or see catalogue.
Map Ref: W, C5
OS Grid Ref: SP033443

WIvo   IVOR MACE NURSERIES ⊠ UK
2 Mace Lane, Ynyswen,
Treorci, Rhondda, Mid Glamorgan,
Wales CF42 6DS
☎ (01443) 775531
Email: ivormacc@hotmail.com
Contact: I Mace
Opening Times: Not open. Plants can be
seen growing. By appt.
Min Mail Order UK: £5.00 + p&p*
Cat. Cost: Sae
Specialities: Large exhibition
chrysanthemums.
*Note: delivery by mail order or collection
during Feb & Mar only.
Map Ref: W, C3

WIvy   IVYCROFT PLANTS
Upper Ivington, Leominster,
Herefordshire HR6 0JN
☎ (01568) 720344
Email: rogerandsue@ivycroft.freeserve.co.uk
Website: www.ivycroft.freeserve.co.uk
Contact: Roger Norman
Opening Times: 0900-1600 Wed & Thu
Mar-Sep. Other times by appt., please
phone.
Cat. Cost: 2 x 1st class
Credit Cards: None
Specialities: *Cyclamen, Galanthus, Salix,*

alpines & herbaceous.
Map Ref: W, C4
OS Grid Ref: SO464562

WJas   PAUL JASPER TREES ▣ ⊠ UK
The Lighthouse, Bridge Street, Leominster,
Herefordshire HR6 8DX
Fax: (01568) 616499 for orders.
Email: enquiries@jaspertrees.co.uk
Website: www.jaspertrees.co.uk
Contact: Paul Jasper
Opening Times: Mail order only.
Min Mail Order UK: £40.00 + p&p
Cat. Cost: 2 x 1st class
Credit Cards: None
Specialities: Full range of fruit &
ornamental trees. Over 100 modern and
traditional apple varieties + 220 others all
direct from the grower. Many unusual
varieties of *Malus domestica*.
Map Ref: W, C4

WJek   JEKKA'S HERB FARM ▣ ⊠ EU ☑ ♠ €
Rose Cottage, Shellards Lane, Alveston,
Bristol BS35 3SY
☎ (01454) 418878
Fax: (01454) 411988
Email: farm@jekkasherbfarm.com
Website: www.jekkasherbfarm.com
Contact: Jekka McVicar
Opening Times: By appt. only.
Min Mail Order UK: Nmc
Min Mail Order EU: Nmc*
Cat. Cost: 4 x 1st class
Credit Cards: Visa, MasterCard, Delta, Switch
Specialities: Culinary, medicinal, aromatic,
decorative herbs.
Note: individual quotations for EU Sales.
Soil Association licensed herb farm.
Map Ref: W, D4

WJun   JUNGLE GIANTS ▣ ⊠ EU ☑ €
Burford House Gardens, Tenbury Wells,
Worcestershire WR15 8HQ
☎ (01584) 819885
Fax: (01584) 819779
Email: bamboo@junglegiants.co.uk
Website: www.junglegiants.co.uk
Contact: Michael Brisbane
Opening Times: 7 days. By appt. only
please.

W

Min Mail Order UK: £20.00 + p&p
Min Mail Order EU: £25.00 + p&p
Cat. Cost: 2 x 1st class
Credit Cards: Access, MasterCard, Visa
Specialities: Bamboo.
Map Ref: W, C4

WKif **KIFTSGATE COURT GARDENS**
Kiftsgate Court, Chipping Camden,
Gloucestershire GL55 6LW
☎ (01386) 438777
Fax: (01386) 438777
Email: kiftsgte@aol.com
Website: www.kiftsgate.co.uk
Contact: Mrs J Chambers
Opening Times: 1400-1800 Wed, Thu &
Sun 1st Apr -30th Sep & B/hol Mons.
Also Sat in Jun & Jul.
Cat. Cost: None issued
Credit Cards: None
Specialities: Small range of unusual plants.
Map Ref: W, C5

W

WKin **KINGSTONE COTTAGE PLANTS** ⊠ EU
Weston-under-Penyard, Ross-on-Wye,
Herefordshire HR9 7PH
☎ (01989) 565267
Contact: Mr M Hughes
Opening Times: By appt. and as under NGS.
Min Mail Order UK: No minimum charge
Min Mail Order EU: Nmc
Cat. Cost: 2 x 1st class
Credit Cards: None
Specialities: National Collection of *Dianthus*.
Map Ref: W, C4

WLav **THE LAVENDER GARDEN** ▣⊠ EU ♦ €
Ashcroft Nurseries, Nr Ozleworth,
Kingscote, Tetbury, Gloucestershire GL8 8YF
☎ (01453) 860356, (01453) 549286
Contact: Andrew Bullock
Opening Times: 1100-1700 Sat & Sun.
Weekdays variable, please phone.
Min Mail Order UK: £10.00 + p&p
Min Mail Order EU: £20.00 + p&p
Cat. Cost: 2 x 1st class
Credit Cards: Visa, MasterCard
Specialities: *Lavandula*, *Buddleja*, plants to
attract butterflies. Herbs, wild flowers.
Map Ref: W, D5

WLeb **LEBA ORCHARD - GREEN'S
LEAVES** ▣⊠ UK ♦
Lea Bailey, Nr Ross-on-Wye,
Herefordshire HR9 5TY
☎ (01989) 750303

Contact: Paul Green
Opening Times: By appt. only, w/ends
preferred.
Min Mail Order UK: £10.00 + p&p
Cat. Cost: 2 x 2nd class
Credit Cards: None
Specialities: Ornamental grasses, sedges &
phormiums. Increasing range of rare &
choice shrubs, also some perennials.
Map Ref: W, C4

WLHH **LAWTON HALL HERBS**
Lawton Hall, Eardisland,
Herefordshire HR6 9AX
☎ (01568) 709215
Email: herbs@lawtonhall.co.uk
Website: www.LawtonHall.co.uk
Contact: Alexandra Fox
Opening Times: 1030-1830 Wed-Mon,
closed Tue.
Cat. Cost: 1 x 1st class
Credit Cards: None
Specialities: Herbs, culinary, aromatic &
medicinal.
Map Ref: W, C4

WLin **LINGEN NURSERY AND
GARDEN** ▣⊠ EU ♦
Lingen, Nr Bucknell,
Shropshire SY7 0DY
☎ (01544) 267720
Fax: (01544) 267720
Email: kim&maggie@lingen.freeserve.co.uk
Website: www.lingennursery.co.uk
Contact: Kim W Davis
Opening Times: 1000-1700 Thu-Mon Feb-
Oct. By appt. Thu-Mon Nov-Jan. Closed
Tue-Wed all year.
Min Mail Order UK: No minimum charge
Min Mail Order EU: £20.00 + p&p
Cat. Cost: 3 x 1st class
Credit Cards: Visa, MasterCard
Specialities: Alpines, rock plants, herbaceous
esp. *Androsace, Aquilegia, Campanula, Iris,
Primula*, auriculas & *Penstemon*. National
Collection of herbaceous *Campanula* &
housing *Iris sibirica*.
Map Ref: W, C4

WLow **LOWER SPRING NURSERY** ▣
Kenley, Shrewsbury, Shropshire SY5 6PA
☎ (01952) 510589
Contact: Bob Hemmings
Opening Times: Sat & Sun Mar-Oct.
Winter w/ends by arrangement, plus B/hols.
Credit Cards: None

Specialities: A good range of cacti &
succulents, plus herbaceous, alpines & shrubs.
Map Ref: W, B4

WLRN LITTLE RHYNDASTON NURSERIES
Hayscastle, Haverfordwest, Pembrokeshire,
Wales SA62 5PT
☎ (01437) 710656
Contact: D A & P Baster
Opening Times: 0900-1700 Mon-Sat,
1100-1700 Sun. Closed Aug.
Cat. Cost: None issued
Credit Cards: Visa, MasterCard, Switch
Specialities: Herbaceous perennials, conifers,
shrubs, alpines, climbers, patio plants, many
suitable for coastal locations.
Map Ref: W, C1

WLun LUNNON NURSERY ◪ ⊠ UK €
Little Lunnon, Broughton Green, Hanbury,
Nr Droitwich, Worcestershire WR9 7EF
☎ (01905) 391316
Fax: (01905) 391316
Contact: John Farmer
Opening Times: By appt. only. Please
phone first.
Min Mail Order UK: No minimum charge
Cat. Cost: 2 x 1st class
Credit Cards: None
Specialities: *Euphorbia*. Grafted trees. Wide
range of hardy perennials, shrubs & trees.
Map Ref: W, C5

**WMal MARSHALL'S
MALMAISON** ◪ ⊠ EU ⊠ ♠ €
4 The Damsells, Tetbury,
Gloucestershire GL8 8JA
☎ (01666) 502589
Contact: J M Marshall
Opening Times: By appt. only
Min Mail Order UK: £17 incl. p&p
Min Mail Order EU: £30 incl p&p
Cat. Cost: 1st class Sae
Credit Cards: None
Specialities: National Collection of
Malmaison carnations.
Map Ref: W, D5

WMaN THE MARCHES NURSERY ⊠ EU ♠
Presteigne, Powys, Wales LD8 2HG
☎ (01544) 260474
Fax: (01544) 260474
Contact: Jane Cooke
Opening Times: Not open, mail order only.
Min Mail Order UK: 6 plants (£18.00)+ p&p*
Min Mail Order EU: 6 plants (£18.00) + p&p

Cat. Cost: Large Sae for list
Credit Cards: None
Specialities: An increasing range of choice
perennials, incl. *Achillea, Chrysanthemum,
Erysimum, Geranium, Papaver, Penstemon* &
Phlox. *Note: mail order only in spring.

WMAq MEREBROOK WATER PLANTS ⊠ EU €
Merebrook Farm, Hanley Swan, Worcester,
Worcestershire WR8 0DX
☎ (01684) 310950
Fax: (01684) 310034
Email: enquiries@pondplants.co.uk
Website: www.pondplants.co.uk
Contact: Roger Kings & Biddi Kings
Opening Times: 1000-1600 Thu-Tue
Easter-Sep.
Min Mail Order UK: No minimum charge
Min Mail Order EU: £20.00
Cat. Cost: Free
Credit Cards: Access, Visa, Switch, Delta
Specialities: *Nymphaea* & other aquatic
plants. Extensive display gardens open to
the public (no charge). International
Waterlily & Water Gardening Society
accredited collection.
Map Ref: W, C5
OS Grid Ref: SO802425

WMnd MYND HARDY PLANTS ◪ ⊠ EU ♠
Delbury Hall Estate, Diddlebury, Craven
Arms, Shropshire SY7 9DH
☎ (01547) 530459
Fax: (01547) 530459
Email: sales@myndplants.co.uk
Website: www.myndplants.co.uk
Contact: Steve Adams
Opening Times: 1000-1700 Wed-Sun
Easter-end Oct. Other times phone for appt.
Min Mail Order UK: No minimum charge
Min Mail Order EU: Nmc
Cat. Cost: 4 x 2nd class
Credit Cards: Visa, MasterCard
Specialities: Herbaceous plants.
Map Ref: W, B4
OS Grid Ref: SO510852

WMoo MOORLAND COTTAGE PLANTS ⊠ UK
Rhyd-y-Groes, Brynberian, Crymych,
Pembrokeshire, Wales SA41 3TT
☎ (01239) 891363

Email: jenny@moorlandcottageplants.co.uk
Website: www.moorlandcottageplants.co.uk
Contact: Jennifer Matthews
Opening Times: 1000-1800 daily excl. Wed
end Feb-end Sep.
Min Mail Order UK: See cat. for details.
Cat. Cost: 4 x 1st class
Credit Cards: None
Specialities: Traditional & unusual hardy
perennials incl. *Aster, Astilbe, Crocosmia,
Geranium, Geum, Persicaria, Potentilla,
Sedum, Sidalcea, Tiarella*, ornamental
grasses, cottage garden & woodland plants,
colourful ground cover
Map Ref: W, C2
OS Grid Ref: SN091343

WMou   MOUNT PLEASANT TREES ▣ €
Rockhampton, Berkeley,
Gloucestershire GL13 9DU
☎ (01454) 260348
Contact: P & G Locke
Opening Times: By appt. only.
Cat. Cost: 3 x 2nd class
Credit Cards: None
Specialities: Wide range of trees for forestry,
hedging, woodlands & gardens esp. *Tilia,
Populus* & *Platanus.*
Map Ref: W, D4

WMul   MULU NURSERIES ▣ ⊠ EU ▣ €
Longdon Hill, Wickhamford, Evesham,
Worcestershire WR11 7RP
☎ (01386) 833171
Fax: (01386) 833136
Email: plants@mulu.co.uk
Website: www.mulu.co.uk
Contact: Andy Bateman
Opening Times: 1000-1800 or dusk 7 days.
Phone first Nov-Mar.
Min Mail Order UK: No minimum charge
Min Mail Order EU: £25.00 + p&p
Cat. Cost: 4 x 1st class
Credit Cards: Visa, MasterCard, Delta
Specialities: Exotic plants, hardy & tender
incl. bananas, gingers, palms, tree ferns,
aroids.
Map Ref: W, C5

WNor   NORFIELDS ▣ ⊠ EU ▣ ṅ €
Llangwm Arboretum, Usk,
Monmouthshire NP15 1NQ
☎ (01291) 650306
Fax: (01291) 650577
Email: andrew@norfield.co.uk
Website: www.Norfields.co.uk

Contact: Andrew Norfield
Opening Times: Not open.
Min Mail Order UK: £3.00 + p&p
Min Mail Order EU: £3.00 + p&p
Cat. Cost: 2 x 1st class
Credit Cards: None
Specialities: Wide range of tree seedlings for
growing on. *Acer, Betula, Stewartia* & pre-
treated seed.

WOBN   OLD BARN NURSERY ▣ ⊠ EU ṅ €
Llwynglas, Llwynteg, Ffynnon-ddrain,
Carmarthen, Wales SA33 6EE
☎ (01267) 237275
Email: oldbarnnursery@aol.com
Contact: G B J Smith & M Scott
Opening Times: Not open. Mail order only.
Min Mail Order UK: £10.00
Min Mail Order EU: £10.00
Cat. Cost: 2 x 1st class
Credit Cards: None
Specialities: Alpines, many unusual, in
small numbers. *Rhodohypoxis* in profusion.
Agapanthus & wide range of *Iris*, some in
small numbers.

WOFF   OLD FASHIONED FLOWERS ⊠ EU
Cleeway, Eardington, Bridgnorth,
Shropshire WV16 5JT
☎ (01746) 766909
Contact: John Snocken
Opening Times: By appt. only.
Min Mail Order UK: No minimum charge
Min Mail Order EU: Nmc
Cat. Cost: 2 x 2nd class
Credit Cards: None
Specialities: Show pansies, fancy pansies &
exhibition violas. National Collection of
Florists' Violas & Pansies. Some bedding
violas.
Map Ref: W, B4
OS Grid Ref: 723907

WOld   OLD COURT NURSERIES ⊠ EU ▣ €
Colwall, Nr Malvern,
Worcestershire WR13 6QE
☎ (01684) 540416
Fax: (01684) 565314
Email: picton@dircon.co.uk
Website: www.autumnasters.co.uk
Contact: Paul & Meriel Picton
Opening Times: 1100-1700 Wed-Sun May-
Oct, 7 days 2nd week Sep-2nd week Oct.
Min Mail Order UK: No minimum charge*
Min Mail Order EU: Nmc
Cat. Cost: 1 x 1st class

Credit Cards: None
Specialities: National Collection of
Michaelmas Daisies. Herbaceous perennials.
*Note: mail order for *Aster* only.
Map Ref: W, C4
OS Grid Ref: SO759430

WOrn **ORNAMENTAL TREE NURSERIES** ▨ ⊠ UK
Broomy Hill Gardens, Cobnash, Kingsland,
Herefordshire HR6 9QZ
☎ (01568) 708016
Fax: (01568) 709022
Email: enquiries@ornamental-trees.co.uk
Website: www.ornamental-trees.co.uk
Contact: Russell Mills
Opening Times: 0900-1700 Mon-Sat.
Min Mail Order UK: £9.95
Cat. Cost: 2 x 2nd class
Credit Cards: Visa, Switch, MasterCard,
Access, Delta, American Express
Specialities: Ornamental trees.
Map Ref: W, C4

WOTO **OGON TORA ORIENTAL
NURSERY** ▨ ♗ €
Pikes Pool Lane, Burcot, Bromsgrove,
Worcestershire B60 1LJ
☎ (0121) 445 3114
Contact: Mr J M Hall
Opening Times: By appt. only 1000-1730
7 days. Please phone before travelling.
Closed Xmas to New Year's Day inclusive.
Cat. Cost: None issued
Credit Cards: None
Specialities: Choice & unusual shrubs, trees,
perennials, ferns, bamboos. Particularly from
Japan & China. Nursery grows trees &
shrubs for the production of Bonsai.
Map Ref: W, C5

WOut **OUT OF THE COMMON WAY** ⊠ EU ♗
(Office) Penhyddgan, Boduan, Pwllheli
Gwynedd, Wales LL53 8YH
☎ (01758) 721577 (Office)
(01407) 720431 (Nursery)
Email: joanna.davidson@virginnet.co.uk
Contact: Joanna Davidson (nursery)
Margaret Mason (office & mail order)
Opening Times: By arrangement.
Min Mail Order UK: No minimum charge
Min Mail Order EU: Nmc
Cat. Cost: Sae 33p (2nd class)
Credit Cards: None
Specialities: *Lobelia, Nepeta, Geranium,
Salvia, Viola, Digitalis, Lavandula, Stachys* &
Veronica. Note: some plants propagated in

small quantities only. Nursery is at Pandy
Treban, Bryngwran, Anglesey.
Map Ref: W, A2
OS Grid Ref: SH370778

WOVN **THE OLD VICARAGE NURSERY** ⊠ UK ♗
Lucton, Leominster,
Herefordshire HR6 9PN
☎ (01568) 780538
Fax: (01568) 780818
Contact: Mrs R M Flake
Opening Times: By appt.
Min Mail Order UK: No minimum charge
Cat. Cost: 2 x 1st class
Credit Cards: None
Specialities: Roses: old roses; climbers &
ramblers; species & ground cover. *Euphorbia*
& half-hardy *Salvia*.
Map Ref: W, C4

WP&B **P & B FUCHSIAS** ⊠ UK ♗ €
Maes y Gwaelod, Penclawdd Road,
Penclawdd, Swansea, Wales SA4 3RB
☎ (01792) 851669
Fax: (01792) 851779
Email: pbfuchsias@fuchsias.u-net.com
Website: www.fuchsias.u-net.com
Contact: Paul Fisher
Opening Times: 0900-1800 7 days 1 Mar-
30 Sep.
Min Mail Order UK: £9.00 (6 plants @
£1.50 incl. p&p)
Cat. Cost: 3 x 1st class
Credit Cards: None
Specialities: Fuchsias. Hybrid & species.
Note: cuttings only available Mar-May. Very
limited quantities of each.
Map Ref: W, D3

WPat **CHRIS PATTISON** ▨ ⊠ UK ♗ €
Brookend, Pendock,
Gloucestershire GL19 3PL
☎ (01531) 650480
Fax: (01531) 650480
Email: cpplants@redmarley.freeserve.co.uk
Website: www.chrispattison.fsnet.co.uk
Contact: Chris Pattison
Opening Times: 0900-1700 Mon-Fri.
W/ends by appt. only.
Min Mail Order UK: £10.00 +p&p*
Cat. Cost: 3 x 1st class

W

Credit Cards: None
Specialities: Choice, rare shrubs & alpines.
Grafted stock esp. Japanese maples &
Liquidambar. Wide range of *Viburnum,*
Phormium, dwarf willows & dwarf
ericaceous shrubs.
*Note: mail order Nov-Feb only.
Map Ref: W, C5

WPen   PENPERGWM PLANTS
Penpergwm Lodge,
Abergavenny, Gwent,
Wales NP7 9AS
☎ (01873) 840422/840208
Fax: (01873) 840470/840208
Email: boyle@penpergwm.co.uk
Website: www.penplants.com
Contact: Mrs J Kerr/Mrs S Boyle
Opening Times: 28th Mar-29 Sep 2002,
27th Mar-28th Sep 2003, Thu-Sun 1400-
1800.
Cat. Cost: 2 x 1st class
Credit Cards: None
Specialities: Hardy perennials.
Map Ref: W, D4

WPer   PERHILL NURSERIES 🏵 ✉ EU 🔥 €
Worcester Road, Great Witley,
Worcestershire WR6 6JT
☎ (01299) 896329
Fax: (01299) 896990
Email: PerhillP@aol.com
Website: www.hartlana.co.uk/perhill/
Contact: Duncan Straw
Opening Times: 0900-1700 Mon-Sat,
1000-1600 Sun, 1st Feb-15th Oct & by
appointment.
Min Mail Order UK: No minimum charge
Min Mail Order EU: £10.00
Cat. Cost: 6 x 2nd class
Credit Cards: MasterCard, Delta, Switch,
EuroCard, Visa, Maestro
Specialities: 2500+ varieties of rare, unusual
alpines & herbaceous perennials incl.
Penstemon, Campanula, Salvia, Thymus,
herbs, *Veronica.*
Map Ref: W, C4

WPGP   PAN-GLOBAL PLANTS ✉ UK
Spoonbed Nursery, Rococo Garden,
Painswick, Gloucestershire GL6 6TH
☎ (01452) 814242
Fax: (01453) 768858
Contact: Nick Macer
Opening Times: 1100-1700 Wed-Sun
10th Jan-30th Nov. Also B/hols.

Min Mail Order UK: please enquire
Cat. Cost: 3 x 1st class
Credit Cards: MasterCard, Visa, Solo,
Delta, American Express
Specialities: Small nursery offering a wide
range of rare, unusual & desirable trees,
shrubs, herbaceous, bamboos, *Hydrangea* &
Magnolia.
Map Ref: W, D5

WPhl   JUST PHLOMIS ✉ UK
Sunningdale, Grange Court, Westbury-on-
Severn, Gloucestershire GL14 1PL
☎ (01452) 760268
Fax: (01452) 760268
Email: phlomis@manntaylor.com
Website: www.manntaylor.com/phlomis.html
Contact: J Mann Taylor
Opening Times: By appt. only.
Min Mail Order UK: £7.50 + p&p
Cat. Cost: 2 x 2nd class
Credit Cards: None
Specialities: National Collection of *Phlomis.*
Map Ref: W, D4
OS Grid Ref: SO727164

**WPic   THE PICTON CASTLE TRUST
NURSERY**
Picton Castle, Haverfordwest,
Pembrokeshire, Wales SA62 4AS
☎ (01437) 751326
Fax: (01437) 751326
Email: pct@pictoncastle.freeserve.co.uk
Website: www.pictoncastle.co.uk
Contact: D L Pryse Lloyd
Opening Times: 1030-1700 7 days except
Mon Apr-Oct. Other times by arrangement.
Cat. Cost: 1 x 1st class
Credit Cards: None
Specialities: Woodland & unusual shrubs.
Herbs.
Map Ref: W, D2

WPnn   THE PERENNIAL NURSERY 🔥
Rhosygilwen, Llanrhian Road,
St Davids, Pembrokeshire,
Wales SA62 6DB
☎ (01437) 721954
Fax: (01437) 721954
Email: Rhosygilwendairy@ukgateway.net
Contact: Mrs Philipa Symons
Opening Times: 0930-1730 every day
Mar-Oct. Nov-Feb by appt.
Credit Cards: None
Specialities: Herbaceous perennials &
alpines especially *Erodium.* Tender perennials

W

especially *Argyranthemum*.
Map Ref: W, C1
OS Grid Ref: SM775292

WPnP **PENLAN PERENNIALS** ⊠ EU ⊠ ⋔ €
Penlan Farm, Penrhiwpal, Llandysul
Ceredigion, Wales SA44 5QH
☎ (01239) 851244
Fax: (01239) 851244
Email: rcain@penlanfarm.co.uk
Website: www.penlanperennials.co.uk
Contact: Richard & Jane Cain
Opening Times: 0930-1730 Wed-Sun
Mar-Sep & B/hols.
Min Mail Order UK: No minimum charge
Min Mail Order EU: Nmc
Cat. Cost: 4 x 2nd class
Credit Cards: None
Specialities: Hardy *Geranium* (200+). Dry
& moist shade lovers & woodland plants,
incl. bulbs, climbers, ferns but esp.
herbaceous perennials.
Note: mail order all year, next day delivery.
Map Ref: W, C2
OS Grid Ref: SN344457

WPPR **PERSHORE PLANT**
RAISERS ⊿ ⊠ EU € ◆
Pensham, Pershore,
Worcestershire WR10 3HB
☎ (01386) 554672
Fax: (01386) 556555
Contact: Edward Wilson
Opening Times: 1000-1600 Mar-Oct,
Mon-Sat.
Min Mail Order UK: £11.00*
Min Mail Order EU: £12.00
Cat. Cost: 2 x 1st class
Credit Cards: None
Specialities: *Penstemon, Salvia, Diascia*.
*Note: mail order Mar-May & Sep-Nov.
Map Ref: W, C5

WPrP **PRIME PERENNIALS** ⊠ EU
Llety Moel, Rhos-y-Garth, Llanilar, Nr
Aberystwyth, Ceredigion, Wales SY23 4SG
☎ (01974) 241505
Contact: Elizabeth Powney
Opening Times: Not open to public.
Min Mail Order UK: No minimum charge
Min Mail Order EU: Nmc
Cat. Cost: 4 x 1st class
Credit Cards: None
Specialities: Unusual & interesting
perennials, bulbs & grasses. *Dierama,
Fritillaria, Tulbaghia, Kniphofia & Tricyrtis*.

Nursery 650ft above sea level.
*Note: mail order Apr-Dec.
Map Ref: W, C3

WRha **RHANDIRMWYN PLANTS**
8 Pannau Street, Rhandirmwyn, Nr
Llandovery, Carmarthenshire,
Wales SA20 0NP
☎ (01550) 760220
Fax: (01550) 760399
Contact: Sara Fox/Thomas Sheppard
Opening Times: Open most days, but
please ring first to avoid disappointment.
Cat. Cost: none issued.
Credit Cards: None
Specialities: 1000+ varieties & species incl.
aquilegias, campanulas, chrysanthemums,
digitalis, geraniums, geums, *Lychnis,
Mentha, Monarda, Origanum*, primulas,
Rosmarinus, salvias & violas. Stock
limited in quantity but not variety!
Map Ref: W, C3

WRHF **RED HOUSE FARM**
Flying Horse Lane, Bradley Green,
Nr Redditch, Worcestershire B96 6QT
☎ (01527) 821269
Fax: (01527) 821674
Email:
contact@redhousefarmgardenandnursery.co.uk
Website:
www.redhousefarmgardenandnursery.co.uk
Contact: Mrs Maureen Weaver
Opening Times: 0900-1700 Mon-Sat all
year. 1000-1700 Sun & B/Hols.
Cat. Cost: 2 x 1st class
Credit Cards: None
Specialities: Cottage garden perennials.
Map Ref: W, C5

WRic **RICKARD'S HARDY FERNS** ⊿ ⊠ EU
Kyre Park, Kyre, Tenbury Wells,
Worcestershire WR15 8RP
☎ (01885) 410282, (01885) 410729
Fax: (01885) 410729
Contact: Martin Rickard
Opening Times: 0900-1700 Mon & Wed-
Fri, 1100-1700 Sat & Sun Mar-Oct. 1100-
1600 Nov-Mar by appt. only.
Min Mail Order UK: £30.00 + p&p*
Min Mail Order EU: £50.00 + p&p

W

KEY		
⊠ Mail order to UK or EU	⋔ Delivers to shows	
⊠ Exports beyond EU	€ Euro accepted	
⊿ Also supplies Wholesale	◆ See Display advertisement	

Cat. Cost: 5 x 1st class or 6 x 2nd class
Credit Cards: None
Specialities: Ferns, hardy & half-hardy, tree ferns. National Collection of *Polypodium*.
*Note: UK customers order with limited cheque. EU customers confirm availability before ordering. Rare items in limited numbers, year round availability not guaranteed.
Map Ref: W, C4

WRos ROSEMARY'S FARMHOUSE NURSERY
Llwyn-y-moel-gau, Llanfihangel, Llanfyllin, Powys, Wales SY22 5JE
☎ (01691) 648196
Fax: (01691) 648196
Email: rosemary@farmhouse-nursery.fsnet.co.uk
Contact: Rosemary Pryce
Opening Times: 1000-1700 most days all year, but advisable to phone to confirm.
Cat. Cost: None issued.
Credit Cards: None
Specialities: Unusual perennials & ornamental grasses. Hardy geraniums.
Map Ref: W, B3
OS Grid Ref: SJ083149

WRus RUSHFIELDS OF LEDBURY ▣ ⋔ €
Ross Road, Ledbury, Herefordshire HR8 2LP
☎ (01531) 632004
Fax: (01531) 633454
Email: rush01531@aol.com
Website: www.rushfields.co.uk
Contact: B & J Homewood
Opening Times: 1100-1700 Wed-Sat. Other times by appt.
Cat. Cost: A5 Sae 31p + £1.00
Credit Cards: Visa, Access
Specialities: Unusual herbaceous incl. *Euphorbia*, hardy *Geranium*, *Helleborus*, *Hosta*, *Penstemon*, primroses & grasses.
Map Ref: W, C4

WSan SANDSTONES COTTAGE GARDEN PLANTS ⊠ EU ⋔ €
58 Bolas Heath, Great Bolas, Shropshire TF6 6PS
☎ (01952) 541657
Fax: (01952) 541657
Email: pbrelsforth@ewcom.net
Website: www.sandstonesplants.mcmail.com
Contact: Joanne Brelsforth
Opening Times: By appt. only.
Min Mail Order UK: £10.00 + p&p
Min Mail Order EU: £25.00 + p&p

Cat. Cost: 4 x 1st class
Credit Cards: None
Specialities: Unusual & interesting hardy perennials. Large range of variegated varieties.
Map Ref: W, B4

WSel THE SELSLEY HERB NURSERY ⋔
Hayhedge Lane, Bisley, Stroud, Gloucestershire GL6 7AN
☎ (01452) 770073
Fax: (01452) 770879
Contact: Rob Wimperis
Opening Times: 1000-1700 Tue-Sat, 1400-1700 Sun & B/hols Mar-Oct. Nov-Feb variable, please phone to check. only.
Cat. Cost: 4 x 1st class
Credit Cards: MasterCard, Visa
Specialities: Culinary, aromatic & medicinal herbs & selected garden plants.
Map Ref: W, D5
OS Grid Ref: SO058906

WSHC STONE HOUSE COTTAGE NURSERIES
Stone, Nr Kidderminster, Worcestershire DY10 4BG
☎ (01562) 69902
Fax: (01562) 69960
Email: louisa@shcn.co.uk
Website: www.shcn.co.uk
Contact: J F & L N Arbuthnott
Opening Times: 1000-1730 Wed-Sat. & B/hol Mon. By appt. only Oct-Mar.
Cat. Cost: Sae
Credit Cards: None
Specialities: Small general range esp. wall shrubs, climbers & unusual plants.
Map Ref: W, C5

WShi JOHN SHIPTON (BULBS) ▣ ⊠ EU ▣ €
Y Felin, Henllan Amgoed, Whitland, Dyfed, Wales SA34 0SL
☎ (01994) 240125
Fax: (01994) 241180
Email: bluebell@zoo.co.uk
Website: www.bluebellbulbs.co.uk
Contact: John Shipton & Alison Foot
Opening Times: By appt. only.
Min Mail Order UK: No minimum charge
Min Mail Order EU: Nmc
Cat. Cost: Sae
Credit Cards: None
Specialities: Native British bulbs, & bulbs & plants for naturalising.
Map Ref: W, D2
OS Grid Ref: SN188207

WSPU   PERSHORE COLLEGE OF
HORTICULTURE ▣
Specialist Plant Unit & Plant Centre,
Avonbank, Pershore,
Worcestershire WR10 3JP
☎ (01386) 561385
Fax: (01386) 555601
Contact: Jo Yates (Plant Centre)
Opening Times: (Plant centre) 0900-1700
Mon-Sat, 1000-1600 Sun.
Cat. Cost: £1.00
Credit Cards: Visa, Access
Specialities: National Collection of
Penstemon. Open for viewing 0800-1630
Mon-Fri.
Map Ref: W, C5

WStI   ST ISHMAEL'S NURSERIES
Haverfordwest Pembrokeshire,
Wales SA62 3SX
☎ (01646) 636343
Fax: (01646) 636343
Email: david@saintishmaels.fsnet.co.uk
Website: www.st-ishmaelsgardencentre.co.uk
Contact: Mr D & Mrs H Phippen
Opening Times: 0900-1730 7 days summer.
0900-1700 7 days winter.
Cat. Cost: None issued
Credit Cards: Visa, Diners, Access, Switch,
Delta, MasterCard, EuroCard
Specialities: Wide general range.
Map Ref: W, D1

WSuV   SUNNYBANK VINE NURSERY ▣ ⊠ EU ⊠
The Old Trout Inn, Dulas,
Herefordshire HR2 0HL
☎ (01981) 240256
Email: http://vinenursery@hotmail.com
Website: vinenursery.netfirms.com
Contact: B R Edwards
Opening Times: Not open, mail order only
Min Mail Order UK: £8.00 incl. p&p
Min Mail Order EU: £10.00 incl. p&p⁺
Cat. Cost: Sae
Credit Cards: None
Specialities: Vines.
⁺Note: EU sales by arrangement.
Map Ref: W, C4

WTan   TAN-Y-LLYN NURSERIES
Meifod, Powys, Wales SY22 6YB
☎ (01938) 500370
Fax: (01938) 500303
Email: callumjohnston@tanyllyn.the-
nursery.co.uk
Contact: Callum Johnston

Opening Times: 1000-1700 Tue-Fri
Mar-Jun and at other times by appt.
Cat. Cost: 2 x 1st class
Credit Cards: None
Specialities: Herbs, alpines, perennials.
Map Ref: W, B3
OS Grid Ref: SJ167125

WTel   TELLING AND COATES ▣ ⊠ UK
64A Church Street, Charlton Kings,
Cheltenham, Gloucestershire GL53 8AS
☎ (01242) 514472
Email: tellingandcoates@freenet.co.uk
Website: www.tellingandcoates.freeola.net
Contact: John Coates
Opening Times: Nursery open 0830-1300
& 1400-1730 Mar-Nov, closed Sun, Wed &
B/hols. Dec-Feb by appt. only
Min Mail Order UK: No minimum charge
Cat. Cost: 3 x 1st class or 4 x 2nd class
Credit Cards: None
Specialities: A traditional hardy plant
nursery offering a wide range of shrubs,
climbers, heathers, alpines & herbaceous
plants at reasonable prices.
Map Ref: W, C5
OS Grid Ref: SO966205

WTin   TINPENNY PLANTS
Tinpenny Farm, Fiddington, Tewkesbury,
Gloucestershire GL20 7BJ
☎ (01684) 292668
Email: plants@tinpenny.totalserve.co.uk
Contact: Elaine Horton
Opening Times: 1200-1700 Tue-Thu or by
appointment.
Cat. Cost: 2 x 1st class
Credit Cards: None
Specialities: Wide range of hardy garden-
worthy plants esp. *Helleborus, Iris* &
Sempervivum. Small nursery will propagate
to order rare plants from own stock.
Map Ref: W, C5

WTMC   TIR MAB CYNAN NURSERY ▣
Brithdir, Dolgellau, Gwynedd,
Wales LL40 2RW
☎ (01341) 450339
Fax: (01341) 450339
Contact: Jim Haunch
Opening Times: 1000-dusk, Easter-1 Oct.

KEY		
⊠ Mail order to UK or EU	🏃 Delivers to shows	
🏹 Exports beyond EU	€ Euro accepted	
▣ Also supplies Wholesale	◆ See Display advertisement	

Cat. Cost: None issued
Specialities: Hardy *Geranium*, *Hemerocallis*, hostas, ferns, *Iris*, a wide range of hardy perennials & sought after plants.
Map Ref: W, B3

WTre   TREASURES OF TENBURY LTD ⊠ EU €
Burford House Gardens, Tenbury Wells, Worcestershire WR15 8HQ
☎ (01584) 810777
Fax: (01584) 810673
Email: treasures@burford.co.uk
Website: www.burford.co.uk
Contact: Mike Humphries
Opening Times: 1000-1800 (dusk in winter) 7 days.
Min Mail Order UK: No minimum charge
Min Mail Order EU: Nmc
Cat. Cost: 4 x 1st class stamps
Credit Cards: Visa, Access, Switch
Specialities: *Clematis* and herbaceous, bamboos, trees & shrubs. National Collection of *Clematis*.
Map Ref: W, C4

WViv   VIV MARSH POSTAL PLANTS ⊠ EU 🖾 € ◆
Walford Heath, Shrewsbury, Shropshire SY4 2HT
☎ (01939) 291475
Fax: (01939) 290743
Email: mail@PostalPlants.co.uk
Website: www.PostalPlants.co.uk
Contact: Mr Viv Marsh
Opening Times: 1000-1600 Sat, Sun & B/hols, Mar-Oct. Please ring to check.
Min Mail Order UK: No minimum charge
Min Mail Order EU: Nmc
Cat. Cost: 5 x 1st class or 2 x IRCs (£1 refund on first order)
Credit Cards: Visa, MasterCard, Switch
Specialities: Rare & routine herbaceous perennials. Worldwide plant introductions, incl. new *Alstroemeria*, *Zantedeschia*, *Gypsophila*, *Aster* & *Solidago*.
Note: mail order beyond Europe Oct-Feb only when plants are dormant.
Map Ref: W, B4

WWal   THE WALLED GARDEN AT PIGEONSFORD 🖾 ⊠ UK €
Llangranog, Llandysul, Ceredigion, Wales SA44 6AF
☎ (01239) 654360
Fax: (01239) 654360
Email: pigeonsford@llangrannog.com

Website: www.llangrannog.com/pigeonsford
Contact: David & Hilary Pritchard
Opening Times: 1000-1800 Easter-end Oct. Phone for appt. Nov-Easter. Closed Mon & Tue.
Min Mail Order UK: £6.00 + p&p
Cat. Cost: 4 x 1st class
Credit Cards: None
Specialities: Good general range specialising in herbaceous plants esp. hardy *Geranium* & *Primula*. *Camellia*.
Map Ref: W, C2
OS Grid Ref: SN325543

WWeb   WEBBS OF WYCHBOLD 🖾 € ◆
Wychbold, Droitwich, Worcestershire WR9 0DG
☎ (01527) 861777
Fax: (01527) 861284
Email: carole@webbsofwychbold.co.uk
Website: www.webbsofwychbold.co.uk
Contact: David Smith/Olly Spencer
Opening Times: 0900-1800 Mon-Fri winter. 0900-2000 Mon-Fri summer. 0900-1800 Sat & 1030-1630 Sun all year. Closed Xmas Day, Boxing Day & Easter Sun.
Cat. Cost: None issued
Credit Cards: Visa, Access, American Express
Specialities: Hardy trees & shrubs, climbers, conifers, alpines, heathers, herbaceous, herbs, roses, fruit & aquatics. National Collection of shrubby *Potentilla*.
Map Ref: W, C5

WWes   WESTONBIRT ARBORETUM ⊠ UK
(Forest Enterprise), The National Arboretum Tetbury Glos GL8 8QS
☎ (01666) 880544   **Fax:** (01666) 880386
Email: plant.centre@forestry.gsi.gov.uk
Website: www.westonbirtarboretum.com
Contact: Glyn R Toplis, Penny Jones
Opening Times: 1000-1730 7 days summer, 1000-1700 winter.
Min Mail Order UK: No minimum charge*
Cat. Cost: None issued.
Credit Cards: Visa, Access, Switch, Solo, Delta
Specialities: Japanese maples & general range of trees & shrubs, many choice & rare. Most plants available in small numbers only.
*Note: mail order Dec-Mar only.
Map Ref: W, D5

WWhi   WHIMBLE NURSERY
Kinnerton, Presteigne, Powys, Wales LD8 2PD
☎ (01547) 560413

W

Email: nursery@whimble.totalserve.co.uk
Contact: Liz Taylor
Opening Times: 1030-1730 Wed-Sun
(closed Mon & Tue except B/hol Mons)
Apr-mid Oct.
Cat. Cost: 5 x 1st class*
Credit Cards: None
Specialities: Mainly herbaceous, some
unusual. Small collections of *Achillea*,
Crocosmia, Geranium, Viola.
*Note: send Sae for plant list (no
descriptions).
Map Ref: W, C4

WWin WINTERGREEN NURSERIES ⋔
Bringsty Common, Bringsty, Worcester,
Worcestershire WR6 5UJ
☎ (01886) 821858 (eves.)
Contact: S Dodd
Opening Times: 1000-1730 Wed-Sun
1st Mar-31st Oct & by appt.
Cat. Cost: 2 x 2nd class
Credit Cards: None
Specialities: General, esp. alpines &
herbaceous.
Map Ref: W, C4
OS Grid Ref: SO708555

WWol WOOLMANS PLANTS LTD ▣ ⊠ EU €
The Plant Centre, Knowle Hill, Evesham,
Worcestershire WR11 7EN
☎ (01386) 833022
Fax: (01386) 832915
Email: sales@woolman.co.uk
Website: www.woolman.co.uk
Contact: John Woolman
Opening Times: 0900-1700 Mon-Sun.
Min Mail Order UK: No minimum charge
Min Mail Order EU: Nmc
Cat. Cost: Free
Credit Cards: MasterCard, Visa, Switch, Solo
Specialities: *Chrysanthemum*, hanging basket
& patio plants, *Dahlia*, perennials.
Map Ref: W, C5

WWpP WATERPUMP PLANTS ⊠ UK
Waterpump Farm, Ryeford, Ross-on-Wye,
Herefordshire HR9 7PU
☎ (01989) 750177
Email: waterpump_plants@hotmail.com
Contact: Mrs E Sugden
Opening Times: 1100-1800 Tues-Sat
Apr-Sep or by appt.
Min Mail Order UK: £15.00
Cat. Cost: 4 x 1st class
Credit Cards: None

Specialities: Hardy geraniums, aquatics,
moisture loving and many unusual
herbaceous plants. Organically grown.
Map Ref: W, C4
OS Grid Ref: SO642226

WWst WESTONBIRT PLANTS ⊠ EU ▣ €
9 Westonbirt Close, Worcester,
Worcestershire WR5 3RX
☎ (01905) 350429 (answerphone)
Fax: (01905) 350429
Contact: Garry Dickerson
Opening Times: Not open, strictly mail
order only.
Min Mail Order UK: No minimum charge
Min Mail Order EU: Nmc
Cat. Cost: 3 x 1st class
Credit Cards: None
Specialities: *Iris, Fritillaria, Erythronium*,
particular interest in *Iris* species, + *Crocus,
Corydalis, Lilium, Arisaema, Trillium, Arum*
& tulip species. Many rare plants in limited
numbers.

WWye WYE VALLEY PLANTS ⋔ ◆
The Nurtons, Tintern, Chepstow, Gwent,
Wales NP16 7NX
☎ (01291) 689253
Fax: (01291) 689253
Email: elsa.adrian@thenurtons.fsnet.co.uk
Website: www.thenurtons.co.uk
Contact: Adrian & Elsa Wood
Opening Times: 1030-1700 Wed-Mon,
mid Feb-mid Oct. Other times by appt.
(closed Tue).
Cat. Cost: 3 x 1st class
Credit Cards: None
Specialities: Wide range of unusual
perennials, aromatic and medicinal herbs,
Salvia, grasses & sedges. Soil Association
symbol. Cert UK 5.
Map Ref: W, D4
OS Grid Ref: SO536011

ABROAD

XB&T B & T WORLD SEEDS ▣ ⊠ EU ▣ €
Paguignan, 34210 Olonzac, France
☎ 00 33 (0) 4689 12963
Fax: 00 33 (0) 4689 13039
Email: lesley@b-and-t-world-seeds.com

KEY		
⊠ Mail order to UK or EU	⋔ Delivers to shows	
▣ Exports beyond EU	€ Euro accepted	
▣ Also supplies Wholesale	◆ See Display advertisement	

Website: www.b-and-t-world-seeds.com
Contact: Lesley Sleigh
Min Mail Order UK: £10.00
Min Mail Order EU: £10.00
Cat. Cost: £10 Europe, £14 elsewhere.
Credit Cards: Visa, MasterCard
Specialities: Master list contains over 40,000 items. 700 sub-lists available.
Note: exports seed only. Catalogue/botanical reference system available on CD Rom. SeedyRom™ catalogue £20 worldwide.

XBlo TABLE BAY VIEW NURSERY ⊠ EU ⊠
(Office) 60 Molteno Road, Oranjezicht, Cape Town 8001, South Africa
☎ 00 27 21 683 5108/424 4854/426 4227
Fax: 00 27 21 683 5108/426 4227
Contact: Terence Bloch
Opening Times: No personal callers.
Min Mail Order UK: £15.00 + p&p
Min Mail Order EU: £15.00
Cat. Cost: £3.30 (cheque/postal order)
Credit Cards: None
Specialities: Tropical & sub-tropical ornamental & fruiting plants. UK customers may contact Cape Town office or UK Agents, see Nursery Code NBlo.

XDoo IGNACE VAN DOORSLAER ⊠ ⊠ EU ⋒ €
Kapellendries 52, B 9090, Melle Gontrode, Belgium
☎ 0032 (09) 252 11 23
Fax: 0032 (09) 252 44 55
Contact: Ignace van Doorslaer
Opening Times: 6 days per week, by appt.
Min Mail Order UK: Depends on weight*
Min Mail Order EU: Depends on weight*
Cat. Cost: Free
Credit Cards: None
Specialities: *Agapanthus.*
*Note: invoice sent when transport charges known. £ stirling accepted. Located 12km south of Ghent. Will deliver to shows in Belgium, France & Holland.

XFro FROSCH EXCLUSIVE PERENNIALS ⊠ ⊠ EU ⊠ €
Am Brunnen 14, D-85551 Kirchheim, Germany
☎ 00 49 172 842 2050

Fax: 00 49 9077 5565
Email: info@cypripedium.de
Website: www.cypripedium.de
Contact: Michael Weinert
Opening Times: Not open, mail order only. 0700-2200.
Min Mail Order UK: £120.00 + p&p
Min Mail Order EU: £120.00 + p&p
Cat. Cost: None issued.
Credit Cards: None
Specialities: *Cypripedium* hybrids. Hardy orchids.
Note: exports beyond the EU.

XJel JELITTO PERENNIAL SEED ⊠ ⊠ EU ⊠ € ◆
PO Box 1264, D-29685 Schwarmstedt, Germany
☎ 00 49 50 71-98 29-0
Fax: 00 49 50 71-98 29-27
Email: info@jelitto.com
Website: www.jelitto.com
Contact: Ulrich Schamp, Georg Uebelhart
Opening Times: Not open. Mail order & Online shop.
Min Mail Order UK: €40 + p&p
Min Mail Order EU: €40 + p&p
Cat. Cost: €5
Credit Cards: Visa, MasterCard, JCB
Specialities: Alpines, perennials, herbs, wild flowers, ornamental grass seed, 2500+ varieties.
UK Agent: Meadows (Fenton) Ltd, PO Box 78, St Ives, PE27 4UQ (Richard Oliver) tel: (01480)463570 Fax: (01480) 466042 Email: richard@jelitto.com

XPab PABIANICE BOTANICAL GARDEN ⊠ UK ⊠ €
PL-95-200, Pabianice, Box 6 Poland
Contact: Roman Plaskota
Opening Times: Please write for catalogue.
Min Mail Order UK: See cat. for details
Cat. Cost: 2 x IRC
Credit Cards: None
Specialities: Botanic Garden offering wide range of seed: lilies, day lilies, perennials, herbs, shrubs, trees, climbers.

Nursery Index by Name

Nurseries that are included in the *RHS Plant Finder* for the first time this year (or have been reintroduced) are marked in **bold type**. Full details of the nurseries will be found in

Nursery Details by Code on page 772. For a key to the geographical codes, see the reverse of the card insert at the start of **Nurseries**.

Coombland Gardens	SCou
Patricia Cooper	ECoo
Ian and Deborah Coppack	**MIDC**
Cotswold Garden Flowers	WCot
Cottage Garden Nursery	LCtg
Cottage Garden Plants	NCot
Cottage Garden Plants and Herbs	CCge
The Cottage Garden	ECot
The Cottage Herbery	WCHb
Cottage Nurseries	ECtt
Country Lady Nursery	MCLN
County Park Nursery	ECou
Cranesbill Nursery	WCra
Creake Plant Centre	ECre
Crescent Plants	MCre
Crin Gardens	**ECri**
Crocknafeola Nursery	ICro
Crofters Nurseries	SCrf
Croftway Nursery	SCro
Croston Cactus	NCro
Crown Nursery	ECrN
Crûg Farm Plants	WCru
CTDA	LCTD
Cwmrhaiadr Nursery	WCwm
D K Plants	MDKP
Dacus Plants	IDac
Daisy Roots	**LDai**
Dalesview Nursery	NDlv
Darasina Nursery	**EDsa**
D'Arcy & Everest	EDAr
David Cheshire Seeds and Plants	MDCh
Martin Davis Plants	WDav
De Jager & Sons	SDeJ
Deacon's Nursery	SDea
Derek Lloyd Dean	LDea
Deanston Nursery	GDea
Deelish Garden Centre	**IDee**
Designer Plants	SDes
Desirable Plants	CDes
Devon & Dorset Bamboo	CDDB
Devon Violet Nursery	CDev
Devonshire Lavenders & Herbs	**CLvH**
DHE Plants	MDHE
Dibley's Nurseries	WDib
Dickson Nurseries Ltd	IDic
Different Plants	**EDif**
Dingle Nurseries	WDin
Samuel Dobie & Son	CDob
Ignace van Doorslaer	XDoo
Dove Cottage Nursery	NDov
Downderry Nursery	SDow
Dragoons Pool Nursery	GDrg
Drake's Alpines	GDra
Drysdale Garden Exotics	SDry
Duchy of Cornwall	CDoC
Dulford Nurseries	CDul
Dunge Valley Gardens	MDun
Dyffryn Gwyddno Nursery	WDyG
Dyffryn Nurseries	WDyf
Dysons Nurseries	SDys
Earlstone Nursery	LEar
East Northdown Farm	SEND
Eastgrove Cottage Garden Nursery	WEas
Ebberly Down Nursery	**CEbD**
Edrom Nurseries	**GEdr**
Edulis	LEdu
Eggesford Gardens & Country Centre Ltd	CEgg
Eggleston Hall	NEgg
Eildon Plants	GEil
Elizabeth House Nursery	**MEHN**
Charles F Ellis	WCFE
Ellwood Penstemons	WEll
Elm Tree Nursery	CElm
Elsworth Herbs	EEls
Elworthy Cottage Plants	CElw
Endsleigh Gardens	CEnd
Equatorial Plant Co.	NEqu
The Europa Nursery	LEur
Evelix Daffodils	GEve
Evergreen Conifer Centre	WEve
Fairhaven Nursery	CFai
Fairholm Plants	GFai
Fairweather's Garden Centre	SFai
Famecheck Special Plants	**EFam**
Family Trees	SFam
Farmyard Nurseries	WFar
Feebers Hardy Plants	CFee
The Fern Nursery	EFer
Fernwood Nursery	CWil
Fibrex Nurseries Ltd	WFib
Field House Nurseries	MFie
Fillan's Plants	CFil
Fillpots Nursery	**EFpt**
Fir Tree Farm Nursery	CFir
Fir Trees Pelargonium Nursery	NFir
The Firs Nursery	MFir
Margery Fish Gardens	CFis
Flaxton House Nursery	**NFla**
Fleurs Plants	GFle
Flora Exotica	EFEx
The Flower Bower	CFwr
Flowers of the Field	WFoF
Foliage Scented & Herb Plants	LFol
Ford Nursery	**CFRD**
Ford Nursery	NFor
Four Seasons	EFou
Four Ways Garden & Nursery	EFWa
Fox Cottage Plants	**MFOX**
Foxley Road Nurseries	CFox
Frogswell Nursery	IFro
From The Garden	**WFTG**
Fron Goch Garden Centre	WGer
Frosch Exclusive Perennials	XFro
Fryer's Nurseries Ltd	MFry
Fulbrooke Nursery	EFul

Rodney Fuller	CFul	Sue Hartfree	SHFr
Gaggini's Plant Centre	MGag	Harts Green Nursery	MHar
Gandy's (Roses) Ltd	MGan	Hartside Nursery Garden	NHar
The Garden at the Bannut	WBan	Harvest Nurseries	SHvs
The Garden at The Elms Nursery	WElm	Harveys Garden Plants	EHrv
Garden Cottage Nursery	GGar	The Hawthornes Nursery	NHaw
Garden House Nurseries	NGdn	Hayward's Carnations	SHay
Garden Plants	SGar	Heather Bank Nursery	CHea
Gardenscape	NGar	The Heather Society	EHea
Garth Cottage Nursery	NGCt	Hellyer's Garden Plants	SHel
Linda Gascoigne Wild Flowers	MGas	Henllys Lodge Plants	WHen
W G Geissler	WGei	The Herb Garden	MHrb
Gilbey's Plants	**NGby**	The Herb Garden & Historical	WHer
Glen Chantry	EGle	Plant Nursery	
Glendoick Gardens Ltd	GGGa	The Herb Nursery	MHer
Glenhirst Cactus Nursery	EGln	Herbs at Myddfai	WHbs
Glenville Nurseries	EGlv	Hergest Croft Gardens	WHCr
Global Orange Groves UK	CGOG	**Heritage Herbs**	**WHHs**
Godly's Roses	LGod	Herterton House Garden Nursery	NHer
Goldbrook Plants	EGol	Hewitt-Cooper Carnivorous Plants	LHew
Golden Cottage Plants	MGol	Hidden Valley Nursery	CHid
Elisabeth Goodwin Nurseries	EGoo	High Banks Nurseries	SHBN
Gordon's Nursery	WGor	High Farm Nurseries	MHFa
Gortkelly Castle Nursery	IGor	The High Garden	CHig
Goscote Nurseries Ltd	MGos	Highdown Nursery	SHDw
Grafted Walnut Trees	**WGWT**	Highfield Hollies	SHHo
Graham's Hardy Plants	CGra	Hill House Nursery & Gardens	CHll
Granby Gardens Nursery	MGrG	Hillview Hardy Plants	WHil
Grange Farm Plants	**EGFP**	Hoecroft Plants	EHoe
Grasmere Plants	EGra	Hofflands Daffodils	EHof
Grass Roots Nursery	**CGsR**	Holden Clough Nursery	NHol
Peter Grayson (Sweet Pea Seedsman)	MPet	Holkham Gardens	EHol
Great Dixter Nurseries	SDix	Holly Gate Cactus Nursery	SHol
The Great Western Gladiolus Nursery	EGrW	Home Plants	SHom
Mary Green Hostas	**NMyG**	Homestead Plants	MHom
& Hardy Perennials		Honeysome Aquatic Nursery	EHon
The Green Garden	MGGn	Hoo House Nursery	WHoo
Green Garden Herbs & Plants	NGHP	Hopleys Plants Ltd	LHop
Greenhead Roses	GGre	Horn's Garden Centre	NHor
Grimsdyke House	**SGrm**	Horton Vale Nursery	CHor
C W Groves & Son	CGro	Hortus Nursery	LHrt
Growing Carpets	LGro	Hull Farm	EHul
Gwynfor Growers	WGwG	Hunts Court Garden & Nursery	WHCG
Hadspen Garden & Nursery	CHad	Hydon Nurseries	LHyd
Halecat Nurseries	NHlc	Hyrons Trees	LHyr
Hall Farm Nursery	WHal	Hythe Alpines	EHyt
Halls of Heddon	NHal	Iden Croft Herbs	SIde
Halsway Nursery	CHal	Tim Ingram	SIgm
Hambrooks Growing Concern	**SHGC**	W E Th. Ingwersen Ltd	SIng
Hampshire Carnivorous Plants	SHmp	Intakes Farm	MInt
Hanging Gardens Nurseries Ltd	EHan	The Iris Garden	LIri
Hardifolia	MHdf	Iris of Sissinghurst	SIri
Hardstoft Herb Garden	NHHG	Iverna Herbs	IIve
Hardy Exotics	CHEx	Ivycroft Plants	WIvy
Hardy Orchids	CHdy	Jackson's Nurseries	MJac
Hardy's Cottage Garden Plants	SHar	Jasmine Cottage Gardens	CJas
Harley Nursery	WHar	Paul Jasper Trees	WJas
Harrells Hardy Plants	WHrl	Jekka's Herb Farm	WJek

Jelitto Perennial Seed	XJel	Lower Icknield Farm Nurseries	LIck
C & K Jones	MJon	Lower Severalls Nursery	CSev
Julia's Garden	WBry	Lower Spring Nursery	WLow
Jungle Giants	WJun	**Lunnon Nursery**	**WLun**
Just Bamboo Ltd	LJus	Lydford Alpine Nursery	CLyd
Just Phlomis	WPhl	M & M Plants	CM&M
Kayes Garden Nursery	MKay	M G H Nurseries	IMGH
Keenan's Nursery & Gash Gardens	IKee	MGW Plants	NMGW
Keepers Nursery	SKee	Ivor Mace Nurseries	WIvo
Kelways Ltd	CKel	Elizabeth MacGregor	GMac
Kent Cacti	SKCa	MacGregors Plants for Shade	SMac
Kent Street Nurseries	SKen	Macpennys Nurseries	CMac
Kenwith Nursery (Gordon Haddow)	CKen	Macplants	GMaP
Kerry's Cottage Garden Plants	**SKCG**	Madrona Nursery	SMad
Kevock Garden Plants & Flowers	**GKev**	**Maidenhead Aquatics**	**LMdh**
Kiftsgate Court Gardens	WKif	Mallet Court Nursery	CMCN
Kingsfield Conservation Nursery	CKin	**Malletts Nurseries**	**EMlt**
Kingstone Cottage Plants	WKin	Manor Nursery	EMan
Kirkdale Nursery	GKir	**Marchants Hardy Plants**	**SMHy**
Knap Hill & Slocock Nurseries	LKna	The Marches Nursery	WMaN
Knoll Gardens	CKno	Lesley Marshall	EMar
Kobakoba	CKob	Marshall's Malmaison	WMal
L W Plants	LLWP	J & D Marston	NMar
Ladybrae Farm Nursery	**GLbr**	Martin Nest Nurseries	EMNN
Landford Trees	CLnd	Marwood Hill Gardens	CMHG
Landlife Wildflowers Ltd	NLan	Mattock's Roses	MMat
Landscape Plants	SLPl	S M McArd (Seeds)	EMcA
Lane End Nursery	MLan	**Hubert McHale**	**IHMH**
Laneside Alpines	NLAp	The Mead Nursery	CMea
Langley Boxwood Nursery	SLan	Meadow Cottage Plants	CMCo
Langthorns Plantery	ELan	Meadows Nursery	CMdw
Larch Cottage Nurseries	NLar	Mendle Nursery	NMen
Laurel Farm Herbs	ELau	Merebrook Water Plants	WMAq
The Laurels Nursery	SLau	Merriments Gardens	SMrm
The Lavender Garden	WLav	Merryfield Nurseries (Canterbury) Ltd	SMer
Lawton Hall Herbs	**WLHH**	Mickfield Watergarden Centre Ltd	EMFW
Layham Garden Centre & Nursery	SLay	Mickfield Hostas	EMic
Lea Rhododendron Gardens Ltd	MLea	Mill Cottage Plants	CMil
Leba Orchard – Green's Leaves	WLeb	Mill Hill Plants	MMil
Lilliesleaf Nursery	GLil	Mill Race Nursery	EMil
Lime Cross Nursery	SLim	Millais Nurseries	LMil
Lincluden Nursery	LLin	**Millrace Nursery**	**NMRc**
Linden Farm Nurseries	**SLFN**	Mills' Farm Plants & Gardens	EMFP
Lingen Nursery and Garden	WLin	Milton Garden Plants	CMGP
Linward Hardy Plants	MLwd	Mires Beck Nursery	NMir
Liscahane Nursery	ILsc	Monksilver Nursery	EMon
Lisdoonan Herbs	ILis	Moor Monkton Nurseries	NMoo
Little Brook Fuchsias	SLBF	Moorland Cottage Plants	WMoo
Little Creek Nursery	CLCN	Morehavens	LMor
Little Red Hen Nurseries	**NLRH**	John Morley	EMor
Little Rhyndaston Nurseries	WLRN	Morton Hall Gardens	MMHG
C S Lockyer	CLoc	Stanley Mossop	NMos
Loder Plants	SLdr	Mount Harry Trees	SMHT
Lodge Lane Nursery & Gardens	MLLN	Mount Pleasant Trees	WMou
Long Acre Plants	CLAP	Mozart House Nursery Garden	MMoz
The Longframlington Centre for Plants & Gardens	NLon	Ken Muir Ltd	EMui
		Mulu Nurseries	WMul
Longstock Park Nursery	SLon	Kathleen Muncaster Fuchsias	EKMF

Potterton & Martin	EPot	Sampford Shrubs	CSam
The Potting Shed	IPot	Sandstones Cottage Garden Plants	WSan
Pound Lane Nurseries	**SPLN**	Scarletts Quality Plants	ESlt
Pounsley Plants	CPou	Scott's Wildflowers	NSco
Poyntzfield Herb Nursery	GPoy	Scree Gardens	SScr
Prime Perennials	WPrP	Seaforde Gardens	ISea
Primrose Cottage Nursery	NPri	Seagate Irises	ESgI
Priory Plants	EPri	Seale Nurseries	SSea
Properplants.com	**CPrp**	Seaside Nursery	ISsi
ProudPlants	NPro	Seeds by Size	LSee
Quality Daffodils	CQua	Select Seeds	LSss
Quinish Garden Nursery	GQui	The Selsley Herb Nursery	WSel
R D Plants	CRDP	Sherston Parva Nursery Ltd	CSPN
Rapkyns Nursery	**SRkn**	Sherwood Cottage	CSdC
Rarer Plants	NRar	John Shipton (Bulbs)	WShi
Raven Valley Plant Nursery	LRav	Shirley's Plants	NShi
Ravensthorpe Nursery	MRav	**Showglads**	**MSGs**
Reads Nursery	ERea	Shrubland Park Nurseries	EShb
Really Wild Flowers	CRea	Silver Dale Nurseries	CSil
The Really Wild Nursery	**CRWN**	Silver Leaf Nurseries	CSLe
Red House Farm	WRHF	Clive Simms	ESim
G Reuthe Ltd	SReu	Sino-Himalayan Plant Association	LSiH
Rezare Nurseries	**CRez**	Siskin Plants	ESis
Rhandirmwyn Plants	WRha	Skipness Plants	GSki
Rhodes & Rockliffe	ER&R	Slack Top Alpines	NSla
Ribblesdale Nurseries	NRib	**Slade Park Plants**	**LSde**
Rickard's Hardy Ferns	WRic	Slipps Garden Centre	CSli
Ringhaddy Daffodils	IRhd	South West Carnivorous Plants	CSWC
(formerly Ballydorn Bulb Farm)		Sourhease Plants	SSth
River Garden Nurseries	SRiv	Southfield Nurseries	ESou
Colin Roberts	**SCnR**	Southview Nurseries	SSvw
Robin Savill Clematis Specialist	ERob	Special Plants	CSpe
Robins Nursery	SRob	Speldhurst Nurseries	SSpe
W Robinson & Sons Ltd	NRob	Spinners Garden	SSpi
Sue Robinson	ERsn	Springbank Nurseries	SSpr
Rodbaston College	MRod	Springhill Plants	MSph
The Rodings Plantery	ERod	Springwood Pleiones	NSpr
R V Roger Ltd	NRog	Stapeley Water Gardens Ltd	MSta
The Romantic Garden	ERom	Starborough Nursery	SSta
Rosedown Mill Palms and Exotics	CRoM	Stenbury Nursery	SSte
Roseholme Nursery	ERos	Steventon Road Nurseries	MSte
Roseland House Nursery	CRHN	Stillingfleet Lodge Nurseries	NSti
Rosemary's Farmhouse Nursery	WRos	Stone House Cottage Nurseries	WSHC
Rosewarne Collections	CRsw	**Stone Lane Gardens**	**CSto**
Rosewood Daylilies	SRos	**Strachan's Plants**	**MSPs**
Rosies' Garden Plants	SRGP	Henry Street Nursery	LStr
Rotherview Nursery	SRot	Sue Strickland Plants	CStr
Rougham Hall Nurseries	ERou	Stuckey's Alpines	CStu
Rowde Mill Nursery	CRde	Style Roses	ESty
Rowden Gardens	CRow	Brian & Pearl Sulman	ESul
Rumsey Gardens	SRms	Sunnybank Vine Nursery	WSuV
Rushfields of Ledbury	WRus	**Sussex Topiary**	**STop**
Ryal Nursery	NRya	Suttons Seeds	CSut
Ryans Nurseries	IRya	Sylvatica Nursery	LSyl
S & S Perennials	MS&S	Table Bay View Nursery	NBlo
St Bridget Nurseries Ltd	**CSBt**	Table Bay View Nursery, Cape Town	XBlo
St Ishmael's Nurseries	WStI	Tan-y-Llyn Nurseries	WTan
Salley Gardens	MSal	**Tavistock Herb Nursery**	**NTHB**

SPECIALIST NURSERIES

Nurseries have classified themselves under the following headings where they *exclusively* or *predominantly* supply this range of plants. Plant groups are set out in alphabetical order. Refer to **Nursery Details by Code** on page 772 for details of the nurseries whose codes are listed under the plant group which interests you. See page 771 for a fuller explanation.

ACID-LOVING PLANTS

CMac CPLG CTrh CWCL
ECho ELan EPar GCrs GDra
GDrg GGGa GGar IBlr
IDac ISea LHyd LMil LNet
MBar MGos MLea NLAp
NMen NNor SBrw SCam
SFai SHmp SLdr SOkd
SRot WAbe WCru WHar

ALPINE/ROCK PLANTS

CAvo CFul CGra CLyd CMea
CNic CPBP CStu CWCL
CWes CWil EBur EHyt ELan
EMNN EMlt EOas EPot
ETow GCrs GDra GDrg
GEdr GFle GGGa GTou
IBlr IDac ITim LBee LGro
LPVe MCre MAln MDHE
MNew MOne NBro NDlv
NHar NHol NJOw NLAp
NLon NMen NNew NPol
NRya NSla NWCA NWoo
SDeJ SIgm SIng SOkd SPop
SRms SRot SScr WAbe WCom
WGor WHoo WLin WLow
WOBN WPat WPer XPab

AQUATIC/MARGINAL

CBen CLAP COld CRow
EHon ELan EMFW EPar
IHMH LPBA MCCP MSta
NLon NNor NOrc SAWi
SBHF SLon SWat WHal
WLin WMAq WRic WWpP

BAMBOOS

CDDB CDul EFul EGln
EPVP EPla GBin LEdu LPan
MBrN MCCP MDCh MHdf

MMoz MPRe MWhi
MWht MWod NBee NGdn
NMoo NNEX NOGN
NPSI NPal SAPC SArc
SDes SDry WJun WMul
WNor WPGP

BRITISH WILD FLOWERS

CArn CKin CNat COld
CRWN CRea GBar GPoy
GWCH Ilve MBSH MGas
MHer NHHG NLan NMir
NMyG NSco NTHB SIde
SWat Walt WBWF WBri
WHbs WMoo WShi

BULBOUS PLANTS

CAvo CBro CElm CLAP
CLCN CMea CQua CStu
CTca CWoo EBot ECho
EDif EFam EGrW EHyt
EMon EMui EPar EPot
ERos ETub GCrs GEdr
GEve GTou IBlr IRhd
LBow LPhx MNrw MS&S
NBlo NCel NMen NOaD
SDeJ STil WCru WDav
WOBN WPrP WShi WWst
XBlo

CACTI & SUCCULENTS

CPhi CTrC CWil EGln
EOas EPln ESou LToo
MPRe NCro NOaD SBrk
SChr SCon SHol SHvs
SKCa WGei

CARNIVOROUS PLANTS

CSWC GTro LHew SHmp
SKCa

CHALK-LOVING PLANTS

CBot CSpe EFam EGoo LGro
SEND SLan SLon SSvw SYvo

CLIMBERS

CRHN CSPN CTri CWhi
EGlv EHan EOrc ERea
ERob ESCh ETWh ETho
ICrw MBar MCCP MCad
MGos MNew NBea NBrk
NGCt NSti NTay SAPC
SApu SArc SBra SHGC
SLau SLay SLim SPla WAct
WBuc WCru WHar WSHC
WTre

COASTAL PLANTS

CPne CPou CTrC GGar
GSki IBal SAPC SChr
SEND SLan SPar WPnn

CONIFERS

CKen CLnd CTho EGlv
EHul EOrn GTre LBee
LCon LLin LPan MAsh
MBar NBee NLar SCoo
SCrf SLim WEve WGor
WHar

CONSERVATORY PLANTS

CBrP CGOG CPhi CPne
CRHN CRoM CSpe CTrC
EBak EGln EOHP ERea
EShb GDrg GFai GGGa
LDea LToo MNew MOak
MPRe NBlo NFir NPal
SArc SHol SLdr SOWG
SYvo WDib WMal WMul
WRic XBlo

DROUGHT TOLERANT

CBot CKno CPne CSLe
ECha EFam EGln EGoo
EOas EPVP LPhx LRav SChr
SEND SIgm SPar SSvw

FERNS

CLAP CRow EFer EHon
EMon GBin GEdr LCaP
LEur LPBA MCCP MMoz
NBro NDlv NHar NHol
NMar NMyG NOGN NOak
NOrc NPal SApp SArc SChu
SHmp SLon SNut SPla
SRms SRot WHal WRic

FRUIT

CAgr CCAT CGOG CTho
CTri ECrN EMui ERea ESim
GTre GTwe LEdu MCoo
NBlo SBdl SCrf SDea SFam
SKee WBuc WHar WJas
WOrn WSuV XBlo

GRASSES

CBig CBrm CKno CMea
COld CPen CRow CTrC
CWCL CWes EBur ECGN
EFul EHoe EHon EHul
EMon EPGN EPPr EPla
EPyc EWsh GBin GCal
GDea GOrn GSki LCaP
LEdu LPhx LRav MBSH
MBrN MCCP MDCh
MHdf MMoz MNrw MWhi
MWod NBea NBee NBro
NGdn NHol NMoo NMyG
NNor NOGN NOak NOrc
NPSI NSti SApp SBHF
SDeJ SDes SHGC SMHy
SPla SUsu SWal WHal
WHer WLeb WMoo WPGP
WPer WPrP WRus WWye

HEDGING

CArn CCVT CDul CKin
CLnd CSil CTrC CTri
ECrN ERom GTre IMGH
LBuc LCon LEar LHyr
LLin LPan MBar MCoo
MGos NBee NGCt SCam
SHGC SHHo SLan SLim
SRiv STop WAct WBad

WBuc WDin WEve WHar
WLav WMou WOrn WWeb

HERBS

CAgr CArn CLvH COld
CRWN CSev EBot ELau
EOHP GBar GDea GPoy
GWCH IHMH IIve ILis
LFol LGro LLWP LMor
MChe MHer MSal MWhi
NGCt NGHP NHHG
NTHB NWoo SHDw SIde
SWat WBad WBri WHbs
WJek WLHH WLav WPer
WSel WWye XPab

ORCHIDS

CBur CHdy CStu EFEx
EPot GUzu LBut LEur
NEqu NSpr WHer XFro

ORGANIC

CBgR COld EBlw GBar
GDea GPoy LEdu LLWP
NMar NPol SKCG WJek
WShi WWpP WWye

ORNAMENTAL TREES

CAgr CCAT CCVT CDul
CLnd CPMA CTho CTri
ECrN EGFP EMui GTre
ICrw IMGH ISea LHyr
LPan LRav MCCP MDCh
MGos NBea NBee NNEX
NPSI SFam SHBN SHGC
SLan SLau SLay SLim WBuc
WCel WGWT WHar WJas
WMou WNor WOrn WPGP

PEAT FREE

CAbx CBgR CKno CKob
CMdw CMea CPen CSam
EBlw ECGN EFer EGoo
GPoy LEdu MEHN MGas
MMoz MPhe NGby NLRH
NSco SCou SFam SKCG
SPar SRob SVen SYvo WGWT
WHbs WJek WPnP WPrP
WSel WShi WWpP WWye

PERIOD PLANTS

CBot CQua EMFP ERob

ETWh ILis LDea MAln
SSvw WAct WCGr WHer
WJek WOFF

PROPAGATE TO ORDER

CAbx CDul CElw CLCN
CLvH CMdw CQua CRWN
CRow CTrC ECho ECrN
EGFP EGlv EOas EPla EPyc
GFai GSki IHMH ILis LLWP
LMil LStr MDCh MMoz
MOak MWod NBlo NCro
NNEX NPol NRya NShi
NTHB NWCA NWoo SBdl
SCou SHDw SHel SLan SLau
SWat WGWT WHer WHil
WJek WOBN WP&B WPrP
WTin WWpP WWye XBlo

SEEDS

CDob CElm CKin CPas
CPla CSpe CStr CSut CTuc
EGrW EMcA EPVP GDea
GDra GPoy LCTD LCha
LChw LSee LSiH LSss MAsh
MBSH MChe MDCh MGol
MPet MPhe NChl NGCt
NLan NPol NRob SCou
SIde WHen WJek WNor
XB&T XJel XPab

SPECIMEN SIZED PLANTS

CArn CCVT CDul CPMA
CPhi CPne CSil CTho CTrh
ECho ECrN EGln EHul
ELau ERom GGGa GTre
IMGH LCon LEar LHyd
LHyr LLin LMil LNet LPVe
LPan MBrN MDCh MLea
MPRe MPhe MWod NGCt
NMar NOrc NPSI NPal
SAPC SArc SBrw SCam SCrf
SDes SEND SFai SFam
SHGC SHHo SHmp SLan
SLdr SLim STop WBad
WDin WEve WHar WHer
WJek WJun WMul WPat
WRic WWeb

TOPIARY

COld CWes ERea ERom LEar
LHyr LPan NGCt NPSI
NPal SAPC SArc SHHo
SLan SRiv STop WEve WWeb

INDEX MAP

The maps on the following pages
show the approximate location of
the nurseries whose details are
listed in this directory.

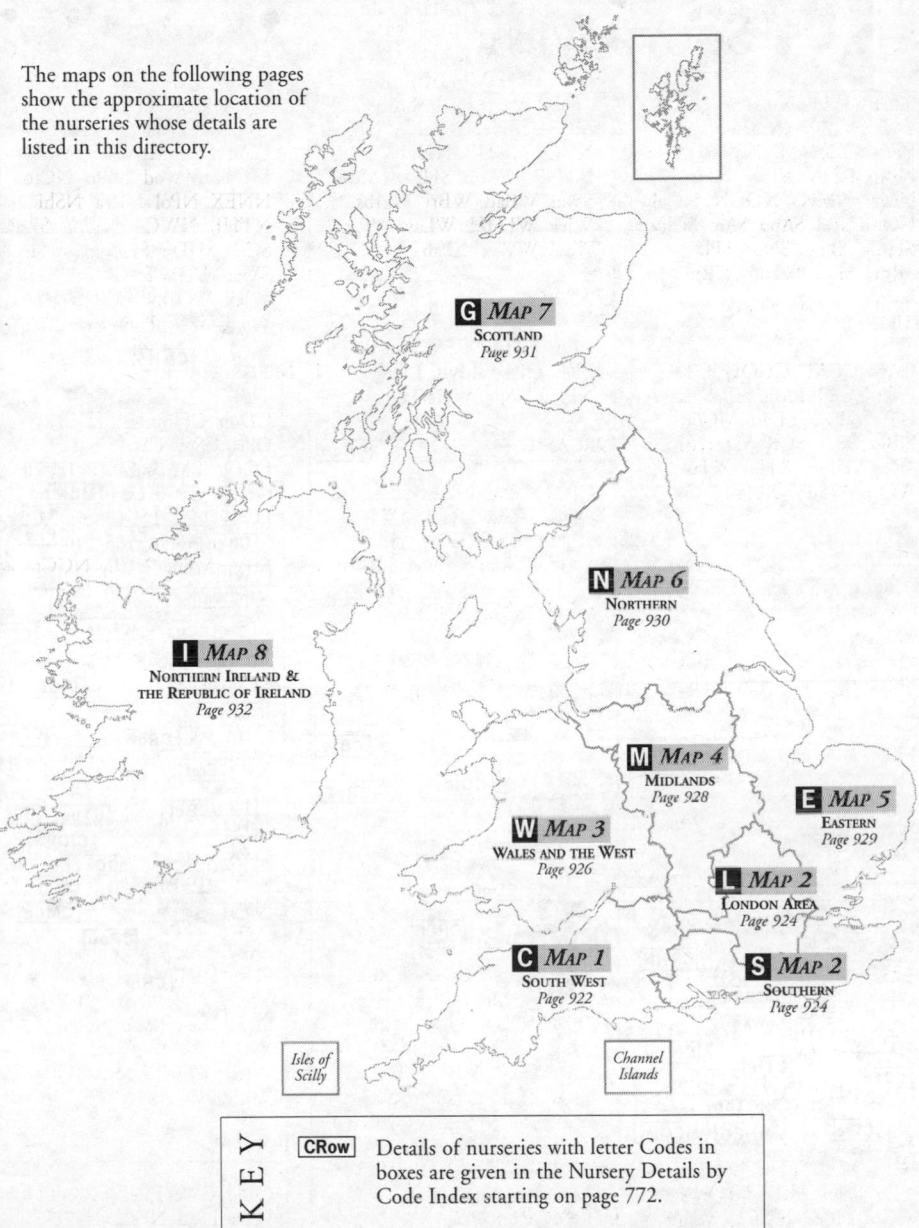

G *MAP 7*
SCOTLAND
Page 931

N *MAP 6*
NORTHERN
Page 930

I *MAP 8*
NORTHERN IRELAND &
THE REPUBLIC OF IRELAND
Page 932

M *MAP 4*
MIDLANDS
Page 928

E *MAP 5*
EASTERN
Page 929

W *MAP 3*
WALES AND THE WEST
Page 926

L *MAP 2*
LONDON AREA
Page 924

C *MAP 1*
SOUTH WEST
Page 922

S *MAP 2*
SOUTHERN
Page 924

*Isles of
Scilly*

*Channel
Islands*

K E Y **CRow** Details of nurseries with letter Codes in
boxes are given in the Nursery Details by
Code Index starting on page 772.

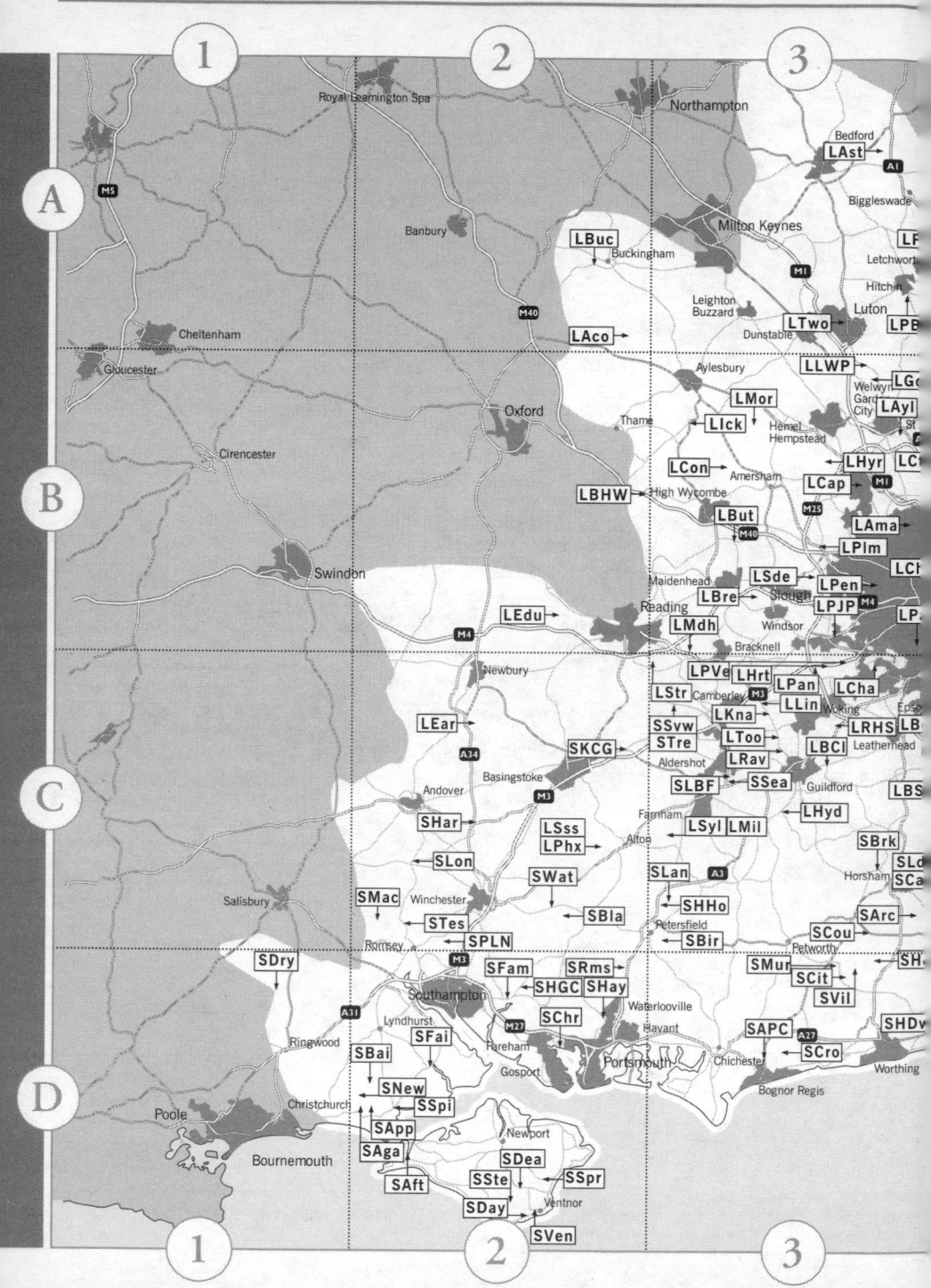

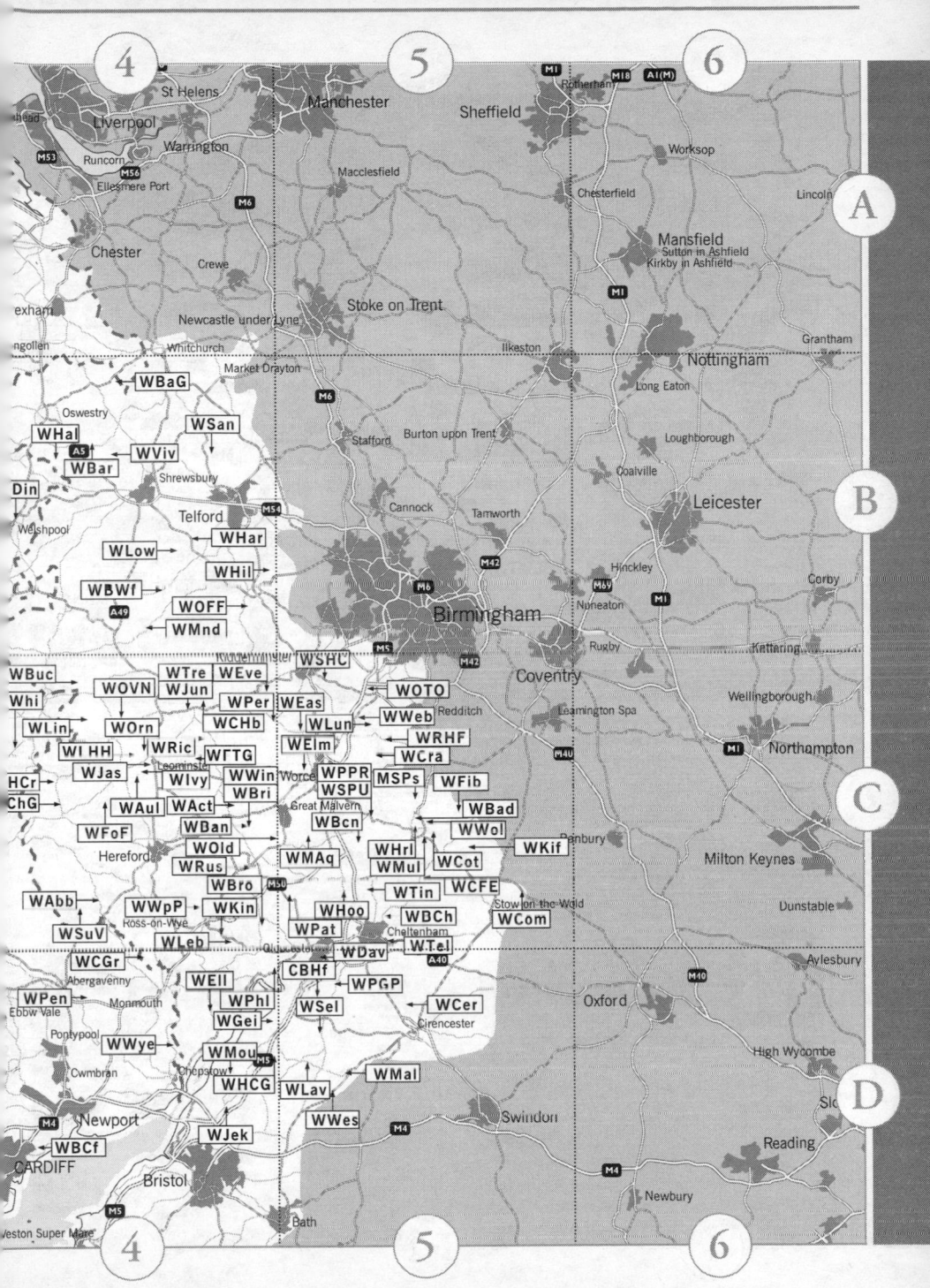

St Helens
Liverpool
Warrington
Manchester
Sheffield
Rotherham
M1
M18
A1(M)
Worksop
Runcorn
M56
Ellesmere Port
Chesterfield
Lincoln
M53
A
Chester
Crewe
Mansfield
Sutton in Ashfield
Kirkby in Ashfield
Newcastle under Lyme
Stoke on Trent
Whitchurch
Ilkeston
Nottingham
Grantham
Market Drayton
M6
Long Eaton
WBaG
Stafford
Burton upon Trent
Loughborough
Oswestry
WHal
WSan
A5
WViv
Shrewsbury
Coalville
Leicester
B
WBar
Din
Cannock
Tamworth
Welshpool
M54
Telford
WHar
Hinckley
Corby
WLow
M6
WHil
Birmingham
Nuneaton
Kettering
WBWf
WOFF
A49
Rugby
WMnd
M5
M42
Coventry
Wellingborough
WBuc
WTre
WEve
WSHC
WOTO
WOVN
WJun
Whi
WPer
WEas
WWeb
Redditch
Leamington Spa
M1
Northampton
WLin
WCHb
WLun
WRHF
M40
Banbury
WI HH
WOrn
WRic
WElm
WCra
Milton Keynes
C
WJas
WrTG
Leominster
WWin
WPPR
MSPs
WFib
WIvy
Worcester
WSPU
HCr
WAul
WAct
WBri
Dunstable
ChG
Great Malvern
WBad
WFoF
WBan
WBcn
WWol
Hereford
WOld
WMAq
WHrl
WCot
WKif
WRus
WMul
WBro
WTin
WCFE
WAbb
WWpP
WKin
WHoo
WBCh
Stow on the Wold
WSuV
Ross-on-Wye
WPat
WCom
Aylesbury
WLeb
Cheltenham
WCGr
M50
WDav
W.Tel
Abergavenny
WEll
CBHf
A40
Oxford
WPen
Monmouth
WPhl
WPGP
M40
Ebbw Vale
WGei
WSel
WCer
High Wycombe
Pontypool
Cirencester
WWye
WMou
Cwmbran
Chepstow
M5
WHCG
WLav
WMal
Slo
D
Newport
WWes
Swindon
M4
Reading
M4
WBCf
CARDIFF
M4
Bristol
Newbury
M5
Weston Super Mare
Bath

1 2 3

A B C D

Blackpool
Lytham St. Anne's
Southport
Keighley
Nelson
Bradford
Leeds
Kingston upon Hull
Preston
Accrington
Burnley
Halifax
Brighouse
Batley
Pudsey
Castleford
Scunthorpe
M6
Blackburn
Darwen
Dewsbury
Wakefield
Wigan
M66
M62
Huddersfield
MANCHESTER
Barnsley
Doncaster
Skelmersdale
Leigh
St. Helens
SHEFFIELD
Rotherham
A1(M)
Lincoln
Crosby
Litherland
Bootle
Wallasey
Birkenhead
Bebington
Liverpool
Widnes
MCad **MLan**
MWar
MPhe
MGGn
MFry
MOne
MBow
MDun
Worksop
MMHG
MNes
Runcorn
M56
MLLN
MArl
MFir
MIDC
Chesterfield
A1
MJon
Chester
MOke
MPWC
Knutsford
M6
MDHE
MFOX
Mansfield
Sutton in Ashfield
Ashfield
Newark-on-Trent
MNrw
Wrexham
MChe
Crewe
Nantwich
Newcastle under Lyme
Macclesfield
MBar
MLEa
MWht
M1
MLwd
MMil
MSta
MInt
MDKP
Ashbourne
Ilkeston
MGrG
MHom
Grantham
MBri
MTis
Nottingham
MApt
Stoke on Trent
A50
Derby
Long Eaton
MSal
Shrewsbury
M6
MHFa
Burton upon Trent
MBlu
Loughborough
MFie
MOak
Melton Mowbray
MHer
Telford
Stafford
MBre
Coalville
MTed
MKay
MBNS
MCau
M54
MRod
MCLN
MPRe
MUlv
MGos
MWgw
Cannock
MJac
MS&S
MCls
Uppingham
Peterborough
MAus
MWod
A5
MWrn
Leicester
MAsh
M42
Tamworth
MMoz
MGas
Corby
Birmingham
Hinckley
M6
Nuneaton
MTho
Kettering
MHar
MBSo
Coventry
MGan
MRav
MTPN
Wellingborough
Kidderminster
M42
MAvo
Rugby
MCCP
MGag
M5
Redditch
MBrN
MWhe
Northampton
Worcester
Great Malvern
MAAq
MWoo
M1
Bedford
Hereford
Banbury
MEHN
Milton Keynes
MPEx
MWya
Chipping Norton
M40
MNFA
Leighton Buzzard
Woodstock
MBlm
Dunstable
Luton
MWhi
Aylesbury
M1
Burford
MWat
Hemel Hempstead
St. Albans
A40
MSph
MMat
EbbwVale
MHrb
Oxford
Watford
High Wycombe
Pontypool
Cwmbran
MBct
Faringdon
MSte
MNew
M40
M25
M4
Newport
M5
MBro
Wallingford
Maidenhead
Slough
CARDIFF
Bristol
MAbH
Swindon
Reading
Windsor
Bath
M4
Bracknell
Staines
Trowbridge
Newbury
Leatherhead
Epso[m]

MAP FOUR
M MIDLANDS

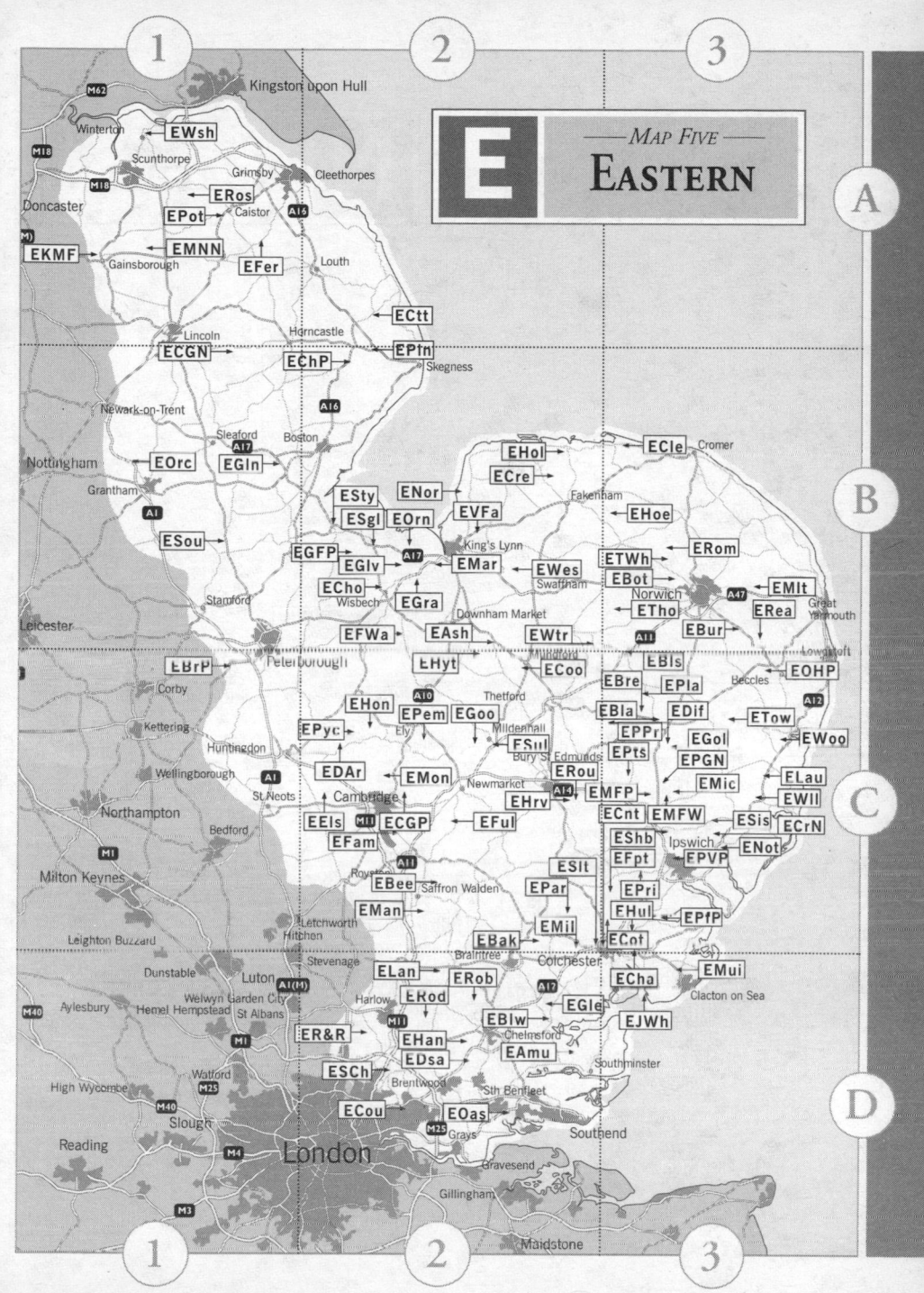

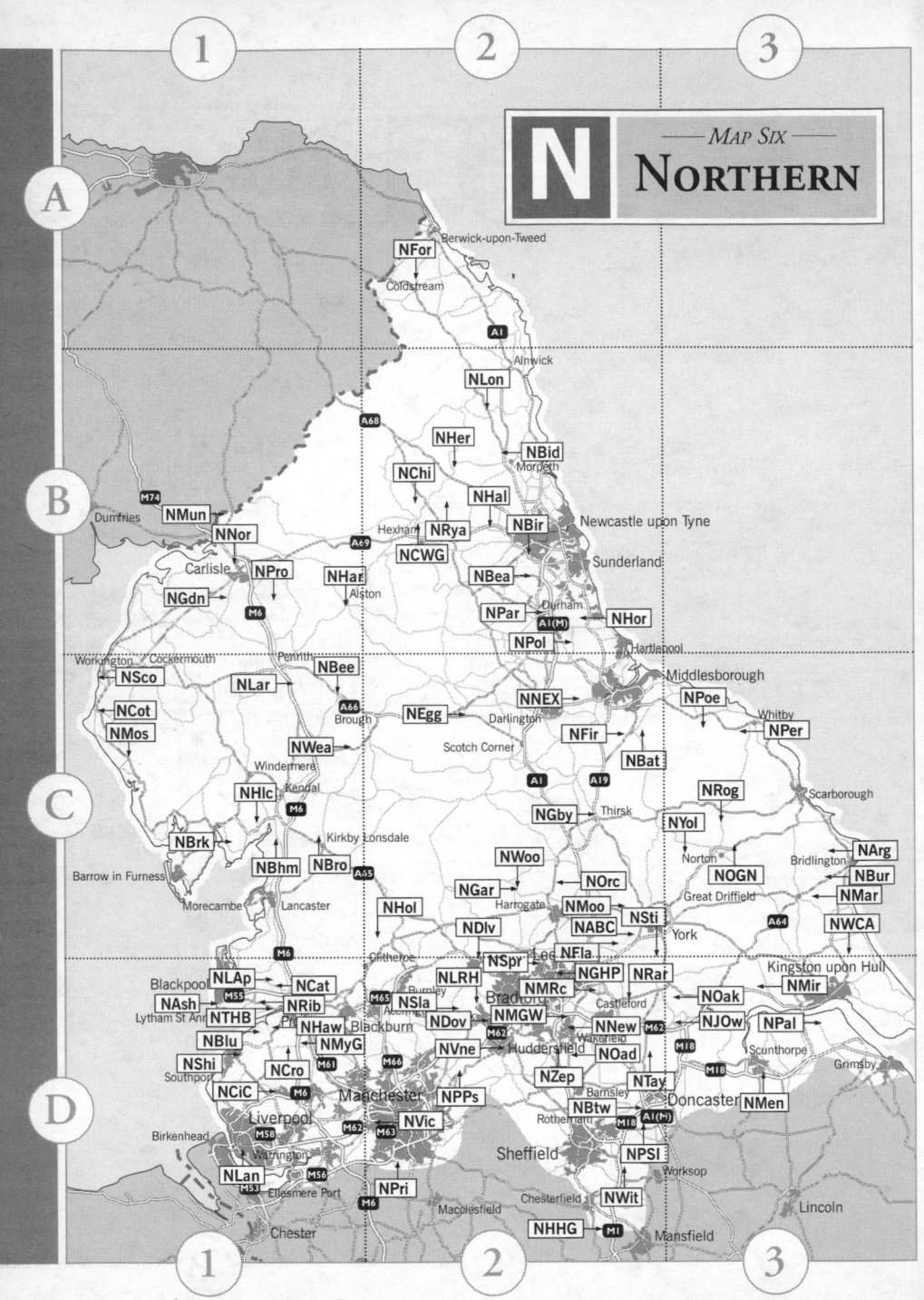

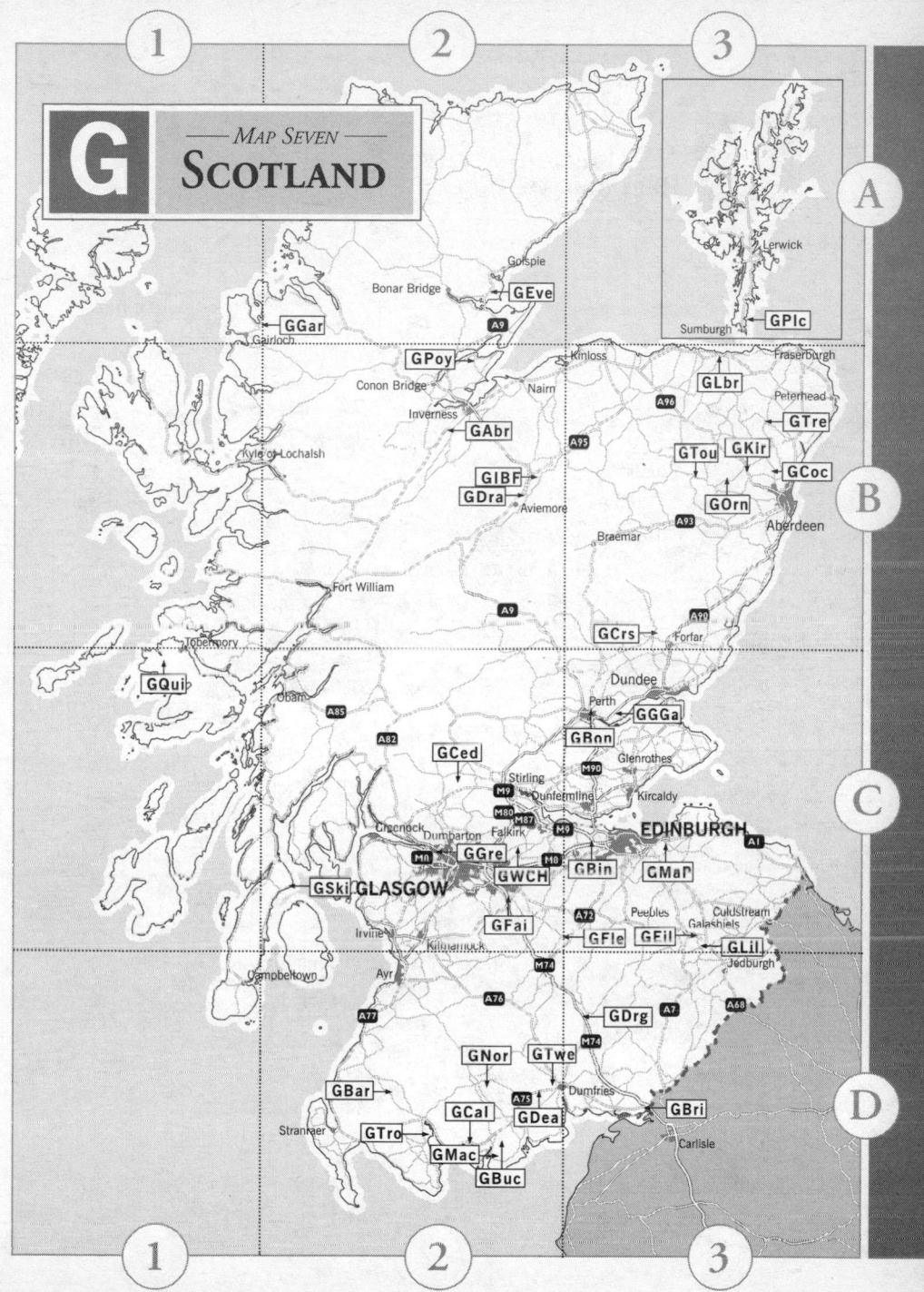

G

— MAP SEVEN —
SCOTLAND

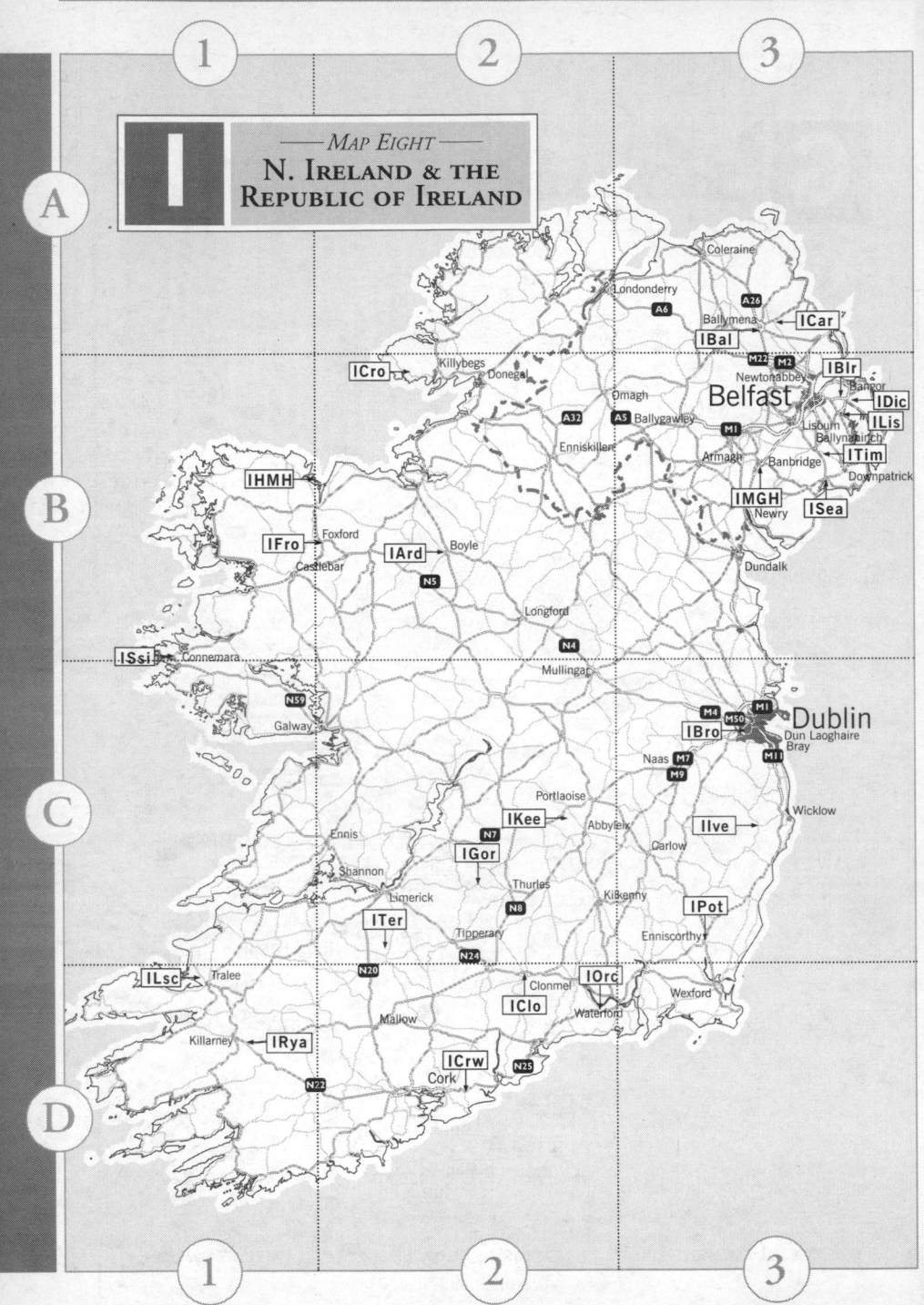

1   **2**   **3**

A

— MAP EIGHT —
N. IRELAND & THE REPUBLIC OF IRELAND

Coleraine

Londonderry

A6

A26

Ballymena

IBal   ICar

ICro   Killybegs   Donegal   M22   M2

Omagh   Newtownabbey   IBlr

Bangor

A32   A5   Ballygawley   Belfast   IDic

ILis

Enniskillen   M1   Lisburn   Ballynahinch

Armagh   Banbridge   ITim

B   IHMH   Downpatrick

IFro   Foxford   Boyle   IMGH   ISea

Castlebar   IArd   Newry

N5   Dundalk

Longford

N4

ISsi   Connemara   Mullingar

N59   M4   M1   **Dublin**

Galway   M50   Dun Laoghaire

IBro   Bray

Naas   M7   M11

M9

C   Portlaoise

IKee   Abbeyleix   IIve   Wicklow

Ennis   N7   Carlow

IGor   Thurles   Kilkenny

Shannon   N8   IPot

Limerick   ITer   Enniscorthy

Tipperary

N20   N24

ILsc   Tralee   Clonmel   IOrc   Wexford

Mallow   IClo   Waterford

IRya   Killarney   ICrw   N25

N22   Cork

D

1   **2**   **3**

Have you found or bred a new plant?

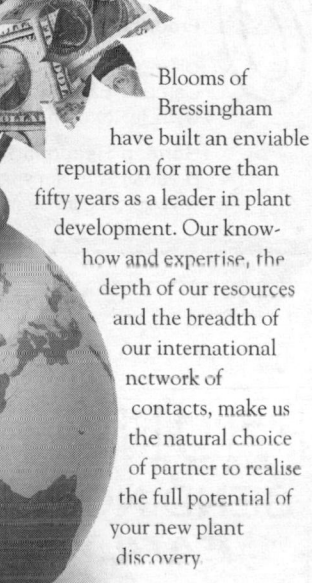

Trust us to realise the full worldwide potential of your new plant discovery.

The new plant that you've found or bred may well have the potential to be developed and marketed to achieve worldwide commercial success.

Blooms of Bressingham have built an enviable reputation for more than fifty years as a leader in plant development. Our know-how and expertise, the depth of our resources and the breadth of our international network of contacts, make us the natural choice of partner to realise the full potential of your new plant discovery.

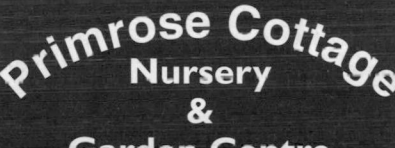

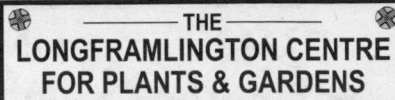

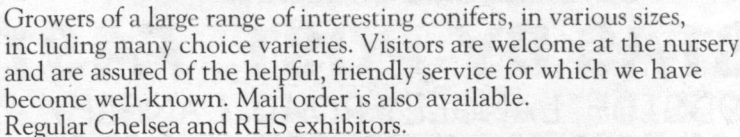

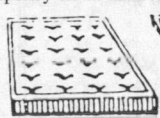

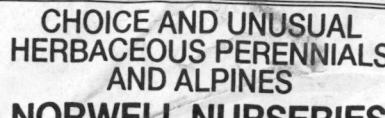

954

INDEX OF ADVERTISERS

The HARDY PLANT SOCIETY

Explores, encourages and conserves all that is best in gardens

The Hardy Plant Society encourages interest in growing hardy perennial plants and provides members with information about familiar and less well known perennial plants that flourish in our gardens, how to grow them and where they may obtained. This friendly society offers a range of activities locally and nationally, giving members plenty of opportunity to meet other keen gardeners to share ideas and information in a convivial atmosphere. The activities and work of the Society inform and encourage the novice gardener, stimulate and enlighten the more knowledgeable, and entertain and enthuse all gardeners bonded by a love for, and an interest in, hardy perennial plants.

LOCAL GROUPS

There are over 40 local groups across the UK and national members are invited to join the group nearest to them. Each group offers a wide range of gardening activities including informative lectures, garden visits and plant plus educational and social events throughout the year. Most groups produce their own newsletters. Full details of how to join a local group are sent out to new members.

SPECIALIST GROUPS AND GARDENING BY POST

Specialist Groups produce their own newsletters and organise meetings and events for fellow enthusiasts. The Correspondents Group ensures that members who are unable to attend meetings can exchange gardening ideas and information.

SEED DISTRIBUTION

Every member can join in the annual Seed Distribution Scheme by obtaining or donating hardy perennial seed. The Seed List offers over 2,500 tempting varieties of rare, unusual and familiar seeds and is sent to every member in December.

SHOWS AND EVENTS

Exhibits at major shows throughout the country let visitors see hardy plants in bloom and leaf in their natural season and more information about the work of the Society is available. Events hosted by local group members are also organised, from plant study days to residential weekends to garden visits. The Society also organises overseas garden tours.

CONSERVATION

The Hardy Plant Society is concerned about the conservation of garden plants and is working towards ensuring that older, rarer and lesser-known perennial plants are conserved and made available to gardeners generally.

PUBLICATIONS AND THE SLIDE LIBRARY

The Society's journal, *The Hardy Plant*, is published twice a year and regular newsletters provide information on all the Society's events, activities, interests and group contacts. The Society also publishes a series of booklets on special plant families which include Hardy Geraniums, Penstemons, Pulmonarias, Hostas, Grasses, Euphorbias, Phlox and Success with Seed. Other publications for members include a B&B list and a gardens to visit list. The Slide Library has a wide range of hardy plant slides available on loan.

INFORMATION ABOUT THE SOCIETY IS AVAILABLE FROM:

The Administrator
Mrs Pam Adams
The Hardy Plant Society
Little Orchard
Great Comberton
Pershore
Worcestershire WR10 3DP

Tel: 01386 710317
Fax: 01386 710117
E-mail: admin@hardy-plant.org.uk
Website: www.hardy-plant.org.uk

Please see overleaf for an application form

The HARDY PLANT SOCIETY

MEMBERSHIP APPLICATION FOR 2001

The Annual Subscriptions are:
Single **£10.00** per year (one member)
Joint **£12.00** per year (two members at the same address)

• Subscriptions are renewable annually on **1 January**.
• Subscriptions of members joining after 1 October are valid until the end of the following year.
• Overseas members are requested to pay in pounds sterling by International Money Order
or by credit card. An optional charge of £6.00 is made for airmail postage outside Western Europe of
all literature, if preferred.

Please fill in the details in BLOCK CAPITALS, tear off this form and send it with your payment to the
Administrator or telephone the Administrator with details of your credit card.

Please tick the type of membership required

☐ Single £10.00 per year (one member)

☐ Joint £12.00 per year (two members at one address)

☐ Airmail postage £6.00 per year (optional for members outside Western Europe)

NAME/S ....

ADDRESS ....

....

.... POST CODE ....

TELEPHONE NUMBER ....

I enclose a cheque/postal order* payable to **THE HARDY PLANT SOCIETY** (in pounds sterling ONLY) for £...........

OR
Please debit my Visa/Master Card* by the sum of £ ....
(* delete as required)

CARD NUMBER ☐☐☐☐ ☐☐☐☐ ☐☐☐☐ ☐☐☐☐

EXPIRY DATE ☐☐☐☐

Name as embossed on card ....

Signature ....

Please print your name and address clearly, tear out the page and send it to
The Administrator at the address overleaf

The Hardy Plant Society is a Registered Charity, number 208080

Royal Horticultural Society

Step into a world of inspirational gardens

Join the Royal Horticultural Society and enjoy free entry to over 90 inspirational gardens in the UK.

Members can receive advice, ideas and inspiration through free entry to the renowned RHS Gardens – Wisley, Rosemoor, Hyde Hall and Harlow Carr – as well as free entry to 88 partner gardens at carefully selected periods of the year. Members also benefit from the excellent monthly magazine *The Garden*, as well as from a free gardening advice service from the RHS experts, available by phone, fax, letter, e-mail or face-to-face. Members also enjoy privileged access and special rate tickets to the world's most famous Flower Shows including Chelsea, Hampton Court Palace and Tatton Park, as well as discounted tickets to RHS talks, events and garden tours across Britain.

RHS Membership Special Offer – Save £5

RHS membership is normally £37 (£30 including a one-off joining fee of £7) but you can save £5 and pay just £32 by calling the Membership Hotline on

0845 130 4646

and quote code 1924

(Lines open 9:00am - 5:00pm Monday to Friday)
Offer expires 31/10/02

www.rhs.org.uk

Registered charity no. 222879

THE Plantsman
THE ROYAL HORTICULTURAL SOCIETY

NEW SERIES VOLUME 1   PART 1 MARCH 2002

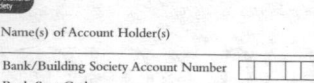